W9-BNB-964

2019
STANDARD POSTAGE
STAMP CATALOGUE

ONE HUNDRED AND SEVENTY-FIFTH EDITION IN SIX VOLUMES

VOLUME 1B

Austria-B

EDITOR	Donna Houseman
MANAGING EDITOR	Charles Snee
EDITOR EMERITUS	James E. Kloetzel
SENIOR EDITOR /NEW ISSUES & VALUING	Martin J. Frankevicz
SENIOR VALUING ANALYST	Steven R. Myers
SENIOR EDITOR	Timothy A. Hodge
ADMINISTRATIVE ASSISTANT/CATALOGUE LAYOUT	Eric Wiessinger
PRINTING AND IMAGE COORDINATOR	Stacey Mahan
SENIOR GRAPHIC DESIGNER	Cinda McAlexander
SALES DIRECTOR	David Pistello
SALES DIRECTOR	Eric Roth

Released April 2018

Includes New Stamp Listings through the February 2018 *Linn's Stamp News Monthly* Catalogue Update

Copyright© 2018 by

AMOS MEDIA

911 Vandemark Road, Sidney, OH 45365-0828
Publishers of *Linn's Stamp News*, *Linn's Stamp News Monthly*, *Coin World* and *Coin World Monthly*.

Table of Contents

See Volumes 1A, 2A through 6B for Countries of the World, United States, United Nations, Abu Dhabi-Australia, C-Z

Volume 1A: United States, United Nations, Abu Dhabi-Australia
Volume 2A: C-Cur; Volume 2B: Cyp-F
Volume 3A: G; Volume 3B: H-I
Volume 4A: J-L; Volume 4B: M
Volume 5A: N-Phil; Volume 5B: Pit-Sam
Volume 6A: San-Tete; Volume 6B: Thai-Z

Scott Catalogue Mission Statement

The Scott Catalogue Team exists to serve the recreational,
educational and commercial hobby needs of stamp collectors and dealers.

We strive to set the industry standard for philatelic information and products by developing and
providing goods that help collectors identify, value, organize and present their collections.

Quality customer service is, and will continue to be, our highest priority.
We aspire toward achieving total customer satisfaction.

SCOTT

What's new for 2019 Scott Standard Volume 1B?

Greetings, Fellow Scott Catalog User:

This year celebrates another milestone in the 150-year history of the Scott catalogs. The 2019 volumes are the 175th edition of the Scott *Standard Postage Stamp Catalogue*. Vol. 1B contains listings for Austria through B countries of the world. Listings for the United States, United Nations, and countries of the world Aden through Australia can be found in Vol. 1A.

• The pattern of the roughly 400 value changes for the Bahamas is one the Scott editors have seen for other British Commonwealth countries for the past five years or so. A modest number of increases are seen in the classic period, up to the 1935 Silver Jubilee issue. The biggest jumps are seen for used stamps. As an example, the 1-shilling 1898 Queen Victoria (Scott 23) jumps from $37.50 used in 2018 to $50 in 2019.

Market activity for stamps from the late 1960s through 2005 is quiet, with small decreases predominating. Scattered increases are seen beginning in 2006. The 2006 Flowers set of 14 (Scott 1182-1195) sees a robust jump — from $50.75 mint and used in 2018 to $61.25 both ways this year.

And don't forget to scan back-of-the-book listings, where several war tax stamps see significant gains. The 1918 1-penny carmine and black (Scott MR5) almost doubles in value in used condition, rising from $6.50 to $11.

• Almost 850 value changes are recorded for Bahrain. Declines are the norm for stamps issued from 1970 up to 2005, while values for stamps issued from 2005 to 2010 trend upward. Among the more robust increases is the 2005 sheet of six celebrating the 50th anniversary of the discovery of Dilmon Civilization artifacts, which advances from $7.50 mint and used in 2018 to $12 both ways this year.

• For the stamps of Belize, the editors made more than 1,300 value changes. Values decline for many stamps issued up to 2005. Among the more recent issues, values are up or are provided for the first time for surcharged stamps. A notable example is the 1980 10¢-on-35¢ with round obliterator (Scott 424Ab), with an initial value of $300.

• More than 700 value changes are recorded for Bermuda. Scattered upward adjustments characterize the classic issues through the mid-1930s.

For stamps issued through the mid-1990s, you will note increases for numerous stamps in used condition. Keep in mind that these values are for stamps with contemporaneous cancellations, not canceled-to-order stamps.

Values for unused stamps from the 1940s through about 2003 are down, albeit modestly. Decreases on the order of 10 percent or less are the norm. Stamps issued during the past decade or so are up about 10 percent to 20 percent. Larger jumps are typically seen for popular topical subjects. For example, the 2012 set of six Paintings stamps (Scott 1047-1052) advances from $12 mint and used last year to $13.50 both ways this year.

• A thorough review of Brazil this year generated more than 4,500 value changes. Numerous value changes were made for stamps issued from 1900 to 1940, resulting in a mix of increases and decreases. Values slide downward from 1940 through the 1990s, but increases in value are the norm among the back-of-the-book listings.

• If you collect British Indian Ocean Territory, be sure to review the higher values for stamps issued during 2006-10. Decreases are seen across the board for the remaining 300 or so value changes.

• A thorough review of Brunei found more than 930 value changes. Issues from 1949 to 2000 are down for the most part. Values for individual stamps within sets have been adjusted to reflect market conditions more precisely.

• A line-by-line review of Bulgaria serves up more than 4,300 value changes. Values for unused stamps from 1920 to 1935 have been adjusted downward to better reflect retail prices in relation to never-hinged stamps. On the whole, value declines of 10 percent to 15 percent predominate through the postage section for issue through mid-2005. Steeper declines are seen for some used stamps issued from 1998 through 2003.

From mid-2005 through late 2016, the value-change arrow takes a sharp turn up. During this time period, value increases of 20 percent or more are common. A standout example is the 2008 Ferrari Race Cars pair (Scott 4487), which rockets up from $2.75 mint and used in the 2018 catalog to $20 both ways this year.

As with many other countries, popular topicals see some gains. The 2004 Butterflies set of four with gauge 14-by-13½ perforations (Scott 4291a-4294a) floats up to $30 mint and used, from $28 both ways last year. Be sure to look at items that are footnoted because many values have been added or updated.

• Burkina Faso, formerly known as Upper Volta, tested the editors' analysis because retail market prices often varied substantially. Of the more than 1,300 value changes, scattered declines outpaced gains for stamps issued during the 1960s to the mid-1980s, with sharper drops seen for stamps issued during 1984-87. Values are added for the first time for numerous stamps from the mid-1990s through 2008. The 1996-98 Handicrafts set of 10, with mint and used values dashed previously, is now valued at $60 mint and at $15 used. Be sure to review the semipostal and airmail listings, which also see myriad value changes.

• A review of Burma yielded slightly more than 300 value changes. Stocks of issues from the 1950s to 1990 are scarce, which drove up values for many of these stamps.

Editorial enhancements for Vol. 1B

• Bahrain's Flag, Map, and Sheik Isa definitive set (Scott 225-240) has been expanded, with new minor-number listings for perforation varieties. Some of these stamps are readily identifiable by the bold printer's imprint in the bottom margin.

A new design type has been added to the 1991 set of eight and souvenir sheet honoring the 30th anniversary of the coronation of Sheik Isa (Scott 373-380 and 381).

It has been determined that two stamps previously listed as war tax stamps are in fact postal tax stamps. The relevant Scott numbers have been changed from MR1-MR2 to RA1-RA2.

• Among the Bhutan listings, numerous editorial notes and footnotes have been added or updated. Two new 2005 surcharges on 1979 Antiques stamps appear for the first time as Scott 1409A-1409B. Both are valued at $35 used.

• Four Botswana Gems and Minerals stamps showing the type I surcharge (thick numerals and "t") at bottom right have been added as Scott 157b, 160b, 166b, and 167b. This quartet issued in 1977 joins the two sets showing the type I and type II (thin numerals and "t") surcharges at top right.

• Bulgaria's imperforate variety of the 1982 50-stotinki Children's Drawing souvenir sheet is now listed as Scott 2870a.

As always, we encourage you to pay special attention to the Number Additions, Deletions & Changes found on page 879 in this volume. We also suggest reading the catalog introduction, which Includes an abundance of useful information.

Enjoy this wonderful hobby every day!

Donna Houseman

Donna Houseman/Catalogue Editor

Acknowledgments

Our appreciation and gratitude go to the following individuals who have assisted us in preparing information included in this year's Scott Catalogues. Some helpers prefer anonymity. These individuals have generously shared their stamp knowledge with others through the medium of the Scott Catalogue.

Those who follow provided information that is in addition to the hundreds of dealer price lists and advertisements and scores of auction catalogues and realizations that were used in producing the catalogue values. It is from those noted here that we have been able to obtain information on items not normally seen in published lists and advertisements. Support from these people goes beyond data leading to catalogue values, for they also are key to editorial changes.

A special acknowledgment to Liane and Sergio Sismondo of The Classic Collector for their assistance and knowledge sharing that have aided in the preparation of this year's Standard and Classic Specialized Catalogues.

Roland Austin
Jim Bardo (Bardo Stamps)
William Barclay (South Sudan Philatelic Society)
John Birkinbine II
Roger S. Brody
Tina & John Carlson (JET Stamps)
Henry Chlanda
Bob Coale
David & Julia Crawford
Tony L. Crumbley (Carolina Coin & Stamp, Inc.)
Christopher Dahle
Ubaldo Del Toro
Leon Djerahian
Bob & Rita Dumaine (Sam Houston Duck Co.)
Sister Theresa Durand
Paul G. Eckman
George Epstein (Allkor Stamp Co.)
Robert A. Fisher
Jeffrey M. Forster
Robert S. Freeman
Ernest E. Fricks
Michael Fuchs
Bob Genisol (Sultan Stamp Center)
Stan Goldfarb
Allen Grant (Rushstamps (Retail) Ltd.)
Daniel E. Grau
Robin Harris
Bruce Hecht (Bruce L. Hecht Co.)
Peter Hoffman
John Hotchner
Armen Hovsepian (Armenstamp)
Doug Iams
Eric Jackson
John Jamieson (Saskatoon Stamp and Coin)
Peter Jeannopoulos
William A. Jones
Allan Katz (Ventura Stamp Co.)
Lewis Kaufman (The Philatelic Foundation)
Patricia Kaufmann (Confederate Stamp Alliance)

Jon Kawaguchi (Ryukyu Philatelic Specialist Society)
Roland Kretschmer
William V. Kriebel (Brazil Philatelic Association)
Frederick P. Lawrence
John R. Lewis (The William Henry Stamp Co.)
Ulf Lindahl
Ignacio Llach (Filatelia Llach S.L.)
Marilyn R. Mattke
William K. McDaniel
Mauricio Mejia
Gary Morris (Pacific Midwest Co.)
Peter Mosiondz, Jr.
Bruce M. Moyer (Moyer Stamps & Collectibles)
Richard H. Muller
Scott Murphy (Professional Stamp Experts)
Leonard Nadybal
Dr. Tiong Tak Ngo
Gerald Nylander
Nik & Lisa Oquist
Dr. Everett Parker
Don Peterson (International Philippine Philatelic Society)
Stanley M. Piller (Stanley M. Piller & Associates)
Virgil Pirvulescu
Todor Drumev Popov
Peter W. W. Powell
Bob Prager (Gary Posner, Inc.)
Siddique Mahmudur Rahman
Ghassan D. Riachi
Mehrdad Sadri (Persiphila)
Theodosios Sampson PhD
Alexander Schauss (Schauss Philatelics)
Jacques C. Schiff, Jr.
Jeff Siddiqui
Sergio & Liane Sismondo (The Classic Collector)
Jay Smith
Peter Thy

Scott R. Trepel (Robert A. Siegel Auction Galleries, Inc.)
Dan Undersander (United Postal Stationery Society)
Herbert R. Volin
Philip T. Wall
Giana Wayman
Don White (Dunedin Stamp Centre)
Ralph Yorio

Addresses, Telephone Numbers, Web Sites, E-Mail Addresses of General & Specialized Philatelic Societies

Collectors can contact the following groups for information about the philately of the areas within the scope of these societies, or inquire about membership in these groups. Aside from the general societies, we limit this list to groups that specialize in particular fields of philately, particular areas covered by the Scott Standard Postage Stamp Catalogue, and topical groups. Many more specialized philatelic society exist than those listed below. These addresses are updated yearly, and they are, to the best of our knowledge, correct and current. Groups should inform the editors of address changes whenever they occur. The editors also want to hear from other such specialized groups not listed. Unless otherwise noted all website addresses begin with http://

American Philatelic Society
100 Match Factory Place
Bellefonte PA 16823-1367
Ph: (814) 933-3803
www.stamps.org
E-mail: apsinfo@stamps.org

American Stamp Dealers Association, Inc.
P.O. Box 692
Leesport PA 19553
Ph: (800) 369-8207
www.americanstampdealer.com
E-mail: asda@americanstampdealer.com

National Stamp Dealers Association
Richard Kostka, President
3643 Private Road 18
Pinckneyville IL 62274-3426
Ph: (800) 875-6633 or (618) 357-5497
www.nsdainc.org
E-mail: nsda@nsdainc.org

International Society of Worldwide Stamp Collectors
Joanne Berkowitz, MD
P.O. Box 19006
Sacramento CA 95819
www.iswsc.org
E-mail: executivedirector@iswsc.org

Royal Philatelic Society
41 Devonshire Place
London, W1G 6JY
UNITED KINGDOM
www.rpsl.org.uk
E-mail: secretary@rpsl.org.uk

Royal Philatelic Society of Canada
P.O. Box 69080
St. Clair Post Office
Toronto, ON, M4T 3A1
CANADA
Ph: (888) 285-4143
www.rpsc.org
E-mail: info@rpsc.org

Young Stamp Collectors of America
Janet Houser
100 Match Factory Place
Bellefonte PA 16823-1367
Ph: (814) 933-3820
www.stamps.org/ysca/intro.htm
E-mail: ysca@stamps.org

Philatelic Research Resources
(The Scott editors encourage any additional research organizations to submit data for inclusion in this listing category)

American Philatelic Research Library
Scott Tiffney
100 Match Factory Place
Bellefonte PA 16823
Ph: (814) 933-3803
www.stamplibrary.org
E-mail: libraryestamps.org

Institute for Analytical Philately, Inc.
P.O. Box 8035
Holland MI 49422-8035
Ph: (616) 399-9299
www.analyticalphilately.org
E-mail: info@analyticalphilately.org

The Western Philatelic Library
P.O. Box 2219
1500 Partridge Ave.
Sunnyvale CA 94087
Ph: (408) 733-0336
www.fwpf.org

Groups focusing on fields or aspects found in worldwide philately (some might cover U.S. area only)

American Air Mail Society
Stephen Reinhard
P.O. Box 110
Mineola NY 11501
www.americanairmailsociety.org
E-mail: sreinhard1@optonline.net

American First Day Cover Society
Douglas Kelsey
P.O. Box 16277
Tucson AZ 85732-6277
Ph: (520) 321-0880
www.afdcs.org
E-mail: afdcs@afdcs.org

American Revenue Association
Eric Jackson
P.O. Box 728
Leesport PA 19533-0728
Ph: (610) 926-6200
www.revenuer.org
E-mail: eric@revenuer.com

American Topical Association
Vera Felts
P.O. Box 8
Carterville IL 62918-0008
Ph: (618) 985-5100
www.americantopicalassn.org
E-mail: americantopical@msn.com

Christmas Seal & Charity Stamp Society
John Denune
234 E. Broadway
Granville OH 43023
Ph: (740) 587-0276
www.seal-society.org
E-mail: john@christmasseals.net

Errors, Freaks and Oddities Collectors Club
Scott Shaulis
P.O. Box 549
Murrysville PA 15668-0549
Ph: (724) 733-4134
www.efocc.org
E-mail: Scott@shaulisstamps.com

First Issues Collectors Club
Kurt Streepy, Secretary
3128 E. Mattatha Drive
Bloomington IN 47401
www.firstissues.org
E-mail: secretary@firstissues.org

International Society of Reply Coupon Collectors
Peter Robin
P.O. Box 353
Bala Cynwyd PA 19004
E-mail: peterrobin@verizon.net

The Joint Stamp Issues Society
Richard Zimmermann
29A Rue Des Eviats
Lalaye F-67220
FRANCE
www.philarz.net
E-mail: richard.zimmermann@club-internet.fr

National Duck Stamp Collectors Society
Anthony J. Monico
P.O. Box 43
Harleysville PA 19438-0043
www.ndscs.org
E-mail: ndscs@ndscs.org

No Value Identified Club
Albert Sauvanet
Le Clos Royal B, Boulevard des Pas Enchantes
St. Sebastien-sur Loire, 44230
FRANCE
E-mail: alain.vailly@irin.univ nantes.fr

The Perfins Club
Ken Masters
111 NW 94th Street Apt. 102
Kansas City MO 64155-2993
Ph: (816) 835-5907
www.perfins.org
E-mail: kmasters@aol.com

Postage Due Mail Study Group
John Rawlins
13, Longacre
Chelmsford, CM1 3BJ
UNITED KINGDOM
E-mail: john.rawlins2@ukonline.co.uk.

Post Mark Collectors Club
Bob Milligan
7014 Woodland Oaks
Magnolia TX 77354
Ph: (281) 259-2735
www.postmarks.org
E-mail: bob.milligan@gmail.net

Postal History Society
Gary Wayne Loew
P.O. Box 468101
Atlanta GA 31146-8101
www.postalhistorysociety.org
E-mail: garywloew@gmail.com

Precancel Stamp Society
Dick Kalmbach
2658 Iron Works Drive
Buford GA 30519
Ph: (610) 248-8844
www.precancels.com
E-mail: promo@precancels.com

United Postal Stationery Society
Stuart Leven
1659 Branham Lane Suite F-307
San Jose CA 95118-2291
www.upss.org
E-mail: poststat@gmail.com

United States Possessions Philatelic Society
Daniel F. Ring
P.O. Box 113
Woodstock IL 60098
www.uspps.net
E-mail: danielfring@hotmail.com

Groups focusing on U.S. area philately as covered in the Standard Catalogue

Canal Zone Study Group
Tom Brougham
737 Neilson St.
Berkeley CA 94707
www.CanalZoneStudyGroup.com
E-mail: czsgsecretary@gmail.com

Carriers and Locals Society
Martin Richardson
P.O. Box 74
Grosse Ile MI 48138
www.pennypost.org
E-mail: martinr362@aol.com

Confederate Stamp Alliance
Patricia A. Kaufmann
10194 N. Old State Road
Lincoln DE 19960
Ph: (302) 422-2656
www.csalliance.org
E-mail: trishkauf@comcast.net

Hawaiian Philatelic Society
Gawwon Sugimura
P.O. Box 10115
Honolulu HI 96816-0115
E-mail: hiphilsoc@gmail.com

Plate Number Coil Collectors Club
Gene Trinks
16415 W. Desert Wren Court
Surprise AZ 85374
Ph: (623) 322-4619
www.pnc3.org
E-mail: gctrinks@cox.net

Ryukyu Philatelic Specialist Society
Laura Edmonds, Secy.
P.O. Box 240177
Charlotte NC 28224-0177
Ph: (336) 509-3739
www.ryukyustamps.org
E-mail: secretary@ryukyustamps.org

United Nations Philatelists
Blanton Clement, Jr.
P.O. Box 146
Morrisville PA 19067-0146
www.unpi.com
E-mail: bclemjunior@gmail.com

United States Stamp Society
Executive Secretary
Larry Ballantyne
P.O. Box 6634
Katy TX 77491-6634
www.usstamps.org

U.S. Cancellation Club
Roger Curran
20 University Avenue
Lewisburg PA 17837
E-mail: rcurran@dejazzd.com

U.S. Philatelic Classics Society
Rob Lund
2913 Fulton St.
Everett WA 98201-3733
www.uspcs.org
E-mail: membershipchairman@uspcs.org

Groups focusing on philately of foreign countries or regions

Aden & Somaliland Study Group
Gary Brown
P.O. Box 106
Briar Hill, Victoria, 3088
AUSTRALIA
E-mail: garyjohn951@optushome.com.au

American Society of Polar Philatelists (Antarctic areas)
Alan Warren
P.O. Box 39
Exton PA 19341-0039
www.polarphilatelists.org

Andorran Philatelic Study Circle
D. Hope
17 Hawthorn Drive
Stalybridge, Cheshire, SK15 1UE
UNITED KINGDOM
www.andorranpsc.org.uk
E-mail: andorranpsc@btinternet.com

Australian States Study Circle of The Royal Sydney Philatelic Club
Ben Palmer
GPO 1751
Sydney, N.S.W., 2001
AUSTRALIA
www.philas.org.au/states

Austria Philatelic Society
Ralph Schneider
P.O. Box 23049
Belleville IL 62223
Ph: (618) 277-6152
www.austriaphilatelicsociety.com
E-mail: rschneiderstamps@att.net

Bechuanalands and Botswana Society
Neville Midwood
69 Porlock Lane
Furzton, Milton Keynes, MK4 1JY
UNITED KINGDOM
www.nevsoft.com
E-mail: bbsoc@nevsoft.com

Bermuda Collectors Society
John Pare
405 Perimeter Road
Mount Horeb WI 53572
www.bermudacollectorssociety.com
E-mail: pare16@mhtc.net

Brazil Philatelic Association
William V. Kriebel
1923 Manning St.
Philadelphia PA 19103-5728
www.brazilphilatelic.org
E-mail: info@brazilphilatelic.org

British Caribbean Philatelic Study Group
Duane Larson
2 Forest Blvd.
Park Forest IL 60466
www.bcpsg.com
E-mail: dlarson283@aol.com

The King George VI Collectors Society (British Commonwealth)
Brian Livingstone
21 York Mansions, Prince of Wales Drive
London, SW11 4DL
UNITED KINGDOM
www.kg6.info
E-mail: livingstone484@btinternet.com

British North America Philatelic Society (Canada & Provinces)
Andy Ellwood
10 Doris Avenue
Gloucester, ON, KIT 3W8
CANADA
www.bnaps.org
E-mail: secretary@bnaps.org

British West Indies Study Circle
John Seidl
4324 Granby Way
Marietta GA 30062
Ph: (404) 229-6863
www.bwisc.org
E-mail: john.seidl@gmail.com

Burma Philatelic Study Circle
Michael Whittaker
1, Ecton Leys, Hillside
Rugby, Warwickshire, CV22 5SL
UNITED KINGDOM
www.burmastamps.homecall.co.uk
E-mail: manningham8@mypostoffice.co.uk

Cape and Natal Study Circle
Dr. Guy Dillaway
P.O. Box 181
Weston MA 02493
www.nzsc.demon.co.uk

Ceylon Study Circle
R. W. P. Frost
42 Lonsdale Road, Cannington
Bridgwater, Somerset, TA5 2JS
UNITED KINGDOM
www.ceylonsc.org
E-mail: rodney.frost@tiscali.co.uk

Channel Islands Specialists Society
Richard Flemming
64, Falconers Green, Burbage
Hinckley, Leicestershire, LE10 2SX
UNITED KINGDOM
www.ciss1950.org.uk
E-mail: secretary@ciss1950.org.uk

China Stamp Society
H. James Maxwell
1050 West Blue Ridge Blvd.
Kansas City MO 64145-1216
www.chinastampsociety.org
E-mail: president@chinastampsociety.org

Colombia/Panama Philatelic Study Group (COPAPHIL)
Thomas P. Myers
P.O. Box 522
Gordonsville VA 22942
www.copaphil.org
E-mail: tpmphil@hotmail.com

Association Filatelic de Costa Rica
Giana Wayman (McCarty)
SJO 4935, P.O. Box 025723
Miami FL 33102-5723
E-mail: scotland@racsa.co.cr

Society for Costa Rica Collectors
Dr. Hector R. Mena
P.O. Box 14831
Baton Rouge LA 70808
www.socorico.org
E-mail: hrmena@aol.com

International Cuban Philatelic Society
Ernesto Cuesta
P.O. Box 34434
Bethesda MD 20827
www.cubafil.org
E-mail: ecuesta@philat.com

Cuban Philatelic Society of America ®
P.O. Box 141656
Coral Gables FL 33114-1656
www.cubapsa.com
E-mail: cpsa.usa@gmail.com

Cyprus Study Circle
Colin Dear
10 Marne Close, Wem
Shropshire, SY4 5YE
UNITED KINGDOM
www.cyprusstudycircle.org/index.htm
E-mail: colindear@talktalk.net

Society for Czechoslovak Philately
Tom Cossaboom
P.O. Box 4124
Prescott AZ 86302
Ph: (928) 771-9097
www.csphilately.org
E-mail: klfck1@aol.com

Danish West Indies Study Unit of the Scandinavian Collectors Club
Arnold Sorensen
7666 Edgedale Drive
Newburgh IN 47630
Ph: (812) 480-6532
www.scc-online.org
E-mail: valbydwi@hotmail.com

East Africa Study Circle
Michael Vesey-Fitzgerald
Gambles Cottage, 18 Clarence Road
Lyndhurst, SO43 7AL
UNITED KINGDOM
www.easc.org.uk
E-mail: secretary@easc.org.uk

Egypt Study Circle
Mike Murphy
109 Chadwick Road
London, SE15 4PY
UNITED KINGDOM
Trent Ruebush: North American Agent
E-mail: tkruebrush@gmail.com
www.egyptstudycircle.org.uk
E-mail: egyptstudycircle@hotmail.com

Estonian Philatelic Society
Juri Kirsimagi
29 Clifford Ave.
Pelham NY 10803
Ph: (914) 738-3713

Ethiopian Philatelic Society
Ulf Lindahl
21 Westview Place
Riverside CT 06878
Ph: (203) 722-0769
http://ethiopianphilatelicsociety.weebly.com
E-mail: ulindahl@optonline.net

Falkland Islands Philatelic Study Group
Carl J. Faulkner
615 Taconic Trail
Williamstown MA 01267-2745
Ph: (413) 458-4421
www.fipsg.org.uk
E-mail: cfaulkner@taconicwilliamstown.com

Faroe Islands Study Circle
Norman Hudson
40 Queen's Road, Vicar's Cross
Chester, CH3 5HB
UNITED KINGDOM
www.faroeislandssc.org
E-mail: jntropics@hotmail.com

Former French Colonies Specialist Society
COLFRA
BP 628
75367 Paris, Cedex 08
FRANCE
www.colfra.org
E-mail: secretaire@colfra.org

France & Colonies Philatelic Society
Edward Grabowski
111 Prospect St., 4C
Westfield NJ 07090
www.franceandcolps.org
E-mail: edjjg@alum.mit.edu

Gibraltar Study Circle
Susan Dare
22, Byways Park, Strode Road,
Clevedon, North Somerset, BS21 6UR
UNITED KINGDOM
www.gibraltarstudycircle.wordpress.com
E-mail: smldare@yahoo.co.uk

Germany Philatelic Society
P.O. Box 6547
Chesterfield MO 63006
www.germanyphilatelicusa.org

Plebiscite-Memel-Saar Study Group of the German Philatelic Society
Clayton Wallace
100 Lark Court
Alamo CA 94507
E-mail: claytonwallace@comcast.net

Great Britain Collectors Club
Steve McGill
10309 Brookhollow Circle
Highlands Ranch CO 80129
www.gbstamps.com/gbcc
E-mail: steve.mcgill@comcast.net

International Society of Guatemala Collectors
Jaime Marckwordt
449 St. Francis Blvd.
Daly City CA 94015-2136
www.guatemalastamps.com
E-mail: membership@guatamalastamps.com

Haiti Philatelic Society
Ubaldo Del Toro
5709 Marble Archway
Alexandria VA 22315
www.haitiphilately.org
E-mail: u007ubi@aol.com

Federacion Filatelica de la Republica de Honduras (Honduran Philatelic Federation, FFRH)
Mauricio Mejia
Apartado postal 1465
Tegucigalpa
HONDURAS

Hong Kong Stamp Society
Ming W. Tsang
P.O. Box 206
Glenside PA 19038
www.hkss.org
E-mail: hkstamps@yahoo.com

Society for Hungarian Philately
Alan Warren
P.O. Box 3024
Andover MA 01810
Ph: (978) 682-0242
www.hungarianphilately.org
E-mail: alan@hungarianstamps.com

India Study Circle
John Warren
P.O. Box 7326
Washington DC 20044
Ph: (202) 488-7443
www.indiastudycircle.org
E-mail: jw-kbw@earthlink.net

Indian Ocean Study Circle
E. S. Hutton
29 Patermoster Close
Waltham Abby, Essex, EN9 3JU
UNITED KINGDOM
www.indianoceanstudycircle.com
E-mail: secretary@indianoceanstudy-circle.com

Society of Indo-China Philatelists
Ron Bentley
2600 N. 24th St.
Arlington VA 22207
www.sicp-online.org
E-mail: ron.bentley@verizon.net

Iran Philatelic Study Circle
Mehdi Esmaili
P.O. Box 750096
Forest Hills NY 11375
www.iranphilatelic.org
E-mail: m.esmaili@earthlink.net

Eire Philatelic Association (Ireland)
David J. Brennan
P.O. Box 704
Bernardsville NJ 07924
www.eirephilatelicassoc.org
E-mail: brennan704@aol.com

Society of Israel Philatelists
Jacqueline Baca
100 Match Factory Place
Bellefonte PA 16823-1367
Ph: (814) 933-3803 ext. 212
www.israelstamps.com
E-mail: israelstamps@gmail.com

Italy and Colonies Study Circle
Richard Harlow
7 Duncombe House, 8 Manor Road
Teddington, TW11 8BE
UNITED KINGDOM
www.icsc.pwp.blueyonder.co.uk
E-mail: richardharlow@outlook.com

International Society for Japanese Philately
William Eisenhauer
P.O. Box 230462
Tigard OR 97281
www.isjp.org
E-mail: secretary@isjp.org

Latin American Philatelic Society
Jules K. Beck
30½ St. #209
St. Louis Park MN 55426-3551

Liberian Philatelic Society
William Thomas Lockard
P.O. Box 106
Wellston OH 45692
Ph: (740) 384-2020
E-mail: tlockard@zoomnet.net

Liechtenstudy USA (Liechtenstein)
Paul Tremaine
410 SW Ninth St.
Dundee OR 97115
Ph: (503) 538-4500
www.liechtenstudy.org
E-mail: editor@liechtenstudy.org

Lithuania Philatelic Society
John Variakojis
8472 Carlisle Court
Burr Ridge IL 60527
Ph: (630) 974-6525
www.lithuanianphilately.com/lps
E-mail: variakojis@sbcglobal.net

Luxembourg Collectors Club
Gary B. Little
7319 Beau Road
Sechelt, BC, V0N 3A8
CANADA
lcc.luxcentral.com
E-mail: gary@luxcentral.com

Malaya Study Group
David Tett
4 Amenbury Court
Harpenden Herts,
Wheathampstead Herts AL5 2BU
UNITED KINGDOM
www.m-s-g.org.uk
E-mail: davidtett@aol.com

Malta Study Circle
Rodger Evans
Ravensbourne, Hook Heath Road
Woking, Surrey, GU22 0LB
UNITED KINGDOM
www.maltastudycircle.org.uk
E-mail: carge@hotmail.co.uk

Mexico-Elmhurst Philatelic Society International
Eric Stovner
P.O. Box 10097
Santa Ana CA 92711-0097
www.mepsi.org
E-mail: treasurer@mepsi.org

Asociacion Mexicana de Filatelia AMEXFIL
Alejando Grossman
Jose Maria Rico, 129, Col. Del Valle
Mexico City DF, 03100
MEXICO
www.amexfil.mx
E-mail: amexfil@gmail.com

Society for Moroccan and Tunisian Philately S.P.L.M.
206, bld Pereire
Paris 75017
FRANCE
splm-philatelie.org
E-mail: splm206@aol.com

Nepal & Tibet Philatelic Study Group
Ken Goss
2643 Wagner Place
EL Dorado Hills CA 95762
Ph: (510) 207-5369
www.fuchs-online.com/ntpsc/
E-mail: kfgoss@comcast.net

American Society for Netherlands Philately
Hans Kremer
50 Rockport Court
Danville CA 94526
Ph: (925) 820-5841
www.asnp1975.com
E-mail: hkremer@usa.net

New Zealand Society of Great Britain
Michael Wilkinson
121 London Road
Sevenoaks, Kent, TN13 1BH
UNITED KINGDOM
www.nzsgb.org.uk
E-mail: mwilkin799@aol.com

Nicaragua Study Group
Erick Rodriguez
11817 SW 11th St.
Miami FL 33184-2501
clubs.yahoo.com/clubs/
nicaraguastudygroup
E-mail: nsgsec@yahoo.com

Society of Australasian Specialists/Oceania
David McNamee
P.O. Box 37
Alamo CA 94507
www.sasoceania.org
E-mail: treasurer@sasoceania.org

Orange Free State Study Circle
J. R. Stroud
24 Hooper Close
Burnham-on-sea, Somerset, TA8 1JQ
UNITED KINGDOM
orangefreestatephilately.org.uk
E-mail: richard@richardstroud.plus.com

Pacific Islands Study Circle
John Ray
24 Woodvale Ave.
London, SE25 4AE
UNITED KINGDOM
www.pisc.org.uk
E-mail: secretary@pisc.org.uk

Pakistan Philatelic Study Circle
Jeff Siddiqui
P.O. Box 7002
Lynnwood WA 98046
E-mail: jeffsiddiqui@msn.com

Asociacion Filatelica de Panama (ASOFILPA)
Edward D. Vianna
Apartado Postal 0819-03400
El Dorado, Panama
PANAMA
www.asociacionfilatelicadepanama.
blogspot.com
E-mail: asofilpa@gmail.com

Papuan Philatelic Society
Steven Zirinsky
P.O. Box 49, Ansonia Station
New York NY 10023
Ph: (718) 706-0616
www.communigate.co.uk/york/pps
E-mail: szirinsky@cs.com

International Philippine Philatelic Society
Donald J. Peterson
P.O. Box 122
Brunswick MD 21716
Ph: (301) 834-6419
www.theipps.info
E-mail: dpeterson4526@gmail.com

Pitcairn Islands Study Group
Dr. Everett L. Parker
117 Cedar Breeze South
Glenburn ME 04401-1734
Ph: (207) 573-1686
www.pisg.net
E-mail: eparker@hughes.net

Polonus Philatelic Society (Poland)
Daniel Lubelski
P.O. Box 2212
Benicia CA 94510
Ph: (419) 410-9115
www.polonus.org
E-mail: info@polonus.org

International Society for Portuguese Philately
Clyde Homen
1491 Bonnie View Road
Hollister CA 95023-5117
www.portugalstamps.com
E-mail: ispp1962@sbcglobal.net

Rhodesian Study Circle
William R. Wallace
P.O. Box 16381
San Francisco CA 94116
www.rhodesianstudycircle.org.uk
E-mail: bwall8rscr@earthlink.net

Rossica Society of Russian Philately
Alexander Kolchinsky
1506 Country Lake Drive
Champaign IL 6821-6428
www.rossica.org
E-mail: alexander.kolchinsky@rossica.org

St. Helena, Ascension & Tristan Da Cunha Philatelic Society
Dr. Everett L. Parker
117 Cedar Breeze South
Glenburn ME 04401-1734
Ph: (207) 573-1686
www.shatps.org
E-mail: eparker@hughes.net

St. Pierre & Miquelon Philatelic Society
James R. (Jim) Taylor
2335 Paliswood Road SW
Calgary, AB, T2V 3P6
CANADA
www.stamps.org/spm

Asociacion Filatelica Salvadorena
Joseph D. Hahn
301 Rolling Ridge Drive, Apt. 111
State College PA 16801-6149
www.elsalvadorphilately.org
E-mail: joehahn100@hotmail.com

Fellowship of Samoa Specialists
Donald Mee
23 Leo St.
Christchurch, 8051
NEW ZEALAND
www.samoaexpress.org
E-mail: donanm@xtra.co.nz

Sarawak Specialists' Society
Stephen Schumann
2417 Cabrillo Drive
Hayward CA 94545
Ph: (510) 785-4794
www.britborneostamps.org.uk
E-mail: stephen.schumann@att.net

Scandinavian Collectors Club
Steve Lund
P.O. Box 16213
St. Paul MN 55116
www.scc-online.org
E-mail: steve88h@aol.com

Slovakia Stamp Society
Jack Benchik
P.O. Box 555
Notre Dame IN 46556

Philatelic Society for Greater Southern Africa
Alan Hanks
34 Seaton Drive
Aurora, ON, L4G 2K1
CANADA
www.psgsa.thestampweb.com

South Sudan Philatelic Society
William Barclay
1370 Spring Hill Road
South Londonderry VT 05155
E-mail: barclayphilatelics@gmail.com

Spanish Philatelic Society
Robert H. Penn
1108 Walnut Drive
Danielsville PA 18038
Ph: (610) 844-8963
E-mail: roberthpenn43@gmail.com

Sudan Study Group
David Sher
5 Ellis Park Road
Toronto, ON, M6S2V1
CANADA
www.sudanstamps.org
e-mail: sh3603@hotmail.com

American Helvetia Philatelic Society (Switzerland, Liechtenstein)
Richard T. Hall
P.O. Box 15053
Asheville NC 28813-0053
www.swiss-stamps.org
E-mail: secretary2@swiss-stamps.org

Tannu Tuva Collectors Society
Ken R. Simon
P.O. Box 385
Lake Worth FL 33460-0385
Ph: (561) 588-5954
www.tuva.tk
E-mail: yurttuva@yahoo.com

Society for Thai Philately
H. R. Blakeney
P.O. Box 25644
Oklahoma City OK 73125
E-mail: HRBlakeney@aol.com

Transvaal Study Circle
Chris Board
36 Wakefield Gardens
London, SE19 2NR
UNITED KINGDOM
www.transvaalstamps.org.uk
E-mail: c.board@macace.net

Ottoman and Near East Philatelic Society (Turkey and related areas)
Bob Stuchell
193 Valley Stream Lane
Wayne PA 19087
www.oneps.org
E-mail: rstuchell@msn.com

Ukrainian Philatelic & Numismatic Society
Martin B. Tatuch
5117 8th Road N.
Arlington VA 22205-1201
www.upns.org
E-mail: treasurer@upns.org

Vatican Philatelic Society
Sal Quinonez
1 Aldersgate, Apt. 1002
Riverhead NY 11901-1830
Ph: (516) 727-6426
www.vaticanphilately.org

British Virgin Islands Philatelic Society
Giorgio Migliavacca
P.O. Box 7007
St. Thomas VI 00801-0007
www.islandsun.com/category/collectables/
E-mail: issun@candwbvi.net

West Africa Study Circle
Martin Bratzel
1233 Virginia Ave.
Windsor, ON, N8S 2Z1
CANADA
www.wasc.org.uk
E-mail: marty_bratzel@yahoo.ca

Western Australia Study Group
Brian Pope
P.O. Box 423
Claremont, Western Australia, 6910
AUSTRALIA
www.wastudygroup.com
E-mail: black5swan@yahoo.com.au

Yugoslavia Study Group of the Croatian Philatelic Society
Michael Lenard
1514 N. Third Ave.
Wausau WI 54401
Ph: (715) 675-2833
E-mail: mjlenard@aol.com

Topical Groups

Americana Unit
Dennis Dengel
17 Peckham Road
Poughkeepsie NY 12603-2018
www.americanaunit.org
E-mail: ddengel@americanaunit.org

Astronomy Study Unit
John Budd
728 Sugar Camp Way
Brooksville FL 34604
Ph: (352) 345-4799
www.astronomystudyunit.net
E-mail: jwgbudd@gmail.com

Bicycle Stamps Club
Steve Andreasen
2000 Alaskan Way, Unit 157
Seattle WA 98121
E-mail: steven.w.andreasen@gmail.com

Biology Unit
Alan Hanks
34 Seaton Drive
Aurora, ON, L4G 2K1
CANADA
Ph: (905) 727-6993

Bird Stamp Society
S. A. H. (Tony) Statham
Ashlyns Lodge, Chesham Road,
Berkhamsted, Hertfordshire HP4 2ST
UNITED KINGDOM
www.bird-stamps.org/bss
E-mail: tony.statham@sky.com

Captain Cook Society
Jerry Yucht
8427 Leale Ave.
Stockton CA 95212
www.captaincooksociety.com
E-mail: US@captaincooksociety.com

The CartoPhilatelic Society
Marybeth Sulkowski
2885 Sanford Ave, SW, #32361
Grandville MI 49418-1342
www.mapsonstamps.org
E-mail: secretary@mapsonstamps.org

Casey Jones Railroad Unit
Jeff Lough
2612 Redbud Lane, Apt. C
Lawrence KS 66046
www.uqp.de/cjr/index.htm
E-mail: jeffydplaugh@gmail.com

Cats on Stamps Study Unit
Robert D. Jarvis
2731 Teton Lane
Fairfield CA 94533
www.catstamps.info
E-mail: bobmarci@aol.com

Chemistry & Physics on Stamps Study Unit
Dr. Roland Hirsch
20458 Water Point Lane
Germantown MD 20874
www.cpossu.org
E-mail: rfhirsch@cpossu.org

Chess on Stamps Study Unit
Ray C. Alexis
608 Emery St.
Longmont CO 80501
E-mail: chessstuff911459@aol.com

Christmas Philatelic Club
Jim Balog
P.O. Box 744
Geneva OH 44041
www.christmasphilatelicclub.org
E-mail: jpb4stamps@windstream.net

Cricket Philatelic Society
A. Melville-Brown, President
11 Weppons, Ravens Road
Shoreham-by-Sea
West Sussex, BN43 5AW
UNITED KINGDOM
www.cricketstamp.net
E-mail: mel.cricket.100@googlemail.com

Dogs on Stamps Study Unit
Morris Raskin
202A Newport Road
Monroe Township NJ 08831
Ph: (609) 655-7411
www.dossu.org
E-mail: mraskin@cellurian.com

Earth's Physical Features Study Group
Fred Klein
515 Magdalena Ave.
Los Altos CA 94024
epfsu.jeffhayward.com

Ebony Society of Philatelic Events and Reflections, Inc. (African-American topicals)
Manuel Gilyard
800 Riverside Drive, Suite 4H
New York NY 10032-7412
www.esperstamps.org
E-mail: gilyardmani@aol.com

Europa Study Unit
Tonny E. Van Loij
3002 S. Xanthia St.
Denver CO 80231-4237
Ph: (303) 752-0189
www.europastudyunit.org
E-mail: tvanloij@gmail.com

Fine & Performing Arts
Deborah L. Washington
6922 S. Jeffery Blvd., #7 - North
Chicago IL 60649
E-mail: brasslady@comcast.net

Fire Service in Philately
John Zaranek
81 Hillpine Road
Cheektowaga NY 14227-2259
Ph: (716) 668-3352
E-mail: jczaranek@roadrunner.com

Gay & Lesbian History on Stamps Club
Joe Petronie
P.O. Box 190842
Dallas TX 75219-0842
www.facebook.com/glhsc
E-mail: glhsc@aol.com

Gems, Minerals & Jewelry Study Unit
Mrs. Gilberte Proteau
138 Lafontaine
Beloeil QC J3G 2G7
CANADA
Ph: (978) 851-8283
E-mail: gilberte.ferland@sympatico.ca

Graphics Philately Association
Mark H. Winnegrad
P.O. Box 380
Bronx NY 10462-0380
www.graphics-stamps.org
E-mail: indybruce1@yahoo.com

Journalists, Authors & Poets on Stamps
Clete Delvaux
800 East River Drive
De Pere WI 54115
E-mail: cdelvaux@msn.com

Lighthouse Stamp Society
Dalene Thomas
1805 S Balsam St., #106
Lakewood CO 80232
Ph: (303) 986-6620
www.lighthousestampsociety.org
E-mail: dalene@lighthousestampsociety.org

Lions International Stamp Club
John Bargus
108-2777 Barry Road RR 2
Mill Bay, BC, V0R 2P2
CANADA
Ph: (250) 743-5782

Mahatma Gandhi On Stamps Study Circle
Pramod Shivagunde
Pratik Clinic, Akluj
Solapur, Maharashtra, 413101
INDIA
E-mail: drnanda@bom6.vsnl.net.in

Masonic Study Unit
Gene Fricks
25 Murray Way
Blackwood NJ 08012-4400
E-mail: genefricks@comcast.net

Mathematical Study Unit
Monty Strauss
4209 88th St.
Lubbock TX 79423-2941
www.mathstamps.org
E-mail: montystrauss@gmail.com

Medical Subjects Unit
Dr. Frederick C. Skvara
P.O. Box 6228
Bridgewater NJ 08807
E-mail: fcskvara@optonline.net

Military Postal History Society
Ed Dubin
1 S. Wacker Drive, Suite 3500
Chicago IL 60606
www.militaryPHS.org
E-mail: dubine@comcast.net

Mourning Stamps and Covers Club
James Camak, Jr.
3801 Acapulco Ct.
Irving TX 75062
www.mscc.ms
E-mail: jamescamak7@gmail.com

Napoleonic Age Philatelists
Ken Berry
4117 NW 146th St.
Oklahoma City OK 73134-1746
Ph: (405) 748-8646
www.nap-stamps.org
E-mail: krb4117@att.net

Old World Archeological Study Unit
Caroline Scannell
11 Dawn Drive
Smithtown NY 11787-1761
www.owasu.org
E-mail: editor@owasu.org

Petroleum Philatelic Society International
Feitze Papa
922 Meander Dr.
Walnut Creek CA 94598-4239
E-mail: oildad@astound.net

Rotary on Stamps Unit
Gerald L. Fitzsimmons
105 Calle Ricardo
Victoria TX 77904
rotaryonstamps.org
E-mail: glfitz@suddenlink.net

Scouts on Stamps Society International
Woodrow (Woody) Brooks
498 Baldwin Road
Akron OH 44312
Ph: (330) 612-1294
www.sossi.org
E-mail: rfrank@sossi.org

Ships on Stamps Unit
Les Smith
302 Conklin Ave.
Penticton, BC, V2A 2T4
CANADA
Ph: (250) 493-7486
www.shipsonstamps.org
E-mail: lessmith440@shaw.ca

Space Unit
David Blog
P.O. Box 174
Bergenfield NJ 07621
www.space-unit.com
E-mail: davidblognj@gmail.com

Sports Philatelists International
Mark Maestrone
2824 Curie Place
San Diego CA 92122-4110
www.sportstamps.org
Email: president@sportstamps.org

Stamps on Stamps Collectors Club
Alf Jordan
156 W. Elm St.
Yarmouth ME 04096
www.stampsonstamps.org
E-mail: ajordan1@maine.rr.com

Windmill Study Unit
Walter J. Hollien
607 N. Porter St.
Watkins Glenn NY 14891-1345
Ph: (607) 229-3541
www.windmillworld.com
E-mail: whollien@earthlink.net

Wine On Stamps Study Unit
David Wolfersberger
768 Chain Ridge Road
St. Louis MO 63122-3259
Ph: (314) 961-5032
www.wine-on-stamps.org
E-mail: dewolf2@swbell.net

Women on Stamps Study Unit
Hugh Gottfried
2232 26th St.
Santa Monica CA 90405-1902
E-mail: hgottfried@adelphia.net

Expertizing Services

The following organizations will, for a fee, provide expert opinions about stamps submitted to them. Collectors should contact these organizations to find out about their fees and requirements before submiting philatelic material to them. The listing of these groups here is not intended as an endorsement by Amos Media Co.

General Expertizing Services

American Philatelic Expertizing Service (a service of the American Philatelic Society)
100 Match Factory Place
Bellefonte PA 16823-1367
Ph: (814) 237-3803
Fax: (814) 237-6128
www.stamps.org
E-mail: twhorn@stamps.org
Areas of Expertise: Worldwide

B. P. A. Expertising, Ltd.
P.O. Box 1141
Guildford, Surrey, GU5 0WR
UNITED KINGDOM
E-mail: sec@bpaexpertising.org
Areas of Expertise: British Commonwealth, Great Britain, Classics of Europe, South America and the Far East

Philatelic Foundation
22 E. 35th St., 4th Floor
New York NY 10016
Ph: (212) 221-6555
Fax: (212) 221-6208
www.philatelicfoundation.org
E-mail: philatelicfoundation@verizon.net
Areas of Expertise: U.S. & Worldwide

Philatelic Stamp Authentication and Grading, Inc.
P.O. Box 41-0880
Melbourne FL 32941-0880
Customer Service: (305) 345-9864
www.psaginc.com
E-mail: info@psaginc.com
Areas of Expertise: U.S., Canal Zone, Hawaii, Philippines, Canada & Provinces

Professional Stamp Experts
P.O. Box 539309
Henderson NV 89053-9309
Ph: (702) 776-6522
www.gradingmatters.com
www.psestamp.com
E-mail: info@gradingmatters.com
Areas of Expertise: Stamps and covers of U.S., U.S. Possessions, British Commonwealth

Royal Philatelic Society Expert Committee
41 Devonshire Place
London, W1N 1PE
UNITED KINGDOM
www.rpsl.org.uk/experts.html
E-mail: experts@rpsl.org.uk
Areas of Expertise: Worldwide

Expertizing Services Covering Specific Fields or Countries

China Stamp Society Expertizing Service
1050 W. Blue Ridge Blvd.
Kansas City MO 64145
Ph: (816) 942-6300
E-mail: hjmesq@aol.com
Areas of Expertise: China

Confederate Stamp Alliance Authentication Service
Gen. Frank Crown, Jr.
P.O. Box 278
Capshaw AL 35742-0396
Ph: (302) 422-2656
Fax: (302) 424-1990
www.csalliance.org
E-mail: csaas@knology.net
Areas of Expertise: Confederate stamps and postal history

Errors, Freaks and Oddities Collectors Club Expertizing Service
138 East Lakemont Drive
Kingsland GA 31548
Ph: (912) 729-1573
Areas of Expertise: U.S. errors, freaks and oddities

Estonian Philatelic Society Expertizing Service
39 Clafford Lane
Melville NY 11747
Ph: (516) 421-2078
E-mail: esto4@aol.com
Areas of Expertise: Estonia

Hawaiian Philatelic Society Expertizing Service
P.O. Box 10115
Honolulu HI 96816-0115
Areas of Expertise: Hawaii

Hong Kong Stamp Society Expertizing Service
P.O. Box 206
Glenside PA 19038
Fax: (215) 576-6850
Areas of Expertise: Hong Kong

International Association of Philatelic Experts United States Associate members:

Paul Buchsbayew
119 W. 57th St.
New York NY 10019
Ph: (212) 977-7734
Fax: (212) 977-8653
Areas of Expertise: Russia, Soviet Union

William T. Crowe
P.O. Box 2090
Danbury CT 06813-2090
E-mail: wtcrowe@aol.com
Areas of Expertise: United States

John Lievsay
(see American Philatelic Expertizing Service and Philatelic Foundation)
Areas of Expertise: France

Robert W. Lyman
P.O. Box 348
Irvington on Hudson NY 10533
Ph and Fax: (914) 591-6937
Areas of Expertise: British North America, New Zealand

Robert Odenweller
P.O. Box 401
Bernardsville NJ 07924-0401
Ph and Fax: (908) 766-5460
Areas of Expertise: New Zealand, Samoa to 1900

Sergio Sismondo
The Regency Tower, Suite 1109
770 James Street
Syracuse NY 13203
Ph: (315) 422-2331
Fax: (315) 422-2956
Areas of Expertise: British East Africa, Camerouns, Cape of Good Hope, Canada, British North America

International Society for Japanese Philately Expertizing Committee
132 North Pine Terrace
Staten Island NY 10312-4052
Ph: (718) 227-5229
Areas of Expertise: Japan and related areas, except WWII Japanese Occupation issues

International Society for Portuguese Philately Expertizing Service
P.O. Box 43146
Philadelphia PA 19129-3146
Ph and Fax: (215) 843-2106
E-mail: s.s.washburne@worldnet.att.net
Areas of Expertise: Portugal and Colonies

Mexico-Elmhurst Philatelic Society International Expert Committee
Expert Committee Administrator
Marc E. Gonzales
P.O. Box 29040
Denver CO 80229-0040
www.mepsi.org/expertization
Areas of Expertise: Mexico

Ukrainian Philatelic & Numismatic Society Expertizing Service
30552 Dell Lane
Warren MI 48092-1862
Areas of Expertise: Ukraine, Western Ukraine

V. G. Greene Philatelic Research Foundation
P.O. Box 204, Station Q
Toronto, ON, M4T 2M1
CANADA
Ph: (416) 921-2073
Fax: (416) 921-1282
www.greenefoundation.ca
E-mail: vggfoundation@on.aibn.com
Areas of Expertise: British North America

Information on Catalogue Values, Grade and Condition

Catalogue Value

The Scott Catalogue value is a retail value; that is, an amount you could expect to pay for a stamp in the grade of Very Fine with no faults. Any exceptions to the grade valued will be noted in the text. The general introduction on the following pages and the individual section introductions further explain the type of material that is valued. The value listed for any given stamp is a reference that reflects recent actual dealer selling prices for that item.

Dealer retail price lists, public auction results, published prices in advertising and individual solicitation of retail prices from dealers, collectors and specialty organizations have been used in establishing the values found in this catalogue. Amos Media Co. values stamps, but Amos Media is not a company engaged in the business of buying and selling stamps as a dealer.

Use this catalogue as a guide for buying and selling. The actual price you pay for a stamp may be higher or lower than the catalogue value because of many different factors, including the amount of personal service a dealer offers, or increased or decreased interest in the country or topic represented by a stamp or set. An item may occasionally be offered at a lower price as a "loss leader," or as part of a special sale. You also may obtain an item inexpensively at public auction because of little interest at that time or as part of a large lot.

Stamps that are of a lesser grade than Very Fine, or those with condition problems, generally trade at lower prices than those given in this catalogue. Stamps of exceptional quality in both grade and condition often command higher prices than those listed.

Values for pre-1900 unused issues are for stamps with approximately half or more of their original gum. Stamps with most or all of their original gum may be expected to sell for more, and stamps with less than half of their original gum may be expected to sell for somewhat less than the values listed. On rarer stamps, it may be expected that the original gum will be somewhat more disturbed than it will be on more common issues. Post-1900 unused issues are assumed to have full original gum. From breakpoints in most countries' listings, stamps are valued as never hinged, due to the wide availability of stamps in that condition. These notations are prominently placed in the listings and in the country information preceding the listings. Some countries also feature listings with dual values for hinged and never-hinged stamps.

Grade

A stamp's grade and condition are crucial to its value. The accompanying illustrations show examples of Very Fine stamps from different time periods, along with examples of stamps in Fine to Very Fine and Extremely Fine grades as points of reference. When a stamp seller offers a stamp in any grade from fine to superb without further qualifying statements, that stamp should not only have the centering grade as defined, but it also should be free of faults or other condition problems.

FINE stamps (illustrations not shown) have designs that are quite off center, with the perforations on one or two sides very close to the design but not quite touching it. There is white space between the perforations and the design that is minimal but evident to the unaided eye. Imperforate stamps may have small margins, and earlier issues may show the design just touching one edge of the stamp design. Very early perforated issues normally will have the perforations slightly cutting into the design. Used stamps may have heavier than usual cancellations.

FINE-VERY FINE stamps will be somewhat off center on one side, or slightly off center on two sides. Imperforate stamps will have two margins of at least normal size, and the design will not touch any edge. For perforated stamps, the perfs are well clear of the design, but are still noticeably off center. *However, early issues of a country may be printed in such a way that the design naturally is very close to the edges. In these cases, the perforations may cut into the design very slightly.* Used stamps will not have a cancellation that detracts from the design.

VERY FINE stamps will be just slightly off center on one or two sides, but the design will be well clear of the edge. The stamp will present a nice, balanced appearance. Imperforate stamps will be well centered within normal-sized margins. *However, early issues of many countries may be printed in such a way that the perforations may touch the design on one or more sides. Where this is the case, a boxed note will be found defining the centering and margins of the stamps being valued.* Used stamps will have light or otherwise neat cancellations. This is the grade used to establish Scott Catalogue values.

EXTREMELY FINE stamps are close to being perfectly centered. Imperforate stamps will have even margins that are slightly larger than normal. Even the earliest perforated issues will have perforations clear of the design on all sides.

Amos Media Co. recognizes that there is no formally enforced grading scheme for postage stamps, and that the final price you pay or obtain for a stamp will be determined by individual agreement at the time of transaction.

Condition

Grade addresses only centering and (for used stamps) cancellation. *Condition* refers to factors other than grade that affect a stamp's desirability.

Factors that can increase the value of a stamp include exceptionally wide margins, particularly fresh color, the presence of selvage, and plate or die varieties. Unusual cancels on used stamps (particularly those of the 19th century) can greatly enhance their value as well.

Factors other than faults that decrease the value of a stamp include loss of original gum, regumming, a hinge remnant or foreign object adhering to the gum, natural inclusions, straight edges, and markings or notations applied by collectors or dealers.

Faults include missing pieces, tears, pin or other holes, surface scuffs, thin spots, creases, toning, short or pulled perforations, clipped perforations, oxidation or other forms of color changelings, soiling, stains, and such man-made changes as reperforations or the chemical removal or lightening of a cancellation.

Grading Illustrations

On the following two pages are illustrations of various stamps from countries appearing in this volume. These stamps are arranged by country, and they represent early or important issues that are often found in widely different grades in the marketplace. The editors believe the illustrations will prove useful in showing the margin size and centering that will be seen on the various issues.

In addition to the matters of margin size and centering, collectors are reminded that the very fine stamps valued in the Scott catalogues also will possess fresh color and intact perforations, and they will be free of defects.

Examples shown are computer-manipulated images made from single digitized master illustrations.

Stamp Illustrations Used in the Catalogue

It is important to note that the stamp images used for identification purposes in this catlaogue may not be indicative of the grade of stamp being valued. Refer to the written discussion of grades on this page and to the grading illustrations on the following two pages for grading information.

Fine-Very Fine →

SCOTT
CATALOGUES
VALUE
STAMPS IN
THIS GRADE

Very Fine →

Extremely Fine →

Fine-Very Fine →

SCOTT
CATALOGUES
VALUE
STAMPS IN
THIS GRADE

Very Fine →

Extremely Fine →

Fine-Very Fine

SCOTT
CATALOGUES
VALUE
STAMPS IN
THIS GRADE

Very Fine

Extremely Fine

Fine-Very Fine

SCOTT
CATALOGUES
VALUE
STAMPS IN
THIS GRADE

Very Fine

Extremely Fine

For purposes of helping to determine the gum condition and value of an unused stamp, Scott presents the following chart which details different gum conditions and indicates how the conditions correlate with the Scott values for unused stamps. Used together, the Illustrated Grading Chart on the previous pages and this Illustrated Gum Chart should allow catalogue users to better understand the grade and gum condition of stamps valued in the Scott catalogues.

Gum Categories:	MINT N.H.	ORIGINAL GUM (O.G.)					NO GUM
	Mint Never Hinged *Free from any disturbance*	**Lightly Hinged** *Faint impression of a removed hinge over a small area*	**Hinge Mark or Remnant** *Prominent hinged spot with part or all of the hinge remaining*	**Large part o.g.** *Approximately half or more of the gum intact*	**Small part o.g.** *Approximately less than half of the gum intact*		**No gum** *Only if issued with gum*
Commonly Used Symbol:	★ ★	★	★	★	★		(★)
Pre-1900 Issues (Pre-1881 for U.S.)	*Very fine pre-1900 stamps in these categories trade at a premium over Scott value*			Scott Value for "Unused"			Scott "No Gum" listings for selected unused classic stamps
From 1900 to breakpoints for listings of never-hinged stamps	Scott "Never Hinged" listings for selected unused stamps	Scott Value for "Unused" (Actual value will be affected by the degree of hinging of the full o.g.)					
From breakpoints noted for many countries	Scott Value for "Unused"						

Never Hinged (NH; ★★): A never-hinged stamp will have full original gum that will have no hinge mark or disturbance. The presence of an expertizer's mark does not disqualify a stamp from this designation.

Original Gum (OG; ★): Pre-1900 stamps should have approximately half or more of their original gum. On rarer stamps, it may be expected that the original gum will be somewhat more disturbed than it will be on more common issues. Post-1900 stamps should have full original gum. Original gum will show some disturbance caused by a previous hinge(s) which may be present or entirely removed. The actual value of a post-1900 stamp will be affected by the degree of hinging of the full original gum.

Disturbed Original Gum: Gum showing noticeable effects of humidity, climate or hinging over more than half of the gum. The significance of gum disturbance in valuing a stamp in any of the Original Gum categories depends on the degree of disturbance, the rarity and normal gum condition of the issue and other variables affecting quality.

Regummed (RG; (★)): A regummed stamp is a stamp without gum that has had some type of gum privately applied at a time after it was issued. This normally is done to deceive collectors and/or dealers into thinking that the stamp has original gum and therefore has a higher value. A regummed stamp is considered the same as a stamp with none of its original gum for purposes of grading.

Understanding the Listings

On the opposite page is an enlarged "typical" listing from this catalogue. Below are detailed explanations of each of the highlighted parts of the listing.

❶ Scott number — Scott catalogue numbers are used to identify specific items when buying, selling or trading stamps. Each listed postage stamp from every country has a unique Scott catalogue number. Therefore, Germany Scott 99, for example, can only refer to a single stamp. Although the Scott catalogue usually lists stamps in chronological order by date of issue, there are exceptions. When a country has issued a set of stamps over a period of time, those stamps within the set are kept together without regard to date of issue. This follows the normal collecting approach of keeping stamps in their natural sets.

When a country issues a set of stamps over a period of time, a group of consecutive catalogue numbers is reserved for the stamps in that set, as issued. If that group of numbers proves to be too few, capital-letter suffixes, such as "A" or "B," may be added to existing numbers to create enough catalogue numbers to cover all items in the set. A capital-letter suffix indicates a major Scott catalogue number listing. Scott generally uses a suffix letter only once. Therefore, a catalogue number listing with a capital-letter suffix will seldom be found with the same letter (lower case) used as a minor-letter listing. If there is a Scott 16A in a set, for example, there will seldom be a Scott 16a. However, a minor-letter "a" listing may be added to a major number containing an "A" suffix (Scott 16Aa, for example).

Suffix letters are cumulative. A minor "b" variety of Scott 16A would be Scott 16Ab, not Scott 16b.

There are times when a reserved block of Scott catalogue numbers is too large for a set, leaving some numbers unused. Such gaps in the numbering sequence also occur when the catalogue editors move an item's listing elsewhere or have removed it entirely from the catalogue. Scott does not attempt to account for every possible number, but rather attempts to assure that each stamp is assigned its own number.

Scott numbers designating regular postage normally are only numerals. Scott numbers for other types of stamps, such as air post, semi-postal, postal tax, postage due, occupation and others have a prefix consisting of one or more capital letters or a combination of numerals and capital letters.

❷ Illustration number — Illustration or design-type numbers are used to identify each catalogue illustration. For most sets, the lowest face-value stamp is shown. It then serves as an example of the basic design approach for other stamps not illustrated. Where more than one stamp use the same illustration number, but have differences in design, the design paragraph or the description line clearly indicates the design on each stamp not illustrated. Where there are both vertical and horizontal designs in a set, a single illustration may be used, with the exceptions noted in the design paragraph or description line.

When an illustration is followed by a lower-case letter in parentheses, such as "A2(b)," the trailing letter indicates which overprint or surcharge illustration applies.

Illustrations normally are 70 percent of the original size of the stamp. Oversized stamps, blocks and souvenir sheets are reduced even more. Overprints and surcharges are shown at 100 percent of their original size if shown alone, but are 70 percent of original size if shown on stamps. In some cases, the illustration will be placed above the set, between listings or omitted completely. Overprint and surcharge illustrations are not placed in this catalogue for purposes of expertizing stamps.

❸ Paper color — The color of a stamp's paper is noted in italic type when the paper used is not white.

❹ Listing styles — There are two principal types of catalogue listings: major and minor.

Major listings are in a larger type style than minor listings. The catalogue number is a numeral that can be found with or without a capital-letter suffix, and with or without a prefix.

Minor listings are in a smaller type style and have a small-letter suffix or (if the listing immediately follows that of the major number) may show only the letter. These listings identify a variety of the major item. Examples include perforation and shade differences, multiples (some souvenir sheets, booklet panes and se-tenant combinations), and singles of multiples.

Examples of major number listings include 16, 28A, B97, C13A, 10N5, and 10N6A. Examples of minor numbers are 16a and C13Ab.

❺ Basic information about a stamp or set — Introducing each stamp issue is a small section (usually a line listing) of basic information about a stamp or set. This section normally includes the date of issue, method of printing, perforation, watermark and, sometimes, some additional information of note. *Printing method, perforation and watermark apply to the following sets until a change is noted.* Stamps created by overprinting or surcharging previous issues are assumed to have the same perforation, watermark, printing method and other production characteristics as the original. Dates of issue are as precise as Scott is able to confirm and often reflect the dates on first-day covers, rather than the actual date of release.

❻ Denomination — This normally refers to the face value of the stamp; that is, the cost of the unused stamp at the post office at the time of issue. When a denomination is shown in parentheses, it does not appear on the stamp. This includes the non-denominated stamps of the United States, Brazil and Great Britain, for example.

❼ Color or other description — This area provides information to solidify identification of a stamp. In many recent cases, a description of the stamp design appears in this space, rather than a listing of colors.

❽ Year of issue — In stamp sets that have been released in a period that spans more than a year, the number shown in parentheses is the year that stamp first appeared. Stamps without a date appeared during the first year of the issue. Dates are not always given for minor varieties.

❾ Value unused and Value used — The Scott catalogue values are based on stamps that are in a grade of Very Fine unless stated otherwise. Unused values refer to items that have not seen postal, revenue or any other duty for which they were intended. Pre-1900 unused stamps that were issued with gum must have at least most of their original gum. Later issues are assumed to have full original gum. From breakpoints specified in most countries' listings, stamps are valued as never hinged. Stamps issued without gum are noted. Modern issues with PVA or other synthetic adhesives may appear ungummed. Unused self-adhesive stamps are valued as appearing undisturbed on their original backing paper. Values for used self-adhesive stamps are for examples either on piece or off piece. For a more detailed explanation of these values, please see the "Catalogue Value," "Condition" and "Understanding Valuing Notations" sections elsewhere in this introduction.

In some cases, where used stamps are more valuable than unused stamps, the value is for an example with a contemporaneous cancel, rather than a modern cancel or a smudge or other unclear marking. For those stamps that were released for postal and fiscal purposes, the used value represents a postally used stamp. Stamps with revenue cancels generally sell for less.

Stamps separated from a complete se-tenant multiple usually will be worth less than a pro-rated portion of the se-tenant multiple, and stamps lacking the attached labels that are noted in the listings will be worth less than the values shown.

❿ Changes in basic set information — Bold type is used to show any changes in the basic data given for a set of stamps. These basic data categories include perforation gauge measurement, paper type, printing method and watermark.

⓫ Total value of a set — The total value of sets of three or more stamps issued after 1900 are shown. The set line also notes the range of Scott numbers and total number of stamps included in the grouping. The actual value of a set consisting predominantly of stamps having the minimum value of 25 cents may be less than the total value shown. Similarly, the actual value or catalogue value of se-tenant pairs or of blocks consisting of stamps having the minimum value of 25 cents may be less than the catalogue values of the component parts.

NYASALAND

A6

King George VI
A7

SCOTT NUMBER ❶

ILLUS. NUMBER ❷

PAPER COLOR ❸

LISTING STYLES ❹ MAJORS
MINORS

5 BASIC INFORMATION ON STAMP OR SET

6 DENOMINATION

7 COLOR OR OTHER DESCRIPTION

8 YEAR OF ISSUE

UNUSED   **9** CATALOGUE VALUES
USED

10 CHANGES IN BASIC SET INFORMATION

11 TOTAL VALUE OF SET

1938-44			**Engr.**	**Perf. 12½**	
54	A6	½p	green	.25	2.00
54A	A6	½p	dk brown ('42)	.25	2.25
55	A6	1p	dark brown	2.50	.35
55A	A6	1p	green ('42)	.25	1.75
56	A6	1½p	dark carmine	5.00	6.00
56A	A6	1½p	gray ('42)	.25	5.75
b.			"A" of CA in watermark missing	1,600.	
57	A6	2p	gray	5.00	1.25
b.			"A" of CA in watermark missing		1,300.
57A	A6	2p	dark car ('42)	.25	2.00
c.			"A" of CA in watermark missing	1,600.	
58	A6	3p	blue	.60	1.00
59	A6	4p	rose lilac	1.75	2.00
60	A6	6p	dark violet	2.00	2.00
61	A6	9p	olive bister	2.00	5.25
62	A6	1sh	orange & blk	2.10	3.25

Typo.
Perf. 14
Chalky Paper

63	A7	2sh	ultra & dl vio, *bl*	7.00	17.50
64	A7	2sh6p	red & blk, *bl*	9.00	24.00
65	A7	5sh	red & grn, *yel*	35.00	30.00
a.			5sh dk red & dp grn, *yel* ('44)	55.00	140.00
66	A7	10sh	red & grn, *grn*	35.00	70.00

Wmk. 3

67	A7	£1	blk & vio, *red*	30.00	52.50
			Nos. 54-67 (18)	138.20	228.85
			Set, never hinged	220.00	

Special Notices

Classification of stamps

The *Scott Standard Postage Stamp Catalogue* lists stamps by country of issue. The next level of organization is a listing by section on the basis of the function of the stamps. The principal sections cover regular postage, semi-postal, air post, special delivery, registration, postage due and other categories. Except for regular postage, catalogue numbers for all sections include a prefix letter (or number-letter combination) denoting the class to which a given stamp belongs. When some countries issue sets containing stamps from more than one category, the catalogue will at times list all of the stamps in one category (such as air post stamps listed as part of a postage set).

The following is a listing of the most commonly used catalogue prefixes.

Prefix	Category
C	Air Post
M	Military
P	Newspaper
N	Occupation - Regular Issues
O	Official
Q	Parcel Post
J	Postage Due
RA	Postal Tax
B	Semi-Postal
E	Special Delivery
MR	War Tax

Other prefixes used by more than one country include the following:

Prefix	Category
H	Acknowledgment of Receipt
I	Late Fee
CO	Air Post Official
CQ	Air Post Parcel Post
RAC	Air Post Postal Tax
CF	Air Post Registration
CB	Air Post Semi-Postal
CBO	Air Post Semi-Postal Official
CE	Air Post Special Delivery
EY	Authorized Delivery
S	Franchise
G	Insured Letter
GY	Marine Insurance
MC	Military Air Post
MQ	Military Parcel Post
NC	Occupation - Air Post
NO	Occupation - Official
NJ	Occupation - Postage Due
NRA	Occupation - Postal Tax
NB	Occupation - Semi-Postal
NE	Occupation - Special Delivery
QY	Parcel Post Authorized Delivery
AR	Postal-fiscal
RAJ	Postal Tax Due
RAB	Postal Tax Semi-Postal
F	Registration
EB	Semi-Postal Special Delivery
EO	Special Delivery Official
QE	Special Handling

New issue listings

Updates to this catalogue appear each month in the *Linn's Stamp News* monthly magazine. Included in this update are additions to the listings of countries found in the *Scott Standard Postage Stamp Catalogue* and the *Specialized Catalogue of United States Stamps and Covers*, as well as corrections and updates to current editions of this catalogue.

From time to time there will be changes in the final listings of stamps from the *Linn's Stamp News* magazine to the next edition of the catalogue. This occurs as more information about certain stamps or sets becomes available.

The catalogue update section of the *Linn's Stamp News* magazine is the most timely presentation of this material available. Annual subscriptions to *Linn's Stamp News* are available from Linn's Stamp News, Box 926, Sidney, OH 45365-0926.

Number additions, deletions & changes

A listing of catalogue number additions, deletions and changes from the previous edition of the catalogue appears in each volume. See Catalogue Number Additions, Deletions & Changes in the table of contents for the location of this list.

Understanding valuing notations

The *minimum catalogue value* of an individual stamp or set is 25 cents. This represents a portion of the cost incurred by a dealer when he prepares an individual stamp for resale. As a point of philatelic-economic fact, the lower the value shown for an item in this catalogue, the greater the percentage of that value is attributed to dealer mark up and profit margin. In many cases, such as the 25-cent minimum value, that price does not cover the labor or other costs involved with stocking it as an individual stamp. The sum of minimum values in a set does not properly represent the value of a complete set primarily composed of a number of minimum-value stamps, nor does the sum represent the actual value of a packet made up of minimum-value stamps. Thus a packet of 1,000 different common stamps — each of which has a catalogue value of 25 cents — normally sells for considerably less than 250 dollars!

The *absence of a retail value* for a stamp does not necessarily suggest that a stamp is scarce or rare. A dash in the value column means that the stamp is known in a stated form or variety, but information is either lacking or insufficient for purposes of establishing a usable catalogue value.

Stamp values in *italics* generally refer to items that are difficult to value accurately. For expensive items, such as those priced at $1,000 or higher, a value in italics indicates that the affected item trades very seldom. For inexpensive items, a value in italics represents a warning. One example is a "blocked" issue where the issuing postal administration may have controlled one stamp in a set in an attempt to make the whole set more valuable. Another example is an item that sold at an extreme multiple of face value in the marketplace at the time of its issue.

One type of warning to collectors that appears in the catalogue is illustrated by a stamp that is valued considerably higher in used condition than it is as unused. In this case, collectors are cautioned to be certain the used version has a genuine and contemporaneous cancellation. The type of cancellation on a stamp can be an important factor in determining its sale price. Catalogue values do not apply to fiscal, telegraph or non-contemporaneous postal cancels, unless otherwise noted.

Some countries have released back issues of stamps in canceled-to-order form, sometimes covering as much as a 10-year period. The Scott Catalogue values for used stamps reflect canceled-to-order material when such stamps are found to predominate in the marketplace for the issue involved. Notes frequently appear in the stamp listings to specify which items are valued as canceled-to-order, or if there is a premium for postally used examples.

Many countries sell canceled-to-order stamps at a marked reduction of face value. Countries that sell or have sold canceled-to-order stamps at *full* face value include United Nations, Australia, Netherlands, France and Switzerland. It may be almost impossible to identify such stamps if the gum has been removed, because official government canceling devices are used. Postally used examples of these items on cover, however, are usually worth more than the canceled-to-order stamps with original gum.

Abbreviations

Scott uses a consistent set of abbreviations throughout this catalogue to conserve space, while still providing necessary information.

COLOR ABBREVIATIONS

amb. amber	crim. crimson	ol ..... olive
anil.. aniline	cr ..... cream	olvn . olivine
ap.... apple	dk .... dark	org... orange
aqua aquamarine	dl ..... dull	pck .. peacock
az .... azure	dp .... deep	pnksh pinkish
bis ... bister	db .... drab	Prus . Prussian
bl..... blue	emer emerald	pur... purple
bld... blood	gldn. golden	redsh reddish
blk... black	gryshgrayish	res ... reseda
bril... brilliant	grn... green	ros ... rosine
brn... brown	grnsh greenish	ryl .... royal
brnsh brownish	hel ... heliotrope	sal ... salmon
brnz. bronze	hn .... henna	saph sapphire
brt.... bright	ind ... indigo	scar . scarlet
brnt . burnt	int .... intense	sep .. sepia
car... carmine	lav ... lavender	sien . sienna
cer ... cerise	lem .. lemon	sil..... silver
chlky chalky	lil ..... lilac	sl...... slate
chamchamois	lt ...... light	stl .... steel
chnt . chestnut	mag. magenta	turq.. turquoise
choc chocolate	man. manila	ultra ultramarine
chr... chrome	mar.. maroon	Ven .. Venetian
cit ... citron	mv ... mauve	ver ... vermilion
cl...... claret	multi multicolored	vio ... violet
cob .. cobalt	mlky milky	yel ... yellow
cop .. copper	myr.. myrtle	yelsh yellowish

When no color is given for an overprint or surcharge, black is the color used. Abbreviations for colors used for overprints and surcharges include: "(B)" or "(Blk)," black; "(Bl)," blue; "(R)," red; and "(G)," green.

Additional abbreviations in this catalogue are shown below:

Adm.	Administration
AFL...............	American Federation of Labor
Anniv.	Anniversary
APS	American Philatelic Society
Assoc.	Association
ASSR.	Autonomous Soviet Socialist Republic
b.	Born
BEP...............	Bureau of Engraving and Printing
Bicent.	Bicentennial
Bklt.	Booklet
Brit...............	British
btwn.	Between
Bur...............	Bureau
c. or ca..........	Circa
Cat.	Catalogue
Cent.	Centennial, century, centenary
CIO	Congress of Industrial Organizations
Conf.	Conference
Cong.	Congress
Cpl.	Corporal
CTO	Canceled to order
d.	Died
Dbl.	Double
EDU..............	Earliest documented use
Engr.	Engraved
Exhib.............	Exhibition
Expo.	Exposition
Fed.	Federation
GB	Great Britain
Gen.	General
GPO	General post office
Horiz.	Horizontal
Imperf.	Imperforate
Impt..............	Imprint

Intl.	International
Invtd.............	Inverted
L	Left
Lieut., lt.........	Lieutenant
Litho.	Lithographed
LL	Lower left
LR	Lower right
mm	Millimeter
Ms.	Manuscript
Natl.	National
No.................	Number
NY	New York
NYC	New York City
Ovpt.	Overprint
Ovptd............	Overprinted
P	Plate number
Perf.	Perforated, perforation
Phil.	Philatelic
Photo............	Photogravure
PO	Post office
Pr.	Pair
P.R.	Puerto Rico
Prec.	Precancel, precanceled
Pres.	President
PTT	Post, Telephone and Telegraph
R	Right
Rio	Rio de Janeiro
Sgt................	Sergeant
Soc.	Society
Souv.	Souvenir
SSR...............	Soviet Socialist Republic, see ASSR
St.	Saint, street
Surch.	Surcharge
Typo.	Typographed
UL.................	Upper left
Unwmkd.	Unwatermarked
UPU..............	Universal Postal Union
UR	Upper Right
US	United States
USPOD	United States Post Office Department
USSR	Union of Soviet Socialist Republics
Vert...............	Vertical
VP	Vice president
Wmk..............	Watermark
Wmkd.	Watermarked
WWI.............	World War I
WWII............	World War II

Examination

Amos Media Co. will not comment upon the genuineness, grade or condition of stamps, because of the time and responsibility involved. Rather, there are several expertizing groups that undertake this work for both collectors and dealers. Neither will Amos Media Co. appraise or identify philatelic material. The company cannot take responsibility for unsolicited stamps or covers sent by individuals.

All letters, E-mails, etc. are read attentively, but they are not always answered due to time considerations.

How to order from your dealer

When ordering stamps from a dealer, it is not necessary to write the full description of a stamp as listed in this catalogue. All you need is the name of the country, the Scott catalogue number and whether the desired item is unused or used. For example, "Japan Scott 422 unused" is sufficient to identify the unused stamp of Japan listed as "422 A206 5y brown."

Catalogue Listing Policy

It is the intent of Amos Media Co. to list all postage stamps of the world in the *Scott Standard Postage Stamp Catalogue*. The only strict criteria for listing is that stamps be decreed legal for postage by the issuing country and that the issuing country actually have an operating postal system. Whether the primary intent of issuing a given stamp or set was for sale to postal patrons or to stamp collectors is not part of our listing criteria. Scott's role is to provide basic comprehensive postage stamp information. It is up to each stamp collector to choose which items to include in a collection.

It is Scott's objective to seek reasons why a stamp should be listed, rather than why it should not. Nevertheless, there are certain types of items that will not be listed. These include the following:

1. Unissued items that are not officially distributed or released by the issuing postal authority. If such items are officially issued at a later date by the country, they will be listed. Unissued items consist of those that have been printed and then held from sale for reasons such as change in government, errors found on stamps or something deemed objectionable about a stamp subject or design.

2. Stamps "issued" by non-existent postal entities or fantasy countries, such as Nagaland, Occusi-Ambeno, Staffa, Sedang, Torres Straits and others. Also, stamps "issued" in the names of legitimate, stamp-issuing countries that are not authorized by those countries.

3. Semi-official or unofficial items not required for postage. Examples include items issued by private agencies for their own express services. When such items are required for delivery, or are valid as prepayment of postage, they are listed.

4. Local stamps issued for local use only. Postage stamps issued by governments specifically for "domestic" use, such as Haiti Scott 219-228, or the United States non-denominated stamps, are not considered to be locals, since they are valid for postage throughout the country of origin.

5. Items not valid for postal use. For example, a few countries have issued souvenir sheets that are not valid for postage. This area also includes a number of worldwide charity labels (some denominated) that do not pay postage.

6. Egregiously exploitative issues such as stamps sold for far more than face value, stamps purposefully issued in artificially small quantities or only against advance orders, stamps awarded only to a selected audience such as a philatelic bureau's standing order customers, or stamps sold only in conjunction with other products. All of these kinds of items are usually controlled issues and/or are intended for speculation. These items normally will be included in a footnote.

7. Items distributed by the issuing government only to a limited group, club, philatelic exhibition or a single stamp dealer or other private company. These items normally will be included in a footnote.

8. Stamps not available to collectors. These generally are rare items, all of which are held by public institutions such as museums. The existence of such items often will be cited in footnotes.

The fact that a stamp has been used successfully as postage, even on international mail, is not in itself sufficient proof that it was legitimately issued. Numerous examples of so-called stamps from non-existent countries are known to have been used to post letters that have successfully passed through the international mail system.

There are certain items that are subject to interpretation. When a stamp falls outside our specifications, it may be listed along with a cautionary footnote.

A number of factors are considered in our approach to analyzing how a stamp is listed. The following list of factors is presented to share with you, the catalogue user, the complexity of the listing process.

Additional printings — "Additional printings" of a previously issued stamp may range from an item that is totally different to cases where it is impossible to differentiate from the original. At least a minor number (a small-letter suffix) is assigned if there is a distinct change in stamp shade, noticeably redrawn design, or a significantly different perforation measurement. A major number (numeral or numeral and capital-letter combination) is assigned if the editors feel the "additional printing" is sufficiently different from the original that it constitutes a different issue.

Commemoratives — Where practical, commemoratives with the same theme are placed in a set. For example, the U.S. Civil War Centennial set of 1961-65 and the Constitution Bicentennial series of 1989-90 appear as sets. Countries such as Japan and Korea issue such material on a regular basis, with an announced, or at least predictable, number of stamps known in advance. Occasionally, however, stamp sets that were released over a period of years have been separated. Appropriately placed footnotes will guide you to each set's continuation.

Definitive sets — Blocks of numbers generally have been reserved for definitive sets, based on previous experience with any given country. If a few more stamps were issued in a set than originally expected, they often have been inserted into the original set with a capital-letter suffix, such as U.S. Scott 1059A. If it appears that many more stamps than the originally allotted block will be released before the set is completed, a new block of numbers will be reserved, with the original one being closed off. In some cases, such as the U.S. Transportation and Great Americans series, several blocks of numbers exist. Appropriately placed footnotes will guide you to each set's continuation.

New country — Membership in the Universal Postal Union is not a consideration for listing status or order of placement within the catalogue. The index will tell you in what volume or page number the listings begin.

"No release date" items — The amount of information available for any given stamp issue varies greatly from country to country and even from time to time. Extremely comprehensive information about new stamps is available from some countries well before the stamps are released. By contrast some countries do not provide information about stamps or release dates. Most countries, however, fall between these extremes. A country may provide denominations or subjects of stamps from upcoming issues that are not issued as planned. Sometimes, philatelic agencies, those private firms hired to represent countries, add these later-issued items to sets well after the formal release date. This time period can range from weeks to years. If these items were officially released by the country, they will be added to the appropriate spot in the set. In many cases, the specific release date of a stamp or set of stamps may never be known.

Overprints — The color of an overprint is always noted if it is other than black. Where more than one color of ink has been used on overprints of a single set, the color used is noted. Early overprint and surcharge illustrations were altered to prevent their use by forgers.

Personalized Stamps — Since 1999, the special service of personalizing stamp vignettes, or labels attached to stamps, has been offered to customers by postal administrations of many countries. Sheets of these stamps are sold, singly or in quantity, only through special orders made by mail, in person, or through a sale on a computer website with the postal administrations or their agents for which an extra fee is charged, though some countries offer to collectors at face value personalized stamps having generic images in the vignettes or on the attached labels. It is impossible for any catalogue to know what images have been chosen by customers. Images can be 1) owned or created by the customer, 2) a generic image, or 3) an image pulled from a library of stock images on the stamp creation website. It is also impossible to know the quantity printed for any stamp having a particular image. So from a valuing standpoint, any image is equivalent to any other image for any personalized stamp having the same catalogue number. Illustrations of personalized stamps in the catalogue are not always those of stamps having generic images.

Personalized items are listed with some exceptions. These include:
1. Stamps or sheets that have attached labels that the customer cannot personalize, but which are nonetheless marketed as "personalized," and are sold for far more than the franking value.
2. Stamps or sheets that can be personalized by the customer, but where a portion of the print run must be ceded to the issuing country for sale to other customers.
3. Stamps or sheets that are created exclusively for a particular commercial client, or clients, including stamps that differ from any similar stamp that has been made available to the public.
4. Stamps or sheets that are deliberately conceived by the issuing authority that have been, or are likely to be, created with an excessive number of different face values, sizes, or other features that are changeable.
5. Stamps or sheets that are created by postal administrations using the same system of stamp personalization that has been put in place for use by the public that are printed in limited quantities and sold above face value.
6. Stamps or sheets that are created by licensees not directly affiliated or controlled by a postal administration.

Excluded items may or may not be footnoted.

Se-tenants — Connected stamps of differing features (se-tenants) will be listed in the format most commonly collected. This includes pairs, blocks or larger multiples. Se-tenant units are not always symmetrical. An example is Australia Scott 508, which is a block of seven stamps. If the stamps are primarily collected as a unit, the major number may be assigned to the multiple, with minors going to each component stamp. In cases where continuous-design or other unit se-tenants will receive significant postal use, each stamp is given a major Scott number listing. This includes issues from the United States, Canada, Germany and Great Britain, for example.

Basic Stamp Information

A stamp collector's knowledge of the combined elements that make a given stamp issue unique determines his or her ability to identify stamps. These elements include paper, watermark, method of separation, printing, design and gum. On the following pages each of these important areas is briefly described.

Paper

Paper is an organic material composed of a compacted weave of cellulose fibers and generally formed into sheets. Paper used to print stamps may be manufactured in sheets, or it may have been part of a large roll (called a web) before being cut to size. The fibers most often used to create paper on which stamps are printed include bark, wood, straw and certain grasses. In many cases, linen or cotton rags have been added for greater strength and durability. Grinding, bleaching, cooking and rinsing these raw fibers reduces them to a slushy pulp, referred to by paper makers as "stuff." Sizing and, sometimes, coloring matter is added to the pulp to make different types of finished paper.

After the stuff is prepared, it is poured onto sieve-like frames that allow the water to run off, while retaining the matted pulp. As fibers fall onto the screen and are held by gravity, they form a natural weave that will later hold the paper together. If the screen has metal bits that are formed into letters or images attached, it leaves slightly thinned areas on the paper. These are called watermarks.

When the stuff is almost dry, it is passed under pressure through smooth or engraved rollers - dandy rolls - or placed between cloth in a press to be flattened and dried.

Wove   Laid   Granite

Quadrille   Oblong   Laid
Quadrille   Batonne

Stamp paper falls broadly into two types: wove and laid. The nature of the surface of the frame onto which the pulp is first deposited causes the differences in appearance between the two. If the surface is smooth and even, the paper will be of fairly uniform texture throughout. This is known as *wove paper*. Early papermaking machines poured the pulp onto a continuously circulating web of felt, but modern machines feed the pulp onto a cloth-like screen made of closely interwoven fine wires. This paper, when held to a light, will show little dots or points very close together. The proper name for this is "wire wove," but the type is still considered wove. Any U.S. or British stamp printed after 1880 will serve as an example of wire wove paper.

Closely spaced parallel wires, with cross wires at wider intervals, make up the frames used for what is known as *laid paper*. A greater thickness of the pulp will settle between the wires. The paper, when held to a light, will show alternate light and dark lines. The spacing and the thickness of the lines may vary, but on any one sheet of paper they are all alike. See Russia Scott 31-38 for examples of laid paper.

Batonne, from the French word meaning "a staff," is a term used if the lines in the paper are spaced quite far apart, like the printed ruling on a writing tablet. Batonne paper may be either wove or laid. If laid, fine laid lines can be seen between the batons.

Quadrille is the term used when the lines in the paper form little squares. *Oblong quadrille* is the term used when rectangles, rather than squares, are formed. Grid patterns vary from distinct to extremely faint. See Mexico-Guadalajara Scott 35-37 for examples of oblong quadrille paper.

Paper also is classified as thick or thin, hard or soft, and by color. Such colors may include yellowish, greenish, bluish and reddish.

Brief explanations of other types of paper used for printing stamps, as well as examples, follow.

Colored — Colored paper is created by the addition of dye in the paper-making process. Such colors may include shades of yellow, green, blue and red. *Surface-colored papers*, most commonly used for British colonial issues in 1913-14, are created when coloring is added only to the surface during the finishing process. Stamps printed on surface-colored paper have white or uncolored backs, while true colored papers are colored through. See Jamaica Scott 71-73.

Pelure — Pelure paper is a very thin, hard and often brittle paper that is sometimes bluish or grayish in appearance. See Serbia Scott 169-170.

Native — This is a term applied to handmade papers used to produce some of the early stamps of the Indian states. Stamps printed on native paper may be expected to display various natural inclusions that are normal and do not negatively affect value. Japanese paper, originally made of mulberry fibers and rice flour, is part of this group. See Japan Scott 1-18.

Manila — This type of paper is often used to make stamped envelopes and wrappers. It is a coarse-textured stock, usually smooth on one side and rough on the other. A variety of colors of manila paper exist, but the most common range is yellowish-brown.

Silk — Introduced by the British in 1847 as a safeguard against counterfeiting, silk paper contains bits of colored silk thread scattered throughout. The density of these fibers varies greatly and can include as few as one fiber per stamp or hundreds. U.S. revenue Scott R152 is a good example of an easy-to-identify silk paper stamp.

Silk-thread paper has uninterrupted threads of colored silk arranged so that one or more threads run through the stamp or postal stationery. See Great Britain Scott 5-6 and Switzerland Scott 14-19.

Granite — Filled with minute cloth or colored paper fibers of various colors and lengths, granite paper should not be confused with either type of silk paper. Austria Scott 172-175 and a number of Swiss stamps are examples of granite paper.

Chalky — A chalk-like substance coats the surface of chalky paper to discourage the cleaning and reuse of canceled stamps, as well as to provide a smoother, more acceptable printing surface. Because the designs of stamps printed on chalky paper are imprinted on what is often a water-soluble coating, any attempt to remove a cancellation will destroy the stamp. *Do not soak these stamps in any fluid.* To remove a stamp printed on chalky paper from an envelope, wet the paper from underneath the stamp until the gum dissolves enough to release the stamp from the paper. See St. Kitts-Nevis Scott 89-90 for examples of stamps printed on this type of chalky paper.

India — Another name for this paper, originally introduced from China about 1750, is "China Paper." It is a thin, opaque paper often used for plate and die proofs by many countries.

Double — In philately, the term double paper has two distinct meanings. The first is a two-ply paper, usually a combination of a thick and a thin sheet, joined during manufacture. This type was used experimentally as a means to discourage the reuse of stamps.

The design is printed on the thin paper. Any attempt to remove a cancellation would destroy the design. U.S. Scott 158 and other Banknote-era stamps exist on this form of double paper.

The second type of double paper occurs on a rotary press, when the end of one paper roll, or web, is affixed to the next roll to save time feeding the paper through the press. Stamp designs are printed over the joined paper and, if overlooked by inspectors, may get into post office stocks.

Goldbeater's Skin — This type of paper was used for the 1866 issue of Prussia, and was a tough, translucent paper. The design was printed in reverse on the back of the stamp, and the gum applied over the printing. It is impossible to remove stamps printed on this type of paper from the paper to which they are affixed without destroying the design.

Ribbed — Ribbed paper has an uneven, corrugated surface made by passing the paper through ridged rollers. This type exists on some copies of U.S. Scott 156-165.

Various other substances, or substrates, have been used for stamp manufacture, including wood, aluminum, copper, silver and gold foil, plastic, and silk and cotton fabrics.

Watermarks

Watermarks are an integral part of some papers. They are formed in the process of paper manufacture. Watermarks consist of small designs, formed of wire or cut from metal and soldered to the surface of the mold or, sometimes, on the dandy roll. The designs may be in the form of crowns, stars, anchors, letters or other characters or symbols. These pieces of metal - known in the paper-making industry as "bits" - impress a design into the paper. The design sometimes may be seen by holding the stamp to the light. Some are more easily seen with a watermark detector. This important tool is a small black tray into which a stamp is placed face down and dampened with a fast-evaporating watermark detection fluid that brings up the watermark image in the form of dark lines against a lighter background. These dark lines are the thinner areas of the paper known as the watermark. Some watermarks are extremely difficult to locate, due to either a faint impression, watermark location or the color of the stamp. There also are electric watermark detectors that come with plastic filter disks of various colors. The disks neutralize the color of the stamp, permitting the watermark to be seen more easily.

Multiple watermarks of Crown Agents and Burma

Watermarks of Uruguay, Vatican City and Jamaica

WARNING: Some inks used in the photogravure process dissolve in watermark fluids (Please see the section on Soluble Printing Inks). Also, see "chalky paper."

Watermarks may be found normal, reversed, inverted, reversed and inverted, sideways or diagonal, as seen from the back of the stamp. The relationship of watermark to stamp design depends on the position of the printing plates or how paper is fed through the press. On machine-made paper, watermarks normally are read from right to left. The design is repeated closely throughout the sheet in a "multiple-watermark design." In a "sheet watermark," the design appears only once on the sheet, but extends over many stamps. Individual stamps

may carry only a small fraction or none of the watermark.

"Marginal watermarks" occur in the margins of sheets or panes of stamps. They occur on the outside border of paper (ostensibly outside the area where stamps are to be printed). A large row of letters may spell the name of the country or the manufacturer of the paper, or a border of lines may appear. Careless press feeding may cause parts of these letters and/or lines to show on stamps of the outer row of a pane.

Soluble Printing Inks

WARNING: Most stamp colors are permanent; that is, they are not seriously affected by short-term exposure to light or water. Many colors, especially of modern inks, fade from excessive exposure to light. There are stamps printed with inks that dissolve easily in water or in fluids used to detect watermarks. Use of these inks was intentional to prevent the removal of cancellations. Water affects all aniline inks, those on so-called safety paper and some photogravure printings - all such inks are known as fugitive colors. *Removal from paper of such stamps requires care and alternatives to traditional soaking.*

Separation

"Separation" is the general term used to describe methods used to separate stamps. The three standard forms currently in use are perforating, rouletting and die-cutting. These methods are done during the stamp production process, after printing. Sometimes these methods are done on-press or sometimes as a separate step. The earliest issues, such as the 1840 Penny Black of Great Britain (Scott 1), did not have any means provided for separation. It was expected the stamps would be cut apart with scissors or folded and torn. These are examples of imperforate stamps. Many stamps were first issued in imperforate formats and were later issued with perforations. Therefore, care must be observed in buying single imperforate stamps to be certain they were issued imperforate and are not perforated copies that have been altered by having the perforations trimmed away. Stamps issued imperforate usually are valued as singles. However, imperforate varieties of normally perforated stamps should be collected in pairs or larger pieces as indisputable evidence of their imperforate character.

PERFORATION

The chief style of separation of stamps, and the one that is in almost universal use today, is perforating. By this process, paper between the stamps is cut away in a line of holes, usually round, leaving little bridges of paper between the stamps to hold them together. Some types of perforation, such as hyphen-hole perfs, can be confused with roulettes, but a close visual inspection reveals that paper has been removed. The little perforation bridges, which project from the stamp when it is torn from the pane, are called the teeth of the perforation.

As the size of the perforation is sometimes the only way to differentiate between two otherwise identical stamps, it is necessary to be able to accurately measure and describe them. This is done with a perforation gauge, usually a ruler-like device that has dots or graduated lines to show how many perforations may be counted in the space of two centimeters. Two centimeters is the space universally adopted in which to measure perforations.

Perforation gauge

perce en arc · perce en lignes · perce en points · oblique roulette · perce en scie · perce serpentin

To measure a stamp, run it along the gauge until the dots on it fit exactly into the perforations of the stamp. If you are using a graduated-line perforation gauge, simply slide the stamp along the surface until the lines on the gauge perfectly project from the center of the bridges or holes. The number to the side of the line of dots or lines that fit the stamp's perforation is the measurement. For example, an "11" means that 11 perforations fit between two centimeters. The description of the stamp therefore is "perf. 11." If the gauge of the perforations on the top and bottom of a stamp differs from that on the sides, the result is what is known as *compound perforations*. In measuring compound perforations, the gauge at top and bottom is always given first, then the sides. Thus, a stamp that measures 11 at top and bottom and 10½ at the sides is "perf. 11 x 10½." See U.S. Scott 632-642 for examples of compound perforations.

Stamps also are known with perforations different on three or all four sides. Descriptions of such items are clockwise, beginning with the top of the stamp.

A perforation with small holes and teeth close together is a "fine perforation." One with large holes and teeth far apart is a "coarse perforation." Holes that are jagged, rather than clean-cut, are "rough perforations." *Blind perforations* are the slight impressions left by the perforating pins if they fail to puncture the paper. Multiples of stamps showing blind perforations may command a slight premium over normally perforated stamps.

The term *syncopated perfs* describes intentional irregularities in the perforations. The earliest form was used by the Netherlands from 1925-33, where holes were omitted to create distinctive patterns. Beginning in 1992, Great Britain has used an oval perforation to help prevent counterfeiting. Several other countries have started using the oval perfs or other syncopated perf patterns.

A new type of perforation, still primarily used for postal stationery, is known as microperfs. Microperfs are tiny perforations (in some cases hundreds of holes per two centimeters) that allows items to be intentionally separated very easily, while not accidentally breaking apart as easily as standard perforations. These are not currently measured or differentiated by size, as are standard perforations.

ROULETTING

In rouletting, the stamp paper is cut partly or wholly through, with no paper removed. In perforating, some paper is removed. Rouletting derives its name from the French roulette, a spur-like wheel. As the wheel is rolled over the paper, each point makes a small cut. The number of cuts made in a two-centimeter space determines the gauge of the roulette, just as the number of perforations in two centimeters determines the gauge of the perforation.

The shape and arrangement of the teeth on the wheels varies. Various roulette types generally carry French names:

Perce en lignes - rouletted in lines. The paper receives short, straight cuts in lines. This is the most common type of rouletting. See Mexico Scott 500.

Perce en points - pin-rouletted or pin-perfed. This differs from a small perforation because no paper is removed, although round, equidistant holes are pricked through the paper. See Mexico Scott 242-256.

Perce en arc and *perce en scie* - pierced in an arc or saw-toothed designs, forming half circles or small triangles. See Hanover (German States) Scott 25-29.

Perce en serpentin - serpentine roulettes. The cuts form a serpentine or wavy line. See Brunswick (German States) Scott 13-18.

Once again, no paper is removed by these processes, leaving the stamps easily separated, but closely attached.

DIE-CUTTING

The third major form of stamp separation is die-cutting. This is a method where a die in the pattern of separation is created that later cuts the stamp paper in a stroke motion. Although some standard stamps bear die-cut perforations, this process is primarily used for self-adhesive postage stamps. Die-cutting can appear in straight lines, such as U.S. Scott 2522, shapes, such as U.S. Scott 1551, or imitating the appearance of perforations, such as New Zealand Scott 935A and 935B.

Printing Processes

ENGRAVING (Intaglio, Line-engraving, Etching)

Master die — The initial operation in the process of line engraving is making the master die. The die is a small, flat block of softened steel upon which the stamp design is recess engraved in reverse.

Master die

Transfer roll

Photographic reduction of the original art is made to the appropriate size. It then serves as a tracing guide for the initial outline of the design. The engraver lightly traces the design on the steel with his graver, then slowly works the design until it is completed. At various points during the engraving process, the engraver hand-inks the die and makes an impression to check his progress. These are known as progressive die proofs. After completion of the engraving, the die is hardened to withstand the stress and pressures of later transfer operations.

Transfer roll — Next is production of the transfer roll that, as the name implies, is the medium used to transfer the subject from the master die to the printing plate. A blank roll of soft steel, mounted on a mandrel, is placed under the bearers of the transfer press to allow it to roll freely on its axis. The hardened die is placed on the bed of the press and the face of the transfer roll is applied to the die, under pressure. The bed or the roll is then rocked back and forth under increasing pressure, until the soft steel of the roll is forced into every engraved line of the die. The resulting impression on the roll is known as a "relief" or a "relief transfer." The engraved image is now positive in appearance and stands out from the steel. After the required number of reliefs are "rocked in," the soft steel transfer roll is hardened.

Different flaws may occur during the relief process. A defective relief may occur during the rocking in process because of a minute piece of foreign material lodging on the die, or some other cause. Imperfections in the steel of the transfer roll may result in a breaking away of parts of the design. This is known as a relief break, which will show up on finished stamps as small, unprinted areas. If a damaged relief remains in use, it will transfer a repeating defect to the plate. Deliberate alterations of reliefs sometimes occur. "Altered reliefs" designate these changed conditions.

Plate — The final step in pre-printing production is the making of the printing plate. A flat piece of soft steel replaces the die on the bed of the transfer press. One of the reliefs on the transfer roll is positioned over this soft steel. Position, or layout, dots determine the correct position on the plate. The dots have been lightly marked on the plate in advance. After the correct position of the relief is determined,

the design is rocked in by following the same method used in making the transfer roll. The difference is that this time the image is being transferred from the transfer roll, rather than to it. Once the design is entered on the plate, it appears in reverse and is recessed. There are as many transfers entered on the plate as there are subjects printed on the sheet of stamps. It is during this process that double and shifted transfers occur, as well as re-entries. These are the result of improperly entered images that have not been properly burnished out prior to rocking in a new image.

Modern siderography processes, such as those used by the U.S. Bureau of Engraving and Printing, involve an automated form of rocking designs in on preformed cylindrical printing sleeves. The same process also allows for easier removal and re-entry of worn images right on the sleeve.

Transferring the design to the plate

Following the entering of the required transfers on the plate, the position dots, layout dots and lines, scratches and other markings generally are burnished out. Added at this time by the siderographer are any required *guide lines*, *plate numbers* or other *marginal markings*. The plate is then hand-inked and a proof impression is taken. This is known as a *plate proof*. If the impression is approved, the plate is machined for fitting onto the press, is hardened and sent to the plate vault ready for use.

On press, the plate is inked and the surface is automatically wiped clean, leaving ink only in the recessed lines. Paper is then forced under pressure into the engraved recessed lines, thereby receiving the ink. Thus, the ink lines on engraved stamps are slightly raised, and slight depressions (debossing) occur on the back of the stamp. Prior to the advent of modern high-speed presses and more advanced ink formulations, paper had to be dampened before receiving the ink. This sometimes led to uneven shrinkage by the time the stamps were perforated, resulting in improperly perforated stamps, or misperfs. Newer presses use drier paper, thus both *wet* and *dry printings* exist on some stamps.

Rotary Press — Until 1914, only flat plates were used to print engraved stamps. Rotary press printing was introduced in 1914, and slowly spread. Some countries still use flat-plate printing.

After approval of the plate proof, older *rotary press plates* require additional machining. They are curved to fit the press cylinder. "Gripper slots" are cut into the back of each plate to receive the "grippers," which hold the plate securely on the press. The plate is then hardened. Stamps printed from these bent rotary press plates are longer or wider than the same stamps printed from flat-plate presses. The stretching of the plate during the curving process is what causes this distortion.

Re-entry — To execute a re-entry on a flat plate, the transfer roll is re-applied to the plate, often at some time after its first use on the press. Worn-out designs can be resharpened by carefully burnishing out the original image and re-entering it from the transfer roll. If the original impression has not been sufficiently removed and the transfer roll is not precisely in line with the remaining impression, the resulting double transfer will make the re-entry obvious. If the registration is true, a re-entry may be difficult or impossible to distinguish. Sometimes a stamp printed from a successful re-entry is identified by having a much sharper and clearer impression than its neighbors. With the advent of rotary presses, post-press re-entries were not possible. After a plate was curved for the rotary press, it was impossible to make a re-entry. This is because the plate had already been bent once (with the design distorted).

However, with the introduction of the previously mentioned modern-style siderography machines, entries are made to the preformed cylindrical printing sleeve. Such sleeves are dechromed and softened. This allows individual images to be burnished out and re-entered on the curved sleeve. The sleeve is then rechromed, resulting in longer press life.

Double Transfer — This is a description of the condition of a transfer on a plate that shows evidence of a duplication of all, or a portion of the design. It usually is the result of the changing of the registration between the transfer roll and the plate during the rocking in of the original entry. Double transfers also occur when only a portion of the design has been rocked in and improper positioning is noted. If the worker elected not to burnish out the partial or completed design, a strong double transfer will occur for part or all of the design.

It sometimes is necessary to remove the original transfer from a plate and repeat the process a second time. If the finished re-worked image shows traces of the original impression, attributable to incomplete burnishing, the result is a partial double transfer.

With the modern automatic machines mentioned previously, double transfers are all but impossible to create. Those partially doubled images on stamps printed from such sleeves are more than likely re-entries, rather than true double transfers.

Re-engraved — Alterations to a stamp design are sometimes necessary after some stamps have been printed. In some cases, either the original die or the actual printing plate may have its "temper" drawn (softened), and the design will be re-cut. The resulting impressions from such a re-engraved die or plate may differ slightly from the original issue, and are known as "re-engraved." If the alteration was made to the master die, all future printings will be consistently different from the original. If alterations were made to the printing plate, each altered stamp on the plate will be slightly different from each other, allowing specialists to reconstruct a complete printing plate.

Dropped Transfers — If an impression from the transfer roll has not been properly placed, a dropped transfer may occur. The final stamp image will appear obviously out of line with its neighbors.

Short Transfer — Sometimes a transfer roll is not rocked its entire length when entering a transfer onto a plate. As a result, the finished transfer on the plate fails to show the complete design, and the finished stamp will have an incomplete design printed. This is known as a "short transfer." U.S. Scott No. 8 is a good example of a short transfer.

TYPOGRAPHY (Letterpress, Surface Printing, Flexography, Dry Offset, High Etch)

Although the word "Typography" is obsolete as a term describing a printing method, it was the accepted term throughout the first century of postage stamps. Therefore, appropriate Scott listings in this catalogue refer to typographed stamps. The current term for this form of printing, however, is "letterpress."

As it relates to the production of postage stamps, letterpress printing is the reverse of engraving. Rather than having recessed areas trap the ink and deposit it on paper, only the raised areas of the design are inked. This is comparable to the type of printing seen by inking and using an ordinary rubber stamp. Letterpress includes all printing where the design is above the surface area, whether it is wood, metal or, in some instances, hardened rubber or polymer plastic.

For most letterpress-printed stamps, the engraved master is made in much the same manner as for engraved stamps. In this instance, however, an additional step is needed. The design is transferred to another surface before being transferred to the transfer roll. In this way, the transfer roll has a recessed stamp design, rather than one done in relief. This makes the printing areas on the final plate raised, or relief areas.

For less-detailed stamps of the 19th century, the area on the die not used as a printing surface was cut away, leaving the surface area raised. The original die was then reproduced by stereotyping or electrotyping. The resulting electrotypes were assembled in the required number and format of the desired sheet of stamps. The plate used in printing the stamps was an electroplate of these assembled electrotypes.

Once the final letterpress plates are created, ink is applied to the raised surface and the pressure of the press transfers the ink impression to the paper. In contrast to engraving, the fine lines of letterpress are impressed on the surface of the stamp, leaving a debossed surface. When viewed from the back (as on a typewritten page), the corresponding line work on the stamp will be raised slightly (embossed) above the surface.

PHOTOGRAVURE (Gravure, Rotogravure, Heliogravure)

In this process, the basic principles of photography are applied to a chemically sensitized metal plate, rather than photographic paper. The design is transferred photographically to the plate through a halftone, or dot-matrix screen, breaking the reproduction into tiny dots. The plate is treated chemically and the dots form depressions, called cells, of varying depths and diameters, depending on the degrees of shade in the design. Then, like engraving, ink is applied to the plate and the surface is wiped clean. This leaves ink in the tiny cells that is lifted out and deposited on the paper when it is pressed against the plate.

Gravure is most often used for multicolored stamps, generally using the three primary colors (red, yellow and blue) and black. By varying the dot matrix pattern and density of these colors, virtually any color can be reproduced. A typical full-color gravure stamp will be created from four printing cylinders (one for each color). The original multicolored image will have been photographically separated into its component colors.

Modern gravure printing may use computer-generated dot-matrix screens, and modern plates may be of various types including metal-coated plastic. The catalogue designation of Photogravure (or "Photo") covers any of these older and more modern gravure methods of printing.

For examples of the first photogravure stamps printed (1914), see Bavaria Scott 94-114.

LITHOGRAPHY (Offset Lithography, Stone Lithography, Dilitho, Planography, Collotype)

The principle that oil and water do not mix is the basis for lithography. The stamp design is drawn by hand or transferred from engraving to the surface of a lithographic stone or metal plate in a greasy (oily) substance. This oily substance holds the ink, which will later be transferred to the paper. The stone (or plate) is wet with an acid fluid, causing it to repel the printing ink in all areas not covered by the greasy substance.

Transfer paper is used to transfer the design from the original stone or plate. A series of duplicate transfers are grouped and, in turn, transferred to the final printing plate.

Photolithography — The application of photographic processes to lithography. This process allows greater flexibility of design, related to use of halftone screens combined with line work. Unlike photogravure or engraving, this process can allow large, solid areas to be printed.

Offset — A refinement of the lithographic process. A rubber-covered blanket cylinder takes the impression from the inked lithographic plate. From the "blanket" the impression is *offset* or transferred to the paper. Greater flexibility and speed are the principal reasons offset printing has largely displaced lithography. The term "lithography" covers both processes, and results are almost identical.

EMBOSSED (Relief) Printing

Embossing, not considered one of the four main printing types, is a method in which the design first is sunk into the metal of the die. Printing is done against a yielding platen, such as leather or linoleum. The platen is forced into the depression of the die, thus forming the design on the paper in relief. This process is often used for metallic inks.

Embossing may be done without color (see Sardinia Scott 4-6); with color printed around the embossed area (see Great Britain Scott 5 and most U.S. envelopes); and with color in exact registration with the embossed subject (see Canada Scott 656-657).

HOLOGRAMS

For objects to appear as holograms on stamps, a model exactly the same size as it is to appear on the hologram must be created. Rather than using photographic film to capture the image, holography records an image on a photoresist material. In processing, chemicals eat away at certain exposed areas, leaving a pattern of constructive and destructive interference. When the photoresist is developed, the result is a pattern of uneven ridges that acts as a mold. This mold is then coated with metal, and the resulting form is used to press copies in much the same way phonograph records are produced.

A typical reflective hologram used for stamps consists of a reproduction of the uneven patterns on a plastic film that is applied to a reflective background, usually a silver or gold foil. Light is reflected off the background through the film, making the pattern present on the film visible. Because of the uneven pattern of the film, the viewer will perceive the objects in their proper three-dimensional relationships with appropriate brightness.

The first hologram on a stamp was produced by Austria in 1988 (Scott 1441).

FOIL APPLICATION

A modern technique of applying color to stamps involves the application of metallic foil to the stamp paper. A pattern of foil is applied to the stamp paper by use of a stamping die. The foil usually is flat, but it may be textured. Canada Scott 1735 has three different foil applications in pearl, bronze and gold. The gold foil was textured using a chemical-etch copper embossing die. The printing of this stamp also involved two-color offset lithography plus embossing.

THERMOGRAPHY

In the 1990s stamps began to be enhanced with thermographic printing. In this process, a powdered polymer is applied over a sheet that has just been printed. The powder adheres to ink that lacks drying or hardening agents and does not adhere to areas where the ink has these agents. The excess powder is removed and the sheet is briefly heated to melt the powder. The melted powder solidifies after cooling, producing a raised, shiny effect on the stamps. See Scott New Caledonia C239-C240.

COMBINATION PRINTINGS

Sometimes two or even three printing methods are combined in producing stamps. In these cases, such as Austria Scott 933 or Canada 1735 (described in the preceding paragraph), the multiple-printing technique can be determined by studying the individual characteristics of each printing type. A few stamps, such as Singapore Scott 684-684A, combine as many as three of the four major printing types (lithography, engraving and typography). When this is done it often indicates the incorporation of security devices against counterfeiting.

INK COLORS

Inks or colored papers used in stamp printing often are of mineral origin, although there are numerous examples of organic-based pigments. As a general rule, organic-based pigments are far more subject to varieties and change than those of mineral-based origin.

The appearance of any given color on a stamp may be affected by many aspects, including printing variations, light, color of paper, aging and chemical alterations.

Numerous printing variations may be observed. Heavier pressure or inking will cause a more intense color, while slight interruptions in the ink feed or lighter impressions will cause a lighter appearance. Stamps printed in the same color by water-based and solvent-based inks can differ significantly in appearance. This affects several stamps in the U.S. Prominent Americans series. Hand-mixed ink formulas (primarily from the 19th century) produced under different conditions (humidity and temperature) account for notable color variations in early printings of the same stamp (see U.S. Scott 248-250, 279B, for example). Different sources of pigment can also result in significant differences in color.

Light exposure and aging are closely related in the way they affect stamp color. Both eventually break down the ink and fade colors, so that a carefully kept stamp may differ significantly in color from an identical copy that has been exposed to light. If stamps are exposed to light either intentionally or accidentally, their colors can be faded or completely changed in some cases.

Papers of different quality and consistency used for the same stamp printing may affect color appearance. Most pelure papers, for example, show a richer color when compared with wove or laid papers. See Russia Scott 181a, for an example of this effect.

The very nature of the printing processes can cause a variety of differences in shades or hues of the same stamp. Some of these shades are scarcer than others, and are of particular interest to the advanced collector.

Luminescence

All forms of tagged stamps fall under the general category of luminescence. Within this broad category is fluorescence, dealing with forms of tagging visible under longwave ultraviolet light, and phosphorescence, which deals with tagging visible only under shortwave light. Phosphorescence leaves an afterglow and fluorescence does not. These treated stamps show up in a range of different colors when exposed to UV light. The differing wavelengths of the light activates the tagging material, making it glow in various colors that usually serve different mail processing purposes.

Intentional tagging is a post-World War II phenomenon, brought about by the increased literacy rate and rapidly growing mail volume. It was one of several answers to the problem of the need for more automated mail processes. Early tagged stamps served the purpose of triggering machines to separate different types of mail. A natural outgrowth was to also use the signal to trigger machines that faced all envelopes the same way and canceled them.

Tagged stamps come in many different forms. Some tagged stamps have luminescent shapes or images imprinted on them as a form of security device. Others have blocks (United States), stripes, frames (South Africa and Canada), overall coatings (United States), bars (Great Britain and Canada) and many other types. Some types of tagging are even mixed in with the pigmented printing ink (Australia Scott 366, Netherlands Scott 478 and U.S. Scott 1359 and 2443).

The means of applying taggant to stamps differs as much as the intended purposes for the stamps. The most common form of tagging is a coating applied to the surface of the printed stamp. Since the taggant ink is frequently invisible except under UV light, it does not interfere with the appearance of the stamp. Another common application is the use of phosphored papers. In this case the paper itself either has a coating of taggant applied before the stamp is printed, has taggant applied during the papermaking process (incorporating it into the fibers), or has the taggant mixed into the coating of the paper. The latter method, among others, is currently in use in the United States.

Many countries now use tagging in various forms to either expedite mail handling or to serve as a printing security device against counterfeiting. Following the introduction of tagged stamps for public use in 1959 by Great Britain, other countries have steadily joined the parade. Among those are Germany (1961); Canada and Denmark (1962); United States, Australia, France and Switzerland (1963); Belgium and Japan (1966); Sweden and Norway (1967); Italy (1968); and Russia (1969). Since then, many other countries have begun using forms of tagging, including Brazil, China, Czechoslovakia, Hong Kong, Guatemala, Indonesia, Israel, Lithuania, Luxembourg, Netherlands, Penrhyn Islands, Portugal, St. Vincent, Singapore, South Africa, Spain and Sweden to name a few.

In some cases, including United States, Canada, Great Britain and Switzerland, stamps were released both with and without tagging. Many of these were released during each country's experimental period. Tagged and untagged versions are listed for the aforementioned countries and are noted in some other countries' listings. For at least a few stamps, the experimentally tagged version is worth far more than its untagged counterpart, such as the 1963 experimental tagged version of France Scott 1024.

In some cases, luminescent varieties of stamps were inadvertently created. Several Russian stamps, for example, sport highly fluorescent ink that was not intended as a form of tagging. Older stamps, such as early U.S. postage dues, can be positively identified by the use of UV light, since the organic ink used has become slightly fluorescent over time. Other stamps, such as Austria Scott 70a-82a (varnish bars) and Obock Scott 46-64 (printed quadrille lines), have become fluorescent over time.

Various fluorescent substances have been added to paper to make it appear brighter. These optical brightners, as they are known, greatly affect the appearance of the stamp under UV light. The brightest of these is known as Hi-Brite paper. These paper varieties are beyond the scope of the Scott Catalogue.

Shortwave UV light also is used extensively in expertizing, since each form of paper has its own fluorescent characteristics that are impossible to perfectly match. It is therefore a simple matter to detect filled thins, added perforation teeth and other alterations that involve the addition of paper. UV light also is used to examine stamps that have had cancels chemically removed and for other purposes as well.

Gum

The Illustrated Gum Chart in the first part of this introduction shows and defines various types of gum condition. Because gum condition has an important impact on the value of unused stamps, we recommend studying this chart and the accompanying text carefully.

The gum on the back of a stamp may be shiny, dull, smooth, rough, dark, white, colored or tinted. Most stamp gumming adhesives use gum arabic or dextrine as a base. Certain polymers such as polyvinyl alcohol (PVA) have been used extensively since World War II.

The Scott Standard Postage Stamp Catalogue does not list items by types of gum. The Scott Specialized Catalogue of United States Stamps and Covers does differentiate among some types of gum for certain issues.

Reprints of stamps may have gum differing from the original issues. In addition, some countries have used different gum formulas for different seasons. These adhesives have different properties that may become more apparent over time.

Many stamps have been issued without gum, and the catalogue

will note this fact. See, for example, United States Scott 40-47. Sometimes, gum may have been removed to preserve the stamp. Germany Scott B68, for example, has a highly acidic gum that eventually destroys the stamps. This item is valued in the catalogue with gum removed.

Reprints and Reissues

These are impressions of stamps (usually obsolete) made from the original plates or stones. If they are valid for postage and reproduce obsolete issues (such as U.S. Scott 102-111), the stamps are *reissues*. If they are from current issues, they are designated as *second, third*, etc., *printing*. If designated for a particular purpose, they are called *special printings*.

When special printings are not valid for postage, but are made from original dies and plates by authorized persons, they are *official reprints*. *Private reprints* are made from the original plates and dies by private hands. An example of a private reprint is that of the 1871-1932 reprints made from the original die of the 1845 New Haven, Conn., postmaster's provisional. *Official reproductions* or imitations are made from new dies and plates by government authorization. Scott will list those reissues that are valid for postage if they differ significantly from the original printing.

The U.S. government made special printings of its first postage stamps in 1875. Produced were official imitations of the first two stamps (listed as Scott 3-4), reprints of the demonetized pre-1861 issues (Scott 40-47) and reissues of the 1861 stamps, the 1869 stamps and the then-current 1875 denominations. Even though the official imitations and the reprints were not valid for postage, Scott lists all of these U.S. special printings.

Most reprints or reissues differ slightly from the original stamp in some characteristic, such as gum, paper, perforation, color or watermark. Sometimes the details are followed so meticulously that only a student of that specific stamp is able to distinguish the reprint or reissue from the original.

Remainders and Canceled to Order

Some countries sell their stock of old stamps when a new issue replaces them. To avoid postal use, the *remainders* usually are canceled with a punch hole, a heavy line or bar, or a more-or-less regular-looking cancellation. The most famous merchant of remainders was Nicholas F. Seebeck. In the 1880s and 1890s, he arranged printing contracts between the Hamilton Bank Note Co., of which he was a director, and several Central and South American countries. The contracts provided that the plates and all remainders of the yearly issues became the property of Hamilton. Seebeck saw to it that ample stock remained. The "Seebecks," both remainders and reprints, were standard packet fillers for decades.

Some countries also issue stamps *canceled-to-order (CTO)*, either in sheets with original gum or stuck onto pieces of paper or envelopes and canceled. Such CTO items generally are worth less than postally used stamps. In cases where the CTO material is far more prevalent in the marketplace than postally used examples, the catalogue value relates to the CTO examples, with postally used examples noted as premium items. Most CTOs can be detected by the presence of gum. However, as the CTO practice goes back at least to 1885, the gum inevitably has been soaked off some stamps so they could pass as postally used. The normally applied postmarks usually differ slightly from standard postmarks, and specialists are able to tell the difference. When applied individually to envelopes by philatelically minded persons, CTO material is known as *favor canceled* and generally sells at large discounts.

Cinderellas and Facsimiles

Cinderella is a catch-all term used by stamp collectors to describe phantoms, fantasies, bogus items, municipal issues, exhibition seals, local revenues, transportation stamps, labels, poster stamps and many other types of items. Some cinderella collectors include in their collections local postage issues, telegraph stamps, essays and proofs, forgeries and counterfeits.

A *fantasy* is an adhesive created for a nonexistent stamp-issuing authority. Fantasy items range from imaginary countries (Occusi-Ambeno, Kingdom of Sedang, Principality of Trinidad or Torres Straits), to non-existent locals (Winans City Post), or nonexistent transportation lines (McRobish & Co.'s Acapulco-San Francisco Line).

On the other hand, if the entity exists and could have issued stamps (but did not) or was known to have issued other stamps, the items are considered *bogus* stamps. These would include the Mormon postage stamps of Utah, S. Allan Taylor's Guatemala and Paraguay inventions, the propaganda issues for the South Moluccas and the adhesives of the Page & Keyes local post of Boston.

Phantoms is another term for both fantasy and bogus issues.

Facsimiles are copies or imitations made to represent original stamps, but which do not pretend to be originals. A catalogue illustration is such a facsimile. Illustrations from the Moens catalogue of the last century were occasionally colored and passed off as stamps. Since the beginning of stamp collecting, facsimiles have been made for collectors as space fillers or for reference. They often carry the word "facsimile," "falsch" (German), "sanko" or "mozo" (Japanese), or "faux" (French) overprinted on the face or stamped on the back. Unfortunately, over the years a number of these items have had fake cancels applied over the facsimile notation and have been passed off as genuine.

Forgeries and Counterfeits

Forgeries and counterfeits have been with philately virtually from the beginning of stamp production. Over time, the terminology for the two has been used interchangeably. Although both forgeries and counterfeits are reproductions of stamps, the purposes behind their creation differ considerably.

Among specialists there is an increasing movement to more specifically define such items. Although there is no universally accepted terminology, we feel the following definitions most closely mirror the items and their purposes as they are currently defined.

Forgeries (also often referred to as *Counterfeits*) are reproductions of genuine stamps that have been created to defraud collectors. Such spurious items first appeared on the market around 1860, and most old-time collections contain one or more. Many are crude and easily spotted, but some can deceive experts.

An important supplier of these early philatelic forgeries was the Hamburg printer Gebruder Spiro. Many others with reputations in this craft included S. Allan Taylor, George Hussey, James Chute, George Forune, Benjamin & Sarpy, Julius Goldner, E. Oneglia and L.H. Mercier. Among the noted 20th-century forgers were Francois Fournier, Jean Sperati and the prolific Raoul DeThuin.

Forgeries may be complete replications, or they may be genuine stamps altered to resemble a scarcer (and more valuable) type. Most forgeries, particularly those of rare stamps, are worth only a small fraction of the value of a genuine example, but a few types, created by some of the most notable forgers, such as Sperati, can be worth as much or more than the genuine. Fraudulently produced copies are known of most classic rarities and many medium-priced stamps.

In addition to rare stamps, large numbers of common 19th- and early 20th-century stamps were forged to supply stamps to the early packet trade. Many can still be easily found. Few new philatelic forgeries have appeared in recent decades. Successful imitation of well-engraved work is virtually impossible. It has proven far easier to produce a fake by altering a genuine stamp than to duplicate a stamp completely.

Counterfeit (also often referred to as *Postal Counterfeit* or *Postal Forgery*) is the term generally applied to reproductions of stamps that have been created to defraud the government of revenue. Such items usually are created at the time a stamp is current and, in some cases, are hard to detect. Because most counterfeits are seized when the perpetrator is captured, postal counterfeits, particularly used on cover, are usually worth much more than a genuine example to specialists. The first postal counterfeit was of Spain's 4-cuarto carmine of 1854 (the real one is Scott 25). Apparently, the counterfeiters were not satisfied with their first version, which is now very scarce, and they soon created an engraved counterfeit, which is common. Postal counterfeits quickly followed in Austria, Naples, Sardinia and the Roman States. They have since been created in many other countries as well, including the United States.

An infamous counterfeit to defraud the government is the 1-shilling Great Britain "Stock Exchange" forgery of 1872, used on telegraph forms at the exchange that year. The stamp escaped detection until a stamp dealer noticed it in 1898.

Fakes

Fakes are genuine stamps altered in some way to make them more desirable. One student of this part of stamp collecting has estimated that by the 1950s more than 30,000 varieties of fakes were known. That number has grown greatly since then. The widespread existence of fakes makes it important for stamp collectors to study their philatelic holdings and use relevant literature. Likewise, collectors should buy from reputable dealers who guarantee their stamps and make full and prompt refunds should a purchased item be declared faked or altered by some mutually agreed-upon authority. Because fakes always have some genuine characteristics, it is not always possible to obtain unanimous agreement among experts regarding specific items. These students may change their opinions as philatelic knowledge increases. More than 80 percent of all fakes on the philatelic market today are regummed, reperforated (or perforated for the first time), or bear forged overprints, surcharges or cancellations.

Stamps can be chemically treated to alter or eliminate colors. For example, a pale rose stamp can be re-colored to resemble a blue shade of high market value. In other cases, treated stamps can be made to resemble missing color varieties. Designs may be changed by painting, or a stroke or a dot added or bleached out to turn an ordinary variety into a seemingly scarcer stamp. Part of a stamp can be bleached and reprinted in a different version, achieving an inverted center or frame. Margins can be added or repairs done so deceptively that the stamps move from the "repaired" into the "fake" category.

Fakers have not left the backs of the stamps untouched either. They may create false watermarks, add fake grills or press out genuine grills. A thin India paper proof may be glued onto a thicker backing to create the appearance an issued stamp, or a proof printed on cardboard may be shaved down and perforated to resemble a stamp. Silk threads are impressed into paper and stamps have been split so that a rare paper variety is added to an otherwise inexpensive stamp. The most common treatment to the back of a stamp, however, is regumming.

Some in the business of faking stamps have openly advertised fool-proof application of "original gum" to stamps that lack it, although most publications now ban such ads from their pages. It is believed that very few early stamps have survived without being hinged. The large number of never-hinged examples of such earlier material offered for sale thus suggests the widespread extent of regumming activity. Regumming also may be used to hide repairs or thin spots. Dipping the stamp into watermark fluid, or examining it under longwave ultraviolet light often will reveal these flaws.

Fakers also tamper with separations. Ingenious ways to add margins are known. Perforated wide-margin stamps may be falsely represented as imperforate when trimmed. Reperforating is commonly done to create scarce coil or perforation varieties, and to eliminate the naturally occurring straight-edge stamps found in sheet margin positions of many earlier issues. Custom has made straight-edged stamps less desirable. Fakers have obliged by perforating straight-edged stamps so that many are now uncommon, if not rare.

Another fertile field for the faker is that of overprints, surcharges and cancellations. The forging of rare surcharges or overprints began in the 1880s or 1890s. These forgeries are sometimes difficult to detect, but experts have identified almost all. Occasionally, overprints or cancellations are removed to create non-overprinted stamps or seemingly unused items. This is most commonly done by removing a manuscript cancel to make a stamp resemble an unused example. "SPECIMEN" overprints may be removed by scraping and repainting to create non-overprinted varieties. Fakers use inexpensive revenues or pencanceled stamps to generate unused stamps for further faking by adding other markings. The quartz lamp or UV lamp and a high-powered magnifying glass help to easily detect removed cancellations.

The bigger problem, however, is the addition of overprints, surcharges or cancellations - many with such precision that they are very difficult to ascertain. Plating of the stamps or the overprint can be an important method of detection.

Fake postmarks may range from many spurious fancy cancellations to a host of markings applied to transatlantic covers, to adding normally appearing postmarks to definitives of some countries with stamps that are valued far higher used than unused. With the increased popularity of cover collecting, and the widespread interest in postal history, a fertile new field for fakers has come about. Some have tried to create entire covers. Others specialize in adding stamps, tied by fake cancellations, to genuine stampless covers, or replacing less expensive or damaged stamps with more valuable ones. Detailed study of postal rates in effect at the time a cover in question was mailed, including the analysis of each handstamp used during the period, ink analysis and similar techniques, usually will unmask the fraud.

Restoration and Repairs

Scott bases its catalogue values on stamps that are free of defects and otherwise meet the standards set forth earlier in this introduction. Most stamp collectors desire to have the finest copy of an item possible. Even within given grading categories there are variances. This leads to a controversial practice that is not defined in any universal manner: stamp *restoration*.

There are broad differences of opinion about what is permissible when it comes to restoration. Carefully applying a soft eraser to a stamp or cover to remove light soiling is one form of restoration, as is washing a stamp in mild soap and water to clean it. These are fairly accepted forms of restoration. More severe forms of restoration include pressing out creases or removing stains caused by tape. To what degree each of these is acceptable is dependent upon the individual situation. Further along the spectrum is the freshening of a stamp's color by removing oxide build-up or the effects of wax paper left next to stamps shipped to the tropics.

At some point in this spectrum the concept of *repair* replaces that of restoration. Repairs include filling thin spots, mending tears by reweaving or adding a missing perforation tooth. Regumming stamps may have been acceptable as a restoration or repair technique many decades ago, but today it is considered a form of fakery.

Restored stamps may or may not sell at a discount, and it is possible that the value of individual restored items may be enhanced over that of their pre-restoration state. Specific situations dictate the resultant value of such an item. Repaired stamps sell at substantial discounts from the value of sound stamps.

Terminology

Booklets — Many countries have issued stamps in small booklets for the convenience of users. This idea continues to become increasingly popular in many countries. Booklets have been issued in many sizes and forms, often with advertising on the covers, the panes of stamps or on the interleaving.

The panes used in booklets may be printed from special plates or made from regular sheets. All panes from booklets issued by the United States and many from those of other countries contain stamps that are straight edged on the sides, but perforated between. Others are distinguished by orientation of watermark or other identifying features. Any stamp-like unit in the pane, either printed or blank, that is not a postage stamp, is considered to be a *label* in the catalogue listings.

Scott lists and values booklet panes. Modern complete booklets also are listed and valued. Individual booklet panes are listed only when they are not fashioned from existing sheet stamps and, therefore, are identifiable from their sheet stamp counterparts.

Panes usually do not have a used value assigned to them because there is little market activity for used booklet panes, even though many exist used and there is some demand for them.

Cancellations — The marks or obliterations put on stamps by postal authorities to show that they have performed service and to prevent their reuse are known as cancellations. If the marking is made with a pen, it is considered a "pen cancel." When the location of the post office appears in the marking, it is a "town cancellation." A "postmark" is technically any postal marking, but in practice the term generally is applied to a town cancellation with a date. When calling attention to a cause or celebration, the marking is known as a "slogan cancellation." Many other types and styles of cancellations exist, such as duplex, numerals, targets, fancy and others. See also "precancels," below.

Coil Stamps — These are stamps that are issued in rolls for use in dispensers, affixing and vending machines. Those coils of the United States, Canada, Sweden and some other countries are perforated horizontally or vertically only, with the outer edges imperforate. Coil stamps of some countries, such as Great Britain and Germany, are perforated on all four sides and may in some cases be distinguished from their sheet stamp counterparts by watermarks, counting numbers on the reverse or other means.

Covers — Entire envelopes, with or without adhesive postage stamps, that have passed through the mail and bear postal or other markings of philatelic interest are known as covers. Before the introduction of envelopes in about 1840, people folded letters and wrote the address on the outside. Some people covered their letters with an extra sheet of paper on the outside for the address, producing the term "cover." Used airletter sheets, stamped envelopes and other items of postal stationery also are considered covers.

Errors — Stamps that have some major, consistent, unintentional deviation from the normal are considered errors. Errors include, but are not limited to, missing or wrong colors, wrong paper, wrong watermarks, inverted centers or frames on multicolor printing, inverted or missing surcharges or overprints, double impressions, missing perforations, unintentionally omitted tagging and others. Factually wrong or misspelled information, if it appears on all examples of a stamp, are not considered errors in the true sense of the word. They are errors of design. Inconsistent or randomly appearing items, such as misperfs or color shifts, are classified as freaks.

Color-Omitted Errors — This term refers to stamps where a missing color is caused by the complete failure of the printing plate to deliver ink to the stamp paper or any other paper. Generally, this is caused by the printing plate not being engaged on the press or the ink station running dry of ink during printing.

Color-Missing Errors — This term refers to stamps where a color or colors were printed somewhere but do not appear on the finished stamp. There are four different classes of color-missing errors, and the catalog indicates with a two-letter code appended to each such listing what caused the color to be missing. These codes are used only for the United States' color-missing error listings.

FO = A *foldover* of the stamp sheet during printing may block ink from appearing on a stamp. Instead, the color will appear on the back of the foldover (where it might fall on the back of the selvage or perhaps on the back of the stamp or another stamp). FO also will be used in the case of foldunders, where the paper may fold underneath the other stamp paper and the color will print on the platen.

EP = A piece of *extraneous paper* falling across the plate or stamp paper will receive the printed ink. When the extraneous paper is removed, an unprinted portion of stamp paper remains and shows partially or totally missing colors.

CM = A misregistration of the printing plates during printing will result in a *color misregistration*, and such a misregistraion may result in a color not appearing on the finished stamp.

PS = A *perforation shift* after printing may remove a color from the finished stamp. Normally, this will occur on a row of stamps at the edge of the stamp pane.

Measurements – When measurements are given in the Scott catalogues for stamp size, grill size or any other reason, the first measurement given is always for the top and bottom dimension, while the second measurement will be for the sides (just as perforation gauges are measured). Thus, a stamp size of 15mm x 21mm will indicate a vertically oriented stamp 15mm wide at top and bottom, and 21mm tall at the sides. The same principle holds for measuring or counting items such as U.S. grills. A grill count of 22x18 points (B grill) indicates that there are 22 grill points across by 18 grill points down.

Overprints and Surcharges — Overprinting involves applying wording or design elements over an already existing stamp. Overprints can be used to alter the place of use (such as "Canal Zone" on U.S. stamps), to adapt them for a special purpose ("Porto" on Denmark's 1913-20 regular issues for use as postage due stamps, Scott J1-J7) or to commemorate a special occasion (United States Scott 647-648).

A *surcharge* is a form of overprint that changes or restates the face value of a stamp or piece of postal stationery.

Surcharges and overprints may be handstamped, typeset or, occasionally, lithographed or engraved. A few hand-written overprints and surcharges are known.

Personalized Stamps — In 1999, Australia issued stamps with se-tenant labels that could be personalized with pictures of the customer's choice. Other countries quickly followed suit, with some offering to print the selected picture on the stamp itself within a frame that was used exclusively for personalized issues. As the picture used on these stamps or labels vary, listings for such stamps are for any picture within the common frame (or any picture on a se-tenant label), be it a "generic" image or one produced especially for a customer, almost invariably at a premium price.

Precancels — Stamps that are canceled before they are placed in the mail are known as precancels. Precanceling usually is done to expedite the handling of large mailings and generally allow the affected mail pieces to skip certain phases of mail handling.

In the United States, precancellations generally identified the point of origin; that is, the city and state. This information appeared across the face of the stamp, usually centered between parallel lines. More recently, bureau precancels retained the parallel lines, but the city and state designations were dropped. Recent coils have a service inscription that is present on the original printing plate. These show the mail service paid for by the stamp. Since these stamps are not intended to receive further cancellations when used as intended, they are considered precancels. Such items often do not have parallel lines as part of the precancellation.

In France, the abbreviation *Affranchts* in a semicircle together with the word *Postes* is the general form of precancel in use. Belgian precancellations usually appear in a box in which the name of the city appears. Netherlands precancels have the name of the city enclosed between concentric circles, sometimes called a "lifesaver." Precancellations of other countries usually follow these patterns, but may be any arrangement of bars, boxes and city names.

Precancels are listed in the Scott catalogues only if the precancel changes the denomination (Belgium Scott 477-478); if the precanceled stamp is different from the non-precanceled version (such as untagged U.S. precancels); or if the stamp exists only precanceled (France Scott 1096-1099, U.S. Scott 2265).

Proofs and Essays — Proofs are impressions taken from an approved die, plate or stone in which the design and color are the same as the stamp issued to the public. Trial color proofs are impressions taken from approved dies, plates or stones in colors that vary from the final version. An essay is the impression of a design that differs in some way from the issued stamp. "Progressive die proofs" generally are considered to be essays.

Provisionals — These are stamps that are issued on short notice and intended for temporary use pending the arrival of regular issues. They usually are issued to meet such contingencies as changes in government or currency, shortage of necessary postage values or military occupation.

During the 1840s, postmasters in certain American cities issued stamps that were valid only at specific post offices. In 1861, postmasters of the Confederate States also issued stamps with limited validity. Both of these examples are known as "postmaster's provisionals."

Se-tenant — This term refers to an unsevered pair, strip or block of stamps that differ in design, denomination or overprint.

Unless the se-tenant item has a continuous design (see U.S. Scott 1451a, 1694a) the stamps do not have to be in the same order as shown in the catalogue (see U.S. Scott 2158a).

Specimens — The Universal Postal Union required member nations to send samples of all stamps they released into service to the International Bureau in Switzerland. Member nations of the UPU received these specimens as samples of what stamps were valid for postage. Many are overprinted, handstamped or initial-perforated "Specimen," "Canceled" or "Muestra." Some are marked with bars across the denominations (China-Taiwan), punched holes (Czechoslovakia) or back inscriptions (Mongolia).

Stamps distributed to government officials or for publicity purposes, and stamps submitted by private security printers for official approval, also may receive such defacements.

The previously described defacement markings prevent postal use, and all such items generally are known as "specimens."

Tete Beche — This term describes a pair of stamps in which one is upside down in relation to the other. Some of these are the result of intentional sheet arrangements, such as Morocco Scott B10-B11. Others occurred when one or more electrotypes accidentally were placed upside down on the plate, such as Colombia Scott 57a. Separation of the tete-beche stamps, of course, destroys the tete beche variety.

Pronunciation Symbols

ə .... banana, collide, abut

ˈə, ˌə .... humdrum, abut

ə .... immediately preceding \l\, \n\, \m\, \ŋ\, as in battle, mitten, eaten, and sometimes open \ˈō-pᵊm\, lock and key \-ᵊŋ-\; immediately following \l\, \m\, \r\, as often in French table, prisme, titre

ər .... further, merger, bird

ˈər-
ˈə-r } .... as in two different pronunciations of hurry \ˈhər-ē, ˈhə-rē\

a .... mat, map, mad, gag, snap, patch

ā .... day, fade, date, aorta, drape, cape

ä .... bother, cot, and, with most American speakers, father, cart

à .... father as pronounced by speakers who do not rhyme it with bother; French patte

aù .... now, loud, out

b .... baby, rib

ch .... chin, nature \ˈnā-chər\

d .... did, adder

e .... bet, bed, peck

ˈē, ˌē .... beat, nosebleed, evenly, easy

ē .... easy, mealy

f .... fifty, cuff

g .... go, big, gift

h .... hat, ahead

hw .... whale as pronounced by those who do not have the same pronunciation for both whale and wail

i .... tip, banish, active

ī .... site, side, buy, tripe

j .... job, gem, edge, join, judge

k .... kin, cook, ache

ḳ .... German ich, Buch; one pronunciation of loch

l .... lily, pool

m .... murmur, dim, nymph

n .... no, own

ⁿ .... indicates that a preceding vowel or diphthong is pronounced with the nasal passages open, as in French un bon vin blanc \œⁿ -bōⁿ -vaⁿ -blä ⁿ\

ŋ .... sing \ˈsiŋ\, singer \ˈsiŋ-ər\, finger \ˈfiŋ-gər\, ink \ˈiŋk\

ō .... bone, know, beau

ȯ .... saw, all, gnaw, caught

œ .... French boeuf, German Hölle

œ̄ .... French feu, German Höhle

ȯi .... coin, destroy

p .... pepper, lip

r .... red, car, rarity

s .... source, less

sh .... as in shy, mission, machine, special (actually, this is a single sound, not two); with a hyphen between, two sounds as in grasshopper \ˈgras-ˌhä-pər\

t .... tie, attack, late, later, latter

th .... as in thin, ether (actually, this is a single sound, not two); with a hyphen between, two sounds as in knighthood \ˈnīt-ˌhùd\

th .... then, either, this (actually, this is a single sound, not two)

ü .... rule, youth, union \ˈyün-yən\, few \ˈfyü\

ù .... pull, wood, book, curable \ˈkyùr-ə-bəl\, fury \ˈfyùr-ē\

ue .... German füllen, hübsch

ūe .... French rue, German fühlen

v .... vivid, give

w .... we, away

y .... yard, young, cue \ˈkyü\, mute \ˈmyüt\, union \ˈyün-yən\

ʸ .... indicates that during the articulation of the sound represented by the preceding character the front of the tongue has substantially the position it has for the articulation of the first sound of yard, as in French digne \dēnʸ\

z .... zone, raise

zh .... as in vision, azure \ˈa-zhər\ (actually, this is a single sound, not two); with a hyphen between, two sounds as in hogshead \ˈhȯgz-ˌhed, ˈhägz-\

\ .... slant line used in pairs to mark the beginning and end of a transcription: \ˈpen\

ˈ .... mark preceding a syllable with primary (strongest) stress: \ˈpen-mən-ˌship\

ˌ .... mark preceding a syllable with secondary (medium) stress: \ˈpen-mən-ˌship\

- .... mark of syllable division

( ) .... indicate that what is symbolized between is present in some utterances but not in others: factory \ˈfak-t(ə-)rē\

÷ .... indicates that many regard as unacceptable the pronunciation variant immediately following: cupola \ˈkyü-pə-lə, ÷-ˌlō\

COMMON DESIGN TYPES

Pictured in this section are issues where one illustration has been used for a number of countries in the Catalogue. Not included in this section are overprinted stamps or those issues which are illustrated in each country. Because the location of Never Hinged breakpoints varies from country to country, some of the values in the listings below will be for unused stamps that were previously hinged.

EUROPA
Europa, 1956

The design symbolizing the cooperation among the six countries comprising the Coal and Steel Community is illustrated in each country.

Belgium		*496-497*
France		*805-806*
Germany		*748-749*
Italy		*715-716*
Luxembourg		*318-320*
Netherlands		*368-369*

Nos. 496-497 (2)	9.00	.70
Nos. 805-806 (2)	5.25	1.00
Nos. 748-749 (2)	7.30	1.20
Nos. 715-716 (2)	11.50	1.25
Nos. 318-320 (3)	65.50	42.00
Nos. 368-369 (2)	72.50	1.75
Set total (13) Stamps	171.05	47.90

Europa, 1958

"E" and
Dove — CD1

European Postal Union at the service of European integration.

1958, Sept. 13

Belgium		527-528
France		889-890
Germany		790-791
Italy		750-751
Luxembourg		341-343
Netherlands		375-376
Saar		317-318

Nos. 527-528 (2)	4.25	.60
Nos. 889-890 (2)	1.65	.55
Nos. 790-791 (2)	3.65	.65
Nos. 750-751 (2)	1.85	.60
Nos. 341-343 (3)	2.35	1.15
Nos. 375-376 (2)	2.50	.75
Nos. 317-318 (2)	1.05	2.30
Set total (15) Stamps	17.30	6.60

Europa, 1959

6-Link Enless
Chain — CD2

1959, Sept. 19

Belgium		536-537
France		929-930
Germany		805-806
Italy		791-792
Luxembourg		354-355
Netherlands		379-380

Nos. 536-537 (2)	1.55	.60
Nos. 929-930 (2)	1.40	.80
Nos. 805-806 (2)	1.55	.65
Nos. 791-792 (2)	.80	.50
Nos. 354-355 (2)	3.50	1.40
Nos. 379-380 (2)	9.90	1.25
Set total (12) Stamps	18.70	5.20

Europa, 1960

19-Spoke
Wheel
CD3

First anniverary of the establishment of C.E.P.T. (Conference Europeenne des Administrations des Postes et des Telecommunications.) The spokes symbolize the 19 founding members of the Conference.

1960, Sept.

Belgium		553-554
Denmark		379
Finland		376-377
France		970-971
Germany		818-820
Great Britain		377-378
Greece		688
Iceland		327-328
Ireland		175-176
Italy		809-810
Luxembourg		374-375
Netherlands		385-386
Norway		387
Portugal		866-867
Spain		941-942
Sweden		562-563
Switzerland		400-401
Turkey		1493-1494

Nos. 553-554 (2)	1.25	.55
No. 379 (1)	.55	.50
Nos. 376-377 (2)	1.70	1.80
Nos. 970-971 (2)	.50	.50
Nos. 818-820 (3)	2.25	1.50
Nos. 377-378 (2)	9.00	5.00
No. 688 (1)	5.00	2.00
Nos. 327-328 (2)	1.30	1.85
Nos. 175-176 (2)	75.00	14.00
Nos. 809-810 (2)	.70	.50
Nos. 374-375 (2)	1.00	.40
Nos. 385-386 (2)	3.65	1.50
No. 387 (1)	1.25	1.25
Nos. 866-867 (2)	2.25	1.25
Nos. 941-942 (2)	1.50	.75
Nos. 562-563 (2)	1.05	.55
Nos. 400-401 (2)	1.25	.65
Nos. 1493-1494 (2)	2.10	1.35
Set total (34) Stamps	111.30	36.30

Europa, 1961

19 Doves
Flying as
One — CD4

The 19 doves represent the 19 members of the Conference of European Postal and Telecommunications Administrations C.E.P.T.

1961-62

Belgium		572-573
Cyprus		201-203
France		1005-1006
Germany		844-845
Great Britain		382-384
Greece		718-719
Iceland		340-341
Italy		845-846
Luxembourg		382-383
Netherlands		387-388
Spain		1010-1011
Switzerland		410-411
Turkey		1518-1520

Nos. 572-573 (2)	.75	.50
Nos. 201-203 (3)	2.10	1.20
Nos. 1005-1006 (2)	.50	.50
Nos. 844-845 (2)	.60	.75
Nos. 382-384 (3)	.75	.90
Nos. 718-719 (2)	.80	.50
Nos. 340-341 (2)	1.10	1.60
Nos. 845-846 (2)	.55	.50
Nos. 382-383 (2)	.70	.70
Nos. 387-388 (2)	.55	.50
Nos. 1010-1011 (2)	.70	.55
Nos. 410-411 (2)	1.25	.60
Nos. 1518-1520 (3)	2.45	1.30
Set total (29) Stamps	12.80	10.10

Europa, 1962

Young Tree
with 19
Leaves
CD5

The 19 leaves represent the 19 original members of C.E.P.T.

1962-63

Belgium		582-583
Cyprus		219-221
France		1045-1046
Germany		852-853
Greece		739-740
Iceland		348-349
Ireland		184-185
Italy		860-861
Luxembourg		386-387
Netherlands		394-395
Norway		414-415
Switzerland		416-417
Turkey		1553-1555

Nos. 582-583 (2)	.65	.65
Nos. 219-221 (3)	76.25	6.75
Nos. 1045-1046 (2)	.60	.50
Nos. 852-853 (2)	.70	.80
Nos. 739-740 (2)	2.25	1.15
Nos. 348-349 (2)	.85	.85
Nos. 184-185 (2)	2.00	1.50
Nos. 860-861 (2)	1.35	.55
Nos. 386-387 (2)	.85	.70
Nos. 394-395 (2)	1.40	.75
Nos. 414-415 (2)	2.25	2.25
Nos. 416-417 (2)	1.65	1.00
Nos. 1553-1555 (3)	3.00	1.55
Set total (28) Stamps	93.80	19.00

Europa, 1963

Stylized
Links,
Symbolizing
Unity — CD6

1963, Sept.

Belgium		598-599
Cyprus		229-231
Finland		419
France		1074-1075
Germany		867-868
Greece		768-769
Iceland		357-358
Ireland		188-189
Italy		880-881
Luxembourg		403-404
Netherlands		416-417
Norway		441-442
Switzerland		429
Turkey		1602-1603

Nos. 598-599 (2)	1.60	.55
Nos. 229-231 (3)	64.00	9.40
No. 419 (1)	1.25	.55
Nos. 1074-1075 (2)	.60	.50
Nos. 867-868 (2)	.50	.55
Nos. 768-769 (2)	5.25	1.90
Nos. 357-358 (2)	1.20	1.20
Nos. 188-189 (2)	4.75	3.25
Nos. 880-881 (2)	.65	.50
Nos. 403-404 (2)	1.00	.80
Nos. 416-417 (2)	2.25	1.00
Nos. 441-442 (2)	4.75	3.00
No. 429 (1)	.90	.60
Nos. 1602-1603 (2)	1.40	.60
Set total (27) Stamps	90.10	24.40

Europa, 1964

Symbolic
Daisy — CD7

5th anniversary of the establishment of C.E.P.T. The 22 petals of the flower symbolize the 22 members of the Conference.

1964, Sept.

Austria		738
Belgium		614-615
Cyprus		244-246
France		1109-1110
Germany		897-898
Greece		801-802
Iceland		367-368
Ireland		196-197
Italy		894-895
Luxembourg		411-412
Monaco		590-591
Netherlands		428-429
Norway		458
Portugal		931-933
Spain		1262-1263
Switzerland		438-439
Turkey		1628-1629

No. 738 (1)	1.20	.80
Nos. 614-615 (2)	1.40	.60
Nos. 244-246 (3)	32.25	5.10
Nos. 1109-1110 (2)	.50	.50
Nos. 897-898 (2)	.50	.50
Nos. 801-802 (2)	5.00	1.90
Nos. 367-368 (2)	1.40	1.15
Nos. 196-197 (2)	20.00	4.25
Nos. 894-895 (2)	.55	.50
Nos. 411-412 (2)	.90	.55
Nos. 590-591 (2)	2.50	.70
Nos. 428-429 (2)	1.80	.60
No. 458 (1)	4.50	4.50
Nos. 931-933 (3)	10.00	2.00
Nos. 1262-1263 (2)	1.30	.80
Nos. 438-439 (2)	1.60	.50
Nos. 1628-1629 (2)	2.65	1.35
Set total (34) Stamps	88.05	26.30

Europa, 1965

Leaves and
"Fruit"
CD8

1965

Belgium		636-637
Cyprus		262-264
Finland		437
France		1131-1132
Germany		934-935
Greece		833-834
Iceland		375-376
Ireland		204-205
Italy		915-916
Luxembourg		432-433
Monaco		616-617
Netherlands		438-439
Norway		475-476
Portugal		958-960
Switzerland		469
Turkey		1665-1666

Nos. 636-637 (2)	.50	.50
Nos. 262-264 (3)	25.35	6.00
No. 437 (1)	1.25	.55
Nos. 1131-1132 (2)	.70	.55
Nos. 934-935 (2)	.50	.50
Nos. 833-834 (2)	2.25	1.15
Nos. 375-376 (2)	2.50	1.75
Nos. 204-205 (2)	20.00	3.35
Nos. 915-916 (2)	.50	.50
Nos. 432-433 (2)	.80	.60
Nos. 616-617 (2)	3.25	1.65
Nos. 438-439 (2)	.75	.55
Nos. 475-476 (2)	4.00	3.10
Nos. 958-960 (3)	10.00	2.75
No. 469 (1)	1.15	.25
Nos. 1665-1666 (2)	3.50	2.10
Set total (32) Stamps	77.00	25.85

Europa, 1966

Symbolic
Sailboat — CD9

1966, Sept.

Andorra, French		172
Belgium		675-676
Cyprus		275-277
France		1163-1164
Germany		963-964

Greece................................862-863
Iceland................................384-385
Ireland................................216-217
Italy................................942-943
Liechtenstein........................415
Luxembourg..........................440-441
Monaco................................639-640
Netherlands..........................441-442
Norway................................496-497
Portugal................................980-982
Switzerland..........................477-478
Turkey................................1718-1719

No. 172 (1)	3.00	3.00
Nos. 675-676 (2)	.80	.50
Nos. 275-277 (3)	4.75	2.75
Nos. 1163-1164 (2)	.55	.50
Nos. 963-964 (2)	.50	.55
Nos. 862-863 (2)	2.25	1.05
Nos. 384-385 (2)	4.50	3.50
Nos. 216-217 (2)	7.00	2.00
Nos. 942-943 (2)	.50	.50
No. 415 (1)	.40	.35
Nos. 440-441 (2)	.80	.60
Nos. 639-640 (2)	2.00	.65
Nos. 441-442 (2)	1.50	.65
Nos. 496-497 (2)	5.00	3.00
Nos. 980-982 (3)	9.75	2.25
Nos. 477-478 (2)	1.60	.60
Nos. 1718-1719 (2)	3.35	1.75
Set total (34) Stamps	48.25	24.20

Europa, 1967

Cogwheels
CD10

1967

Andorra, French 174-175
Belgium................................688-689
Cyprus................................297-299
France................................1178-1179
Germany................................969-970
Greece................................891-892
Iceland................................389-390
Ireland................................232-233
Italy................................951-952
Liechtenstein........................420
Luxembourg..........................449-450
Monaco................................669-670
Netherlands..........................444-447
Norway................................504-505
Portugal................................994-996
Spain................................1465-1466
Switzerland..........................482
Turkey................................B120-B121

Nos. 174-175 (2)	10.75	6.25
Nos. 688-689 (2)	1.05	.55
Nos. 297-299 (3)	4.25	2.50
Nos. 1178-1179 (2)	.55	.50
Nos. 969-970 (2)	.55	.55
Nos. 891-892 (2)	3.75	1.00
Nos. 389-390 (2)	3.00	2.00
Nos. 232-233 (2)	6.15	2.30
Nos. 951-952 (2)	.60	.50
No. 420 (1)	.45	.40
Nos. 449-450 (2)	1.00	.70
Nos. 669-670 (2)	2.75	.70
Nos. 444-447 (4)	5.00	1.85
Nos. 504-505 (2)	3.25	2.75
Nos. 994-996 (3)	9.50	1.85
Nos. 1465-1466 (2)	.50	.50
No. 482 (1)	.70	.25
Nos. B120-B121 (2)	3.50	2.75
Set total (38) Stamps	57.30	27.90

Europa, 1968

Golden Key
with
C.E.P.T.
Emblem
CD11

1968

Andorra, French 182-183
Belgium................................705-706
Cyprus................................314-316
France................................1209-1210
Germany................................983-984
Greece................................916-917
Iceland................................395-396
Ireland................................242-243
Italy................................979-980

Liechtenstein 442
Luxembourg 466-467
Monaco 689-691
Netherlands 452-453
Portugal 1019-1021
San Marino 687
Spain 1526
Switzerland 488
Turkey 1775-1776

Nos. 182-183 (2)	16.50	10.00
Nos. 705-706 (2)	1.25	.50
Nos. 314-316 (3)	2.90	2.50
Nos. 1209-1210 (2)	.85	.55
Nos. 983-984 (2)	.50	.55
Nos. 916-917 (2)	3.75	1.65
Nos. 395-396 (2)	3.00	2.20
Nos. 242-243 (2)	3.75	3.00
Nos. 979-980 (2)	.50	.50
No. 442 (1)	.45	.40
Nos. 466-467 (2)	.80	.70
Nos. 689-691 (3)	5.40	.95
Nos. 452-453 (2)	2.10	.70
Nos. 1019-1021 (3)	9.75	2.10
No. 687 (1)	.55	.35
No. 1526 (1)	.25	.25
No. 488 (1)	.45	.25
Nos. 1775-1776 (2)	5.00	2.00
Set total (35) Stamps	57.75	29.15

Europa, 1969

"EUROPA"
and "CEPT"
CD12

Tenth anniversary of C.E.P.T.

1969

Andorra, French 188-189
Austria................................837
Belgium................................718-719
Cyprus................................326-328
Denmark................................458
Finland................................483
France................................1245-1246
Germany................................996-997
Great Britain........................585
Greece................................947-948
Iceland................................406-407
Ireland................................270-271
Italy................................1000-1001
Liechtenstein........................453
Luxembourg..........................475-476
Monaco................................722-724
Netherlands..........................475-476
Norway................................533-534
Portugal................................1038-1040
San Marino..........................701-702
Spain................................1567
Sweden................................814-816
Switzerland..........................500-501
Turkey................................1799-1800
Vatican................................470-472
Yugoslavia..........................1003-1004

Nos. 188-189 (2)	18.50	12.00
No. 837 (1)	.65	.30
Nos. 718-719 (2)	.75	.50
Nos. 326-328 (3)	3.00	2.25
No. 458 (1)	.75	.75
No. 483 (1)	3.50	.75
Nos. 1245-1246 (2)	.55	.50
Nos. 996-997 (2)	.80	.50
No. 585 (1)	.25	.25
Nos. 947-948 (2)	5.00	1.50
Nos. 406-407 (2)	4.20	2.40
Nos. 270-271 (2)	4.00	2.00
Nos. 1000-1001 (2)	.70	.50
No. 453 (1)	.45	.45
Nos. 475-476 (2)	1.00	.70
Nos. 722-724 (3)	10.50	2.00
Nos. 475-476 (2)	2.60	1.15
Nos. 533-534 (2)	3.75	2.35
Nos. 1038-1040 (3)	17.75	2.40
Nos. 701-702 (2)	.90	.90
No. 1567 (1)	.25	.25
Nos. 814-816 (3)	4.00	2.85
Nos. 500-501 (2)	1.85	.60
Nos. 1799-1800 (2)	3.85	2.25
Nos. 470-472 (2)	.75	.75
Nos. 1003-1004 (2)	4.00	4.00
Set total (51) Stamps	94.30	44.85

Europa, 1970

Interwoven
Threads
CD13

1970

Andorra, French 196-197
Belgium................................741-742
Cyprus................................340-342
France................................1271-1272
Germany................................1018-1019
Greece................................985, 987
Iceland................................420-421
Ireland................................279-281
Italy................................1013-1014
Liechtenstein........................470
Luxembourg..........................489-490
Monaco................................768-770
Netherlands..........................483-484
Portugal................................1060-1062
San Marino..........................729-730
Spain................................1607
Switzerland..........................515-516
Turkey................................1848-1849
Yugoslavia..........................1024-1025

Nos. 196-197 (2)	20.00	8.50
Nos. 741-742 (2)	1.10	.55
Nos. 340-342 (3)	2.70	2.75
Nos. 1271-1272 (2)	.65	.50
Nos. 1018-1019 (2)	.60	.50
Nos. 985, 987 (2)	7.75	2.00
Nos. 420-421 (2)	6.00	4.00
Nos. 279-281 (3)	9.50	3.30
Nos. 1013-1014 (2)	.65	.50
No. 470 (1)	.45	.45
Nos. 489-490 (2)	.80	.80
Nos. 768-770 (3)	6.35	2.10
Nos. 483-484 (2)	2.50	1.15
Nos. 1060-1062 (3)	9.75	2.35
Nos. 729-730 (2)	.90	.55
No. 1607 (1)	.25	.25
Nos. 515-516 (2)	1.85	.60
Nos. 1848-1849 (2)	5.00	2.25
Nos. 1024-1025 (2)	.80	.80
Set total (40) Stamps	77.60	33.90

Europa, 1971

"Fraternity,
Cooperation,
Common
Effort"
CD14

1971

Andorra, French 205-206
Belgium................................803-804
Cyprus................................365-367
Finland................................504
France................................1304
Germany................................1064-1065
Greece................................1029-1030
Iceland................................429-430
Ireland................................305-306
Italy................................1038-1039
Liechtenstein........................485
Luxembourg..........................500-501
Malta................................425-427
Monaco................................797-799
Netherlands..........................488-489
Portugal................................1094-1096
San Marino..........................749-750
Spain................................1675-1676
Switzerland..........................531-532
Turkey................................1876-1877
Yugoslavia..........................1052-1053

Nos. 205-206 (2)	20.00	7.75
Nos. 803-804 (2)	1.30	.55
Nos. 365-367 (3)	2.60	3.25
No. 504 (1)	5.00	.75
No. 1304 (1)	.45	.40
Nos. 1064-1065 (2)	.60	.50
Nos. 1029-1030 (2)	4.00	1.80
Nos. 429-430 (2)	5.00	3.75
Nos. 305-306 (2)	5.00	1.50
Nos. 1038-1039 (2)	.65	.50
No. 485 (1)	.45	.45
Nos. 500-501 (2)	1.00	.80
Nos. 425-427 (3)	.80	.80
Nos. 797-799 (3)	15.00	2.80
Nos. 488-489 (2)	2.50	1.15
Nos. 1094-1096 (3)	9.75	1.75
Nos. 749-750 (2)	.65	.55
Nos. 1675-1676 (2)	.75	.55
Nos. 531-532 (2)	1.85	.65
Nos. 1876-1877 (2)	5.60	2.50
Nos. 1052-1053 (2)	.50	.50
Set total (43) Stamps	83.45	33.25

Europa, 1972

Sparkles, Symbolic
of Communications
CD15

1972

Andorra, French 210-211
Andorra, Spanish 62
Belgium................................825-826
Cyprus................................380-382
Finland................................512-513
France................................1341
Germany................................1089-1090
Greece................................1049-1050
Iceland................................439-440
Ireland................................316-317
Italy................................1065-1066
Liechtenstein........................504
Luxembourg..........................512-513
Malta................................450-453
Monaco................................831-832
Netherlands..........................494-495
Portugal................................1141-1143
San Marino..........................771-772
Spain................................1718
Switzerland..........................544-545
Turkey................................1907-1908
Yugoslavia..........................1100-1101

Nos. 210-211 (2)	21.00	7.00
No. 62 (1)	45.00	45.00
Nos. 825-826 (2)	.95	.55
Nos. 380-382 (3)	5.95	4.25
Nos. 512-513 (2)	7.00	1.40
No. 1341 (1)	.50	.35
Nos. 1089-1090 (2)	1.30	.50
Nos. 1049-1050 (2)	2.00	1.55
Nos. 439-440 (2)	2.90	2.65
Nos. 316-317 (2)	13.00	4.50
Nos. 1065-1066 (2)	.65	.50
No. 504 (1)	.45	.45
Nos. 512-513 (2)	1.00	.80
Nos. 450-453 (4)	1.05	1.40
Nos. 831-832 (2)	5.00	1.40
Nos. 494-495 (2)	3.25	1.15
Nos. 1141-1143 (3)	9.75	1.50
Nos. 771-772 (2)	.70	.50
No. 1718 (1)	.50	.40
Nos. 544-545 (2)	1.65	.60
Nos. 1907-1908 (2)	7.50	3.00
Nos. 1100-1101 (2)	1.20	1.20
Set total (44) Stamps	132.30	80.65

Europa, 1973

Post Horn
and Arrows
CD16

1973

Andorra, French 219-220
Andorra, Spanish 76
Belgium................................839-840
Cyprus................................396-398
Finland................................526
France................................1367
Germany................................1114-1115
Greece................................1090-1092
Iceland................................447-448
Ireland................................329-330
Italy................................1108-1109
Liechtenstein 528-529
Luxembourg..........................523-524
Malta................................469-471
Monaco................................866-867
Netherlands..........................504-505
Norway................................604-605
Portugal................................1170-1172
San Marino..........................802-803
Spain................................1753
Switzerland..........................580-581
Turkey................................1935-1936
Yugoslavia..........................1138-1139

Nos. 219-220 (2)	20.00	11.00
No. 76 (1)	.65	.55
Nos. 839-840 (2)	1.00	.65
Nos. 396-398 (3)	4.25	3.85
No. 526 (1)	1.25	.55
No. 1367 (1)	1.25	.75
Nos. 1114-1115 (2)	.90	.55
Nos. 1090-1092 (3)	2.10	1.40
Nos. 447-448 (2)	6.65	3.35

Nos. 329-330 (2)	5.25	2.00
Nos. 1108-1109 (2)	.65	.50
Nos. 528-529 (2)	.60	.60
Nos. 523-524 (2)	.90	1.00
Nos. 469-471 (3)	.90	1.20
Nos. 866-867 (2)	15.00	2.40
Nos. 504-505 (2)	2.85	1.10
Nos. 604-605 (2)	6.25	2.40
Nos. 1170-1172 (3)	13.00	2.15
No. 1753 (1)	.35	.25
Nos. 580-581 (2)	1.55	.60
Nos. 1935-1936 (2)	10.00	4.50
Nos. 1138-1139 (2)	1.15	1.10
Set total (46) Stamps	97.50	43.00

Europa, 2000

CD17

2000

Albania	2621-2622
Andorra, French	522
Andorra, Spanish	262
Armenia	610-611
Austria	1814
Azerbaijan	698-699
Belarus	350
Belgium	1818
Bosnia & Herzegovina (Moslem)	358
Bosnia & Herzegovina (Serb)	111-112
Croatia	428-429
Cyprus	959
Czech Republic	3120
Denmark	1189
Estonia	394
Faroe Islands	376
Finland	1129
Aland Islands	166
France	2771
Georgia	228-229
Germany	2086-2087
Gibraltar	837-840
Great Britain (Jersey)	935-936
Great Britain (Isle of Man)	883
Greece	1959
Greenland	363
Hungary	3699-3700
Iceland	910
Ireland	1230-1231
Italy	2349
Latvia	504
Liechtenstein	1178
Lithuania	668
Luxembourg	1035
Macedonia	187
Malta	1011-1012
Moldova	355
Monaco	2161-2162
Poland	3519
Portugal	2358
Portugal (Azores)	455
Portugal (Madeira)	208
Romania	4370
Russia	6589
San Marino	1480
Slovakia	355
Slovenia	424
Spain	3036
Sweden	2394
Switzerland	1074
Turkey	2762
Turkish Rep. of Northern Cyprus	500
Ukraine	379
Vatican City	1152

Nos. 2621-2622 (2)	11.00	11.00
No. 522 (1)	2.00	1.00
No. 262 (1)	1.60	.70
Nos. 610-611 (2)	4.75	4.75
No. 1814 (1)	1.40	1.40
Nos. 698-699 (2)	6.00	6.00
No. 350 (1)	1.75	1.75
No. 1818 (1)	1.40	.60
No. 358 (1)	4.75	4.75
Nos. 111-112 (2)	110.00	110.00
Nos. 428-429 (2)	6.25	6.25
No. 959 (1)	2.10	1.40
No. 3120 (1)	1.20	.40
No. 1189 (1)	3.50	2.25
No. 394 (1)	1.25	1.25
No. 376 (1)	2.40	2.40
No. 1129 (1)	2.00	.60
No. 166 (1)	2.00	1.10
No. 2771 (1)	1.25	.40
Nos. 228-229 (2)	9.00	9.00
Nos. 2086-2087 (2)	4.15	1.90
Nos. 837-840 (4)	5.50	5.30

Nos. 935-936 (2)	2.40	2.40
No. 883 (1)	1.50	1.50
No. 363 (1)	1.90	1.90
Nos. 3699-3700 (2)	6.50	2.50
No. 910 (1)	1.60	1.60
Nos. 1230-1231 (2)	4.75	4.75
No. 2349 (1)	1.50	.40
No. 504 (1)	5.00	2.40
No. 1178 (1)	2.25	1.75
No. 668 (1)	1.50	1.50
No. 1035 (1)	1.40	1.00
No. 187 (1)	3.25	3.25
Nos. 1011-1012 (2)	4.35	4.35
No. 355 (1)	3.50	3.50
Nos. 2161-2162 (2)	2.80	1.40
No. 3519 (1)	1.10	.50
No. 2358 (1)	1.25	.65
No. 455 (1)	1.25	.50
No. 208 (1)	1.25	.50
No. 4370 (1)	2.50	1.25
No. 6589 (1)	2.00	.85
No. 1480 (1)	1.00	1.00
No. 355 (1)	1.25	.55
No. 424 (1)	3.25	1.60
No. 3036 (1)	.75	.40
No. 2394 (1)	3.00	2.25
No. 1074 (1)	2.10	.75
No. 2762 (1)	2.00	2.00
No. 500 (1)	2.50	2.50
No. 379 (1)	4.50	3.00
No. 1152 (1)	1.25	1.25
Set total (68) Stamps	260.40	227.95

The Gibraltar stamps are similar to the stamp illustrated, but none have the design shown above. All other sets listed above include at least one stamp with the design shown, but some include stamps with entirely different designs. Bulgaria Nos. 4131-4132, Guernsey Nos. 802-803 and Yugoslavia Nos. 2485-2486 are Europa stamps with completely different designs.

PORTUGAL & COLONIES
Vasco da Gama

Fleet Departing
CD20

Fleet Arriving at
Calicut — CD21

Embarking at
Rastello
CD22

Muse of
History
CD23

San Gabriel,
da Gama and
Camoens
CD24

Archangel
Gabriel, the
Patron Saint
CD25

Flagship San
Gabriel — CD26

Vasco da
Gama — CD27

Fourth centenary of Vasco da Gama's discovery of the route to India.

1898

Azores	93-100
Macao	67-74
Madeira	37-44
Portugal	147-154
Port. Africa	1-8
Port. Congo	75-98
Port. India	189-196
St. Thomas & Prince Islands	170-193
Timor	45-52

Nos. 93-100 (8)	122.00	76.25
Nos. 67-74 (8)	136.00	96.75
Nos. 37-44 (8)	44.55	34.00
Nos. 147-154 (8)	169.30	43.45
Nos. 1-8 (8)	24.75	21.70
Nos. 75-98 (24)	50.50	34.45
Nos. 189-196 (8)	20.25	12.95
Nos. 170-193 (24)	38.75	34.30
Nos. 45-52 (8)	19.50	8.75
Set total (104) Stamps	625.60	362.60

Pombal
POSTAL TAX
POSTAL TAX DUES

Marquis de
Pombal — CD28

Planning
Reconstruction
of Lisbon,
1755 — CD29

Pombal Monument,
Lisbon — CD30

Sebastiao Jose de Carvalho e Mello, Marquis de Pombal (1699-1782), statesman, rebuilt Lisbon after earthquake of 1755. Tax was for the erection of Pombal monument. Obligatory on all mail on certain days throughout the year. Postal Tax Dues are inscribed "Multa."

1925

Angola	RA1-RA3, RAJ1-RAJ3
Azores	RA9-RA11, RAJ2-RAJ4
Cape Verde	RA1-RA3, RAJ1-RAJ3
Macao	RA1-RA3, RAJ1-RAJ3
Madeira	RA1-RA3, RAJ1-RAJ3
Mozambique	RA1-RA3, RAJ1-RAJ3
Nyassa	RA1-RA3, RAJ1-RAJ3
Portugal	RA11-RA13, RAJ2-RAJ4
Port. Guinea	RA1-RA3, RAJ1-RAJ3
Port. India	RA1-RA3, RAJ1-RAJ3
St. Thomas & Prince Islands	RA1-RA3, RAJ1-RAJ3
Timor	RA1-RA3, RAJ1-RAJ3

Nos. RA1-RA3, RAJ1-RAJ3 (6)	6.60	6.60
Nos. RA9-RA11, RAJ2-RAJ4 (6)	6.60	9.30
Nos. RA1-RA3, RAJ1-RAJ3 (6)	6.00	5.40
Nos. RA1-RA3, RAJ1-RAJ3 (6)	18.50	10.50
Nos. RA1-RA3, RAJ1-RAJ3 (6)	4.35	12.45
Nos. RA1-RA3, RAJ1-RAJ3 (6)	2.55	2.70
Nos. RA1-RA3, RAJ1-RAJ3 (6)	52.50	38.25
Nos. RA11-RA13, RAJ2-RAJ4 (6)	5.80	5.20
Nos. RA1-RA3, RAJ1-RAJ3 (6)	3.30	2.70
Nos. RA1-RA3, RAJ1-RAJ3 (6)	3.45	3.45
Nos. RA1-RA3, RAJ1-RAJ3 (6)	3.60	3.60
Nos. RA1-RA3, RAJ1-RAJ3 (6)	2.10	3.90
Set total (72) Stamps	115.35	104.05

Vasco da Gama
CD34

Mousinho de
Albuquerque
CD35

Dam
CD36

Prince Henry
the Navigator
CD37

Affonso de
Albuquerque
CD38

Plane over
Globe
CD39

1938-39

Angola	274-291, C1-C9
Cape Verde	234-251, C1-C9
Macao	289-305, C7-C15
Mozambique	270-287, C1-C9
Port. Guinea	233-250. C1-C9
Port. India	439-453, C1-C8
St. Thomas & Prince Islands	302-319, 323-340, C1-C18
Timor	223-239, C1-C9

Nos. 274-291,C1-C9 (27)	132.90	22.85
Nos. 234-251,C1-C9 (27)	100.00	31.20
Nos. 289-305,C7-C15 (26)	701.70	135.60
Nos. 270-287,C1-C9 (27)	63.45	11.20
Nos. 233-250,C1-C9 (27)	88.05	30.70
Nos. 439-453,C1-C8 (23)	74.75	25.50
Nos. 302-319,323-340,C1-C18 (54)	319.25	190.35
Nos. 223-239,C1-C9 (26)	149.25	73.15
Set total (237) Stamps	1,629.	520.55

Lady of Fatima

Our Lady of the
Rosary, Fatima,
Portugal — CD40

1948-49

Angola	315-318
Cape Verde	266
Macao	336
Mozambique	325-328
Port. Guinea	271
Port. India	480
St. Thomas & Prince Islands	351
Timor	254

Nos. 315-318 (4)	68.00	17.25
No. 266 (1)	8.50	4.50
No. 336 (1)	40.00	12.00
Nos. 325-328 (4)	20.00	4.50
No. 271 (1)	3.25	3.00
No. 480 (1)	2.50	2.25
No. 351 (1)	7.25	6.50
No. 254 (1)	2.75	2.75
Set total (14) Stamps	152.25	52.75

A souvenir sheet of 9 stamps was issued in 1951 to mark the extension of the 1950 Holy Year. The sheet contains: Angola No. 316, Cape Verde No. 266, Macao No. 336, Mozambique No. 325, Portuguese Guinea No. 271, Portuguese India Nos. 480, 485, St. Thomas & Prince Islands No. 351, Timor No. 254. The sheet also contains a portrait of Pope Pius XII and is inscribed "Encerramento do

Ano Santo, Fatima 1951." It was sold for 11 escudos.

Holy Year

Church Bells and Dove CD41 — Angel Holding Candelabra CD42

Holy Year, 1950.

1950-51

Angola		331-332
Cape Verde		268-269
Macao		339-340
Mozambique		330-331
Port. Guinea		273-274
Port. India	490-491,	496-503
St. Thomas & Prince Islands		353-354
Timor		258-259

Nos. 331-332 (2)	7.60	1.35
Nos. 268-269 (2)	4.75	2.20
Nos. 339-340 (2)	55.00	12.50
Nos. 330-331 (2)	1.75	.85
Nos. 273-274 (2)	3.50	2.60
Nos. 490-491,496-503 (10)	12.80	5.40
Nos. 353-354 (2)	7.50	4.40
Nos. 258-259 (2)	3.75	3.25
Set total (24) Stamps	96.65	32.55

A souvenir sheet of 8 stamps was issued in 1951 to mark the extension of the Holy Year. The sheet contains: Angola No. 331, Cape Verde No. 269, Macao No. 340, Mozambique No. 331, Portuguese Guinea No. 275, Portuguese India No. 490, St. Thomas & Prince Islands No. 354, Timor No. 258, some with colors changed. The sheet contains doves and is inscribed 'Encerramento do Ano Santo, Fatima 1951.' It was sold for 17 escudos.

Holy Year Conclusion

Our Lady of Fatima — CD43

Conclusion of Holy Year. Sheets contain alternate vertical rows of stamps and labels bearing quotation from Pope Pius XII, different for each colony.

1951

Angola		357
Cape Verde		270
Macao		352
Mozambique		356
Port. Guinea		275
Port. India		506
St. Thomas & Prince Islands		355
Timor		270

No. 357 (1)	5.25	1.50
No. 270 (1)	1.50	1.25
No. 352 (1)	37.50	10.00
No. 356 (1)	2.25	1.00
No. 275 (1)	1.00	.65
No. 506 (1)	1.60	1.00
No. 355 (1)	2.50	2.00
No. 270 (1)	2.00	1.75
Set total (8) Stamps	53.60	19.15

Medical Congress

CD44

First National Congress of Tropical Medicine, Lisbon, 1952. Each stamp has a different design.

1952

Angola		358
Cape Verde		287
Macao		364

Mozambique		359
Port. Guinea		276
Port. India		516
St. Thomas & Prince Islands		356
Timor		271

No. 358 (1)	1.50	.50
No. 287 (1)	.70	.50
No. 364 (1)	9.75	4.25
No. 359 (1)	1.10	.55
No. 276 (1)	.45	.35
No. 516 (1)	4.75	2.00
No. 356 (1)	.30	.30
No. 271 (1)	1.00	1.00
Set total (8) Stamps	19.55	9.45

Postage Due Stamps

CD45

1952

Angola		J37-J42
Cape Verde		J31-J36
Macao		J53-J58
Mozambique		J51-J56
Port. Guinea		J40-J45
Port. India		J47-J52
St. Thomas & Prince Islands		J52-J57
Timor		J31-J36

Nos. J37-J42 (6)	4.05	3.15
Nos. J31-J36 (6)	2.80	2.30
Nos. J53-J58 (6)	17.45	6.85
Nos. J51-J56 (6)	1.80	1.55
Nos. J40-J45 (6)	2.55	2.55
Nos. J47-J52 (6)	6.10	6.10
Nos. J52-J57 (6)	4.15	4.15
Nos. J31-J36 (6)	6.20	3.50
Set total (48) Stamps	45.10	30.15

Sao Paulo

Father Manuel da Nobrega and View of Sao Paulo — CD46

Founding of Sao Paulo, Brazil, 400th anniv.

1954

Angola		385
Cape Verde		297
Macao		382
Mozambique		395
Port. Guinea		291
Port. India		530
St. Thomas & Prince Islands		369
Timor		279

No. 385 (1)	.80	.50
No. 297 (1)	.70	.60
No. 382 (1)	14.00	3.00
No. 395 (1)	.40	.30
No. 291 (1)	.35	.25
No. 530 (1)	.80	.40
No. 369 (1)	.80	.60
No. 279 (1)	.85	.70
Set total (8) Stamps	18.70	6.35

Tropical Medicine Congress

CD47

Sixth International Congress for Tropical Medicine and Malaria, Lisbon, Sept. 1958. Each stamp shows a different plant.

1958

Angola		409
Cape Verde		303
Macao		392
Mozambique		404
Port. Guinea		295
Port. India		569
St. Thomas & Prince Islands		371

Timor		289

No. 409 (1)	3.50	1.10
No. 303 (1)	5.50	2.10
No. 392 (1)	8.00	3.00
No. 404 (1)	4.00	.85
No. 295 (1)	2.75	1.10
No. 569 (1)	1.75	.75
No. 371 (1)	2.75	2.25
No. 289 (1)	3.00	2.75
Set total (8) Stamps	31.25	13.90

Sports

CD48

Each stamp shows a different sport.

1962

Angola		433-438
Cape Verde		320-325
Macao		394-399
Mozambique		424-429
Port. Guinea		299-304
St. Thomas & Prince Islands		374-379
Timor		313-318

Nos. 433-438 (6)	5.50	3.20
Nos. 320-325 (6)	15.25	5.20
Nos. 394-399 (6)	74.00	14.60
Nos. 424-429 (6)	5.70	2.45
Nos. 299-304 (6)	4.95	2.15
Nos. 374-379 (6)	6.75	3.20
Nos. 313-318 (6)	6.40	3.70
Set total (42) Stamps	118.55	34.50

Anti-Malaria

Anopheles Funestus and Malaria Eradication Symbol — CD49

World Health Organization drive to eradicate malaria.

1962

Angola		439
Cape Verde		326
Macao		400
Mozambique		430
Port. Guinea		305
St. Thomas & Prince Islands		380
Timor		319

No. 439 (1)	1.75	.90
No. 326 (1)	1.40	.90
No. 400 (1)	6.50	2.00
No. 430 (1)	1.40	.40
No. 305 (1)	1.25	.45
No. 380 (1)	2.00	1.50
No. 319 (1)	.75	.60
Set total (7) Stamps	15.05	6.75

Airline Anniversary

Map of Africa, Super Constellation and Jet Liner — CD50

Tenth anniversary of Transportes Aereos Portugueses (TAP).

1963

Angola		490
Cape Verde		327
Mozambique		434
Port. Guinea		318
St. Thomas & Prince Islands		381

No. 490 (1)	1.00	.35
No. 327 (1)	1.10	.70
No. 434 (1)	.40	.25

No. 318 (1)	.65	.35
No. 381 (1)	.70	.60
Set total (5) Stamps	3.85	2.25

National Overseas Bank

Antonio Teixeira de Sousa — CD51

Centenary of the National Overseas Bank of Portugal.

1964, May 16

Angola		509
Cape Verde		328
Port. Guinea		319
St. Thomas & Prince Islands		382
Timor		320

No. 509 (1)	.90	.30
No. 328 (1)	1.10	.75
No. 319 (1)	.65	.40
No. 382 (1)	.70	.50
No. 320 (1)	.75	.60
Set total (5) Stamps	4.10	2.55

ITU

ITU Emblem and the Archangel Gabriel — CD52

International Communications Union, Cent.

1965, May 17

Angola		511
Cape Verde		329
Macao		402
Mozambique		464
Port. Guinea		320
St. Thomas & Prince Islands		383
Timor		321

No. 511 (1)	1.25	.65
No. 329 (1)	2.10	1.40
No. 402 (1)	5.00	2.00
No. 464 (1)	.40	.25
No. 320 (1)	1.90	.75
No. 383 (1)	1.50	1.00
No. 321 (1)	1.50	.90
Set total (7) Stamps	13.65	6.95

National Revolution

CD53

40th anniv. of the National Revolution. Different buildings on each stamp.

1966, May 28

Angola		525
Cape Verde		338
Macao		403
Mozambique		465
Port. Guinea		329
St. Thomas & Prince Islands		392
Timor		322

No. 525 (1)	.50	.25
No. 338 (1)	.60	.45
No. 403 (1)	5.00	2.00
No. 465 (1)	.50	.30
No. 329 (1)	.55	.35
No. 392 (1)	.75	.50
No. 322 (1)	1.50	.90
Set total (7) Stamps	9.40	4.75

Navy Club

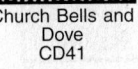

CD54

Centenary of Portugal's Navy Club. Each stamp has a different design.

1967, Jan. 31

Angola	527-528
Cape Verde	339-340
Macao	412-413
Mozambique	478-479
Port. Guinea	330-331
St. Thomas & Prince Islands	393-394
Timor	323-324

Nos. 527-528 (2)	1.75	.75
Nos. 339-340 (2)	2.00	1.40
Nos. 412-413 (2)	9.50	3.75
Nos. 478-479 (2)	1.20	.65
Nos. 330-331 (2)	1.20	.90
Nos. 393-394 (2)	3.20	1.25
Nos. 323-324 (2)	4.00	2.00
Set total (14) Stamps	22.85	10.70

Admiral Coutinho

CD55

Centenary of the birth of Admiral Carlos Viegas Gago Coutinho (1869-1959), explorer and aviation pioneer. Each stamp has a different design.

1969, Feb. 17

Angola	547
Cape Verde	355
Macao	417
Mozambique	484
Port. Guinea	335
St. Thomas & Prince Islands	397
Timor	335

No. 547 (1)	.85	.35
No. 355 (1)	.35	.25
No. 417 (1)	3.75	1.50
No. 484 (1)	.25	.25
No. 335 (1)	.35	.25
No. 397 (1)	.50	.35
No. 335 (1)	1.10	.85
Set total (7) Stamps	7.15	3.80

Administration Reform

Luiz Augusto Rebello da Silva — CD56

Centenary of the administration reforms of the overseas territories.

1969, Sept. 25

Angola	549
Cape Verde	357
Macao	419
Mozambique	491
Port. Guinea	337
St. Thomas & Prince Islands	399
Timor	338

No. 549 (1)	.35	.25
No. 357 (1)	.35	.25
No. 419 (1)	5.00	1.00
No. 491 (1)	.25	.25
No. 337 (1)	.25	.25
No. 399 (1)	.45	.45
No. 338 (1)	.40	.25
Set total (7) Stamps	7.05	2.70

Marshal Carmona

CD57

Birth centenary of Marshal Antonio Oscar Carmona de Fragoso (1869-1951), President of Portugal. Each stamp has a different design.

1970, Nov. 15

Angola	563
Cape Verde	359
Macao	422
Mozambique	493
Port. Guinea	340
St. Thomas & Prince Islands	403
Timor	341

No. 563 (1)	.45	.25
No. 359 (1)	.55	.35
No. 422 (1)	2.25	1.25
No. 493 (1)	.40	.25
No. 340 (1)	.35	.25
No. 403 (1)	.75	.45
No. 341 (1)	.25	.25
Set total (7) Stamps	5.00	3.05

Olympic Games

CD59

20th Olympic Games, Munich, Aug. 26-Sept. 11. Each stamp shows a different sport.

1972, June 20

Angola	569
Cape Verde	361
Macao	426
Mozambique	504
Port. Guinea	342
St. Thomas & Prince Islands	408
Timor	343

No. 569 (1)	.65	.25
No. 361 (1)	.65	.30
No. 426 (1)	3.25	1.00
No. 504 (1)	.30	.25
No. 342 (1)	.45	.25
No. 408 (1)	.35	.25
No. 343 (1)	.50	.50
Set total (7) Stamps	6.15	2.80

Lisbon-Rio de Janeiro Flight

CD60

50th anniversary of the Lisbon to Rio de Janeiro flight by Arturo de Sacadura and Coutinho, March 30-June 5, 1922. Each stamp shows a different stage of the flight.

1972, Sept. 20

Angola	570
Cape Verde	362
Macao	427
Mozambique	505
Port. Guinea	343
St. Thomas & Prince Islands	409
Timor	344

No. 570 (1)	.35	.25
No. 362 (1)	1.50	.30
No. 427 (1)	22.50	7.50
No. 505 (1)	.25	.25
No. 343 (1)	.25	.25
No. 409 (1)	.35	.25
No. 344 (1)	.25	.40
Set total (7) Stamps	25.45	9.20

WMO Centenary

WMO Emblem — CD61

Centenary of international meterological cooperation.

1973, Dec. 15

Angola	571
Cape Verde	363
Macao	429
Mozambique	509
Port. Guinea	344
St. Thomas & Prince Islands	410

Timor	345

No. 571 (1)	.45	.25
No. 363 (1)	.65	.30
No. 429 (1)	6.25	1.75
No. 509 (1)	.30	.25
No. 344 (1)	.45	.35
No. 410 (1)	.60	.25
No. 345 (1)	1.75	2.00
Set total (7) Stamps	10.45	5.40

FRENCH COMMUNITY
Upper Volta can be found under
Burkina Faso in Vol. 1
Madagascar can be found under
Malagasy in Vol. 3
Colonial Exposition

People of French Empire CD70

Women's Heads CD71

France Showing Way to Civilization CD72

"Colonial Commerce" CD73

International Colonial Exposition, Paris.

1931

Cameroun	213-216
Chad	60-63
Dahomey	97-100
Fr. Guiana	152-155
Fr. Guinea	116-119
Fr. India	100-103
Fr. Polynesia	76-79
Fr. Sudan	102-105
Gabon	120-123
Guadeloupe	138-141
Indo-China	140-142
Ivory Coast	92-95
Madagascar	169-172
Martinique	129-132
Mauritania	65-68
Middle Congo	61-64
New Caledonia	176-179
Niger	73-76
Reunion	122-125
St. Pierre & Miquelon	132-135
Senegal	138-141
Somali Coast	135-138
Togo	254-257
Ubangi-Shari	82-85
Upper Volta	66-69
Wallis & Futuna Isls.	85-88

Nos. 213-216 (4)	23.00	18.25
Nos. 60-63 (4)	22.00	22.00
Nos. 97-100 (4)	26.00	26.00
Nos. 152-155 (4)	22.00	22.00
Nos. 116-119 (4)	19.75	19.75
Nos. 100-103 (4)	18.00	18.00
Nos. 76-79 (4)	30.00	30.00
Nos. 102-105 (4)	19.00	19.00
Nos. 120-123 (4)	17.50	17.50
Nos. 138-141 (4)	19.00	19.00
Nos. 140-142 (3)	11.50	11.50
Nos. 92-95 (4)	22.50	22.50
Nos. 169-172 (4)	7.90	5.00
Nos. 129-132 (4)	21.00	21.00
Nos. 65-68 (4)	22.00	22.00
Nos. 61-64 (4)	20.50	20.50
Nos. 176-179 (4)	24.00	24.00
Nos. 73-76 (4)	21.50	21.50
Nos. 122-125 (4)	24.00	24.00
Nos. 132-135 (4)	24.00	24.00
Nos. 138-141 (4)	20.00	20.00
Nos. 135-138 (4)	22.00	22.00
Nos. 254-257 (4)	22.00	22.00

Nos. 82-85 (4)	21.00	21.00
Nos. 66-69 (4)	19.00	19.00
Nos. 85-88 (4)	35.00	35.00
Set total (103) Stamps	552.15	544.50

Paris International Exposition
Colonial Arts Exposition

"Colonial Resources"
CD74   CD77

Overseas Commerce CD75

Exposition Building and Women CD76

"France and the Empire" CD78

Cultural Treasures of the Colonies CD79

Souvenir sheets contain one imperf. stamp.

1937

Cameroun	217-222A
Dahomey	101-107
Fr. Equatorial Africa	27-32, 73
Fr. Guiana	162-168
Fr. Guinea	120-126
Fr. India	104-110
Fr. Polynesia	117-123
Fr. Sudan	106-112
Guadeloupe	148-154
Indo-China	193-199
Inini	41
Ivory Coast	152-158
Kwangchowan	132
Madagascar	191-197
Martinique	179-185
Mauritania	69-75
New Caledonia	208-214
Niger	77-83
Reunion	167-173
St. Pierre & Miquelon	165-171
Senegal	172-178
Somali Coast	139-145
Togo	258-264
Wallis & Futuna Isls.	89

Nos. 217-222A (7)	18.80	20.30
Nos. 101-107 (7)	23.60	27.60
Nos. 27-32, 73 (7)	28.10	32.10
Nos. 162-168 (7)	22.50	24.50
Nos. 120-126 (7)	24.00	28.00
Nos. 104-110 (7)	21.15	36.50
Nos. 117-123 (7)	58.50	75.00
Nos. 106-112 (7)	23.60	27.60
Nos. 148-154 (7)	19.55	21.05
Nos. 193-199 (7)	17.70	19.70
No. 41 (1)	19.00	22.50
Nos. 152-158 (7)	22.20	26.20
No. 132 (1)	9.25	11.00
Nos. 191-197 (7)	19.25	21.75
Nos. 179-185 (7)	19.95	21.70
Nos. 69-75 (7)	20.50	24.50
Nos. 208-214 (7)	39.00	50.50
Nos. 73-83 (11)	42.70	46.70
Nos. 167-173 (7)	21.70	23.20
Nos. 165-171 (7)	49.60	64.00
Nos. 172-178 (7)	21.00	23.80
Nos. 139-145 (7)	25.60	32.60
Nos. 258-264 (7)	20.40	20.40
No. 89 (1)	28.50	37.50
Set total (154) Stamps	616.15	738.70

Curie

Pierre and Marie Curie
CD80

40th anniversary of the discovery of radium. The surtax was for the benefit of the Intl. Union for the Control of Cancer.

1938

Cameroun		B1
Cuba		B1-B2
Dahomey		B2
France		B76
Fr. Equatorial Africa		B1
Fr. Guiana		B3
Fr. Guinea		B2
Fr. India		B6
Fr. Polynesia		B5
Fr. Sudan		B1
Guadeloupe		B3
Indo-China		B14
Ivory Coast		B2
Madagascar		B2
Martinique		B2
Mauritania		B3
New Caledonia		B4
Niger		B1
Reunion		B4
St. Pierre & Miquelon		B3
Senegal		B3
Somali Coast		B2
Togo		B1

No. B1 (1)	10.00	10.00
Nos. B1-B2 (2)	12.00	3.35
No. B2 (1)	9.50	9.50
No. B76 (1)	21.00	12.50
No. B1 (1)	24.00	24.00
No. B3 (1)	13.50	13.50
No. B2 (1)	8.75	8.75
No. B6 (1)	10.00	10.00
No. B5 (1)	20.00	20.00
No. B1 (1)	12.50	12.50
No. B3 (1)	11.00	10.50
No. B14 (1)	12.00	12.00
No. B2 (1)	11.00	7.50
No. B2 (1)	11.00	11.00
No. B2 (1)	13.00	13.00
No. B3 (1)	7.75	7.75
No. B4 (1)	16.50	17.50
No. B1 (1)	15.00	15.00
No. B4 (1)	14.00	14.00
No. B3 (1)	21.00	22.50
No. B3 (1)	10.50	10.50
No. B2 (1)	7.75	7.75
No. B1 (1)	20.00	20.00
Set total (24) Stamps	311.75	293.10

Caillie

Rene Caillie and Map of Northwestern Africa — CD81

Death centenary of Rene Caillie (1799-1838), French explorer. All three denominations exist with colony name omitted.

1939

Dahomey		108-110
Fr. Guinea		161-163
Fr. Sudan		113-115
Ivory Coast		160-162
Mauritania		109-111
Niger		84-86
Senegal		188-190
Togo		265-267

Nos. 108-110 (3)	1.20	3.60
Nos. 161-163 (3)	1.20	3.20
Nos. 113-115 (3)	1.20	3.20
Nos. 160-162 (3)	1.05	2.55
Nos. 109-111 (3)	1.05	3.80
Nos. 84-86 (3)	1.05	2.35
Nos. 188-190 (3)	1.05	2.90
Nos. 265-267 (3)	1.05	3.30
Set total (24) Stamps	8.85	24.90

New York World's Fair

Natives and New York Skyline
CD82

1939

Cameroun		223-224
Dahomey		111-112
Fr. Equatorial Africa		78-79
Fr. Guiana		169-170
Fr. Guinea		164-165
Fr. India		111-112
Fr. Polynesia		124-125
Fr. Sudan		116-117
Guadeloupe		155-156
Indo-China		203-204
Inini		42-43
Ivory Coast		163-164
Kwangchowan		133-134
Madagascar		209-210
Martinique		186-187
Mauritania		112-113
New Caledonia		215-216
Niger		87-88
Reunion		174-175
St. Pierre & Miquelon		205-206
Senegal		191-192
Somali Coast		179-180
Togo		268-269
Wallis & Futuna Isls.		90-91

Nos. 223-224 (2)	2.80	2.40
Nos. 111-112 (2)	1.60	3.20
Nos. 78-79 (2)	1.60	3.20
Nos. 169-170 (2)	2.60	2.60
Nos. 164-165 (2)	1.60	3.20
Nos. 111-112 (2)	3.00	8.00
Nos. 124-125 (2)	4.80	4.80
Nos. 116-117 (2)	1.60	3.20
Nos. 155-156 (2)	2.50	2.50
Nos. 203-204 (2)	2.05	2.05
Nos. 42-43 (2)	7.50	9.00
Nos. 163-164 (2)	1.50	3.00
Nos. 133-134 (2)	2.50	2.50
Nos. 209-210 (2)	1.50	2.50
Nos. 186-187 (2)	2.35	2.35
Nos. 112-113 (2)	1.40	2.80
Nos. 215-216 (2)	3.35	3.35
Nos. 87-88 (2)	1.40	2.80
Nos. 174-175 (2)	2.80	2.80
Nos. 205-206 (2)	4.80	6.00
Nos. 191-192 (2)	1.40	2.80
Nos. 179-180 (2)	1.40	2.80
Nos. 268-269 (2)	1.40	2.80
Nos. 90-91 (2)	6.00	6.00
Set total (48) Stamps	63.45	86.65

French Revolution

Storming of the Bastille
CD83

French Revolution, 150th anniv. The surtax was for the defense of the colonies.

1939

Cameroun		B2-B6
Dahomey		B3-B7
Fr. Equatorial Africa		B4-B8, CB1
Fr. Guiana		B4-B8, CB1
Fr. Guinea		B3-B7
Fr. India		B7-B11
Fr. Polynesia		B6-B10, CB1
Fr. Sudan		B2-B6
Guadeloupe		B4-B8
Indo-China		B15-B19, CB1
Inini		B1-B5
Ivory Coast		B3-B7
Kwangchowan		B1-B5
Madagascar		B3-B7, CB1
Martinique		B3-B7
Mauritania		B4-B8
New Caledonia		B5-B9, CB1
Niger		B2-B6
Reunion		B5-B9, CB1
St. Pierre & Miquelon		B4-B8
Senegal		B4-B8, CB1
Somali Coast		B3-B7
Togo		B2-B6
Wallis & Futuna Isls.		B1-B5

Nos. B2-B6 (5)	60.00	60.00
Nos. B3-B7 (5)	47.50	47.50
Nos. B4-B8,CB1 (6)	120.00	120.00
Nos. B4-B8,CB1 (6)	79.50	79.50
Nos. B3-B7 (5)	47.50	47.50
Nos. B7-B11 (5)	28.75	32.50
Nos. B6-B10,CB1 (6)	122.50	122.50
Nos. B2-B6 (5)	50.00	50.00
Nos. B4-B8 (5)	50.00	50.00
Nos. B15-B19,CB1 (6)	85.00	85.00
Nos. B1-B5 (5)	75.00	87.50
Nos. B3-B7 (5)	43.75	43.75
Nos. B1-B5 (5)	46.25	46.25
Nos. B3-B7,CB1 (6)	65.50	65.50
Nos. B3-B7 (5)	52.50	52.50
Nos. B4-B8 (5)	42.50	42.50
Nos. B5-B9,CB1 (6)	101.50	101.50
Nos. B2-B6 (5)	60.00	60.00
Nos. B5-B9,CB1 (6)	87.50	87.50
Nos. B4-B8 (5)	67.50	72.50
Nos. B4-B8,CB1 (6)	56.50	56.50
Nos. B3-B7 (5)	45.00	45.00
Nos. B2-B6 (5)	42.50	42.50
Nos. B1-B5 (5)	95.00	95.00
Set total (128) Stamps	1,572.	1,593.

Plane over Coastal Area
CD85

All five denominations exist with colony name omitted.

1940

Dahomey		C1-C5
Fr. Guinea		C1-C5
Fr. Sudan		C1-C5
Ivory Coast		C1-C5
Mauritania		C1-C5
Niger		C1-C5
Senegal		C12-C16
Togo		C1-C5

Nos. C1-C5 (5)	4.00	4.00
Nos. C1-C5 (5)	4.00	4.00
Nos. C1-C5 (5)	4.00	4.00
Nos. C1-C5 (5)	3.80	3.80
Nos. C1-C5 (5)	3.50	3.50
Nos. C1-C5 (5)	3.50	3.50
Nos. C12-C16 (5)	3.50	3.50
Nos. C1-C5 (5)	3.15	3.15
Set total (40) Stamps	29.45	29.45

Defense of the Empire

Colonial Infantryman — CD86

1941

Cameroun		B13B
Dahomey		B13
Fr. Equatorial Africa		B8B
Fr. Guiana		B10
Fr. Guinea		B13
Fr. India		B13
Fr. Polynesia		B12
Fr. Sudan		B12
Guadeloupe		B10
Indo-China		B19B
Inini		B7
Ivory Coast		B13
Kwangchowan		B7
Madagascar		B9
Martinique		B9
Mauritania		B14
New Caledonia		B11
Niger		B12
Reunion		B11
St. Pierre & Miquelon		B8B
Senegal		B14
Somali Coast		B9
Togo		B10B
Wallis & Futuna Isls.		B7

No. B13B (1)	1.60	
No. B13 (1)	1.20	
No. B8B (1)	3.50	
No. B10 (1)	1.40	
No. B13 (1)	1.40	
No. B13 (1)	1.25	
No. B12 (1)	3.50	
No. B12 (1)	1.40	
No. B10 (1)	1.00	
No. B19B (1)	1.60	
No. B7 (1)	1.75	
No. B13 (1)	1.25	
No. B7 (1)	.85	

No. B9 (1)	1.50	
No. B9 (1)	1.40	
No. B14 (1)	.95	
No. B12 (1)	1.40	
No. B11 (1)	1.60	
No. B8B (1)	4.50	
No. B14 (1)	1.25	
No. B9 (1)	1.60	
No. B10B (1)	1.10	
No. B7 (1)	2.40	
Set total (23) Stamps	39.40	

Each of the CD86 stamps listed above is part of a set of three stamps. The designs of the other two stamps in the set vary from country to country. Only the values of the Common Design stamps are listed here.

Colonial Education Fund

CD86a

1942

Cameroun		CB3
Dahomey		CB4
Fr. Equatorial Africa		CB5
Fr. Guiana		CB4
Fr. Guinea		CB4
Fr. India		CB3
Fr. Polynesia		CB4
Fr. Sudan		CB4
Guadeloupe		CB5
Indo-China		CB5
Inini		CB3
Ivory Coast		CB4
Kwangchowan		CB5
Malagasy		CB5
Martinique		CB4
Mauritania		CB4
New Caledonia		CB4
Niger		CB4
Reunion		CB4
St. Pierre & Miquelon		CB3
Senegal		CB5
Somali Coast		CB3
Togo		CB3
Wallis & Futuna		CB3

No. CB3 (1)	1.10	
No. CB4 (1)	.80	5.50
No. CB5 (1)	.80	
No. CB4 (1)	1.10	
No. CB4 (1)	.40	5.50
No. CB3 (1)	.90	
No. CB4 (1)	2.00	
No. CB4 (1)	.40	5.50
No. CB5 (1)	1.10	
No. CB5 (1)	1.10	
No. CB3 (1)	1.25	
No. CB4 (1)	1.00	5.50
No. CB5 (1)	1.00	
No. CB5 (1)	.65	
No. CB4 (1)	1.00	
No. CB4 (1)	.80	
No. CB4 (1)	2.25	
No. CB4 (1)	.35	
No. CB4 (1)	.90	
No. CB3 (1)	7.00	
No. CB5 (1)	.80	6.50
No. CB3 (1)	.70	
No. CB3 (1)	.35	
No. CB3 (1)	2.25	
Set total (24) Stamps	30.00	28.50

Cross of Lorraine & Four-motor Plane
CD87

1941-5

Cameroun		C1-C7
Fr. Equatorial Africa		C17-C23
Fr. Guiana		C9-C10
Fr. India		C1-C6
Fr. Polynesia		C3-C9
Fr. West Africa		C1-C3
Guadeloupe		C1-C2
Madagascar		C37-C43

Martinique.................................. C1-C2
New Caledonia........................ C7-C13
Reunion.................................. C18-C24
St. Pierre & Miquelon............... C1-C7
Somali Coast.............................. C1-C7

Nos. C1-C7 (7)	6.30	6.30
Nos. C17-C23 (7)	10.40	6.35
Nos. C9-C10 (2)	3.80	3.10
Nos. C1-C6 (6)	9.30	15.00
Nos. C3-C9 (7)	13.75	10.00
Nos. C1-C3 (3)	9.50	3.90
Nos. C1-C2 (2)	3.75	2.50
Nos. C37-C43 (7)	5.60	3.80
Nos. C1-C2 (2)	3.00	1.60
Nos. C7-C13 (7)	8.85	7.30
Nos. C18-C24 (7)	7.05	5.00
Nos. C1-C7 (7)	11.60	9.40
Nos. C1-C7 (7)	13.95	11.10
Set total (71) Stamps	106.85	85.35

Somali Coast stamps are inscribed "Djibouti".

Transport
Plane
CD88

Caravan
and Plane
CD89

1942

Dahomey C6-C13
Fr. Guinea C6-C13
Fr. Sudan C6-C13
Ivory Coast C6-C13
Mauritania............................... C6-C13
Niger....................................... C6-C13
Senegal C17-C25
Togo C6-C13

Nos. C6-C13 (8)	7.15
Nos. C6-C13 (8)	5.75
Nos. C6-C13 (8)	8.00
Nos. C6-C13 (8)	11.15
Nos. C6-C13 (8)	9.75
Nos. C6-C13 (8)	6.90
Nos. C17-C25 (9)	9.45
Nos. C6-C13 (8)	6.75
Set total (65) Stamps	64.90

Red Cross

Marianne
CD90

The surtax was for the French Red Cross
and national relief.

1944

Cameroun.................................... B28
Fr. Equatorial Africa B38
Fr. Guiana B12
Fr. India B14
Fr. Polynesia B13
Fr. West Africa B1
Guadeloupe................................ B12
Madagascar................................ B15
Martinique.................................. B11
New Caledonia............................. B13
Reunion..................................... B15
St. Pierre & Miquelon.................... B13
Somali Coast.............................. B13
Wallis & Futuna Isls. B9

No. B28 (1)	2.00	1.60
No. B38 (1)	1.60	1.20
No. B12 (1)	1.75	1.25
No. B14 (1)	1.50	1.25
No. B13 (1)	2.00	1.60
No. B1 (1)	6.50	4.75
No. B12 (1)	1.40	1.00
No. B15 (1)	.90	.90
No. B11 (1)	1.20	1.20
No. B13 (1)	1.50	1.50
No. B15 (1)	1.60	1.10
No. B13 (1)	2.40	2.40
No. B13 (1)	1.75	2.00
No. B9 (1)	4.50	3.25
Set total (14) Stamps	30.60	25.00

Eboue

CD91

Felix Eboue, first French colonial administrator to proclaim resistance to Germany after
French surrender in World War II.

1945

Cameroun..............................296-297
Fr. Equatorial Africa 156-157
Fr. Guiana 171-172
Fr. India 210-211
Fr. Polynesia.........................150-151
Fr. West Africa 15-16
Guadeloupe..........................187-188
Madagascar..........................259-260
Martinique.............................196-197
New Caledonia.......................274-275
Reunion................................238-239
St. Pierre & Miquelon..............322-323
Somali Coast.........................238-239

Nos. 296-297 (2)	2.40	1.95
Nos. 156-157 (2)	2.55	2.00
Nos. 171-172 (2)	2.45	2.00
Nos. 210-211 (2)	2.20	1.95
Nos. 150-151 (2)	3.60	2.85
Nos. 15-16 (2)	2.40	2.40
Nos. 187-188 (2)	2.05	1.60
Nos. 259-260 (2)	2.00	1.45
Nos. 196-197 (2)	2.05	1.55
Nos. 274-275 (2)	3.40	3.00
Nos. 238-239 (2)	2.40	2.00
Nos. 322-323 (2)	4.40	3.45
Nos. 238-239 (2)	2.45	2.10
Set total (26) Stamps	34.35	28.30

Victory

Victory — CD92

European victory of the Allied Nations in
World War II.

1946, May 8

Cameroun...................................... C8
Fr. Equatorial Africa C24
Fr. Guiana C11
Fr. India C7
Fr. Polynesia C10
Fr. West Africa C4
Guadeloupe.................................. C3
Indo-China................................. C19
Madagascar................................ C44
Martinique.................................... C3
New Caledonia............................. C14
Reunion..................................... C25
St. Pierre & Miquelon...................... C8
Somali Coast................................ C8
Wallis & Futuna Isls. C1

No. C8 (1)	1.60	1.20
No. C24 (1)	1.60	1.25
No. C11 (1)	1.75	1.25
No. C7 (1)	1.00	4.00
No. C10 (1)	2.75	2.00
No. C4 (1)	1.60	1.20
No. C3 (1)	1.25	1.00
No. C19 (1)	1.00	.55
No. C44 (1)	1.00	.35
No. C3 (1)	1.30	1.00
No. C14 (1)	1.50	1.25
No. C25 (1)	1.10	.90
No. C8 (1)	2.10	2.10
No. C8 (1)	1.75	1.40
No. C1 (1)	2.50	1.90
Set total (15) Stamps	23.80	21.35

Chad to Rhine

Leclerc's Departure from
Chad — CD93

Battle at Cufra Oasis — CD94

Tanks in Action, Mareth — CD95

Normandy Invasion — CD96

Entering Paris — CD97

Liberation of Strasbourg — CD98

"Chad to the Rhine" march, 1942-44, by
Gen. Jacques Leclerc's column, later French
2nd Armored Division.

1946, June 6

Cameroun................................ C9-C14
Fr. Equatorial Africa C25-C30
Fr. Guiana C12-C17
Fr. India C8-C13
Fr. Polynesia C11-C16
Fr. West Africa C5-C10
Guadeloupe.............................. C4-C9
Indo-China............................ C20-C25
Madagascar.......................... C45-C50
Martinique................................ C4-C9
New Caledonia....................... C15-C20
Reunion............................... C26-C31
St. Pierre & Miquelon.............. C9-C14
Somali Coast......................... C9-C14
Wallis & Futuna Isls. C2-C7

Nos. C9-C14 (6)	12.05	9.70
Nos. C25-C30 (6)	14.70	10.80
Nos. C12-C17 (6)	12.65	10.35
Nos. C8-C13 (6)	12.80	15.00
Nos. C11-C16 (6)	17.55	13.40
Nos. C5-C10 (6)	16.05	11.95
Nos. C4-C9 (6)	12.00	9.60
Nos. C20-C25 (6)	6.40	6.40
Nos. C45-C50 (6)	10.30	8.40
Nos. C4-C9 (6)	8.85	7.30
Nos. C15-C20 (6)	13.40	11.90
Nos. C26-C31 (6)	10.25	6.55
Nos. C9-C14 (6)	17.30	14.35

Nos. C9-C14 (6)	18.10	12.65
Nos. C2-C7 (6)	13.75	10.45
Set total (90) Stamps	196.15	158.80

UPU

French Colonials, Globe and
Plane — CD99

Universal Postal Union, 75th anniv.

1949, July 4

Cameroun.................................... C29
Fr. Equatorial Africa C34
Fr. India C17
Fr. Polynesia C20
Fr. West Africa C15
Indo-China................................. C26
Madagascar................................ C55
New Caledonia............................. C24
St. Pierre & Miquelon.................... C18
Somali Coast.............................. C18
Togo C18
Wallis & Futuna Isls. C10

No. C29 (1)	8.00	4.75
No. C34 (1)	16.00	12.00
No. C17 (1)	11.50	8.75
No. C20 (1)	20.00	15.00
No. C15 (1)	12.00	8.75
No. C26 (1)	4.75	4.00
No. C55 (1)	4.00	2.75
No. C24 (1)	7.50	5.00
No. C18 (1)	20.00	12.00
No. C18 (1)	14.00	10.50
No. C18 (1)	8.50	7.00
No. C10 (1)	12.50	8.25
Set total (12) Stamps	138.75	98.75

Tropical Medicine

Doctor
Treating
Infant
CD100

The surtax was for charitable work.

1950

Cameroun.................................... B29
Fr. Equatorial Africa B39
Fr. India B15
Fr. Polynesia B14
Fr. West Africa B3
Madagascar................................ B17
New Caledonia............................. B14
St. Pierre & Miquelon.................... B14
Somali Coast.............................. B14
Togo B11

No. B29 (1)	7.25	5.50
No. B39 (1)	7.25	5.50
No. B15 (1)	6.00	4.00
No. B14 (1)	10.50	8.00
No. B3 (1)	9.50	7.25
No. B17 (1)	5.50	5.50
No. B14 (1)	6.75	5.25
No. B14 (1)	14.00	13.00
No. B14 (1)	7.75	6.25
No. B11 (1)	5.00	3.50
Set total (10) Stamps	79.50	63.75

Military Medal

Medal, Early Marine
and Colonial
Soldier — CD101

Centenary of the creation of the French Military Medal.

1952

Cameroun.................................... 322
Comoro Isls. 39
Fr. Equatorial Africa 186

Fr. India 233
Fr. Polynesia 179
Fr. West Africa 57
Madagascar 286
New Caledonia 295
St. Pierre & Miquelon................345
Somali Coast..........................267
Togo....................................327
Wallis & Futuna Isls. 149

No. 322 (1)	7.25	3.25
No. 39 (1)	50.00	40.00
No. 186 (1)	8.00	5.50
No. 233 (1)	5.50	7.00
No. 179 (1)	13.50	10.00
No. 57 (1)	8.75	6.50
No. 286 (1)	3.75	2.50
No. 295 (1)	6.50	6.00
No. 345 (1)	12.00	12.00
No. 267 (1)	9.00	8.00
No. 327 (1)	5.50	4.75
No. 149 (1)	9.50	7.00
Set total (12) Stamps	139.25	112.50

Liberation

Allied Landing, Victory Sign and Cross of Lorraine — CD102

Liberation of France, 10th anniv.

1954, June 6

Cameroun..............................C32
Comoro Isls. C4
Fr. Equatorial Africa C38
Fr. India C18
Fr. Polynesia C22
Fr. West Africa C17
Madagascar C57
New Caledonia C25
St. Pierre & Miquelon................C19
Somali Coast..........................C19
Togo....................................C19
Wallis & Futuna Isls. C11

No. C32 (1)	7.25	4.75
No. C4 (1)	35.00	20.00
No. C38 (1)	12.00	8.00
No. C18 (1)	11.00	8.00
No. C22 (1)	10.00	8.00
No. C17 (1)	12.00	5.50
No. C57 (1)	3.25	2.00
No. C25 (1)	7.50	5.00
No. C19 (1)	20.00	12.00
No. C19 (1)	10.50	8.50
No. C19 (1)	7.00	5.50
No. C11 (1)	12.50	8.25
Set total (12) Stamps	148.00	95.50

FIDES

Plowmen CD103

Efforts of FIDES, the Economic and Social Development Fund for Overseas Possessions (Fonds d' Investissement pour le Developpement Economique et Social). Each stamp has a different design.

1956

Cameroun.........................326-329
Comoro Isls. 43
Fr. Equatorial Africa 189-192
Fr. Polynesia 181
Fr. West Africa 65-72
Madagascar 292-295
New Caledonia 303
St. Pierre & Miquelon................350
Somali Coast.......................268-269
Togo....................................331

Nos. 326-329 (4)	6.90	3.20
No. 43 (1)	2.25	1.60
Nos. 189-192 (4)	3.20	1.65
No. 181 (1)	4.00	2.00
Nos. 65-72 (8)	16.00	6.35
Nos. 292-295 (4)	2.25	1.20
No. 303 (1)	1.90	1.10
No. 350 (1)	5.50	3.50

Nos. 268-269 (2)	5.35	3.15
No. 331 (1)	4.25	2.10
Set total (27) Stamps	51.60	25.85

Flower

CD104

Each stamp shows a different flower.

1958-9

Cameroun..............................333
Comoro Isls. 45
Fr. Equatorial Africa 200-201
Fr. Polynesia 192
Fr. So. & Antarctic Terr. 11
Fr. West Africa 79-83
Madagascar 301-302
New Caledonia 304-305
St. Pierre & Miquelon................357
Somali Coast..........................270
Togo.................................348-349
Wallis & Futuna Isls. 152

No. 333 (1)	1.60	.80
No. 45 (1)	5.50	4.50
Nos. 200-201 (2)	3.60	1.60
No. 192 (1)	6.50	4.00
No. 11 (1)	8.75	7.50
Nos. 79-83 (5)	10.45	5.60
Nos. 301-302 (2)	1.60	.60
Nos. 304-305 (2)	8.00	3.00
No. 357 (1)	4.25	2.10
No. 270 (1)	4.25	1.40
Nos. 348-349 (2)	1.10	.50
No. 152 (1)	4.50	2.50
Set total (20) Stamps	60.10	34.10

Human Rights

Sun, Dove and U.N. Emblem CD105

10th anniversary of the signing of the Universal Declaration of Human Rights.

1958

Comoro Isls. 44
Fr. Equatorial Africa 202
Fr. Polynesia 191
Fr. West Africa 85
Madagascar 300
New Caledonia 306
St. Pierre & Miquelon................356
Somali Coast..........................274
Wallis & Futuna Isls. 153

No. 44 (1)	11.00	11.00
No. 202 (1)	2.40	1.25
No. 191 (1)	13.00	8.75
No. 85 (1)	2.40	2.00
No. 300 (1)	.80	.40
No. 306 (1)	2.00	1.50
No. 356 (1)	3.50	2.50
No. 274 (1)	3.50	2.10
No. 153 (1)	5.75	4.00
Set total (9) Stamps	44.35	33.50

C.C.T.A.

CD106

Commission for Technical Cooperation in Africa south of the Sahara, 10th anniv.

1960

Cameroun..............................339
Cent. Africa 3
Chad....................................66
Congo, P.R.............................90
Dahomey 138
Gabon 150
Ivory Coast............................180
Madagascar 317

Mali 9
Mauritania 117
Niger...................................104
Upper Volta............................89

No. 339 (1)	1.60	.75
No. 3 (1)	1.90	.65
No. 66 (1)	1.90	.50
No. 90 (1)	1.00	1.00
No. 138 (1)	.50	.25
No. 150 (1)	1.40	1.10
No. 180 (1)	1.10	.50
No. 317 (1)	.60	.30
No. 9 (1)	1.20	.50
No. 117 (1)	.75	.40
No. 104 (1)	.85	.45
No. 89 (1)	.65	.40
Set total (12) Stamps	13.45	6.80

Air Afrique, 1961

Modern and Ancient Africa, Map and Planes — CD107

Founding of Air Afrique (African Airlines).

1961-62

Cameroun..............................C37
Cent. Africa C5
Chad....................................C7
Congo, P.R.............................C5
Dahomey C17
Gabon C5
Ivory Coast............................C18
Mauritania C17
Niger...................................C22
Senegal C31
Upper Volta............................C4

No. C37 (1)	1.00	.50
No. C5 (1)	1.00	.55
No. C7 (1)	1.00	.25
No. C5 (1)	1.75	.90
No. C17 (1)	.80	.40
No. C5 (1)	11.00	6.00
No. C18 (1)	2.00	1.25
No. C17 (1)	2.50	1.25
No. C22 (1)	1.75	.90
No. C31 (1)	.80	.30
No. C4 (1)	3.50	1.75
Set total (11) Stamps	27.10	14.05

Anti-Malaria

CD108

World Health Organization drive to eradicate malaria.

1962, Apr. 7

Cameroun..............................B36
Cent. Africa B1
Chad....................................B1
Comoro Isls. B1
Congo, P.R.............................B3
Dahomey B15
Gabon B4
Ivory Coast............................B15
Madagascar B19
Mali B1
Mauritania B16
Niger...................................B14
Senegal B16
Somali Coast..........................B15
Upper Volta............................B1

No. B36 (1)	1.00	.45
No. B1 (1)	1.40	1.40
No. B1 (1)	1.25	.50
No. B1 (1)	4.00	4.00
No. B3 (1)	1.40	1.00
No. B15 (1)	.75	.75
No. B4 (1)	1.00	1.00
No. B15 (1)	1.25	1.25
No. B19 (1)	.75	.50
No. B1 (1)	1.25	.60
No. B16 (1)	.80	.80
No. B14 (1)	.60	.60

No. B16 (1)	1.10	.65
No. B15 (1)	7.00	7.00
No. B1 (1)	.75	.70
Set total (15) Stamps	24.30	21.20

Abidjan Games

CD109

Abidjan Games, Ivory Coast, Dec. 24-31, 1961. Each stamp shows a different sport.

1962

Cent. Africa 19-20, C6
Chad...............................83-84, C8
Congo, P.R....................103-104, C7
Gabon 163-164, C6
Niger...............................109-111
Upper Volta.......................103-105

Nos. 19-20, C6 (3)	3.90	2.60
Nos. 83-84, C8 (3)	6.30	1.55
Nos. 103-104, C7 (3)	3.85	1.80
Nos. 163-164, C6 (3)	5.00	3.00
Nos. 109-111 (3)	2.60	1.10
Nos. 103-105 (3)	2.80	1.75
Set total (18) Stamps	24.45	11.80

African and Malagasy Union

Flag of Union CD110

First anniversary of the Union.

1962, Sept. 8

Cameroun..............................373
Cent. Africa 21
Chad....................................85
Congo, P.R.............................105
Dahomey 155
Gabon 165
Ivory Coast............................198
Madagascar 332
Mauritania 170
Niger...................................112
Senegal 211
Upper Volta............................106

No. 373 (1)	2.00	.75
No. 21 (1)	1.25	.60
No. 85 (1)	1.25	.25
No. 105 (1)	1.50	.50
No. 155 (1)	1.25	.90
No. 165 (1)	1.60	1.25
No. 198 (1)	2.10	.75
No. 332 (1)	.80	.80
No. 170 (1)	.75	.50
No. 112 (1)	.80	.40
No. 211 (1)	.80	.50
No. 106 (1)	1.10	.75
Set total (12) Stamps	15.20	7.95

Telstar

Telstar and Globe Showing Andover and Pleumeur-Bodou — CD111

First television connection of the United States and Europe through the Telstar satellite, July 11-12, 1962.

1962-63

Andorra, French 154
Comoro Isls. C7
Fr. Polynesia C29
Fr. So. & Antarctic Terr. C5
New Caledonia C33
St. Pierre & Miquelon................C26
Somali Coast..........................C31
Wallis & Futuna Isls. C17

No. 154 (1)	2.00	1.60
No. C7 (1)	5.00	3.00
No. C29 (1)	11.50	8.00

No. C5 (1)	29.00	21.00
No. C33 (1)	25.00	18.50
No. C26 (1)	6.00	4.50
No. C31 (1)	1.00	1.00
No. C17 (1)	3.50	3.50
Set total (8) Stamps	83.00	61.10

Freedom From Hunger

World Map and Wheat Emblem CD112

U.N. Food and Agriculture Organization's "Freedom from Hunger" campaign.

1963, Mar. 21

Cameroun	B37-B38
Cent. Africa	B2
Chad	B2
Congo, P.R.	B4
Dahomey	B16
Gabon	B5
Ivory Coast	B16
Madagascar	B21
Mauritania	B17
Niger	B15
Senegal	B17
Upper Volta	B2

Nos. B37-B38 (2)	2.25	.75
No. B2 (1)	1.25	1.25
No. B2 (1)	2.00	.50
No. B4 (1)	1.40	1.00
No. B16 (1)	.80	.80
No. B5 (1)	1.00	1.00
No. B16 (1)	1.50	1.50
No. B21 (1)	.60	.45
No. B17 (1)	.80	.80
No. B15 (1)	.60	.60
No. B17 (1)	.80	.50
No. B2 (1)	.75	.70
Set total (13) Stamps	13.75	9.85

Red Cross Centenary

CD113

Centenary of the International Red Cross.

1963, Sept. 2

Comoro Isls.	55
Fr. Polynesia	205
New Caledonia	328
St. Pierre & Miquelon	367
Somali Coast	297
Wallis & Futuna Isls.	165

No. 55 (1)	9.50	7.00
No. 205 (1)	15.00	12.00
No. 328 (1)	8.00	6.75
No. 367 (1)	12.00	5.50
No. 297 (1)	6.25	6.25
No. 165 (1)	4.00	3.50
Set total (6) Stamps	54.75	41.00

African Postal Union, 1963

UAMPT Emblem, Radio Masts, Plane and Mail CD114

Establishment of the African and Malagasy Posts and Telecommunications Union.

1963, Sept. 8

Cameroun	C47
Cent. Africa	C10
Chad	C9
Congo, P.R.	C13

Dahomey	C19
Gabon	C13
Ivory Coast	C25
Madagascar	C75
Mauritania	C22
Niger	C27
Rwanda	36
Senegal	C32
Upper Volta	C9

No. C47 (1)	2.25	1.00
No. C10 (1)	1.90	.85
No. C9 (1)	2.40	.60
No. C13 (1)	1.40	.75
No. C19 (1)	.75	.25
No. C13 (1)	1.90	.80
No. C25 (1)	2.50	1.50
No. C75 (1)	1.25	.80
No. C22 (1)	1.50	.60
No. C27 (1)	1.25	.60
No. 36 (1)	.90	.55
No. C32 (1)	1.75	.50
No. C9 (1)	1.50	.75
Set total (13) Stamps	21.25	9.55

Air Afrique, 1963

Symbols of Flight — CD115

First anniversary of Air Afrique and inauguration of DC-8 service.

1963, Nov. 19

Cameroun	C48
Chad	C10
Congo, P.R.	C14
Gabon	C18
Ivory Coast	C26
Mauritania	C26
Niger	C35
Senegal	C33

No. C48 (1)	1.25	.40
No. C10 (1)	2.40	.60
No. C14 (1)	1.60	.60
No. C18 (1)	1.40	.65
No. C26 (1)	1.00	.50
No. C26 (1)	.70	.25
No. C35 (1)	.90	.50
No. C33 (1)	2.00	.65
Set total (8) Stamps	11.25	4.15

Europafrica

Europe and Africa Linked — CD116

Signing of an economic agreement between the European Economic Community and the African and Malagasy Union, Yaounde, Cameroun, July 20, 1963.

1963-64

Cameroun	402
Cent. Africa	C12
Chad	C11
Congo, P.R.	C16
Gabon	C19
Ivory Coast	217
Niger	C43
Upper Volta	C11

No. 402 (1)	2.25	.60
No. C12 (1)	2.50	1.75
No. C11 (1)	2.00	.50
No. C16 (1)	1.60	1.00
No. C19 (1)	1.40	.75
No. 217 (1)	1.10	.35
No. C43 (1)	.85	.50
No. C11 (1)	1.50	.80
Set total (8) Stamps	13.20	6.25

Human Rights

Scales of Justice and Globe CD117

15th anniversary of the Universal Declaration of Human Rights.

1963, Dec. 10

Comoro Isls.	56
Fr. Polynesia	206
New Caledonia	329
St. Pierre & Miquelon	368
Somali Coast	300
Wallis & Futuna Isls.	166

No. 56 (1)	9.50	7.50
No. 205 (1)	15.00	12.00
No. 329 (1)	7.00	6.00
No. 368 (1)	7.00	3.50
No. 300 (1)	8.50	8.50
No. 166 (1)	8.00	7.50
Set total (6) Stamps	55.00	45.00

PHILATEC

Stamp Album, Champs Elysees Palace and Horses of Marly CD118

Intl. Philatelic and Postal Techniques Exhibition, Paris, June 5-21, 1964.

1963-64

Comoro Isls.	60
France	1078
Fr. Polynesia	207
New Caledonia	341
St. Pierre & Miquelon	369
Somali Coast	301
Wallis & Futuna Isls.	167

No. 60 (1)	4.50	4.00
No. 1078 (1)	.25	.25
No. 206 (1)	15.00	10.00
No. 341 (1)	6.50	6.50
No. 369 (1)	11.00	8.00
No. 301 (1)	7.75	7.75
No. 167 (1)	3.50	3.50
Set total (7) Stamps	48.50	40.00

Cooperation

CD119

Cooperation between France and the French-speaking countries of Africa and Madagascar.

1964

Cameroun	409-410
Cent. Africa	39
Chad	103
Congo, P.R.	121
Dahomey	193
France	1111
Gabon	175
Ivory Coast	221
Madagascar	360
Mauritania	181
Niger	143
Senegal	236
Togo	495

Nos. 409-410 (2)	2.50	.50
No. 39 (1)	1.00	.55
No. 103 (1)	1.00	.25
No. 121 (1)	.80	.35
No. 193 (1)	.80	.35
No. 1111 (1)	.25	.25
No. 175 (1)	.90	.60
No. 221 (1)	1.10	.35

No. 360 (1)	.60	.25
No. 181 (1)	.60	.35
No. 143 (1)	.80	.40
No. 236 (1)	1.60	.85
No. 495 (1)	.70	.25
Set total (14) Stamps	12.65	5.30

ITU

Telegraph, Syncom Satellite and ITU Emblem CD120

Intl. Telecommunication Union, Cent.

1965, May 17

Comoro Isls.	C14
Fr. Polynesia	C33
Fr. So. & Antarctic Terr.	C8
New Caledonia	C40
New Hebrides	124-125
St. Pierre & Miquelon	C29
Somali Coast	C36
Wallis & Futuna Isls.	C20

No. C14 (1)	20.00	10.00
No. C33 (1)	80.00	52.50
No. C8 (1)	200.00	160.00
No. C40 (1)	10.00	8.00
Nos. 124-125 (2)	40.50	34.00
No. C29 (1)	20.00	10.00
No. C36 (1)	15.00	9.00
No. C20 (1)	21.00	15.00
Set total (9) Stamps	406.50	298.50

French Satellite A-1

Diamant Rocket and Launching Installation — CD121

Launching of France's first satellite, Nov. 26, 1965.

1965-66

Comoro Isls.	C16a
France	1138a
Reunion	359a
Fr. Polynesia	C41a
Fr. So. & Antarctic Terr.	C10a
New Caledonia	C45a
St. Pierre & Miquelon	C31a
Somali Coast	C40a
Wallis & Futuna Isls.	C23a

No. C16a (1)	11.00	11.00
No. 1138a (1)	.65	.65
No. 359a (1)	3.50	3.00
No. C41a (1)	14.00	14.00
No. C10a (1)	29.00	24.00
No. C45a (1)	7.00	7.00
No. C31a (1)	12.50	12.50
No. C40a (1)	7.00	7.00
No. C23a (1)	9.25	9.25
Set total (9) Stamps	93.90	88.40

French Satellite D-1

D-1 Satellite in Orbit — CD122

Launching of the D-1 satellite at Hammaguir, Algeria, Feb. 17, 1966.

1966

Comoro Isls.	C17
France	1148

Fr. Polynesia		C42
Fr. So. & Antarctic Terr.		C11
New Caledonia		C46
St. Pierre & Miquelon		C32
Somali Coast		C49
Wallis & Futuna Isls.		C24

No. C17 (1)	4.00	4.00
No. 1148 (1)	.25	.25
No. C42 (1)	7.00	4.75
No. C11 (1)	57.50	40.00
No. C46 (1)	2.25	2.00
No. C32 (1)	8.00	6.00
No. C49 (1)	4.25	2.75
No. C24 (1)	3.50	3.50
Set total (8) Stamps	86.75	63.25

Air Afrique, 1966

Planes and Air Afrique
Emblem — CD123

Introduction of DC-8F planes by Air Afrique.

1966

Cameroun		C79
Cent. Africa		C35
Chad		C26
Congo, P.R.		C42
Dahomey		C42
Gabon		C47
Ivory Coast		C32
Mauritania		C57
Niger		C63
Senegal		C47
Togo		C54
Upper Volta		C31

No. C79 (1)	.80	.25
No. C35 (1)	1.00	.40
No. C26 (1)	1.00	.25
No. C42 (1)	1.00	.25
No. C42 (1)	.75	.25
No. C47 (1)	.90	.35
No. C32 (1)	1.00	.60
No. C57 (1)	.80	.30
No. C63 (1)	.65	.35
No. C47 (1)	.80	.30
No. C54 (1)	.80	.25
No. C31 (1)	.75	.50
Set total (12) Stamps	10.25	4.05

African Postal Union, 1967

Telecommunications Symbols and Map
of Africa — CD124

Fifth anniversary of the establishment of the African and Malagasy Union of Posts and Telecommunications, UAMPT.

1967

Cameroun		C90
Cent. Africa		C46
Chad		C37
Congo, P.R.		C57
Dahomey		C61
Gabon		C58
Ivory Coast		C34
Madagascar		C85
Mauritania		C65
Niger		C75
Rwanda		C1-C3
Senegal		C60
Togo		C81
Upper Volta		C50

No. C90 (1)	2.40	.65
No. C46 (1)	2.25	.85
No. C37 (1)	2.00	.60
No. C57 (1)	1.60	.60
No. C61 (1)	1.75	.95
No. C58 (1)	2.25	.95
No. C34 (1)	3.50	1.50
No. C85 (1)	1.25	.60
No. C65 (1)	1.25	.60
No. C75 (1)	1.40	.60

Nos. C1-C3 (3)	2.30	1.25
No. C60 (1)	1.75	.50
No. C81 (1)	1.90	.30
No. C50 (1)	1.80	.70
Set total (16) Stamps	27.40	10.65

Monetary Union

Gold Token of the
Ashantis, 17-18th
Centuries — CD125

West African Monetary Union, 5th anniv.

1967, Nov. 4

Dahomey		244
Ivory Coast		259
Mauritania		238
Niger		204
Senegal		294
Togo		623
Upper Volta		181

No. 244 (1)	.65	.65
No. 259 (1)	.85	.40
No. 238 (1)	.45	.25
No. 204 (1)	.45	.25
No. 294 (1)	.60	.25
No. 623 (1)	.60	.25
No. 181 (1)	.65	.35
Set total (7) Stamps	4.25	2.40

WHO Anniversary

Sun,
Flowers
and WHO
Emblem
CD126

World Health Organization, 20th anniv.

1968, May 4

Afars & Issas		317
Comoro Isls.		73
Fr. Polynesia		241-242
Fr. So. & Antarctic Terr.		31
New Caledonia		367
St. Pierre & Miquelon		377
Wallis & Futuna Isls.		169

No. 317 (1)	3.00	3.00
No. 73 (1)	2.75	2.00
Nos. 241-242 (2)	22.00	12.75
No. 31 (1)	62.50	47.50
No. 367 (1)	4.00	2.25
No. 377 (1)	10.00	8.00
No. 169 (1)	6.50	4.50
Set total (8) Stamps	110.75	80.00

Human Rights Year

Human Rights
Flame — CD127

1968, Aug. 10

Afars & Issas		322-323
Comoro Isls.		76
Fr. Polynesia		243-244
Fr. So. & Antarctic Terr.		32
New Caledonia		369
St. Pierre & Miquelon		382
Wallis & Futuna Isls.		170

Nos. 322-323 (2)	6.75	4.00
No. 76 (1)	3.50	3.50
Nos. 243-244 (2)	24.00	14.00
No. 32 (1)	55.00	47.50
No. 369 (1)	2.75	1.50
No. 382 (1)	8.00	5.50
No. 170 (1)	3.75	3.75
Set total (9) Stamps	103.75	79.75

2nd PHILEXAFRIQUE

CD128

Opening of PHILEXAFRIQUE, Abidjan, Feb. 14. Each stamp shows a local scene and stamp.

1969, Feb. 14

Cameroun		C118
Cent. Africa		C65
Chad		C48
Congo, P.R.		C77
Dahomey		C94
Gabon		C82
Ivory Coast		C38-C40
Madagascar		C92
Mali		C65
Mauritania		C80
Niger		C104
Senegal		C68
Togo		C104
Upper Volta		C62

No. C118 (1)	3.25	1.25
No. C65 (1)	1.90	1.90
No. C48 (1)	2.40	1.00
No. C77 (1)	2.00	1.75
No. C94 (1)	2.25	2.25
No. C82 (1)	2.25	2.25
Nos. C38-C40 (3)	14.50	14.50
No. C92 (1)	1.75	.85
No. C65 (1)	1.75	1.00
No. C80 (1)	1.90	.75
No. C104 (1)	2.75	1.90
No. C68 (1)	2.00	1.40
No. C104 (1)	2.25	.45
No. C62 (1)	4.00	3.25
Set total (16) Stamps	44.95	34.50

Concorde

Concorde in
Flight
CD129

First flight of the prototype Concorde supersonic plane at Toulouse, Mar. 1, 1969.

1969

Afars & Issas		C56
Comoro Isls.		C29
France		C42
Fr. Polynesia		C50
Fr. So. & Antarctic Terr.		C18
New Caledonia		C63
St. Pierre & Miquelon		C40
Wallis & Futuna Isls.		C30

No. C56 (1)	26.00	16.00
No. C29 (1)	24.00	16.00
No. C42 (1)	.75	.35
No. C50 (1)	55.00	35.00
No. C18 (1)	55.00	37.50
No. C63 (1)	27.50	20.00
No. C40 (1)	30.00	11.00
No. C30 (1)	15.00	10.00
Set total (8) Stamps	233.25	145.85

Development Bank

Bank
Emblem — CD130

African Development Bank, fifth anniv.

1969

Cameroun		499
Chad		217
Congo, P.R.		181-182

Ivory Coast		281
Mali		127-128
Mauritania		267
Niger		220
Senegal		317-318
Upper Volta		201

No. 499 (1)	.80	.25
No. 217 (1)	.70	.25
Nos. 181-182 (2)	.80	.50
No. 281 (1)	.70	.40
Nos. 127-128 (2)	1.00	.50
No. 267 (1)	.60	.25
No. 220 (1)	.60	.30
Nos. 317-318 (2)	1.55	.50
No. 201 (1)	.65	.30
Set total (12) Stamps	7.40	3.25

ILO

ILO Headquarters, Geneva, and
Emblem — CD131

Intl. Labor Organization, 50th anniv.

1969-70

Afars & Issas		337
Comoro Isls.		83
Fr. Polynesia		251-252
Fr. So. & Antarctic Terr.		35
New Caledonia		379
St. Pierre & Miquelon		396
Wallis & Futuna Isls.		172

No. 337 (1)	2.75	2.00
No. 83 (1)	1.25	.75
Nos. 251-252 (2)	24.00	12.50
No. 35 (1)	15.00	10.00
No. 379 (1)	2.25	1.10
No. 396 (1)	8.50	5.50
No. 172 (1)	3.00	2.90
Set total (8) Stamps	56.75	34.75

ASECNA

Map of
Africa,
Plane and
Airport
CD132

10th anniversary of the Agency for the Security of Aerial Navigation in Africa and Madagascar (ASECNA, Agence pour la Securite de la Navigation Aerienne en Afrique et a Madagascar).

1969-70

Cameroun		500
Cent. Africa		119
Chad		222
Congo, P.R.		197
Dahomey		269
Gabon		260
Ivory Coast		287
Mali		130
Niger		221
Senegal		321
Upper Volta		204

No. 500 (1)	2.00	.60
No. 119 (1)	2.25	.80
No. 222 (1)	1.00	.25
No. 197 (1)	2.00	.40
No. 269 (1)	.90	.55
No. 260 (1)	1.75	.75
No. 287 (1)	.90	.40
No. 130 (1)	.90	.40
No. 221 (1)	1.25	.70
No. 321 (1)	1.60	.50
No. 204 (1)	1.75	1.00
Set total (11) Stamps	16.30	6.35

U.P.U. Headquarters

CD133

New Universal Postal Union headquarters, Bern, Switzerland.

1970

Afars & Issas 342
Algeria 443
Cameroun 503-504
Cent. Africa 125
Chad 225
Comoro Isls. 84
Congo, P.R. 216
Fr. Polynesia 261-262
Fr. So. & Antarctic Terr. 36
Gabon 258
Ivory Coast 295
Madagascar 444
Mali 134-135
Mauritania 283
New Caledonia 382
Niger 231-232
St. Pierre & Miquelon 397-398
Senegal 328-329
Tunisia 535
Wallis & Futuna Isls. 173

No. 342 (1)	2.50	1.40
No. 443 (1)	1.10	.40
Nos. 503-504 (2)	2.60	.55
No. 125 (1)	1.90	.70
No. 225 (1)	1.00	.25
No. 84 (1)	5.50	2.00
No. 216 (1)	.80	.25
Nos. 261-262 (2)	20.00	10.00
No. 36 (1)	40.00	27.50
No. 258 (1)	.90	.55
No. 295 (1)	1.10	.50
No. 444 (1)	.55	.25
Nos. 134-135 (2)	1.05	.50
No. 283 (1)	.60	.30
No. 382 (1)	3.00	1.50
Nos. 231-232 (2)	1.20	.60
Nos. 397-398 (2)	28.00	17.00
Nos. 328-329 (2)	1.55	.55
No. 535 (1)	.60	.25
No. 173 (1)	4.00	4.00
Set total (26) Stamps	117.95	69.05

De Gaulle

CD134

First anniversary of the death of Charles de Gaulle, (1890-1970), President of France.

1971-72

Afars & Issas 356-357
Comoro Isls. 104-105
France 1325a
Fr. Polynesia 270-271
Fr. So. & Antarctic Terr. 52-53
New Caledonia 393-394
Reunion 380a
St. Pierre & Miquelon 417-418
Wallis & Futuna Isls. 177-178

Nos. 356-357 (2)	12.50	7.50
Nos. 104-105 (2)	9.00	5.75
No. 1325a (1)	3.00	2.50
Nos. 270-271 (2)	51.50	29.50
Nos. 52-53 (2)	40.00	29.50
Nos. 393-394 (2)	23.00	11.75
No. 380a (1)	9.25	8.00
Nos. 417-418 (2)	40.00	30.00
Nos. 177-178 (2)	24.00	16.25
Set total (16) Stamps	212.25	140.75

African Postal Union, 1971

UAMPT Building, Brazzaville, Congo — CD135

10th anniversary of the establishment of the African and Malagasy Posts and Telecommunications Union, UAMPT. Each stamp has a different native design.

1971, Nov. 13

Cameroun C177
Cent. Africa C89
Chad C94
Congo, P.R. C136
Dahomey C146
Gabon C120
Ivory Coast C47
Mauritania C113
Niger C164
Rwanda C8
Senegal C105
Togo C166
Upper Volta C97

No. C177 (1)	2.00	.50
No. C89 (1)	2.25	.85
No. C94 (1)	1.50	.50
No. C136 (1)	1.60	.75
No. C146 (1)	1.75	.80
No. C120 (1)	1.75	.70
No. C47 (1)	2.00	1.00
No. C113 (1)	1.20	.65
No. C164 (1)	1.25	.60
No. C8 (1)	2.75	2.25
No. C105 (1)	1.60	.50
No. C166 (1)	1.25	.40
No. C97 (1)	1.50	.50
Set total (13) Stamps	22.40	10.20

West African Monetary Union

African Couple, City, Village and Commemorative Coin — CD136

West African Monetary Union, 10th anniv.

1972, Nov. 2

Dahomey 300
Ivory Coast 331
Mauritania 299
Niger 258
Senegal 374
Togo 825
Upper Volta 280

No. 300 (1)	.65	.25
No. 331 (1)	1.00	.50
No. 299 (1)	.75	.25
No. 258 (1)	.55	.30
No. 374 (1)	.50	.30
No. 825 (1)	.60	.25
No. 280 (1)	.60	.25
Set total (7) Stamps	4.65	2.10

African Postal Union, 1973

Telecommunications Symbols and Map of Africa — CD137

11th anniversary of the African and Malagasy Posts and Telecommunications Union (UAMPT).

1973, Sept. 12

Cameroun 574
Cent. Africa 194
Chad 294
Congo, P.R. 289
Dahomey 311
Gabon 320
Ivory Coast 361
Madagascar 500
Mauritania 304
Niger 287
Rwanda 540
Senegal 393
Togo 849
Upper Volta 297

No. 574 (1)	1.75	.40
No. 194 (1)	1.25	.75
No. 294 (1)	1.75	.40
No. 289 (1)	1.60	.50
No. 311 (1)	1.25	.55
No. 320 (1)	1.40	.75
No. 361 (1)	2.50	1.00
No. 500 (1)	1.10	.35
No. 304 (1)	1.10	.40
No. 287 (1)	.90	.60
No. 540 (1)	3.75	2.00
No. 393 (1)	1.60	.50
No. 849 (1)	1.00	.35
No. 297 (1)	1.25	.70
Set total (14) Stamps	22.20	9.25

Philexafrique II — Essen

CD138

CD139

Designs: Indigenous fauna, local and German stamps. Types CD138-CD139 printed horizontally and vertically se-tenant in sheets of 10 (2x5). Label between horizontal pairs alternately commemorates Philexafrique II, Libreville, Gabon, June 1978, and 2nd International Stamp Fair, Essen, Germany, Nov. 1-5.

1978-1979

Benin C286a
Central Africa C201a
Chad C239a
Congo Republic C246a
Djibouti C122a
Gabon C216a
Ivory Coast C65a
Mali C357a
Mauritania C186a
Niger C292a
Rwanda C13a
Senegal C147a
Togo C364a

No. C286a (1)	9.00	8.50
No. C201a (1)	7.50	7.50
No. C239a (1)	8.00	4.00
No. C246a (1)	7.00	7.00
No. C122a (1)	8.50	8.50
No. C216a (1)	6.50	4.00
No. C65a (1)	9.00	9.00
No. C357a (1)	5.00	3.00
No. C186a (1)	4.50	4.00
No. C292a (1)	6.00	5.00
No. C13a (1)	4.00	4.00
No. C147a (1)	10.00	4.00
No. C364a (1)	3.00	1.50
Set total (13) Stamps	88.00	70.00

BRITISH COMMONWEALTH OF NATIONS

The listings follow established trade practices when these issues are offered as units by dealers. The Peace issue, for example, includes only one stamp from the Indian state of Hyderabad. The U.P.U. issue includes the Egypt set. Pairs are included for those varieties issued with bilingual designs se-tenant.

Silver Jubilee

Windsor Castle and King George V CD301

Reign of King George V, 25th anniv.

1935

Antigua 77-80
Ascension 33-36
Bahamas 92-95
Barbados 186-189
Basutoland 11-14
Bechuanaland Protectorate......117-120
Bermuda 100-103
British Guiana 223-226
British Honduras 108-111
Cayman Islands 81-84
Ceylon 260-263
Cyprus 136-139
Dominica 90-93
Falkland Islands 77-80
Fiji 110-113
Gambia 125-128
Gibraltar 100-103
Gilbert & Ellice Islands 33-36
Gold Coast 108-111
Grenada 124-127
Hong Kong 147-150
Jamaica 109-112
Kenya, Uganda, Tanzania 42-45
Leeward Islands 96-99
Malta 184-187
Mauritius 204-207
Montserrat 85-88
Newfoundland 226-229
Nigeria 34-37
Northern Rhodesia 18-21
Nyasaland Protectorate............47-50
St. Helena 111-114
St. Kitts-Nevis 72-75
St. Lucia 91-94
St. Vincent 134-137
Seychelles 118-121
Sierra Leone 166-169
Solomon Islands 60-63
Somaliland Protectorate...........77-80
Straits Settlements 213-216
Swaziland 20-23
Trinidad & Tobago 43-46
Turks & Caicos Islands 71-74
Virgin Islands 69-72

The following have different designs but are included in the omnibus set:

Great Britain 226-229
Offices in Morocco (Sp. Curr.) 67-70
Offices in Morocco (Br. Curr.) 226-229
Offices in Morocco (Fr. Curr.) 422-425
Offices in Morocco (Tangier)....508-510
Australia 152-154
Canada 211-216
Cook Islands 98-100
India 142-148
Nauru 31-34
New Guinea 46-47
New Zealand 199-201
Niue 67-69
Papua 114-117
Samoa 163-165
South Africa 68-71
Southern Rhodesia 33-36
South-West Africa 121-124

Nos. 77-80 (4)	20.25	23.25
Nos. 33-36 (4)	58.50	127.50
Nos. 92-95 (4)	25.00	46.00
Nos. 186-189 (4)	30.00	46.80
Nos. 11-14 (4)	11.60	21.25
Nos. 117-120 (4)	15.75	36.00
Nos. 100-103 (4)	16.80	58.50
Nos. 223-226 (4)	18.35	35.50
Nos. 108-111 (4)	15.25	16.35
Nos. 81-84 (4)	21.60	21.60
Nos. 260-263 (4)	10.40	21.60
Nos. 136-139 (4)	39.75	34.40
Nos. 90-93 (4)	18.85	19.85
Nos. 77-80 (4)	55.00	14.75
Nos. 110-113 (4)	15.25	27.90
Nos. 125-128 (4)	12.20	25.25
Nos. 100-103 (4)	28.75	42.75
Nos. 33-36 (4)	31.50	50.00
Nos. 108-111 (4)	26.25	62.85
Nos. 124-127 (4)	16.70	40.60
Nos. 147-150 (4)	59.00	18.75
Nos. 109-112 (4)	17.00	39.00
Nos. 42-45 (4)	8.75	11.00
Nos. 96-99 (4)	35.75	49.60
Nos. 184-187 (4)	22.00	33.70
Nos. 204-207 (4)	47.60	58.25
Nos. 85-88 (4)	10.25	30.25
Nos. 226-229 (4)	17.50	12.05
Nos. 34-37 (4)	13.25	25.75
Nos. 18-21 (4)	16.75	16.25
Nos. 47-50 (4)	39.75	80.25
Nos. 111-114 (4)	31.15	33.25
Nos. 72-75 (4)	11.55	18.50
Nos. 91-94 (4)	16.00	20.80
Nos. 134-137 (4)	9.45	21.25
Nos. 118-121 (4)	17.50	32.50
Nos. 166-169 (4)	24.25	56.00
Nos. 60-63 (4)	27.25	38.00
Nos. 77-80 (4)	17.00	48.25
Nos. 213-216 (4)	15.00	25.10
Nos. 20-23 (4)	6.80	18.25
Nos. 43-46 (4)	14.05	27.75
Nos. 71-74 (4)	8.40	14.50
Nos. 69-72 (4)	25.00	55.25
Nos. 226-229 (4)	7.25	7.45

Nos. 67-70 (4)	14.35	*26.10*
Nos. 226-229 (4)	8.20	*28.90*
Nos. 422-425 (4)	3.90	*2.00*
Nos. 508-510 (3)	18.80	*23.85*
Nos. 152-154 (3)	45.75	*60.35*
Nos. 211-216 (6)	24.85	*13.35*
Nos. 98-100 (3)	9.65	*12.00*
Nos. 142-148 (7)	23.25	*11.80*
Nos. 31-34 (4)	9.90	*9.90*
Nos. 46-47 (2)	4.35	*1.70*
Nos. 199-201 (3)	21.75	*31.75*
Nos. 67-69 (3)	11.30	*26.50*
Nos. 114-117 (4)	9.20	*17.00*
Nos. 163-165 (3)	4.40	*5.50*
Nos. 68-71 (4)	57.00	*155.00*
Nos. 33-36 (4)	27.75	*45.25*
Nos. 121-124 (4)	13.00	*36.10*
Set total (245) Stamps	1,313.	*2,108.*

Coronation

Queen
Elizabeth
and King
George VI
CD302

1937

Aden	13-15
Antigua	81-83
Ascension	37-39
Bahamas	97-99
Barbados	190-192
Basutoland	15-17
Bechuanaland Protectorate	121-123
Bermuda	115-117
British Guiana	227-229
British Honduras	112-114
Cayman Islands	97-99
Ceylon	275-277
Cyprus	140-142
Dominica	94-96
Falkland Islands	81-83
Fiji	114-116
Gambia	129-131
Gibraltar	104-106
Gilbert & Ellice Islands	37-39
Gold Coast	112-114
Grenada	128-130
Hong Kong	151-153
Jamaica	113-115
Kenya, Uganda, Tanzania	60-62
Leeward Islands	100-102
Malta	188-190
Mauritius	208-210
Montserrat	89-91
Newfoundland	230-232
Nigeria	50-52
Northern Rhodesia	22-24
Nyasaland Protectorate	51-53
St. Helena	115-117
St. Kitts-Nevis	76-78
St. Lucia	107-109
St. Vincent	138-140
Seychelles	122-124
Sierra Leone	170-172
Solomon Islands	64-66
Somaliland Protectorate	81-83
Straits Settlements	235-237
Swaziland	24-26
Trinidad & Tobago	47-49
Turks & Caicos Islands	75-77
Virgin Islands	73-75

The following have different designs but are included in the omnibus set:

Great Britain	234
Offices in Morocco (Sp. Curr.)	82
Offices in Morocco (Fr. Curr.)	439
Offices in Morocco (Tangier)	514
Canada	237
Cook Islands	109-111
Nauru	35-38
Newfoundland	233-243
New Guinea	48-51
New Zealand	223-225
Niue	118-121
Papua	118-121
South Africa	74-78
Southern Rhodesia	38-41
South-West Africa	125-132

Nos. 13-15 (3)	2.70	*5.65*
Nos. 81-83 (3)	1.85	*8.00*
Nos. 37-39 (3)	2.75	*2.75*
Nos. 97-99 (3)	1.05	*3.05*
Nos. 190-192 (3)	1.10	*1.95*
Nos. 15-17 (3)	1.15	*3.00*
Nos. 121-123 (3)	.95	*3.35*
Nos. 115-117 (3)	1.25	*5.00*
Nos. 227-229 (3)	1.45	*3.05*
Nos. 112-114 (3)	1.20	*2.40*
Nos. 97-99 (3)	1.10	*2.70*
Nos. 275-277 (3)	8.25	*10.35*

Nos. 140-142 (3)	3.75	*6.50*
Nos. 94-96 (3)	.85	*2.40*
Nos. 81-83 (3)	2.90	*2.30*
Nos. 114-116 (3)	1.50	*5.75*
Nos. 129-131 (3)	.95	*3.95*
Nos. 104-106 (3)	2.25	*6.45*
Nos. 37-39 (3)	.85	*2.00*
Nos. 112-114 (3)	3.10	*10.00*
Nos. 128-130 (3)	1.00	*.85*
Nos. 151-153 (3)	23.00	*12.50*
Nos. 113-115 (3)	1.25	*1.25*
Nos. 60-62 (3)	1.00	*2.35*
Nos. 100-102 (3)	1.55	*4.00*
Nos. 188-190 (3)	1.25	*1.60*
Nos. 208-210 (3)	2.05	*3.75*
Nos. 89-91 (3)	1.00	*3.35*
Nos. 230-232 (3)	7.00	*2.80*
Nos. 50-52 (3)	3.25	*8.50*
Nos. 22-24 (3)	.95	*2.25*
Nos. 51-53 (3)	1.05	*1.30*
Nos. 115-117 (3)	1.45	*2.05*
Nos. 76-78 (3)	.95	*2.05*
Nos. 107-109 (3)	1.05	*2.05*
Nos. 138-140 (3)	.80	*4.75*
Nos. 122-124 (3)	1.20	*1.90*
Nos. 170-172 (3)	1.95	*5.65*
Nos. 64-66 (3)	.90	*2.00*
Nos. 81-83 (3)	1.10	*3.40*
Nos. 235-237 (3)	3.25	*1.60*
Nos. 24-26 (3)	1.05	*1.75*
Nos. 47-49 (3)	1.00	*1.00*
Nos. 75-77 (3)	1.30	*1.15*
Nos. 73-75 (3)	2.20	*6.90*

No. 234 (1)	.25	*.25*
No. 82 (1)	.80	*.80*
No. 439 (1)	.35	*.25*
No. 514 (1)	.55	*.55*
No. 237 (1)	.35	*.25*
Nos. 109-111 (3)	.85	*.80*
Nos. 35-38 (4)	1.10	*5.50*
Nos. 233-243 (11)	41.90	*30.40*
Nos. 48-51 (4)	1.40	*7.90*
Nos. 223-225 (3)	1.40	*2.75*
Nos. 70-72 (3)	.80	*2.05*
Nos. 118-121 (4)	1.60	*5.25*
Nos. 74-78 (5)	9.25	*10.80*
Nos. 38-41 (4)	3.55	*15.50*
Nos. 125-132 (8)	5.00	*8.40*
Set total (189) Stamps	172.65	*262.80*

Peace

King
George VI
and
Parliament
Buildings,
London
CD303

Return to peace at the close of World War II.

1945-46

Aden	28-29
Antigua	96-97
Ascension	50-51
Bahamas	130-131
Barbados	207-208
Bermuda	131-132
British Guiana	242-243
British Honduras	127-128
Cayman Islands	112-113
Ceylon	293-294
Cyprus	156-157
Dominica	112-113
Falkland Islands	97-98
Falkland Islands Dep.	1L9-1L10
Fiji	137-138
Gambia	144-145
Gibraltar	119-120
Gilbert & Ellice Islands	52-53
Gold Coast	128-129
Grenada	143-144
Jamaica	136-137
Kenya, Uganda, Tanzania	90-91
Leeward Islands	116-117
Malta	206-207
Mauritius	223-224
Montserrat	104-105
Nigeria	71-72
Northern Rhodesia	46-47
Nyasaland Protectorate	82-83
Pitcairn Islands	9-10
St. Helena	128-129
St. Kitts-Nevis	91-92
St. Lucia	127-128
St. Vincent	152-153
Seychelles	149-150
Sierra Leone	186-187
Solomon Islands	80-81
Somaliland Protectorate	108-109
Trinidad & Tobago	62-63
Turks & Caicos Islands	90-91
Virgin Islands	88-89

The following have different designs but are included in the omnibus set:

Great Britain	264-265

Offices in Morocco (Tangier)	523-524
Aden	
Kathiri State of Seiyun	12-13
Qu'aiti State of Shihr and Mukalla	
	12-13
Australia	200-202
Basutoland	29-31
Bechuanaland Protectorate	137-139
Burma	66-69
Cook Islands	127-130
Hong Kong	174-175
India	195-198
Hyderabad	51-53
New Zealand	247-257
Niue	90-93
Pakistan-Bahawalpur	O16
Samoa	191-194
South Africa	100-102
Southern Rhodesia	67-70
South-West Africa	153-155
Swaziland	38-40
Zanzibar	222-223

Nos. 28-29 (2)	.95	*2.50*
Nos. 96-97 (2)	.50	*.80*
Nos. 50-51 (2)	.80	*2.00*
Nos. 130-131 (2)	.50	*1.40*
Nos. 207-208 (2)	.50	*1.10*
Nos. 131-132 (2)	.55	*.55*
Nos. 242-243 (2)	1.05	*1.40*
Nos. 127-128 (2)	.50	*.50*
Nos. 112-113 (2)	.60	*.80*
Nos. 293-294 (2)	.60	*2.10*
Nos. 156-157 (2)	.90	*.70*
Nos. 112-113 (2)	.50	*.50*
Nos. 97-98 (2)	.90	*1.35*
Nos. 1L9-1L10 (2)	1.30	*1.00*
Nos. 137-138 (2)	.50	*1.75*
Nos. 144-145 (2)	.50	*.95*
Nos. 119-120 (2)	.75	*1.00*
Nos. 52-53 (2)	.50	*.50*
Nos. 128-129 (2)	1.85	*3.75*
Nos. 143-144 (2)	.50	*.95*
Nos. 136-137 (2)	.80	*12.50*
Nos. 90-91 (2)	.65	*.65*
Nos. 116-117 (2)	.50	*1.50*
Nos. 206-207 (2)	.65	*2.00*
Nos. 223-224 (2)	.50	*1.05*
Nos. 104-105 (2)	.50	*.50*
Nos. 71-72 (2)	.70	*2.75*
Nos. 46-47 (2)	1.25	*2.00*
Nos. 82-83 (2)	.50	*.50*
Nos. 9-10 (2)	1.40	*1.40*
Nos. 128-129 (2)	.65	*.70*
Nos. 91-92 (2)	.50	*.50*
Nos. 127-128 (2)	.50	*.60*
Nos. 152-153 (2)	.50	*.50*
Nos. 149-150 (2)	.55	*.50*
Nos. 186-187 (2)	.50	*.50*
Nos. 80-81 (2)	.50	*1.50*
Nos. 108-109 (2)	.70	*.50*
Nos. 62-63 (2)	.50	*.50*
Nos. 90-91 (2)	.50	*.50*
Nos. 88-89 (2)	.50	*.50*

Nos. 264-265 (2)	.50	*.70*
Nos. 523-524 (2)	1.50	*3.00*
Nos. 12-13 (2)	.50	*.90*
Nos. 12-13 (2)	.50	*1.25*
Nos. 200-202 (3)	1.60	*3.00*
Nos. 29-31 (3)	2.10	*2.60*
Nos. 137-139 (3)	2.05	*4.75*
Nos. 66-69 (4)	1.60	*1.30*
Nos. 127-130 (4)	2.00	*1.85*
Nos. 174-175 (2)	6.75	*3.15*
Nos. 195-198 (4)	4.75	*3.60*
Nos. 51-53 (3)	1.50	*1.70*
Nos. 247-257 (11)	3.95	*3.90*
Nos. 90-93 (4)	1.70	*2.20*
No. O16 (1)	5.50	*7.00*
Nos. 191-194 (4)	2.05	*1.00*
Nos. 100-102 (2)	1.20	*4.00*
Nos. 67-70 (4)	1.40	*1.75*
Nos. 153-155 (3)	1.85	*3.25*
Nos. 38-40 (3)	2.40	*5.50*
Nos. 222-223 (2)	.65	*1.00*
Set total (151) Stamps	74.35	*114.65*

Silver Wedding

King George VI and Queen
Elizabeth

CD304   CD305

1948-49

Aden	30-31
Kathiri State of Seiyun	14-15
Qu'aiti State of Shihr and Mukalla	
	14-15

Antigua	98-99
Ascension	52-53
Bahamas	148-149
Barbados	210-211
Basutoland	39-40
Bechuanaland Protectorate	147-148
Bermuda	133-134
British Guiana	244-245
British Honduras	129-130
Cayman Islands	116-117
Cyprus	158-159
Dominica	114-115
Falkland Islands	99-100
Falkland Islands Dep.	1L11-1L12
Fiji	139-140
Gambia	146-147
Gibraltar	121-122
Gilbert & Ellice Islands	54-55
Gold Coast	142-143
Grenada	145-146
Hong Kong	178-179
Jamaica	138-139
Kenya, Uganda, Tanzania	92-93
Leeward Islands	118-119
Malaya	
Johore	128-129
Kedah	55-56
Kelantan	44-45
Malacca	1-2
Negri Sembilan	36-37
Pahang	44-45
Penang	1-2
Perak	99-100
Perlis	1-2
Selangor	74-75
Trengganu	47-48
Malta	223-224
Mauritius	229-230
Montserrat	106-107
Nigeria	73-74
North Borneo	238-239
Northern Rhodesia	48-49
Nyasaland Protectorate	85-86
Pitcairn Islands	11-12
St. Helena	130-131
St. Kitts-Nevis	93-94
St. Lucia	129-130
St. Vincent	154-155
Sarawak	174-175
Seychelles	151-152
Sierra Leone	188-189
Singapore	21-22
Solomon Islands	82-83
Somaliland Protectorate	110-111
Swaziland	48-49
Trinidad & Tobago	64-65
Turks & Caicos Islands	92-93
Virgin Islands	90-91
Zanzibar	224-225

The following have different designs but are included in the omnibus set:

Great Britain	267-268
Offices in Morocco (Sp. Curr.)	93-94
Offices in Morocco (Tangier)	525-526
Bahrain	62-63
Kuwait	82-83
Oman	25-26
South Africa	106
South-West Africa	159

Nos. 30-31 (2)	40.40	*47.25*
Nos. 14-15 (2)	17.85	*16.00*
Nos. 14-15 (2)	18.55	*12.50*
Nos. 98-99 (2)	13.55	*15.75*
Nos. 52-53 (2)	55.55	*50.45*
Nos. 148-149 (2)	45.25	*40.30*
Nos. 210-211 (2)	18.35	*13.05*
Nos. 39-40 (2)	52.80	*55.25*
Nos. 147-148 (2)	42.85	*47.75*
Nos. 133-134 (2)	47.75	*55.25*
Nos. 244-245 (2)	24.25	*28.45*
Nos. 129-130 (2)	25.25	*53.20*
Nos. 116-117 (2)	25.25	*33.50*
Nos. 158-159 (2)	58.50	*78.05*
Nos. 114-115 (2)	25.25	*32.75*
Nos. 99-100 (2)	112.10	*76.10*
Nos. 1L11-1L12 (2)	4.25	*6.00*
Nos. 139-140 (2)	17.00	*11.50*
Nos. 146-147 (2)	21.25	*21.25*
Nos. 121-122 (2)	61.00	*78.00*
Nos. 54-55 (2)	14.25	*22.75*
Nos. 142-143 (2)	35.25	*37.75*
Nos. 145-146 (2)	21.75	*21.75*
Nos. 178-179 (2)	303.50	*96.50*
Nos. 138-139 (2)	27.85	*60.25*
Nos. 92-93 (2)	50.25	*67.75*
Nos. 118-119 (2)	7.00	*8.25*
Nos. 128-129 (2)	29.25	*53.25*
Nos. 55-56 (2)	35.25	*50.25*
Nos. 44-45 (2)	35.75	*62.75*
Nos. 1-2 (2)	35.40	*49.75*
Nos. 36-37 (2)	28.10	*38.20*
Nos. 44-45 (2)	28.00	*38.05*
Nos. 1-2 (2)	40.50	*37.80*

Nos. 99-100 (2)	27.80	37.75
Nos. 1-2 (2)	33.50	58.00
Nos. 74-75 (2)	30.25	25.30
Nos. 47-48 (2)	35.25	62.75
Nos. 223-224 (2)	40.55	45.25
Nos. 229-230 (2)	17.75	45.25
Nos. 106-107 (2)	9.25	18.25
Nos. 73-74 (2)	17.85	22.80
Nos. 238-239 (2)	35.30	45.75
Nos. 48-49 (2)	92.80	90.25
Nos. 85-86 (2)	18.25	30.25
Nos. 11-12 (2)	44.75	48.50
Nos. 130-131 (2)	32.80	42.80
Nos. 93-94 (2)	11.25	7.25
Nos. 129-130 (2)	22.25	45.25
Nos. 154-155 (2)	27.75	30.25
Nos. 174-175 (2)	50.40	52.90
Nos. 151-152 (2)	16.25	45.75
Nos. 188-189 (2)	24.75	26.25
Nos. 21-22 (2)	116.00	45.40
Nos. 82-83 (2)	13.40	13.40
Nos. 110-111 (2)	8.40	8.75
Nos. 48-49 (2)	40.30	47.75
Nos. 64-65 (2)	32.75	38.25
Nos. 92-93 (2)	11.25	16.25
Nos. 90-91 (2)	16.25	22.25
Nos. 224-225 (2)	29.60	38.00
Nos. 267-268 (2)	40.40	40.25
Nos. 93-94 (2)	20.10	25.35
Nos. 525-526 (2)	23.10	29.25
Nos. 62-63 (2)	38.50	57.75
Nos. 82-83 (2)	45.50	45.50
Nos. 25-26 (2)	46.00	47.50
No. 106 (1)	.90	1.25
No. 159 (1)	1.10	.35
Set total (136) Stamps	2,491.	2,675.

U.P.U.

Mercury and Symbols of Communications — CD306

Plane, Ship and Hemispheres — CD307

Mercury Scattering Letters over Globe CD308

U.P.U. Monument, Bern CD309

Universal Postal Union, 75th anniversary.

1949

Aden	32-35
Kathiri State of Seiyun	16-19
Qu'aiti State of Shihr and Mukalla	
	16-19
Antigua	100-103
Ascension	57-60
Bahamas	150-153
Barbados	212-215
Basutoland	41-44
Bechuanaland Protectorate	149-152
Bermuda	138-141
British Guiana	246-249
British Honduras	137-140
Brunei	79-82
Cayman Islands	118-121
Cyprus	160-163
Dominica	116-119
Falkland Islands	103-106
Falkland Islands Dep.	1L14-1L17
Fiji	141-144
Gambia	148-151
Gibraltar	123-126

Gilbert & Ellice Islands	56-59
Gold Coast	144-147
Grenada	147-150
Hong Kong	180-183
Jamaica	142-145
Kenya, Uganda, Tanzania	94-97
Leeward Islands	126-129
Malaya	
Johore	151-154
Kedah	57-60
Kelantan	46-49
Malacca	18-21
Negri Sembilan	59-62
Pahang	46-49
Penang	23-26
Perak	101-104
Perlis	3-6
Selangor	76-79
Trengganu	49-52
Malta	225-228
Mauritius	231-234
Montserrat	108-111
New Hebrides, British	62-65
New Hebrides, French	79-82
Nigeria	75-78
North Borneo	240-243
Northern Rhodesia	50-53
Nyasaland Protectorate	87-90
Pitcairn Islands	13-16
St. Helena	132-135
St. Kitts-Nevis	95-98
St. Lucia	131-134
St. Vincent	170-173
Sarawak	176-179
Seychelles	153-156
Sierra Leone	190-193
Singapore	23-26
Solomon Islands	84-87
Somaliland Protectorate	112-115
Southern Rhodesia	71-72
Swaziland	50-53
Tonga	87-90
Trinidad & Tobago	66-69
Turks & Caicos Islands	101-104
Virgin Islands	92-95
Zanzibar	226-229

The following have different designs but are included in the omnibus set:

Great Britain	276-279
Offices in Morocco (Tangier)	546-549
Australia	223
Bahrain	68-71
Burma	116-121
Ceylon	304-306
Egypt	281-283
India	223-226
Kuwait	89-92
Oman	31-34
Pakistan-Bahawalpur	26-29, O25-O28
South Africa	109-111
South-West Africa	160-162

Nos. 32-35 (4)	5.85	8.45
Nos. 16-19 (4)	2.75	5.50
Nos. 16-19 (4)	2.60	4.20
Nos. 100-103 (4)	3.60	7.70
Nos. 57-60 (4)	11.10	9.00
Nos. 150-153 (4)	5.35	9.30
Nos. 212-215 (4)	4.40	14.15
Nos. 41-44 (4)	4.75	10.00
Nos. 149-152 (4)	3.35	7.25
Nos. 138-141 (4)	4.75	6.15
Nos. 246-249 (4)	2.75	4.20
Nos. 137-140 (4)	3.30	6.35
Nos. 79-82 (4)	9.50	8.45
Nos. 118-121 (4)	3.60	7.25
Nos. 160-163 (4)	4.60	10.70
Nos. 116-119 (4)	2.30	5.65
Nos. 103-106 (4)	14.00	17.10
Nos. 1L14-1L17 (4)	14.60	14.50
Nos. 141-144 (4)	3.35	14.75
Nos. 148-151 (4)	3.10	7.10
Nos. 123-126 (4)	5.90	8.75
Nos. 56-59 (4)	4.70	7.85
Nos. 144-147 (4)	3.05	6.95
Nos. 147-150 (4)	2.15	3.55
Nos. 180-183 (4)	57.25	18.25
Nos. 142-145 (4)	2.25	2.45
Nos. 94-97 (4)	2.90	3.40
Nos. 126-129 (4)	3.05	9.60
Nos. 151-154 (4)	4.70	8.90
Nos. 57-60 (4)	4.80	12.00
Nos. 46-49 (4)	4.25	11.00
Nos. 18-21 (4)	4.25	17.30
Nos. 59-62 (4)	3.50	10.75
Nos. 46-49 (4)	3.00	7.25
Nos. 23-26 (4)	5.10	11.75
Nos. 101-104 (4)	3.65	10.75
Nos. 3-6 (4)	3.95	14.25
Nos. 76-79 (4)	4.90	12.30
Nos. 49-52 (4)	4.95	9.75
Nos. 225-228 (4)	4.50	4.85
Nos. 231-234 (4)	4.35	6.70
Nos. 108-111 (4)	3.40	3.85
Nos. 62-65 (4)	1.60	4.25
Nos. 79-82 (4)	24.25	24.25

Nos. 75-78 (4)	2.80	9.25
Nos. 240-243 (4)	7.15	6.50
Nos. 50-53 (4)	5.00	6.50
Nos. 87-90 (4)	4.05	4.05
Nos. 13-16 (4)	18.50	16.50
Nos. 132-135 (4)	4.85	7.10
Nos. 95-98 (4)	3.35	4.70
Nos. 131-134 (4)	2.55	3.85
Nos. 170-173 (4)	2.20	5.05
Nos. 176-179 (4)	8.15	10.85
Nos. 153-156 (4)	3.25	4.10
Nos. 190-193 (4)	3.00	5.10
Nos. 84-87 (4)	18.00	13.20
Nos. 112-115 (4)	4.05	4.90
Nos. 71-72 (2)	3.95	8.70
Nos. 50-53 (4)	1.95	2.25
Nos. 87-90 (4)	2.80	4.65
Nos. 66-69 (4)	3.00	5.25
Nos. 101-104 (4)	3.15	3.15
Nos. 92-95 (4)	2.70	4.10
Nos. 226-229 (4)	2.60	5.90
Nos. 276-279 (4)	5.45	13.50
Nos. 546-549 (4)	1.35	2.10
No. 223 (1)	3.20	10.15
Nos. 68-71 (4)	.60	.55
Nos. 116-121 (6)	4.75	16.50
Nos. 304-306 (3)	7.30	5.35
Nos. 281-283 (3)	3.35	4.25
Nos. 223-226 (4)	5.75	2.70
Nos. 89-92 (4)	35.50	10.50
Nos. 31-34 (4)	6.10	10.25
Nos. 26-29,O25-O28 (8)	5.55	15.75
Nos. 109-111 (3)	2.00	42.00
Nos. 160-162 (3)	2.20	3.00
Set total (313) Stamps	3.00	5.50
	469.15	687.85

University

Arms of University College CD310   Alice, Princess of Athlone CD311

1948 opening of University College of the West Indies at Jamaica.

1951

Antigua	104-105
Barbados	228-229
British Guiana	250-251
British Honduras	141-142
Dominica	120-121
Grenada	164-165
Jamaica	146-147
Leeward Islands	130-131
Montserrat	112-113
St. Kitts-Nevis	105-106
St. Lucia	149-150
St. Vincent	174-175
Trinidad & Tobago	70-71
Virgin Islands	96-97

Nos. 104-105 (2)	1.35	3.75
Nos. 228-229 (2)	1.85	1.55
Nos. 250-251 (2)	1.10	1.25
Nos. 141-142 (2)	1.40	2.20
Nos. 120-121 (2)	1.40	1.75
Nos. 164-165 (2)	1.20	1.60
Nos. 146-147 (2)	.90	.70
Nos. 130-131 (2)	1.35	4.00
Nos. 112-113 (2)	.85	1.50
Nos. 105-106 (2)	.90	1.50
Nos. 149-150 (2)	1.40	1.50
Nos. 174-175 (2)	1.00	2.15
Nos. 70-71 (2)	.75	.75
Nos. 96-97 (2)	1.50	3.75
Set total (28) Stamps	16.95	27.95

Coronation

Queen Elizabeth II — CD312

1953

Aden	47
Kathiri State of Seiyun	28

Qu'aiti State of Shihr and Mukalla	28
Antigua	106
Ascension	61
Bahamas	157
Barbados	234
Basutoland	45
Bechuanaland Protectorate	153
Bermuda	142
British Guiana	252
British Honduras	143
Cayman Islands	150
Cyprus	167
Dominica	141
Falkland Islands	121
Falkland Islands Dependencies	1L18
Fiji	145
Gambia	152
Gibraltar	131
Gilbert & Ellice Islands	60
Gold Coast	160
Grenada	170
Hong Kong	184
Jamaica	153
Kenya, Uganda, Tanzania	101
Leeward Islands	132
Malaya	
Johore	155
Kedah	82
Kelantan	71
Malacca	27
Negri Sembilan	63
Pahang	71
Penang	27
Perak	126
Perlis	28
Selangor	101
Trengganu	74
Malta	241
Mauritius	250
Montserrat	127
New Hebrides, British	77
Nigeria	79
North Borneo	260
Northern Rhodesia	60
Nyasaland Protectorate	96
Pitcairn Islands	19
St. Helena	139
St. Kitts-Nevis	119
St. Lucia	156
St. Vincent	185
Sarawak	196
Seychelles	172
Sierra Leone	194
Singapore	27
Solomon Islands	88
Somaliland Protectorate	127
Swaziland	54
Trinidad & Tobago	84
Tristan da Cunha	13
Turks & Caicos Islands	118
Virgin Islands	114

The following have different designs but are included in the omnibus set:

Great Britain	313-316
Offices in Morocco (Tangier)	579-582
Australia	259-261
Bahrain	92-95
Canada	330
Ceylon	317
Cook Islands	145-146
Kuwait	113-116
New Zealand	280-284
Niue	104-105
Oman	52-55
Samoa	214-215
South Africa	192
Southern Rhodesia	80
South-West Africa	244-248
Tokelau Islands	4

No. 47 (1)	1.25	1.25
No. 28 (1)	.75	1.50
No. 28 (1)	1.10	.60
No. 106 (1)	.40	.75
No. 61 (1)	1.25	2.75
No. 157 (1)	1.40	.75
No. 234 (1)	1.00	.25
No. 45 (1)	.50	.60
No. 153 (1)	.75	.35
No. 142 (1)	.85	.50
No. 252 (1)	.45	.25
No. 143 (1)	.60	.40
No. 150 (1)	.40	1.75
No. 167 (1)	1.60	.75
No. 141 (1)	.40	.40
No. 121 (1)	.90	1.50
No. 1L18 (1)	1.80	1.40
No. 145 (1)	1.00	.60
No. 152 (1)	.50	.50
No. 131 (1)	.50	.50
No. 60 (1)	.65	2.25
No. 160 (1)	.95	.95

No. 170 (1)	.30	.25
No. 184 (1)	6.00	.35
No. 153 (1)	.70	.25
No. 101 (1)	.40	.25
No. 132 (1)	1.00	2.25
No. 155 (1)	1.40	.30
No. 82 (1)	2.25	.60
No. 71 (1)	1.60	1.60
No. 27 (1)	1.10	1.50
No. 63 (1)	1.40	.65
No. 71 (1)	2.25	.25
No. 27 (1)	1.75	.30
No. 126 (1)	1.60	.25
No. 28 (1)	1.75	4.00
No. 101 (1)	1.75	.25
No. 74 (1)	1.50	1.00
No. 241 (1)	.50	.25
No. 250 (1)	1.00	.25
No. 127 (1)	.65	.50
No. 77 (1)	.75	.60
No. 79 (1)	.45	.25
No. 260 (1)	2.00	1.00
No. 60 (1)	.70	.25
No. 96 (1)	.75	.75
No. 19 (1)	2.25	2.25
No. 139 (1)	1.25	1.25
No. 119 (1)	.35	.25
No. 156 (1)	.70	.35
No. 185 (1)	.50	.30
No. 196 (1)	2.00	1.75
No. 172 (1)	.80	.80
No. 194 (1)	.40	.40
No. 27 (1)	2.50	.40
No. 88 (1)	1.00	1.00
No. 127 (1)	.40	.25
No. 54 (1)	.30	.25
No. 84 (1)	.25	.25
No. 13 (1)	1.00	1.75
No. 118 (1)	.40	1.10
No. 114 (1)	.40	1.00
Nos. 313-316 (4)	16.35	8.75
Nos. 579-582 (4)	7.40	5.20
Nos. 259-261 (3)	4.60	3.25
Nos. 92-95 (4)	15.25	12.75
No. 330 (1)	.25	.25
No. 317 (1)	1.50	.25
Nos. 145-146 (2)	2.65	2.65
Nos. 113-116 (4)	16.00	8.50
Nos. 280-284 (5)	5.65	6.85
Nos. 104-105 (2)	1.60	1.60
Nos. 52-55 (4)	15.25	6.50
Nos. 214-215 (2)	2.10	1.00
No. 192 (1)	.30	.25
No. 80 (1)	7.25	7.25
Nos. 244-248 (5)	3.00	2.35
No. 4 (1)	2.75	2.75
Set total (106) Stamps	168.95	121.25

Separate designs for each country for the visit of Queen Elizabeth II and the Duke of Edinburgh.

Royal Visit 1953

1953

Aden		62
Australia		267-269
Bermuda		163
Ceylon		318
Fiji		146
Gibraltar		146
Jamaica		154
Kenya, Uganda, Tanzania		102
Malta		242
New Zealand		286-287

No. 62 (1)	.65	1.25
Nos. 267-269 (3)	2.35	1.90
No. 163 (1)	.50	.25
No. 318 (1)	1.25	.25
No. 146 (1)	.65	.35
No. 146 (1)	.50	.30
No. 154 (1)	.50	.25
No. 102 (1)	.50	.25
No. 242 (1)	.35	.25
Nos. 286-287 (2)	.50	.50
Set total (13) Stamps	7.75	5.55

West Indies Federation

Map of the Caribbean
CD313

Federation of the West Indies, April 22, 1958.

1958

Antigua		122-124
Barbados		248-250
Dominica		161-163
Grenada		184-186
Jamaica		175-177
Montserrat		143-145
St. Kitts-Nevis		136-138
St. Lucia		170-172

St. Vincent		198-200
Trinidad & Tobago		86-88

Nos. 122-124 (3)	5.80	3.80
Nos. 248-250 (3)	1.60	2.90
Nos. 161-163 (3)	1.95	1.85
Nos. 184-186 (3)	1.50	1.20
Nos. 175-177 (3)	2.65	3.45
Nos. 143-145 (3)	2.35	1.35
Nos. 136-138 (3)	3.00	1.85
Nos. 170-172 (3)	2.05	2.80
Nos. 198-200 (3)	1.50	1.75
Nos. 86-88 (3)	.75	.90
Set total (30) Stamps	23.15	21.85

Freedom from Hunger

Protein Food
CD314

U.N. Food and Agricultural Organization's "Freedom from Hunger" campaign.

1963

Aden		65
Antigua		133
Ascension		89
Bahamas		180
Basutoland		83
Bechuanaland Protectorate		194
Bermuda		192
British Guiana		271
British Honduras		179
Brunei		100
Cayman Islands		168
Dominica		181
Falkland Islands		146
Fiji		198
Gambia		172
Gibraltar		161
Gilbert & Ellice Islands		76
Grenada		190
Hong Kong		218
Malta		291
Mauritius		270
Montserrat		150
New Hebrides, British		93
North Borneo		296
Pitcairn Islands		35
St. Helena		173
St. Lucia		179
St. Vincent		201
Sarawak		212
Seychelles		213
Solomon Islands		109
Swaziland		108
Tonga		127
Tristan da Cunha		68
Turks & Caicos Islands		138
Virgin Islands		140
Zanzibar		280

No. 65 (1)	1.50	1.75
No. 133 (1)	.35	.35
No. 89 (1)	1.00	.50
No. 180 (1)	.65	.65
No. 83 (1)	.50	.25
No. 194 (1)	.50	.50
No. 192 (1)	1.00	.50
No. 271 (1)	.45	.25
No. 179 (1)	.60	.25
No. 100 (1)	3.25	2.25
No. 168 (1)	.55	.30
No. 181 (1)	.30	.30
No. 146 (1)	10.50	2.50
No. 198 (1)	3.50	2.25
No. 172 (1)	.50	.25
No. 161 (1)	4.00	2.25
No. 76 (1)	1.40	.40
No. 190 (1)	.30	.25
No. 218 (1)	47.50	7.50
No. 291 (1)	2.00	2.00
No. 270 (1)	.50	.50
No. 150 (1)	.55	.45
No. 93 (1)	.60	.25
No. 296 (1)	1.90	.75
No. 35 (1)	10.00	4.50
No. 173 (1)	2.25	1.10
No. 179 (1)	.40	.40
No. 201 (1)	.90	.50
No. 212 (1)	1.60	1.75
No. 213 (1)	.85	.35
No. 109 (1)	3.00	.85
No. 108 (1)	.50	.50
No. 127 (1)	.60	.35
No. 68 (1)	.75	.35
No. 138 (1)	.50	.25
No. 140 (1)	.50	.50
No. 280 (1)	1.50	.80
Set total (37) Stamps	107.25	39.40

Red Cross Centenary

Red Cross and Elizabeth II
CD315

1963

Antigua		134-135
Ascension		90-91
Bahamas		183-184
Basutoland		84-85
Bechuanaland Protectorate		195-196
Bermuda		193-194
British Guiana		272-273
British Honduras		180-181
Cayman Islands		169-170
Dominica		182-183
Falkland Islands		147-148
Fiji		203-204
Gambia		173-174
Gibraltar		162-163
Gilbert & Ellice Islands		77-78
Grenada		191-192
Hong Kong		219-220
Jamaica		203-204
Malta		292-293
Mauritius		271-272
Montserrat		151-152
New Hebrides, British		94-95
Pitcairn Islands		36-37
St. Helena		174-175
St. Kitts-Nevis		143-144
St. Lucia		180-181
St. Vincent		202-203
Seychelles		214-215
Solomon Islands		110-111
South Arabia		1-2
Swaziland		109-110
Tonga		134-135
Tristan da Cunha		69-70
Turks & Caicos Islands		139-140
Virgin Islands		141-142

Nos. 134-135 (2)	1.00	2.00
Nos. 90-91 (2)	6.75	3.35
Nos. 183-184 (2)	2.30	2.80
Nos. 84-85 (2)	1.20	.90
Nos. 195-196 (2)	.95	.85
Nos. 193-194 (2)	3.00	2.80
Nos. 272-273 (2)	1.05	.80
Nos. 180-181 (2)	1.00	2.50
Nos. 169-170 (2)	1.10	3.00
Nos. 182-183 (2)	.70	1.05
Nos. 147-148 (2)	18.00	5.50
Nos. 203-204 (2)	3.25	2.80
Nos. 173-174 (2)	.75	1.00
Nos. 162-163 (2)	6.25	5.40
Nos. 77-78 (2)	2.25	3.25
Nos. 191-192 (2)	.80	.50
Nos. 219-220 (2)	35.00	7.35
Nos. 203-204 (2)	.75	1.65
Nos. 292-293 (2)	2.50	4.75
Nos. 271-272 (2)	.90	.90
Nos. 151-152 (2)	1.00	.80
Nos. 94-95 (2)	1.00	.50
Nos. 36-37 (2)	6.50	5.50
Nos. 174-175 (2)	1.70	2.30
Nos. 143-144 (2)	.90	.90
Nos. 180-181 (2)	1.25	1.25
Nos. 202-203 (2)	.90	.90
Nos. 214-215 (2)	1.10	.90
Nos. 110-111 (2)	1.25	1.15
Nos. 1-2 (2)	1.25	1.25
Nos. 109-110 (2)	1.10	1.10
Nos. 134-135 (2)	1.00	1.25
Nos. 69-70 (2)	1.15	.80
Nos. 139-140 (2)	.85	.75
Nos. 141-142 (2)	.80	1.25
Set total (70) Stamps	111.25	73.75

Shakespeare

Shakespeare Memorial Theatre, Stratford-on-Avon — CD316

400th anniversary of the birth of William Shakespeare.

1964

Antigua		151
Bahamas		201
Bechuanaland Protectorate		197
Cayman Islands		171

Dominica		184
Falkland Islands		149
Gambia		192
Gibraltar		164
Montserrat		153
St. Lucia		196
Turks & Caicos Islands		141
Virgin Islands		143

No. 151 (1)	.35	.25
No. 201 (1)	.60	.35
No. 197 (1)	.35	.35
No. 171 (1)	.35	.30
No. 184 (1)	.35	.35
No. 149 (1)	1.60	.50
No. 192 (1)	.35	.25
No. 164 (1)	.65	.55
No. 153 (1)	.35	.25
No. 196 (1)	.45	.25
No. 141 (1)	.40	.25
No. 143 (1)	.45	.45
Set total (12) Stamps	6.25	4.10

ITU

ITU Emblem
CD317

Intl. Telecommunication Union, cent.

1965

Antigua		153-154
Ascension		92-93
Bahamas		219-220
Barbados		265-266
Basutoland		101-102
Bechuanaland Protectorate		202-203
Bermuda		196-197
British Guiana		293-294
British Honduras		187-188
Brunei		116-117
Cayman Islands		172-173
Dominica		185-186
Falkland Islands		154-155
Fiji		211-212
Gibraltar		167-168
Gilbert & Ellice Islands		87-88
Grenada		205-206
Hong Kong		221-222
Mauritius		291-292
Montserrat		157-158
New Hebrides, British		108-109
Pitcairn Islands		52-53
St. Helena		180-181
St. Kitts-Nevis		163-164
St. Lucia		197-198
St. Vincent		224-225
Seychelles		218-219
Solomon Islands		126-127
Swaziland		115-116
Tristan da Cunha		85-86
Turks & Caicos Islands		142-143
Virgin Islands		159-160

Nos. 153-154 (2)	1.45	1.35
Nos. 92-93 (2)	1.90	1.30
Nos. 219-220 (2)	1.35	1.50
Nos. 265-266 (2)	1.50	1.25
Nos. 101-102 (2)	.85	.65
Nos. 202-203 (2)	1.10	.75
Nos. 196-197 (2)	2.15	2.25
Nos. 293-294 (2)	.60	.55
Nos. 187-188 (2)	.75	.75
Nos. 116-117 (2)	1.75	1.75
Nos. 172-173 (2)	1.00	.85
Nos. 185-186 (2)	.55	.55
Nos. 154-155 (2)	6.75	3.15
Nos. 211-212 (2)	2.00	1.05
Nos. 167-168 (2)	9.00	5.95
Nos. 87-88 (2)	.95	.75
Nos. 205-206 (2)	.50	.50
Nos. 221-222 (2)	24.50	3.80
Nos. 291-292 (2)	1.20	.65
Nos. 157-158 (2)	1.25	1.15
Nos. 108-109 (2)	.65	.50
Nos. 52-53 (2)	6.25	4.30
Nos. 180-181 (2)	.80	.60
Nos. 163-164 (2)	.60	.60
Nos. 197-198 (2)	1.25	1.25
Nos. 224-225 (2)	.80	.90
Nos. 218-219 (2)	.90	.90
Nos. 126-127 (2)	.70	.55
Nos. 115-116 (2)	.75	.75
Nos. 85-86 (2)	1.00	.65
Nos. 142-143 (2)	.75	.50
Nos. 159-160 (2)	.85	.85
Set total (64) Stamps	76.40	42.55

Intl. Cooperation Year

ICY Emblem CD318

1965

Antigua	155-156
Ascension	94-95
Bahamas	222-223
Basutoland	103-104
Bechuanaland Protectorate	204-205
Bermuda	199-200
British Guiana	295-296
British Honduras	189-190
Brunei	118-119
Cayman Islands	174-175
Dominica	187-188
Falkland Islands	156-157
Fiji	213-214
Gibraltar	169-170
Gilbert & Ellice Islands	104-105
Grenada	207-208
Hong Kong	223-224
Mauritius	293-294
Montserrat	176-177
New Hebrides, British	110-111
New Hebrides, French	126-127
Pitcairn Islands	54-55
St. Helena	182-183
St. Kitts-Nevis	165-166
St. Lucia	199-200
Seychelles	220-221
Solomon Islands	143-144
South Arabia	17-18
Swaziland	117-118
Tristan da Cunha	87-88
Turks & Caicos Islands	144-145
Virgin Islands	161-162

Nos. 155-156 (2)	.55	.50
Nos. 94-95 (2)	1.30	1.40
Nos. 222-223 (2)	.65	1.90
Nos. 103-104 (2)	.75	.85
Nos. 204-205 (2)	.85	1.00
Nos. 199-200 (2)	2.05	1.25
Nos. 295-296 (2)	.65	.60
Nos. 189-190 (2)	.60	.55
Nos. 118-119 (2)	.85	.85
Nos. 174-175 (2)	1.00	.75
Nos. 187-188 (2)	.55	.55
Nos. 156-157 (2)	6.00	1.65
Nos. 213-214 (2)	1.95	1.25
Nos. 169-170 (2)	1.25	2.75
Nos. 104-105 (2)	.95	.60
Nos. 207-208 (2)	.50	.50
Nos. 223-224 (2)	22.00	3.10
Nos. 293-294 (2)	.70	.70
Nos. 176-177 (2)	.80	.65
Nos. 110-111 (2)	.50	.50
Nos. 126-127 (2)	12.00	12.00
Nos. 54-55 (2)	6.35	4.50
Nos. 182-183 (2)	.95	.50
Nos. 165-166 (2)	.70	.60
Nos. 199-200 (2)	.55	.55
Nos. 220-221 (2)	.90	.65
Nos. 143-144 (2)	.70	.60
Nos. 17-18 (2)	1.20	.50
Nos. 117-118 (2)	.75	.75
Nos. 87-88 (2)	1.05	.65
Nos. 144-145 (2)	.65	.50
Nos. 161-162 (2)	.65	.50
Set total (64) Stamps	70.90	44.20

Churchill Memorial

Winston Churchill and St. Paul's, London, During Air Attack CD319

1966

Antigua	157-160
Ascension	96-99
Bahamas	224-227
Barbados	281-284
Basutoland	105-108
Bechuanaland Protectorate	206-209
Bermuda	201-204
British Antarctic Territory	16-19
British Honduras	191-194
Brunei	120-123
Cayman Islands	176-179
Dominica	189-192
Falkland Islands	158-161
Fiji	215-218

Gibraltar	171-174
Gilbert & Ellice Islands	106-109
Grenada	209-212
Hong Kong	225-228
Mauritius	295-298
Montserrat	178-181
New Hebrides, British	112-115
New Hebrides, French	128-131
Pitcairn Islands	56-59
St. Helena	184-187
St. Kitts-Nevis	167-170
St. Lucia	201-204
St. Vincent	241-244
Seychelles	222-225
Solomon Islands	145-148
South Arabia	19-22
Swaziland	119-122
Tristan da Cunha	89-92
Turks & Caicos Islands	146-149
Virgin Islands	163-166

Nos. 157-160 (4)	3.05	3.05
Nos. 96-99 (4)	10.00	6.40
Nos. 224-227 (4)	2.30	3.20
Nos. 281-284 (4)	3.00	4.45
Nos. 105-108 (4)	2.80	3.25
Nos. 206-209 (4)	2.50	2.50
Nos. 201-204 (4)	4.00	4.75
Nos. 16-19 (4)	37.85	18.00
Nos. 191-194 (4)	2.45	1.30
Nos. 120-123 (4)	7.65	6.55
Nos. 176-179 (4)	3.10	3.65
Nos. 189-192 (4)	1.15	1.15
Nos. 158-161 (4)	12.75	9.55
Nos. 215-218 (4)	4.40	3.00
Nos. 171-174 (4)	3.05	5.30
Nos. 106-109 (4)	1.75	1.30
Nos. 209-212 (4)	1.10	1.10
Nos. 225-228 (4)	52.50	11.40
Nos. 295-298 (4)	4.05	4.05
Nos. 178-181 (4)	1.60	1.55
Nos. 112-115 (4)	2.30	1.00
Nos. 128-131 (4)	10.25	10.25
Nos. 56-59 (4)	11.00	6.75
Nos. 184-187 (4)	1.85	1.95
Nos. 167-170 (4)	1.70	1.70
Nos. 201-204 (4)	1.50	1.50
Nos. 241-244 (4)	1.50	1.75
Nos. 222-225 (4)	3.20	3.60
Nos. 145-148 (4)	1.50	1.60
Nos. 19-22 (4)	2.95	2.20
Nos. 119-122 (4)	1.70	2.55
Nos. 89-92 (4)	5.95	2.70
Nos. 146-149 (4)	1.60	1.75
Nos. 163-166 (4)	1.90	1.90
Set total (136) Stamps	209.95	136.70

Royal Visit, 1966

Queen Elizabeth II and Prince Philip CD320

Caribbean visit, Feb. 4 - Mar. 6, 1966.

1966

Antigua	161-162
Bahamas	228-229
Barbados	285-286
British Guiana	299-300
Cayman Islands	180-181
Dominica	193-194
Grenada	213-214
Montserrat	182-183
St. Kitts-Nevis	171-172
St. Lucia	205-206
St. Vincent	245-246
Turks & Caicos Islands	150-151
Virgin Islands	167-168

Nos. 161-162 (2)	3.50	2.60
Nos. 228-229 (2)	3.05	3.05
Nos. 285-286 (2)	3.00	2.00
Nos. 299-300 (2)	3.35	1.60
Nos. 180-181 (2)	3.45	1.80
Nos. 193-194 (2)	3.00	.60
Nos. 213-214 (2)	.80	.50
Nos. 182-183 (2)	1.70	1.00
Nos. 171-172 (2)	.80	.75
Nos. 205-206 (2)	1.50	1.35
Nos. 245-246 (2)	2.75	1.35
Nos. 150-151 (2)	1.20	.55
Nos. 167-168 (2)	1.75	1.75
Set total (26) Stamps	29.85	18.90

World Cup Soccer

Soccer Player and Jules Rimet Cup CD321

World Cup Soccer Championship, Wembley, England, July 11-30.

1966

Antigua	163-164
Ascension	100-101
Bahamas	245-246
Bermuda	205-206
Brunei	124-125
Cayman Islands	182-183
Dominica	195-196
Fiji	219-220
Gibraltar	175-176
Gilbert & Ellice Islands	125-126
Grenada	230-231
New Hebrides, British	116-117
New Hebrides, French	132-133
Pitcairn Islands	60-61
St. Helena	188-189
St. Kitts-Nevis	173-174
St. Lucia	207-208
Seychelles	226-227
Solomon Islands	167-168
South Arabia	23-24
Tristan da Cunha	93-94

Nos. 163-164 (2)	.80	.85
Nos. 100-101 (2)	2.50	2.00
Nos. 245-246 (2)	.65	.65
Nos. 205-206 (2)	1.75	1.75
Nos. 124-125 (2)	1.30	1.25
Nos. 182-183 (2)	.75	.65
Nos. 195-196 (2)	1.20	.75
Nos. 219-220 (2)	1.70	.60
Nos. 175-176 (2)	1.85	1.75
Nos. 125-126 (2)	.80	.60
Nos. 230-231 (2)	.65	.95
Nos. 116-117 (2)	1.00	1.00
Nos. 132-133 (2)	7.00	7.00
Nos. 60-61 (2)	5.50	5.00
Nos. 188-189 (2)	1.25	.60
Nos. 173-174 (2)	.85	.80
Nos. 207-208 (2)	1.15	.90
Nos. 226-227 (2)	.85	.85
Nos. 167-168 (2)	1.10	1.10
Nos. 23-24 (2)	1.90	.55
Nos. 93-94 (2)	1.90	1.90
Set total (42) Stamps	35.80	30.40

WHO Headquarters

World Health Organization Headquarters, Geneva — CD322

1966

Antigua	165-166
Ascension	102-103
Bahamas	247-248
Brunei	126-127
Cayman Islands	184-185
Dominica	197-198
Fiji	224-225
Gibraltar	180-181
Gilbert & Ellice Islands	127-128
Grenada	232-233
Hong Kong	229-230
Montserrat	184-185
New Hebrides, British	118-119
New Hebrides, French	134-135
Pitcairn Islands	62-63
St. Helena	190-191
St. Kitts-Nevis	177-178
St. Lucia	209-210
St. Vincent	247-248
Seychelles	228-229
Solomon Islands	169-170
South Arabia	25-26
Tristan da Cunha	99-100

Nos. 165-166 (2)	1.15	.55
Nos. 102-103 (2)	6.60	3.35
Nos. 247-248 (2)	.80	.80
Nos. 126-127 (2)	1.35	1.35
Nos. 184-185 (2)	2.25	1.20
Nos. 197-198 (2)	.75	.75
Nos. 224-225 (2)	4.70	3.30
Nos. 180-181 (2)	6.50	4.50
Nos. 127-128 (2)	.80	.70
Nos. 232-233 (2)	.80	.50
Nos. 229-230 (2)	11.25	2.30
Nos. 184-185 (2)	.75	1.00
Nos. 118-119 (2)	.75	.50
Nos. 134-135 (2)	8.75	8.75
Nos. 62-63 (2)	7.25	6.50
Nos. 190-191 (2)	3.50	1.50
Nos. 177-178 (2)	.65	.65
Nos. 209-210 (2)	.80	.80
Nos. 247-248 (2)	1.15	1.05
Nos. 228-229 (2)	1.25	.75
Nos. 169-170 (2)	.95	.80

Nos. 25-26 (2)	2.10	.70
Nos. 99-100 (2)	1.90	1.25
Set total (46) Stamps	67.00	43.55

UNESCO Anniversary

"Education" — CD323

"Science" (Wheat ears & flask enclosing globe). "Culture" (lyre & columns). 20th anniversary of the UNESCO.

1966-67

Antigua	183-185
Ascension	108-110
Bahamas	249-251
Barbados	287-289
Bermuda	207-209
Brunei	128-130
Cayman Islands	186-188
Dominica	199-201
Gibraltar	183-185
Gilbert & Ellice Islands	129-131
Grenada	234-236
Hong Kong	231-233
Mauritius	299-301
Montserrat	186-188
New Hebrides, British	120-122
New Hebrides, French	136-138
Pitcairn Islands	64-66
St. Helena	192-194
St. Kitts-Nevis	179-181
St. Lucia	211-213
St. Vincent	249-251
Seychelles	230-232
Solomon Islands	171-173
South Arabia	27-29
Swaziland	123-125
Tristan da Cunha	101-103
Turks & Caicos Islands	155-157
Virgin Islands	176-178

Nos. 183-185 (3)	1.90	2.50
Nos. 108-110 (3)	11.00	5.80
Nos. 249-251 (3)	2.35	2.35
Nos. 287-289 (3)	2.50	2.15
Nos. 207-209 (3)	3.80	3.90
Nos. 128-130 (3)	4.65	5.40
Nos. 186-188 (3)	2.50	1.50
Nos. 199-201 (3)	1.60	.75
Nos. 183-185 (3)	6.50	3.25
Nos. 129-131 (3)	2.50	1.65
Nos. 234-236 (3)	1.10	1.20
Nos. 231-233 (3)	69.50	17.50
Nos. 299-301 (3)	2.10	1.50
Nos. 186-188 (3)	2.40	2.40
Nos. 120-122 (3)	1.90	1.90
Nos. 136-138 (3)	7.75	7.75
Nos. 64-66 (3)	7.10	4.75
Nos. 192-194 (3)	5.25	3.65
Nos. 179-181 (3)	.90	.90
Nos. 211-213 (3)	1.15	1.15
Nos. 249-251 (3)	2.30	1.35
Nos. 230-232 (3)	2.40	2.40
Nos. 171-173 (3)	2.00	1.50
Nos. 27-29 (3)	5.50	5.50
Nos. 123-125 (3)	1.45	1.45
Nos. 101-103 (3)	2.00	1.40
Nos. 155-157 (3)	1.05	.90
Nos. 176-178 (3)	1.40	1.30
Set total (84) Stamps	156.55	87.75

Silver Wedding, 1972

Queen Elizabeth II and Prince Philip — CD324

Designs: borders differ for each country.

1972

Anguilla	161-162
Antigua	295-296
Ascension	164-165
Bahamas	344-345
Bermuda	296-297
British Antarctic Territory	43-44
British Honduras	306-307
British Indian Ocean Territory	48-49

Brunei 186-187
Cayman Islands......................304-305
Dominica 352-353
Falkland Islands 223-224
Fiji 328-329
Gibraltar 292-293
Gilbert & Ellice Islands............206-207
Grenada 466-467
Hong Kong 271-272
Montserrat 286-287
New Hebrides, British 169-170
New Hebrides, French 188-189
Pitcairn Islands 127-128
St. Helena 271-272
St. Kitts-Nevis 257-258
St. Lucia 328-329
St.Vincent 344-345
Seychelles 309-310
Solomon Islands.....................248-249
South Georgia 35-36
Tristan da Cunha 178-179
Turks & Caicos Islands 257-258
Virgin Islands 241-242

Nos. 161-162 (2)	1.30	1.50
Nos. 295-296 (2)	.50	.50
Nos. 164-165 (2)	.70	.70
Nos. 344-345 (2)	.60	.60
Nos. 296-297 (2)	.50	.65
Nos. 43-44 (2)	7.75	6.10
Nos. 306-307 (2)	.80	.80
Nos. 48-49 (2)	2.00	1.00
Nos. 186-187 (2)	.70	.70
Nos. 304-305 (2)	.75	.75
Nos. 352-353 (2)	.65	.65
Nos. 223-224 (2)	1.00	1.15
Nos. 328-329 (2)	.70	.70
Nos. 292-293 (2)	.50	.50
Nos. 206-207 (2)	.50	.50
Nos. 466-467 (2)	.70	.70
Nos. 271-272 (2)	1.70	1.50
Nos. 286-287 (2)	.55	.55
Nos. 169-170 (2)	.50	.50
Nos. 188-189 (2)	1.05	1.05
Nos. 127-128 (2)	.90	.85
Nos. 271-272 (2)	.70	1.20
Nos. 257-258 (2)	.65	.50
Nos. 328-329 (2)	.75	.75
Nos. 344-345 (2)	.55	.55
Nos. 309-310 (2)	.95	.95
Nos. 248-249 (2)	.50	.50
Nos. 35-36 (2)	1.40	1.40
Nos. 178-179 (2)	.70	.70
Nos. 257-258 (2)	.50	.50
Nos. 241-242 (2)	.50	.50
Set total (62) Stamps	31.55	29.50

Princess Anne's Wedding

Princess Anne and Mark Phillips — CD325

Wedding of Princess Anne and Mark Phillips, Nov. 14, 1973.

1973

Anguilla 179-180
Ascension 177-178
Belize......................................325-326
Bermuda..................................302-303
British Antarctic Territory............60-61
Cayman Islands.......................320-321
Falkland Islands 225-226
Gibraltar 305-306
Gilbert & Ellice Islands............216-217
Hong Kong 289-290
Montserrat 300-301
Pitcairn Islands 135-136
St. Helena 277-278
St. Kitts-Nevis 274-275
St. Lucia 349-350
St. Vincent 358-359
St. Vincent Grenadines 1-2
Seychelles 311-312
Solomon Islands......................259-260
South Georgia 37-38
Tristan da Cunha 189-190
Turks & Caicos Islands 286-287
Virgin Islands 260-261

Nos. 179-180 (2)	.55	.55
Nos. 177-178 (2)	.60	.60
Nos. 325-326 (2)	.50	.50
Nos. 302-303 (2)	.50	.50
Nos. 60-61 (2)	1.10	1.10
Nos. 320-321 (2)	.50	

Nos. 225-226 (2)	.70	.60
Nos. 305-306 (2)	.55	.55
Nos. 216-217 (2)	.50	.50
Nos. 289-290 (2)	2.65	2.00
Nos. 300-301 (2)	.65	.65
Nos. 135-136 (2)	.70	.60
Nos. 277-278 (2)	.50	.50
Nos. 274-275 (2)	.50	.50
Nos. 349-350 (2)	.50	.50
Nos. 358-359 (2)	.50	.50
Nos. 1-2 (2)	.50	.50
Nos. 311-312 (2)	.70	.70
Nos. 259-260 (2)	.70	.70
Nos. 37-38 (2)	.75	.75
Nos. 189-190 (2)	.50	.50
Nos. 286-287 (2)	.50	.50
Nos. 260-261 (2)	.50	.50
Set total (46) Stamps	15.65	14.80

Elizabeth II Coronation Anniv.

CD326

CD327

CD328

Designs: Royal and local beasts in heraldic form and simulated stonework. Portrait of Elizabeth II by Peter Grugeon. 25th anniversary of coronation of Queen Elizabeth II.

1978

Ascension..................................229
Barbados 474
Belize..397
British Antarctic Territory.................71
Cayman Islands.........................404
Christmas Island...........................87
Falkland Islands 275
Fiji...384
Gambia 380
Gilbert Islands 312
Mauritius 464
New Hebrides, British 258
New Hebrides, French 278
St. Helena 317
St. Kitts-Nevis...........................354
Samoa.......................................472
Solomon Islands........................368
South Georgia 51
Swaziland 302
Tristan da Cunha.......................238
Virgin Islands 337

No. 229 (1)	2.00	2.00
No. 474 (1)	1.35	1.35
No. 397 (1)	1.40	1.75
No. 71 (1)	6.00	6.00
No. 404 (1)	2.00	2.00
No. 87 (1)	3.50	4.00
No. 275 (1)	4.00	5.50
No. 384 (1)	1.75	1.75
No. 380 (1)	1.50	1.50
No. 312 (1)	1.25	1.25
No. 464 (1)	2.75	2.75
No. 258 (1)	1.75	1.75
No. 278 (1)	3.50	3.50
No. 317 (1)	1.75	1.75
No. 354 (1)	1.00	1.00
No. 472 (1)	2.00	2.00
No. 368 (1)	2.50	2.50
No. 51 (1)	3.00	3.00
No. 302 (1)	1.75	1.75
No. 238 (1)	1.50	1.50
No. 337 (1)	1.80	1.80
Set total (21) Stamps	48.05	50.40

Queen Mother Elizabeth's 80th Birthday

CD330

Designs: Photographs of Queen Mother Elizabeth. Falkland Islands issued in sheets of 50; others in sheets of 9.

1980

Ascension.................................261
Bermuda...................................401
Cayman Islands........................443
Falkland Islands........................305
Gambia.....................................412
Gibraltar....................................393
Hong Kong................................364
Pitcairn Islands.........................193
St. Helena.................................341
Samoa.......................................532
Solomon Islands.......................426
Tristan da Cunha.......................277

No. 261 (1)	.40	.40
No. 401 (1)	.45	.75
No. 443 (1)	.40	.40
No. 305 (1)	.40	.40
No. 412 (1)	.40	.50
No. 393 (1)	.35	.35
No. 364 (1)	1.10	1.00
No. 193 (1)	.60	.60
No. 341 (1)	.50	.50
No. 532 (1)	.55	.55
No. 426 (1)	.50	.50
No. 277 (1)	.45	.45
Set total (12) Stamps	6.10	6.40

Royal Wedding, 1981

CD331a

Prince Charles and Lady Diana — CD331

Wedding of Charles, Prince of Wales, and Lady Diana Spencer, St. Paul's Cathedral, London, July 29, 1981.

1981

Antigua 623-627
Ascension 294-296
Barbados 547-549
Barbuda 497-501
Bermuda...................................412-414
Brunei.......................................268-270
Cayman Islands........................471-473
Dominica...................................701-705
Falkland Islands 324-326
Falkland Islands Dep...........1L59-1L61
Fiji...442-444
Gambia 426-428
Ghana 759-764
Grenada 1051-1055
Grenada Grenadines................440-443
Hong Kong 373-375
Jamaica 500-503
Lesotho.....................................335-337
Maldive Islands.........................906-909
Mauritius 520-522
Norfolk Island 280-282
Pitcairn Islands.........................206-208
St. Helena 353-355
St. Lucia 543-549
Samoa.......................................558-560
Sierra Leone.............................509-518
Solomon Islands.......................450-452
Swaziland 382-384
Tristan da Cunha......................294-296
Turks & Caicos Islands 486-489
Caicos Islands...............................8-11
Uganda 314-317
Vanuatu....................................308-310
Virgin Islands............................406-408

Nos. 623-627 (5)	6.55	2.55
Nos. 294-296 (3)	1.00	1.00

Nos. 547-549 (3)	.90	.90
Nos. 497-501 (5)	10.95	10.95
Nos. 412-414 (3)	2.00	2.00
Nos. 268-270 (3)	2.15	4.50
Nos. 471-473 (3)	1.20	1.30
Nos. 701-705 (5)	8.35	2.35
Nos. 324-326 (3)	1.65	1.70
Nos. 1L59-1L61 (3)	1.45	1.45
Nos. 442-444 (3)	1.35	1.35
Nos. 426-428 (3)	.80	.80
Nos. 759-764 (9)	6.20	6.20
Nos. 1051-1055 (5)	9.85	1.85
Nos. 440-443 (4)	2.35	2.35
Nos. 373-375 (3)	3.30	3.10
Nos. 500-503 (4)	1.45	1.35
Nos. 335-337 (3)	.90	.90
Nos. 906-909 (4)	1.55	1.55
Nos. 520-522 (3)	2.75	2.75
Nos. 280-282 (3)	1.35	1.35
Nos. 206-208 (3)	1.10	1.10
Nos. 353-355 (3)	.85	.85
Nos. 543-549 (5)	8.50	8.50
Nos. 558-560 (3)	.85	.85
Nos. 509-518 (10)	15.50	15.50
Nos. 450-452 (3)	1.25	1.25
Nos. 382-384 (3)	1.30	1.25
Nos. 294-296 (3)	.90	.90
Nos. 486-489 (4)	2.20	2.20
Nos. 8-11 (4)	5.00	5.00
Nos. 314-317 (4)	3.30	3.00
Nos. 308-310 (3)	1.15	1.15
Nos. 406-408 (3)	1.10	1.10
Set total (131) Stamps	111.05	94.90

Princess Diana

CD332

CD333

Designs: Photographs and portrait of Princess Diana, wedding or honeymoon photographs, royal residences, arms of issuing country. Portrait photograph by Clive Friend. Souvenir sheet margins show family tree, various people related to the princess. 21st birthday of Princess Diana of Wales, July 1.

1982

Antigua 663-666
Ascension 313-316
Bahamas 510-513
Barbados 585-588
Barbuda 544-547
British Antarctic Territory...........92-95
Cayman Islands........................486-489
Dominica...................................773-776
Falkland Islands 348-351
Falkland Islands Dep............1L72-1L75
Fiji...470-473
Gambia 447-450
Grenada 1101A-1105
Grenada Grenadines................485-491
Lesotho.....................................372-375
Maldive Islands.........................952-955
Mauritius 548-551
Pitcairn Islands.........................213-216
St. Helena 372-375
St. Lucia 591-594
Sierra Leone.............................531-534
Solomon Islands.......................471-474
Swaziland 406-409
Tristan da Cunha......................310-313
Turks and Caicos Islands 531-534
Virgin Islands............................430-433

Nos. 663-666 (4)	8.25	7.35
Nos. 313-316 (4)	3.50	3.50
Nos. 510-513 (4)	6.00	3.85
Nos. 585-588 (4)	3.40	3.25
Nos. 544-547 (4)	9.75	7.70
Nos. 92-95 (4)	5.30	3.45
Nos. 486-489 (4)	4.75	2.70
Nos. 773-776 (4)	7.05	7.05
Nos. 348-351 (4)	2.95	2.95
Nos. 1L72-1L75 (4)	2.50	2.60
Nos. 470-473 (4)	3.25	2.95
Nos. 447-450 (4)	2.85	2.85
Nos. 1101A-1105 (7)	16.05	15.55

Nos. 485-491 (7)	17.65	17.65
Nos. 372-375 (4)	4.00	4.00
Nos. 952-955 (4)	5.50	3.90
Nos. 548-551 (4)	5.50	5.50
Nos. 213-216 (4)	2.15	2.15
Nos. 372-375 (4)	2.95	2.95
Nos. 591-594 (4)	9.90	9.90
Nos. 531-534 (4)	7.20	7.20
Nos. 471-474 (4)	2.90	2.90
Nos. 406-409 (4)	3.85	2.25
Nos. 310-313 (4)	3.65	1.45
Nos. 486-489 (4)	2.20	2.20
Nos. 430-433 (4)	3.00	3.00
Set total (110) Stamps	146.05	130.80

250th anniv. of first edition of Lloyd's List (shipping news publication) & of Lloyd's marine insurance.

CD335

Designs: First page of early edition of the list; historical ships, modern transportation or harbor scenes.

1984

Ascension	351-354
Bahamas	555-558
Barbados	627-630
Cayes of Belize	10-13
Cayman Islands	522-526
Falkland Islands	404-407
Fiji	509-512
Gambia	519-522
Mauritius	587-590
Nauru	280-283
St. Helena	412-415
Samoa	624-627
Seychelles	538-541
Solomon Islands	521-524
Vanuatu	368-371
Virgin Islands	466-469

Nos. 351-354 (4)	2.90	2.55
Nos. 555-558 (4)	4.15	2.95
Nos. 627-630 (4)	6.10	5.15
Nos. 10-13 (4)	2.65	2.65
Nos. 522-526 (5)	9.30	8.45
Nos. 404-407 (4)	3.50	3.65
Nos. 509-512 (4)	5.30	4.90
Nos. 519-522 (4)	4.20	4.30
Nos. 587-590 (4)	8.95	8.95
Nos. 280-283 (4)	2.40	2.35
Nos. 412-415 (4)	2.40	2.40
Nos. 624-627 (4)	2.75	2.55
Nos. 538-541 (4)	5.25	5.25
Nos. 521-524 (4)	4.65	3.95
Nos. 368-371 (4)	2.40	2.40
Nos. 466-469 (4)	4.25	4.25
Set total (65) Stamps	71.15	66.70

Queen Mother 85th Birthday

CD336

Designs: Photographs tracing the life of the Queen Mother, Elizabeth. The high value in each set pictures the same photograph taken of the Queen Mother holding the infant Prince Henry.

1985

Ascension	372-376
Bahamas	580-584
Barbados	660-664
Bermuda	469-473
Falkland Islands	420-424
Falkland Islands Dep.	1L92-1L96
Fiji	531-535
Hong Kong	447-450
Jamaica	599-603
Mauritius	604-608
Norfolk Island	364-368
Pitcairn Islands	253-257
St. Helena	428-432
Samoa	649-653

Seychelles	567-571
Zil Elwannyen Sesel	101-105
Solomon Islands	543-547
Swaziland	476-480
Tristan da Cunha	372-376
Vanuatu	392-396

Nos. 372-376 (5)	4.65	4.65
Nos. 580-584 (5)	7.70	6.45
Nos. 660-664 (5)	8.00	6.70
Nos. 469-473 (5)	9.40	9.40
Nos. 420-424 (5)	7.35	6.65
Nos. 1L92-1L96 (5)	8.00	8.00
Nos. 531-535 (5)	6.15	6.15
Nos. 447-450 (4)	10.25	8.50
Nos. 599-603 (5)	6.15	7.00
Nos. 604-608 (5)	11.80	11.80
Nos. 364-368 (5)	5.05	5.05
Nos. 253-257 (5)	5.25	5.95
Nos. 428-432 (5)	5.25	5.25
Nos. 649-653 (5)	8.65	7.80
Nos. 567-571 (5)	8.70	8.70
Nos. 101-105 (5)	7.15	7.15
Nos. 543-547 (5)	3.95	3.95
Nos. 476-480 (5)	8.00	7.50
Nos. 372-376 (5)	5.40	5.40
Nos. 392-396 (5)	5.25	5.25
Set total (99) Stamps	142.10	137.30

Queen Elizabeth II, 60th Birthday

CD337

1986, April 21

Ascension	389-393
Bahamas	592-596
Barbados	675-679
Bermuda	499-503
Cayman Islands	555-559
Falkland Islands	441-445
Fiji	544-548
Hong Kong	465-469
Jamaica	620-624
Kiribati	470-474
Mauritius	629-633
Papua New Guinea	640-644
Pitcairn Islands	270-274
St. Helena	451-455
Samoa	670-674
Seychelles	592-596
Zil Elwannyen Sesel	114-118
Solomon Islands	562-566
South Georgia	101-105
Swaziland	490-494
Tristan da Cunha	388-392
Vanuatu	414-418
Zambia	343-347

Nos. 389-393 (5)	2.80	3.30
Nos. 592-596 (5)	2.75	3.70
Nos. 675-679 (5)	3.35	3.20
Nos. 499-503 (5)	4.65	5.15
Nos. 555-559 (5)	4.55	5.60
Nos. 441-445 (5)	3.95	4.95
Nos. 544-548 (5)	3.00	3.00
Nos. 465-469 (5)	9.60	6.85
Nos. 620-624 (5)	2.75	2.70
Nos. 470-474 (5)	2.10	2.10
Nos. 629-633 (5)	3.70	3.70
Nos. 640-644 (5)	4.50	4.50
Nos. 270-274 (5)	2.70	2.70
Nos. 451-455 (5)	3.05	3.05
Nos. 670-674 (5)	2.90	2.90
Nos. 592-596 (5)	2.70	2.70
Nos. 114-118 (5)	2.25	2.25
Nos. 562-566 (5)	2.90	2.90
Nos. 101-105 (5)	3.30	3.65
Nos. 490-494 (5)	2.30	2.30
Nos. 388-392 (5)	3.00	3.00
Nos. 414-418 (5)	3.10	3.10
Nos. 343-347 (5)	1.75	1.75
Set total (115) Stamps	77.65	79.05

Royal Wedding

Marriage of Prince Andrew and Sarah Ferguson
CD338

1986, July 23

Ascension	399-400
Bahamas	602-603
Barbados	687-688

Cayman Islands	560-561
Jamaica	629-630
Pitcairn Islands	275-276
St. Helena	460-461
St. Kitts	181-182
Seychelles	602-603
Zil Elwannyen Sesel	119-120
Solomon Islands	567-568
Tristan da Cunha	397-398
Zambia	348-349

Nos. 399-400 (2)	1.60	1.60
Nos. 602-603 (2)	2.75	2.75
Nos. 687-688 (2)	2.25	1.25
Nos. 560-561 (2)	1.70	2.35
Nos. 629-630 (2)	1.35	1.35
Nos. 275-276 (2)	2.40	2.40
Nos. 460-461 (2)	1.05	1.05
Nos. 181-182 (2)	1.50	1.50
Nos. 602-603 (2)	2.50	2.50
Nos. 119-120 (2)	2.30	2.30
Nos. 567-568 (2)	1.00	1.00
Nos. 397-398 (2)	1.40	1.40
Nos. 348-349 (2)	1.10	1.30
Set total (26) Stamps	22.90	22.75

Queen Elizabeth II, 60th Birthday

Queen Elizabeth II & Prince Philip, 1947 Wedding Portrait — CD339

Designs: Photographs tracing the life of Queen Elizabeth II.

1986

Anguilla	674-677
Antigua	925-928
Barbuda	783-786
Dominica	950-953
Gambia	611-614
Grenada	1371-1374
Grenada Grenadines	749-752
Lesotho	531-534
Maldive Islands	1172-1175
Sierra Leone	760-763
Uganda	495-498

Nos. 674-677 (4)	8.00	8.00
Nos. 925-928 (4)	5.50	6.20
Nos. 783-786 (4)	23.15	23.15
Nos. 950-953 (4)	7.25	7.25
Nos. 611-614 (4)	8.25	7.90
Nos. 1371-1374 (4)	6.80	6.80
Nos. 749-752 (4)	6.75	6.75
Nos. 531-534 (4)	5.25	5.25
Nos. 1172-1175 (4)	6.25	6.25
Nos. 760-763 (4)	6.30	6.30
Nos. 495-498 (4)	8.50	8.50
Set total (44) Stamps	92.00	92.35

Royal Wedding, 1986

CD340

Designs: Photographs of Prince Andrew and Sarah Ferguson during courtship, engagement and marriage.

1986

Antigua	939-942
Barbuda	809-812
Dominica	970-973
Gambia	635-638
Grenada	1385-1388
Grenada Grenadines	758-761
Lesotho	545-548
Maldive Islands	1181-1184
Sierra Leone	769-772
Uganda	510-513

Nos. 939-942 (4)	7.00	8.75
Nos. 809-812 (4)	14.55	14.55
Nos. 970-973 (4)	7.25	7.25
Nos. 635-638 (4)	8.55	8.55
Nos. 1385-1388 (4)	8.30	8.30
Nos. 758-761 (4)	9.00	9.00

Nos. 545-548 (4)	7.45	7.45
Nos. 1181-1184 (4)	8.45	8.45
Nos. 769-772 (4)	5.35	5.35
Nos. 510-513 (4)	9.25	10.00
Set total (40) Stamps	85.15	87.65

Lloyds of London, 300th Anniv.

CD341

Designs: 17th century aspects of Lloyds, representations of each country's individual connections with Lloyds and publicized disasters insured by the organization.

1986

Ascension	454-457
Bahamas	655-658
Barbados	731-734
Bermuda	541-544
Falkland Islands	481-484
Liberia	1101-1104
Malawi	534-537
Nevis	571-574
St. Helena	501-504
St. Lucia	923-926
Seychelles	649-652
Zil Elwannyen Sesel	146-149
Solomon Islands	627-630
South Georgia	131-134
Trinidad & Tobago	484-487
Tristan da Cunha	439-442
Vanuatu	485-488

Nos. 454-457 (4)	5.00	5.00
Nos. 655-658 (4)	8.90	4.95
Nos. 731-734 (4)	12.50	8.35
Nos. 541-544 (4)	8.00	6.60
Nos. 481-484 (4)	5.45	3.85
Nos. 1101-1104 (4)	4.25	4.25
Nos. 534-537 (4)	11.00	7.85
Nos. 571-574 (4)	8.35	8.35
Nos. 501-504 (4)	8.70	7.15
Nos. 923-926 (4)	9.40	9.40
Nos. 649-652 (4)	13.10	13.10
Nos. 146-149 (4)	11.25	11.25
Nos. 627-630 (4)	7.00	4.45
Nos. 131-134 (4)	6.30	3.70
Nos. 484-487 (4)	10.25	6.35
Nos. 439-442 (4)	7.60	7.60
Nos. 485-488 (4)	5.90	5.90
Set total (68) Stamps	142.95	118.10

Moon Landing, 20th Anniv.

CD342

Designs: Equipment, crew photographs, spacecraft, official emblems and report profiles created for the Apollo Missions. Two stamps in each set are square in format rather than like the stamp shown; see individual country listings for more information.

1989

Ascension	468-472
Bahamas	674-678
Belize	916-920
Kiribati	517-521
Liberia	1125-1129
Nevis	586-590
St. Kitts	248-252
Samoa	760-764
Seychelles	676-680
Zil Elwannyen Sesel	154-158
Solomon Islands	643-647
Vanuatu	507-511

Nos. 468-472 (5)	9.40	8.60
Nos. 674-678 (5)	23.00	19.70
Nos. 916-920 (5)	22.85	18.10
Nos. 517-521 (5)	12.50	12.50
Nos. 1125-1129 (5)	8.50	8.50
Nos. 586-590 (5)	7.50	7.50

Nos. 248-252 (5)	8.00	8.00
Nos. 760-764 (5)	9.60	9.05
Nos. 676-680 (5)	16.05	16.05
Nos. 154-158 (5)	26.85	26.85
Nos. 643-647 (5)	9.00	6.75
Nos. 507-511 (5)	9.90	9.90
Set total (60) Stamps	163.15	151.50

Queen Mother, 90th Birthday

CD343   CD344

Designs: Portraits of Queen Elizabeth, the Queen Mother. See individual country listings for more information.

1990

Ascension	491-492
Bahamas	698-699
Barbados	782-783
British Antarctic Territory	170-171
British Indian Ocean Territory	106-107
Cayman Islands	622-623
Falkland Islands	524-525
Kenya	527-528
Kiribati	555-556
Liberia	1145-1146
Pitcairn Islands	336-337
St. Helena	532-533
St. Lucia	969-970
Seychelles	710-711
Zil Elwannyen Sesel	171-172
Solomon Islands	671-672
South Georgia	143-144
Swaziland	565-566
Tristan da Cunha	480-481

Nos. 491-492 (2)	4.75	4.75
Nos. 698-699 (2)	5.25	5.25
Nos. 782-783 (2)	4.00	3.70
Nos. 170-171 (2)	6.75	6.75
Nos. 106-107 (2)	18.00	18.50
Nos. 622-623 (2)	4.00	5.50
Nos. 524-525 (2)	4.75	4.75
Nos. 527-528 (2)	7.00	7.00
Nos. 555-556 (2)	4.75	4.75
Nos. 1145-1146 (2)	3.25	3.25
Nos. 336-337 (2)	4.25	4.25
Nos. 532-533 (2)	5.25	5.25
Nos. 969-970 (2)	5.25	5.25
Nos. 710-711 (2)	6.60	6.60
Nos. 171-172 (2)	8.25	8.25
Nos. 671-672 (2)	5.00	5.30
Nos. 143-144 (2)	5.50	6.50
Nos. 565-566 (2)	4.35	4.35
Nos. 480-481 (2)	5.60	5.60
Set total (38) Stamps	112.55	115.55

Queen Elizabeth II, 65th Birthday, and Prince Philip, 70th Birthday

CD345

CD346

Designs: Portraits of Queen Elizabeth II and Prince Philip differ for each country. Printed in sheets of 10 + 5 labels (3 different) between. Stamps alternate, producing 5 different triptychs.

1991

Ascension	506a
Bahamas	731a
Belize	970a
Bermuda	618a
Kiribati	572a
Mauritius	734a
Pitcairn Islands	349a
St. Helena	555a
St. Kitts	319a
Samoa	791a
Seychelles	724a
Zil Elwannyen Sesel	178a
Solomon Islands	689a
South Georgia	150a
Swaziland	587a
Vanuatu	541a

No. 506a (1)	3.50	3.75
No. 731a (1)	4.00	4.00
No. 970a (1)	3.75	3.75
No. 618a (1)	3.50	4.00
No. 572a (1)	4.00	4.00
No. 734a (1)	3.75	3.75
No. 349a (1)	3.25	3.25
No. 555a (1)	2.75	2.75
No. 319a (1)	3.00	3.00
No. 791a (1)	4.25	4.25
No. 724a (1)	5.00	5.00
No. 178a (1)	6.50	6.50
No. 689a (1)	3.75	3.75
No. 150a (1)	4.75	7.00
No. 587a (1)	4.25	4.25
No. 541a (1)	2.50	2.50
Set total (16) Stamps	62.50	65.50

Royal Family Birthday, Anniversary

CD347

Queen Elizabeth II, 65th birthday, Charles and Diana, 10th wedding anniversary: Various photographs of Queen Elizabeth II, Prince Philip, Prince Charles, Princess Diana and their sons William and Henry.

1991

Antigua	1446-1455
Barbuda	1229-1238
Dominica	1328-1337
Gambia	1080-1089
Grenada	2006-2015
Grenada Grenadines	1331-1340
Guyana	2440-2451
Lesotho	871-875
Maldive Islands	1533-1542
Nevis	666-675
St. Vincent	1485-1494
St. Vincent Grenadines	769-778
Sierra Leone	1387-1396
Turks & Caicos Islands	913-922
Uganda	918-927

Nos. 1446-1455 (10)	21.70	20.05
Nos. 1229-1238 (10)	125.00	119.50
Nos. 1328-1337 (10)	30.20	30.20
Nos. 1080-1089 (10)	24.65	24.40
Nos. 2006-2015 (10)	25.45	22.10
Nos. 1331-1340 (10)	23.85	23.35
Nos. 2440-2451 (12)	21.40	21.15
Nos. 871-875 (5)	13.55	13.55
Nos. 1533-1542 (10)	28.10	28.10
Nos. 666-675 (10)	25.65	25.65
Nos. 1485-1494 (10)	26.75	25.90
Nos. 769-778 (10)	25.40	25.40
Nos. 1387-1396 (10)	26.55	26.55
Nos. 913-922 (10)	27.50	25.30
Nos. 918-927 (10)	26.60	26.60
Set total (147) Stamps	472.35	457.80

Queen Elizabeth II's Accession to the Throne, 40th Anniv.

CD348

Various photographs of Queen Elizabeth II with local Scenes.

1992

Antigua	1513-1518
Barbuda	1306-1311
Dominica	1414-1419
Gambia	1172-1177
Grenada	2047-2052
Grenada Grenadines	1368-1373
Lesotho	881-885
Maldive Islands	1637-1642
Nevis	702-707
St. Vincent	1582-1587
St. Vincent Grenadines	829-834
Sierra Leone	1482-1487
Turks and Caicos Islands	978-987
Uganda	990-995
Virgin Islands	742-746

Nos. 1513-1518 (6)	15.00	15.10
Nos. 1306-1311 (6)	125.25	83.65
Nos. 1414-1419 (6)	12.50	12.50
Nos. 1172-1177 (6)	16.60	16.35
Nos. 2047-2052 (6)	15.95	15.95
Nos. 1368-1373 (6)	17.00	15.35
Nos. 881-885 (5)	11.90	11.90
Nos. 1637-1642 (6)	17.55	17.55
Nos. 702-707 (6)	13.80	13.80
Nos. 1582-1587 (6)	14.40	14.40
Nos. 829-834 (6)	19.65	19.65
Nos. 1482-1487 (6)	22.50	22.50
Nos. 913-922 (10)	27.50	25.30
Nos. 990-995 (6)	19.50	19.50
Nos. 742-746 (5)	15.50	15.50
Set total (92) Stamps	364.60	319.00

CD349

1992

Ascension	531-535
Bahamas	744-748
Bermuda	623-627
British Indian Ocean Territory	119-123
Cayman Islands	648-652
Falkland Islands	549-553
Gibraltar	605-609
Hong Kong	619-623
Kenya	563-567
Kiribati	582-586
Pitcairn Islands	362-366
St. Helena	570-574
St. Kitts	332-336
Samoa	805-809
Seychelles	734-738
Zil Elwannyen Sesel	183-187
Solomon Islands	708-712
South Georgia	157-161
Tristan da Cunha	508-512
Vanuatu	555-559
Zambia	561-565

Nos. 531-535 (5)	6.10	6.10
Nos. 744-748 (5)	6.90	4.70
Nos. 623-627 (5)	7.40	7.55
Nos. 119-123 (5)	22.75	19.25
Nos. 648-652 (5)	7.60	6.60
Nos. 549-553 (5)	5.95	5.90
Nos. 605-609 (5)	5.15	5.50
Nos. 619-623 (5)	5.65	2.65
Nos. 563-567 (5)	9.10	9.10
Nos. 582-586 (5)	3.85	3.85
Nos. 362-366 (5)	5.35	5.35
Nos. 570-574 (5)	5.70	5.70
Nos. 332-336 (5)	6.60	5.50
Nos. 805-809 (5)	8.10	6.15
Nos. 734-738 (5)	10.80	10.80
Nos. 183-187 (5)	9.40	9.40
Nos. 708-712 (5)	5.00	5.30
Nos. 157-161 (5)	5.60	5.90
Nos. 508-512 (5)	8.75	8.30
Nos. 555-559 (5)	3.65	3.65
Nos. 561-565 (5)	5.35	5.35
Set total (105) Stamps	155.00	142.85

Royal Air Force, 75th Anniversary

CD350

1993

Ascension	557-561
Bahamas	771-775
Barbados	842-846
Belize	1003-1008
Bermuda	648-651
British Indian Ocean Territory	136-140
Falkland Is.	573-577
Fiji	687-691
Montserrat	830-834
St. Kitts	351-355

Nos. 557-561 (5)	15.60	14.60
Nos. 771-775 (5)	24.65	21.45
Nos. 842-846 (5)	13.65	12.35
Nos. 1003-1008 (6)	16.55	16.50
Nos. 648-651 (4)	9.65	10.45
Nos. 136-140 (5)	16.10	16.10
Nos. 573-577 (5)	10.85	10.85
Nos. 687-691 (5)	17.75	17.40
Nos. 830-834 (5)	14.35	14.35
Nos. 351-355 (5)	24.45	23.95
Set total (50) Stamps	163.60	158.00

Royal Air Force, 80th Anniv.

Design CD350 Re-inscribed

1998

Ascension	697-701
Bahamas	907-911
British Indian Ocean Terr	198-202
Cayman Islands	754-758
Fiji	814-818
Gibraltar	755-759
Samoa	957-961
Turks & Caicos Islands	1258-1265
Tuvalu	763-767
Virgin Islands	879-883

Nos. 697-701 (5)	16.10	16.10
Nos. 907-911 (5)	13.60	12.35
Nos. 136-140 (5)	16.10	16.10
Nos. 754-758 (5)	15.25	15.25
Nos. 814-818 (5)	14.00	12.75
Nos. 755-759 (5)	9.70	9.70
Nos. 957-961 (5)	16.70	15.90
Nos. 1258-1265 (2)	27.50	27.50
Nos. 763-767 (5)	9.75	9.75
Nos. 879-883 (5)	15.00	15.00
Set total (47) Stamps	153.70	150.70

End of World War II, 50th Anniv.

CD351

CD352

1995

Ascension	613-617
Bahamas	824-828
Barbados	891-895
Belize	1047-1050
British Indian Ocean Territory	163-167
Cayman Islands	704-708
Falkland Islands	634-638
Fiji	720-724
Kiribati	662-668
Liberia	1175-1179
Mauritius	803-805
St. Helena	646-654
St. Kitts	389-393
St. Lucia	1018-1022
Samoa	890-894
Solomon Islands	799-803
South Georgia	198-200
Tristan da Cunha	562-566

Nos. 613-617 (5)	21.50	21.50

Nos. 824-828 (5)	22.00	18.70
Nos. 891-895 (5)	14.20	11.90
Nos. 1047-1050 (4)	6.05	5.90
Nos. 163-167 (5)	16.25	16.25
Nos. 704-708 (5)	17.65	13.95
Nos. 634-638 (5)	18.65	17.15
Nos. 720-724 (5)	17.50	14.50
Nos. 662-668 (7)	16.30	16.30
Nos. 1175-1179 (5)	15.25	11.15
Nos. 803-805 (3)	7.50	7.50
Nos. 646-654 (9)	26.10	26.10
Nos. 389-393 (5)	13.60	13.60
Nos. 1018-1022 (5)	14.25	11.15
Nos. 890-894 (5)	14.25	13.50
Nos. 799-803 (5)	14.75	14.75
Nos. 198-200 (3)	14.50	15.50
Nos. 562-566 (5)	20.10	20.10
Set total (91) Stamps	290.40	269.50

UN, 50th Anniv.

CD353

1995

Bahamas	839-842	
Barbados	901-904	
Belize	1055-1058	
Jamaica	847-851	
Liberia	1187-1190	
Mauritius	813-816	
Pitcairn Islands	436-439	
St. Kitts	398-401	
St. Lucia	1023-1026	
Samoa	900-903	
Tristan da Cunha	568-571	
Virgin Islands	807-810	

Nos. 839-842 (4)	7.15	6.40
Nos. 901-904 (4)	7.00	5.75
Nos. 1055-1058 (4)	4.70	4.70
Nos. 847-851 (5)	5.40	5.45
Nos. 1187-1190 (4)	9.65	9.65
Nos. 813-816 (4)	3.90	3.90
Nos. 436-439 (4)	8.15	8.15
Nos. 398-401 (4)	6.15	6.15
Nos. 1023-1026 (4)	7.50	7.25
Nos. 900-903 (4)	9.35	8.20
Nos. 568-571 (4)	13.50	13.50
Nos. 807-810 (4)	7.45	7.45
Set total (49) Stamps	89.90	86.55

Queen Elizabeth, 70th Birthday

CD354

1996

Ascension	632-635	
British Antarctic Territory	240-243	
British Indian Ocean Territory	176-180	
Falkland Islands	653-657	
Pitcairn Islands	446-449	
St. Helena	672-676	
Samoa	912-916	
Tokelau	223-227	
Tristan da Cunha	576-579	
Virgin Islands	824-828	

Nos. 632-635 (4)	5.30	5.30
Nos. 240-243 (4)	10.50	8.90
Nos. 176-180 (5)	11.50	11.50
Nos. 653-657 (5)	13.55	11.20
Nos. 446-449 (4)	8.60	8.60
Nos. 672-676 (5)	12.70	12.70
Nos. 912-916 (5)	11.50	11.50
Nos. 223-227 (5)	10.50	10.50
Nos. 576-579 (4)	8.35	8.35
Nos. 824-828 (5)	11.30	11.30
Set total (46) Stamps	103.80	99.85

Diana, Princess of Wales (1961-97)

CD355

1998

Ascension	696	
Bahamas	901A-902	
Barbados	950	
Belize	1091	
Bermuda	753	
Botswana	659-663	
British Antarctic Territory	258	
British Indian Ocean Terr.	197	
Cayman Islands	752A-753	
Falkland Islands	694	
Fiji	819-820	
Gibraltar	754	
Kiribati	719A-720	
Namibia	909	
Niue	706	
Norfolk Island	644-645	
Papua New Guinea	937	
Pitcairn Islands	487	
St. Helena	711	
St. Kitts	437A-438	
Samoa	955A-956	
Seychelles	802	
Solomon Islands	866-867	
South Georgia	220	
Tokelau	252B-253	
Tonga	980	
Niuafo'ou	201	
Tristan da Cunha	618	
Tuvalu	762	
Vanuatu	718A-719	
Virgin Islands	878	

No. 696 (1)	5.25	5.25
Nos. 901A-902 (2)	5.30	5.30
No. 950 (1)	5.00	5.00
No. 1091 (1)	5.00	5.00
No. 753 (1)	5.00	5.00
Nos. 659-663 (5)	8.25	8.80
No. 258 (1)	6.25	6.25
No. 197 (1)	5.50	5.50
Nos. 752A-753 (3)	7.40	7.40
No. 694 (1)	5.00	5.00
Nos. 819-820 (2)	5.25	5.25
No. 754 (1)	4.75	4.75
Nos. 719A-720 (2)	4.85	4.85
No. 909 (1)	1.75	1.75
No. 706 (1)	5.50	5.50
Nos. 644-645 (2)	5.25	5.25
No. 937 (1)	6.50	6.50
No. 487 (1)	4.75	4.75
No. 711 (1)	4.25	4.25
Nos. 437A-438 (2)	5.15	5.15
Nos. 955A-956 (2)	7.00	7.00
No. 802 (1)	6.25	6.25
Nos. 866-867 (2)	5.40	5.40
No. 220 (1)	4.50	5.00
Nos. 252B-253 (2)	5.50	5.50
No. 980 (1)	5.75	5.75
No. 201 (1)	6.50	6.50
No. 618 (1)	5.00	5.00
No. 762 (1)	4.00	4.00
Nos. 718A-719 (2)	8.00	8.00
No. 878 (1)	4.50	4.50
Set total (46) Stamps	168.35	169.40

Wedding of Prince Edward and Sophie Rhys-Jones

CD356

1999

Ascension	729-730	
Cayman Islands	775-776	
Falkland Islands	729-730	
Pitcairn Islands	505-506	
St. Helena	733-734	
Samoa	971-972	
Tristan da Cunha	636-637	

Virgin Islands	908-909	

Nos. 729-730 (2)	4.50	4.50
Nos. 775-776 (2)	4.95	4.95
Nos. 729-730 (2)	14.00	14.00
Nos. 505-506 (2)	7.00	7.00
Nos. 733-734 (2)	5.00	5.00
Nos. 971-972 (2)	5.00	5.00
Nos. 636-637 (2)	7.50	7.50
Nos. 908-909 (2)	7.50	7.50
Set total (16) Stamps	55.45	55.45

1st Manned Moon Landing, 30th Anniv.

CD357

1999

Ascension	731-735	
Bahamas	942-946	
Barbados	967-971	
Bermuda	778	
Cayman Islands	777-781	
Fiji	853-857	
Jamaica	889-893	
Kirbati	746-750	
Nauru	465-469	
St. Kitts	460-464	
Samoa	973-977	
Solomon Islands	875-879	
Tuvalu	800-804	
Virgin Islands	910-914	

Nos. 731-735 (5)	12.80	12.80
Nos. 942-946 (5)	14.10	14.10
Nos. 967-971 (5)	8.65	7.75
No. 778 (1)	9.00	9.00
Nos. 777-781 (5)	9.25	9.25
Nos. 853-857 (5)	9.25	8.45
Nos. 889-893 (5)	8.30	7.18
Nos. 746-750 (5)	8.85	8.85
Nos. 465-469 (5)	8.90	10.15
Nos. 460-464 (5)	12.00	12.00
Nos. 973-977 (5)	13.45	13.30
Nos. 875-879 (5)	7.50	7.50
Nos. 800-804 (5)	7.45	7.45
Nos. 910-914 (5)	11.75	11.75
Set total (66) Stamps	141.25	139.53

Queen Mother's Century

CD358

1999

Ascension	736-740	
Bahamas	951-955	
Cayman Islands	782-786	
Falkland Islands	734-738	
Fiji	858-862	
Norfolk Island	688-692	
St. Helena	740-744	
Samoa	978-982	
Solomon Islands	880-884	
South Georgia	231-235	
Tristan da Cunha	638-642	
Tuvalu	805-809	

Nos. 736-740 (5)	15.50	15.50
Nos. 951-955 (5)	13.75	12.65
Nos. 782-786 (5)	8.35	8.35
Nos. 734-738 (5)	30.00	28.25
Nos. 858-862 (5)	12.80	13.25
Nos. 688-692 (5)	10.30	10.30
Nos. 740-744 (5)	16.15	16.15
Nos. 978-982 (5)	12.50	12.10
Nos. 880-884 (5)	7.50	7.00
Nos. 231-235 (5)	29.75	30.00
Nos. 638-642 (5)	18.00	18.00
Nos. 805-809 (5)	8.65	8.65
Set total (60) Stamps	183.25	180.20

Prince William, 18th Birthday

CD359

2000

Ascension	755-759	
Cayman Islands	797-801	
Falkland Islands	762-766	
Fiji	889-893	
South Georgia	257-261	
Tristan da Cunha	664-668	
Virgin Islands	925-929	

Nos. 755-759 (5)	15.50	15.50
Nos. 797-801 (5)	11.15	10.90
Nos. 762-766 (5)	24.60	22.50
Nos. 889-893 (5)	12.90	12.90
Nos. 257-261 (5)	29.00	28.75
Nos. 664-668 (5)	21.50	21.50
Nos. 925-929 (5)	14.50	14.50
Set total (35) Stamps	129.15	126.55

Reign of Queen Elizabeth II, 50th Anniv.

CD360

2002

Ascension	790-794	
Bahamas	1033-1037	
Barbados	1019-1023	
Belize	1152-1156	
Bermuda	822-826	
British Antarctic Territory	307-311	
British Indian Ocean Territory	239-243	
Cayman Islands	844-848	
Falkland Islands	804-808	
Gibraltar	896-900	
Jamaica	952-956	
Nauru	491-495	
Norfolk Island	758-762	
Papua New Guinea	1019-1023	
Pitcairn Islands	552	
St. Helena	788-792	
St. Lucia	1146-1150	
Solomon Islands	931-935	
South Georgia	274-278	
Swaziland	706-710	
Tokelau	302-306	
Tonga	1059	
Niuafo'ou	239	
Tristan da Cunha	706-710	
Virgin Islands	967-971	

Nos. 790-794 (5)	14.10	14.10
Nos. 1033-1037 (5)	15.25	15.25
Nos. 1019-1023 (5)	13.15	13.15
Nos. 1152-1156 (5)	12.65	12.25
Nos. 822-826 (5)	18.00	18.00
Nos. 307-311 (5)	25.00	25.00
Nos. 239-243 (5)	19.40	19.40
Nos. 844-848 (5)	13.25	13.25
Nos. 804-808 (5)	23.00	22.00
Nos. 896-900 (5)	6.65	6.65
Nos. 952-956 (5)	16.65	16.65
Nos. 491-495 (5)	18.75	18.75
Nos. 758-762 (5)	19.50	19.50
Nos. 1019-1023 (5)	14.50	14.50
No. 552 (1)	9.25	9.25
Nos. 788-792 (5)	19.75	19.75
Nos. 1146-1150 (5)	12.25	12.25
Nos. 931-935 (5)	12.40	12.40
Nos. 274-278 (5)	28.00	28.50
Nos. 706-710 (5)	12.75	12.75
Nos. 302-306 (5)	14.50	14.50
No. 1059 (1)	8.50	8.50
No. 239 (1)	8.75	8.75
Nos. 706-710 (5)	18.50	18.50
Nos. 967-971 (5)	16.50	16.50
Set total (113) Stamps	391.00	390.10

Queen Mother Elizabeth (1900-2002)

CD361

2002

Ascension		799-801
Bahamas		1044-1046
Bermuda		834-836
British Antarctic Territory		312-314
British Indian Ocean Territory		245-247
Cayman Islands		857-861
Falkland Islands		812-816
Nauru		499-501
Pitcairn Islands		561-565
St. Helena		808-812
St. Lucia		1155-1159
Seychelles		830
Solomon Islands		945-947
South Georgia		281-285
Tokelau		312-314
Tristan da Cunha		715-717
Virgin Islands		979-983

Nos. 799-801 (3)	8.85	8.85
Nos. 1044-1046 (3)	9.10	9.10
Nos. 834-836 (3)	12.25	12.25
Nos. 312-314 (3)	19.25	19.25
Nos. 245-247 (3)	17.35	17.35
Nos. 857-861 (5)	15.00	15.00
Nos. 812-816 (5)	28.50	28.50
Nos. 499-501 (3)	16.00	16.00
Nos. 561-565 (5)	15.25	15.25
Nos. 808-812 (5)	12.00	12.00
Nos. 1155-1159 (5)	13.00	13.00
No. 830 (1)	6.50	6.50
Nos. 945-947 (3)	9.25	9.25
Nos. 281-285 (5)	19.50	19.50
Nos. 312-314 (3)	11.85	11.85
Nos. 715-717 (3)	16.25	16.25
Nos. 979-983 (5)	23.50	23.50
Set total (63) Stamps	253.40	253.40

Head of Queen Elizabeth II

CD362

2003

Ascension		822
Bermuda		865
British Antarctic Territory		322
British Indian Ocean Territory		261
Cayman Islands		878
Falkland Islands		828
St. Helena		820
South Georgia		294
Tristan da Cunha		731
Virgin Islands		1003

No. 822 (1)	12.50	12.50
No. 865 (1)	50.00	50.00
No. 322 (1)	10.00	10.00
No. 261 (1)	11.00	11.00
No. 878 (1)	14.00	14.00
No. 828 (1)	9.00	9.00
No. 820 (1)	9.00	9.00
No. 294 (1)	8.50	8.50
No. 731 (1)	10.00	10.00
No. 1003 (1)	10.00	10.00
Set total (10) Stamps	144.00	144.00

Coronation of Queen Elizabeth II, 50th Anniv.

CD363

2003

Ascension		823-825

Bahamas		1073-1075
Bermuda		866-868
British Antarctic Territory		323-325
British Indian Ocean Territory		262-264
Cayman Islands		879-881
Jamaica		970-972
Kiribati		825-827
Pitcairn Islands		577-581
St. Helena		821-823
St. Lucia		1171-1173
Tokelau		320-322
Tristan da Cunha		732-734
Virgin Islands		1004-1006

Nos. 823-825 (3)	12.50	12.50
Nos. 1073-1075 (3)	13.00	13.00
Nos. 866-868 (3)	14.25	14.25
Nos. 323-325 (3)	26.00	26.00
Nos. 262-264 (3)	28.00	28.00
Nos. 879-881 (3)	19.25	19.25
Nos. 970-972 (3)	10.00	10.00
Nos. 825-827 (3)	13.50	13.50
Nos. 577-581 (5)	14.40	14.40
Nos. 821-823 (3)	7.25	7.25
Nos. 1171-1173 (3)	8.75	8.75
Nos. 320-322 (3)	17.25	17.25
Nos. 732-734 (3)	16.75	16.75
Nos. 1004-1006 (3)	25.00	25.00
Set total (44) Stamps	225.90	225.90

Prince William, 21st Birthday

CD364

2003

Ascension		826
British Indian Ocean Territory		265
Cayman Islands		882-884
Falkland Islands		829
South Georgia		295
Tokelau		323
Tristan da Cunha		735
Virgin Islands		1007-1009

No. 826 (1)	7.25	7.25
No. 265 (1)	8.00	8.00
Nos. 882-884 (3)	6.95	6.95
No. 829 (1)	13.50	13.50
No. 295 (1)	8.50	8.50
No. 323 (1)	7.25	7.25
No. 735 (1)	6.00	6.00
Nos. 1007-1009 (3)	10.00	10.00
Set total (12) Stamps	67.45	67.45

British Commonwealth of Nations

Dominions, Colonies, Territories, Offices and Independent Members

Comprising stamps of the British Commonwealth and associated nations.

A strict observance of technicalities would bar some or all of the stamps listed under Burma, Ireland, Kuwait, Nepal, New Republic, Orange Free State, Samoa, South Africa, South-West Africa, Stellaland, Sudan, Swaziland, the two Transvaal Republics and others but these are included for the convenience of collectors.

1. Great Britain

Great Britain: Including England, Scotland, Wales and Northern Ireland.

2. The Dominions, Present and Past

AUSTRALIA

The Commonwealth of Australia was proclaimed on January 1, 1901. It consists of six former colonies as follows:

New South Wales	Victoria
Queensland	Tasmania
South Australia	Western Australia

The following islands and territories are, or have been, administered by Australia: Australian Antarctic Territory, Christmas Island, Cocos (Keeling) Islands, Nauru, New Guinea, Norfolk Island, Papua.

CANADA

The Dominion of Canada was created by the British North America Act in 1867. The following provinces were former sepa- rate colonies and issued postage stamps:

British Columbia and Vancouver Island	Newfoundland
New Brunswick	Nova Scotia
	Prince Edward Island

FIJI

The colony of Fiji became an independent nation with dominion status on Oct. 10, 1970.

GHANA

This state came into existence Mar. 6, 1957, with dominion status. It consists of the former colony of the Gold Coast and the Trusteeship Territory of Togoland. Ghana became a republic July 1, 1960.

INDIA

The Republic of India was inaugurated on January 26, 1950. It succeeded the Dominion of India which was proclaimed August 15, 1947, when the former Empire of India was divided into Pakistan and the Union of India. The Republic is composed of about 40 predominantly Hindu states of three classes: governor's provinces, chief commissioner's provinces and princely states. India also has various territories, such as the Andaman and Nicobar Islands.

The old Empire of India was a federation of British India and the native states. The more important princely states were autonomous. Of the more than 700 Indian states, these 43 are familiar names to philatelists because of their postage stamps.

CONVENTION STATES

Chamba	Jhind
Faridkot	Nabha
Gwalior	Patiala

FEUDATORY STATES

Alwar	Jammu and Kashmir
Bahawalpur	Jasdan
Bamra	Jhalawar
Barwani	Jhind (1875-76)
Bhopal	Kashmir
Bhor	Kishangarh
Bijawar	Kotah
Bundi	Las Bela
Bussahir	Morvi
Charkhari	Nandgaon
Cochin	Nowanuggur
Dhar	Orchha
Dungarpur	Poonch
Duttia	Rajasthan
Faridkot (1879-85)	Rajpeepla
Hyderabad	Sirmur
Idar	Soruth
Indore	Tonk
Jaipur	Travancore
Jammu	Wadhwan

NEW ZEALAND

Became a dominion on September 26, 1907. The following islands and territories are, or have been, administered by New Zealand:

Aitutaki	Ross Dependency
Cook Islands (Rarotonga)	Samoa (Western Samoa)
Niue	Tokelau Islands
Penrhyn	

PAKISTAN

The Republic of Pakistan was proclaimed March 23, 1956. It succeeded the Dominion which was proclaimed August 15, 1947. It is made up of all or part of several Moslem provinces and various districts of the former Empire of India, including Bahawalpur and Las Bela. Pakistan withdrew from the Commonwealth in 1972.

SOUTH AFRICA

Under the terms of the South African Act (1909) the self-governing colonies of Cape of Good Hope, Natal, Orange River Colony and Transvaal united on May 31, 1910, to form the Union of South Africa. It became an independent republic May 3, 1961.

Under the terms of the Treaty of Versailles, South-West Africa, formerly German South-West Africa, was mandated to the Union of South Africa.

SRI LANKA (CEYLON)

The Dominion of Ceylon was proclaimed February 4, 1948. The island had been a Crown Colony from 1802 until then. On May 22, 1972, Ceylon became the Republic of Sri Lanka.

3. Colonies, Past and Present; Controlled Territory and Independent Members of the Commonwealth

Aden	Bechuanaland
Aitutaki	Bechuanaland Prot.
Anguilla	Belize
Antigua	Bermuda
Ascension	Botswana
Bahamas	British Antarctic Territory
Bahrain	British Central Africa
Bangladesh	British Columbia and
Barbados	Vancouver Island
Barbuda	British East Africa
Basutoland	British Guiana
Batum	

British Honduras
British Indian Ocean Territory
British New Guinea
British Solomon Islands
British Somaliland
Brunei
Burma
Bushire
Cameroons
Cape of Good Hope
Cayman Islands
Christmas Island
Cocos (Keeling) Islands
Cook Islands
Crete,
  British Administration
Cyprus
Dominica
East Africa & Uganda
  Protectorates
Egypt
Falkland Islands
Fiji
Gambia
German East Africa
Gibraltar
Gilbert Islands
Gilbert & Ellice Islands
Gold Coast
Grenada
Griqualand West
Guernsey
Guyana
Heligoland
Hong Kong
Indian Native States
  (see India)
Ionian Islands
Jamaica
Jersey

Kenya
Kenya, Uganda & Tanzania
Kuwait
Labuan
Lagos
Leeward Islands
Lesotho
Madagascar
Malawi
Malaya
  Federated Malay States
  Johore
  Kedah
  Kelantan
  Malacca
  Negri Sembilan
  Pahang
  Penang
  Perak
  Perlis
  Selangor
  Singapore
  Sungei Ujong
  Trengganu
Malaysia
Maldive Islands
Malta
Man, Isle of
Mauritius
Mesopotamia
Montserrat
Muscat
Namibia
Natal
Nauru
Nevis
New Britain
New Brunswick
Newfoundland
New Guinea

New Hebrides
New Republic
New South Wales
Niger Coast Protectorate
Nigeria
Niue
Norfolk Island
North Borneo
Northern Nigeria
Northern Rhodesia
North West Pacific Islands
Nova Scotia
Nyasaland Protectorate
Oman
Orange River Colony
Palestine
Papua New Guinea
Penrhyn Island
Pitcairn Islands
Prince Edward Island
Queensland
Rhodesia
Rhodesia & Nyasaland
Ross Dependency
Sabah
St. Christopher
St. Helena
St. Kitts
St. Kitts-Nevis-Anguilla
St. Lucia
St. Vincent
Samoa
Sarawak
Seychelles
Sierra Leone
Solomon Islands
Somaliland Protectorate
South Arabia
South Australia
South Georgia

Southern Nigeria
Southern Rhodesia
South-West Africa
Stellaland
Straits Settlements
Sudan
Swaziland
Tanganyika
Tanzania
Tasmania
Tobago
Togo
Tokelau Islands
Tonga
Transvaal
Trinidad
Trinidad and Tobago
Tristan da Cunha
Trucial States
Turks and Caicos
Turks Islands
Tuvalu
Uganda
United Arab Emirates
Victoria
Virgin Islands
Western Australia
Zambia
Zanzibar
Zululand

POST OFFICES IN FOREIGN COUNTRIES
Africa
  East Africa Forces
  Middle East Forces
Bangkok
China
Morocco
Turkish Empire

Colonies, Former Colonies, Offices, Territories Controlled by Parent States

Belgium
Belgian Congo
Ruanda-Urundi

Denmark
Danish West Indies
Faroe Islands
Greenland
Iceland

Finland
Aland Islands

France
COLONIES PAST AND PRESENT, CONTROLLED TERRITORIES
Afars & Issas, Territory of
Alaouites
Alexandretta
Algeria
Alsace & Lorraine
Anjouan
Annam & Tonkin
Benin
Cambodia (Khmer)
Cameroun
Castellorizo
Chad
Cilicia
Cochin China
Comoro Islands
Dahomey
Diego Suarez
Djibouti (Somali Coast)
Fezzan
French Congo
French Equatorial Africa
French Guiana
French Guinea
French India
French Morocco
French Polynesia (Oceania)
French Southern & Antarctic Territories
French Sudan
French West Africa
Gabon
Germany
Ghadames
Grand Comoro
Guadeloupe
Indo-China
Inini
Ivory Coast
Laos
Latakia
Lebanon
Madagascar
Martinique
Mauritania
Mayotte
Memel
Middle Congo
Moheli
New Caledonia
New Hebrides
Niger Territory

Nossi-Be
Obock
Reunion
Rouad, Ile
Ste.-Marie de Madagascar
St. Pierre & Miquelon
Senegal
Senegambia & Niger
Somali Coast
Syria
Tahiti
Togo
Tunisia
Ubangi-Shari
Upper Senegal & Niger
Upper Volta
Viet Nam
Wallis & Futuna Islands

POST OFFICES IN FOREIGN COUNTRIES
China
Crete
Egypt
Turkish Empire
Zanzibar

Germany
EARLY STATES
Baden
Bavaria
Bergedorf
Bremen
Brunswick
Hamburg
Hanover
Lubeck
Mecklenburg-Schwerin
Mecklenburg-Strelitz
Oldenburg
Prussia
Saxony
Schleswig-Holstein
Wurttemberg

FORMER COLONIES
Cameroun (Kamerun)
Caroline Islands
German East Africa
German New Guinea
German South-West Africa
Kiauchau
Mariana Islands
Marshall Islands
Samoa
Togo

Italy
EARLY STATES
Modena
Parma
Romagna
Roman States
Sardinia
Tuscany
Two Sicilies
  Naples
  Neapolitan Provinces
  Sicily

FORMER COLONIES, CONTROLLED TERRITORIES, OCCUPATION AREAS
Aegean Islands
  Calimno (Calino)
  Caso
  Cos (Coo)
  Karki (Carchi)
  Leros (Lero)
  Lipso
  Nisiros (Nisiro)
  Patmos (Patmo)
  Piscopi
  Rodi (Rhodes)
  Scarpanto
  Simi
  Stampalia
Castellorizo
Corfu
Cyrenaica
Eritrea
Ethiopia (Abyssinia)
Fiume
Ionian Islands
  Cephalonia
  Ithaca
  Paxos
Italian East Africa
Libya
Oltre Giuba
Saseno
Somalia (Italian Somaliland)
Tripolitania

POST OFFICES IN FOREIGN COUNTRIES
"ESTERO"*
Austria
China
  Peking
  Tientsin
Crete
Tripoli
Turkish Empire
  Constantinople
  Durazzo
  Janina
Jerusalem
Salonika
Scutari
Smyrna
Valona
*Stamps overprinted "ESTERO" were used in various parts of the world.

Netherlands
Aruba
Caribbean Netherlands
Curacao
Netherlands Antilles (Curacao)
Netherlands Indies
Netherlands New Guinea
St. Martin
Surinam (Dutch Guiana)

Portugal
COLONIES PAST AND PRESENT, CONTROLLED TERRITORIES
Angola
Angra
Azores

Cape Verde
Funchal
Horta
Inhambane
Kionga
Lourenco Marques
Macao
Madeira
Mozambique
Mozambique Co.
Nyassa
Ponta Delgada
Portuguese Africa
Portuguese Congo
Portuguese Guinea
Portuguese India
Quelimane
St. Thomas & Prince Islands
Tete
Timor
Zambezia

Russia
ALLIED TERRITORIES AND REPUBLICS, OCCUPATION AREAS
Armenia
Aunus (Olonets)
Azerbaijan
Batum
Estonia
Far Eastern Republic
Georgia
Karelia
Latvia
Lithuania
North Ingermanland
Ostland
Russian Turkestan
Siberia
South Russia
Tannu Tuva
Transcaucasian Fed. Republics
Ukraine
Wenden (Livonia)
Western Ukraine

Spain
COLONIES PAST AND PRESENT, CONTROLLED TERRITORIES
Aguera, La
Cape Juby
Cuba
Elobey, Annobon & Corisco
Fernando Po
Ifni
Mariana Islands
Philippines
Puerto Rico
Rio de Oro
Rio Muni
Spanish Guinea
Spanish Morocco
Spanish Sahara
Spanish West Africa

POST OFFICES IN FOREIGN COUNTRIES
Morocco
Tangier
Tetuan

Dies of British Colonial Stamps

DIE A:

1. The lines in the groundwork vary in thickness and are not uniformly straight.

2. The seventh and eighth lines from the top, in the groundwork, converge where they meet the head.

3. There is a small dash in the upper part of the second jewel in the band of the crown.

4. The vertical color line in front of the throat stops at the sixth line of shading on the neck.

DIE B:

1. The lines in the groundwork are all thin and straight.

2. All the lines of the background are parallel.

3. There is no dash in the upper part of the second jewel in the band of the crown.

4. The vertical color line in front of the throat stops at the eighth line of shading on the neck.

DIE I:

1. The base of the crown is well below the level of the inner white line around the vignette.

2. The labels inscribed "POSTAGE" and "REVENUE" are cut square at the top.

3. There is a white "bud" on the outer side of the main stem of the curved ornaments in each lower corner.

4. The second (thick) line below the country name has the ends next to the crown cut diagonally.

DIE Ia.	DIE Ib.
1 as die II.	1 and 3 as die II.
2 and 3 as die I.	2 as die I.

DIE II:

1. The base of the crown is aligned with the underside of the white line around the vignette.

2. The labels curve inward at the top inner corners.

3. The "bud" has been removed from the outer curve of the ornaments in each corner.

4. The second line below the country name has the ends next to the crown cut vertically.

Wmk. 1
Crown and C C

Wmk. 2
Crown and C A

Wmk. 3
Multiple Crown
and C A

Wmk. 4
Multiple Crown
and Script C A

Wmk. 4a

Wmk. 46

Wmk. 314
St. Edward's Crown
and C A Multiple

Wmk. 373

Wmk. 384

Wmk. 406

British Colonial and Crown Agents Watermarks

Watermarks 1 to 4, 314, 373, 384 and 406, common to many British territories, are illustrated here to avoid duplication.

The letters "CC" of Wmk. 1 identify the paper as having been made for the use of the Crown Colonies, while the letters "CA" of the others stand for "Crown Agents." Both Wmks. 1 and 2 were used on stamps printed by De La Rue & Co.

Wmk. 3 was adopted in 1904; Wmk. 4 in 1921; Wmk. 46 in 1879; Wmk. 314 in 1957; Wmk. 373 in 1974; Wmk. 384 in 1985; Wmk 406 in 2008.

In Wmk. 4a, a non-matching crown of the general St. Edwards type (bulging on both sides at top) was substituted for one of the Wmk. 4 crowns which fell off the dandy roll. The non-matching crown occurs in 1950-52 printings in a horizontal row of crowns on certain regular stamps of Johore and Seychelles, and on various postage due stamps of Barbados, Basutoland, British Guiana, Gold Coast, Grenada, Northern Rhodesia, St. Lucia, Swaziland and Trinidad and Tobago. A variation of Wmk. 4a, with the non-matching crown in a horizontal row of crown-CA-crown, occurs on regular stamps of Bahamas, St. Kitts-Nevis and Singapore.

Wmk. 314 was intentionally used sideways, starting in 1966. When a stamp was issued with Wmk. 314 both upright and sideways, the sideways varieties usually are listed also – with minor numbers. In many of the later issues, Wmk. 314 is slightly visible.

Wmk. 373 is usually only faintly visible.

2017 Scott Series Supplement Releases

Come check out our newest 2017 Scott supplement releases on our brand NEW website! Customers are able to see sample pages along with the suggested mounts page for the National and Minuteman series. We are dedicated to improve the shopping experience for all of our customers!

United States National Series

Item#	Description	Retail	AA	Release
100S017	U.S. National	$22.99	**$19.99**	February
130S017	U.S. Commemorative Singles	$16.99	**$13.99**	February
114S017	U.S. Plate Number Coils–Comprehensive	$19.99	**$16.99**	January
113S017	U.S. Plate Number Coils–Simplified	$11.99	**$9.99**	January
101S017	U.S. Booklet Panes	$16.99	**$13.99**	April
118S017	U.S. Small Panes	$34.99	**$29.99**	April
110S017	U.S. Postal Cards	$11.99	**$9.99**	April
120S017	U.S. Commemorative & Air Plate Blocks	$19.99	**$16.99**	April
125S017	U.S. Regular & Air Plate Blocks	$11.99	**$9.99**	April
105S017	U.S. Postal Stationery	$11.99	**$9.99**	March

United Nations National Series

Item#	Description	Retail	AA	Release
552S017	U.N. Imprint Blocks	$19.99	**$16.99**	March
551S017	U.N. Singles & Postal Stationery	$25.99	**$21.99**	March

Territories National Series

Item#	Description	Retail	AA	Release
111MI17	Federated States of Micronesia	$34.99	**$29.99**	April
111PA17	Republic of Palau	$34.99	**$29.99**	April
111MA17	Republic of the Marshall Islands	$22.99	**$19.99**	April

Standard U.S. PNC Series

Item#	Description	Retail	AA	Release
117S017	U.S. Plate Number Coil Singles	$19.99	**$16.99**	January

Specialty Series

Item#	Description	Retail	AA	Release
170S017	American (includes U.N.)	$34.99	**$29.99**	March

Minuteman Series

Item#	Description	Retail	AA	Release
180S017	U.S. Minuteman	$22.99	**$19.99**	February
181S017	U.N. Minuteman	$25.99	**$21.99**	March

Pony Express Series

Item#	Description	Retail	AA	Release
178S017	U.S. Pony Express (double-sided)	$22.99	**$19.99**	March

United States - Hingeless

Item#	Description	Retail	AA	Release
199S017	U.S. Platinum - Hingeless	$78.99	**$67.99**	April
HUSA2017	U.S. Scott/Schaubek - Hingeless	$78.99	**$67.99**	April

2017 U.S. Mount Packs

Item#	Description	Retail	AA	Release
2017 B	2017 U.S. Scott Mount Pack, Black	$49.99	**$39.99**	February
2017 C	2017 U.S. Scott Mount Pack, Clear	$49.99	**$39.99**	February
100S017BB	U.S. National+U.S. Scott Mount Set, Black	$69.98	**$47.98**	February
100S017BC	U.S. National+U.S. Scott Mount Set, Clear	$69.98	**$47.98**	February
180S017BB	U.S. Minuteman+U.S. Scott Mount Set, Black	$69.98	**$47.98**	February
180S017BC	U.S. Minuteman+U.S. Scott Mount Set, Clear	$69.98	**$47.98**	February

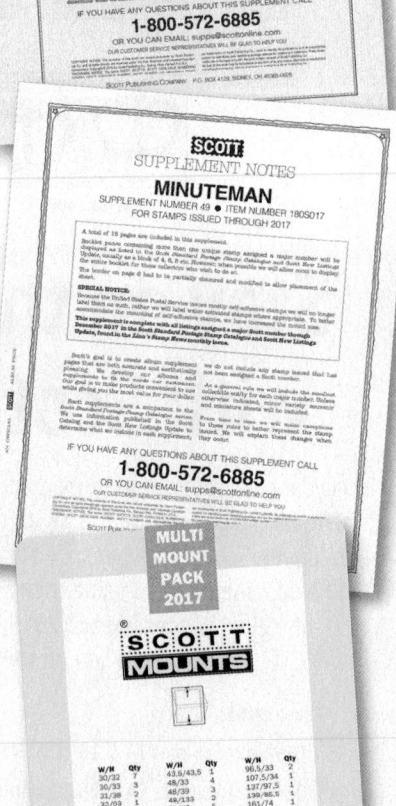

Call 800-572-6885 - Outside U.S. & Canada call: (937) 498-0800
Visit AmosAdvantage.com

AUSTRIA

ˈos-trē-ə

LOCATION — Central Europe
GOVT. — Republic
AREA — 32,378 sq. mi.
POP. — 8,139,299 (1999 est.)
CAPITAL — Vienna

Before 1867 Austria was an absolute monarchy, which included Hungary and Lombardy-Venetia. In 1867 the Austro-Hungarian Monarchy was established, with Austria and Hungary as equal partners. After World War I, in 1918, the different nationalities established their own states and only the German-speaking parts remained, forming a republic under the name "Deutschoster-reich" (German Austria), which name was shortly again changed to "Austria." In 1938 German forces occupied Austria, which became part of the German Reich. After the liberation by Allied troops in 1945, an independent republic was re-established.

60 Kreuzer = 1 Gulden
100 Neu-Kreuzer = 1 Gulden (1858)
100 Heller = 1 Krone (1899)
100 Groschen = 1 Schilling (1925)
100 Cents = 1 Euro (2002)

Catalogue values for unused stamps in this country are for Never Hinged items, beginning with Scott 432 in the regular postage section, Scott B165 in the semi-postal section, Scott C47 in the airpost section, Scott J175 in the postage due section, and Scott 4N1 in the AMG section.

Unused stamps without gum sell for about one-third or less of the values quoted.

Watermarks

Wmk. 91 — "BRIEF-MARKEN" In Double-lined Capitals Across the Middle of the Sheet

Wmk. 140 — Crown

Issues of the Austrian Monarchy (including Hungary)

Coat of Arms — A1

NINE KREUZER
Type I. One heavy line around coat of arms center. On the 9kr the top of "9" is about on a level with "Kreuzer" and not near the top of the label. Each cliche has the "9" in a different position.
Type IA. As type I, but with 1¼mm between "9" and "K."

Type II. One heavy line around coat of arms center. On the 9kr the top of "9" is much higher than the top of the word "Kreuzer" and nearly touches the top of the label.
Type III. As type II, but with two, thinner, lines around the center.

Wmk. K.K.H.M. in Sheet or Unwmk.
1850   Typo.   Imperf.

The stamps of this issue were at first printed on a rough hand-made paper, varying in thickness and having a watermark in script letters K.K.H.M., the initials of Kaiserlich Königliches Handels-Ministerium (Imperial and Royal Ministry of Commerce), vertically in the gutter between the panes. Parts of these letters show on margin stamps in the sheet. From 1854 a thick, smooth machine-made paper without watermark was used.

Thin to Thick Paper

1	A1 1kr yellow	1,650.	115.00
a.	Printed on both sides	2,000.	150.00
b.	1kr orange	2,350.	150.00
c.	1kr brown orange	3,475.	625.00
2	A1 2kr black	1,375.	82.50
a.	Ribbed paper	—	4,550.
b.	2kr gray black	2,350.	120.00
d.	Half used as 1kr on cover		52,500.
3	A1 3kr red	825.00	4.00
a.	Ribbed paper	4,000.	160.00
b.	Laid paper	—	19,000.
c.	Printed on both sides		10,000.
4	A1 6kr brown	1,000.	6.00
a.	Ribbed paper		2,450.
c.	Diagonal half used as 3kr on cover		20,000.
5	A1 9kr blue, type II	2,350.	9.00
a.	9kr blue, type I	2,250.	19.00
b.	9kr blue, type IA	15,000.	1,250.
c.	Laid paper, type III		15,000.
d.	Printed on both sides, type II		9,250.

1854
Machine-made Paper, Type III

1d	A1 1kr yellow	1,450.	100.00
2c	A1 2kr black	1,750.	80.00
3e	A1 3kr red	475.00	4.25
f.	3kr red, type I	4,650.	52.50
4b	A1 6kr brown	975.00	8.25
5e	A1 9kr blue	1,025.	4.25

In 1852-54, Nos. 1-5, rouletted 14, were used in Tokay and Homonna. A 12kr blue exists, but was not issued. Value, $100,000.
The reprints are type III in brighter colors, some on paper watermarked "Briefmarken" in the sheet.
For similar design see Lombardy-Venetia A1.

A2

A3

Emperor Franz Josef — A4

A5

A6

Two Types of Each Value.
Type I. Loops of the bow at the back of the head broken, except the 2kr. In the 2kr, the "2" has a flat foot, thinning to the right. The frame line in the UR corner is thicker than the line below. In the 5kr the top frame line is unbroken.
Type II. Loops complete. Wreath projects further at top of head. In the 2kr, the "2" has a more curved foot of uniform thickness, with a shading line in the upper and lower curves. The frame line UR is thicker than the line below. In the 5kr the top frame line is broken.

1858-59   Embossed   Perf. 14½

6	A2 2kr yellow, type II	1,225.	55.00
a.	2kr yellow, type II	3,000.	400.00
b.	2kr orange, type II	3,750.	450.00
c.	Half used as 1kr on cover		41,500.
7	A3 3kr black, type II	2,500.	175.00
a.	3kr black, type I	2,000.	240.00
8	A3 3kr green, type II ('59)	1,350.	140.00

9	A4 5kr red, type II	475.00	2.40
a.	5kr red, type I	2,000.	20.00
b.	5kr red, type II with type I frame	950.00	32.50
10	A5 10kr brown, type II	875.00	4.75
a.	10kr brown, type I	2,400.	24.00
b.	Half used as 5kr on cover		16,000.
11	A6 15kr blue, type II	800.00	2.00
a.	Type I	2,400.	24.00
b.	Half used as 7kr on cover		24.00

The reprints are of type II and are perforated 10½, 11, 12, 12½ and 13. There are also imperforate reprints of Nos. 6 to 8.
For similar designs see Lombardy-Venetia A2-A6.

Franz Josef — A7

1860-61   Embossed   Perf. 14

12	A7 2kr yellow	450.00	35.00
a.	Half used as 1kr on cover		25,000.
13	A7 3kr green	375.00	30.00
14	A7 5kr red	290.00	1.00
15	A7 10kr brown	325.00	3.00
a.	Half used as 5kr on cover		9,000.
16	A7 15kr blue	475.00	3.00

The reprints are perforated 9, 9½, 10, 10½, 11, 11½, 12, 12½, 13 and 13½.
There are also imperforate reprints of the 2 and 3kr.
For similar design see Lombardy-Venetia A7.

Coat of Arms — A8

1863

17	A8 2kr yellow	675.00	110.00
a.	Half used as 1kr on cover		
18	A8 3kr green	525.00	100.00
19	A8 5kr rose	625.00	15.00
20	A8 10kr blue	1,650.	18.50
21	A8 15kr yellow brown	1,650.	18.00

For similar design see Lombardy-Venetia A1.

Wmk. 91, or, before July 1864, Unwmkd.

1863-64			Perf. 9½
22	A8 2kr yellow ('64)	190.00	15.00
a.	Ribbed paper		550.00
b.	Half used as 1kr on cover		27,500.
23	A8 3kr green ('64)	190.00	15.00
24	A8 5kr rose	55.00	.75
a.	Ribbed paper		775.00
25	A8 10kr blue	250.00	3.50
a.	Half used as 5kr on cover		22,500.
26	A8 15kr yellow brown	225.00	2.25
	Nos. 22-26 (5)	910.00	36.50

The reprints are perforated 10½, 11½, 13 and 13½. There are also imperforate reprints of the 2 and 3kr.

Issues of Austro-Hungarian Monarchy

From 1867 to 1871 the independent postal administrations of Austria and Hungary used the same stamps.

A9

A10

5 kr:

Type I. In arabesques in lower left corner, the small ornament at left of the curve nearest the figure "5" is short and has three points at bottom.

Type II. The ornament is prolonged within the curve and has two points at bottom. The corresponding ornament at top of the lower left corner does not touch the curve (1872).

Type III. Similar to type II but the top ornament is joined to the curve (1881). Two different printing methods were used for the 1867-74 issues. The first produced stamps on which the hair and whiskers were coarse and thick, from the second they were fine and clear.

1867-72   Wmk. 91   Typo.   Perf. 9½
Coarse Print

27	A9	2kr yellow	120.00	3.00
a.		Half used as 1kr on cover		
28	A9	3kr green	140.00	2.90
29	A9	5kr rose, type II	87.50	.25
a.		5kr rose, type I	95.00	.25
b.		Perf. 10½, type II	190.00	
c.		Cliché of 3kr in plate of 5kr		37,500.
30	A9	10kr blue	290.00	2.40
a.		Half used as 5kr on cover		
31	A9	15kr brown	290.00	6.50
32	A9	25kr lilac	87.50	21.00
b.		25kr brown violet	325.00	65.00

Perf. 12

33	A10	50kr light brown	40.00	130.00
a.		50kr pale red brown	500.00	210.00
b.		50kr brownish rose	500.00	325.00
c.		Pair, imperf. btwn., vert. or horizontal	725.00	1,700.

Issues for Austria only

1874-80   Fine Print   Perf. 9½

34	A9	2kr yellow ('76)	14.50	.90
35	A9	3kr green ('76)	65.00	.90
36	A9	5kr rose, type III	4.50	.25
37	A9	10kr blue ('75)	160.00	.60
38	A9	15kr brown ('77)	8.75	7.75
39	A9	25kr gray lil ('78)	1.10	190.00
40	A10	50kr red brown	14.50	190.00

Perf. 9

34a	A9	2kr	250.00	65.00
35a	A9	3kr	225.00	30.00
36a	A9	5kr	87.50	3.50
37a	A9	10kr	440.00	35.00
38a	A9	15kr	625.00	130.00

Perf. 10½

34b	A9	2kr	60.00	4.50
35b	A9	3kr	100.00	2.75
36b	A9	5kr	14.50	.90
37b	A9	10kr	225.00	2.75
38b	A9	15kr	250.00	27.50

Perf. 12

34c	A9	2kr	275.00	160.00
35c	A9	3kr	250.00	27.50
36c	A9	5kr	60.00	5.00
37c	A9	10kr	525.00	130.00
38c	A9	15kr	825.00	190.00
40b	A10	50kr brown ('80)	19.00	190.00
c.		Perf. 10½x12	325.00	—

Perf. 13

34d	A9	2kr	325.00	360.00
35d	A9	3kr	225.00	36.00
36d	A9	5kr	130.00	21.00
37d	A9	10kr	275.00	100.00
38d	A9	15kr	625.00	475.00
40a	A10	50kr	30.00	250.00

Perf. 9x10½

34e	A9	2kr	440.00	87.50
35e	A9	3kr	360.00	77.50
36e	A9	5kr	140.00	18.00
37e	A9	10kr	410.00	105.00

Various compound perforations exist.

Values are for stamps that do not show the watermark. Stamps showing the watermark often sell for more.

For similar designs see Offices in the Turkish Empire A1-A2.

A11

Perf. 9, 9½, 10, 10½, 11½, 12, 12½
1883   Inscriptions in Black

41	A11	2kr brown	6.00	.45
42	A11	3kr green	6.00	.35
43	A11	5kr rose	75.00	.30
a.		Vert. pair, imperf. btwn.	190.00	425.00
44	A11	10kr blue	4.50	.35
45	A11	20kr gray	55.00	4.25
46	A11	50kr red lilac, perf 9½	375.00	80.00

The last printings of Nos. 41-46 are watermarked "ZEITUNGS-MARKEN" instead of "BRIEF-MARKEN." Values are for stamps that do not show watermark. Stamps with watermarks that are identifiable as being from "BRIEFMARKEN" sheets often sell for slightly more, while those with watermarks identifying stamps from "ZEITUNGS-MARKEN" sheets sell for significantly more. See the *Scott Classic Specialized Catalogue of Stamps and Covers* for detailed listings.

The 5kr has been reprinted in a dull red rose, perforated 10½.

For similar design see Offices in the Turkish Empire A3.

For surcharges see Offices in the Turkish Empire Nos. 15-19.

A12

A13

Perf. 9 to 13½, also Compound
1890-96   Unwmk.   Granite Paper
Numerals in black, Nos. 51-61

51	A12	1kr dark gray	1.50	.30
a.		Pair, imperf. between	225.00	540.00
b.		Half used as ½kr on cover		150.00
52	A12	2kr light brown	.35	.30
53	A12	3kr gray green	.45	.30
a.		Pair, imperf. between	325.00	650.00
54	A12	5kr rose	.45	.30
a.		Pair, imperf. between	260.00	450.00
55	A12	10kr ultramarine	1.10	.30
a.		Pair, imperf. between	360.00	650.00
56	A12	12kr claret	2.60	.40
a.		Pair, imperf. between		800.00
57	A12	15kr lilac	2.60	.40
a.		Pair, imperf. between	475.00	900.00
58	A12	20kr olive green	37.50	2.40
59	A12	24kr gray blue	2.25	1.50
a.		Pair, imperf. between	475.00	700.00
60	A12	30kr dark brown	2.75	.80
61	A12	50kr violet, perf 10	6.00	11.00

Engr.

62	A13	1gld dark gray	3.00	3.00
63	A13	1gld pale lilac ('96)	45.00	4.50
64	A13	2gld carmine	3.25	24.00
65	A13	2gld gray green ('96)	15.00	47.50
		Nos. 51-65 (15)	123.80	97.00

Nearly all values of the 1890-1907 issues are found with numerals missing in one or more corners, some with numerals printed on the back.

For surcharges see Offices in the Turkish Empire Nos. 20-25, 28-31.

A14

Perf. 9 to 13½, also Compound
1891   Typo.   Numerals in black

66	A14	20kr olive green	1.90	.30
67	A14	24kr gray blue	3.25	.95
68	A14	30kr brown	1.90	.30
a.		Pair, imperf. between	275.00	700.00
b.		Perf. 9	110.00	55.00
69	A14	50kr violet	1.90	.40
		Nos. 66-69 (4)	8.95	1.95

For surcharges see Offices in the Turkish Empire Nos. 26-27.

A15

A16

A17

A18

Perf. 10½ to 13½ and Compound
1899   Without Varnish Bars
Numerals in black, Nos. 70-82

70	A15	1h lilac	.75	.25
b.		Imperf.	60.00	150.00
c.		Perf. 10½	32.50	8.00
d.		Numerals inverted	2,250.	3,400.
71	A15	2h dark gray	2.75	.65
72	A15	3h bister brown	6.50	.25
b.		"3" in lower right corner sideways		3,000.
73	A15	5h blue green	7.25	.25
c.		Perf. 10½	22.50	4.75
74	A15	6h orange	.75	.25
75	A16	10h rose	16.00	.25
b.		Perf. 10½	875.00	210.00
76	A16	20h brown	5.25	.25
77	A16	25h ultramarine	60.00	.35
78	A16	30h red violet	19.00	2.75
b.		Horiz. pair, imperf. btwn.	600.00	
80	A17	40h green	32.50	3.50
81	A17	50h gray blue	17.50	4.25
b.		All four "50's" parallel		3,100.
82	A17	60h brown	50.00	1.25
b.		Horiz. pair, imperf. btwn.	550.00	
c.		Perf. 10½	105.00	5.40

Engr.

83	A18	1k carmine rose	6.00	.45
a.		1k carmine	6.00	.25
b.		Vert. pair, imperf. btwn.	250.00	350.00
84	A18	2k gray lilac	52.50	.45
a.		Vert. pair, imperf. btwn.	440.00	725.00
85	A18	4k gray green	10.50	18.00
		Nos. 70-85 (15)	287.25	33.15

For surcharges see Offices in Crete Nos. 1-7, Offices in the Turkish Empire Nos. 32-45.

1901   With Varnish Bars

70a	A15	1h lilac	1.60	.45
71a	A15	2h dark gray	6.50	.40
72a	A15	3h bister brown	.80	.25
73a	A15	5h blue green	.80	.25
74a	A15	6h orange	.80	.25
75a	A16	10h rose	.80	.25
76a	A16	20h brown	.80	.25
77a	A16	25h ultra	.80	.25
78a	A16	30h red violet	3.25	.80
79	A17	35h green	.80	.25
80a	A17	40h green	3.25	4.75
81a	A17	50h gray blue	4.75	11.00
82a	A17	60h brown	3.25	1.60
		Nos. 70a-78a,79,80a-82a (13)	28.20	20.75

The diagonal yellow bars of varnish were printed across the face to prevent cleaning.

A19

A20

A21

Perf. 12½ to 13½ and Compound
1905-07   Typo.
Without Varnish Bars
Colored Numerals

86	A19	1h lilac	.25	.35
87	A19	2h dark gray	.25	.25
88	A19	3h bister brown	.25	.25
89	A19	5h dk blue green	12.00	.25
90	A19	5h yellow grn ('06)	.25	.25
91	A19	6h deep orange	.25	.25
92	A20	10h carmine ('06)	.50	.25
93	A20	12h violet ('07)	1.20	.80
94	A20	20h brown ('06)	4.00	.25
95	A20	25h ultra ('06)	4.00	.40
96	A20	30h red violet ('06)	8.00	.40

Black Numerals

97	A20	10h carmine	16.00	.25
98	A20	20h brown	40.00	1.60
99	A20	25h ultra	40.00	2.40
100	A20	30h red violet	55.00	4.75

White Numerals

101	A21	35h green	2.00	.25
102	A21	40h deep violet	2.00	.80
103	A21	50h dull blue	2.00	3.50
104	A21	60h yellow brown	2.00	.80
105	A21	72h rose	2.00	1.75
		Nos. 86-105 (20)	191.95	19.80
		Set, never hinged	650.00	

For surcharges see Offices in Crete Nos. 8-14.

1904   Perf. 13x13½
With Varnish Bars

86a	A19	1h lilac	.35	.95
87a	A19	2h dark gray	1.40	.95
88a	A19	3h bister brown	2.00	.25
89a	A19	5h dk blue green	3.25	.25
91a	A19	6h deep orange	8.00	.30
97a	A20	10h carmine	1.75	.25
98a	A20	20h brown	29.00	1.20
99a	A20	25h ultra	29.00	.80
100a	A21	30h red violet	45.00	1.60
101a	A21	35h green	29.00	.55
102a	A21	40h deep violet	27.50	4.00
103a	A21	50h dull blue	29.00	9.50
104a	A21	60h yellow brown	40.00	1.60
105a	A21	72h rose	2.00	2.25
		Nos. 86a-105a (14)	247.25	24.45
		Set, never hinged	875.00	

Stamps of the 1901, 1904 and 1905 issues perf. 9 or 10½, also compound with 12½, were not sold at any post office, but were supplied only to some high-ranking officials. This applies also to the contemporaneous issues of Austrian Offices Abroad.

Karl VI — A22

Franz Josef — A23

Schönbrunn Palace — A24

Franz Josef — A25

Designs: 2h, Maria Theresa. 3h, Joseph II. 5h, 10h, 25h, Franz Josef. 6h, Leopold II. 12h, Franz I. 20h, Ferdinand I. 30h, Franz Josef as youth. 35h, Franz Josef in middle age. 60h, Franz Josef on horseback. 1k, Franz Josef in royal robes. 5k, Hofburg, Vienna.

1908-16   Typo.   Perf. 12½

110a	A22	1h gray black	.25	.25
111a	A22	2h violet	.25	.25
112	A22	3h magenta	.25	.25
113	A22	5h yellow green	.25	.25
a.		Booklet pane of 6	27.50	
114a	A22	6h buff ('13)	.55	.80
115	A22	10h rose	.25	.25
a.		Booklet pane of 6	82.50	
116a	A22	12h scarlet	.80	1.20
117a	A22	20h chocolate	4.75	.45
118a	A22	25h deep blue	2.00	.45
119a	A22	30h olive green	9.50	.65
120	A22	35h slate	2.40	

Engr.

121	A23	50h dark green	.55	.25
a.		Vert. pair, imperf. btwn.	200.00	400.00
b.		Horiz. pair, imperf. btwn.	200.00	400.00
122	A23	60h deep carmine	.25	.25
a.		Vert. pair, imperf. btwn.	160.00	400.00
b.		Horiz. pair, imperf. btwn.	160.00	400.00
123	A23	72h dk brown	1.60	.40
124	A23	1k purple	12.00	.25
a.		Vert. pair, imperf. btwn.	200.00	350.00
b.		Horiz. pair, imperf. btwn.	200.00	350.00
125	A24	2k lake & olive grn	20.00	.40
126	A24	5k bister & dk vio	40.00	6.00

127	A25	10k blue, bis & dp brn	190.00	65.00
		Nos. 110a-127 (18)	285.65	77.60
		Set, never hinged	875.00	

Definitive set issued for the 60th year of the reign of Emperor Franz Josef.

The 1h-35h exist on both ordinary (1913) and chalk-surfaced (1908) paper. The cheaper varieties are listed above. For detailed listings, see the *Scott Classic Specialized Catalogue of Stamps and Covers.*

All values exist imperforate. They were not sold at any post office, but presented to a number of high government officials. This applies also to all imperforate stamps of later issues, including semi-postals, etc., and those of the Austrian Offices Abroad.

Litho. forgeries of No. 127 exist.

For overprint and surcharge see #J47-J48.

For similar designs see Offices in Crete A5-A6, Offices in the Turkish Empire A16-A17.

Birthday Jubilee Issue

No. 144

Similar to 1908 Issue, but designs enlarged by labels at top and bottom bearing dates "1830" and "1910"

		1910		**Typo.**
128	A22	1h gray black	4.00	8.00
129	A22	2h violet	4.75	16.00
130	A22	3h magenta	4.00	12.00
131	A22	5h yellow green	.25	.35
132	A22	6h buff	3.25	12.00
133	A22	10h rose	.25	.35
134	A22	12h scarlet	3.25	12.00
135	A22	20h chocolate	3.25	12.00
136	A22	25h deep blue	1.60	2.40
137	A22	30h olive green	3.25	12.00
138	A22	35h slate	3.25	12.00
		Engr.		
139	A23	50h dark green	5.50	12.00
140	A23	60h deep car	5.50	12.00
141	A23	1k purple	5.50	16.00
142	A24	2k lake & ol grn	140.00	225.00
143	A24	5k bister & dk vio	110.00	225.00
144	A25	10k blue, bis & dp brn	175.00	325.00
		Nos. 128-144 (17)	472.60	914.10
		Set, never hinged	1,050.	

80th birthday of Emperor Franz Josef. All values exist imperforate.

Litho. forgeries of Nos. 142-144 exist.

Austrian Crown — A37

Franz Josef — A38

A39

Coat of Arms — A40

		1916-18		**Typo.**
145	A37	3h brt violet	.25	.25
146	A37	5h lt green	.25	.25
a.		Booklet pane of 6	15.50	
b.		Booklet pane of 4 + 2 labels	30.00	
147	A37	6h deep orange	.25	.80
148	A37	10h magenta	.25	.25
a.		Booklet pane of 6	30.00	
149	A37	12h light blue	.25	.90
150	A38	15h rose red	.40	.25
a.		Booklet pane of 6	16.50	
151	A38	20h chocolate	.25	.25
152	A38	25h blue	4.00	.80

153	A38	30h slate	6.50	.65
154	A39	40h olive green	.25	.25
155	A39	50h blue green	.25	.25
156	A39	60h deep blue	.25	.25
157	A39	80h orange brown	.25	.25
158	A39	90h red violet	.25	.25
159	A39	1k car, yel ('18)	.25	.25
		Engr.		
160	A40	2k dark blue	4.00	.40
161	A40	3k claret	24.00	1.20
162	A40	4k deep green	8.00	2.40
163	A40	10k deep violet	27.50	52.50
		Nos. 145-163 (19)	81.15	62.40
		Set, never hinged	240.00	

Stamps of type A38 have two varieties of the frame. Stamps of type A40 have various decorations about the shield.

Nos. 145-163 exist imperf. Value set, $475 hinged, $875 never hinged.

		1917		**Ordinary Paper**
164	A40	2k lt blue	2.00	.80
165	A40	3k car rose	47.50	.80
166	A40	4k yel grn	3.25	1.25
167	A40	10k violet	140.00	110.00
		Nos. 164-167 (4)	192.75	112.85
		Set, never hinged	475.00	

Nos. 164-167 exist imperf. Value set, $325 unused, $650 never hinged.

See Nos. 172-175 (granite paper). For overprints and surcharges see Nos. 181-199, C1-C3, J60-J63, N1-N5, N10-N19, N33-N37, N42-N51. Western Ukraine 2-7, 11-15, 19-28, 57-58, 85-89, 94-103, N3-N14, NJ13.

Emperor Karl I — A42

		1917-18		**Typo.**
168	A42	15h dull red	.40	.40
a.		Booklet pane of 6	16.50	
169	A42	20h dk green ('18)	.40	.40
a.		20h green ('17)	.80	.65
170	A42	25h blue	.40	.40
171	A42	30h dull violet	2.00	.40
		Nos. 168-171 (4)	3.20	1.60
		Set, never hinged	13.50	

Nos. 168-171 exist imperf. Value set, $160 unused, $400 never hinged.

For overprints and surcharges see Nos. N6-N9, N20, N38-N41, N52, N64. Western Ukraine 1, 8, 16-18, 90-93, N15-N18.

		1918-19	**Engr.**	**Granite Paper**
172	A40	2k lt blue	1.20	.45
a.		Perf. 11½	725.00	1,200.
		Never hinged	1,600.	
173	A40	3k car rose	.40	.80
174	A40	4k yel grn ('19)	4.00	20.00
175	A40	10k lt vio ('19)	8.00	32.50
		Nos. 172-175 (4)	13.60	53.75
		Set, never hinged	40.00	

Issues of the Republic

Austrian Stamps of 1916-18 Overprinted

		1918-19	**Unwmk.**	**Perf. 12½**
181	A37	3h bright violet	.25	.25
182	A37	5h light green	.25	.25
183	A37	6h deep orange	.80	3.25
184	A37	10h magenta	.25	.25
185	A37	12h light blue	.40	2.40
186	A42	15h dull red	.80	2.00
187	A42	20h deep green	.40	.25
188	A42	25h blue	.80	.25
189	A42	30h dull violet	.80	.25
190	A39	40h olive green	.80	.25
191	A39	50h deep green	.80	2.00
192	A39	60h deep blue	1.20	2.00
193	A39	80h orange brown	.40	.80
a.		Inverted overprint	275.00	325.00
		Never hinged	650.00	
194	A39	90h red violet	1.20	.80
195	A39	1k carmine, yel	1.40	.80
		Granite Paper		
196	A40	2k lt blue	.25	.25
a.		Horiz. pair, imperf. between	240.00	
		Never hinged	400.00	
b.		Vert. pair, imperf. between	1,200.	
		Never hinged		
c.		Perf. 11½	95.00	110.00
		Never hinged	175.00	

197	A40	3k car rose	.35	.80
198	A40	4k yel grn	1.60	3.25
a.		Perf. 11½	16.00	35.00
		Never hinged	32.50	
199	A40	10k deep vio	9.50	20.00
		Nos. 181-199 (19)	22.25	40.10
		Set, never hinged	62.50	

Nos. 181, 182, 184, 187-191, 194, 197 and 199 exist imperforate.

Post Horn — A43

Coat of Arms — A44

Allegory of New Republic — A45

		1919-20	**Typo.**	**Perf. 12½**
		Ordinary Paper		
200	A43	3h gray	.25	.25
201	A44	5h yellow green	.25	.25
202	A44	5h gray ('20)	.25	.25
203	A43	6h orange	.25	.50
204	A44	10h deep rose	.25	.25
205	A44	10h red ('20)	.25	.25
a.		Thick grayish paper ('20)	.25	.40
206	A44	12h grnsh blue	.25	4.00
207	A43	15h bister ('20)	.35	.80
a.		Thick grayish paper ('20)	.25	.40
208	A44	20h dark green	.25	.25
a.		20h yellow green	.25	.25
b.		As "a," thick grysh paper ('20)	1.60	4.00
209	A44	25h blue	.25	.25
210	A43	25h violet ('20)	.25	.25
211	A45	30h dark brown	.25	.25
212	A45	40h violet	.25	.25
213	A45	40h lake ('20)	.25	.25
214	A44	45h olive green	.30	.80
215	A45	50h dark blue	.25	.25
a.		Thick grayish paper ('20)	.40	.95
216	A43	60h ol grn ('20)	.25	.25
217	A44	1k carmine, yel	.25	.25
218	A44	1k light blue ('20)	.25	.25
		Nos. 200-218 (19)	4.90	9.85
		Set, never hinged	4.00	

All values exist imperf. (For regularly issued imperfs, see Nos. 227-235.)

For overprints and surcharge see Nos. B11-B19, B30-B38, J102, N21, N27, N53, N58, N65, N71.

Parliament Building A46

		1919-20	**Engr.**	**Perf. 12½, 11½**
		Granite Paper		
219	A46	2k ver & blk	.25	.80
a.		Center inverted	2,750.	
		Never hinged	6,500.	
b.		Perf. 11½	1.60	3.25
220	A46	2½k ol bis ('20)	.30	.25
221	A46	3k bl & blk brn	.25	.25
a.		Perf. 11½	5.75	20.00
222	A46	4k car & blk	.25	.25
a.		Center inverted	2,100.	3,250.
		Never hinged	2,750.	
b.		Perf. 11½	2.00	6.50
223	A46	5k black ('20)	.25	.25
a.		Perf. 11½x12½	55.00	87.50
		Never hinged	160.00	
b.		Perf. 11½	2.75	7.25
224	A46	7½k plum	.30	.40
a.		Perf. 11½x12½	120.00	240.00
		Never hinged	290.00	
b.		Perf. 11½x12½	80.00	240.00
		Never hinged	240.00	
225	A46	10k olive grn & blk brn	.30	.40
a.		Perf. 11½x12½	160.00	300.00
		Never hinged	475.00	
b.		Perf. 11½	13.50	30.00
		Never hinged	32.50	
226	A46	20k lil & red ('20)	.25	.40
a.		Center inverted	60,000.	40,000.
b.		Perf. 11½	72.50	175.00
		Never hinged	175.00	
		Nos. 219-226 (8)	2.15	3.00
		Set, never hinged	6.75	

Nos. 220-222, 225-226 exist imperforate between. Values, per pair: unused $200-$350; never hinged $400-$725.

See No. 248. For overprints and surcharge see Nos. B23-B29, B43-B49.

		1920	**Typo.**	**Imperf.**
		Ordinary Paper		
227	A44	5h yellow green	.35	.95
228	A44	5h gray	.25	.25
229	A44	10h deep rose	.25	.25
230	A44	10h red	.25	.25
231	A43	15h bister	.25	.25
232	A43	25h violet	.25	.25
233	A45	30h dark brown	.25	.25
234	A45	40h violet	.25	.25
235	A43	50h olive green	.25	.25
		Nos. 227-235 (9)	2.35	2.95
		Set, never hinged	2.00	

Arms

A47   A48

		1920-21	**Typo.**	**Perf. 12½**
		White Paper		
238	A47	80h rose	.25	.25
239	A47	1k black brown	.25	.25
241	A47	1½k green ('21)	.30	.25
242	A47	2k blue	.25	.30
243	A48	3k yel grn & dk grn ('21)	.25	.30
244	A48	4k red & clar ('21)	.25	.25

245	A48	5k vio & clar ('21)	.25	.25
246	A48	7½k yel & brn ('21)	.25	.30
247	A48	10k ultra & bl ('21)	.25	.25
		Nos. 238-247 (9)	2.30	2.40
		Set, never hinged	4.75	

Nos. 238-245, 247 exist on white paper of good quality and on thick grayish paper of inferior quality; No. 246 exists only on white paper. Values are for the cheaper varieties.
See the *Scott Classic Specialized Catalogue of Stamps and Covers* for detailed listings.
For overprints and surcharges see Nos. B20-B22, B39-B42.

1921
			Engr.	
248	A46	50k dk violet, *yel*	.95	1.60
		Never hinged	1.60	
a.		Perf. 11½	14.50	77.50
		Never hinged	23.00	

Symbols of Agriculture A49

Symbols of Labor and Industry A50

1922-24 Typo. Perf. 12½
250	A49	½k olive bister	.25	.65
251	A50	1k brown	.25	.25
252	A50	2k cobalt blue	.25	.25
253	A49	2½k orange brown	.25	.25
254	A50	4k dull violet	.25	1.00
255	A50	5k gray green	.25	.25
256	A49	7½k gray violet	.25	.25
257	A50	10k claret	.25	.25
258	A49	12½k gray green	.25	.25
259	A49	15k bluish green	.25	.25
260	A49	20k dark blue	.25	.25
261	A49	25k claret	.25	.25
262	A50	30k pale gray	.25	.25
263	A50	45k pale red	.25	.25
264	A50	50k orange brown	.25	.25
265	A50	60k yellow green	.25	.25
266	A50	75k ultramarine	.25	.25
267	A50	80k yellow	.25	.25
268	A49	100k gray	.25	.25
269	A49	120k brown	.25	.25
270	A49	150k orange	.25	.25
271	A49	160k light green	.25	.25
272	A49	180k red	.25	.25
273	A49	200k pink	.25	.25
274	A49	240k dark violet	.25	.25
275	A49	300k light blue	.25	.25
276	A49	400k deep green	1.20	.80
a.		400k gray green	.90	.40
277	A49	500k yellow	.25	.25
278	A49	600k slate	.25	.25
279	A49	700k brown ('24)	2.40	.25
280	A49	800k violet ('24)	1.60	2.10
281	A50	1000k violet ('23)	2.40	.25
282	A50	1200k car rose ('23)	.80	.50
283	A50	1500k orange ('24)	2.00	.25
284	A50	1600k slate ('23)	3.25	3.25
285	A50	2000k dp bl ('23)	4.75	2.75
286	A50	3000k lt blue ('23)	12.00	2.40
287	A50	4000k dk bl, *bl* ('24)	2.75	2.75
		Nos. 250-287 (38)	43.40	23.45
		Set, never hinged	175.00	

Nos. 250-287 exist imperf. Value set, $600 unused, $1,200 never hinged.

Symbols of Art and Science — A51

1922-24 Engr. Perf. 12½
288	A51	20k dark brn, 26x29mm	.25	.25
289	A51	25k blue, 26x29mm	.25	.25
290	A51	50k brown red, 26x29mm	.25	.25
b.		Vert. pair, imperf. btwn.	250.00	350.00
f.		brown red, 25x29½mm	.25	.25
291	A51	100k green, 26x29mm	2.50	.25
b.		Vert. pair, imperf. btwn.	—	475.00
e.		green, 25x29½mm	.25	.25
292	A51	200k dk violet, 26x29mm	1.50	.25
b.		Vert. pair, imperf. btwn.	250.00	
c.		dk violet, 25x29½mm	.50	.25
293	A51	500k dp orange, 25x29½mm	.25	.25
a.		dp orange, 26x29mm	15.00	15.00

294	A51	1000k blk vio, *yel,* 25x29½mm	.25	.25
b.		Vert. pair, imperf. btwn.	360.00	
c.		Horiz. pair, imperf. btwn.	360.00	
295	A51	2000k ol grn, *yel*	.25	.25
a.		Vert. pair, imperf. btwn.	360.00	
296	A51	3000k clar brn, 25x29½mm ('23)	10.00	.40
297	A51	5000k gray blk, 25x29½mm ('23)	6.50	.80

Granite Paper
298	A51	10,000k red brn, 26x29mm ('24)	4.50	4.50
		Nos. 288-298 (11)	26.50	7.70
		Set, never hinged	72.50	

1922-24 Perf. 11½
288a	A51	20k dk brown, 26x29mm	1.60	1.60
289a	A51	25k blue, 26x29mm	1.25	1.25
290a	A51	50k brown red, 26x29mm	1.60	1.60
291a	A51	100k grn, 26x29mm	4.75	4.75
i.		100k green, 25x29½mm	15.00	15.00
292a	A51	200k dk violet, 26x29mm	5.50	5.50
294a	A51	1000k bk violet, 25x29½mm	240.00	240.00

Nos. 288-298 come in two design sizes: 25x29½mm and 26x29mm.
On Nos. 281-287, 291-298 "kronen" is abbreviated to "k" and transposed with the numerals.
Nos. 288-298 exist imperf. Value set, $410 hinged, $750 never hinged.

Numeral A52

Fields Crossed by Telegraph Wires A53

Golden Eagle — A54

Church of Minorite Friars — A55

1925-32 Typo. Perf. 12
303	A52	1g dark gray	.40	.25
304	A52	2g claret	.40	.25
305	A52	3g scarlet	.40	.25
306	A52	4g grnsh blue ('27)	1.20	.25
307	A52	5g brown orange	1.60	.25
308	A52	6g ultramarine	1.60	.25
309	A52	7g chocolate	1.60	.25
310	A52	8g yellow green	4.00	.25
311	A53	10g orange	.80	.25
313	A53	15g red lilac	.80	.25
314	A53	16g dark blue	.80	.25
315	A53	18g olive green	1.20	.80
316	A54	20g dark violet	1.20	.25
317	A54	24g carmine	1.20	.40
318	A54	30g dark brown	1.20	.25
319	A54	40g ultramarine	1.20	.25
320	A54	45g yellow brown	1.60	.25
321	A54	50g gray	1.60	.30
322	A54	80g turquoise blue	3.50	4.50

Perf. 12½ Engr.
323	A55	1s deep green	20.00	1.60
a.		1s light green	375.00	24.00
		Never hinged	1,750.	
b.		As "a," pair, imperf between	925.00	
324	A55	2s brown rose	8.00	10.50
		Nos. 303-324 (21)	54.30	21.85
		Set, never hinged	225.00	

Nos. 303-324 exist imperf. Value, set unused $475; never hinged $2,000.
For type A52 surcharged see No. B118.

Güssing — A56

National Library, Vienna — A57

15g, Hochosterwitz. 16g, 20g, Durnstein. 18g, Traunsee. 24g, Salzburg. 30g, Seewiesen. 40g, Innsbruck. 50g, Worthersee. 60g, Hohenems. 2s, St. Stephen's Cathedral, Vienna.

1929-30 Typo. Perf. 12½
Size: 25½x21½mm
326	A56	10g brown orange	.65	.25
327	A56	10g bister ('30)	.65	.25
328	A56	15g violet brown	.65	1.40
329	A56	16g dark gray	.25	.25
330	A56	18g blue green	.40	.50
331	A56	20g dark gray ('30)	.80	.25
332	A56	24g maroon	6.50	8.00
333	A56	24g lake ('30)	6.50	.50
334	A56	30g dark violet	6.50	.25
335	A56	40g dark blue	8.00	.25
336	A56	50g gray violet ('30)	27.50	.25
337	A56	60g olive green	17.50	.25

Engr.
Size: 21x26mm
338	A57	1s black brown	8.00	.25
a.		Horiz. pair, imperf. btwn.	260.00	
		Never hinged	450.00	
b.		Vert. pair, imperf. btwn.	260.00	
		Never hinged	450.00	
339	A57	2s dark green	16.00	12.00
a.		Horiz. pair, imperf. btwn.	325.00	
		Never hinged	575.00	
		Nos. 326-339 (14)	99.90	24.65
		Set, never hinged	675.00	

Nos. 326, 328-330 and 332-339 exist imperf. Values, set of 12 unused hinged $1,450, never hinged $2,000.

Type of 1929-30 Issue
Designs: 12g, Traunsee. 64g, Hohenems.

1932 Perf. 12
Size: 21x16½mm
340	A56	10g olive brown	.80	.25
341	A56	12g blue green	1.60	.25
342	A56	18g blue green	1.60	3.25
343	A56	20g dark gray	.80	.25
344	A56	24g carmine rose	8.00	.25
345	A56	24g dull violet	4.75	.25
346	A56	30g dark violet	20.00	.25
347	A56	30g carmine rose	8.00	.25
a.		Vert. pair, imperf. btwn.	45.00	
		Never hinged, #347a	60.00	
348	A56	40g dark blue	24.00	1.60
349	A56	40g dark violet	8.00	.40
350	A56	50g gray violet	24.00	.40
351	A56	50g dull blue	8.00	.40
352	A56	60g gray green	65.00	4.00
353	A56	64g gray green	24.00	.40
		Nos. 340-353 (14)	198.55	12.20
		Set, never hinged	750.00	

For overprints and surcharges see Nos. B87-B92, B119-B121.
Nos. 340-353 exist imperf. Values, set unused hinged, $575, never hinged $1,200.

Used values for Nos. 354-389 are for stamps with philatelic favor cancels. Values for postally used examples are 50%-100% more.

Burgenland A67

Tyrol A68

Costumes of various districts: 3g, Burgenland. 4g, 5g, Carinthia. 6g, 8g, Lower Austria. 12g, 20g, Upper Austria. 24g, 25g, Salzburg. 30g, 35g, Styria. 45g, Tyrol. 60g, Vorarlberg bridal couple. 64g, Vorarlberg. 1s, Viennese family. 2s, Military.

1934-35 Typo. Perf. 12
354	A67	1g dark violet	.25	.25
355	A67	3g scarlet	.25	.25
356	A67	4g olive green	.25	.25
357	A67	5g red violet	.25	.25
358	A67	6g ultramarine	.25	.25
359	A67	8g green	.25	.25

360	A67	12g dark brown	.25	.25
361	A67	20g yellow brown	.25	.25
362	A67	24g grnsh blue	.25	.25
363	A67	25g violet	.25	.25
364	A67	30g maroon	.25	.25
365	A67	35g rose carmine	.35	.35

Perf. 12½
366	A68	40g slate gray	.30	.25
367	A68	45g brown red	.30	.25
368	A68	60g ultramarine	.55	.40
369	A68	64g brown	.80	.25
370	A68	1s deep violet	1.20	.65
371	A68	2s dull green	45.00	45.00

Designs Redrawn
Perf. 12 (6g), 12½ (2s)
372	A67	6g ultra ('35)	.25	.25
373	A68	2s emerald ('35)	3.50	3.50
		Nos. 354-373 (20)	55.00	53.65
		Set, never hinged	200.00	

The design of No. 358 looks as though the man's ears were on backwards, while No. 372 appears correctly.
On No. 373 there are seven feathers on each side of the eagle instead of five.
Nos. 354-373 exist imperf. Values, set unused hinged $410, never hinged $700.
For surcharges see Nos. B128-B131.

Dollfuss Mourning Issue

Engelbert Dollfuss — A85

1934-35 Engr. Perf. 12½
374	A85	24g greenish black	.35	.35
		Never hinged	1.60	
375	A85	24g indigo ('35)	.80	.80
		Never hinged	3.25	

Nos. 374-375 exist imperf. Value, each unused hinged $200, never hinged $400.

"Mother and Child," by Joseph Danhauser A86

1935, May 1
376	A86	24g dark blue	.80	.35
		Never hinged	2.00	
a.		Vert. pair, imperf. btwn.	300.00	
		Never hinged	425.00	
b.		Horiz. pair, imperf. btwn.	275.00	
		Never hinged	400.00	

Mother's Day. No. 376 exists imperf. Value, unused hinged $200, never hinged $475.

"Madonna and Child," after Painting by Dürer — A87

1936, May 5 Photo.
377	A87	24g violet blue	.65	.55
		Never hinged	1.75	

Mother's Day. No. 377 exists imperf. Value, unused hinged $250, never hinged $400.

Farm Workers — A88

Design: 5s, Construction workers.

1936, June   Engr.   *Perf. 12½*

378	A88	3s red orange	13.50 13.50
		Never hinged	32.50
379	A88	5s brown black	32.50 *32.50*
		Never hinged	52.50

Nos. 378-379 exist imperf. Values, set unused hinged $350, never hinged $800.

Engelbert Dollfuss — A90

1936, July 25

380	A90	10s dark blue	725.00 *725.00*
		Never hinged	1,100.

Second anniv. of death of Engelbert Dollfuss, chancellor.
Value, used, is for CTO examples.
Exists imperf. Value, $1,900, never hinged $3,250.

Mother and Child — A91

1937, May 5   Photo.   *Perf. 12*

381	A91	24g henna brown	.65 .80
		Never hinged	1.60

Mother's Day. Exists imperf. Values, unused hinged $200, never hinged $325.

S.S. Maria Anna A92

1937, June 9

Steamships: 24g, Uranus, 64g, Oesterreich.

382	A92	12g red brown	1.10 .55
383	A92	24g deep blue	1.10 .55
384	A92	64g dark green	1.10 *.55*
		Nos. 382-384 (3)	3.30 *1.65*
		Set, never hinged	14.50

Centenary of steamship service on Danube River. Exist imperf. Value, set never hinged $3,500.

First Locomotive, "Austria" A95

Designs: 25g, Modern steam locomotive. 35g, Modern electric train.

1937, Nov. 22

385	A95	12g black brown	.25 .25
386	A95	25g dark violet	.65 .65
387	A95	35g brown red	2.00 2.00
		Nos. 385-387 (3)	2.90 *2.90*
		Set, never hinged	15.00

Centenary of Austrian railways. Exist imperf. Value, set never hinged $325.

Rose and Zodiac Signs — A98

1937   Engr.   *Perf. 13x12½*

388	A98	12g dark green	.25 .25
389	A98	24g dark carmine	.25 .25
		Set, never hinged	1.60

Nos. 388-389 exist imperf. Value, set never hinged $275.

Used values for Nos. 390-454 are for stamps with philatelic favor cancels. Postally used examples sell for substantially more.

German stamps were in use in Austria until mid-1945, when they were replaced by issues of the Russian (May) and American-British-French (June) occupation authorities.

For Use in Vienna, Lower Austria and Burgenland

Germany Nos. 509-511 and 511B Overprinted in Black

      a   b

1945   Unwmk.   *Perf. 14*

390	A115(a)	5pf dp yellow green	.25 .85
391	A115(b)	6pf purple	.25 .85
392	A115(a)	8pf red	.25 .45
393	A115(c)	12pf carmine	.25 .45
		Nos. 390-393 (4)	2.60
		Set, never hinged	1.00

Nos. 390-393 exist with overprint inverted or double.
Germany No. 507, the 3pf, with overprint "a" was prepared, not issued, but sold to collectors after the definitive Republic issue had been placed in use. Values, $30 hinged, $65 never hinged.

German Semi-Postal Stamps, #B207, B209, B210, B283 Surcharged in Black

c

d

1945   *Perf. 14, 14x13½, 13½x14*

394	SP181(c)	5pf on 12pf + 88pf	.25 2.00
395	SP184(d)	6pf on 6pf + 14pf	2.10 17.50
396	SP242(d)	8pf on 42pf + 108pf	.25 3.50
397	SP183(d)	12pf on 3pf + 7pf	.25 2.00
		Nos. 394-397 (4)	2.85 25.00
		Set, never hinged	9.75

The surcharges are spaced to fit the stamps.

Stamps of Germany, Nos. 509 to 511, 511B, 519 and 529 Overprinted

     e   f

1945   Typo.   *Perf. 14*
Size: 18½x22½mm

398	A115(e)	5pf dp yel grn	.85 8.00
399	A115(f)	5pf dp yel grn	3.50 27.50
400	A115(e)	6pf purple	.30 3.50
401	A115(e)	8pf red	.30 3.50

402	A115(e)	12pf carmine	.85 4.00

Engr.
Size: 21½x26mm

403	A115(e)	30pf olive green	6.00
a.		Thin bar at bottom	15.00
		Never hinged	47.50
404	A118(e)	42pf brt green	20.00
a.		Thin bar at bottom	9.00
		Never hinged	50.00
		Nos. 398-404 (7)	31.80 *46.50*
		Set, never hinged	98.00

On Nos. 403a and 404a, the bottom bar of the overprint is 2½mm wide, and, as the overprint was applied in two operations, "Osterreich" is usually not exactly centered in its diagonal slot. On Nos. 403 and 404, the bottom bar is 3mm wide, and "Osterreich" is always well centered.
Germany Nos. 524-527 (the 1m, 2m, 3m and 5m), overprinted with vertical bars and "Osterreich" similar to "e" and "f," were prepared, not issued, but sold to collectors after the definitive Republic issue had been placed in use. Value for set, $70 hinged, $150 never hinged.
Counterfeits exist of Nos. 403-404, 403a-404a and 1m-5m overprints.

For Use in Styria

Germany Nos. 506 to 511, 511A, 511B, 514 to 523 and 529 Ovptd. in Black

1945   Unwmk.   Typo.   *Perf. 14*
Size: 18½x22½mm

405	A115	1pf gray black	1.25 8.00
406	A115	3pf lt brown	.75 8.00
407	A115	4pf slate	4.50 27.50
408	A115	5pf dp yel grn	1.00 8.00
409	A115	6pf purple	.25 1.60
410	A115	8pf red	.25 2.50
411	A115	10pf dark brown	1.00 8.00
412	A115	12pf carmine	.25 2.50

Engr.

413	A115	15pf brown lake	.40 4.00
414	A115	16pf pck green	10.00 65.00
415	A115	20pf blue	1.00 6.50
416	A115	24pf org brn	10.00 65.00

Size: 22½x26mm

417	A115	25pf brt ultra	1.25 8.00
418	A115	30pf olive green	1.25 8.00
419	A115	40pf brt red violet	1.25 8.00
420	A118	42pf brt green	2.00 16.00
421	A115	50pf myrtle green	1.75 12.00
422	A115	60pf dk red brown	1.75 12.00
423	A115	80pf indigo	1.50 12.00
		Nos. 405-423 (19)	41.40 282.60
		Set, never hinged	130.00

Overprinted on Nos. 524-527
Perf. 12½, 14

424	A116	1m dk slate grn	6.50 50.00
a.		Perf. 12½	2,000.
		Never hinged	6,500.
425	A116	2m violet	6.50 50.00
a.		Perf. 14	25.00 80.00
426	A116	3m copper red	40.00 150.00
427	A116	5m dark blue	150.00 1,200.
		Nos. 424-427 (4)	203.00 1,450.
		Set, never hinged	650.00

On the preceding four stamps the innermost vertical lines are 11.1-11.4mm apart; on the pfennig values 6½mm apart.
Counterfeits exist of Nos. 405-427 overprints.

Germany Nos. 524 to 527 Overprinted in Black

Perf. 14

428	A116	1m dk slate grn	9.00 50.00
429	A116	2m violet	12.50 60.00

Perf. 12½

430	A116	3m copper red	15.00 90.00
431	A116	5m dark blue	100.00 650.00
		Nos. 428-431 (4)	136.50 850.00
		Set, never hinged	400.00

On the preceding four stamps, "Osterreich" is thinner, measuring 16mm. On the previous set of 23 values it measures 18mm.
Counterfeits exist of Nos. 428-431 overprints.

Catalogue values for unused stamps in this section, from this point to the end of the section, are for Never Hinged items.

For Use in Vienna, Lower Austria and Burgenland

Coat of Arms
A99   A100

Typographed or Lithographed
1945, July 3   Unwmk.   *Perf. 14x13½*
Size: 21x25mm

432	A99	3pf brown	.25 .25
433	A99	4pf slate	.25 .25
434	A99	5pf dark green	.25 .25
435	A99	6pf deep violet	.25 .25
436	A99	8pf orange brown	.25 .25
437	A99	10pf deep brown	.25 .25
438	A99	12pf rose carmine	.25 .25
439	A99	15pf orange red	.25 .25
440	A99	16pf dull blue green	.25 .25

Perf. 14
Size: 24x28½mm

441	A99	20pf light blue	.25 .25
442	A99	24pf orange	.25 .25
443	A99	25pf dark blue	.25 .25
444	A99	30pf deep gray grn	.25 .25
445	A99	38pf ultramarine	.25 .25
446	A99	40pf brt red vio	.25 .25
447	A99	42pf sage green	.25 .25
448	A99	50pf blue green	.25 .25
449	A99	60pf maroon	.25 .25
450	A99	80pf dull lilac	.25 .30

Engr.   *Perf. 14x13½*

451	A100	1m dark green	.25 .25
452	A100	2m dark purple	.25 .25
453	A100	3m dark violet	.25 .25
454	A100	5m brown red	.30 .30
		Nos. 432-454 (23)	5.80 5.85

Nos. 432, 433, 437, 439, 440, 443, 446, 448, 449 are typographed. Nos. 434, 435, 441. 442 are lithographed; the other values exist both ways.
For overprint see No. 604.

For General Use

Lermoos, Winter Scene — A101   The Prater Woods, Vienna — A105

Wolfgang See, near Salzburg A106   Lake Constance A110

Dürnstein, Lower Austria A124

Designs: 4g, Eisenerz surface mine. 5g, Leopoldsberg, near Vienna. 6g, Hohen-salzburg, Salzburg Province. 10g, Hochos-terwitz, Carinthia. 15g, Forchtenstein Castle, Burgenland. 16g, Gesäuse Valley. 24g, Höl-drichs Mill, Lower Austria. 25g, Oetz Valley Outlet, Tyrol. 30g, Neusiedler Lake, Burgen-land. 35g, Belvedere Palace, Vienna. 38g, Langbath Lake. 40g, Mariazell, Styria. 42g, Traunkirchen. 45g, Hartenstein Castle. 50g, Silvretta Mountains, Vorarlberg. 60g, Railroad viaducts near Semmering.

70g, Waterfall of Bad-Gastein, Salzburg. 80g, Kaiser Mountains, Tyrol. 90g, Wayside Shrine, Tragöss, Styria. 2s, St. Christof am Arlberg, Tyrol. 3s, Heiligenblut, Carinthia. 5s, Schönbrunn, Vienna.

Perf. 14x13½

			Unwmk.	
1945-46		**Photo.**		
455	A101	3g sapphire	.25	.25
456	A101	4g dp orange ('46)	.25	.25
457	A101	5g dk carmine rose	.25	.25
458	A101	6g dk slate green	.25	.25
459	A105	8g golden brown	.25	.25
460	A106	10g dark green	.25	.25
461	A106	12g dark brown	.25	.25
462	A106	15g dk slate bl ('46)	.25	.25
463	A106	16g chnt brn ('46)	.25	.25

Perf. 13½x14

464	A110	20g dp ultra ('46)	.25	.25
465	A110	24g dp yellow grn ('46)	.25	.25
466	A110	25g gray black ('46)	.25	.25
467	A110	30g dark red ('46)	.25	.25
468	A110	35g brown red ('46)	.25	.25
469	A110	38g brn olive ('46)	.25	.25
470	A110	40g gray	.25	.25
471	A110	42g brn org ('46)	.25	.25
472	A110	45g dark blue ('46)	.35	1.60
473	A110	50g dark blue	.25	.25
474	A110	60g dark violet ('46)	.25	.25
a.		Imperf., pair	75.00	85.00
475	A110	70g Prus blue ('46)	.25	.40
476	A110	80g brown	.35	.55
477	A110	90g Prussian green	.80	2.40
478	A124	1s dk red brn ('46)	.80	.80
479	A124	2s blue gray ('46)	2.40	4.50
480	A124	3s dk slate grn ('46)	1.00	5.00
481	A124	5s dark red ('46)	1.60	4.00
		Nos. 455-481 (27)	12.30	24.00

See Nos. 482, 486-488, 496-515. For over-prints and surcharges see Nos. 492-493, B166, B280, B287.

No. 461 Overprinted in Carmine

1946, Sept. 26
482 A106 12g dark brown .40 .40
Meeting of the Soc. for Cultural and Eco-nomic Relations with the USSR, Vienna, Sept. 26-29.

City Hall Park, Vienna
A128

Hochosterwitz, Carinthia
A129

Perf. 14x13½

			Unwmk.	
1946-47		**Photo.**		
483	A128	8g deep plum	.25	.25
484	A128	8g olive brown	.25	.25
a.		8g dark olive green		
485	A129	10g dk brn vio ('47)	.25	.25

Perf. 13½x14

486	A110	30g blue gray ('47)	.40	.40
487	A110	50g brown violet ('47)	.80	.80
488	A110	60g violet blue ('47)	2.50	2.50
		Nos. 483-488 (6)	4.45	4.45

See No. 502.

Franz Grillparzer
A130

1947 **Engr.** **Perf. 14x13½**
489 A130 18g chocolate .40 .40

Photo.
490 A130 18g dk violet brn .65 .65
Death of Grillparzer, dramatic poet, 75th anniv.
A second printing of No. 490 on thicker paper was made in June 1947. It has a darker frame and clearer delineation of the portrait.
Issue dates: No. 489, Feb. 10; No. 490, Mar. 31.

Franz Schubert — A131

1947, Mar. 31 **Engr.**
491 A131 12g dark green .40 .65
150th birth anniv. of Franz Schubert, musi-cian and composer.

Nos. 469 and 463 Surcharged in Brown

1947, Sept. 1 **Photo.** **Perf. 14**
492 A110 75g on 38g brown ol .25 .85
493 A106 1.40s on 16g chnt brn .25 .45
The surcharge on No. 493 varies from brown to black brown.

Symbols of Global Telegraphic Communication A132

1947, Nov. 5 **Engr.** **Perf. 14x13½**
495 A132 40g dark violet .40 .40
Centenary of the telegraph in Austria.

Scenic Type of 1946

1946, Aug. **Photo.** **Perf. 13½x14**
496	A124	1s dark brown	1.60	4.00
497	A124	2s dark blue	9.50	4.00
498	A124	3s dark slate green	3.25	4.25
499	A124	5s dark red	40.00	20.00
		Nos. 496-499 (4)	54.35	32.25

On Nos. 478 to 481 the upper and lower panels show a screen effect. On Nos. 496 to 499 the panels appear to be solid color.

Scenic Types of 1945-46

1947-48 **Photo.** **Perf. 14x13½**
500	A101	3g bright red	.25	.25
501	A101	5g bright red	.25	.25
502	A129	10g bright red	.25	.25
503	A106	15g brt red ('48)	2.00	1.75

Perf. 13½x14

504	A110	20g bright red	.40	.25
505	A110	30g bright red	.40	.25
506	A110	40g bright red	.40	.25
507	A110	50g bright red	.80	.25
508	A110	60g brt red ('48)	9.50	2.00
509	A110	70g brt red ('48)	4.00	.25
510	A110	80g brt red ('48)	4.00	.25
511	A110	90g brt red ('48)	4.75	.80
512	A124	1s dark violet	1.60	.25
513	A124	2s dark violet	1.20	.25
514	A124	3s dk violet ('48)	24.00	2.00
515	A124	5s dk violet ('48)	24.00	2.00
		Nos. 500-515 (16)	77.80	11.30
		Set, hinged	16.00	

Carl Michael Ziehrer (1843-1922), Composer
A133

Designs: No. 517, Adalbert Stifter (1805-68), novelist. No. 518, Anton Bruckner (1824-96), composer. 60g, Friedrich von Amerling (1803-87), painter.

1948-49 **Engr.**
516	A133	20g dull green	.40	.25
517	A133	40g chocolate	8.00	4.50
518	A133	40g dark green	8.00	8.00
519	A133	60g rose brown	.40	.35
		Nos. 516-519 (4)	16.80	13.10

Issue dates: 20g, Jan. 21, No. 517, Sept. 6, No. 518, Sept. 3, 1949, 60g, Jan. 26.

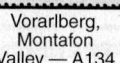

Vorarlberg, Montafon Valley — A134

Costume of Vienna, 1850 — A135

Austrian Costumes: 3g, Tyrol, Inn Valley. 5g, Salzburg, Pinzgau. 10g, Styria, Salzkam-mergut. 15g, Burgenland, Lutzmannsburg. 25g, Vienna, 1850. 30g, Salzburg, Pongau. 40g, Vienna, 1840. 45g, Carinthia, Lesach Valley. 50g, Vorarlberg, Bregenzer Forest. 60g, Carinthia, Lavant Valley. 70g, Lower Aus-tria, Wachau. 75g, Styria, Salzkammergut. 80g, Styria, Enns Valley. 90g, Central Styria. 1s, Tyrol, Puster Valley. 1.20s, Lower Austria, Vienna Woods. 1.40s, Upper Austria, Inn Dis-trict. 1.45s, Wilten. 1.50s, Vienna, 1853. 1.60s, Vienna, 1830. 1.70s, East Tyrol, Kals. 2s, Upper Austria. 2.20s, Ischl, 1820. 2.40s, Kitzbuhel. 2.50s, Upper Steiermark, 1850. 2.70s, Little Walser Valley. 3s, Burgenland. 3.50s, Lower Austria, 1850. 4.50s, Gail Valley. 5s, Ziller Valley. 7s, Steiermark, Sulm Valley.

Perf. 14x13½

			Unwmk.	Photo.
1948-52		**On Toned Paper, with Glossy Yellowish Gum**		
520	A134	3g gray ('50)	.65	.80
521	A134	5g dk grn ('49)	.25	.25
522	A134	10g deep blue	.25	.25
523	A134	15g brown	.40	.25
524	A134	20g yellow green	.25	.25
525	A134	25g brown ('49)	.25	.25
526	A134	30g dk car rose	4.00	.25
527	A134	30g dk vio ('50)	.85	.25
528	A134	40g violet	3.25	.25
529	A134	40g green ('49)	.65	.25
530	A134	45g violet blue	3.25	.40
531	A134	50g org brn ('49)	1.00	.25
532	A134	60g scarlet	.65	.25
533	A134	70g brt bl grn ('49)	.65	.25
534	A134	75g blue	5.50	.40
535	A134	80g car rose ('49)	.95	.25
536	A134	90g brn vio ('49)	45.00	.35
537	A134	1s ultramarine	16.00	
538	A134	1s rose red ('50)	105.00	.25
539	A134	1s dk violet ('50)	.65	.25
540	A134	1.20s violet ('49)	.95	.25
541	A134	1.40s brown	2.40	.25
542	A134	1.45s dk car ('51)	3.25	.25
543	A134	1.50s ultra ('51)	.20	.25
544	A134	1.60s org red ('49)	.65	.25
545	A134	1.70s vio bl ('50)	3.25	.80
546	A134	2s blue green	1.25	.25
547	A134	2.20s slate ('52)	6.50	.25
548	A134	2.40s blue ('51)	2.00	.25
549	A134	2.50s brown ('52)	5.50	3.25
550	A134	2.70s dk brn ('51)	.80	1.60
551	A134	3s brn car ('49)	3.25	.25
552	A134	3.50s dull grn ('51)	24.00	.25
553	A134	4.50s brn vio ('51)	.80	1.60
554	A134	5s dark red vio	1.20	.25
555	A134	7s olive ('52)	4.75	2.40

Engr.
556	A135	10s gray ('50)	40.00	5.50
b.		Flat white gum	275.00	17.50
		Nos. 520-556 (37)	292.00	23.85
		Set, hinged	62.50	

1958-59
On White Paper, with Flat White Gum

521a	A134	5g dk grn	.25	.25
522a	A134	10g deep blue	.25	.25
524a	A134	20g dp yel grn	.25	.25
525a	A134	25g dk brown ('59)	.55	.55
527a	A134	30g dk vio	.80	.25
529a	A134	40g dp bl grn	.65	.25
531a	A134	50g org brn	.95	.25
532a	A134	60g scarlet	.95	.65
533a	A134	70g brt bl grn	.95	.25
535a	A134	80g car rose	.95	.25
540a	A134	1.20s violet	1.60	.25
542a	A134	1.45s dk car	3.25	.65
543a	A134	1.50s ultramarine	4.00	.45
544a	A134	1.60s brn org	4.00	3.00
547a	A134	2.20s slate	6.50	.25
548a	A134	2.40s blue	2.00	.90
549a	A134	2.50s brown	6.50	3.25
551a	A134	3s brn car	4.00	.25
552a	A134	3.50s dull grn	24.00	.25
554a	A134	5s dark red vio ('59)	1.60	.25
555a	A134	7s olive ('59)	4.75	2.40
		Nos. 521a-555a (21)	68.75	15.50
		Set, hinged	15.00	

Designs of the 1958-59 printing are clearer and on most values appear sharper than on the 1948-52 printings.

Pres. Karl Renner — A136

1948, Nov. 12 **Perf. 14x13½**
557 A136 1s deep blue 2.50 2.00
Founding of the Austrian Republic, 30th anniv. See Nos. 573, 636.

Franz Gruber and Josef Mohr
A137

1948, Dec. 18 **Perf. 13½x14**
558 A137 60g red brown 6.00 4.50
130th anniv. of the hymn "Silent Night, Holy Night".

Symbolical of Child Welfare — A138

1949, May 14 **Photo.** **Perf. 14x13½**
559 A138 1s bright blue 12.00 3.25
1st year of activity of UNICEF in Austria.

Johann Strauss, the Younger — A139

Designs: 30g, Johann Strauss, the elder. No. 561, Johann Strauss, the younger. No. 562, Karl Millöcker.

1949

				Engr.
560	A139	30g violet brown	1.60	2.00
561	A139	1s dark blue	3.25	2.25
562	A139	1s dark blue	16.00	12.50
	Nos. 560-562 (3)		20.85	16.75

Johann Strauss, the elder (1804-49), Johann Strauss, the younger (1825-99), and Karl Millöcker (1842-1899), composers. See No. 574.

Issue dates: No. 560, 9/24; No. 561, 6/3; No. 562, 12/31.

Esperanto Star, Olive Branches — A140

1949, June 25 Photo.
563	A140	20g blue green	.95	.95

Austrian Esperanto Congress at Graz.

St. Gebhard — A141

1949, Aug. 6 Engr.
564	A141	30g dark violet	1.60	1.60

St. Gebhard (949-995), Bishop of Vorarlberg.

Letter, Roses and Post Horn A142

UPU, 75th Anniv.: 60g, Plaque. 1s, "Austria," wings and monogram.

1949, Oct. 8 Perf. 13½x14
565	A142	40g dark green	4.00	4.00
566	A142	60g dk carmine	4.00	3.25
567	A142	1s dk violet blue	8.00	7.25
	Nos. 565-567 (3)		16.00	14.50

Andreas Hofer — A143

Moritz Michael Daffinger — A144

Designs: 30g, Alexander Girardi (1850-1918), actor. No. 569, Moritz Michael Daffinger (1790-1849), painter. No. 570, Andreas Hofer (1767-1810), patriot. No. 571, Josef Madersperger (1768-1850), inventor.

1950 Unwmk. Perf. 14x13½
568	A143	30g dark blue	1.60	1.20
569	A144	60g red brown	8.00	6.50
570	A143	60g dark violet	13.00	9.50
571	A143	60g purple	7.25	4.00
	Nos. 568-571 (4)		29.85	21.20

Issue dates: 30g, Dec. 5; No. 569, Jan. 25; No. 570, Feb. 20; No. 571, Oct. 2.

Austrian Stamp of 1850 — A146

1950, May 20 Perf. 14½
572	A146	1s black, *straw*	2.00	1.60

Centenary of Austrian postage stamps.

Renner Type of 1948
Frame and Inscriptions Altered
1951, Mar. 3
573	A136	1s black, *straw*	1.20	.45

In memory of Pres. Karl Renner, 1870-1950.

Strauss Type of 1949
Portrait: 60g, Joseph Lanner.

1951, Apr. 12
574	A139	60g dk blue green	4.75	2.40

Joseph Lanner (1801-43), composer.

Martin Johann Schmidt — A147

1951, June 28 Engr. Perf. 14x13½
575	A147	1sh brown red	6.50	2.40

150th death anniv. of Martin Johann Schmidt, painter.

7th World Scout Jamboree A148

1951, Aug. 3 Engr. and Litho.
576	A148	1sh dk grn, ocher & pink	4.75	4.75

Bad Ischl-St. Wolfgang, Aug. 3-13, 1951.

Wilhelm Kienzl — A149

Josef Schrammel A150

Design: 1s, Karl von Ghega.

1951-52 Engr. Unwmk.
577	A149	1s deep green ('52)	6.50	1.60
578	A149	1.50s indigo	3.25	2.00
579	A150	1.50s violet blue ('52)	6.50	2.00
	Nos. 577-579 (3)		16.25	5.60

Ghega (1802-60), civil engineer; Kienzl (1857-1941), composer; Schrammel (1852-95), composer. See No. 582.

Issued: 1s, 3/2; No. 578, 10/3; No. 579, 3/3.

Breakfast Pavilion, Schönbrunn A151

1952, May 24 Perf. 13½x14
580	A151	1.50s dark green	6.50	2.00

Vienna Zoological Gardens, 200th anniv.

Globe as Dot Over "i" — A152

1952, July 1 Perf. 14x13½
581	A152	1.50s dark blue	6.50	1.20

Formation of the Intl. Union of Socialist Youth Camp, Vienna, July 1-10, 1952.

Type Similar to A150
Portrait: 1s, Nikolaus Lenau.

1952, Aug. 13
582	A150	1s deep green	6.50	1.60

Nikolaus Lenau, pseudonym of Nikolaus Franz Niembsch von Strehlenau (1802-50), poet.

School Girl — A153

1952, Sept. 6
583	A153	2.40s dp violet blue	12.00	2.40

Issued to stimulate letter-writing between Austrian and foreign school children.

Hugo Wolf — A154

1953, Feb. 21 Engr. Perf. 14x13½
587	A154	1.50s dark blue	6.50	1.60

Hugo Wolf, composer, 50th death anniv.

Pres. Theodor Körner — A155

1953, Apr. 24
588	A155	1.50s dk violet blue	6.50	1.20

80th birthday of Pres. Theodor Körner. See Nos. 591, 614.

State Theater, Linz, and Masks A156

1953, Oct. 17 Perf. 13½x14
589	A156	1.50s dark gray	16.00	2.40

State Theater at Linz, 150th anniv.

Child and Christmas Tree — A157

1953, Nov. 30 Perf. 14x13½
590	A157	1s dark green	1.25	.65

See No. 597.

Type Similar to A155
Portrait: 1.50s, Moritz von Schwind.

1954, Jan. 21 Perf. 14x13½
591	A155	1.50s purple	12.00	2.40

Moritz von Schwind, painter, 150th birth anniv.

Karl von Rokitansky A158

1954, Feb. 19
592	A158	1.50s purple	14.50	2.75

Karl von Rokitansky, physician, 150th birth anniv. See No. 595.

Esperanto
Star and
Wreath
A159

Engr. and Photo.
1954, June 5   **Perf. 13½x14**
593 A159 1s dk brown & emer   4.00 .55
Esperanto movement in Austria, 50th anniv.

A160

1954, Aug. 4   Engr.   Perf. 14x13½
594 A160 1s dark blue green 12.00 2.75
300th birth anniv. of Johann Michael
Rottmayr von Rosenbrunn, painter.

Type Similar to A158
Portrait: 1.50s, Carl Auer von Welsbach.
1954, Aug. 4
595 A158 1.50s violet blue   24.00 2.75
25th death anniv. of Carl Auer von Welsbach (1858-1929), chemist.

2nd Intl. Congress
for Catholic
Church Music,
Vienna, Oct. 4-
10 — A161

Organ, St. Florian Monastery and Cherub.

1954, Oct. 2   **Unwmk.**
596 A161 1s brown   2.40 .40

Christmas Type of 1953
1954, Nov. 30
597 A157 1s dark blue   4.00 .55

Arms of
Austria and
Official
Publication
A162

1954, Dec. 18   **Engr.**
598 A162 1s salmon & black   2.40 .40
Austria's State Printing Plant, 150th anniv.,
and Wiener Zeitung, government newspaper,
250th year of publication.

Parliament
Building
A163

Designs: 1s, Western railroad station,
Vienna. 1.45s, Letters forming flag. 1.50s,
Public housing, Vienna. 2.40s, Limberg dam.

1955, Apr. 27   **Perf. 13½x14**
599 A163 70g rose violet   1.60 .80
600 A163 1s deep ultra   4.75 .25
601 A163 1.45s scarlet   9.50 2.75

---

602 A163 1.50s brown   24.00 .40
603 A163 2.40s dk blue green   9.50 5.50
   Nos. 599-603 (5)   49.35 9.70
10th anniv. of Austria's liberation.

Type of 1945
Overprinted in
Blue

1955, May 15   **Perf. 14x13½**
604 A100 2s blue gray   2.40 .65
Signing of the state treaty with the US,
France, Great Britain and Russia, 5/15/55.

Workers of
Three
Races
Climbing
Globe
A164

1955, May 20   **Perf. 13½x14**
605 A164 1s indigo   2.40 2.00
4th congress of the Intl. Confederation of
Free Trade Unions, Vienna, May.

Burgtheater,
Vienna
A165

Design: 2.40s, Opera House, Vienna.

1955, July 25
606 A165 1.50s light sepia   4.00 .40
607 A165 2.40s dark blue   4.75 2.40
Re-opening of the Burgtheater and Opera
House in Vienna.

Symbolic of
Austria's
Desire to
Join the
UN — A166

1955, Oct. 24   **Unwmk.**
608 A166 2.40s green   13.00 3.25
Tenth anniversary of UN.

Wolfgang
Amadeus Mozart,
Birth
Bicent. — A167

1956, Jan. 21   **Perf. 14x13½**
609 A167 2.40s slate blue   4.75 1.20

Symbolic of
Austria's Joining
the UN — A168

1956, Feb. 20
610 A168 2.40s chocolate   10.50 2.00
Austria's admission to the UN.

Globe
Showing
Energy of
the Earth
A169

1956, May 8   **Perf. 13½x14**
611 A169 2.40s deep blue   11.00 2.40
Fifth Intl. Power Conf., Vienna, June 17-23.

Map of Europe
and City
Maps — A170

Photo. and Typo.
1956, June 8   **Perf. 14x13½**
612 A170 1.45s lt grn blk & red 3.25 .80
23rd Intl. Housing and Town Planning Congress, Vienna, July 22-28.

J.B. Fischer von
Erlach, Architect,
300th Birth
Anniv. — A171

1956, July 20   **Engr.**
613 A171 1.50s brown   .80 .80

Körner Type of 1953
1957, Jan. 11
614 A155 1.50s gray black   1.75 1.60
Death of Pres. Theodor Körner.

Dr. Julius
Wagner-Jauregg,
Psychiatrist, Birth
Cent. — A172

1957, Mar. 7   **Perf. 14x13½**
615 A172 2.40s brn violet   4.00 2.40

Anton Wildgans,
Poet, 25th Death
Anniv. — A173

1957, May 3   **Unwmk.**
616 A173 1s violet blue   .55 .55

Old and New
Postal Motor
Coach
A174

1957, June 14   **Perf. 13½x14**
617 A174 1s black, yellow   .55 .55
Austrian Postal Motor Coach Service, 50th
anniv.

Gasherbrum
II and
Glacier
A175

1957, July 27
618 A175 1.50s gray blue   .55 .65
Austrian Karakorum Expedition, which
climbed Mount Gasherbrum II on July 7, 1956.

A176   A177

Designs: 20g, Farmhouse at Mörbisch. 50g,
Heiligenstadt, Vienna. 1s, Mariazell. 1.40s,
County seat, Klagenfurt. 1.50s, Rabenhof
Building, Erdberg, Vienna. 1.80s, The Mint,
Hall, Tyrol. 2s, Christkindl Church. 3.40s,
Steiner Gate, Krems. 4s, Vienna Gate,
Hainburg. 4.50s, Schwechat Airport, Vienna.
5.50s, Chur Gate, Feldkirch. 6s, County seat,
Graz. 6.40s, "Golden Roof," Innsbruck. 10s,
Heidenreichstein Castle.

1957-61   **Litho.   Perf. 14x13½**
                          Size: 20x25mm
618A A176 20g violet blk
                    ('61)   .25 .25
619 A176 50g bluish blk
                    ('59)   .40 .25
                          Engr.
620 A176 1s chocolate   1.60 .55
                          Typo.
621 A176 1s chocolate   1.60 .65
                          Litho.
622 A176 1s choc ('59)   .40 .25
622A A176 1.40s brt greenish
              bl ('60)   .40 .25
623 A176 1.50s rose lake
              ('58)   .40 .25
624 A176 1.80s brt ultra ('60)   .40 .25
625 A176 2s dull blue
                    ('58)   3.00 .25
626 A176 3.40s yel grn ('60)   1.60 1.20
627 A176 4s brt red lil
                    ('60)   1.75 .25
627A A176 4.50s dl green ('60)   2.00 1.20
628 A176 5.50s grnsh gray
                    ('60)   1.60 1.20
629 A176 6s brt vio ('60)   1.60 .80
629A A176 6.40s brt blue ('60)   2.75 2.75
                          Engr.
                          Size: 22x28mm
630 A177 10s dk bl grn   2.75 1.00
   Nos. 618A-630 (16)   22.50 11.35
Of the three 1s stamps above, Nos. 620 and
621 have two names in imprint (designer H.

Strohofer, engraver G. Wimmer). No. 622 has
only Strohofer's name.
  Values for Nos. 618A-624, 626-630 are for
stamps on white paper. Most denominations
also come on grayish paper with yellowish
gum.
  See Nos. 688-702.

1960-65   Photo.   Perf. 14½x14
Size: 17x21mm
630A A176 50g slate ('64)   .25   .25
Size: 18x21½mm
630B A176 1s chocolate   .25   .25
Size: 17x21mm
630C A176 1.50s dk car ('65)   .35   .25
  Nos. 630A-630C (3)   .85   .75
Nos. 630A-630C issued in sheets and coils.

Graukogel,
Badgastein
A180

1958, Feb. 1   Engr.   Perf. 14x13½
631 A180 1.50s dark blue   .45   .45
  Intl. Ski Federation Alpine championships,
Badgastein, Feb. 2-7.

Plane over
Map of
Austria
A181

1958, Mar. 27   Perf. 13½x14
632 A181 4s red   .80   .80
  Re-opening of Austrian Airlines.

Mother and
Daughter — A182

1958, May 8   Unwmk.   Perf. 14x13½
633 A182 1.50s dark blue   .45   .45
  Issued for Mother's Day.

Walther von der
Vogelweide
A183

1958, July 17   Litho. and Engr.
634 A183 1.50s multicolored   .45   .45
  3rd Austrian Song Festival, Vienna, 7/17-20.

Oswald Redlich
(1858-1944),
Historian — A184

1958, Sept. 17   Engr.
635 A184 2.40s ultramarine   .65   .45

Renner Type of 1948
1958, Nov. 12
636 A136 1.50s deep green   .65   .65
  Austrian Republic, 40th anniv.

Giant "E" on
Map — A185

1959, Mar. 9
637 A185 2.40s emerald   1.20   .55
  Idea of a United Europe.

Cigarette Machine
and Trademark of
Tobacco
Monopoly — A186

1959, May 8   Unwmk.   Perf. 13½
638 A186 2.40s dark olive bister .45 .40
  Austrian tobacco monopoly, 175th anniv.

Archduke
Johann — A187

1959, May 11   Perf. 14x13½
639 A187 1.50s deep green   .45   .45
  Archduke Johann of Austria, military leader
and humanitarian, death cent.

Capercaillie
A188

  Animals: 1.50s, Roe buck. 2.40s, Wild boar.
3.50s, Red deer, doe and fawn.
1959, May 20   Engr.
640 A188 1s rose violet   .25   .25
641 A188 1.50s blue violet   .45   .45
642 A188 2.40s dk bl green   .65   .65
643 A188 3.50s dark brown   .65   .65
  Nos. 640-643 (4)   2.00 2.00
  Congress of the Intl. Hunting Council,
Vienna, May 20-24.

Joseph Haydn
(1732-1809),
Composer
A189

1959, May 30   Unwmk.
644 A189 1.50s violet brown   .45   .45

Coat of Arms,
Tyrol — A190

1959, June 13   Perf. 14x13½
645 A190 1.50s rose red   .45   .45
  Fight for liberation of Tyrol, 150th anniv.

Antenna,
Zugspitze — A191

1959, June 19   Perf. 13½
646 A191 2.40s dk bl grn   .45   .45
  Inauguration of Austria's relay system.

Field Ball
Player — A192

  1s, Runner. 1.80s, Gymnast on vaulting
horse. 2s, Woman hurdler. 2.20s, Hammer
thrower.

1959-70   Engr.   Perf. 14x13½
647 A192   1s lilac   .35   .25
648 A192 1.50s blue green   .55   .45
648A A192 1.80s carmine ('62) .35   .35
648B A192   2s rose lake ('70).25   .25
648C A192 2.20s bluish blk ('67).35 .35
  Nos. 647-648C (5)   1.85 1.65

Orchestral
Instruments
A193

1959, Aug. 19   Litho. and Engr.
**   Perf. 14x13½**
649 A193 2.40s dull bl & blk   .45   .45
  World tour of the Vienna Philharmonic
Orchestra.

Family
Fleeing over
Mountains
A194

1960, Apr. 7   Engr.   Perf. 13½x14
650 A194 3s Prussian green   .55   .80
  WRY, July 1, 1959-June 30, 1960.

President Adolf
Schärf — A195

1960, Apr. 20   Perf. 14x13½
651 A195 1.50s gray olive   .45   .45
  Pres. Adolf Scharf, 70th birthday.

Young
Hikers and
Hostel
A196

1960, May 20   Perf. 13½x14
652 A196 1s carmine rose   .40   .40
  Youth hiking; youth hostel movement.

Anton Eiselsberg,
Surgeon, Birth
Cent. — A197

**   Litho. and Engr.**
1960, June 20   Perf. 14x13½
653 A197 1.50s buff & dk brn   .65   .40

Gustav Mahler
(1860-1911),
Composer
A198

1960, July 7   Engr.
654 A198 1.50s chocolate   .65   .40

Jakob Prandtauer,
Architect, 300th
Birth
Anniv. — A199

1960, July 16   Unwmk.
655 A199 1.50s Melk Abbey   .65   .40

Gross Glockner
Mountain Road,
25th
Anniv. — A200

1960, Aug. 3
656 A200 1.80s dark blue   1.25 .40

Ionic
Capital — A201

1960, Aug. 29   Perf. 14x13½
657 A201 3s black   1.25 1.25
Europa: Idea of a United Europe.

Griffen,
Carinthia
A202

1960, Oct. 10   Engr.   Perf. 13½x14
658 A202 1.50s slate green   .40 .40
40th anniv. of the plebiscite which kept
Carinthia with Austria.

Flame and Broken
Chain — A203

1961, May 8   Unwmk.   Perf. 14x13½
659 A203 1.50s scarlet   .35 .25
Victims in Austria's fight for freedom.

First
Austrian
Mail Plane,
1918
A204

1961, May 15   Perf. 13½x14
660 A204 5s violet blue   .95 .55
Airmail Phil. Exhib., LUPOSTA 1961,
Vienna, May.

Transportation by
Road, Rail and
Waterway
A205

Engraved and Typographed
1961, May 29   Perf. 13½
661 A205 3s rose red & olive   .80 .55
13th European Conference of Transportation ministers, Vienna, May 29-31.

Society of
Creative Artists,
Künstlerhaus,
Vienna,
Cent. — A206

Designs: 1s, Mountain Mower, by Albin
Egger-Lienz. 1.50s, The Kiss, by August von
Pettenkofen. 3s, Girl, by Anton Romako. 5s,
Ariadne's Triumph, by Hans Makart.

1961, June 12 Engr. Perf. 13½x14
Inscriptions in Red Brown
662 A206 1s rose lake   .25 .25
663 A206 1.50s dull violet   .40 .25
664 A206 3s olive green   .80 .95
665 A206 5s blue violet   1.40 .65
  Nos. 662-665 (4)   2.85 2.10

Sonnblick
Mountain and
Observatory
A207

1961, Sept. 1   Perf. 14x13½
666 A207 1.80s violet blue   .40 .35
Sonnblick meteorological observatory, 75th
anniv.

Mercury and
Globe — A208

1961, Sept. 18
667 A208 3s black   .55 .45
Intl. Banking Congress, Vienna, Sept. 1961.
English inscription listing UN financial groups.

Coal Mine
Shaft — A209

Designs: 1.50s, Generator. 1.80s, Iron blast
furnace. 3s, Pouring steel. 5s, Oil refinery.

1961, Sept. 15   Engr.   Perf. 14x13½
668 A209 1s black   .25 .25
669 A209 1.50s green   .25 .25
670 A209 1.80s dark car rose .55 .45
671 A209 3s bright lilac   .65 .55
672 A209 5s blue   .80 .75
  Nos. 668-672 (5)   2.50 2.25
15th anniversary of nationalized industry.

Arms of
Burgenland
A210

1961, Oct. 9   Engr. and Litho.
673 A210 1.50s blk, yel & dk red   .35 .25
Burgenland as part of the Austrian Republic,
40th anniv.

Franz Liszt (1811-
86), Composer
A211

1961, Oct. 20   Engr.
674 A211 3s dark brown   .80 .45

Parliament
A212

1961, Dec. 18   Perf. 13½x14
675 A212 1s brown   .25 .25
Austrian Bureau of Budget, 200th anniv.

Kaprun-Mooserboden
Reservoir — A213

Hydroelectric Power Plants: 1.50s, Ybbs-
Persenbeug dam and locks. 1.80s, Lünersee
dam and reservoir. 3s, Grossraming dam. 4s,
Bisamberg transformer plant. 6.40s, St. Andrä
power plant.

1962, Mar. 26   Unwmk.
676 A213 1s violet blue   .25 .25
677 A213 1.50s red lilac   .30 .25
678 A213 1.80s green   .55 .55
679 A213 3s brown   .55 .40
680 A213 4s rose red   .65 .40
681 A213 6.40s gray   1.20 1.20
  Nos. 676-681 (6)   3.50 3.05
Nationalization of the electric power industry, 15th anniv.

Johann
Nestroy — A214

1962, May 25   Perf. 14x13½
682 A214 1s violet   .35 .35
Johann Nepomuk Nestroy, Viennese playwright, author and actor, death cent.

Friedrich
Gauermann
(1807-1862),
Landscape
Painter — A215

1962, July 6   Engr.
683 A215 1.50s intense blue   .35 .35

Scout Emblem
and Handshake
A216

1962, Oct. 5
684 A216 1.50s dark green   .40 .35
Austria's Boy Scouts, 50th anniv.

Lowlands
Forest
A217

1.50s, Deciduous forest. 3s, Fir & larch
forest.

1962, Oct. 12   Perf. 13½x14
685 A217 1s greenish gray   .40 .40
686 A217 1.50s reddish brown .45 .45
687 A217 3s dk slate green 1.10 1.10
  Nos. 685-687 (3)   1.95 1.95

Buildings Types of 1957-61
Designs: 30g, City Hall, Vienna. 40g, Porcia
Castle, Spittal on the Drau. 60g, Tanners'
Tower, Wels. 70g, Residenz Fountain, Salz-
burg. 80g, Old farmhouse, Pinzgau. 1s,
Romanesque columns, Millstatt Abbey. 1.20s,
Kornmesser House, Bruck on the Mur. 1.30s,
Schatten Castle, Feldkirch, Vorarlberg. 2s,
Dragon Fountain, Klagenfurt. 2.20s, Beetho-
ven House, Vienna. 2.50s, Danube Bridge,
Linz. 3s, Swiss Gate, Vienna. 3.50s, Ester-
hazy Palace, Eisenstadt. 8s, City Hall, Steyr.
20s, Melk Abbey.

1962-70   Litho.   Perf. 14x13½
Size: 20x25mm
688 A176 30g greenish gray   .40 .25
689 A176 40g rose red   .25 .25
690 A176 60g violet brown   .40 .25
691 A176 70g dark blue   .40 .25
692 A176 80g yellow brown   .25 .25
693 A176 1s brown ('70)   .35 .25
694 A176 1.20s red lilac   .40 .25
695 A176 1.30s green ('67)   .40 .40
696 A176 3s dk blue ('68)   .40 .30
697 A176 2.20s green   .80 .30
698 A176 2.50s violet   .80 .30
699 A176 3s bright blue   .90 .25
700 A176 3.50s rose carmine   1.20 .25
701 A176 8s claret ('65)   1.60 .55

Perf. 13½
Engr.
Size: 28x36½mm
702 A177 20s rose claret ('63) 3.50 2.00
  Nos. 688-702 (15)   12.05 6.10
Values for Nos. 688-702 are for stamps on
white paper. Some denominations also come
on grayish paper with yellowish gum.

Electric Locomotive and Train of
1837 — A218

Lithographed and Engraved
1962, Nov. 9   *Perf. 13½x14*
703 A218 3s buff & black   1.20 1.20
125th anniversary of Austrian railroads.

Postilions and Postal Clerk, 1863 — A219

1963, May 7   **Photo.**   *Perf. 14x13½*
704 A219 3s dk brn & citron   .75 .55
First Intl. Postal Conference, Paris, cent.

Hermann Bahr, Writer, Birth Cent. — A220

Lithographed and Envraved
1963, July 19   *Perf. 14x13½*
705 A220 1.50s blue & black   .35 .35

St. Florian Statue, Kefermarkt, Contemporary and Old Fire Engines — A221

1963, Aug. 30   **Unwmk.**
706 A221 1.50s brt rose & blk   .45 .45
Austrian volunteer fire brigades, cent.

Factory, Flag and "ÖGB" on Map of Austria A222

1963, Sept. 23   **Litho.**   *Perf. 13½x14*
707 A222 1.50s gray, red & dk brn .35 .35
5th Congress of the Austrian Trade Union Federation (ÖGB), Sept. 23-28.

Arms of Austria and Tyrol A223

1963, Sept. 27   **Unwmk.**
708 A223 1.50s tan, blk, red & yel .35 .35
Tyrol's union with Austria, 600th anniv.

Prince Eugene of Savoy (1663-1736), Austrian General — A224

1963, Oct. 18   **Engr.**   *Perf. 14x13½*
709 A224 1.50s violet   .35 .35

Intl. Red Cross, Cent. — A225

1963, Oct. 25   **Engr. and Photo.**
710 A225 3s blk, sil & red   .55 .55

Slalom A226

Sports: 1.20s, Biathlon (skier with rifle). 1.50s, Ski jump. 1.80s, Women's figure skating. 2.20s, Ice hockey. 3s, Tobogganing. 4s, Bobsledding.

Photo. and Engr.
1963, Nov. 11   *Perf. 13½x14*
711 A226 1s multi   .25 .25
712 A226 1.20s multi   .25 .25
713 A226 1.50s multi   .35 .35
714 A226 1.80s multi   .35 .35
715 A226 2.20s multi   .45 .45
716 A226 3s multi   .55 .55
717 A226 4s multi   .65 .65
Nos. 711-717 (7)   2.85 2.85
9th Winter Olympic Games, Innsbruck, Jan. 29-Feb. 9, 1964.

Baroque Creche by Josef Thaddäus Stammel — A227

1963, Nov. 29   **Engr.**   *Perf. 14x13½*
718 A227 2s dark Prus green   .40 .40

Flowers A228

1964, Apr. 17   **Litho.**   *Perf. 14*
719 A228 1s Nasturtium   .25 .25
720 A228 1.50s Peony   .35 .35
721 A228 1.80s Clematis   .25 .25
722 A228 2.20s Dahlia   .40 .40
723 A228 3s Morning glory   .65 .65
724 A228 4s Hollyhock   .95 .95
Nos. 719-724 (6)   2.85 2.85
Vienna Intl. Garden Show, Apr. 16-Oct. 11.

St. Mary Magdalene and Apostle — A229

1964, May 21   **Engr.**   *Perf. 13½*
725 A229 1.50s bluish black   .35 .35
Romanesque art in Austria. The 12th century stained-glass window is from the Weitensfeld Church, the bust of the Apostle from the portal of St. Stephen's Cathedral, Vienna.

Pallas Athena and National Council Chamber — A230

Engr. and Litho.
1964, May 25   *Perf. 14x13½*
726 A230 1.80s black & emer   .35 .35
2nd Parliamentary and Scientific Conf., Vienna.

The Kiss, by Gustav Klimt A231

1964, June 5   **Litho.**   *Perf. 13½*
727 A231 3s multicolored   .55 .55
Re-opening of the Vienna Secession, a museum devoted to early 20th century art (art nouveau).

Brother of Mercy and Patient — A232

1964, June 11   **Engr.**   *Perf. 14x13½*
728 A232 1.50s dark blue   .35 .35
Brothers of Mercy in Austria, 350th anniv.

"Bringing the News of Victory at Kunersdorf" by Bernardo Bellotto — A233

"The Post in Art": 1.20s, Changing Horses at Relay Station, by Julius Hörmann. 1.50s, The Honeymoon Trip, by Moritz von Schwind. 1.80s, After the Rain, by Ignaz Raffalt. 2.20s, Mailcoach in the Mountains, by Adam Klein. 3s, Changing Horses at Bavarian Border, by Friedrich Gauermann. 4s, Postal Sleigh (Truck) in the Mountains, by Adalbert Pilch. 6.40s, Saalbach Post Office, by Adalbert Pilch.

1964, June 15   *Perf. 13½x14*
729 A233 1s rose claret   .25 .25
730 A233 1.20s sepia   .25 .25
731 A233 1.50s violet blue   .35 .35
732 A233 1.80s brt violet   .35 .35
733 A233 2.20s black   .40 .40
734 A233 3s dl car rose   .55 .55
735 A233 4s slate green   .65 .65
736 A233 6.40s dull claret   1.40 1.40
Nos. 729-736 (8)   4.20 4.20
15th UPU Cong., Vienna, May-June 1964.

Workers — A234

1964, Sept. 4   *Perf. 14x13½*
737 A234 1s black   .25 .25
Centenary of Austrian Labor Movement.

Common Design Types pictured following the introduction.

Europa Issue, 1964
Common Design Type
1964, Sept. 14   **Litho.**   *Perf. 12*
Size: 21x36mm
738 CD7 3s dark blue   1.20 .80

Emblem of Radio Austria and Transistor Radio Panel A235

1964, Oct. 1   **Photo.**   *Perf. 13½*
739 A235 1s black brn & red   .25 .25
Forty years of Radio Austria.

6th Congress of the Intl. Graphic Federation, Vienna, Oct. 12-17 — A236

Litho. and Engr.
1964, Oct. 12   *Perf. 14x13½*
740 A236 1.50s Old printing press   .35 .35

Dr. Adolf Schärf (1890-1965), Pres. of Austria (1957-65) A237

Pres. Adolf Schärf, Schärf Student Center.

Typo. and Engr.
1965, Apr. 20   *Perf. 12*
741 A237 1.50s bluish black   .35 .25

Ruins and New Buildings — A238

1965, Apr. 27   Engr.   Perf. 14x13½
742 A238 1.80s carmine lake   .35 .35
Twenty years of reconstruction.

Oldest Seal of Vienna University — A239

Photo. and Engr.
1965, May 10   Perf. 14x13½
743 A239 3s gold & red   .55 .55
University of Vienna, 600th anniv.

St. George, 16th Century Wood Sculpture A240

1965, May 17   Engr.
744 A240 1.80s bluish black   .35 .35
Art of the Danube Art School, 1490-1540, exhibition, May-Oct. 1965. The stamp background shows an engraving by Albrecht Altdorfer.

ITU Emblem, Telegraph Key and TV Antenna — A241

1965, May 17   Unwmk.
745 A241 3s violet blue   .55 .55
ITU, cent.

Dr. Ignaz Philipp Semmelweis A242

Ferdinand Raimund — A242a

Portraits: No. 747, Bertha von Suttner. No. 749, Ferdinand Georg Waldmüller.

1965   Engr.   Perf. 14x13½
746 A242   1.50s violet   .35 .25
747 A242   1.50s bluish black   .35 .35
748 A242a 3s dark brown   .55 .55
749 A242a 3s greenish blk   .55 .55
  Nos. 746-749 (4)   1.80 1.70
Semmelweis (1818-65), who discovered the cause of puerperal fever and introduced antisepsis into obstetrics (No. 746). 60th anniv. of the awarding of the Nobel Prize for Peace to von Suttner (1843-1914), pacifist and author (No. 747). Raimund (1790-1836), actor and playwright (No. 748). Waldmüller (1793-1865), painter (No. 749).
Issued: No. 746, Aug. 13; No. 747, Dec. 1; No. 748, June 1; No. 749, Aug. 23.

4th Gymnaestrada, Intl. Athletic Meet, Vienna, July 20-24 — A243

1.50s, Male gymnasts with practice bars. 3s, Dancers with tambourines.

1965, July 20   Photo. and Engr.
750 A243 1.50s gray & black   .35 .35
751 A243 3s bister & blk   .55 .55

Red Cross and Strip of Gauze — A244

1965, Oct. 1   Litho.   Perf. 14x13½
752 A244 3s black & red   .55 .40
20th Intl. Red Cross Conference, Vienna.

Austrian Flag and Eagle with Mural Crown — A245

1965, Oct. 7   Photo. and Engr.
753 A245 1.50s gold, red & blk   .35 .35
50th anniv. of the Union of Austrian Towns.

Austrian Flag, UN Headquarters and Emblem A246

Lithographed and Engraved
1965, Oct. 25   Unwmk.   Perf. 12
754 A246 3s blk, brt bl & red   .55 .40
Austria's admission to the UN, 10th anniv.

University of Technology, Vienna A247

1965, Nov. 8   Engr.   Perf. 13½x14
755 A247 1.50s violet   .35 .35
Vienna University of Technology, 150th anniv.

Map of Austria with Postal Zone Numbers — A248

1966, Jan. 14   Photo.   Perf. 12
756 A248 1.50s yel, red & blk   .35 .35
Introduction of postal zone numbers, 1/1/66.

PTT Building, Emblem and Churches of Sts. Maria Rotunda and Barbara — A249

Lithographed and Engraved
1966, Mar. 4   Perf. 14x13½
757 A249 1.50s blk, dull yellow   .35 .35
Headquarters of the Post and Telegraph Administration, cent.

Maria von Ebner Eschenbach (1830-1916), Novelist, Poet — A250

1966, Mar. 11   Engr.
758 A250 3s plum   .55 .40

Ferris Wheel, Prater — A251

1966, Apr. 19   Engr.   Perf. 14x13½
759 A251 1.50s slate green   .35 .35
Opening of the Prater (park), Vienna, to the public by Emperor Joseph II, 200th anniv.

Josef Hoffmann (1870-1956), Architect A252

1966, May 6   Unwmk.   Perf. 12
760 A252 3s dark brown   .55 .40

Wiener Neustadt Arms — A253

Photo. and Engr.
1966, May 27   Perf. 14
761 A253 1.50s multicolored   .35 .35
Wiener Neustadt Art Exhib., centered around the time and person of Frederick III (1440-93).

Austrian Eagle and Emblem of National Bank A254

1966, May 27   Perf. 14
762 A254 3s gray grn, dk brn & dk green   .55 .55
Austrian National Bank, 150th anniv.

Puppy — A255

Litho. and Engr.
1966, June 16   Perf. 12
763 A255 1.80s yellow & black   .35 .35
120th anniv. of the Vienna Humane Society.

Alpine Flowers — A256

1.50s, Columbine. 1.80s, Turk's cap. 2.20s, Wulfenia carinthiaca. 3s, Globeflowers. 4s, Fire lily. 5s, Pasqueflower.

1966, Aug. 17   Litho.   Perf. 13½
Flowers in Natural Colors
764 A256 1.50s dark blue   .35 .35
765 A256 1.80s dark blue   .35 .35
766 A256 2.20s dark blue   .40 .40
767 A256 3s dark blue   .55 .50
768 A256 4s dark blue   .55 .50
769 A256 5s dark blue   1.00 1.00
  Nos. 764-769 (6)   3.20 3.10

Fair Building A257

1966, Aug. 26   Engr.   Perf. 13½x13
770 A257 3s violet blue   .55 .40
First International Fair at Wels.

Peter Anich (1723-1766), Tirolean Cartographer and Books — A258

1966, Sept. 1   *Perf. 14x13½*
771 A258 1.80s black   .35   .35

Sick Worker and Health Emblem — A259

1966, Sept. 19   **Engr. and Litho.**
772 A259 3s black & vermilion   .55   .40
15th Occupational Medicine Congress, Vienna, Sept. 19-24.

Theater Collection: "Eunuchus" by Terence from a 1496 Edition A260

Designs: 1.80s, Map Collection: Title page of Geographia Blavania (Cronus, Hercules and celestial sphere). 2.20s, Picture Archive and Portrait Collection: View of Old Vienna after a watercolor by Anton Stutzinger. 3s, Manuscript Collection: Illustration from the 15th century "Livre du Cuer d'Amours Espris" of the Duke René d'Anjou.

Photogravure and Engraved
1966, Sept. 28   *Perf. 13½x14*
773 A260 1.50s multicolored   .35   .40
774 A260 1.80s multicolored   .35   .40
775 A260 2.20s multicolored   .35   .40
776 A260 3s multicolored   .55   .80
    Nos. 773-776 (4)   1.60 2.00
Austrian National Library.

Young Girl — A261

Litho. and Engr.
1966, Oct. 3   *Perf. 14x13½*
777 A261 3s light blue & black   .55   .40
"Save the Child" society, 10th anniv.

Strawberries — A262

1966, Nov. 25   **Photo.**   *Perf. 13½x13*
778 A262 50g shown   .25   .25
779 A262 1s Grapes   .25   .25
780 A262 1.50s Apple   .35   .25
781 A262 1.80s Blackberries   .40   .40
782 A262 2.20s Apricots   .50   .50
783 A262 3s Cherries   .55   .55
    Nos. 778-783 (6)   2.30 2.20

Coat of Arms of University of Linz — A263

Photo. and Engr.
1966, Dec. 9   *Perf. 14x13½*
784 A263 3s multi   .55   .40
Inauguration of the Universary of Linz, Oct. 8, 1966.

Vienna Ice Skating Club, Cent. — A264

Photo. and Engr.
1967, Feb. 3   *Perf. 14x13½*
785 A264 3s Skater, 1866   .55   .40

Ballet Dancer — A265

1967, Feb. 15   **Engr.**   *Perf. 11½x12*
786 A265 3s deep claret   .75   .75
  a.   Perf. 12   2.40 2.40
"Blue Danube" waltz by Johann Strauss, cent.

Dr. Karl Schönherr (1867-1943), Poet, Playwright and Physician — A266

1967, Feb. 24   **Engr.**   *Perf. 14x13½*
787 A266 3s gray brown   .55   .40

Ice Hockey Goalkeeper A267

Photogravure and Engraved
1967, Mar. 17   *Perf. 13½x14*
788 A267 3s pale grn & dk bl   .55   .65
Ice Hockey Championships, Vienna, Mar. 18-29.

Violin, Organ and Laurel — A268

1967, Mar. 28   **Engr.**   *Perf. 13½*
789 A268 3.50s indigo   .55   .40
Vienna Philharmonic Orchestra, 125th anniv.

Motherhood, Watercolor by Peter Fendi — A269

1967, Apr. 28   **Litho.**   *Perf. 14*
790 A269 2s multicolored   .40   .40
Mother's Day.

Gothic Mantle Madonna A270

1967, May 19   **Engr.**   *Perf. 13½x14*
791 A270 3s slate   .55   .40
"Austrian Gothic," art exhibition, Krems, 1967. The Gothic wood carving is from Frauenstein in Upper Austria.

Medieval Gold Cross — A271

Litho. and Engr.
1967, June 9   *Perf. 13½*
792 A271 3.50s Prus grn & multi   .55   .40
Salzburg Treasure Chamber; exhibition at Salzburg Cathedral, June 12-Sept. 15.

Swan, Tapestry by Oscar Kokoschka — A272

1967, June 9   **Photo.**
793 A272 2s multicolored   .40   .40
Nibelungen District Art Exhibition, Pöchlarn, celebrating the 700th anniversary of Pöchlarn as a city. The design is from the border of the Amor and Psyche tapestry at the Salzburg Festival Theater.

View and Arms of Vienna A273

Engraved and Photogravure
1967, June 12   *Perf. 14x13½*
794 A273 3s black & red   .55   .40
10th Europa Talks, "Science and Society in Europe," Vienna, June 13-17.

Prize Bull "Mucki" A274

1967, Aug. 28   **Engr.**   *Perf. 13½*
795 A274 2s deep claret   .35   .35
Centenary of the Ried Festival and the Agricultural Fair.

Potato Beetle A275

Engraved and Photogravure
1967, Aug. 29   *Perf. 13½x14*
796 A275 3s black & multi   .55   .40
6th Intl. Congress for Plant Protection, Vienna.

First Locomotive Used on Brenner Pass A276

1967, Sept. 23   **Photo.**   *Perf. 12*
797 A276 3.50s tan & slate grn   .55   .40
Centenary of railroad over Brenner Pass.

Christ in Glory — A277

1967, Oct. 9   *Perf. 13½*
798 A277 2s multicolored   .35   .35
Restoration of the Romanesque (11th century) frescoes in the Lambach monastery church.

Main Gate to Fair, Prater, Vienna A278

1967, Oct. 24   **Photo.**   *Perf. 13½x14*
799 A278 2s choc & buff   .25   .35
Congress of Intl. Trade Fairs, Vienna, Oct., 1967.

Medal Showing Minerva and Art Symbols — A279

Litho. & Engr.
1967, Oct. 25   **Perf. 13½**
800 A279 2s dk brn, dk bl & yel   .25   .35
Vienna Academy of Fine Arts, 275th anniv. The medal was designed by Georg Raphael Donner (1693-1741) and is awarded as an artist's prize.

Frankfurt Medal for Reformation, 1717 — A280

1967, Oct. 31   Engr.   Perf. 14x13½
801 A280 3.50s blue black   .55   .35
450th anniversary of the Reformation.

Mountain Range and Stone Pines A281

1967, Nov. 7   **Perf. 13½**
802 A281 3.50s green   .55   .40
Centenary of academic study of forestry.

Land Survey Monument, 1770 — A282

1967, Nov. 7   **Photo.**
803 A282 2s olive black   .25   .35
150th anniversary of official land records.

St. Leopold, Window, Heiligenkreuz Abbey — A283

1967, Nov. 15   Engr. & Photo.
804 A283 1.80s multicolored   .25   .35
Margrave Leopold III (1075-1136), patron saint of Austria.

Tragic Mask and Violin — A284

1967, Nov. 17   **Perf. 13½**
805 A284 3.50s bluish lil & blk   .55   .55
Academy of Music and Dramatic Art, 150th anniv.

Nativity from 15th Century Altar — A285

1967, Nov. 27   Engr.   Perf. 14x13½
806 A285 2s green   .35   .35
Christmas.
The design shows the late Gothic carved center panel of the altar in St. John's Chapel in Nonnberg Convent, Salzburg.

Innsbruck Stadium, Alps and FISU Emblem — A286

1968, Jan. 22   Engr.   Perf. 13½
807 A286 2s dark blue   .40   .35
Winter University Games under the auspices of FISU (Fédération Internationale du Sport Universitaire), Innsbruck, Jan. 21-28.

Camillo Sitte (1843-1903), Architect, City Planner — A287

1968, Apr. 17   **Perf. 13½**
808 A287 2s black brown   .25   .35

Mother and Child — A288

1968, May 7
809 A288 2s slate green   .25   .35
Mother's Day.

Cup and Serpent Emblem — A289

1968, May 7   **Photo.**
810 A289 3.50s dp plum, gray & gold   .55   .35
Bicentenary of the Veterinary College.

Bride with Lace Veil — A290

1968, May 24   Engr.   Perf. 12
811 A290 3.50s blue black   .55   .35
Embroidery industry of Vorarlberg, cent.

Horse Race A291

1968, June 4   **Perf. 13½**
812 A291 3.50s sepia   .55   .40
Centenary of horse racing at Freudenau, Vienna.

Dr. Karl Landsteiner A292

1968, June 14   **Perf. 14x13½**
813 A292 3.50s dark blue   .55   .35
Birth cent. of Dr. Karl Landsteiner (1868-1943), pathologist, discoverer of the four main human blood types.

Peter Rosegger (1843-1918), Poet and Writer — A293

1968, June 26
814 A293 2s slate green   .25   .35

Angelica Kauffmann, Self-portrait A294

1968, July 15   Engr.   Perf. 14x13½
815 A294 2s intense black   .35   .35
"Angelica Kauffmann and her Contemporaries," art exhibitions, Bregenz, July 28-Oct. 13, and Vienna, Oct. 22, 1968-Jan. 6, 1969.

Bronze Statue of Young Man, 1st Century B.C. — A295

1968, July 15   Litho. & Engr.
816 A295 2s grnsh gray & blk   .25   .35
20 years of excavations on Magdalene Mountain, Carinthia.

Bishop, Romanesque Bas-relief — A296

1968, Sept. 20   Engr.   Perf. 14x13½
817 A296 2s blue gray   .35   .35
Graz-Seckau Bishopric, 750th anniv.

Koloman Moser (1868-1918), Stamp Designer, Painter — A297

Engr. & Photo.
1968, Oct. 18   **Perf. 12**
818 A297 2s black brn & ver   .35   .35

Intl. Human Rights Year — A298

1968, Oct. 18   Photo.   Perf. 14x13½
819 A298 1.50s gray, dp car & dk green   .55   .35

Republic of Austria, 50th Anniv. — A299

Designs: No. 820, Pres. Karl Renner and States' arms. No. 821, Coats of arms of Austria and Austrian states. No. 822, Article I of Austrian Constitution and States' coats of arms.

Engr. & Photo.
1968, Nov. 11   **Perf. 13½**
820 A299 2s black & multi   .40   .45
821 A299 2s black & multi   .40   .45
822 A299 2s black & multi   .40   .45
   Nos. 820-822 (3)   1.20 1.35

Hymn "Silent
Night, Holy Night,"
150th
Anniv. — A300

Crèche, Memorial Chapel, Oberndorf-
Salzburg.

1968, Nov. 29   Engr.   Perf. 14x13½
823 A300 2s slate green   .35   .35
Christmas.

Angels, from Last Judgment by Troger
(Röhrenbach-Greillenstein
Chapel) — A301

Baroque Frescoes: No. 825, Vanquished
Demons, by Paul Troger, Altenburg Abbey. No.
826, Sts. Peter and Paul, by Troger, Melk
Abbey. No. 827, The Glorification of Mary, by
Franz Anton Maulbertsch, Maria Treu Church,
Vienna. No. 828, St. Leopold Carried into
Heaven, by Maulbertsch, Ebenfurth Castle
Chapel. No. 829, Symbolic figures from The
Triumph of Apollo, by Maulbertsch, Halbthurn
Castle.

Engr. & Photo.
1968, Dec. 11   Perf. 13½x14
824 A301 2s multicolored   .40   .40
825 A301 2s multicolored   .40   .40
826 A301 2s multicolored   .40   .40
827 A301 2s multicolored   .40   .40
828 A301 2s multicolored   .40   .40
829 A301 2s multicolored   .40   .40
    Nos. 824-829 (6)   2.40 2.40

St.
Stephen — A302

Statues in St. Stephen's Cathedral, Vienna:
No. 831, St. Paul. No. 832, Mantle Madonna.
No. 833, St. Christopher. No. 834, St. George
and the Dragon. No. 835, St. Sebastian.

1969, Jan. 28   Engr.   Perf. 13½
830 A302 2s black   .40   .40
831 A302 2s rose claret   .40   .40
832 A302 2s gray violet   .40   .40
833 A302 2s slate blue   .40   .40
834 A302 2s slate green   .40   .40
835 A302 2s dk red brn   .40   .40
    Nos. 830-835 (6)   2.40 2.40

500th anniversary of Diocese of Vienna.

Parliament
and Pallas
Athena
Fountain,
Vienna
A303

1969, Apr. 8   Engr.   Perf. 13½
836 A303 2s greenish black   .25   .30
Interparliamentary Union Conf., Vienna,
4/7-13.

Europa Issue, 1969
Common Design Type
1969, Apr. 28   Photo.   Perf. 12
837 CD12 2s gray grn, brick red
         & blue   .65   .30

Council of
Europe
Emblem
A304

1969, May 5
838 A304 3.50s gray, ultra, blk &
         yel   .55   .30
20th anniversary of Council of Europe.

Frontier
Guards — A305

Engr. & Photo.
1969, May 14   Perf. 12
839 A305 2s sepia & red   .35   .35
Austrian Federal Army.

Don Giovanni, by Mozart — A306

Cent. of Vienna Opera House: a, Don Giovanni, Mozart. b, Magic Flute, Mozart. c, Fide-
lio, Beethoven. d, Lohengrin, Wagner. e, Don
Carlos, Verdi. f, Carmen, Bizet. g, Rosen-
cavalier, Richard Strauss. h, Swan Lake, Ballet by Tchaikovsky.

1969, May 23   Perf. 13½
840   A306 Sheet of 8   4.75 4.75
 a.-h.   2s, any single   .50   .50
Centenary of Vienna Opera House.
  No. 840 contains 8 stamps arranged around
gold and red center label showing Opera
House. Printed in sheets containing 4 Nos.
840 with wide gutters between.

Emperor
Maximilian I
Exhibition,
Innsbruck, May
30-Oct.
5 — A307

Gothic armor of Maximilian I.

1969, June 4   Engr.
841 A307 2s bluish black   .35   .35

19th Cong. of the
Intl. Org. of
Municipalities,
Vienna — A308

Oldest Municipal Seal of Vienna.

1969, June 16   Photo.   Perf. 13½
842 A308 2s tan, red & black   .25   .35

SOS Children's
Villages in
Austria, 20th
Anniv. — A309

Girl's head and village house.

Engraved and Photogravure
1969, June 16   Perf. 13½x14
843 A309 2s yel grn & sepia   .25   .35

ILO, 50th
Anniv. — A310

Hands holding wrench, and UN emblem.

1969, Aug. 22 Photo.   Perf. 13x13½
844 A310 2s deep green   .25   .35

Year of Austrians
Living Abroad,
1969 — A311

Austria's flag and shield circling the world.

Engraved and Lithographed
1969, Aug. 22   Perf. 14x13½
845 A311 3.50s slate & red   .55   .35

Etching
Collection in the
Albertina,
Vienna,
Bicent. — A312

Etchings: No. 846, Young Hare, by Dürer.
No. 847, El Cid Killing a Bull, by Francisco de
Goya. No. 848, Madonna with the Pomegran-
ate, by Raphael. No. 849, The Painter, by
Peter Brueghel. No. 850, Rubens' Son Nico-
las, by Rubens. No. 851, Self-portrait, by
Rembrandt. No. 852, Lady Reading, by Fran-
cois Guerin. No. 853, Wife of the Artist, by
Egon Schiele.

Engraved and Photogravure
1969, Sept. 26   Perf. 13½
Gray Frame, Buff Background
846 A312 2s black & brown   .40   .45
847 A312 2s black   .40   .45
848 A312 2s black   .40   .45
849 A312 2s black   .40   .45
850 A312 2s black & salmon   .40   .45
851 A312 2s black   .40   .45
852 A312 2s black & salmon   .40   .45
853 A312 2s black   .40   .45
    Nos. 846-853 (8)   3.20 3.60

President Franz
Jonas — A313

1969, Oct. 3
854 A313 2s gray & vio blue   .25   .35
70th birthday of Franz Jonas, Austrian Pres.

Post Horn,
Globe and
Lightning
A314

1969, Oct. 17   Perf. 13½x14
855 A314 2s multicolored   .25   .35
Union of Postal and Telegraph employees,
50th anniv.

Savings Box, about
1450 — A315

1969, Oct. 31 Photo.   Perf. 13x13½
856 A315 2s silver & slate green .25 .35
The importance of savings.

Madonna, by
Albin Egger-Lienz
A316

Engr. & Photo.
1969, Nov. 24   Perf. 12
857 A316 2s dp claret & pale yel .25 .35
Christmas.

Josef
Schöffel — A317

1970, Feb. 6   Engr.   Perf. 14x13½
858 A317 2s dull purple   .25   .25
60th death anniv. of Josef Schöffel, (1832-
1910), who saved the Vienna Woods.

St. Klemens M.
Hofbauer — A318

Engraved and Photogravure
1970, Mar. 13   Perf. 14x13½
859 A318 2s dk brn & lt tan   .25 .25

150th death anniv. St. Klemens Maria
Hofbauer (1751-1820); Redemptorist preacher
in Poland and Austria, canonized in 1909.

Chancellor Leopold Figl — A319

Belvedere Palace, Vienna — A320

1970, Apr. 27   Engr.   Perf. 13½
860 A319 2s dark olive gray   .35 .25
861 A320 2s dark rose brown   .35 .25

25th anniversary of Second Republic.

European
Nature
Conservation
Year,
1970 — A321

1970, May 19   Engr.   Perf. 13½
862 A321 2s Krimml waterfalls   .40 .25

Leopold
Franzens
University,
Innsbruck, 300th
Anniv. — A322

St. Leopold on oldest seal of Innsbruck
University.

Litho. & Engr.
1970, June 5   Perf. 13½
863 A322 2s red & black   .25 .25

Organ, Great Hall, Music
Academy — A323

Photo. & Engr.
1970, June 5   Perf. 14
864 A323 2s gold & deep claret   .25 .25
Vienna Music Academy Building, cent.

Tower Clock,
1450-1550
A324

Old Clocks from Vienna Horological
Museum: No. 866, Lyre clock, 1790-1815. No.
867, Pendant clock 1600-50. No. 868, Pendant
watch, 1800-30. No. 869, Bracket clock, 1720-
60. No. 870, French column clock, 1820-50.

1970
865 A324 1.50s buff & sepia   .35 .35
866 A324 1.50s greenish & grn   .25 .35
867 A324 2s pale bl & dk bl   .40 .40
868 A324 2s pale rose & lake   .35 .45
869 A324 3.50s buff & brown   .70 .70
870 A324 3.50s pale lil & brn vio   .55 .80
        Nos. 865-870 (6)   2.60 3.05

Issued: Nos. 865, 867, 869, 6/22; others,
10/23.

The Beggar
Student, by Carl
Millöcker — A325

Operettas: No. 872, Fledermaus, by Johann
Strauss. No. 873, The Dream Waltz, by Oscar
Straus. No. 874, The Bird Seller, by Carl
Zeller. No. 875, The Merry Widow, by Franz
Lehar. No. 876, Two Hearts in Three-quarter
Time, by Robert Stolz.

1970   Photo. & Engr.   Perf. 13½
871 A325 1.50s pale grn & grn   .35 .35
872 A325 1.50s yel & vio blue   .25 .25
873 A325 2s pale rose & vio
                 brn   .40 .40
874 A325 2s pale grn & sep   .35 .35
875 A325 3.50s pale bl & ind   .70 .70
876 A325 3.50s beige & slate   .55 .45
        Nos. 871-876 (6)   2.60 2.50

Issued: Nos. 871, 873, 875, 7/3; others 9/11.

Bregenz
Festival
Stage — A326

1970, July 23   Photo.
877 A326 3.50s dark blue & buff   .55 .40
25th anniversary of Bregenz Festival.

Salzburg
Festival
Emblem — A327

1970, July 27   Perf. 14
878 A327 3.50s blk, red, gold &
                 gray   .55 .40
50th anniversary of Salzburg Festival.

A328

1970, Aug. 31   Engr.
879 A328 3.50s dark gray   .55 .35

13th General Assembly of the World Veter-
ans Federation, Aug. 28-Sept. 4. The head of
St. John is from a sculpture showing the
Agony in the Garden in the chapel of the Par-
ish Church in Ried. It is attributed to Thomas
Schwanthaler (1634-1702).

Thomas Koschat
(1845-1914),
Carinthian Song
Composer
A329

1970, Sept. 16   Perf. 14x13½
880 A329 2s chocolate   .25 .25

Mountain
Scene
A330

1970, Sept. 16 Photo. Perf. 14x13½
881 A330 2s vio bl & pink   .25 .25
Hiking and mountaineering in Austria.

Alfred Cossmann
(1870-1951),
Engraver — A331

1970, Oct. 2   Engr.   Perf. 14x13½
882 A331 2s dark brown   .25 .25

Arms of
Carinthia — A332

Photo. & Engr.
1970, Oct. 2   Perf. 14
883 A332 2s ol, red, gold, blk &
                 sil   .25 .25
Carinthian plebiscite, 50th anniversary.

UN Emblem
A333

1970, Oct. 23   Litho.   Perf. 14x13½
884 A333 3.50s lt blue & blk   .55 .35
25th anniversary of the United Nations.

Adoration of
the
Shepherds,
Carving
from
Garsten
Vicarage
A334

1970, Nov. 27   Engr.   Perf. 13½x14
885 A334 2s dk violet blue   .25 .25
Christmas.

Karl Renner
(1870-1950),
Austrian
Pres. — A335

1970, Dec. 14   Engr.   Perf. 14x13½
886 A335 2s deep claret   .25 .25

Beethoven, by
Georg
Waldmüller
A336

Photo. & Engr.
1970, Dec. 16   Perf. 13½
887 A336 3.50s black & buff   .55 .40
Ludwig van Beethoven (1770-1827), composer, birth bicentenary.

Enrica Handel-
Mazzetti (1871-
1955), Novelist,
Poet — A337

1971, Jan. 11   Engr.   Perf. 14x13½
888 A337 2s sepia   .25 .25

"Watch
Out for
Children!"
A338

1971, Feb. 18   Photo.   Perf. 13½
889 A338 2s blk, red brn & brt
                 grn   .35 .25
Traffic safety.

Saltcellar,
by
Benvenuto
Cellini
A339

Art Treasures: 1.50s, Covered vessel, made
of prase, gold and precious stones, Florentine,
1580. 2s, Emperor Joseph I, ivory statue by
Matthias Steinle, 1693.

Photo. & Engr.
1971, Mar. 22   **Perf. 14**
890 A339 1.50s gray & slate grn   .40   .40
891 A339 2s gray & dp plum   .50   .50
892 A339 3.50s gray, blk & bister   .70   .70
    Nos. 890-892 (3)   1.60   1.60

Emblem of Austrian Wholesalers' Organization A340

1971, Apr. 16   **Photo.**   **Perf. 13½**
893 A340 3.50s multicolored   .55   .35
    Intl. Chamber of Commerce, 23rd Congress, Vienna, Apr. 17-23.

Jacopo de Strada, by Titian — A341

Paintings in Vienna Museum: 2s, Village Feast, by Peter Brueghel, the Elder. 3.50s, Young Venetian Woman, by Albrecht Dürer.

1971, May 6   **Engr.**   **Perf. 13½**
894 A341 1.50s rose lake   .25   .40
895 A341 2s greenish black   .35   .45
896 A341 3.50s deep brown   .55   .70
    Nos. 894-896 (3)   1.15   1.55

Seal of Paulus of Franchenfordia, 1380 — A342

Photo. & Engr.
1971, May 6   **Perf. 13½x14**
897 A342 3.50s dk brn & bister   .55   .35
    Congress commemorating the centenary of the Austrian Notaries' Statute, May 5-8.

St. Matthew — A343

1971, May 27   **Perf. 12½x13½**
898 A343 2s brt rose lil & brn   .25   .25
    Exhibition of "1000 Years of Art in Krems." The statue of St. Matthew is from the Lentl Altar, created about 1520 by the Master of the Pulkau Altar.

August Neilreich — A344

1971, June 1   **Engr.**   **Perf. 14x13½**
899 A344 2s brown   .25   .25
    August Neilreich (1803-71), botanist.

Singer with Lyre — A345

Photo. & Engr.
1971, July 1   **Perf. 13½x14**
900 A345 4s lt bl, vio bl & gold   .55   .50
    Intl. Choir Festival, Vienna, July 1-4.

Coat of Arms of Kitzbuhel — A346

1971, Aug. 23   **Perf. 14**
901 A346 2.50s gold & multi   .35   .25
    700th anniversary of the town of Kitzbuhel.

Vienna Stock Exchange — A347

1971, Sept. 1   **Engr.**   **Perf. 13½x14**
902 A347 4s reddish brown   .55   .35
    Bicentenary of the Vienna Stock Exchange.

First and Latest Exhibition Halls A348

1971, Sept. 6   **Photo.**   **Perf. 13½x13**
903 A348 2.50s dp rose lilac   .35   .25
    Vienna Intl. Fair, 50th anniv.

Trade Union Emblem — A349

1971, Sept. 20   **Perf. 14x13½**
904 A349 2s gray, buff & red   .25   .25
    Austrian Trade Union Assoc., 25th anniv.

Arms of Burgenland A350

1971, Oct. 1
905 A350 2s dk bl, gold, red & blk   .25   .25
    50th anniv. of Burgenland joining Austria.

Marcus Car — A351

Photo. & Engr.
1971, Oct. 1   **Perf. 14**
906 A351 4s pale green & blk   .55   .40
    Austrian Automobile, Motorcycle and Touring Club, 75th anniv.

Europa Bridge — A352

1971, Oct. 8   **Engr.**   **Perf. 14x13½**
907 A352 4s violet blue   .55   .40
    Opening of highway over Brenner Pass.

Styria's Iron Mountain A353

Designs: 2s, Austrian Nitrogen Products, Ltd., Linz. 4s, United Austrian Iron and Steel Works, Ltd. (VOEST), Linz Harbor.

1971, Oct. 15   **Perf. 13½**
908 A353 1.50s reddish brown   .35   .40
909 A353 2s bluish black   .35   .40
910 A353 4s dk slate grn   .65   .80
    Nos. 908-910 (3)   1.35   1.60
    25 years of nationalized industry.

High-speed Train on Semmering A354

1971, Oct. 21   **Perf. 14**
911 A354 2s claret   .35   .25
    Inter-city rapid train service.

Trout Fisherman A355

1971, Nov. 15   **Perf. 13½**
912 A355 2s dark red brn   .25   .25

Dr. Erich Tschermak-Seysenegg (1871-1962), Botanist — A356

Photo. & Engr.
1971, Nov. 15   **Perf. 14x13½**
913 A356 2s pale ol & dk pur   .25   .25

Infant Jesus as Savior, by Dürer — A357

1971, Nov. 26   **Perf. 13½**
914 A357 2s gold & multi   .25   .25
    Christmas.

Franz Grillparzer, by Moritz Daffinger — A358

Litho. & Engr.
1972, Jan. 21   **Perf. 14x13½**
915 A358 2s buff, gold & blk   .35   .25
    Death cent. of Franz Grillparzer (1791-1872), dramatic poet.

Fountain, Main Square, Friesach — A359

Designs: 2s, Fountain, Heiligenkreuz Abbey. 2.50s, Leopold Fountain, Innsbruck.

1972, Feb. 23   **Engr.**   **Perf. 14x13½**
916 A359 1.50s rose lilac   .35   .25
917 A359 2s brown   .35   .25
918 A359 2.50s olive   .45   .65
    Nos. 916-918 (3)   1.15   1.15

Cardiac Patient and Monitor A360

1972, Apr. 11 *Perf. 13½x14*
919 A360 4s violet brown   .65 .40
World Health Day.

Conference of European Post and Telecommunications Ministers, Vienna, Apr. 11-14 — A361

St. Michael's Gate, Royal Palace, Vienna.

1972, Apr. 11 *Perf. 14x13½*
920 A361 4s violet blue   .65 .40

Gurk (Carinthia) Diocese, 900th Anniv. — A362

Photo. & Engr.
1972, May 5 *Perf. 14*
921 A362 2s Sculpture, Gurk Cathedral   .35 .25
The design is after the central column supporting the sarcophagus of St. Hemma in Gurk Cathedral.

City Hall, Congress Emblem A363

1972, May 23 **Litho. & Engr.**
922 A363 4s red, blk & yel   .65 .40
9th Intl. Congress of Public and Cooperative Economy, Vienna, May 23-25.

Power Line in Carnic Alps — A364

2.50s, Power Station, Semmering. 4s, Zemm Power Station (lake in Zillertaler Alps).

1972, June 28 *Perf. 13½x14*
923 A364   70g gray & violet   .25 .35
924 A364   2.50s gray & red brn   .40 .45
925 A364   4s gray & slate   .65 .80
   Nos. 923-925 (3)   1.30 1.60
Nationalization of the power industry, 25th anniv.

Runner with Olympic Torch — A365

Engr. & Photo.
1972, Aug. 21 *Perf. 14x13½*
926 A365 2s sepia & red   .35 .25
Olympic torch relay from Olympia, Greece, to Munich, Germany, passing through Austria.

St. Hermes, by Conrad Laib — A366

1972, Aug. 21 **Engr.**
927 A366 2s violet brown   .35 .25
Exhibition of Late Gothic Art, Salzburg.

Pears A367

1972, Sept. *Perf. 14*
928 A367 2.50s dk blue & multi   .40 .25
World Congress of small plot Gardeners, Vienna, Sept. 7-10.

Souvenir Sheet

Spanish Riding School, Vienna, 400th Anniv. — A368

1972, Sept. 12 *Perf. 13½*
929 A368   Sheet of 6   2.75 4.00
a. 2s Spanish walk   .35 .25
b. 2s Piaffe   .35 .25
c. 2.50s Levade   .40 .25
d. 2.50s On long rein   .40 .25
e. 4s Capriole   .65 .55
f. 4s Courbette   .65 .55

Arms of University of Agriculture A369

Photo. & Engr.
1972, Oct. 17 *Perf. 14x13½*
930 A369 2s black & multi   .35 .25
University of Agriculture, Vienna, cent.

Church and Old University — A370

1972, Nov. 7 **Engr.**
931 A370 4s red brown   .65 .40
Paris Lodron University, Salzburg, 350th anniv.

Carl Michael Ziehrer — A371

1972, Nov. 14
932 A371 2s rose claret   .35 .25
50th death anniv. of Carl Michael Ziehrer (1843-1922), composer.

Virgin and Child, Wood, 1420-30 A372

Photo. & Engr.
1972, Dec. 1 *Perf. 13½*
933 A372 2s olive & chocolate   .35 .25
Christmas.

Racing Sleigh, 1750 A373

Designs: 2s, Coronation landau, 1824. 2.50s, Imperial state coach, 1763.

1972, Dec. 12
934 A373 1.50s pale gray & brn   .25 .25
935 A373   2s pale gray & sl grn   .40 .45
936 A373 2.50s pale gray & plum .50 .65
   Nos. 934-936 (3)   1.15 1.35
Collection of historic state coaches and carriages in Schönbrunn Palace.

Map of Austrian Telephone System A374

1972, Dec. 14 **Photo.** *Perf. 14*
937 A374 2s yellow & blk   .35 .25
Completion of automation of Austrian telephone system.

"Drugs are Death" A375

1973, Jan. 26 Photo. *Perf. 13½x14*
938 A375 2s scarlet & multi   .35 .25
Fight against drug abuse.

Alfons Petzold (1882-1923), Poet — A376

1973, Jan. 26 Engr. *Perf. 14x13½*
939 A376 2s reddish brn   .35 .25

Theodor Körner (1873-1957), Austrian Pres. — A377

Photo. & Engr.
1973, Apr. 24 *Perf. 14x13½*
940 A377 2s gray & deep claret   .35 .25

Douglas DC-9 A378

1973, May 14 *Perf. 13½x14*
941 A378 2s vio bl & rose red   .35 .25
First intl. airmail service, Vienna to Kiev, Mar. 31, 1918, 55th anniv.; Austrian Aviation Corporation, 50th anniv.; Austrian Airlines, 15th anniv.

Otto Loewi (1873-1961), Pharmacologist, Nobel Laureate — A379

1973, June 4 Engr. *Perf. 14x13½*
942 A379 4s deep violet   .65 .40

"Support" — A380

1973, June 25
943 A380 2s dark blue   .35 .25
Federation of Austrian Social Insurance Institutes, 25th anniv.

Europa Issue

Post Horn and Telephone
A381

1973, July 9   Photo.   Perf. 14
944 A381 2.50s ocher, blk & yel   .80 .40

Dornbirn Fair Emblem
A382

1973, July 27   Perf. 13½x14
945 A382 2s multicolored   .35 .25
Dornbirn Trade Fair, 25th anniversary.

23rd Intl. Military Pentathlon Championships, Wiener Neustadt, Aug. 13-18 — A383

1973, Aug. 13   Engr.   Perf. 14x13½
946 A383 4s Hurdles   .65 .40

Leo Slezak (1873-1946), Operatic Tenor — A384

1973, Aug. 17   Perf. 14
947 A384 4s dark brown   .65 .40

Gate, Vienna Hofburg, and ISI Emblem — A385

Photogravure and Engraved
1973, Aug. 20   Perf. 14x13½
948 A385 2s gray, dk brn & ver   .35 .25
39th Congress of Intl. Statistical Institute, Vienna, Aug. 20-30.

Tegetthoff off Franz Josef Land, by Julius Payer
A386

1973, Aug. 30   Engr.   Perf. 13½x14
949 A386 2.50s Prussian grn   .40 .25
Discovery of Franz Josef Land by an Austrian North Pole expedition, cent.

Academy of Science, by Canaletto
A387

1973, Sept. 4
950 A387 2.50s violet   .40 .25
World Meteorological Organization, cent.

Arms of Viennese Tanners — A388

Photo. & Engr.
1973, Sept. 4   Perf. 14
951 A388 4s red & multi   .65 .40
13th Congress of the Intl. Union of Leather Chemists' Societies, Vienna, Sept. 1-7.

Max Reinhardt (1873-1943), Theatrical Director — A389

1973, Sept. 7   Engr.   Perf. 13x13½
952 A389 2s rose magenta   .35 .25

Trotter
A390

1973, Sept. 28   Perf. 13½
953 A390 2s green   .35 .25
Centenary of Vienna Trotting Association.

Ferdinand Hanusch (1866-1923), Secretary of State — A391

1973, Sept. 28   Perf. 14x13½
954 A391 2s rose brown   .35 .25

Police Radio Operator
A392

1973, Oct. 2   Perf. 13½x14
955 A392 4s violet blue   .65 .40
50th anniv. of Intl. Criminal Police Org. (INTERPOL).

Josef Petzval's Photographic Lens — A393

Litho. & Engr.
1973, Oct. 8   Perf. 14
956 A393 2.50s blue & multi   .40 .25
EUROPHOT Photographic Cong., Vienna.

Emperor's Spring, Hell Valley
A394

Photo. & Engr.
1973, Oct. 23   Perf. 13½x14
957 A394 2s sepia, blue & red   .35 .25
Vienna's first mountain spring water supply system, cent.

Almsee, Upper Austria — A395

Hofburg and Prince Eugene Statue, Vienna — A395a

Designs: 50g, Farmhouses, Zillertal, Tirol. 1s, Kahlenbergerdorf. 1.50s, Bludenz, Vorarlberg. 2s, Inn Bridge, Alt Finstermunz. 2.50s, Murau, Styria. 3s, Bischofsmütze, Salzburg. 3.50s, Easter Church, Oberwart. 4.50s, Windmill, Retz. 5s, Aggstein Castle, Lower Austria. 6s, Lindauer Hut, Vorarlberg. 6.50s, Holy Cross Church, Villach, Carinthia. 7s, Falkenstein Castle, Carinthia. 7.50s, Hohensalzburg. 8s, Votive column, Reiteregg, Styria. 10s, Lake Neusiedl, Burgenland. 11s, Old Town, Enns. 16s, Openair Museum, Bad Tatzmannsdorf. 20s, Myra waterfalls.

Photo. & Engr.
1973-78   Perf. 13½x14

Size: 23x29mm

958	A395	50g gray & slate green	.25	.25
959	A395	1s brn & dk brown	.30	.25
960	A395	1.50s rose & brown	.40	.25
961	A395	2s gray bl & dk blue	.50	.25
962	A395	2.50s vio & dp violet	.55	.25
963	A395	3s lt ultra & vio	.65	.25
963A	A395	3.50s dl org & brown	.75	.25
964	A395	4s brt lil & pur	.65	.25
965	A395	4.50s brt grn & bl green	.80	.25
966	A395	5s lilac & vio	.80	.25
967	A395	6s dp rose & dk violet	1.40	.25
968	A395	6.50s bl grn & indigo	1.20	.25
969	A395	7s sage grn & sl green	1.60	.25
970	A395	7.50s lil rose & claret	2.00	.25
971	A395	8s dl red & dp brown	1.75	.25
972	A395	10s gray grn & dk green	2.10	.25
973	A395	11s ver & dk carmine	2.00	.25
974	A395	16s bister & brown	3.25	.35
975	A395	20s ol bis & ol grn	4.00	.40
976	A395a	50s gray vio & vio bl	12.00	2.40
		Nos. 958-976 (20)	36.95	7.45

Issued: Nos. 960-963, 1974; Nos. 958-959, 967, 976, 1975; Nos. 965, 971, 973, 1976; Nos. 968, 970, 974-975, 1977; No. 963A, 1978. See Nos. 1100-1109.

Nativity — A396

1973, Nov. 30   Perf. 14
977 A396 2s multicolored   .35 .25
Christmas. Design from 14th century stained-glass window.

Pregl — A397

1973, Dec. 12   Engr.   Perf. 14x13½
978 A397 4s deep blue   .65 .40
50th anniv. of the awarding of the Nobel prize for chemistry to Fritz Pregl (1869-1930).

Radio Austria, 50th Anniv. — A398

1974, Jan. 14   Photo.   Perf. 14x13½
979 A398 2.50s Telex Machine   .40 .25

Hugo Hofmannsthal (1874-1929), Poet and Playwright
A399

1974, Feb. 1   Engr.   Perf. 14
980 A399 4s violet blue   .65 .45

Anton Bruckner and Bruckner House
A400

1974, Mar. 22   Engr.   Perf. 14
981 A400 4s brown   .65 .40
Founding of Anton Bruckner House (concert hall), Linz, and birth of Anton Bruckner (1824-1896), composer, 150th anniv.

Vegetables
A401

Photo. & Engr.
1974, Apr. 18　　　　　　*Perf. 14*
982 A401　2s shown　　　　　.35　.25
983 A401　2.50s Fruits　　　　.40　.40
984 A401　4s Flowers　　　　.80　.95
　　Nos. 982-984 (3)　　　　1.55 1.60
Intl. Garden Show, Vienna, Apr. 18-Oct. 14.

Seal of Judenburg
A402

1974, Apr. 24　Photo.　Perf. 14x13½
985 A402　2s plum & multi　　　.35　.25
　　750th anniversary of Judenburg.

Karl Kraus (1874-
1936), Poet and
Satirist — A403

1974, Apr. 6　　　　　　Engr.
986 A403　4s dark red　　　　.65　.40

St. Michael, by
Thomas
Schwanthaler
A404

1974, May 3
987 A404　2.50s slate green　　.40　.25
　　Exhibition of the works by the Schwanthaler Family of sculptors, (1633-1848), Reichersberg am Inn, May 3-Oct. 13.

A405

Europa: King Arthur, from tomb of
Maximilian I

1974, May 8　　　　　*Perf. 13½*
988 A405　2.50s ocher & slate blue　*.65　.40*

Austrian
Automobile
Assoc., 75th
Anniv. — A406

De Dion Bouton motor tricycle.

Photo. & Engr.
1974, May 17　　　　*Perf. 14x13½*
989 A406　2s gray & vio brn　　.35　.25

Satyr's
Head,
Terracotta
A407

1974, May 22　　　　*Perf. 13½x14*
990 A407　2s org brn, gold & blk　.35　.25
　　Exhibition, "Renaissance in Austria," Schallaburg Castle, May 22-Nov. 14.

Road Transport
Union
Emblem — A408

1974, May 24　Photo.　Perf. 14x13½
991 A408　4s deep orange & blk　.65　.40
　　14th Congress of the Intl. Road Transport Union, Innsbruck.

Franz Anton
Maulbertsch
(1724-96),
Painter — A409

1974, June 7　Engr.　Perf. 14x13½
992 A409　2s Self-portrait　　.35　.25

Gendarmes,
1824 and
1974
A410

1974, June 7　Photo.　Perf. 13½x14
993 A410　2s red & multi　　　.35　.25
　　125th anniversary of Austrian gendarmery.

Fencing
A411

Photo. & Engr.
1974, June 14　　　　*Perf. 13½*
994 A411　2.50s red org & blk　.40　.25

Transportation
Symbols — A412

1974, June 18　Photo.　Perf. 14x13½
995 A412　4s lt ultra & multi　.65　.40
　　European Conference of Transportation Ministers, Vienna, June 18-21.

St. Virgil,
Sculpture from
Nonntal
Church — A413

1974, June 28　Engr.　Perf. 13½x14
996 A413　2s violet blue　　.35　.25
　　Consecration of the Cathedral of Salzburg by Scotch-Irish Bishop Feirgil (St. Virgil), 1200th anniv. Salzburg was a center of Christianization in the 8th century.

Franz Jonas
and Austrian
Eagle — A414

1974, June 28
997 A414　2s black　　　　.35　.25
　　Jonas (1899-1974), Austrian Pres., 1965-1974.

Franz Stelzhamer
A415

1974, July 12　Engr.　Perf. 14x13½
998 A415　2s indigo　　　　.35　.25
　　Franz Stelzhamer (1802-1874), poet who wrote in Upper Austrian vernacular, death cent.

Diver — A416

Photo. & Engr.
1974, Aug. 16　　　　*Perf. 13x13½*
999 A416　4s blue & sepia　　.65　.40
　　13th European Swimming, Diving and Water Polo Championships, Vienna, Aug. 18-25.

Ferdinand Ritter
von
Hebra — A417

1974, Sept. 10　Engr.　Perf. 14x13½
1000 A417　4s brown　　　.65　.40
　　30th Meeting of the Assoc. of German-speaking Dermatologists, Graz, Sept. 10-14. Dr. von Hebra (1816-1880) was a founder of modern dermatology.

Arnold
Schonberg
A418

1974, Sept. 13　　　　*Perf. 13½x14*
1001 A418　2.50s purple　　.40　.25
　　Schönberg (1874-1951), composer.

Radio
Station,
Salzburg
A419

1974, Oct. 1　Photo.　Perf. 13½x14
1002 A419　2s multicolored　.35　.25
　　50th anniversary of Austrian broadcasting.

Edmund Eysler
(1874-1949),
Composer
A420

1974, Oct. 4　Engr.　Perf. 14x13½
1003 A420　2s dark olive　　.25　.25

Mailman,
Mail Coach
and Train,
UPU
Emblem
A421

4s, Mailman, jet, truck, 1974, & UPU emblem.

1974, Oct. 9　Photo.　Perf. 13½
1004 A421　2s deep claret & lil　.35　.25
1005 A421　4s dark blue & gray　.65　.40
　　Centenary of Universal Postal Union.

Gauntlet
Protecting
Rose
A422

1974, Oct. 23　Photo.　Perf. 13½x14
1006 A422　2s multicolored　.35　.25
　　Environment protection.

Austrian
Sports Pool
Emblem
A423

1974, Oct. 23   Photo.   Perf. 13½x14
1007 A423 70g multicolored   .35 .25
Austrian Sports Pool (lottery), 25th anniv.

Carl Ditters von
Dittersdorf (1739-
1799), Composer
A424

1974, Oct. 24   Engr.   Perf. 14x13½
1008 A424 2s Prussian green   .35 .25

Virgin and Child,
Wood, c.
1600 — A425

1974, Nov. 29   Photo. & Engr.
1009 A425 2s brown & gold   .35 .25
Christmas.

Franz Schmidt
(1874-1939),
Composer
A426

1974, Dec. 18
1010 A426 4s gray & black   .65 .40

European
Architectural
Heritage
Year — A427

Photo. & Engr.
1975, Jan. 24   Perf. 13½
1011 A427 2.50s St. Christopher   .40 .25
The design shows part of a wooden figure
from central panel of the retable in the
Kefermarkt Church, 1490-1497.

Safety Belt and
Skeleton
Arms — A428

1975, Apr. 1   Photo.   Perf. 14x13½
1012 A428 70g violet & multi   .25 .25
Introduction of obligatory use of automobile
safety belts.

Stained Glass
Window, Vienna
City Hall — A429

1975, Apr. 2   Perf. 14
1013 A429 2.50s multicolored   .40 .25
11th meeting of the Council of European
Municipalities, Vienna, Apr. 2-5.

Austria as
Mediator
A430

1975, May 2   Litho.   Perf. 14
1014 A430   2s blk, gray & ol brn .35 .25
2nd Republic of Austria, 30th anniv.

National Forests,
50th
Anniv. — A431

1975, May 6   Engr.
1015 A431 2s green   .35 .25

Europa Issue

High Priest, by
Michael
Pacher — A432

Photo. & Engr.
1975, May 27   Perf. 14x13½
1016 A432 2.50s multicolored   .40 .25
Design is detail from painting "The Marriage
of Joseph and Mary," by Michael Pacher (c.
1450-1500).

Gosaukamm
Funicular — A433

1975, June 23   Perf. 14x13½
1017 A433 2s slate & red   .35 .25
4th Intl. Funicular Cong., Vienna, 6/23-27.

Josef Misson and Mühlbach am
Manhartsberg — A434

1975, June 27   Perf. 13½x14
1018 A434 2s choc & redsh brn   .35 .25
Josef Misson (1803-1875), poet who wrote
in Lower Austrian vernacular, death cent.

Setting Sun and
"P" — A435

1975, Aug. 27   Litho.   Perf. 14x13½
1019 A435 1.50s org, blk & bl   .25 .25
Austrian Assoc. of Pensioners 25th anniv.
meeting, Vienna, Aug. 1975.

Ferdinand
Porsche
(1875-1951),
Engineer,
Auto Maker
A436

Photo. & Engr.
1975, Sept. 3   Perf. 13½x14
1020 A436 1.50s gray & purple   .25 .25

Leo Fall (1873-
1925), Composer
A437

1975, Sept. 16   Engr.   Perf. 14x13½
1021 A437 2s violet   .35 .25

10th World Judo
Championships,
Vienna — A438

1975, Oct. 20   Photo.   Perf. 14x13½
1022 A438 2.50s Judo Throw   .40 .25

Heinrich Angeli
(1840-1925),
Painter — A439

1975, Oct. 21   Engr.   Perf. 14x13½
1023 A439 2s rose lake   .35 .25

Johann
Strauss and
Dancers
A440

Photo. & Engr.
1975, Oct. 24   Perf. 13½x14
1024 A440 4s ocher & sepia   .65 .40
Johann Strauss (1825-1899), composer.

Stylized Musician
Playing a
Viol — A441

1975, Oct. 30   Perf. 14x13½
1025 A441 2.50s silver & vio bl .40 .25
Vienna Symphony Orchestra, 75th anniv.

Symbolic
House — A442

1975, Oct. 31   Photo.
1026 A442 2s multicolored   .35 .25
Austrian building savings societies, 50th
anniv.

Fan with
"Hanswurst"
Scene, 18th
Century
A443

1975, Nov. 14   Photo.   Perf. 13½x14
1027 A443 1.50s green & multi   .25 .25
Salzburg Theater bicentenary.

Virgin and Child,
from 15th Century
Altar — A444

Photo. & Engr.
1975, Nov. 28   Perf. 13x13½
1028 A444 2s gold & dull purple .35 .25
Christmas.

"The Spiral Tree," by Hundertwasser — A445

Photo., Engr. & Typo.
1975, Dec. 11   *Perf. 13½x14*
1029 A445 4s multicolored   .80 .35
Austrian modern art. Friedenstreich Hundertwasser is the pseudonym of Friedrich Stowasser (1928-2000).

Old Burgtheater — A446

No. 1030b, Grand staircase, new Burgtheater.

Perf. 14 (pane), 13½x14 (stamps)
1976, Apr. 8   **Engr.**
1030   Pane of 2 + label   1.20 1.40
   a. A446 3s violet blue   .65 .25
   b. A446 3s deep brown   .65 .25
Bicentenary of Vienna Burgtheater. Label (head of Pan) and inscription in vermilion.

Dr. Robert Barany (1876-1936), Winner of Nobel Prize for Medicine, 1914 — A447

Photo. & Engr.
1976, Apr. 22   *Perf. 14x13½*
1031 A447 3s blue & brown   .55 .25

Ammonite — A448

1976, Apr. 30 Photo. *Perf. 13½x14*
1032 A448 3s red & multi   .55 .25
Vienna Museum of Natural History, Centenary Exhibition.

Carinthian Dukes' Coronation Chair — A449

Photo. & Engr.
1976, May 6   *Perf. 14x13½*
1033 A449 3s grnsh blk & org   .55 .25
Millennium of Carinthia.

Siege of Linz, 17th Century Etching — A450

1976, May 14
1034 A450 4s blk & gray grn   .65 .40
Upper Austrian Peasants' War, 350th anniv.

Skittles — A451

1976, May 14   *Perf. 13½x14*
1035 A451 4s black & org   .65 .40
11th World Skittles Championships, Vienna.

Duke Heinrich II, Stained-glass Window — A452

1976, May 14   *Perf. 14*
1036 A452 3s multicolored   .55 .25
Babenberg Exhibition, Lilienfeld.

St. Wolfgang, from Pacher Altar — A453

1976, May 26   **Engr.**   *Perf. 13½*
1037 A453 6s bright violet   1.10 .55
Intl. Art Exhibition at St. Wolfgang.

Europa Issue

Tassilo Cup, Kremsmunster, 777 — A454

Photo. & Engr.
1976, Aug. 13   *Perf. 14x13½*
1038 A454 4s ultra & multi   .65 .40

Timber Fair Emblem — A455

1976, Aug. 13   **Photo.**
1039 A455 3s green & multi   .55 .25
Austrian Timber Fair, Klagenfurt, 25th anniv.

Constantin Economo, M.D. (1876-1931), Neurologist — A456

1976, Aug. 23   **Engr.**
1040 A456 3s dark red brown   .55 .25

Administrative Court, by Salomon Klein — A457

1976, Oct. 25 Engr. *Perf. 13½x14*
1041 A457 6s deep brown   1.10 .55
Austrian Central Administrative Court, cent.

Souvenir Sheet

Coats of Arms of Austrian Provinces — A458

Millennium of Austria: a, Lower Austria. b, Upper Austria. c, Styria. d, Carinthia. e, Tyrol. f, Voralberg. g, Salzburg. h, Burgenland. i, Vienna.

Photo. & Engr.
1976, Oct. 25   *Perf. 14*
1042 A458   Sheet of 9   3.25 3.50
   a.-i.   2s any single   .35 .40

"Cancer" — A459

1976, Nov. 17 Photo. *Perf. 14x13½*
1043 A459 2.50s multicolored   .40 .25
Fight against cancer.

UN Emblem and Bridge — A460

1976, Nov. 17
1044 A460 3s blue & gold   .55 .25
UN Industrial Development Org. (UNIDO), 10th anniv.

Punched Tape, Map of Europe — A461

1976, Nov. 17   *Perf. 14*
1045 A461 1.50s multicolored   .25 .25
Austrian Press Agency (APA), 30th anniv.

Viktor Kaplan, Kaplan Turbine — A462

Photo. & Engr.
1976, Nov. 26   *Perf. 13½x14*
1046 A462 2.50s multicolored   .40 .25
Viktor Kaplan (1876-1934), inventor of Kaplan turbine, birth centenary.

Nativity, by Konrad von Friesach, c. 1450 — A463

1976, Nov. 26   *Perf. 13½*
1047 A463 3s multicolored   .55 .25
Christmas.

Augustin, the Piper — A464

Photo. & Engr.
1976, Dec. 29   *Perf. 13½*
1048 A464 6s multicolored   1.10 .55
Modern Austrian art.

Rainer Maria Rilke (1875-1926), Poet — A465

1976, Dec. 29   **Engr.**   *Perf. 14x13½*
1049 A465 3s deep violet   .55 .25

Vienna City Synagogue — A466

1976, Dec. 29   **Photo.**   *Perf. 13½*
1050 A466 1.50s multicolored   .25 .25
Sesquicentennial of Vienna City Synagogue.

Nikolaus Joseph von Jacquin (1727-1817), Botanist — A467

1977, Feb. 16 Engr. *Perf. 14x13½*
1051 A467 4s chocolate .65 .40

Oswald von Wolkenstein (1377-1445), Poet — A468

Photo. & Engr.
1977, Feb. 16 *Perf. 14*
1052 A468 3s multicolored .55 .25

Handball A469

1977, Feb. 25 Photo. *Perf. 13½x14*
1053 A469 1.50s multicolored .25 .25
World Indoor Handball Championships, Austria, Feb. 5-Mar. 6.

Alfred Kubin (1877-1959), Illustrator and Writer — A470

1977, Apr. 12 Engr. *Perf. 14x13½*
1054 A470 6s dk violet blue 1.10 .55

Great Spire, St. Stephen's Cathedral A471

Designs: 3s, Heathen Tower and Frederick's Gable. 4s, Interior view with Albertinian Choir.

1977, Apr. 22 Engr. *Perf. 13½*
1055 A471 2.50s dark brown .55 .30
1056 A471 3s dark blue .65 .40
1057 A471 4s rose lake .80 .55
Nos. 1055-1057 (3) 2.00 1.25
Restoration and re-opening of St. Stephen's Cathedral, Vienna, 25th anniversary.

Fritz Hermanovsky-Orlando (1877-1954), Poet and Artist — A472

Photo. & Engr.
1977, Apr. 29 *Perf. 13½x14*
1058 A472 6s Prus green & gold 1.10 .55

Intl. Atomic Energy Agency (IAEA), 20th Anniv. — A473

1977, May 2 Photo. *Perf. 14*
1059 A473 3s IAEA Emblem .55 .25

Schwanenstadt, 350th Anniv. — A474

1977, June 10 Photo. *Perf. 14x13½*
1060 A474 3s Town arms .55 .25

Europa Issue

Attersee, Upper Austria — A475

1977, June 10 Engr. *Perf. 14*
1061 A475 6s olive green 1.20 .55

Globe, by Vincenzo Coronelli, 1688 — A476

Photo. & Engr.
1977, June 29 *Perf. 14*
1062 A476 3s black & buff .55 .25
5th Intl. Symposium of the Coronelli World Fed. of Friends of the Globe, Austria, June 29-July 3.

Kayak Race A477

1977, July 15 Photo. *Perf. 13½x14*
1063 A477 4s multicolored .65 .40
3rd Kayak Slalom White Water Race on Lieser River, Spittal.

The Good Samaritan, by Francesco Bassano A478

1977, Sept. 16 Photo. & Engr.
1064 A478 1.50s brown & red .25 .25
Workers' Good Samaritan Org., 50th anniv.

Papermakers' Coat of Arms — A479

1977, Oct. 10 *Perf. 14x13½*
1065 A479 3s multicolored .55 .25
17th Conf. of the European Committee of Pulp and Paper Technology (EUCEPA), Vienna.

Man with Austrian Flag Lifting Barbed Wire — A480

1977, Nov. 3 *Perf. 14*
1066 A480 2.50s slate & red .40 .25
Honoring the martyrs for Austria's freedom.

"Austria," First Steam Locomotive in Austria — A481

Designs: 2.50s, Steam locomotive 214. 3s, Electric locomotive 1044.

Photo. & Engr.
1977, Nov. 17 *Perf. 13½*
1067 A481 1.50s multicolored .40 .25
1068 A481 2.50s multicolored .65 .25
1069 A481 3s multicolored .95 .40
Nos. 1067-1069 (3) 2.00 .90
140th anniversary of Austrian railroads.

Christmas — A482

Virgin and Child, wood statue, Mariastein, Tyrol.

1977, Nov. 25 *Perf. 14x13½*
1070 A482 3s multicolored .55 .25

Modern Austrian Art — A483

The Danube Maiden, by Wolfgang Hutter.

1977, Dec. 2 *Perf. 13½x14*
1071 A483 6s multicolored 1.10 .55

Egon Friedell (1878-1938), Writer and Historian A484

1978, Jan. 23 Photo. & Engr.
1072 A484 3s lt blue & blk .55 .25

Subway Train A485

1978, Feb. 24 Photo. *Perf. 13½x14*
1073 A485 3s multicolored .65 .25
New Vienna subway system.

Biathlon Competition A486

1978, Feb. 28 Photo. & Engr.
1074 A486 4s multicolored .65 .40
Biathlon World Championships, Hochfilzen, Tyrol, Feb. 28-Mar. 5.

Leopold Kunschak (1871-1953), Political Leader — A487

1978, Mar. 13 Engr. *Perf. 14x13½*
1075 A487 3s violet blue .55 .25

Coyote, Aztec Feather Shield A488

1978, Mar. 13 Photo. *Perf. 13½x14*
1076 A488 3s multicolored .55 .25
Ethnographical Museum, 50th anniv. exhibition.

Alpine Farm, Woodcut by Suitbert Lobisser — A489

1978, Mar. 23 Engr. *Perf. 13½*
1077 A489 3s dark brown, *buff* .55 .25
Lobisser (1878-1943), graphic artist.

Capercaillie, Hunting Bag, 1730, and Rifle, 1655 — A490

Photo. & Engr.
1978, Apr. 28   *Perf. 13½*
1078 A490 6s multicolored   1.10 .55
Intl. Hunting Exhibition, Marchegg.

Europa Issue

Riegersburg, Styria — A491

1978, May 3   **Engr.**
1079 A491 6s deep rose lilac   *1.60* .55

Parliament, Vienna, and Map of Europe — A492

1978, May 3 Photo.   *Perf. 14x13½*
1080 A492 4s multicolored   .65 .40
3rd Interparliamentary Conference for European Cooperation and Security, Vienna.

Admont Pietà, c. 1410 — A493

1978, May 26   **Photo. & Engr.**
1081 A493 2.50s ocher & black   .40 .25
Gothic Art in Styria Exhibition, St. Lambrecht, 1978.

Ort Castle, Gmunden — A494

1978, June 9
1082 A494 3s multicolored   .55 .25
700th anniversary of Gmunden City.

Child with Flowers and Fruit — A495

Photo. & Engr.
1978, June 30   *Perf. 14x13½*
1083 A495 6s gold & multi   1.10 .55
25 years of Social Tourism.

Lehar and his Home, Bad Ischl — A496

1978, July 14   **Engr.**   *Perf. 14x13½*
1084 A496 6s slate   1.10 .55
International Lehar Congress, Bad Ischl. Franz Lehar (1870-1948), operetta composer.

Congress Emblem A497

1978, Aug. 21 Photo.   *Perf. 13½x14*
1085 A497 1.50s black, red & yel   .25 .25
Cong. of Intl. Fed. of Building Construction and Wood Workers, Vienna, Aug. 20-24.

Ottokar of Bohemia and Rudolf of Hapsburg A498

1978, Aug. 25   **Photo. & Engr.**
1086 A498   3s multicolored   .55 .25
Battle of Durnkrut and Jedenspeigen (Marchfeld), which established Hapsburg rule in Austria, 700th anniversary.

First Documentary Reference to Villach, "ad pontem uillah" — A499

1978, Sept. 8 Litho.   *Perf. 13½x14*
1087 A499 3s multicolored   .55 .25
1100th anniversary of Villach, Carinthia.

Seal of Graz, 1440 — A500

Photo. & Engr.
1978, Sept. 13   *Perf. 14x13½*
1088 A500 4s multicolored   .65 .40
850th anniversary of Graz.

Emperor Maximilian Fishing — A501

1978, Sept. 15   *Perf. 14x13½*
1089 A501 4s multicolored   .65 .40
World Fishing Championships, Vienna, Sept. 1978.

"Aid to the Handicapped" — A502

1978, Oct. 2 Photo.   *Perf. 13½x14*
1090 A502 6s orange brn & blk   1.10 .55

Symbolic Column — A503

1978, Oct. 9 Photo.   *Perf. 13½*
1091 A503 2.50s orange, blk & gray .40 .25
9th Intl. Congress of Concrete and Prefabrication Industries, Vienna, Oct. 8-13.

Grace, by Albin Egger-Lienz A504

1978, Oct. 27   *Perf. 13½x14*
1092 A504 6s multicolored   1.10 .55
European Family Congress, Vienna, Oct. 26-29.

Lise Meitner (1878-1968), Physicist, and Atom Symbol — A505

1978, Nov. 7 Engr.   *Perf. 14x13½*
1093 A505 6s dark violet   1.10 .55

Viktor Adler, by Anton Hanak A506

Photo. & Engr.
1978, Nov. 10   *Perf. 13½x14*
1094 A506 3s vermilion & black   .55 .25
Viktor Adler (1852-1918), leader of Social Democratic Party, 60th death anniversary.

Franz Schubert, by Josef Kriehuber A507

1978, Nov. 17   **Engr.**   *Perf. 14*
1095 A507 6s reddish brown   1.25 .55
Franz Schubert (1797-1828), composer.

Virgin and Child, Wilhering Church — A508

Photo. & Engr.
1978, Dec. 1   *Perf. 12½x13½*
1096 A508 3s multicolored   .55 .25
Christmas.

Archduke Johann Shelter, Grossglockner — A509

1978, Dec. 6   *Perf. 13½x14*
1097 A509 1.50s gold & dk vio bl   .25 .25
Austrian Alpine Club, centenary.

Modern Austrian Art — A510

Adam, by Rudolf Hausner.

1978, Dec. 6 Photo.   *Perf. 13½x14*
1098 A510 6s multicolored   1.10 .55

Universal Declaration of Human Rights, 30th Anniv. — A511

1978, Dec. 6   *Perf. 14x13½*
1099 A511 6s Bound Hands   1.10 .55

Type of 1973

Designs: 20g, Freistadt, Upper Austria. 3s, Bishofsmutze, Salzburg. 4.20s, Hirschegg, Kleinwalsertal. 5.50s, Peace Chapel, Stoderzinken. 5.60s, Riezlern, Kleinwalsertal. 9s, Asten Carinthia. 12s, Kufstein Fortress. 14s, Weiszsee, Salzburg.

Photo. & Engr.
1978-83   *Perf. 13½x14*
Size: 23x29mm
1100 A395 20g vio bl & dk bl   .50 .25
Size: 17x21mm
1102 A395 3s lt ultra & vio bl   .40 .25

Size: 23x29mm

1104	A395	4.20s blk & grysh bl	.95	.40
1105	A395	5.50s lilac & pur	1.50	.50
1106	A395	5.60s yel grn & ol grn	1.50	.70
1107	A395	9s rose & car	2.10	.40
1108	A395	12s ocher & vio brn	2.40	.35
1109	A395	14s lt green & green	3.25	.25
	Nos. 1100-1109 (8)		12.60	3.10

Issued: 3s, 12/7/78; 4.20s, 6/22/79; 20g, 6/27/80; 12s, 10/3/80; 14s, 1/27/82; 5.50s, 5.60s, 7/1/82; 9s, 2/9/83.

Child and IYC Emblem A512

Photo. & Engr.
1979, Jan. 16   **Perf. 14**
1110 A512 2.50s multicolored   .40 .25
International Year of the Child.

CCIR Emblem A513

1979, Jan. 16   **Photo.**   **Perf. 13½x14**
1111 A513 6s multicolored   .80 .50
Intl. Radio Consultative Committee (CCIR) of the ITU, 50th anniv.

Air Rifle, Air Pistol and Club Emblem A514

Photo. & Engr.
1979, Mar. 7   **Perf. 13½**
1112 A514 6s multicolored   1.10 .55
Austrian Shooting Club, cent., and European Air Rifle and Air Pistol Championships, Graz.

Figure Skater — A515

1979, Mar. 7   **Photo.**   **Perf. 14x13½**
1113 A515 4s multicolored   .65 .40
World Ice Skating Championships, Vienna.

Steamer Franz I A516

Designs: 2.50s, Tugboat Linz. 3s, Passenger ship Theodor Körner.

1979, Mar. 13   **Engr.**   **Perf. 13½**
1114	A516	1.50s violet blue	.35	.25
1115	A516	2.50s sepia	.50	.35
1116	A516	3s magenta	.80	.25
	Nos. 1114-1116 (3)		1.65	.85

1st Danube Steamship Company, 150th anniv.

Fashion Design, by Theo Zasche, 1900 — A517

Photo. & Engr.
1979, Mar. 26   **Perf. 13x13½**
1117 A517 2.50s multicolored   .40 .25
50th Intl. Fashion Week, Vienna.

Wiener Neustadt Cathedral, 700th Anniv. — A518

1979, Mar. 27   **Engr.**   **Perf. 13½**
1118 A518 4s violet blue   .65 .40

Teacher and Pupils, by Franz A. Zauner — A519

Photo. & Engr.
1979, Mar. 30   **Perf. 14x13½**
1119 A519 2.50s multicolored   .40 .25
Education of the deaf in Austria, 200th anniv.

Population Chart and Baroque Angel — A520

1979, Apr. 6
1120 A520 2.50s multicolored   .40 .25
Austrian Central Statistical Bureau, 150th anniv.

Europa Issue

Laurenz Koschier — A521

1979, May 4
1121 A521 6s ocher & purple   1.20 .55

Diesel Motor — A522

1979, May 4   **Photo.**
1122 A522 4s multicolored   .65 .40
13th CIMAC Congress (Intl. Org. for Internal Combustion Machines).

Arms of Ried, Schärding and Braunau — A523

Photo. & Engr.
1979, June 1   **Perf. 14x13½**
1123 A523 3s multicolored   .55 .25
200th anniversary of Innviertel District.

Stream and City — A524

1979, June 1   **Perf. 13½x14**
1124 A524 2.50s multicolored   .40 .25
Control and eliminate water pollution.

Arms of Rottenmann A525

Photo. & Engr.
1979, June 22   **Perf. 14x13½**
1125 A525 3s multicolored   .95 .25
700th anniversary of Rottenmann.

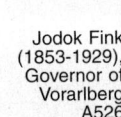

Jodok Fink (1853-1929), Governor of Vorarlberg A526

1979, June 29   **Engr.**   **Perf. 14**
1126 A526 3s brown carmine   .55 .25

Arms of Wels, Returnees' Emblem, "Europa Sail" — A527

1979, July 6   **Photo.**   **Perf. 14x13½**
1127 A527 4s yellow grn & blk   .65 .40
5th European Meeting of the Intl. Confederation of Former Prisoners of War, Wels, July 6-8.

Symbolic Flower, Conference Emblem — A528

1979, Aug. 20   **Litho.**   **Perf. 14x13½**
1128 A528 4s turq blue   .65 .40
UN Conf. for Science and Technology, Vienna, Aug. 20-31.

Donaupark, UNIDO and IAEA Emblems A529

1979, Aug. 24   **Engr.**   **Perf. 13½x14**
1129 A529 6s grayish blue   1.10 .55
Opening of the Donaupark Intl. Center in Vienna, seat of the UN Industrial Development Org. (UNIDO) and the Intl. Atomic Energy Agency (IAEA).

Diseased Eye and Blood Vessels A530

1979, Sept. 10   **Photo.**   **Perf. 14**
1130 A530 2.50s multicolored   .40 .25
10th World Congress of Intl. Diabetes Federation, Vienna, Sept. 9-14.

View of Stanz Valley through East Portal of Arlberg Tunnel A531

1979, Sept. 14   **Photo. & Engr.**
1131 A531 4s multicolored   .65 .40
16th World Road Cong., Vienna, 9/16-21.

Steam Printing Press A532

Photo. & Engr.
1979, Sept. 18   **Perf. 13½x14**
1132 A532 3s multicolored   .40 .25
Austrian Government Printing Office, 175th anniv.

Richard Zsigmondy (1865-1929), Chemist — A533

1979, Sept. 21 Engr.   Perf. 14x13½
1133 A533 6s multicolored   1.10 .55

"Save Energy" A534

1979, Oct. 1 Photo.   Perf. 14x13½
1134 A534 2.50s multicolored   .40 .25

Festival and Convention Center, Bregenz (Model) — A535

1979, Oct. 1 Engr.   Perf. 14
1135 A535 2.50s purple   .40 .25

Lions International Emblem A536

1979, Oct. 11 Photo. & Engr.
1136 A536 4s multicolored   .65 .40
25th Lions Europa Forum, Vienna, 10/11-13.

A537

Photo. & Engr.
1979, Oct. 19   Perf. 13½x14
1137 A537 2.50s Wilhelm Exner   .40 .25
Centenary of Technological Handicraft Museum, founded by Wilhelm Exner.

Modern Austrian Art — A538

The Compassionate Christ, by Hans Fronius.
1979, Oct. 23 Litho.   Perf. 13½x14
1138 A538 4s olive & ol blk   .65 .40

Locomotive and Arms — A539

1979, Oct. 24 Photo.   Perf. 13½x14
1139 A539 2.50s multicolored   .55 .25
Raab-Odenburg-Ebenfurt railroad, cent.

August Musger — A540

Photo. & Engr.
1979, Oct. 30   Perf. 14x13½
1140 A540 2.50s bl gray & blk   .40 .25
August Musger (1868-1929), developer of slow-motion film technique.

Nativity, St. Barbara's Church A541

1979, Nov. 30   Perf. 13½x14
1141 A541 4s multicolored   .65 .40
Christmas.

Arms of Baden — A542

1980, Jan. 25   Perf. 14
1142 A542 4s multicolored   .65 .40
Baden, 500th anniversary.

Fight Rheumatism A543

1980, Feb. 21   Perf. 13½
1143 A543 2.50s red & aqua   .40 .25

Austrian Exports — A544

1980, Feb. 21 Photo.   Perf. 14x13½
1144 A544 4s dark blue & red   .65 .40

Austrian Red Cross Centenary A545

1980, Mar. 14 Photo.   Perf. 13½x14
1145 A545 2.50s multicolored   .40 .25

Rudolph Kirchschlager A546

Photo. & Engr.
1980, Mar. 20   Perf. 14x13½
1146 A546 4s sepia & red   .65 .40

Robert Hamerling (1830-1889), Poet — A547

1980, Mar. 24 Engr.   Perf. 13½x14
1147 A547 2.50s olive green   .40 .25

Seal of Hallein — A548

Photo. & Engr.
1980, Apr. 30   Perf. 14x13½
1148 A548 4s red & black   .65 .40
Hallein, 750th anniversary.

Empress Maria Theresa (1717-80) A549

Paintings by: 2.50s, Andreas Moller. 4s, Martin van Meytens. 6s, Josef Ducreux.

1980, May 13 Engr.   Perf. 13½
1149 A549 2.50s violet brown   .65 .25
1150 A549 4s dark blue   .90 .40
1151 A549 6s rose lake   1.50 .80
  Nos. 1149-1151 (3)   3.05 1.45

Flags of Austria and Four Powers A550

1980, May 14 Photo.   Perf. 13½x14
1152 A550 4s multicolored   .65 .40
State Treaty, 25th anniversary.

St. Benedict, by Meinrad Guggenbichler A551

1980, May 16 Engr.   Perf. 14½
1153 A551 2.50s olive green   .40 .25
Congress of Benedictine Order of Austria.

Hygeia by Gustav Klimt — A552

1980, May 20 Photo.   Perf. 14
1154 A552 4s multicolored   .65 .40
Academic teaching of hygiene, 175th anniv.

Aflenz Ground Satellite Receiving Station A553

1980, May 30 Photo.   Perf. 14
1155 A553 6s multicolored   1.10 .55

Steyr, Etching, 1693 A554

Photo. & Engr.
1980, June 4   Perf. 13½
1156 A554 4s multicolored   .65 .40
Millennium of Steyr.

Worker, Oil Drill Head — A555

1980, June 12
1157 A555 2.50s multicolored   .40 .25
Austrian oil production, 25th anniversary.

Seal of Innsbruck, 1267 A556

1980, June 23   Perf. 13½x14½
1158 A556 2.50s multicolored   .40 .25
Innsbruck, 800th anniversary.

Duchy of Styria, 800th Anniv. — A557

Perf. 14½x13½
1980, June 23 **Photo.**
1159 A557 4s Duke's hat .65 .40

Leo Ascher (1880-1942), Composer A558

1980, Aug. 18 **Engr.** **Perf. 14**
1160 A558 3s dark purple .40 .25

Bible Illustration, Book of Genesis — A559

1980, Aug. 25 **Perf. 13½**
1161 A559 4s multicolored .65 .40
10th Intl. Cong. of the Org. for Old Testament Studies.

Europa Issue

Robert Stolz (1880-1975), Composer A560

1980, Aug. 25 **Engr.** **Perf. 14x13½**
1162 A560 6s red brown 1.20 .55

Old and Modern Bridges A561

1980, Sept. 1 **Photo.** **Perf. 13½**
1163 A561 4s multicolored .65 .40
11th Congress of the Intl. Assoc. for Bridge and Structural Engineering, Vienna.

Moon Figure, by Karl Brandstätter A562

Photo. & Engr.
1980, Oct. 10 **Perf. 14x13½**
1164 A562 4s multicolored .65 .40

Customs Service, Sesquicentennial A563

1980, Oct. 13 **Photo.**
1165 A563 2.50s multicolored .40 .25

Gazette Masthead, 1810 A564

1980, Oct. 23 **Photo.** **Perf. 13½**
1166 A564 2.50s multicolored .40 .25
Official Gazette of Linz, 350th anniversary.

Waidhofen Town Book Title Page, 14th Century — A565

1980, Oct. 24 **Perf. 14**
1167 A565 2.50s multicolored .40 .25
Waidhofen on Thaya, 750th anniversary.

Federal Austrian Army, 25th Anniversary A566

1980, Oct. 24 **Photo.** **Perf. 13½x14**
1168 A566 2.50s grnsh black & red .40 .25

Alfred Wegener A567

1980, Oct. 31 **Engr.**
1169 A567 4s violet blue .65 .40
Alfred Wegener (1880-1930), scientist, formulated theory of continental drift.

Robert Musil (1880-1942), Writer — A568

1980, Nov. 6 **Perf. 14x13½**
1170 A568 4s dark red brown .65 .40

Christmas — A569

Nativity, stained glass window, Klagenfurt.

Photo. & Engr.
1980, Nov. 28 **Perf. 13½**
1171 A569 4s multicolored .65 .40

25th Anniversary of Social Security A570

1981, Jan. 19 **Litho.** **Perf. 13½x14**
1172 A570 2.50s multicolored .35 .25

Niebelungen Saga, 1926, by Dachauer — A571

1981, Apr. 6 **Engr.** **Perf. 14x13½**
1173 A571 3s sepia .40 .25
Wilhelm Dachauer (1881-1951), artist and engraver.

Machinist in Wheelchair A572

1981, Apr. 6 **Photo. & Engr.**
1174 A572 6s multicolored .80 .55
Rehabilitation Intl., 3rd European Regional Conf.

Sigmund Freud (1856-1939), Psychoanalyst A573

1981, May 6 **Engr.**
1175 A573 3s rose violet .40 .25

Heating Engineers Union Congress, Vienna — A574

1981, May 11 **Photo.**
1176 A574 4s multicolored .55 .40

Kuenringer Exhibition, Zwettl Monastery A575

Azzo (founder of House of Kuenringer) and his followers, bear-skin manuscript.

1981, May 15 **Photo. & Engr.**
1177 A575 3s multicolored .40 .25

Europa — A576

1981, May 22 **Photo.**
1178 A576 6s Maypole 1.20 .55

Telephone Service Centenary A577

Photo. and Engr.
1981 May 29 **Perf. 13½x14**
1179 A577 4s multicolored .55 .40

Seibersdorf Research Center, 25th Anniv. — A578

1981, June 29 **Photo.** **Perf. 13½**
1180 A578 4s multicolored .55 .40

The Frog King (Child's Drawing) A579

1981, June 29 **Perf. 13½x14**
1181 A579 3s multicolored .40 .25

Town Hall and Town Seal of 1250 A580

Photo. & Engr.
1981, July 17 **Perf. 13½x14**
1182 A580 4s multicolored .55 .40
St. Veit an der Glan, 800th anniv.

Johann Florian Heller (1813-1871), Pioneer of Urinalysis — A581

1981, Aug. 31   *Perf. 14x13½*
1183 A581 6s red brown   .80 .55
11th Intl. Clinical Chemistry Congress.

Ludwig Boltzmann (1844-1906), Physicist — A582

1981, Sept. 4 Engr.   *Perf. 14x13½*
1184 A582 3s dark green   .40 .25

Intl. Pharmaceutical Federation World Congress, Vienna — A583

Photo. & Engr.
1981, Sept. 7   *Perf. 14*
1185 A583 6s Scale   .80 .55

Otto Bauer, Politician, Birth Centenary A584

1981, Sept. 7 Photo.   *Perf. 14x13½*
1186 A584 4s multicolored   .55 .40

Escher's Impossible Cube — A585

1981, Sept. 14
1187 A585 4s dk blue & brt blue   .55 .40
10th Intl. Mathematicians' Cong., Innsbruck.

Kneeling Virgin, Detail of Coronation of Mary Altarpiece, St. Wolfgang, 500th Anniv. — A586

1981, Sept. 25 Engr.   *Perf. 14x13½*
1188 A586 3s dark blue   .40 .25

South-East Fair, Graz, 75th Anniv. A587

1981, Sept. 25 Photo.   *Perf. 13½x14*
1189 A587 4s multicolored   .55 .40

Holy Trinity, 12th Cent. Byzantine Miniature A588

1981, Oct. 5
1190 A588 6s multicolored   .80 .55
16th Intl. Byzantine Congress.

Hans Kelsen (1881-1973), Co-author of Federal Constitution A589

1981, Oct. 9   *Engr.*
1191 A589 3s dark carmine   .40 .25

Edict of Tolerance Bicen. — A590

Photo. & Engr.
1981, Oct. 9   *Perf. 14*
1192 A590 4s Joseph II   .55 .40

World Food Day A591

1981, Oct. 16 Photo.   *Perf. 13½*
1193 A591 6s multicolored   .80 .55

Between the Times, by Oscar Asboth A592

1981, Oct. 22 Litho.   *Perf. 13½x14*
1194 A592 4s multicolored   .55 .40

Intl. Catholic Workers' Day — A593

Photo. & Engr.
1981, Oct. 23   *Perf. 14x13½*
1195 A593 3s multicolored   .40 .25

Baron Josef Hammer-Purgstall, Founder of Oriental Studies, 125th Death Anniv. — A594

Photo. & Engr.
1981, Nov. 23   *Perf. 14*
1196 A594 3s multicolored   .40 .25

Julius Raab (1891-1964), Politician A595

1981, Nov. 27 Engr.   *Perf. 13½*
1197 A595 6s rose lake   .75 .55

Nativity, Corn Straw Figures A596

1981, Nov. 27   **Photo. & Engr.**
1198 A596 4s multicolored   .50 .40
Christmas.

Stefan Zweig (1881-1942), Writer — A597

1981, Nov. 27 Engr.   *Perf. 14x13½*
1199 A597 4s dull violet   .50 .40

800th Anniv. of St. Nikola on the Danube A598

1981, Dec. 4   **Photo. & Engr.**
1200 A598 4s multicolored   .50 .40

Vienna Emergency Medical Service Centenary A599

1981, Dec. 9 Photo.   *Perf. 13½x14*
1201 A599 3s multicolored   .40 .25

Schladming-Haus Alpine World Skiing Championship — A600

1982, Jan. 27   *Perf. 14*
1202 A600 4s multicolored   .50 .35

Dorotheum (State Auction Gallery), 275th Anniv. — A601

Photo. & Engr.
1982, Mar. 12   *Perf. 14*
1203 A601 4s multicolored   .50 .35

Water Rescue Service, 25th Anniv. — A602

1982, Mar. 19 Photo.   *Perf. 14x13½*
1204 A602 5s multicolored   .65 .50

St. Severin and the End of the Roman Era Exhibition — A603

Photo. & Engr.
1982, Apr. 23   *Perf. 14x13½*
1205 A603 3s St. Severin   .40 .25

Intl. Kneipp Hydropathy Congress, Vienna — A604

1982, May 4   *Perf. 14*
1206 A604 4s multicolored   .50 .40

Printing in Austria, 500th Anniv. — A605

1982, May 7
1207 A605 4s Printers' guild arms   .50 .40

5th European Urology Soc. Cong., Vienna — A606

Design: Urine analysis, Canone di Avicenna manuscript.

1982, May 12   Photo.
1208 A606 6s multicolored   .75 .55

St. Francis of Assisi, 800th Birth Anniv. — A607

1982, May 14   Photo. & Engr.
1209 A607 3s multicolored   .40 .25

Haydn and His Time Exhibition, Rohrau — A608

1982, May 19   Engr.   *Perf. 13½*
1210 A608 3s olive green   .50 .25

25th World Milk Day — A609

1982, May 25   Photo.   *Perf. 14x13½*
1211 A609 7s multicolored   .95 .65

800th Anniv of Gfohl (Market Town) — A610

Photo. & Engr.
1982, May 28   *Perf. 14*
1212 A610 4s multicolored   .50 .40

Tennis Player and Austrian Tennis Federation Emblem — A611

1982, June 11
1213 A611 3s multicolored   .40 .25

900th Anniv. of City of Langenlois A612

Photo. & Engr.
1982, June 11   *Perf. 13½x14*
1214 A612 4s multicolored   .50 .35

800th Anniv. of City of Weiz — A613

1982, June 18   Photo.   *Perf. 14x13½*
1215 A613 4s Arms   1.10 .35

Ignaz Seipel (1876-1932), Statesman A614

1982, July 30   Engr.   *Perf. 14x13½*
1216 A614 3s brown violet   .40 .25

Europa Issue

Sesquicentennial of Linz-Freistadt-Budweis Horse-drawn Railroad — A615

1982, July 30   *Perf. 13½*
1217 A615 6s brown   1.60 .55

Mail Bus Service, 75th Anniv. — A616

1982, Aug. 6   Photo.   *Perf. 14x13½*
1218 A616 4s multicolored   .50 .40

Rocket Lift-off — A617

1982, Aug. 9   *Perf. 14*
1219 A617 4s multicolored   .50 .40
2nd UN Conference on Peaceful Uses of Outer Space, Vienna, Aug. 9-21.

Geodesists' Day — A618

Photo. & Engr.
1982, Sept. 1   *Perf. 13½x14*
1220 A618 3s Tower, Office of Standards   .40 .25

Protection of Endangered Species — A619

1982, Sept. 9   *Perf. 14*
1221 A619 3s Bustard   .40 .40
1222 A619 4s Beaver   .55 .55
1223 A619 6s Capercaillie   .80 .80
   Nos. 1221-1223 (3)   1.75 1.75

10th Anniv. of Intl. Institute for Applied Systems Analysis, Vienna A620

1982, Oct. 4   Photo.
1224 A620 3s Laxenburg Castle   .35 .25

St. Apollonia (Patron Saint of Dentists) A621

1982, Oct. 11   Photo. & Engr.
1225 A621 4s multicolored   .50 .40
70th Annual World Congress of Dentists.

Emmerich Kalman (1882-1953), Composer A622

1982, Oct. 22   Engr.   *Perf. 13½*
1226 A622 3s dark blue   .40 .25

Max Mell (1882-1971), Poet — A623

1982, Nov. 10   Photo.   *Perf. 14x13½*
1227 A623 3s multicolored   .40 .25

Christmas A624

Design: Christmas crib, Damuls Church, Vorarlberg, 1630.

Photo. & Engr.
1982, Nov. 25   *Perf. 13½*
1228 A624 4s multicolored   .50 .40

Centenary of St. George's College, Istanbul — A625

1982, Nov. 26   Litho.   *Perf. 14*
1229 A625 4s Bosporus   .50 .40

Portrait of a Girl, by Ernst Fuchs — A626

1982, Dec. 10   Photo. & Engr.
1230 A626 4s multicolored   .50 .40

Postal Savings Bank Centenary A627

Photo. & Engr.
1983, Jan. 12   *Perf. 14*
1231 A627 4s Bank   .50 .40

Hildegard Burjan (1883-1933), Founder of Caritas Socialis A628

1983, Jan. 28   Engr.
1232 A628 4s rose lake   .50 .40

World Communications Year — A629

1983, Feb. 18   Photo.   Perf. 13½x14
1233 A629 7s multicolored   .90   .55

75th Anniv. Children's Friends Org. — A630

Photo. & Engr.
1983, Feb. 23   Perf. 14x13½
1234 A630 4s multicolored   .50   .40

Josef Matthias Hauer (1883-1959), Composer A631

1983, Mar. 18   Engr.   Perf. 14
1235 A631 3s deep lilac rose   .35   .25

25th Anniv. of Austrian Airlines A632

1983, Mar. 31   Photo.   Perf. 13½x14
1236 A632 6s multicolored   .75   .55

Work Inspection Centenary A633

1983, Apr. 8   Photo.   Perf. 13½
1237 A633 4s multicolored   .50   .40

Upper Austria Millennium Provincial Exhibition — A634

3s, Wels Castle, by Matthaus Merian.

1983, Apr. 28   Photo.   Perf. 13½
1238 A634 3s multicolored   .35   .25

Gottweig Monastery, 900th Anniv. — A635

Photo. & Engr.
1983, Apr. 29   Perf. 13½
1239 A635 3s multicolored   .40   .25

7th World Pacemakers Symposium A636

1983, Apr. 29   Photo.   Perf. 14x13½
1240 A636 4s multicolored   .50   .40

Catholic Students' Org. A637

1983, May 20   Photo.   Perf. 14
1241 A637 4s multicolored   .50   .40

Weitra, 800th Anniv. A638

Photo. & Engr.
1983, May 20   Perf. 13½
1242 A638 4s multicolored   .50   .40

Granting of Town Rights to Hohenems, 650th Anniv. — A639

1983, May 27   Photo.   Perf. 14
1243 A639 4s multicolored   .50   .40

25th Anniv. of Stadthall, Vienna A640

1983, June 24   Photo.   Perf. 14
1244 A640 4s multicolored   .50   .40

Viktor Franz Hess (1883-1964), 1936 Nobel Prize Winner in Physics — A641

1983, June 24   Engr.   Perf. 14x13½
1245 A641 6s dark green   1.20   .55

Europa.

Kiwanis Intl. Convention, Vienna — A642

1983, July 1   Photo.   Perf. 13½
1246 A642 5s multicolored   .65   .50

7th World Congress of Psychiatry, Vienna — A643

4s, Emblem, St. Stephen's Cathedral.

1983, July 11   Photo.   Perf. 14
1247 A643 4s multicolored   .50   .35

Baron Carl von Hasenauer (1833-1894), Architect A644

3s, Natural History Museum, Vienna.

1983, July 20   Engr.   Perf. 13½x14
1248 A644 3s chocolate   .40   .25

27th Intl. Chamber of Commerce Professional Competition, Linz — A645

1983, Aug. 16   Photo.
1249 A645 4s Chamber building   .55   .40

13th Intl. Chemotherapy Congress, Vienna, Aug. 28-Sept. 2 — A646

5s, Penicillin test on cancer.

1983, Aug. 26
1250 A646 5s multicolored   .55   .50

Catholics' Day — A647

1983, Sept. 9   Photo.   Perf. 14x13½
1251 A647 3s multicolored   .40   .25

Visit of Pope John Paul II — A648

Photo. & Engr.
1983, Sept. 9   Perf. 13½
1252 A648 6s multicolored   .95   .55

Souvenir Sheet

Battle of 1683 to Relieve Vienna, by Frans Geffel — A649

1983, Sept. 9   Perf. 14
1253 A649 6s multicolored   .95 1.20

300th anniv. of Vienna's relief from Turkish siege.

Vienna Rathaus Centenary A650

1983, Sept. 23   Perf. 13½x14
1254 A650 4s multicolored   .55   .35

Karl von Terzaghi (1883-1963), Founder of Soil Mechanics A651

1983, Oct. 3   Engr.
1255 A651 3s dark blue   .40   .25

10th Trade Unions Federal Congress, Oct. 3-8 A652

1983, Oct. 3   Photo.   Perf. 13½
1256 A652 3s black & red   .40   .25

Evening Sun in Burgenland, by Gottfried Kumpf — A653

Photo. & Engr.
1983, Oct. 7 *Perf. 13½x14*
1257 A653 4s multicolored .50 .40

Modling-Hinterbruhl Electric Railroad Centenary — A654

1983, Oct. 21 Photo.
1258 A654 3s multicolored .50 .25

Provincial Museum of Upper Austria Sesquicentennial — A655

4s, Francisco-Carolinum Museum.

1983, Nov. 4 Photo. & Engr.
1259 A655 4s multicolored .55 .40

Creche, St. Andreas Parish Church, Kitzbuhel A656

1983, Nov. 25 *Perf. 14*
1260 A656 4s multicolored .50 .40
Christmas.

Parliament Bldg. Vienna, 100th Anniv. — A657

1983, Dec. 2 Engr.
1261 A657 4s slate blue .55 .40

Altar Picture, St. Nikola/Pram Church — A658

1983, Dec. 6 Photo. *Perf. 14x13½*
1262 A658 3s multicolored .40 .25

Wolfgang Pauli (1900-58), Physicist, Nobel Laureate — A659

1983, Dec. 15 Engr. *Perf. 14½x13½*
1263 A659 6s dark red brn .80 .55

Gregor Mendel (1822-1884), Genetics Founder — A660

Photo. & Engr.
1984, Jan. 5 *Perf. 13½*
1264 A660 4s multicolored .50 .40

Anton Hanak (1875-1934), Sculptor — A661

1984, Jan. 5
1265 A661 3s red brown & blk .40 .25

50th Anniv. of 1934 Uprising — A662

4.50s, Memorial, Woellersdorf.

1984, Feb. 10 Photo. *Perf. 14*
1266 A662 4.50s black & red .55 .40

Wernher von Reichersberg Family, Bas-relief, 15th Cent. — A663

Photo. & Engr.
1984, Apr. 25 *Perf. 14x13½*
1267 A663 3.50s brown & blue .40 .35
900th anniv. of Reichersberg Monastery.

Tobacco Monopoly Bicentenary A665

4.50s, Cigar wrapper, tobacco plant.

1984, May 4 *Perf. 13½*
1269 A665 4.50s multicolored .55 .40

1200th Anniv. of Kostendorf Municipality A666

1984, May 4
1270 A666 4.50s View, arms .55 .40

Automobile Engineers World Congress A667

5s, Wheel bearing cross-section.

1984, May 4 Photo. *Perf. 13½x14*
1271 A667 5s multicolored .65 .40

Europa (1959-1984) A668

1984, May 4 *Perf. 13½*
1272 A668 6s multicolored 1.60 .65

Archduke Johann (1782-1859), by S. von Carolsfeld A669

Photo. & Engr.
1984, May 11 *Perf. 14*
1273 A669 4.50s multicolored .55 .40

Ore and Iron Provincial Exhibition A670

1984, May 11 *Perf. 13½*
1274 A670 3.50s Aragonite .40 .25

Era of Emperor Francis Joseph Exhibition A671

Design: Cover of Viribus Unitis, publ. by Max Herzig, 1898.

1984, May 18
1275 A671 3.50s red & gold .50 .35

City of Vocklabruck, 850th Anniv. — A672

Photo. & Engr.
1984, May 30 *Perf. 14x13½*
1276 A672 4.50s Tower, arms .55 .40

Museum of Carinthia, Cent. — A673

Dionysius, Virinum mosaic.

1984, June 1 *Perf. 13½*
1277 A673 3.50s multicolored .40 .25

Erosion Prevention Systems Centenary A674

4.50s, Stone reinforcement wall.

1984, June 5 Engr. *Perf. 14*
1278 A674 4.50s grnish black .55 .40

Tyrol Provincial Celebration, 1809-1984 A675

Art Exhibition: Meeting of Imperial Troops with South Tyrolean Reserves under Andreas Hofer near Sterzing in April 1809, by Ludwig Schnorr von Carolsfeld, 1830.

Photo. & Engr.
1984, June 5 *Perf. 14x13½*
1279 A675 3.50s multicolored .40 .25

Ralph Benatzky (1884-1957), Composer A676

1984, June 5 Engr.
1280 A676 4s violet brown .50 .40

Christian von Ehrenfels (1859-1932), Philosopher A677

1984, June 22   Photo.   Perf. 14
1281 A677 3.50s multicolored   .40   .25

25th Anniv. of Minimundus (Model City) A678

4s, Eiffel Tower, Tower of Pisa, ferris wheel.

1984, June 22   Perf. 13½x14
1282 A678 4s multicolored   .50   .40

Blockheide Eibenstein Nature Park A679

1984   Photo. & Engr.
1283 A679 4s shown   .50   .40
1284 A679 4s Lake Neusiedl   .50   .40

Issued: No. 1283, June 29; No. 1284, Aug. 13.
See Nos. 1349-1354, 1492-1499, 1744, 1777, 1813, 1843.

Monasteries and Abbeys — A679a

Designs: 3.50s, Geras Monastery, Lower Austria. 4s, Stams. 4.50s, Schlagl. 5s, Benedictine Abbey of St. Paul, Levanttal. 6s, Rein-Hohenfurth.

1984-85   Perf. 14
1285 A679a 3.50s multi   .80   .25
1286 A679a 4s multi   .80   .25
1287 A679a 4.50s multi   .80   .25
1288 A679a 5s multi   .80   .25
1288A A679a 6s multi   1.10   .25
   Nos. 1285-1288A (5)   4.30 1.25

Issued: 3.50s, 4/27/84; 4s, 9/28/84; 4.50s, 5/18/84; 5s, 9/27/85; 6s, 10/4/84.
See Nos. 1361-1365, 1465-1472.

Schanatobel Railroad Bridge — A680

Railroad Anniversaries: 3.50s, Arlberg centenary. 4.50s, Falkenstein Bridge, Tauern, 75th.

1984, July 6   Perf. 14
1289 A680 3.50s shown   .65   .40
1290 A680 4.50s multicolored   .80   .50

Balloon Flight in Austria Bicent. — A681

6s, Johan Stuwer's balloon.

1984, July 6   Photo.
1291 A681 6s multicolored   .75   .55

Intl. Lawyers' Congress, Vienna — A682

7s, Vienna Palace of Justice, emblem.

1984, Aug. 31   Photo. & Engr.
1292 A682 7s multicolored   .95   .75

7th European Anatomy Congress, Innsbruck — A683

6s, Josef Hyrtl, anatomist.

1984, Sept. 3   Photo.
1293 A683 6s multicolored   .80   .50

Window, by Karl Korab — A684

1984, Oct. 12
1294 A684 4s multicolored   .50   .35

Johannes of Gmunden, Mathematician, 600th Birth Anniv. — A685

3.50s, Clock (Immset Uhr), 1555.

1984, Oct. 18
1295 A685 3.50s multicolored   .40   .35

Concordia Press Club, 125th Anniv. — A686

1984, Nov. 9   Photo.   Perf. 13½
1296 A686 4.50s Quill   .55   .40

Fanny Eissler, Dancer, Death Centenary — A687

1984, Nov. 23   Photo. & Engr.
1297 A687 4s multicolored   .55   .35

Christmas A688

Design: Christ is Born, Aggsbacher Altar, Herzogenburg Monastery.

1984, Nov. 30   Perf. 14
1298 A688 4.50s multicolored   .55   .40

Karl Franzens University, Graz, 400th Anniv. — A689

1985, Jan. 4   Perf. 14x13½
1299 A689 3.50s Seal   .40   .35

Dr. Lorenz Bohler, Surgeon, Birth Cent. — A690

1985, Jan. 15   Engr.
1300 A690 4.50s dk rose lake   .55   .40

Nordic Events, Ski Championships, Seefeld — A691

4s, Ski jumper, cross country racer.

1985, Jan. 17   Photo.   Perf. 13½
1301 A691 4s multicolored   .55   .40

Linz Diocese Bicentenary A692

4.50s, Linz Cathedral interior.

1985, Jan. 25
1302 A692 4.50s gold & multi   .55   .40

Alban Berg (1885-1935), Composer A693

1985, Feb. 8   Engr.
1303 A693 6s bluish black   .80   .55

Vocational Training Inst., 25th Anniv. A694

1985, Feb. 15   Photo.   Perf. 13½x14
1304 A694 4.50s multicolored   .55   .40

City of Bregenz, Bimillennium A695

1985, Feb. 22   Perf. 14x13½
1305 A695 4s multicolored   .50   .35

Austrian Registration Labels Cent. A696

1985, Mar. 15   Perf. 13½x14
1306 A696 4.50s Label, 1885   .55   .40

Josef Stefan (1835-1893), Physicist — A697

Photo. & Engr.
1985, Mar. 22   Perf. 14x13½
1307 A697 6s buff, dl red brn &
            dk brn   .80   .55

St. Leopold Exhibition, Klosterneuberg A698

St. Leopold 16th-17th cent. embroidery.

1985, Mar. 29
1308 A698 3.50s multicolored .40 .35

Liberation From German Occupation, 40th Anniv. — A699

1985, Apr. 26 Photo.
1309 A699 4.50s multicolored .55 .40

Painter Franz von Defregger (1835-1921) A700

3.50s, Fairy tale teller.

1985, Apr. 26
1310 A700 3.50s gold & multi .40 .35

Europa Issue

Johann Joseph Fux (1660-1741), Composer, Violin and Trombone A701

Photo. & Engr.
1985, May 3 Perf. 13½
1311 A701 6s lil gray & dk brn 1.60 .65

Boheimkirchen (Market Town) Millennium — A702

4.50s, View, coat of arms.

1985, May 10 Perf. 14
1312 A702 4.50s gold & multi .55 .40

European Free Trade Assoc., 25th Anniv. — A703

Mercury staff, flags of member and affiliate nations.

1985, May 10 Photo. Perf. 13½
1313 A703 4s multicolored .50 .40

St. Polten Diocese, Bicent. — A704

Episcopal residence gate, St. Polten diocese arms.

1985, May 15 Photo. & Engr.
1314 A704 4.50s multicolored .55 .40

The Gumpp Family of Builders, Innsbruck — A705

Perf. 14½x13½
1985, May 17 Photo.
1315 A705 3.50s multicolored .40 .35

Garsten Market Town Millennium A706

Design: 17th century engraving by George Matthaus Fischer (1628-1696).

Photo. & Engr.
1985, June 7 Perf. 13½x14
1316 A706 4.50s multicolored .55 .40

UN, 40th Anniv. A707

Perf. 13½x14½
1985, June 26 Photo.
1317 A707 4s multicolored .55 .40
Austrian membership, 30th anniv.

Intl. Assoc. for the Prevention of Suicide, 13th Congress A708

Photo. & Engr.
1985, June 28 Perf. 14
1318 A708 5s brn, lt ap grn & yel .65 .50

Souvenir Sheet

Year of the Forest — A709

6s, Healthy and damaged woodland.

1985, June 28 Perf. 13½
1319 A709 6s multicolored 1.10 1.10

Kurhaus, Bad Ischl Operetta Activities Emblem A710

1985, July 5 Perf. 14
1320 A710 3.50s multicolored .50 .40
Bad Ischl Festival, 25th anniv.

Intl. Competition of Fire Brigades, Vocklabruck A711

4.50s, Fireman, emblem.

1985, July 18 Photo. Perf. 14x13½
1321 A711 4.50s multicolored .80 .40

Grossglockner Alpine Motorway, 50th Anniv. — A712

4s, View of Fuschertorl.

Photo. & Engr.
1985, Aug. 2 Perf. 13½
1322 A712 4s multicolored .50 .40

World Chess Federation Congress, Graz — A713

4s, Checkered globe, emblem.

1985, Aug. 28 Photo. Perf. 13½
1323 A713 4s multicolored .50 .40

The Legendary Foundation of Konigstetten by Charlemagne, by Auguste Stephan, c. 1870 — A714

Photo. & Engr.
1985, Aug. 30 Perf. 14
1324 A714 4.50s multicolored .55 .40
Konigstetten millennium.

Hofkirchen-Taufkirchen-Weibern Municipalities, 1200th Anniv. — A715

4.50s, View of Weibern, municipal arms.

1985, Aug. 30 Perf. 13½x14
1325 A715 4.50s multi .55 .40

Dr. Adam Politzer (1835-1923), Physician A716

1985, Sept. 12 Engr. Perf. 14
1326 A716 3.50s blue violet .50 .35
Politzer pioneered aural therapy for auditory disorders.

Intl. Assoc. of Forwarding Agents, World Congress, Vienna — A717

1985, Oct. 7 Photo. Perf. 13½
1327 A717 6s multicolored .80 .55

Carnival Figures Riding High Bicycles, By Paul Flora A718

Photo. & Engr.
1985, Oct. 25 Perf. 14
1328 A718 4s multicolored .55 .40

St. Martin on Horseback A719

1985, Nov. 8 Photo.
1329 A719 4.50s multicolored .55 .40
Eisenstadt Diocese, 25th anniv.

Creche, Marble Bas-relief, Salzburg — A720

Photo. & Engr.
1985, Nov. 29   *Perf. 13½*
1330 A720 4.50s gold, dl vio & buff   .55 .35
Christmas.

Hanns Horbiger (1860-1931), Inventor A721

1985, Nov. 29   *Perf. 14*
1331 A721 3.50s gold & sepia   .40 .35

Aqueduct, Hundsau Brook, Near Gostling A722

1985, Nov. 29   *Perf. 13½x14½*
1332 A722 3.50s red, bluish blk & brt ultra   .40 .35
Vienna Aqueduct, 75th anniv.

Chateau de la Muette, Paris Headquarters — A723

1985, Dec. 13
1333 A723 4s sep, rose lil & gold   .50 .40
Org. for Economic Cooperation and Development, 25th anniv.

Johann Bohm (1886-1959), Pres. Austrian Trade Fed. — A724

1986, Jan. 24   **Photo.**   *Perf. 14*
1334 A724 4.50s blk, ver & grayish black   .55 .45

Intl. Peace Year — A725

Perf. 13½x14½
1986, Jan. 24   **Photo.**
1335 A725 6s multicolored   .75 .50

Digital Telephone Service Introduction A726

5s, Push-button keyboard.

1986, Jan. 29   **Photo.**
1336 A726 5s multicolored   .55 .40

Johann Georg Albrechtsberger (b. 1736), Composer — A727

3.50s, Klosterneuberg organ.

Photo. & Engr.
1986, Jan. 31   *Perf. 13½x14½*
1337 A727 3.50s multicolored   .40 .35

Korneuburg, 850th Anniv. — A728

1986, Feb. 7   **Photo.**   *Perf. 14*
1338 A728 5s multicolored   .65 .40

Self-portrait, by Oskar Kokoschka (b.1886) — A729

Perf. 14½x13½
1986, Feb. 28   **Photo.**
1339 A729 4s multicolored   .55 .35

Admission to Council of Europe, 30th Anniv. — A730

1986, Feb. 28 **Photo.** *Perf. 13x13½*
1340 A730 6s multicolored   .80 .55

Clemens Holzmeister (b. 1886), Architect, Salzburg Festival Theater, 1926 — A731

Photo. & Engr.
1986, Mar. 27   *Perf. 13½*
1341 A731 4s sepia & redsh brn   .50 .40

3rd Intl. Geotextile Congress, Vienna A732

1986, Apr. 7 Photo. *Perf. 13½x14½*
1342 A732 5s multicolored   .65 .40

Prince Eugen and Schlosshof Castle A733

Photo. & Engr.
1986, Apr. 21   *Perf. 14*
1343 A733 4s multicolored   .50 .40
Prince Eugen Exhibition, Schlosshof and Niederweiden.

St. Florian Monastery, Upper Austria A734

1986, Apr. 24
1344 A734 4s multicolored   .50 .40
The World of Baroque provincial exhibition, St. Florian.

Herberstein Castle, Arms of Styria A735

1986, May 2   *Perf. 13½x14½*
1345 A735 4s multicolored   .50 .40

Pasque Flower — A736

1986, May 2   *Perf. 13½*
1346 A736 6s multicolored   1.60 .55
Europa 1986.

Antimonite A738

1986, May 23   *Perf. 13½x14½*
1348 A738 4s multicolored   .50 .40
Burgenland Provincial Minerals Exhibition.

Scenery Type of 1984
No. 1349, Martinswall, Tyrol. No. 1350, Tschauko Falls, Carinthia. No. 1351, Dachstein Ice Caves. No. 1352, Gauertal, Montafon. No. 1353, Krimmler Waterfalls. No. 1354, Lusthauswasser.

1986-89 Photo. & Engr. *Perf. 14*
1349 A679 5s multicolored   .75 .50
1350 A679 5s multicolored   .65 .50
1351 A679 5s multicolored   .65 .40
1352 A679 5s multicolored   .65 .40
1353 A679 5s multicolored   .65 .50
1354 A679 5s multicolored   .65 .40
Nos. 1349-1354 (6)   4.00 2.70
Issued: No. 1349, 6/13/86; No. 1350, 7/4/86; No. 1351, 6/11/87; No. 1352, 8/21/87; No. 1353, 8/19/88; No. 1354, 9/1/89.

Waidhofen on Ybbs Township, 800th Anniv. — A739

1986, June 20   Photo.   *Perf. 13½*
1355 A739 4s multicolored   .55 .40

Salzburg Local Railway, Cent. A740

1986, Aug. 8   Photo.   *Perf. 14*
1356 A740 4s multicolored   .55 .40

Seals of Dukes Leopold Of Austria, Otakar of Styria, and Georgenberg Church — A741

1986, Aug. 14   Photo. & Engr.
1357 A741 5s multicolored   .65 .50
Georgenberg Treaty, 800th anniv.

Julius Tandler (1869-1936), Social Reformer A742

1986, Aug. 22
1358 A742 4s multicolored   .50 .40

Sonnblick Observatory, Cent. A743

4s, Observatory, 1886.

Photo. & Engr.
1986, Sept. 5   *Perf. 13½x14½*
1359 A743 4s multicolored   .50   .40

Discovery of Mandrake Root — A744

1986, Sept. 8   *Perf. 14½x13½*
1360 A744 5s multicolored   .65   .40
European Assoc. for Anesthesiology, 7th cong.

Monasteries and Abbeys Type of 1984

Designs: 5.50s, St. Gerold's Provostry, Vorarlberg. 7s, Loretto Monastery, Burgenland. 7.50s, Dominican Convent, Vienna. 8s, Zwettl Monastery. 10s, Wilten Monastery.

1986-88 **Photo. & Engr.** *Perf. 14*
1361 A679a 5.50s multicolored   1.10   .25
1362 A679a 7s multicolored   1.60   .25
1363 A679a 7.50s multicolored   1.60   .25
1364 A679a 8s multicolored   1.60   .25
1365 A679a 10s multicolored   1.90   .25
    Nos. 1361-1365 (5)   7.80 1.25

Issued: 5.50s, 9/12/86; 7.50s, 10/3; 7s, 8/14/87; 8s, 5/27/88; 10s, 3/18/88.

Otto Stoessl (d. 1936), Writer — A745

Photo. & Engr.
1986, Sept. 19   *Perf. 14*
1366 A745 4s multicolored   .50   .40

Vienna Fire Brigade, 300th Anniv. — A746

1986, Sept. 19   *Photo.*
1367 A746 4s Fireman, 1686   .80   .40

Silk Viennese Hunting Tapestry A747

Photo. & Engr.
1986, Sept. 19   *Perf. 14*
1368 A747 5s multicolored   .65   .50
Intl. conf. on Oriental Carpets, Vienna, Budapest.

Minister at Pulpit — A748

Photo. & Engr.
1986, Oct. 10   *Perf. 14*
1369 A748 5s blk & rose lilac   .65   .50
Protestant Act, 25th anniv., and Protestant Patent of Franz Josef I ensuring religious equality, 125th anniv.

Disintegration, by Walter Schmogner A749

1986, Oct. 17   *Perf. 13½x14*
1370 A749 4s multicolored   .55   .40

Franz Liszt, Composer, and Birthplace, Burgenland A750

1986, Oct. 17   *Perf. 13½*
1371 A750 5s green & sepia   .65   .40

Souvenir Sheet

European Security Conference, Vienna — A751

1986, Nov. 4   *Perf. 13½x14*
1372 A751 6s Vienna   .90 1.20

Strettweg Cart, 7th Cent. B.C. A752

Photo. & Engr.
1986, Nov. 26   *Perf. 14*
1373 A752 4s multicolored   .50   .40
Joanneum Styrian Land Museum, 175th anniv.

Christmas A753

Design: The Little Crib, bas-relief by Schwanthaler (1740-1810), Schlierbach Monastery.

1986, Nov. 28
1374 A753 5s gold & rose lake   .65   .50

Federal Chamber of Commerce, 40th Anniv. — A754

1986, Dec. 2   *Photo.*
1375 A754 5s multicolored   .65   .50

Industry A755

No. 1376, Steel workers. No. 1377, Office worker, computer. No. 1378, Lab assistant. No. 1379, Textile worker. No. 1380, Bricklayer.

1986-91   *Perf. 14x13½*
1376 A755 4s multicolored   .50   .40
1377 A755 4s multicolored   .55   .40
1378 A755 4s multicolored   .55   .35
1379 A755 4.50s multicolored   .55   .40
1380 A755 5s multicolored   .50   .50
    Nos. 1376-1380 (5)   2.80 2.05

Issued: No. 1376, 12/4/86; No. 1377, 10/5/87; No. 1378, 10/21/88; 5s, 10/10/89; 4.50s, 10/11/91.

The Educated Eye, by Arnulf Rainer — A756

1987, Jan. 22 Photo.   *Perf. 13½x14*
1386 A756 5s multicolored   .80   .60
Adult education in Vienna, cent.

The Large Blue Madonna, by Anton Faistauer (1887-1970) — A757

Paintings: 6s, Self-portrait, 1922, by A. Paris Gutersloh (1887-1973).

1987, Feb. 13   *Perf. 14*
1387 A757 4s multicolored   .60   .40
1388 A757 6s multicolored   1.00   .70

Hundertwasser House — A758

Photo. & Engr.
1987, Apr. 6   *Perf. 13½x14*
1389 A758 6s multicolored   2.00 1.00
Europa 1987.

World Ice Hockey Championships, Vienna — A759

Perf. 13½x14½
1987, Apr. 17   *Photo.*
1390 A759 5s multicolored   1.00   .60

Opening of the Austria Center, Vienna A760

1987, Apr. 22
1391 A760 5s multicolored   1.00   .60

Salzburg City Charter, 700th Anniv. A761

1987, Apr. 24
1392 A761 5s multicolored   1.10   .70

Work-Men-Machines, Provincial Exhibition, Upper Austria — A762

Photo. & Engr.
1987, Apr. 29   *Perf. 14*
1393 A762 4s Factory, 1920   .70   .40

Equal Rights for Men and Women — A763

1987, Apr. 29 Photo.   *Perf. 13½*
1394 A763 5s multicolored   .80   .60

Adele Block-Bauer I, Abstract by Gustav Klimt — A764

Photo. & Engr.

1987, May 8   *Perf. 13½*
1395 A764 4s multicolored   .70   .40
The Era of Emperor Franz Joseph, provincial exhibition, Lower Austria.

Arthur Schnitzler (1862-1931), Poet — A765

1987, May 15   *Perf. 14½x13½*
1396 A765 6s multicolored   .90   .70

Von Raitenau, View of Salzburg A766

1987, May 15   *Perf. 14*
1397 A766 4s multicolored   .60   .50
Prince Archbishop Wolf Dietrich von Raitenau, patron of baroque architecture in Salzburg, provincial exhibition.

Lace, Lustenau Municipal Arms A767

1987, May 22
1398 A767 5s multicolored   .80   .60
Lustenau, 1100th anniv.

Souvenir Sheet

Austrian Railways Sesquicentenary — A768

1987, June 5   Photo.   *Perf. 13½*
1399 A768 6s multicolored   1.10 1.10

8th Intl. Congress of Engravers, Vienna A769

Photo. & Engr.

1987, June 17   *Perf. 14*
1400 A769 5s gray, gray brn & dull rose   .80 .50

Dr. Karl Josef Bayer (1847-1904), Chemist — A770

1987, June 22   *Perf. 14x13½*
1401 A770 5s multicolored   .80   .60
Eighth Intl. Light Metals Congress, June 22-26, Leoben and Vienna; Bayer Technique for producing aluminum oxide from bauxite, cent.

Shipping on Achensee, Cent. — A771

1987, June 26   Photo.
1402 A771 4s multicolored   .60   .50

Ombudsmen's Office, 10th Anniv. — A772

5s, Palais Rottal, Vienna.

1987, July 1
1403 A772 5s multicolored   .80   .60

Dr. Erwin Schrodinger (1887-1961), 1933 Nobel Laureate in Physics — A773

1987, Aug. 11   **Photo. & Engr.**
1404 A773 5s dull olive bister, choc & buff   .80 .60

Freistadt Exhibitions, 125th Anniv. A774

1987, Aug. 11   *Perf. 14x14½*
1405 A774 5s multicolored   .80   .60

Arbing, 850th Anniv. — A775

1987, Aug. 21   *Perf. 13½*
1406 A775 5s multicolored   .80   .60

1987 World Cycling Championships, Villach to Vienna — A776

1987, Aug. 25   *Perf. 14*
1407 A776 5s multicolored   .80   .60

World Congress of Savings Banks, Vienna A777

Perf. 13½x14½
1987, Sept. 9   Photo.
1408 A777 5s multicolored   .80   .60

Johann Michael Haydn (1737-1806), Composer A778

Perf. 13½x14½
1987, Sept. 14   Engr.
1409 A778 4s dull violet   .60   .50

Paul Hofhaymer (1459-1537), Composer A779

Photo. & Engr.
1987, Sept. 11   *Perf. 14*
1410 A779 4s gold, blk & ultra   .60   .50

Bearded Vulture — A780

1987, Sept. 25
1411 A780 4s multicolored   .60   .50
Innsbruck Zoo, 25th anniv.

Baumgottinnen, by Arnulf Neuwirth — A781

1987, Oct. 9   *Perf. 14x13½*
1412 A781 5s multicolored   .80   .60
Modern Art.

Gambling Monopoly, 200th Anniv. — A782

Perf. 14½x13½
1987, Oct. 30   Photo.
1413 A782 5s Lottery drum   .80   .60

Christoph Willibald Gluck (1714-1787), Composer A784

Photo. & Engr.
1987, Nov. 13   *Perf. 14*
1415 A784 5s cream & blk   .80   .60

Oskar Helmer (b. 1887), Politician — A785

1987, Nov. 13
1416 A785 4s multicolored   .60   .50

Joseph Mohr (1792-1848) and Franz Gruber (1787-1863), Opening Bars of "Silent Night, Holy Night" — A786

1987, Nov. 27
1417 A786 5s multicolored   1.20   .60
Christmas.

Intl. Education Congress of Salesian Fathers — A787

5s, St. John Bosco, children.

Photo. & Engr.
1988, Jan. 12   *Perf. 13½*
1418 A787 5s multicolored   .80   .60

Ernst Mach (1838-1916), Physicist — A788

Photo. & Engr.
1988, Feb. 19 Perf. 14½x13½
1419 A788 6s multicolored .90 .60

Village with Bridge (1904), by Franz von Zulow (1883-1963), Painter — A789

1988, Feb. 25 Photo. Perf. 14½x14
1420 A789 4s multicolored .70 .50

Biedermeier Provincial Exhibition, Vormarz in Vienna — A790

Painting: Confiscation, by Ferdinand Georg Waldmuller (1793-1865).

Photo. & Engr.
1988, Mar. 11 Perf. 14
1421 A790 4s multicolored .70 .50

Anschluss of March 11, 1938 — A791

1988, Mar. 11 Photo. Perf. 13½
1422 A791 5s gray olive, brn blk & ver .80 .50

No. 2 Aigen Steam Locomotive, 1887 A792

5s, Electric train, Josepsplatz.

1988, Mar. 22 Perf. 13½x14½
1423 A792 4s shown .80 .50
1424 A792 5s multicolored 1.00 .60

Muhlkreis Railway, cent. (4s); Vienna Local Railway, cent. (5s).

World Wildlife Fund — A793

Photo. & Engr.
1988, Apr. 15 Perf. 13½x14
1425 A793 5s Bee eater .90 .60

Styrian Provincial Exhibition on Glass and Coal, Barnbach A794

1988, Apr. 29 Perf. 13½
1426 A794 4s Frosted glass .70 .50

Intl. Red Cross, 125th Anniv. — A795

1988, May 6 Photo. Perf. 14
1427 A795 12s grn, brt red & blk 1.90 1.25

Gothic Silver Censer — A796

1988, May 6 Photo. & Engr.
1428 A796 4s multicolored .60 .50

Art and Monasticism at the Birth of Austria, lower Austrian provincial exhibition, Seitenstetten.

Europa 1988 A797

Communication and transportation.

1988, May 13 Photo.
1429 A797 6s multicolored 1.50 .60

Mattsee Monastery and Lion of Alz — A798

1988, May 18 Photo. & Engr.
1430 A798 4s multicolored .70 .50

Provincial exhibition at Mattsee Monastery: Bavarian Tribes in Salzburg.

Weinberg Castle A799

Perf. 13½x14½
1988, May 20 Photo.
1431 A799 4s multicolored .70 .50

Upper Austrian provincial exhibition: Weinberg Castle.

Odon von Horwath (1901-1938), Dramatist — A800

Photo. & Engr.
1988, June 1 Perf. 14½x13½
1432 A800 6s olive bis & slate grn .90 .60

Stockerau Festival, 25th Anniv. — A801

5s, Stockerau Town Hall.

1988, June 17 Perf. 14
1433 A801 5s multicolored .80 .50

Tauern Motorway Opening — A802

1988, June 24 Photo. Perf. 13½x14
1434 A802 4s multicolored .70 .50

Brixlegg, 1200th Anniv. A803

Photo. & Engr.
1988, July 1 Perf. 13½x14½
1435 A803 5s multicolored .90 .60

View of Klagenfurt, Engraving by Matthaus Merian (1593-1650) — A804

Photo. & Engr.
1988, Aug. 12 Perf. 14
1436 A804 5s multicolored .80 .60

Carinthian Postal Service, 400th Anniv.

Brixen-im-Thale, 1200th Anniv. — A805

1988, Aug. 12
1437 A805 5s multicolored .80 .50

Feldkirchen, 1100th Anniv. — A806

1988, Sept. 2 Perf. 13½
1438 A806 5s multicolored .80 .50

Feldbach, 800th Anniv. A807

1988, Sept. 15 Photo. & Engr.
1439 A807 5s multicolored .80 .60

Ansfelden, 1200th Anniv. — A808

1988, Sept. 23 Perf. 14
1440 A808 5s multicolored .80 .50

Exports A809

1988, Oct. 18 Photo. Perf. 14x13½
1441 A809 8s multicolored 2.25 2.00

No. 1441 has a holographic image. Soaking in water may affect the hologram.

Vienna Concert Hall, 75th Anniv. A810

Photo. & Engr.
1988, Oct. 19 Perf. 13½
1442 A810 5s multicolored .80 .60

The Watchmen, by Giselbert Hoke — A811

1988, Oct. 21   *Perf. 14*
1443 A811 5s multicolored   .80   .60

Social Democrats Unification Party Congress, Cent. — A812

1988, Nov. 11 Photo. *Perf. 14½x14*
1444 A812 4s multicolored   .70   .60

Leopold Schonbauer (1888-1963), Physician — A813

Photo. & Engr.
1988, Nov. 11   *Perf. 14½x13½*
1445 A813 4s multicolored   .65   .50

Christmas A814

Nativity painting from St. Barbara's Church.

1988, Nov. 25   *Perf. 14*
1446 A814 5s multicolored   .80   .60

Benedictine Monastery, Melk, 900th Anniv. — A815

Design: Fresco by Paul Troger.

1989, Mar. 17   Photo. & Engr.
1447 A815 5s multicolored   .80   .50

Madonna and Child, by Lucas Cranach (1472-1553) A816

1989, Mar. 17   *Perf. 14½x13½*
1448 A816 4s multicolored   .60   .50
Diocese of Innsbruck, 25th anniv.

Marianne Hainisch (1839-1936), Women's Rights Activist — A817

1989, Mar. 24   *Perf. 14x13½*
1449 A817 6s multicolored   1.00   .70

Glider Plane and Parachutist A818

1989, Mar. 31 Photo. *Perf. 14*
1450 A818 6s multicolored   1.00   .70
World Gliding Championships, Wiener Neustadt, and World Parachuting Championships, Damuls.

Bruck an der Leitha Commune, 750th Anniv. — A819

Painting by Georg Matthaus Vischer (1628-1696).

1989, Apr. 21
1451 A819 5s multicolored   .80   .50

Die Malerei, 1904, by Rudolf Jettmar (1869-1939) A820

Perf. 14½x13½
1989, Apr. 21   Photo.
1452 A820 5s multicolored   .80   .50

Holy Trinity Church, Stadl-Paura A821

1989, Apr. 26   Photo. & Engr.
1453 A821 5s multicolored   .80   .50
Michael Prunner (1669-1739), baroque architect.

Eduard Suess (1831-1914), Structural Geologist and Map — A822

Portrait by J. Krieher (1800-1876).

1989, Apr. 26
1454 A822 6s multicolored   .90   .80

Ludwig Wittgenstein (1889-1951), Philosopher A823

1989, Apr. 26
1455 A823 5s multicolored   .80   .50

Styrian Provincial Exhibition, Judenburg A824

Design: Judenburg, 17th cent., an engraving by Georg Matthaus Vischer.

1989, Apr. 28   *Perf. 14x13½*
1456 A824 4s multicolored   .70   .50

Industrial Technology Exhibition, Pottenstein — A825

1989, Apr. 28 Photo. *Perf. 13½*
1457 A825 4s Steam engine   .70   .50

Radstadt Township, 700th Anniv. A826

1989, May 3 Photo. *Perf. 13½x14½*
1458 A826 5s multicolored   .80   .50

Toy Boat A827

1989, May 5
1459 A827 6s multicolored   1.50   .60
Europa 1989.

Monastery Church at Lambach, 900th Anniv. — A828

Photo. & Engr.
1989, May 19   *Perf. 14*
1460 A828 4s multicolored   .70   .50

Paddle Steamer *Gisela* A829

1989, May 19 Photo. *Perf. 13½*
1461 A829 5s multicolored   1.25   .60
Shipping on the Traunsee, 150th anniv.

St. Andra im Lavanttal, 650th Anniv. A830

Period cityscape by Matthaus Merian.

1989, May 26   Photo. & Engr.
1462 A830 5s multicolored   .80   .60

Richard Strauss (1864-1949), Composer A831

Photo. & Engr.
1989, June 1   *Perf. 14½x13½*
1463 A831 6s dark brn, gold & red brn   1.00   .70

Achensee Railway, Cent. A832

1989, June 8 Photo. *Perf. 13½*
1464 A832 5s multicolored   1.00   .50

Monastery Type of 1984

Design: 50g, Vorau Abbey, Styria. 1s, Monastery of Mehrerau, Vorarlberg. 1.50s, Monastery of the German Order in Vienna. 2s, Bendictine Monastery, Michaelbeuern. 11s, Engelszell Abbey. 12s, Monastery of the Hospitalers, Eisenstadt. 17s, St. Peter, Salzburg. 20s, Wernberg Monastery.

1989-92 Photo. & Engr. *Perf. 14*
1465 A679a 50g multi   .25   .25
1466 A679a 1s multi   .25   .25
1467 A679a 1.50s multi   .25   .25
1468 A679a 2s multi   .50   .25
1469 A679a 11s multi   2.50   .50
1470 A679a 12s multi   4.00   .90
1471 A679a 17s multi   4.50   .90
1472 A679a 20s multi   6.00   .60
    Nos. 1465-1472 (8)   18.25 3.90

Issued: 1s, 9/1/89; 17s, 6/29/89; 11s, 3/9/90; 50g, 10/12/90; 20s, 5/3/91; 2s, 9/27/91; 1.50s, 10/23/92; 12s, 6/17/92.

Interparliamentary Union, Cent. — A833

Photo. & Engr.
1989, June 30   *Perf. 14*
1475 A833 6s Parliament, Vienna 1.00 .70

Social Security in Austria, Cent. — A834

1989, Aug. 1   **Photo.**
1476 A834 5s multicolored   .80 .50

UN Offices in Vienna, 10th Anniv. A835

1989, Aug. 23
1477 A835 8s multicolored   1.50 .80

Wildalpen, 850th Anniv. A836

5s, Foundry, coat of arms.

Photo. & Engr.
1989, Sept. 15   *Perf. 13½x14*
1478 A836 5s multicolored   .80 .60

33rd Congress of the Association for Quality Assurance (EOQC) — A837

1989, Sept. 18 Photo.   *Perf. 14x13½*
1479 A837 6s multicolored   .90 .70

14th World Congress of the Soc. for Criminal Law (AIDP) A838

6s, Justice Palace, Vienna.

Photo. & Engr.
1989, Oct. 2   *Perf. 13½*
1480 A838 6s multicolored   .90 .70

Lebensbaum, by Ernst Steiner — A839

1989, Oct. 10   *Perf. 13½x14*
1481 A839 5s multicolored   .80 .60

Georg Trakl (1887-1914), Expressionist Poet — A840

1989, Nov. 6 Photo.   *Perf. 14½x13½*
1482 A840 4s Trakl   .70 .50
1483 A840 4s Anzengruber   .70 .50
Ludwig Anzengruber (1839-1889), playwright and novelist.

Alfred Fried (1864-1921), Pacifist, Publisher and 1911 Nobel Laureate — A841

1989, Nov. 10   **Photo. & Engr.**
1484 A841 6s multicolored   1.00 .70

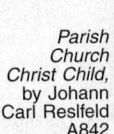

Parish Church Christ Child, by Johann Carl Reslfeld A842

1989, Dec. 1   *Perf. 13½x14½*
1485 A842 5s multicolored   .80 .60
Christmas.

Postal Communications in Europe, 500th Anniv. — A843

The Young Post Rider, an Engraving by Albrecht Durer

Photo. & Engr.
1990, Jan. 12   *Perf. 14*
1486 A843 5s multicolored   1.00 .60
See Belgium No. 1332, Germany No. 1592, Berlin No. 9N584 and German Democratic Republic No. 2791.

Hahnenkamm Alpine Competition, Kitzbuhel, 50th Anniv. — A844

Perf. 13½x14½
1990, Jan. 12   **Photo.**
1487 A844 5s multicolored   .90 .65

Salomon Sulzer (1804-90), Cantor and Composer A845

Perf. 14½x13½
1990, Jan. 17   **Photo.**
1488 A845 4.50s multicolored   .75 .55

Friedrich Emich (1860-1940), Chemist — A846

1990, Jan. 22   **Photo. & Engr.**
1489 A846 6s claret & pale green 1.00 .75

Miniature from the *Market Book of Grein,* by Ulrich Schreier, c. 1490 A847

1990, Mar. 9   *Perf. 14*
1490 A847 5s multicolored   .90 .65
City of Linz, 500th anniv.

University Seals — A848

1990, Apr. 6
1491 A848 5s multicolored   .90 .65
625th Anniv. of Vienna University and 175th anniv. of Vienna Technical University.

Scenery Type of 1984
No. 1492, Styrian Vineyards. No. 1493, Obir Caverns. No. 1494, Natural Bridge, Vorarlberg. No. 1495, Wilder Kaiser Mountain, Tyrol. No. 1496, Peggau Cave, Styria. No. 1497, Moorland, swamp, Heidenreichstein. No. 1498, Hohe Tauern Natl. Park. No. 1499, Nussberg Vineyards.

1990-97   *Perf. 14*
1492 A679 5s multicolored   .90 .65
1493 A679 5s multicolored   .90 .65
1494 A679 5s multicolored   .90 .65
1495 A679 6s multicolored   1.10 .80
1496 A679 6s multicolored   .90 .75
1497 A679 6s multicolored   .90 .55
1498 A679 6s multicolored   1.00 .60
1499 A679 6s multicolored   1.10 1.10
    Nos. 1492-1499 (8)   7.70 5.75

Issued: No. 1492, 4/27; No. 1493, 3/26/91; No. 1494, 2/5/92; No. 1495, 2/19/93; No. 1496, 4/29/94; No. 1497, 5/19/95; No. 1498, 3/29/96; No. 1499, 2/21/97.

Anthering, 1200th Anniv. — A849

Church and municipal arms.

1990, Apr. 27 Photo.   *Perf. 14x13½*
1500 A849 7s multicolored   1.10 .70

Labor Day, Cent. — A850

1990, Apr. 30 Photo.   *Perf. 13½*
1501 A850 4.50s multicolored   .80 .65

Seckau Abbey, 850th Anniv. — A851

1990, May 4 Engr.   *Perf. 14x13½*
1502 A851 4.50s bluish black   .80 .60

Ebene Reichenau Post Office A852

1990, May 4 Photo.   *Perf. 13½x14*
1503 A852 7s multicolored   2.25 1.10
Europa.

Hans Makart (1840-84), Self-Portrait A853

Self Portrait: 5s, Egon Schiele (1890-1918).

Photo. & Engr.
1990, May 29   *Perf. 14*
1504 A853 4.50s multicolored   .80 .70
1505 A853 5s multicolored   1.00 1.00

Ferdinand Raimund (1790-1836), Actor — A854

1990, June 1 Photo.   *Perf. 14x13½*
1506 A854 4.50s multicolored   .80 .65

Christ Healing the Sick by Rembrandt A855

Photo. & Engr.

1990, June 5   *Perf. 14*
1507 A855 7s multicolored   1.25 1.00
2nd Intl. Christus Medicus Cong., Bad Ischl.

Hardegg, 700th Anniv. — A856

Photo. & Engr.

1990, June 8   *Perf. 13½x14*
1508 A856 4.50s multicolored   .80 .65

Oberdrauburg, 750th Anniv. — A857

1990, June 8   **Photo.**
1509 A857 5s multicolored   1.00 .65

Gumpoldskirchen, 850th Anniv. — A858

Photo. & Engr.

1990, June 15   *Perf. 13½*
1510 A858 5s multicolored   1.00 .65

Mathias Zdarsky (1856-1940), Alpine Skier — A859

1990, June 20   *Perf. 14x13½*
1511 A859 5s multicolored   .90 .65

Telegraph, 1880, Anton Tschechow, 1978 — A860

1990, June 28   **Photo.**   *Perf. 14*
1512 A860 9s multicolored   1.50 1.10
Modern shipbuilding in Austria, 150th anniv.

Joseph Friedrich Perkonig (1890-1959), Novelist — A861

Photo. & Engr.

1990, Aug. 3   *Perf. 14x13½*
1513 A861 5s gold & brown   .85 .65

Herr des Regenbogens, by Robert Zeppel-Sperl A862

Photo. & Engr.

1990, Aug. 30   *Perf. 13½x14*
1514 A862 5s multicolored   .85 .65

European Dialysis and Transplantation Society, 27th Congress — A863

1990, Sept. 4   **Photo.**   *Perf. 14*
1515 A863 7s multicolored   1.25 .80

Franz Werfel (1890-1945), Writer — A864

Photo. & Engr.

1990, Sept. 11   *Perf. 14x13½*
1516 A864 5s multicolored   .90 .65

Austrian Forces in UN Peace Keeping Forces, 30th Anniv. A865

1990, Sept. 20   **Photo.**   *Perf. 13½*
1517 A865 7s multicolored   1.25 .80

Federal and State Arms A866

1990, Sept. 24   **Photo. & Engr.**
1518 A866 5s multicolored   .90 .55
Federalism in Austria.

Mining Univ., Leoben, 150th Anniv. — A867

Photo. & Engr.

1990, Oct. 22   *Perf. 14*
1519 A867 4.50s blk, bl grn & red   .80 .45

Karl Freiherr von Vogelsang (1818-90), Politician — A868

Photo. & Engr.

1990, Nov. 8   *Perf. 14x13½*
1520 A868 4.50s multicolored   .80 .45

Metalworkers and Miners Trade Union, Cent. — A869

1990, Nov. 16   *Perf. 14*
1521 A869 5s multicolored   .90 .65

3rd World Curling Championships A870

1990, Nov. 23   **Photo.**   *Perf. 14x13½*
1522 A870 7s multicolored   1.25 .80

Palmhouse at Schonbrunn — A871

1990, Nov. 30   *Perf. 14*
1523 A871 5s multicolored   .90 .65

Christmas A872

Altar in Klosterneuburg Abbey by the Master from Verdun.

Photo. & Engr.

1990, Nov. 23   *Perf. 13½*
1524 A872 5s multicolored   .90 .55

Franz Grillparzer (1791-1872), Dramatic Poet — A873

Photo. & Engr.

1991, Jan. 15   *Perf. 14x13½*
1525 A873 4.50s multicolored   .80 .55

A874

1991, Jan. 21   *Perf. 13½*
1526 A874 5s multicolored   .90 .65
Alpine Skiing World Championship, Saalbach-Hinterglemm.

Bruno Kreisky (1911-90), Chancellor A875

1991, Jan. 21   **Photo.**   *Perf. 14x13½*
1527 A875 5s multicolored   .95 .70

Friedrich Freiherr von Schmidt (1825-1891), Architect — A876

1991, Jan. 21   *Perf. 14*
1528 A876 7s multicolored   1.40 1.10

Visual Arts A877

Designs: 4.50s, Donner Fountain, Vienna, by Raphael Donner (1693-1741), sculptor. 5s, Kitzbuhel in Winter, by Alfons Walde (1891-1958), painter. 7s, Vienna Stock Exchange, Theophil Hansen (1813-1891), architect.

1991, Feb. 8
1529 A877 4.50s multicolored   .75 .75
1530 A877 5s multicolored   .85 .85
1531 A877 7s multicolored   1.10 1.10
   Nos. 1529-1531 (3)   2.70 2.70

See No. 1543.

Marie von Ebner Eschenbach (1830-1916), Novelist
A878

1991, Mar. 12   Engr.   Perf. 13½x14½
1532 A878 4.50s rose violet   .80 .55

Miniature Sheet

A879

Design: a, Wolfgang Amadeus Mozart (1756-1791), Composer. b, Magic Flute Fountain, Vienna.

Photo. & Engr.
1991, Mar. 22   Perf. 13½
1533 A879 Sheet of 2 + label   2.40 3.25
 a.-b.   5s any single   .80 .80

Spittal an der Drau, 800th Anniv.
A880

1991, Apr. 11   Perf. 14
1534 A880 4.50s multicolored   .75 .60

Europa
A881

1991, May 3   Photo.   Perf. 14
1535 A881 7s ERS-1 satellite   2.75 1.00

Garden Banquet by Anthony Bays
A882

1991, May 10   Photo.   Perf. 13½
1536 A882 5s multicolored   .90 .65
Vorarlberg Provincial Exhibition, Hohenems.

Museum of Military History, Cent.
A883

7s, Interior of Museum of Art History.

Photo. & Engr.
1991, May 24   Perf. 13½
1537 A883 5s multicolored   .95 .95
1538 A883 7s multicolored   1.40 1.40
Museum of Art History, Cent. (No. 1538).

Grein, 500th Anniv.
A884

1991, May 24   Photo.   Perf. 14
1539 A884 4.50s multicolored   .80 .65

Tulln, 1200th Anniv.
A885

1991, May 24   Perf. 13½x14
1540 A885 5s multicolored   .95 .65

Completion of Karawanken Tunnels — A886

1991, May 31   Perf. 14x13½
1541 A886 7s multicolored   1.25 1.00

5th Anniv. of St. Polten as Provincial Capital of Lower Austria
A887

1991, July 5   Photo.   Perf. 14
1542 A887 5s multicolored   1.00 .65

Visual Arts Type of 1991
Design: 4.50s, Karlsplatz Station of Vienna Subway by Otto Wagner (1841-1918), Architect.

1991, July 12   Photo. & Engr.
1543 A877 4.50s multicolored   .75 .60

Rowing and Junior Canoeing World Championships, Vienna — A888

1991, Aug. 20 Photo. Perf. 13½x14
1544 A888 5s multicolored   .85 .70

European Congress of Radiologists — A889

1991, Sept. 13   Perf. 14
1545 A889 7s multicolored   1.20 1.00

Paracelsus (1493-1541), Physician — A890

1991, Sept. 27   Perf. 14x13½
1546 A890 4.50s multicolored   .75 .60

Joint Austrian-Soviet Space Mission
A891

1991, Oct. 2   Perf. 14
1547 A891 9s multicolored   1.50 1.25

Austrian Folk Festivals
A892

4.50s, Almabtrieb, Tyrol. 5s, Winzerkrone, Vienna. 7s, Ernte-Monstranz, Styria.

1991, Oct. 4   Photo. & Engr.
1548 A892 4.50s multicolored   .75 .60
1549 A892 5s multicolored   .90 .75
1550 A892 7s multicolored   1.20 1.00
 Nos. 1548-1550 (3)   2.85 2.35

See Nos. 1577-1579, 1619-1621, 1633-1635, 1671-1673, 1694, 1705-1706, 1714, 1730, 1741, 1752-1753, 1762, 1778, 1799-1800, 1805-1806, 1824, 1836-1838, 1954, 2020, 2050.

The General by Rudolph Pointner
A893

Photo. & Engr.
1991, Oct. 11   Perf. 13½x14
1551 A893 5s multicolored   .85 .70

Birth of Christ, Baumgartenberg Church — A894

1991, Nov. 29
1552 A894 5s multicolored   .85 .85
Christmas.

Julius Raab, Politician, Birth Cent. — A895

1991, Nov. 29   Perf. 14x13½
1553 A895 4.50s red brn & brn   .75 .60

1992 Winter and Summer Olympic Games
A897

1992, Jan. 14   Photo.   Perf. 14
1555 A897 7s multicolored   1.25 1.00

Trade Union of Clerks in Private Enterprises, Cent. — A898

1992, Jan. 14
1556 A898 5.50s multicolored   .95 .80

8th Natural Run Toboggan World Championships
A899

1992, Jan. 29   Perf. 14x13½
1557 A899 5s multicolored   .90 .75

George Saiko, Writer, Birth Cent. — A900

1992, Feb. 5   Engr.   Perf. 14x13½
1558 A900 5.50s brown   .95 .80

Worker's Sports, Cent. — A901

1992, Feb. 5   Photo.   Perf. 14
1559 A901 5.50s multicolored   .95 .80

Souvenir Sheet

Vienna Philharmonic Orchestra, 150th Anniv. — A902

Photo. & Engr.

1992, Mar. 27   **Perf. 14**
1560   A902   5.50s multicolored   1.25   1.60

Scientists A903

Designs: 5s, Franz Joseph Muller von Reichenstein (1742-1825), discoverer of tellurium. 5.50s, Dr. Paul Kitaibel (1757-1817), botanist. 6s, Christian Johann Doppler (1803-1853), physicist. 7s, Richard Kuhn (1900-1967), chemist.

1992, Mar. 27   **Photo.**
1561   A903   5s   multicolored   .90   .75
1562   A903   5.50s multicolored   .90   .75
1563   A903   6s   multicolored   1.10   .85
1564   A903   7s   multicolored   1.25   1.10
    Nos. 1561-1564 (4)   4.15   3.45

Railway Workers Union, Cent. A904

1992, Apr. 2   **Perf. 14x13½**
1565   A904   5.50s black & red   1.00   .65

Norbert Hanrieder (1842-1913), Poet — A905

Photo. & Engr.

1992, Apr. 30   **Perf. 14x13½**
1566   A905   5.50s purple & buff   1.10   .90

Carl Zeller (1842-1898) and Karl Millocker (1842-1899), Operetta Composers A906

Photo. & Engr.

1992, Apr. 30   **Perf. 14**
1567   A906   6s multicolored   1.10   .85

LD Steel Mill, 40th Anniv. A907

1992, May 8   **Photo.**   **Perf. 14x13½**
1568   A907   5s multicolored   .95   .70

Discovery of America, 500th Anniv. A908

Photo. & Engr.

1992, May 8   **Perf. 14**
1569   A908   7s multicolored   2.25   1.10

Europa.

Austro-Swiss Treaty on Regulation of Rhine River, Cent. — A909

1992, May 8   **Photo.**   **Perf. 13½x14**
1570   A909   7s multicolored   1.25   1.10

Protection of the Alps — A910

1992, May 22   **Perf. 14x13½**
1571   A910   5.50s multicolored   1.00   .85

See Switzerland No. 916.

Dr. Anna Dengel (1892-1980), Physician — A911

1992, May 22   **Photo. & Engr.**
1572   A911   5.50s multicolored   1.00   .65

Sebastian Rieger (1867-1953), Poet — A912

1992, May 22   **Engr.**
1573   A912   5s red brown   .85   .70

Lienz, 750th Anniv. A913

1992, June 17   **Photo.**   **Perf. 14x13½**
1574   A913   5s Town Hall   .90   .70

Intl. Congress of Austrian Society of Surgeons A914

Photo. & Engr.

1992, June 17   **Perf. 14**
1575   A914   6s multicolored   1.10   .90

Dr. Kurt Waldheim, President of Austria, 1986-92 — A915

1992, June 22   **Perf. 14x13½**
1576   A915   5.50s multicolored   1.00   .85

Folk Festivals Type of 1991

Designs: 5s, Marksman's target, Lower Austria. 5.50s, Peasant's chest, Carinthia. 7s, Votive icon, Vorarlberg.

Photo. & Engr.

1992, Sept. 18   **Perf. 14**
1577   A892   5s   multicolored   .90   .90
1578   A892   5.50s multicolored   1.10   1.10
1579   A892   7s   multicolored   1.25   1.25
    Nos. 1577-1579 (3)   3.25   3.25

Marchfeld Canal — A917

1992, Oct. 9   **Photo.**   **Perf. 13½x14**
1580   A917   5s multicolored   .90   .70

5th Intl. Ombudsman Conference, Vienna — A918

Photo & Engr.

1992, Oct. 9   **Perf. 14**
1581   A918   5.50s multicolored   .95   .65

The Clearance of Seawater, by Peter Pongratz A919

1992, Oct. 9
1582   A919   5.50s multicolored   .95   .75

Academy of Fine Arts, 300th Anniv. — A920

Photo. & Engr.

1992, Oct. 23   **Perf. 14**
1583   A920   5s red & blue   .90   .75

Birth of Christ, by Johann Georg Schmidt A921

1992, Nov. 27   **Perf. 14x13½**
1584   A921   5.50s multicolored   1.10   .65

Christmas.

Veit Koniger, Sculptor, Death Bicent. A922

Photo. & Engr.

1992, Nov. 27   **Perf. 14**
1585   A922   5s multicolored   .90   .80

Herman Potocnik, Theoretician of Geosynchronous Satellite Orbit, Birth Cent. — A923

1992, Nov. 27   **Photo.**
1586   A923   10s multicolored   2.00   1.60

Famous Buildings A924

5s, Statues & dome of Imperial Palace, Vienna, designed by Joseph Emanuel Fischer von Erlach. 5.50s, Kinsky Palace, designed by

Lukas von Hildebrandt. 7s, Vienna State Opera, designed by Eduard van der Null & August Siccard von Siccardsburg.

1993, Jan. 22 **Photo. & Engr.**
1587	A924	5s multicolored	1.00	.80
1588	A924	5.50s multicolored	1.10	.90
1589	A924	7s multicolored	1.40	1.10
		Nos. 1587-1589 (3)	3.50	2.80

Joseph Emanuel Fischer von Erlach, 300th birth anniv. (No. 1587). Johann Lukas von Hildebrandt, 325th birth anniv. (No. 1588). Eduard van der Null, August Siccard von Siccardsburg, 125th death anniv. (No. 1589).

Radio Dispatched Medical Service, 25th Anniv. — A925

1993, Feb. 19 **Photo.**
1590 A925 5s multicolored 1.00 .80

Typewriter Made by Peter Mitterhofer (1822-1893) A926

1993, Feb. 19 **Perf. 13½x14**
1591 A926 17s multicolored 3.50 2.75

Popular Entertainers — A927

Strada del Sole, by Rainhard Fendrich.

1993, Mar. 19 **Photo.** **Perf. 14**
1592 A927 5.50s multicolored 1.00 .80
See Nos. 1626, 1639.

Charles Sealsfield (1793-1864), Writer A928

Photo. & Engr.
1993, Mar. 19 **Perf. 13½x14**
1593 A928 10s multicolored 1.75 1.40

Rights of the Child — A930

1993, Apr. 16 **Photo.** **Perf. 13½x14**
1595 A930 7s multicolored 1.25 1.00

Flying Harlequin, by Paul Flora A931

1993, Apr. 16 **Photo. & Engr.**
1596 A931 7s multicolored 3.75 1.00
Europa.

Monastery of Admont — A932

Designs: 1s, Detail of abbesse's crosier, St. Gabriel Abbey, Styria. 5.50s, Death, wooden statue by Josef Stammel (1695-1765). 6s, Stained glass, Mariastern-Gwiggen Monastery. 7s, Marble lion, Franciscan Monastery, Salzburg. 7.50s, Cupola fresco, by Paul Troger, Monastery of Altenburg. 8s, Gothic entry, Wilhering Monastery, Upper Austria. 10s, Altarpiece, St. Peregrinus praying, Maria Luggau Monastery. 20s, Crosier, Fiecht Monastery. 26s, Sculpture of Mater Dolorosa, Franciscan Monastery, Schwaz, Tirol. 30s, Madonna of Scottish Order, Schottenstift Monastery, Vienna.

Photo. & Engr.
1993-95 **Perf. 13¾x14**
1599	A932	1s multicolored	.25	.25
1600	A932	5.50s multicolored	2.00	.25
1601	A932	6s multicolored	1.25	.25
1602	A932	7s multicolored	1.75	.25
1603	A932	7.50s multicolored	2.00	.55
1604	A932	8s multicolored	2.25	.65
1605	A932	10s multicolored	2.50	.50
1606	A932	20s multicolored	5.00	.55
1607	A932	26s multicolored	6.00	.75
1608	A932	30s multicolored	8.00	1.25
		Nos. 1599-1608 (10)	31.00	5.25

Issued: 5.50s, 4/16; 6s, 9/17; 20s, 10/8; 7.50s, 4/4/94; 10s, 8/26/94; 30s, 10/7/94; 7s, 11/18/94; 8s, 9/15/95; 26s, 10/6/95; 1s, 4/28/95.

Peter Rosegger (1843-1918), Poet — A933

1993, May 5 **Photo.** **Perf. 14x13½**
1617 A933 5.50s green & black 1.00 .80

Lake Constance Steamer Hohentwiel A934

1993, May 5 **Photo.** **Perf. 14**
1618 A934 6s multicolored 1.50 .85
See Germany No. 1786, Switzerland No. 931.

Folk Festivals Type of 1991
Designs: 5s, Corpus Christi Day Procession, Upper Austria. 5.50s, Blockdrawing, Burgenland. 7s, Cracking whip when snow is melting, Salzburg.

Photo. & Engr.
1993, June 11 **Perf. 14**
1619	A892	5s multicolored	.90	.70
1620	A892	5.50s multicolored	1.00	.80
1621	A892	7s multicolored	1.10	1.00
		Nos. 1619-1621 (3)	3.00	2.50

UN Conference on Human Rights, Vienna A935

1993, June 11 **Photo.**
1622 A935 10s multicolored 1.75 1.40

Franz Jagerstatter (1907-1943), Conscientious Objector — A936

1993, Aug. 6 **Photo.** **Perf. 14x13½**
1623 A936 5.50s multicolored 1.00 .80

Schafberg Railway, Cent. A937

1993, Aug. 6 **Perf. 13½x14**
1624 A937 6s multicolored 1.10 .90

Self-portrait with Puppet, by Rudolf Wacker (1893-1939) A938

1993, Aug. 6 **Perf. 14**
1625 A938 6s multicolored 1.10 .90

Popular Entertainers Type of 1993
Design: 5.50s, Granny, by Ludwig Hirsch.

1993, Sept. 3 **Photo.** **Perf. 14**
1626 A927 5.50s multicolored 1.00 .80

Vienna Mens' Choral Society, 150th Anniv. A940

1993, Sept. 17 **Photo.** **Perf. 14**
1627 A940 5s multicolored .90 .75

Easter, by Max Weiler — A941

Photo. & Engr.
1993, Oct. 8 **Perf. 13½x14**
1628 A941 5.50s multicolored 1.00 .80

99 Heads, by Hundertwasser A942

1993, Oct. 8
1629 A942 7s multicolored 2.00 1.00
Council of Europe Conference, Vienna.

Austrian Republic, 75th Anniv. — A943

Design: 5.50s, Statue of Pallas Athena.

Photo. & Engr.
1993, Nov. 12 **Perf. 13½x14**
1630 A943 5.50s multicolored 1.00 .80

Trade Unions in Austria, Cent. A944

1993, Nov. 12 **Photo.** **Perf. 14**
1631 A944 5.50s multicolored 1.00 .80

Birth of Christ, by Master of the Krainburger Altar — A945

Photo. & Engr.
1993, Nov. 26 **Perf. 13½x14**
1632 A945 5.50s multicolored 1.00 .80
Christmas.

Folklore and Customs Type of 1991
Antiques: 5.50s, Dolls, cradle, Vorarlberg. 6s, Sled, Steiermark. 7s, Godparent's bowl, Upper Austria.

Photo. & Engr.
1994, Jan. 28 **Perf. 14**
1633	A892	5.50s multicolored	.90	.70
1634	A892	6s multicolored	1.10	.80
1635	A892	7s multicolored	1.25	.90
		Nos. 1633-1635 (3)	3.25	2.40

1994 Winter Olympics, Lillehammer, Norway — A946

1994, Feb. 9
1636 A946 7s multicolored 1.25 1.00

Vienna Mint, 800th Anniv. A947

1994, Feb. 18
1637 A947 6s multicolored   1.10   .90

Lying Lady, by Herbert Boeckl (1894-1966) — A948

1994, Mar. 18 Photo. Perf. 14x13½
1638 A948 5.50s multicolored   1.00   .70

Popular Entertainers Type of 1993
Design: 6s, Rock Me Amadeus, by Falco.

1994, Mar. 18   Perf. 14
1639 A927 6s multicolored   1.00   .80

Wiener Neustadt, 800th Anniv. — A949

1994, Mar. 18
1640 A949 6s multicolored   1.00   .80

Lake Rudolph, Teleki-Hohnel Expedition — A950

Photo. & Engr.
1994, May 27   Perf. 14x13½
1641 A950 7s multicolored   1.40 1.00
Europa.

Daniel Gran, 300th Birth Anniv. A951

Fresco: 20s, Allegory of Theology, Jurisprudence and Medicine.

1994, May 27
1642 A951 20s multicolored   3.75 2.00

Carinthian Summer Festival, 25th Anniv. — A952

Design: 5.50s, Scene from The Prodigal Son.

Photo. & Engr.
1994, June 17   Perf. 14
1643 A952 5.50s lake & gold   1.00   .75

Railway Centennials — A953

1994   Photo. & Engr.   Perf. 14
1647 A953 5.50s Gailtal   1.00   .80
1648 A953   6s Murtal   1.25   .80
Issued: 5.50s, 6s, 6/17/94.

Hermann Gmeiner, 75th Birth Anniv. — A954

1994, June 17   Perf. 14x13½
1656 A954 7s multicolored   1.25 1.00

Karl Seitz (1869-1950) Politician A955

1994, Aug. 12 Photo.   Perf. 14
1657 A955 5.50s multicolored   1.00   .80

Karl Bohm (1894-1981), Conductor A956

Photo. & Engr.
1994, Aug. 26   Perf. 14x13½
1658 A956 7s gold & dk blue   1.25 1.00

Ethnic Minorities in Austria A957

1994, Sept. 9 Photo.   Perf. 13½
1659 A957 5.50s multicolored   1.00   .80

Franz Theodor Csokor (1885-1969), Writer — A958

7s, Joseph Roth (1894-1939), writer.

1994, Sept. 9   Perf. 14x13½
1660 A958 6s multicolored   1.00   .80
1661 A958 7s multicolored   1.25 1.00

Savings Banks in Austria, 175th Anniv. — A959

Photo. & Engr.
1994, Oct. 7   Perf. 14x13½
1662 A959 7s Coin bank   1.25 1.00

Modern Art — A960

Design: 6s, "Head," by Franz Ringel.

1994, Oct. 7   Perf. 13½x14
1663 A960 6s multicolored   1.10   .90

Austrian Working Environment — A961

1994, Nov. 18 Photo.   Perf. 14
1664 A961 6s Stewardess, child   1.10   .90
See Nos. 1690, 1703, 1736, 1773, 1828, 1859.

Richard Coudenhove Kalergi, Founder of PanEuropean Union, Birth Cent. — A962

Photo. & Engr.
1994, Nov. 18   Perf. 13½
1665 A962 10s multicolored   1.90 1.50

Birth of Christ, by Anton Wollenek A963

1994, Nov. 25   Perf. 14
1666 A963 6s multicolored   1.10   .90
Christmas.

Membership in European Union — A964

1995, Jan. 13 Photo.   Perf. 14
1667 A964 7s multicolored   1.25 1.00

Adolf Loos (1870-1933), Architect A965

1995, Jan. 13
1668 A965 10s House, Vienna   1.90 1.50

Official Representation for Workers, 75th Anniv. — A966

1995, Feb. 24   Perf. 14x13½
1669 A966 6s multicolored   1.10   .90

Austrian Gymnastics and Sports Assoc., 50th Anniv. — A967

1995, Feb. 24
1670 A967 6s multicolored   1.10   .90

Folklore and Customs Type of 1991
Designs: 5.50s, Belt, Gailtal, Carinthia. 6s, Vineyard watchman's costume, Vienna. 7s, Bonnet, Wachau, Lower Austria.

Photo. & Engr.
1995, Mar. 24   Perf. 14
1671 A892 5.50s multicolored   1.00   .60
1672 A892   6s multicolored   1.00   .70
1673 A892   7s multicolored   1.25   .80
  Nos. 1671-1673 (3)   3.25 2.10

Second Republic, 50th Anniv. — A968

1995, Apr. 27
1674 A968 6s State seal   1.25 1.00

History of Mining & Industry A969

Design: Blast furnaces, old Heft ironworks.

1995, Apr. 28　　Perf. 13½x14
1675 A969 5.50s multicolored　1.10　.90

Carinthian Provincial Exhibition.

Nature Lovers Club, Cent. — A970

1995, Apr. 28　　Perf. 14
1676 A970 5.50s multicolored　1.10　.90

Europa — A971

1995, May 19　　Perf. 14
1677 A971 7s multicolored　1.50 1.25

1995 Conference of Ministers of Transportation, Vienna — A972

1995, May 26　Photo.　Perf. 14
1678 A972 7s multicolored　1.40 1.25

Bregenz Festival, 50th Anniv. A973

1995, June 9
1679 A973 6s multicolored　1.25 1.00

St. Gebhard (949-995) A974

Stained glass window, by Martin Hausle.

1995, June 9
1680 A974 7.50s multicolored　1.50 1.25

UN, 50th Anniv. — A975

1995, June 26　Photo.　Perf. 14
1681 A975 10s multicolored　2.00　.70

Josef Loschmidt (1821-95), Chemist — A976

Photo. & Engr.
1995, June 26　Perf. 14x13½
1682 A976 20s multicolored　4.50 1.50

Salzburg Festival, 75th Anniv. — A977

Photo. & Engr.
1995, Aug. 18　Perf. 13½x14
1683 A977 6s multicolored　1.25 1.00

Kathe Leichter, Resistance Member, Birth Cent. — A978

1995, Aug. 18　Perf. 14x13½
1684 A978 6s buff, black & red　1.25 1.00

Europaisches Landschaftsbild, by Adolf Frohner — A979

1995, Aug. 18
1685 A979 6s multicolored　1.25 1.00

Operetta Composers A980

Designs: 6s, Franz von Suppe (1819-95), scene from "The Beautiful Galathea." 7s, Nico Dostal (b. 1895), scene from "The Hungarian Wedding."

1995, Sept. 15　　Perf. 14
1686 A980 6s multicolored　1.00　.60
1687 A980 7s multicolored　1.25　.70

See Croatia No. 253.

University of Klagenfurt, 25th Anniv. — A981

1995, Oct. 6　Photo.　Perf. 14
1688 A981 5.50s multicolored　1.10　.90

Carinthian Referendum, 75th Anniv. — A982

1995, Oct. 6　Photo. & Engr.
1689 A982 6s multicolored　1.25 1.00

Austria Working Environment Type of 1994

1995, Oct. 20
1690 A961 6s Post office official　1.25 1.00

Composers A983

6s, Anton von Webern (1883-1945). 7s, Ludwig van Beethoven (1770-1827).

1995, Oct. 20　　Perf. 13½x14
1691 A983 6s orange & blue　1.00　.60
1692 A983 7s orange & red　1.25　.70

Christmas A984

Photo. & Engr.
1995, Dec. 1　　Perf. 13½
1693 A984 6s Christ Child　1.25 1.00

Folklore and Customs Type of 1991

Design: Roller and Scheller in "Procession of Masked Groups in Imst," Tyrol.

Photo. & Engr.
1996, Feb. 9　　Perf. 14
1694 A892 6s multicolored　1.25 1.00

Maria Theresa Academy, 250th Anniv. — A985

1996, Feb. 9
1695 A985 6s multicolored　1.25 1.00

1996 World Ski Jumping Championships A986

1996, Feb. 9　　Photo.
1696 A986 7s multicolored　1.40 1.10

New Western Pier, Vienna Intl. Airport A987

1996, Mar. 28　Photo.　Perf. 14
1697 A987 7s multicolored　1.40 1.10

A988

6s, Mother with Child, by Peter Fendi (1796-1842). 7s, Self-portrait, by Leopold Kupelwieser (1795-1862).

1996, Mar. 29
1698 A988 6s multicolored　1.25 1.00
1699 A988 7s multicolored　1.40 1.10

Anton Bruckner (1824-96), Composer, Organist A989

Photo. & Engr.
1996, Apr. 26　　Perf. 14
1700 A989 5.50s Organ, music　1.10　.90

Georg Matthäus Vischer, 300th Death Anniv. A990

1996, Apr. 26
1701 A990 10s Kollmitz Castle　2.00 1.50

City of Klagenfurt, 800th Anniv. — A991

1996, May 3
1702 A991 6s Ancient square　1.25 1.00

Austrian Working Environment Type of 1994

1996, May 17
1703 A961 6s Chef, waitress   1.25 1.00

Paula von Preradovic, Author
A992

1996, May 17   *Perf. 13½x14*
1704 A992 7s black, gray & buff   *1.50 1.10*

Europa.

Folklore and Customs Type of 1991

Designs: 5.50s, Corpus Christi poles, Salzburg. 7s, Tyrolian riflemen.

Photo. & Engr.

1996, June 21   *Perf. 14*
1705 A892 5.50s multicolored   1.00 .80
1706 A892 7s multicolored   1.25 1.00

1996 Summer Olympic Games, Atlanta — A993

1996, June 21
1707 A993 10s multicolored   1.90 1.50

Burgenland Province, 75th Anniv. — A994

1996, Sept. 20
1708 A994 6s multicolored   1.10 .90

Austrian Mountain Rescue Service, Cent. — A995

1996, Sept. 27
1709 A995 6s multicolored   1.10 .90

Austria Millennium A996

Designs: a, Deed by Otto III. b, Empress Maria Theresa, Josef II. c, Duke Henry II. d, 1848 Revolution. e, Rudolf IV. f, Dr. Karl Renner, 1st Republic. g, Emperor Maximilian I. h, State Treaty of 1955, 2nd Republic. i, Imperial Crown of Rudolf II. j, Austria, Europe.

Photo. & Engr.

1996, Oct. 25   *Perf. 14*
1710   Sheet of 10   19.00 20.00
  a.-b.   A996 6s any single   .90 .90
  c.-f.   A996 7s any single   1.10 1.10
  g.-h.   A996 10s any single   1.50 1.50
  i.-j.   A996 20s any single   3.00 3.00

Power Station, by Reinhard Artberg A997

1996, Nov. 22
1711 A997 7s multicolored   1.25 1.25

UNICEF, 50th Anniv. — A998

1996, Nov. 22   *Photo.*
1712 A998 10s multicolored   1.90 1.90

Christmas A999

1996, Nov. 29   *Photo. & Engr.*
1713 A999 6s multicolored   1.25 1.00

Folklore and Customs Type of 1991

Epiphany Carol Singers, Burgenland.

Photo. & Engr.

1997, Jan. 17   *Perf. 14*
1714 A892 7s multicolored   1.25 1.00

Theodor Kramer, Poet, Birth Cent. — A1000

1997, Jan. 17   *Engr.*
1715 A1000 5.50s deep blue   1.00 .80

Austrian Academy of Sciences, 150th Anniv. — A1001

1997, Feb. 21   *Photo.*   *Perf. 14*
1716 A1001 10s multicolored   1.75 1.40

Austrian Electricity Board, 50th Anniv. A1002

1997, Mar. 21
1717 A1002 6s multicolored   1.00 .80

The Cruel Lady of Forchtenstein Castle, Burgenland A1003

Photo. & Engr.

1997, Mar. 21   *Perf. 14*
1718 A1003 7s multicolored   1.10 .95

See Nos. 1731, 1733, 1745-1746, 1763, 1775, 1794, 1802, 1804, 1810-1811.

Erich Wolfgang Korngold (1897-1957), Composer A1004

Design: Scene from opera, "The Dead City."

1997, Mar. 21
1719 A1004 20s bl, blk & gold   4.50 2.00

Vienna Rapid, Austrian Soccer Champions — A1005

1997, Apr. 25   *Photo.*   *Perf. 14*
1720 A1005 7s multicolored   1.25 1.00

See Nos. 1754, 1779, 1807, 1839.

Deer Feeding in Wintertime A1006

1997, Apr. 25
1721 A1006 7s multicolored   1.25 1.00

See Nos. 1747, 1782, 1808, 1835.

St. Peter Canisius (1521-97) A1007

1997, Apr. 25   *Photo. & Engr.*
1722 A1007 7.50s Canisius Altar, Innsbruck   1.25 1.10

Composers — A1008

Designs: 6s, Johannes Brahms (1833-1897). 10s, Franz Schubert (1797-1828).

1997, May 9
1723 A1008 6s gold & vio bl   1.00 .80
1724 A1008 10s purple & gold   1.75 1.40

Stamp Day — A1009

1997, May 9   *Perf. 13½*
1725 A1009 7s "A" and "E"   1.25 1.00

See Nos. B357-B362, 1765, 1791, 1818. The 1st letters spell "Briefmarke," the 2nd "Philatelie."

Child's View of "Town Band of Bremen" A1010

1997, May 23   *Photo.*
1726 A1010 7s multicolored   *1.50 1.00*

Europa.

Technical Surveyance Assoc., 125th Anniv. A1011

1997, June 13   *Photo.*   *Perf. 14*
1727 A1011 7s multicolored   1.40 1.10

Railways A1012

Designs: 6s, Hochschneeberg Cog Railway. 7.50s, Wiener Neustadt-Odenburg Railway.

1997, June 13   *Photo. & Engr.*
1728 A1012 6s multicolored   1.25 .95
1729 A1012 7.50s multicolored   1.50 1.25

Folklore and Customs Type of 1991

6.50s, Marching band, Tyrol.

Photo. & Engr.

1997, July 11   *Perf. 14*
1730 A892 6.50s multicolored   1.25 1.00

Stories and Legends Type of 1997
Design: Dragon of Klagenfurt.

1997, July 11
1731 A1003 6.50s multicolored   1.60 1.00

Karl Heinrich Waggerl, Birth Cent. — A1013

1997, July 11
1732 A1013 7s multicolored   1.40 1.00

Stories and Legends Type of 1997
Design: Danube water nymph rescuing ferryman, Upper Austria.

Photo. & Engr. Perf. 14
1997, Sept. 19
1733 A1003 14s multicolored   3.25 2.10

1997 Orthopedics Congress, Vienna — A1014

1997, Sept. 19 Photo. Perf. 14
1734 A1014 8s Adolph Lorenz   1.60 1.25

Vienna Agricultural University, 125th Anniv. A1015

1997, Sept. 19
1735 A1015 9s multicolored   1.75 1.40

Austrian Working Environment Type of 1994
Photo. & Engr. Perf. 14
1997, Oct. 17
1736 A961 6.50s Nurse, patient 1.25 1.00

"House in Wind," by Helmut Schickhofer — A1016

1997, Oct. 17
1737 A1016 7s multicolored   1.40 1.00

Blind Persons Assocs. in Austria, Cent. — A1017

Photo. & Embossed
1997, Oct. 17
1738 A1017 7s multicolored   1.40 1.00
No. 1738 has embossed Braille inscription.

Dr. Thomas Klestil, Pres. of Austria, 65th birthday — A1018

Photo. & Engr.
1997, Oct. 31 Perf. 14x13½
1739 A1018 7s multicolored   1.40 1.00

Oskar Werner (1922-84), Actor — A1019

1997, Oct. 31 Perf. 14
1740 A1019 7s multicolored   1.40 1.00

Folklore and Customs Type of 1991
Upper Austria tower wind players, Steyr.

Photo. & Engr.
1997, Nov. 21 Perf. 14
1741 A892 6.50s multicolored   1.25 1.00

Light Into Darkness Relief Organization, 25th Anniv. — A1020

1997, Nov. 28 Photo. Perf. 14
1742 A1020 7s multicolored   1.40 1.00

Christmas A1021

7s, Mariazell Madonna.

Photo. & Engr.
1997, Nov. 28 Perf. 14
1743 A1021 7s multicolored   1.40 1.00

Scenery Type of 1984
Kalkalpen Natl. Park, Upper Austria.

Photo. & Engr.
1998, Jan. 23 Perf. 14
1744 A679 7s multicolored   1.10 .85

Stories and Legends Type of 1997
Designs: 9s, The Charming Augustin. 13s, Pied Piper from Korneuburg.

1998, Jan. 23
1745 A1003 9s multicolored   2.25 1.00
1746 A1003 13s multicolored   3.25 1.50

Hunting and Environment Type
1998, Feb. 6 Photo.
1747 A1006 9s Black cocks 1.50 1.00

1998 Winter Olympic Games, Nagano — A1022

1998, Feb. 6 Photo. & Engr.
1748 A1022 14s multicolored   2.50 1.60

Lithographic Printing, Bicent. A1023

Portrait of Aloys Senefelder (1771-1834), inventor of lithography, on printing stone.

1998, Mar. 13 Litho. Perf. 13½
1749 A1023 7s multicolored   1.25 1.00

Joseph Binder (1898-1972), Graphic Artist — A1024

1998, Mar. 13 Photo. Perf. 14
1750 A1024 7s Poster   1.40 1.00

Wiener Secession, Cent. (Assoc. of Artists in Austria-Viennese Secession) A1025

1998, Mar. 13 Photo. & Engr.
1751 A1025 8s multicolored   1.40 1.25

Folklore and Customs Type of 1991
6.50s, Fiacre, Vienna. 7s, Christ figure, Palm Sunday Donkey Procession, Tyrol.

1998, Apr. 3
1752 A892 6.50s multicolored   1.25 .95
1753 A892 7s multicolored   1.40 1.00

Soccer Champions Type of 1997
7s, Austria-Memphis Club.

1998, Apr. 17 Photo.
1754 A1005 7s multicolored   1.40 1.00

Salzburg Archdiocese, 1200th Anniv. A1026

1998, Apr. 17 Photo. & Engr.
1755 A1026 7s multicolored   1.40 1.00

St. Florian, Patron Saint of Fire Brigades A1027

1998, Apr. 17 Photo.
1756 A1027 7s multicolored   1.40 1.00

Railway Centennials A1028

No. 1757, Ybbs Railway. No. 1758, Pöstlingberg Railway. No. 1759, Pinzgau Railway.

1998 Photo. & Engr. Perf. 14
1757 A1028 6.50s multicolored   1.25 1.00
1758 A1028 6.50s multicolored   1.25 1.00
1759 A1028 6.50s multicolored   1.25 1.00
  Nos. 1757-1759 (3)   3.75 3.00
  Issued: No. 1757, 5/15; No. 1758, 6/12; No. 1759, 7/17.

Ferdinandeum, Federal Museum of Tyrol, 175th Anniv. A1029

1998, May 15
1760 A1029 7s multicolored   1.40 1.00

Vienna Festival Weeks — A1030

1998, May 15
1761 A1030 7s Townhall   1.60 1.00
  Europa.

Folklore and Customs Type of 1991
Samson figure & the Zwergin, Lungau district, Salzburg.

1998, June 5
1762 A892 6.50s multicolored   1.25 1.00

Stories and Legends Type of 1997

Design: 25s, Saint Konrad collecting spring water in his handkerchief, Ems Castle.

1998, June 5
1763 A1003 25s multicolored   6.00 2.50

Christine Lavant, Poet, 25th Death Anniv. A1031

1998, June 5   **Photo.**
1764 A1031 7s multicolored   1.40 1.00

Stamp Day Type of 1997
Photo. & Engr.
1998, June 12   **Perf. 13½**
1765 A1009 7s "R" and "L"   1.40 1.00

See Nos. 1725, 1791, 1818, B357-B362. The 1st letters spell "Briefmarke," the 2nd "Philatelie."

Austrian Presidency of the European Union — A1032

1998, July 1   **Photo.**   **Perf. 13½x14**
1766 A1032 7s multicolored   1.40 1.00

The People's Opera, Vienna, Centennial & Franz Lehar (1870-1948), Composer — A1033

1998, Sept. 10   **Photo.**   **Perf. 14**
1767 A1033 6.50s multicolored   1.25 .85

Elizabeth, Empress of Austria (1837-98) A1034

1998, Sept. 10   **Photo. & Engr.**
1768 A1034 7s multicolored   1.40 .90

Vienna University for Commercial Sudies, Cent. — A1035

1998, Sept. 10   **Photo.**
1769 A1035 7s multicolored   1.40 .90

Hans Kudlich, Emancipator of Peasants, 175th Birth Anniv. A1036

Photo. & Engr.
1998, Oct. 23   **Perf. 14**
1770 A1036 6.50s multicolored   1.25 .90

"My Garden," by Hans Staudacher A1037

1998, Oct. 23
1771 A1037 7s multicolored   1.25 .90

City of Eisenstadt, 350th Anniv. — A1038

1998, Oct. 23
1772 A1038 7s multicolored   1.25 .90

Austrian Working Environment Type of 1994

6.50s, Reporter, photographer.

Photo. & Engr.
1998, Nov. 6   **Perf. 14**
1773 A961 6.50s multicolored   1.10 .85

Christmas A1039

1423 Fresco from Tainach/Tinje Church, Carinthia.

1998, Nov. 27
1774 A1039 7s multicolored   1.25 .85

Stories and Legends Type of 1997

The Dark Maiden of Hardegg Castle.

Photo. & Engr.
1999, Feb. 19   **Perf. 14**
1775 A1003 8s multicolored   1.25 .85

1999 Nordic Skiing World Championships, Mt. Dachstein, Ramsau A1040

1999, Feb. 19
1776 A1040 7s multicolored   1.10 .85

Scenery Type of 1984

Bohemian Forest, Upper Austria.

Photo. & Engr.
1999, Mar. 19   **Perf. 14**
1777 A679 7s multicolored   1.10 .85

Folklore and Customs Type of 1991

Traditional walking pilgrimage to Mariazell.

1999, Mar. 19
1778 A892 6.50s multicolored   1.00 .75

Soccer Champions Type of 1997

Design: Soccer Club SK Puntigamer Sturm Graz.

1999, Apr. 16   **Photo.**   **Perf. 14**
1779 A1005 7s multicolored   1.10 .85

Schönnbrun Palace, UNESCO World Heritage Site — A1041

Photo. & Engr.
1999, Apr. 16   **Perf. 14**
1780 A1041 13s multicolored   2.25 1.50

See Nos. 1826, 1845, 1928.

Austrian Patent Office, Cent. — A1042

1999, Apr. 16
1781 A1042 7s multicolored   1.10 .85

Hunting and Environment Type of 1997

1999, May 7   **Litho.**   **Perf. 14**
1782 A1006 6.50s Partridges   1.00 .75

Austrian General Sport Federation, 50th Anniv. — A1043

1999, May 7   **Engr.**   **Perf. 14**
1783 A1043 7s multicolored   1.10 .80

Council of Europe, 50th Anniv. A1044

1999, May 7   **Photo.**   **Perf. 13½x14**
1784 A1044 14s multicolored   2.50 2.00

Karl Jenschke (1899-1969), Automobile Designer A1045

1999, May 28
1785 A1045 7s Steyr automobile   1.10 .80

Marble Relief of St. Martin A1046

Design: 9s, St. Anne, Mary and Jesus.

1999   **Photo. & Engr.**   **Perf. 14**
1786 A1046 8s multicolored   1.40 .95
           Perf. 13¾
1787 A1046 9s multicolored   1.75 1.10

Issued: 8s, 5/28; 9s, 9/17. See Nos. 1817, 1830, 1851-1852.

Austrian Social Welfare Service, 125th Anniv. A1047

1999, June 4   **Litho.**   **Perf. 13¾**
1788 A1047 7s multicolored   1.25 .80

Johann Strauss, the Younger (1825-99), Composer A1048

8s, Johann Strauss, the Elder (1804-49).

1999, June 4   **Photo. & Engr.**
1789 A1048 7s multicolored   1.25 .80
1790 A1048 8s multicolored   1.30 .95

Stamp Day Type of 1997

1999, June 18   **Perf. 13½**
1791 A1009 7s "K" and "I"   1.25 .80

See Nos. 1725, 1765, 1818, B357-B362. The 1st letters spell "Briefmarke," the 2nd "Philatelie."

Donau-Auen Natl. Park — A1049

1999, June 18   **Perf. 13¾**
1792 A1049 7s multicolored   *1.60 1.00*

Europa.

Natl. Gendarmery, 150th Anniv. — A1050

1999, June 18
1793 A1050 7s multicolored   1.25   .80

Stories and Legends Type of 1997
Design: The Holy Notburga.

Photo. & Engr.
1999, Aug. 27   *Perf. 13¾x14*
1794 A1003 20s multicolored   5.00 2.50

Graz Opera House, 100th Anniv. — A1051

Photo. & Engr.
1999, Sept. 17   *Perf. 13¾*
1795 A1051 6.50s multicolored   1.25   .75

International Year of Older Persons — A1052

1999, Sept. 17   Photo.   *Perf. 13¾*
1796 A1052 7s multicolored   1.25   .85

Federation of Austrian Trade Unions, 14th Congress A1053

1999, Oct. 15   Litho.   *Perf. 13¾*
1797 A1053 6.50s multicolored   1.25   .75

"Caffee Girardi," by Wolfgang Herzig — A1054

Photo. & Engr.
1999, Oct. 22   *Perf. 13¾x14*
1798 A1054 7s multicolored   1.25   .85

Folklore & Customs Type of 1991
7s, The Pummerin, Bell in St. Stephen's Cathedral, Vienna. 8s, Pumpkin Festival, Lower Austria.

1999   Photo. & Engr.   *Perf. 13¾*
1799 A892 7s multicolored   1.25   .85
1800 A892 8s multicolored   1.40   .95
   Issued: 8s, 10/22; 7s, 11/12.

National Institute of Geology, 150th Anniv. A1055

Photo. & Engr.
1999, Nov. 12   *Perf. 13¾x14*
1801 A1055 7s multicolored   1.25   .85

Stories & Legends Type of 1997
Design: 32s, Discovery of Erzberg.

Photo. & Engr.
1999, Nov. 12   *Perf. 13¾x14*
1802 A1003 32s multicolored   9.00 4.00

Christmas A1056

Photo. & Engr.
1999, Nov. 26   *Perf. 13¾*
1803 A1056 7s Pinkafeld creche   1.25   .85

Stories & Legends Type of 1997
Design: 10s, House of the Basilisk, Vienna.

Photo. & Engr.
2000, Jan. 21   *Perf. 13¾x14*
1804 A1003 10s multi   2.50 1.50
   a.   Souvenir sheet of 1   35.00 35.00
No. 1804a was sold only with the purchase of an 80s ticket to the Vienna Intl. Philatelic Exhibition.

Folklore & Customs Type of 1991
Designs: 6.50s, Schleicherlaufen Festival, Telfs. 7s, Carrying miniature churches, Bad Eisenkappel.

2000   Photo. & Engr.   *Perf. 13¾*
1805 A892 6.50s multi   1.25 1.25
1806 A892   7s multi   1.25 1.25
   Issued: 6.50s, 2/11; 7s, 1/21.

Soccer Champions Type of 1997
Design: Tirol Soccer Club.

2000, Mar. 3   Photo.   *Perf. 13¾*
1807 A1005 7s multi   1.25 1.00

Hunting and Environment Type of 1997
2000, Mar. 3   *Perf. 14x14¼*
1808 A1006 7s Ibex   1.25 1.00

Intl. Gardening Exhibition, Graz — A1057

Photo. & Embossed
2000, Mar. 3   *Perf. 13½x13¾*
1809 A1057 7s multi   1.25 1.25

Stories & Legends Type of 1997
Designs: 22s, The Witch's Ride. 23s, The Bread Loaf Monument.

2000   Photo. & Engr.   *Perf. 13¾x14*
1810 A1003 22s multi   4.50 4.50
1811 A1003 23s multi   4.50 6.00
   Issued: 22s, 4/28. 23s, 6/16.

First Ascent of Grossglockner, Bicent. A1058

2000, Apr. 28   *Perf. 13¾*
1812 A1058 7s multi   1.25 1.00

Scenery Type of 1984
Design: Sonnblick Glacier, Granatspitze, Weissee, Salzburg.

2000, May 9   *Perf. 13¾x14*
1813 A679 7s multi   1.25 1.25

Europa, 2000
Common Design Type
2000, May 9   Photo.   *Perf. 14¼x13½*
1814 CD17 7s multi   1.40 1.40

Klagenfurt Airport, 75th Anniv. A1059

2000, May 19   *Perf. 13¾*
1815 A1059 7s multi   1.25 1.25

Protection of Historical Monuments, 150th Anniv. — A1060

Photo. & Engr.
2000, May 19   *Perf. 14x13¼*
1816 A1060 8s multi   1.40 1.10

Religious Art Type of 1999
Design: 9s, Illustration of St. Malachy from book, *The Life of Bishop Malachy.*

2000, May 19   *Perf. 13¾*
1817 A1046 9s multi   1.65 1.25

Stamp Day Type of 1997
2000, May 30   *Perf. 13½*
1818 A1009 7s "E" and "E"   1.25 1.25
   See Nos. 1725, 1765, 1791, B357-B362. The 1st letters spell "Briefmarke," the 2nd "Philatelie."

Austrian Postage Stamps, 150th Anniv. A1061

2000, May 30   *Perf. 13¾*
1819 A1061 7s Nos. 5, 1818   1.25 1.25

Children's Television Character, Confetti A1062

2000, May 31
1820 A1062 7s multi   1.25 1.25
   See Nos. 1841, 1893, 1914.

Blue Blues, by Friedensreich Hundertwasser (1928-2000), Artist — A1063

Colors of seven solid vertical panels at top: a, Silver. b, Red. c, Red violet. d, Black.

2000, June 2
1821   Sheet of 4   8.00 10.00
   a.-d.   A1063 7s Any single   1.50 1.25

Discovery of Human Blood Types, Cent. A1064

       Perf. 13¾x13½
2000, June 16   *Photo.*
1822 A1064 8s multi   1.40 1.40

Scheduled Motorized Vehicle Passenger Transportation, Cent. — A1065

Photo. & Engr.
2000, June 16   *Perf. 14*
1823 A1065 9s multi   1.75 1.75

Folklore & Customs Type of 1991
7s, Intl. meeting of rafters, Carinthia.

Photo. & Engr.
2000, Aug. 25   *Perf. 13¾*
1824 A892 7s multi   1.25 1.25

Vienna Philharmonic Orchestra, Cent. — A1066

2000, Sept. 15
1825 A1066 7s multi   1.25 1.25

World Heritage Site Type of 1999
Hallstatt-Dachstein and Salzkammergut

2000, Sept. 15
1826 A1041 7s multi   1.25 1.25

2000 Summer Olympics,
Sydney — A1068

2000, Sept. 15   Perf. 14x13¾
1827 A1068 9s multi   1.60 1.60

Working Environment Type of 1994
6.50s, Papermaker, printer.

2000, Sept. 29
1828 A961 6.50s multi   1.25 1.25

Turf Turkey, by
Ida Szigethy
A1069

2000, Oct. 13   Perf. 13¾
1829 A1069 7s multi   1.25 1.25

Religious Art Type of 1999
Design: 8s, Illuminated text, Codex 965.

2000, Oct. 13
1830 A1046 8s multi   1.50 1.50

Association of
Austrian Adult
Education
Centers, 50th
Anniv.
A1070

Photo. & Engr.
2000, Nov. 24   Perf. 13¾
1831 A1070 7s multi   1.25 1.25

Vaccinations in
Austria,
Bicent. — A1071

2000, Nov. 24   Perf. 14¼x13½
1832 A1071 7s multi   1.25 1.25

Christmas
A1072

Altar sidewing, St. Martin's Church,
Ludesch.

2000, Dec. 1   Perf. 13¾
1833 A1072 7s multi   1.25 1.25

2001 Alpine Skiing World
Championships, St. Anton am
Arlberg — A1073

2000, Dec. 15   Perf. 14x13¾
1834 A1073 7s multi   1.25 1.25

**Hunting & Environment Type of
1997**
2001, Feb. 16 Photo. Perf. 14x14¼
1835 A1006 7s Ducks   1.25 1.25

Folklore & Customs Type of 1991
Designs: No. 1836, Lenten altar cloths,
Eastern Tyrol. No. 1837, Water disk shooting,
Prebersee. No. 1838, Boat Mill, Mureck.

2001   Photo. & Engr.   Perf. 13¾
1836 A892 7s multi   1.25 1.25
1837 A892 7s multi   1.25 1.25
1838 A892 8s multi   1.40 1.40
       Nos. 1836-1838 (3)   3.90 3.90

Issued: No. 1836, 5/4/01. No. 1838,
3/30/01. No. 1837, 8/24/01.

Soccer Champions Type of 1997
7s, Wustenrot Salzburg.

2001, Mar. 30 Photo. Perf. 13¾
1839 A1005 7s multi   1.25 1.25

Zilltertal
Railway,
Cent.
A1074

Photo. & Engr.
2001, Mar. 30   Perf. 13¾
1840 A1074 7s multi   1.25 1.25

**Children's Television Character
Type of 2000**
2001, Apr. 20 Photo. Perf. 13¾
1841 A1062 7s Rolf Rüdiger   1.25 1.25

Salzburg
Airport,
75th Anniv.
A1075

Photo. & Engr.
2001, Apr. 20   Perf. 13½x14¼
1842 A1075 14s multi   2.75 2.75

Scenery Type of 1984
Design: Bärenschützkamm, Styria.

Photo. & Engr.
2001, May 4   Perf. 13¾
1843 A679 7s multi   1.40 1.40

Europa
A1076

2001, May 18 Photo. Perf. 13¾
1844 A1076 15s multi   2.50 2.50

**UNESCO World Heritage Type of
1999**
Design: Semmering Railway.

Photo. & Engr.
2001, June 8   Perf. 13¾
1845 A1041 35s multi   8.50 8.50

Austrian Aero
Club,
Cent. — A1077

2001, June 8   Perf. 13¾x14
1846 A1077 7s multi   1.40 1.40

UN High Commissioner for Refugees,
50th Anniv. — A1078

2001, June 8   Perf. 14x13¾
1847 A1078 21s multi   4.25 4.25

7th IVV
Hiking
Olympics
A1079

2001, June 22 Photo. Perf. 13¾
1848 A1079 7s multi   1.40 1.40

Military
Post
Offices
Abroad
A1080

2001, June 22
1849 A1080 7s multi   1.40 1.40

Conversion of
East-West
Railway to
Four Tracks
A1081

Photo. & Engr.
2001, Aug. 31   Perf. 13¾
1850 A1081 7s multi   1.40 1.40

Religious Art Type of 1999
Designs: 7s, Church vestment cut from
Turkish tent, 1683. 10s, Pluvial.

2001   Photo. & Engr.   Perf. 13¾
1851 A1046 7s multi   1.40 1.40
1852 A1046 10s multi   1.90 1.90

Issued: 7s, 10/5; 10s, 9/14.

Johann
Nestroy
(1801-62),
Playwright
A1082

2001, Sept. 14
1853 A1082 7s multi   1.40 1.40

The Continents
(Detail), by
Helmut
Leherb — A1083

2001, Sept. 14
1854 A1083 7s multi   1.40 1.40

Joseph Ritter von Führich (1800-76),
Painter — A1084

2001, Sept. 14   Perf. 14
1855 A1084 8s multi   1.60 1.60

Leopold Ludwig
Döbler (1801-
64), Magician
A1085

2001, Oct. 5
1856 A1085 7s multi   1.40 1.40

Meteorology and Geodynamics
Institute, 150th Anniv. — A1086

2001, Oct. 5
1857 A1086 12s multi   2.50 2.50

Cat King, by
Manfred
Deix — A1087

2001, Oct. 5   Perf. 13¾
1858 A1087 19s multi   4.25 4.25
See No. 1903.

Working Environment Type of 1994

2001, Oct. 16   *Perf. 14*
1859 A961 7s Public servants   1.40 1.40

Christmas
A1088

Photo. & Engr.

2001, Nov. 30   *Perf. 14*
1860 A1088 7s multi   1.40 1.40

100 Cents = 1 Euro (€)

Introduction of the Euro — A1089

Photo. & Embossed with Foil Application

2002, Jan. 1   *Perf. 13½x13¾*
1861 A1089 €3.27 multi   8.50 8.50

Austrian Scenes — A1090

Designs: 4c, Schönlaterngasse, Vienna. 7c, Stations of the Cross, Lower Austria Province. 13c, Cow in pasture, Tyrol Province. 17c, Street, Hadres. 20c, Sailboats on Wörther See, Carinthia. 25c, Rock with crosses, Mondsee, Upper Austria. 27c, Farmhouse, Salzburg Province. 45c, St. Martin's Chapel, Kleinwalser Valley, Vorarlberg. 51c, Schönlaterngasse, Vienna. 55c, Houses, Steyr. 58c, Street, Hadres. 73c, Farmhouse, Salzburg Province. 75c, Ship in Lake Constance (Bodensee), Vorarlberg Province. 87c, Cow in pasture, Tyrol Province. €1, Farmhouse, Rossegg. €1.25, Wine press house, Eisenberg. €2.03, Stations of the Cross, Lower Austria Province. €3.75, Roadside shrine, Carinthia Province.

2002-03   **Photo.**   *Perf. 13¾x14*
1862	A1090	4c multi	.25	.25
1863	A1090	7c multi	.25	.25
1863A	A1090	13c multi	.35	.35
1864	A1090	17c multi	.45	.45
1865	A1090	20c multi	.55	.50
1865A	A1090	25c multi	.65	.50
1866	A1090	27c multi	.70	.50
1866A	A1090	45c multi	1.25	1.25
1867	A1090	51c multi	1.40	.70
1868	A1090	55c multi	1.50	1.40
1869	A1090	58c multi	1.50	.70
1872	A1090	73c multi	1.90	.90
1873	A1090	75c multi	2.00	1.40
1875	A1090	87c multi	2.25	1.10
1876	A1090	€1 multi	2.75	2.10
1877	A1090	€1.25 multi	3.25	2.50
1879	A1090	€2.03 multi	5.25	2.50
1880	A1090	€3.75 multi	9.75	8.50

Nos. 1862-1880 (18)   36.00 25.85

Issued: 51c, 58c, 73c, 87c, €2.03, 1/1/02. 4c, 7c, 13c, 17c, 27c, 6/2/03; 55c, 75c, €1, €1.25, €3.75, 5/30/03. 20c, 25c, 7/18/03. 45c, 12/5/03.
For surcharges see Nos. 1969, 1979-1986, 2047, B376.

2002 Winter Olympics, Salt Lake City — A1091

Photo. & Engr.

2002, Feb. 8   *Perf. 14x13¾*
1882 A1091 73c multi   1.90 1.90

Love — A1092

2002, Feb. 14   **Photo.**   *Perf. 14¼x14*
1883 A1092 87c multi   2.25 2.25

Intl. Women's Day — A1093

2002, Mar. 8   *Perf. 13¾*
1884 A1093 51c multi   1.40 1.40

Promotion of Youth Philately — A1094

Cartoon characters: No. 1885, Girls Mel and Lucy. No. 1886, Sisco and Mauritius (boy and dog). No. 1887, Edison and Gogo (girl and boy).

2002   **Photo.**   *Perf. 14x13¾*
1885	A1094	58c multi	1.75	1.75
1886	A1094	58c multi	1.75	1.75
1887	A1094	58c multi	1.75	1.75

Nos. 1885-1887 (3)   5.25 5.25

Issued: No. 1885, 4/5. No. 1886, 5/10. No. 1887, 11/22.

Roses — A1095

2002, Apr. 5   **Photo.**   *Perf. 14x13¾*
1888 A1095 58c multi   1.75 1.75

80th Anniversary of Marianneum, by Alfred Kubin — A1096

2002, Apr. 10   *Perf. 13½x13¾*
1889 A1096 87c black & buff   2.25 2.25

Caritas — A1097

2002, Apr. 26
1890 A1097 51c multi   1.40 1.40

Europa A1098

2002, May 3   *Perf. 13¾*
1891 A1098 87c multi   2.25 2.25

Lilienfeld Monastery, 800th Anniv. A1099

Photo. & Engr.

2002, May 17   *Perf. 13¾*
1892 A1099 €2.03 multi   5.25 5.25

Children's Television Character Type of 2000

2002, May 23   **Photo.**   *Perf. 13¾*
1893 A1062 51c Mimi   1.40 1.40

Souvenir Sheet

Schönbrunn Zoo, 250th Anniv. — A1100

No. 1894: a, Orangutan, leopard, lioness, zebras. b, Various birds. c, Lion, antelope, turtle, crocodile, jellyfish. d, Antelope, elephant, birds, jellyfish, fish, ray.

Photo. & Engr.

2002, June 3   *Perf. 13½x14¼*
1894	A1100	Sheet of 4	11.50 11.50
a.		51c multi	1.50 1.50
b.		58c multi	1.75 1.75
c.		87c multi	2.50 2.50
d.		€1.38 multi	4.00 4.00

Teddy Bears, Cent. — A1101

2002, June 4   **Photo.**   *Perf. 14¼x14*
1895 A1101 51c multi   1.40 1.40

Crystal Cup from Innsbruck Glassworks A1102

Photo. & Engr.

2002, June 21   *Perf. 13¾*
1896 A1102 €1.60 multi   4.25 4.25

Traditional arts and crafts.

Chair by Michael Thonet, 1860 — A1103

2002, June 21   **Photo.**
1897 A1103 €1.38 multi   3.75 3.75

Austrian design.

Museum of Contemporary Art, Vienna — A1104

2002, Sept. 4   **Photo.**   *Perf. 14x13¾*
1898 A1104 58c multi   1.50 1.50

Austrians Living Abroad — A1105

Photo. & Engr.

2002, Sept. 5   *Perf. 13¾x14*
1899 A1105 €2.47 multi   6.50 6.50

Clown Doctor
A1106

2002, Sept. 10   Photo.   Perf. 13¾
1900 A1106 51c multi   1.40 1.40

Linz "Sound Cloud"
A1107

2002, Sept. 13
1901 A1107 58c multi   1.50 1.50

OAF Gräf & Stift Type 40/45 Automobile
A1108

2002, Sept. 27
1902 A1108 51c multi   1.40 1.40
See No. 1925.

Pet Type of 2001
Design: Dog King, by Manfred Deix.

2002, Oct. 4   Photo.   Perf. 13¾
1903 A1087 51c multi   1.40 1.40

Train at Vienna South Railway Station
A1109

2002, Oct. 4   Photo. & Engr.
1904 A1109 51c multi   1.40 1.40
See Nos. 1921, 1958, 2023, 2059, 2105, 2114, 2166, 2171, 2215, 2249, 2279, 2330, 2337, 2521, 2582, 2634, 2682, 2687.

Schützenhaus, by Karl Goldammer
A1110

2002, Oct. 11
1905 A1110 51c multi   1.40 1.40

Souvenir Sheet

National Lottery, 250th Anniv. — A1111

2002, Oct. 17   Photo.   Perf.
1906 A1111 87c multi   2.50 2.50

Thayatal Natl. Park
A1112

Photo. & Engr.
2002, Oct. 25   Perf. 13¾
1907 A1112 58c multi   1.60 1.60

Puch 175 SV Motorcycle
A1113

2002, Nov. 8   Photo.   Perf. 14x13¾
1908 A1113 58c multi   1.60 1.60

One Eye, by Wolfgang Homola
A1114

2002, Nov. 15   Perf. 13¾
1909 A1114 €1.38 multi   3.75 3.75
Austrian design.

Christmas — A1115

Photo. & Engr.
2002, Nov. 29   Perf. 14x14¼
1910 A1115 51c multi   1.40 1.40

A1115a

2003, Jan. 22   Litho.   Perf. 13¾x14
1910A A1115a 45c multi   8.00 8.00

Graz, 2003 European Cultural Capital
A1116

Perf. 13½x14¼
2003, Mar. 14   Photo.
1911 A1116 58c multi   1.60 1.60

Heart, Wedding Rings and Pigeons — A1117

2003, Mar. 21   Perf. 14¼x13½
1912 A1117 58c multi   1.60 1.60

Billy Wilder (1906-2002), Movie Director — A1118

2003, Mar. 21
1913 A1118 58c gray black   1.50 1.50

Children's Television Character Type of 2000
2003, Apr. 11   Photo.   Perf. 13¾
1914 A1062 51c Kasperl   1.40 1.40

Implementation of Waste Recycling System, 10th Anniv. — A1119

2003, Apr. 11
1915 A1119 55c multi   1.40 1.40

Bar Service No. 248, Glassware by Adolf Loos — A1120

2003, Apr. 11
1916 A1120 €1.38 multi   3.50 3.50
Austrian design.

Souvenir Sheet

Panda Research in Austria — A1121

2003, Apr. 14   Perf. 14x14¼
1917 A1121   Sheet of 2   5.25 5.25
  a. 75c Two pandas   2.25 2.25
  b. €1 Two pandas, diff.   3.00 3.00
  No. 1917b is 38mm in diameter.

St. Georgen am Längsee Convent, 1000th Anniv.
A1122

2003, Apr. 25   Perf. 13¾
1918 A1122 87c multi   2.25 2.25

Souvenir Sheet

Marcel Prawy (1911-2003), Musical Impresario — A1123

2003, Apr. 25
1919 A1123 €1.75 multi   5.25 5.25

Europa
A1124

2003, May 9
1920 A1124 €1.02 multi   2.75 2.75

Railways Type of 2002
75c, OEBB Series 5045.

Photo. & Engr.
2003, June 6   Perf. 13¾
1921 A1109 75c multi   2.00 2.00

Salzach River Bridge, Laufen, Germany — Oberndorf, Austria — A1125

Photo. & Engr.
2003, June 12   Perf. 13½
1922 A1125 55c multi   1.50 1.50
See Germany No. 2245.

Souvenir Sheet

Ford Motor Company, Cent. — A1126

No. 1923: a, Model T. b, Henry Ford (1863-1947). c, 2003 Ford Streetka.

Perf. 13½x14¼

2003, June 16			**Photo.**
1923	A1126	Sheet of 3 + label	5.00 5.00
a.-c.		55c Any single	1.50 1.50

Souvenir Sheet

Rolling Stones — A1127

No. 1924: a, Guitarist Keith Richards. b, Singer Mick Jagger. c, Drummer Charlie Watts. d, Guitarist Ron Wood smoking cigarette.

2003, June 18			**Perf. 14x13½**
1924	A1127	Sheet of 4	6.50 6.50
a.-d.		55c Any single	1.60 1.60

Vehicle Type of 2002

Design: Rosenbauer Panther 8x8 airport fire engine.

2003, June 20		**Perf. 13¾**
1925	A1108 55c multi	1.50 1.50

Bible Year — A1128

2003, June 20		
1926	A1128 55c multi	1.50 1.50

Prenez le Temps d'Aimer, by Kiki Kogelnik (1935-97) A1129

2003, July 3		**Photo. & Engr.**
1927	A1129 55c multi	1.50 1.50

UNESCO World Heritage Type of 1999

Design: Neusiedler See.

Photo. & Engr.		
2003, July 11		**Perf. 13¾**
1928	A1041 €1 multi	2.75 2.75

Samurai and Geisha A1130

2003, July 19	**Photo.**	**Perf. 13¾**
1929	A1130 55c multi	1.50 1.50

Exhibition of Japanese Shogun Era Culture, Leoben Kunsthalle, Vienna.

Performance of Turandot at St. Margarethen Opera Festival — A1131

2003, July 24		**Perf. 14x13¾**
1930	A1131 55c multi	1.50 1.50

Children's Welfare — A1132

2003, Sept. 12	**Photo.**	**Perf. 13x13½**
1931	A1132 55c multi	1.50 1.50

Water Tower, Wiener Neustadt A1133

2003, Sept. 18		**Perf. 13¾**
1932	A1133 55c multi	1.40 1.40

50th Austrian Local Government Conference.

Thank You A1134

2003, Sept. 19		
1933	A1134 55c multi	1.40 1.40

Mail Order Business A1135

2003, Sept. 24		**Perf. 13¾x14**
1934	A1135 55c multi	1.40 1.40

Werner Schlager, 2003 Table Tennis World Champion — A1136

2003, Sept. 25		**Perf. 14x13¾**
1935	A1136 55c multi	1.40 1.40

Jugend-Phila Graz '03 Youth Philatelic Exhibition — A1137

2003, Sept. 26		
1936	A1137 55c multi	1.40 1.40

Performance of Musical "Elisabeth," Theater an der Wien, Vienna — A1138

2003, Oct. 1		
1937	A1138 55c multi	1.40 1.40

Souvenir Sheet

Judith I, by Gustav Klimt — A1139

Photo. & Engr.		
2003, Oct. 10		**Perf. 13½x13¾**
1938	A1139 €2.10 multi	6.25 6.25

Licht Ins Dunkel Fund-Raising Campaign for the Handicapped, 30th Anniv. — A1140

		Perf. 13¾x13½
2003, Nov. 11		**Photo.**
1939	A1140 55c multi	1.40 1.40

Bösendorfer Piano A1141

Jazz Pianist Oscar Peterson and Bösendorfer Piano — A1142

Photo. & Engr.		
2003, Nov. 19		**Perf. 13¾**
1940	A1141 75c multi	2.00 2.00
Photo.		
2003, Nov. 19		**Perf. 13½x12¾**
1941	A1142 €1.25 multi	3.25 3.25

Bösendorfer pianos, 175th anniv.

Christmas A1143

Photo. & Engr.		
2003, Nov. 28		**Perf. 13¾x14**
1942	A1143 55c multi	1.40 1.40

Personalized Stamps A1145

A1144

2003, Dec. 5	**Photo.**	**Perf. 13¾**
1943	A1144 55c multi	1.40 1.40
1944	A1145 55c multi	1.40 1.40

Stamp vignettes could be personalized by customers, presumably for an extra fee.

A quantity of Nos. 1943 and 1944 were later imprinted with various commercial themes and offered by Austria Post in full panes at a premium over face value. Only examples as illustrated, bearing generic vignettes, were sold at the face value shown on the stamp. In 2006, Nos. 1943 and 1944 were offered with other denominations that lacked the euro sign. Stamps with similar frames in colors other than yellow and blue, as seen on No. 2036, and stamps with country names and denominations in white were created starting in 2013.

2004 New Year's Concert with Conductor Riccardo Muti — A1146

2004, Jan. 1   Photo.   Perf. 13¾
1945 A1146 €1 multi   2.50 2.50

Seiji Ozawa, Conductor of Vienna State Opera A1147

2004, Jan. 16   Photo.   Perf. 13¾
1946 A1147 €1 multi   2.75 2.75

José Carreras, 30th Anniv. at Vienna State Opera A1148

2004, Feb. 23   Photo.   Perf. 13¾
1947 A1148 €1 multi   2.50 2.50

Austrian Soccer Association, Cent. — A1149

No. 1948: a, Gerhard Hanappi. b, Mathias Sindelar. c, Soccer ball, centenary emblem. d, Bruno Pezzey. e, Ernst Ocwirk. f, Walter Zeman. g, Herbert Prohaska. h, Hans Krankl. i, Andreas Herzog. j, Anton Polster.

2004, Mar. 18
1948 A1149   Sheet of 10   15.00 15.00
a.-j.   55c Any single   1.40 1.40

Easter — A1150

2004, Mar. 26
1949 A1150 55c multi   1.40 1.40

Life Ball, Charity Ball for AIDS Research — A1151

2004, Mar. 29   Perf. 14x13¾
1950 A1151 55c multi   1.40 1.40

Franz Cardinal König (1905-2004) A1152

Photo. & Engr.
2004, Mar. 30   Perf. 14¼
1951 A1152 €1 multi   2.75 2.75

Souvenir Sheet

Wedding of Emperor Franz Joseph and Empress Elizabeth von Wittelsbach, 150th Anniv. — A1153

No. 1952: a, Emperor and Empress on honeymoon in Laxenburg (29x36mm). b, Wedding procession (29x36mm). c, Emperor and Empress (31x38mm).

2004, Apr. 23   Perf. 14¼x14
1952 A1153   Sheet of 3   12.50 12.50
a.   €1.25 multi   3.25 3.25
b.   €1.50 multi   4.00 4.00
c.   €1.75 multi   4.50 4.50

Souvenir Sheet

Central European Catholics' Day — A1154

No. 1953: a, Catholics' Day emblem. b, Pope John Paul II. c, Madonna and Child, Mariazell Basilica (silver panel at bottom). d, Mother of God on the Column of the Blessed Virgin, Mariazell Basilica. e, Virgin Mary and Child, Mariazell Basilica (gold frame). f, Altar crucifix, Mariazell Basilica.

Photo. (55c), Photo. & Engr.
2004, Apr. 28   Perf. 14
1953 A1154   Sheet of 6   17.50 17.50
a.   55c multi   1.50 1.50
b.-f.   €1.25 Any single   3.25 3.25

Folklore & Customs Type of 1991

Design: Barrel sliding, Klosterneuburg.

Photo. & Engr.
2004, May 8   Perf. 13¾
1954 A892 55c multi   1.40 1.40

Joe Zawinul, Jazz Musician A1155

2004, May 24   Photo.   Perf. 13¾
1955 A1155 55c multi   1.40 1.40

Europa A1156

2004, June 4   Perf. 13¾x14
1956 A1156 75c multi   2.00 2.00

Papal Order of the Holy Sepulchre of Jerusalem A1157

Photo. & Engr.
2004, June 4   Perf. 13¾
1957 A1157 125c multi   3.50 3.50

Railways Type of 2002

55c, Engerth locomotive.

Photo. & Engr.
2004, June 19   Perf. 13¾
1958 A1109 55c multi   1.40 1.40

21st Danube Island Festival, Vienna A1158

2004, June 25   Photo.   Perf. 13¾x14
1959 A1158 55c multi   1.40 1.40

Theodor Herzl (1860-1904), Zionist Leader A1159

2004, July 6   Perf. 13¾
1960 A1159 55c multi   1.40 1.40
See Hungary No. 3903, Israel No. 1566.

Arnold Schwarzenegger, Governor of California, Actor — A1160

2004, July 30   Photo.
1961 A1160 100c multi   2.75 2.75

Ernst Happel (1925-92), Soccer Coach — A1161

2004, Aug. 17   Perf. 14x13½
1962 A1161 100c red & black   2.50 2.50

Winning Entry in Tom Turbo Television Show Children's Stamp Design Contest A1162

2004, Sept. 9   Photo.   Perf. 13¾
1963 A1162 55c multi   1.40 1.40

Tom Tom, Tom Tomette and Schneckodemus, Cartoon by Thomas Kostron — A1163

2004, Sept. 10   Perf. 14¼x14
1964 A1163 55c multi   1.40 1.40

Incorporation of Floridsdorf into Vienna, Cent. — A1164

Photo. & Engr.
2004, Sept. 17   Perf. 14x13¾
1965 A1164 55c multi   1.40 1.40

Souvenir Sheet

Swarovski Crystal — A1165

No. 1966: a, Crystal. b, Swan.

Photo. With Glass Crystals Affixed
2004, Sept. 20   Perf. 14x14¼
1966 A1165   Sheet of 2   20.00 20.00
a.-b.   375c Either single   10.00 10.00
   Six crystals are affixed to each stamp. Sheet was sold with a protective sleeve.

AUSTRIA

55

Hermann Maier, Skier — A1166

2004, Sept. 25 Photo. Perf. 14x13¾
1967 A1166 55c multi   1.40 1.40

Kaspar's Winter Scene, by Josef Bramer A1167

Photo. & Engr.
2004, Oct. 8 Perf. 13½x13¾
1968 A1167 55c multi   1.50 1.50

No. 1867 Surcharged

2004, Oct. 13 Photo. Perf. 13¾x14
1969 A1090 55c on 51c #1867   1.50 1.50

Woman Waiting, by Silvia Gredenberg A1168

2004, Oct. 15 Photo. Perf. 13¾x14
1970 A1168 55c multi   1.50 1.50

Souvenir Sheet

Young Sunflower, by Max Weiler — A1169

Photo. & Engr.
2004, Oct. 18 Perf. 13¾
1971 A1169 210c multi   6.00 6.00

Poster for Danube Meadows National Park, by Friedensreich Hundertwasser A1170

Photo. & Engr.
2004, Oct. 22 Perf. 13½x13¾
1972 A1170 55c multi   1.50 1.50

Federal Army, 50th Anniv. — A1171

2004, Oct. 26 Photo. Perf. 13¾
1973 A1171 55c multi   1.50 1.50

Nikolaus Harnoncourt, Conductor, 75th Birthday — A1172

2004, Oct. 29
1974 A1172 100c multi   2.75 2.75

Christmas A1173

Photo. & Engr.
2004, Nov. 26 Perf. 13½x13¾
1975 A1173 55c multi   1.50 1.50

2005 New Year's Concert With Conductor Lorin Maazel A1174

2005, Jan. 1 Photo. Perf. 13¾
1976 A1174 €1 multi   2.75 2.75

Herbert von Karajan Center, 10th Anniv. A1175

2005, Jan. 14 Perf. 14x14¼
1977 A1175 55c multi   1.50 1.50

Examples of No. 1977 with a lighter background were given away as gifts to standing order customers.

Stephan Eberharter, Skier — A1176

2005, Jan. 20 Perf. 14x13¾
1978 A1176 55c multi   1.50 1.50

Nos. 1863A, 1864, 1866, 1867, 1869, 1872, 1875 and 1879 Surcharged

g   h

i   j

k   l

m   n

2005 Photo. Perf. 13¾x14
1979 A1090(g) 55c on 13c multi   1.50 1.50
1980 A1090(h) 55c on 17c multi   1.50 1.50
1981 A1090(i) 55c on 27c multi   1.50 1.50
1982 A1090(j) 55c on 51c multi   1.50 1.50
1983 A1090(k) 55c on 58c multi   1.50 1.50
1984 A1090(l) 55c on 73c multi   1.50 1.50
1985 A1090(m) 55c on 87c multi   1.50 1.50
1986 A1090(n) 55c on €2.03 multi 1.50 1.50
  Nos. 1979-1986 (8)   12.00 12.00
Issued: Nos. 1979, 1980, 2/11; Nos. 1981, 1986, 2/18; Nos. 1982, 1983, 2/4; Nos. 1984, 1985, 1/25.

Rotary International, Cent. — A1177

2005, Feb. 23 Photo. Perf. 14x14¼
1987 A1177 55c multi   1.50 1.50

Max Schmeling (1905-2005), Boxer A1178

Photo. & Engr.
2005, Mar. 1 Perf. 13¾x14
1988 A1178 100c multi   2.75 2.75

Venus at a Mirror, by Peter Paul Rubens A1179

2005, Mar. 7 Perf. 13¾
1989 A1179 125c multi   3.00 3.00
  See Liechtenstein No. 1314.

Souvenir Sheet

Carl Djerassi, Chemist and Novelist — A1180

2005, Mar. 8 Photo. Perf. 14
1990 A1180 100c multi   2.75 2.75

Pope John Paul II (1920-2005) A1181

Photo. & Engr.
2005, Apr. 14 Perf. 13½x14¼
1991 A1181 €1 multi   2.75 2.75

Zodiac A1182   New Year 2005 (Year of the Rooster) A1183

Die Cut Perf. 14 Syncopated
2005-06 Self-Adhesive Photo.
Booklet Stamps

1992	A1182	55c Taurus	4.00	4.00
1993	A1182	55c Gemini	4.00	4.00
1994	A1182	55c Cancer	4.00	4.00
1995	A1183	55c Red rooster	4.00	4.00
a.		Booklet pane, 2 each #1992-1995		35.00
1996	A1182	55c Leo	4.00	4.00
1997	A1182	55c Virgo	4.00	4.00
1998	A1182	55c Libra	4.00	4.00
1999	A1183	55c Yellow rooster	4.00	4.00
a.		Booklet pane, 2 each #1996-1999		35.00
2000	A1182	55c Scorpio	4.00	4.00
2001	A1182	55c Sagittarius	4.00	4.00
2002	A1182	55c Capricorn	4.00	4.00
2003	A1183	55c Orange roost-er	4.00	4.00
a.		Booklet pane, 2 each #2000-2003		35.00
2004	A1182	55c Aquarius	4.00	4.00
2005	A1182	55c Pisces	4.00	4.00
2006	A1182	55c Aries	4.00	4.00
2007	A1183	55c Red dog	4.00	4.00
a.		Booklet pane, 2 each #2004-2007		35.00

Issued: Nos. 1992-1995, 4/21. Nos. 1996-1999, 7/22; 2000-2003, 10/24; Nos. 2004-2007, 1/20/06.

Austrian Imperial Post Office, Jerusalem A1184

Photo. & Engr.
2005, Apr. 22 **Perf. 13¾**
2008 A1184 100c multi 2.75 2.75

Patron Saints of Austrian Regions A1185

Designs: No. 2009, St. Florian, patron saint of Upper Austria. No. 2010, St. Joseph, patron saint of Styria.

2005 Photo. & Engr. Perf. 13½x14
2009 A1185 55c multi 1.50 1.50
2010 A1185 55c multi 1.50 1.50

Issued: No. 2009, 5/4; No. 2010, 6/10.
See Nos. 2053, 2062, 2089, 2120, 2162, 2187, 2232.

Liberation of Mauthausen Concentration Camp, 60th Anniv. — A1186

2005, May 6 **Perf. 13¾**
2011 A1186 55c multi 1.50 1.50

Souvenir Sheet

Second Republic, 60th Anniv. — A1187

No. 2012: a, Heraldic eagle and "60" (35x35mm). b, Signatures on State Treaty (42x35mm).

2005, May 15 **Perf. 13¾**
2012 A1187 Sheet of 2 3.00 3.00
a.-b. 55c Either single 1.50 1.50

Heidi Klum, 2005 Life Ball Attendee — A1188

2005, May 20 Photo. Perf. 14x13¾
2013 A1188 75c multi 2.00 2.00

Europa A1189

2005, May 28 **Perf. 13¾**
2014 A1189 75c multi 1.50 1.50

Jochen Rindt, Formula I Race Car Driver — A1190

2005, June 11 Photo. Perf. 14x13¾
2015 A1190 55c multi 1.50 1.50

Niki Lauda, Formula I Race Car Driver — A1191

2005, Sept. 13 Photo. Perf. 14x13¾
2016 A1191 55c multi 1.50 1.50

A €1.25 stamp picturing the Dalai Lama exists. Advance complimentary examples were sent out before the issue was canceled. It is believed approximately 30 examples are extant. An auction sale in 2008 realized €5,683 for the first public sale of the stamp.

Premiere of Animated Movie "Madagascar" A1192

2005, July 7 Photo. Perf. 14
2017 A1192 55c multi 1.50 1.50

Inachis Io — A1193

Photo. & Engr.
2005, July 15 **Perf. 13½x14¼**
2018 A1193 55c multi 1.50 1.50

Edelweiss A1194

2005, July 19 Embroidered Imperf. Self-Adhesive
2019 A1194 375c green & white 11.00 11.00

Folklore & Customs Type of 1991

Design: Frankenburger Dice Game, Upper Austria.

Photo. & Engr.
2005, July 29 **Perf. 13¾**
2020 A892 55c multi 1.50 1.50

Halloween A1195

2005, Sept. 16 Photo. Perf. 13¾
2021 A1195 55c multi 1.50 1.50

Souvenir Sheet

Row of Houses, by Egon Schiele (1890-1918) — A1196

Photo. & Engr.
2005, Sept. 21 **Perf. 13¾**
2022 A1196 210c multi 6.25 6.25

Railways Type of 2002

55c, Montafon Railway ET 10.103.

2005, Sept. 30
2023 A1109 55c multi 1.50 1.50

Montafon Railway, cent.

Landhaus, Klagenfurt A1197

Photo. & Engr.
2005, Oct. 7 **Perf. 13¾x13½**
2024 A1197 75c multi 2.00 2.00

Master of Woods, by Karl Hodina A1198

2005, Oct. 14 **Perf. 13½x13¾**
2025 A1198 55c multi 1.50 1.50

Adalbert Stifter (1805-68), Writer — A1199

2005, Oct. 21 Photo. Perf. 13¾
2026 A1199 55c multi 1.50 1.50

Souvenir Sheet

Reopening of National Theater and State Opera House, 50th Anniv. — A1200

No. 2027: a, National Theater. b, State Opera House.

2005, Oct. 25 Engr. Perf. 13½x14¼
2027 A1200 Sheet of 2 + central label 3.25 3.25
a.-b. 55c Either single 1.60 1.60

Souvenir Sheet

Cyclorama of Salzburg, by Johann Sattler — A1201

No. 2028: a, Denomination at left. b, Denomination at right.

Photo. & Engr.
2005, Oct. 26 **Perf. 13¾x13½**
2028 A1201 Sheet of 2 8.00 8.00
a.-b. 125c Either single 3.75 3.75

Expectation, by Veronika Zillner — A1202

Perf. 13½x13¾

2005, Oct. 28   Photo.
2029 A1202 55c multi   1.50 1.50

Opening of Film, *The Chronicles of Narnia: The Lion, the Witch and the Wardrobe* A1203

2005, Nov. 8   **Perf. 13¾**
2030 A1203 55c multi   1.50 1.50

Visitation of Mary Chapel, by Reinhold Stecher A1204

2005, Nov. 14   **Perf. 13¾x14**
2031 A1204 55c multi   1.50 1.50

Advent and Christmas.

Teutonic Order in Austria, 800th Anniv. A1205

Photo. & Engr.
2005, Nov. 18   **Perf. 14**
2032 A1205 55c multi   1.50 1.50

Christmas A1206

2005, Nov. 25 Photo.   **Perf. 14x14¼**
2033 A1206 55c multi   1.50 1.50

2006 New Year's Concert With Conductor Mariss Jansons A1207

2006, Jan. 1 Photo.   **Perf. 13¾x14**
2034 A1207 75c multi   1.75 1.75

Austrian Presidency of European Union A1208

Photo. & Engr.
2006, Jan. 1   **Perf. 14x14¼**
2035 A1208 75c multi   2.25 2.25

Personalized Stamp — A1209

2006, Jan. 1 Photo.   **Perf. 14x13¾**
2036 A1209 55c multi   1.50 1.50

Stamp vignettes could be personalized by customers, presumably for an extra fee.
A quantity of No. 2036 was later imprinted with various commercial themes and offered by Austria Post in full panes at a substantial premium over face value.
Other denominations could be ordered, as well as stamps with vertically oriented frames, but the example of No. 2036 shown is the only stamp with a "generic" vignette that sold for the face value shown on the stamp.
See note after No. 1944.

Muhammad Ali, Boxer — A1211

2006, Jan. 14 Photo.   **Perf. 13¾x14**
2038 A1211 125c multi   3.00 3.00

Wolfgang Amadeus Mozart (1756-91), Composer A1212

Photo. & Embossed
2006, Jan. 27   **Perf. 13½x13¾**
2039 A1212 55c multi   1.50 1.50

Europa Stamps, 50th Anniv. — A1213

2006, Mar. 3 Photo.   **Perf. 14**
2040 A1213 125c multi   3.75 3.75

Lost in Her Dreams, by Friedrich von Amerling A1214

Photo. & Engr.
2006, Mar. 6   **Perf. 13¾**
2041 A1214 125c multi   3.75 3.75

See Liechtenstein No. 1342.

Souvenir Sheet

Meteor — A1215

2006, Mar. 24 Photo.   **Perf.**
2042 A1215 375c multi   11.00 11.00

Meteorite particles are embedded in the ink used on the meteor.

Karlheinz Böhm, Founder of Menschen für Menschen Foundation, and His Wife, Almaz A1216

2006, Mar. 30   **Perf. 14**
2043 A1216 100c multi   3.00 3.00

Menschen für Menschen Foundation, 25th anniv.

Souvenir Sheet

Freemasonry in Austria — A1217

2006, Apr. 6   **Photo. & Engr.**
2044 A1217 100c multi   3.00 3.00

Couch of Sigmund Freud (1856-1939), Psychoanalyst A1218

2006, Apr. 10   **Photo.**
2045 A1218 55c multi   1.60 1.60

Franz Beckenbauer, by Andy Warhol A1219

2006, Apr. 12   **Perf. 13¾**
2046 A1219 75c multi   2.25 2.25

No. 1863 Surcharged

2006, May 15 Photo.   **Perf. 13¾x14**
2047 A1090 55c on 7c #1863   1.60 1.60

Falco (Hans Hölzl, 1957-98), Rock Musician — A1220

Photo. & Engr.
2006, May 18   **Perf. 14¼x13½**
2048 A1220 55c multi   1.60 1.60

Naomi Campbell, 2006 Life Ball Attendee — A1221

2006, May 20 Photo.   **Perf. 14x13¾**
2049 A1221 75c multi   2.25 2.25

Folklore & Customs Type of 1991

Design: Kranzelreiten, Weitensfeld.

Photo. & Engr.
2006, June 4   **Perf. 13¾**
2050 A892 55c multi   1.60 1.60

Miniature Sheet

Formula I Race Car Drivers — A1222

No. 2051: a, Jim Clark (1936-68). b, Jacky Ickx. c, Jackie Stewart. d, Alain Prost. e, Stirling Moss. f, Mario Andretti. g, Bruce McLaren (1937-70). h, Jack Brabham.

2006, June 7 Photo. Perf. 14x13¾
2051	A1222	Sheet of 8	25.00	25.00
a.-d.		55c Any single	1.60	1.60
e.-f.		75c Either single	2.25	2.25
g.		100c multi	3.00	3.00
h.		125c multi	3.75	3.75

Compare with types A1190-A1191.

Initial Stock Offering of Austria Post — A1223

2006, June 8 Perf. 13¾
2052 A1223 55c multi 1.60 1.60

Patron Saints Type of 2005

Design: St. Hemma, patron saint of Carinthia.

Photo. & Engr.
2006, June 27 Perf. 13¾
2053 A1185 55c multi 1.60 1.60

Federal Chamber of Industry and Commerce, 60th Anniv. — A1224

2006, June 28 Photo. Perf. 14
2054 A1224 55c sil, blk & red 1.60 1.60

Wolfgang Amadeus Mozart and Salzburg — A1225

2006, June 30
2055 A1225 55c multi 1.60 1.60

Activities in Salzburg commemorating 250th anniv. of the birth of Mozart.

Ottfried Fischer, Television Actor — A1226

2006, July 1 Perf. 13¾x14
2056 A1226 55c multi 1.60 1.60

Europa A1227

2006, July 1 Perf. 14
2057 A1227 75c multi 1.75 1.75

St. Anne's Column, Innsbruck, 300th Anniv. — A1228

Photo. & Engr.
2006, July 26 Perf. 14
2058 A1228 55c multi 1.60 1.60

Railways Type of 2002

55c, Pyhrn Railway locomotive.

2006, Aug. 19 Perf. 13¾
2059 A1109 55c multicolored 1.60 1.60

Pyhrn Railway, cent.

Souvenir Sheet

Fireworks — A1229

No. 2060: a, Fireworks over Hong Kong Harbor. b, Fireworks over Prater Ferris wheel, Vienna.

Photo. With Glass Beads Affixed
2006, Aug. 22 Perf. 14
2060	A1229	Sheet of 2	22.50	22.50
a.-b.		375c Either single	11.00	11.00
c.		Sheet, Austria #2060b, Hong Kong #1208a	32.50	32.50

See Hong Kong Nos. 1206-1208. No. 2060c, sold for €12.40 in Austria and for $120 in Hong Kong and is identical to Hong Kong No. 1208c.

Lynx Lynx A1230

Photo. & Engr.
2006, Aug. 25 Perf. 13½x14¼
2061 A1230 55c multi 1.60 1.60

Patron Saints Type of 2005

Design: St. Gebhard, patron saint of Vorarlberg.

Photo. & Engr.
2006, Sept. 1 Perf. 13¾
2062 A1185 55c multi 1.60 1.60

Steyr 220 Automobile — A1231

2006, Sept. 9 Photo.
2063 A1231 55c multi 1.60 1.60

KTM R 125 Tarzan Motorcycle A1232

2006, Sept. 10 Perf. 14¼
2064 A1232 55c multi 1.60 1.60

Benjamin Raich, Skier — A1233

2006, Sept. 23 Perf. 14
2065 A1233 55c multi 1.60 1.60

Musical Instruments A1234

Designs: No. 2066, Seven-stringed qin, China. No. 2067, Bösendorfer piano, Austria.

2006, Sept. 26 Perf. 13½x14¼
2066 A1234 55c multi 1.60 1.60
2067 A1234 55c multi 1.60 1.60

See People's Republic of China Nos. 3531-3532.

Youngboy Vienna Austria 2005, by Cornelia Schlesinger — A1235

2006, Sept. 29 Perf. 14x14¼
2068 A1235 55c multi 1.60 1.60

Homo Sapiens, by Valentin Oman — A1236

Photo. & Engr.
2006, Oct. 9 Perf. 13¾x14
2069 A1236 55c multi 1.60 1.60

Wildlife — A1237

Designs: No. 2070, Emys orbicularis. No. 2071, Geronticus eremita. No. 2072, Ursus arctos.

Die Cut Perf. 13¾x13½
2006, Nov. 6 Coil Stamp Photo.
Self-Adhesive
2070 A1237 55c multi 1.60 1.60

Booklet Stamps
Size: 32x27mm
Die Cut Perf. 14 Syncopated
2071	A1237	55c multi	1.60	1.60
2072	A1237	55c multi	1.60	1.60
a.		Booklet pane, 5 each #2071-2072	16.00	
		Nos. 2070-2072 (3)	4.80	4.80

See Nos. 2092-2094, 2122, 2140-2141, 2154-2155, 2164-2165, 2216-2217, 2235-2237, 2259-2260.

Holy Family at Rest, by Franz Weiss — A1238

Christkindl Pilgrimage Church, by Bishop Reinhold Stecher — A1239

2006 Perf. 14x14¼
2073 A1238 55c multi 1.60 1.60
Perf. 14¼x13½
2074 A1239 55c multi 1.60 1.60

Christmas. Issued: No. 2073, 11/10; No. 2074, 11/24.

1,000 imperf examples of No. 2074 were sold to benefit a charity.

Lviv, Ukraine, 750th Anniv. — A1240

Photo. & Engr.
2006, Dec. 1 Perf. 14x13¾
2075 A1240 55c multi 1.60 1.60

No. 2075 was printed in sheets of 10 stamps and 5 labels. See Ukraine No. 651.

Michael Schumacher, Formula I Race Car Driver — A1241

2006, Dec. 4 Photo. Perf. 13½x14
2076 A1241 75c multi 2.25 2.25

Compare with No. 2103A.

Austrian Stamp and Coin Dealers Association, Cent. — A1242

Photo. & Engr.
2006, Dec. 8 *Perf. 13¾*
2077 A1242 55c Type N1 1.60 1.60

2007 New Year's Concert With Conductor Zubin Mehta A1243

2007, Jan. 1 Photo. *Perf. 13¾*
2078 A1243 75c multi 2.25 2.25

Flowers — A1244

Designs: 55c, Alpine rose, edelweiss, and blue gentian. 75c, Christmas rose. 125c, Liverwort, tall cowslip, and daphne.

2007, Jan. 26 *Perf. 13¾x14*
2079 A1244 55c multi 1.60 1.60
2080 A1244 75c multi 2.25 2.25
2081 A1244 125c multi 3.75 3.75
Nos. 2079-2081 (3) 7.60 7.60
See Nos. 2096-2101, 2130, 2169.

"Mankind and Technology" A1245

Serpentine Die Cut 13¾x14
2007, Feb. 15 *Litho.*
Coil Stamp
Self-Adhesive
2082 A1245 55c multi 1.60 1.60

Lower Austria Fire and Earth Exhibition — A1246

2007, Feb. 16 Litho. *Perf. 13¾*
2083 A1246 55c multi 1.60 1.60

Miniature Sheet

Scouting, Cent. — A1247

No. 2084: a, Scout. b, Campfire. c, Tent. d, Guitar.

2007, Feb. 22
2084 A1247 Sheet of 4 6.50 6.50
a.-d. 55c Any single 1.60 1.60

Roe Deer — A1248

2007, Feb. 23 Photo. *Perf. 14¼x14*
2085 A1248 75c multi 2.25 2.25

Portrait of a Lady, by Bernardino Zaganelli da Cotignola A1249

Photo. & Engr.
2007, Mar. 5 *Perf. 13¾x13½*
2086 A1249 125c multi 3.75 3.75
Printed in sheets of 8. See Liechtenstein No. 1370.

Campaign to End Violence Against Women A1250

2007, Mar. 8 Litho. *Perf. 13¾x14*
2087 A1250 55c multi 1.60 1.60

Easter Rattles A1251

2007, Mar. 9 *Perf. 13¾*
2088 A1251 55c multi 1.60 1.60

Patron Saints Type of 2005
Design: St. Klemens Maria Hofbauer, patron saint of Vienna.

Photo. & Engr.
2007, Mar. 15 *Perf. 13¾x14*
2089 A1185 55c multi 1.60 1.60

Roses — A1252

2007, Mar. 17 Litho. *Perf. 14*
2090 A1252 (55c) multi 1.60 1.60

Congratulations — A1253

2007, Mar. 30 *Perf. 13¾*
2091 A1253 (55c) multi 1.60 1.60

Wildlife Type of 2006
Designs: No. 2092, Myotis brandtii. No. 2093, Salamandra salamandra. No. 2094, Astacus astacus.

Serpentine Die Cut 13½
2007 Self-Adhesive Photo.
Coil Stamp
2092 A1237 55c multi 1.60 1.60

Booklet Stamps
Size: 32x27mm
Die Cut Perf. 14 Syncopated
2093 A1237 55c multi 1.60 1.60
2094 A1237 55c multi 1.60 1.60
a. Booklet pane, 5 each #2093-2094 16.00
Issued: No. 2092, 4/20; Nos. 2093-2094, 3/31.

Pope Benedict XVI, 80th Birthday — A1254

2007, Apr. 12 Photo. *Perf. 14*
2095 A1254 100c multi 3.00 3.00

Flowers Type of 2004
Designs: 4c, Dandelions (Löwenzahn). 10c, Scotch laburnum (Alpen-goldregen). 65c, Guelder rose (Gewöhnlicher schneeball). 100c, Violets (veilchen). 115c, Gentian (Fransenenzian). 140c, Clematis (Waldrebe).

2007 *Perf. 13¾x14*
2096 A1244 4c multi .25 .25
2097 A1244 10c multi .30 .25
2098 A1244 65c multi 1.90 1.90
2099 A1244 100c multi 3.00 3.00
2100 A1244 115c multi 3.50 3.50
2101 A1244 140c multi 4.25 4.25
Nos. 2096-2101 (6) 13.20 13.15
Issued: 100c, 4/27. 4c, 10c, 65c, 115c, 140c, 8/25.

Austrian Workers' Samaritan Federation, 80th Anniv. A1255

Photo. & Engr.
2007, May 18 *Perf. 13¾*
2102 A1255 55c multi 1.60 1.60

Opening of Hermann Nitsch Museum, Mistelbach — A1256

2007, May 25 *Imperf.*
2103 A1256 100c multi 3.00 3.00

Michael Schumacher Type of 2006 Redrawn
2007, May 29 Photo. *Perf. 13¾x14*
2103A A1241 75c multi 3.00 3.00
No. 2076 is inscribed "Weltmeister 1994 1995." No. 2103A is inscribed "Weltmeister 1995 1996," and has a thicker signature and grayer hair.

Miniature Sheet

Formula I Race Car Drivers — A1257

No. 2104: a, Phil Hill. b, Clay Regazzoni (1939-2006). c, Gerhard Berger. d, Juan Manuel Fangio (1911-95). e, John Surtees. f, Mika Häkkinen. g, Graham Hill (1929-75). h, Emerson Fittipaldi.

2007, May 29 Litho. *Perf. 14*
2104 A1257 Sheet of 8 13.00 13.00
a.-h. 55c Any single 1.60 1.60

Railroads Type of 2002
55c, Mariazell Railway locomotive.

Photo. & Engr.
2007, May 31 *Perf. 13¾*
2105 A1109 55c multi 1.60 1.60
Mariazell Railway, cent.

Mariazell Basilica, 850th Anniv. A1258

2007, June 1 *Litho.*
2106 A1258 55c multi 1.60 1.60

Souvenir Sheet

UEFA European Soccer Championships, Austria and Switzerland — A1259

No. 2107 — Mascots Trix and Flix: a, Chasing ball. b, Holding trophy. c, Running toward each other. d, Celebrating.

2007, June 5   *Perf. 13¼x12¾*
2107 A1259 Sheet of 4   3.50 3.50
a.   20c multi   .60 .60
b.   25c multi   .75 .75
c.   30c multi   .90 .90
d.   35c multi   1.00 1.00

Souvenir Sheet

Self-Portrait of Angelika Kauffmann — A1260

Photo. & Engr.
2007, June 15   *Perf. 13½*
2108 A1260 210c multi   6.25 6.25

Europa A1261

2007, June 16 Litho. *Perf. 14¼x14*
2109 A1261 55c multi   1.60 1.60

Ignaz Joseph Pleyel (1757-1831), Composer A1262

Photo. & Engr.
2007, June 17   *Perf. 14*
2110 A1262 €1 multi   3.00 3.00

Premiere of Animated Movie, "Shrek the Third" — A1263

Perf. 13½x13¾
2007, June 21   Litho.
2111 A1263 55c multi   1.60 1.60

Essl Museum, Klosterneuberg A1264

Serpentine Die Cut 13½
2007, July 2 Coil Stamp Photo.
Self-Adhesive
2112 A1264 55c multi   1.60 1.60

Wilhelm Kienzl (1857-1941), Composer — A1265

2007, July 13 Photo. *Perf. 13¾*
2113 A1265 75c multi   2.25 2.25

Railways Type of 2002
75c, Bregenz Forest Railway.

Photo. & Engr.
2007, Aug. 4   *Perf. 13¾*
2114 A1109 75c multi   2.25 2.25

Man, by Astrid Bernhart A1266

2007, Aug. 24 Photo. *Perf. 13¾*
2115 A1266 55c multi   1.60 1.60

Haliaeetus Albicilla A1267

2007, Sept. 7
2116 A1267 55c multi   1.60 1.60
   Printed in sheets of 8 + central label. See Serbia No. 399.

Necklace by Josef Hoffmann (1870-1956) — A1268

Litho. & Embossed With Foil Application
2007, Sept. 14   *Imperf.*
2117 A1268 265c multi   7.50 5.25

Oil Production in Austria, 75th Anniv. A1269

2007, Sept. 17 Litho. *Perf. 14x13¾*
2118 A1269 75c multi   1.80 1.80
   Portions of the design were applied by a thermographic process producing a shiny, raised effect.

Deer, by Friedrich Gauermann (1807-62) — A1270

2007, Sept. 20   **Photo. & Engr.**
2119 A1270 55c multi   1.60 1.50

Patron Saints Type of 2005
   Design: St. Rupert, patron saint of Salzburg.

2007, Sept. 24   *Perf. 13¾x14*
2120 A1185 55c multi   1.60 1.50

Niki Hosp, Skier — A1271

2007, Sept. 29 Litho. *Perf. 14x13¾*
2121 A1271 55c multi   1.60 1.50

Wildlife Type of 2006
Serpentine Die Cut 13½
2007, Oct. 10 Coil Stamp Photo.
Self-Adhesive
2122 A1237 75c Lucanus cervus 2.25 2.25

Linz Cathedral Key, Carved by Michael Blümelhuber (1865-1936) A1272

Photo. & Engr.
2007, Oct. 12   *Perf. 13¾x14*
2123 A1272 75c multi   2.10 1.75

Christiane Hörbiger, Actress — A1273

2007, Oct. 13 Litho. *Perf. 14x13¾*
2124 A1273 55c multi   1.60 1.50

Vienna State Opera's Performance of Queen of Spades, by P. I. Tchaikovsky — A1274

2007, Oct. 28   *Perf. 13¾*
2125 A1274 55c multi   1.60 .60

Nativity Scene, Chapel of Sts. Peter and Paul, Oberwöllan A1275

Nativity Scene, St. Barbara's Church, Vienna — A1276

2007   **Photo.**   *Perf. 13¾*
2126 A1275 55c multi   1.60 1.60
            Perf. 14¼x14
2127 A1276 65c multi   1.90 1.90
   Christmas. Issued: 55c, 11/23; 65c, 11/9.

House of the Sea Aquarium, Vienna — A1277

Perf. 13½x13¼
2007, Nov. 29   Litho.
2128 A1277 55c multi   1.60 1.60
   Portions of the design were applied by a thermographic process, producing a shiny, raised effect.

Thomas Gottschalk, Television Personality — A1278

2007, Dec. 8   *Perf. 13½x13¾*
2129 A1278 65c multi   1.90 1.90

Flowers Type of 2004
   Design: 15c, Lady's slippers (Frauenschuh).

2008, Jan. 15 Photo. *Perf. 13¾x14*
2130 A1244 15c multi   .45 .45

Miniature Sheet

Venues of UEFA Euro 2008 Soccer
Championships — A1279

No. 2131: a, Vienna. b, Salzburg. c, Klagenfurt. d, Innsbruck-Tirol. e, Zurich. f, Basel. g,
Bern. h, Geneva.

2008, Jan. 17   Litho.   Perf. 14
2131   A1279   Sheet of 8   14.00 14.00
a.-d.   55c Any single   1.60 1.60
e.-h.   65c Any single   1.90 1.90

Mascots Trix   Emblem
and Flix   A1281
A1280

Serpentine Die Cut 13¾
2008, Jan. 22   Coil Stamps   Photo.
Self-Adhesive
2132   A1280   55c multi   1.75 1.75
2133   A1281   65c multi   2.00 2.00

UEFA Euro 2008 Soccer Championships,
Austria and Switzerland.

Martina, by
Hans Robert
Pippal (1915-98)
A1282

2008, Jan. 31   Photo.   Perf. 13¾x14
2134   A1282   65c multi   2.00 2.00

A1283

Children's
Art
A1284

2008, Feb. 4   Litho.   Perf. 13¾
2135   A1283   55c multi   1.75 1.75
2136   A1284   55c multi   1.75 1.75

UEFA Euro 2008 Soccer Championships,
Austria and Switzerland.

Vienna Landmarks Type of Semi-Postals
Souvenir Sheet
2008, Feb. 15   Photo.   Perf. 13¾
2137   Sheet of 3 + 2 labels   5.50 5.50
a.   SP209 55c multi   1.75 1.75
b.   SP211 55c multi   1.75 1.75
c.   SP213 65c multi   2.00 2.00

2008 Vienna Intl. Stamp Exhibition (WIPA).

Children's
Art
A1285

2008, Feb. 19   Litho.   Perf. 13¾
2138   A1285   65c multi   2.00 2.00

UEFA Euro 2008 Soccer Championships,
Austria and Switzerland.

Defense, by
Maria Lassnig
A1286

2008, Feb. 21
2139   A1286   55c multi   1.75 1.75

UEFA Euro 2008 Soccer Championships,
Austria and Switzerland.

Wildlife Type of 2006
Designs: No. 2140, Hyla arborea. No. 2141,
Alcedo atthis.

Die Cut Perf. 14 Syncopated
2008, Feb. 25   Photo.
Booklet Stamps
Self-Adhesive
Size: 32x27mm
2140   A1237   65c multi   2.00 2.00
2141   A1237   65c multi   2.00 2.00
a.   Booklet pane of 10, 5 each
        #2140-2141, + 10 eti-
        quettes   20.00

Austrian Airlines, 50th Anniv. — A1287

Litho. With Foil Application
2008, Feb. 28   Perf. 14
2142   A1287   140c multi   4.25 4.25

Vienna State Opera Production of
"The Force of Destiny," by Giuseppe
Verdi
A1288

2008, Mar. 1   Litho.   Perf. 13¾
2143   A1288   55c multi   1.75 1.75

Sleeping
Princess Maria
Franziska, by
Friedrich von
Amerling
A1289

Photo. & Engr.
2008, Mar. 3   Perf. 13¾x13½
2144   A1289   125c multi   4.00 4.00

See Liechtenstein No. 1407.

Painting by
Soshana
A1290

2008, Mar. 7   Photo.   Perf. 13½x13¾
2145   A1290   55c multi   1.75 1.75

Soccer
Ball — A1291

Silk-screened
2008, Mar. 12   Die Cut
Self-Adhesive
2146   A1291   375c multi   11.50 11.50

No. 2146 is printed on the same poly-
urethane foam material used to make soccer
balls for the UEFA Euro 2008 Soccer
Championships.

Soccer Player, Ball and Field — A1292

2008, Mar. 20   Litho.   Perf. 14
2147   A1292   55c multi   1.75 1.75

UEFA Euro 2008 Soccer Championships,
Austria and Switzerland.

Children's
Art
A1293

2008, Apr. 2   Litho.   Perf. 13¾
2148   A1293   125c multi   4.00 4.00

UEFA Euro 2008 Soccer Championships,
Austria and Switzerland.

Wachau
UNESCO
World
Heritage
Site
A1294

2008, Apr. 9   Photo. & Engr.
2149   A1294   100c multi   3.25 3.25

A1295

Children's
Art — A1296

2008   Litho.
2150   A1295   55c multi   1.75 1.75
2151   A1296   100c multi   3.25 3.25

Issued: 55c, 4/18; 100c, 4/19. UEFA 2008
Soccer Championships, Austria and
Switzerland.

Tyrolean Federation of Traditional
Provincial Costumes, Cent. — A1297

2008, Apr. 26   Perf. 14x13¾
2152   A1297   75c multi   2.40 2.40

Miniature Sheet

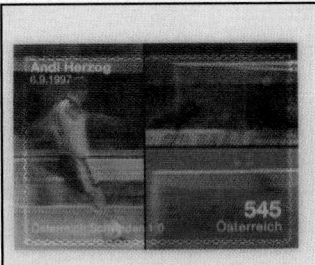

Goal by Andreas Herzog Against
Sweden In 1997 World Cup Qualifying
Match — A1298

Litho. With Three-Dimensional
Plastic Affixed
2008, May 5   *Serpentine Die Cut 9*
Self-Adhesive
2153   A1298   545c multi   17.00 17.00

UEFA 2008 Soccer Championships, Austria
and Switzerland.

Wildlife Type of 2006

Designs: No. 2154, Erinaceus concolor. No. 2155, Lepus europaeus.

Die Cut Perf. 14 Syncopated

2008, May 5		**Photo.**

Booklet Stamps
Self-Adhesive
Size: 32x27mm

2154	A1237	55c multi	1.75 1.75
2155	A1237	55c multi	1.75 1.75
a.		Booklet pane of 10, 5 each	
		#2154-2155	17.50

Federal Stud Farm, Piber — A1299

2008, May 9		**Litho.**	**Perf. 14**
2156	A1299	55c multi	1.75 1.75

Grass of Soccer Field — A1300

2008, May 10			**Perf. 13¾**
2157	A1300	75c multi	2.40 2.40

UEFA 2008 Soccer Championships, Austria and Switzerland.

Soccer Ball and Chairs A1301

2008, May 16			
2158	A1301	55c multi	1.75 1.75

UEFA 2008 Soccer Championships, Austria and Switzerland.

Miniature Sheets

Face Painted with Flags of Countries — A1302

No. 2159: a, Italy. b, Croatia. c, Sweden. d, Greece. e, Austria. f, Portugal. g, Spain. h, Czech Republic.

No. 2160: a, Switzerland. b, Germany. c, Romania. d, Turkey. e, Netherlands. f, Poland. g, Russia. h, France.

2008, May 16			**Perf. 14**
2159	A1302	Sheet of 8	7.00 7.00
a.-b.		10c Either single	.30 .30
c.-d.		15c Either single	.45 .45
e.-f.		20c Either single	.65 .65
g.-h.		65c Either single	2.10 2.10
2160	A1302	Sheet of 8	9.25 9.25
a.-b.		25c Either single	.80 .80
c.-d.		30c Either single	.95 .95
e.-f.		35c Either single	1.10 1.10
g.-h.		55c Either single	1.75 1.75

UEFA 2008 Soccer Championships, Austria and Switzerland.

Souvenir Sheet

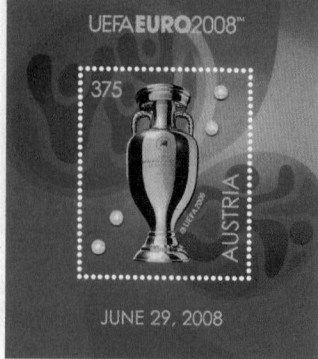

Henri Delaunay Cup — A1303

Photo. With Synthetic Crystals Affixed

2008, June 5			**Perf. 13¾**
2161	A1303	375c multi	12.00 12.00

UEFA 2008 Soccer Championships, Austria and Switzerland.

Patron Saints Type of 2005

Design: St. Notburga, patron saint of Tyrol.

2008, June 6			**Photo. & Engr.**
2162	A1185	55c multi	1.75 1.75

Europa A1304

2008, June 6			**Photo.**
2163	A1304	65c multi	1.60 1.60

Wildlife Type of 2006

Designs: No. 2164, Upupa epops. No. 2165, Hemaris fuciformis.

Booklet Stamps
Self-Adhesive

Die Cut Perf. 14 Syncopated

2008, June 13			**Size: 32x27mm**
2164	A1237	75c multi	2.40 2.40
2165	A1237	75c multi	2.40 2.40
a.		Booklet pane of 10, 5 each	
		#2164-2165	24.00

Railways Type of 2002

75c, Vienna Urban Railway locomotive.

2008, June 20			**Photo. & Engr.** **Perf. 13¾**
2166	A1109	75c multi	2.40 2.40

Vienna Urban Railway, 110th anniv.

Letterbox, by Josef Maria Olbrich (1867-1908) — A1305

2008, Aug. 5		**Litho.**	**Perf. 14**
2167	A1305	65c multi	2.00 2.00

Souvenir Sheet

Willendorf Venus — A1306

Litho. with Three-Dimensional Plastic Affixed

2008, Aug. 8	**Serpentine Die Cut 9¼**		
2168	A1306	375c multi	11.50 11.50

This stamp was a gift for standing order customers. It was not made available for sale.

Flowers Type of 2004

Design: 50c, Columbine (Akelei).

2008, Sept. 1		**Photo.**	**Perf. 13¾**
2169	A1244	50c multi	1.50 1.50

Vienna Skyline — A1307

Coil Stamp

Photo. With Foil Application
Serpentine Die Cut 13½x14

2008, Sept. 2		**Self-Adhesive**	
2170	A1307	55c multi	1.60 1.60

2008 Vienna Intl. Stamp Exhibition (WIPA).

Railways Type of 2002

100c, Princess Elizabeth Western Railway train.

2008, Sept. 10		**Photo. & Engr.**	**Perf. 13¾**
2171	A1109	100c multi	3.00 3.00

Princess Elizabeth Western Railway, 150th anniv.

Souvenir Sheet

Mail Coach — A1308

2008, Sept. 12			
2172	A1308	265c multi	7.75 7.75

Praga 2008 Intl. Stamp Exhibition, Prague, and 2008 Vienna Intl. Stamp Exhibition. See Czech Republic No. 3398.

Miniature Sheet

Art by Friedensreich Hundertwasser (1928-2000) — A1309

Various unnamed works of art.

2008, Sept. 18			**Perf. 13¾x14**
2173	A1309	Sheet of 4	10.50 10.50
a.		55c multi	1.60 1.60
b.		75c multi	2.25 2.25
c.		€1 multi	3.00 3.00
d.		€1.25 multi	3.50 3.50

Nude Woman, by Dina Larot — A1310

2008, Sept. 19		**Litho.**	**Perf. 13¾x14**
2174	A1310	55c multi	1.60 1.60

Gentian Flower A1311

Embroidered

2008, Sept. 19			**Self-Adhesive** **Imperf.**
2175	A1311	375c tan & dark blue	11.00 11.00

Maximilian Schell, Actor A1312

2008, Sept. 20		**Litho.**	**Perf. 13¾**
2176	A1312	100c multi	3.00 3.00

Romy Schneider (1938-82), Actress A1313

2008, Sept. 21   Photo.
2177 A1313 100c multi   3.00 3.00

Spain, UEFA Euro 2008 Soccer Champions — A1314

2008, Sept. 27   Litho.
2178 A1314 65c multi   1.90 1.90

Markus Rogan, Swimmer A1315

2008. Sept. 27
2179 A1315 100c multi   3.00 3.00

Thomas Morgenstern, Skier — A1316

2008, Sept. 27   Perf. 14x13¾
2180 A1316 100c multi   3.00 3.00

70th Birthday of Pres. Heinz Fischer — A1317

2008, Oct. 7   Litho.   Perf. 14¼x13½
2181 A1317 55c multi   1.50 1.50

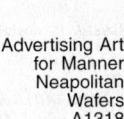

Advertising Art for Manner Neapolitan Wafers A1318

2008, Oct. 16   Perf. 13¾
2182 A1318 55c multi   1.40 1.40

Koloman Moser (1868-1918), Artist — A1319

2008, Oct. 31   Perf. 14¼x13½
2183 A1319 130c multi   3.50 3.50

Lobby of Imperial Post Office, Trieste A1320

2008, Nov. 3   Perf. 13¾
2184 A1320 65c multi   1.75 1.75

Adoration of the Magi, by Unknown Artist A1321

The First Christmas Tree in Ried, by Felix Ignaz Pollinger A1322

2008   Photo.
2185 A1321 55c multi   1.40 1.40
2186 A1322 65c multi   1.75 1.75

Issued: 55c, 11/21; 65c, 11/5.

Patron Saints Type of 2005

Design: St. Martin, patron saint of Burgenland.

2008, Nov. 7   Photo. & Engr.
2187 A1185 55c multi   1.40 1.40

70th Birthday of Karl Schranz, Olympic Skier A1323

2008, Nov. 11   Litho.
2188 A1323 65c multi   1.75 1.75

Souvenir Sheet

Salt and Pepper Shaker by Benvenulto Cellini — A1324

No. 2189: a, Female figure. b, Male figure.

Litho. & Embossed
2009, Jan. 24   Perf. 14
2189 A1324 Sheet of 2   11.00 11.00
a.-b.   210c Either single   5.50 5.50

Landskron Castle — A1325

Serpentine Die Cut 13¾x13½
2009, Jan. 30   Coil Stamp   Photo.
Self-Adhesive
2190 A1325 55c multi   1.40 1.40

Advertising Art for Pez Candy A1326

2009, Feb. 6   Litho.   Perf. 13¾
2191 A1326 55c multi   1.40 1.40

Imperial Post Office, Cracow A1327

2009, Feb. 13
2192 A1327 100c multi   2.60 2.60

Raimondo Montecuccoli (1609-80), Military Leader A1328

2009, Feb. 20
2193 A1328 130c multi   3.50 3.50

SOS Children's Villages, 60th Anniv. — A1329

2009, Mar. 6   Litho.   Perf. 14x13¾
2194 A1329 55c multi   1.40 1.40

Lewis Hamilton, 2008 Formula 1 Racing Champion — A1330

2009, Mar. 17
2195 A1330 100c multi   2.60 2.60

Mercedes Silver Arrow at Vienna Technical Museum — A1331

Litho. With Three-Dimensional Plastic Affixed
Serpentine Die Cut 9¼
2009, Mar. 17   Self-Adhesive
2196 A1331 265c multi   6.75 6.75

Schönbrunn Palace, Vienna — A1332

2009, Mar. 20   Litho.   Perf. 13½x13
2197 A1332 65c multi   1.75 1.75

Preservation of Polar Regions and Glaciers A1333

2009, Mar. 26   Perf. 14¼
2198 A1333 65c multi   1.75 1.75

Steyr-Daimler-Puch Haflinger, 50th Anniv. — A1334

2009, Mar. 27   Perf. 13¾
2199 A1334 55c multi   1.40 1.40

Joseph Haydn (1732-1809), Composer A1335

2009, Mar. 31
2200 A1335 65c multi   1.75 1.75

Tyto Alba — A1336

Serpentine Die Cut 13½
2009, Apr. 5   Coil Stamp   Litho.
Self-Adhesive
2201 A1336 55c multi   1.50 1.50

Souvenir Sheet

Art By Christo — A1337

No. 2202: a, Drawing of wrapped Flak Tower. b, Model of building with tower.

2009, Apr. 15		**Perf. 14**	
2202 A1337	Sheet of 2	3.00	3.00
a.-b.	55c Either single	1.50	1.50

Fred Zinnemann (1907-97), Film Director A1338

2009, Apr. 29		**Perf. 13¾**	
2203 A1338	55c multi	1.50	1.50

St. Pölten, 850th Anniv. A1339

2009, May 2 Litho.		**Perf. 13¼x13¾**	
2204 A1339	55c multi	1.50	1.50

Vienna State Opera Production of *The Ring of the Nibelungen* A1340

2009, May 2		**Perf. 13½x13¾**	
2205 A1340	100c multi	2.75	2.75

Propeller Steamer Thalia, Cent. — A1341

2009, May 7		**Perf. 14x13¼**	
2206 A1341	55c multi	1.50	1.50

Baptismal Font, Old Cathedral, Linz — A1342

Litho. & Engr.

2009, May 8		**Perf. 13¾**	
2207 A1342	55c multi	1.50	1.50

Vienna State Opera House, 140th Anniv. — A1343

2009, May 25 Litho.		**Perf. 14x13¼**	
2208 A1343	100c multi	2.75	2.75

Miniature Sheet

Formula 1 Personalities — A1344

No. 2209: a, Wolfgang Graf Berghe von Trips (1928-61), race car driver. b, Gilles Villeneuve (1950-82), race car driver. c, James Hunt (1947-93), race car driver. d, Bernie Ecclestone, president of Formula One Management.

2009, May 27		**Perf. 14x13¾**	
2209 A1344	Sheet of 4	6.00	6.00
a.-d.	55c Any single	1.50	1.50

Souvenir Sheet

Battle of Aspern and Essling, Bicent. — A1345

2009, June 4 Litho.		**Perf. 14**	
2210 A1345	110c multi	3.25	3.25

Europa A1346

2009, June 5		**Perf. 13¾**	
2211 A1346	65c multi	1.90	1.90
	Intl. Year of Astronomy.		

Graz Historic Center UNESCO World Heritage Site A1347

2009, June 12		**Photo. & Engr.**	
2212 A1347	100c multi	3.00	3.00

Wiener Neustadt Airfield, Cent. — A1348

2009, June 12 Litho.		**Perf. 14**	
2213 A1348	140c multi	4.00	4.00

Rosalia Alpina — A1349

Serpentine Die Cut 13½x14

2009, June 19 Coil Stamp Photo.			
Self-Adhesive			
2214 A1349	75c multi	2.10	2.10

Railways Type of 2002

75c, Wachau Railway train.

Photo & Engr.

2009, June 20		**Perf. 13¾**	
2215 A1109	75c multi	2.10	2.10
	Wachau Railway, cent.		

Wildlife Type of 2006

Designs: No. 2216, Apis mellifera. No. 2217, Merops apiaster.

Die Cut Perf. 14 Syncopated

2009, Aug. 28		**Photo.**	
Booklet Stamps			
Self-Adhesive			
Size: 32x27mm			
2216 A1237	55c multi	1.60	1.60
2217 A1237	55c multi	1.60	1.60
a.	Booklet pane of 10, 5 each #2216-2217	16.00	

This stamp, released Sept. 1, 2009, was a gift for standing order customers. It was not made available for sale.

Premiere of Movie, *The Third Man*, 60th Anniv. — A1350

2009, Sept. 2 Litho.		**Perf. 14**	
2218 A1350	65c multi	1.90	1.90

Opening of Border Between Austria and Hungary, 20th Anniv. A1351

2009, Sept. 10		**Perf. 12**	
2219 A1351	65c multi	1.90	1.90
	See Germany No. 2548, Hungary No. 4136.		

Souvenir Sheet

Archaeological Excavations of Roman Military Camps — A1352

Litho. & Engr.

2009, Sept. 11		**Perf. 13¾x14**	
2220 A1352	Sheet of 2	3.50	3.50
a.	55c Carnuntum	1.60	1.60
b.	65c Gerulata	1.90	1.90
	See Slovakia No. 579.		

Bertha von Suttner (1843-1914), Novelist, 1905 Nobel Peace Laureate A1353

2009, Sept. 12 Litho.		**Perf. 14¼x14**	
2221 A1353	55c multi	1.60	1.60

Souvenir Sheet

Rosary Triptych, by Ernst Fuchs — A1354

No. 2222: a, Glorious Rosary. b, Joyful Rosary. c, Sorrowful Rosary.

Litho. & Engr.

2009, Sept. 18		**Perf. 14x13¾**	
2222 A1354	Sheet of 3	7.00	7.00
a.	55c multi	1.60	1.60
b.	75c multi	2.25	2.25
c.	100c multi	3.00	3.00

Gregor Schlierenzauer, Ski
Jumper — A1355

Wolfgang Loitzl, Ski Jumper — A1356

2009, Sept. 26 Litho. *Perf. 14x13¼*
2223 A1355 100c multi   3.00 3.00
2224 A1356 100c multi   3.00 3.00

Drösing-Zistersdorf Local Railway,
120th Anniv. — A1357

2009, Oct. 4 Litho. *Perf. 13¼x13¾*
2225 A1357 100c multi   3.00 3.00

Woman Rocking
on a Chair, by
Leander
Kaiser — A1358

2009, Oct. 9   *Perf. 13¾*
2226 A1358 55c multi   1.75 1.75

Souvenir Sheet

Austria - Japan Year — A1359

No. 2227 — Paintings: a, Portrait of Emilie
Flöge, by Gustav Klimt. b, Autumn Clothing, by
Shoen Uemura.

2009, Oct. 16   *Perf. 13½*
2227 A1359   Sheet of 2   8.50 8.50
a.-b.   140c Either single   4.25 4.25
            See Japan No. 3166.

Souvenir Sheet

Paintings by Diego
Velázquez — A1360

No. 2228: a, The Royal Family of Felipe IV.
b, The Infanta Margarita Teresa in a Blue
Dress.

2009, Oct. 22 Photo. *Perf. 14x13¾*
2228 A1360   Sheet of 2   3.75 3.75
a.   55c multi   1.75 1.75
b.   65c multi   2.00 2.00

A1361

Christmas
A1362

2009   Litho.   *Perf. 14x13¾*
2229 A1361 55c multi   1.75 1.75
            Perf. 14
2230 A1362 65c multi   2.00 2.00
Issued: No. 2229, 11/20; No. 2230, 11/6.

Advertising Art
for Palmers
Underwear
A1363

2009, Nov. 12   *Perf. 13¾*
2231 A1363 55c multi   1.75 1.75

Patron Saint Type of 2005
Design: St. Leopold, patron saint of Lower
Austria.

Photo. & Engr.
2009, Nov. 13   *Perf. 13½x14*
2232 A1185 55c multi   1.75 1.75

Essl Museum,
10th Anniv.
A1364

2009, Nov. 21 Litho. *Perf. 14*
2233 A1364 55c multi   1.75 1.75

Souvenir Sheet

Charles Darwin (1809-82),
Naturalist — A1365

No. 2234: a, Monkey with book. b, Boy and
mirror held by monkey. c, Monkey with arm
extended.

Photo. & Engr.
2009, Nov. 24   *Perf. 14¼x13½*
2234 A1365   Sheet of 3   5.25 5.25
a.-c.   55c Any single   1.75 1.75

Wildlife Type of 2006
Designs: 65c, Felis silvestris. No. 2236,
Lutra lutra. No. 2237, Salmo trutta fario.

Coil Stamp
Serpentine Die Cut 13½x14
2010   Litho.   Self-Adhesive
2235 A1237 65c multi   1.90 1.90
Booklet Stamps
Size: 32x27mm
Die Cut Perf. 14 Syncopated
2236 A1237 75c multi   2.10 2.10
2237 A1237 75c multi   2.10 2.10
a.   Booklet pane of 10, 5 each
       #2236-2237   21.00
Issued: Nos. 2236-2237, 1/8; No. 2235, 1/13.

Salzburg
Old Town
Center
UNESCO
World
Heritage
Site
A1366

Photo. & Engr.
2010, Jan. 29   *Perf. 13¾*
2238 A1366 100c multi   2.75 2.75

Otto Preminger
(1905-86), Film
Director
A1367

2010, Feb. 5 Litho. *Perf. 13¾*
2239 A1367 55c multi   1.50 1.50

Roger
Federer,
Tennis
Player
A1368

2010, Feb. 8   *Perf. 14x13¾*
2240 A1368 65c multi   1.75 1.75

Annual Rings
of Scent and
Bliss, by
Helmut
Kand — A1369

2010, Feb. 10   *Perf. 13¾*
2241 A1369 55c multi   1.50 1.50

Prince Eugene
of Savoy
(1663-1736)
A1370

2010, Feb. 12
2242 A1370 65c multi   1.75 1.75

Advertising Art
for Kleinbahn
A1371

2010, Feb. 16
2243 A1371 55c multi   1.50 1.50

Souvenir Sheet

The Tyrolean Land Army - Year Nine,
by Joseph Anton Koch — A1372

2010, Feb. 19   *Perf. 14*
2244 A1372 175c multi   4.75 4.75

Andreas Hofer (1767-1810), leader of 1809
Tyrolean Uprising.

Vienna
State
Opera
Production
of
"Medea,"
by Aribert
Reimann
A1373

2010, Feb. 24   *Perf. 14x13¾*
2245 A1373 100c multi   2.75 2.75

Soon the Sun
Will Rise, by
Max Weiler
(1910-2001)
A1374

2010, Mar. 18　　Litho.　　Perf. 14
2246 A1374 75c multi　　　　　2.10 2.10

Lady in Yellow,
by Max
Kurzweil
(1867-1916)
A1375

2010, Mar. 19　　Perf. 14x13½
2247 A1375 65c multi　　　　　1.75 1.75

Belvedere
Castle,
Vienna
A1376

2010, Mar. 24　　Perf. 13½x12¾
2248 A1376 65c multi　　　　　1.75 1.75

Railways Type of 2002

100c, Graz-Köflacher Railway train.

Photo. & Engr.
2010, Apr. 10　　Perf. 13¾
2249 A1109 100c multi　　　　2.75 2.75

Graz-Köflacher Railway, 150th anniv.

Hradcany
Castle,
Prague
A1377

2010, Apr. 16　　Litho.
2250 A1377 65c multi　　　　　1.75 1.75

Souvenir Sheet

Empress Elizabeth, by F. X.
Winterhalter — A1378

2010, Apr. 30　　Perf. 13¼x14
2251 A1378 55c multi　　　　　1.50 1.50

Expo 2010, Shanghai.

Mendel
Funicular
Railway
A1379

2010, May 8　　　Perf. 13¾
2252 A1379 65c multi　　　　　1.75 1.75

Austria Post
Collection Box
on Postman's
Legs
A1380

2010, May 10　　Litho.　　Perf. 13¾
2253 A1380 55c multi　　　　　1.40 1.40

Hof Palace — A1381

2010, May 13　　Litho.　　Perf. 14x13¼
2254 A1381 55c multi　　　　　1.40 1.40

Maria Taferl,
350th Anniv.
A1382

2010, May 16　　Perf. 13¾
2255 A1382 55c multi　　　　　1.40 1.40

Gustav Mahler (1860-1911),
Composer — A1383

2010, May 18　　Perf. 14x13¾
2256 A1383 100c multi　　　　2.60 2.60

Salzburg
Festival, 90th
Anniv.
A1384

2010, May 20　　Perf. 13¾
2257 A1384 55c multi　　　　　1.40 1.40

Crozier of
Archbishop
Gebhard of
Salzburg
A1385

2010, May 28　　Photo. & Engr.
2258 A1385 75c multi　　　　　1.90 1.90

Wildlife Type of 2006

Designs: 55c, Coracias garrulus. 75c,
Aquila chrysaetos.

Self-Adhesive

Serpentine Die Cut 13½x14
2010, May 28　　Coil Stamps　　Litho.
2259 A1237 55c multi　　　　　1.40 1.40
2260 A1237 75c multi　　　　　1.90 1.90

Europa
A1386

2010, June 11　　Litho.　　Perf. 13¾
2261 A1386 65c multi　　　　　1.60 1.60

Self-portrait, by Egon Schiele (1890-
1918) — A1387

2010, June 12　　Photo. & Engr.
2262 A1387 140c multi　　　　3.50 3.50

Second Viennese Mountain Spring
Pipeline, Cent. — A1388

2010, June 14　　Litho.　　Perf. 14x13½
2263 A1388 55c multi　　　　　1.40 1.40

Simon Wiesenthal (1908-2005), Hunter
of Nazi War Criminals — A1389

2010, June 14　　Perf. 12½x12¾
2264 A1389 75c multi　　　　　1.90 1.90

The Star of David is made up of tiny holes
made by a laser. See Israel No. 1820.

Ioan Holender, Vienna State Opera
Director, 75th Birthday — A1390

2010, June 20　　Perf. 14x13¾
2265 A1390 100c multi　　　　2.50 2.50

Palatinate
Church,
Karnburg
A1391

2010, June 25　　Litho.　　Perf. 13¾
2266 A1391 100c multi　　　　2.50 2.50

Johann Joseph Fux (1660-1741),
Composer — A1392

2010, June 26　　Perf. 14
2267 A1392 100c multi　　　　2.50 2.50

Grete Rehor (1910-87),
Politician — A1393

2010, June 29　　Perf. 13¾
2268 A1393 55c multi　　　　　1.40 1.40

Vienna
Rainbow
Parade,
15th
Anniv.
A1394

2010, July 3　　Perf. 14x14¼
2269 A1394 55c multi　　　　　1.40 1.40

Spielfeld Strass - Bad Radkersburg
Railway, 125th Anniv. — A1395

2010, July 10　　Perf. 13¾
2270 A1395 65c multi　　　　　1.75 1.75

Grafenegg Castle — A1396

Coil Stamp
Serpentine Die Cut 13¾
2010, July 17   **Self-Adhesive**
2271 A1396 55c multi   1.50 1.50

La Plume, by Alphonse Mucha (1860-1939), Illustrator A1397

2010, July 23   *Perf. 13¾*
2272 A1397 115c multi   3.00 3.00

Diocese of Eisenstadt, 50th Anniv. — A1398

2010, Aug. 12   **Litho.**   *Perf. 13¾*
2273 A1398 55c multi   1.50 1.50

Mother Teresa (1910-97), Humanitarian — A1399

2010, Aug. 26   *Perf. 14*
2274 A1399 130c multi   3.50 3.50

This stamp, released Sept. 3, 2010, was a gift for standing order customers. It was not made available for sale.

Souvenir Sheet

Orient Express — A1400

No. 2275 — Locomotives and views of: a, Sinaia, Romania. b, Salzburg, Austria.

2010, Sept. 6   **Litho.**   *Perf. 14x14¼*
2275 A1400   Sheet of 2   3.50 3.50
a.-b.   65c Either single   1.75 1.75
See Romania Nos. 5205-5206.

Crucifix by Jakob Adlhart, St. Peter's Archabbey, Salzburg A1401

Photo. & Engr.
2010, Sept. 14   *Perf. 13¾*
2276 A1401 100c multi   2.75 2.75

Organization of Petroleum Exporting Countries, 50th Anniv. A1402

2010, Sept. 14   **Litho.**   *Perf. 13¾*
2277 A1402 140c multi   4.00 4.00

Petit Point Embroidery — A1403

Litho. With Embroidery Affixed
2010, Sept. 17   *Imperf.*
2278 A1403 265c multi   7.50 7.50

Railways Type of 2002
100c, Wechsel Railway train.
Photo. & Engr.
2010, Sept. 19   *Perf. 13¾*
2279 A1109 100c multi   2.75 2.75
Wechsel Railway, cent.

Andreas and Wolfgang Linger, Lugers — A1404

2010, Sept. 25   **Litho.**   *Perf. 14x13¾*
2280 A1404 100c multi   2.75 2.75

Modern Furniture by Peter Zuchi A1405

2010, Oct. 1   **Litho.**   *Perf. 13¾*
2281 A1405 65c multi   1.90 1.90

Archduchess Maria Theresa (1717-80) A1406

2010, Oct. 8
2282 A1406 65c multi   1.90 1.90

Souvenir Sheet

Weather Stations in Austria and Argentina — A1407

No. 2283 — Weather station in: a, Stadtpark, Vienna. b, Buenos Aires Botanical Garden.

2010, Oct. 13
2283 A1407   Sheet of 2   5.75 5.75
a.   65c multi   1.90 1.90
b.   140c multi   3.75 3.75
See Argentina No. 2596.

Ornithopter of Jakob Degen (1760-1848), Inventor A1408

2010, Oct. 15
2284 A1408 125c multi   3.50 3.50

Missions Abroad for Austrian Armed Forces, 50th Anniv. — A1409

2010, Oct. 26   *Perf. 14x13½*
2285 A1409 65c multi   1.90 1.90

Historic Center of Vienna UNESCO World Heritage Site A1410

Photo. & Engr.
2010, Nov. 5   *Perf. 13¾*
2286 A1410 100c multi   3.00 3.00

Nativity A1411

Innsbruck Buildings, Christmas Tree — A1412

Adoration of the Magi — A1413

2010   **Litho.**   *Perf. 14¼*
2287 A1411 55c multi   1.50 1.50
   Perf. 13¾x14
2288 A1412 65c multi   1.75 1.75
Coil Stamp
Self-Adhesive
Serpentine Die Cut 13¾x13½
2289 A1413 (55c) multi   1.50 1.50
Christmas. Issued: No. 2287, 11/19; No. 2288, 11/11; No. 2289, 11/12.

Emperor Franz Josef and Dr. Anton Freiherr von Eiselsberg A1414

2011, Jan. 21   *Perf. 13¾x14*
2290 A1414 55c multi   1.50 1.50
Austria Cancer Aid, cent.

Imperial Post Office, Maribor A1415

2011, Jan. 21   *Perf. 13¾*
2291 A1415 65c multi   1.75 1.75

Violin and Bow
A1416

2011, Jan. 21   *Perf. 13½x14¼*
2292 A1416 75c multi   2.10 2.10

Chancellor Bruno Kreisky (1911-90)
A1417

2011, Jan. 22   *Perf. 13¾*
2293 A1417 55c multi   1.50 1.50

Miniature Sheet

Joanneum, Graz, Bicent. — A1418

2011, Jan. 26   *Perf.*
2294 A1418 100c multi   2.75 2.75

Franz Liszt (1811-86), Composer
A1419

2011, Jan. 29   *Perf. 13½x14*
2295 A1419 65c multi   1.75 1.75

Hedy Lamarr (1914-2000), Actress
A1420

2011, Feb. 4   *Perf. 13¾*
2296 A1420 55c multi   1.50 1.50

Advertising Art for Schweden-Bomben Confections — A1421

2011, Feb. 15   *Perf. 13¾*
2297 A1421 55c multi   1.50 1.50

Austria Wien Soccer Team, Cent.
A1422

2011, Mar. 15   *Perf. 13¾x14*
2298 A1422 65c multi   1.90 1.90

KTM 125 D.O.H.C. Apfelbeck Motorcycle — A1423

2011, Mar. 15   *Perf. 14x13¾*
2299 A1423 75c multi   2.25 2.25

Puch 500 Automobile — A1424

2011, Mar. 17
2300 A1424 65c multi   1.90 1.90

Karl Gölsdorf (1861-1916), Locomotive Designer — A1425

2011, Mar. 22   *Perf. 13¼x13¾*
2301 A1425 65c multi   1.90 1.90

Vienna Kunsthaus, 20th Anniv. — A1426

Photo. & Engr.
2011, Apr. 8   *Perf. 13¾*
2302 A1426 175c multi   5.25 5.25

Café Hewelka, Vienna
A1427

2011, Apr. 11   *Litho.*
2303 A1427 62c multi   1.90 1.90

Manned Space Flight, 50th Anniv.
A1428

2011, Apr. 12   *Perf. 13¼x13¾*
2304 A1428 65c multi   1.90 1.90

2011 Lower Austrian Regional Exhibition
A1429

2011, Apr. 16   *Perf. 13¾x14*
2305 A1429 62c multi   1.75 1.75

Architecture
A1430

Designs: 7c, Ars Electronica Center, Linz. No. 2307, Kunsthaus and Universal Museum Joanneum, Graz. No. 2308, Lentos Kunstmuseum, Linz. No. 2309, Forum Stadtpark, Graz. No. 2310, Museum Moderner Kunst Stiftung Ludwig (Ludwig Foundation Museum of Modern Art), Vienna. No. 2311, Kunsthaus, Bregenz, vert. No. 2312, Kunsthalle, Krems, vert. No. 2313, Museum der Moderne Mönchsberg (Mönchsberg Museum of Modern Art), Salzburg. No. 2314, Essl Museum Klosterneuburg. 145c, Project Space Karlsplatz, Kunsthalle, Vienna. 170c, MAK Center Schindler Chase House, Los Angeles. 340c, Austrian Cultural Forum, New York City, vert.

Die Cut Perf. 13¼
2011, May 1   Coil Stamps   Litho.
Self-Adhesive
Background Color
Without Name of Architect
2306 A1430 7c gray   .25 .25
2307 A1430 62c light blue   1.75 1.75
2308 A1430 70c yel org   2.00 2.00
2309 A1430 90c lilac   2.60 2.60
    Nos. 2306-2309 (4)   6.60 6.60

Booklet Stamps
2310 A1430 62c light blue   1.75 1.75
   a.   Booklet pane of 4   7.00
2311 A1430 62c light blue   1.75 1.75
2312 A1430 62c light blue   1.75 1.75
   a.   Booklet pane of 10, 5 each
     #2311-2312   17.50
2313 A1430 70c yel org   2.00 2.00
   a.   Booklet pane of 4 + 4 etiquettes   8.00
2314 A1430 90c lilac   2.60 2.60
   a.   Booklet pane of 4   10.50
2315 A1430 145c blue green   4.25 4.25
   a.   Booklet pane of 4   17.00
2316 A1430 170c pale orange   5.00 5.00
   a.   Booklet pane of 4 + 4 etiquettes   20.00
2317 A1430 340c yellow   9.75 9.75
   a.   Booklet pane of 4   39.00
    Nos. 2310-2317 (8)   28.85 28.85

See Nos. 2325, 2357-2364, 2393-2394.

Budweis-Linz-Gmunden Horse-Drawn Railway, 175th Anniv. — A1431

2011, May 1   Litho.   *Perf. 14x13¾*
2318 A1431 62c multi   1.75 1.75

CARE Austria, 25th Anniv. — A1432

2011, May 1
2319 A1432 70c multi   2.00 2.00

Mekhitarists In Vienna, 200th Anniv.
A1433

2011, May 1   *Perf. 14¼x14*
2320 A1433 90c multi   2.60 2.60

Pöllauberg Pilgrimage Church — A1434

2011, May 20   *Perf. 14x13¾*
2321 A1434 62c multi   1.75 1.75

The Tower of Babel, by Pieter Brueghel the Elder
A1435

Photo. & Engr.
2011, June 11   *Perf. 13¾*
2322 A1435 145c multi   4.25 2.10

Souvenir Sheet

Paintings by Hans Makart (1840-84) — A1436

No. 2323: a, Portrait of Dora Fournier-Gabillon. b, The Triumph of Ariadne.

2011, June 9   Litho.   *Perf. 14*
2323 A1436   Sheet of 2   7.00 7.00
   a.   70c multi   2.00 1.00
   b.   170c multi   5.00 2.50

Miniature Sheet

Austria, Country of Forests A1437

2011, June 15   **Perf.**
2324 A1437 90c multi   2.60 1.25
Values are for stamp with surrounding selvage.

Architecture Type of 2011

Design: Liaunig Museum, Neuhaus.

2011, June 20   **Litho.**   **Perf. 14x13¾**
2325 A1430 5c black   .25 .25

Austrian Military Aviation, Cent. A1438

2011, July 1   **Litho.**   **Perf. 14**
2326 A1438 62c multi   1.75 1.75

Tassilo Chalice, Kremsmünster Monastery A1439

Litho. & Engr.
2011, July 1   **Perf. 13¾**
2327 A1439 145c multi   4.25 4.25

St. Christopher Brotherhood, 625th Anniv. — A1440

2011, July 9   **Litho.**   **Perf. 14**
2328 A1440 62c multi   1.75 1.75

Organization for Economic Cooperation and Development, 50th Anniv. A1441

2011, July 11   **Perf. 13¾**
2329 A1441 70c multi   2.00 2.00

Railways Type of 2002

90c, Stammersdorf Railway train.

2011, July 15   **Photo. & Engr.**
2330 A1109 90c multi   2.60 2.60
Stammersdorf Local Railway, cent.

Bronze Relief by Ulrich Henn, Rankweil Basilica A1442

2011, Sept. 2   **Perf. 13¾**
2331 A1442 90c multi   2.50 2.50

Ferdinand Raimund (1790-1836), Playwright — A1443

2011, Sept. 4   **Litho.**   **Perf. 14x13¾**
2332 A1443 62c multi   1.75 1.75

Austrian Soccer Championships, Cent. — A1444

2011, Sept. 6   **Perf. 13¼x13¾**
2333 A1444 62c multi   1.75 1.75

Künstlerhaus, Vienna, Cent. — A1445

2011, Sept. 7   **Perf. 14x13¾**
2334 A1445 62c multi   1.75 1.75

Souvenir Sheet

Austrian Lotto, 25th Anniv. — A1446

2011, Sept. 7   **Perf.**
2335 A1446 145c multi   4.00 4.00
The top of No. 2335, separated by a row of rouletting, serves as a voucher for a free bet in the Austrian Lotto.

Souvenir Sheet

Europa — A1447

2011, Sept. 8   **Perf. 13¾**
2336 A1447 170c multi   4.75 4.75
Intl. Year of Forests. No. 2336 is an envelope containing spruce seeds. Rouletting around the souvenir sheet allows it to be removed from the rest of the envelope. Unused values are for the complete envelope with seeds.

Railways Type of 2002

90c, Erzberg Railway train.

Photo. & Engr.
2011, Sept. 10   **Perf. 13¾**
2337 A1109 90c multi   2.50 2.50
Erzberg Railway, 120th anniv.

Carbon Dioxide Neutral Delivery of Mail — A1448

2011, Sept. 10   **Litho.**
2338 A1448 62c multi   1.75 1.75

Portrait of Walburga Neuzil, by Egon Schiele A1449

2011. Sept. 23   **Perf. 13¾**
2339 A1449 62c multi   1.75 1.75
Leopold Museum, Vienna, 10th anniv.

Elisabeth Görgl, 2011 Women's Super-G Skiing World Champion — A1450

2011, Sept. 24   **Perf. 14x13¾**
2340 A1450 62c multi   1.75 1.75

Angst, Painting by Arnulf Rainer — A1451

O.T. 014, 2003, Photograph by Eva Schlegel A1452

2011, Oct. 1   **Perf. 13¾**
2341 A1451 62c multi   1.75 1.75
2342 A1452 70c multi   1.90 1.90

Trademark Austria A1453

2011, Oct. 4   **Perf. 14**
2343 A1453 62c multi   1.75 1.75

Loisium Wine Center, Langenlois — A1454

2011, Oct. 7   **Perf. 14x13¾**
2344 A1454 62c multi   1.75 1.75

The Song of Songs, Painting by Arik Brauer — A1455

Photo. & Engr.
2011, Oct. 14   **Perf. 13½**
2345 A1455 170c multi   4.75 4.75

Burgenland Statehood, 90th Anniv. — A1456

2011, Oct. 21   **Litho.**   **Perf. 13¾**
2346 A1456 90c multi   2.50 2.50

Nativity, by Unknown Artist — A1457

Chapel of St. Quirinus A1458

Madonna and Child — A1459

2011   **Perf. 13¾x14**
2347 A1457 62c multi   1.75 1.75
2348 A1458 70c multi   1.90 1.90

Coil Stamp
Self-Adhesive
Die Cut Perf. 13½x13¼
2349 A1459 62c multi   1.75 1.75
   Christmas. Issued: No. 2347, 11/25; No. 2348, 11/11; No. 2349, 11/18.

Reopening of Vienna Western Railway Station — A1460

2011, Nov. 23   **Perf. 14x13¾**
2350 A1460 70c multi   1.90 1.90

Wolfgang Amadeus Mozart (1756-91), Composer A1461

2011, Dec. 5   **Perf. 13½x14**
2351 A1461 70c multi   1.90 1.90

Miniature Sheet

Vienna Music Association, Bicent. — A1462

2012, Jan. 1   **Litho.**   **Perf.**
2352 A1462 90c multi   2.40 2.40

1959 Lohner L 125 Scooter A1463

2012, Jan. 2   **Perf. 13¾**
2353 A1463 145c multi   3.75 3.75

Carl Ritter von Ghega (1802-60), Railway Builder, and Kalte Rinne Viaduct — A1464

2012, Jan. 10   **Perf. 13½x13¾**
2354 A1464 70c multi   1.90 1.90
   Kalte Rinne Viaduct, 160th anniv.

Alpine Association, 150th Anniv. — A1465

2012, Jan. 12   **Perf. 14x13¾**
2355 A1465 62c multi   1.75 1.75

Vienna Rapid Transit Railway, 50th Anniv. A1466

2012, Jan. 17   **Perf. 14x14¼**
2356 A1466 62c multi   1.75 1.75

Architecture Type of 2011 With Names of Architects Added

   Designs: No. 2357, Like #2307, Spacelab Cook-Fournier architect. No. 2358, Like #2308, Weber Hofer Partner AG architect. No. 2359, Like #2309, Giselbrecht & Zinganel architect. No. 2360, Frauenmuseum (Women's Museum), Hittisau, Cukrowicz Nachbaur Architekten architect. No. 2361, Like #2311, Peter Zumthor architect, vert. No. 2362, Like #2310, Ortner & Ortner architect. No. 2363, Like #2313, Friedrich Hoff Zwink architect. No. 2364, Like #2316, Rudolph M. Schindler architect.

2012   **Litho.**   *Die Cut Perf. 13¼*
Self-Adhesive
Coil Stamps
Background Color
2357 A1430   62c light blue   1.75 1.75
2358 A1430   70c yel org   1.90 1.90
2359 A1430   90c lilac   2.40 2.40
2360 A1430   145c blue green   3.75 3.75
  a.   Booklet pane of 4   15.00
   Nos. 2357-2360 (4)   9.80 9.80
Booklet Stamps
2361 A1430   62c light blue   1.75 1.75
  a.   Booklet pane of 10   17.50
2362 A1430   62c light blue   1.60 1.60
  a.   Booklet pane of 4   6.50
2363 A1430   70c yel org   1.90 1.90
  a.   Booklet pane of 4 + 4 etiquettes   7.75
2364 A1430   170c pale orange   4.50 4.50
  a.   Booklet pane of 4 + 4 etiquettes   18.00
   Nos. 2361-2364 (4)   9.75 9.75
   Issued: Nos. 2357, 2361, 2/3; No. 2358, 1/30; Nos. 2359, 2360, 2363, 4/27; Nos. 2360a, 2364, 1/18; No. 2362, 5/18.

   This stamp, released Feb. 15, 2012, was a gift for standing order customers. It was not made available for sale.

2012 Vienna Opera Ball — A1467

2012, Feb. 16   **Litho.**   **Perf. 13¾**
2365 A1467 70c multi   1.90 1.90

Stöckl, Photograph by Elfie Semotan — A1468

2012, Feb. 24   **Perf. 14x13¾**
2366 A1468 70c multi   1.90 1.90

Steyr XII Taxi-Landaulet — A1469

2012, Mar. 26   **Perf. 13¾**
2367 A1469 70c multi   1.90 1.90

Viennese Oboe A1470

2012, Mar. 26   **Perf. 13½x14¼**
2368 A1470 90c multi   2.40 2.40

Character From Children's Book "I Am Me," by Mira Lobe A1471

2012, Mar. 27   **Perf. 13¾**
2369 A1471 62c multi   1.75 1.75

Turhan Bey, Actor A1472

2012, Mar. 30   **Litho.**
2370 A1472 70c multi   1.90 1.90

Enns, 800th Anniv. — A1473

Litho. & Engr.
2012, Apr. 22   **Perf. 13¾x14**
2371 A1473 145c multi   3.75 3.75

Bavaria-Upper Austria Provincial Exhibition — A1474

2012, Apr. 26   **Litho.**   **Perf. 13½x14¼**
2372 A1474 70c multi   1.90 1.90

Herzogenburg Priory, 900th Anniv. — A1475

2012, May 5   **Perf. 13¾**
2373 A1475 90c multi   2.25 2.25

Discovery of Cosmic Radiation by Victor F. Hess (1883-1964) — A1476

Litho. With Foil Application
2012, May 5   **Perf. 14x13¾**
2374 A1476 145c multi   3.75 3.75

SV Ried Soccer Team, Cent. — A1477

2012, May 6 **Litho.** **Perf. 13¾**
2375 A1477 62c multi   1.60 1.60

Souvenir Sheet

Prater Ferris Wheel, Vienna — A1478

2012, May 11 **Perf. 13½x14¼**
2376 A1478 70c multi   1.75 1.75

Europa.

Paddlewheel Steamship Schönbrunn, Cent. A1479

2012, May 12 **Perf. 13¾**
2377 A1479 90c multi   2.25 2.25

Johann Nepomuk Nestroy (1801-62), Playwright and Actor — A1480

2012, May 24 **Litho. & Engr.**
2378 A1480 145c multi   3.75 3.75

Self-portrait, by Anton Faistauer (1887-1930) A1481

2012, June 2 **Litho.**
2379 A1481 70c multi   1.75 1.75

Stockerau, 1000th Anniv. A1482

2012, June 3
2380 A1482 62c multi   1.60 1.60

Stained-Glass Window, Lilienfeld Monastery A1483

2012, June 8 **Litho. & Engr.**
2381 A1483 145c multi   3.75 3.75

Johann Puch (1862-1914), Bicycle Manufacturer A1484

2012, June 27 **Litho.** **Perf. 13¾x14**
2382 A1484 145c multi   3.75 3.75

Caritas Austria Charity Anti-Hunger Campaign — A1485

2012, July 2 **Perf. 14x14¼**
2383 A1485 62c multi   1.60 1.60

A1486

A1487

Austria on Maps A1488

2012, June 6 **Die Cut Perf. 13¼**
Coil Stamps
Self-Adhesive
2384 A1486   (62c) multi   1.60 1.60
2385 A1487   (70c) multi   1.75 1.75
2386 A1488   (€1.70) multi   4.25 4.25
  Nos. 2384-2386 (3)   7.60 7.60

Wolkenturm Open-air Stage, Grafenegg A1489

2012, July 14 **Perf. 13¾**
2387 A1489 70c multi   1.75 1.75

Portrait of Fritza Riedler, by Gustav Klimt (1862-1918) A1490

2012, July 14
2388 A1490 170c multi   4.25 4.25

Imperial Post Office, Zagreb A1491

2012, July 17
2389 A1491 70c multi   1.75 1.75

Votive Church, Vienna, Painting by Rudolf von Alt (1812-1905) A1492

Litho. & Engr.
2012, Aug. 23 **Perf. 13¾**
2390 A1492 170c multi   4.50 4.50

Gmundner Ceramics A1493

2012, Aug. 24 **Litho.**
2391 A1493 62c multi   1.60 1.60

Steigl Brewery, Salzburg, Horse-drawn Barrel Cart and Beer Stein — A1494

2012, Aug. 26
2392 A1494 62c multi   1.60 1.60

Architecture Type of 2011 With Names of Architects Added

Designs: No. 2393, Like #2314, Heinz Tesar architect. No. 2394, Like #2317, Raimund Abraham architect.

Die Cut Perf. 13¼
2012, Sept. 14 **Litho.**
Self-Adhesive
Booklet Stamps
Background Color
2393 A1430 90c lilac   2.40 2.40
  a.   Booklet pane of 4   9.75
2394 A1430 340c yellow   8.75 8.75
  a.   Booklet pane of 4   35.00

Vulpes Vulpes A1495

2012, Sept. 14 **Litho.** **Perf. 14x14¼**
2395 A1495 90c multi   2.40 2.40

St. Stephan's Church, Baden, 700th Anniv. A1496

2012, Sept. 16 **Perf. 13¾x14**
2396 A1496 90c multi   2.40 2.40

Alpenzoo, Innsbruck, 50th Anniv. — A1497

2012, Sept. 22 **Perf. 13¼x14**
2397 A1497 70c multi   1.90 1.90

Gerlinde Kaltenbrunner, Mountaineer — A1498

2012, Sept. 29 **Perf. 14x13¾**
2398 A1498 62c multi   1.60 1.60

St. Michael
From
Mondsee
Basilica
Altarpiece
A1499

Litho. & Engr.
2012, Sept. 29   *Perf. 13¾*
2399 A1499 145c multi   3.75 3.75

Mittenwald Railway, Cent. — A1500

2012, Sept. 29   *Perf. 14x13¾*
2400 A1500 145c multi   3.75 3.75

Miniature Sheet

Characters From Movie *Madagascar 3:
Europe's Most Wanted* — A1501

No. 2401: a, Penguin lighting fuse of cannon, mouth of Alex the Lion. b, Marty the Zebra, and Gloria the Hippo, in cannon. c, Penguins, part of head of Alex the Lion. d, Part of head of Alex the Lion, Melman the Giraffe.

Serpentine Die Cut 14
2012, Oct. 5   Litho.   Self-Adhesive
2401 A1501 Sheet of 4   7.50
  a.-b.   62c Either single   1.60 1.60
  c.   70c multi   1.90 1.90
  d.   90c multi   2.40 2.40

Sleeping
Child, by
Bernardo
Strozzi
A1502

Litho. & Engr.
2012, Oct. 6   *Perf. 13¾*
2402 A1502 170c multi   4.50 4.50

Souvenir Sheet

Ants, Painting by Peter
Kogler — A1503

2012, Oct. 6   Litho.   Perf. 14
2403 A1503 Sheet of 2   3.50 3.50
  a.   62c gray, brt org red & blk 1.60 1.60
  b.   70c brt org red, gray & blk 1.90 1.90

Self-Portrait With
Red Hat, by
Marie-Louise
von Motesiczky
A1504

2012, Oct. 10   *Perf. 13¾x14*
2404 A1504 62c multi   1.60 1.60

Carl Auer von
Welsbach (1858-
1929), Inventor,
and Gas
Lamp — A1505

2012, Oct. 13   *Perf. 13¼x14*
2405 A1505 62c multi   1.60 1.60

Concession for Raab-Oedenberg-
Ebenfurth Railroad, 140th
Anniv. — A1506

2012, Oct. 15   *Perf. 14x13¼*
2406 A1506 62c multi   1.60 1.60

Wine Glass,
Wine, Grapes
and Windmill
A1507

2012, Oct. 19   *Perf. 13¼x14*
2407 A1507 62c multi   1.60 1.60

Vienna International Film Festival, 50th
Anniv. — A1508

2012, Oct. 25   *Perf. 14x13¾*
2408 A1508 70c multi   1.90 1.90

Souvenir Sheet

Meeting of Emperor Franz Josef and
King Chulalongkorn of Thailand, 115th
Anniv. — A1509

No. 2409: a, Emperor Franz Josef. b, King Chulalongkorn.

2012, Nov. 10   *Perf. 14¼x13½*
2409 A1509 Sheet of 2   6.50 6.50
  a.   70c multi   1.90 1.90
  b.   170c multi   4.50 4.50

See Thailand No. 2714.

Arndorfer Altar,
Maria Saal
Cathedral
A1510

Church of St.
George, Kals
am
Grossglockner
A1511

Hunters in
Snow, by
Pieter
Breughel,
the Elder
A1512

Adoration
of the
Magi, by
Jacopo
Bassano
A1513

2012   *Perf. 13¾*
2410 A1510 62c multi   1.60 1.60
          Perf. 13¾x14
2411 A1511 70c multi   1.90 1.90
Coil Stamps
Self-Adhesive
Die Cut Perf. 13
2412 A1512 62c multi   1.60 1.60
2413 A1513 70c multi   1.90 1.90
Christmas. Issued: Nos. 2410, 2412, 11/30; Nos. 2411, 2413, 11/16.

Lenz Moser
Wines
A1514

2012, Nov. 17   *Perf. 13¾x14*
2414 A1514 62c multi   1.60 1.60

Railways in Austria, 175th
Anniv. — A1515

2012, Nov. 23   *Perf. 14x13¾*
2415 A1515 90c multi   2.40 2.40

2013 World
Alpine Skiing
Championships,
Schladming
A1516

Paintings by Christian Ludwig Attersee: 62c, Freedom in the Snow. 70c, Styrian Heart. 90c, Slalom Dance.

2013, Jan. 2   *Perf. 13¾x14*
Panel Color
2416 A1516 62c orange   1.75 1.75
2417 A1516 70c dark red   1.90 1.90
2418 A1516 90c yel green   2.40 2.40
  Nos. 2416-2418 (3)   6.05 6.05

Bergisel Ski
Jump,
Innsbruck
A1517

2013, Jan. 4   *Perf. 13¾*
2419 A1517 62c multi   1.75 1.75

Diversity
in Unity
A1518

2013, Jan. 21
2420 A1518 70c multi   1.90 1.90

1953 Halleiner Motor Works 250 BJ Motorbike A1519

2013, Jan. 21
2421 A1519 220c multi 6.00 6.00

This stamp, released Feb. 13, 2013, was a gift for standing order customers. It was not made available for sale.

Best Wishes A1520

2013, Feb. 20 Litho. Perf. 14
2422 A1520 (62c) multi 1.60 1.60

Salzburg Marionette Theater, Cent. — A1521

2013, Feb. 27 Perf. 13¾x14
2423 A1521 62c multi 1.60 1.60

1948 Porsche 356 No. 1 Roadster A1522

2013, Feb. 28 Perf. 13¾
2424 A1522 70c multi 1.90 1.90

Valie Export - Smart Export, Photograph by Valie Export A1523

2013, Mar. 13
2425 A1523 70c black 1.90 1.90

Bruck Locomotive at Baden Station, c. 1846 — A1524

2013, Mar. 13 Perf. 14x13¾
2426 A1524 145c multi 4.50 4.50

Rupicapra Rupicapra A1525

Litho. & Engr.
2013, Mar. 14 Perf. 14x14¼
2427 A1525 90c multi 2.40 2.40

Page Illumination, St. Florian Monastery A1526

2013, Mar. 15 Perf. 13¾
2428 A1526 90c multi 2.40 2.40

Senta Berger, Actress A1527

2013, Mar. 22 Litho.
2429 A1527 70c multi 1.90 1.90

Preseren Square, Ljubljana, Slovenia A1528

2013, Apr. 6
2430 A1528 62c multi 1.60 1.60

Souvenir Sheet

Underground Post Office in Postojna Cave, Slovenia — A1529

2013, Apr. 6 Perf. 13¾
2431 A1529 70c multi 1.90 1.90
See Slovenia No. 982.

Music Theater at Landestheater, Linz — A1530

2013, Apr. 11
2432 A1530 62c multi 1.60 1.60

Landhaus Bacher Restaurant, Mautern — A1531

2013, Apr. 11
2433 A1531 62c multi 1.60 1.60

30th Vienna City Marathon — A1532

2013, Apr. 14 Perf. 14
2434 A1532 62c multi 1.60 1.60

Vienna Horn A1533

2013, Apr. 15 Perf. 13½x14¼
2435 A1533 90c multi 2.40 2.40

Julius Lott (1836-83), Builder of Arlberg Railroad A1534

2013, Apr. 17 Perf. 13¼x13¾
2436 A1534 70c multi 1.90 1.90

Toboggan Ride, Wurstelprater Amusement Park, Vienna, Cent. — A1535

2013, Apr. 19 Perf. 13¾
2437 A1535 62c multi 1.60 1.60

Souvenir Sheet

Attersee Area Transportation Centenaries — A1536

No. 2438: a, Shipping on Attersee, cent. b, Attergau Railway, cent.

2013, Apr. 19 Perf. 14x13¾
2438 A1536 Sheet of 2 3.50 3.50
a. 62c multi 1.60 1.60
b. 70c multi 1.90 1.90

Hohentwiel Paddle-wheeled Steamer, Cent. — A1537

2013, May 4 Perf. 13¾
2439 A1537 62c multi 1.75 1.75

Austrian Open-Air Museum, Stübing, 50th Anniv. A1538

2013, May 5 Perf. 14x14¼
2440 A1538 70c multi 1.90 1.90

Souvenir Sheet

Europa — A1539

2013, May 6 Die Cut
Self-Adhesive
2441 A1539 70c multi 1.90 1.90

International Red Cross, 150th Anniv. — A1540

2013, May 8 Perf. 14
2442 A1540 62c multi 1.75 1.75

Vienna Concert House, Cent. — A1541

2013, May 11 Litho.
2443 A1541 90c multi 2.40 2.40

Robert Jungk (1913-94), Journalist A1542

2013, May 13   *Perf. 13¾*
2444 A1542 90c multi   2.40 2.40

Franz West (1947-2012), Artist — A1543

2013, May 14
2445 A1543 70c black   1.90 1.90

South Styrian Wine Region — A1544

2013, May 24   *Perf. 13¼x14*
2446 A1544 62c multi   1.75 1.75

St. Theodul, Patron Saint of the Walsers A1545

    Litho. & Engr.
2013, May 29   *Perf. 13¾*
2447 A1545 145c multi   4.00 4.00
   Walser settlements in Vorarlberg, 700th anniv.

Souvenir Sheet

Pilgrimage to Maria Luggau, 500th Anniv. — A1546

2013, May 31   **Litho.**   *Perf. 13x13¼*
2448 A1546 170c multi   4.75 4.75

St. Anna's Children's Cancer Research Institute, 25th Anniv. — A1547

2013, June 6   *Perf. 14*
2449 A1547 62c multi   1.75 1.75

Austrian Nature Protection League, Cent. — A1548

2013, June 7
2450 A1548 90c multi   2.40 2.40

Fairtrade Austria, 20th Anniv. — A1549

2013, June 21   *Perf. 13¾*
2451 A1549 62c multi   1.60 1.60

Lorenz I. Bordogna von Taxis (1510-59), Tyrolean Postmaster A1550

2013, June 25   **Litho. & Engr.**
2452 A1550 145c multi   3.75 3.75

Self-portrait, by Richard Gerstl (1883-1908) A1551

2013, June 27   **Litho.**   *Perf. 14*
2453 A1551 62c multi   1.60 1.60

Vorau Monastery, 850th Anniv. — A1552

    Perf. 13¾x13½
2013, June 28   **Litho. & Engr.**
2454 A1552 145c brown & blk   3.75 3.75

Wacker Soccer Team, Innsbruck, Cent. — A1553

2013, July 5   **Litho.**   *Perf. 13¾*
2455 A1553 62c multi   1.60 1.60

Ausserfern Railway, Cent. A1554

2013, July 6   *Perf. 13½x14¼*
2456 A1554 70c multi   1.90 1.90

Traditional Women's Clothing From Gmunden A1555

2013, Aug. 23   *Perf. 13¼x14*
2457 A1555 62c multi   1.75 1.75

Volunteer Fire Departments in Austria, 150th Anniv. A1556

    Perf. 13½x14¼
2013, Sept. 7   **Litho. & Engr.**
2458 A1556 90c multi   2.40 2.40

Stylized Landmarks A1557

   Austrian flag and: No. 2459, Lindwurm Fountain, Brunnen. No. 2460, Hohensalzburg Fortress, Salzburg. No. 2461, Pöstlingberg Church, Linz. No. 2462, Goldenes Dachl (Golden Roof), Innsbruck, vert. No. 2463, St. Martin's Tower, Bregenz, vert. No. 2464, Bergkirche, Eisenstadt, vert. No. 2465, Landhaus, St. Pölten, vert.

    Die Cut Perf. 14
2013, Sept. 12   **Litho.**
    Coil Stamps
    Self-Adhesive
2459 A1557 62c multi   1.75 1.75
2460 A1557 90c multi   2.40 2.40
2461 A1557 145c multi   4.00 4.00
   Nos. 2459-2461 (3)   8.15 8.15
    Booklet Stamps
2462 A1557 62c multi   1.75 1.75
   a. Booklet pane of 4   7.00
2463 A1557 62c multi   1.75 1.75
   a. Booklet pane of 10   17.50
2464 A1557 90c multi   2.40 2.40
   a. Booklet pane of 4   9.75

2465 A1557 145c multi   4.00 4.00
   a. Booklet pane of 4   16.00
   Nos. 2462-2465 (4)   9.90 9.90
    See Nos. 2488-2491.

Souvenir Sheet

Holiday Travel with the Express Mail, Painting by Karl Schnorpfeil (1875-1937) — A1558

2013, Sept. 12   *Perf. 14*
2466 A1558 70c multi   1.90 1.90

Helene Winterstein-Kamberesky (1900-66), Inventor of Waterproof Mascara — A1559

2013, Sept. 13   *Perf. 13¼x14*
2467 A1559 70c multi   1.90 1.90

Advertising Art for Engelhofer Bonbons A1560

2013, Sept. 13   *Perf. 13¾x14*
2468 A1560 70c multi   1.90 1.90

Icon of St. Nicholas of Myra, Russian Orthodox Cathedral, Vienna A1561

    Litho. & Engr.
2013, Sept. 20   *Perf. 13¾*
2469 A1561 145c multi   4.00 4.00

Madonna and Child, Painting by Lorenzo Lotto (1480-1557) — A1562

2013, Sept. 26
2470 A1562 170c multi   4.75 4.75

Tyrolean Ski Federation, Cent. — A1563

2013, Oct. 11 Litho. Perf. 14
2471 A1563 62c multi   1.75 1.75

St. Martin's Church, Linz — A1564

2013, Oct. 11 Litho. Perf. 14
2472 A1564 62c multi   1.75 1.75

Burgtheater, Vienna, 125th Anniv. — A1565

2013, Oct. 11 Litho. Perf. 13¾
2473 A1565 70c multi   1.90 1.90

Scene From "Orient, 1st Part," Video Art by Markus Schinwald A1566

2013, Oct. 14 Litho. Perf. 14
2474 A1566 145c multi   4.00 4.00

Miniature Sheet

Halloween — A1567

No. 2475 — Haunted house and: a, Ghost, witch on broom, spider. b, Bats, vampire. c, Skeleton, graveyard. d, Jack o'lanterns.

Serpentine Die Cut 14¼
2013, Oct. 14 Litho.
Self-Adhesive
2475 A1567 Sheet of 4   7.00
a.-d.   62c Any single   1.75 1.75

Adoration of the Shepherds from Altarpiece of St. Michael's Church, Lungau A1568

St. Georgenberg-Fiecht Abbey — A1569

Franz Xaver Gruber (1787-1863), Composer of "Silent Night," and Silent Night Chapel, Oberndorf — A1570

The Nativity, Painting by Joos van Cleve — A1571

2013 Litho. Perf. 13¾x14
2476 A1568 62c multi   1.75 1.75
2477 A1569 70c multi   2.00 2.00
Coil Stamps
Self-Adhesive
Die Cut Perf. 14x14¼
2478 A1570 62c multi   1.75 1.75
Die Cut Perf. 13x13½
2479 A1571 70c multi   2.00 2.00

Christmas. No. 2479 lacks country name. Issued: Nos. 2476, 2478, 11/29; Nos. 2477, 2479, 11/15.

E.V.A., by Franz Graf — A1572

2013, Dec. 5 Litho. Perf. 13¾x14
2480 A1572 145c black   4.00 4.00

Colorable Stamp A1573

2014, Jan. 22 Litho. Perf. 13¾x13¼
2481 A1573 62c multi   1.75 1.75
No. 2481 was pritned in sheets of 6.

Austro Daimler ADR 22/70 A1574

2014, Jan. 22 Litho. Perf. 14¼
2482 A1574 170c multi   4.75 4.75

KTM Ponny II Motorcycle A1575

2014, Jan. 31 Litho. Perf. 14¼
2483 A1575 145c multi   4.00 4.00

This stamp, released Feb. 7, 2014, was a gift for standing order customers. It was not made available for sale.

Romy Awards, 25th Anniv. — A1576

Litho. & Embossed With Foil Application
2014, Feb. 7 Perf. 14x13¾
2484 A1576 145c multi   4.00 4.00

Imperial Post Office, Gablonz (Jablonec), Bohemia A1577

2014, Feb. 28 Litho. Perf. 14¼
2485 A1577 62c multi   1.75 1.75

Hospital of the Brothers of Charity, Vienna, 400th Anniv. A1578

2014, Mar. 8 Litho. Perf. 14¼
2486 A1578 62c multi   1.75 1.75

Vienna Double Bass — A1579

Litho. & Engr.
2014, Mar. 13 Perf. 14
2487 A1579 175c multi   4.75 4.75

Stylized Landmarks Type of 2013
Designs: No. 2488, Schönbrunn Castle, Vienna. No. 2489, St. Stephen's Cathedral, Vienna, vert. 170c, Riesenrad (Ferris Wheel), Vienna, vert. 340c, Clock tower, Graz, vert.

Die Cut Perf. 14
2014, Mar. 19 Litho.
Coil Stamp
Self-Adhesive
2488 A1557 70c multi   2.00 2.00
Booklet Stamps
2489 A1557 70c multi   2.00 2.00
a.   Booklet pane of 4 + 4 eti-
      quettes   8.00
2490 A1557 170c multi   4.75 4.75
a.   Booklet pane of 4 + 4 eti-
      quettes   19.00
2491 A1557 340c multi   9.50 9.50
a.   Booklet pane of 4   38.00
   Nos. 2488-2491 (4)   18.25 18.25

Rose — A1580

Silk-Screened on Porcelain Tile
2014, Mar. 20 Imperf.
Self-Adhesive
2492 A1580 590c multi   16.50 16.50

European Organization for Nuclear Research (CERN), 60th Anniv. — A1581

2014, Apr. 4 Litho. Perf. 14
2493 A1581 90c multi   2.50 2.50

Zum Schwarzen Kameel (Black Camel) Restaurant, Vienna — A1582

2014, Apr. 10   Litho.   Perf. 14¼
2494 A1582 70c multi   2.00 2.00

Eric Pleskow,
Movie Producer
A1583

2014, Apr. 12   Litho.   Perf. 13¾x13½
2495 A1583 70c multi   2.00 2.00

Charlie Chaplin
(1889-1977),
Film
Actor — A1584

2014, Apr. 12   Litho.   Perf. 13¾x14
2496 A1584 90c gray & blk   2.50 2.50

Klosterneuberg Monastery, 900th
Anniv. — A1585

Litho. & Engr.
2014, Apr. 24   Perf. 14x13¾
2497 A1585 145c multi   4.00 4.00

Wachau Wine
Region — A1586

2014, May 3   Litho.   Perf. 13¾x14
2498 A1586 62c multi   1.75 1.75

Zither — A1587

2014, May 9   Litho.   Perf. 13½
2499 A1587 70c multi   1.90 1.90

Europa.

Scolopax
Rusticola
A1588

Litho. & Engr.
2014, May 16   Perf. 14x14¼
2500 A1588 170c multi   4.75 4.75

Steamboats
on
Traunsee,
175th
Anniv.
A1589

2014, May 17   Litho.   Perf. 14¼x14
2501 A1589 62c multi   1.75 1.75

Erzberg
Motorcycle
Rodeo, 19th
Anniv. — A1590

2014, May 29   Litho.   Perf. 13¾x14
2502 A1590 62c multi   1.75 1.75

Souvenir Sheet

Popes — A1591

No. 2503: a, St. John XXIII. b, St. John Paul
II. c, Pope Francis.

2014, June 5   Litho.   Perf. 13x13½
2503 A1591   Sheet of 3   5.50 5.50
  a.-b.   62c Either single   1.75 1.75
  c.   70c multi   1.90 1.90
Canonization of Popes John XXIII and John
Paul II.

Josef
Madersperger
(1768-1850),
and His Sewing
Machine
A1592

2014, June 6   Litho.   Perf. 13¾x14
2504 A1592 70c multi   1.90 1.90

Museum of Applied Arts (MAK),
Vienna, 150th Anniv. — A1593

2014, June 10   Litho.   Perf. 14x13¾
2505 A1593 62c multi   1.75 1.75

Hans Moser
(1880-1964),
Actor — A1594

2014, June 10   Litho.   Perf. 13¼x13
2506 A1594 70c multi   1.90 1.90

Richard Strauss (1864-1949),
Composer — A1595

2014, June 11   Litho.   Perf. 14x13¾
2507 A1595 62c multi   1.75 1.75

Austrian Referendum on Joining the
European Union, 20th Anniv. — A1596

2014, June 12   Litho.   Perf. 13¾
2508 A1596 62c multi   1.75 1.75

Dormition
Icon,
Hochfeistritz
Fortress
Church
A1597

Litho. & Engr.
2014, June 13   Perf. 13¾
2509 A1597 90c multi   2.50 2.50

Souvenir Sheet

June 28, 1914 Royal
Assassinations — A1598

No. 2510: a, Archduke Franz Ferdinand
(1863-1914). b, Duchess Sophie of
Hohenberg (1868-1914).

2014, June 28   Litho.   Perf. 13¼x14
2510 A1598   Sheet of 2   3.75 3.75
  a.   62c multi   1.75 1.75
  b.   70c multi   1.90 1.90

Traditional
Clothing of
Ausseerland
A1599

2014, July 18   Litho.   Perf. 13¾x14
2511 A1599 70c multi   1.90 1.90

Miniature Sheet

Characters From *Maya the Bee*
Animated Television Show — A1600

No. 2512: a, Willy the Bee. b, Maya the Bee.
c, Thekla the Spider. d, Flip the Grasshopper.

Serpentine Die Cut 14
2014, Aug. 29   Litho.
        Self-Adhesive
2512 A1600   Sheet of 4   6.50
  a.-d.   62c Any single   1.60 1.60

Museum
Angerlehner,
Thalheim bei
Wels — A1601

2014, Sept. 12   Litho.   Perf. 14¼
2513 A1601 62c multi   1.60 1.60

Mariatrost
Basilica, Graz,
300th Anniv.
A1602

2014, Sept. 19   Litho.   Perf. 14¼
2514 A1602 62c multi   1.60 1.60

Austrian Horse-Drawn Parcel Post
Carriage, c. 1830 — A1603

2014, Sept. 20   Litho.   Perf. 14x13¾
2515 A1603 90c multi   2.25 2.25

Souvenir Sheet

Steyr Valley Railway, 125th
Anniv. — A1604

Perf. 13¾x13¼
2014, Sept. 20   Litho.
2516 A1604 145c multi   3.75 3.75

Map of Trans-
Alpine Route of
Fussach
Messenger
Courier Service
A1605

Litho. & Engr.
2014, Sept. 27   Perf. 13¾
2517 A1605 90c multi   2.25 2.25

Vienna Sales
Board, 150th
Anniv.
A1606

2014, Oct. 1   Litho.   Perf. 14¼
2518 A1606 62c multi   1.60 1.60

Portrait of
Isabella Reisser,
by Anton
Romako
A1607

2014, Oct. 10   Litho.   Perf. 14
2519 A1607 62c multi   1.60 1.60

Opening of Vienna Central Railroad
Station — A1608

2014, Oct. 10   Litho.   Perf. 14
2520 A1608 90c multi   2.25 2.25

Railways Type of 2002
Perf. 13¾x13½
2014, Oct. 10   Litho. & Engr.
2521 A1109 145c Murtal Railway
                        train   3.75 3.75
Murtal Railway, 120th anniv.

Udo Jürgens, Singer, 80th
Birthday — A1609

2014, Oct. 18   Litho.   Perf. 14
2522 A1609 70c multi   1.75 1.75

1656 Portrait of
Infanta
Margarita
Teresa in a
White Dress, by
Diego
Velazquez
A1610

Litho. & Engr.
2014, Oct. 18   Perf. 13¾
2523 A1610 145c multi   3.75 3.75

Interiors,
Film by
Ursula
Mayer
A1611

2014, Oct. 22   Litho.   Perf. 14¼
2524 A1611 90c black   2.25 2.25

Mona Lisa, by
Gelatin Art
Collective
A1612

2014, Oct. 22   Litho.   Perf. 14
2525 A1612 170c multi   4.25 4.25

Media Poet,
Film by Peter
Weibel — A1613

2014, Oct. 25   Litho.   Perf. 14¼x14½
2526 A1613 62c multi   1.60 1.60

Souvenir Sheet

Vienna Philharmonic Gold Coins, 25th
Anniv. — A1614

2014 coin: a, Obverse (pipe organ). b,
Reverse (various musical instruments).

**Litho. & Embossed With Foil
Application**
2014, Nov. 5   Perf.
2527 A1614   Sheet of 2   4.00 4.00
  a.   70c blue & gold   1.75 1.75
  b.   90c maroon & gold 2.25 2.25

Hirschegg Parish
Church
Altarpiece Detail
Depicting
Adoration of the
Magi — A1615

Madonna of
Krumlov, c.
1400 — A1616

Adoration of
the Magi,
by Jan
Brueghel
the Elder
(1568-1625)
A1617

Winter Landscape, by Lucas I. van
Valckenborch (c. 1535-97) — A1618

2014   Litho.   Perf. 13¾x14
2528 A1615 62c multi   1.60 1.60
2529 A1616 70c multi   1.75 1.75

Coil Stamps
Self-Adhesive
Die Cut Perf. 13½x13¾
2530 A1617 62c multi   1.60 1.60
Die Cut Perf. 13¼
2531 A1618 70c multi   1.75 1.75
   Christmas. Issued: Nos. 2528, 2530, 11/28;
Nos. 2529, 2531, 11/14.

Travel Poster by
Arthur Zelger
(1914-2004),
Graphic
Designer
A1619

2014, Dec. 5   Litho.   Perf. 13¼x14
2532 A1619 170c multi   4.25 4.25

Souvenir Sheet

Skiing — A1620

   No. 2533: a, Toni Sailer, skier. b, Trophy for
Hahnenkamm Races.

2015, Jan. 20   Litho.   Perf. 13¾x13½
2533 A1620   Sheet of 2   3.00 3.00
  a.   62c multi   1.40 1.40
  b.   70c multi   1.60 1.60
   Toni Sailer, 80th birthday; Hahnenkamm
Races, 75th anniv.

"Osterreich 62 Cent" — A1621

2015, Jan. 21   Litho.   Perf. 13¾
2534 A1621 62c red   1.40 1.40

Timpani Drums — A1622

Litho. & Engr.
2015, Jan. 21   *Perf. 14*
2535 A1622 145c multi   3.25 3.25

Austrian
Landmarks
A1623

Part of map of Austria and: 6c, Riesenrad, Vienna. 10c, Bergkirche, Eisenstadt. 20c, Statue of Athena, Parliament, Vienna. 40c, Sailboarder, Neusiedler See, Burgenland. No. 2540, Clock tower, Graz. No. 2541, Goldenes Dachl (Golden Roof), Innsbruck. No. 2542, Martinsturm, Bregenz. No. 2543, Grossglockner, Hohe Tauern Range.

No. 2544, Heidentor, Carnuntum. No. 2545, Hohensalzburg Castle, Salzburg. No. 2546, St. Stephen's Cathedral, Vienna. No. 2547, Pöstlingberg Church, Linz. 150c, Lindwurm (Dragon Fountain), Klagenfurt. No. 2549, Murinsel, Graz. 170c, Bergisel Ski Jump, Innsbruck. 400c, Forchtenstein Castle.

Die Cut Perf. 13¾
2015, Mar. 1   Litho.
Coil Stamps
Self-Adhesive
2536 A1623   6c multi   .25 .25
2537 A1623   10c multi   .25 .25
2538 A1623   20c multi   .45 .45
2539 A1623   40c multi   .90 .90
2540 A1623   68c multi   1.50 1.50
2541 A1623   80c multi   1.75 1.75
2542 A1623   100c multi   2.25 2.25
2543 A1623   160c multi   3.50 3.50
    Nos. 2536-2543 (8)   10.85 10.85

Booklet Stamps
2544 A1623   68c multi   1.50 1.50
   a.   Booklet pane of 4   6.00
2545 A1623   68c multi   1.50 1.50
   a.   Booklet pane of 10   15.00
2546 A1623   80c multi   1.75 1.75
   a.   Booklet pane of 4   7.00
2547 A1623   100c multi   2.25 2.25
   a.   Booklet pane of 4   9.00
2548 A1623   150c multi   3.50 3.50
   a.   Booklet pane of 4   14.00
2549 A1623   160c multi   3.50 3.50
   a.   Booklet pane of 4   14.00
2550 A1623   170c multi   3.75 3.75
   a.   Booklet pane of 4   15.00
2551 A1623   400c multi   9.00 9.00
   a.   Booklet pane of 4   36.00
    Nos. 2544-2551 (8)   26.75 26.75

A self-adhesive sheet of four containing die cut examples of Nos. 2536-2539 and a self-adhesive sheet of 11 containing die cut examples of Nos. 2540-2551 were given away to standing order customers. The stamps in the sheets were not valid for postage.

Advertising Art
for Schartner
Bombe
Beverages
A1624

2015, Mar. 1   Litho.   *Perf. 13¾*
2552 A1624 68c multi   1.50 1.50

Joseph
Hardtmuth
(1758-1816),
Pencil
Manufacturer
A1625

2015, Mar. 1   Litho.   *Perf. 14*
2553 A1625 80c multi   1.75 1.75

1953 Delta-Gnom LM 125
Motorcycle — A1626

2015, Mar. 7   Litho.   *Perf. 13¾*
2554 A1626 220c multi   5.00 5.00

Miniature Sheet

Easter — A1627

No. 2555: a, Purple rabbit pointing to Easter eggs in tower. b, Brown and gray rabbits on blanket. c, Yellow rabbit and two mice. d, Pink rabbit and Easter eggs.

Serpentine Die Cut 14
2015, Mar. 7   Litho.
Self-Adhesive
2555 A1627   Sheet of 4   6.00
   a.-d.   68c Any single   1.50 1.50

This stamp, released Mar. 7, 2015, was a gift for standing order customers. It was not made available for sale.

University of
Vienna, 650th
Anniv. — A1628

2015, Mar. 13   Litho.   *Perf. 13¾*
2556 A1628 100c multi   2.25 2.25

St. Teresa of
Avila (1515-82)
A1629

Litho. & Engr.
2015, Mar. 28   *Perf. 13¾*
2557 A1629 170c multi   3.75 3.75

Literature
Museum of the
Austrian
National Library,
Vienna — A1630

2015, Apr. 18   Litho.   *Perf. 13¾x14*
2558 A1630 68c multi   1.60 1.60

Maria Schell
(1926-2005),
Actress
A1631

2015, Apr. 24   Litho.   *Perf. 13½*
2559 A1631 68c multi   1.60 1.60

2015 Eurovision Song Contest,
Vienna — A1632

2015, Apr. 24   Litho.   *Perf. 14x13¾*
2560 A1632 80c multi   1.90 1.90

Museum
Liaunig,
Neuhaus
A1633

2015, Apr. 26   Litho.   *Perf. 14x13¾*
2561 A1633 68c multi   1.60 1.60

Traditional
Tyrolean
Costumes
A1634

2015, May 2   Litho.   *Perf. 13¾x14*
2562 A1634 68c multi   1.60 1.60

Europa — A1635

2015, May 7   Litho.   *Perf. 14x13¾*
2563 A1635 80c multi   1.75 1.75

Souvenir Sheet

After the Rain, by Hubert
Schmalix — A1636

2015, May 7   Litho.   *Perf. 14*
2564 A1636 100c multi   2.25 2.25

Souvenir Sheet

Penny Black, 175th Anniv. — A1637

2015, May 7   Litho.   *Perf. 14¼x14*
2565 A1637 220c multi   5.00 5.00

Steyr
Puch IMP
700 GT
Coupe
A1638

2015, May 29   Litho.   *Perf. 13¾*
2566 A1638 100c multi   2.25 2.25

Congress of
Vienna, 200th
Anniv.
A1639

2015, June 9   Litho.   *Perf. 13¾*
2567 A1639 68c black   1.50 1.50

Chalice Veil,
Diocesan
Museum of St.
Polten
A1640

Litho. & Engr.
2015, June 19   *Perf. 13¾*
2568 A1640 100c multi   2.25 2.25

Lepus Europaeus
A1641

Litho. & Engr.
2015, June 19   *Perf. 14x14¼*
2569 A1641 160c multi   3.50 3.50

Spanish Riding School, Vienna, 450th Anniv.
A1642

2015, June 26   Litho.   Perf. 13¾
2570 A1642 80c multi   1.75 1.75

Rankweil Basilica
A1643

2015, Aug. 21   Litho.   Perf. 13¾
2571 A1643 68c multi   1.50 1.50

Souvenir Sheet

Horse-Drawn Mail Wagon — A1644

2015, Aug. 27   Litho.   Perf. 13¼x13
2572 A1644 100c multi   2.25 2.25

Lady With a Dark Hat, by Anton Faistauer
A1645

2015, Aug. 28   Litho.   Perf. 13¾
2573 A1645 68c multi   1.50 1.50

Carnuntum Wine Region — A1646

2015, Sept. 5   Litho.   Perf. 14
2574 A1646 80c multi   1.90 1.90

St. John Bosco (1815-88), Founder of Salesians Society
A1647

2015, Sept. 12   Litho.   Perf. 13¾
2575 A1647 150c multi   3.50 3.50

Alpine-Adriatic Philately, 20th Anniv. — A1648

2015, Sept. 18   Litho.   Perf. 14x13¼
2576 A1648 80c multi   1.90 1.90

Haas House, Vienna, 25th Anniv.
A1649

2015, Sept. 19   Litho.   Perf. 13¾
2577 A1649 68c multi   1.60 1.60

Vexations, Photograph by Gregor Schmoll — A1650

Perf. 14¼x13½
2015, Sept. 19   Litho.
2578 A1650 68c black   1.60 1.60

Friedrich Kiesler (1890-1965), Architect — A1651

2015, Sept. 22   Litho.   Perf. 14x14¼
2579 A1651 80c multi   1.90 1.90

Lederhosen
A1652

Embossed on Brown Leather With Glass Crystals Affixed
Serpentine Die Cut 7¾
2015, Sept. 24   Self-Adhesive
2580 A1652 630c black   14.50 14.50

Univerity of Leoben, 175th Anniv. — A1653

Litho. With Foil Application
2015, Oct. 2   Perf. 13¾x14¼
2581 A1653 80c multi   1.90 1.90

Railways Type of 2002
Perf. 13¾x13½
2015, Oct. 3   Litho. & Engr.
2582 A1109 160c Semmerling
          Railway train   3.75 3.75

Schiebel Camcopter S-100 — A1654

2015, Oct. 17   Litho.   Perf. 14
2583 A1654 68c multi   1.60 1.60

Painting by Svenja Deininger
A1655

2015, Oct. 21   Litho.   Perf. 13¾
2584 A1655 80c multi   1.75 1.75

Susanna and the Elders, by Tintoretto
A1656

2015, Oct. 21   Perf. 13¾
Litho. & Engr.
2585 A1656 160c multi   3.50 3.50

Vienna University of Technology, 200th Anniv. — A1657

2015, Nov. 6   Litho.   Perf. 13¾x14
2586 A1657 68c multi   1.50 1.50

Rotes Haus Restaurant, Dornbirn — A1658

2015, Nov. 6   Litho.   Perf. 13¾
2587 A1658 150c multi   3.25 3.25

Nativity, by Master of Liefering
A1659

Stylized Christmas Tree — A1660

Reindeer
A1661

Madonna and Child, Gampern Triptych
A1662

2015   Litho.   Perf. 14x13¾
2588 A1659 68c multi   1.50 1.50
Perf. 13¾x13½
2589 A1660 80c multi   1.75 1.75
Coil Stamps
Self-Adhesive
Die Cut Perf. 14
2590 A1661 68c multi   1.50 1.50
Die Cut Perf. 13¼
2591 A1662 80c multi   1.75 1.75

Christmas. Issued: Nos. 2588, 2590, 11/27;
Nos. 2589, 2591, 11/13.

Austrian National Bank, 200th Anniv. A1663

Litho. & Embossed With Foil Application

2016, Jan. 18		Perf. 13¾
2592	A1663 100c multi	2.25 2.25

Austrian Automobile, Motorcycle and Touring Club, 120th Anniv. — A1664

2016, Jan. 20	Litho.	Perf. 14¼x14
2593	A1664 68c multi	1.50 1.50

Turmhutfrau, Digital Painting by Dorothee Golz — A1665

2016, Jan. 28	Litho.	Perf. 14
2594	A1665 68c multi	1.50 1.50

Future Factor, by Anna Liska and Andreas Wesle A1666

Litho. & Embossed

2016, Jan. 28		Perf. 14¼x13¾
2595	A1666 80c gray & white	1.75 1.75

Viennese Trumpet — A1667

Litho. & Embossed

2016, Jan. 28		Perf. 14
2596	A1667 160c multi	3.50 3.50

Advertising Art for Fritze Lacquer A1668

2016, Feb. 18	Litho.	Perf. 14
2597	A1668 100c multi	2.25 2.25

Josef Ressel (1793-1857), Inventor of Ship Propeller A1669

2016, Feb. 19	Litho.	Perf. 14
2598	A1669 80c multi	1.75 1.75

Crown of the Archduke of Austria, 400th Anniv. — A1670

2016, Mar. 4	Litho.	Perf. 14x13¼
2599	A1670 150c multi	3.50 3.50

This stamp, released Mar. 5, 2016, was a gift for standing order customers. It was not made available for sale.

Dog and Marie von Ebner-Eschenbach (1830-1916), Writer — A1671

Litho. & Engr.

2016, Mar. 5		Perf. 13¾
2600	A1671 160c multi	3.75 3.75

Kunsthistorisches Museum, Vienna, 125th Anniv. — A1672

2016, Mar. 8	Litho.	Perf. 13¾
2601	A1672 100c multi	2.25 2.25

Untitled Art by Esther Stocker — A1673

2016, Mar. 16	Litho.	Perf. 14
2602	A1673 80c black	1.90 1.90

Untitled Art from Fundraising Series, by Martha Jungwirth — A1674

2016, Mar. 6	Litho.	Perf. 14
2603	A1674 100c multi	2.25 2.25

Cross From Melk Abbey A1675

Litho. & Engr.

2016, Mar. 17		Perf. 13¾
2604	A1675 170c multi	4.00 4.00

1923 Puch 125 LM Motorcycle — A1676

2016, Mar. 23	Litho.	Perf. 14¼x14
2605	A1676 220c multi	5.00 5.00

Postal Agreement of 1516, 500th Anniv. A1677

2016, Apr. 2	Litho.	Perf. 13¾
2606	A1677 68c multi	1.60 1.60

Souvenir Sheet

Stamps of 1850 — A1678

No. 2607: a, Lombardy-Venetia #4b. b, Austria #2.

2016, Apr. 2	Litho.	Perf. 13
2607	A1678 Sheet of 2	6.75 6.75
a.	68c multi	1.60 1.60
b.	220c multi	5.00 5.00

Michael Haneke, Movie Director A1679

2016, Apr. 4	Litho.	Perf. 13½
2608	A1679 68c multi	1.60 1.60

Untitled Painting by Erwin Bohatsch A1680

2016, Apr. 4	Litho.	Perf. 13¾
2609	A1680 80c multi	1.90 1.90

Prater Park, Vienna, 250th Anniv. — A1681

2016, Apr. 9	Litho.	Perf. 14
2610	A1681 80c multi	1.90 1.90

Traditional Clothing of Montafon A1682

2016, Apr. 30	Litho.	Perf. 14
2611	A1682 68c multi	1.60 1.60

Return of Salzburg to Austria, 200th Anniv. A1683

2016, Apr. 30   Engr.   Perf. 13¾
2612 A1683 100c multi   2.40 2.40

Mariazell Basilica A1684

2016, May 12   Litho.   Perf. 14
2613 A1684 80c multi   1.90 1.90

Europa — A1685

2016, May 14   Litho.   Perf. 14
2614 A1685 80c multi   1.90 1.90
Think Green Issue.

Postcrossing A1686

2016, May 21   Litho.   Perf. 13¾
2615 A1686 80c multi   1.90 1.90

Traditional Clothing of Schärding A1687

2016, May 29   Litho.   Perf. 14
2616 A1687 68c multi   1.60 1.60

International Day of United Nations Peacekeepers A1688

2016, May 29   Litho.   Perf. 14
2617 A1688 68c multi   1.60 1.60

Schärding, 700th Anniv. — A1689

2016, June 4   Litho.   Perf. 14
2618 A1689 80c multi   1.90 1.90

2016 European Soccer Championships, France — A1690

2016, June 10   Litho.   Perf. 14
2619 A1690 80c multi   1.90 1.90

Pieta — A1691

Screen Printed on Back of Piece of Glass
2016, June 10   Imperf.
Self-Adhesive
2620 A1691 630c multi   14.00 14.00

Concrete Boat, Sculpture by Michael Schuster — A1692

2016, June 15   Litho.   Perf. 14
2621 A1692 68c multi   1.50 1.50

Madonna and Child Stained-Glass Window From Parish Church, Steyr — A1693

Litho. & Engr.
2016, June 17   Perf. 13¾
2622 A1693 100c multi   2.25 2.25

Revival to New Life, by Ferdinand Georg Waldmüller (1793-1865) — A1694

Litho. & Engr.
2016, July 13   Perf. 13¾
2623 A1694 160c multi   3.75 3.75

Post Office Savings Bank, Vienna, Designed by Otto Wagner (1841-1918) A1695

2016, July 13   Litho.   Perf. 13¾x14¼
2624 A1695 170c multi   3.75 3.75

Mittelburgenland Wine Region — A1696

2016, July 16   Litho.   Perf. 14
2625 A1696 80c multi   1.90 1.90

Souvenir Sheet

Postman on Tricycle — A1697

2016, Aug. 25   Litho.   Perf. 13¼x14
2626 A1697 100c multi   2.25 2.25

Denzel WD Super 1300 A1698

Perf. 13½x13¾
2016, Aug. 26   Litho.
2627 A1698 100c multi   2.25 2.25

Emperor Franz Joseph I (1830-1916) A1699

2016, Aug. 27   Litho.   Perf. 13¾
2628 A1699 80c multi   1.90 1.90

Liebespaar, by Koloman Moser (1868-1918) A1700

2016, Sept. 7   Litho.   Perf. 14
2629 A1700 68c multi   1.60 1.60

Lentia Chair, by March Gut — A1701

2016, Sept. 16   Litho.   Perf. 13½
2630 A1701 68c multi   1.60 1.60

Flower and "Thank You" A1702

2016, Sept. 22   Litho.   Perf. 14x13¼
2631 A1702 (68c) multi   1.60 1.60

Dirndl — A1703

Embroidered
2016, Sept. 22   Imperf.
Self-Adhesive
2632 A1703 630c multi   14.00 14.00

Maria Locherboden Church, Mötz — A1704

2016, Sept. 23   Litho.   Perf. 14x13¼
2633 A1704 68c multi   1.60 1.60

Railways Type of 2002

Design: Gleichenberger Railway train.

Perf. 13¾x13½
2016, Oct. 7   Litho. & Engr.
2634 A1109 170c multicolored   3.75 3.75

1945 Rescue of Art Treasures from Salt Mines — A1705

2016, Oct. 12   Litho.   Perf. 14x14¼
2635 A1705 170c multi   3.75 3.75

Souvenir Sheet

Stamps of 1858 — A1706

No. 2636: a, Lombardy-Venetia #8. b, Austria #9.

2016, Oct. 12   Litho.   Perf. 13¼x13
2636 A1706   Sheet of 2   6.50 6.50
a.   68c multi   1.50 1.50
b.   220c multi   5.00 5.00

Institute for High Energy Physics, 50th Anniv. — A1707

2016, Oct. 19   Litho.   Perf. 14
2637 A1707 80c multi   1.75 1.75

T-Center, Vienna A1708

2016, Oct. 19   Litho.   Perf. 13¼x13¾
2638 A1708 80c multi   1.75 1.75

Meles Meles A1709

Litho. & Engr.
2016, Oct. 22   Perf. 14x14¼
2639 A1709 160c multi   3.75 3.75

Gasthof Post Hotel, Lech am Arlberg A1710

2016, Nov. 7   Litho.   Perf. 13¼x13¾
2640 A1710 68c multi   1.50 1.50

Silent Night, Hymn by Joseph Mohr and Franz Gruber, 200th Anniv. A1711

Symbols of Christmas A1712

Adoration of the Magi, Painting by Unknown Artist, Mariapfarr Church A1713

Nativity, by Master of Raigern A1714

Christmas — A1715

No. 2645: a, Girl behind chair, denomination at LR. b, Boy behind chair, denomination at LL. c, Angel. d, Santa Claus.

2016   Litho.   Perf. 13½
2641 A1711 68c multi   1.50 1.50
2642 A1712 80c red   1.75 1.75
Coil Stamps
Self-Adhesive
Die Cut Perf. 13¼
2643 A1713 68c multi   1.50 1.50
Die Cut Perf. 14
2644 A1714 80c multi   1.75 1.75
Miniature Sheet
Serpentine Die Cut 14
2645 A1715   Sheet of 4   6.50
a.-b.   68c Either single   1.50 1.50
c.-d.   80c Either single   1.75 1.75

Issued: Nos. 2641, 2643, 11/25; Nos. 2642, 2644, 2645, 11/11.

Helicopter Police Force, 60th Anniv. A1716

2016, Nov. 16   Litho.   Perf. 13¾
2646 A1716 170c multi   3.75 3.75

Details From State Coats of Arms — A1717

Designs: 25c, Salzburg (lion's feet). No. 2648, Lower Austria (Niederösterreich, eagle's head). No. 2649, Burgenland (eagle's head and tongue). No. 2650, Tyrol (Tirol, crowned eagle). No. 2651, Styria (Steiermark, panther's head). No. 2652, Lower Austria (eagle). No. 2653, Carinthia (Kärnten, lion). No. 2654, Salzburg (lion's head). No. 2655, Upper Austria (Oberösterreich, eagle's head). 170c, Burgenland (eagle feathers). 175c, Tyrol (eagle tail and claws). 210c, Styria (panther's claws). No. 2659, Vorarlberg (rings and banner). No. 2660, Vienna (Wien, cross). 400c, Vorarlberg (banner fringes).

Die Cut Perf. 13½
2017, Jan. 1   Litho.
            Coil Stamps
2647 A1717 25c multi   .55   .55
2648 A1717 68c multi   1.40 1.40
            Booklet Stamps
2649 A1717 68c multi   1.40 1.40
a.   Booklet pane of 4   5.75
2650 A1717 68c multi   1.40 1.40
a.   Booklet pane of 10   14.00
2651 A1717 68c multi   1.40 1.40
a.   Booklet pane of 25   35.00
2652 A1717 80c multi   1.75 1.75
a.   Booklet pane of 4   7.00
2653 A1717 80c multi   1.75 1.75
a.   Booklet pane of 50   87.50
2654 A1717 125c multi   2.60 2.60
a.   Booklet pane of 4   10.50
2655 A1717 125c multi   2.60 2.60
a.   Booklet pane of 50   130.00
2656 A1717 170c multi   3.50 3.50
a.   Booklet pane of 4   14.00
2657 A1717 175c multi   3.75 3.75
a.   Booklet pane of 4   15.00
2658 A1717 210c multi   4.50 4.50
a.   Booklet pane of 4   18.00
2659 A1717 250c multi   5.25 5.25
a.   Booklet pane of 4   21.00
2660 A1717 250c multi   5.25 5.25
a.   Booklet pane of 25   135.00
2661 A1717 400c multi   8.25 8.25
a.   Booklet pane of 4   33.00
Nos. 2649-2661 (13)   43.40 43.40

Villach Carnival, 150th Anniv. — A1718

2017, Jan. 7   Litho.   Perf. 14x14¼
2662 A1718 80c multi   1.75 1.75

Staples Repairing Tear A1719

2017, Jan. 18   Litho.   Perf. 14¼x14
2663 A1719 68c multi   1.50 1.50

Protestant Reformation, 500th Anniv. — A1720

2017, Jan. 24   Litho.   Perf. 14
2664 A1720 68c multi   1.50 1.50

Photograph of Hochtannberg, by Margherita Spiluttini — A1721

2017, Feb. 8   Litho.   Perf. 14x13½
2665 A1721 80c black   1.75 1.75

Falco (1957-98), Rock Musician A1722

2017, Feb. 19   Litho.   Perf. 13¼x14
2666 A1722 80c multi   1.75 1.75

Peter Mitterhofer (1822-93), and His Vienna Typewriter A1723

2017, Feb. 22   Litho.   Perf. 14
2667 A1723 80c multi   1.75 1.75

Harp and G Clef — A1724

Photo. & Engr.
2017, Feb. 22   Perf. 13¾
2668 A1724 210c multi   4.50 4.50

Untitled (Autumn), by Tobias Pils — A1725

2017, Mar. 3 Litho. *Perf. 13¼x14*
2669 A1725 68c multi   1.50 1.50

Miniature Sheet

Birthday Party — A1726

No. 2670: a, Boy and dog. b, Boy, girl, cake with candles. c, Girl holding gift. d, Boy and piece of cake.

Serpentine Die Cut 14
2017, Mar. 4   Litho.
Self-Adhesive
2670 A1726 Sheet of 4   6.00
a.-d. 68c Any single   1.50 1.50

This stamp, released Mar. 4, 2017, was a gift for standing order customers. It was not made available for sale.

Vienna Wine Region — A1727

2017, Mar. 15 Litho. *Perf. 14*
2671 A1727 68c multi   1.50 1.50

Crafts and Trade Code for Goldsmiths and Silversmiths, 650th Anniv. A1728

Litho. With Foil Application
2017, Apr. 12 *Perf. 13¼x14*
2672 A1728 175c multi   4.00 4.00

Souvenir Sheet

Stamps of 1860-62 — A1729

No. 2673: a, Lombardy-Venetia #14. b, Austria #16.

2017, Apr. 12 Litho. *Perf. 13*
2673 A1729 Sheet of 2   6.25 6.25
a. 68c multi   1.50 1.50
b. 220c multi   4.75 4.75

Traditional Clothing of Pöttsching A1730

2017, Apr. 19 Litho. *Perf. 14*
2674 A1730 68c multi   1.50 1.50

Emblem of Schlierbach Cheese A1731

2017, Apr. 28 Litho. *Perf. 13¾*
2675 A1731 68c multi   1.50 1.50

Schönbrunn Palace, Vienna — A1732

2017, May 9 Litho. *Perf. 14¼x13¾*
2676 A1732 68c multi   1.50 1.50

Europa.

Souvenir Sheet

Holy Roman Empress Maria Theresa (1717-80) — A1733

Litho. With Foil Application
2017, May 13 *Perf. 14x13¼*
2677 A1733 170c multi   4.00 4.00
See Croatia No. 1038, Hungary No. 4433, Slovenia No. 1219, Ukraine No.

Lions Clubs International, Cent. — A1734

2017, May 19 Litho. *Perf. 13¾x14¼*
2678 A1734 80c multi   1.90 1.90

Puch Vehicles A1735

Designs: 68c, 1919-20 Alpenwagen XII. 220c, 1961 150 SR motor scooter.

2017 Litho. *Perf. 13½x13¾*
2679 A1735 68c multi   1.60 1.60
2680 A1735 220c multi   5.00 5.00
Issued: 68c, 5/20; 220c, 5/19.

Vienna Philharmonic Orchestra, 175th Anniv. — A1736

2017, May 25 Litho. *Perf. 14*
2681 A1736 80c multi   1.90 1.90

Railways Type of 2002
2017, May 28 Litho. *Perf. 13¾x13½*
2682 A1109 125c Stainzerbahn train   2.75 2.75

White Act, by Herbert Boeckl (1894-1966) — A1737

2017, June 7 Litho. *Perf. 13½x13¾*
2683 A1737 68c multi   1.60 1.60

Untitled Painting by Walter Vopava A1738

2017, July 1 Litho. *Perf. 13¼x14*
2684 A1738 125c multi   3.00 3.00

Christoph Waltz, Actor — A1739

2017, July 12 Litho. *Perf. 13½*
2685 A1739 80c multi   1.90 1.90

St. Thomas Touching Christ, by Thomas von Villach, St. Andrew Parish Church, Thörl-Maglern A1740

Photo. & Engr.
2017, July 14 *Perf. 13¾*
2686 A1740 170c sliver & multi   4.00 4.00

Railways Type of 2002
2017, July 15 Litho. *Perf. 13½x13¾*
2687 A1109 175c Brennerbahn train   4.25 4.25

Oak Tree — A1741

Silk-Screened on Wood Veneer
2017, July 28 *Laser Cut*
Self-Adhesive
2688 A1741 690c multi   16.50 16.50

Souvenir Sheet

19th Century Horse-drawn Post Wagon — A1742

2017, Aug. 24   Litho.   Perf. 13¼x14
2689 A1742 210c multi   5.00 5.00

Souvenir Sheet

1867 Stamps of the Austro-Hungarian Empire — A1743

No. 2690: a, 68c, Austria #29. b, 220c, Austria #33.

2017, Aug. 25   Litho.   Perf. 13¼x13
2690 A1743 Sheet of 2   7.00 7.00
  a.   68c multi   1.75 1.75
  b.   220c multi   5.25 5.25

See Hungary No. 4441.

Maria Kirchental, St. Martin bei Lofer — A1744

Perf. 13¾x13¼
2017, Sept. 10   Litho.
2691 A1744 80c multi   1.90 1.90

New Austria Post Headquarters, Vienna — A1745

Perf. 13¼x13¾
2017, Sept. 21   Litho.
2692 A1745 80c multi   1.90 1.90

SEMI-POSTAL STAMPS

Issues of the Monarchy

Emperor Franz Josef — SP1

Perf. 12½
1914, Oct. 4   Typo.   Unwmk.
B1 SP1 5h green   .40   .80
B2 SP1 10h rose   .80 1.60
  Set, never hinged   2.75

Nos. B1-B2 were sold at an advance of 2h each over face value. Exist imperf.; value, set $120.

The Firing Step — SP2

Designs: 5h+2h, Cavalry. 10h+2h, Siege gun. 20h+3h, Battleship. 35h+3h, Airplane.

1915, May 1
B3 SP2 3h + 1h violet brn   1.20   .40
B4 SP2 5h + 2h green   .25   .25
B5 SP2 10h + 2h deep rose   .25   .25
B6 SP2 20h + 3h Prus blue   4.00 2.40
B7 SP2 35h + 3h ultra   6.50 5.50
  Nos. B3-B7 (5)   12.20 8.80
  Set, never hinged   35.00

Exist imperf. Value, set $325 hinged and $525 never hinged.

Issues of the Republic

Types of Austria, 1919-20, Overprinted in Black

1920, Sept. 16   Perf. 12½
B11 A44 5h gray, *yellow*   .55 1.60
B12 A44 10h red, *pink*   .55 1.25
B13 A43 15h bister, *yel*   .25   .80
B14 A45 20h dark grn, *bl*   .25   .65
B15 A43 25h violet, *pink*   .25   .75
B16 A45 30h brown, *buff*   1.40 2.90
B17 A45 40h carmine, *yel*   .25   .80
B18 A45 50h dark bl, *blue*   .25   .65
B19 A43 60h ol grn, *azure* 1.40 2.75
B20 A47 80h red   .35   .75
B21 A47 1k orange brown   .35   .80
B22 A47 2k pale blue   .35   .80

Granite Paper
Imperf
B23 A46 2½k brown red   .40 1.00
B24 A46 3k dk blue & green   .50 1.25
B25 A46 4k carmine & violet   .65 1.50
B26 A46 5k blue   .50 1.25
B27 A46 7½k yellow green   .55 1.25
B28 A46 10k gray grn & red   .55 1.40
B29 A46 20k lilac & orange   .75 1.75
  Nos. B11-B29 (19)   10.15 23.90
  Set, never hinged   26.00

Carinthia Plebiscite. Sold at three times face value for the benefit of the Plebiscite Propaganda Fund.
Nos. B11-B19 exist imperf. Values, set unused hinged $290, never hinged $400.

Types of Regular Issues of 1919-21 Overprinted

1921, Mar. 1   Perf. 12½
B30 A44 5h gray, *yellow*   .25   .80
B31 A44 10h orange brown   .25   .80
B32 A43 15h gray   .25   .80
B33 A45 20h green, *yellow*   .25   .80
B34 A43 25h blue, *yellow*   .25   .80
B35 A45 30h violet, *bl*   .50 1.60
B36 A45 40h org brn, *pink*   .55 2.00
B37 A45 50h green, *blue*   1.25 3.25
B38 A43 50h lilac, *yellow*   .50 1.60
B39 A47 80h pale blue   .50 1.60
B40 A47 1k red org, *blue*   .40 1.60
B41 A47 1⅛k brown   .25   .80
B42 A47 2k lilac brown   .25   .80

Overprinted

B43 A46 2½k light blue   .25   .80
B44 A46 3k ol grn & brn red   .25   .80
B45 A46 4k lilac & orange   .80 2.75
B46 A46 5k olive green   .25 1.60
B47 A46 7½k brown red   .30 1.60
B48 A46 10k blue & olive grn .30 1.60
B49 A46 20k car rose & vio   .50 2.40
  Nos. B30-B49 (20)   8.10 28.80
  Set, never hinged   18.00

Nos. B30-B49 were sold at three times face value, the excess going to help flood victims. Exists imperf. Values, set unused hinged $300, never hinged $525.

Nos. B50-B76, B93-B98, B112-B117, B122-B127, B132-B137 and B146-B164 exist imperf, on handmade paper, printed in black or in colors other than those of the issued stamps. These are proofs.

Franz Joseph Haydn — SP9

Musicians: 5k, Mozart. 7½k, Beethoven. 10k, Schubert. 25k, Anton Bruckner. 50k, Johann Strauss (son). 100k, Hugo Wolf.

1922, Apr. 24   Engr.   Perf. 12½
B50 SP9 2½k brn, perf.
    11½   7.25 7.25
  a.   Perf. 12½   11.00 12.00
    Never hinged   30.00
B51 SP9 5k dark blue   1.25 1.25
B52 SP9 7½k black   2.00 2.00
  a.   Perf. 11½   110.00 110.00
    Never hinged   240.00
B53 SP9 10k dark violet   2.75 2.40
  a.   Perf. 11½   3.25 3.25
    Never hinged   16.00
B54 SP9 25k dark green   4.75 4.75
  a.   Perf. 11½   4.75 4.75
    Never hinged   16.00
B55 SP9 50k claret   2.40 2.40
B56 SP9 100k brown olive   8.00 8.00
  a.   Perf. 11½   10.50 10.50
    Never hinged   47.50
  Nos. B50-B56 (7)   28.40 28.05
  Set, never hinged   72.50

These stamps were sold at 10 times face value, the excess being given to needy musicians.
Used values are for examples with philatelic favor cancels. Postally used stamps are worth 50%-100% more.
All values exist imperf. Values, set unused hinged $900, never hinged $1,750.
A 1969 souvenir sheet without postal validity contains reprints of the 5k in black, 7½k in claret and 50k in dark blue, each overprinted "NEUDRUCK" in black at top. It was issued for the Vienna State Opera Centenary Exhibition.

View of Bregenz — SP16

Designs: 120k, Mirabelle Gardens, Salzburg. 160k, Church at Eisenstadt. 180k, Assembly House, Klagenfurt. 200k, "Golden Roof," Innsbruck. 240k, Main Square, Linz. 400k, Castle Hill, Graz. 600k, Abbey at Melk. 1000k, Upper Belvedere, Vienna.

Various Frames

1923, May 22   Perf. 12½
B57 SP16 100k dk green   4.00 4.00
B58 SP16 120k deep blue   4.00 4.00
B59 SP16 160k dk violet   4.00 4.00
B60 SP16 180k red violet   4.00 4.00
B61 SP16 200k lake   4.00 4.00
B62 SP16 240k red brown   4.00 4.00
B63 SP16 400k dark brown   4.00 4.00

B64 SP16 600k olive brn   4.00 4.00
B65 SP16 1000k black   4.00 4.00
  Nos. B57-B65 (9)   36.00 36.00
  Set, never hinged   100.00

Nos. B57-B65 were sold at five times face value, the excess going to needy artists.
Used values are for examples with philatelic favor cancels. Values for postally used: Nos. B57-B64, each $8; No. B65 $14.
All values exist imperf. on both regular and handmade papers. Values, set hinged $700, never hinged $1,000.

Feebleness — SP25

Designs: 300k+900k, Aid to industry. 500k+1500k, Orphans and widow. 600k+1800k, Indigent old man. 1000k+3000k, Alleviation of hunger.

1924, Sept. 6   Photo.
B66 SP25 100k + 300k yel
    grn   4.00 4.00
B67 SP25 300k + 900k red
    brn   4.00 4.00
B68 SP25 500k + 1500k brn
    vio   4.00 4.00
B69 SP25 600k + 1800k pck
    bl   8.00 6.50
B70 SP25 1000k + 3000k brn
    org   9.50 8.00
  Nos. B66-B70 (5)   29.50 26.50
  Set, never hinged   67.50

The surtax was for child welfare and antituberculosis work.
Used values are for examples with philatelic favor cancels. Values for postally used are 2-2.5 times values shown.
Set exists imperf. Values, set unused hinged $350, never hinged $525.

Siegfried Slays the Dragon — SP30

Designs: 8g+2g, Gunther's voyage to Iceland. 15g+5g, Brunhild accusing Kriemhild. 20g+5g, Nymphs telling Hagen the future. 24g+6g, Rudiger von Bechelaren welcomes the Nibelungen. 40g+10g, Dietrich von Bern vanquishes Hagen.

1926, Mar. 8   Engr.
B71 SP30 3g + 2g olive blk   .95   .80
B72 SP30 8g + 2g indigo   .40   .40
B73 SP30 15g + 5g dk claret   .35   .35
B74 SP30 20g + 5g olive grn   .50   .50
B75 SP30 24g + 6g dk violet   .50   .50
B76 SP30 40g + 10g red brn   2.40 2.40
  Nos. B71-B76 (6)   5.10 4.95
  Set, never hinged   15.00

Nibelungen issue. The surtax was for child welfare.
Nos. B71-B76 were printed in two sizes: 27 ½x28 ½mm and 28 ½x27 ½mm.
Used values are for examples with philatelic favor cancels. Values for postally used are 1.5 times values shown.
Nos. B71-B76 exist imperf. Values, set unused hinged $350, never hinged $500.

Pres. Michael Hainisch — SP36

1928, Nov. 5
B77 SP36 10g dark brown   5.50 4.75
B78 SP36 15g red brown   5.50 4.75
B79 SP36 30g black   5.50 4.75
B80 SP36 40g indigo   5.50 4.75
  Nos. B77-B80 (4)   22.00 19.00
  Set, never hinged   37.50

Tenth anniversary of Austrian Republic. Sold at double face value, the premium aiding war orphans and children of war invalids.

Used values are for examples with philatelic favor cancels. Values for postally used are 2.5 times values shown.

Set exists imperf, without gum. Value, set $625.

Pres. Wilhelm
Miklas — SP37

1930, Oct. 4

B81	SP37	10g light brown	7.25	7.25
B82	SP37	20g red	7.25	7.25
B83	SP37	30g brown violet	7.25	7.25
B84	SP37	40g indigo	7.25	7.25
B85	SP37	50g dark green	7.25	7.25
B86	SP37	1s black brown	7.25	7.25
	Nos. B81-B86 (6)		43.50	43.50
	Set, never hinged		125.00	

Nos. B81-B86 were sold at double face value. The excess aided the anti-tuberculosis campaign and the building of sanatoria in Carinthia.

Used values are for examples with philatelic favor cancels. Values for postally used are 3 times values shown.

Set exists imperf, without gum. Value, set $950.

Regular Issue of
1929-30
Overprinted in
Various Colors

1931, June 20

B87	A56	10g bister (Bl)	27.50	27.50
B88	A56	20g dk gray (R)	27.50	27.50
B89	A56	30g dk violet (Gl)	27.50	27.50
B90	A56	40g dk blue (Gl)	27.50	27.50
B91	A56	50g gray vio (O)	27.50	27.50
B92	A57	1s black brn (Bk)	27.50	27.50
	Nos. B87-B92 (6)		165.00	165.00
	Set, never hinged		550.00	

Rotary convention, Vienna.

Nos. B87 to B92 were sold at double their face value. The excess was added to the beneficent funds of Rotary International.

Used values are for examples with philatelic favor cancels. Values for postally used are 2 times values shown.

Ferdinand
Raimund — SP38

Poets: 20g, Franz Grillparzer. 30g, Johann Nestroy. 40g, Adalbert Stifter. 50g, Ludwig Anzengruber. 1s, Peter Rosegger.

1931, Sept. 12

B93	SP38	10g dark violet	13.50	11.00
B94	SP38	20g gray black	13.50	11.00
B95	SP38	30g orange red	13.50	11.00
B96	SP38	40g dull blue	13.50	11.00
B97	SP38	50g gray green	13.50	11.00
B98	SP38	1s yellow brown	13.50	11.00
	Nos. B93-B98 (6)		81.00	66.00
	Set, never hinged		160.00	

Nos. B93-B98 were sold at double face value. The surtax aided unemployed young people.

Used values are for examples with philatelic favor cancels. Values for postally used are 3 times values shown.

Set exists imperf, without gum. Value, set $950.

Chancellor Ignaz
Seipel — SP44

1932, Oct. 12   Perf. 13

B99	SP44	50g ultra	12.00	9.50
	Never hinged		27.50	

Msgr. Ignaz Seipel, Chancellor of Austria, 1922-29. Sold at double face value, the excess aiding wounded veterans of World War I.

Used value is for a cancelled-to-order example. Value for postally used $27.50.

Exists imperf, without gum. Value $800.

Ferdinand Georg
Waldmüller
SP45

Artists: 24g, Moritz von Schwind. 30g, Rudolf von Alt. 40g, Hans Makart. 64g, Gustav Klimt. 1s, Albin Egger-Lienz.

1932, Nov. 21

B100	SP45	12g slate green	20.00	16.00
B101	SP45	24g dp violet	20.00	16.00
B102	SP45	30g dark red	20.00	16.00
B103	SP45	40g dark gray	20.00	16.00
B104	SP45	64g dark brown	20.00	16.00
B105	SP45	1s claret	20.00	16.00
	Nos. B100-B105 (6)		120.00	96.00
	Set, never hinged		525.00	

Nos. B100 to B105 were sold at double their face values. The surtax was for the assistance of charitable institutions.

Used values are for examples with philatelic favor cancels. Values for postally used, each $60.

Set exists imperf, without gum. Value, set $1,200.

Mountain
Climbing
SP51

Designs: 24g, Ski gliding. 30g, Walking on skis. 50g, Ski jumping.

1933, Jan. 9   Photo.   Perf. 12½

B106	SP51	12g dark green	6.50	6.50
B107	SP51	24g dark violet	95.00	75.00
B108	SP51	30g brown red	12.00	12.00
B109	SP51	50g dark blue	95.00	75.00
	Nos. B106-B109 (4)		208.50	168.50
	Set, never hinged		525.00	

Meeting of the Intl. Ski Federation, Innsbruck, Feb. 8-13.

These stamps were sold at double their face value. The surtax was for the benefit of "Youth in Distress."

Used values are for examples with philatelic favor cancels. Values for postally used, 25%-80% higher.

Set exists imperf, without gum. Value, set $4,000.

Stagecoach, after Painting by Moritz
von Schwind — SP55

1933, June 23   Engr.   Perf. 12½
Ordinary Paper

B110	SP55	50g dp ultra	150.00	150.00
	Never hinged		260.00	
a.	Granite paper		325.00	325.00
	Never hinged		600.00	

Sheets of 25.

Used values are for examples with philatelic favor cancels. Values for postally used, 50% higher.

Nos. B110 and B110a exist imperf. Value, No. B110 unused hinged, $2,400.

Souvenir Sheet
Perf. 12
Granite Paper

B111	Sheet of 4		2,500.	2,400.
	Never hinged		3,050.	
a.	SP55 50g deep ultra		475.00	475.00
	Never hinged		650.00	

Intl. Phil. Exhib., Vienna, 1933. In addition to the postal value of 50g the stamp was sold at a premium of 50g for charity and of 1.60s for the admission fee to the exhibition.

Size of No. B111: 126x103mm.

Used values are for examples with philatelic favor cancels. Values for postally used, 35% higher.

A 50g dark red in souvenir sheet, with dark blue overprint ("NEUDRUCK WIPA 1965"), had no postal validity.

Sheet margins of No. B111 are uniformly gummed. When sold at the WIPA exhibition, each example of No. B111 was affixed to a heavy dark bluish gray folder with 3 dabs of water soluable glue. When removed these glue spots appear similar to hinge marks. Some consider No. B111 to be never hinged if no additional hinge marks appear beyond the three dissolved glue spots.

No. B111 exists imperf.

St. Stephen's   Marco d'Aviano,
Cathedral in   Papal
1683 — SP56   Legate — SP57

Designs: 30g, Count Ernst Rudiger von Starhemberg. 40g, John III Sobieski, King of Poland. 50g, Karl V, Duke of Lorraine. 64g, Burgomaster Johann Andreas von Liebenberg.

1933, Sept. 6   Photo.   Perf. 12½

B112	SP56	12g dark green	24.00	20.00
B113	SP57	24g dark violet	20.00	16.00
B114	SP57	30g brown red	20.00	16.00
B115	SP57	40g blue black	32.50	20.00
B116	SP57	50g dark blue	20.00	16.00
B117	SP57	64g olive brown	27.50	16.00
	Nos. B112-B117 (6)		144.00	104.00
	Set, never hinged		350.00	

Deliverance of Vienna from the Turks, 250th anniv., and Pan-German Catholic Congress, Sept. 6, 1933.

The stamps were sold at double their face value, the excess being for the aid of Catholic works of charity.

Used values are for examples with philatelic favor cancels. Values for postally used, 2-3 times values shown.

Types of Regular Issue of 1925-30
Surcharged

a   b

c

1933, Dec. 15

B118	A52(a)	5g + 2g ol grn	.25	.25
B119	A56(b)	12g + 3g lt blue	.25	.25
B120	A56(b)	24g + 6g brn org	.25	.25
B121	A57(c)	1s + 50g org red	35.00	32.50
	Nos. B118-B121 (4)		35.75	33.25
	Set, never hinged		75.00	

Winterhelp.

Used values are for examples with philatelic favor cancels. Values for postally used, 2-3 times values shown.

Anton
Pilgram — SP62

Architects: 24g, J. B. Fischer von Erlach. 30g, Jakob Prandtauer. 40g, A. von Siccardsburg & E. van der Null. 60g, Heinrich von Ferstel. 64g, Otto Wagner.

1934, Dec. 2   Engr.   Perf. 12½
Thick Yellowish Paper

B122	SP62	12g black	9.50	8.00
B123	SP62	24g dull violet	9.50	8.00
B124	SP62	30g carmine	9.50	8.00
B125	SP62	40g brown	9.50	8.00
B126	SP62	60g blue	9.50	8.00
B127	SP62	64g dull green	9.50	8.00
	Nos. B122-B127 (6)		57.00	48.00
	Set, never hinged		120.00	

Used values are for examples with philatelic favor cancels. Values for postally used, each $20.

Exist imperf. Values, set unused hinged $650, never hinged $850.

Nos. B124-B127 exist in horiz. pairs imperf. between. Value, each $250-$325.

These stamps were sold at double their face value. The surtax on this and the following issues was devoted to general charity.

Types of Regular Issue of 1934
Surcharged in Black

c   d

1935, Nov. 11   Perf. 12, 12½

B128	A67(d)	5g + 2g emerald	.50	.80
B129	A67(d)	12g + 3g blue	.95	.95
B130	A67(d)	24g + 6g lt brown	.50	.80
B131	A68(c)	1s + 50g ver	32.50	32.50
	Nos. B128-B131 (4)		34.45	35.05
	Set, never hinged		80.00	

Winterhelp. Set exists imperf. Values, set unused hinged $175, never hinged $260.

Set without surcharge unused hinged $250, never hinged $325.

Prince Eugene of
Savoy — SP68

Military Leaders: 24g, Field Marshal Laudon. 30g, Archduke Karl. 40g, Field Marshal Josef Radetzky. 60g, Admiral Wilhelm Tegetthoff. 64g, Field Marshal Franz Conrad Hotzendorff.

1935, Dec. 1   Perf. 12½

B132	SP68	12g brown	10.50	9.50
B133	SP68	24g dark green	10.50	9.50
B134	SP68	30g claret	10.50	9.50
B135	SP68	40g slate	10.50	9.50
B136	SP68	60g deep ultra	10.50	9.50
B137	SP68	64g dark violet	10.50	9.50
	Nos. B132-B137 (6)		63.00	57.00
	Set, never hinged		125.00	

These stamps were sold at double their face value.

Used values are for examples with philatelic favor cancels. Values for postally used, each $20.

Set exists imperf. Values, set unused hinged $650, never hinged $850.

Slalom Turn — SP74

Designs: 24g, Jumper taking off. 35g, Slalom turn. 60g, Innsbruck view.

1936, Feb. 20   **Photo.**
B138	SP74	12g Prus green	1.60	1.60
B139	SP74	24g dp violet	2.40	2.40
B140	SP74	35g rose car	24.00	24.00
B141	SP74	60g sapphire	24.00	24.00
		Nos. B138-B141 (4)	52.00	52.00
		Set, never hinged	130.00	

Ski concourse issue. These stamps were sold at twice face value.

Used values are for examples with philatelic favor cancels. Value for postally used set, $110.

Set exists imperf. Values, set unused hinged $600, never hinged $750.

St. Martin of Tours — SP78

Designs: 12g+3g, Medical clinic. 24g+6g, St. Elizabeth of Hungary. 1s+1s, "Flame of Charity."

1936, Nov. 2   **Unwmk.**
B142	SP78	5g + 2g dp green	.25	.25
B143	SP78	12g + 3g dp violet	.25	.25
B144	SP78	24g + 6g dp blue	.35	.35
B145	SP78	1s + 1s dk car	7.50	7.50
		Nos. B142-B145 (4)	8.35	8.35
		Set, never hinged	14.00	

Winterhelp.

Used values are for examples with philatelic favor cancels. Values for postally used: Nos. B142-B144, each 80¢; No. B145, $19.

Set exists imperf. Values, set unused hinged $400, never hinged $500.

Josef Ressel — SP82

Inventors: 24g, Karl von Ghega. 30g, Josef Werndl. 40g, Carl Auer von Welsbach. 60g, Robert von Lieben. 64g, Viktor Kaplan.

1936, Dec. 6   **Engr.**
B146	SP82	12g dk brown	2.75	2.75
B147	SP82	24g dk violet	2.75	2.75
B148	SP82	30g dp claret	2.75	2.75
B149	SP82	40g gray violet	2.75	2.75
B150	SP82	60g vio blue	2.75	2.75
B151	SP82	64g dk slate green	2.75	2.75
		Nos. B146-B151 (6)	16.50	16.50
		Set, never hinged	47.50	

These stamps were sold at double their face value.

Used values are for examples with philatelic favor cancels. Values for postally used: each $6.75.

Exists imperf, without gum. Value, set unused hinged $800, never hinged $1,000.

Nurse and Infant — SP88

12g+3g, Mother and child. 24g+6g, Nursing the aged. 1s+1s, Sister of Mercy with patient.

1937, Oct. 18   **Photo.**
B152	SP88	5g + 2g dk green	.30	.25
B153	SP88	12g + 3g dk brown	.30	.25
B154	SP88	24g + 6g dk blue	.30	.25
B155	SP88	1s + 1s dk carmine	4.00	3.50
		Nos. B152-B155 (4)	4.90	4.25
		Set, never hinged	11.00	

Winterhelp.

Used values are for examples with philatelic favor cancels. Values for postally used: Nos. B152-B154, each 40c; No. B155, $13.50.

Set exists imperf. Values, set unused hinged $125, never hinged $160.

Gerhard van Swieten — SP92

Physicians: 8g, Leopold Auenbrugger von Auenbrugg. 12g, Karl von Rokitansky. 20g, Joseph Skoda. 24g, Ferdinand von Hebra. 30g, Ferdinand von Arlt. 40g, Joseph Hyrtl. 60g, Theodor Billroth. 64g, Theodor Meynert.

1937, Dec. 5   **Engr.**   **Perf. 12½**
B156	SP92	5g choc	2.40	2.00
B157	SP92	8g dk red	2.40	2.00
B158	SP92	12g brown blk	2.40	2.00
B159	SP92	20g dk green	2.40	2.00
B160	SP92	24g dk violet	2.40	2.00
B161	SP92	30g brown car	2.40	2.00
B162	SP92	40g dp olive grn	2.40	2.00
B163	SP92	60g indigo	2.40	2.00
B164	SP92	64g brown vio	2.40	2.00
		Nos. B156-B164 (9)	21.60	18.00
		Set, never hinged	52.50	

These stamps were sold at double their face value.

Used values are for examples with philatelic favor cancels. Values for postally used: each $5.25.

Set exists imperf, without gum. Value, set $2,250.

> **Catalogue values for unused stamps in this section, from this point to the end of the section, are for Never Hinged items.**

The Dawn of Peace — SP101

1945, Sept. 10   **Photo.**   **Perf. 14**
B165	SP101	1s + 10s dk green	1.25	.80

Used value is for examples with philatelic favor cancels. Postally used value $2.40.

No. 467 Surcharged in Black

1946, June 25
B166	A110	30g + 20g dk red	2.50	2.50

First anniversary of United Nations.

Used value is for examples with philatelic favor cancels. Postally used value $4.75.

Pres. Karl Renner SP102

1946   **Engr.**   **Perf. 13½x14**
B167	SP102	1s + 1s dk slate grn	4.75	.80
B168	SP102	2s + 2s dk blue vio	4.75	.80
B169	SP102	3s + 3s dk purple	4.75	.80
B170	SP102	5s + 5s dk vio brn	4.75	.80
		Nos. B167-B170 (4)	19.00	3.20

Used values are for examples with philatelic favor cancels. Postally used values, each $8. See Nos. B185-B188.

Nazi Sword Piercing Austria — SP103   Sweeping Away Fascist Symbols — SP104

Designs: 8g+6g, St. Stephen's Cathedral in Flames. 12g+12g, Pleading hand in concentration camp. 30g+30g, Hand choking Nazi serpent. 42g+42g, Hammer breaking Nazi pillar. 1s+1s, Oath of allegiance. 2s+2s, Austrian eagle and burning swastika.

Unwmk.

1946, Sept. 16   **Photo.**   **Perf. 14**
B171	SP103	5g + (3g) dk brown	.40	.40
B172	SP104	6g + (4g) dk slate grn	.25	.25
B173	SP104	8g + (6g) orange red	.25	.25
B174	SP104	12g + (12g) slate blk	.25	.25
B175	SP104	30g + (30g) violet	.25	.25
B176	SP104	42g + (42g) dull brn	.25	.25
B177	SP104	1s + 1s dk red	.40	.40
B178	SP104	2s + 2s dk car rose	.80	.80
		Nos. B171-B178 (8)	2.85	2.85

Anti-fascist propaganda.

Used values are for examples with philatelic favor cancels. Postally used values approx. 2-3 times values shown.

A 5g + 3g black olive brown stamp showing SS lightning bolt striking map of Austria and 12g + 12g black gray blue depicting skull with Hitler mask were prepared but not issued. Value, each $1,050.

Race Horse with Foal SP111

Various Race Horses.

1946, Oct. 20   **Engr.**   **Perf. 13½x14**
B179	SP111	16g + 16g rose brown	1.60	1.60
B180	SP111	24g + 24g dk purple	1.60	1.60
B181	SP111	60g + 60g dk green	1.60	1.60
B182	SP111	1s + 1s dk blue gray	1.60	1.60
B183	SP111	2s + 2s yel brown	5.75	4.00
		Nos. B179-B183 (5)	12.15	10.40

Austria Prize race, Vienna.

Used values are for examples with philatelic favor cancels. Postally used values 2-2.5 times values shown.

St. Ruprecht's Church, Vienna — SP116

1946, Oct. 30   **Perf. 14x13½**
B184	SP116	30g + 70g dark red	.40	.40

Founding of Austria, 950th anniv. The surtax aided the Stamp Day celebration.

Used value is for examples with philatelic favor cancels. Postally used value $2.

Renner Type of 1946
Souvenir Sheets

1946, Sept. 5   **Imperf.**
B185		Sheet of 8	500.00	450.00
	a.	SP102 1s+1s dk slate grn	62.50	32.50
B186		Sheet of 8	500.00	450.00
	a.	SP102 2s+2s dk blue vio	62.50	32.50
B187		Sheet of 8	500.00	450.00
	a.	SP102 3s+3s dark purple	62.50	32.50
B188		Sheet of 8	500.00	450.00
	a.	SP102 5s+5s dk vio brown	62.50	32.50

First anniv. of Austria's liberation. Sheets of 8 plus center label showing arms.

Values for used examples are for those with philatelic favor cancels. Postally used values: singles, each $275; sheets, each $3,250.

Statue of Rudolf IV the Founder — SP118

Designs: 5g+20g, Tomb of Frederick III. 6g+24g, Main pulpit. 8g+32g, Statue of St. Stephen. 10g+40g, Madonna of the Domestics statue. 12g+48g, High altar. 30g+1.20s, Organ, destroyed in 1945. 50g+1.80s, Anton Pilgram statue. 1s+5s, Cathedral from northeast. 2s+10s, Southwest corner of cathedral.

1946, Dec. 12   **Engr.**   **Perf. 14x13½**
B189	SP118	3g + 12g brown	.25	.25
B190	SP118	5g + 20g dk vio brown	.25	.25
B191	SP118	6g + 24g dk blue	.25	.25
B192	SP118	8g + 32g dk grn	.25	.25
B193	SP118	10g + 40g dp blue	.25	.25
B194	SP118	12g + 48g dk vio	.25	.25
B195	SP118	30g + 1.20s car	1.25	1.25
B196	SP118	50g + 1.80s dk bl	1.60	1.60
B197	SP118	1s + 5s brn vio	2.00	2.00
B198	SP118	2s + 10s vio brn	4.00	4.00
		Nos. B189-B198 (10)	10.35	10.35

The surtax aided reconstruction of St. Stephen's Cathedral, Vienna.

Values for used examples are for those with philatelic favor cancels. Postally used value, set $24.

Reaping Wheat — SP128

Designs: 8g+2g, Log raft. 10g+5g, Cement factory. 12g+8g, Coal mine. 18g+12g, Oil derricks. 30g+10g, Textile machinery. 35g+15g, Iron furnace. 60g+20g, Electric power lines.

1947, Mar. 23   **Perf. 14x13½**
B199	SP128	3g + 2g yel brown	.40	.30
B200	SP128	8g + 2g dk bl grn	.40	.30
B201	SP128	10g + 5g slate blk	.40	.30
B202	SP128	12g + 8g dark pur	.40	.30
B203	SP128	18g + 12g ol green	.40	.30
B204	SP128	30g + 10g deep cl	.40	.30
B205	SP128	35g + 15g crimson	.40	.30
B206	SP128	60g + 20g dk blue	.40	.30
		Nos. B199-B206 (8)	3.20	2.40

Vienna International Sample Fair, 1947.

Values for used examples are for those with philatelic favor cancels. Postally used value, set $8.

Race Horse and Jockey SP136

1947, June 29   *Perf. 13½x14*
B207 SP136 60g + 20g dp bl,
                                     .40 .40
                 pale pink

Value for used is for examples with philatelic favor cancels. Postally used value $1.25.

Cup of Corvinus SP137

Designs: 8g+2g, Statue of Providence, Vienna. 10g+5g, Abbey at Melk. 12g+8g, Picture of a Woman, by Kriehuber. 18g+12g, Children at the Window, by Waldmuller. 20g+10g, Entrance, Upper Belvedere Palace. 30g+10g, Nymph Egeria, Schönbrunn Castle. 35g+15g, National Library, Vienna. 48g+12g, "Workshop of a Printer of Engravings," by Schmutzer. 60g+20g, Girl with Straw Hat, by Amerling.

1947, June 20   *Perf. 14x13½*
B208 SP137   3g + 2g brown   .40 .30
B209 SP137   8g + 2g dk blue
                        grn   .40 .30
B210 SP137 10g + 5g dp claret   .40 .30
B211 SP137 12g + 8g dk purple   .40 .30
B212 SP137 18g + 12g golden
                        brn   .40 .30
B213 SP137 20g + 10g sepia   .40 .30
B214 SP137 30g + 10g dk yel
                        grn   .40 .30
B215 SP137 35g + 15g deep car   .40 .30
B216 SP137 48g + 12g dk brn
                        vio   .65 .50
B217 SP137 60g + 20g dp blue   .65 .50
           Nos. B208-B217 (10)   4.50 3.40

Values for used examples are for those with philatelic favor cancels. Postally used value, double values shown.

Prisoner of War — SP147

12g+8g, Prisoners' Mail, 18g+12g, Prison camp visitor. 35g+15g, Family reunion. 60g+20g, "Industry" beckoning. 1s+40g, Sower.

1947, Aug. 30
B218 SP147   8g + 2g dk green   .25 .25
B219 SP147 12g + 8g dk vio brn   .25 .25
B220 SP147 18g + 12g black brn   .25 .25
B221 SP147 35g + 15g rose brn   .25 .25
B222 SP147 60g + 20g dp blue   .25 .25
B223 SP147   1s + 40g redsh brn .25 .25
           Nos. B218-B223 (6)   1.50 1.50

Values for used examples are for those with philatelic favor cancels. Postally used value, set $5.50.

Olympic Flame and Emblem — SP153

1948, Jan. 16   **Engr.**
B224 SP153 1s + 50g dark blue   .55 .55
The surtax was used to help defray expenses of Austria's 1948 Olympics team.

Laabenbach Bridge Neulengbach SP154

Designs: 20g+10g, Dam, Vermunt Lake. 30g+10g, Danube Port, Vienna. 40g+20g, Mining, Erzberg. 45g+20g, Tracks, Southern Railway Station, Vienna. 60g+30g, Communal housing project, Vienna. 75g+35g, Gas Works, Vienna. 80g+40g, Oil refinery. 1s+50g, Gesäuse Highway, Styria. 1.40s+70g, Parliament Building, Vienna.

1948, Feb. 18   *Perf. 14x13½*
B225 SP154 10g + 5g slate blk   .25 .25
B226 SP154 20g + 10g lilac   .25 .25
B227 SP154 30g + 10g dull grn   .50 .50
B228 SP154 40g + 20g ol brn   .25 .25
B229 SP154 45g + 20g dk blue   .25 .25
B230 SP154 60g + 30g dk red   .25 .25
B231 SP154 75g + 35g dk vio
                        brn   .25 .25
B232 SP154 80g + 40g vio brn   .25 .25
B233 SP154   1s + 50g dp blue   .25 .25
B234 SP154 1.40s + 70g dp car   .50 .50
           Nos. B225-B234 (10)   3.00 3.00
The surtax was for the Reconstruction Fund.

Violet — SP155

Designs: 20g+10g, Anemone. 30g+10g, Crocus. 40g+20g, Yellow primrose. 45g+20g, Pasqueflower. 60g+30g, Rhododendron. 75g+35g, Dogrose. 80g+40g, Cyclamen. 1s+50g, Alpine Gentian. 1.40s+70g, Edelweiss.

1948, May 14   **Engr. & Typo.**
B235 SP155 10g + 5g multi   .35 .35
B236 SP155 20g + 10g multi   .25 .25
B237 SP155 30g + 10g multi   3.25 3.00
B238 SP155 40g + 20g multi   .65 .40
B239 SP155 45g + 20g multi   .25 .25
B240 SP155 60g + 30g multi   .25 .25
B241 SP155 75g + 35g multi   .25 .25
B242 SP155 80g + 40g multi   .25 .25
B243 SP155   1s + 50g multi   .35 .35
B244 SP155 1.40s + 70g multi   1.60 1.60
           Nos. B235-B244 (10)   7.45 6.95

Hans Makart — SP156

Designs: 20g+10g, Künstlerhaus, Vienna. 40g+20g, Carl Kundmann. 50g+25g, A. S. von Siccardsburg. 60g+30g, Hans Canon. 1s+50g, William Unger. 1.40s+70g, Friedrich von Schmidt.

1948, June 15   **Unwmk.**   **Engr.**
B245 SP156 20g + 10g dp
                        yel green   8.00 6.50
B246 SP156 30g + 15g dark
                        brown   2.50 2.50
B247 SP156 40g + 20g ind   4.00 *5.50*
B248 SP156 50g + 25g dk
                        vio   4.75 3.25
B249 SP156 60g + 30g dk
                        red   5.50 3.25
B250 SP156   1s + 50g dk
                        blue   5.50 5.50
B251 SP156 1.40s + 70g red
                        brown   12.50 16.00
           Nos. B245-B251 (7)   42.75 42.50
Kunstlerhaus, home of the leading Austrian Artists Association, 80th anniv.

St. Rupert — SP157

Designs: 30g+15g, Cathedral and Fountain. 40g+20g, Facade of Cathedral. 50g+25g, Cathedral from South. 60g+30g, Abbey of St. Peter. 80g+40g, Inside Cathedral. 1s+50g, Salzburg Cathedral and Castle. 1.40s+70g, Madonna by Michael Pacher.

1948, Aug. 6   *Perf. 14x13½*
B252 SP157 20g + 10g dp
                        grn   8.00 8.00
B253 SP157 30g + 15g red
                        brn   2.50 *3.25*
B254 SP157 40g + 20g sl blk   2.75 *3.25*
B255 SP157 50g + 25g choc   .40 .80
B256 SP157 60g + 30g dk
                        red   .40 .80
B257 SP157 80g + 40g dk
                        brn vio   .40 .80
B258 SP157   1s + 50g dp
                        blue   .80 .80
B259 SP157 1.40s + 70g dk
                        grn   2.50 3.25
           Nos. B252-B259 (8)   17.75 20.95
The surtax was to aid in the reconstruction of Salzburg Cathedral.

Easter — SP158

Designs: 60g+20g, St. Nicholas Day. 1s+25g, Birthday. 1.40s+35g, Christmas.

Inscribed: "Gluckliche Kindheit"

1949, Apr. 13   **Unwmk.**
B260 SP158 40g + 10g brn
                        vio   16.00 18.00
B261 SP158 60g + 20g brn
                        red   16.00 18.00
B262 SP158   1s + 25g dp
                        ultra   16.00 18.00
B263 SP158 1.40s + 35g dk
                        grn   16.00 18.00
           Nos. B260-B263 (4)   64.00 72.00
The surtax was for Child Welfare.

Arms of Austria, 1230 — SP159

1949, Aug. 17   **Engr. & Photo.**
B264 SP159 40g + 10g 1230   9.50 9.50

Engraved and Typographed
B265 SP159 60g + 15g 1450   8.00 8.00
B266 SP159   1s + 25g 1600   8.00 8.00
B267 SP159 1.60s + 40g 1945   12.00 12.00
           Nos. B264-B267 (4)   37.50 37.50
Surtax was for returned prisoners of war.

SP160

Laurel Branch, Stamps and Magnifier

1949, Dec. 3   **Engr.**
B268 SP160 60g + 15g dark red   3.25 2.75
Stamp Day, Dec. 3-4.

Arms of Austria and Carinthia SP161

Carinthian with Austrian Flag — SP162

Design: 1.70s+40g, Casting ballot.

1950, Oct. 10 Photo.   *Perf. 14x13½*
B269 SP161 60g + 15g   32.50 27.50
B270 SP162   1s + 25g   40.00 32.50
B271 SP162 1.70s + 40g   47.50 35.00
           Nos. B269-B271 (3)   120.00 95.00
Plebiscite in Carinthia, 30th anniv.

Collector Examining Cover — SP163

1950, Dec. 2   **Engr.**
B272 SP163 60g + 15g blue grn   9.50 8.00
Stamp Day.

Miner and Mine — SP164

60g+15g, Mason holding brick and trowel. 1s+25g, Bridge builder with hook and chain. 1.70s+40g, Electrician, pole and insulators.

1951, Mar. 10   **Unwmk.**
B273 SP164 40g + 10g dark
                        brown   16.00 14.50
B274 SP164 60g + 15g dk
                        grn   12.00 14.50

B275 SP164   1s + 25g red
                            brown   12.00 14.50
B276 SP164 1.70s + 40g vio bl 16.00 14.50
    Nos. B273-B276 (4)   56.00 58.00

Issued to publicize Austrian reconstruction.

Laurel Branch and Olympic Circles SP165

1952, Jan. 26   *Perf. 13½x14*
B277 SP165 2.40s + 60g grnsh
                            black   20.00 20.00

The surtax was used to help defray expenses of Austria's athletes in the 1952 Olympic Games.

Cupid as Postman SP166

1952, Mar. 10   *Perf. 14x13½*
B278 SP166 1.50s + 35g dark
                            brn car   20.00 20.00
Stamp Day.

Sculpture, "Christ, The Almighty" SP167

1952, Sept. 6   *Perf. 13½x14*
B279 SP167 1s + 25g grnsh
                            gray   11.50 12.00
Austrian Catholic Conv., Vienna, 9/11-14.

Type of 1945-46 Ovptd. in Gold

1953, Aug. 29   Unwmk.
B280 A124 1s + 25g on 5s dl bl 2.50 2.50
60th anniv. of labor unions in Austria.

Bummerlhaus Steyr — SP168

Designs: 1s+25g, Johannes Kepler. 1.50s+40g, Lutheran Bible, 1st edition. 2.40s+60g, Theophil von Hansen. 3s+75g, Reconstructed Lutheran School, Vienna.

1953, Nov. 5   Engr.   *Perf. 14x13½*
B281 SP168   70g + 15g vio
                            brn   .25   .25
B282 SP168   1s + 25g dk
                            gray blue   .25   .25
B283 SP168 1.50s + 40g choc   .80   .80
B284 SP168 2.40s + 60g dk
                            grn   3.25   3.25

B285 SP168   3s + 75g dk
                            pur   6.50   6.50
    Nos. B281-B285 (5)   11.05 11.05
The surtax was used toward reconstruction of the Lutheran School, Vienna.

Globe and Philatelic Accessories SP169

1953, Dec. 5
B286 SP169 1s + 25g chocolate 6.50 6.50
Stamp Day.

Type of 1945-46 with Denomination Replaced by Asterisks

Overprinted in Brown

1954, Feb. 19   *Perf. 13½x14*
B287 A124 1s + 20g blue gray   .40   .50
Surtax for aid to avalanche victims.

Patient Under Sun Lamp — SP170

Designs: 70g+15g, Physician using microscope. 1s+25g, Mother and children. 1.45s+35g, Operating room. 1.50s+35g, Baby on scale. 2.40s+60g, Nurse.

1954   Engr.   *Perf. 14x13½*
B288 SP170   30g + 10g pur   1.25   1.60
B289 SP170   70g + 15g dk
                            brn   .25   .25
B290 SP170   1s + 25g dk bl   .25   .25
B291 SP170 1.45s + 35g dk bl
                            green   .55   .35
B292 SP170 1.50s + 35g dk
                            red   5.50   5.50
B293 SP170 2.40s + 60g dk
                            red brown   6.50   8.00
    Nos. B288-B293 (6)   14.30 15.95
The surtax was for social welfare.

Early Vienna-Ulm Ferryboat SP171

1954, Dec. 4   *Perf. 13½x14*
B294 SP171 1s + 25g dk gray
                            grn   6.50   6.50
Stamp Day.

"Industry" Welcoming Returned Prisoner of War SP172

1955, June 29
B295 SP172 1s + 25g red brn   2.50 2.50
Surtax for returned prisoners of war and relatives of prisoners not yet released.

Collector Looking at Album — SP173

1955, Dec. 3   *Perf. 14x13½*
B296 SP173 1s + 25g vio brn   4.00 4.00
Stamp Day. The surtax was for the promotion of Austrian philately.

Ornamental Shield and Letter — SP174

1956, Dec. 1   Engr.
B297 SP174 1s + 25g scarlet   3.25 3.25
Stamp Day. See note after No. B296.

Arms of Austria, 1945 — SP175

Engr. & Typo.
1956, Dec. 21   *Perf. 14x13½*
B298 SP175 1.50s + 50g on 1.60s
                            + 40g gray &
                            red   .65   .65
The surtax was for Hungarian refugees.

New Post Office, Linz 2 SP176

Design: 2.40s+60g, Post office, Kitzbuhel.

1957-58   Engr.   *Perf. 13½x14*
B299 SP176   1s + 25g dk sl
                            grn   2.40   3.25
B300 SP176 2.40s + 60g blue   .95   .95
Stamp Day. See note after B296. Issue dates: 1s, Nov. 30, 1957. 2.40s, Dec. 6, 1958. See No. B303.

Roman Carriage from Tomb at Maria Saal SP177

Litho. & Engr.
1959, Dec. 5   *Perf. 13½x14*
B301 SP177 2.40s + 60g pink &
                            blk   .80   1.00
Stamp Day.

Progressive Die Proof under Magnifying Glass SP178

1960, Dec. 2   Engr.   *Perf. 13½x14*
B302 SP178 3s + 70g vio brn   .95   .95
Stamp Day.

Post Office Type of 1957
Design: 3s+70g, Post Office, Rust.

1961, Dec. 1   Unwmk.   *Perf. 13½*
B303 SP176 3s + 70g dk bl grn   .95   .95
Stamp Day. See note after No. B296.

Hands of Stamp Engraver at Work SP179

1962, Nov. 30   *Perf. 13½x14*
B304 SP179 3s + 70g dull pur 1.25 1.25
Stamp Day.

Railroad Exit, Post Office Vienna 101 SP180

1963, Nov. 29   Litho. & Engr.
B305 SP180 3s + 70g tan & blk   .65   .65
Stamp Day.

View of Vienna, North SP181

Designs: Various view of Vienna with compass indicating direction.

1964, July 20   Litho.   *Perf. 13½x14*
B306 SP181 1.50s + 30g ("N")   .35   .40
B307 SP181 1.50s + 30g ("NO")   .35   .40
B308 SP181 1.50s + 30g ("O")   .35   .40
B309 SP181 1.50s + 30g ("SO")   .35   .40
B310 SP181 1.50s + 30g ("S")   .35   .40
B311 SP181 1.50s + 30g ("SW")   .35   .40
B312 SP181 1.50s + 30g ("W")   .35   .40
B313 SP181 1.50s + 30g ("NW")   .35   .40
    Nos. B306-B313 (8)   2.80   3.20
Vienna Intl. Phil. Exhib. (WIPA 1965).

Post Bus Terminal, St. Gilgen, Wolfgangsee — SP182

1964, Dec. 4   Unwmk.   *Perf. 13½*
B314 SP182 3s + 70g multi   .55   .55
Stamp Day.

Wall Painting, Tomb at Thebes — SP183

Development of Writing: 1.80s+50g, Cuneiform writing on stone tablet and man's head from Assyrian palace. 2.20s+60g, Wax tablet with Latin writing, Corinthian column. 3s+80g, Gothic writing on sealed letter, Gothic window from Munster Cathedral. 4s+1s, Letter with seal and postmark and upright desk. 5s+1.20s, Typewriter.

Litho. & Engr.

1965, June 4 ***Perf. 14x13½***

B315	SP183	1.50s + 40g multi	.35	.35
B316	SP183	1.80s + 50g multi	.35	.35
B317	SP183	2.20s + 60g multi	.50	.50
B318	SP183	3s + 80g multi	.55	.55
B319	SP183	4s + 1s multi	.65	.65
B320	SP183	5s + 1.20s multi	.95	.95
		Nos. B315-B320 (6)	3.35	3.35

Vienna Intl. Phil. Exhib., WIPA, June 4-13.

Mailman Distributing Mail SP184

1965, Dec. 3 **Engr.** ***Perf. 13½x14***

B321 SP184 3s + 70g blue grn .50 .80

Stamp Day.

Letter Carrier, 16th Century — SP185

Litho. & Engr.

1966, Dec. 2 ***Perf. 13½***

B322 SP185 3s + 70g multi .55 .55

Stamp Day. Design is from Ambras Heroes' Book, Austrian National Library.

Letter Carrier, 16th Century Playing Card — SP186

Engr. & Photo.

1967, Dec. 1 ***Perf. 13x13½***

B323 SP186 3.50s + 80g multi .55 .80

Stamp Day.

Mercury, Bas-relief from Purkersdorf SP187

1968, Nov. 29 **Engr.** ***Perf. 13½***

B324 SP187 3.50s + 80g slate green .55 .80

Stamp Day.

Unken Post Station Sign, 1710 — SP188

Engr. & Photo.

1969, Dec. 5 ***Perf. 12***

B325 SP188 3.50s + 80g tan, red & blk .55 1.20

Stamp Day. Design is from a watercolor by Friedrich Zeller.

Saddle, Bag, Harness and Post Horn — SP189

Engr. & Litho.

1970, Dec. 4 ***Perf. 13½x14***

B326 SP189 3.50s + 80g gray blk & yel .55 1.20

Stamp Day.

"50 Years" SP190

Engr. & Photo.

1971, Dec. 3 ***Perf. 13½***

B327 SP190 4s + 1.50s gold & red brn .75 1.20

50th anniversary of the Federation of Austrian Philatelic Societies.

Local Post Carrier — SP191

1972, Dec. 1 **Engr.** ***Perf. 14x13½***

B328 SP191 4s + 1s olive green .75 .65

Stamp Day.

Gabriel, by Lorenz Luchsperger, 15th Century — SP192

1973, Nov. 30

B329 SP192 4s + 1s maroon .65 1.10

Stamp Day.

Mail Coach Leaving Old PTT Building — SP193

1974, Nov. 29 **Engr.** ***Perf. 14x13½***

B330 SP193 4s + 2s violet blue .75 .75

Stamp Day.

Alpine Skiing, Women's SP194

Designs: 1.50s+70g, Ice hockey. 2s+90g, Ski jump. 4s+1.90s, Bobsledding.

1975, Mar. 14 **Photo.** ***Perf. 13½x14***

B331	SP194	1s + 50g multi	.25	.25
B332	SP194	1.50s + 70g multi	.25	.25
B333	SP194	2s + 90g multi	.40	.40
B334	SP194	4s + 1.90s multi	.80	.80
		Nos. B331-B334 (4)	1.70	1.70

1975, Nov. 14

Designs: 70g+30g, Figure skating, pair. 2s+1s, Cross-country skiing. 2.50s+1s, Luge. 4s+2s, Biathlon.

B335	SP194	70g + 30g multi	.25	.40
B336	SP194	2s + 1s multi	.40	.65
B337	SP194	2.50s + 1s multi	.40	.65
B338	SP194	4s + 2s multi	.75	1.20
		Nos. B335-B338 (4)	1.80	2.90

12th Winter Olympic Games, Innsbruck, Feb. 4-15, 1976.

Austria Nos. 5, 250, 455 — SP195

Photo. & Engr.

1975, Nov. 28 ***Perf. 14***

B339 SP195 4s + 2s multi .75 1.20

Stamp Day; 125th anniv. of Austrian stamps.

Postilion's Gala Hat and Horn SP196

1976, Dec. 3 ***Perf. 13½x14***

B340 SP196 6s + 2s blk & lt vio 1.10 1.00

Stamp Day.

Emanuel Herrmann SP197

1977, Dec. 2 ***Perf. 14x13½***

B341 SP197 6s + 2s multi 1.25 1.10

Stamp Day. Emanuel Herrmann (1839-1902), economist, invented postal card. Austria issued first postal card in 1869.

Post Bus, 1913 SP198

1978, Dec. 1 **Photo.** ***Perf. 13½x14***

B342 SP198 10s + 5s multi 2.00 1.20

Stamp Day.

Heroes' Square, Vienna SP199

Photo. & Engr.

1979, Nov. 30 ***Perf. 13½***

B343 SP199 16s + 8s multi 3.00 2.40

No. B343 Inscribed "2. Phase"

1980, Nov. 21

B344 SP199 16s + 8s multi 3.25 2.40

Souvenir Sheet

1981, Feb. 20

B345 SP199 16s + 8s multi 2.75 2.75

WIPA 1981 Phil. Exhib., Vienna, May 22-31. No. B345 contains one stamp without inscription.

Mainz-Weber Mailbox, 1870 — SP200

1982, Nov. 26 **Photo. & Engr.**

B346 SP200 6s + 3s multi 1.40 1.25

Stamp Day.

Boy Examining Cover SP201

Photo. & Engr.

1983, Oct. 21 ***Perf. 14***

B347 SP201 6s + 3s multi 1.25 1.00

Stamp Day. See Nos. B349-B352, B354-B355.

World Winter Games for the Handicapped — SP202

1984, Jan. 5 **Photo.** ***Perf. 13½x13***

B348 SP202 4s + 2s Downhill skier .75 .75

Stamp Day Type of 1983

Designs: No. B349, Seschemnofer III burial chamber detail, pyramid of Cheops, Gizeh. No. B350, Roman messenger on horseback. No. B351, Nuremberg messenger, 16th cent. No. B352, *The Postmaster* (detail), 1841, lithograph by Carl Schuster.

1984-87   Photo. & Engr.   Perf. 14
B349 SP201 6s +3s multi   1.25 1.10
B350 SP201 6s +3s multi   1.25 1.00
B351 SP201 6s +3s multi   1.25 1.00
B352 SP201 6s +3s multi   1.25 1.10
        Nos. B349-B352 (4)   5.00 4.20

Issued: No. B349, 11/30/84; No. B350, 11/28/85; No. B351, 11/28/86; No. B352, 11/19/87.

4th World Winter Sports Championships for the Disabled, Innsbruck — SP203

1988, Jan. 15   Photo.   Perf. 13½
B353 SP203 5s + 2.50s multi   1.40 1.10

Stamp Day Type of 1983

Designs: No. B354, Railway mail car. No. B355, Hansa-Brandenburg CI mail plane.

1988-89   Photo. & Engr.   Perf. 14
B354 SP201 6s +3s multi   1.75 1.40
B355 SP201 6s +3s multi   1.75 1.40

Issued: No. B354, Nov. 17; No. B355, May 24, 1989.

Stamp Day — SP204

1990, May 25   Photo.   Perf. 13½
B356 SP204 7s +3s multi   1.75 1.40

SP205

1991, May 29   Photo. & Engr.
B357 SP205 7s +3s B & P   1.75 1.75
1992, May 22
B358 SP205 7s +3s R & H   1.75 1.75
1993, May 5
B359 SP205 7s +3s I & I   1.75 1.75
1994, May 27
B360 SP205 7s +3s E & L   1.90 1.90

SP205a

1995, May 26
B361 SP205a 10s +5s F & A   2.40 2.40
1996, May 17
B362 SP205a 10s +5s M & T   2.60 2.60
        Nos. B357-
        B362,1725,1765,1791 (9) 16.05 14.95

Stamp Day. The 1st letters spell "Briefmarke," the 2nd "Philatelie."
For "A" & "E," see No. 1725; "R" & "L," No. 1765; "K" & "I," No. 1791; "E" & "E," No. 1818.

Special Olympics Winter Games SP206

1993, Mar. 19   Photo.   Perf. 13½x14
B367 SP206 6s +3s multi   1.90 1.90

Vienna Intl. Postage Stamp Exhibition (WIPA), 2000 — SP207

Designs: No. B368, #5, postman on bicycle. No. B369, #339, early mail truck. No. B370, #525, airplane, service vehicles.

1997-2000   Photo. & Engr.   Perf. 14
B368 SP207 27s +13s multi   7.00 7.00
B369 SP207 32s +13s multi   8.00 8.00
B370 SP207 32s +16s multi   9.00 9.00
a.   Souvenir sheet, #B368-
        B370 + label   30.00 30.00
        Nos. B368-B370 (3)   24.00 24.00

Stamps from No. B370a are dated "2000."
Issued: No. B368, 5/23; No. B369, 11/6/98; No. B370, 9/17/99. No. B370a, 2000.

Stamp Day — SP208

Designs: No. B372, 1919 Mail car. No. B373, Siemens M 320 mail wagon, 1987. No B374, Oeffag C II mail plane. No. B375, Junkers F13 airplane.

Photo. & Engr.
2001, May 18   Perf. 13¾
B371 SP208 20s +10s multi
        + label   8.50 8.50
2002, May 24
B372 SP208 €1.60 +80c multi
        + label   7.25 7.25
2003, May 23
B373 SP208 €2.54 +€1.26
        multi + la-
        bel   11.50 11.50
2004, May 7
B374 SP208 €2.65 +€1.30
        multi + la-
        bel   12.00 12.00
2005, May 27
B375 SP208 265c +130c mul-
        ti + label   12.00 12.00
        See No. B377.

No. 1865A Surcharged

2006, Apr. 21   Photo.   Perf. 13¾x14
B376 A1090 75c +425c on 25c
        #1865A   11.00 11.00

Surtax was for flood relief. Standing order customers were able to purchase this stamp for the 75c franking value.

Stamp Day Type of 2001

Design: Airbus A310-300.

Photo. & Engr.
2006, July 2   Perf. 13¾
B377 SP208 265c +130c multi
        + label   10.00 10.00
Printed in sheets of 5 stamps + 5 labels.

Ferris Wheel, Vienna SP209

2006, Aug. 26   Photo.   Perf. 13¾
B378 SP209 55c +20c multi   2.25 2.25
a.   Inscribed "OSTERREICH"
        (from #B382a)   2.25 2.25

2008 Vienna Intl. Stamp Exhibition (WIPA), Vienna. See No. 2137a.
No. B378 is inscribed "Osterrreich."

German and Austrian Philatelic Exhibition, Bad Reichenhall SP210

2006, Oct. 6   Photo.   Perf. 14¼x14
B379 SP210 55c +20c multi   2.25 2.25

Gloriette, Schönbrunn Palace — SP211

2007, Mar. 16   Photo.   Perf. 13¾
B380 SP211 55c +20c multi   2.25 2.25

2008 Vienna Intl. Stamp Exhibition (WIPA). See No. 2137b.

Steamer Wien SP212

2007, June 15
B381 SP212 265c +130c multi 11.50 11.50
Stamp Day.

St. Stephen's Cathedral, Vienna — SP213

2008, Jan. 18   Photo.   Perf. 13¾
B382 SP213 55c +20c multi   2.25 2.25
a.   Souvenir sheet, #B378, B380,
        B382   7.25 7.25

2008 Vienna Intl. Stamp Exhibition (WIPA). See No. 2137c.
No. B382a issued 9/18.

Paddle-wheel Steamer Schönbrunn — SP214

2008, Sept. 18   Photo.   Perf. 13¾
B383 SP214 265c +130c multi 11.50 11.50
Stamp Day.

MS Osterreich SP215

2009, Sept. 11   Litho.   Perf. 13¾
B384 SP215 265c +130c multi 11.50 11.50
Stamp Day.

Gmunden SP216

2010, Aug. 27   Litho.   Perf. 13¾
B385 SP216 265c +130c multi 10.50 10.50
Stamp Day.

Graz SP217

2011, May 13   Perf. 13¾
B386 SP217 272c+136c multi   11.50 11.50
Stamp Day.

Federation of Austrian Philatelist Societies, 90th Anniv. — SP218

2011, Sept. 10   Perf. 14¼x14
B387 SP218 62c+20c multi   2.25 2.25

Breast Cancer Research SP219

2011, Sept. 28   Perf. 13¾
B388 SP219 90c+10c multi   2.75 2.75
Surtax for Austrian Cancer Aid Society.

Karlsplatz
SP220

2012, May 11
B389 SP220 272c +136c multi 10.50 10.50
Stamp Day.

Winning Drawing in "Children for Integration" Stamp Design Contest SP221

2012, Aug. 31
B390 SP221 62c +20c multi 2.10 2.10

Winning Art in "Protection of Nature" Children's Stamp Design Contest SP222

2013, June 13
B391 SP222 62c +20c multi 2.25 2.25

Salzburg
SP223

2013, Aug. 22
B392 SP223 282c+141c multi 11.50 11.50
Stamp Day.

Winniing Art in "Youth for Sport and Exercise" Stamp Design Contest SP224

2014, June 26   Litho.   Perf. 14¼
B393 SP224 62c+20c multi 2.25 2.25

Irises and Basilica of Rankweil SP225

2014, Sept. 26   Litho.   Perf. 14¼
B394 SP225 282c +141c multi 11.00 11.00
Stamp Day.

Winning Art in "Healthy Eating" Children's Stamp Design Contest SP226

2015, June 3   Litho.   Perf. 13¾
B395 SP226 68c +20c multi 2.00 2.00
Surtax for promotion of youth philately.

Tulln an der Donau SP227

2015, June 18   Litho.   Perf. 13¾
B396 SP227 288c +144c multi 9.50 9.50
Stamp Day.

Child — SP228

2016, Feb. 18   Litho.   Perf. 14
B397 SP228 68c +232c multi 6.50 6.50
Surtax was for UNICEF refugee assistance projects in Syria.

Szombathely, Hungary to Pinkafelder, Austria Train and Stations — SP229

2016, Oct. 21   Litho.   Perf. 13¾
B398 SP229 288c +144c multi 9.75 9.75
Stamp Day. Surtax was for promotion of philately.

AIR POST STAMPS

Issues of the Monarchy

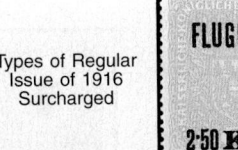

Types of Regular Issue of 1916 Surcharged

1918, Mar. 30   Unwmk.   Perf. 12½
C1 A40 1.50k on 2k lilac 1.60 7.50
C2 A40 2.50k on 3k ocher 10.50 32.50
  a. Inverted surcharge 1,200.
     Never hinged 2,400.
  b. Perf. 11½ 725.00 1,100.
     Never hinged 1,600.
  c. Perf. 12½x11½ 65.00 140.00
     Never hinged 160.00

Overprinted

C3 A40 4k gray 4.75 20.00
  Nos. C1-C3 (3) 16.85 60.00
  Set, never hinged 40.00
Exist imperf, without gum. Value, set $450.

Nos. C1-C3 also exist without surcharge or overprint. Values, set perf unused hinged $475, never hinged $1,050. Values, set imperf, unused hinged $425, never hinged $850.
Nos. C1-C3 were printed on grayish and on white paper. See the *Scott Classic Specialized Catalogue of Stamps and Covers* for detailed listing.
A 7k on 10k red brown was prepared but not regularly issued. Values: perf, $650 unused hinged, $1,600 never hinged; imperf, without gum, $1,050.

Issues of the Republic

Hawk — AP1

Wilhelm Kress — AP2

1922-24   Typo.   Perf. 12½
C4 AP1 300k claret .35 .35
C5 AP1 400k green ('24) 5.00 4.75
C6 AP1 600k bister .25 .25
C7 AP1 900k brn orange .25 .25

Engr.
C8 AP2 1200k brn violet .25 .25
C9 AP2 2400k slate .25 .25
C10 AP2 3000k dp brn ('23) 3.25 2.75
C11 AP2 4800k dark bl ('23) 2.75 2.75
  Nos. C4-C11 (8) 12.35 11.60
  Set, never hinged 29.00

Values for used are for stamps with philatelic favor cancels. Postally used value, set $45.
Set exists imperf. Values, set unused hinged $350, never hinged $500.

Plane and Pilot's Head — AP3

Airplane Passing Crane — AP4

1925-30   Typo.   Perf. 12½
C12 AP3 2g gray brown .40 .40
C13 AP3 5g red .40 .40
  a. Horiz. pair, imperf. btwn. 800.00
     Never hinged 1,250.
C14 AP3 6g dark blue .80 .80
C15 AP3 8g yel green .80 .80
C16 AP3 10g dp org ('26) .80 .80
  a. Horiz. pair, imperf. btwn. 800.00
     Never hinged 1,250.
C17 AP3 15g red vio ('26) .40 .40
  a. Horiz. pair, imperf. btwn. 800.00
     Never hinged 1,250.
C18 AP3 20g org brn ('30) 11.00 11.00
C19 AP3 25g blk vio ('30) 4.75 4.75
C20 AP3 30g bister ('26) 8.00 8.00
C21 AP3 50g bl gray ('26) 13.50 13.50
C22 AP3 80g dk grn ('30) 2.40 2.40

Photo.
C23 AP4 10g orange red .80 .80
  a. Horiz. pair, imperf. btwn. 800.00
     Never hinged 1,250.
C24 AP4 15g claret .80 .80
C25 AP4 30g brn violet .80 .80
C26 AP4 50g gray black .80 .80
C27 AP4 1s deep blue 8.00 8.00

C28 AP4 2s dark green 1.60 1.60
  a. Vertical pair, imperf.
     btwn. 800.00
     Never hinged 1,250.
C29 AP4 3s red brn ('26) 52.50 52.50
C30 AP4 5s indigo ('26) 13.50 13.50

Size: 25½x32mm
C31 AP4 10s blk brown,
          gray ('26) 8.00 8.00
  Nos. C12-C31 (20) 130.05 130.05
  Set, never hinged 325.00
Values for used are for stamps with philatelic favor cancels. Postally used value, set $200.
Exists imperf. Values, set unused hinged $850, never hinged $1,100.

Airplane over Güssing Castle — AP5

Airplane over the Danube — AP6

Designs (each includes plane): 10g, Maria-Worth. 15g, Durnstein. 20g, Hallstatt. 25g, Salzburg. 30g, Upper Dachstein and Schladminger Glacier. 40g, Lake Wetter. 50g, Arlberg. 60g, St. Stephen's Cathedral. 80g, Church of the Minorites. 2s, Railroad viaduct, Carinthia. 3s, Gross Glockner mountain. 5s, Aerial railway. 10s, Seaplane and yachts.

1935, Aug. 16   Engr.   Perf. 12½
C32 AP5 5g rose violet .25 .25
C33 AP5 10g red orange .25 .25
C34 AP5 15g yel green .80 .80
C35 AP5 20g gray blue .25 .25
C36 AP5 25g violet brn .25 .25
C37 AP5 30g brn orange .25 .25
C38 AP5 40g gray green .25 .25
C39 AP5 50g light sl bl .25 .25
C40 AP5 60g black brn .35 .35
C41 AP5 80g light brown .40 .40
C42 AP6 1s rose red .35 .35
C43 AP6 2s olive green 2.00 2.00
C44 AP6 3s yellow brn 12.00 8.00
C45 AP6 5s dark green 4.00 2.75
C46 AP6 10s slate blue 52.50 52.50
  Nos. C32-C46 (15) 74.55 68.90
  Set, never hinged 150.00

Values for used are for stamps with philatelic favor cancels. Postally used value, set $175.
Set exists imperf. Values, set unused hinged $375, never hinged $475.

Catalogue values for unused stamps in this section, from this point to the end of the section, are for Never Hinged items.

Windmill, Neusiedler Lake Shore — AP20

1s, Roman arch, Carnuntum. 2s, Town Hall, Gmund. 3s, Schieder Lake, Hinterstoder. 4s, Praegraten, Eastern Tyrol. 5s, Torsäule, Salzburg. 10s, St. Charles Church, Vienna.

1947   Unwmk.   Perf. 14x13½
C47 AP20 50g black brown .40 .40
C48 AP20 1s dark brn vio .40 .40
C49 AP20 2s dark green .40 .40
C50 AP20 3s chocolate 2.40 2.40
C51 AP20 4s dark green 2.00 2.00
C52 AP20 5s dark blue 2.00 2.00
C53 AP20 10s dark blue .80 .80
  Nos. C47-C53 (7) 8.40 8.40
Used values for examples with philatelic favor cancels. Postally used value, set $27.50.

Rooks
AP27

Birds: 1s, Barn swallows. 2s, Blackheaded gulls. 3s, Great cormorants. 5s, Buzzard. 10s, Gray heron. 20s, Golden eagle.

1950-53   Perf. 13½x14

C54	AP27	60g dark bl vio	1.60	1.60
C55	AP27	1s dark vio blue ('53)	16.00	16.00
C56	AP27	2s dark blue	12.50	9.50
C57	AP27	3s dk slate green ('53)	120.00	95.00
C58	AP27	5s red brn ('53)	120.00	95.00
C59	AP27	10s gray vio ('53)	52.50	47.50
C60	AP27	20s brn blk ('52)	10.00	8.50
		Nos. C54-C60 (7)	332.60	273.10
		Set, hinged	190.00	

Value at lower left on Nos. C59 and C60.
No. C60 exists imperf.

Etrich "Dove" AP28

Designs: 3.50s, Twin-engine jet airliner. 5s, Four-engine jet airliner.

1968, May 31   Engr.   Perf. 13½x14

C61	AP28	2s olive bister	.35	.35
C62	AP28	3.50s slate green	.55	.65
C63	AP28	5s dark blue	1.10	1.40
		Nos. C61-C63 (3)	2.00	2.40

IFA WIEN 1968 (International Air Post Exhibition), Vienna, May 30-June 4.

POSTAGE DUE STAMPS

Issues of the Monarchy

D1

Perf. 10 to 13½

1894-95   Typo.   Wmk. 91

J1	D1	1kr brown	2.00	1.25
a.		Perf. 13½	45.00	62.50
b.		Half used as ½kr on cover		80.00
J2	D1	2kr brown ('95)	2.75	2.40
a.		Pair, imperf. btwn.	200.00	300.00
b.		Half used as 1kr on cover		200.00
J3	D1	3kr brown	3.25	1.25
a.		Half used as 1½kr on cover		160.00
J4	D1	5kr brown	3.25	.80
a.		Perf. 13½	25.00	25.00
b.		Pair, imperf. btwn.	160.00	250.00
J5	D1	6kr brown ('95)	2.75	6.50
a.		Half used as 3kr on cover		200.00
J6	D1	7kr brown ('95)	.80	6.00
a.		Vert. pair, imperf. btwn.	275.00	550.00
b.		Horiz. pair, imperf. btwn.	275.00	550.00
J7	D1	10kr brown	4.75	.95
a.		Half used as 5kr on cover		140.00
J8	D1	20kr brown	.80	6.00
J9	D1	50kr brown	35.00	72.50
		Nos. J1-J9 (9)	55.35	97.65

Values for Nos. J1-J9 are for stamps that do not show the watermark. Stamps showing the watermark often sell for more.
See Nos. J204-J231.

D2

1899-1900   Imperf.

J10	D2	1h brown	.25	.40
J11	D2	2h brown	.25	.55
J12	D2	3h brown ('00)	.25	.40
J13	D2	4h brown	2.00	2.00
J14	D2	5h brown ('00)	1.60	1.25
J15	D2	6h brown	.25	.40
J16	D2	10h brown	.25	.50

J17	D2	12h brown	.35	2.40
J18	D2	15h brown	.35	1.60
J19	D2	20h brown	24.00	4.75
J20	D2	40h brown	2.40	2.60
J21	D2	100h brown	4.75	3.25
		Nos. J10-J21 (12)	36.70	20.20

Perf. 10½, 12½, 13½ and Compound

J22	D2	1h brown	.55	.25
J23	D2	2h brown	.40	.25
J24	D2	3h brown ('00)	.40	.25
J25	D2	4h brown	.65	.25
J26	D2	5h brown ('00)	.55	.25
J27	D2	6h brown	.40	.25
J28	D2	10h brown	.55	.55
J29	D2	12h brown	.55	.75
J30	D2	15h brown	.80	.80
J31	D2	20h brown	.95	.25
J32	D2	40h brown	1.25	.75
J33	D2	100h brown	24.00	2.00
		Nos. J22-J33 (12)	31.05	6.30

Nos. J10-J33 exist on unwmkd. paper.
For surcharges see Offices in the Turkish Empire Nos. J1-J5.

D3

Ordinary Thin Paper

1910-13   Unwmk.   Perf. 12½

J34	D3	1h carmine	.80	1.60
J35	D3	2h carmine	.50	.35
d.		Half used as 1h on cover		95.00
J36	D3	4h carmine	.50	.25
c.		Half used as 2h on cover		95.00
J37	D3	6h carmine	.50	.25
J38	D3	10h carmine	.50	.25
c.		Half used as 5h on cover		47.50
J39	D3	14h carmine ('13)	4.00	2.75
J40	D3	20h carmine	8.00	.25
c.		Half used as 10h on cover		95.00
J41	D3	25h carmine ('10)	8.00	6.50
J42	D3	30h carmine	8.00	.35
J43	D3	50h carmine	12.00	.40
J44	D3	100h carmine	16.00	.80
		Never hinged	65.00	
		Nos. J34-J44 (11)	58.80	13.75

All values exist on ordinary paper, Nos. J34-J38, J40, J42-J44 on chalky paper and Nos. J34-J38, J40, J44 on thin ordinary paper. In most cases, values are for the least expensive stamp of the types. Some of the expensive types sell for considerably more.
All values exist imperf.
See Offices in the Turkish Empire type D3.

1911, July 16

J45	D3	5k violet	80.00	12.50
J46	D3	10k violet	240.00	4.00

Nos. J45-J46 exist imperf. Value set: unused hinged $900; never hinged $1,200.

Regular Issue of 1908 Overprinted or Surcharged in Carmine or Black

No. J47   No. J48

1916, Oct. 21

J47	A22	1h gray (C)	.25	.25
a.		Pair, one without overprint	210.00	
		Never hinged	300.00	
J48	A22	15h on 2h vio (Bk)	.25	.55
a.		Inverted surcharge	400.00	
		Never hinged	750.00	
		Set, never hinged	1.60	

D4   D5

Perf. 12½, 12½x13 (#J57-J59)

1916, Oct. 1

J49	D4	5h rose red	.25	.25
J50	D4	10h rose red	.25	.25
a.		Half used as 5h on cover		65.00
J51	D4	15h rose red	.25	.25
J52	D4	20h rose red	.25	.25
J53	D4	25h rose red	.25	.95
J54	D4	30h rose red	.25	.25
a.		Half used as 15h on cover		160.00
J55	D4	40h rose red	.25	.25
a.		Half used as 20h on cover		140.00
J56	D4	50h rose red	.95	3.25
J57	D5	1k ultramarine	.25	.40
a.		Horiz. pair, imperf. btwn.	250.00	550.00
		Never hinged	550.00	
J58	D5	5k ultramarine	2.75	3.25
J59	D5	10k ultramarine	3.50	1.60
		Nos. J49-J59 (11)	9.20	11.25
		Set, never hinged	32.50	

Exists imperf. Value set: unused hinged $150, never hinged $400.
For overprints see J64-J74, Western Ukraine Nos. 54-55, NJ1-NJ6, Poland Nos. J1-J10.

Type of Regular Issue of 1916 Surcharged

1917

J60	A38	10h on 24h blue	1.60	.55
J61	A38	15h on 36h violet	.50	.25
J62	A38	20h on 54h orange	.25	.40
J63	A38	50h on 42h chocolate	.35	.25
		Nos. J60-J63 (4)	2.70	1.55
		Set, never hinged	14.00	

All values of this issue are known imperforate, also without surcharge, perforated and imperforate. Value set imperf unused hinged $160, never hinged $250. Value of set without surcharge imperf unused hinged $200, never hinged $350. Same values for set without surcharge, perf 12½.
For surcharges see Poland Nos. J11-J12

Issues of the Republic

Postage Due Stamps of 1916 Overprinted

1919

J64	D4	5h rose red	.25	.25
a.		Inverted overprint	250.00	325.00
		Never hinged	325.00	
J65	D4	10h rose red	.25	.25
J66	D4	15h rose red	.25	.40
J67	D4	20h rose red	.25	.40
J68	D4	25h rose red	8.00	27.50
J69	D4	30h rose red	.25	.40
J70	D4	40h rose red	.25	.80
J71	D4	50h rose red	.30	1.25
J72	D5	1k ultramarine	4.50	16.00
J73	D5	5k ultramarine	8.75	16.00
J74	D5	10k ultramarine	10.50	4.00
		Nos. J64-J74 (11)	33.55	67.25
		Set, never hinged	100.00	

Nos. J64, J65, J67, J70 exist imperf. Value, 4 values hinged $325.

D6   D7

1920-21   Perf. 12½

J75	D6	5h bright red	.25	.35
J76	D6	10h bright red	.25	.25
J77	D6	15h bright red	.25	1.60
J78	D6	20h bright red	.25	.25
J79	D6	25h bright red	.25	1.60
J80	D6	30h bright red	.25	.35
J81	D6	40h bright red	.25	.35
J82	D6	50h bright red	.25	.25
J83	D6	80h bright red	.25	.45
J84	D7	1k ultramarine	.25	.35
J85	D7	1½k ultra ('21)	.25	.35
J86	D7	2k ultra ('21)	.25	.35
J87	D7	3k ultra ('21)	.25	.95
J88	D7	4k ultra ('21)	.25	.95

J89	D7	5k ultramarine	.25	.35
J90	D7	8k ultra ('21)	.25	.95
J91	D7	10k ultra ('21)	.25	.45
J92	D7	20k ultra ('21)	.30	2.00
		Nos. J75-J92 (18)		12.25
		Set, never hinged	4.75	

Nos. J84-J92 exist on white paper and on grayish white paper. Values are for the cheaper varieties. See the *Scott Classic Specialized Catalogue* for detailed listings.
Nos. J84 to J92 exist imperf. Values, set unused hinged $150, never hinged $250.

Imperf

J93	D6	5h bright red	.25	.65
J94	D6	10h bright red	.25	.40
J95	D6	15h bright red	.25	1.60
J96	D6	20h bright red	.25	.40
J97	D6	25h bright red	.25	1.60
J98	D6	30h bright red	.25	.25
J99	D6	40h bright red	.25	.65
J100	D6	50h bright red	.25	1.10
J101	D6	80h bright red	.25	.85
		Nos. J93-J101 (9)		8.50
		Set, never hinged	3.25	

No. 207a Surcharged in Dark Blue

1921, Dec.   Perf. 12½

J102	A43	7½k on 15h bister	.25	.25
		Never hinged	.25	
a.		Inverted surcharge	450.00	500.00

D8

1922

J103	D8	1k reddish buff	.25	.35
J104	D8	2k reddish buff	.25	.40
J105	D8	4k reddish buff	.25	.65
J106	D8	5k reddish buff	.25	.35
J107	D8	7½k reddish buff	.25	1.20
J108	D8	10k blue green	.25	.50
J109	D8	15k blue green	.25	.75
J110	D8	20k blue green	.25	1.25
J111	D8	25k blue green	.25	1.25
J112	D8	30k blue green	.25	1.25
J113	D8	50k blue green	.25	1.25
		Nos. J103-J113 (11)		7.65
		Set, never hinged	5.25	

Issue date: Nos. J108-J113, June 2.

D9

D10

1922-24

J114	D9	10k cobalt blue	.25	.40
J115	D9	15k cobalt blue	.25	.55
J116	D9	20k cobalt blue	.25	.55
J117	D9	50k cobalt blue	.25	.55
J118	D10	100k plum	.25	.25
J119	D10	150k plum	.25	.25
J120	D10	200k plum	.25	.25
J121	D10	400k plum	.25	.25
J122	D10	600k plum ('23)	.25	.40
J123	D10	800k plum	.25	.25
J124	D10	1,000k plum ('23)	.25	.25
J125	D10	1,200k plum ('23)	1.00	4.75
J126	D10	1,500k plum ('24)	.25	.80
J127	D10	1,800k plum ('24)	3.25	12.00
J128	D10	2,000k plum ('23)	.40	1.60
J129	D10	3,000k plum ('24)	5.50	24.00

J130	D10	4,000k plum ('24)	3.25	20.00
J131	D10	6,000k plum ('24)	3.25	27.50
		Nos. J114-J131 (18)	19.65	94.60
		Set, never hinged		70.00

J103-J131 sets exist imperf. Values, both sets unused hinged $450, never hinged $650.

D11   D12

1925-34   Perf. 12½

J132	D11	1g red	.25	.25
J133	D11	2g red	.25	.25
J134	D11	3g red	.25	.25
J135	D11	4g red	.25	.25
J136	D11	5g red ('27)	.25	.25
J137	D11	6g red	.25	.25
J138	D11	8g red	.25	.25
J139	D11	10g dark blue	.25	.25
J140	D11	12g dark blue	.25	.25
J141	D11	14g dark blue ('27)	.25	.25
J142	D11	15g dark blue	.25	.25
J143	D11	16g dark blue ('29)	.25	.25
J144	D11	18g dark blue ('34)	1.25	2.75
J145	D11	20g dark blue	.25	.25
J146	D11	23g dark blue	.40	.25
J147	D11	24g dark blue ('32)	1.60	.25
J148	D11	28g dark blue ('27)	1.60	.25
J149	D11	30g dark blue	.25	.25
J150	D11	31g dark blue ('29)	1.25	.25
J151	D11	35g dark blue ('30)	1.25	.25
J152	D11	39g dark blue ('32)	1.60	.25
J153	D11	40g dark blue	2.00	2.50
J154	D11	60g dark blue	2.00	2.00
J155	D12	1s dark green	2.75	1.25
J156	D12	2s dark green	25.00	4.00
J157	D12	5s dark green	87.50	45.00
J158	D12	10s dark green	35.00	8.00
		Nos. J132-J158 (27)	166.70	70.50
		Set, never hinged		575.00

Issues of 1925-27 exist imperf. Values, set of 18 unused hinged $600, never hinged $800.
Issued: 3g, 2s-10s, Dec; 5g, 28g, 1/1; 14g, June; 31g, 2/1; 35g, Jan; 24g, 39g, Sept; 16g, May; 18g, 6/25; others, 6/1.

Coat of Arms
D13   D14

1935, June 1

J159	D13	1g red	.25	.25
J160	D13	2g red	.25	.25
J161	D13	3g red	.25	.25
J162	D13	5g red	.25	.25
J163	D13	10g blue	.25	.25
J164	D13	12g blue	.25	.25
J165	D13	15g blue	.25	.50
J166	D13	20g blue	.25	.25
J167	D13	24g blue	.25	.25
J168	D13	30g blue	.25	.25
J169	D13	39g blue	.35	.25
J170	D13	60g blue	.50	1.25
J171	D14	1s green	.80	.35
J172	D14	2s green	1.50	1.00
J173	D14	5s green	3.00	4.00
J174	D14	10s green	4.75	.65
		Nos. J159-J174 (16)	13.40	10.25
		Set, never hinged		55.00

On Nos. J163-J170, background lines are horiz.
Nos. J159-J174 exist imperf. Values, set unused hinged $160, never hinged $350.

Catalogue values for unused stamps in this section, from this point to the end of the section, are for Never Hinged items.

D15

1945   Unwmk.   Typo.   Perf. 10½

J175	D15	1g vermilion	.25	.25
J176	D15	2g vermilion	.25	.25
J177	D15	3g vermilion	.25	.25
J178	D15	5g vermilion	.25	.25
J179	D15	10g vermilion	.25	.25
J180	D15	12g vermilion	.25	.25
J181	D15	20g vermilion	.25	.25

J182	D15	24g vermilion	.25	.40
J183	D15	30g vermilion	.25	.40
J184	D15	60g vermilion	.25	.40
J185	D15	1s violet	.25	.40
J186	D15	2s violet	.25	.80
J187	D15	5s violet	.25	.80
J188	D15	10s violet	.25	.80
		Nos. J175-J188 (14)	3.50	5.75

Issued: 1g-60g, Sept. 10; 1s-10s, Sept. 24.

Occupation Stamps of the Allied Military Government Overprinted in Black

1946   Perf. 11

J189	OS1	3g deep orange	.25	.25
J190	OS1	5g bright green	.25	.25
J191	OS1	6g red violet	.25	.25
J192	OS1	8g rose pink	.25	.25
J193	OS1	10g light gray	.25	.25
J194	OS1	12g pale buff brown	.25	.25
J195	OS1	15g rose red	.25	.25
J196	OS1	20g copper brown	.25	.25
J197	OS1	25g deep blue	.25	.25
J198	OS1	30g bright violet	.25	.25
J199	OS1	40g light ultra	.25	.25
J200	OS1	60g light olive grn	.25	.25
J201	OS1	1s dark violet	.25	.25
J202	OS1	2s yellow	.50	.80
J203	OS1	5s deep ultra	.50	.80
		Nos. J189-J203 (15)	4.25	4.85

Nos. J189-J203 were issued by the Renner Government. Inverted overprints exist on about half of the denominations.
Issued: 3g-60g, Apr. 23; 1s-5s, May 20.

Type of 1894-95
Inscribed "Republik Osterreich"

1947   Typo.   Perf. 14

J204	D1	1g chocolate	.25	.40
J205	D1	2g chocolate	.25	.40
J206	D1	3g chocolate	.25	.40
J207	D1	5g chocolate	.25	.25
J208	D1	8g chocolate	.25	.25
J209	D1	10g chocolate	.25	.40
J210	D1	12g chocolate	.25	.25
J211	D1	15g chocolate	.25	.25
J212	D1	16g chocolate	.30	.95
J213	D1	17g chocolate	.30	.95
J214	D1	18g chocolate	.30	.95
J215	D1	20g chocolate	.75	.25
J216	D1	24g chocolate	.35	.95
J217	D1	30g chocolate	.25	.25
J218	D1	36g chocolate	.75	1.40
J219	D1	40g chocolate	.25	.25
J220	D1	42g chocolate	.80	1.40
J221	D1	48g chocolate	.80	1.40
J222	D1	50g chocolate	.75	.35
J223	D1	60g chocolate	.25	.35
J224	D1	70g chocolate	.25	.35
J225	D1	80g chocolate	4.50	1.60
J226	D1	1s blue	.25	.35
J227	D1	1.15s blue	3.25	.50
J228	D1	1.20s blue	3.25	1.25
J229	D1	2s blue	.35	.35
J230	D1	5s blue	.35	.35
J231	D1	10s blue	.75	.35
		Nos. J204-J231 (28)	20.45	17.20

Issue dates: 1g, 20g, 50g, 80g, 1.15s, 1.20s, Sept. 25, others, Aug. 14.

D16

1949-57

J232	D16	1g carmine	.35	.25
J233	D16	2g carmine	.35	.25
J234	D16	4g carmine ('51)	.50	.35
J235	D16	5g carmine	1.90	.40
J236	D16	8g carmine ('51)	1.90	1.60
J237	D16	10g carmine	.25	.25
J238	D16	20g carmine	.35	.25
J239	D16	30g carmine	.35	.25
J240	D16	40g carmine	.35	.25
J241	D16	50g carmine	.35	.25
J242	D16	60g carmine ('50)	10.50	.40
J243	D16	63g carmine ('57)	4.75	3.50
J244	D16	70g carmine	.40	.25
J245	D16	80g carmine	.35	.25
J246	D16	90g carmine ('50)	.55	.25
J247	D16	1s carmine	.50	.25
J248	D16	1.20s purple	.55	.40
J249	D16	1.30s purple ('51)	.40	.40
J250	D16	1.40s purple ('51)	.40	.40
J251	D16	1.50s purple ('53)	.40	.40
J252	D16	1.65s purple ('50)	.40	.40
J253	D16	1.70s purple ('50)	.40	.25
J254	D16	2s purple	1.40	.25

J255	D16	2.50s purple ('51)	.75	.25
J256	D16	3s purple ('51)	.80	.25
J257	D16	4s purple ('51)	1.00	1.00
J258	D16	5s purple	1.25	.25
J259	D16	10s purple	2.40	.25
		Nos. J232-J259 (28)	33.85	13.45

Issued: 60g, 90g, 1.65s, 8/7; 4g, 8g, 1.40s, 2.50s-4s, 12/4; 1.50s, 2/18; 63g, 4/30; others, 11/17.

D17

1985-89   Photo.   Perf. 14
Background Color

J260	D17	10g brt yel ('86)	.25	.25
J261	D17	20g violet ('86)	.25	.25
J262	D17	50g orange ('86)	.25	.25
J263	D17	1s lt blue ('86)	.25	.35
J264	D17	2s pale brn ('86)	.25	.50
J265	D17	3s violet ('86)	.40	.55
J266	D17	5s ocher	.85	.65
J267	D17	10s pale grn ('89)	1.75	1.75
		Nos. J260-J267 (8)	4.25	4.55

Issue dates: 5s, Dec. 12. 20g, 1s, 3s, Mar. 19. 10g, 50g, 2s, Oct. 3. 10s, June 30.

MILITARY STAMPS

Issues of the Austro-Hungarian Military Authorities for the Occupied Territories in World War I

See Bosnia and Herzegovina for similar designs inscribed "MILITARPOST" instead of "FELDPOST."

Stamps of Bosnia of 1912-14 Overprinted

1915   Unwmk.   Perf. 12½

M1	A23	1h olive green	.25	.40
M2	A23	2h bright blue	.25	.40
M3	A23	3h claret	.25	.40
M4	A23	5h green	.25	.40
M5	A23	6h dark gray	.25	.40
M6	A23	10h rose carmine	.25	.25
M7	A23	12h deep ol grn	.25	.80
M8	A23	20h orange brn	.35	.80
M9	A23	25h ultramarine	.25	.80
M10	A23	30h orange red	3.25	6.50
M11	A24	35h myrtle grn	2.50	4.75
M12	A24	40h dark violet	2.50	4.75
M13	A24	45h olive brown	2.50	4.75
M14	A24	50h slate blue	2.50	4.75
M15	A24	60h brn violet	.40	.80
M16	A24	72h dark blue	2.50	4.75
M17	A25	1k brn vio, straw	2.50	4.75
M18	A25	2k dk gray, blue	2.50	4.75
M19	A26	3k car, green	20.00	47.50
M20	A25	5k dk vio, gray	20.00	40.00
M21	A25	10k dk ultra, gray	150.00	300.00
		Nos. M1-M21 (21)	213.50	432.55
		Set, never hinged		420.00

Exists imperf. Values, set unused hinged $450, never hinged $875.
Nos. M1-M21 also exist with overprint double, inverted and in red. These varieties were made by order of an official but were not regularly issued. Values, each set: unused $325; never hinged $650.

M1   M2

Design: Emperor Franz Josef.

Perf. 11½, 12½ and Compound
1915-17   Engr.

M22	M1	1h olive green	.25	.25
M23	M1	2h dull blue	.25	.35
M24	M1	3h claret	.25	.25

M25	M1	5h green	.25	.25
a.		Perf. 11½	100.00	150.00
		Never hinged	200.00	
b.		Perf. 11½x12½	150.00	240.00
		Never hinged	325.00	
c.		Perf. 12½x11½	200.00	325.00
		Never hinged	400.00	
M26	M1	6h dark gray	.25	.35
M27	M1	10h rose carmine	.25	.25
M28	M1	10h gray bl ('17)	.25	.25
M29	M1	12h deep olive grn	.25	.40
M30	M1	15h car rose ('17)	.25	.40
a.		Perf. 11½	8.00	27.50
		Never hinged	27.50	
M31	M1	20h orange brn	.35	.40
M32	M1	20h ol green ('17)	.25	.50
M33	M1	25h ultramarine	.25	.35
M34	M1	30h vermilion	.35	.50
M35	M1	35h dark green	.35	.65
M36	M1	40h dark violet	.35	.65
M37	M1	45h olive brown	.35	.65
M38	M1	50h myrtle green	.35	.65
M39	M1	60h brown violet	.35	.65
M40	M1	72h dark blue	.35	.65
M41	M1	80h org brn ('17)	.35	.35
M42	M1	90h magenta ('17)	.80	1.25
M43	M2	1k brn vio, straw	1.60	2.50
M44	M2	2k dk gray, blue	.80	1.60
M45	M2	3k car, green	.80	6.50
M46	M2	4k dk vio, gray ('17)	.80	8.00
M47	M2	5k dk vio, gray	20.00	37.50
M48	M2	10k dk ultra, gray	4.00	16.00
		Nos. M22-M48 (27)	34.70	82.20
		Set, never hinged		125.00

Nos. M22-M48 exist imperf. Values, set unused hinged $250, never hinged $475.
For overprints see Montenegro Nos. 1N1-1N4.

Emperor Karl I
M3   M4

1917-18   Perf. 12½

M49	M3	1h grnsh blue ('18)	.25	.25
a.		Perf. 11½	5.50	16.00
		Never hinged	16.00	
M50	M3	2h red org ('18)	.25	.25
M51	M3	3h olive gray	.25	.25
a.		Perf. 11½	20.00	47.50
		Never hinged	47.50	
b.		Perf. 11½x12½	32.50	80.00
		Never hinged	80.00	
M52	M3	5h olive green	.25	.25
M53	M3	6h violet	.25	.25
M54	M3	10h orange brn	.25	.25
M55	M3	12h blue	.25	.25
a.		Perf. 11½	4.00	12.00
		Never hinged	12.00	
M56	M3	15h bright rose	.25	.25
M57	M3	20h red brown	.25	.25
M58	M3	25h ultramarine	.25	.55
M59	M3	30h slate	.25	.25
M60	M3	40h olive bister	.25	.25
a.		Perf. 11½	2.50	6.50
		Never hinged	6.50	
M61	M3	50h deep green	.25	.25
a.		Perf. 11½	8.00	32.50
		Never hinged	32.50	
M62	M3	60h car rose	.25	.40
M63	M3	80h dull blue	.25	.25
M64	M3	90h dk violet	.35	.80
M65	M4	2k rose, straw	.25	.25
a.		Perf. 11½	4.00	12.00
		Never hinged	12.00	
M66	M4	3k green, blue	1.25	2.75
M67	M4	4k rose, green	16.00	24.00
a.		Perf. 11½	40.00	80.00
		Never hinged	80.00	
M68	M4	10k dl vio, gray	1.25	8.00
a.		Perf. 11½	16.00	47.50
		Never hinged	47.50	
		Nos. M49-M68 (20)	22.85	40.00
		Set, never hinged		87.50

Nos. M49-M68 exist imperf. Values, set unused hinged $160, never hinged $325. Also exist in pairs, imperf between. Values, each: unused $60, never hinged $120.

See No. M82. For surcharges and overprints see Italy Nos. N1-N19, N33, Western Ukraine Nos. 44-63, 75, 95-101, Poland Nos. 30-40, Romania Nos. 1N1-1N17.

Emperor Karl I — M5

1918 — Typo. — Perf. 12½

M69	M5	1h grnsh blue	24.00
M70	M5	2h orange	9.50
M71	M5	3h olive gray	9.50
M72	M5	5h yellow green	.40
M73	M5	10h dark brown	.40
M74	M5	20h red	.80
M75	M5	25h blue	.80
M76	M5	30h bister	95.00
M77	M5	45h dark slate	95.00
M78	M5	50h deep green	47.50
M79	M5	60h violet	95.00
M80	M5	80h rose	65.00
M81	M5	90h brown violet	1.60

Engr.

M82	M4	1k ol bister, *blue*	.40
		Nos. M69-M82 (14)	444.90
		Set, never hinged	1,050.

Nos. M69-M82 were on sale at the Vienna post office for a few days before the Armistice signing. They were never issued at the Army Post Offices. They exist imperf. Values, set unused hinged $800, never hinged $1,600.

For surcharges see Italy Nos. N20-N33, Romania 1N35-1N47.

MILITARY SEMI-POSTAL STAMPS

Emperor Karl I — MSP7   Empress Zita — MSP8

Perf. 12½x13

1918, July 20 — Unwmk. — Typo.

MB1	MSP7	10h gray green	.40	.80
MB2	MSP8	20h magenta	.40	.80
MB3	MSP7	45h blue	.40	.80
		Nos. MB1-MB3 (3)	1.20	2.40
		Set, never hinged	3.00	

These stamps were sold at a premium of 10h each over face value. The surtax was for "Karl's Fund."

For overprints see Western Ukraine Nos. 31-33.

Exist imperf. Values, set hinged unused $95, never hinged $240.

MILITARY NEWSPAPER STAMPS

Mercury — MN1

1916 — Unwmk. — Typo. — Perf. 12½

MP1	MN1	2h blue	.25	.35
a.		Perf. 11½	1.25	2.00
		Never hinged	3.25	
b.		Perf. 12½x11½	240.00	240.00
		Never hinged	450.00	
MP2	MN1	6h orange	.50	1.50
MP3	MN1	10h carmine	.55	1.50
MP4	MN1	20h brown	1.25	1.50
a.		Perf. 11½	4.00	8.00
		Never hinged	8.00	
		Nos. MP1-MP4 (4)	2.55	4.85
		Set, never hinged	8.00	

Exist imperf. Values, Nos. MP2-MP3, unused hinged each $1.60, never hinged $6.50; Nos. MP1, MP4, unused hinged each $40, never hinged $120.

For surcharges see Italy Nos. NP1-NP4.

NEWSPAPER STAMPS

From 1851 to 1866, the Austrian Newspaper Stamps were also used in Lombardy-Venetia.

> Values for unused stamps 1851-67 are for fine examples with original gum. Examples without gum sell for about a third or less of the figures quoted.

Issues of the Monarchy

Mercury — N1

Three Types
Type I — The "G" has no crossbar.
Type II — The "G" has a crossbar.
Type IIa — as type II but the rosette is deformed. Two spots of color in the "G."

1851-56 — Unwmk. Typo. Imperf. Machine-made Paper

P1	N1	(0.6kr) bl, type IIa	175.00	110.00
a.		Blue, type I	250.00	130.00
b.		Ribbed paper	625.00	240.00
c.		Blue, type II	600.00	250.00
P2	N1	(6kr) yel, type I	31,000.	10,000.
P3	N1	(30kr) rose, type I	—	13,000.
P4	N1	(6kr) scar, type II ('56)	85,000.	13,500.

From 1852 No. P3 and from 1856 No. P2 were used as 0.6 kreuzer values.

Values for Nos. P2-P3 unused are for stamps without gum. Pale shades sell at considerably lower values.

Originals of Nos. P2 and P3 are usually in pale colors and poorly printed. Values are for stamps clearly printed and in bright colors. Numerous reprints of Nos. P1 to P4 were made between 1866 and 1904. Those of Nos. P2 and P3 are always well printed and in much deeper colors. All reprints are in type I, but occasionally show faint traces of a crossbar on "G" of "ZEITUNGS."

N2

Two Types of the 1858-59 Issue
Type I — Loops of the bow at the back of the head broken.
Type II — Loops complete. Wreath projects further at top of head.

1858-59 — Embossed

P5	N2	(1kr) blue, type I	650.00	625.00
P6	N2	(1kr) lilac, type II ('59)	875.00	300.00

N3

1861

P7	N3	(1kr) gray	175.00	175.00
a.		(1kr) gray lilac	625.00	240.00
b.		(1kr) deep lilac	2,500.	800.00

The embossing on the reprints of the 1858-59 and 1861 issues is not as sharp as on the originals.

N4

Wmk. 91, or, before July 1864, Unwmkd.

1863

P8	N4	(1.05kr) gray	45.00	16.50
a.		Tete beche pair	125,000.	
b.		(1.05kr) gray lilac	100.00	20.00

Values are for stamps that do not show the watermark. Stamps showing the watermark often sell for more.

The embossing of the reprints is not as sharp as on the originals.

Mercury — N5

Three Types
Type I — Helmet not defined at back, more or less blurred. Two thick short lines in front of wing of helmet. Shadow on front of face not separated from hair.
Type II — Helmet distinctly defined. Four thin short lines in front of wing. Shadow on front of face clearly defined from hair.
Type III — Outer white circle around head is open at top (closed on types I and II). Greek border at top and bottom is wider than on types I and II.

Coarse Print

1867-73 — Typo. — Wmk. 91

P9	N5	(1kr) vio, type I	75.00	8.50
a.		(1kr) violet, type II ('73)	225.00	25.00

1874-76 — Fine Print

P9B	N5	(1kr) vio, type III ('76)	.55	.40
c.		(1kr) gray lilac, type I ('76)	225.00	32.50
d.		(1kr) violet, type II	65.00	8.50
e.		Double impression, type III	175.00	

Stamps of this issue, except No. P9Bc, exist in many shades, from gray to lilac brown and deep violet. Stamps in type III exist also privately perforated or rouletted.

Mercury — N6

1880

P10	N6	½kr blue green	8.50	1.25

Nos. P9B and P10 also exist on thicker paper without sheet watermark and No. P10 exists with unofficial perforation.

N7

Without Varnish Bars

1899 — Unwmk. — Imperf.

P11	N7	2h dark blue	.25	.25
P12	N7	6h orange	1.60	2.00
P13	N7	10h brown	1.60	.95
P14	N7	20h rose	1.60	2.00
		Nos. P11-P14 (4)	5.05	5.20

1901 — With Varnish Bars

P11a	N7	2h dark blue	2.40	.25
P12a	N7	6h orange	16.00	24.00
P13a	N7	10h brown	16.00	8.00
P14a	N7	20h rose	20.00	65.00
		Nos. P11a-P14a (4)	54.40	97.25

Nos. P11-P14 were re-issued in 1905. They exist privately perforated.

Mercury — N8

1908 — Imperf.

P15	N8	2h dark blue	.80	.25
a.		Tete beche pair	200.00	325.00
P16	N8	6h orange	3.25	.50
P17	N8	10h carmine	3.25	.40
P18	N8	20h brown	3.25	.40
		Nos. P15-P18 (4)	10.55	1.55

All values are found on chalky, regular and thin ordinary paper. They exist privately perforated.

Mercury — N9

1916 — Imperf.

P19	N9	2h brown	.25	.40
P20	N9	4h green	.35	1.25
P21	N9	6h dark blue	.55	1.25
P22	N9	10h orange	.60	1.25
P23	N9	30h claret	.55	1.60
		Nos. P19-P23 (5)	2.30	5.75
		Set, never hinged	9.50	

Nos. P19-P23 exist privately perforated.

Issues of the Republic

Newspaper Stamps of 1916 Overprinted

1919

P24	N9	2h brown	.25	.80
P25	N9	4h green	.40	6.50
P26	N9	6h dark blue	.25	8.00
P27	N9	10h orange	.40	9.50
P28	N9	30h claret	.25	16.00
		Nos. P24-P28 (5)	1.55	40.80
		Set, never hinged	3.25	

Nos. P24-P28 exist privately perforated.

Mercury — N10

1920-21 — Imperf.

P29	N10	2h violet	.25	.25
P30	N10	4h brown	.25	.25
P31	N10	5h slate	.25	.25
P32	N10	6h turq blue	.25	.25
P33	N10	8h green	.25	.40
P34	N10	9h yellow ('21)	.25	.25
P35	N10	10h red	.25	.25
P36	N10	12h blue	.25	.40
P37	N10	15h lilac ('21)	.25	.25
P38	N10	18h blue grn ('21)	.25	.25
P39	N10	20h orange	.25	.25
P40	N10	30h yellow brn ('21)	.25	.25
P41	N10	45h green ('21)	.25	.40
P42	N10	60h claret	.25	.25
P43	N10	72h chocolate ('21)	.25	.40
P44	N10	90h violet ('21)	.25	.80
P45	N10	1.20k red ('21)	.25	.80
P46	N10	2.40k yellow grn ('21)	.25	.80
P47	N10	3k gray ('21)	.25	.80
		Nos. P29-P47 (19)		7.55
		Set, never hinged	4.00	

Nos. P37-P40, P42, P44 and P47 exist also on thick grayish paper. Values are for the cheaper varieties. See the *Scott Classic Specialized Catalogue* for detailed listings.

Nos. P29-P47 exist privately perforated.

Mercury — N11

1921-22

P48	N11	45h gray	.25	.25
P49	N11	75h brown org ('22)	.25	.25
P50	N11	1.50k ol bister ('22)	.25	.25
P51	N11	1.80k gray blue ('22)	.25	.25
P52	N11	2.25k light brown	.25	.25
P53	N11	3k dull green ('22)	.25	.25
P54	N11	6k claret ('22)	.25	.25
P55	N11	7.50k bister	.25	.40
		Nos. P48-P55 (8)		2.15
		Set, never hinged	4.75	

Used values are for cancelled-to-order stamps. Postally used examples are worth much more.

Nos. P48-P55 exist privately perforated.

NEWSPAPER TAX STAMPS

Values for unused stamps 1853-59 are for examples in fine condition with gum. Examples without gum sell for about one-third or less of the figures quoted.

Issues of the Monarchy

NT1

Unwmk.

1853, Mar. 1   Typo.   Imperf.

PR1	NT1 2kr green	1,800.	57.50

The reprints are in finer print than the more coarsely printed originals, and on a smooth toned paper.

Values for Nos. PR2-PR9 are for stamps that do not show the watermark. Stamps showing the watermark often sell for more.

NT2

Two Types.
Type I — The banderol on the Crown of the left eagle touches the beak of the eagle.
Type II — The banderol does not touch the beak.

Wmk. 91, or, before July 1864, Unwmkd.

1858-59

PR2	NT2 1kr blue, type II	50.00	5.50
('59)			
a.	1kr blue, type I	1,225.	190.00
b.	Printed on both sides, type II		
PR3	NT2 2kr brn, type II	47.50	6.75
('59)			
a.	2kr red brown, type II	600.00	240.00
PR4	NT2 4kr brn, type I	425.00	1,100.

Nos. PR2a, PR3a, and PR4 were printed only on unwatermarked paper. Nos. PR2 and PR3 exist on unwatermarked and watermarked paper.

Nos. PR2 and PR3 exist in coarse and (after 1874) in fine print, like the contemporary postage stamps.

The reprints of the 4kr brown are of type II and on a smooth toned paper.

Issue date: 4kr, Nov. 1.

See Lombardy-Venetia for the 1kr in black and the 2kr, 4fk in red.

NT3

1877   Redrawn

PR5	NT3 1kr blue	12.50	1.40
a.	1kr pale ultramarine		2,900.
PR6	NT3 2kr brown	14.00	6.75

In the redrawn stamps the shield is larger and the vertical bar has eight lines above the white square and nine below, instead of five.

Nos. PR5 and PR6 exist also watermarked "WECHSEL-MARKEN." instead of "ZEITUNGS-MARKEN."

NT4

1890, June 1

PR7	NT4 1kr brown	9.00	1.00
PR8	NT4 2kr green	10.00	1.50

#PR5-PR8 exist with private perforation.

NT5

1890, June 1   Wmk. 91   Perf. 12½

PR9	NT5 25kr carmine	95.00	200.00

Nos. PR1-PR9 did not pay postage, but were a fiscal tax, collected by the postal authorities on newspapers.

SPECIAL HANDLING STAMPS

(For Printed Matter Only)
Issues of the Monarchy

Mercury
SH1

1916   Unwmk.   Perf. 12½

QE1	SH1 2h claret, *yellow*	1.20	4.00
QE2	SH1 5h dp green, *yellow*	1.20	4.00
	Set, never hinged	6.50	

SH2

1917   Perf. 12½

QE3	SH2 2h claret, *yellow*	.25	.40
a.	Pair, imperf. between	325.00	650.00
	Never hinged	650.00	
b.	Perf. 11½x12½	150.00	260.00
	Never hinged	800.00	
c.	Perf. 12½x11½	225.00	325.00
	Never hinged	950.00	
d.	Perf. 11½	1.60	4.00
	Never hinged	4.00	
QE4	SH2 5h dp grn, *yel*	.25	.40
a.	Pair, imperf. between	325.00	650.00
	Never hinged	650.00	
b.	Perf. 11½x12½	120.00	150.00
	Never hinged	800.00	
c.	Perf. 12½x11½	190.00	260.00
	Never hinged	950.00	
d.	Perf. 11½	1.60	4.00
	Never hinged	4.00	
	Set, never hinged	1.60	

Nos. QE1-QE4 exist imperforate.

Issues of the Republic

Nos. QE3 and QE4 Overprinted

1919

QE5	SH2 2h claret, *yellow*	.35	.25
a.	Inverted overprint	325.00	
	Never hinged	650.00	
b.	Perf. 11½x12½	6.00	12.00
	Never hinged	10.50	
c.	Perf. 12½x11½	110.00	290.00
	Never hinged	325.00	
d.	Perf. 11½	.40	1.25
	Never hinged	1.25	
QE6	SH2 5h dp grn, *yel*	.35	.25
a.	Perf. 11½x12½	1.60	4.50
	Never hinged	4.00	
b.	Perf. 12½x11½	40.00	95.00
	Never hinged	87.50	
c.	Perf. 11½	.35	.80
	Never hinged	.80	
	Set, never hinged	1.60	

Nos. QE5 and QE6 exist imperforate. Value, set unused hinged $175; never hinged $360.

No. QE3 Surcharged in Dark Blue

1921

QE7	SH2 50h on 2h claret, *yel*	.25	.80
	Never hinged	.80	

SH4

1922   Perf. 12½

QE8	SH4 50h lilac, *yellow*	.25	.25
	Never hinged	.40	

Nos. QE5-QE8 exist in vertical pairs, imperf between. No. QE8 exists imperf. Value: unused hinged $125; never hinged $250.

OCCUPATION STAMPS

Issued under Italian Occupation

Issued in Trieste

Austrian Stamps of 1916-18 Overprinted

1918   Unwmk.   Perf. 12½

N1	A37 3h bright vio	1.60	1.60
a.	Double overprint	57.50	57.50
b.	Inverted overprint	57.50	57.50
N2	A37 5h light grn	1.60	1.60
a.	Inverted overprint	57.50	57.50
c.	Double overprint	—	57.50
N3	A37 6h dp orange	2.50	2.50
N4	A37 10h magenta	25.00	4.00
a.	Inverted overprint	57.50	57.50
N5	A37 12h light bl	3.25	3.25
a.	Inverted overprint	57.50	57.50
N6	A42 15h dull red	1.60	1.60
a.	Inverted overprint	57.50	57.50
b.	Double overprint	57.50	57.50
N7	A42 20h dark green	1.60	1.60
a.	Inverted overprint	57.50	57.50
c.	Double overprint	140.00	
N8	A42 25h deep blue	12.50	12.50
a.	Inverted overprint	225.00	225.00
N9	A42 30h dl violet	3.25	3.25
N10	A39 40h olive grn	275.00	290.00
N11	A39 50h dark green	12.50	12.50
N12	A39 60h deep blue	29.00	29.00
N13	A39 80h orange brn	20.00	20.00
a.	Inverted overprint	—	
N14	A39 1k car, *yel*	20.00	20.00
a.	Double overprint	130.00	
N15	A40 2k light bl	450.00	500.00
	Never hinged	900.00	
N16	A40 4k yellow grn	1,050.	1,250.
	Never hinged	2,600.	

Handstamped

N17	A40 10k dp violet	30,000.	52,000.
	Never hinged	45,000.	

Granite Paper

N18	A40 2k light blue	675.00	
	Never hinged	1,350.	
N19	A40 3k car rose	650.00	700.00
	Never hinged	1,300.	
	Nos. N1-N14 (14)	409.40	403.40
	Set, never hinged	975.00	

Some authorities question the authenticity of No. N18.

Counterfeits of Nos. N10, N15-N19 are plentiful.

A variety of N19 exists on ordinary paper. Only 50 examples are known. Values, $8,250 unused, $12,250 never hinged.

A 90h stamp was printed but not issued because the Austrian stamps were replaced by Italian stamps. Only 50 90h were printed. Values, $4,100 unused, $8,000 never hinged.

Italian Stamps of 1901-18 Overprinted

Wmk. 140   Perf. 14

N20	A42 1c brown	3.25	8.25
a.	Inverted overprint	32.50	32.50
N21	A43 2c orange brn	3.25	8.25
a.	Inverted overprint	29.00	29.00
N22	A48 5c green	2.50	2.50
a.	Inverted overprint	57.50	57.50
b.	Double overprint	140.00	
N23	A48 10c claret	2.50	2.50
a.	Inverted overprint	85.00	85.00
b.	Double overprint	140.00	
N24	A50 20c brn orange	2.50	3.25
a.	Inverted overprint	110.00	110.00
b.	Double overprint	130.00	130.00
N25	A49 25c blue	2.50	4.00
a.	Double overprint	—	
b.	Inverted overprint	130.00	130.00

N26	A49 40c brown	16.00	29.00
a.	Inverted overprint	—	
N27	A45 45c olive grn	6.50	10.00
		160.00	160.00
N28	A49 50c violet	12.50	12.50
N29	A49 60c brown car	85.00	160.00
a.	Inverted overprint	—	
b.	Double overprint	375.00	
N30	A46 1 l brn & green	40.00	57.50
a.	Inverted overprint	—	
	Nos. N20-N30 (11)	176.50	297.75
	Set, never hinged	525.00	

Italian Stamps of 1901-18 Surcharged

N31	A48 5h on 5c green	1.60	3.25
	Never hinged	4.00	
a.	"5" omitted	125.00	125.00
b.	Inverted surcharge	125.00	125.00
N32	A50 20h on 20c brn org	1.60	3.25
	Never hinged	4.00	
a.	Double surcharge	125.00	125.00

Issued in the Trentino

Austrian Stamps of 1916-18 Overprinted

1918   Unwmk.   Perf. 12½

N33	A37 3h bright vio	12.50	12.50
a.	Double overprint	130.00	130.00
b.	Inverted overprint	125.00	125.00
N34	A37 5h light grn	10.00	5.00
a.	"8 nov. 1918"	3,400.	
b.	Inverted overprint	125.00	125.00
N35	A37 6h dp orange	125.00	110.00
N36	A37 10h magenta	10.00	8.25
a.	"8 nov. 1918"	250.00	250.00
N37	A37 12h light blue	325.00	290.00
N38	A42 15h dull red	12.50	10.00
N39	A42 20h dk grn	8.25	8.25
a.	"8 nov. 1918"	325.00	325.00
b.	Double overprint	130.00	130.00
c.	Inverted overprint	57.50	57.50
	Never hinged	1,900.	
N40	A42 25h deep blue	75.00	65.00
N41	A42 30h dl violet	29.00	25.00
		42.50	
N42	A39 40h olive grn	100.00	90.00
N43	A39 50h dk grn	65.00	50.00
a.	Inverted overprint	325.00	325.00
N44	A39 60h deep blue	110.00	90.00
		325.00	325.00
N45	A39 80h org brn	160.00	130.00
N46	A39 90h red violet	2,250.	3,100.
N47	A39 1k car, *yel*	150.00	125.00
N48	A40 2k light blue	750.00	900.00
N49	A40 4k yel green	3,400.	4,100.
N50a	A40 10k dp vio, gray ovpt.	25,000.	25,000.

Granite Paper

N51	A40 2k light blue	1,650.	2,250.
	Never hinged	3,300.	

Counterfeits of Nos. N33-N51 are plentiful.

Italian Stamps of 1901-18 Overprinted

Wmk. 140   Perf. 14

N52	A42 1c brown	4.00	11.50
a.	Inverted overprint	110.00	110.00
b.	Double overprint	125.00	
N53	A43 2c orange brn	4.00	11.50
a.	Inverted overprint	110.00	110.00
N54	A48 5c green	4.00	11.50
a.	Inverted overprint	110.00	110.00
b.	Double overprint	125.00	125.00
N55	A48 10c claret	4.00	11.50
a.	Inverted overprint	160.00	160.00
b.	Double overprint	125.00	125.00
N56	A50 20c brn orange	4.00	11.50
a.	Inverted overprint	160.00	160.00
N57	A49 40c brown	130.00	85.00
N58	A45 45c olive grn	65.00	85.00
		375.00	375.00
N59	A49 50c violet	65.00	85.00
N60	A46 1 l brn & green	65.00	85.00
a.	Double overprint	375.00	375.00
	Nos. N52-N60 (9)	345.00	397.50

Italian Stamps of 1906-18 Surcharged

N61	A48	5h on 5c green	2.50	4.00
N62	A48	10h on 10c claret	2.50	4.00
a.		Inverted overprint	110.00	110.00
N63	A50	20h on 20c brn org	2.50	4.00
a.		Double surcharge	110.00	110.00
		Nos. N61-N63 (3)	7.50	12.00

General Issue

Italian Stamps of 1901-18 Surcharged

1919

N64	A42	1c on 1c brown	1.60	4.00
a.		Inverted surcharge	25.00	25.00
N65	A43	2c on 2c org brn	1.60	4.00
a.		Double surcharge	375.00	
b.		Inverted surcharge	20.00	20.00
N66	A48	5c on 5c green	1.60	1.60
a.		Inverted surcharge	65.00	65.00
b.		Double surcharge	125.00	
N67	A48	10c on 10c claret	1.60	1.60
a.		Inverted surcharge	65.00	65.00
b.		Double surcharge	125.00	125.00
N68	A50	20c on 20c brn org	1.60	1.60
a.		Double surcharge	160.00	160.00
b.		Half used as 10c on cover		400.00
N69	A49	25c on 25c blue	1.60	2.50
a.		Double surcharge	160.00	
N70	A49	40c on 40c brown	1.60	4.00
a.		"ccrona"	150.00	150.00
N71	A49	45c on 45c ol grn	1.60	4.00
a.		Inverted surcharge	180.00	180.00
N72	A49	50c on 50c violet	1.60	4.00
a.		Inverted surcharge	180.00	180.00
N73	A49	60c on 60c brn car	1.60	4.00
a.		"00" for "60"	180.00	180.00

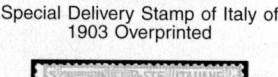

Italian No. 87 Surcharged

N74	A46	1cor on 1 l brn & green	5.00	10.00
		Nos. N64-N74 (11)	21.00	41.30

Surcharges similar to these but differing in style or arrangement of type were used in Dalmatia.

OCCUPATION SPECIAL DELIVERY STAMPS

Issued in Trieste

Special Delivery Stamp of Italy of 1903 Overprinted

1918　　　　Wmk. 140　　　　Perf. 14

NE1	SD1	25c rose red	75.00	130.00
a.		Inverted overprint	400.00	400.00

General Issue

Special Delivery Stamps of Italy of 1903-09 Surcharged

1919

NE2	SD1	25c on 25c rose	2.50	3.25
a.		Double surcharge	130.00	130.00
NE3	SD2	30c on 30c bl & rose	4.00	6.50
a.		Pair, on stamp without surcharge	1,500.	

OCCUPATION POSTAGE DUE STAMPS

Issued in Trieste

Postage Due Stamps of Italy, 1870-94, Overprinted

1918　　　　Wmk. 140　　　　Perf. 14

NJ1	D3	5c buff & mag	1.60	1.60
a.		Inverted overprint	29.00	29.00
b.		Double overprint	260.00	
NJ2	D3	10c buff & mag	1.60	1.60
a.		Inverted overprint	110.00	110.00
NJ3	D3	20c buff & mag	3.25	3.25
a.		Double overprint	260.00	
b.		Inverted overprint	110.00	110.00
NJ4	D3	30c buff & mag	6.50	6.50
NJ5	D3	40c buff & mag	50.00	60.00
a.		Inverted overprint	375.00	375.00
NJ6	D3	50c buff & mag	110.00	160.00
a.		Inverted overprint	450.00	450.00
NJ7	D3	1 l bl & mag	250.00	500.00
		Nos. NJ1-NJ7 (7)	422.95	732.95

General Issue

Postage Due Stamps of Italy, 1870-1903 Surcharged

1919　　　　Buff & Magenta

NJ8	D3	5c on 5c	2.50	2.50
a.		Inverted overprint	37.50	37.50
NJ9	D3	10c on 10c	2.50	2.50
a.		Center and surcharge invtd.	260.00	260.00
NJ10	D3	20c on 20c	4.00	2.50
a.		Double overprint	260.00	260.00
NJ11	D3	30c on 30c	4.00	5.00
NJ12	D3	40c on 40c	4.00	5.00
NJ13	D3	50c on 50c	6.50	8.25

Surcharged

NJ14	D3	1cor on 1 l bl & mag	6.50	12.50
NJ15	D2	2cor on 2 l bl & mag	75.00	160.00
NJ16	D3	5cor on 5 l bl & mag	75.00	160.00
		Nos. NJ8-NJ16 (9)	180.00	358.25

A. M. G. ISSUE FOR AUSTRIA

> Catalogue values for unused stamps in this section are for Never Hinged items.

Issued jointly by the Allied Military Government of the US and Great Britain, for civilian use in areas under American, British and French occupation. (Upper Austria, Salzburg, Tyrol, Vorarlberg, Styria and Carinthia).

OS1

1945　　　Unwmk.　　Litho.　　Perf. 11

4N1	OS1	1g aquamarine	.25	.25
4N2	OS1	3g deep orange	.25	.25
4N3	OS1	4g buff	.25	.25
4N4	OS1	5g bright green	.25	.25
4N5	OS1	6g red violet	.25	.25
4N6	OS1	8g rose pink	.25	.25
4N7	OS1	10g light gray	.25	.25
4N8	OS1	12g pale buff brown	.25	.25
4N9	OS1	15g rose red	.25	.25
4N10	OS1	20g copper brown	.25	.25
4N11	OS1	25g deep blue	.30	.30
4N12	OS1	30g bright violet	.30	.30
4N13	OS1	40g light ultra	.30	.30
4N14	OS1	60g light olive grn	.40	.40
4N15	OS1	1s dark violet	.40	.40

4N16	OS1	2s yellow	.95	.95
4N17	OS1	5s deep ultra	.95	.95
		Nos. 4N1-4N17 (17)	6.10	6.10

Used values are for examples with philatelic favor cancels. Postally used are worth much more.

For Nos. 4N2, 4N4-4N17 overprinted "PORTO" see Nos. J189-J203.

AUSTRIAN OFFICES ABROAD

These stamps were on sale and usable at all Austrian post-offices in Crete and in the Turkish Empire.

100 Centimes = 1 Franc

OFFICES IN CRETE

> Used values are italicized for stamps often found with false cancellations.

Stamps of Austria of 1899-1901 Issue, Surcharged in Black

a　　　　　　　　　b

c　　　　　　　　　d

On Nos. 73a, 75a, 77a, 81a Granite Paper With Varnish Bars

1903-04　　Unwmk.　　Perf. 12½, 13½

1	A15(a)	5c on 5h blue green	1.00	3.00
2	A16(b)	10c on 10h rose	.45	4.00
3	A16(b)	25c on 25h ultra	40.00	25.00
4	A17(c)	50c on 50h gray blue	8.00	110.00

On Nos. 83, 83a, 84, 85 Without Varnish Bars

5	A18(d)	1fr on 1k car rose	1.25	85.00
a.		1fr on 1k carmine	8.00	85.00
b.		Horiz. pair, imperf. btwn.	225.00	—
c.		Vert. pair, imperf. btwn.	—	—
6	A18(d)	2fr on 2k ('04)	7.75	325.00
7	A18(d)	4fr on 4k ('04)	11.00	600.00
		Nos. 1-7 (7)	69.45	1,152.

Surcharged on Austrian Stamps of 1904-05 On Nos. 89, 97

1905　　　Without Varnish Bars

8a	A19(a)	5c on 5h blue green	50.00	45.00
9	A20(b)	10c on 10h car	1.00	11.50

On Nos. 89a, 97a, 99a, 103a With Varnish Bars

8	A19(a)	5c on 5h bl grn	3.00	6.00
9a	A20(b)	10c on 10h carmine	32.50	32.50
10	A20(b)	25c on 25h ultra	1.00	110.00
11	A21(b)	50c on 50h dl bl	2.50	475.00

Surcharged on Austrian Stamps and Type of 1906-07 Without Varnish Bars

1907　　　　　Perf. 12½, 13½

12	A19(a)	5c on 5h yel green (#90)	1.00	3.00
13	A20(b)	10c on 10h car (#92)	1.40	20.00
14	A20(b)	10c on 15h vio	1.75	22.00
		Nos. 12-14 (3)	4.15	45.00

A5　　　　　　　　　A6

1908　　　　Typo.　　　　Perf. 12½

15	A5	5c green, yellow	.35	1.00
16	A5	10c scarlet, rose	.40	1.00
17	A5	15c brown, buff	.45	4.75
18	A5	25c dp blue, blue	15.00	3.75

Engr.

19	A6	50c lake, yellow	2.75	30.00
20	A6	1fr brown, gray	6.75	57.50
a.		Vert. pair, imperf. btwn.	225.00	
		Nos. 15-20 (6)	25.70	98.00

Nos. 15-18 are on paper colored on the surface only. All values exist imperforate. Value, each pair $75.

60th year of the reign of Emperor Franz Josef, for permanent use.

Paper Colored Through

1914　　　　　　　　　Typo.

21	A5	10c rose, rose	1.20	2,000.
22	A5	25c ultra, blue	2.00	150.00

Nos. 21 and 22 exist imperforate. Value, each pair $75.

OFFICES IN THE TURKISH EMPIRE

From 1863 to 1867 the stamps of Lombardy-Venetia (Nos. 15 to 24) were used at the Austrian Offices in the Turkish Empire.

100 Soldi = 1 Florin

40 Paras = 1 Piaster

> Values for unused stamps are for examples with gum. Examples without gum sell for about one-third or less of the figures quoted. Used values are italicized for stamps often found with false cancellations.

For similar designs in Kreuzers, see early Austria.

A1　　　　　　　　　A2

Two different printing methods were used, as in the 1867-74 issues of Austria. They may be distinguished by the coarse or fine lines of the hair and whiskers and by the paper, which is more transparent on the later issue.

1867　Typo.　Wmk. 91　Perf. 9½ Coarse Print

1	A1	2sld orange	2.40	27.50
a.		2sld yellow	65.00	80.00
2	A1	3sld green	150.00	67.50
a.		3sld dark green	325.00	200.00
3	A1	5sld red	240.00	14.00
a.		5sld carmine	325.00	40.00
b.		5sld red lilac	275.00	24.00
4	A1	10sld blue	200.00	2.40
a.		10sld light blue	275.00	3.25
b.		10sld dark blue	240.00	3.25
5	A1	15sld brown	24.00	8.00
a.		15sld dark brown	95.00	65.00
b.		15sld reddish brown	40.00	16.00
c.		15sld gray brown	80.00	16.00
6	A1	25sld violet	24.00	40.00
a.		25sld brown violet	40.00	60.00
b.		25sld gray lilac	120.00	47.50
7	A2	50sld brn, perf. 10½	1.25	65.00
a.		Perf. 12	100.00	110.00
b.		Perf. 13	325.00	—
k.		Perf. 9	27.50	140.00
l.		50sld pale red brn, perf. 12	160.00	160.00
m.		Vert. pair, imperf. btwn.	300.00	550.00
n.		Horiz. pair, imperf. btwn.	300.00	550.00
o.		Perf. 10½x9	85.00	160.00

Perf. 9, 9½, 10½ and Compound

1876-83   **Fine Print**

7C	A1	2sld yellow ('83)	.40	3,000.
7D	A1	3sld green ('78)	1.20	27.50
7E	A1	5sld red ('78)	.40	24.00
7F	A1	10sld blue	100.00	1.25
7I	A1	15sld org brn ('81)	12.00	160.00
7J	A1	25sld gray lil ('83)	.80	360.00
		Nos. 7C-7J (6)	114.80	3,573.

The 10 soldi was reprinted in deep dull blue, perforated 10½. Value, $6.50.

A3

1883   **Perf. 9½**

8	A3	2sld brown	.25	190.00
9	A3	3sld green	1.20	35.00
10	A3	5sld rose	.25	20.00
11	A3	10sld blue	.80	.80
12	A3	20sld gray, perf. 10	6.50	600.00
a.		Perf. 9½	1.60	9.50
13	A3	50sld red lilac	1.25	20.00
		Nos. 8-13 (6)	10.25	865.80

No. 9 Surcharged

10 PARAS ON 3 SOLDI:
Type I — Surcharge 16½mm across. "PARA" about ½mm above bottom of "10." 2mm space between "10" and "P"; 1½mm between "A" and "10." Perf. 9½ only.
Type II — Surcharge 15¼ to 16mm across. "PARA" on same line with figures or slightly higher or lower. 1½mm space between "10" and "P"; 1mm between "A" and "10." Perf. 9½ and 10.

1886   **Perf. 9½, 10**

14	A4	10pa on 3sld grn, type II, perf. 10	.35	8.00
a.		10pa on 3sld green, type I	200.00	500.00
b.		Inverted surcharge, type I		2,000.

Surcharged on Austria Nos. 42-46

1888

15	A11	10pa on 3kr grn	4.00	12.00
a.		"01 PARA 10"		1,200.
16	A11	20pa on 5kr rose	.40	12.00
a.		Double surcharge	400.00	
		Never hinged	1,200.	
17	A11	1pi on 10kr blue	65.00	1.60
a.		Perf. 13½		800.00
b.		Double surcharge		—
18	A11	2pi on 20kr gray	1.60	6.50
19	A11	5pi on 50kr vio	2.00	20.00
		Nos. 15-19 (5)	73.00	52.10

Austria Nos. 52-55, 58, 61 Surcharged

1890-92   **Unwmk. Perf. 9 to 13½**
Granite Paper

20	A12	8pa on 2kr brn ('92)	.25	.65
a.		Perf. 9½	12.00	16.00
21	A12	10pa on 3kr green	.55	.65
a.		Pair, imperf. between		550.00
22	A12	20pa on 5kr rose	.35	.65
23	A12	1pi on 10kr ultra	.40	.25
a.		Pair, imperf. between		550.00
24	A12	2pi on 20kr ol grn	8.00	32.50
25	A12	5pi on 50kr vio	12.00	72.50
		Nos. 20-25 (6)	21.55	107.20

See note after Austria No. 65 on missing numerals, etc.

Austria Nos. 66, 69 Surcharged

1891   **Perf. 10 to 13½**

26	A14	2pi on 20kr green	6.50	1.60
a.		Perf. 9¼	200.00	160.00
27	A14	5pi on 50kr violet	3.25	3.25

Two types of the surcharge on No. 26 exist.

Austria Nos. 62-65 Surcharged

1892   **Perf. 10½, 11½**

28	A13	10pi on 1gld blue	12.00	32.50
29	A13	20pi on 2gld car	16.00	60.00
a.		Double surcharge		—

1896   **Perf. 10½, 11½, 12½**

30	A13	10pi on 1gld pale lil	18.50	22.50
31	A13	20pi on 2gld gray grn	37.50	75.00

Austria Nos. 73, 75, 77, 81, 83-85 Surcharged

#32-35   #36-38

Perf. 12½, 13½ and Compound

1900   **Without Varnish Bars**

32	A15	10pa on 5h bl grn	4.75	.80
33	A16	20pa on 10h rose	5.50	.80
b.		Perf. 12½x10½	400.00	350.00
34	A16	1pi on 25h ultra	3.25	.40
35	A17	2pi on 50h gray bl	8.00	4.00
36	A18	5pi on 1k car rose	.55	.40
a.		5pi on 1k carmine	.80	1.20
b.		Horiz. or vert. pair, imperf. btwn.	160.00	
37	A18	10pi on 2k gray lil	2.00	3.50
38	A18	20pi on 4k gray grn	1.60	8.00
		Nos. 32-38 (7)	25.65	17.90

In the surcharge on Nos. 37 and 38 "piaster" is printed "PIAST."

1901   **With Varnish Bars**

32a	A15	10pa on 5h blue green	1.60	2.75
33a	A16	20pa on 10h rose	2.40	400.00
34a	A16	1pi on 25h ultra	1.20	.80
35b	A17	2pi on 50h gray blue	2.75	8.00
		Nos. 32a-35b (4)	7.95	411.55

A4   A5

A6

1906   **Perf. 12½ to 13½**
Without Varnish Bars

39	A4	10pa dark green	12.00	4.00
40	A5	20pa rose	.80	1.20
41	A5	1pi ultra	.80	.60
42	A6	2pi gray blue	.80	1.20
		Nos. 39-42 (4)	14.40	6.80

1903   **With Varnish Bars**

39a	A4	10pa dark green	4.75	2.00
40a	A5	20pa rose	3.25	.80
41a	A5	1pi ultra	2.40	.40
42a	A6	2pi gray blue	160.00	3.25
		Nos. 39a-42a (4)	170.40	6.45

1907   **Without Varnish Bars**

43	A4	10pa yellow green	.55	2.00
45	A5	30pa violet	.55	4.00

A7   A8

1908   **Typo.**   **Perf. 12½**

46	A7	10pa green, yellow	.25	.40
47	A7	20pa scarlet, rose	.25	.40
48	A7	30pa brown, buff	.40	2.00
49	A7	1pi deep bl, blue	14.50	.25
50	A7	60pa vio, bluish	.65	5.50

Engr.

51	A8	2pi lake, yellow	.65	.25
52	A8	5pi brown, gray	.65	.95
53	A8	10pi green, yellow	.95	2.40
54	A8	2pi blue, gray	2.40	4.75
		Nos. 46-54 (9)	20.70	16.90

Nos. 46-50 are on paper colored on the surface only. 60th year of the reign of Emperor Franz Josef I, for permanent use.
Nos. 46-50 exist imperforate. Values, set: unused $275, never hinged $650.

Paper Colored Through

1913-14   **Typo.**

57	A7	20pa rose, rose ('14)	.55	650.00
58	A7	1pi ultra, blue	.35	.55

Nos. 57 and 58 exist imperforate.

POSTAGE DUE STAMPS

Type of Austria D2 Surcharged in Black

1902   **Unwmk.**   **Perf. 12½, 13½**

J1	D2	10pa on 5h gray green	1.60	8.00
J2	D2	20pa on 10h gray green	1.60	12.00
J3	D2	1pi on 20h gray green	1.60	12.00
J4	D2	2pi on 40h gray green	1.60	12.00
J5	D2	5pi on 100h gray green	1.60	8.00
		Nos. J1-J5 (5)	8.00	52.00

Shades of Nos. J1-J5 exist, varying from yellowish to dark green.

D3

1908   **Typo.**   **Perf. 12½**
Chalky Paper

J6	D3	¼pi pale green	3.25	13.50
J7	D3	½pi pale green	2.00	11.00
J8	D3	2pi pale green	2.40	8.00
J9	D3	1½pi pale green	1.20	24.00
J10	D3	2pi pale green	1.60	20.00
J11	D3	5pi pale green	2.40	14.50
J12	D3	10pi pale green	16.00	150.00
J13	D3	20pi pale green	11.00	160.00
J14	D3	30pi pale green	16.00	14.50
		Nos. J6-J14 (9)	55.85	415.50

Nos. J6-J14 exist in distinct shades of green and on thick chalky, regular and thin ordinary paper. Values are for the least expensive variety. For comprehensive listings, see Scott Classic Specialized Catalogue.
No. J6-J14 exist imperforate.
Forgeries exist.

LOMBARDY-VENETIA

Formerly a kingdom in the north of Italy forming part of the Austrian Empire. Milan and Venice were the two principal cities. Lombardy was annexed to Sardinia in 1859, and Venetia to the kingdom of Italy in 1866.

100 Centesimi = 1 Lira
100 Soldi = 1 Florin (1858)

Unused examples without gum of Nos. 1-24 are worth approximately 20% of the values given, which are for stamps with original gum as defined in the catalogue introduction.

For similar designs in Kreuzers, see early Austria.

Coat of Arms — A1

15 CENTESIMI:
Type I — "5" is on a level with the "1." One heavy line around coat of arms center.
Type II — As type I, but "5" is a trifle sideways and is higher than the "1."
Type III — As type II, but two, thinner, lines around center.

45 CENTESIMI:
Type I — Lower part of "45" is lower than "Centes." One heavy line around coat of arms center. "45" varies in height and distance from "Centes."
Type II — One heavy line around coat of arms center. Lower part of "45" is on a level with lower part of "Centes."
Type III — As type II, but two, thinner, lines around center.

Wmk. K.K.H.M. in Sheet or Unwmkd.

1850   **Typo.**   **Imperf.**
Thick to Thin Paper

1	A1	5c buff	6,000.	200.00
		On cover, single franking		625.00
a.		Printed on both sides	21,500.	675.00
b.		5c yellow	11,250.	650.00
c.		5c orange	6,500.	225.00
d.		5c lemon yellow		2,500.
3	A1	10c black	6,000.	200.00
a.		10c gray black		175.00
4	A1	15c red, type III	1,900.	7.50
		15c red, type I	4,500.	29.00
c.		Ribbed paper, type II		900.00
d.		Ribbed paper, type I	27,500.	275.00
f.		15c red, type II	2,400.	30.00
5	A1	30c brown	6,750.	26.50
a.		Ribbed paper	13,500.	175.00
6	A1	45c blue, type III	20,000.	60.00
a.		45c blue, type I	21,250.	60.00
b.		Ribbed paper, type I		750.00
c.		45c blue, type II	190,000.	75.00

1854
Machine-made Paper, Type III

3c	A1	10c black	12,250.	500.00
4g	A1	15c pale red	2,100.	6.00
5b	A1	30c brown ('55)	7,500.	26.50
6d	A1	45c blue	18,000.	75.00

See note about the paper of the 1850 issue of Austria. *The reprints are type III, in brighter colors.*

A2   A3

A4   A5

A6

Two Types of Each Value.
Type I — Loops of the bow at the back of the head broken.
Type II — Loops complete. Wreath projects further at top of head.

		1858-62 Embossed	Perf. 14½	
7	A2	2s yel, type II	2,400.	150.00
a.		2s yellow, type I	12,000.	900.00
8	A3	3s black, type II	18,000.	190.00
a.		3s black, type I	6,750.	375.00
b.		Perf. 16, type I	—	2,250.
c.		Perf. 15x16 or 16x15, type I	12,500.	750.00
9	A3	3s grn, type II ('62)	1,325.	140.00
10	A4	5s red, type II	750.00	12.00
a.		5s red, type I	2,400.	45.00
b.		Printed on both sides, type II		6,750.
11	A5	10s brn, type II	5,250.	24.00
a.		10s brown, type I	1,500.	140.00
12	A6	15s blue, type II	6,000.	125.00
		No gum	1,500.	
a.		15s blue, type I	12,000.	225.00
b.		Printed on both sides, type II		18,750.

The reprints are of type II and are perforated 10½, 11, 11½, 12, 12½ and 13. There are also imperforate reprints of Nos. 7-9.

A7

		1861-62	Perf. 14	
13	A7	5s red	7,125.	7.00
14	A7	10s brown ('62)	13,000.	75.00

The reprints are perforated 9, 9 ½, 10½, 11, 12, 12½ and 13. There are also imperforate reprints of the 2 and 3s.
The 2, 3 and 15s of this type exist only as reprints.

A8

		1863		
15	A8	2s yellow	425.00	225.00
16	A8	3s green	5,250.	125.00
17	A8	5s rose	6,750.	37.50
18	A8	10s blue	14,000.	90.00
19	A8	15s yellow brown	12,000.	340.00

		1864-65 Wmk. 91	Perf. 9½	
20	A8	2s yellow ('65)	640.00	900.00
21	A8	3s green	55.00	52.50
22	A8	5s rose	9.00	11.50
23	A8	10s blue	110.00	22.50
24	A8	15s yellow brown	1,250.	210.00

Nos. 15-24 reprints are perforated 10½ and 13. There are also imperforate reprints of the 2s and 3s.

NEWSPAPER TAX STAMPS

From 1853 to 1858 the Austrian Newspaper Tax Stamp 2kr green (No. PR1) was also used in Lombardy-Venetia, at the value of 10 centesimi.

NT1

Type I — The banderol of the left eagle touches the beak of the eagle.
Type II — The banderol does not touch the beak.

		1858-59 Unwmk. Typo.	Imperf.	
PR1	NT1	1kr black, type I ('59)	3,750.	4,750.
PR2	NT1	2kr red, type II ('59)	500.00	75.00
a.		Watermark 91	1,650.	115.00
PR3	NT1	4kr red, type I	150,000.	5,500.

The reprints are on a smooth toned paper and are all of type II.

AZERBAIJAN

ˌa-zər-ˌbī-'jän

(Azerbaidjan)

LOCATION — Southernmost part of Russia in Eastern Europe, bounded by Georgia, Dagestan, Caspian Sea, Iran and Armenia
GOVT. — A Soviet Socialist Republic
AREA — 33,430 sq. mi.
POP. — 7,908,224 (1999 est)
CAPITAL — Baku

With Armenia and Georgia, Azerbaijan made up the Transcaucasian Federation of Soviet Republics.
Stamps of Azerbaijan were replaced in 1923 by those of Transcaucasian Federated Republics.
With the breakup of the Soviet Union on Dec. 26, 1991, Azerbaijan and ten former Soviet republics established the Commonwealth of Independent States.

100 Kopecks = 1 Ruble
100 Giapiks = 1 Manat (1992)

Catalogue values for unused stamps in this country are for Never Hinged items, beginning with Scott 350 in the regular postage section, and Scott C1 in the air post section.

National Republic

Standard Bearer — A1

Farmer at Sunset — A2

Baku — A3

Temple of Eternal Fires — A4

		1919 Unwmk. Litho. Imperf. On White Paper		
1	A1	10k multicolored	.40	.40
2	A1	20k multicolored	.40	.40
3	A2	40k green, yellow & blk	.40	.40
4	A2	60k red, yellow & blk	.55	.55
5	A2	1r blue, yellow & blk	.90	.90
6	A3	2r red, bister & blk	.90	.90
7	A3	5r blue, bister & blk	1.90	2.00
8	A3	10r olive grn, bis & blk	1.90	1.90

9	A4	25r blue, red & black	3.25	50.00
10	A4	50r ol grn, red & black	4.50	4.75
		Nos. 1-10 (10)	15.10	62.20

For surcharges see Nos. 57-64, 75-80.

1920

		On Grayish Paper		
1A	A1	10k multicolored	.25	20.00
2A	A1	20k multicolored	.25	20.00
3A	A2	40k green, yellow & blk	.25	30.00
4A	A2	60k red, yellow & blk	.25	30.00
5A	A2	1r blue, yellow & blk	.40	30.00
6A	A3	2r red, bister & blk	.40	40.00
7A	A3	5r blue, bister & blk	.45	40.00
8A	A3	10r olive grn, bis & blk	.65	40.00
9A	A4	25r blue, red & black	1.10	225.00
10A	A4	50r ol grn, red & black	1.40	175.00
		Nos. 1A-10A (10)	5.40	650.00

Soviet Socialist Republic

Symbols of Labor — A5

Oil Well — A6

Bibi Eibatt Oil Field — A7

Khan's Palace, Baku — A8

Globe and Workers — A9

Maiden's Tower, Baku — A10

Goukasoff House A11

Blacksmiths — A12

Hall of Judgment, Baku — A13

1922

15	A5	1r gray green	.25	.35
16	A6	2r olive black	.60	.60
17	A7	5r gray brown	.25	.35
18	A8	10r gray	.60	.60
19	A9	25r orange brown	.25	.40
20	A10	50r violet	.25	.40
21	A11	100r dull red	.35	.50
22	A12	150r blue	.35	.50
23	A9	250r violet & buff	.35	.50
24	A13	400r dark blue	.40	.50
25	A12	500r gray vio & blk	.40	.50
26	A13	1000r dk blue & rose	.40	.60
27	A8	2000r blue & black	.40	.45
28	A7	3000r brown & blue	.45	.50
a.		Tete beche pair	18.00	18.00
29	A11	5000r black, ol grn	.75	.90
		Nos. 15-29 (15)	6.05	7.80

Counterfeits exist of Nos. 1-29. They generally sell for more than genuine examples.
For overprints and surcharges see Nos. 32-41, 43, 45-55, 65-72, 300-304, 307-333.

Nos. 15, 17, 23, 28, 27 Handstamped from Metal Dies in a Numbering Machine

1922

32	A5	10,000r on 1r	19.50	17.50
33	A7	15,000r on 5r	19.50	27.50
34	A9	33,000r on 250r	6.25	6.25
35	A7	50,000r on 3000r	32.50	10.00
36	A8	66,000r on 2000r	19.50	12.00
		Nos. 32-36 (5)	97.25	73.25

Same Surcharges on Regular Issue and Semi-Postal Stamps of 1922

1922-23

36A	A7	500r on 5r	180.00	190.00
37	A6	1000r on 2r	30.00	36.00
38	A8	2000r on 10r	18.00	9.00
39	A8	5000r on 2000r	9.00	3.75
40	A11	15,000r on 5000r	15.00	12.00
41	A5	20,000r on 1r	24.00	14.50
42	SP1	25,000r on 500r	60.00	—
43	A7	50,000r on 5r	60.00	60.00
44	SP2	50,000r on 1000r	60.00	—
45	A11	50,000r on 5000r	18.00	18.00
45A	A8	60,000r on 2000r	120.00	225.00
46	A11	70,000r on 5000r	150.00	47.50
47	A6	100,000r on 2r	18.00	18.00
48	A8	200,000r on 10r	12.00	12.00
49	A8	200,000r on 25r	18.00	19.00
50	A7	300,000r on 3000r	50.00	50.00
51	A8	500,000r on 2000r	30.00	30.00

Regular Issue Stamps of 1922-23 Surcharged

52	A7	500r on #33	650.00	700.00
53	A11	15,000r on #46	650.00	700.00
54	A7	300,000r on #35	750.00	800.00
55	A8	500,000r on #36	650.00	700.00

The surcharged semi-postal stamps were used for regular postage.

Same Surcharges on Stamps of 1919

57	A1	25,000r on 10k	.85	1.50
58	A1	50,000r on 20k	.85	1.50
59	A2	75,000r on 40k	2.00	4.00
60	A2	100,000r on 60k	.85	1.50
61	A2	200,000r on 1r	.85	1.50
62	A3	300,000r on 2r	1.10	1.50

63	A3	500,000r on 5r	1.10	1.50
64	A2	750,000r on 40k	4.25	5.50
		Nos. 57-64 (8)	11.85	18.50

Handstamped from Settings of Rubber Type in Black or Violet

Nos. 65-66, 72-80   Nos. 67-70

On Stamps of 1922

65	A6	100,000r on 2r	27.50	27.50
66	A8	200,000r on 10r	80.00	80.00
67	A8	200,000r on 10r (V)	80.00	80.00
68	A9	200,000r on 25r (V)	80.00	80.00
a.		Black surcharge	80.00	80.00
69	A7	300,000r on 3000r (V)	80.00	80.00
70	A8	500,000r on 2000r (V)	72.50	72.50
a.		Black surcharge	90.00	90.00
72	A11	1,500,000r on 5000r	140.00	140.00
a.		Black surcharge	120.00	120.00

On Stamps of 1919

75	A1	50,000r on 20k	4.00	
76	A2	75,000r on 40k	4.00	
77	A2	100,000r on 60k	4.00	
78	A2	200,000r on 1r	4.00	
79	A3	300,000r on 2r	4.00	
80	A3	500,000r on 5r	4.00	

Inverted and double surcharges of Nos. 32-80 sell for twice the normal price.
Counterfeits exist of Nos. 32-80.

Baku Province

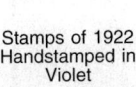

Regular and Semi-Postal Stamps of 1922 Handstamped in Violet or Black

The overprint reads "Bakinskoi P(ochtovoy) K(ontory)," meaning Baku Post Office.

1922		Unwmk.		Imperf.
300	A5	1r gray green	100.00	
301	A7	5r gray brown	100.00	200.00
302	A12	150r blue	100.00	100.00
303	A9	250r violet & buff	100.00	200.00
304	A13	400r dark blue	75.00	75.00
305	SP1	500r bl & pale bl	100.00	150.00
306	SP2	1000r brown & bis	100.00	
307	A8	2000r blue & black	120.00	150.00
308	A7	3000r brown & blue	100.00	
309	A11	5000r black, ol grn	120.00	
		Nos. 300-309 (10)	1,015.	

Stamps of 1922 Handstamped in Violet

Бакинскаго Г.-П.-Т.О.Xξ1

Ovpt. reads: Baku Post, Telegraph Office No. 1.

1924		Overprint 24x2mm	
312	A12	150r blue	65.00
313	A9	250r violet & buff	65.00
314	A13	400r dark blue	65.00
317	A8	2000r blue & black	65.00
318	A7	3000r brn & blue	65.00
319	A11	5000r black, ol grn	200.00

		Overprint 30x3½mm		
323	A12	150r blue	100.00	125.00
324	A9	250r violet & buff	100.00	
325	A13	400r dark blue	100.00	100.00
328	A8	2000r blue & black		
329	A7	3000r brn & blue	100.00	150.00
330	A11	5000r black, ol grn	100.00	

		Overprinted on Nos. 32-33, 35	
331	A5	10,000r on 1r	500.00
332	A7	15,000r on 5r	500.00
333	A7	50,000r on 3000r	500.00
		Nos. 312-333 (15)	2,625.

The overprinted semipostal stamps were used for regular postage.
A 24x2mm handstamp on #17, B1-B2, and 30x3½mm on Nos. 15, 17, B1-B2, was of private origin.

> **Catalogue values for unused stamps in this section, from this point to the end of the section, are for Never Hinged items.**

Flag, Map — A20

Unwmk.

1992, Mar. 26		Litho.	Perf. 14	
350	A20	35k multicolored	1.50	1.50

For surcharge, see No. 733.

Caspian Sea — A21

1992, May 7			Perf. 12	
351	A21	25g on 15k multi	.40	.40
a.		Booklet pane of 12	5.00	
		Complete booklet, #351a	6.00	
352	A21	35g on 15k multi	.50	.50
353	A21	50g on 15k multi	.65	.65
354	A21	1.50m on 15k multi	2.25	2.25
355	A21	2.50m on 15k multi	3.50	3.50
		Nos. 351-355 (5)	7.30	7.30

Nos. 351-355 are sucharged on the Azerbaijan value of a National Park series featuring one stamp for each republic, prepared by the Soviet Union but not issued. Value for the unoverprinted Azerbaijan stamp, $1.25.
For additional surcharges see Nos. 435, 501-504.

Iran-Azerbaijan Telecommunications — A21a

1993		Photo.	Perf. 13x13½	
355A	A21a	15g multicolored	1.25	1.25

See Iran No. 2544.
For surcharges see Nos. 403-406.

Horses A22

1993, Feb. 1		Litho.	Perf. 13	
356	A22	20g shown	.25	.25
357	A22	30g Kabarda	.25	.25
358	A22	50g Qarabair	.25	.25
359	A22	1m Don	.25	.25
360	A22	2.50m Yakut	.40	.40
361	A22	5m Orlov	.80	.80
362	A22	10m Diliboz	1.75	1.75
		Nos. 356-362 (7)	3.95	3.95

Perf. 12½

Souvenir Sheet

362A	A5	8m Qarabag	1.50	1.50

For overprints see Nos. 629-636.

Maiden's Tower — A23

1992-93		Litho.	Perf. 12½x12	
363	A23	10g blk & blue grn	.25	.25
365	A23	20g black & red	.25	.25
367	A23	50g black & blue grn	.25	.25
368	A23	50g black & yellow	.50	.50
370	A23	1m black & rose lilac	.25	.25
372	A23	1.50m black & blue	1.00	1.00
373	A23	2.50m black & yellow	.50	.50
374	A23	5m black & green	.75	.75
		Nos. 363-374 (8)	3.75	3.75

Issued: 10g, 20g, 1.50m, No. 367, Dec. 20; No. 368, 1m, 2.50m, 5m, June 20, 1993.
For surcharges see Nos. 550-557, 757.

Government Building — A24

1993, Oct. 12		Litho.	Perf. 12½	
375	A24	25g yellow & black	.30	.30
376	A24	30g green & black	.30	.30
377	A24	50g blue & black	.40	.40
378	A24	1m red & black	.80	.80
		Nos. 375-378 (4)	1.80	1.80

For surcharges see No. 407-414.

Flowers — A25

1993, Aug. 12		Litho.	Perf. 12½	
379	A25	25g multi	.25	.25
380	A25	50g multi	.25	.25
381	A25	1m multi	.25	.25
382	A25	1.50m multi	.35	.35
383	A25	5m multi	.85	.85
384	A25	10m multi	1.60	1.60
		Nos. 379-384 (6)	3.55	3.55

Souvenir Sheet
Perf. 13

385	A25	10m multi	1.75	1.75

No. 385 contains one 32x40mm stamp.
For surcharge, see No. 809.

25g, Tulipa eichleri. 50g, Puschkinia scilloides. 1m, Iris elegantissima. 1.50m, Iris acutiloba. 5m, Tulipa florenskyii. 10m, Iris reticulata.
No. 385, Muscari elecostomum.

Fish A26

25g, Acipenser guldenstadti. 50g, Acipenser stellatus. 1m, Rutilus frisii kutum. 1.50m, Rutilus rutilus caspicus. 5m, Salmo trutta caspius. No. 391, Alosa kessleri. No. 392, Huso huso.

1993, Aug. 27			Perf. 12½	
386	A26	25g multicolored	.25	.25
387	A26	50g multicolored	.25	.25
388	A26	1m multicolored	.25	.25
389	A26	1.50m multicolored	.35	.35
390	A26	5m multicolored	.85	.85
391	A26	10m multicolored	1.60	1.60
		Nos. 386-391 (6)	3.55	3.55

Souvenir Sheet
Perf. 13

392	A26	10m multicolored	1.75	1.75

No. 392 contains one 40x32mm stamp.
For surcharges, see Nos. 810, 813.

Pres. Heydar A. Aliyev — A27

Design: No. 394, Map of Nakhichevan.

1993, Sept. 12		Litho.	Perf. 12½x13	
393	A27	25m multicolored	2.00	1.60
394	A27	25m multicolored	2.00	1.60
a.		Pair, #393-394	4.25	4.25
b.		Souv. sheet, #393-394, perf. 12	90.00	
c.		Souv. sheet, #393-394, perf. 12	15.00	

Name on map spelled "Naxcivan" on No. 394c. It is spelled "Haxcivan" on Nos. 394-394b.
No. 394c issued Sept. 20, 1993.

Shirvanshah's Palace, UNESCO World Heritage Site, Baku — A28

Style of tombs: 2m, Shirvanshah's Palace, 13th-14th cent. 4m, Turbe mausoleum, 15th cent. 8m, Divan-Khana, 15th cent.

1994, Jan. 17		Litho.	Perf. 11	
395	A28	2m red, silver & black	.25	.25
396	A28	4m green, silver & black	.35	.35
397	A28	8m blue, silver & black	.75	.75
		Nos. 395-397 (3)	1.35	1.35

For surcharges, see Nos. 753, 758-759, 808.

A29

5m, Natl. Colors, Star, Crescent. 8m, Natl. coat of arms.

1994, Jan. 17			Perf. 12½	
398	A29	5m multicolored	.45	.45
399	A29	8m multicolored	.80	.80

For surcharges, see Nos. 816, 817.

A30

1994, Jan. 17   **Perf. 12½**
400 A30 10m multi + label   .75   .75
Mohammed Fizuli (1494-1556), poet.

Mammed Amin Rasulzade (1884-
1955), 1st President — A31

Jalil Mamedkulizade, Writer, 125th
Birth Anniv. — A32

1994, May 21   **Perf. 12½, 13 (#402)**
401 A31 15m blk, yel & brown   1.25 1.25
402 A32 20m black, blue & gold   1.25 1.25
No. 402 printed se-tenant with label.
For surcharges, see Nos. 814, 867.

No. 355A Surcharged

1994, Jan. 18 Photo.   Perf. 13x13½
403 A21a 2m on 15g   .50   .50
404 A21a 20m on 15g   1.00 1.00
405 A21a 25m on 15g   1.50 1.50
406 A21a 50m on 15g   3.00 3.00
  a.   Vert. strip of 4, #403-406   5.00 5.00
       Nos. 403-406 (4)   6.00 6.00

**Nos. 375-378
Surcharged**

1994, Feb. 22   Litho.   Perf. 12½
407 A24   5m on 1m #375   .50   .50
408 A24   10m on 30g #377   .50   .50
409 A24   15m on 30g #377   .50   .50
  a.   Pair, #408-409   1.25 1.25
410 A24   20m on 50g #378   .50   .50
411 A24   25m on 1m #375   .60   .60
  a.   Pair, #407, 411   1.40 1.40
412 A24   40m on 50g #378   1.10 1.10
  a.   Pair, #410, 412   1.75 1.75
413 A24   50m on 25g #376   1.50 1.50
414 A24   100m on 25g #376   2.25 2.25
  a.   Pair, #413-414   4.00 4.00
       Nos. 407-414 (8)   7.45 7.45

Baku Oil Fields — A33

Designs: 15m, Temple of Eternal Fires.
20m, Oil derricks. 25m, Early tanker. 50m,
Ludwig Nobel, Robert Nobel, Petr Bilderling,
Alfred Nobel.

1994, June 10   Photo.   Perf. 13
415 A33 15m multicolored   .30   .30
416 A33 20m multicolored   .30   .30
417 A33 25m multicolored   .40   .40
418 A33 50m multicolored   1.00 1.00
  a.   Souvenir sheet of 1   1.50 1.50
       Nos. 415-418 (4)   2.00 2.00
See Turkmenistan Nos. 39-43.

Minerals — A34

1994, June 15   Litho.   Perf. 13¼x13
419 A34   5m Laumontite   .30   .30
420 A34   10m Epidot calcite   .50   .50
421 A34   15m Andradite   .75   .75
422 A34   20m Amethyst   1.00 1.00
  a.   Souvenir sheet, #419-422 + 2 la-
       bels, perf. 12   2.50 2.50
       Nos. 419-422 (4)   2.55 2.55
For surcharges, see Nos. 760, 762-764.

Posthorn — A35

1994, June 28   Litho.   Perf. 12½
426 A35   5m black & red   .25   .25
427 A35   10m black & green   .25   .25
428 A35   20m black & blue   .40   .40
429 A35   25m black & yellow   .40   .40
431 A35   40m black & brown   .75   .75
       Nos. 426-431 (5)   2.05 2.05
For surcharges see Nos. 487-489A, 752,
761, 765, 811.

No. 351
Surcharged

Unwmk.
1994, Oct. 17   Litho.   Perf. 12
435 A21 400m on 25g multi   2.50 2.50

Souvenir Sheet

Pres. Heydar A. Aliyev — A36

1994, Oct. 28   Litho.   Perf. 14
436 A36 150m multicolored   3.00 3.00

Ships of
the
Caspian
Sea
A37

Designs: a, Tugboat, "Captain Racebov." b,
"Azerbaijan." c, Balt Ro Ro line, "Merkuri I." d,
Tanker, "Tovuz." e, Tanker.

1994, Oct. 28
437 A37 50m Strip of 5, #a.-e.   1.75 1.75
Issued in sheets of 15 stamps. The background of the sheet shows a nautical chart,
giving each stamp a different background.
Value $7.

1994 World Cup Soccer
Championships, U.S. — A38

Various soccer plays. Denominations: 5m,
10m, 20m, 25m, 30m, 50m, 80m.

1994, June 17   Perf. 13
438-444 A38 Set of 7   3.50 3.50
Souvenir Sheet
445 A38 100m multicolored   1.75 1.75
No. 445 contains one 32x40mm stamp and
is a continuous design.

Dinosaurs — A39

Designs: 5m, Coelophysis, segisaurus.
10m, Pentaceratops, tyrannosaurids. 20m,
Segnosaurus, oviraptor. 25m, Albertosaurus,
corythosaurus. 30m, Iguanodons. 50m, Stegosaurus, allosaurus. 80m, Tyrannosaurus,
saurolophus.
100m, Phobetor.

1994, Sept. 15
446-452 A39 Set of 7   3.25 3.25
Souvenir Sheet
Perf. 12½
453 A39 100m multicolored   2.10 2.10
No. 453 contains one 40x32mm stamp and
is a continuous design.

Lyrurus Mlokosiewickzi — A40

a, 50m, Female on nest. b, 80m, Female on
mountain cliff. c, 100m, 2 males. d, 120m,
Male.

1994, Dec. 15   Litho.   Perf. 12½
454 A40 Block of 4, #a.-d.   5.00 5.00
World Wildlife Fund.

Raptors
A41

10m, Haliaeetus albicilla. 15m, Aguila
heliaca. 20m, Aguila rapax. 25m, Gypaetus
barbatus, vert. 50m, Falco cherrug, vert.
100m, Aguila chrysaetos.

1994, Nov. 15   Litho.   Perf. 13
458-462 A41 Set of 5   3.25 3.25
Souvenir Sheet
Perf. 12½
463 A41 100m multicolored   1.75 1.75
No. 463 contains one 40x32mm stamp and
is a continuous design.

Cats
A42

Designs: 10m, Felis libica, vert. 15m, Felis
otocolobus, vert. 20m, Felis lyns, vert. 25m,
Felis pardus. 50m, Panthera tigrus.
100m, Panthera tigrus adult and cub, vert.

1994, Dec. 14   Perf. 13
464-468 A42 Set of 5   3.25 3.25
Souvenir Sheet
469 A42 100m multicolored   1.75 1.75
No. 469 contains one 32x40mm stamp and
is a continuous design.
For overprints see Nos. 637-642.

Butterflies
A43

Designs: 10m, Parnassius apollo. 25m,
Zegris menestho. 50m, Manduca atropos.
60m, Pararge adrastoides.

1995, Jan. 23   Litho.   Perf. 14
470 A43 10m multicolored   .30   .30
471 A43 25m multicolored   .65   .65
472 A43 50m multicolored   1.15 1.15
473 A43 60m multicolored   1.50 1.50
  a.   Souvenir sheet of 4, #470-473 4.00 4.00
       Nos. 470-473 (4)   3.60 3.60
For surcharges, see Nos. 783-786a.

Intl. Olympic Committee, Cent. — A44

Designs: No. 474, Pierre de Coubertin. No.
475, Discus. No. 476, Javelin.

1994, Dec. 15   Litho.   Perf. 12
474-476 A44 100m Set of 3   2.00 2.00

A45

1994 Winter Olympic medalists, Lillehammer: 10m, Aleksei Urmanov, Russia, figure skating, 25, Nancy Kerrigan, US, figure skating. 40m Bonnie Blair, US, speed skating, horiz. 50m, Takanori Kano, Japan, ski jumping, horiz. 80m, Philip LaRouche, Canada, freestyle skiing. 100m, Four-man bobsled, Germany.
200m, Katja Seizinger, skiing, Germany, vert.

1995, Feb. 10   Litho.   Perf. 14
478-483 A45 Set of 6   3.50 3.50
Souvenir Sheet
484 A45 200m multicolored   3.25 3.25

Miniature Sheet

A46

No. 485, 100m: a, Mary Cleave, U.S. b, Valentina Tereshkova, Russia. c, Tamara Jernigan, U.S. d, Wendy Lawrence, U.S.
No. 486, 100m: a, Mae Jemison, U.S. b, Catherine Coleman, U.S. c, Ellen Shulman, U.S. d, M.E. Weber, U.S.

1995, Feb. 21
485-486 A46 Set of 2, #a-d   6.00 6.00
First manned moon landing, 25th anniv. (in 1994).

Nos. 426-428 Surcharged

1995   Litho.   Perf. 12½
487   A35 100m on 5m #426   .25   .25
488   A35 250m on 10m #427   .40   .40
488A A35 400m on 25m No. 429   .75   .75
489   A35 500m on 20m #428   .65   .65
489A A35 900m on 40m No. 431   1.75 1.75
     Nos. 487-489A (5)   3.80 3.80
Issued: No. 488A, 7/7; Nos. 487-488, 489, 2/28.

Mushrooms — A47

Designs: 100m, Gymnopilus spectabilis. 250m, Fly agaris. 300m, Lepiota procera. 400m, Hygrophurus spectosus.
500m, Fly agaris, diff.

1995, Sept. 1   Litho.   Perf. 14
490-493 A47 Set of 4   3.75 3.75
Souvenir Sheet
494 A47 500m multicolored   2.25 2.25

Singapore '95 — A48

Orchids: 100m, Paphiopedilum argus, paphiopedilum barbatum. 250m, Maxillaria picta. 300m, Laeliocattleya. 400m, Dendrobium nobile.
500m, Cattleya gloriette.

1995, Sept. 1
495-498 A48 Set of 4   3.75 3.75
Souvenir Sheet
499 A48 500m multicolored   2.25 2.25

UN, 50th Anniv. A49

Design: 250m, Azerbaijan Pres. Heydar A. Aliyev, UN Sec. Gen. Boutros Boutros-Ghali.

1995, Sept. 15
500 A49 250m multicolored   2.50 2.50

Nos. 352-355 Surcharged

1995   Litho.   Perf. 12
501 A21 200m on 2.50m #355   .50   .50
502 A21 600m on 35g #352   1.50 1.50
503 A21 800m on 50g #353   2.00 2.00
504 A21 1000m on 1.50m #354   2.50 2.50
     Nos. 501-504 (4)   6.50 6.50

Uzeyir Hacibeyov (1885-1948) A50

400m, Ali Aga Iskenderov (1895-1965).

1995, June 30   Litho.   Perf. 12x12½
505 A50 250m silver gray & black .40 .40
506 A50 400m gold bister & brn   .85 .85

Balloons and Airships A51

100m, First hydrogen balloon, 1784. 150m, 1st motorized balloon, 1883. 250m, First elliptical balloon, 1784. 300m, 1st Scott Baldwin dirigible, 1904. 400m, US Marine balloon, 1917. 500m, Pedal-powered dirigible, 1909.
800m, 1st rigid dirigible designed by Hugo Eckener, 1924.

1995, July 20   Litho.   Perf. 13
507 A51 100m multi, vert.   .25   .25
508 A51 150m multi, vert.   .35   .35
509 A51 250m multi   .50   .50
510 A51 300m multi   .60   .60
511 A51 400m multi   .90   .90
512 A51 500m multi   1.25 1.25
     Nos. 507-512 (6)   3.85 3.85
Souvenir Sheet
513 A51 800m multicolored   2.75 2.75

Marine Life A52

50m, Loligo vulgaris. 100m, Orchistoma pileus. 150m, Pegea confoederata. 250m, Polyorchis karafutoensis. 300m, Agalma okeni.
500m, Corolla spectabillis.

1995, June 2   Litho.   Perf. 13
514 A52 50m multi   .25   .25
515 A52 100m multi   .45   .45
516 A52 150m multi   .60   .60
517 A52 250m multi, vert.   1.10 1.10
518 A52 300m multi, vert.   1.25 1.25
     Nos. 514-518 (5)   3.65 3.65
Souvenir Sheet
519 A52 500m multicolored   2.50 2.50

Turtles A53

Designs: 50m, Chelus fimbriatus. 100m, Caretta caretta. 150m, Geochelone pardalis. 250m, Geochelone elegans. 300m, Testudo hermanni.
500m, Macroclemys temmincki.

1995, June 12   Litho.   Perf. 13
520 A53 50m multicolored   .25   .25
521 A53 100m multicolored   .45   .45
522 A53 150m multicolored   .60   .60
523 A53 250m multicolored   1.10 1.10
524 A53 300m multicolored   1.25 1.25
     Nos. 520-524 (5)   3.65 3.65
Souvenir Sheet
525 A53 500m multicolored   2.50 2.50

1998 World Cup Soccer Championships, France — A54

Various soccer plays.

1995, Sept. 30   Litho.   Perf. 12½
526 A54 100m orange & multi   .40   .40
527 A54 150m green & multi   .55   .55
528 A54 250m yel org & multi   .80   .80
529 A54 300m yellow & multi   1.00 1.00
530 A54 400m blue & multi   1.40 1.40
     Nos. 526-530 (5)   4.15 4.15
Souvenir Sheet
Perf. 13
531 A54 600m multicolored   2.25 2.25

Domestic Cats — A55

100m, Persian. 150m, Chartreux. 250m, Somali. 300m, Longhair Scottish fold. 400m, Cumric. 500m, Turkish angora.
800m, Birman.

1995, Oct. 30   Perf. 12½
532 A55 100m multicolored   .35   .35
533 A55 150m multicolored   .50   .50
534 A55 250m multicolored   .65   .65
535 A55 300m multicolored   .80   .80
536 A55 400m multicolored   1.00 1.00
537 A55 500m multicolored   1.25 1.25
     Nos. 532-537 (6)   4.55 4.55
Souvenir Sheet
538 A55 800m multicolored   2.00 2.00
No. 538 contains one 32x40mm stamp.

Fauna and Flora — A56

Designs: 100m, Horse. 200m, Muscari elecostomum, vert. 250m, Huso huso. 300m, Aquila chrysaetos. 400m, Panthera tigris. 500m, Lyrurus miokosiewickzi, facing right. 1000m, Lyrurus miokosiewickzi, facing left.

1995, Nov. 30
539 A56 100m multicolored   .25   .25
540 A56 200m multicolored   .50   .50
541 A56 250m multicolored   .60   .60
542 A56 300m multicolored   .75   .75
543 A56 400m multicolored   1.00 1.00
544 A56 500m multicolored   1.50 1.50
545 A56 1000m multicolored   2.50 2.50
     Nos. 539-545 (7)   7.10 7.10

John Lennon (1940-80) A57

1995, Dec. 8   Perf. 14½
546 A57 500m multicolored   1.60 1.60
Issued in sheet of 16 plus label.

Miniature Sheet

Locomotives — A58

Designs: No. 547a, 4-4-0, America. b, J3 Hudson, US. c, 2-8-2. d, 2-6-2, Germany. e, 2-8-2, Germany. f, 2-6-2, Italy. g, G-C5, Japan. h, 2-10-2 QJ, China. i, 0-10-0, China.
500m, Electric passenger train, vert.

1996, Feb. 1   Perf. 14
547 A58 100m Sheet of 9, #a.-i. 6.50 6.50
Souvenir Sheet
548 A58 500m multicolored   3.25 3.25

Dr. M. Topchibashev, Surgeon — A59

1996, Feb. 1
549 A59 300m multicolored   1.25 1.25

Nos. 363, 365, 367-368, 370, 372-374 Surcharged

1995, Jan. 4   Litho.   Perf. 12½x12
550 A23 250m on 10g #363   .75   .75
551 A23 250m on 20g #365   .75   .75
552 A23 250m on 50g #368   .75   .75
553 A23 250m on 1.50m #372   .75   .75
554 A23 500m on 50g #367   1.50 1.50
555 A23 500m on 1m #370   1.50 1.50
556 A23 500m on 2.50m #373   1.50 1.50
557 A23 500m on 5m #374   1.50 1.50
     Nos. 550-557 (8)   9.00 9.00

1996 Olympic Games, Atlanta A60

50m, Carl Lewis. 100m, Muhammed Ali. 150m, Li Ning. 200m, Said Aouita. 250m, Olga Korbut. 300m, Nadia Comaneci. 400m, Greg Louganis.
500m, Nazim Hüseynov, vert.

1996, Apr. 9   Litho.   Perf. 14
568 A60 50m multicolored   .25   .25
569 A60 100m multicolored   .40   .40
570 A60 150m multicolored   .40   .40
571 A60 200m multicolored   .55   .55
572 A60 250m multicolored   .70   .70
573 A60 300m multicolored   .90   .90
574 A60 400m multicolored   1.00   1.00
        Nos. 568-574 (7)   4.20   4.20
Souvenir Sheet
575 A60 500m multicolored   1.90   1.90

Husein Aliyev (1911-91), Artist A61

Paintings: 100m, Water bird, swamp. 200m, Landscape.

1996, Apr. 16   Litho.   Perf. 14
576 A61 100m multicolored   1.00   1.00
577 A61 200m multicolored   1.50   1.50
  a. Pair, #576-577 + label   2.50   2.50

No. 577a issued in sheets of 6 stamps.

Resid Behbudov (1915-89), Singer — A62

1996, Apr. 22   Perf. 12½
578 A62 100m multicolored   1.30   1.30

Novruz Bayrami, Natl. Holiday — A63

1996, Mar. 20
579 A63 250m multicolored   1.25   1.25

Independence, 5th Anniv. — A64

1996, May 28   Litho.   Perf. 14
580 A64 250m multicolored   1.25   1.25

A65

1996, Apr. 22   Litho.   Perf. 12½
581 A65 100m multicolored   1.25   1.25

Yusif Memmedeliyev (1905-95), chemist.

A66

Jerusalem, 3000th Anniv.: a, 100m, Wailing Wall. b, 250m, Inside cathedral. c, 300m, Dome of the Rock. 500m, Windmill.

1996, June 7   Perf. 14
582 A66 Sheet of 3, #a.-c.   4.00   4.00
Souvenir Sheet
583 A66 500m multicolored   3.00   3.00

For overprints see Nos. 643-644.

Dogs A67

Designs: 50m, German shepherd. 100m, Basset hound. 150m, Collie. 200m, Bull terrier. 300m, Boxer. 400m, Cocker spaniel. 500m, Sharpei.

1996, June 18   Perf. 13
584-589 A67 Set of 6   3.75   3.75
Souvenir Sheet
590 A67 500m multicolored   2.00   2.00

Birds — A68

Designs: 50m, Tetraenura regia. 100m, Coliuspasser macrourus. 150m, Oriolus xanthornus. 200m, Oriolus oriolus. 300m, Sturnus vulgaris. 400m, Serinus mozambicus. 500m, Merops apiaster.

1996, June 19   Perf. 13
591-596 A68 Set of 6   3.75   3.75
Souvenir Sheet
597 A68 500m multicolored   2.00   2.00

Roses — A69

Designs: 50m, Burgundy. 100m, Virgo. 150m, Rose gaujard. 200m, Luna. 300m, Lady rose. 400m, Landora. 500m, Lougsor, horiz.

1996, June 19
598-603 A69 Set of 6   3.75   3.75
Souvenir Sheet
604 A69 500m multicolored   2.00   2.00

UNICEF, 50th Anniv. — A70

1996, July 8   Litho.   Perf. 14
605 A70 500m multicolored   1.00   1.00

A71

Competing teams: 100m, Spain, Bulgaria. 150m, Romania, France. 200m, Czech Republic, Germany. 250m, England, Israel. 300m, Croatia, Turkey. 400m, Italy, Russia. 500m, Trophy cup.

1996, July 22
606-611 A71 Set of 6   4.00   4.00
Souvenir Sheet
612 A71 500m multicolored   2.00   2.00

Euro '96, European Soccer Championships, Great Britain.

Ships A72

Ship, home country: 100m, Chinese junk. 150m, Danmark, Denmark. 200m, Nippon Maru, Japan. 250m, Mircea, Romania. 300m, Kruzenshtern, Russia. 400m, Ariadne, Germany. 500m, Tovarishch, Russia, vert.

1996, Aug. 26   Litho.   Perf. 14
613-618 A72 Set of 6   4.50   4.50
Souvenir Sheet
619 A72 500m multicolored   3.00   3.00

For overprints see Nos. 645-651.

Baxram Gur Kills a Dragon, Sculpture — A73

1997, Mar. 6   Litho.   Perf. 13½x13
620 A73 250m black & yellow   .35   .35
621 A73 400m black & vermilion   .55   .55
622 A73 500m black & green   .75   .75
623 A73 1000m black & purple   1.50   1.50
        Nos. 620-623 (4)   3.15   3.15
        See No. 671.

Famous Personalities — A74

No. 624, Aziz Mamed-Kerim Ogli Aliyev (1897-1962), politician. No. 625, Illyas Efendiyev (1914-96), writer. No. 626, Fatali Khan-Khoyski (1875-1920), politician. No. 627, Nariman Narimanov (1870-1925), politician, writer.

1997, Mar. 25   Litho.   Perf. 14
Background Color
624 A74 250m tan   .80   .80
625 A74 250m gray blue   .80   .80
626 A74 250m pale red   .80   .80
627 A74 250m pale olive   .80   .80
        Nos. 624-627 (4)   3.20   3.20

Qobustan Prehistoric Art — A75

Rock carvings: a, Oxen. b, Large horned animals. c, Six figures.

1997, May 19   Litho.   Perf. 14
628 A75 500m Sheet of 3, #a.-c.   3.50   3.50

For overprint see No. 674.

#356-362A, 464-469 Ovptd. in Red

1997, June 2   Litho.   Perf. 13
Denominations as Before
629-635 A22 Set of 7   9.00   9.00
Souvenir Sheet
636 A22 8m multicolored   4.00   4.00

Location of overprint varies. No. 636 is ovptd. both on stamp and in sheet margin.

1997, June 2
Denominations as Before
637-641 A42 Set of 5   6.00   6.00
Souvenir Sheet
642 A42 100m multicolored   4.50   4.50

Location of overprint varies. No. 642 is ovptd. both on stamp and in sheet margin.

Nos. 582-583, 613-619 Ovptd.

1997, June 2   Perf. 14
643 A66 Sheet of 3, #a.-c.   5.00   5.00
Souvenir Sheet
644 A66 500m multicolored   5.00   5.00

Size and location of overprint varies. Overprint appears both on stamp and in sheet margin.

1997, June 2   Perf. 14
Denominations as Before
645-650 A72 Set of 6   5.00   5.00
Souvenir Sheet
651 A72 500m multicolored   5.00   5.00

Location of overprint varies. No. 651 is ovptd. both on stamp and in sheet margin.

Grimm's Fairy Tales — A76

The Town Musicians of Bremen: No. 652: a, Dog. b, Dancing donkey, cat. c, Rooster.
500m, Animals looking through window at treaure chest, man.

1997, July 1 **Perf. 13½x14**
652 A76 250m Sheet of 3, #a.-c. 4.50 4.50
Souvenir Sheet
653 A76 500m multicolored 3.50 3.50

Caspian Seals A77

Designs: a, Seal looking right. b, Mountain top, seal looking forward. c, Seal, seagull. d, Seal looking left. e, Seal looking forward. f, Small seal.
500m, Mother nursing pup.

1997, July 1
654 A77 250m Sheet of 6, #a.-f. 4.50 4.50
Souvenir Sheet
655 A77 500m multicolored 3.50 3.50

Traditional Musical Instruments — A77a

1997, Aug. 4 **Litho.** **Perf. 14**
656 A77a 250m Qaval .90 .90
657 A77a 250m Tanbur .90 .90
658 A77a 500m Cenq 1.75 1.75
Nos. 656-658 (3) 3.55 3.55

A78

Azerbaijan Oil Industry: a, Early oil derricks, building. b, Off-shore oil drilling platform.

1997, Aug. 18 **Perf. 14½**
Souvenir Sheet
659 A78 500m Sheet of 2, #a.-b. 3.25 3.25

Hagani Shirvany, Poet — A79

1997, Sept. 12 **Perf. 14x13½**
660 A79 250m multicolored 1.00 1.00
Issued in sheets of 4 + 5 labels. Value $5.

Mosques A80

No. 661, Ashaqi Qovgar-agi, Shusha, 1874-75. No. 662, Momuna-Zatun, Naxcivan, 1187. No. 663, Taza-pir, Baku (1905-14).

1997, Sept. 18 **Litho.** **Perf. 14**
661 A80 250m multicolored 1.00 1.00
662 A80 250m multicolored 1.00 1.00
663 A80 250m multicolored 1.00 1.00
Nos. 661-663 (3) 3.00 3.00

H.C. Rasulbekov (1917-1984), Communications Official — A81

1997, Oct. 6 **Litho.** **Perf. 14**
664 A81 250m multicolored .90 .90

1998 World Cup Soccer Championships, France — A82

Winning team photos: No. 665: a, Italy, 1938. b, Argentina, 1986. c, Uruguay, 1930. d, Brazil, 1994. e, England, 1966. f, Germany, 1990.
1500m, Tofiq Bahramov, "Golden Whistle" prize winner, 1966, vert.

1997, Oct. 15
665 A82 250m Sheet of 6, #a.-f. 4.00 4.00
Souvenir Sheet
666 A82 1500m multicolored 3.50 3.50

A83

Figure skaters: No. 667: a, Katarina Witt, Germany. b, Elvis Stojko, Canada. c, Midori Ito, Japan. d, Silhouettes of various winter sports against natl. flag. e, Hand holding Olympic torch. f, Kristi Yamaguchi, US. g, John Curry, England. h, Lu Chen, China.
No. 668, Gordeyeva and Grinkov, Russia.

1998, Jan. 13 **Litho.** **Perf. 14**
667 A83 250m Sheet of 8, #a.-h. 4.50 4.50
Souvenir Sheet
668 A83 500m multicolored 3.50 3.50
1998 Winter Olympic Games, Nagano.

A84

Diana, Princess of Wales (1961-97): No. 669, Wearing black turtleneck. No. 670, Wearing violet dress.

1998, Feb. 4 **Perf. 13½**
669 A84 400m multicolored .70 .70
670 A84 400m multicolored .70 .70
Nos. 669-670 were each issued in sheets of 6. Value, set of 2 sheets $10.

Sculpture Type of 1997
1998, Mar. 23 Litho. Perf. 13½x13
671 A73 100m blk & bright pink 1.00 1.00

Hasan Aliyev, Ecologist, 90th Birth Anniv. A85

1998, Apr. 3 **Perf. 14**
672 A85 500m multicolored 1.00 1.00

Souvenir Sheet

Pres. Heydar Aliyev, 75th Birthday — A86

1998, May 10 **Perf. 13½**
673 A86 500m multicolored 3.00 3.00

No. 628 Ovptd.

1998, May 13 **Perf. 14**
674 A75 500m Sheet of 3, #a.-c. 8.00 8.00
Additional inscription in sheet margin reads "ISRAEL 98 — WORLD STAMP EXHIBITION / TEL-AVIV 13-21 MAY 1998."

Artists A87

No. 675, Gara Garayev, composer. No. 676, Ashug Alesker, folk musician, poet. No. 677, Mohammad-Hossein Shahriar, poet.

1998, June 7 **Litho.** **Perf. 14**
675 A87 250m multicolored .90 .90
676 A87 250m multicolored .90 .90
677 A87 250m multicolored .90 .90
Nos. 675-677 (3) 2.70 2.70

Bul-Bul, Singer, Birth Cent. — A88

1998, July 7
678 A88 500m multicolored 1.00 1.00

Disney Characters at World Rapid Chess Championship — A89

Designs: 250m, Minnie, Mickey.
No. 679: a, Minnie, Mickey. b, Goofy. c, Donald. d, Pluto. e, Minnie. f, Daisy. g, Goofy, Donald. h, Mickey.
No. 680, 4000m, Donald, Mickey. No. 681, 4000m, Minnie, Mickey.

1998 **Perf. 13½**
678A A89 250m multicolored 4.50 4.50
Perf. 13½x14
679 A89 500m Sheet of 8, #a.-h. 32.50 32.50
Souvenir Sheets
680-681 A89 Set of 2 50.00 50.00
Issued: 250m, 12/28; others, 11/13.

New Year Holiday A90

Europa: 1000m, Woman rolling dough. 3000m, Men performing at holiday festival.

1998, Dec. 29 **Litho.** **Perf. 13x12½**
682 A90 1000m multicolored 1.50 1.50
683 A90 3000m multicolored 3.50 3.50

Nos. 682-683 Ovptd.

1999, Apr. 27 **Litho.** **Perf. 13x12½**
684 A90 1000m on #682 1.50 1.50
685 A90 3000m on #683 3.50 3.50

A91

Europa: 1000m, Rose flamingo, Gizilagach Natl. Park. 3000m, Deer, Girkan Natl. Park.

1999, Apr. 28 **Perf. 12½x12¾**
686 A91 1000m multicolored 1.75 1.75
687 A91 3000m multicolored 3.75 3.75

A92

Towers: 1000m, Dord Kundge, 14th cent. 3000m, Danravy, 13th cent.

1999, Aug. 3   Litho.   Perf. 11¼x11¾
688 A92 1000m black & blue   .75   .75
689 A92 3000m black & red   2.00 2.00

See Nos. 701-702, 717-718, 731-732, 744, 754.
For surcharge, see No. 812, 815.

A93

Naxçivan Autonomous Republic, 75th anniv.: a, Pres. Heydar Aliyev, flag. b, Map of Naxçivan.

1999, Oct. 9   Perf. 12
690 A93 1000m Pair, #a.-b.   3.00 3.00
 c.   Souvenir sheet, pair, #a.-b.   3.00 3.00

A94

1999, Oct. 20   Perf. 12½x12
691 A94 250m multicolored   1.10 1.10
Jafar Jabbarly (1899-1934), playwright.

Souvenir Sheet

A95

80th anniv. of Azerbaijan postage stamps: a, #1. b, #3. c, #7. d, #10. b-d horiz.

Perf. 14¾x14½ (a), 14½x13¾ (b-d)
1999, Oct. 30
692 A95 500m Sheet of 4, #a.-d.   3.50 3.50
Exists imperf. Value, $20.

Baku Caravansary — A96

No. 693, Inner courtyard. No. 694, Facade, camels.

1999, Dec. 29   Litho.   Perf. 13
693-694 A96 500m Set of 2   3.50 3.50

A97

1999, Dec. 29   Perf. 12
695 A97 1000m multi   1.75 1.75
Council of Europe, 50th anniv.

UPU, 125th Anniv. — A98

Azerbaijan flag, UPU emblem and: a, 250m, Dove. b, 3000m, Computer, satellite.

1999, Dec. 29
696 A98 Pair, #a.-b.   3.50 3.50

Souvenir Sheet

Epic Legend Kitabi Dede Gorgud, 1300th Anniv. — A99

Designs: a, Beyrek fights with camel. b, Wounded Tural on horseback. c, Gazan Khan sleeping, horse.

1999, Dec. 29   Perf. 12¼x11¾
697 A99 1000m Sheet of 3, #a.-
      c.   3.50 3.50

Europa, 2000
Common Design Type
2000, Feb. 7   Litho.   Perf. 12¾x13
698 CD17 1000m multi   1.00 1.00
699 CD17 3000m multi   5.00 5.00

Souvenir Sheet

Baku Transportation — A100

Designs: a, Phaeton. b, Horse-drawn tram. c, Electric tram. d, Trolleybus.

2000, Feb. 15   Litho.   Perf. 12½x12
700 A100 500m Sheet of 4, #a-d   4.50 4.50

Tower Type of 1999
100m, Ramany Castle, 14th cent, horiz.
250m, Nardaran Castle, 14th cent, horiz.

2000, May 5   Litho.   Perf. 11¾x11¼
701 A92 100m black & orange   .35   .35
702 A92 250m black & green   .85   .85

World Meteorological Organization, 50th Anniv. — A101

2000, May 5   Perf. 12
703 A101 1000m multi   1.00 1.00

Worldwide Fund for Nature — A102

Aythya nyroca: a, One in flight. b, Two on rocks, three in water. c, One on rocks, three in water. d, One in water, three in flight.

2000, May 5   Perf. 12½x12
704 A102 500m Block of 4, #a-d   3.50 3.50

2000 Summer Olympics, Sydney — A103

Designs: a, Wrestling. b, Weight lifting. c, Boxing. d, Running.

2000, May 5   Perf. 12x12½
705 A103 500m Block of 4, #a-d   5.00 5.00

Souvenir Sheet

Phasianus Colchicus — A104

2000, June 21   Litho.   Perf. 13½x13
706 A104 2000m multi   4.00 4.00

Fruit A105

No. 707: a, Cydonia oblonga. b, Punica granatum. c, Persica L. d, Ficus carica.

2000, June 21   Perf. 13x13¼
707   Sheet of 4   4.50 4.50
 a.-d. A105 500m Any single   1.10 1.10

Rasul Rza (1911-81), Poet A106

2000, Sept. 28   Litho.   Perf. 13x13¼
708 A106 250m multi   1.00 1.00

Reptiles A107

No. 709: a, Vipera lebetina. b, Laserta saxcola. c, Vipera xanthina. d, Phrynocephalus mystaceus.
No. 710, Natrix tessellata, Phrynocephalus helioscopus, vert.

2000, Sept. 28   Perf. 13½x13
709   Sheet of 4   6.50 6.50
 a.-d. A107 500m Any single   1.50 1.50
Souvenir Sheet
Perf. 13x13½
710 A107 500m multi   3.00 3.00

Sabit Rahman (1910-70), Writer A108

2000, Nov. 17   Perf. 13x13¼
711 A108 1000m multi   1.60 1.60

Intl. Year for the Culture of Peace — A109

2000, Nov. 17   Perf. 13¼x13
712 A109 3000m multi   3.50 3.50

Souvenir Sheet

2000 Olympic Medalists — A110

No. 713: a, Namig Abdullaev, 54kg free-style wrestling gold medalist. b, Zemfira Meftahaddinova, women's skeet shooting gold medalist. c, Vugar Alakbarov, middleweight boxing bronze medalist.

2001, Jan. 26 Litho.   *Perf. 13½x13¾*
713 A110 1000m Sheet of 3,
        #a-c   4.50 4.50
      Dated 2000.

Europa — A111

Caspian Sea and: 1000m, Seal. 3000m, Sturgeon, crab, jellyfish.

        Perf. 13½x13¼
2001, Mar. 28   **Litho.**
714-715 A111   Set of 2   6.00 6.00
715a Pane, 4 each #714-715   32.50
    Stamps in the middle two columns of No. 715a are tete beche. No. 715a was sold with booklet cover, but unattached to it.

Admission
of
Azerbaijan
to Council
of Europe
A112

2001, Apr. 25   ***Perf. 13¼x13½***
716 A112 1000m multi   1.75 1.75

Tower Type of 1999
    Designs: 100m, Sheki, 18th cent., horiz. 250m, Sheki, 12th-13th cent., horiz.

2001, July 27   ***Perf. 14x13¾***
717 A92 100m black & lilac   .45 .45
718 A92 250m black & yellow 1.00 1.00

Souvenir Sheet

UN High Commissioner for Refugees, 50th Anniv. — A113

2001, Aug. 22   ***Perf. 13¼x13½***
719 A113 3000m multi   3.50 3.50

Souvenir Sheet

Nasir ad-Din at-Tusi (1201-74), Scientist — A114

2001, Sept. 7   ***Perf. 13¼***
720 A114 3000m multi   3.50 3.50

Commonwealth of Independent States, 10th Anniv. — A115

2001, Oct. 8 Litho.   *Perf. 13½x13¼*
721 A115 1000m multi   1.60 1.60

Souvenir Sheet

First Manned Space Flight, 40th Anniv. — A116

2001, Nov. 6   ***Perf. 13¼x13½***
722 A116 3000m multi   3.50 3.50

Independence, 10th Anniv. — A117

Litho. & Embossed with Foil Application
2001, Dec. 1   ***Perf. 13¼***
723 A117 5000m gold & multi 10.00 10.00

Owls — A118

    No. 724: a, Asio flammeus. b, Strix aluco. c, Otus scops. d, Asio otus. e, Bubo bubo, wings at side. f, Athene noctua.
    No. 725, Bubo bubo, wings extended.

2001, Dec. 1 Litho.   *Perf. 13¼x13*
724 A118 1000m Sheet of 6, #a-f 6.50 6.50
Souvenir Sheet
725 A118 1000m shown   3.50 3.50

Visit of Russian Pres. Vladimir Putin A119

2001, Dec. 20   ***Perf. 13***
726 A119 1000m multi   1.50 1.50

Natl. Olympic Committee, 10th Anniv. — A120

2002, Mar. 6   ***Perf. 13¼x13½***
727 A120 3000m multi   3.00 3.00

Europa — A121

    Designs: 1000m, Tight rope walker, musicians, strong man, acrobat. 3000m, Trapeze artist, juggler, horse trainer.

2002, Mar. 11   ***Perf. 13½x13¼***
728-729 A121   Set of 2   5.50 5.50
729a Booklet pane, 2 each #728-729,
    perf. 13½x13¼ on 3 sides   11.00 —
    Complete booklet, #729a   11.00

Azerbaijan — People's Republic of China Diplomatic Relations, 10th Anniv. A122

2002, Mar. 28   **Litho.**   ***Perf. 12***
730 A122 1000m multi   1.20 1.20

Tower Type of 1999
    Designs: 100m, Molla Panah Vagif Mausoleum, Shusha. 250m, Mosque, Agdam.

2002, Apr. 23   ***Perf. 13½x14***
731 A92 100m blk & ol grn   .30 .30
732 A92 250m blk & tan   .60 .60
    For surcharge, see No. 812.

No. 350 Surcharged in Red

Method & Perf. As Before
2002, May 8
733 A20 1000m on 35k multi 1.20 1.20

New Azerbaijan Party, 10th Anniv. — A123

2002, June 1   ***Perf. 13½***
734 A123 3000m multi   3.00 3.00

Butterflies — A124

    No. 735: a, Danaus chrysippus. b, Papilio orientalis. c, Thaleropis jonia. d, Vanessa atalanta. e, Argynnis alexandra. f, Brahmaea christophi.

2002, June 19   ***Perf. 13***
735 A124 1000m Sheet of 6, #a-f 7.50 7.50

In Remembrance of Sept. 11, 2001 Terrorist Attacks — A125

2002, Sept. 18   ***Perf. 13½x13¼***
736 A125 1500m multi   1.50 1.50
    Printed in sheets of 3. Value $4.50.

Baku Telegraph Office, 70th Anniv. — A126

2002, Sept. 18   ***Perf. 14¼x14***
737 A126 3000m multi   3.00 3.00

Rauf Gadjiev, Composer, 80th Anniv. of Birth A127

2002, Sept. 18   ***Perf. 14x14¼***
738 A127 5000m multi   3.50 3.50

Souvenir Sheet

Visit of Pope John Paul II — A128

2002, Sept. 18   *Perf. 13¼x13½*
739 A128 1500m multi   3.00 3.00

Souvenir Sheet

European Junior Chess
Championships — A129

Baku skyline and stylized chess pieces: a, King, queen, pawns. b, Knights, pawn. c, Two elephants, rook, pawn. d, King, queen, rook, pawn.

2002, Sept. 18   *Perf. 12¾x13¼*
740 A129 1500m Sheet of 4,
     #a-d   7.00 7.00

Souvenir Sheet

Turkey's Third Place Finish in 2002
World Cup Soccer
Championships — A130

2002, Oct. 16   *Perf. 13¼x13*
741 A130 5000m multi   4.50 4.50

Women for
Peace — A131

2002, Nov. 1   *Perf. 14¼x14*
742 A131 3000m multi   3.00 3.00

Souvenir Sheet

Aquarium Fish — A132

No. 743: a, Betta splendens. b, Symphysodon aequifasciatus. c, Pterophylium scalare. d, Carassius auratus auratus. e, Melanotaenia boesemani. f, Cichlasoma meeki.

2002, Dec. 27   Litho.   *Perf. 13½*
743 A132 1000m Sheet of 6,
     #a-f   6.50 6.50

Tower Type of 1999

Design: Askeran Towers, 18th cent., horiz.

2003, Jan. 8   *Perf. 14x13½*
744 A92 250m black & lt blue   .60 .60

Europa
A133

Posters: 1000m, Stop Terrorism. 3000m, Sport is the Health of the Nation

2003, Mar. 12   *Perf. 13½*
745-746 A133 Set of 2   6.00 6.00
746a   Booklet pane, 2 each #745-
     746, perf. 13½ on 3 sides   12.00 12.00

No. 746a was sold with booklet cover, but unattached to it.

Admission to UPU,
10th Anniv. — A134

2003, Apr. 8   *Perf. 14¼x14*
747 A134 3000m multi   3.00 3.00

Nakhichevan — A135

2003, Apr. 8   *Perf. 14x14¼*
748 A135 3000m multi   2.75 2.75

For surcharge see No. 851.

Baku — Tbilisi — Ceyhan Oil
Pipeline — A136

2003, Apr. 8   *Perf. 13¾x14¼*
749 A136 3000m multi   3.00 3.00

Zarifa Aliyeva (1923-85),
Ophthalmologist — A137

2003, Apr. 28   *Perf. 14x14¼*
750 A137 3000m multi   2.75 2.75

Souvenir Sheet

Pres. Heydar Aliyev, 80th
Birthday — A138

Litho. With Foil Application

2003, May 2   *Perf. 11½*
751 A138 10,000m multi   9.00 9.00

Nos. 397, 429
Surcharged

Methods and Perfs As Before
2003, May 27
752 A35   500m on 25m #429   .70 .70
753 A28 1000m on 8m #397   1.30 1.30

Towers Type of 1999

Design: 1000m, Ganja Doors on tower walls, Shusha.

2003, Aug. 13   Litho.   *Perf. 13¾*
754 A92 1000m black   1.00 1.00

Souvenir Sheet

Automobiles — A139

No. 755: a, QAZ-11-73. b, QAZ-M-20 Pobeda. c, QAZ-12 Zim. d, QAZ-21 Volqa.

2003, Aug. 13   *Perf. 11½*
755   A139 500m Sheet of 4, #a-
     d   3.00 3.00

Arshin Mal Alan,
Musical Comedy by
Uzeyir Hadjibekov,
90th Anniv. — A140

2003, Nov. 21   Litho.   *Perf. 14¼x14*
756 A140 10,000m multi   7.00 7.00

Nos. 757-759, 761,
765 Surcharged

Nos. 760, 762-
764 Surcharged

Methods and Perfs as Before
2003, Dec. 11
757 A23 500m on 50g #367   .75 .75
758 A28 500m on 2m #395   .75 .75
759 A28 500m on 4m #396   .75 .75
760 A34 500m on 5m #419   .75 .75
761 A35 500m on 5m #426   .75 .75
762 A34 500m on 10m #420   .75 .75
763 A34 500m on 15m #421   .75 .75
764 A34 500m on 20m #422   .75 .75
   a.   On #422a   4.75 4.75
765 A35 500m on 40m #431   .75 .75
   Nos. 757-765 (9)   6.75 6.75

Souvenir Sheet

Sheki National Park — A141

No. 766: a, Bear. b, Raccoon. c, Boar. d, Fox.

2003, Dec. 30   Litho.   *Perf. 11½*
766 A141 3000m Sheet of 4,
     #a-d   9.00 9.00

Nakhichevan
Autonomous
Republic, 80th
Anniv. — A142

2004, Jan. 3   *Perf. 14¼x14*
767 A142 3000m multi   2.25 2.25

For surcharge see No. 852.

Dove of Peace
Monument,
Sumgayit — A143

2004, Jan. 31   *Perf. 13¼x13¾*
768 A143 500m blk & blue   .80 .80

See No. 788.

Europa
A144

Designs: 1000m, Geygel Lake. 3000m, Baku.

2004, Mar. 16   *Perf. 13¼x13½*
769-770 A144   Set of 2   4.50 4.50
770a   Booklet pane, 2 each
     #769-770, perf. 13¼x13½
     on 3 sides   12.00 —

No. 770a was sold with booklet cover, but unattached to it.

Molla
Juma, Poet,
150th
Anniv. of
Birth
A145

2004, Mar. 25   *Perf. 14x14¼*
771 A145 500m multi   1.25 1.25

2004 Summer Olympics,
Athens — A146

No. 772: a, Pole vault. b, Wrestling. c, Running. d, Greek amphora.

2004, Apr. 15   *Perf. 14¼x14*
772 A146 500m Block of 4, #a-d   4.00 4.00

FIFA (Fédération Internationale de
Football Association), Cent. — A147

No. 773 — Soccer stadium, FIFA emblem
and: a, World Cup. b, Player wearing jersey
#11. c, Player wearing jersey #9. d, Goalie.

2004, Apr. 15   *Perf. 14x14¼*
773 A147 500m Block of 4, #a-d   4.00 4.00

Pres. Heydar
Aliyev (1923-2003)
A148

2004, May 10   Litho.   *Perf. 14¼x14*
774 A148 500m multi   .95 .95
See Nos. 794, 818.

Great Silk
Way — A149

2004, June 7
775 A149 3000m multi   2.75 2.75

Costumes of the
19th
Century — A150

Man and woman from: No. 776, 500m, Baku
(Baki). No. 777, 500m, Karabakh (Qarabag).
No. 778, 500m, Nakhichevan (Naxçivan). No.
779, 500m, Shemakha (Samaxi).

2004, July 8
776-779 A150   Set of 4   4.25 4.25
779a   Miniature sheet, 2 each   8.50 8.50
    #776-779

Internet,
35th Anniv.
A151

2004, Sept. 29 Litho.   *Perf. 14x14¼*
780 A151 3000m multi   2.75 2.75

Souvenir Sheet

Pres. Heydar Aliyev (1923-
2003) — A152

2004, Dec. 10   *Perf. 11½*
781 A152 10,000m multi   6.00 6.00

Worldwide Fund for Nature
(WWF) — A153

No. 782 — Panthera pardus ciscaucasica:
a, Adult on tree branch. b, Two cubs behind
branch. c, Adult with mouth open. d, Adult and
cub.

2005, Jan. 7   *Perf. 14x14¼*
782 A153 1000m Block of 4, #a-d 3.25 3.25

**Nos. 470-473, 473a Surcharged in
Red**

2005, Feb. 1   Litho.   *Perf. 14*
783 A43 1000m on 10m #470   .90 .90
784 A43 1000m on 25m #471   .90 .90
785 A43 1000m on 50m #472   .90 .90
786 A43 1000m on 60m #473   .90 .90
   a.   Souvenir sheet, #783-786   3.50 3.50
    Nos. 783-786 (4)   3.60 3.60

Taxation Ministry,
5th Anniv. — A154

2005, Feb. 5   *Perf. 14¼x14*
787 A154 3000m multi   2.75 2.75

Local Monuments Type of 2004
Design: Observatory, Samaxi.

2005, Mar. 10   *Perf. 13¼x13¾*
788 A143 500m blk & red vio   .75 .75

Orchids — A155

Designs: 500m, Cephalanthera rubra.
1000m, Orchis papilionacea. 1500m, Epipactis atrorubens. 3000m, Orchis purpurea.

2005, Mar. 10   *Perf. 13¼x13*
789-792 A155   Set of 4   6.50 6.50
   a.   Souvenir sheet, #789-792   6.50 6.50

End of
World War
II, 60th
Anniv.
A156

2005, Apr. 6   *Perf. 14x14¼*
793 A156 1000m multi   1.50 1.50

Pres. Aliyev Type of 2004
2005, Apr. 18   *Perf. 14¼x14*
794 A148 1000m bl grn & multi 1.50 1.50

Europa
A157

Designs: 1000m, Plov. 3000m, Dolma.

2005, Apr. 18   *Perf. 13¾x14*
795-796 A157   Set of 2   5.00 5.00

Booklet Stamps
797 A157 1000m Like #795   1.50 1.50
798 A157 3000m Like #796   4.50 4.50
   a.   Booklet pane of 4, 2 each   12.00 —
    #797-798
   b.   Booklet pane of 6, 3 each   18.00 —
    #797-798
    Complete booklet, #798a-798b 30.00

For surcharges see Nos. 838-839.

National
Academy
of
Sciences,
60th Anniv.
A158

2005, May 5 Litho.   *Perf. 14x14¼*
799 A158 1000m multi   1.50 1.50

Souvenir Sheet

First Spacewalk, 40th Anniv. — A159

2005, June 1   *Perf. 11½*
800 A159 3000m multi   4.00 4.00

World
Summit on
the
Information
Society,
Tunis
A160

2005, June 24   *Perf. 14x14¼*
801 A160 1000m multi   1.50 1.50

Pope John Paul II (1920-
2005) — A161

2005, June 24
802 A161 3000m multi   3.00 3.00
For surcharge see No. 853.

Souvenir Sheet

Bees — A162

No. 803: a, 500m, Paravespula germanica.
b, 1000m, Bombus terrestris. c, 1500m, Vespa
crabro. d, 3000m, Apis mellifera caucasica.

2005, July 27
803 A162   Sheet of 4, #a-d   5.50 5.50

European Philatelic Cooperation, 50th
Anniv. (in 2006) — A163

Emblem and vignettes of Europa stamps:
No. 804, France #805, Germany #748. No.

805, Azerbaijan #682-683. No. 806, Azerbaijan #698-699. No. 807, Stamps similar to Azerbaijan #745-746.

2005, Oct. 25   **Perf. 12¾x13**
Background Color

804	A163	3000m gray green	1.75	1.75
	a.	Souvenir sheet of 1	1.75	1.75
	b.	Pair, imperf.	4.00	4.00
805	A163	3000m tan	1.75	1.75
	a.	Souvenir sheet of 1	1.75	1.75
	b.	Pair, imperf.	4.00	4.00
806	A163	3000m yel green	1.75	1.75
	a.	Souvenir sheet of 1	1.75	1.75
	b.	Pair, imperf.	4.00	4.00
807	A163	3000m red orange	1.75	1.75
	a.	Souvenir sheet of 1	1.75	1.75
	b.	Pair, imperf.	4.00	4.00
		Nos. 804-807 (4)	7.00	7.00

For surcharges see Nos. 854-857.

Nos. 381, 387-388, 395, 398-399, 402, 429, 689, and 731 Srchd. in Black, Blue or Red

Methods and Perfs As Before
2006, Jan. 1

808	A28	5g on 8m #395	.35	.35
809	A25	10g on 1m #381	.35	.35
810	A26	10g on 1m #388	.35	.35
811	A35	10g on 25m #429	.35	.35
812	A92	10g on 100m #731	.35	.35
813	A26	20g on 50g #387	.85	.85
814	A92	20g on 20m #402 (Bl)	.85	.85
815	A92	20g on 3000m #689	.85	.85
816	A29	60g on 5m #398 (R)	3.25	3.25
817	A29	60g on 8m #399 (R)	3.25	3.25
		Nos. 808-817 (10)	10.80	10.80

Pres. Aliyev Type of 2004
2006, Jan. 1   **Litho.**   **Perf. 14¼x14**
818 A148 60g multi   2.50 2.50

Mosque, Länkäran — A164

2006, Jan. 1   **Litho.**   **Perf. 13½x14**
819 A164 10g blk & blue   .40 .40

Fortress, Lachin — A165

2006, Jan. 1   **Litho.**   **Perf. 13½x14**
820 A165 20g blk & bister   1.00 1.00

OPEC Intl. Development Fund, 30th Anniv. — A166

2006, Jan. 30   **Litho.**   **Perf. 14¼x14**
821 A166 5g multi   .85 .85

Europa — A167

Monuments and: 20g, Hands, circle of stars. 60g, Dancers, man at computer, oil well, globes.

2006, Mar. 1   **Perf. 13½x13¼**
822-823 A167 Set of 2   5.00 5.00
823a   Booklet pane, 2 each #822-823, perf. 13½x13¾ on 3 sides   22.50 22.50

No. 823a was sold with booklet cover, but unattached to it. The middle columns of the booklet are tete-beche.

2006 World Cup Soccer Championships, Germany — A168

No. 824 — Soccer players and: a, 20g, 2006 World Cup emblem. b, 60g, Emblem, map of Germany.

2006, Mar. 14   **Perf. 13½**
824 A168 Horiz. pair, #a-b   3.50 3.50

Poets A169

Designs: 10g, Samed Vurgun. 20g, Suleyman Rustam.

2006, Mar. 16   **Perf. 14x14¼**
825-826 A169 Set of 2   1.40 1.40

Russia Year in Azerbaijan — A170

No. 827: a, 10g, St. Basil's Cathedral, Moscow, Russian flag and arms. b, 20g, Taza Pir Mosque, Azerbaijani flag and arms. c, 30g, Maiden Tower, Azerbaijani flag and arms. d, 60g, Kremlin, Moscow, Russian flag and arms.

2006, Apr. 17   **Perf. 14x14¼**
827 A170 Block of 4, #a-d   4.00 4.00

Printed in sheets containing two each of Nos. 827a-827d, and 2 labels.

Gulistan Mausoleum, Nakhichevan A171

2006, May 22   **Litho.**   **Perf. 14¼x14**
828 A171 20g multi   .85 .85

World Information Organization Day — A172

2006, June 12
829 A172 1m multi   3.25 3.25

Karabakh Horses A173

Designs: Nos. 830, 834a, 20g, Khan, 1867. Nos. 831, 834b, 20g, Zaman, 1952. Nos. 832, 834c, 20g, Sarvan, 1987. Nos. 833, 834d, 20g, Qar-qar, 2001. 60g, Aliyetmaz, 1867, vert.

2006, June 27   **Perf. 14x14¼**
Size: 40x28mm
830-833 A173 Set of 4   3.50 3.50
Miniature Sheet
Stamp Size: 52x37mm
Perf. 13½
834 A173 20g Sheet of 4, #a-d   3.50 3.50
Souvenir Sheet
Stamp Size: 28x40mm
Perf. 14¼x14
835 A173 60g multi   2.75 2.75

Summuqqala Tower, Qax — A174

Mausoleum of Nezami, Gäncä — A175

2006, Aug. 3   **Perf. 13½x14**
836 A174 10g blk & lilac   .40 .40
837 A175 20g blk & rose   .85 .85

Nos. 797-798 Surcharged

Methods and Perfs As Before
2006, Sept. 28   **Size: 45x35mm**
838 A157 20g on 1000m #797   1.25 1.25
839 A157 60g on 3000m #798   3.00 3.00
   a.   Sheet of 4, 2 each #838-839   8.50 8.50
   b.   Sheet of 6, 3 each #838-839   17.00 17.00

Nos. 839a-839b were not sold in a booklet, like the unsurcharged stamps. The margins of Nos. 839a-839b, have an overprint commemorating the 50th anniversary of Europa stamps.

Regional Communications Commonwealth, 15th Anniv. — A176

2006, Oct. 9   **Litho.**   **Perf. 14x14¼**
840 A176 20g multi   1.20 1.20

Independence, 15th Anniv. — A177

2006, Oct. 18
841 A177 20g multi   1.20 1.20

Miniature Sheet

Fire Trucks — A178

No. 842: a, 10g, AMO-F15, 1926. b, 20g, PMQ-1, 1932. c, 60g, PMQ-9, 1950. d, 1m, ATS 2, 5-40, 1998.

2006, Dec. 28
842 A178 Sheet of 4, #a-d   5.50 5.50

Pigeons — A179

No. 843, horiz.: a, Three pigeons. b, Sogani and Qara Ebres pigeons. c, Qirmizi and Qirmizi Cep pigeons. d, Ag Dugus and Qarabas pigeons. e, Two Qara pigeons. f, Qara and Qirmizi Cil pigeons. 1m, Ag Leleyli pigeon.

2007, Jan. 24   **Perf. 14x14¼**
843 A179 20g Sheet of 6, #a-f   5.00 5.00
Souvenir Sheet
Perf. 14¼x14
844 A179 1m multi   3.00 3.00

Customs Service Buidings — A180

No. 845 — Building for: a, 20g, Baku Customs. b, 60g, Azerbaijan Customs.

2007, Jan. 30   **Perf. 14¼x14**
845 A180 Horiz. pair, #a-b, + central label   3.75 3.75

Souvenir Sheet

Fall of Khojali, 15th Anniv. — A181

2007, Feb. 26   Litho.   Perf. 14¼x14
846 A181 1m multi + 2 labels   3.50 3.50

Europa — A182

Scouting emblem and: 20g, Dove, tents. 60g, Scout, kite.

2007, Apr. 2   Perf. 13½x13¼
847-848 A182   Set of 2   5.50 5.50
848a   Booklet pane, 4 each #847-
       848, perf. 13½x13¼ on 3
       sides   21.00 21.00

Scouting, cent. No. 848a was sold with booklet cover, but unattached to it. The middle columns of the booklet are tete-beche.

Friendship
Between
Azerbaijan
and Japan
A183

2007, Apr. 5   Perf. 14x14¼
849 A183 1m multi   3.50 3.50

Mosque,
Göyçay — A184

2007, Apr. 20   Perf. 14x13½
850 A184 10g blk & yellow   .40 .40

**Nos. 748, 767, 802, 804-807
Surcharged in Black or Red**

Methods and Perfs As Before
2007, Apr. 20
851 A135 60g on 3000m #748   2.25 2.25
852 A142 60g on 3000m #767
         (R)   2.25 2.25
853 A161 60g on 3000m #802   2.40 2.40
854 A163 60g on 3000m #804
         (R)   2.00 2.00
  a.   Pair, imperf.   4.00 4.00
855 A163 60g on 3000m #805
         (R)   2.00 2.00
  a.   Pair, imperf.   4.00 4.00
856 A163 60g on 3000m #806
         (R)   2.00 2.00
  a.   Pair, imperf.   4.00 4.00
857 A163 60g on 3000m #807
         (R)   2.00 2.00
  a.   Pair, imperf.   4.00 4.00
       Nos. 851-857 (7)   14.90 14.90

Dog Fight,
by Azim
Azimade
A185

Wedding,
by Azim
Azimade
A186

2007, June 5   Litho.   Perf. 14x14¼
858   Horiz. pair with central
         label   2.10 2.10
  a.   A185 20g multi   1.00 1.00
  b.   A186 20g multi   1.00 1.00

Azermarka, 15th
Anniv. — A187

2007, July 14   Perf. 14¼x14
859 A187 50g multi   2.75 2.75

Knut, Polar
Bear Cub
Born in
Berlin Zoo
A188

2007, Aug. 15   Perf. 13x13¼
860 A188 60g shown   3.00 3.00
  a.   Souvenir sheet of 4 12.00 12.00
       Souvenir Sheet
861 A188 1m Knut, vert.   5.00 5.00

No. 861 contains one 30x38mm stamp.

Flowers — A189

No. 862: a, 10g, Gagea alexeenkoana. b, 20g, Centaurea ficher. c, 40g, Galanthus caucasicus. d, 60g, Ophrys caucasica. 1m, Ophrys caucasica, diff.

2007, Aug. 20   Perf. 14x14¼
862 A189   Sheet of 4, #a-d 3.50 3.50
       Souvenir Sheet
863 A189 1m multi   3.00 3.00

Hüseyn Cavid (1882-1941),
Writer — A190

2007, Sept. 19
864 A190 20g multi   1.20 1.20

Bridges — A191

No. 865: a, 10g, Xudaferin Bridge. b, 20g, Qazançi Bridge. c, 30g, Qudyalçay Bridge. d, 50g, Gancaçay Bridge. 60g, Xudaferin Bridge, diff.

2007, Nov. 1   Litho.   Perf. 14x14¼
865 A191   Sheet of 4, #a-d 4.25 4.25
       Souvenir Sheet
866 A191 60g multi   2.50 2.50

No. 401 Surcharged

Methods and Perfs As Before
2007, Nov. 28
867 A31 10g on 15m #401   .40 .40

Xudaferin Bridge,   Fortress,
Jabrayil — A192   Kalbacar — A193

2007, Nov. 28   Litho.   Perf. 14x13½
868 A192 10g blk & pale org   .50 .50
869 A193 20g blk & green   .90 .90

Souvenir Sheet

Launch of Sputnik 1, 50th
Anniv. — A194

2007, Nov. 28   Perf. 14¼x14
870 A194 1m multi   4.50 4.50

Souvenir Sheet

Lt. Gen. Karim Karimov (1917-2003),
USSR Space Flight Commission
Chairman — A195

2007, Dec. 30
871 A195 1m multi   4.25 4.25

2008 Summer Olympics,
Beijing — A196

No. 872: a, 20g, Judo. b, 30g, Weight lifting. c, 40g, Wrestling. d, 60g, Boxing.

2008, Feb. 25   Perf. 14x14¼
872 A196   Block of 4, #a-d 5.50 5.50

Europa — A197

Designs: 20g, Open envelope. 60g, Computer monitor. 1m, Dove.

2008, Mar. 13   Litho.   Perf. 13½
873-874 A197   Set of 2   5.50 5.50
874a   Booklet pane, 4 each #873-
       874, perf. 13½ on 3 sides 22.00 22.00
       Souvenir Sheet
              Perf. 13¼x13¾
875 A197 1m multi   5.50 5.50

No. 874a was sold with booklet cover, but unattached to it. The middle columns of the booklet are tete-beche.
No. 875 contains one 18x25mm stamp.

Tower, Qazak — A198

2008, Apr. 8   Perf. 13½x14
876 A198 10g blk & sal pink   .40 .40

Nakhichevan Drama Theater, 125th
Anniv. — A199

2008, Apr. 9   **Perf. 14x14¼**
877 A199 20g multi   1.20 1.20

Zarifa Aliyeva (1923-85),
Ophthalmologist, Wife of Pres. Heydar
Aliyev — A200

Pres. Heydar Aliyev (1923-
2003) — A201

No. 878 — Mrs. Aliyeva: a, Plain background. b, Flower in background.
No. 879 — Pres. Aliyev: a, And Azerbaijan
flag. b, Blue and green background.

2008   Litho.   Perf. 14¼x14
878 A200 1m Pair, #a-b   7.50 7.50
879 A201 1m Pair, #a-b   7.50 7.50

Issued: No. 878, 4/28; No. 879, 5/2. Nos.
878 and 879 were each printed in sheets containing four of each stamp of that particular
pair and a central label.

Azerbaijan
Republic,
90th Anniv.
A202

2008, May 28   **Perf. 14x14¼**
880 A202 20g multi   1.20 1.20

Mikayil
Müsfiq
(1908-39),
Poet
A203

2008, June 6
881 A203 20g multi   1.20 1.20

Physicists
A204

Designs: No. 882, 20g, Lev Landau (1908-
68). No. 883, 20g, Hasan Abdullayev (1918-
93).

2008, July 21   Litho.   Perf. 14x14¼
882-883 A204   Set of 2   2.50 2.50

Miniature Sheet

Caspian Shipping Company, 150th
Anniv. — A205

No. 884: a, 20g, Tanker Heydar Aliyev. b,
30g, Ferry Azerbaijan. c, 50g, Cargo ship
Bestekar Qara Qarayev. d, 60g, Cargo ship
Maestro Niyaz. e, 1m, Tanker Vandal.

2008, Sept. 21   **Perf. 13½**
884 A205   Sheet of 5, #a-e, +   9.00 9.00
                   4 labels

Jewelry — A206

No. 885: a, Earring 12th-13th cent. b, Pendant, 19th cent.

2008, Sept. 18   **Perf. 11½**
885 A206 60g Horiz. pair, #a-b, +   5.25 5.25
                   central label
           See Ukraine No. 742.

Khanagah   Garabaghla
Mausoleum,   Mausoleum,
Culfa   Sarur
A207   A208

2008, Oct. 3   Litho.   Perf. 14x13½
886 A207 10g blk & brown   .40 .40
                              Perf. 13½x14
887 A208 20g blk & gray   .85 .85

Arachnids — A209

No. 888: a, 5g, Galeodes araneoides. b,
10g, Buthus occitanus. c, 20g, Pisaura
mirabilis. d, 30g, Latrodectus tredecimgut-
tatus. e, 40g, Araneus diadematus. f, 60g,
Tegenaria domestica.
1m, Argyroneta aquatica.

2008, Dec. 2   **Perf. 14¼x14**
888 A209   Sheet of 6, #a-f   6.00 6.00
              Souvenir Sheet
889 A209 1m multi   4.00 4.00

Mir Jalal (1908-
78),
Writer — A210

2008, Dec. 17
890 A210 60g multi   2.25 2.25

Azerbaijan postal authorities
declared as illegal miniature sheets
dated 2008 depicting the Pope and
Princess Diana, Mushrooms, Dinosaurs, Horses, Dogs, Animals and
Cats.

Miniature Sheet

Nakhichevan Autonomous Republic,
85th Anniv. — A211

No. 891 — Buildings: a, H. Javid Mausoleum (white building with steps at left). b,
Heydar Aliyev School (with curved front, flowers at right). c, Nakhichevan Ministry of Economy building (with island gardens). d, Library,
Nakhichevan State University (with red roof
and striped curbs). e, Conservatory, Nakhichevan State University (with striped curbs). f,
Physiotherapy Center (with curved front and
circular garden). g, Tebriz Hotel (with dome at
right). h, Medical Center of Nakhichevan (with
curved front with brown vertical lines on
wings).

2009, Feb. 7
891 A211 20g Sheet of 8, #a-h, +   6.50 6.50
                   central label

Baku, Center of Islamic
Culture — A212

Designs: 10g, Emblem. 20g, Emblem and
Maiden Tower, Baku.

2009, Feb. 18   **Perf. 13½x14**
892-893 A212   Set of 2   1.25 1.25

Souvenir Sheet

Preservation of Polar Regions and
Glaciers — A213

No. 894 — Emblem and map of: a, Antarctica. b, Greenland and Arctic region.

2009, Mar. 3   **Perf. 13¾x13½**
894 A213 1m Sheet of 2, #a-b   7.00 7.00

10th Economic
Cooperation
Organization
Summit,
Tehran — A214

2009, Apr. 2   **Perf. 14¼x14**
895 A214 1m multi   3.50 3.50
See Iran 2981, compare with Pakistan 1111.

Europa — A215

Designs: 20g, Nasir ad-Din at-Tusi (1201-
74), scientist. 60g, Samaxi Observatory and
Moon.
1m, Earth, Moon, telescope of Galileo.

2009, Apr. 13   **Perf. 13½x13¼**
896-897 A215   Set of 2   5.50 5.50
897a   Booklet pane of 8, 4 each
         #896-897, perf. 13½x13¼
         on 3 sides   22.00
              Souvenir Sheet
898 A215 1m multi   5.50 5.50

Intl. Year of Astronomy. No. 897a was sold
with booklet cover, but unattached to it. The
middle columns of the booklet pane are tete-
beche.

Azerbaijan's Cooperation With NATO,
15th Anniv. — A216

2009, May 4   Litho.   Perf. 14x14¼
899 A216 20g multi   .85 .85
Printed in sheets of 8 + 2 labels.

European
Council,
60th Anniv.
A217

2009, May 5
900 A217 60g multi   2.75 2.75

European
Court of
Human
Rights,
50th Anniv.
A218

2009, May 5
901 A218 60g multi   2.75 2.75

Sumqayit, 60th Anniv. — A219

2009, June 1   *Perf. 13½x14*
902 A219 10g multi   .75 .75

Butterflies — A220

Designs: 10g, Vanessa atalanta. 20g, Papilio alexanor orientalis.

2009, June 1
903-904 A220   Set of 2   1.25 1.25
See Nos.913-914, 928-929, 939.

Diplomatic Service, 90th Anniv. — A221

2009, July 9   Litho.   *Perf. 14¼x14*
905 A221 60g multi   2.50 2.50
Printed in sheets of 8 + central label.

Jalil Mammadguluzadeh (1869-1932), Writer — A222

2009, July 10
906 A222 20g multi   1.25 1.25

Leyla Mammadbeyova (1909-89), Test Pilot — A223

2009, Sept. 19   Litho.   *Perf. 14x14¼*
907 A223 20g multi   1.00 1.00

State Oil Fund, 10th Anniv. — A224

2009, Oct. 8   *Perf. 14¼x14*
908 A224 60g multi   2.00 2.00
Printed in sheets of 8 + central label.

Universal Postal Union, 135th Anniv. A225

No. 909 — Background color: a, 20g, Pale orange. b, 60g, Rose pink.

2009, Oct. 9   *Perf. 14x14¼*
909 A225   Pair, #a-b   3.25 3.25

Miniature Sheet

Birds — A226

No. 910: a, 10g, Platalea leucorodia. b, 20g, Phalacrocorax pygmaeus. c, 60g, Numenius tenuirostris. d, 1m, Porphyrio porphyrio.

2009, Oct. 19   Litho.
910 A226   Sheet of 4, #a-d   6.50 6.50

Souvenir Sheet

Azerbaijan, 2009 European Chess Champions — A227

No. 911 — Chess pieces and map of: a, 50g, Europe. b, 1m, Azerbaijan.

2009, Oct. 8   *Perf. 14¼x14*
911 A227   Sheet of 2, #a-b   5.00 5.00

Miniature Sheet

Paintings by Sattar Bahlulzadeh (1909-74) — A228

No. 912: a, Qedim Samaxi (Ancient Shamakhi). b, Zeferanla Narlar (Saffron with Pomegranates). c, Buzovna Sahil (Buzovna Shore). d, Menzere (View). e, Laleler (Poppies). f, Qirmizi Menzere (Red View).

2009, Dec. 15   *Perf. 14x14¼*
912 A228 20g Sheet of 6, #a-f, +   5.50 5.50
     3 central labels

Butterflies Type of 2009

Designs: 10g, Thaleropis jonia. 20g, Danaus chrysippus.

2010, Jan. 11   *Perf. 13½x14*
913-914 A220   Set of 2   1.25 1.25

Souvenir Sheet

January 20, 1990 Baku Massacre — A229

2010, Jan. 20   *Perf. 14¼x14*
915 A229 1m multi + 2 labels   3.50 3.50

Ministry of Taxation, 10th Anniv. A230

2010, Feb. 11   *Perf. 14x14¼*
916 A230 60g multi   2.25 2.25

New Year 2010 (Year of the Tiger) — A231

Litho. With Foil Application
2010, Mar. 1   *Perf. 14¼x14*
917 A231 60g multi   2.25 2.25

Azerbaijan Red Crescent Society, 90th Anniv. A232

2010, Mar. 10   Litho.   *Perf. 14x14¼*
918 A232 60g multi   2.25 2.25

Europa — A233

Characters from children's stories: 20g, Boy, dog and bear. 60g, Lion, wolf, duck, fox. 1m, Ogre and children.

2010, Mar. 16   *Perf. 13x13¼*
919-920 A233   Set of 2   5.00 5.00
920a   Booklet pane of 8, 4 each   20.00 —
     #919-920, perf. 13 on 3
     sides
Souvenir Sheet
Perf. 13
921 A233 1m multi   6.00 6.00
No. 920a was sold with booklet cover, but unattached to it. The middle columns of the booklet pane are tete-beche.

Peonies — A234

No. 922 — Flower color: a, Yellow. b, Pink. c, White. d, Red.
20g, Peonies in vase.

2010, Apr. 10   *Perf. 13¼*
922 A234 10g Sheet of 4, #a-d   2.50 2.50
Souvenir Sheet
923 A234 20g multi   1.50 1.50

Victory in World War II, 65th Anniv. — A235

No. 924 — 65th anniversary emblem and: a, 10g, Soviet soldiers in front of statue in Berlin. b, 20g; Soviet soldiers raising Soviet flag over Reichstag building, Berlin. c, 60g, Soviet airplane, rail tanker.

2010, Apr. 20   Litho.   *Perf. 14¼x14*
924 A235   Horiz. strip of 3   3.50 3.50
Printed in sheets containing two strips separated by a horizontal strip of three labels.

2010 World Cup Soccer Championships, South Africa — A236

No. 925 — Soccer player and 2010 World Cup: a, 20g, Emblem. b, 60g, Mascot.

2010, May 18   *Perf. 14x14¼*
925 A236   Pair, #a-b   3.25 3.25

Souvenir Sheet

Azerbaijan Pavilion, Expo 2010, Shanghai — A237

2010, May 18   *Perf. 13¼*
926 A237 60g multi   2.50 2.50

Alesker Alekberov (1910-63), Actor A238

2010, June 18   *Perf. 14x14¼*
927 A238 20g multi   1.25 1.25

Butterflies Type of 2009

Designs: 10g, Argynnis alexandra. 20g, Brahmaea christophi.

2010, July 15   *Perf. 13½x14*
928-929 A220   Set of 2   1.25 1.25

Mausoleum of
Noah,
Nakhichevan
A239

2010, July 19   *Perf. 14¼x14*
930 A239 60g multi   2.50 2.50

Buildings in Baku's Old City — A240

No. 931: a, 10g, Shirvanshah Palace, 12th-
15th cent. b, 20g, Bazaar Square, 15th cent. c,
30g, Fortress archways, 19th cent. d, 40g,
Came Mosque, 14th cent. e, 50g, Qasim Bey
Bathhouse, 15th cent. f, 60g, Multam and
Bukhara Caravansaries, 15th cent.
No. 932: a, 10g, Maiden Tower, 6th
cent. b, 20g, Muhammad Mosque, 11th cent.
c, 30g, Fortress walls, 12th cent. d, 40g, Palace Mosque, 15th cent. e, 50g, Shirvanshah
Tomb, 15th cent. f, 60g, Divankhana, 15th
cent.
1m, Shirvanshah Palace complex, 12th-15th
cent.

2010, July 26   *Perf. 13½*
Sheets of 6, #a-f
931-932 A240 Set of 2   17.00 17.00
Souvenir Sheet
Perf. 14¼x14
933 A240 1m multi   5.00 5.00
No. 933 contains one 56x40mm stamp.

Souvenir Sheet

Temples — A241

No. 934: a, Ateshgah, Baku, Azerbaijan. b,
Pyramid of the Sun, Teotihuacan, Mexico.

2010, Oct. 12 Litho. *Perf. 14x14¼*
934 A241 60g Sheet of 2   5.00 5.00
See Mexico No. 2699.

Shafaat
Mehdiyev
(1910-93),
Geologist
A242

2010, Nov. 5   *Perf. 14x14¼*
935 A242 60g multi   2.25 2.25

Cats — A243

No. 936: a, 10g, Scottish fold cat. b, 2g,
Persian cat. c, 30g, Somali cat. d, 40g, British
shorthaired cat. e, 50g, Burmese cat. f, 60g,
Maine Coon cat.
1m, Angora cat.

2010, Nov. 8   *Perf. 14¼x14*
936 A243   Sheet of 6, #a-f   7.00 7.00
Souvenir Sheet
937 A243 1m multi   3.50 3.50

Birds of the Caspian Sea — A244

No. 938: a, Ardeola ralloides. b, Phoenicopterus roseus.

2010, Nov. 24   *Perf. 14¼x14*
938 A244 60g Pair, #a-b   4.00 4.00
See Kazakhstan No. 632.

Butterflies Type of 2009
2010, Dec. 15   *Perf. 13½x14*
939 A220 10g Parnassius apollo   .90 .90

Flowers — A245

Designs: 20g, Centaurea fischeri. 50g,
Gagea alexeenkoana.

2011, Mar. 10   *Perf. 13½x14*
940-941 A245   Set of 2   2.50 2.50
See Nos. 951-952.

Novruz
Festival — A246

2011, Mar. 18 Litho. *Perf. 14¼x14*
942 A246 30g multi   1.25 1.25

New Year 2011
(Year of the
Rabbit) — A247

Litho. With Foil Application
2011, Mar. 18
943 A247 1m multi   3.50 3.50

Admission of Azerbaijan to European
Council, 10th Anniv. — A248

2011, Mar. 18 Litho. *Perf. 14x14¼*
944 A248 1m multi   3.50 3.50

Europa
A249

Designs: 20g, Ulmus densa. 60g, Platanus
orientalis.
1m, Parrotia persica.

2011, Apr. 8   *Perf. 13¼x13*
945 A249 20g multi   1.00 1.00
  a.   Perf. 13 on 3 sides   1.00 1.00
946 A249 60g multi   4.00 4.00
  a.   Perf. 13 on 3 sides   4.00 4.00
  b.   Booklet pane of 8, 4 each
       #945a-946a   20.00   —
Souvenir Sheet
947 A249 1m multi   5.50 5.50
Intl. Year of Forests. No. 946b was sold with
booklet cover, but unattached to it. The middle
columns of the booklet pane are tete-beche.

Souvenir Sheet

First Manned Space Flight, 50th
Anniv. — A250

No. 948: a, 20g, International Space Station
(40x28mm). b, 50g, Vostok 1 (40x28mm). c,
1m, To You Mankind, painting by Tahir
Salakhov (79x28mm).

Perf. 14x14¼, 14 Horiz. (1m)
2011, Apr. 12
948 A250   Sheet of 3, #a-c   6.00 6.00

Huseyn Aliyev
(1911-91),
Painter — A251

2011, Apr. 22   *Perf. 14¼x14*
949 A251 60g multi   2.25 2.25

Musical Instruments — A252

No. 950: a, Hurdy-gurdy (tekerli lira),
Belarus. b, Tar, Azerbaijan.

2011, May 25 Litho.   *Perf. 14x14¼*
950 A252 50g Pair, #a-b   3.50 3.50
See Belarus No. 770.

Flowers Type of 2011
Designs: 10g, Ophrys caucasica. 30g,
Galanthus caucasicus.

2011, June 20   *Perf. 13½x14*
951-952 A245   Set of 2   1.75 1.75

Souvenir Sheet

Victory of Eldar Qasimov and Nigar
Camal in 2011 Eurovision Song
Contest — A253

2011, July 5   *Perf. 14¼x14*
953 A253 1m multi   3.75 3.75

Heydar Aliyev Palace,
Nakhchivan — A254

2011, July 15   *Perf. 14x14¼*
954 A254 60g multi   2.00 2.00

A255

No. 955: a, Behbud Aga Sahtaxtinski (1881-
1924), Minister of State Control. b, Map of
Azerbaijan at 1921 signing of Treaty of Kars.

2011, July 15
955 A255 60g Horiz. pair, #a-b   4.00 4.00

Chrysanthemums — A256

No. 956 — Chrysanthemums at: a, 10g, Right. b, 20g, Left.

2011, Aug. 3   **Perf. 12¾x13**
956 A256   Horiz. pair, #a-b   1.25 1.25
Printed in sheets containing 3 pairs.

Miniature Sheet

Medals and Orders of Azerbaijan — A257

No. 957: a, Order of Heydar Aliyev. b, Gold Star medal. c, Order of Independence (Istiqlal). d, Order of Shah Ismail (Sah Ismayil). e, Order of the Azerbaijani Flag (Azerbaycan Bayragi). f, Order of Honor (Seref). g, Order of Glory (Söhret). h, Order of Friendship (Dostluq). i, Order of Service to the Motherland (Vetene Xidmete Göre).

2011, Sept. 5   **Perf. 13½**
957 A257 60g Sheet of 9, #a-i   17.50 17.50

Miniature Sheets

A258

Items in Customs Museum — A259

No. 958: a, Two daggers, 12th-7th cent. B.C. b, Curved dagger with thin blade and scabbard, 19th cent. c, Curved sword, scabbard, sword handle, 19th cent. d, Dagger with wide blade and scabbard, 19th cent. e, Straight dagger and scabbard, 20th cent. f, Rifle and pistol, 19th cent. g, Rifle, 19th cent. h, Rifle and powder horn, 19th cent.

No. 959: a, Belt with oval and rectanuglar panels, 19th cent. b, Belt with loops at bottom and oval buckle, 19th cent. c, Belt with round buttons, 19th cent. d, Cylindrical case with chain and pendants, 19th cent. e, Belt with loops at bottom and round buckle, 19th cent. f, Decorative statues depicting people on amimals, 1st cent. B.C. g, Rübab, 19th cent. h, Decorative statues depicting two-headed animal and horseman, 1st cent. B.C.

2011, Sept. 5
958 A258 20g Sheet of 8, #a-h, + central label   5.00 5.00
959 A259 60g Sheet of 8, #a-h, + central label   15.00 15.00

Nizami Ganjavi (1141-1209), Poet — A260

No. 960 — Ganjavi facing: a, Right. b, Left.

2011, Sept. 21   **Litho.**
960 A260 30g Horiz. pair, #a-b, + central label   2.50 2.50

Regional Communications Commonwealth, 20th Anniv. — A261

2011, Sept. 23   **Perf. 14x14¼**
961 A261 50g multi   2.00 2.00

Commonwealth of Independent States, 20th Anniv. — A262

2011, Sept. 23
962 A262 60g multi   2.50 2.50

Independence, 20th Anniv. — A263

No. 963: a, Azerbaijan coat of arms. b, Azerbaijan flag. c, Azerbaijan national anthem. d, Azerbaijan map.
No. 964, 2m, Flag and map of Azerbaijan.
No. 965, 2m, Pres. Heydar Aliyev and flag.

Litho. & Embossed With Foil Application
2011, Oct. 11   **Perf. 13½x13**
963 A263 1m Sheet of 4, #a-d   12.50 12.50
Souvenir Sheets
964-965 A263   Set of 2   12.50 12.50

Azerbaijan's Candidacy for Seat on United Nations Security Council — A264

2011, Oct. 21   **Litho.**   **Perf. 14x14¼**
966 A264 60g multi   2.25 2.25

Worldwide Fund for Nature (WWF) — A265

No. 967 — Circaetus gallicus: a, 20g, Two birds in flight. b, 30g, Two adults and chick. c, 50g, Two adults. d, 60g, One adult attacking prey.

2011, Oct. 28
967 A265   Block of 4, #a-d   5.00 5.00
   e.   Souvenir sheet of 4, #967a-967d   5.00 5.00
   f.   Souvenir sheet of 8, 2 separated vertical rows of #967a-967d   10.00 10.00

Flag Day — A266

2011, Nov. 9   **Perf. 14¼x14**
968 A266 30g multi   1.25 1.25

Karabakh Horses — A267

Various horses: 10g, 20g, 30g, 50g.

2011, Nov. 16   **Perf. 14x13½**
969-972 A267   Set of 4   3.75 3.75

Abbas Zamanov (1911-93), Literary Critic — A268

2011, Dec. 1   **Perf. 14¼x14**
973 A268 60g multi   2.25 2.25

First Use of Telephone in Azerbaijan, 130th Anniv. — A269

2011, Dec. 6   **Perf. 14x14¼**
974 A269 1m multi   3.00 3.00

Dogs — A270

No. 975: a, 10g, Shar Pei. b, 20g, Dalmatian. c, 30g, Labrador retriever. d, 40g, Doberman Pinscher. e, 50g, Chow Chow. f, 60g, German Shepherd.
1m, Caucasian Shepherds, horiz.

2011, Dec. 10   **Perf. 14¼x14**
975 A270   Sheet of 6, #a-f   6.50 6.50
Souvenir Sheet
   Perf. 14¼x14
976 A270 1m multi   3.00 3.00

Souvenir Sheet

World Championship of Rabita Baku Women's Volleyball Team — A271

2011, Dec. 26   **Perf. 14¼x14**
977 A271 1m multi   3.75 3.75

New Year 2012 (Year of the Dragon) A272

2012, Jan. 5   **Litho.**   **Perf. 13¼**
978 A272 20g multi   .90 .90

Central Bank of Azerbaijan, 20th Anniv. A273

2012, Feb. 12   **Perf. 14x14¼**
979 A273 50g multi   2.10 2.10

Bahruz Kengerli (1892-1922), Painter — A274

2012, Mar. 15   **Perf. 14¼x14**
980 A274 20g multi   1.00 1.00

Designs: 20g, Beach on Caspian Sea, airplane, sailboat. 60g, Skier and chairlift. 1m, Baku International Airport, vert.

2012, Mar. 15   **Perf. 13¼x13**
981-982 A275   Set of 2   5.00 5.00
982a   Booklet pane of 8, 4 each
    #981-982, perf. 13 on 3
    sides   20.00 —

Souvenir Sheet
Perf. 13x13¼
983 A275 1m multi   6.00 6.00

No. 982a was sold with, but unattached to, a booklet cover.

A276

A277

2012 Eurovision Song Contest, Baku — A278

No. 984: a, 10g, Flame Towers. b, 20g, Heydar Aliyev Center. c, 30g, SOCAR (State Oil Company of Azerbaijan) Tower. d, 40g, Baku Hilton Hotel. e, 50g, Port Baku Residences. f, 60g, Absheron Marriott Hotel.

No. 985: a, 10g, Heydar Aliyev Palace. b, 20g, Opera and Ballet Theater. c, 30g, Philharmonic Hall. d, 40g, Green Theater. e, 50g, Mugam Center. f, 60g, Rashid Behbudov State Song Theater.

No. 986: a, 10g, Shirvansahlar Palace. b, 20g, Government House. c, 30g, Baku City Hall. d, 40g, Nizami Museum of Azerbaijani Literature. e, 50g, Heydar Aliyev Foundation Building. f, 60g, Presidium of Azerbaijan National Academy of Sciences.

No. 987, Eurovision Song Contest emblem, Shirvansahlar Palace. No. 988, Flame, Eurovision Song Contest emblem.

Litho. & Embossed With Foil Application
2012, May 14
984 A276   Sheet of 6, #a-f   6.00 6.00
985 A277   Sheet of 6, #a-f   6.00 6.00
986 A278   Sheet of 6, #a-f   6.00 6.00
   Nos. 984-986 (3)   18.00 18.00
Souvenir Sheets
987 A278 60g multi   2.00 2.00
988 A278 60g multi   2.00 2.00

Diplomatic Relations Between Azerbaijan and People's Republic of China, 20th Anniv.
A279

2012, June 13   Litho.   Perf. 14x14¼
989 A279 50g multi   2.00 2.00

Mirza Fatali Axundzade (1812-78), Writer — A280

2012, June 30   **Perf. 14¼x14**
990 A280 20g multi   1.20 1.20

Mirza Alakbar Sabir (1862-1911), Philosopher A281

2012, July 10
991 A281 20g multi   1.20 1.20

Souvenir Sheet

Azermarka, 20th Anniv. — A282

2012, July 14   **Perf. 14x14¼**
992 A282 1m multi   3.50 3.50

Mammed Said Ordubadi (1872-1950), Writer — A283

2012, Aug. 17   **Perf. 14¼x14**
993 A283 50g multi   1.75 1.75

Müslüm Magomayev (1942-2008), Singer — A284

2012, Aug. 17
994 A284 50g multi   1.75 1.75

Aythya Nyroca — A285

Various depictions of Aythya nyroca.

2012, Sept. 12   **Perf. 14x13½**
Frame Color
995 A285 10g yellow   .40 .40
996 A285 20g rose lilac   .75 .75
997 A285 50g light blue   1.75 1.75
   Nos. 995-997 (3)   2.90 2.90

Baku and Arms — A286

National Flag and Symbol — A287

2012, Apr. 6   **Perf. 14xx14¼**
998 A286 60g multi + label   2.00 2.00
Perf. 14¼x14
999 A287 60g multi + label   2.00 2.00

Souvenir Sheet

Diplomatic Relations Between Azerbaijan and Egypt, 20th Anniv. — A288

No. 1000: a, Maiden's Tower, Azerbaijan. b, Sphinx and Pyramids, Egypt.

2012, June 13   **Perf. 14x14¼**
1000 A288 60g Sheet of 2, #a-b   4.25 4.25

Huseyn Javid (1882-1941), Poet — A289

2012, Oct. 24   **Perf. 14¼x14**
1001 A289 20g multi   1.00 1.00

Souvenir Sheet

Karabakh Costumes of the 19th Century — A290

No. 1002 — Emblem of Regional Communications Commonwealth and: a, Woman and girl. b, Man and boy.

2012, Oct. 29
1002 A290 50g Sheet of 2, #a-b   3.50 3.50

Souvenir Sheet

Diplomatic Relations Between Azerbaijan and Poland, 540th Anniv. — A291

No. 1003: a, Sultan Uzun Hasan (1423-78). b, King Casimir IV of Poland (1427-92).

2012, Oct. 29
1003 A291 60g Sheet of 2, #a-b   4.00 4.00

Birds — A292

No. 1004: a, 10g, Goose. b, 20g, Turkey. c, 30g, Chicken. d, 40g, Guinea fowl. e, 50g, Duck. f, 60g, Quail.
1m, Rooster, hen and chick.

2012, Nov. 5
1004 A292   Sheet of 6, #a-f   7.00 7.00
Souvenir Sheet
1005 A292 1m multi   3.00 3.00

Azerbaijan Olympic Committee, 20th Anniv. A293

2012, Nov. 7   **Perf. 14x14¼**
1006 A293 20g multi   1.00 1.00

Souvenir Sheet

Baku-Tbilisi-Kars Railway — A294

No. 1007 — Map of: a, Western Azerbaijan showing Kars and Tbilisi. b, Eastern Azerbaijan showing Baku.

2012, Nov. 12
1007 A294 60g Sheet of 2, #a-b 4.50 4.50

Developmental Partnership With World Bank, 20th Anniv. — A295

2012, Dec. 14
1008 A295 50g multi 1.75 1.75

Souvenir Sheet

First Azerbaijan Telecommunications Satellite — A296

2013, Jan. 15   **Perf. 12x12¼**
1009 A296 1m multi 3.50 3.50

Miniature Sheet

New Year 2013 (Year of the Snake) — A297

No. 1010: a, Fish on Chinese character. b, Deer on Chinese character. c, Cranes on Chinese character. d, Bird on Chinese character. e, Snake.

2013, Jan. 23   **Perf. 13¼**
1010 A297 20g Sheet of 20,
#1010a-
1010d, 16
#1010e   12.50 12.50

Europa A298

Postal vehicles: 20g, Truck. 60g, Van. 1m, Horse-drawn carriage.

2013, Feb. 25   **Perf. 13¼x13**
1011-1012 A298   Set of 2   5.00 5.00
1012a   Booklet pane of 8, 4
each #1011-1012, perf.
13 on 3 sides   20.00 20.00
Souvenir Sheet
1013 A298 1m multi   5.00 5.00

No. 1012a was sold with, but unattached to, a booklet cover. The two different stamps are found tete-beche within the booklet.

Intl. Association of Academies of Science, 20th Anniv. — A299

2013, Apr. 10   **Perf. 14¼x14**
1014 A299 20g multi   .90 .90

Miniature Sheet

Lighthouses — A300

No. 1015: a, Süvelan Lighthouse. b, Amburan Lighthouse. c, Böyük Zire Lighthouse. d, Abseron Lighthouse. e, Cilov Lighthouse.

2013, Apr. 11   **Perf. 12**
1015 A300 50g Sheet of 5, #a-e,
+ label   7.75 7.75

Islam Safarli (1923-74), Poet — A301

Alimardan Topchubashov (1863-1934), Politician — A302

Hokuma Gurbanova (1913-88), Actress A303

Nigar Rafibeyli (1913-81), Writer A304

2013, Apr. 19   **Perf. 14¼x14**
1016 A301 20g multi   .75 .75
      Perf. 14x14¼
1017 A302 20g multi   .75 .75
1018 A303 20g multi   .75 .75
1019 A304 20g multi   .75 .75
Nos. 1016-1019 (4)   3.00 3.00

Souvenir Sheet

Dancers — A305

No. 1020: a, Terekeme dancers, Azerbaijan. b, Kryzhachok dancers, Belarus.

2013, Apr. 24   **Perf. 13½x13**
1020 A305 50g Sheet of 2, #a-b 3.25 3.25
See Belarus No. 855.

Souvenir Sheet

Zarifa Aliyeva (1923-85), Ophthalmologist, Wife of Pres. Heydar Aliyev — A306

Litho. & Embossed With Foil Application
2013, Apr. 28
1021 A306 1m multi   3.25 3.25

Pres. Heydar Aliyev (1923-2003), Order of St. Andrew the Apostle — A307

2013, May 6   Litho.   Perf. 13½
1022 A307 50g multi   1.90 1.90
See Russia No. 7442.

A308

A309

Pres. Heydar Aliyev (1923-2003) — A310

No. 1023 — Pres. Aliyev: a, As young man in suit and tie. b, As young man in army uniform. c, As older man, wearing medals. d, Waving. e, Behind microphone, with hand on book. f, With soldiers, holding binoculars.
No. 1024 — Pres. Aliyev with: a, Turkish Pres. Süleyman Demirel, seated on red chairs. b, U.S. Pres. Bill Clinton. c, German Chancellor Helmut Kohl, paneled wall in background. d, Russian Pres. Vladimir Putin, picture frame behind Putin's head. e, French Pres. Jacques Chirac, seated on sofa. f, People's Republic of China Pres. Jiang Zemin.
1m, Pres. Aliyev and flag of Azerbaijan.

Litho. & Embossed With Foil Application
Perf. 13½x13, 13x13½ (#1024)
2013, May 10
1023 A308 50g Sheet of 6, #a-f 9.50 9.50
1024 A309 50g Sheet of 6, #a-f 9.50 9.50
Souvenir Sheet
1025 A310 1m multi   3.25 3.25

Mahsati Ganjavi (c. 1089-1159), Poet — A311

2013, May 14   Litho.   Perf. 14¼x14
1026 A311 60g multi   2.00 2.00

Souvenir Sheet

Diplomatic Relations Between Belarus and Azerbaijan, 20th Anniv. — A312

Litho. (Sheet Margin Litho. With Foil Application)
2013, June 11   *Perf. 12*
1027 A312 1m multi   3.00 3.00
See Belarus No. 862.

Souvenir Sheet

Fabric Designs Depicting Peacocks — A313

No. 1028 — Peacock from: a, Hungarian embroidered pillow cover (white background). b, Azeri woven horse blanket (tan background).

2013, June 15 Litho. *Perf. 14x14¼*
1028 A313 60g Sheet of 2, #a-b 3.50 3.50
See Hungary No. 4287.

Souvenir Sheet

Space Flight of Valentina Tereshkova, First Woman in Space, 50th Anniv. — A314

2013, June 16
1029 A314 1m multi   3.25 3.25

Souvenir Sheet

Armed Forces of Azerbaijan, 95th Anniv. — A315

2013, June 26   *Perf. 14¼x14*
1030 A315 1m multi   3.25 3.25

Birds — A316

Designs: 10g, Merops persicus. 20g, Coracias garrulus. 30g, Alcedo atthis. 50g, Upupa epops. 60g, Garrulus glandarius.

2013, July 16 Litho. *Perf. 13x13¼*
1031 A316 10g multi   .35 .35
1032 A316 20g multi   .70 .70
1033 A316 30g multi   1.10 1.10

1034 A316 50g multi   1.75 1.75
1035 A316 60g multi   2.10 2.10
    Nos. 1031-1035 (5)   6.00 6.00

State Management of Radio Frequencies, 45th Anniv. — A317

2013, Sept. 3 Litho. *Perf. 13*
1036 A317 60g multi   2.10 2.10

State Committee for Securities, 15th Anniv. A318

2013, Sept. 6 Litho. *Perf. 14x14¼*
1037 A318 60g multi   2.10 2.10

Memmed Araz (1933-2004), Poet — A319

2013, Sept. 10 Litho. *Perf. 14¼x14*
1038 A319 20g multi   .85 .85

Souvenir Sheet

Communications — A320

No. 1039: a, Building, people in office, wagon. b, Transmission tower, satellite, satellite dish, women at computers.

2013, Sept. 17 Litho. *Perf. 14¼x14*
1039 A320 50g Sheet of 2, #a-b 3.50 3.50

Miniature Sheets

Wildlife in Hirkan National Park — A321

No. 1040: a, 20g, Cervus nippon. b, 30g, Capreolus. c, 50g, Lynx lynx. d, 60g, Martes foina.
No. 1041: a, 20g, Dendrocopos major. b, 30g, Ciconia nigra. c, 50g, Pelecanus crispus. d, 60g, Marmaronetta angustirostris.

2013, Nov. 15   Litho.   *Perf. 12*
         Sheets of 4, #a-d
1040-1041 A321 Set of 2 10.00 10.00

Mehdi Huseynzade (1918-44), Soldier — A322

2013, Dec. 12 Litho. *Perf. 14¼x14*
1042 A322 60g multi   2.10 2.10
See Slovenia No. 1022.

2014 Winter Olympics, Sochi, Russia — A323

No. 1043: a, 20g, Alpine skiing. b, 30g, Ice hockey. c, 50g, Speed skating. d, 60g, Pairs figure skating.

2014, Jan. 15   Litho.   *Perf. 14¼x14*
1043 A323   Block or horiz. strip
             of 4, #a-d   5.50 5.50

Miniature Sheet

New Year 2014 (Year of the Horse) — A324

No. 1044: a, Yellow rocking horse facing right. b, Yellow rocking horse facing left. c, Blue rocking horse facing left. d, Blue rocking horse facing right.

2014, Jan. 16   Litho.   *Perf. 14x14¼*
1044 A324 20g Sheet of 4, #a-d 2.75 2.75

Souvenir Sheet

Azerbaijan's Chess Team's Victory at 2013 European Championships — A325

2014, Jan. 16 Litho. *Perf. 14x14¼*
1045 A325 1m multi   3.25 3.25

Mammad Amin Rasulzade (1884-1955), President of Democratic Republic of Azerbaijan — A326

2014, Jan. 31 Litho. *Perf. 14¼x14*
1046 A326 20g multi   .85 .85

Europa A327

Musical instruments: 20g, Zurna, tar and balaban. 60g, Kamança, qaval and tütak. 1m, Man playing qaval, vert.

2014, Feb. 17 Litho. *Perf. 14x14¼*
1047-1048 A327 Set of 2   5.00 5.00
1048a   Booklet pane of 8, 4
            each #1047-1048, perf.
            14x14¼ on 3 sides   20.00 20.00
            Souvenir Sheet
            Perf. 14¼x14
1049 A327 1m multi   5.00 5.00
No. 1048a was sold with, but unattached to, a booklet cover. The two different stamps are found tete-beche within the booklet pane.

Heydar Aliyev Memorial, Sumgayit A328

2014, Mar. 7 Litho. *Perf. 14x14¼*
1050 A328 20g multi   .85 .85
Sumgayit, 65th anniv.

Souvenir Sheet

Nakhchivan Autonomous Republic, 90th Anniv. — A329

2014, Mar. 7   Litho.   Perf. 14x14¼
1051 A329 60g multi   2.00 2.00

Cats — A330

Designs: 10g, Tabby cat. 20g, British Shorthair cat. 30g, Maine Coon cat. 50g, Scottish Fold cat. 60g, Birman cat.

2014, Apr. 8   Litho.   Perf. 13¼x13
1052 A330 10g multi   .35   .35
1053 A330 20g multi   .65   .65
1054 A330 30g multi   1.00 1.00
1055 A330 50g multi   1.60 1.60
1056 A330 60g multi   1.90 1.90
    Nos. 1052-1056 (5)   5.50 5.50

International Dialogue for Environmental Action — A331

No. 1057: a, 10g, Gazella subgutturosa. b, 20g, Panthera pardus. c, 30g, Aquila heliaca. d, 50g, Ursus arctos. e, 60g, Canis lupus. 1m, Hands holding seedling, vert.

2014, May 7   Litho.   Perf. 14x14¼
1057 A331 Sheet of 5, #a-e, +
    label   5.75 5.75
Souvenir Sheet
Perf. 14¼x14
1058 A331 1m multi   3.25 3.25

Ilyas Afandiyev (1914-96), Writer A332

2014, May 26   Litho.   Perf. 14x14¼
1059 A332 20g multi   1.00 1.00

Roses — A333

No. 1060 — Color of rose: a, Pink. b, Pinkish orange. c, Red. d, White. 1m, Red roses, vert.

2014, July 25   Litho.   Perf. 14¼
1060 A333 30g Sheet of 4, #a-d   4.00 4.00
Souvenir Sheet
Perf. 14¼x14
1061 A333 1m multi   3.00 3.00
No. 1061 contains one 28x40mm stamp.

Dogs — A334

Puppies of various breeds.

2014, Aug. 27   Litho.   Perf. 13¼x13
1062 A334 10g multi   .30   .30
1063 A334 20g multi   .65   .65
1064 A334 30g multi   .95   .95
1065 A334 50g multi   1.50 1.50
1066 A334 60g multi   1.90 1.90
    Nos. 1062-1066 (5)   5.30 5.30

Souvenir Sheet

Butterflies — A335

No. 1067: a, Heodes vigaureae. b, Polyommatus icarus.

2014, Aug. 27   Litho.   Perf. 13¼
1067 A335 60g Sheet of 2, #a-b   4.00 4.00

Souvenir Sheet

"Contract of the Century" Oil Production Contract, 20th Anniv. — A336

2014, Sept. 20   Litho.   Perf. 14¼x14
1068 A336 1m multi   3.25 3.25

Souvenir Sheet

Winter Sports — A337

No. 1069: a, Snowboarding. b, Skiing.

2014, Oct. 24   Litho.   Perf. 14¼x14
1069 A337 50g Sheet of 2, #a-b   4.00 4.00

First Global Forum on Youth Policies, Baku A338

2014, Oct. 28   Litho.   Perf. 14x14¼
1070 A338 60g multi   2.00 2.00

Souvenir Sheets

Venues of 2015 European Games, Baku — A339

No. 1071, 60g: a, National Stadium. b, Tofiq Bahramov Stadium. c, National Gymnastics Arena.
No. 1072, 60g: a, Crystal Hall. b, Baku Aquatics Center. c, Heydar Aliyev Arena.

2014, Nov. 19   Litho.   Perf. 12
Sheets of 3, #a-c
1071-1072 A339 Set of 2   12.00 12.00

Miniature Sheets

Famous People — A340

Historic Buildings — A341

No. 1073: a, Molla Panah Vagif (1717-97), poet. b, Khurshidbanu Natavan (1832-97), poet. c, Bulbul (1897-1961), singer. d, Uzeyir Hajibeyov (1885-1948), composer. e, Khan Shushinski (1901-79), singer. f, Abdurrahim Hagverdiyev (1870-1933), writer.
No. 1074: a, Khotavang Christian complex, 6th-13th cent. b, Ganzanar Christian complex, 13th cent. c, Malik Azdhar Mausoleum, 14th cent. d, Ashaga Govhar Agha Mosque, 1874-75. e, Allah-Allah Mausoleum, Barda, 1322. f, Mosque, Agdam, 1868-70.

2014, Nov. 25   Litho.   Perf. 14x14¼
1073 A340 50g Sheet of 6, #a-f   8.50 8.50
Perf. 14¼x14
1074 A341 50g Sheet of 6, #a-f   8.50 8.50

Souvenir Sheet

Handicrafts — A342

No. 1075: a, Copper vessel from Lahich, Azerbaijan. b, Pottery jug from Horezu, Romania.

2014, Dec. 19   Litho.   Perf. 14¼x14
1075 A342 60g Sheet of 2, #a-b   4.25 4.25
See Romania Nos. 5640-5641.

New Year 2015 (Year of the Goat) — A343

No. 1076 — Head of goat facing: a, Left. b, Right.

2015, Jan. 12   Litho.   Perf. 14x14¼
1076 A343 20g Pair, #a-b   1.60 1.60
Printed in sheets containing two pairs.

Europa — A344

Designs: 20g, Teddy bear, tower of rings, ball. 60g, Blocks, wooden train. 1m, Stuffed rabbit in toy car.

2015, Mar. 6   Litho.   Perf. 14¼x14
1077-1078 A344 Set of 2   4.75 4.75
1078a Booklet pane of 8, 4 each
    #1077-1078, perf. 14¼x14
    on 3 sides   19.00   —
Souvenir Sheet
1079 A344 1m multi   5.75 5.75
No. 1078a was sold with, but unattached to, a booklet cover. The two different stamps are found tete-beche within the booklet pane.

Aziz Sharif (1895-1988), Writer — A345

2015, Mar. 29   Litho.   Perf. 14¼x14
1080 A345 50g multi   1.50 1.50

Penny Black, 175th Anniv. — A346

2015, Apr. 1   Litho.   Perf. 14x14¼
1081 A346 20g multi   .70   .70
No. 1081 was printed in sheets of 4.

Marmara Group Foundation, 30th Anniv. A347

2015, Apr. 7   Litho.   Perf. 14x14¼
1082 A347 50g multi   1.50 1.50

Miniature Sheets

A348

Sports of 2015 European Games, Baku — A349

No. 1083 (purple background): a, Rhythmic gymnastics (gymnast holding ball). b, Aerobic gymnastics (gymnast running with arm raised). c, Trampoline (athlete flipping in air). d, Track (athlete running).
No. 1084 (blue background): a, Swimming. b, Boxing. c, Fencing. d, Diving.
No. 1085 (red background): a, Kayaking. b, Shooting. c, Triathlon. d, Mountain biking.
No. 1086 (green background): a, Archery. b, Wrestling. c, Badminton. d, Table tennis.
No. 1087: a, Artistic gymnastics (gymnast leaping). b, Volleyball. c, BMX cycling. d, Sambo.

2015, Apr. 23   Litho.   Perf. 12
1083 A348 20g Sheet of 4, #a-
          d   3.00 3.00
1084 A348 20g Sheet of 4, #a-
          d   3.00 3.00
1085 A348 20g Sheet of 4, #a-
          d   3.00 3.00
1086 A348 20g Sheet of 4, #a-
          d   3.00 3.00
1087 A349 20g Sheet of 4, #a-
          d   3.00 3.00
      Nos. 1083-1087 (5)   15.00 15.00

Victory in World War II, 70th Anniv. A350

2015, May 9   Litho.   Perf. 12
1088 A350 20g multi   .95   .95

Intl. Telecommunication Union, 150th Anniv. — A351

2015, May 17   Litho.   Perf. 14x14¼
1089 A351 50g multi   1.60 1.60

Jamshid Nakhchivanski (1895-1938), Military Commander A352

2015, July 16   Litho.   Perf. 14¼x14
1090 A352 50g multi   1.60 1.60

Souvenir Sheet

2015 Chess World Cup, Baku — A353

2015, Sept. 10   Litho.   Perf. 14¼x14
1091 A353 1m multi   3.00 3.00

Architecture A354

No. 1092: a, Maiden's Tower, Baku (denomination at LL). b, Kremlin, Moscow (denomination at LR).

2015, Sept. 22   Litho.   Perf. 13
1092 A354 60g Pair, #a-b   3.75 3.75
Printed in sheets of 4 pairs + central label.
See Russia No. 7677.

National Academy of Sciences, 70th Anniv. — A355

2015, Oct. 1   Litho.   Perf. 14¼x14
1093 A355 30g multi   1.00 1.00

Dancers — A356

No. 1094: a, Dancers from Azerbaijan (denomination at LL). b, Dancers from Moldova (denomination at UR).

2015, Oct. 16   Litho.   Perf. 13¼x13
1094   Horiz. pair   3.00 3.00
 a.-b. A356 50g Either single   1.50 1.50
      See Moldova No. 883.

United Nations, 70th Anniv. A357

2015, Oct. 24   Litho.   Perf. 14x14¼
1095 A357 50g multi   1.60 1.60

National Flag Square — A358

2015, Nov. 9   Litho.   Perf. 14¼x14
1096 A358 50g multi   1.60 1.60

Book of Dede Korkut — A359

2015, Nov. 16   Litho.   Perf. 14¼x14
1097 A359 50g multi   1.60 1.60

Souvenir Sheet

Buildings on Nizami Street, Baku — A360

No. 1098 — Various buildings with denomination at: a, LL. b, LR.

2015, Nov. 16   Litho.   Perf. 14¼x14
1098 A360 50g Sheet of 2, #a-b,
          + central label   3.75 3.75

Souvenir Sheet

Satellites — A361

No. 1099: a, 50g, DZZ satellite, Belarus. b, 1m, Azerspace-1 satellite, Azerbaijan.

Litho., Sheet Margin Litho. With Foil Application
2015, Dec. 3   Perf.
1099 A361 Sheet of 2, #a-b   4.75 4.75
      See Belarus No. 967.

Rashid Behbudov (1915-89), Singer and Actor A362

2015, Dec. 14   Litho.   Perf. 14x14¼
1100 A362 50g multi   1.40 1.40

Miniature Sheet

New Year 2016 (Year of the Monkey) — A363

No. 1101 — Monkey facing: a, Right, denomination at LL. b, Left, denomination at LR. c, Left, denomination at LL. d, Right, denomination at LR.

2016, Jan. 12   Litho.   Perf. 14x14¼
1101 A363 20g Sheet of 4, #a-d   3.00 3.00

Europa A364

Frame color: 20g, Bluish gray. 60g, Apple green.
1m, No frame.

2016, Jan. 25   Litho.   Perf. 14x14¼
1102-1103 A364 Set of 2   5.00 5.00
1103a   Booklet pane of 8, 4 each
            #1102-1103, perf.
            14x14¼ on 3 sides   20.00 20.00
Souvenir Sheet
1104 A364 1m multi   5.75 5.75
      Think Green Issue.
No. 1103a was sold with, but unattached to, a booklet cover. Tete-beche pairs of Nos. 1102-1103 are found in No. 1103a.

Broadcasting
Anniversaries
A365

2016, Feb. 22   Litho.   Perf. 14¼x14
1105 A365 50g multi   1.60 1.60
Radio broadcasting in Azerbaijan, 90th
anniv.; television broadcasting, 60th anniv.

Regional
Communications
Commonwealth,
25th
Anniv. — A366

2016, Mar. 2   Litho.   Perf. 14¼x14
1106 A366 50g multi   1.60 1.60

Eynali bey
Sultanov (1866-
1935),
Writer — A367

2016, May 5   Litho.   Perf. 14¼x14
1107 A367 20g multi   .60 .60

Architects and Their Buildings — A368

Union of Architects 80th Anniv.
Emblem — A369

No. 1108, 50g: a, Ajami Nakhchivani (12th-
13th cent.). b, Ustad Mahmud ibn Saad (13th-
14th cent.). c, Karbalayi Safikhan Karabakhi
(1817-1910). d, Zivar bey Ahmadbeyov (1873-
1925).
No. 1109, 50g: a, I. V. Qoslavskiy (1865-
1904). b, I. K. Plosko (1866-1931). c, M. C.
Hasinski (1875-1931). d, N. A. fon der Nonne
(1836-1906).
No. 1110, 50g: a, Sadig Dadashov (1905-
46). b, Mikayil Huseynov (1905-92), c, Enver
Kasim-zade (1912-69). d, Hasan Mejidov
(1914-78).

2016, May 6   Litho.   Perf. 14x14¼
Sheets of 4, #a-d
1108-1110 A368 Set of 3   14.50 14.50
Souvenir Sheet
1111 A369 1m multi   2.40 2.40
See Nos. 1131-1133.

Eagles — A370

No. 1112: a, Aquila chrysaetos. b, Aquila
nipalensis.

2016, May 12   Litho.   Perf. 14x14¼
1112 A370 60g Pair, #a-b   3.00 3.00
See Belarus No. 984.

A371

2016 Formula 1 Grand Prix Races,
Baku — A372

No. 1113: a, Red car, front view. b, Blue car,
front view. c, Dark blue car, front and side
view. d, Orange car, rear view.
1m, Red car, emblem of Baku City Circuit.

2016, June 10   Litho.   Perf. 14x14¼
1113 A371 50g Block of 4, #a-d   5.00 5.00
Souvenir Sheet
Perf. 14¼x14
1114 A372 1m multi   2.40 2.40

2016 Summer Olympics, Rio de
Janeiro — A373

No. 1115: a, Boxing. b, Weight lifting. c,
Wrestling, country name at left. d, Wrestling,
country name ar right.

2016, Aug. 1   Litho.   Perf. 14x14¼
1115 A373 50g Block of 4, #a-d   5.00 5.00

Miniature Sheet

42nd Chess Olympiad, Baku — A374

No. 1116 — Chess pieces: a, Seated
swordsman, rook. b, Swordsman on elephant.
c, Kneeling and standing swordsmen. d, Man
on horseback. e, Seated and standing
swordsmen.

2016, Sept. 1   Litho.   Perf. 14¼x14
1116 A374 50g Sheet of 5, #a-e   6.00 6.00

Worldwide Fund for Nature
(WWF) — A375

No. 1117 — Manul: a, One animal, country
name at left. b, One animal, country name at
right. c, Two animals. d, Three animals.

2016, Sept. 5   Litho.   Perf. 14x14¼
1117 A375 50g Block of 4, #a-d   4.00 4.00
  e   Souvenir sheet of 4, #1117a-
      1117d   4.00 4.00

Independence,
25th
Anniv. — A376

2016, Nov. 15   Litho.   Perf. 14x14¼
1118 A376 10g multi   .25 .25

Souvenir Sheet

Restoration of Trapezitsa Architectural
Museum Reserve, Veliko Tarnovo,
Bulgaria — A377

2016, Nov. 22   Litho.   Perf. 13¼x13
1119 A377 1.50m multi   3.50 3.50
See Bulgaria No. 4774.

Telephone Communication in
Azerbaijan, 135th Anniv. — A378

2016, Dec. 6   Litho.   Perf. 14x14¼
1120 A378 10g multi   .25 .25

Souvenir Sheet

Visit of Pope Francis to
Azerbaijan — A379

2016, Dec. 20   Litho.   Perf. 14x14¼
1121 A379 1.50m multi   3.75 3.75

Souvenir Sheet

National Cuisine — A380

No. 1122: a, Piti. b, Dolma.

2016, Dec. 22   Litho.   Perf. 14¼x14
1122 A380 50g Sheet of 2, #a-b 2.75 2.75

Ganja,
2016
European
Youth
Capital
A381

2017, Jan. 30   Litho.   Perf. 14x14¼
1123 A381 30g multi   .60 .60

New Year 2017 (Year of the
Rooster) — A382

No. 1124: a, Head of rooster. b, Rooster.

2017, Apr. 14   Litho.   Perf. 14x14¼
1124 A382 30g Pair, #a-b   1.60 1.60
Printed in sheets containing two pairs.

Novruz Festival — A383

No. 1125: a, Lake and mountain. b, Fire. c, Mountain. d, Flowers.

2017, Apr. 14 Litho. *Perf. 14¼x14*
1125 A383 30g Block of 4, #a-d 3.25 3.25

Khojaly Massacre, 25th Anniv. A384

2017, Apr. 14 Litho. *Perf. 14x14¼*
1126 A384 10g multi .25 .25

Europa A385

Designs: 20g, Mardakan Castle. 60g, Ramana Castle. 1m, Maiden's Tower, Baku.

2017, Apr. 14 Litho. *Perf. 14x14¼*
1127-1128 A385 Set of 2 5.25 5.25
1128a Booklet pane of 8, 4 each #1127-1128, perf. 14x14¼ on 3 sides 21.00

Souvenir Sheet
1129 A385 1m multi 6.25 6.25

No. 1128a was sold with, but unattached to, a booklet cover. Tete-beche pairs of Nos. 1127-1128 are found in No. 1128a.

4th Islamic Solidarity Games, Baku — A386

No. 1130: a, Tennis. b, Gymnastics. c, Boxing. d, Soccer.

2017, May 5 Litho. *Perf. 14x14¼*
1130 A386 50g Block of 4, #a-d 4.25 4.25

Architects and Their Buildings Type of 2016
Miniature Sheets

No. 1131, 50g: a, Qasim bey Hajibababeyov (1811-74). b, Adolf V. Eichler (1869-1911). c, Lev V. Rudnev (1885-1956). d, Alexander A. Vesnin (1883-1959) and Viktor A. Vesnin (1882-1950).

No. 1132, 50g: a, Anvar A. Ismayilov (1916-88). b, Hanifa A. Alasgarov (1912-91). c, Tahir A. Abdullayev (1915-2004). d, Ghazanfar M. Ali-zadeh (1910-94).

No. 1133, 50g: a, Talat A. Khanlarov (1927-2004). b, Juzef I. Gadimov (1928-2012). c, Konstantin I. Senchikhin (1905-85). d, Shafiga M. Zeynalova (1922-78).

2017, June 22 Litho. *Perf. 14x14¼*
Sheets of 4, #a-d
1131-1133 A368 Set of 3 13.50 13.50

Emblem of Azerbaijan — A387

2017, July 12 Litho. *Perf. 13¼x13¾*
Background Color
1134 A387 10g white .25 .25
1135 A387 20g dull green .45 .45
1136 A387 30g salmon .65 .65
1137 A387 50g light blue 1.10 1.10
Nos. 1134-1137 (4) 2.45 2.45

2017 Scouting Events in Azerbaijan — A388

No. 1138: a, 13th World Scout Youth Forum, Gabala. b, 41st World Scout Conference, Baku.

2017, Aug. 14 Litho. *Perf. 14¼x14*
1138 A388 20g Pair, #a-b 1.10 1.10

Souvenir Sheet

Azermarka (Printer of Azerbaijan Postage Stamps), 25th Anniv. — A389

2017, Aug. 22 Litho. *Perf. 14x14¼*
1139 A389 1m multi 2.75 2.75

Partnership for Development Between Azerbaijan and World Bank — A390

2017, Sept. 19 Litho. *Perf. 12x12¼*
1140 A390 50g multi 1.10 1.10

SEMI-POSTAL STAMPS

Carrying Food to Sufferers SP1

1922 Unwmk. *Imperf.*
B1 SP1 500r blue & pale blue .40 190.00

For overprint and surcharge see Nos. 42, 305.

Widow and Orphans — SP2

1922
B2 SP2 1000r brown & bister .75 190.00
Counterfeits exist.

For overprint and surcharge see Nos. 44, 306.

Eagle — AP1

1995, Oct. 16 Litho. *Perf. 14*
C1 AP1 2200m multicolored 4.00 4.00

AZORES

'ā-ˌzōrz

LOCATION — Group of islands in the North Atlantic Ocean, due west of Portugal
AREA — 922 sq. mi.
POP. — 253,935 (1930)
CAPITAL — Ponta Delgada

Azores stamps were supplanted by those of Portugal in 1931.

In 1934-45, #RA5-RA11, RAJ1-RAJ4, and many stamps between #155-223 were used for regular postage in Portugal.

The Azores were declared an autonomous, or self-governing, region of Portugal in 1976. See Portugal for issues since 1980.

1000 Reis = 1 Milreis
100 Centavos = 1 Escudo (1912)

Stamps of Portugal Overprinted in Black or Carmine

A second type of this overprint has a broad "O" and open "S."

1868		**Unwmk.**		*Imperf.*
1	A14	5r black	3,500.	2,400.
2	A14	10r yellow	13,750.	10,000.
3	A14	20r bister	200.00	140.00
4	A14	50r green	200.00	140.00
5	A14	80r orange	200.00	150.00
6	A14	100r lilac	200.00	150.00

The reprints are on thick chalky white wove paper, ungummed, and on thin ivory paper with shiny white gum. Value $35-42.50 each.

1868-70 *Perf. 12½*

5 REIS:
Type I — The "5" at the right is 1mm from end of label.
Type II — The "5" is 1½mm from end of label.

7	A14	5r black, type I (C)	60.00	30.00
a.		Type II	70.00	70.00
8	A14	10r yellow	120.00	40.00
a.		Inverted overprint	250.00	150.00
9	A14	20r bister	50.00	65.00
10	A14	25r rose	50.00	11.00
a.		Inverted overprint	—	—
11	A14	50r green	160.00	150.00
12	A14	80r orange	160.00	150.00
13	A14	100r lilac ('69)	160.00	150.00
14	A14	120r blue	150.00	130.00
15	A14	240r violet	800.00	400.00

The reprints are on thick chalky white paper ungummed, perf 13½, and on thin ivory paper with shiny white gum, perf 13½. Value $30 each.

AÇORES

1871-75			*Perf. 12½*	
21	A15	5r black (C)	13.50	8.75
a.		Inverted overprint	47.50	42.50
23	A15	10r yellow	40.00	25.00
a.		Inverted overprint	—	—
b.		Double overprint	60.00	47.50
24	A15	20r bister	30.00	26.00
25	A15	25r rose	17.00	4.25
a.		Inverted overprint	—	—
b.		Double overprint	40.00	
c.		Perf. 14	190.00	85.00
d.		Dbl. impression of stamp	—	—
26	A15	50r green	85.00	42.50
27	A15	80r orange	90.00	50.00
28	A15	100r lilac	100.00	60.00
a.		Perf. 14	195.00	150.00
29	A15	120r blue	200.00	125.00
a.		Inverted overprint	—	—
30	A15	240r violet	1,000.	675.00

Nos. 21-29 exist with overprint "b."

The reprints are of type "b." All values exist are on thick chalky white paper ungummed, perf 13½ (value, each $29) and also on thin white paper with shiny white gum and perforated 13½ (value, each $30). The 5r, 10r, 15r, 50r and 120r also exist on thick chalky white paper ungummed, perf 12½. Value, each $80.

Overprinted in Black — c

AÇORES

15 REIS:
Type I — The figures of value, 1 and 5, at the right in upper label are close together.
Type II — The figures of value at the right in upper label are spaced.

1875-80			*Perf. 13½*	
31	A15	10r blue green	150.00	125.00
32	A15	10r yellow green	150.00	125.00
33b	A15	15r lilac brown	20.00	18.00
a.		Inverted overprint	150.00	
34	A15	50r blue	140.00	60.00
35	A15	150r blue	200.00	175.00
36	A15	150r yellow	300.00	175.00
37	A15	300r violet	95.00	65.00

The reprints have the same papers, gum and perforations as those of the preceding issue.

Black Overprint

1880			*Perf. 12½*	
38	A17	25r bluish gray	150.00	95.00
39	A18	25r red lilac	60.00	9.50
b.		25r gray	—	—
d.		As "c," double overprint	—	—

Overprint in Carmine or Black

1881-82				
40	A16	5r black (C)	29.00	12.00
41	A23	25r brown ('82)	55.00	8.00
a.		Double overprint	—	—
42	A19	50r blue	190.00	47.50
		Nos. 40-42 (3)	274.00	67.50

Reprints of Nos. 38, 39, 39a, 40 and 42 have the same papers, gum and perforations as those of preceding issues.

Overprinted in Red or Black — d

AÇORES

15, 20 REIS:
Type I — The figures of value are some distance apart and close to the end of the label.
Type II — The figures are closer together and farther from the end of the label. On the 15 reis this is particularly apparent in the upper right figures.

1882-85			*Perf. 12½*	
43	A16	5r black (R)	20.00	10.00
44	A21	5r slate	19.00	4.50
a.		Double overprint	—	—
c.		Inverted overprint	—	—
45	A15	10r green	90.00	50.00
a.		Inverted overprint	—	—

46	A22	10r green ('84)	32.50	14.00
a.		Double overprint		
47	A15	15r lilac brn	35.00	20.00
b.		Inverted overprint		
48	A15	20r bister	70.00	40.00
a.		Inverted overprint		
49	A15	20r car ('85)	150.00	125.00
a.		Double overprint	190.00	
50	A23	25r brown	30.00	4.50
51	A15	50r blue	2,500.	1,250.
52	A24	50r blue	24.00	3.50
a.		Double overprint		
53	A15	80r yellow	80.00	62.50
a.		Double overprint	125.00	110.00
b.		80r orange		
54	A15	100r lilac	125.00	95.00
55	A15	150r blue	2,500.	900.00
56b	A15	150r yellow	65.00	57.50
57b	A15	300r violet	87.50	77.50
58	A21	5r slate (R)	25.00	6.00
59	A24a	500r black	300.00	175.00
60	A15	1000r black (R)	225.00	125.00

This set was issued on both ordinary and enamel surfaced papers. Nos. 51 and 55 exist only on ordinary paper, Nos. 44, 46, 49 and 53 only on surfaced paper, and the other values on both types of paper. Values for Nos. 56b and 57b are for stamps printed on surfaced paper. Stamps on ordinary paper are worth more.

For specialized listings of this issue and other early Azore stamps, see the *Scott Classic Specialized Catalogue.*

Reprints of the 1882-85 issues have the same papers, gum and perforations as those of preceding issues.

1887   Black Overprint

61	A25	20r pink	50.00	19.00
a.		Inverted overprint	—	—
b.		Double overprint	—	—
62	A26	25r lilac rose	60.00	3.00
a.		Inverted overprint	—	—
b.		Double ovpt., one invtd.	—	—
63	A26	25r red violet	60.00	3.00
64	A24a	500r red violet	250.00	110.00
a.		Perf. 13½	400.00	240.00
		Nos. 61-64 (4)	420.00	135.00

Nos. 58-64 inclusive have been reprinted on thin white paper with shiny white gum and perforated 13½. Value: Nos. 58, 61-64, each $22.50; No. 59, $85; No. 60, $50.

Prince Henry the Navigator Issue
Portugal Nos. 97-109 Overprinted

1894, Mar. 4   Perf. 14

65	A46	5r orange yel	3.50	3.00
a.		Inverted overprint	60.00	60.00
66	A46	10r violet rose	3.50	3.00
a.		Double overprint	—	—
b.		Inverted overprint	—	—
67	A46	15r brown	4.25	4.00
68	A46	20r violet	4.50	4.25
a.		Double overprint	—	—
69	A47	25r green	5.00	4.50
a.		Double overprint	75.00	75.00
b.		Inverted overprint	75.00	75.00
70	A47	50r blue	12.50	6.75
71	A47	75r dp carmine	22.50	9.50
72	A47	80r yellow orn	30.00	10.00
73	A47	100r lt brn, *pale buff*	30.00	8.00
a.		Double overprint	—	—
74	A48	150r lt car, *pale rose*	60.00	19.00
75	A48	300r dk bl, *sal buff*	100.00	30.00
76	A48	500r brn vio, *pale lil*	140.00	45.00
77	A48	1000r gray blk, *yelsh*	200.00	70.00
a.		Double overprint	700.00	500.00
		Nos. 65-77 (13)	615.75	217.00

St. Anthony of Padua Issue
Portugal Nos. 132-146 Overprinted in Red or Black

No. 78

No. 79

1895, June 13   Perf. 12

78	A50	2½r black (R)	3.00	1.25
79	A51	5r brown yel	9.50	3.00
80	A51	10r red lilac	9.50	4.50
81	A51	15r red brown	14.50	7.00
82	A51	20r gray lilac	16.00	9.50
83	A51	25r grn & vio	10.00	3.00
84	A52	50r blue & brn	32.50	15.00
85	A52	75r rose & brn	47.50	40.00
86	A52	80r lt grn & brn	75.00	47.50
87	A52	100r choc & blk	75.00	42.50
88	A53	150r vio rose & bis	200.00	100.00
89	A53	200r blue & bis	200.00	100.00
90	A53	300r slate & bis	250.00	110.00
91	A53	500r vio brn & grn	500.00	150.00
92	A53	1000r vio & grn	800.00	225.00
		Nos. 78-92 (15)	2,243.	858.25

7th cent. of the birth of Saint Anthony of Padua.

Common Design Types pictured following the introduction.

Vasco da Gama Issue
Common Design Types

1898, Apr. 1   Perf. 14, 15

93	CD20	2½r blue green	3.50	1.25
94	CD21	5r red	3.50	1.50
95	CD22	10r gray lilac	7.00	3.00
96	CD23	25r yel grn	7.00	3.00
97	CD24	50r dark blue	10.00	9.50
98	CD25	75r vio brn	21.00	14.00
99	CD26	100r bis brn	27.50	14.00
100	CD27	150r bister	42.50	30.00
		Nos. 93-100 (8)	122.00	76.25

For overprints and surcharges see Nos. 141-148.

King Carlos — A28

1906   Typo.   Perf. 11½x12

101	A28	2½r gray	.45	.40
a.		Inverted overprint	35.00	35.00
102	A28	5r orange yel	.45	.40
a.		Inverted overprint	35.00	35.00
103	A28	10r yellow grn	.45	.40
104	A28	20r gray vio	.70	.50
105	A28	25r carmine	.70	.40
106	A28	50r ultra	6.00	4.75
107	A28	75r brown, *straw*	2.10	1.25
108	A28	100r dk blue, *bl*	2.10	1.40
109	A28	200r red lilac, *pnksh*	2.25	1.40
110	A28	300r dk blue, *rose*	6.75	5.75
111	A28	500r black, *blue*	16.00	14.00
		Nos. 101-111 (11)	37.95	30.65

"Acores" and letters and figures in the corners are in red on the 2½, 10, 20, 75 and 500r and in black on the other values.

King Manuel II — A29

1910, Apr. 1   Perf. 14x15

112	A29	2½r violet	.50	.40
113	A29	5r black	.50	.40
114	A29	10r dk green	.50	.40
115	A29	15r lilac brn	.90	.65
116	A29	20r carmine	1.25	1.00
117	A29	25r violet brn	.50	.50
a.		Perf. 11½	3.00	1.60
118	A29	50r blue	3.00	1.60
119	A29	75r bister brn	3.00	1.60
120	A29	80r slate	3.00	1.60
121	A29	100r brown, *lt grn*	5.00	3.75
122	A29	200r green, *sal*	5.00	3.75
123	A29	300r black, *blue*	3.00	2.75
124	A29	500r olive & brown	9.50	10.00
125	A29	1000r blue & black	21.00	19.00
		Nos. 112-125 (14)	56.65	47.40

The errors of color 10r black, 15r dark green, 25r black and 50r carmine are considered to be proofs.

Stamps of 1910 Overprinted in Carmine or Green

1910

126	A29	2½r violet	.40	.35
a.		Inverted overprint	12.50	12.50
127	A29	5r black	.40	.35
a.		Inverted overprint	12.50	12.50
128	A29	10r dk green	.40	.35
a.		Inverted overprint	12.50	12.50
129	A29	15r lilac brn	1.90	1.40
a.		Inverted overprint	12.50	12.50
130	A29	20r carmine (G)	1.90	1.40
a.		Inverted overprint	22.50	22.50
b.		Double overprint	22.50	22.50
131	A29	25r violet brn	.40	.30
a.		Perf. 11½	65.00	57.50
132	A29	50r blue	1.40	1.25
133	A29	75r bister brn	1.40	.95
a.		Double overprint	12.50	12.50
134	A29	80r slate	1.40	.95
135	A29	100r brown, *grn*	1.10	.90
136	A29	200r green, *sal*	1.10	.95
137	A29	300r black, *blue*	3.50	2.25
138	A29	500r olive & brn	4.50	3.25
139	A29	1000r blue & blk	11.00	7.00
		Nos. 126-139 (14)	30.80	21.65

Vasco da Gama Issue Overprinted or Surcharged in Black

 e

 f

 g

1911   Perf. 14, 15

141	CD20(e)	2½r blue green	.65	.50
142	CD21(f)	15r on 5r red	.65	.50
143	CD23(e)	25r yellow grn	.65	.50
144	CD24(e)	50r dk blue	2.25	1.40
145	CD25(e)	75r violet brn	1.90	1.75
146	CD27(f)	80r on 10r bister	2.00	1.90
147	CD26(e)	100r yellow brn	2.10	1.90
a.		Double surcharge	40.00	40.00
148	CD22(g)	1000r on 10r lil	20.00	15.00
		Nos. 141-148 (8)	30.20	23.45

Postage Due Stamps of Portugal Overprinted or Surcharged in Black

1911   Perf. 12

149	D1	5r black	1.25	1.10
150	D1	10r magenta	2.75	1.10
a.		"Acores" double	30.00	15.00
151	D1	20r orange	5.25	3.75
152	D1	200r brn, *buff*	30.00	20.00
a.		"Acores" inverted	100.00	
153	D1	300r on 50r slate	30.00	19.00
154	D1	500r on 100r car, *pink*	30.00	18.00
		Nos. 149-154 (6)	99.25	62.95

Ceres Issue of Portugal Overprinted in Black or Carmine

With Imprint
Chalky Paper

1912-21   Perf. 15x14

155	A64	¼c olive brown	3.00	1.25
156	A64	½c black (C)	3.00	1.25
157	A64	1c dp grn ('13)	3.00	1.25
158	A64	1½c choc ('13)	4.00	3.00
159	A64	2c car ('13)	6.00	3.00
160	A64	2½c violet	5.00	1.10
161	A64	5c dp blue ('13)	5.00	1.10
162	A64	7½c yel brn ('13)	12.00	7.00
163	A64	8c slate ('13)	12.00	7.00
164	A64	10c org brn ('13)	13.00	7.50
165	A64	15c plum ('13)	17.00	7.50
166	A64	20c vio brn, *grn* ('13)	15.00	7.00
167	A64	30c brn, *pink* ('13)	80.00	60.00
168	A64	30c brn, *yel* ('19)	2.25	1.90
169	A64	50c org, *sal* ('13)	6.50	2.75
170	A64	50c org, *yel* ('13)	6.50	2.75
171	A64	1e dp grn, *bl* ('13)	7.00	6.00

Nos. 155 and 160 also exist on glazed non-chalky paper.

Perf. 12x11½

172	A64	14c dk bl, *yel* ('21)	3.00	1.90
		Nos. 155-172 (18)	203.25	123.25

Nos. 155 and 160 exist on glazed paper.

Ordinary Paper

1917-21   Perf. 15x14

173	A64	¼c olive brown	.55	.40
a.		Inverted overprint	12.50	9.50
174	A64	½c black (C)	.55	.40
a.		Inverted overprint	12.50	
175	A64	1c deep green	1.10	.80
a.		Inverted overprint	17.50	
176	A64	1c dp brn ('18)	.55	.40
177	A64	1½c choc	1.10	.80
a.		Inverted overprint	13.00	
178	A64	1½c dp grn ('18)	.55	.50
a.		Inverted overprint	17.50	
179	A64	2c carmine	.80	.65
a.		Inverted overprint	20.00	
180	A64	2c orange ('19)	.55	.50
a.		Inverted overprint	25.00	
181	A64	2½c violet	.80	.65
182	A64	3c rose	.80	.65
183	A64	3½c lt grn ('18)	.55	.50
184	A64	4c lt grn ('19)	.55	.50
185	A64	5c deep blue	.80	.65
186	A64	5c yel brn ('21)	.75	.65
187	A64	6c dull rose ('20)	.55	.50
188	A64	7½c yellow brown	6.75	3.75
189	A64	7½c dp bl ('19)	1.90	1.75
190	A64	8c slate	.80	.70
191	A64	10c orange brown	8.00	4.00
192	A64	15c plum	.85	.65
193	A64	30c gray brn ('21)	1.90	1.60
194	A64	60c blue ('21)	1.90	1.50
		Never hinged	2.75	
		Nos. 173-194 (22)	32.65	22.50

Examples of thick carton paper varieties exist. See *Scott Classic Specialized Catalogue of Stamps & Covers 1840-1940* for listings.

1918-26   Perf. 12x11½

195	A64	¼c olive brown	.55	.55
196	A64	½c black (R)	.55	.40
197	A64	1c deep brown	.55	.40
198	A64	1½c deep green	.90	.70
199	A64	2c org ('19)	.55	.50
a.		Inverted overprint	24.00	
200	A64	3c rose	.90	.65
201	A64	3c dull ultra ('25)	.40	.30
202	A64	4c lt grn ('19)	.55	.50
a.		Inverted overprint	21.00	
203	A64	5c ol brn ('21)	.55	.50
204A	A64	6c dull rose ('20)	.55	.50
204	A64	6c choc ('25)	.55	.50
205	A64	7½c dp bl ('19)	75.00	50.00
206	A64	8c bl grn ('24)	.80	.55
207	A64	8c org ('25)	1.00	.95
208	A64	10c org brn	.55	.50
209	A64	12c bl gray ('20)	2.75	1.75
210	A64	12c dp grn ('22)	.90	.50
a.		Inverted overprint	20.00	
211	A64	13½c chlky bl ('20)	2.75	1.90
212	A64	15c blk (R) ('24)	.55	.50
213	A64	16c brt ultra ('26)	.95	.90
214	A64	20c choc ('21)	.90	.65
215	A64	20c dp grn ('24)	1.25	.95
a.		Double overprint	22.50	22.50
216	A64	20c gray ('24)	.80	.60
217	A64	24c grnsh bl ('21)	.90	.55
218	A64	25c sal ('23)	.70	.50

219	A64	30c gray brn ('21)	1.90	1.60
220	A64	32c dp grn ('26)	2.75	2.40
221	A64	36c red ('21)	.85	.65
222	A64	40c dp bl ('23)	1.00	.70
223	A64	40c blk brn ('24)	1.90	1.00
224	A64	48c brt rose ('26)	5.00	3.00
225	A64	50c yellow ('23)	1.90	1.50
226	A64	60c blue ('21)	1.90	1.50
227	A64	64c pale ultra ('26)	5.00	2.25
228	A64	75c dull rose ('24)	5.00	4.00
229	A64	80c dull rose ('21)	2.50	2.10
230	A64	80c violet ('24)	2.50	1.90
231	A64	90c chlky bl ('21)	2.50	2.10
232	A64	96c dp rose ('21)	7.50	3.50
233	A64	1e violet ('21)	2.50	2.10
234	A64	1.10e yel brn ('21)	2.75	2.10
235	A64	1.20e yel grn ('22)	3.25	2.10
236	A64	2e slate grn ('22)	10.00	6.50
		Nos. 195-236 (42)	156.55	107.15

Examples of thick carton paper and other varieties exist. See *Scott Classic Specialized Catalogue of Stamps & Covers 1840-1940* for listings.

1924-30			**Perf. 12x11½**	
		Glazed Paper		
237	A64	1e gray vio	3.75	3.25
237A	A64	1.20e buff	8.25	6.00
237B	A64	1.50e blk vio	9.75	6.75
237C	A64	1.50e lilac ('25)	8.50	6.75
237D	A64	1.60e dp bl ('25)	8.50	7.00
237E	A64	2.40e apple grn ('30)	125.00	60.00
237F	A64	3e lil pink ('28)	150.00	60.00
237G	A64	3.20e gray grn ('26)	9.75	9.50
237H	A64	5e emer ('25)	19.00	10.00
237I	A64	10e pink ('25)	125.00	27.50
237J	A64	20e pale turq ('25)	300.00	82.50
		Nos. 237-237J (11)	767.50	279.25

For same overprint on surcharged stamps, see Nos. 300-306. For same design without imprint see Nos. 307-313.

Castello-Branco Issue

Stamps of Portugal, 1925, Overprinted in Black or Red

1925, Mar. 29			**Perf. 12½**	
238	A73	2c orange	.25	.25
239	A73	3c green	.25	.25
240	A73	4c ultra (R)	.25	.25
241	A73	5c scarlet	.25	.25
242	A74	10c pale blue	.25	.25
243	A74	16c red orange	.40	.30
244	A75	25c car rose	.40	.30
245	A74	32c green	.50	.50
246	A75	40c grn & blk (R)	.50	.50
247	A74	48c red brn	1.10	1.10
248	A76	50c blue green	1.10	1.00
249	A76	64c orange brn	1.10	1.00
250	A76	75c gray blk (R)	1.10	1.00
251	A75	80c brown	1.10	1.00
252	A76	96c car rose	1.40	1.10
253	A77	1.50e dk bl, *bl* (R)	1.40	1.10
254	A75	1.60e indigo (R)	1.50	1.40
255	A77	2e dk grn, *grn* (R)	2.50	2.10
256	A77	2.40e red, *org*	3.25	2.40
257	A77	3.20e blk, *grn* (R)	6.00	5.25
		Nos. 238-257 (20)	24.60	21.30

First Independence Issue

Stamps of Portugal, 1926, Overprinted in Red

1926, Aug. 13			**Perf. 14, 14½**	
		Center in Black		
258	A79	2c orange	.35	.35
259	A80	3c ultra	.35	.35
260	A79	4c yellow brn	.35	.35
261	A80	5c black brn	.35	.35
262	A79	6c ocher	.35	.35
263	A80	15c dk green	.75	.70
264	A81	20c dull violet	.75	.70
265	A82	25c scarlet	.75	.70

266	A81	32c deep green	.75	.70
267	A82	40c yellow brn	.75	.70
268	A82	50c olive bis	3.00	2.00
269	A82	75c brown	3.00	2.10
270	A83	1e black violet	4.00	3.00
271	A84	4.50e olive green	15.00	10.00
		Nos. 258-271 (14)	30.50	22.35

The use of these stamps instead of those of the regular issue was obligatory on Aug. 13 and 14, Nov. 30 and Dec. 1, 1926.

Centering is vital to the value of Nos. 258-299. Stamps in grades of less than VF sell at significant discounts from the values here.

Second Independence Issue
Same Overprint on Stamps of Portugal, 1927, in Red

1927, Nov. 29			**Center in Black**	
272	A86	2c lt brown	.30	.30
273	A87	3c ultra	.30	.30
274	A86	4c orange	.30	.30
275	A88	5c dk brown	.30	.30
276	A89	6c orange brn	.30	.30
277	A87	15c black brn	.30	.30
278	A86	25c gray	1.25	1.25
279	A89	32c blue grn	1.25	1.25
280	A90	40c yellow grn	1.00	.75
281	A90	96c red	5.00	3.25
282	A88	1.60e myrtle grn	5.00	3.25
283	A91	4.50e bister	15.00	8.75
		Nos. 272-283 (12)	30.30	20.30

Third Independence Issue
Same Overprint on Stamps of Portugal, 1928, in Red

1928, Nov. 27			**Center in Black**	
284	A93	2c lt blue	.30	.30
285	A94	3c lt green	.30	.30
286	A95	4c lake	.30	.30
287	A96	5c olive grn	.30	.30
288	A97	6c orange brn	.30	.30
289	A94	15c slate	.65	.60
290	A95	16c dk violet	.75	.75
291	A93	25c ultra	.75	.75
292	A97	32c dk green	.80	.80
293	A94	40c olive brn	.80	.80
294	A95	50c red orange	2.00	1.75
295	A94	80c lt gray	2.00	1.75
296	A97	96c carmine	4.00	3.00
297	A96	1e claret	4.00	3.00
298	A93	1.60e dk blue	4.00	3.00
299	A98	4.50e yellow	9.00	8.50
		Nos. 284-299 (16)	30.25	26.20

Types of Portugal Nos. 285, 296 & 298F Overprinted & Surcharged in Black

1929-30			**Perf. 12x11½, 15x14**	
300	A64	4c on 25c pink ('30)	.75	.75
301	A64	40c on 60c dp blue	1.40	1.40
a.		Perf. 15x14	4.75	4.75
302	A64	10c on 25c pink	1.50	1.50
303	A64	12c on 25c pink	1.40	1.40
304	A64	15c on 25c pink	1.40	1.40
305	A64	20c on 25c pink	2.50	2.40
306	A64	40c on 1.10e yel brn	5.00	4.75
		Nos. 300-306 (7)	13.95	13.60

Portugal Nos. 400-401, 403-404, 408, 412, 416 Overprinted in Black or Red

1930			**Perf. 14**	
		Without Imprint at Foot		
307	A85	4c orange	.90	.70
308	A85	5c dp brown	3.00	2.75
309	A85	10c orange red	1.50	1.10
310	A85	15c black (R)	1.50	1.10
311	A85	40c brt green	1.40	.90
312	A85	80c violet	15.00	12.00
313	A85	1.60e dk blue	4.00	1.75
		Nos. 307-313 (7)	27.30	20.30

Black or Red Overprint

1930-31			**Perf. 12x11½**	
		With Imprint at Foot		
313A	A64	4c orange	.55	.50
313B	A64	5c blk brn ('31)	4.00	3.00
313C	A64	6c red brn ('31)	.40	.30
313D	A64	15c black (R)	.95	.70
313E	A64	16c dp blue ('31)	2.75	1.90
313F	A64	32c deep green	3.25	2.25
313G	A64	40c brt grn ('31)	1.50	.70
313H	A64	48c dull pink ('31)	3.50	3.00
313I	A64	50c bister ('31)	4.75	3.50

313J	A64	50c red brn ('31)	4.75	3.50
313K	A64	64c brn rose ('31)	9.00	5.00
313L	A64	75c car rose ('31)	4.75	3.50
313M	A64	80c dk grn ('31)	4.75	3.00
313N	A64	1e brn lake	40.00	27.50
313O	A64	1.25e dk blue	2.75	2.25
		Nos. 313A=313O (15)	87.65	60.90

The original stamps (Portugal Nos. 496A-496R) were printed at the Lisbon Mint from new plates produced from the original dies. The paper is whiter than the paper used for earlier Ceres stamps. The gum is white.

POSTAGE DUE STAMPS

Portugal Nos. J7-J13 Overprinted in Black

1904		**Unwmk.**	**Perf. 12**	
J1	D2	5r brown	1.25	1.10
J2	D2	10r orange	1.40	1.10
J3	D2	20r lilac	2.25	1.10
J4	D2	30r gray green	2.25	1.75
a.		Double overprint		
J5	D2	40r gray violet	4.00	2.40
J6	D2	50r carmine	6.75	4.50
J7	D2	100r dull blue	8.50	8.25
		Nos. J1-J7 (7)	26.40	20.20

Same Overprinted in Carmine or Green (Portugal Nos. J14-J20)

1911				
J8	D2	5r brown	.75	.65
J9	D2	10r orange	.75	.65
J10	D2	20r lilac	.95	.85
J11	D2	30r gray green	.95	.85
J12	D2	40r gray violet	1.50	1.10
J13	D2	50r carmine (G)	7.75	7.50
J14	D2	100r dull blue	2.75	2.75
		Nos. J8-J14 (7)	15.40	14.35

Portugal Nos. J21-J27 Overprinted in Black

1918				
J15	D3	½c brown	.75	.75
a.		Inverted overprint	6.00	
b.		Double overprint	6.00	
J16	D3	1c orange	.75	.75
a.		Inverted overprint	6.00	
b.		Double overprint	6.00	
J17	D3	2c red lilac	.95	.85
a.		Inverted overprint	4.00	
b.		Double overprint	6.00	
J18	D3	3c green	.75	.75
a.		Inverted overprint	6.00	
b.		Double overprint	6.00	
J19	D3	4c gray	.75	.75
a.		Inverted overprint	6.00	
b.		Double overprint	6.00	
J20	D3	5c rose	.75	.75
b.		Double overprint	6.00	
J21	D3	10c dark blue	.75	.75
		Nos. J15-J21 (7)	5.45	5.35

Stamps and Type of Portugal Postage Dues, 1921-27, Overprinted in Black

1922-24			**Perf. 11½x12**	
J30	D3	½c gray green ('23)	.35	.35
J31	D3	1c gray green ('23)	.55	.45
J32	D3	2c gray green ('23)	.55	.45
J33	D3	3c gray green ('24)	.90	.45
J34	D3	8c gray green ('24)	.90	.45
J35	D3	10c gray green ('24)	.90	.45
J36	D3	12c gray green ('24)	.90	.45
J37	D3	16c gray green ('24)	.95	.45
J38	D3	20c gray green ('24)	.95	.45
J39	D3	24c gray green ('24)	.95	.45
J40	D3	32c gray green ('24)	.95	.45
J41	D3	36c gray green	.95	.60
J42	D3	40c gray green ('24)	.95	.60
J43	D3	48c gray green ('24)	.95	.60
J44	D3	50c gray green	.95	.60
J45	D3	60c gray green	1.50	.70
J46	D3	72c gray green	1.50	.70

J47	D3	80c gray green ('24)	5.00	4.25
J48	D3	1.20e gray green	5.75	4.75
		Nos. J30-J48 (19)	26.40	17.65

NEWSPAPER STAMPS

Newspaper Stamps of Portugal, Nos. P1, P1a, Overprinted Types c & d in Black or Red and

N3

		Perf. 12½, 13½ (#P4)		
1876-88			**Unwmk.**	
P1	N1	(c) 2½r olive	13.00	5.50
a.		Inverted overprint	—	
P2	N1	(d) 2½r olive ('82)	5.75	1.90
a.		Inverted overprint	—	
b.		Double overprint	—	
P3	N3	2r black ('85)	6.00	3.00
a.		Inverted overprint	—	
P4	N1	(d) 2½r bister ('82)	5.75	1.90
a.		Double overprint	9.00	
P5	N3	2r black (R) ('88)	19.00	16.00
		Nos. P1-P5 (5)	49.50	28.30

Reprints of the newspaper stamps have the same papers, gum and perforations as reprints of the regular issues. Value $2 each.

PARCEL POST STAMPS

Portugal Nos. Q1-Q17 Ovptd. in Black or Red

1921-22		**Unwmk.**	**Perf. 12**	
Q1	PP1	1c lilac brown	.50	.45
a.		Inverted overprint	6.00	
Q2	PP1	2c orange	.50	.45
a.		Inverted overprint	6.00	
Q3	PP1	5c light brown	.50	.45
a.		Inverted overprint	6.00	
Q4	PP1	10c red brown	.75	.45
a.		Inverted overprint	6.00	
b.		Double overprint	6.00	
Q5	PP1	20c gray blue	.75	.45
a.		Inverted overprint	6.00	
b.		Double overprint	6.00	
Q6	PP1	40c carmine	.75	.45
a.		Double overprint	8.00	
Q7	PP1	50c black (R)	1.00	1.90
Q8	PP1	60c dark blue (R)	1.00	1.90
Q9	PP1	70c gray brown	2.50	1.25
a.		Double overprint	6.00	
Q10	PP1	80c ultra	2.50	1.25
Q11	PP1	90c light violet	2.50	1.25
Q12	PP1	1e light green	2.50	1.25
Q13	PP1	2e pale lilac	7.00	3.50
Q14	PP1	3e olive	12.00	3.75
Q15	PP1	4e ultra	15.00	3.75
Q16	PP1	5e gray	15.00	7.25
Q17	PP1	10e chocolate	50.00	25.00
		Nos. Q1-Q17 (17)	114.75	54.75

POSTAL TAX STAMPS

These stamps represent a special fee for the delivery of postal matter on certain days in the year. The money derived from their sale is applied to works of public charity.

Nos. 128 and 157 Overprinted in Carmine

1911-13 Unwmk. Perf. 14x15
RA1 A29 10r dark green 1.50 1.10
The 20r of this type was for use on telegrams. Value $2.25 unused, $1.90 used.

Perf. 15x14
RA2 A64 1c deep green 5.00 3.75
The 2c of this type was for use on telegrams. Value $7.00 unused, $5.00 used.

Portugal No. RA4 Overprinted in Black

1915 Perf. 12
RA3 PT2 1c carmine .65 .35
The 2c of this type was for use on telegrams. Value $1.10 unused, 85c used.

Postal Tax Stamp of 1915 Surcharged

1924
RA4 PT2 15c on 1c rose 1.10 .90
The 30c on 2c of this type was for use on telegrams. Value $3.00 unused, $1.90 used.

Comrades of the Great War Issue

Postal Tax Stamps of Portugal, 1925, Overprinted

1925, Apr. 8 Perf. 11
RA5 PT3 10c brown 1.10 1.10
RA6 PT3 10c green 1.10 1.10
RA7 PT3 10c rose 1.10 1.10
RA8 PT3 10c ultra 1.10 1.10
Nos. RA5-RA8 (4) 4.40 4.40
The use of Nos. RA5-RA11 in addition to the regular postage was compulsory on certain days. If the tax represented by these stamps was not prepaid, it was collected by means of Postal Tax Due Stamps.

Pombal Issue
Common Design Types

1925 Perf. 12½
RA9 CD28 20c dp grn & blk 1.10 1.10
RA10 CD29 20c dp grn & blk 1.10 1.10
RA11 CD30 20c dp grn & blk 1.10 1.10
Nos. RA9-RA11 (3) 3.30 3.30

POSTAL TAX DUE STAMPS

Portugal No. RAJ1 Ovptd. in Black

1925, Apr. 8 Unwmk. Perf. 11x11½
RAJ1 PTD1 20c brown orange 1.10 .95
See note after No. RA8.

Pombal Issue
Common Design Types

1925, May 8 Perf. 12½
RAJ2 CD28 40c dp grn & blk 1.10 2.00
RAJ3 CD29 40c dp grn & blk 1.10 2.00
RAJ4 CD30 40c dp grn & blk 1.10 2.00
Nos. RAJ2-RAJ4 (3) 3.30 6.00
See note after No. RA8.

BAHAMAS

bə-'hä-məs

LOCATION — A group of about 700 islands and 2,000 rocks in the West Indies, off the coast of Florida. Only 30 islands are inhabited.
GOVT. — Independent state in British Commonwealth
AREA — 5,382 sq. mi.
POP. — 283,705 (1999 est.)
CAPITAL — Nassau

The principal island, on which the capital is located, is New Providence. The Bahamas obtained internal self-government on January 7, 1964, and independence on July 10, 1973.

12 Pence = 1 Shilling
20 Shillings = 1 Pound
100 Cents = 1 Dollar (1966)

> **Catalogue values for unused stamps in this country are for Never Hinged items, beginning with Scott 130, and Scott C1 in the air post section.**

Values for unused stamps are for examples with original gum as defined in the catalogue introduction. Very fine examples of Nos. 2-26 will have perforations touching the design or frameline on at least one side due to the narrow spacing of the stamps on the plates. Stamps with perfs clear of the design or framelines on all four sides are extremely scarce and will command higher prices.

Pen cancellations usually indicate revenue use. Such stamps sell for much less than postally canceled examples. Beware of stamps with revenue or pen cancellations removed and forged postal cancellations added.

Queen Victoria — A1

1859-60 Unwmk. Engr. Imperf.
1 A1 1p dull lake, thin paper ('60) 75.00 1,900.
a. 1p reddish lake, thick paper 6,000. 2,850.
b. 1p brownish lake, thick paper 6,000. 2,850.
Most unused examples of No. 1 are remainders, and false cancellations are plentiful.

Queen Victoria — A2

1861 Rough Perf. 14 to 16
2 A1 1p lake 925. 425.
a. Clean-cut perf. ('60) 7,250. 950.
3 A2 4p dull rose 1,800. 500.
a. Imperf. between, pair 40,000.
4 A2 6p gray lilac 5,500. 800.
a. Pale lilac 4,250. 650.
No. 2 exists perf 11 to 12½. This is a trial perforation by Perkins, Bacon and was not sent to the colony. Value, $2,850.

1862 Perf. 11½, 12
5 A1 1p lake 1,250. 225.
a. Pair, imperf. between 6,250.
6 A2 4p dull rose 4,500. 500.
7 A2 6p gray violet 13,500. 625.
No.5a was not issued in the Bahamas. It is unique and faulty.
Nos. 5-7 exist with perf. 11½ or 12 compound with 11. See the *Scott Classic Specialized Catalogue.*

Perf. 13
8 A1 1p brown lake 950. 160.
a. 1p carmine lake 1,150. 200.
9 A2 4p rose 3,500. 475.
10 A2 6p gray violet 4,250. 600.
a. 6p dull violet 3,500. 575.

Queen Victoria — A3

Engr., Typo. (A3)
1863-65 Wmk. 1 Perf. 12½
11 A1 1p lake 140.00 90.00
a. 1p brown lake 120.00 85.00
b. 1p rose lake 160.00 95.00
c. 1p rose red 70.00 55.00
d. 1p red 75.00 55.00
12 A1 1p vermilion 90.00 57.50
13 A2 4p rose 375.00 75.00
a. 4p rose lake 575.00 100.00
b. 4p bright rose 375.00 75.00
14 A2 6p dk violet 200.00 85.00
a. 6p violet 325.00 115.00
b. 6p rose lilac 8,500. 3,500.
c. 6p lilac 475.00 90.00
15 A3 1sh green ('65) 3,250. 375.00
For surcharge see No. 26.

1863-81 Engr., Typo. (A3) Perf. 14
16 A1 1p vermilion 70.00 20.00
17 A1 1p car lake (anil.) 1,500.
18 A2 4p rose 475.00 50.00
a. 4p deep rose ('76) 550.00 50.00
b. 4p dull rose 1,900. 50.00
19 A3 1sh green ('80) 10.00 11.00
a. 1sh dark green 400.00 50.00
Some examples of No. 16 show a light aniline appearance and care should be taken not to confuse these with No. 17. All known used examples of No. 17 bear fiscal cancels.

Engr., Typo. (A3)
1882-98 Wmk. 2
20 A1 1p vermilion 575.00 75.00
21 A2 4p rose 1,500. 75.00
22 A3 1sh green 50.00 18.00
23 A3 1sh blue grn ('98) 45.00 50.00
Perf. 12
24 A1 1p vermilion 60.00 22.50
25 A2 4p rose 925.00 60.00

No. 14a Surcharged in Black

1883 Engr. Wmk. 1 Perf. 12½
26 A2 4p on 6p violet 725. 500.
a. Inverted surcharge 25,000. 12,000.
The surcharge, being handstamped, is found in various positions. Counterfeit surcharges exist.

Queen Victoria — A5

1884-90 Typo. Wmk. 2 Perf. 14
27 A5 1p carmine rose 9.00 3.25
a. 1p pale rose 95.00 16.00
b. 1p car (aniline) 6.25 8.50
28 A5 2½p ultra 15.50 3.00
a. 2½p dull blue 95.00 22.50
b. 2½p bright blue 55.00 9.50
29 A5 4p yellow 12.50 5.00
30 A5 6p violet 7.50 40.00
31 A5 5sh olive green 90.00 100.00
32 A5 £1 brown 350.00 275.00
Revenue cancellation 55.00
Nos. 27-32 (6) 484.50 426.25
Cleaned fiscally used examples of No. 32 are often found with forged postmarks of small post offices added, especially dated "AU 29 94."

Queen's Staircase — A6

1901-03 Engr. Wmk. 1
33 A6 1p carmine & blk 15.00 4.00
34 A6 5p org & blk ('03) 11.00 65.00
35 A6 2sh ultra & blk ('03) 35.00 65.00
36 A6 3sh green & blk ('03) 50.00 75.00
Nos. 33-36 (4) 111.00 209.00
See Nos. 48, 58-62, 71, 78, 81-82.

Edward VII — A7

1902 Wmk. 2 Typo.
37 A7 1p carmine rose 2.00 3.25
38 A7 2½p ultra 12.50 1.75
39 A7 4p orange 20.00 77.50
40 A7 6p bister brn 8.50 37.50
41 A7 1sh gray blk & car 26.00 65.00
42 A7 5sh violet & ultra 85.00 110.00
43 A7 £1 green & blk 325.00 425.00
Nos. 37-43 (7) 479.00 720.00
Beware of forged postmarks, especially dated "2 MAR 10."

1906-11 Wmk. 3
44 A7 ½p green 6.25 4.00
45 A7 1p car rose ('07) 32.50 1.75
46 A7 2½p ultra ('07) 32.50 32.50
47 A7 6p bister brn ('11) 30.00 60.00
Nos. 44-47 (4) 101.25 98.25

1911-19 Engr.
48 A6 1p red & gray blk ('16) 6.00 3.25
a. 1p carmine & black ('11) 23.00 3.50
For overprints see Nos. B1-B2.

George V — A8

1912-19 Typo.
49 A8 ½p green 1.00 12.50
50 A8 1p car rose (aniline) 4.50 .45
50A A8 2p gray ('19) 3.00 3.75
51 A8 2½p ultra 6.00 35.00
52 A8 4p orange 3.25 22.50
53 A8 6p bister brown 2.25 9.25

Chalky Paper
54 A8 1sh black & car 2.25 11.50
55 A8 5sh violet & ultra 50.00 90.00
56 A8 £1 dull grn & blk 250.00 425.00
Nos. 49-56 (9) 322.25 609.95

1917-19 Engr.
58 A6 3p reddish pur, *buff* 7.75 13.50
59 A6 3p brown & blk ('19) 4.00 5.00

60	A6	5p violet & blk	3.50	9.00
61	A6	2sh ultra & black	37.50	70.00
62	A6	3sh green & black	82.50	70.00
		Nos. 58-62 (5)	135.25	167.50

Peace Commemorative Issue

King George V
and Seal of
Bahamas — A9

1920, Mar. 1		**Engr.**	**Perf. 14**	
65	A9	½p gray green	1.25	7.00
66	A9	1p deep red	3.50	1.25
67	A9	2p gray	3.50	9.50
68	A9	3p brown	3.50	11.50
69	A9	1sh dark green	22.50	45.00
		Nos. 65-69 (5)	34.25	74.25

Types of 1901-12
Typo., Engr. (A6)

1921-34			**Wmk. 4**	
70	A8	½p green ('24)	.65	.50
71	A6	1p car & black	3.50	4.75
72	A8	1p car rose	1.25	.25
73	A8	1½p fawn ('34)	13.00	1.25
74	A8	2p gray ('27)	1.90	3.00
75	A8	2½p ultra ('22)	1.25	3.00
76	A8	3p violet, *yel* ('31)	8.25	20.00
77	A8	4p yellow ('24)	1.90	5.25
78	A6	5p red vio & gray blk ('29)	5.50	57.50
79	A8	6p bister brn ('22)	1.25	3.00
80	A8	1sh blk & red ('26)	9.75	7.25
81	A6	2sh ultra & blk ('22)	30.00	27.50
82	A6	3sh grn & blk ('24)	60.00	82.50
83	A8	5sh vio & ultra ('24)	45.00	85.00
84	A8	£1 grn & blk ('26)	215.00	425.00
		Nos. 70-84 (15)	398.20	725.75

The 3p, 1sh, 5sh and £1 are on chalky paper.

Seal of
Bahamas — A10

1930, Jan. 2		**Engr.**	**Perf. 12**	
85	A10	1p red & black	4.25	3.50
86	A10	3p dp brown & blk	5.50	19.00
87	A10	5p dk vio & blk	5.50	19.00
88	A10	2sh ultra & black	22.50	62.50
89	A10	3sh dp green & blk	52.50	110.00
		Nos. 85-89 (5)	90.25	214.00

The dates on the stamps commemorate important events in the history of the colony. The 1st British occupation was in 1629. The Bahamas were ceded to Great Britain in 1729 and a treaty of peace was signed by that country, France and Spain.

Type of 1930 Issue
Without Dates at Top

1931-46				
90	A10	2sh ultra & black	15.00	9.00
a.		2sh ultra & slate purple	30.00	37.50
91	A10	3sh dp green & blk	10.00	7.00
a.		3sh deep grn & slate purple	37.50	35.00

Nos. 90a-91a are on thicker paper with yellowish gum. Later printings are on thinner white paper with colorless gum.
For overprints see Nos. 126-127.

Common Design Types pictured following the introduction.

Silver Jubilee Issue
Common Design Type

1935, May 6			**Perf. 13½x14**	
92	CD301	1½p car & blue	1.25	4.00
93	CD301	2½p brn & brn	6.25	10.00
94	CD301	6p ol grn & lt bl	8.75	16.50
95	CD301	1sh brt vio & ind	8.75	15.50
		Nos. 92-95 (4)	25.00	46.00
		Set, never hinged	35.00	

Flamingos
in Flight
A11

1935, May 22			**Perf. 12½**	
96	A11	8p car & ultra	7.25	4.25
		Never hinged	10.00	

Coronation Issue
Common Design Type

1937, May 12			**Perf. 13½x14**	
97	CD302	½p dp green	.25	.25
98	CD302	1½p brown	.30	1.40
99	CD302	2½p brt ultra	.50	1.40
		Nos. 97-99 (3)	1.05	3.05
		Set, never hinged	1.50	

George VI — A12

Sea
Gardens,
Nassau
A13

Fort
Charlotte
A14

Flamingos
in Flight
A15

1938-46		**Typo.**	**Wmk. 4**	**Perf. 14**
100	A12	½p green	1.00	1.60
101	A12	1p carmine	7.00	4.50
		Complete booklet, 12 #101 in blocks of 6 and 8 #102 in folded block	—	
101A	A12	1p pale gray ('41)	.50	.90
102	A12	1½p red brown	1.25	1.60
103	A12	2p gray	14.00	5.75
103B	A12	2p carmine ('41)	.85	.85
c.		"TWO PENCE" double		15,000.
104	A12	2½p ultra	2.75	1.90
104A	A12	2½p lt violet ('43)	1.10	1.60
b.		"2½ PENNY" double	3,250.	
105	A12	3p lt violet	13.00	5.00
105A	A12	3p ultra ('43)	.50	1.60
		Engr.		
		Perf. 12½		
106	A13	4p red org & blue	.80	1.25
107	A14	6p blue & ol grn	.65	1.25
108	A15	8p car & ultra	7.25	3.25
		Typo.		
		Perf. 14		
109	A12	10p yel org ('46)	2.25	.55
110	A12	1sh blk & brt red	11.50	1.00
112	A12	5sh pur & ultra	17.50	17.50
113	A12	£1 bl grn & blk	45.00	60.00
		Nos. 100-113 (17)	126.90	110.10
		Set, never hinged	190.00	

Nos. 110-113 printed on chalky and ordinary paper.
See the *Scott Classic Specialized Catalogue of Stamps & Covers* for listings of shades.
See Nos. 154-156. For overprints see Nos. 116-125, 128-129.

No. 104 Surcharged in
Black

3d.

1940, Nov. 28			**Perf. 14**	
115	A12	3p on 2½p ultra	1.10	3.25
		Never hinged		1.75

Stamps of 1931-42
Overprinted in Black

**1492
LANDFALL
OF
COLUMBUS
1942**

1942, Oct. 12			**Perf. 14, 12½, 12**	
116	A12	½p green	.25	.75
117	A12	1p gray	.25	.75
118	A12	1½p red brn	.35	.75
119	A12	2p carmine	.40	.80
120	A12	2½p ultra	.40	.80
121	A12	3p ultra	.25	.80
122	A13	4p red org & blue	.35	1.10
123	A14	6p blue & ol grn	.35	2.10
124	A15	8p car & ultra	1.10	.85
125	A12	1sh blk & car (#110c)	6.50	11.00
126	A10	2sh dk ultra & blk	6.75	11.50
127	A10	3sh dp grn & sl pur (#91a)	6.50	8.00
128	A12	5sh lilac & ultra (#112a)	17.50	16.00
129	A12	£1 grn & blk	22.50	27.50
		Nos. 116-129 (14)	63.45	82.70
		Set, never hinged	95.00	

450th anniv. of the discovery of America by Columbus.
Nos. 125, 128-129 printed on chalky and original paper.
Two printings of the basic stamps were overprinted, the first with dark gum, the second with white gum.
For shades, see the *Scott Classic Catalogue.*

Catalogue values for unused stamps in this section, from this point to the end of the section, are for Never Hinged items.

Peace Issue
Common Design Type
Perf. 13½x14

1946, Nov. 11		**Engr.**	**Wmk. 4**	
130	CD303	1½p brown	.25	.70
131	CD303	3p deep blue	.25	.70

Infant
Welfare
Clinic
A16

Designs: 1p, Modern agriculture. 1½p, Sisal. 2p, Native straw work. 2½p, Modern dairying. 3p, Fishing fleet. 4p, Out island settlement. 6p, Tuna fishing. 8p, Paradise Beach. 10p, Modern hotel. 1sh, Yacht racing. 2sh, Water skiing. 3sh, Shipbuilding. 5sh, Modern transportation. 10sh, Modern salt production. £1, Parliament Building.

1948, Oct. 11		**Unwmk.**	**Perf. 12**	
132	A16	½p orange	.40	1.75
133	A16	1p olive green	.40	.45
134	A16	1½p olive bister	.40	1.00
135	A16	2p vermilion	.40	.50
136	A16	2½p red brown	.85	1.00
137	A16	3p brt ultra	3.25	1.10
138	A16	4p gray black	.75	.90
139	A16	6p emerald	2.75	1.00
140	A16	8p violet	1.25	.90
141	A16	10p rose car	.75	.75
142	A16	1sh olive brn	3.00	1.25
143	A16	2sh claret	6.25	11.00
144	A16	3sh brt blue	12.50	11.00
145	A16	5sh purple	20.00	6.50
146	A16	10sh dk gray	15.00	13.00
147	A16	£1 red orange	16.50	18.00
		Nos. 132-147 (16)	84.95	70.10

300th anniv., in 1947, of the settlement of the colony.

Silver Wedding Issue
Common Design Type
Perf. 14x14½

1948, Dec. 1		**Wmk. 4**	**Photo.**	
148	CD304	1½p red brown	.25	.30
		Engr.; Name Typo.		
		Perf. 11½x11		
149	CD305	£1 gray green	45.00	40.00

UPU Issue
Common Design Types
Engr.; Name Typo. on #151 & 152

1949, Oct. 10			**Perf. 13½, 11x11½**	
150	CD306	2½p violet	.45	.80
151	CD307	3p indigo	2.75	3.75
152	CD308	6p blue gray	.90	3.50
153	CD309	1sh rose car	1.25	1.25
		Nos. 150-153 (4)	5.35	9.30

George VI Type of 1938
Perf. 13½x14

1951-52		**Wmk. 4**	**Typo.**	
154	A12	½p claret ('52)	1.25	3.75
a.		Wmk. 4a (error)	4,750.	3,250.
		Lightly hinged	3,250.	
155	A12	2p ultra	2.00	1.00
156	A12	3p rose red ('52)	1.00	4.00
		Nos. 154-156 (3)	4.25	8.75

Coronation Issue
Common Design Type

1953, June 3		**Engr.**	**Perf. 13½x13**	
157	CD312	6p blue & black	1.40	.75

Infant
Welfare
Clinic
A17

Designs: 1p, Modern Agriculture. 1½p, Out island settlement. 2p, Native strawwork. 3p, Fishing fleet. 4p, Water skiing. 5p, Modern dairying. 6p, Modern transportation. 8p, Paradise Beach. 10p, Modern hotels. 1sh, Yacht racing. 2sh, Sisal. 2sh6p, Shipbuilding. 5sh, Tuna fishing. 10sh, Modern salt production. £1, Parliament Building.

1954, Jan. 1			**Perf. 11x11½**	
158	A17	½p red org & blk	.25	1.75
159	A17	1p org brn & ol grn	.25	.35
160	A17	1½p black & blue	.25	.60
161	A17	2p dk grn & brn org	.25	.35
		Complete booklet, 8 each #159, 160, 161, in blocks of 4	30.00	
162	A17	3p dp car & blk	.60	.75
163	A17	4p lil rose & bl green	.30	.30
164	A17	5p dp ultra & brn	1.60	2.40
165	A17	6p blk & aqua	2.00	.25
166	A17	8p rose vio & blk	.75	.40
		Complete booklet, 4 each #163, 165, 166, in blocks of 4	40.00	
167	A17	10p ultra & blk	.35	.25
168	A17	1sh ol brn & ultra	1.35	.25
169	A17	2sh blk & brn org	2.25	.60
170	A17	2sh6p dp bl & blk	4.00	2.40
171	A17	5sh dp org & emer	20.00	.75
172	A17	10sh grnsh blk & black	27.00	3.50
173	A17	£1 vio & grnsh black	25.00	8.50
		Nos. 158-173 (16)	86.20	23.40

See No. 203. For types overprinted or surcharged see Nos. 181-182, 185-200, 202.

Queen
Elizabeth II — A18

1959, June 10		**Wmk. 314**		
		Engr.	**Perf. 13**	
174	A18	1p dk red & black	.30	.25
175	A18	2p green & black	.30	.25
176	A18	6p blue & black	.50	.50
177	A18	10p brown & black	.80	.80
		Nos. 174-177 (4)	1.90	1.80

Cent. of the 1st postage stamp of Bahamas.

Christ Church Cathedral,
Nassau — A19

Perf. 14x13

1962, Jan. 30	Photo.	Unwmk.	
178	A19	8p shown	.55	.55
179	A19	10p Public library	.60	.60

Centenary of the city of Nassau.

Freedom from Hunger Issue
Common Design Type

Perf. 14x14½

1963, June 4			Wmk. 314	
180	CD314	8p sepia	.65	.65
a.	"8d," "BAHAMAS" omitted		1,200.	2,000.

**Nos. 166-167 Overprinted:
"BAHAMAS TALKS/ 1962"**

Perf. 11x11½

1963, July 15	Engr.	Wmk. 4	
181	A17	8p rose vio & black	.65	.65
182	A17	10p ultra & black	.65	.65

Meeting of Pres. Kennedy and Prime Minister Harold Macmillan, Dec. 1962.

Red Cross Centenary Issue
Common Design Type

Wmk. 314

1963, Sept. 2	Litho.	Perf. 13	
183	CD315	1p black & red	.30	.30
184	CD315	10p ultra & red	2.00	2.50

Type of 1954 Overprinted: "NEW CONSTITUTION/ 1964"

Designs as Before

Perf. 11x11½

1964, Jan. 7	Engr.	Wmk. 314	
185	A17	½p red org & blk	.30	1.40
186	A17	1p org brn & ol grn	.30	.30
187	A17	1½p black & blue	.90	1.40
188	A17	2p dk grn & brn org	.30	.30
189	A17	3p dp car & blk	1.75	1.75
190	A17	4p lil rose & bl grn	.50	.70
191	A17	5p dp ultra & brn	.50	1.75
192	A17	6p blk & aqua	2.40	.40
193	A17	8p rose vio & blk	.90	.40
194	A17	10p ultra & black	.40	.40
195	A17	1sh ol brn & ultra	1.40	.30
196	A17	2sh blk & brn org	1.75	1.75
197	A17	2sh6p dp bl & blk	3.00	3.00
198	A17	5sh dp org & emer	7.00	3.25
199	A17	10sh grnsh blk & black	7.25	5.50
200	A17	£1 vio & grnsh black	8.50	25.00
		Nos. 185-200 (16)	37.15	47.50

Shakespeare Issue
Common Design Type

Perf. 14x14½

1964, Apr. 23	Photo.	Wmk. 314	
201	CD316	6p greenish blue	.60	.35

Type of 1954 Surcharged with Olympic Rings, New Value and Bars

Perf. 11x11½

1964, Oct. 1	Engr.	Wmk. 314	
202	A17	8p on 1sh ol brn & ultra	.90	.90

18th Olympic Games, Tokyo, Oct. 10-25.

Queen Type of 1954

1964, Oct. 6		Wmk. 314	
203	A17	2p dk grn & brn org	1.10	.50

Colony Badge A21

Designs: 1p, Out Island Regatta. 1½p, Princess Margaret Hospital. 2p, High School. 3p, Flamingo. 4p, Liner "Queen Elizabeth." 6p, Island development. 8p, Yachting. 10p, Public

---

Square, Nassau. 1sh, Sea Garden, Nassau. 2sh, Cannons at Fort Charlotte. 2sh6p, Sea plane and jetliner. 5sh, 1914 Williamson film project and 1939 underwater post office. 10sh, Conch shell. £1, Columbus' flagship.

Engr. and Litho.

1965, Jan. 7		Perf. 13½x13	
204	A21	½p multi, bluish	.25	2.00
205	A21	1p multi	.25	1.10
206	A21	1½p multi	.25	3.00
207	A21	2p multi	.25	.25
	Complete booklet, 8 each #205, 206, 207, in blocks of 4		22.50	
208	A21	3p multi	2.00	.25
209	A21	4p multi	2.50	3.00
210	A21	6p multi	.30	.25
211	A21	8p multi	.40	.40
	Complete booklet, 4 each #209, 210, 211, in blocks of 4		22.50	
212	A21	10p multi	.30	.25
213	A21	1sh multi, grnsh	.40	.25
214	A21	2sh multi, grnsh	.90	1.40
215	A21	2sh6p multi	2.25	3.75
216	A21	5sh multi	2.25	1.10
217	A21	10sh multi	14.00	4.00
218	A21	£1 multi	15.00	11.00
	Nos. 204-218 (15)		41.30	32.00

Booklet panes were issued Mar. 23, 1965.
See Nos. 252-266. For surcharges see Nos. 221, 230-244.

ITU Issue
Common Design Type

Perf. 11x11½

1965, May 17	Litho.	Wmk. 314	
219	CD317	1p emerald & org	.25	.25
220	CD317	2sh lilac & olive	1.10	1.25

No. 211
Surcharged

Engr. & Litho.

1965, July 12		Perf. 13½x13	
221	A21	9p on 8p multi	.45	.30

Intl. Cooperation Year Issue
Common Design Type

Wmk. 314

1965, Oct. 25	Litho.	Perf. 14½	
222	CD318	½p blue grn & clar	.25	1.25
223	CD318	1sh lt violet & grn	.40	.65

Churchill Memorial Issue
Common Design Type

1966, Jan. 24	Photo.	Perf. 14	
224	CD319	1p multicolored	.25	.25
225	CD319	2p multicolored	.45	.25
226	CD319	10p multicolored	.80	1.10
227	CD319	1sh multicolored	.80	1.60
	Nos. 224-227 (4)		2.30	3.20

Royal Visit Issue
Common Design Type Inscribed "Royal Visit / 1966"

1966, Feb. 4	Litho.	Perf. 11x12	
228	CD320	6p violet blue	.80	.80
229	CD320	1sh dk car rose	2.25	2.25

Nos. 204-218 Surcharged

Engr. & Litho.

1966, May 25		Wmk. 314	
		Perf. 13½x13	
230	A21	1c on ½p multi	.25	.25
231	A21	2c on 1p multi	.25	.25
232	A21	3c on 2p multi	.25	.25
233	A21	4c on 3p multi	.25	.25
234	A21	5c on 4p multi	.25	.25
a.	Surch. omitted, vert. strip of 7-10		3,250.	
235	A21	8c on 6p multi	.25	.25
236	A21	10c on 8p multi	.25	.25
237	A21	11c on 1½p multi	.45	.25
238	A21	12c on 10p multi	.50	.30
239	A21	15c on 1sh multi	.60	.35
240	A21	22c on 2sh multi	.75	.40
241	A21	50c on 2sh6p multi	1.60	1.35
242	A21	$1 on 5sh multi	3.00	2.75

243	A21	$2 on 10sh multi	6.50	5.50
244	A21	$3 on £1 multi	9.50	8.00
	Nos. 230-244 (15)		24.65	20.65

The denominations are next to the bars instead of below on Nos. 232, 235-240; the length of the bars varies to cover old denomination.

No. 234a, if single, is identical with No. 209, but distinguishable if in vertical strip of 7 to 10. No. 234 was printed in sheets of 100 (10x10); No. 209 in sheets of 60 (10x6).

World Cup Soccer Issue
Common Design Type

1966, July 1	Litho.	Perf. 14	
245	CD321	8c multicolored	.25	.25
246	CD321	15c multicolored	.40	.40

WHO Headquarters Issue
Common Design Type

1966, Sept. 20	Litho.	Perf. 14	
247	CD322	11c multicolored	.30	.30
248	CD322	15c multicolored	.50	.50

UNESCO Anniversary Issue
Common Design Type

1966, Dec. 1	Litho.	Perf. 14	
249	CD323	3c "Education"	.25	.25
250	CD323	15c "Science"	.35	.35
251	CD323	$1 "Culture"	1.75	1.75
	Nos. 249-251 (3)		2.35	2.35

**Type of 1965
Values in Cents and Dollars**

1c, Colony badge. 2c, Out Island Regatta. 3c, High School. 4c, Flamingo. 5c, Liner "Oceanic." 8c, Island development. 10c, Yachting. 11c, Princess Margaret Hospital. 12c, Public Square, Nassau. 15c, Sea Garden, Nassau. 22c, Cannon at Fort Charlotte. 50c, Sea plane, jetliner. $1, 1914 Williamson film project, 1939 underwater post office. $2, Conch shell. $3, Columbus' flagship.

Engr. & Litho.

1967, May 25		Perf. 13½x13	
		Toned Paper	
252	A21	1c brown & multi	.30	4.00
253	A21	2c grn, slate & bl	.30	1.00
254	A21	3c grn, indigo & vio	.30	.35
255	A21	4c ultra, blue & red	4.25	.80
256	A21	5c pur, bl & indigo	1.10	4.50
257	A21	8c dk brn, bl & dl grn	.30	.35
258	A21	10c car rose, bl & pur	.35	1.10
259	A21	11c bl, grn & rose red	.30	1.40
260	A21	12c ol grn, bl & lt brn	.30	.35
261	A21	15c rose & multi	.65	.35
262	A21	22c rose red, brn & bl	.75	1.10
263	A21	50c emer, ol & bl	2.25	1.25
264	A21	$1 sep, brn org & dk blue	2.25	1.10
265	A21	$2 green & multi	14.00	5.00
266	A21	$3 pur, bl & brn org	4.25	3.00
	Nos. 252-266 (15)		31.65	25.65

1970-71		White Paper	
252a	A21	1c brown & multi	.50	4.25
253a	A21	2c grn, slate & bl	1.60	10.00
254a	A21	3c grn, indigo & vio	55.00	6.00
255a	A21	4c ultra, blue & red	14.00	22.50
256a	A21	5c pur, bl & indigo	1.60	9.50
257a	A21	8c dk brn, bl & dl grn	190.00	20.00
258a	A21	10c car rose, bl & pur	1.10	5.00
259a	A21	11c bl, grn & rose red	.95	3.00
260a	A21	12c ol grn, bl & lt brn ('71)	14.00	30.00
261a	A21	15c rose & multi	220.00	26.00
262a	A21	22c rose red, brn & bl	1.60	9.50
263a	A21	50c emer, ol & bl	2.50	6.00
264a	A21	$1 sep, brn org & dk blue ('71)	22.00	70.00
265a	A21	$2 green & multi ('71)	32.50	92.50
266a	A21	$3 pur, bl & brn org ('71)	32.50	92.50
	Nos. 252a-266a (15)		589.85	406.75

Nos. 252-266 are on off-white toned paper. Nos. 252a-266a are on very white, untinted paper. Because of the difference in papers and the use of some new plates, there are noticeable differences in shade on most values.

Seal of Bahamas, Queen Elizabeth II and Lord Baden-Powell — A22

60th anniv. of world Scouting: 15c, Scout emblem and portraits as on 3c.

Perf. 14x13½

1967, Sept. 1	Photo.	Wmk. 314	
267	A22	3c multicolored	.25	.25
268	A22	15c multicolored	.60	.25

Human Rights Flame and Globe A23

Intl. Human Rights Year: 12c, Human rights flame and scales of justice. $1, Human rights flame and Seal of Bahamas.

1968, May 13	Litho.	Perf. 14	
269	A23	3c multicolored	.25	.25
270	A23	12c multicolored	.30	.30
271	A23	$1 multicolored	.90	.90
	Nos. 269-271 (3)		1.45	1.45

Golf — A24

Tourist Publicity: 11c, Yachting. 15c, Horse racing. 50c, Water skiing.

1968, Aug. 20	Unwmk.	Perf. 13½	
272	A24	5c multicolored	2.00	2.00
273	A24	11c multicolored	2.00	2.00
274	A24	15c multicolored	2.50	2.50
275	A24	50c multicolored	3.50	3.50
	Nos. 272-275 (4)		10.00	10.00

Olympic Monument and Sailboat — A25

Olympic Monument, San Salvador Island, Bahamas, and: 11c, Long jump. 50c, Running. $1, Sailing.

1968, Sept. 30	Photo.	Perf. 14½x14	
276	A25	5c multicolored	.45	.45
277	A25	11c multicolored	.75	.75
278	A25	50c multicolored	1.00	1.00
279	A25	$1 multicolored	2.50	2.50
	Nos. 276-279 (4)		4.70	4.70

19th Olympic Games, Mexico City, 10/12-27.

Legislative Building — A26

Designs: 10c, Bahamas mace and Big Ben, London, vert. 12c, Local straw market, vert. 15c, Horse-drawn surrey.

Perf. 14½
1968, Nov. 1   Unwmk.   Litho.
280	A26	3c brt blue & multi	.25	.25
281	A26	10c yel, blk & blue	.25	.25
282	A26	12c brt rose & multi	.25	.25
283	A26	15c green & multi	.25	.25
		Nos. 280-283 (4)	1.00	1.00

14th Commonwealth Parliamentary Conf., Nassau, Nov. 1-8.

$100 Coin with Queen Elizabeth II and Landing of Columbus — A27

Gold Coins with Elizabeth II on Obverse: 12c, $50 coin and Santa Maria flagship. 15c, $20 coin and Nassau Harbor Lighthouse. $1, $10 coin and Fort.

Engr. on Gold Paper
1968, Dec. 2   Unwmk.   Perf. 13½
284	A27	3c dark red	.55	.55
285	A27	12c dark green	.90	.90
286	A27	15c lilac	1.10	1.10
287	A27	$1 black	2.75	2.75
		Nos. 284-287 (4)	5.30	5.30

First gold coinage in the Bahamas.

Bahamas Postal Card and Airplane Wing — A28

Design: 15c, Seaplane, 1929.

Perf. 14½x14
1969, Jan. 30   Litho.   Unwmk.
288	A28	12c multicolored	.75	.75
289	A28	15c multicolored	.90	.90

50th anniv. of the 1st flight from Nassau, Bahamas, to Miami, Fla., Jan. 30, 1919.

Game Fishing Boats A29

Designs: 11c, Paradise Beach. 12c, Sunfish sailboats. 15c, Parade on Rawson Square.

1969, Aug. 26   Litho.   Wmk. 314
290	A29	3c multicolored	.25	.25
291	A29	11c multicolored	.55	.55
292	A29	12c multicolored	.60	.60
293	A29	15c multicolored	.75	.75
a.		Souvenir sheet of 4, #290-293	4.00	4.00
		Nos. 290-293 (4)	2.15	2.15

Tourist publicity.

Holy Family, by Nicolas Poussin — A30

Paintings: 3c, Adoration of the Shepherds, by Louis Le Nain. 12c, Adoration of the Kings, by Gerard David. 15c, Adoration of the Kings, by Vincenzo Foppa.

1969, Oct. 15   Photo.   Perf. 12
294	A30	3c red & multi	.25	.25
295	A30	11c emerald & multi	.25	.25
296	A30	12c ultra & multi	.30	.30
297	A30	15c multicolored	.40	.40
		Nos. 294-297 (4)	1.20	1.20

Christmas.

Girl Guides, Globe and Flags A31

Designs: 12c, Yellow elder and Brownie emblem. 15c, Ranger emblem.

1970, Feb. 23   Wmk. 314   Perf. 14½
298	A31	3c vio blue, yel & red	.25	.25
299	A31	12c dk brn, grn & yel	.50	.50
300	A31	15c vio bl, bluish grn & yel	.70	.70
		Nos. 298-300 (3)	1.45	1.45

60th anniversary of the Girl Guides.

Opening of UPU Headquarters, Bern — A32

1970, May 20   Litho.   Perf. 14½
301	A32	3c vermilion & multi	.25	.25
302	A32	15c orange & multi	.35	.35

Bus and Globe A33

Globe and: 11c, Train. 12c, Sailboat and ship. 15c, Plane.

1970, July 14   Perf. 13½x13
303	A33	3c orange & multi	.85	.85
304	A33	11c emerald & multi	1.75	1.75
305	A33	12c multicolored	1.75	1.75
306	A33	15c blue & multi	1.75	1.75
a.		Souvenir sheet of 4, #303-306	11.50	11.50
		Nos. 303-306 (4)	6.10	6.10

Issued to promote good will through world-wide travel and tourism.

People, Palms and Flamingo — A34

15c, Red Cross Headquarters, Nassau & marlin.

1970, Aug. 18   Perf. 14x14½
307	A34	3c multicolored	1.00	.65
308	A34	15c multicolored	1.00	1.60

Centenary of British Red Cross Society.

Nativity by G. B. Pittoni — A35

Christmas: 11c, Holy Family, by Anton Raphael Mengs. 12c, Adoration of the Shepherds, by Giorgione. 15c, Adoration of the Shepherds, School of Seville.

Perf. 12½x13
1970, Nov. 3   Litho.   Wmk. 314
309	A35	3c multicolored	.25	.25
310	A35	11c red org & multi	.30	.30
311	A35	12c emerald & multi	.30	.30
312	A35	15c blue & multi	.45	.45
a.		Souv. sheet of 4, #309-312 + 3 labels	2.25	2.25
		Nos. 309-312 (4)	1.30	1.30

International Airport A36

2c, Breadfruit. 3c, Straw market. 4c, 6c, Hawksbill turtle. 5c, Grouper. 7c, 12c, Hibiscus. 8c, Yellow elder. 10c, Bahamian sponge boat. 11c, Flamingos. 15c, Bonefish. 18c, 22c, Royal poinciana. 50c, Post office, Nassau. $1, Pineapple, vert. $2, Crayfish, vert. $3, "Junkanoo" (costumed drummer), vert.

Wmk. 314 Upright (Sideways on $1, $2, $3)
1971   Perf. 14½x14, 14x14½
313	A36	1c blue & multi	.25	.30
314	A36	2c red & multi	.25	.35
315	A36	3c lilac & multi	.25	.30
316	A36	4c brown & multi	1.75	10.00
317	A36	5c dp org & multi	.70	.55
318	A36	6c brown & multi	.45	1.10
319	A36	7c green & multi	1.90	4.25
320	A36	8c yel & multi	.65	1.40
321	A36	10c red & multi	.60	.30
322	A36	11c red & multi	2.40	3.00
323	A36	12c green & multi	1.90	2.75
324	A36	15c gray & multi	.60	.35
325	A36	18c multicolored	.70	.55
326	A36	22c green & multi	2.90	15.00
327	A36	50c multicolored	1.40	1.50
328	A36	$1 red & multi	6.50	2.25
329	A36	$2 blue & multi	4.75	5.75
330	A36	$3 vio bl & multi	3.75	9.00
		Nos. 313-330 (18)	31.70	58.70

See Nos. 398-401, 426-443.

Wmk. 314 Sideways (Upright on $1, $2, $3)
1973
317a	A36	5c	17.50	24.00
320a	A36	8c	4.25	6.75
327a	A36	50c	3.25	5.00
328a	A36	$1	3.25	5.00
329a	A36	$2	3.25	5.00
330a	A36	$3	4.50	7.25
		Nos. 317a-330a (6)	36.00	53.00

1976   Wmk. 373
313a	A36	1c	.25	.25
314a	A36	2c	.25	.25
315a	A36	3c	.25	.25
317b	A36	5c	.25	.25
320b	A36	8c	.25	.25
321a	A36	10c	.25	.25
327b	A36	50c	3.25	4.25
328b	A36	$1	6.75	8.75
329b	A36	$2	13.50	16.00
330b	A36	$3	20.00	26.00
		Nos. 313a-330b (10)	45.00	56.50

Snowflake with Peace Signs A37

Christmas: 11c, "Peace on Earth" with doves. 15c, Christmas wreath around old Bahamas coat of arms. 18c, Star of Bethlehem over palms.

Perf. 14x14½
1971   Photo.   Wmk. 314
331	A37	3c dp lil rose, gold & org	.25	.25
332	A37	11c violet & gold	.30	.30
333	A37	15c gold embossed & multi	.30	.30
334	A37	18c brt bl, gold & vio bl	.35	.35
a.		Souv. sheet, #331-334, perf 15	2.25	2.25
		Nos. 331-334 (4)	1.20	1.20

High Jump, Arms of Bahamas — A38

Olympic Rings, Compass, Arms of Bahamas and: 11c, Bicycling. 15c, Running. 18c, Sailing.

1972, June 27   Litho.   Perf. 13x13½
335	A38	10c lt violet & multi	.50	.50
336	A38	11c ocher & multi	.65	.65
337	A38	15c yel green & multi	.90	.90
338	A38	18c blue & multi	1.30	1.30
a.		Souvenir sheet of 4, #335-338	5.50	5.50
		Nos. 335-338 (4)	3.35	3.35

20th Olympic Games, Munich, 8/26-9/10.

Shepherd and Star of Bethlehem — A39

Designs: 6c, Bells. 15c, Holly and monstrance. 20c, Poinsettia.

1972, Oct. 3   Wmk. 314   Perf. 14
339	A39	3c gold & multi	.25	.25
340	A39	6c black & multi	.25	.25
341	A39	15c black & multi	.30	.30
342	A39	20c gold & multi	.50	.50
a.		Souvenir sheet of 4, #339-342	2.50	2.50
		Nos. 339-342 (4)	1.30	1.30

Christmas. Gold on 15c is embossed.

Souvenir Sheet

Map of Bahama Islands — A40

1972, Nov. 1   Litho.   Perf. 15
343	A40	Sheet of 4	6.25	6.25
a.		11c blue & multi	.50	.50
b.		15c blue & multi	.75	.75
c.		18c blue & multi	.90	.90
d.		50c blue & multi	2.75	2.75

Tourism Year of the Americas.

Silver Wedding Issue, 1972
Common Design Type

Design: Queen Elizabeth II, Prince Philip, mace and galleon.

Perf. 14x14½
1972, Nov. 13   Photo.   Wmk. 314
344	CD324	11c car rose & multi	.25	.25
345	CD324	18c violet & multi	.35	.35

Weather Satellite, WMO Emblem A41

1973, Apr. 3   Litho.   Perf. 14
346 A41 15c shown   .55 .45
347 A41 18c Weather radar .75 .65

Intl. meteorological cooperation, cent.

Clarence A. Bain — A42

Independence: 11c, New Bahamian coat of arms. 15c, New flag and Government House. $1, Milo B. Butler, Sr.

1973   Wmk. 314   Perf. 14½x14
348 A42 3c lilac & multi   .25 .25
349 A42 11c lt blue & multi   .35 .35
350 A42 15c lt green & multi .60 .60
351 A42 $1 yel & multi   1.25 1.25
   a. Souvenir sheet of 4, #348-351 3.00 3.00
        Nos. 348-351 (4)   2.45 2.45

Issued: Nos. 348-350, 7/10; Nos. 351, 351a, 8/1.

Virgin in Prayer, by Sassoferrato A43

Christmas: 11c, Virgin and Child with St. John, by Filippino Lippi. 15c, Choir of Angels, by Marmion. 18c, The Two Trinities, by Murillo.

1973, Oct. 16   Litho.   Perf. 14
352 A43 3c blue & multi   .25 .25
353 A43 11c multicolored   .30 .30
354 A43 15c gray grn & multi .30 .30
355 A43 18c lil rose & multi .40 .40
   a. Souvenir sheet of 4, #352-355 1.50 2.00
        Nos. 352-355 (4)   1.25 1.25

Agriculture, Science and Medicine — A44

18c, Symbols of engineering, art, and law.

1974, Feb. 5   Litho.   Perf. 13½x14
356 A44 15c dull grn & multi .35 .35
357 A44 18c multicolored   .50 .50

University of the West Indies, 25th anniv.

UPU Emblem A45

Designs: 13c, UPU emblem, vert. 14c, UPU emblem. 18c, UPU monument, Bern, vert.

1974, Apr. 23   Perf. 14
358 A45 3c multicolored   .25 .25
359 A45 13c multicolored   .30 .30
360 A45 14c olive bis & multi .30 .30
361 A45 18c multicolored   .35 .35
   a. Souvenir sheet of 4, #358-361 1.30 2.00
        Nos. 358-361 (4)   1.20 1.20

Centenary of Universal Postal Union.

Roseate Spoonbills, Trust Emblem — A46

Protected Birds (National Trust Emblem and): 14c, White-crowned pigeons. 21c, White-tailed tropic birds. 36c, Bahamian parrot.

1974, Sept. 10   Litho.   Perf. 14
362 A46 13c multicolored   1.50 .65
363 A46 14c multicolored   1.50 .55
364 A46 21c multicolored   2.00 1.00
365 A46 36c multicolored   2.50 4.25
   a. Souvenir sheet of 4, #362-365 11.00 11.00
        Nos. 362-365 (4)   7.50 6.45

Bahamas National Trust, 15th anniv.

Holy Family, by Jacques de Stella A47

Christmas: 10c, Virgin and Child, by Girolamo Romanino. 12c, Virgin and Child with St. John and St. Catherine, by Andrea Previtali. 21c, Virgin and Child with Angels, by Previtali.

1974, Oct. 29   Wmk. 314   Perf. 13
366 A47 8c black & multi   .25 .25
367 A47 10c green & multi   .30 .30
368 A47 12c red & multi   .30 .30
369 A47 21c ultra & multi   .40 .40
   a. Souvenir sheet of 4, #366-369 1.75 2.25
        Nos. 366-369 (4)   1.25 1.25

Anteos Maerula A48

14c, Eurema nicippe. 18c, Papilio andraemon. 21c, Euptoieta hegesia.

1975, Feb. 4   Litho.   Perf. 14x13½
370 A48 3c shown   .50 .30
371 A48 14c multicolored   1.40 .75
372 A48 18c multicolored   1.50 .95
373 A48 21c multicolored   1.75 1.40
   a. Souvenir sheet of 4, #370-373 11.00 11.00
        Nos. 370-373 (4)   5.15 3.40

Sheep Raising A49

Designs: 14c, Electric reel fishing, vert. 18c, Growing food. 21c, Crude oil refinery, vert.

Unwmk.
1975, May 27   Litho.   Perf. 14
374 A49 3c dull grn & multi .25 .25
375 A49 14c green & multi   .25 .25
376 A49 18c brown & multi   .25 .25
377 A49 21c vio bl & multi   .80 .45
   a. Souvenir sheet of 4, #374-377 1.40 1.40
        Nos. 374-377 (4)   1.55 1.20

Economic diversification.

Rowena Rand, Staff and Chrismon — A50

Plant and IWY Emblem — A51

Wmk. 373
1975, July 22   Litho.   Perf. 14
378 A50 14c multicolored   .30 .40
379 A51 18c multicolored   .35 .60

International Women's Year.

Adoration of the Shepherds, by Perugino — A52

Christmas: 8c, 18c, Adoration of the Kings, by Ghirlandaio. 21c, like 3c.

1975, Dec. 2   Litho.   Perf. 13½
380 A52 3c dk green & multi .25 .25
381 A52 8c dk violet & multi .25 .25
382 A52 18c purple & multi   .65 .65
383 A52 21c maroon & multi   .70 .70
   a. Souvenir sheet of 4, #380-383 2.50 3.00
        Nos. 380-383 (4)   1.85 1.85

Telephones, 1876 and 1976 — A53

Designs: 16c, Radio-telephone link, Deleporte, Nassau (radar). 21c, Alexander Graham Bell. 25c, Communications satellite.

1976, Mar. 23   Litho.   Perf. 14
384 A53 3c multicolored   .25 .25
385 A53 16c multicolored   .35 .35
386 A53 21c multicolored   .50 .50
387 A53 25c multicolored   .60 .60
        Nos. 384-387 (4)   1.70 1.70

Centenary of first telephone call by Alexander Graham Bell, Mar. 10, 1876.

Bicycling and Olympic Rings — A54

Olympic Rings and: 16c, Long jump. 25c, Sailing. 40c, Boxing.

1976, July 13   Litho.   Perf. 14
388 A54 8c magenta & blue   1.75 .30
389 A54 16c orange & brn   .50 .40
390 A54 25c magenta & blue   .65 .65
391 A54 40c orange & brn   .80 1.00
   a. Souvenir sheet of 4, #388-391 4.00 4.00
        Nos. 388-391 (4)   3.70 2.35

21st Olympic Games, Montreal, Canada, July 17-Aug. 1.

John Murray, Earl of Dunmore A55

Design: 16c, Map of US and Bahamas.

1976, June 1   Wmk. 373   Perf. 14
392 A55 16c multicolored   .45 .45
393 A55 $1 multicolored   1.75 1.75
   a. Souvenir sheet of 4, #393 8.25 9.25

American Bicentennial.

Virgin and Child, Filippo Lippi — A56

Christmas: 21c, Adoration of the Shepherds, School of Seville. 25c, Adoration of the Kings, by Vincenzo Foppa. 40c, Virgin and Child, by Vivarini.

1976, Oct. 19   Litho.   Perf. 14½x14
394 A56 3c brt blue & multi .25 .25
395 A56 21c dp org & multi   .25 .25
396 A56 25c emerald & multi .25 .25
397 A56 40c red lilac & multi .40 .40
   a. Souvenir sheet of 4, #394-397 1.75 1.75
        Nos. 394-397 (4)   1.15 1.15

Type of 1971

16c, Hibiscus. 21c, Breadfruit. 25c, Hawksbill turtle. 40c, Bahamian sponge boat.

1976, Nov. 2   Litho.   Wmk. 373
398 A36 16c emerald & multi 1.40 1.75
399 A36 21c vermilion & multi 1.75 4.25
400 A36 25c brown & multi   2.00 2.10
401 A36 40c vermilion & multi 6.00 3.25
        Nos. 398-401 (4)   11.15 11.35

Elizabeth II Seated under Gold Canopy — A57

16c, Coronation. 21c, Taking and signing of oath. 40c, Queen holding orb and scepter.

1977, Feb. 7   Perf. 12
402 A57 8c silver & multi   .25 .25
403 A57 16c silver & multi   .25 .25
404 A57 21c silver & multi   .25 .25
405 A57 40c silver & multi   .30 .30
   a. Souvenir sheet of 4, #402-405 2.00 2.00
        Nos. 402-405 (4)   1.05 1.05

Reign of Queen Elizabeth II, 25th anniv. For surcharges see Nos. 412-415.

Featherduster — A58

Marine Life: 8c, Porkfish. 16c, Elkhorn coral. 21c, Soft coral and sponge.

1977, May 24   Litho.   Perf. 13½
406 A58 3c multicolored   .65 .40
407 A58 8c multicolored   1.10 .55
408 A58 16c multicolored   1.25 .85
409 A58 21c multicolored   1.40 1.10
   a. Souv. sheet of 4, #406-409, perf 14½ 5.50 5.50
        Nos. 406-409 (4)   4.40 2.90

Campfire and Shower A59

1977, Sept. 27   Litho.   Wmk. 373
410 A59 16c shown   .65 .55
411 A59 21c Boating   1.00 .70

6th Caribbean Jamboree, Kingston, Jamaica, Aug. 5-14.

Nos. 402-405a Overprinted "Royal Visit / October 1977"

1977, Oct. 19   Litho.   Perf. 12
412 A57 8c silver & multi   .25 .25
413 A57 16c silver & multi   .25 .25
414 A57 21c silver & multi   .25 .25
415 A57 40c silver & multi   .35 .35
  a. Souvenir sheet of 4   1.50 2.00
      Nos. 412-415 (4)   1.10 1.10

Caribbean visit of Queen Elizabeth II, Oct. 19-20.

Virgin and Child — A60

Crèche Figurines: 16c, Three Kings. 21c, Adoration of the Kings. 25c, Three Kings.

1977, Oct. 25   Litho.   Perf. 13½
416 A60 3c gold & multi   .25 .25
417 A60 16c gold & multi   .25 .25
418 A60 21c gold & multi   .25 .25
419 A60 25c gold & multi   .30 .25
  a. Souv. sheet #416-419, perf 14½ 1.60 3.25
      Nos. 416-419 (4)   1.05 1.05

Christmas.

Nassau Public Library — A61

Architectural Heritage: 8c, St. Matthew's Church. 16c, Government House. 18c, The Hermitage, Cat Island.

1978, Mar. 28   Litho.   Perf. 14½x14
420 A61 3c black & yel green   .25 .25
421 A61 8c black & lt blue   .25 .25
422 A61 16c black & lilac rose   .25 .25
423 A61 18c black & salmon   .25 .25
  a. Souvenir sheet of 4, #420-423 1.00 1.60
      Nos. 420-423 (4)   1.00 1.00

Scepter, St. Edward's Crown, Orb — A62

Perf. 14x13½
1978, June 27   Litho.   Wmk. 373
424 A62 16c Elizabeth II   .25 .25
425 A62 $1 Elizabeth II   1.00 .55
  a. Souvenir sheet of 2, #424-425 1.75 1.75

Coronation of Queen Elizabeth II, 25th anniv.

Type of 1971

Designs as before and: 16c, Hibiscus. 25c, Hawksbill turtle.

Perf. 14½x14, 14x14½
1978, June   Unwmk.
426 A36 1c blue & multi   1.25 1.40
430 A36 5c dp org & multi   1.90 2.10
436 A36 16c brt grn & multi   2.50 3.00
439 A36 25c brown & multi   10.50 13.50
440 A36 50c lemon & multi   4.50 5.75
441 A36 $1 lemon & multi   4.50 5.75
442 A36 $2 blue & multi   7.50 10.00
443 A36 $3 vio bl & multi   7.50 10.00
      Nos. 426-443 (8)   40.15 51.50

Angels and Palms A63

Christmas: 5c, Coat of arms within wreath, and sailing ships.

Perf. 14x14½
1978, Nov. 14   Litho.   Wmk. 373
444 A63 5c car, pink & gold   .25 .25
445 A63 21c ultra, dk bl & gold   .30 .30
  a. Souvenir sheet of 2, #444-445 4.00 4.00

Baby Walking, IYC Emblem — A64

IYC Emblem and: 16c, Children playing leapfrog. 21c, Girl skipping rope. 25c, Building blocks with "IYC" and emblem.

Perf. 13½x13
1979, May 15   Litho.   Wmk. 373
446 A64 5c multicolored   .25 .25
447 A64 16c multicolored   .30 .30
448 A64 21c multicolored   .50 .50
449 A64 25c multicolored   .60 .60
  a. Souv. sheet #446-449, perf 14 2.00 2.00
      Nos. 446-449 (4)   1.65 1.65

International Year of the Child.

Rowland Hill and Penny Black — A65

21c, Stamp printing press, 1840, Bahamas #7. 25c, Great Britain #27 with 1850's Nassau cancellation, Great Britain #29. 40c, Early mailboat, Bahamas #1.

1979, Aug. 14   Perf. 13½x14
450 A65 10c multicolored   .50 .30
451 A65 21c multicolored   .65 .50
452 A65 25c multicolored   .65 .65
453 A65 40c multicolored   .70 .70
  a. Souvenir sheet of 4, #450-453 2.75 2.75
      Nos. 450-453 (4)   2.50 2.15

Sir Rowland Hill (1795-1879), originator of penny postage.

Commonwealth Plaque over Map of Bahamas — A66

Designs: 21c, Parliament buildings. 25c, Legislative chamber. $1, Senate chamber.

1979, Sept. 27   Litho.   Perf. 13½
454 A66 16c multicolored   .30 .30
455 A66 21c multicolored   .35 .35
456 A66 25c multicolored   .35 .35
457 A66 $1 multicolored   1.40 1.40
  a. Souvenir sheet of 4, #454-457 3.50 3.50
      Nos. 454-457 (4)   2.40 2.40

Parliament of Bahamas, 250th anniv.

Headdress A67

Christmas: Goombay Carnival costumes.

1979, Nov. 6   Litho.   Perf. 13
458 A67 5c multicolored   .25 .25
459 A67 10c multicolored   .25 .25
460 A67 16c multicolored   .25 .25
461 A67 21c multicolored   .25 .25
462 A67 25c multicolored   .30 .25
463 A67 40c multicolored   .45 .40
  a. Souv. sheet, 458-463, perf 13½ 2.50 3.75
      Nos. 458-463 (6)   1.75 1.65

Columbus' Landing, 1492 A68

3c, Blackbeard. 5c, Articles, 1647. Eleuthera map. 10c, Ceremonial mace. 12c, Col. Andrew Deveaux. 15c, Slave trading, Vendue House. 16c, Shipwreck salvage, 19th cent. 18c, Blockade runner, 1860s. 21c, Bootlegging, 1919-1929. 25c, Pineapple cultivation. 40c, Sponge clipping. 50c, Victoria & Colonial Hotels. $1, Modern agriculture. $2, Ship, jet. $3, Central Bank, Arms. $5, Prince Charles, Prime Minister Pindling.

1980, July 9   Perf. 15
464 A68 1c shown   .60 2.40
465 A68 3c multicolored   .25 2.40
466 A68 5c multicolored   .25 1.25
467 A68 10c multicolored   .25   .40
468 A68 12c multicolored   .25 1.90
469 A68 15c multicolored   1.75 1.25
470 A68 16c multicolored   .30 1.25
471 A68 18c multicolored   .35 2.40
472 A68 21c multicolored   .40 2.40
473 A68 25c multicolored   .45 2.40
474 A68 40c multicolored   .70 1.90
475 A68 50c multicolored   .95 1.40
476 A68 $1 multicolored   1.75 4.00
477 A68 $2 multicolored   3.50 5.50
478 A68 $3 multicolored   5.50 3.75
479 A68 $5 multicolored   9.00 5.75
      Nos. 464-479 (16)   26.25 40.35

For overprints and surcharges see Nos. 496-499, 532-535.

1985, Nov. 6   Wmk. 384
464a A68 1c   3.75 2.50
465a A68 3c   5.00 3.50
467a A68 10c   5.50 4.00
473a A68 25c   11.00 9.00
      Nos. 464a-473a (4)   25.25 19.00

Virgin and Child, Straw Figures — A69

1980, Oct. 28   Litho.   Perf. 14½
480 A69 5c shown   .25 .25
481 A69 21c Three kings   .35 .35
482 A69 25c Angel   .30 .25
483 A69 $1 Christmas tree   1.00 .90
  a. Souvenir sheet of 4, #480-483 1.75 2.50
      Nos. 480-483 (4)   1.80 1.75

Christmas.

Man with Crutch, Sun Rays A70

1981, Feb. 10   Litho.   Perf. 14½
484 A70 5c shown   .25 .25
485 A70 $1 Man in wheelchair   1.25 1.25
  a. Souvenir sheet of 2, #484-485 1.75 2.50

International Year of the Disabled.

Grand Bahama Tracking Station A71

Satellite Views: 20c, Bahamas. 25c, Eleuthera. 50c, Andros and New Providence.

1981, Apr. 21   Litho.   Wmk. 373   Perf. 13½
486 A71 10c multi   .25 .25
487 A71 20c multi, vert.   .40 .40
488 A71 25c multi   .60 .60
489 A71 50c multi, vert.   1.25 1.25
  a. Souvenir sheet of 4, #486-489 2.75 2.75
      Nos. 486-489 (4)   2.50 2.50

ROYAL WEDDING

Prince Charles and Lady Diana — A72

$2, Charles, Prime Minister.

Wmk. 373
1981, July 22   Litho.   Perf. 14½
490 A72 30c shown   .40 .25
491 A72 $2 multicolored   3.75 1.75
  a. Souvenir sheet of 2, #490-491 7.25 3.25

Royal wedding.

Bahama Ducks A73

20c, Reddish egrets. 25c, Brown boobies. $1, West Indian tree ducks.

Wmk. 373
1981, Aug. 25   Litho.   Perf. 14
492 A73 5c shown   1.40 .75
493 A73 20c multicolored   2.50 1.00
494 A73 25c multicolored   2.50 1.25
495 A73 $1 multicolored   4.50 4.50
  a. Souvenir sheet of 4, #492-495 11.00 11.00
      Nos. 492-495 (4)   10.90 7.50

See Nos. 514-517.

Nos. 466-467, 473, 475 Overprinted:"COMMONWEALTH FINANCE MINISTERS' MEETING 21-23 SEPTEMBER 1981"

1981, Sept.   Litho.   Perf. 15
496 A68 5c multicolored   .35 .35
497 A68 10c multicolored   .35 .35
498 A68 25c multicolored   .60 .60
499 A68 50c multicolored   1.25 1.25
      Nos. 496-499 (4)   2.55 2.55

World Food Day A74

Perf. 13x13½

1981, Oct. 16   **Wmk. 373**

500	A74	5c Chickens	.25	.25
501	A74	20c Sheep	.30	.30
502	A74	30c Lobster	.50	.50
503	A74	50c Pigs	1.00	1.00
a.		Souvenir sheet of 4, #500-503	3.25	3.25
		Nos. 500-503 (4)	2.05	2.05

Christmas — A75

Wmk. 373

1981, Nov. 23   **Litho.**   **Perf. 14**

504		Sheet of 9	7.25	7.25
a.		5c Father Christmas	.50	.50
b.		5c shown	.50	.50
c.		5c St. Nicholas, Holland	.50	.50
d.		25c Lussibruden, Sweden	.75	.75
e.		25c Mother and child	.75	.75
f.		25c King Wenceslas, Czechoslovakia	.75	.75
g.		30c Mother and child	.75	.75
h.		30c Mother and child standing	.75	.75
i.		$1 Christkindl angel, Germany	1.60	1.60

TB Bacillus Centenary A76

1982, Feb. 3   **Litho.**   **Perf. 14**

505	A76	5c Koch	.70	.70
506	A76	16c X-ray	1.40	1.40
507	A76	21c Microscopes	1.60	1.60
508	A76	$1 Mantoux test	3.25	3.25
a.		Souv. sheet, #505-508, perf 14½	7.50	7.50
		Nos. 505-508 (4)	6.95	6.95

Flamingoes A77

Designs: a, Females. b, Males. c, Nesting. d, Juvenile birds. e, Immature birds. No. 509 in continuous design.

Wmk. 373

1982, Apr. 28   **Litho.**   **Perf. 14**

509		Strip of 5	12.00	12.00
a.-e.		A77 25c any single	2.25	2.25

Princess Diana Issue
Common Design Type

1982, July 1   **Litho.**   **Perf. 14**

510	CD333	16c Arms	.55	.25
511	CD333	25c Diana	1.10	.60
512	CD333	40c Wedding	1.60	1.00
513	CD333	$1 Portrait	2.75	2.00
		Nos. 510-513 (4)	6.00	3.85

Bird Type of 1981

1982, Aug. 18   **Wmk. 373**
Litho.   **Perf. 14**

514	A73	10c Bat	1.00	.35
515	A73	16c Hutia	1.40	.45
516	A73	21c Racoon	1.60	.90
517	A73	$1 Dolphins	4.25	2.40
a.		Souvenir sheet of 4, #514-517	8.50	8.50
		Nos. 514-517 (4)	8.25	4.10

28th Commonwealth Parliamentary Conference A78

Perf. 14x13½

1982, Oct. 16   **Litho.**   **Wmk. 373**

518	A78	5c Plaque	.25	.25
519	A78	25c Assoc. arms	.65	.65
520	A78	40c Natl. arms	1.00	1.00
521	A78	50c House of Assembly	1.25	1.25
		Nos. 518-521 (4)	3.15	3.15

Christmas A79

Designs: 5c, Wesley Methodist Church, Baillou Hill Road. 12c, Centerville Seventh Day Adventist Church. 15c, Church of God of Prophecy, East Street. 21c, Bethel Baptist Church, Meeting Street. 25c, St. Francis Xavier Catholic Church, West Hill Street. $1, Holy Cross Anglican Church, Highbury Park.

1982, Nov. 3   **Perf. 14**

522	A79	5c multicolored	.25	.25
523	A79	12c multicolored	.25	.25
524	A79	15c multicolored	.30	.30
525	A79	21c multicolored	.40	.40
526	A79	25c multicolored	.40	.40
527	A79	$1 multicolored	1.40	1.40
		Nos. 522-527 (6)	3.00	3.00

A80

1983, Mar. 14   **Litho.**

528	A80	5c Lynden O. Pindling	.25	.25
529	A80	25c Flags	.50	.50
530	A80	35c Map	.50	.50
531	A80	$1 Ocean liner	1.35	1.35
		Nos. 528-531 (4)	2.60	2.60

Commonwealth Day.

Nos. 469-472 Surcharged

1983, Apr. 5   **Litho.**   **Perf. 15**

532	A68	20c on 15c multi	.60	.60
533	A68	31c on 21c multi	.70	.70
534	A68	35c on 16c multi	1.50	1.50
535	A68	80c on 18c multi	2.10	2.10
		Nos. 532-535 (4)	4.90	4.90

30th Anniv. of Customs Cooperation Council — A81

Perf. 14x13½

1983, May 31   **Wmk. 373**

536	A81	31c Officers, ship	1.75	.55
537	A81	$1 Officers, jet	3.50	2.40

10th Anniv. of Independence A82

1983, July 6   **Litho.**   **Perf. 14**

538	A82	$1 Flag raising	1.50	1.50
a.		Souvenir sheet, perf. 12	2.25	2.25

Local Butterflies A83

5c, Carters skipper. 25c, Giant southern white. 31c, Large orange sulphur. 50c, Flambeau.

1983, Aug. 24   **Perf. 14½x14**

539	A83	5c multicolored	1.40	.30
540	A83	25c multicolored	2.60	.55
541	A83	31c multicolored	2.60	.85
542	A83	50c multicolored	2.75	1.40
a.		Souvenir sheet of 4	10.00	10.00
		Nos. 539-542 (4)	9.35	3.10

No. 542a contains Nos. 539-542, perf. 14 and perf. 14½x14.

American Loyalists Arrival Bicentenary — A84

Paintings by Alton Lowe: 5c, Loyalist Dreams, vert. 31c, New Plymouth, Abaco. 35c, New Plymouth Hotel. 50c, Island Hope, vert.

1983, Sept. 28   **Perf. 14**

543	A84	5c multicolored	.25	.25
544	A84	31c multicolored	.55	.55
545	A84	35c multicolored	.65	.65
546	A84	50c multicolored	.90	.90
a.		Souvenir sheet of 4, #543-546	2.25	2.25
		Nos. 543-546 (4)	2.35	2.35

Christmas — A85

Children's designs: 5c, Christmas Bells, by Monica Pinder. 20c, The Flamingo by Cory Bullard. 25c, The Yellow Hibiscus with Christmas Candle by Monique A. Bailey. 31c, Santa goes a Sailing by Sabrina Seiler, horiz. 35c, Silhouette scene with palm trees by James Blake. 50c, Silhouette scene with Pelicans, by Erik Russell, horiz.

1983, Nov. 1   **Perf. 14**

547	A85	5c multicolored	.25	.25
548	A85	20c multicolored	.40	.40
549	A85	25c multicolored	.50	.50
550	A85	31c multicolored	.65	.65
551	A85	35c multicolored	.75	.75
552	A85	50c multicolored	.90	.90
		Nos. 547-552 (6)	3.45	3.45

125th Anniv. of Bahamas Stamps — A86

1984, Feb. 22   **Litho.**   **Perf. 14**

553	A86	5c No. 3	.25	.25
554	A86	$1 No. 1	2.25	2.25

Lloyd's List Issue
Common Design Type

5c, Trent. 31c, Orinoco. 35c, Nassau Harbor. 50c, Container ship Oropesa.

Wmk. 373

1984, Apr. 25   **Litho.**   **Perf. 14½**

555	CD335	5c multicolored	.50	.25
556	CD335	31c multicolored	.90	.60
557	CD335	35c multicolored	1.15	.70
558	CD335	50c multicolored	1.60	1.40
		Nos. 555-558 (4)	4.15	2.95

1984 Summer Olympics A87

1984, June 20   **Litho.**   **Perf. 14x14½**

559	A87	5c Running	.30	.30
560	A87	25c Discus	.60	.60
561	A87	31c Boxing	.60	.60
562	A87	$1 Basketball	4.25	4.25
a.		Souvenir sheet of 4, #559-562	6.50	6.50
		Nos. 559-562 (4)	5.75	5.75

Flags of Bahamas and Caribbean Community — A88

Wmk. 373

1984, July 4   **Litho.**   **Perf. 14**

563	A88	50c multicolored	1.15	1.15

Conference of Heads of Government of Caribbean Community, 5th Meeting.

Allen's Cay Iguana A89

25c, Curly-tailed lizard. 35c, Greenhouse frog. 50c, Atlantic green turtle.

1984, Aug. 15   **Perf. 14**

564	A89	5c shown	.45	.25
565	A89	25c multicolored	2.10	.75
566	A89	35c multicolored	2.60	1.10
567	A89	50c multicolored	2.75	2.75
a.		Souvenir sheet of 4, #564-567	8.75	8.75
		Nos. 564-567 (4)	7.90	4.85

25th Anniv. of Natl. Trust — A90

Wildlife: a, Calliphlox evelynae. b, Megaceryle alcyon, Eleutherodactylus planirostris. c, Phoebis sennae, Phoenicopterus ruber, Himantopus himantopus, Phoebus sennae. d, Urbanus proteus, Chelonia mydas. e, Pandion haliaetus.
Continuous design.

1984, Aug. 15   Litho.   Perf. 14
568   Strip of 5   19.00 19.00
a.-e. A90 31c any single   3.75 3.75

Christmas — A91

Madonna and Child Paintings.

1984, Nov. 7   Litho.   Perf. 13½x13
569 A91 5c Titian   .50   .40
570 A91 31c Anais Colin   1.40 1.25
571 A91 35c Elena Caula   1.60 1.40
a.   Souvenir sheet of 3, #569-571 2.50 2.50
        Nos. 569-571 (3)   3.50 3.05

Girl Guides, 75th Anniv., Intl. Youth Year A92

1985, Feb. 22   Litho.   Perf. 14
572 A92 5c Brownies   .70   .40
573 A92 25c Camping   1.40   .85
574 A92 31c Girl Guides   1.75 1.10
575 A92 35c Rangers   2.25 1.60
a.   Souvenir sheet of 4, #572-575 6.75 6.75
        Nos. 572-575 (4)   6.10 3.95

Audubon Birth Bicentenary — A93

5c, Killdeer. 31c, Mourning dove, vert. 35c, Mourning doves, diff., vert. $1, Killdeers, diff.

Wmk. 373
1985, Apr. 24   Litho.   Perf. 14
576 A93 5c multicolored   1.10   .85
577 A93 31c multicolored   2.50   .85
578 A93 35c multicolored   2.50 1.00
579 A93 $1 multicolored   4.75 4.75
        Nos. 576-579 (4)   10.85 7.45

Queen Mother 85th Birthday
Common Design Type

5c, Portrait, 1927. 25c, At christening of Peter Phillips. 35c, Portrait, 1985. 50c, Holding Prince Henry.
$1.25, In a pony and trap.

Perf. 14½x14
1985, June 7   Litho.   Wmk. 384
580 CD336 5c multicolored   .40   .25
581 CD336 25c multicolored   .80   .45
582 CD336 35c multicolored   .90   .65
583 CD336 50c multicolored   1.60 1.60
        Nos. 580-583 (4)   3.70 2.95

Souvenir Sheet
584 CD336 $1.25 multicolored   4.00 3.50

UN and UN Food and Agriculture Org., 40th Annivs. — A94

Wmk. 373
1985, Aug. 26   Litho.   Perf. 14
585 A94 25c Wheat, emblems   1.10 1.10

Commonwealth Heads of Government Meeting, 1985 — A95

31c, Queen Elizabeth II. 35c, Flag, Commonwealth emblem.

1985, Oct. 16   Wmk. 373   Perf. 14½
586 A95 31c multicolored   3.00 3.00
587 A95 35c multicolored   3.00 3.00

Christmas A96

Paintings by Alton Roland Lowe: 5c, Grandma's Christmas Bouquet. 25c, Junkanoo Romeo and Juliet, vert. 31c, Bunce Girl, vert. 35c, Home for Christmas.

1985, Nov. 5   Perf. 13
588 A96 5c multicolored   .70   .90
589 A96 25c multicolored   1.60 1.10
590 A96 31c multicolored   1.90 1.40
591 A96 35c multicolored   1.90 1.90
a.   Souv. sheet, #588-591, perf 14 5.50 5.50
        Nos. 588-591 (4)   6.10 4.80

Queen Elizabeth II 60th Birthday
Common Design Type

Designs: 10c, Age 1, 1927. 25c, Coronation, Westminster Abbey, 1953. 35c, Giving speech, royal visit, Bahamas. 40c, At Djakova, Yugoslavia, state visit, 1972. $1, Visiting Crown Agents, 1983.

1986, Apr. 21   Wmk. 384   Perf. 14½
592 CD337 10c scar, blk & sil   .25   .30
593 CD337 25c ultra & multi   .80   .40
594 CD337 35c green & multi   .45   .60
595 CD337 40c violet & multi   .50   .65
596 CD337 $1 rose vio & multi   1.25 1.75
        Nos. 592-596 (5)   2.75 3.70

AMERIPEX '86 — A97

1986, May 19   Perf. 14
597 A97 5c Nos. 464, 471   1.10   .45
598 A97 25c Nos. 288-289   2.40   .45
599 A97 31c No. 392   2.60   .60
600 A97 50c No. 489a   3.50 3.00
601 A97 $1 Statue of Liberty, vert.
                                       4.25 4.75
a.   Souvenir sheet of one   8.00 8.00
        Nos. 597-601 (5)   13.85 9.25

Statue of Liberty, cent.

Royal Wedding Issue, 1986
Common Design Type

Designs: 10c, Formal engagement. $1, Andrew in dress uniform.

1986, July 23   Perf. 14½x14
602 CD338 10c multicolored   .25   .25
603 CD338 $1 multicolored   2.50 2.50

Fish A98

5c, Rock beauty. 10c, Stoplight parrotfish. 15c, Jacknife fish. 20c, Flamefish. 25c, Swissguard basslet. 30c, Spotfin butterflyfish. 35c, Queen triggerfish. 40c, Four-eyed butterflyfish. 45c, Fairy basslet. 50c, Queen angelfish. 60c, Blue chromis. $1, Spanish hogfish. $2, Harlequin bass. $3, Blackbar soldierfish. $5, Pygmy angelfish. $10, Red hind.

1986-87   Wmk. 384   Perf. 14
604 A98 5c multi   1.10   .60
605 A98 10c multi   1.10   .65
606 A98 15c multi   1.90 1.40
607 A98 20c multi   1.75 1.40
608 A98 25c multi   2.10 1.40
609 A98 30c multi   1.50 1.40
610 A98 35c multi   1.75 2.10
611 A98 40c multi   1.75 1.50
612 A98 45c multi   1.90 1.25
613 A98 50c multi   2.75 2.75
614 A98 60c multi   3.00 4.25
615 A98 $1 multi   3.75 3.00
616 A98 $2 multi   4.00 6.75
617 A98 $3 multi   7.75 6.00
618 A98 $5 multi   8.75 7.75
618A A99 $10 multi ('87)   21.00 19.00
        Nos. 604-618A (16)   65.85 61.20

Issue dates: $10, Jan. 2, others, Aug. 5.

1988, Aug. 15   Inscribed "1988"
611a A98 40c   2.50 2.50
615a A98 $1   5.50 5.50
616a A98 $2   25.00 20.00
        Nos. 611a-616a (3)   33.00 28.00

1990, Aug.   Inscribed "1990"
605b A98 10c   2.00 2.50
608b A98 25c   2.25 2.50
611b A98 40c
612b A98 45c   2.75 3.00
613b A98 50c   3.50 3.00
615b A98 $1
617b A98 $3   8.00 15.00
618b A98 $5   11.00 16.00
        Nos. 605b-618b (6)   29.50 42.00

1987, June 25   Wmk. 373
Inscribed "1987"
604c   5c   .80 1.00
d.   Inscribed "1989"
605c   10c   .90   .45
d.   Inscribed "1988"
606c   15c   1.00   .60
611c   40c   2.50 1.25
612c   45c   3.00 1.75
613c   50c   3.25 2.00
614c   60c   3.75 2.25
615c $1   6.50 4.25
616c $2   12.00 8.00
        Nos. 604c-616c (9)   33.70 21.55

Christ Church Cathedral — A99

Wmk. 373
1986, Sept. 16   Litho.   Perf. 14½
619 A99 10c View, 19th cent.   .45   .40
620 A99 40c View, 1986   1.00   .90
a.   Souvenir sheet of 2, #619-620 5.00 5.00

City of Nassau, Diocese of Nassau and the Bahamas and Christ Church, 125th anniv.

Christmas, Intl. Peace Year A100

10c, Nativity. 40c, Flight to Egypt. 45c, Children praying. 50c, Exchanging gifts.

Wmk. 384
1986, Nov. 4   Litho.   Perf. 14
621 A100 10c multicolored   .45   .25
622 A100 40c multicolored   1.30 1.00
623 A100 45c multicolored   1.50 1.40
624 A100 50c multicolored   1.90 2.25
a.   Souvenir sheet of 4, #621-624
                                      10.00 10.00
        Nos. 621-624 (4)   5.15 4.90

Pirates of the Caribbean — A101

A102

10c, Anne Bonney. 40c, Blackbeard (d. 1718). 45c, Capt. Edward England. 50c, Capt. Woodes Rogers (c. 1679-1732).
$1.25, Map of the Bahamas.

Wmk. 373
1987, June 2   Litho.   Perf. 14½
625 A101 10c multi   3.50 1.60
626 A101 40c multi   7.75 7.75
627 A101 45c multi   7.75 5.00
628 A101 50c multi   8.25 8.25
        Nos. 625-628 (4)   27.25 22.60

Souvenir Sheet
629 A102 $1.25 multi   16.00 16.00

Paintings of Lighthouses by Alton Roland Lowe A103

1987, Mar. 31   Wmk. 384
630 A103 10c Great Isaac   4.25 1.25
631 A103 40c Bird Rock   7.50 1.75
632 A103 45c Castle Is.   8.25 1.90
633 A103 $1 Hole in the Wall   12.50 12.50
        Nos. 630-633 (4)   32.50 17.40

Tourist Transportation A104

Ships: No. 634a, Cruise ship, sailboat. b, Cruise ships, tugboat, speedboat. c, Pleasure boat leaving harbor, sailboat. d, Pleasure boat docked, sailboats. e, Sailboats.
Aircraft: No. 635a, Bahamasair plane. b, Bahamasair and Pan Am aircraft. c, Aircraft, radar tower. d, Control tower, aircraft. e, Helicopter, planes.

1987, Aug. 26   Wmk. 373   Perf. 14
634   Strip of 5   13.50 13.50
a.-e. A104 40c any single   2.50 2.50
635   Strip of 5   13.50 13.50
a.-e. A104 40c any single   2.50 2.50

Orchids
Painted by
Alton Roland
Lowe
A105

10c, Cattleyopis lindenii. 40c, Encyclia lucayana. 45c, Encyclia hodgeana. 50c, Encyclia lleidae.

1987, Oct. 20   Wmk. 384   Perf. 14½
636	A105	10c multicolored	2.25	.85
637	A105	40c multicolored	4.25	1.40
638	A105	45c multicolored	4.25	1.40
639	A105	50c multicolored	4.25	4.25
a.		Souvenir sheet of 4, #636-639	15.00	15.00
		Nos. 636-639 (4)	15.00	7.90

Christmas.

Discovery of
America, 500th
Anniv. (in
1992) — A106

10c, Ferdinand & Isabella. 40c, Columbus before the Talavera Committee. 45c, Lucayan village. 50c, Lucayan potters. $1.50, Map, c. 1500.

Perf. 14x14½
1988, Feb. 23   Litho.   Wmk. 373
640	A106	10c multicolored	1.40	1.00
641	A106	40c multicolored	2.50	2.50
642	A106	45c multicolored	3.00	3.00
643	A106	50c multicolored	3.00	3.00
		Nos. 640-643 (4)	9.90	9.50

Souvenir Sheet
644	A106	$1.50 multicolored	11.00	11.00

See Nos. 663-667, 688-692, 725-729, 749-753, 762.

World
Wildlife
Fund
A107

Whistling ducks, Dendrocygna arborea: 5c, Ducks in flight. 10c, Among marine plants. 20c, Adults, ducklings. 45c, Wading.

1988, Apr. 29   Perf. 14½
645	A107	5c multi	3.25	1.25
646	A107	10c multi	3.75	1.25
647	A107	20c multi	6.00	1.50
648	A107	45c multi	9.25	2.75
		Nos. 645-648 (4)	22.25	6.75

Abolition of
Slavery,
150th Anniv.
A108

10c, African hut. 40c, Basket weavers in hut, Grantstown.

1988, Aug. 9   Perf. 14
649	A108	10c multicolored	.75	.50
650	A108	40c multicolored	2.00	1.40

1988
Summer
Olympics,
Seoul
A109

Games emblem and details of painting by James Martin: 10c, Olympic flame, high jump,

hammer throw, basketball and gymnastics. 40c, Swimming, boxing, weight lifting, archery and running. 45c, Gymnastics, shot put and javelin. $1, Running, cycling and gymnastics.

Wmk. 384
1988, Aug. 30   Litho.   Perf. 14
651	A109	10c multicolored	.90	.40
652	A109	40c multicolored	1.25	.55
653	A109	45c multicolored	1.25	.55
654	A109	$1 multicolored	4.50	4.50
a.		Souvenir sheet of 4, #651-654	8.75	8.75
		Nos. 651-654 (4)	7.90	6.00

Lloyds of London, 300th Anniv.
Common Design Type

Designs: 10c, Lloyds List No. 560, 1740. 40c, Freeport Harbor, horiz. 45c, Space shuttle over the Bahamas, horiz. $1, Supply ship Yarmouth Castle on fire.

1988, Oct. 4   Wmk. 373
655	CD341	10c multicolored	.65	.45
656	CD341	40c multicolored	2.25	.75
657	CD341	45c multicolored	2.25	.75
658	CD341	$1 multicolored	3.75	3.00
		Nos. 655-658 (4)	8.90	4.95

Christmas
Carols — A110

Designs: 10c, O' Little Town of Bethlehem. 40c, Little Donkey. 45c, Silent Night. 50c, Hark! The Herald Angels Sing.

1988, Nov. 21   Wmk. 384   Perf. 14½
659	A110	10c multicolored	.80	.30
660	A110	40c multicolored	2.10	.75
661	A110	45c multicolored	2.25	.90
662	A110	50c multicolored	2.50	2.50
a.		Souvenir sheet of 4, #659-662	5.50	5.50
		Nos. 659-662 (4)	7.65	4.45

Discovery of America Type

Design: 10c, Columbus as chartmaker. 40c, Development of the caravel. 45c, Navigational tools. 50c, Arawak artifacts. $1.50, Caravel under construction, an illumination from the Nuremburg Chronicles, 15th cent.

Perf. 14½x14
1989, Jan. 25   Litho.   Wmk. 373
663	A106	10c multicolored	2.40	.65
664	A106	40c multicolored	3.50	1.25
665	A106	45c multicolored	3.50	1.25
666	A106	50c multicolored	3.50	3.50
		Nos. 663-666 (4)	12.90	6.65

Souvenir Sheet
667	A106	$1.50 multicolored	6.75	6.75

Hummingbirds
A111

10c, Cuban emerald. 40c, Ruby-throated. 45c, Bahama woodstar. 50c, Rufous.

Wmk. 384
1989, Mar. 29   Litho.   Perf. 14½
668	A111	10c multi	3.00	1.60
669	A111	40c multi	4.50	2.50
670	A111	45c multi	5.00	2.50
671	A111	50c multi	6.00	6.00
		Nos. 668-671 (4)	18.50	12.60

Intl. Red Cross and Red Crescent
Organizations, 125th Annivs. — A112

1989, May 31   Perf. 14x14½
672	A112	10c Water safety	2.50	.85
673	A112	$1 Dunant, Battle of Solferino	5.75	3.50

Moon Landing, 20th Anniv.
Common Design Type

Apollo 8: 10c, Apollo Communications System, Grand Bahama Is. 40c, James Lovell Jr., William Anders and Frank Borman. 45c, Mission emblem. $1, The Rising Earth (photograph). $2, Astronaut practicing lunar surface activities at Manned Spacecraft Center, Houston, in training for Apollo 11 mission.

1989, July 20   Perf. 14x13½
Size of Nos. 674-675: 29x29mm
674	CD342	10c multicolored	1.60	.65
675	CD342	40c multicolored	2.40	1.40
676	CD342	45c multicolored	2.75	1.40
677	CD342	$1 multicolored	4.25	4.25
		Nos. 674-677 (4)	11.00	7.70

Souvenir Sheet
678	CD342	$2 multicolored	12.00	12.00

Christmas
A113

Designs: 10c, Church of the Nativity, Bethlehem. 40c, Basilica of the Annunciation, Nazareth. 45c, By the Sea of Galilee, Tabgha. $1, Church of the Holy Sepulcher, Jerusalem.

Perf. 14½x14
1989, Oct. 16   Wmk. 373
679	A113	10c multicolored	1.25	.35
680	A113	40c multicolored	2.10	.65
681	A113	45c multicolored	2.10	.65
682	A113	$1 multicolored	5.25	5.25
a.		Souvenir sheet of 4, #679-682	12.00	12.00
		Nos. 679-682 (4)	10.70	6.90

World
Stamp
Expo '89
A114

Expo emblem and: 10c, Earth, #359. 40c, UPU Headquarters, #301. 45c, US Capitol, #601. $1, Passenger jet, #150. $2, Washington, DC, on map.

1989, Nov. 17   Wmk. 384   Perf. 14
683	A114	10c multicolored	.90	.40
684	A114	40c multicolored	2.10	.70
685	A114	45c multicolored	2.10	.75
686	A114	$1 multicolored	7.00	7.00
		Nos. 683-686 (4)	12.10	8.85

Souvenir Sheet
Perf. 14½x14
687	A114	$2 multicolored	12.50	12.50

No. 687 contains one 31x38mm stamp.

Discovery of America Type of 1988

10c, Caravel launch. 40c, Provisioning ships. 45c, Shortening sails. 50c, Lucayan fishermen. $1.50, Columbus's fleet departing from Cadiz.

Perf. 14½x14
1990, Jan. 24   Litho.   Wmk. 373
688	A106	10c multicolored	2.25	.85
689	A106	40c multicolored	2.25	1.60
690	A106	45c multicolored	2.75	1.60
691	A106	50c multicolored	2.75	3.50
		Nos. 688-691 (4)	10.00	7.55

Souvenir Sheet
692	A106	$1.50 multicolored	9.00	9.00

Organization of American States,
Cent. — A115

1990, Mar. 14   Wmk. 384   Perf. 14
693	A115	40c multicolored	3.25	3.25

Souvenir Sheet

Stamp World London '90 — A116

Aircraft: a, Spitfire I. b, Hurricane IIc.

1990, May 3   Wmk. 384
694	A116	Sheet of 2	14.00	14.00
a.-b.		$1 any single	4.75	4.75

For surcharge see No. B3.

Intl.
Literacy
Year
A117

10c, Teacher helping student. 40c, Children reading to each other. 50c, Children reading aloud.

1990, June 27   Wmk. 384   Perf. 14
695	A117	10c multicolored	2.00	.45
696	A117	40c multicolored	2.50	1.40
697	A117	50c multicolored	2.50	4.50
		Nos. 695-697 (3)	7.00	6.35

Queen Mother, 90th Birthday
Common Design Types

40c, Portrait, c. 1938. $1.50, At garden party, 1938.

1990, Aug. 4   Perf. 14x15
698	CD343	40c multicolored	1.25	1.25

Perf. 14½
699	CD344	$1.50 multicolored	4.00	4.00

Bahamian
Parrot — A118

40c, In flight. 45c, Head. 50c, On branch. $1.50, On branch with flowers.

1990, Sept. 26   Wmk. 373   Perf. 14
700	A118	10c shown	1.75	.60
701	A118	40c multicolored	3.25	1.25
702	A118	45c multicolored	3.50	1.25
703	A118	50c multicolored	4.00	4.00
		Nos. 700-703 (4)	12.50	7.10

Souvenir Sheet
704	A118	$1.50 multicolored	13.00	13.00

Christmas
A119

10c, Angel appears to Mary. 40c, Nativity. 45c, Angel appears to shepherds. $1, Three kings.

Wmk. 373
1990, Nov. 5   Litho.   Perf. 13½

705	A119	10c multi	1.00	.55
706	A119	40c multi	1.60	.65
707	A119	45c multi	1.60	.65
708	A119	$1 multi	4.50	4.50
a.		Souvenir sheet of 4, #705-708	16.00	16.00
		Nos. 705-708 (4)	8.70	6.35

Birds — A120

5c, Green heron. 10c, Turkey vulture. 15c, Osprey. 20c, Clapper rail. 25c, Royal tern. 30c, Key West quail dove. 40c, Smooth-billed ani. 45c, Burrowing owl. 50c, Hairy woodpecker. 55c, Mangrove cuckoo. 60c, Bahama mockingbird. 70c, Red-winged blackbird. $1, Thick-billed vireo. $2, Bahama yellowthroat. $5, Stripe-headed tanager. $10, Greater Antillean bullfinch.

Wmk. 384
1991, Feb. 4   Litho.   Perf. 14

709	A120	5c multi	1.90	1.90
710	A120	10c multi	2.25	2.25
711	A120	15c multi	1.75	.70
712	A120	20c multi	2.25	.80
713	A120	25c multi	1.40	.70
714	A120	30c multi	3.75	.80
715	A120	40c multi	4.00	.70
716	A120	45c multi	6.00	.80
717	A120	50c multi	4.75	.80
718	A120	55c multi	4.00	.80
719	A120	60c multi	4.50	.80
720	A120	70c multi	4.50	1.75
721	A120	$1 multi	5.25	1.50
722	A120	$2 multi	11.50	8.25
723	A120	$5 multi	14.50	10.50
724	A120	$10 multi	27.50	17.00
		Nos. 709-724 (16)	99.80	50.05

Issued: $10, 7/1/91; others, 2/4/91.

1993   Dated "1993"   Wmk. 373

710a	10c multicolored	.45	.45
713a	25c multicolored	1.10	1.10
714a	30c multicolored	1.40	1.40
715a	40c multicolored	1.75	1.75
718a	55c multicolored	2.50	2.50
723a	$5 multicolored	22.50	22.50
	Nos. 710a-723a (6)	29.70	29.70

Issued: 40c, 12/31/93; others, 9/23/93.

1995   Dated "1995"

711b	15c multicolored	1.75	.75
713b	25c multicolored	1.10	1.10
715b	40c multicolored	2.50	2.50
718b	55c multicolored	2.50	2.50
723b	$5 multicolored	14.50	14.50
	Nos. 711b-723b (5)	22.35	21.35

Discovery of America Type

Designs: 15c, Columbus practices celestial navigation. 40c, The fleet in rough seas. 55c, Natives on the beach. 60c, Map of voyage. $1.50, Pinta's crew sights land.

Perf. 14½x14
1991, Apr. 9   Litho.   Wmk. 384

725	A106	15c multicolored	1.90	.80
726	A106	40c multicolored	3.25	2.00
727	A106	55c multicolored	3.50	2.40
728	A106	60c multicolored	4.25	4.25
		Nos. 725-728 (4)	12.90	9.45

Souvenir Sheet

729	A106	$1.50 multicolored	13.00	13.00

Elizabeth & Philip, Birthdays
Common Design Types
Wmk. 384
1991, June 17   Litho.   Perf. 14½

730	CD346	15c multicolored	1.25	1.25
731	CD345	$1 multicolored	2.75	2.75
a.		Pair, #730-731 + label	4.00	4.00

Hurricane Awareness — A121

Designs: 15c, Weather radar image of Hurricane Hugo. 40c, Anatomy of hurricane rotating around eye. 55c, Flooding caused by Hurricane David. 60c, Lockheed WP-3D Orion.

1991, Aug. 28   Perf. 14

732	A121	15c multicolored	1.75	.55
733	A121	40c multicolored	2.60	1.50
734	A121	55c multicolored	3.25	2.40
735	A121	60c multicolored	4.00	4.00
		Nos. 732-735 (4)	11.60	8.45

Christmas
A122

Designs: 15c, The Annunciation. 55c, Mary and Joseph traveling to Bethlehem. 60c, Angel appearing to shepherds. $1, Adoration of the Magi.

1991, Oct. 28   Wmk. 373   Perf. 14

736	A122	15c multicolored	.80	.30
737	A122	55c multicolored	2.10	.90
738	A122	60c multicolored	2.25	1.25
739	A122	$1 multicolored	3.50	3.50
a.		Souvenir sheet of 4, #736-739	11.00	11.00
		Nos. 736-739 (4)	8.65	5.95

Majority Rule, 25th Anniv.
A123

Designs: 15c, First Progressive Liberal Party cabinet. 40c, Signing of Independence Constitution. 55c, Handing over constitutional instrument, vert. 60c, First Bahamian Governor-General, Sir Milo Butler, vert.

Wmk. 373
1992, Jan. 10   Litho.   Perf. 14

740	A123	15c multicolored	1.00	.55
741	A123	40c multicolored	2.00	1.60
742	A123	55c multicolored	2.10	2.10
743	A123	60c multicolored	2.50	3.00
		Nos. 740-743 (4)	7.60	7.25

Queen Elizabeth II's Accession to the Throne, 40th Anniv.
Common Design Type
Wmk. 373
1992, Feb. 6   Litho.   Perf. 14

744	CD349	15c multicolored	.75	.30
745	CD349	40c multicolored	1.25	.55
746	CD349	55c multicolored	1.25	.70
747	CD349	60c multicolored	1.75	1.25
748	CD349	$1 multicolored	1.90	1.90
		Nos. 744-748 (5)	6.90	4.70

Discovery of America Type

Designs: 15c, Lucayans first sight of fleet. 40c, Approaching Bahamas coastline. 55c, Lucayans about to meet Columbus. 60c, Columbus gives thanks for safe arrival. $1.50, Monument to Columbus' landing.

Perf. 14½x14
1992, Mar. 17   Wmk. 384

749	A106	15c multicolored	1.50	.80
750	A106	40c multicolored	2.10	1.60

751	A106	55c multicolored	2.25	2.10
752	A106	60c multicolored	2.50	3.25
		Nos. 749-752 (4)	8.35	7.75

Souvenir Sheet

753	A106	$1.50 multicolored	6.00	6.00

Templeton, Galbraith and Hansberger Ltd. Building — A124

Wmk. 384
1992, Apr. 22   Litho.   Perf. 14½

754	A124	55c multicolored	2.25	2.25

Templeton Prize for Progress in Religion, 20th Anniv.

1992 Summer Olympics, Barcelona
A125

Perf. 14½x14
1992, June 2   Wmk. 373

755	A125	15c Pole vault	.75	.35
756	A125	40c Javelin	1.10	.90
757	A125	55c Hurdling	1.40	1.40
758	A125	60c Basketball	6.75	6.00
		Nos. 755-758 (4)	10.00	8.65

Souvenir Sheet

759	A125	$2 Sailing	9.50	9.50

Intl. Conference on Nutrition — A126

15c, Drought-affected earth, starving child. 55c, Hand holding plant, stalks of grain.

Perf. 14½x13
1992, Aug. 11   Litho.   Wmk. 373

760	A126	15c multicolored	1.40	1.10
761	A126	55c multicolored	3.00	2.75

Discovery of America Type
Souvenir Sheet
Perf. 14x13½
1992, Oct. 12   Litho.   Wmk. 384

762	A106	$2 Coming ashore	7.50	7.50

Christmas
A127

15c, The Annunciation. 55c, Nativity Scene. 60c, Angel, shepherds. 70c, The Magi.

1992, Nov. 2   Wmk. 373   Perf. 14

763	A127	15c multicolored	.80	.30
764	A127	55c multicolored	2.00	.90
765	A127	60c multicolored	2.25	1.25
766	A127	70c multicolored	2.50	2.50
a.		Souvenir sheet of 4, #763-766	9.00	9.00
		Nos. 763-766 (4)	7.55	4.95

The Contract, Farm Labor Program, 50th Anniv.
A128

Bahamian, American flags and: 15c, Silhouette of worker's head. 55c, Onions. 60c, Citrus fruits. 70c, Apples.

Perf. 14x14½
1993, Mar. 16   Wmk. 384

767	A128	15c multicolored	1.90	.75
768	A128	55c multicolored	2.75	1.50
769	A128	60c multicolored	2.75	2.50
770	A128	70c multicolored	3.50	3.50
		Nos. 767-770 (4)	10.90	8.25

Royal Air Force, 75th Anniv.
Common Design Type

Designs: 15c, Westland Wapiti. 40c, Gloster Gladiator. 55c, DeHavilland Vampire. 70c, English Electric Lightning.
No. 775a, Avro Shackleton. b, Fairey Battle. c, Douglas Boston. d, DeHavilland DH9a.

Wmk. 373
1993, Apr. 1   Litho.   Perf. 14

771	CD350	15c multicolored	1.90	.85
772	CD350	40c multicolored	2.75	1.60
773	CD350	55c multicolored	3.25	2.25
774	CD350	70c multicolored	4.25	4.25
		Nos. 771-774 (4)	12.15	8.95

Souvenir Sheet of 4

775	CD350	60c #a.-d.	12.50	12.50

Coronation of Queen Elizabeth II, 40th Anniv.
A129

Wmk. 373
1993, June 2   Litho.   Perf. 13½

776	A129	15c Nos. 424-425	.90	.65
777	A129	55c No. 157	2.25	2.25
778	A129	60c Nos. 402-403	2.40	2.40
779	A129	70c Nos. 404-405	2.75	2.75
		Nos. 776-779 (4)	8.30	8.05

A130

Natl. symbols: 15c, Lignum vitae. 55c, Yellow elder. 60c, Blue marlin. 70c, Flamingo.

1993, July 8   Litho.   Perf. 14

780	A130	15c multicolored	.60	.35
781	A130	55c multicolored	1.75	1.75
782	A130	60c multicolored	2.10	2.10
783	A130	70c multicolored	3.00	3.00
		Nos. 780-783 (4)	7.45	7.20

Independence, 20th anniv.

A131

Wildflowers: 15c, Cordia. 55c, Seaside morning glory. 60c, Poinciana. 70c, Spider lily.

1993, Sept. 8   Litho.   Perf. 14
784	A131 15c multicolored	1.60	.55
785	A131 55c multicolored	3.75	1.60
786	A131 60c multicolored	4.00	2.50
787	A131 70c multicolored	4.25	4.25
	Nos. 784-787 (4)	13.60	8.90

Christmas
A132

15c, Angel, Mary. 55c, Shepherds, angel. 60c, Holy family. 70c, Three wise men. $1, Madonna and Child.

1993, Nov. 1   Litho.   Perf. 14
788	A132 15c multi	1.25	.55
789	A132 55c multi	2.75	1.90
790	A132 60c multi	3.50	3.25
791	A132 70c multi	4.00	4.00
	Nos. 788-791 (4)	11.50	9.70

Souvenir Sheet
792	A132 $1 multi	8.50	8.50

Intl. Year of the Family
A133

55c, Children studying. 60c, Son, father fishing. 70c, Children, grandmother.

Wmk. 384

1994, Feb. 18   Litho.   Perf. 13½
793	A133 15c shown	1.25	.45
794	A133 55c multi	2.50	1.40
795	A133 60c multi	3.50	2.10
796	A133 70c multi	4.25	4.50
	Nos. 793-796 (4)	11.50	8.45

Hong Kong '94.

Royal
Visit — A134

Designs: 15c, Bahamas, United Kingdom flags. 55c, Royal Yacht Britannia. 60c, Queen Elizabeth II. 70c, Prince Philip, Queen.

Perf. 14x13½

1994, Mar. 7   Wmk. 373
797	A134 15c multicolored	1.10	.35
798	A134 55c multicolored	3.25	1.60
799	A134 60c multicolored	3.25	1.90
800	A134 70c multicolored	3.25	3.25
	Nos. 797-800 (4)	10.85	7.10

Natl. Family Island Regatta, 40th Anniv.
A135

Designs: 15c, 55c, 60c, 70c, Various sailing boats at sea. $2, Beached yacht, vert.

Wmk. 373

1994, Apr. 27   Litho.   Perf. 14
801	A135 15c multicolored	1.00	.35
802	A135 55c multicolored	2.25	1.10
803	A135 60c multicolored	2.25	2.25
804	A135 70c multicolored	4.00	4.00
	Nos. 801-804 (4)	9.50	7.70

Souvenir Sheet
805	A135 $2 multicolored	11.00	11.00

Intl. Olympic Committee, Cent. — A136

Flag, Olympic rings, and: 15c, Nos. 276-279, horiz. 55c, Nos. 388-391. 60c, Nos. 559-562, horiz. 70c, Nos. 755-758.

Wmk. 373

1994, May 31   Litho.   Perf. 14
806	A136 15c multicolored	2.00	.60
807	A136 55c multicolored	3.25	1.40
808	A136 60c multicolored	3.25	3.25
809	A136 70c multicolored	3.75	3.75
	Nos. 806-809 (4)	12.25	9.00

Souvenir Sheet

First Recipients of the Order of the Caribbean Community — A137

The 13th. Heads of Government Conference conferred the first CARICOM honours on the following three distinguished persons:
William Demas • Derek Walcott • Sir Shridath Ramphal

Perf. 13x14

1994, July 5   Litho.   Wmk. 373
810	A137 $2 multicolored	8.00	8.00

A138

Butterfly, flower: 15c, Canna skipper, canna. 55c, Cloudless sulphur, cassia. 60c, White peacock, passion flower. 70c, Devillier's swallowtail, calico flower.

1994, Aug. 16   Litho.   Perf. 14
811	A138 15c multicolored	1.60	.40
812	A138 55c multicolored	3.00	1.25
813	A138 60c multicolored	3.00	3.00
814	A138 70c multicolored	3.50	3.50
	Nos. 811-814 (4)	11.10	8.15

A139

Marine Life: a, Cuban hogfish, Spanish hogfish. b, Tomate, squirrelfish. c, French angelfish. d, Queen angelfish. e, Rock beauty. $2, Rock beauty, queen angelfish.

1994, Sept. 13   Perf. 13½x14
815	A139 40c Strip of 5, #a.-e.	8.25	8.25

Souvenir Sheet
816	A139 $2 multicolored	9.00	9.00

Christmas — A140

1994, Oct. 31   Litho.   Perf. 14
817	A140 15c Angel	.45	.30
818	A140 55c Holy family	1.40	1.40
819	A140 60c Shepherds	1.60	1.60
820	A140 70c Magi	2.10	2.10
	Nos. 817-820 (4)	5.55	5.40

Souvenir Sheet
821	A140 $2 Christ Child, vert.	6.00	6.00

College of the Bahamas, 20th Anniv. — A141

Designs: 15c, Lion. 70c, Queen Elizabeth II, college facade.

Wmk. 373

1995, Feb. 8   Litho.   Perf. 14
822	A141 15c multicolored	.35	.35
823	A141 70c multicolored	2.10	2.10

End of World War II, 50th Anniv.
Common Design Types

Designs: 15c, Bahamian soldiers on parade. 55c, Neutrality patrols flown by PBY-5A flying boats. 60c, Bahamian women in all three services. 70c, B-24 Liberator, Bahamians in RAF. $2, Reverse of War Medal 1939-45.

Wmk. 373

1995, May 8   Litho.   Perf. 13½
824	CD351 15c multicolored	1.25	.45
825	CD351 55c multicolored	3.75	1.25
826	CD351 60c multicolored	3.75	3.75
827	CD351 70c multicolored	4.75	4.75
	Nos. 824-827 (4)	13.50	10.20

Souvenir Sheet
Perf. 14
828	CD352 $2 multicolored	8.50	8.50

Kirtland's Warbler — A142

No. 829, 15c, Female at nest. No. 829A, 15c Singing male. No. 829B, 25c, Female feeding young. No. 829C, 25c, Immature bird feeding, prior to migration.
$2, Female on branch overlooking lake.

Wmk. 373

1995, June 7   Litho.   Perf. 13½
829	A142 15c multi	1.25	1.25
829A	A142 15c multi	1.25	1.25
829B	A142 25c multi	1.25	1.25
829C	A142 25c multi	1.25	1.25
d.	Strip of 4, as #829-829C, wmk. inverted	5.25	5.25

Souvenir Sheet
Perf. 13
830	A142 $2 multicolored	10.00	10.00

World Wildlife Fund (No. 829).
Nos. 829-829C were printed both in individual sheets of 50, with watermark upright, and in sheets of 16, containing four No. 829d.
No. 830 contains one 42x28mm stamp and has continuous design.

Tourism
A143

Designs: 15c, Eleuthera Cliffs. 55c, Clarence Town, Long Island. 60c, Albert Lowe Museum. 70c, Yachting.

Wmk. 384

1995, July 18   Litho.   Perf. 14½
831	A143 15c multicolored	1.10	.60
832	A143 55c multicolored	2.75	1.25
833	A143 60c multicolored	3.25	3.25
834	A143 70c multicolored	4.00	4.00
	Nos. 831-834 (4)	11.10	9.10

FAO, 50th Anniv.
A144

Designs: 15c, Pig, poultry farming. 55c, Horticultural methods. 60c, Healthy eating. 70c, Sustainable fishing.

Perf. 13½x13

1995, Sept. 5   Litho.   Wmk. 373
835	A144 15c multicolored	1.00	.35
836	A144 55c multicolored	2.00	1.00
837	A144 60c multicolored	2.50	2.50
838	A144 70c multicolored	3.50	3.50
	Nos. 835-838 (4)	9.00	7.35

UN, 50th Anniv.
Common Design Type

Designs: 15c, Sikorsky S-55, UNEF, Sinai, 1957. 55c, Ferret armored car, UNEF, Sinai, 1957. 60c, Fokker F-27, UNAMIC/UNTAC, Cambodia, 1991-93. 70c, Lockheed Hercules.

Wmk. 373

1995, Oct. 25   Litho.   Perf. 14
839	CD353 15c multicolored	.90	.40
840	CD353 55c multicolored	2.00	1.75
841	CD353 60c multicolored	2.00	2.00
842	CD353 70c multicolored	2.25	2.25
	Nos. 839-842 (4)	7.15	6.40

Christmas — A145

Designs: 15c, St. Agnes Anglican Church. 55c, Church of God. 60c, Sacred Heart Roman Catholic Church. 70c, Salem Union Baptist Church.

1995, Nov. 17
843	A145 15c multicolored	.50	.40
844	A145 55c multicolored	1.75	1.75
845	A145 60c multicolored	1.75	1.75
846	A145 70c multicolored	2.10	2.40
	Nos. 843-846 (4)	6.10	6.30

World AIDS Day
A146

1995, Dec. 1
847	A146 25c Virus in blood	.90	.90
848	A146 70c Scientific research	2.00	2.00

Shells
A147

Designs: 5c, Sunrise tellin. 10c, Queen conch. 15c, Angular triton. 20c, True tulip. 25c, Reticulated cowrie-helmet. 30c, Sand dollar. 40c, Lace short-frond murex. 45c, Inflated sea biscuit. 50c, West Indian top shell (magpie). 55c, Spiny oyster. 60c, King helmet. 70c, Lion's paw. $1, Crown cone. $2, Atlantic partridge tun. $5, Wide-mouthed purpura. $10, Triton's trumpet.

Wmk. 373 sideways

		1996	Litho.	Perf. 14	
849	A147	5c multicolored		.25	.25
850	A147	10c multicolored		.30	.25
851	A147	15c multicolored		.40	.35
852	A147	20c multicolored		.65	.45
853	A147	25c multicolored		.70	.50
854	A147	30c multicolored		2.10	.55
855	A147	40c multicolored		1.25	.55
856	A147	45c multicolored		2.75	.60
857	A147	50c multicolored		1.40	.60
858	A147	55c multicolored		3.25	.75
859	A147	60c multicolored		1.75	.75
860	A147	70c multicolored		2.10	.95
a.		Souvenir sheet of 1		4.00	4.00
861	A147	$1 multicolored		3.50	1.00
a.		Souvenir sheet of 1		4.00	4.00
862	A147	$2 multicolored		7.25	1.90
863	A147	$5 multicolored		14.50	4.00
864	A147	$10 multicolored		29.00	9.50
		Nos. 849-864 (16)		71.15	22.95

Issued: $10, 7/1; others, 1/2.
No. 860a issued 6/20/97 for return of Hong Kong to China.
No. 861a issued 2/3/97 for Hong Kong '97.
See Nos. 962-964.

1997			Wmk. 373 upright		
		Inscribed "1997"			
849b	A147	5c multicolored		1.50	1.20
850b	A147	10c multicolored		.90	.80
851b	A147	15c multicolored		1.50	.30
852b	A147	20c multicolored		1.50	.55
853b	A147	25c multicolored		1.75	.50
854b	A147	30c multicolored		1.75	.65
855b	A147	40c multicolored		2.75	.85
856b	A147	45c multicolored		2.50	1.25
857b	A147	50c multicolored		2.75	1.00
858b	A147	55c multicolored		2.75	1.25
859b	A147	60c multicolored		3.75	1.25
860b	A147	70c multicolored		3.75	1.90
861b	A147	$1 multicolored		5.00	2.50
862b	A147	$2 multicolored		9.00	6.25
863b	A147	$5 multicolored		16.00	13.00
864b	A147	$10 multicolored		30.00	24.00
		Nos. 849b-864b (16)		87.15	57.25

Issued: Nos. 861b-864b, 7/1; Nos. 849b-860b, 9/22.

1999			Inscribed "1999"		
849c	A147	5c multicolored		1.50	1.20
850c	A147	10c multicolored		.90	.80
851c	A147	15c multicolored		1.50	.30
852c	A147	20c multicolored		1.50	.55
853c	A147	25c multicolored		1.75	.50
855c	A147	40c multicolored		2.75	.85
857c	A147	50c multicolored		2.75	1.00
859c	A147	60c multicolored		3.75	1.25
860c	A147	70c multicolored		3.75	1.90
861c	A147	$1 multicolored		5.00	2.50
862c	A147	$2 multicolored		9.00	6.25
863c	A147	$5 multicolored		16.00	13.00
864c	A147	$10 multicolored		30.00	24.00
		Nos. 849c-864c (13)		80.15	54.10

2000			Inscribed "2000"		
849d	A147	5c multicolored		1.10	1.20
851d	A147	15c multicolored		1.10	.30
853d	A147	25c multicolored		1.35	.50
857d	A147	50c multicolored		2.25	1.00
859d	A147	60c multicolored			
860d	A147	70c multicolored		3.00	1.90
862d	A147	$2 multicolored		7.00	6.25
		Nos. 849d-862d (6)		15.80	11.15

2001			Inscribed "2001"		
851e	A147	15c multicolored		1.50	.30
853e	A147	25c multicolored		1.75	.50
857e	A147	50c multicolored		2.75	1.00
861e	A147	$1 multicolored		5.00	2.50
862e	A147	$2 multicolored		9.00	6.25
		Nos. 851e-862e (5)		20.00	10.55

Radio, Cent. — A148

Designs: 15c, East Goodwin Lightship, Marconi apparatus suspended from masthead. 55c, Arrest of Dr. Crippen, newspaper headline telling of wireless message from SS Montrose. 60c, SS Philadelphia, first readable transatlantic messages. 70c, Yacht Elettra, Guglielmo Marconi. $2, SS Titanic, SS Carpathia.

1996, Feb. 4		Litho.	Perf. 13½	
865	A148	15c multicolored	2.00	.50
866	A148	55c multicolored	2.75	1.50
867	A148	60c multicolored	3.00	2.75
868	A148	70c multicolored	3.25	3.75
		Nos. 865-868 (4)	11.00	8.50

Souvenir Sheet

869	A148	$2 multicolored	10.00	10.00

A149

Wmk. 384

1996, June 25		Litho.	Perf. 13½	
870	A149	15c Swimming	.60	.40
871	A149	55c Track	1.25	1.00
872	A149	60c Basketball	2.50	1.75
873	A149	70c Long jump	1.90	2.40
		Nos. 870-873 (4)	6.25	5.55

Souvenir Sheet

874	A149	$2 Javelin, 1896	6.00	6.00

Modern Olympic Games, cent.

A150

Reptiles: 15c, Green anole. 55c, Fowl snake. 60c, Inagua freshwater turtle. 70c, Acklins rock iguana.

Wmk. 384

1996, Sept. 3		Litho.	Perf. 14	
875	A150	15c multicolored	.90	.90
876	A150	55c multicolored	1.75	1.75
877	A150	60c multicolored	2.50	2.50
878	A150	70c multicolored	3.00	3.00
a.		Souvenir sheet, #875-878	8.25	8.25
		Nos. 875-878 (4)	8.15	8.15

Environmental protection.

Christmas — A151

Designs: 15c, Angel Gabriel and Mary. 55c, Mary and Joseph. 60c, Shepherds. 70c, Magi. $2, Presentation at the Temple.

Wmk. 373

1996, Nov. 4		Litho.	Perf. 14	
879	A151	15c multicolored	1.10	.40
880	A151	55c multicolored	2.75	.90
881	A151	60c multicolored	3.00	1.40
882	A151	70c multicolored	3.25	3.25
		Nos. 879-882 (4)	10.10	5.95

Souvenir Sheet

883	A151	$2 multicolored	5.50	5.50

Archives Dept., 25th Anniv. — A152

Perf. 14½x14

1996, Dec. 9		Litho.	Wmk. 384	
884	A152	55c shown	2.25	2.25

Souvenir Sheet
Perf. 14x13½

885	A152	$2 Building, horiz.	6.50	6.50

Queen Elizabeth II and Prince Philip, 50th Wedding Anniv. — A153

Designs: No. 886, Queen. No. 887, Grenadier Guards. No. 888, Prince Philip. No. 889, Queen reviewing Grenadier Guards. No. 890, Prince holding trophy, Queen opening jewel box. No. 891, Prince on polo pony.
$2, Queen, Prince riding in open carriage, horiz.

Wmk. 373

1997, July 9		Litho.	Perf. 13	
886	A153	50c multicolored	2.00	2.00
887	A153	50c multicolored	2.00	2.00
a.		Pair, #886-887	4.25	4.25
888	A153	60c multicolored	2.40	2.40
889	A153	60c multicolored	2.40	2.40
a.		Pair, #888-889	5.00	5.00
890	A153	70c multicolored	2.50	2.50
891	A153	70c multicolored	2.50	2.50
a.		Pair, #890-891	5.25	5.25
		Nos. 886-891 (6)	13.80	13.80

Souvenir Sheet

892	A153	$2 multicolored	8.00	8.00

Intl. Year of the Reefs A154

Various pictures of marine life and coral.

Perf. 14x14½

1997, Sept. 3		Litho.	Wmk. 384	
893	A154	15c multicolored	1.25	.55
894	A154	55c multicolored	2.75	1.25
895	A154	60c multicolored	2.75	1.75
896	A154	70c multicolored	3.25	3.25
		Nos. 893-896 (4)	10.00	6.80

Christmas — A155

15c, Angel. 55c, Madonna & Child. 60c, Shepherd. 70c, Magi. $2, Christ Child.

Perf. 13x13½

1997, Oct. 6		Litho.	Wmk. 373	
897	A155	15c multi	1.25	.30
898	A155	55c multi	2.50	.95
899	A155	60c multi	2.75	1.60
900	A155	70c multi	3.50	3.50
		Nos. 897-900 (4)	10.00	6.35

Souvenir Sheet

901	A155	$2 multi	10.00	10.00

Diana, Princess of Wales (1961-97)
Common Design Type

Various portraits: 902: a, 55c. b, 60c. c, 70c.

Perf. 14½x14

1998, Mar. 31		Litho.	Wmk. 373	
901A	CD355	15c multicolored	.80	.80

Sheet of 4

902	CD355	#a.-c., 901A	4.50	4.50

Organization of American States, 50th Anniv. — A156

Map of North and South America, national flags, and: 15c, "New Vision" paper. 55c, Building.

1998, Apr. 14			Perf. 13½x14	
903	A156	15c multicolored	.40	.40
904	A156	55c multicolored	2.00	2.00

University of the West Indies, 50th Anniv. — A157

1998, Apr. 14				
905	A157	55c multicolored	2.00	2.00

Universal Declaration of Human Rights, 50th Anniv. — A158

1998, Apr. 14				
906	A158	55c multicolored	2.25	2.25

Royal Air Force, 80th Anniv.
Common Design Type of 1993
Re-Inscribed

Designs: 15c, Handley Page Hyderabad. 55c, Hawker Demon. 60c, Gloster Meteor F.8. 70c, Lockheed Neptune MR.1.
No. 911: a, Sopwith Camel. b, Short 184. c, Supermarine Spitfire PR.19. d, North American Mitchell III.

1998, Apr. 1				
907	CD350	15c multicolored	.80	.55
908	CD350	55c multicolored	1.80	1.10
909	CD350	60c multicolored	1.75	1.75
910	CD350	70c multicolored	2.25	2.25
		Nos. 907-910 (4)	6.60	5.65

Souvenir Sheet

911	CD350	50c Sheet of 4, #a.-d.	7.00	7.00

Independence, 25th Anniv. — A159

15c, Supreme Court Building. 55c, Nassau Library. 60c, Government House. 70c, Gregory Arch.
$2, Exuma-Family Island Regatta, George Town.

Wmk. 373

1998, July 10		Litho.	Perf. 13½	
912	A159	15c multicolored	1.00	.75
913	A159	55c multicolored	2.10	1.50
914	A159	60c multicolored	2.25	2.25
915	A159	70c multicolored	2.75	2.75
		Nos. 912-915 (4)	8.10	7.25

Souvenir Sheet

916	A159	$2 multicolored	7.00	7.00

Castaway Cay, Disney Cruise Lines A160

1998, Aug. 1   *Perf. 14*

917	A160 55c Daytime	2.25	2.25
918	A160 55c Nighttime	2.25	2.25
a.	Pair, #917-918	4.50	4.50
b.	Bklt. pane, 5 each #917-918	22.50	
	Complete booklet, #918b	25.00	

MS Ryndam, Half Moon Cay — A161

1998, Aug. 19   *Perf. 13½x13*

919	A161 55c multicolored	5.25	2.50

Roses A162

Wmk. 373

1998, Sept. 8   **Litho.**   *Perf. 14*

920	A162 55c Yellow cream	1.90	1.90
921	A162 55c Big red	1.90	1.90
922	A162 55c Seven sisters	1.90	1.90
923	A162 55c Barrel pink	1.90	1.90
924	A162 55c Island beauty	1.90	1.90
a.	Bklt. pane, 2 each #920-924	19.00	
	Complete booklet, #924a	19.00	
	Nos. 920-924 (5)	9.50	9.50

Souvenir Sheet

925	A162 55c like #924	2.75	2.75

No. 925 has parts of other roses extending into center left and upper left area of stamp.

Intl. Year of the Ocean — A163

Wmk. 373

1998, Nov. 24   **Litho.**   *Perf. 14*

926	A163 15c Killer whale	1.25	.75
927	A163 55c Tropical fish	2.00	2.00

Christmas A164

15c, The Annunciation. 55c, Shepherds, star. 60c, Magi. 70c, Flight into Egypt. $2, Nativity scene.

1998, Dec. 11

928	A164 15c multicolored	.75	.40
929	A164 55c multicolored	1.60	.70
930	A164 60c multicolored	1.90	1.60
931	A164 70c multicolored	2.25	2.25
	Nos. 928-931 (4)	6.50	4.95

Souvenir Sheet

932	A164 $2 multicolored	6.00	6.00

Timothy Gibson, Composer of Natl. Anthem A165

1998   **Litho.**   **Wmk. 373**   *Perf. 13½*

933	A165 60c multicolored	1.75	1.75

Independence, 25th anniv.

National Trust, 40th Anniv. — A166

Flamingos on the beach: a, One chick, adults. b, Two chicks, adults. c, One chick spreading wings, adults. d, Six in flight over others. e, Three ascending into flight.

Wmk. 384

1999, Feb. 9   **Litho.**   *Perf. 14*

934	A166 55c Strip of 5, #a.-e.	9.25	9.25

No. 934 is a continuous design. See Nos. 940, 961, 969.

Australia '99, World Stamp Expo A167

Maritime history: 15c, Arawak Indians. 55c, Santa Maria. 60c, Blackbeard's ship, Queen Anne's Revenge. 70c, Banshee running Union blockade, US Civil War. $2, American invasion of Fort Nassau, 1776.

Perf. 14x14½

1999, Mar. 9   **Wmk. 373**

935	A167 15c multicolored	.50	.45
936	A167 55c multicolored	1.90	1.60
937	A167 60c multicolored	2.50	1.90
938	A167 70c multicolored	2.75	2.75
	Nos. 935-938 (4)	7.65	6.70

Souvenir Sheet

939	A167 $2 multicolored	7.00	7.00

National Trust, 40th Anniv. Type

Marine life: a, Dolphin. b, Large fish, four in background. c, Several fish, coral. d, Turtle, fish, coral. e, Lobster, coral.

Wmk. 384

1999, Apr. 6   **Litho.**   *Perf. 14*

940	A166 55c Strip of 5, #a.-e.	11.00	11.00

No. 940 is a continuous design.

Bahamas Historical Society, 40th Anniv. A168

1999, June 9   **Litho.**   *Perf. 13*

941	A168 $1 multicolored	2.00	2.00

1st Manned Moon Landing, 30th Anniv.

Common Design Type

15c, Ascent module in assembly area. 65c, Apollo command & service module. 70c, Descent stage. 80c, Module turns to dock with service module.
$2, Looking at earth from moon.

Perf. 14x13¾

1999, July 20   **Litho.**   **Wmk. 384**

942	CD357 15c multicolored	.80	.80
943	CD357 65c multicolored	2.10	2.10
944	CD357 70c multicolored	2.10	2.10
945	CD357 80c multicolored	2.10	2.10
	Nos. 942-945 (4)	7.10	7.10

Souvenir Sheet

Perf. 14

946	CD357 $2 multicolored	7.00	7.00

No. 946 contains one 40mm circular stamp 40mm.

UPU, 125th Anniv. A170

15c, Mail Packet Delaware. 65c, S.S. Atlantis. 70c, M.V. Queen of Bermuda. 80c, USS Saufley.

Wmk. 384

1999, Aug. 17   **Litho.**   *Perf. 13½*

947	A170 15c multi	1.10	.65
948	A170 65c multi	2.50	1.75
949	A170 70c multi	3.00	2.00
950	A170 80c multi	3.25	3.25
	Nos. 947-950 (4)	9.85	7.65

Queen Mother's Century

Common Design Type

Queen Mother: 15c, At Hertfordshire Hospital. 65c, With Princess Elizabeth. 70c, With Prince Andrew. 80c, With Irish Guards.
$2, With brother David and 1966 British World Cup team members.

Wmk. 373

1999, Aug.   **Litho.**   *Perf. 13½*

951	CD358 15c multicolored	.75	.50
952	CD358 65c multicolored	2.25	1.40
953	CD358 70c multicolored	2.25	2.25
954	CD358 80c multicolored	2.25	2.25
	Nos. 951-954 (4)	7.50	6.40

Souvenir Sheet

955	CD358 $2 multicolored	6.25	6.25

Environmental Protection — A171

15c, Turtle pond. 65c, Green turtles, limestone cliffs. 70c, Barracudas. 80c, Sea fans on reef.
$2, Atlantic bottlenose dolphin.

Wmk. 373

1999, Sept. 21   **Litho.**   *Perf. 13¾*

956	A171 15c multicolored	.75	.50
957	A171 65c multicolored	1.75	1.50
958	A171 70c multicolored	2.25	2.25
959	A171 80c multicolored	2.50	2.50
	Nos. 956-959 (4)	7.25	6.75

Souvenir Sheet

960	A171 $2 multicolored	7.00	7.00

National Trust Type of 1999

Designs: a, Tern. b, Heron. c, Hummingbird, orange flower. d, Duck. e, Parrot.

Wmk. 384

1999, Oct. 8   **Litho.**   *Perf. 14¼*

961	A166 65c Strip of 5, #a.-e.	11.00	11.00

Shell Type of 1996

1999   **Litho.**   **Wmk. 373**   *Perf. 14*

962	A147 35c Like #854	1.50	1.50
963	A147 65c Like #856	6.00	2.75
a.	Inscribed "2001"		
964	A147 80c Like #858	3.75	3.75
	Nos. 962-964 (3)	11.25	8.00

Christmas A172

People in various Junkanoo costumes.

Perf. 14½x14¼

1999, Oct. 25   **Litho.**   **Wmk. 373**

965	A172 15c multicolored	.50	.50
966	A172 65c multicolored	1.25	1.25
967	A172 70c multicolored	2.25	2.25
968	A172 80c multicolored	2.50	2.50
	Nos. 965-968 (4)	6.50	6.50

National Trust Type of 1999

Designs: a, Orchid. b, Rodent. c, Hummingbird, red flowers. d, Lizard. e, Hibiscus.

Wmk. 384

1999, Oct. 8   **Litho.**   *Perf. 14¼*

969	A166 65c Strip of 5, #a.-e.	13.50	13.50

Historic Fishing Villages A173

15c, New Plymouth. 65c, Cherokee Sound. 70c, Hope Town. 80c, Spanish Wells.

Perf. 13¼x13

2000, Jan. 25   **Litho.**   **Wmk. 373**

970	A173 15c multi	1.00	.65
971	A173 65c multi	2.40	1.50
972	A173 70c multi	3.25	3.25
973	A173 80c multi	3.75	3.75
	Nos. 970-973 (4)	10.40	9.15

Souvenir Sheet

1999 World Champions in Women's 4x100-Meter Relay Race — A174

Wmk. 373

2000, Feb. 22   **Litho.**   *Perf. 14½*

974	A174 $2 multi	4.50	4.50

Bush Medicine Plants A175

Perf. 14¼x14½

2000, May 2   **Litho.**   **Wmk. 373**

975	A175 15c Prickly pear	.65	.65
976	A175 65c Buttercup	1.50	1.50
977	A175 70c Shepherd's needle	1.90	1.90
978	A175 80c Five fingers	2.25	2.25
	Nos. 975-978 (4)	6.30	6.30

See Nos. 1040-1043, 1076-1079, 1131-1134.

The Stamp Show 2000, London A176

Battle of Britain, 60th anniv.: 15c, Quick turnaround, rearm and refuel. 65c, Squadron leader R. Stanford-Tuck in Hurricane 1. 70c, Melee. 80c, Tally ho.
$2, Airplanes in flight.

2000, May 22   ***Perf. 13¼x13½***
979	A176	15c multi	1.00 .75
980	A176	65c multi	2.10 2.10
981	A176	70c multi	2.25 2.25
982	A176	80c multi	2.25 2.25

Nos. 979-982 (4)   7.60 7.35

Souvenir Sheet

983 A176 $2 multi   6.75 6.75

Souvenir Sheet

Bahamas Cooperatives — A177

2000, June 27   Litho.   ***Perf. 14***

984 A177 $2 multi   6.00 6.00

2000 Summer Olympics, Sydney A178

15c, Swimming. 65c, Triple jump. 70c, Women's 4x100 meter relay. 80c, Yachting.

2000, July 17   ***Perf. 14¼x14½***

985-988 A178 Set of 4   5.75 5.75

Christmas A179

Orchids: 15c, Cockle-shell orchid. 65c, Pleated encyclia. 70c, Pine pink. 80c, Graceful encyclia.

2000, Nov. 7   ***Perf. 14½x14¼***

989-992 A179 Set of 4   7.75 7.75

Bahamas Humane Society, 76th Anniv. A180

Designs: 15c, Education. 65c, Fund raising. 70c, Veterinary care. 80c, Animal rescue.

Wmk. 373

2000, Dec. 12   Litho.   ***Perf. 14***

993-996 A180 Set of 4   10.00 10.00

Early Settlements A181

Designs: 15c, Meadow St., Inagua. 65c, Bain Town. 70c, Hope Town, Abaco. 80c, The Blue Hills.

Wmk. 373

2001, Feb. 6   Litho.   ***Perf. 14¼***

997-1000 A181 Set of 4   6.75 6.75

Sir Lynden Pindling (1930-2000), Prime Minister — A182

Pindling and: 15c, Microphone. 65c, Flag.

2001, Mar. 22   ***Perf. 14½x14¼***
1001-1002	A182	Set of 2	2.25 2.25
1001a		Inscribed "10th July, 1973"	1.25 1.25

No. 1001 is inscribed "10th July, 1972." Issued: No. 1001a, 8/6/01.

Edible Wild Fruits A183

Designs: 15c, Cocoplum. 65c, Guana berry. 70c, Mastic. 80c, Seagrape.

2001, May 15   ***Perf. 14¼x14½***

1003-1006 A183 Set of 4   6.50 6.50

Birds and Eggs A184

Designs: 5c, Reddish egret. 10c, Purple gallinule. 15c, Antillean nighthawk. 20c, Wilson's plover. 25c, Killdeer. 30c, Bahama woodstar. 40c, Bahama swallow. 50c, Bahama mockingbird. 60c, Black-cowled oriole. 65c, Great lizard cuckoo. 70c, Audubon's shearwater. 80c, Gray kingbird. $1, Bananaquit. $2, Yellow warbler. $5, Antillean bullfinch. $10, Roseate spoonbill.

Wmk. 373

2001, July 1   Litho.   ***Perf. 14***
Inscribed "2001"
1007	A184	5c multi	.25 .25
1008	A184	10c multi	.25 .25
1009	A184	15c multi	.50 .50
1010	A184	20c multi	.65 .65
1011	A184	25c multi	.80 .80
1012	A184	30c multi	1.00 1.00
1013	A184	40c multi	1.25 1.25
1014	A184	50c multi	1.60 1.60
1015	A184	60c multi	2.00 2.00
1016	A184	65c multi	2.00 2.00
1017	A184	70c multi	2.25 2.25
1018	A184	80c multi	2.50 2.50
1019	A184	$1 multi	3.25 3.25
1020	A184	$2 multi	6.50 6.50
1021	A184	$5 multi	16.00 16.00
1022	A184	$10 multi	32.50 32.50

Nos. 1007-1022 (16)   73.30 73.30

Name of Bird in Black
Inscribed "2004"

1022A A184 25c multi   7.50 7.50

Issued: Nos. 1007-1022 7/1/01; No. 1022A, 9/04.
Name of bird on No. 1011 is in brown.

2002   **Inscribed "2002"**
1010a	A184	20c multi	.65 .65
1011a	A184	25c multi	.80 .80
1013a	A184	40c multi	1.25 1.25
1022b	A184	$10 multi	32.50 32.50

Nos. 1010a-1022b (4)   35.20 35.20

2005   **Inscribed "2005"**

1022Aa A184 25c multi   8.50 8.50

Visits of Royal Navy Ships A185

HMS: 15c, Norfolk, 1933. 25c, Scarborough, 1930s. 50c, Bahamas, 1944. 65c, Battleaxe,

---

1979. 70c, Invincible, 1997. 80c, Norfolk, 2000.

Wmk. 373

2001, Aug. 21   Litho.   ***Perf. 14***

1023-1028 A185 Set of 6   13.00 13.00

Christmas — A186

Paintings: 15c, The Adoration of the Shepherds, by Peter Paul Rubens. 65c, Adoration of the Magi, by Rubens and Anthony Van Dyck. 70c, The Holy Virgin in the Wreath of Flowers, by Rubens and Jan Breughel. 80c, The Holy Virgin Adored by Angels, by Rubens.

2001, Nov. 6

1029-1032 A186 Set of 4   7.00 7.00

Reign Of Queen Elizabeth II, 50th Anniv. Issue
Common Design Type

Designs: Nos. 1033, 1037a, 15c, Princess Elizabeth, 1946. Nos. 1034, 1037b, 65c, In 1992. Nos. 1035, 1037c, 70c, With Prince Edward, 1965. Nos. 1036, 1037d, 80c, In 1996. No. 1037e, $2, 1955 portrait by Annigoni (38x50mm).

Perf. 14¼x14½, 13¾ (#1037e)

2002, Feb. 6   Litho.   **Wmk. 373**
With Gold Frames
1033	CD360	15c multicolored	.50 .50
1034	CD360	65c multicolored	1.00 1.00
1035	CD360	70c multicolored	1.75 1.75
1036	CD360	80c multicolored	2.00 2.00

Nos. 1033-1036 (4)   5.25 5.25

Souvenir Sheet
Without Gold Frames

1037 CD360 Sheet of 5, #a-e   10.00 10.00

Souvenir Sheet

Avard Moncur, Runner — A187

Perf. 14x13¾

2002, Apr. 16   Litho.   **Wmk. 373**

1038 A187 $2 multi   5.25 5.25

In Remembrance of Sept. 11, 2001 Terrorist Attacks — A188

Wmk. 373

2002, May 14   Litho.   ***Perf. 13¾***

1039 A188 $1 multi   4.50 4.50

Printed in sheets of four.

Bush Medicine Plants Type of 2000

Designs: 15c, Wild sage (lantana). 65c, Seaside maho. 70c, Sea ox-eye. 80c, Mexican poppy thistle.

Perf. 14¼x14½

2002, July 2   Litho.   **Wmk. 373**

1040-1043 A175 Set of 4   7.50 7.50

Queen Mother Elizabeth (1900-2002)
Common Design Type

Designs: 15c, Wearing hat and maple leaf brooch. 65c, Wearing black hat.
No. 1046: a, 70c, Wearing flowered hat. b, 80c, Wearing blue hat.

Wmk. 373

2002, Aug. 5   Litho.   ***Perf. 14¼***
With Purple Frames
1044	CD361	15c multicolored	.50 .50
1045	CD361	65c multicolored	2.60 2.60

Souvenir Sheet
Without Purple Frames
Perf. 14½x14¼

1046 CD361 Sheet of 2, #a-b   6.00 6.00

Flora and Fauna — A189

Plates from *The Natural History of Carolina, Florida and the Bahama Islands*, by Mark Catesby: 15c, Rice birds and rice. 25c, Alligator and red mangrove. 50c, Parrotfish. 65c, Ilatehera duck and sea oxeye. 70c, Flamingo and gorgonian coral. 80c, Crested bittern and inkberry.

Wmk. 373

2002, Oct. 1   Litho.   ***Perf. 14¼***

1047-1052 A189 Set of 6   11.00 11.00

Christmas A190

Carols: 15c, While Shepherds Watched Their Flocks. 65c, We Three Kings of Orient Are. 70c, Once in Royal David's City. 80c, I Saw Three Ships.

2002, Oct. 29   ***Perf. 14¼x14½***

1053-1056 A190 Set of 4   8.00 8.00

Inagua National Park A191

Photos of various birds by: 15c, Alexander Sprunt IV. 25c, Mrs. Lynn Holowesko. 50c, Bahamas National Trust. 65c, Terra Aqua. 70c, Terra Aqua, diff. 80c, Henry Nixon.

Wmk. 373

2003, Feb. 18   Litho.   ***Perf. 14***

1057-1062 A191 Set of 6   8.50 8.50

Pirates — A192

Designs: 15c, Capt. Edward Teach ("Blackbeard"). 25c, Capt. John Rackham ("Calico Jack"). 50c, Anne Bonney. 65c, Capt. Woodes Rogers. 70c, Sir John Hawkins. 80c, Capt. Bartholomew Roberts ("Black Bart").

2003, Mar. 18
1063-1068 A192   Set of 6   12.00 12.00

50th Natl. Family Island Regatta — A193

Arms, birds and various sailors and sailboats: 15c, 65c, 70c, 80c.

2003, Apr. 30   *Perf. 13¾*
1069-1072 A193   Set of 4   8.25 8.25

Coronation of Queen Elizabeth II, 50th Anniv.
Common Design Type

Designs: Nos. 1073, 65c, 1075a, 15c, Queen with crown, orb and scepter. Nos. 1074, 80c, 1075b, 70c, Queen and family on Buckingham Palace balcony.

Perf. 14¼x14½
2003, June 2   Litho.   Wmk. 373
Vignettes Framed, Red Background
1073 CD363 65c multicolored   2.75 2.75
1074 CD363 80c multicolored   3.75 3.75

Souvenir Sheet
Vignettes Without Frame, Purple Panel
1075 CD363   Sheet of 2, #a-b   6.50 6.50

Bush Medicine Plants Type of 2000

Designs: 15c, Asystasia. 65c, Cassia. 70c, Lignum vitae. 80c, Snowberry.

Wmk. 373
2003, July 8   Litho.   *Perf. 13¾*
1076-1079 A175   Set of 4   7.25 7.25

Powered Flight, Cent. — A194

Designs: 15c, Piper Cub. 25c, DH Tiger Moth. 50c, Lockheed SR-71A Blackbird. 65c, Supermarine S6B. 70c, North American "Miss America" P-51D Mustang. 80c, Douglas DC3 Dakota.

Perf. 13¼x13¾
2003, Sept. 16   Litho.
Stamps + Label
1080-1085 A194   Set of 6   10.50 10.50

Christmas A195

St. Matthew's Anglican Church, Nassau: 15c, Altar. 65c, Altar, horiz. 70c, Exterior, horiz. 80c, Exterior.

Perf. 14¾x14, 14x14¾
2003, Oct. 28   Litho.   Wmk. 373
1086-1089 A195   Set of 4   7.00 7.00

Waters of Life — A196

Paintings by Alton Roland Lowe: 15c, Crawfishin'. 65c, Summer. 70c, The Whelkers. 80c, Annual Visit.

2003, Nov. 24   *Perf. 13¾*
1090-1093 A196   Set of 4   7.25 7.25

Harrold and Wilson Ponds A197

Designs: 15c, Birds on and near dead tree. 25c, Bird in water, bird on branch. 50c, Kayakers. 65c, Birds in water. 70c, Birds in water, diff. 80c, Bird watchers.

Wmk. 373
2004, Feb. 24   Litho.   *Perf. 13¾*
1094-1099 A197   Set of 6   9.75 9.75

John Wesley (1703-91), Religious Leader A198

Designs: 15c, Methodist Church, Cupid's Bay, Governor's Harbor. 25c, Methodist Church, Grants Town, Nassau. 50c, Chapel, Marsh Harbor, vert. 65c, Ebeneezer Methodist Church. 70c, Trinity Methodist Church. 80c, Portrait of Wesley, by Antonius Roberts.

Wmk. 373
2004, Apr. 27   Litho.   *Perf. 13¾*
1100-1105 A198   Set of 6   9.25 9.25

Royal Horticultural Society, Bicent. — A199

Flowers: 15c, Cattleya orchid. 65c, Hibiscus. 70c, Canna lily. 80c, Thunbergia.

Wmk. 373
2004, May 25   Litho.   *Perf. 14*
1106-1109 A199   Set of 4   9.25 9.25
1109a   Sheet, 5 each #1106-1109,
           + 5 labels   47.50 47.50

Lighthouses A200

Designs: 15c, Elbow Reef. 50c, Great Stirrup. 65c, Great Isaac. 70c, Hole in the Wall. 80c, Hog Island.

Wmk. 373
2004, July 7   Litho.   *Perf. 14*
1110-1114 A200   Set of 5   10.50 10.50
See Nos. 1154-1158.

2004 Summer Olympics, Athens — A201

Designs: 15c, Boxing. 50c, Swimming. 65c, Tennis. 70c, Track.

Perf. 13½x13¼
2004, Aug. 24   Litho.   Wmk. 373
1115-1118 A201   Set of 4   8.75 8.75

Children's Junkanoo and Christmas — A202

Designs: 15c, Anticipation. 25c, First time. 50c, On the move, vert. 65c, I'm ready, vert. 70c, Trumpet player, vert. 80c, Drummer boy, vert.

Wmk. 373
2004, Oct. 26   Litho.   *Perf. 14*
1119-1124 A202   Set of 6   8.25 8.25

Merchant Ships A203

Designs: 15c, RMS Mauretania. 25c, MV Adonia. 50c, MS Royal Princess. 65c, SS Queen of Nassau. 70c, RMS Transvaal Castle. 80c, SS Norway.

Wmk. 373
2004, Dec. 7   Litho.   *Perf. 13¼*
1125-1130 A203   Set of 6   12.50 12.50

Bush Medicine Plants Type of 2000

Designs: 15c, Aloe. 25c, Red stopper. 50c, Blue flower. 65c, Bay lavender.

2005, Feb. 8   *Perf. 13¾*
1131-1134 A175   Set of 4   4.25 4.25

Royal Bahamas Defense Force, 25th Anniv. A204

Designs: 15c, Soliders training in camouflage uniforms. 25c, HMBS Abaco. 50c, HMDS Bahamas. 65c, Six defense force members in various uniforms.

2005, Mar. 29   *Perf. 14*
1135-1138 A204   Set of 4   5.50 5.50

Connections Between Bahamas and Key West, Florida — A205

Paintings by Alton Roland Lowe: 15c, William Curry. 25c, Captain John Bartlum's

House, horiz. 50c, Captain John Bartlum. 65c, Captain Tuggy Roberts' House, horiz.

2005, Apr. 26
1139-1142 A205   Set of 4   5.50 5.50

Battle of Trafalgar, Bicent. — A206

Designs: 15c, 1801 RN Pattern Tower Sea Service pistols. 25c, Royal Marine, 1805. 50c, HMS Boreas off Bahamas, 1787, horiz. 65c, The death of Nelson, horiz. 70c, HMS Victory, horiz. 80c, The Achille surrendering to HMS Polyphemus, horiz.
No. 1149: a, Admiral Cuthbert Collingwood. b, HMS Polyphemus.

Wmk. 373, Unwmkd. (70c)
2005, Apr. 29   *Perf. 13¼*
1143-1148 A206   Set of 6   12.00 12.00
Souvenir Sheet
1149 A206 $1 Sheet of 2, #a-b   8.25 8.25

No. 1147 has particles of wood from the HMS Victory embedded in areas covered by a thermographic process that produces a raised, shiny effect.

European Philatelic Cooperation, 50th Anniv. (in 2006) — A207

Flags of Bahamas and European Union, seascape, map of Europe in: 15c, Blue violet. 25c, Dull blue green. 50c, Yellow bister. $5, Green.

Unwmk.
2005, June 1   Litho.   *Perf. 14*
1150-1153 A207   Set of 4   18.00 18.00
1153a   Souvenir sheet, #1150-
           1153   18.00 18.00

Europa stamps, 50th anniv. (in 2006).

Lighthouses Type of 2004

Designs: 15c, Bird Rock. 50c, Castle Island. 65c, San Salvador. 70c, Great Inagua. 80c, Cay Lobos.

Wmk. 373
2005, July 6   Litho.   *Perf. 14*
1154-1158 A200   Set of 5   10.50 10.50

Pope John Paul II (1920-2005) A208

Wmk. 373
2005, Aug. 18   Litho.   *Perf. 14*
1159 A208 $1 multi   4.00 4.00

Souvenir Sheet

College of the Bahamas, 30th
Anniv. — A209

Wmk. 373

2005, Oct. 18		**Litho.**		***Perf. 14***
1160 A209	$2 multi		7.00	7.00

Christmas — A210

Stories by Hans Christian Andersen (1805-75): 15c, The Little Fir Tree. 25c, The Princess and the Pea. 50c, The Tin Soldier. 65c, Thumbelina.

2005, Nov. 8			
1161-1164 A210	Set of 4	5.00	5.00

BirdLife
International
A211

Various depictions of Bahama nuthatch: 15c, 25c, 50c, 65c, 70c, 80c.

Wmk. 373

2006, Mar. 28		**Litho.**		***Perf. 13¾***
1165-1170 A211	Set of 6		12.00	12.00
1170a	Souvenir sheet, #1165-1170		14.00	14.00

Queen
Elizabeth
II, 80th
Birthday
A212

Queen Elizabeth II: 15c, As child. 25c, Wearing tiara. 50c, Wearing blue hat. 65c, Wearing white hat.
No. 1175: a, Like 25c. b, Like 50c.

2006, Apr. 21			***Perf. 14***
1171-1174 A212	Set of 4	5.25	5.25
Souvenir Sheet			
1175 A212	$1.50 Sheet of 2, #a-b	8.50	8.50

ZNS Broadcasting Network, 70th
Anniv. — A213

Designs: 15c, Map of Bahamas, Harcourt R. Bethel, ZNS General Manager. 25c, Map of Bahamas, ZNS Network emblem. 50c, ZNS building. 65c, ZNS building and tower. 70c, Map of Bahamas and radio antenna. 80c, Map of Bahamas, ZNS Radio emblem and microphone.

2006, May 26			
1176-1181 A213	Set of 6	8.00	8.00

Flowers
A214

Designs: 5c, Amaryllis. 10c, Barleria. 15c, Yesterday, today and tomorrow. 25c, Desert rose. 35c, Poor man's orchid. 40c, Frangipani. 55c, Herald's trumpet. 65c, Oleander. 75c, Bird of paradise. 80c, Plumbago. 90c, Rose. $1, Rubber vine. $2, Star of Bethlehem. $5, Angel's trumpet. $10, Wine lily.

Wmk. 373

2006, July 3		**Litho.**		***Perf. 14***
		Inscribed "2006"		
1182 A214	5c multi		.30	.30
1183 A214	10c multi		.30	.30
1184 A214	25c multi		.70	.70
1185 A214	35c multi		.95	.95
1186 A214	40c multi		1.10	1.10
1187 A214	55c multi		1.50	1.50
1188 A214	65c multi		1.75	1.75
1189 A214	75c multi		1.90	1.90
1190 A214	80c multi		1.50	1.50
1191 A214	90c multi		2.50	2.50
1192 A214	$1 multi		2.75	2.75
1193 A214	$2 multi		5.50	5.50
1194 A214	$5 multi		13.00	13.00
1195 A214	$10 multi		27.50	27.50
	Nos. 1182-1195 (14)		61.25	61.25

Wmk. 406

1195B A214	15c multi	1.40	1.40

2007	**Wmk. 373**	**Inscribed "2007"**		
1182a A214	5c multi		2.50	2.50
1183a A214	10c multi		2.50	2.50

2008	**Wmk. 373**	**Inscribed "2008"**		
1192b A214	$1 multi		2.00	2.00
1193b A214	$2 multi		4.00	4.00
1194b A214	$5 multi		10.00	10.00
1195c A214	$10 multi		20.00	20.00
	Nos. 1192b-1195c (4)		36.00	36.00

2008, Aug.		**Wmk. 406**	
1182b	5c	.25	.25
1183b	10c	.25	.25
1186a	40c	.80	.80
1187a	55c	1.10	1.10
1188a	65c	1.40	1.40
1189a	75c	1.50	1.50
1190a	80c	1.60	1.60
1191a	90c	1.90	1.90
1192a	$1	2.00	2.00
1193a	$2	4.00	4.00
1194a	$5	10.00	10.00
1195a	$10	20.00	20.00
	Nos. 1182b-1195a (12)	44.80	44.80

	Dated "2009"		
	Wmk. 406		
1182c	5c multi	1.00	1.00
1183c	10c multi	1.00	1.00

Flowering
Vines
A215

Designs: 15c, Blue pea. 50c, Allamanda. 65c, Morning glory. 70c, Sky vine.

		Perf. 12½x13		
2006, Oct. 31		**Litho.**		**Wmk. 373**
1196-1199 A215	Set of 4		5.25	5.25

Christmas
A216

Designs: 15c, Christmas Sunday. 25c, Christmas dinner. 50c, Bay Street shopping. 65c, Boxing Day Junkanoo. 70c, Watch Night service. 80c, New Year's Day Junkanoo.

2006, Nov. 28		***Perf. 13x13¼***		
1200-1205 A216	Set of 6		7.75	7.75

Worldwide Fund for Nature
(WWF) — A217

Blaineville's beaked whales: 15c, Whale breaching surface of water. 25c, Three whales. 50c, One whale underwater. 60c, Three whales, diff.

Wmk. 373

2007, Jan. 23		**Litho.**		***Perf. 14***
1206-1209 A217	Set of 4		4.50	4.50
1209a	Miniature sheet, 4 each #1206-1209		19.00	19.00

Wedding of
Queen Elizabeth
II and Prince
Philip, 60th
Anniv. — A218

Designs: 15c, Portrait of couple. 25c, Couple in coach. 50c, Couple on balcony. 65c, Couple passing line of people. $5, Color portrait of couple.

Wmk. 373

2007, June 1		**Litho.**		***Perf. 13¾***
1210-1213 A218	Set of 4		4.25	4.25
	Souvenir Sheet			
	Perf. 14			
1214 A218	$5 multi		13.00	13.00

No. 1214 contains one 43x57mm stamp.

Scouting,
Cent.
A219

Designs: 15c, Two Scouts at church service, hands of bugler. 25c, Scout on rope, hands tying knot. 50c, Scouts at campfire, hand holding compass. 65c, Scouts at attention, hand giving salute.
No. 1219, vert.: a, 70c, Scouts playing baseball. b, 80c, Lord Robert Baden-Powell.

2007, July 9		***Perf. 13¾***	
1215-1218 A219	Set of 4	5.00	5.00
	Souvenir Sheet		
1219 A219	Sheet of 2, #a-b	3.25	3.25

Governor
General's Youth
Award, 20th
Anniv. — A220

Designs: 15c, Youths building walkway. 25c, Youths painting. 50c, Youths in kayak. 65c, Youths on hike. 70c, Award emblem.

		Perf. 12½x13		
2007, Sept. 18		**Litho.**		**Wmk. 373**
1220-1224 A220	Set of 5		6.00	6.00

Christmas — A221

Various Christmas ornaments made of seashells with background colors of: 15c, Purple. 25c, Red violet. 50c, Orange. 65c, Red brown. 70c, Lemon. 80c, Green.

2007, Nov. 13				***Perf. 14***
1225-1230 A221	Set of 6		7.25	7.25

Rev.
Charles
Wesley
(1707-88),
Hymn
Writer
A222

Designs: 15c, Church choir, cross. 50c, Stained glass window showing Charles Wesley and brother, John, vert. 65c, Charles Wesley and frontispiece of *Hymns and Sacred Poems in Two Volumes*, vert. 70c, Harbour Island Methodist Church.

	Perf. 12½x13¼, 13¼x12½		
2007, Dec. 13			
1231-1234 A222	Set of 4	5.75	5.75

Butterflies
A223

Designs: 15c, Zebra longwing. 25c, Julia. 50c, Cloudless sulphur. 65c, Queen. 70c, Long-tailed skipper. 80c, Gulf fritillary.

Wmk. 373

2008, Feb. 18		**Litho.**		***Perf. 14***
1235-1240 A223	Set of 6		8.00	8.00
1240a	Miniature sheet, #1235-1240		8.00	8.00

Military
Uniforms — A224

Designs: 15c, His Majesty's Independent Company. 25c, 47th Regiment of Foot. 50c, 99th Regiment of Foot. 65c, Royal Artillery. 70c Black Garrison Companies.

2008, Mar. 20			
1241-1245 A224	Set of 5	6.00	6.00

2008
Summer
Olympics,
Beijing
A225

Designs: 15c, Bamboo, runner. 50c, Dragon, high jump. 65c, Lanterns, javelin. 70c, Fish, runner.

Wmk. 373

2008, Apr. 30		**Litho.**		***Perf. 13½***
1246-1249 A225	Set of 4		5.00	5.00

Royal Bank of Canada in the Bahamas, Cent. A226

Designs: 15c, Anniversary emblem. 25c, Regional head office. 50c, Main branch office, Nassau, early 1900s. 65c, New Carmichael Road office. 70c, Bankers Ross McDonald and Nathaniel Beneby Jr.

Perf. 12½x13¼
2008, Sept. 22　Litho.　Wmk. 406
1250-1254　A226　Set of 5　　6.50　6.50

National Aeronautics and Space Administration, 50th Anniv. — A227

Designs: 15c, Launch of Space Shuttle Discovery. 25c, Apollo 16 over Moon. 50c, Skylab 3. 65c, Hubble Space Telescope. 70c, Swan Nebula. 80c, Carina Nebula.

Wmk. 373
2008, Oct. 1　Litho.　Perf. 13¾
1255-1260　A227　Set of 6　　7.50　7.50

Christmas A228

Paintings by Leonhard Diefenbach: 15c, Adoration of the Magi. 50c, Magi at the Court of King Herod. 65c, Shepherds. 70c, Adoration of the Shepherds.

Perf. 12½x13
2008, Nov. 11　Litho.　Wmk. 406
1261-1264　A228　Set of 4　　6.00　6.00

University of the West Indies, 60th Anniv. A229

Anniversary emblem and: 15c, Men and women in doctor's jackets. 25c, Plaque honoring renaming of Clinical Training Program. 65c, Arms and diploma.

2008, Nov. 25
1265-1267　A229　Set of 3　　3.00　3.00

Treaty of Paris, 225th Anniv. A230

Designs: 15c, Battle of Lexington. 50c, Washington Crossing the Delaware. 65c, Signatories of the Treaty of Paris, by Benjamin West. 70c, Signed treaty.

2008, Dec. 9
1268-1271　A230　Set of 4　　4.50　4.50

Rare Birds — A231

Designs: 15c, Bahamas oriole. 50c, Rose-throated parrot. 65c, Great lizard cuckoo. 70c, Audubon's shearwater.

Wmk. 373
2009, Jan. 6　Litho.　Perf. 13¾
1272-1275　A231　Set of 4　　6.50　6.50

Potcake Dogs A232

Dogs named: 15c, Tripod. 50c, Amigo. 65c, Turtle. 70c, Oreo.

Perf. 12½x13¼
2009, May 1　　Wmk. 406
1276-1279　A232　Set of 4　　6.50　6.50

Miniature Sheet

Peonies — A233

No. 1280 — Panel color: a, Pale yellow. b, White. c, Pink. d, Pale blue. e, Pale orange. f, Light green. g, Light yellow. h, Bluish gray.

Perf. 13¼
2009, Apr. 10　Litho.　Unwmk.
1280　A233　50c Sheet of 8, #a-h　9.00　9.00

First Bahamas Postage Stamp, 150th Anniv. — A234

No. 1281 — Bahamas #1b with background color of: a, Pink. b, Light blue. c, Light green. d, Lilac.

2009, May 26　Wmk. 406　Perf. 13
1281　A234　15c Block of 4, #a-d　1.50　1.50
　e.　Souvenir sheet, #1281　1.50　1.50

Naval Aviation, Cent. A235

Royal Navy airplanes: 15c, Hawker Sea Hurricane. 65c, Hawker Sea Fury. 70c, Fairey Gannet. 80c, De Havilland Sea Vampire.
$2, Airplane on Merchant Aircraft Carrier MV Empire MacKendrick.

2009, June 16　Wmk. 406　Perf. 14
1282-1285　A235　Set of 4　　5.00　5.00
Souvenir Sheet
1286　A235　$2 multi　　4.50　4.50

Nos. 1282-1285 each were printed in sheets of 8 + central label.

Christmas A236

Designs: 15c, Church of God of Prophecy. 25c, Mission Baptist Church. 50c, Grant's Town Seventh-Day Adventist Church. 65c, Wesley Methodist Church. 70c, St. Francis Xavier Cathedral. 80c, St. Ambrose Anglican Church.

Wmk. 406
2009, Nov. 18　Litho.　Perf. 13¾
1287-1292　A236　Set of 6　　6.75　6.75

Souvenir Sheet

British Commonwealth, 60th Anniv. — A237

2009, Nov. 24
1293　A237　$2 multi　　4.50　4.50

Friends of the Environment — A238

Designs: 15c, Whale, dolphin. 50c, Parrot, conch. 65c, Lizard, turtle. 70c, Stork, tree.

2010, Mar. 3　　Perf. 12¾x13
1294-1297　A238　Set of 4　　4.25　4.25

Battle of Britain, 70th Anniv. — A239

Various photographs of Sir Winston Churchill and words from his speeches: 15c, "We shall never surrender." 25c, "The Battle of Britain is about to begin." 50c, "Never in the field of human conflict was so much owed by so many to so few." 65c, "This was their finest hour." 70c, "Upon this battle depends the survival of Christian civilization." 80c, "We shall fight on the beaches."
$2, Sir Douglas Bader.

2010, June 18　　Perf. 12¾
1298-1303　A239　Set of 6　　6.75　6.75
Souvenir Sheet
1303A　A239　$2 black & gray　　4.50　4.50

Hurricane Awareness A240

Designs: 15c, Palm trees in hurricane. 50c, Map of hurricane track. 65c, Hurricane, reconnaissance airplane. 70c, National Emergency Management Agency emblem as eye of hurricane.

Perf. 12½x13
2010, Sept. 28　　Wmk. 406
1304-1307　A240　Set of 4　　7.00　7.00

Christmas — A241

Fireworks and: 15c, Palm tree, cruise ship. 50c, Atlantis Hotel. 65c, Tail of jet airplane. 70c, Fort Fincastle, Water Tower.

Unwmk.
2010, Nov. 10　Litho.　Perf. 14
1308-1311　A241　Set of 4　　7.00　7.00

Sir Victor Sassoon Heart Foundation — A242

Designs: 15c, Heart Ball. 50c, Doctor examining child. 65c, Doctor examining child, diff. 70c, Sir Victor Sassoon (1881-1961), businessman.

Unwmk.
2011, Feb. 12   Litho.   Perf. 14
1312-1315 A242 Set of 4   4.00 4.00

Service of Queen Elizabeth II and
Prince Philip — A243

Designs: 15c, Queen Elizabeth II. 50c,
Queen and Prince Philip. 65c, Queen and
Prince Philip, diff. 70c, Queen and Prince
Philip, diff. $1, Queen and Prince Philip, diff.
$2, Prince Philip.
$2.50, Queen and Prince Philip, diff.

2011, Mar. 23   Litho.   Perf. 13¼
1316-1321 A243 Set of 6   10.00 10.00
1321a   Sheet of 6, #1316-1321,
        + 3 labels   10.00 10.00
Souvenir Sheet
1322 A243 $2.50 multi   5.00   5.00

Wedding of Prince William and
Catherine Middleton — A244

Couple: 15c, In 2008. 50c, At St. James's
Palace. 65c, Kissing on Buckingham Palace
balcony after wedding.
$5, After wedding at Westminster Abbey,
vert.

2011, June 21   Perf. 14
1323-1325 A244 Set of 3   2.60 2.60
Souvenir Sheet
Perf. 14¾x14¼
1326 A244 $5 multi   10.00 10.00
No. 1326 contains one 29x46mm stamp.

Establishment
of City of
Nassau and
Anglican
Diocese, 150th
Anniv. — A245

Designs: 15c, Christ Church Cathedral. 50c,
Rawson Square. 65c, Government House.
70c, Bay Street. $1, Bishop Charles Caulfield.
$2, Royal Governor Charles Bayley.

2011, Sept. 12   Perf. 12½x13
1327-1332 A245 Set of 6   10.00 10.00

Christmas
A246

Angel and: 15c, Virgin Mary. 25c, Mary and
Joseph. 50c, Magi. 65c, Infant Jesus and
lambs. 70c, Shepherds. 80c, Mary and Jesus.

2011, Nov. 17   Perf. 13½x13¼
1333-1338 A246 Set of 6   6.25 6.25

Marine
Life
A247

Designs: 5c, Sea fan. 10c, Christmas tree
worm. 15c, Elkhorn coral. 20c, Cushion sea
star. 25c, Queen conch. 30c, Hawksbill turtle.
40c, Green moray eel. 50c, Bonefish. 60c,
Spidder crab. 65c, Spiny lobster. 70c, Nassau
grouper. 80c, Yellowtail snapper. $1, Great
barracuda. $2, Spotted eagle ray. $5, Caribbean reef shark. $10, Bottlenose dolphin.

2012, Jan. 3   Perf. 13¼x13½
1339 A247   5c multi   .25   .25
1340 A247 10c multi   .25   .25
1341 A247 15c multi   .30   .30
1342 A247 20c multi   .40   .40
1343 A247 25c multi   .50   .50
1344 A247 30c multi   .60   .60
1345 A247 40c multi   .80   .80
1346 A247 50c multi   1.00 1.00
1347 A247 60c multi   1.25 1.25
1348 A247 65c multi   1.40 1.40
1349 A247 70c multi   1.40 1.40
1350 A247 80c multi   1.60 1.60
1351 A247 $1 multi   2.00 2.00
1352 A247 $2 multi   4.00 4.00
1353 A247 $5 multi   10.00 10.00
1354 A247 $10 multi   20.00 20.00
        Nos. 1339-1354 (16) 45.75 45.75

Worldwide Fund
for Nature
(WWF) — A248

Caribbean flamingo: Nos. 1355, 1359a, 15c,
Head. Nos. 1356, 1359b, 50c, Chick and egg.
Nos. 1357, 1359c, 65c, Adults feeding. Nos.
1358, 1359d, 70c, Adults standing, facing
right.
$5, Adults standing, facing left.

2012, Mar. 21   Perf. 14
Stamps With White Frames
1355-1358 A248 Set of 4   4.00 4.00
Stamps Without White Frames
1359 A248   Horiz. strip of 4,
            #a-d   4.00 4.00
Souvenir Sheet
1360 A248 $5 multi   10.00 10.00

2012 Summer
Olympics,
London — A249

Emblem of 2012 Summer Olympics and:
15c, Boxing, Houses of Parliament. 50c, High
jump, Nelson's Column. 65c, Swimming,
Tower Bridge. 70c, Runner, Olympic Stadium.

2012, July 11   Litho.   Perf. 13½
1361-1364 A249 Set of 4   4.00 4.00

Royal Visit of
Prince
Harry — A250

Diamond and: 15c, Prince Harry in uniform.
50c, Prince Harry holding Bahamian flags.

65c, Prince Harry and young girl. 70c, Queen
Elizabeth II.

2012, Aug. 16   Litho.   Perf. 14
1365-1368 A250 Set of 4   4.00 4.00
Reign of Queen Elizabeth II, 60th anniv.

Woman
Suffragists — A251

Designs: 15c, Mary Ingraham (1901-82).
25c, Georgianna Symonette (1902-65). 50c,
Mabel Walker (1902-87). 65c, Eugenia Lock-
hart (1908-89). 70c, Dame Albertha Isaacs
(1900-97). 80c, Dr. Doris Johnson (1921-83).

2012, Oct. 10
1369-1374 A251 Set of 6   6.25 6.25

Christmas
A252

Designs: 15c, Annunciation. 25c, Mary and
Joseph arrive in Bethlehem. 50c, Holy Family.
65c, Shepherds. 70c, Magi. 80c, Flight into
Egypt.

2012, Nov. 1   Perf. 13½
1375-1380 A252 Set of 6   6.25 6.25

Items Produced for
Coronations — A253

Coronation of Queen Elizabeth II, 60th
Anniv. — A254

Items produced for coronation of: 65c,
Queen Victoria. 70c, King Edward VII. 80c,
King George V. $1, King George VI. $2,
Queen Elizabeth II.

2013, Feb. 6   Perf. 14
1381-1385 A253 Set of 5   10.50 10.50
Souvenir Sheet
Perf. 14¾x14
1386 A254 $3 multi   6.00 6.00
Nos. 1381-1385 each were printed in sheets
of 8 + label.

Royal
Bahamas
Police
Force
Band,
120th
Anniv.
A255

Designs: 15c, Sir William Murphy presenting
gallantry medal to Constable Fred Neville Seymour (first conductor of band), 1948. 25c,
Band greeting Royal Yacht Britannia, 1975.

50c, Band, building in background. 65c, Band,
water and buildings in background. 70c, Drummer. 80c, Band passing under arch.

2013, May 15
1387-1392 A255 Set of 6   6.25 6.25

Independence, 40th Anniv. — A256

Designs: 15c, Bahamas Independence
Conference. 25c, Sir Milo Butler (1906-79),
Governor-General, Butler inspecting troops.
50c, Sir Lynden Pindling (1930-2000), Prime
Minister, arms of Bahamas. 65c, HMBS Fla-
mingo and four crewmen killed in 1980 sinking
of ship by Cuban Air Force. 70c, Rhodes
Scholars Christian Campbell, Desiree Cox and
Myron Rolle.

2013, July 8
1393-1397 A256 Set of 5   4.50 4.50

Bahamas Reef Environment
Educational Foundation, 20th
Anniv. — A257

No. 1398: a, Foundation emblem. b, Angelfish and coral.
No. 1399: a, Diver photographing sea turtle.
b, Sea turtle.
No. 1400: a, Diver feeding fish. b, Fish and
coral.
No. 1401: a, Diver and shark. b, Hammerhead shark.

2013, Oct. 29   Litho.   Perf. 12½
1398   Horiz. pair + central la-
           bel   .60   .60
  a.-b. A257 15c Either single .30   .30
1399   Horiz. pair + central la-
           bel   2.00 2.00
  a.-b. A257 50c Either single 1.00 1.00
1400   Horiz. pair + central la-
           bel   2.60 2.60
  a.-b. A257 65c Either single 1.30 1.30
1401   Horiz. pair + central la-
           bel   2.80 2.80
  a.-b. A257 70c Either single 1.40 1.40
        Nos. 1398-1401 (4)   8.00 8.00

Christmas
A258

Inscriptions: 15c, Gabriel Visits Mary. 25c,
The Road to Bethlehem. 50c, No Room at the
Inn. 65c, Jesus in a Manger. 70c, The Angel
Visits the Shepherds. 80c, The Three Kings.

Perf. 13¼x12½
2013, Nov. 19   Litho.
1402-1407 A258 Set of 6   6.25 6.25

Royal
Christenings
A259

Photograph from christening of: 15c, Queen
Elizabeth II, 1926. 50c, Prince Charles, 1948.
65c, Prince William, 1982. 70c, Prince
George, 2013.

2014, May 21   Litho.   Perf. 13¼x13
1408-1411 A259 Set of 4   4.00 4.00

Bahamas National Geographic Information Systems Center, 10th Anniv. — A260

Emblem and: 15c, Map of Bahamas with delineated maritime boundaries. 50c, 1960-2012 hurricane distribution map. 65c, Surveyors verifying maritime boundaries. 70c, Data collection on Inagua Island.

2014, July 21   Litho.   Perf. 12¾x13
1412-1415 A260   Set of 4   4.00 4.00

World's First Undersea Post Office, 75th Anniv. — A261

Inscriptions: 15c, The 1914 Williamson Photosphere Film Project (observation chamber under boat). 50c, Underwater photography (film, photographer, octopus). 65c, The Williamson Photosphere (fish near observation chamber). 70c, John Ernest Williamson (1881-1966), Bahamas #106.

Perf. 12¾x13¼
2014, Aug. 16   Litho.
1416-1419 A261   Set of 4   4.00 4.00

Ministry of Tourism. 50th Anniv. A262

Hotels: No. 1420, 50c, Peace & Plenty Hotel, Exuma. No. 1421, 50c, Princess Resort & Casino, Freeport. No. 1422, 50c, Baha Mar Hotel, Nassau. No. 1423, 50c, Atlantis Hotel, Paradise Island.

2014, Oct. 27   Litho.   Perf. 14
1420-1423 A262   Set of 4   4.00 4.00

Christmas — A263

Inscriptions: 15c, "Peace on Earth." 50c, "Tidings of Great Joy." 65c, "A Time for Giving." 70c, "A Saviour is Born."

Perf. 14¼x14¾
2014, Nov. 11   Litho.
1424-1427 A263   Set of 4   4.00 4.00

World Day of Prayer — A264

Art: 15c, Never Forget How to Serve, by Jessica Colebrooke. 50c, Blessed, by Chantal Bethel. 65c, The Master Key, by Tyrone Ferguson.

2015, Mar. 6   Litho.   Perf. 14
1428-1430 A264   Set of 3   2.60 2.60

Magna Carta, 800th Anniv. A265

Designs: 15c, King John examining Magna Carta. 50c, Bahamas Supreme Court, Nassau. 65c, Bahamas House of Assembly, Nassau. 70c, King John on coin.

Perf. 13¼x13½
2015, June 15   Litho.
1431-1434 A265   Set of 4   4.00 4.00

Queen Elizabeth II, Longest-Reigning British Monarch — A266

Queen Elizabeth II and events during her reign: 15c, Bahamas #157 and cover with coronation cachet. 50c, Visit of Princess Margaret to Bahamas General Hospital, 1966. 65c, Meeting with Governor-General Sir Milo Butler, 1975. 70c, Prince Harry meeting with Boy Scouts, 2012.

2015, Sept. 9   Litho.   Perf. 14
1435-1438 A266   Set of 4   4.00 4.00

Bahamas Girl Guides, Cent. A267

Emblem and: 15c, Rangers, Guides, Brownies and Sunflower at Camp Discovery. 25c, Patrol pitching camp tent at Gwen French site. 50c, Guides building campfire. 65c, Rangers in kayaks. 70c, Brownies with grandmother. 80c, Four early Girl Guide Commissioners.

2015, Oct. 1   Litho.   Perf. 14
1439-1444 A267   Set of 6   6.25 6.25

Christmas — A268

Designs: 15c, Holy Family. 50c, Shepherds. 65c, Magi. 70c, Infant Jesus in manger.

Perf. 13½x13¼
2015, Nov. 19   Litho.
1445-1448 A268   Set of 4   4.00 4.00

Bahamas Marine Mammal Research Organization, 25th Anniv. — A269

Designs: 15c, Pantropical spotted dolphins. 50c, Bottlenose dolphins. 65c, Atlantic spotted dolphin. 70c, Rough-toothed dolphin.

2016, Mar. 31   Litho.   Perf. 14
1449-1452 A269   Set of 4   4.00 4.00
    See Nos. 1466-1469.

Queen Elizabeth II, 90th Birthday — A270

Photographs of Queen Elizabeth II from: 15c, 1965. 50c, 1961. 65c, 2007. 70c, 1992. $4, Queen Elizabeth II in 1966.

2016, Apr. 21   Litho.   Perf. 14
1453-1456 A270   Set of 4   4.00 4.00
Souvenir Sheet
1457 A270 $4 multi   8.00 8.00

2016 Summer Olympics, Rio de Janeiro A271

Designs: 15c, High jump. 50c, Sprinter. 65c, Relay race. 70c, Triple jump.

2016, Aug. 10   Litho.   Perf. 13¼
1458-1461 A271   Set of 4   4.00 4.00

Christmas A272

Designs: 15c, Adoration of the Shepherds. 50c, Holy Family at manger. 65c, Adoration of the Magi. 70c, Holy Family in stable.

2016, Nov. 14   Litho.   Perf. 13¼
1462-1465 A272   Set of 4   4.00 4.00

Bahamas Marine Mammal Research Organization Type of 2016
Designs: 15c, Sperm whale. 50c, Short-finned pilot whale. 65c, Blainville's beaked whales. 70c, Dwarf sperm whale.

2017, Apr. 10   Litho.   Perf. 13¼
1466-1469 A269   Set of 4   4.00 4.00

SEMI-POSTAL STAMPS

No. 48 Overprinted in Red

1917, May 18   Wmk. 3   Perf. 14
B1 A6 1p car & black   .50 2.50

Type of 1911 Overprinted in Red

1919, Jan. 1
B2 A6 1p red & black   .40 3.25
  a. Double overprint   2,750.

This stamp was originally scheduled for release in 1918.

No. 694 Surcharged
Souvenir Sheet

Wmk. 384
1992, Nov. 16   Litho.   Perf. 14
B3 A116 Sheet of 2, #a.-b.   19.00 19.00

AIR POST STAMPS

Catalogue values for all unused stamps in this section are for Never Hinged items.

Manned Flight Bicentenary — AP1

Airplanes — 10c, Consolidated Catalina. 25c, Avro Tudor IV. 31c, Avro Lancastrian. 35c, Consolidated Commodore.

Wmk. 373
1983, Oct. 13   Litho.   Perf. 14
C1 AP1 10c multicolored   .65 .25
  a. Without emblem ('85)   3.00 .50
  b. Without emblem, wmk. 384 ('86) 2.50 1.00
C2 AP1 25c multicolored   .85 .40
  a. Without emblem ('85)   6.00 1.00
  b. Without emblem, wmk. 384 ('86) 5.00 2.00
C3 AP1 31c multicolored   1.00 .55
  a. Without emblem ('85)   1.75 .55
C4 AP1 35c multicolored   .80 .60
  a. Without emblem ('85)   3.25 .65
    Nos. C1-C4 (4)   3.30 1.80

Aircraft AP2

15c, Bahamasair Boeing 737. 40c, Eastern Boeing 757. 45c, Pan Am Airbus A300 B4. 50c, British Airways Boeing 747.

1987, July 7
C5 AP2 15c multicolored   3.50 2.50
C6 AP2 40c multicolored   4.50 3.00
C7 AP2 45c multicolored   4.50 3.00
C8 AP2 50c multicolored   4.50 4.50
    Nos. C5-C8 (4)   17.00 13.00

SPECIAL DELIVERY STAMPS

No. 34 Overprinted

1916   **Wmk. 1**   *Perf. 14*

E1	A6	5p orange & black	7.50	47.50
a.		Double overprint	*1,000.*	*1,500.*
b.		Inverted overprint	*1,750.*	*1,800.*
c.		Double ovpt., one invtd.	*1,550.*	*1,750.*
d.		Pair, one without overprint	*35,000.*	*50,000.*

The No. E1 overprint exists in two types. Type I (illustrated) is much scarcer. Type II shows "SPECIAL" farther right, so that the letter "I" is slightly right of the vertical line of the "E" below it.

Type of Regular Issue of 1903 Overprinted

1917, July 2   **Wmk. 3**

E2	A6	5p orange & black	.80	11.00

No. 60 Overprinted in Red

1918

E3	A6	5p violet & black	.60	4.25

WAR TAX STAMPS

Stamps of 1912-18 Overprinted

1918, Feb. 21   **Wmk. 3**   *Perf. 14*

MR1	A8	½p green	14.00	55.00
a.		Double overprint	*1,000.*	
b.		Inverted overprint	—	—
MR2	A8	1p car rose	1.25	1.00
a.		Double overprint	—	—
b.		Inverted overprint	—	—
MR3	A6	3p brown, *yel*	3.75	3.50
a.		Inverted overprint	*1,400.*	*1,500.*
b.		Double overprint	*2,000.*	*2,150.*
MR4	A8	1sh black & red	125.00	175.00
a.		Double overprint	—	—
		Nos. MR1-MR4 (4)	*144.00*	*234.50*

Same Overprint on No. 48a

1918, July 10

MR5	A6	1p car & black	4.75	11.00
a.		Double overprint	*2,150.*	*2,400.*
b.		Double ovpt., one invtd.	*1,100.*	—
c.		Inverted overprint	*1,900.*	*2,000.*

Nos. 49-50, 54 Overprinted in Black or Red

MR6	A8	½p green	2.25	2.25
MR7	A8	1p car rose	4.50	.65
a.		Watermarked sideways	400.00	
MR8	A8	1sh black & red (R)	14.00	7.50
		Nos. MR6-MR8 (3)	*20.75*	*10.40*

Nos. 58-59 Overprinted

1918-19

MR9	A6	3p brown, *yel*	1.00	3.25
MR10	A6	3p brown & blk ('19)	2.25	7.00

Nos. 49-50, 54 Overprinted in Red or Black

1919, July 14

MR11	A8	½p green (R)	.40	1.60
MR12	A8	1p car rose	1.90	2.25
MR13	A8	1sh blk & red (R)	27.50	60.00
		Nos. MR11-MR13 (3)	*29.80*	*63.85*

No. 59 Overprinted

MR14	A6	3p brn & blk	2.00	10.00

BAHRAIN

bä-'rän

LOCATION — An archipelago in the Persian Gulf, including the islands of Bahrain, Muharraq, Sitra, Nebi Saleh, Kasasifeh and Arad.
GOVT. — Independent sheikdom
AREA — 255 sq. mi.
POP. — 629,090 (1999 est.)
CAPITAL — Manama

Bahrain was a British-protected territory until it became an independent state on August 15, 1971.

12 Pies = 1 Anna
16 Annas = 1 Rupee
100 Naye Paise = 1 Rupee (1957)
1000 Fils = 1 Dinar (1966)

Catalogue values for unused stamps in this country are for Never Hinged items, beginning with Scott 62.

Indian Postal Administration

Stamps of India, 1926-32, Overprinted in Black — a

Wmk. Multiple Stars (196)

1933, Aug. 10   *Perf. 14*

1	A46	3p gray	4.50	.90
2	A47	½a green	12.00	5.25
3	A68	9p dark green	5.00	5.50
4	A48	1a dark brown	11.00	3.75
5	A69	1a3p violet	18.00	5.00
6	A60	2a vermilion	12.00	22.50
7	A51	3a blue	22.50	80.00
8	A70	3a6p deep blue	7.00	.75
9	A61	4a olive green	20.00	82.50
10	A54	8a red violet	10.00	.55
11	A55	12a claret	9.00	3.25

Overprinted in Black — b

12	A56	1r green & brown	20.00	17.00
13	A56	2r brn org & car rose	37.50	50.00
14	A56	5r dk violet & ultra	300.00	250.00
		Nos. 1-14 (14)	*488.50*	*526.95*

No. 14 is more common with an inverted watermark. Value $175.

Stamps of India, 1926-32, Overprinted Type "a" in Black

1934

15	A72	1a dark brown	15.00	.65
a.		Complete booklet, containing 16 #15, wmk inverted, in four blocks of 4	*1,500.*	
16	A51	3a carmine rose	8.50	.80
17	A52	4a olive green	9.75	.75
		Nos. 15-17 (3)	*33.25*	*2.20*

The cover of No. 15a is red and black on tan, with Mysore Sandal Soup advertisement on front.

India Nos. 138, 111, 111a Overprinted Type "a" in Black

1935-37   *Perf. 13½x14, 14*

18	A71	½a green	10.00	2.25
19	A49	2a vermilion	65.00	10.00
a.		Small die ('37)	100.00	.30

India Stamps of 1937 Overprinted Type "a" in Black

1938-41   **Wmk. 196**   *Perf. 13½x14*

20	A80	3p slate	12.00	9.00
21	A80	½a brown	7.00	.35
22	A80	9p green	9.00	15.00
23	A80	1a carmine	8.00	.35
24	A81	2a scarlet	4.00	6.50
26	A81	3a yel grn ('41)	8.00	13.00
27	A81	3a6p ultra	4.00	11.00
28	A81	4a dk brn ('41)	125.00	95.00
30	A81	8a bl vio ('40)	180.00	45.00
31	A81	12a car lake ('40)	105.00	60.00

Overprinted Type "b" in Black

32	A82	1r brn & slate	4.75	3.00
33	A82	2r dk brn & dk vio	12.00	12.00
34	A82	5r dp ultra & dk grn	10.00	17.50
35	A82	10r rose car & dk vio ('41)	60.00	65.00
36	A82	15r dk grn & dk brn ('41)	60.00	97.50
37	A82	25r dk vio & bl vio ('41)	95.00	120.00
		Nos. 20-37 (16)	*703.75*	*570.20*
		Set, never hinged	*1,000.*	

India Stamps of 1941-43 Overprinted Type "a" in Black

1942-44   **Wmk. 196**   *Perf. 13½x14*

38	A83	3p slate	2.00	2.75
39	A83	½a rose vio ('44)	3.00	4.75
40	A83	9p lt green ('43)	11.00	27.50
41	A83	1a car rose ('44)	5.00	1.25
42	A84	1a3p bister ('43)	6.50	25.00
43	A84	1½a dk pur ('43)	4.25	9.00
44	A84	2a scarlet ('43)	4.25	2.25
46	A84	3a violet ('43)	14.00	8.50
47	A84	3½a ultra	4.50	30.00
48	A85	4a chocolate	3.00	.275
49	A85	6a peacock blue	14.00	13.50
50	A85	8a blue vio ('43)	7.00	4.75
51	A85	12a car lake	10.00	6.75
		Nos. 38-51 (13)	*88.50*	*136.28*
		Set, never hinged	*135.00*	

British Postal Administration

See Oman (Muscat) for similar stamps with surcharge of new value only.

Great Britain Nos. 258 to 263, 243 and 248 Surcharged in Black — c

1948-49   **Wmk. 251**   *Perf. 14½x14*

52	A101	½a on ½p green	.50	1.75
53	A101	1a on 1p vermilion	.50	3.50
54	A101	1½a on 1½p lt red brn	.50	4.75
55	A101	2a on 2p lt orange	.50	.30
56	A101	2½a on 2½p ultra	.75	7.00
57	A101	3a on 3p violet	.50	.30
58	A102	6a on 6p rose lilac	.50	.30
59	A103	1r on 1sh brown	1.25	.35

Great Britain Nos. 249A, 250 and 251A Surcharged in Black

Wmk. 259   *Perf. 14*

60	A104	2r on 2sh6p yel grn	4.50	8.00
61	A104	5r on 5sh dull red	4.75	8.50
61A	A105	10r on 10sh ultra	65.00	70.00
		Nos. 52-61A (11)	*79.25*	*104.75*
		Set, never hinged	115.00	

Surcharge bars at bottom on No. 61A.
Issued: 10r, 7/4/49; others, 4/1/48.

Catalogue values for unused stamps in this section, from this point to the end of the section, are for Never Hinged items.

Silver Wedding Issue
Great Britain Nos. 267 and 268 Surcharged in Black

Perf. 14½x14, 14x14½

1948, Apr. 26   **Wmk. 251**

62	A109	2½a on 2½p	1.00	2.75
63	A110	15r on £1	37.50	55.00

Three bars obliterate the original denomination on No. 63.

Olympic Issue

1948, July 29   *Perf. 14½x14*

64	A113	2½a on 2½p brt ultra	1.40	4.75
a.		Double surcharge	*3,500.*	*4,250.*
65	A114	3a on 3p dp vio	1.10	4.25
66	A115	6a on 6p red vio	1.75	4.25
67	A116	1r on 1sh dk brn	2.75	4.25
		Nos. 64-67 (4)	*7.00*	*17.50*

A square of dots obliterates the original denomination on No. 67.

UPU Issue

Great Britain No. 276 Srchd. in Black

Great Britain Nos. 277-279 Srchd. in Black

1949, Oct. 10   Photo.   *Perf. 14½x14*

68	A117	2½a on 2½p brt ultra	.90	3.50
69	A118	3a on 3p brt vio	1.10	5.25
70	A119	6a on 6p red vio	1.00	3.75
71	A120	1r on 1sh brown	1.75	4.00
		Nos. 68-71 (4)	*4.75*	*16.50*

Great Britain Nos. 280-285 Surcharged Type "c" in Black

1950-51   **Wmk. 251**

72	A101	½a on ½p lt org	3.00	3.00
73	A101	1a on 1p ultra	3.50	.35
74	A101	1½a on 1½p green	3.50	17.50
75	A101	2a on 2p lt red brn	2.00	.35
76	A101	2½a on 2½p ver	3.75	17.50
77	A102	4a on 4p ultra	5.00	1.90

Great Britain Nos. 286-288 Surcharged in Black

Type I

Three types of surcharge on No. 78: Type I, "2" level with "RUPEES;" Type II, "2" raised higher than "RUPEES," 15mm between "BAHRAIN" and "2 RUPEES;" Type III, as type II, but 16mm between "BAHRAIN" and "2 RUPEES."

Perf. 11x12
Wmk. 259

78	A121	2r on 2sh6p green, type I ('51)	45.00	17.50
a.		2r on 2sh6p, type III ('55)	140.00	55.00
b.		2r on 2sh6p, type III ('55)	1,750.	150.00
79	A121	5r on 5sh dl red	17.50	7.00
80	A122	10r on 10sh ultra	42.50	12.00
		Nos. 72-80 (9)	125.75	77.10

Longer bars, at lower right, on No. 80.
Issued: 4a, Nov. 2, 1950; others, May 3, 1951.

Great Britain 1952-54 Stamps Surcharged in Black or Dark Blue

1952-54		Wmk. 298	Perf. 14½x14	
81	A126	½a on ½p red org ('53)	.25	.25
a.		"½" omitted	225.00	400.00
82	A126	1a on 1p red	.45	.25
83	A126	1½a on 1½p grn	.45	.25
84	A126	2a on 2p red brn	.45	.25
85	A127	2½a on 2½p scar	.60	1.75
86	A127	3a on 3p dk pur (Dk Bl)	1.25	.25
87	A128	4a on 4p ultra	6.75	.50
88	A129	6a on 6p lil rose	6.00	.45
89	A132	12a on 1sh3p dk grn	6.00	.75
90	A131	1r on 1sh6p dk bl	6.00	1.00
		Nos. 81-90 (10)	28.20	5.70

Issued: Nos. 83, 85, 12/5; Nos. 81-82, 84, 8/31/53; Nos. 87, 89-90, 11/2/53; Nos. 86, 88, 1/18/54.

Six stamps of this design picturing Sheik Sulman bin Hamad Al Kalifah were for local use in 1953-57. Value, mint set $30.
Six stamps of similar design (same sheik, "Bahrain" vertical at left) were issued in 1961 for local use. Value, mint set, $12.50.

Coronation Issue
Great Britain Nos. 313-316 Surcharged "BAHRAIN" and New Value in Black
Perf. 14½x14

1953, June 3			Wmk. 298	
92	A134	2½a on 2½p scar	1.25	1.00
93	A135	4a on 4p brt ultra	2.00	5.00
94	A136	12a on 1sh3p dk grn	5.75	4.50
95	A137	1r on 1sh6p dk bl	6.25	2.25
		Nos. 92-95 (4)	15.25	12.75

Squares of dots obliterate the original denominations on Nos. 94-95.

Great Britain Nos. 309-311 Surcharged "BAHRAIN" and New Value in Black

1955	Wmk. 308	Engr.	Perf. 11x12	
96	A133	2r on 2sh6p dk brn	5.50	2.00
97	A133	5r on 5sh crimson	8.75	3.00
98	A133	10r on 10sh brt ultra	22.50	3.00
		Nos. 96-98 (3)	36.75	8.00

Three slightly different types of surcharge are found on the 2r; two on 5r and 10r.

Great Britain Nos. 317, 323, 325, 332-333 Surcharged "BAHRAIN" and New Value
Perf. 14½x14

1956-57		Wmk. 308	Photo.	
99	A126	½a on ½p red org	.55	.25
100	A128	4a on 4p ultra	6.50	22.50
101	A129	6a on 6p lil rose	1.00	.80
102	A132	12a on 1sh3p dk green	7.75	12.00
103	A131	1r on 1sh6p dk bl ('57)	11.50	.25
		Nos. 99-103 (5)	27.30	35.80

No. 103 exists with double surcharge. Value $5,000.

Great Britain Nos. 317-325, 328, 332 Surcharged "BAHRAIN" and New Value

1957, Apr. 1				
104	A129	1np on 5p lt brown	.25	.25
105	A126	3np on ½p red org	.50	3.00
106	A126	6np on 1p ultra	.50	3.00
107	A126	9np on 1½p green	.50	3.00
108	A126	12np on 2p red brn	.35	.70
109	A127	15np on 2½p scar, type I	.40	.25
a.		Type II	1.10	5.50
110	A127	20np on 3p dk pur	.25	.25
111	A128	25np on 4p ultra	1.00	2.50
112	A129	40np on 6p lil rose	.75	.25
113	A130	50np on 9p dp ol grn	3.75	4.50
114	A132	75np on 1sh3p dk grn	2.50	.60
		Nos. 104-114 (11)	10.75	18.30

The arrangement of the surcharge varies on different values: there are three bars through value on No. 113.

Jubilee Jamboree Issue
Great Britain Nos. 334-336 Surcharged "BAHRAIN," New Value and Square of Dots in Black
Perf. 14½x14

1957, Aug. 1		Photo.	Wmk. 308	
115	A138	15np on 2½p scar	.35	.35
116	A138	25np on 4p ultra	.50	.50
117	A138	75np on 1sh3p dk grn	.75	.75
		Nos. 115-117 (3)	1.60	1.60

Great Britain No. 357 Surcharged "BAHRAIN/ NP 15 NP" in Black

1960		Wmk. 322	Perf. 14½x14	
118	A127	15np on 2½p scar, type II	5.00	12.00

A1

Sheik Sulman bin Hamad Al Khalifah — A2

Perf. 14½x14

1960, July 1		Photo.	Unwmk.	
119	A1	5np lt ultra	.25	.25
120	A1	15np orange	.25	.25
121	A1	20np lt violet	.25	.25
122	A1	30np olive bister	.25	.25
123	A1	40np gray	.25	.25
124	A1	50np emerald	.25	.25
125	A1	75np red brown	.35	.25

Engr.
Perf. 13x13½

126	A2	1r gray	2.50	.35
127	A2	2r carmine	3.50	2.50
128	A2	5r ultra	5.50	3.50
129	A2	10r olive green	15.50	6.00
		Nos. 119-129 (11)	28.85	14.10

Sheik Isa bin Sulman Al Khalifah A3

Bahrain Airport A4

Designs: 5r, 10r, Deep water jetty.

1964, Feb. 22		Photo.	Perf. 14½x14	
130	A3	5np ultra	.25	.25
131	A3	15np orange	.25	.25
132	A3	20np brt purple	.25	.25
133	A3	30np brown olive	.25	.25
134	A3	40np slate	.25	.25
135	A3	50np emerald	.25	.90
136	A3	75np chestnut	.30	.25

Engr.
Perf. 13½x13

137	A4	1r black	9.00	2.40
138	A4	2r rose red	11.00	3.00
139	A4	5r violet blue	15.00	15.00
140	A4	10r dull green	19.00	20.00
		Nos. 130-140 (11)	55.80	42.80

Bahrain Postal Administration

Sheik Isa bin Sulman Al Khalifah — A5

Sheik and Bahrain International Airport — A6

Pearl Divers — A7

Bab al Bahrain, Suq Al-Khamis Mosque, Sheik, Emblem, etc. — A8

Designs: 50f, 75f, Pier, Mina Sulman harbor. 200f, Falcon and horse race. 500f, "Hospitality," pouring coffee and Sheik's Palace.

Perf. 14½x14

1966, Jan. 1		Photo.	Unwmk.	
141	A5	5f green	.50	.35
142	A5	10f dark red	.50	.35
143	A5	15f ultra	.50	.35
144	A5	20f magenta	.50	.35

Perf. 13½x14

145	A6	30f green & black	.60	.35
146	A6	40f blue & black	.70	.35
147	A6	50f dp car rose & blk	.80	.55
148	A6	75f violet & black	1.00	.70

Perf. 14½x14

149	A7	100f dk blue & yel	3.25	1.25
150	A7	200f dk green & org	14.00	2.75
151	A7	500f red brown & yel	12.00	5.00
152	A8	1d multicolored	21.00	10.00
		Nos. 141-152 (12)	55.35	22.35

Produce, Date Palm, Ship, Truck and Plane — A9

1966, Mar. 28		Litho.	Perf. 13x13½	
153	A9	10f red & blue green	.80	.35
154	A9	20f green & vio	1.25	.75
155	A9	40f olive bis & lt bl	2.75	1.50
156	A9	200f vio blue & pink	11.00	9.00
		Nos. 153-156 (4)	15.80	11.60

6th Bahrain Trade Fair & Agricultural Show.

Map of Bahrain and WHO Emblem — A10

1968, June		Unwmk.	Perf. 13½x14	
157	A10	20f gray & black	.90	.60
158	A10	40f blue grn & black	3.00	1.75
159	A10	150f dp rose & black	12.00	6.00
		Nos. 157-159 (3)	15.90	8.35

20th anniv. of the WHO.

Isa Town A11

1968, Nov. 18		Litho.	Perf. 14½	
160	A11	50f shown	5.00	2.00
161	A11	80f Market	7.50	2.75
162	A11	120f Stadium	12.00	5.00
163	A11	150f Mosque	13.50	7.25
		Nos. 160-163 (4)	38.00	17.00

Education Symbol — A12

1969, Apr.		Litho.	Perf. 13	
164	A12	40f multicolored	1.90	1.40
165	A12	60f multicolored	4.00	2.25
166	A12	150f multicolored	9.25	4.75
		Nos. 164-166 (3)	15.15	8.40

50th anniversary of education in Bahrain.

Map of Arabian Gulf, Radar and Emblem A13

Designs: 40f, 150f, Radar installation and emblem of Cable & Wireless Ltd., vert.

Perf. 14x13½, 13½x14

1969, July 14   Litho.
167 A13 20f lt green & multi   3.00   .85
168 A13 40f vio blue & multi   5.50   2.00
169 A13 100f ocher & multi   12.00   5.25
170 A13 150f rose lilac & multi 20.00   8.50
        Nos. 167-170 (4)   40.50 16.60

Opening of the satellite earth station (connected through the Indian Ocean satellite Intelsat III) at Ras Abu Jarjur, July 14.

Municipal Building, Arms and Map of Bahrain A14

1970, Feb. 23   Litho.   Perf. 12x12½
171 A14 30f blue & multi   3.00   3.00
172 A14 150f multicolored   14.50 14.50

2nd Conf. of the Arab Cities' Org.

Copper Bull's Head A15

Conf. Emblem and: 80f, Gateway to Qalat al Bahrain, 7th cent. B.C. 120f, Aerial view of grave mounds, Bahrain. 150f, Dilmun seal, 2000 B.C.

1970, Mar. 1   Photo.   Perf. 14½
173 A15 60f multicolored   5.00   2.25
174 A15 80f multicolored   7.00   2.50
175 A15 120f multicolored   8.50   4.00
176 A15 150f multicolored   10.00   4.75
        Nos. 173-176 (4)   30.50 13.50

3rd Intl. Asian Archaeological Conf., Bahrain.

Vickers VC 10, Big Ben and Minaret A16

1970, Apr. 5   Litho.   Perf. 14½x14
177 A16 30f multicolored   4.25   .90
178 A16 60f multicolored   7.50   2.00
179 A16 120f multicolored   13.00   6.25
        Nos. 177-179 (3)   24.75   9.15

1st flight to London from the Arabian Gulf Area by Gulf Aviation Company.

Intl. Education Year Emblem A17

120f, Education Year emblem & students.

1970, Nov. 1   Litho.   Perf. 14½x14
180 A17 60f blk, blue & org   6.00   3.50
181 A17 120f multicolored   11.50   7.00

Independent State

Declaration of Bahrain Independence, Aug. 15, 1971 — A18

Designs: 30f, "Freedom" with dove and torch, and globe. 60f, Government House, Manama. 120f, 150f, Bahrain coat of arms.

1971, Oct. 2   Photo.   Perf. 14½x14
182 A18 30f gold & multi   2.80   1.25
183 A18 60f gold & multi   5.00   2.75
184 A18 120f gold & multi   11.00   6.00
185 A18 150f gold & multi   15.00   7.50
        Nos. 182-185 (4)   33.80 17.50

UN Emblem and Sails — A19

30f, 60f, Dhow with sails showing UN and Arab League emblems, horiz. 150f, as 120f.

Perf. 14x14½, 14½x14

1972, Feb. 1   Litho.
186 A19 30f multicolored   5.50   5.00
187 A19 60f red, gray & multi   9.00   8.50
188 A19 120f dull blue & multi 12.00 11.00
189 A19 150f multicolored   22.00 21.00
        Nos. 186-189 (4)   48.50 45.50

Bahrain's admission to the Arab League and the United Nations.

"Your Heart is your Health" — A20

1972, Apr. 7   Litho.   Perf. 14½x14
190 A20 30f black & multi   6.00   6.00
191 A20 60f gray & multi   11.00 11.00

World Health Day.

UN and FAO Emblems A21

1973, May 12   Litho.   Perf. 12½x13
192 A21 30f org red, pur & grn   5.75   5.25
193 A21 60f ocher, brn & grn   9.75   9.50

World Food Programs, 10th anniversary.

People of Various Races, Human Rights Flame — A22

1973, Nov.   Litho.   Perf. 14x14½
194 A22 30f blue, blk & brn   5.75   5.75
195 A22 60f lake, blk & brn   10.00 10.00

25th anniversary of the Universal Declaration of Human Rights.

Flour Mill A23

60f, Intl. Airport. 120f, Sulmaniya Medical Center. 150f, ALBA aluminum smelting plant.

1973, Dec. 16   Photo.   Perf. 14½
196 A23 30f multicolored   2.00   1.25
197 A23 60f multicolored   3.00   2.50
198 A23 120f multicolored   6.00   4.25
199 A23 150f multicolored   6.50   5.00
        Nos. 196-199 (4)   17.50 12.50

National Day.

Letters and UPU Emblem — A24

Carrier Pigeon and UPU Emblem A25

60f, UPU emblem & letters. 150f, Like 120f.

1974, Feb. 4   Litho.   Perf. 13½
200 A24 30f blue & multi   2.00   2.00
201 A24 60f emerald & multi   3.50   3.50

Perf. 12½x13½
202 A25 120f ultra & multi   3.75   3.75
203 A25 150f yellow & multi   5.50   5.50
        Nos. 200-203 (4)   14.75 14.75

Bahrain's admission to UPU.

Traffic Signals — A26

1974, May 4   Litho.   Perf. 14½
204 A26 30f org brown & multi   4.00   4.00
205 A26 60f brt blue & multi   8.00   8.00

International Traffic Day.

Jet, Globe, Mail Coach and UPU Emblem — A27

1974, Sept. 1   Photo.   Perf. 14x14½
206 A27 30f multicolored   1.00   1.00
207 A27 60f multicolored   1.50   1.50
208 A27 120f multicolored   3.75   3.75
209 A27 150f multicolored   4.50   4.50
        Nos. 206-209 (4)   10.75 10.75

Centenary of Universal Postal Union.

National Day Emblem, Sitra Power Station — A28

National Day: 120f, 150f, Bahrain dry dock.

1974, Dec. 16   Litho.   Perf. 14½
210 A28 30f blue & multi   .90   .90
211 A28 60f green & multi   2.40   2.40
212 A28 120f lil rose & multi   4.00   4.00
213 A28 150f ver & multi   5.25   5.25
        Nos. 210-213 (4)   12.55 12.55

Woman's Silk Gown — A29

Various women's costumes.

Photo.; Gold Embossed
1975, Feb. 1   Perf. 14½x14
214 A29 30f blue grn & multi   .95   .95
215 A29 60f vio blue & multi   1.75   1.75
216 A29 120f rose red & multi   3.75   3.75
217 A29 150f multicolored   4.50   4.50
        Nos. 214-217 (4)   10.95 10.95

Pendant — A30

Designs: Various jewelry.

1975, Apr. 1   Photo.   Perf. 14½x14
218 A30 30f olive & multi   1.10   1.10
219 A30 60f dp pur & multi   2.50   2.50
220 A30 120f dp car & multi   4.25   4.25
221 A30 150f dp blue & multi   5.50   5.50
        Nos. 218-221 (4)   13.35 13.35

Woman Planting Flower, IWY Emblem — A31

60f, Educated woman holding IWY emblem.

1975, July 28   Litho.   Perf. 14½
222 A31 30f multicolored   2.25 2.25
223 A31 60f multicolored   5.50 5.50

International Women's Year.

Miniature Sheet

Arabian Stallion — A32

No. 224 — Arabian horses: a, Brown head. b, White mare. c, Mare and foal. d, White head. e, White mare. f, Mare and stallion. g, Bedouins on horseback. Nos. 224a, 224b, 224d are vert.

Perf. 14x14½, 14½x14
1975, Sept. 1   Photo.
224 A32 Sheet of 8   62.50 62.50
a.-h.   60f any single   6.25   6.25

Flag of Bahrain — A33

Map of Bahrain — A34

Sheik Isa — A35

1976-2000   Litho.   Perf. 14½
225 A33 5f red & ultra   .35   .35
a.   Perf. 14½x13½
226 A33 10f red & green   .35   .35
a.   Perf. 14½x13½
227 A33 15f red & black   .35   .35
a.   Perf. 14½x13½
228 A33 20f red & brown   .55   .35
b.   Perf. 14½x13½   .65   .35
228A A34 25f gray & blk
         ('79)   .65   .65
229 A34 40f blue & black   .65   .45
229A A34 50f yel grn & blk
         ('79)   .65   .55
a.   Bold imprint ('88)   4.25   .90
230 A34 60f dl grn & blk
         ('77)   1.15   .65
231 A34 80f rose lil & blk   1.75   .80
a.   Bold imprint ('88)   4.25 1.50
232 A34 100f lt red brn &
         blk ('77)   1.75   .95
a.   Bold imprint ('88)   4.25 2.00

233 A34 150f org & black   3.25 1.60
a.   Bold imprint ('88)   4.25 3.75
234 A34 200f yel & black   4.00 1.75
a.   Bold imprint ('88)   4.25 4.25

Engr.
Perf. 12x12½
235 A35 300f lt grn & grn   4.50 2.50
a.   Perf. 13½x14 ('90)   6.00 2.75
236 A35 400f pink & red
         brn   6.50 4.00
a.   Perf. 13½x14 ('90)   8.00 4.50
b.   Perf. 14½ ('94)   67.50 45.00
237 A35 500f lt bl & dk bl   9.00 4.25
a.   Perf. 13½x14 ('90)   9.75 5.25
238 A35 1d gray & sepia   14.50 7.50
a.   Perf. 13½x14 ('90)   16.50 8.50
b.   1d cream & sepia ('93)   37.50 25.00
c.   As b, perf. 13½x14 ('90) 15.50 8.00
d.   1d pale grn & sepia ('00) 37.50 25.00
239 A35 2d rose & vio
         ('80)   22.50 10.00
a.   Perf. 13½x14 ('96)   23.00 12.50
240 A35 3d buff & brn
         ('80)   40.00 20.00
a.   Perf. 13½x14 ('96)   45.00 21.00
Nos. 225-240 (18)   112.45 56.75

Nos. 229Ab, 231a-234a have printer's imprint in bold in bottom margin, with narrower spacing, and a hyphen after "PRESS."
The 300f-1d stamps were reprinted in slightly different shades with new denominations (2d-3d) in 1980. All are on thicker paper with matte gum; original printings have shiny gum. Values, each: $22 unused, and $11 used.

Concorde at London Airport — A36

Designs: No. 245, Concorde at Bahrain Airport. No. 246, Concorde over London to Bahrain map. No. 247, Concorde on runway at night.

1976, Jan. 22   Photo.   Perf. 13x14
244 A36 80f gold & multi   3.75 2.50
245 A36 80f gold & multi   3.75 2.50
246 A36 80f gold & multi   3.75 2.50
247 A36 80f gold & multi   3.75 2.50
a.   Souvenir sheet of 4   17.00 17.00
b.   Block of 4, #244-247   16.00 15.00

1st commercial flight of supersonic jet Concorde, London to Bahrain, Jan. 21. No. 247a contains 4 stamps with simulated perfs.

Soldier, Flag and Arms of Bahrain — A37

1976, Feb. 5   Litho.   Perf. 14½
248 A37 40f yellow & multi   3.00 3.00
249 A37 80f lt blue & multi   5.00 5.00

Defense Force Day.

Sheik Isa, King Khalid, Bahrain and Saudi Flags A38

1976, Mar. 23   Litho.   Perf. 14½
250 A38 40f gold & multi   3.00 1.50
251 A38 80f silver & multi   5.50 2.75

Visit of King Khalid of Saudi Arabia.

New Housing, Housing Ministry's Seal — A39

1976, Dec. 16   Litho.   Perf. 14½
252 A39 40f rose & multi   2.25 1.20
253 A39 80f blue & multi   4.50 2.25

National Day.

APU Emblem A40

1977, Apr. 12   Litho.   Perf. 14½
254 A40 40f silver & multi   1.80 1.50
255 A40 80f rose & multi   4.50 3.25

Arab Postal Union, 25th anniversary.

Miniature Sheet

Saluki dogs — A41

No. 256 — Saluki dogs: a, Dogs on Beach and Dhow. b, Dog and camels. c, Dog and gazelles. d, Dog and Ruler's Palace. e, Dog's head. f, Heads of two dogs. g, Dog in dunes. h, Playing dogs.

1977, July   Photo.   Perf. 14x14½
256 A41 Sheet of 8   35.00 20.00
a.-h.   80f any single   3.50 2.25

Students and Candle A42

1977, Sept. 8   Litho.   Perf. 14½
257 A42 40f multicolored   2.00 2.00
258 A42 80f multicolored   4.50 4.50

International Literacy Day.

Shipyard and Flags A43

1977, Dec. 16   Litho.   Perf. 14½
259 A43 40f multicolored   2.00 1.50
260 A43 80f multicolored   4.50 3.00

Inauguration of Arab Shipbuilding and Repair Yard Co.

Antenna, ITU Emblem A44

1978, May 17   Litho.   Perf. 14½
261 A44 40f yellow & multi   2.00 1.75
262 A44 80f silver & multi   4.25 3.50

10th World Telecommunications Day.

Ghanja Dhow — A45

Dhows of the Arabian Gulf. Nos. 267-270 vertical.

Perf. 14x14½, 14½x14
1979, June 16   Photo.
263 A45 100f shown   6.00 6.00
264 A45 100f Zarook   6.00 6.00
265 A45 100f Shu'ai   6.00 6.00
266 A45 100f Jaliboot   6.00 6.00
267 A45 100f Baghla   6.00 6.00
268 A45 100f Sambuk   6.00 6.00
269 A45 100f Boom   6.00 6.00
270 A45 100f Kotia   6.00 6.00
a.   Block of 8, #263-270   75.00 75.00

Learning to Walk — A46

IYC Emblem and: 100f, Hands surrounding girl, UN emblem.

1979   Litho.   Perf. 14½
271 A46 50f multicolored   2.00 1.50
272 A46 100f multicolored   4.50 3.00

International Year of the Child.

Hegira, 1,500th Anniv. — A47

1980   Photo.   Perf. 13x13½
273 A47 50f multicolored   .95   .65
274 A47 100f multicolored   1.90 1.35
a.   Miniature sheet of 1   10.50 10.50
275 A47 150f multicolored   2.25 1.60
276 A47 200f multicolored   3.50 2.40
Nos. 273-276 (4)   8.60 6.00

Falcon A48

Various falcons.

Perf. 13½x14, 14x13½
1980, Nov. 1   Photo.
277   Block of 8   35.00 20.00
a.-h.   A48 100f any single   4.00 2.00

IYD Emblem, Sheik Isa A49

1981, Mar. 21   Litho.   Perf. 14½
278 A49 50f multicolored   2.75 1.50
279 A49 100f multicolored   5.25 3.50
International Year of the Disabled.

50th Anniversary of Electricity in Bahrain — A50

1981, Apr. 26   Litho.   Perf. 14½
280 A50 50f multicolored   2.75 1.40
281 A50 100f multicolored   5.25 3.00

Stone Cutting — A51

1981, July 1   Photo.   Perf. 14x13½
282 A51 50f shown   1.25   .65
283 A51 100f Pottery   1.75 1.20
284 A51 150f Weaving   3.00 2.50
285 A51 200f Basket making   3.75 3.00
        Nos. 282-285 (4)   9.75 7.35

Hegira (Pilgrimage Year) — A52

Various mosques.

1981, Oct. 1   Photo.   Perf. 14x13½
286 A52 50f multicolored   1.25 1.00
287 A52 100f multicolored   2.00 1.25
288 A52 150f multicolored   2.25 2.00
289 A52 200f multicolored   3.75 2.75
        Nos. 286-289 (4)   9.25 6.65

Sheik Isa, 20th Anniv. of Coronation A53

1981, Dec. 16   Photo.   Perf. 14x13½
290 A53 15f multicolored   .65   .55
291 A53 50f multicolored   1.20 1.00
292 A53 100f multicolored   2.00 1.75
293 A53 150f multicolored   3.25 3.00
294 A53 200f multicolored   4.00 3.50
        Nos. 290-294 (5)   11.10 9.80

Wildlife in al Areen Park — A54

No. 295: a, Gazelle. b, Oryx. c, Dhub lizard. d, Arabian hares. e, Oryxes. f, Reems.

1982, Mar. 1   Photo.   Perf. 13½x14
295   Sheet of 6   16.50 16.50
  a.-f. A54 100f any single   2.50 2.50
Nos. 295a-b and 295e-f exist with blue omitted.

3rd Session of Gulf Supreme Council, Nov. — A55

1982, Nov. 9   Litho.   Perf. 14½
296 A55 50f blue & multi   1.00 1.00
297 A55 100f green & multi   2.75 2.75

Opening of Madinat Hamad Housing Development — A56

1983, Dec. 1   Litho.   Perf. 14½
298 A56 50f multicolored   1.75   .90
299 A56 100f multicolored   4.00 2.75

Al Khalifa Dynasty Bicentenary — A57

No. 300 — Sheiks or emblems: a, 500fr, Isa bin Sulman. b, Emblem (tan & multi). c, Isa bin Ali, 1869-1932. d, Hamad bin Isa, 1932-42. e, Sulman bin Hamad, 1942-61. f, Emblem (pale green & multi). g, Emblem (lemon & multi). h, Emblem (light blue & multi). i, Emblem (gray & multi).

1983, Dec. 16   Litho.   Perf. 14½
300   Sheet of 9   14.00 14.00
  a.-i. A57 100f any single   1.35 1.35
        Souvenir Sheet
301 A57 500f multicolored   12.00 12.00
No. 301 contains one stamp 60x38mm.

Gulf Co-operation Council Traffic Week — A58

1984, Apr. 30   Litho.   Perf. 14½
302 A58 15f multicolored   .60   .45
303 A58 50f multicolored   1.45 1.00
304 A58 100f multicolored   2.50 2.00
        Nos. 302-304 (3)   4.55 3.45

1984 Summer Olympics A59

1984, Sept. 15   Perf. 14½
305 A59 15f Hurdles   .30   .30
306 A59 50f Equestrian   1.00 1.00
307 A59 100f Diving   2.00 2.00
308 A59 150f Fencing   2.50 2.50
309 A59 200f Shooting   4.00 4.00
        Nos. 305-309 (5)   9.80 9.80

Postal Service Cent. A60

1984, Dec. 8   Photo.   Perf. 12x11½
310 A60 15f multicolored   .55   .45
311 A60 50f multicolored   1.75 1.75
312 A60 100f multicolored   3.00 3.00
        Nos. 310-312 (3)   5.30 5.30

Miniature Sheet

Coastal Fish — A61

Various fish.

1985, Feb. 10   Photo.   Perf. 13½x14
313   A61 Sheet of 10   25.00 25.00
  a.-j. 100f any single   2.00 2.00

1st Arab Gulf States Week for Social Work A62

1985, Oct. 15   Litho.   Perf. 14½
314 A62 15f multicolored   .55   .45
315 A62 50f multicolored   1.35 1.35
316 A62 100f multicolored   3.50 3.00
        Nos. 314-316 (3)   5.40 4.80

Intl. Youth Year A63

1985, Nov. 16
317 A63 15f multicolored   .45   .30
318 A63 50f multicolored   1.20 1.10
319 A63 100f multicolored   3.50 2.25
        Nos. 317-319 (3)   5.15 3.65

Bahrain-Saudi Arabia Causeway Opening — A64

15f, Causeway, aerial view. 50f, Island. 100f, Causeway.

1986, Nov.   Litho.   Perf. 14½
320 A64 15f multicolored   .55   .55
321 A64 50f multicolored   1.45 1.45
322 A64 100f multicolored   2.50 2.50
        Nos. 320-322 (3)   4.50 4.50

Sheik Isa, 25th Anniv. as the Emir — A65

1986, Dec. 16
323 A65 15f multicolored   .50   .50
324 A65 50f multicolored   1.30 1.30
325 A65 100f multicolored   2.25 2.25
  a. Souvenir sheet of 3, #323-325   8.25 8.25
        Nos. 323-325 (3)   4.05 4.05

WHO, 40th Anniv. A66

1988, Apr. 30   Litho.   Perf. 14½
326 A66 50f multicolored   .80   .80
327 A66 150f multicolored   2.25 2.25

Opening of Ahmed Al Fateh Islamic Center A67

1988, June 2   Litho.   Perf. 14½
328 A67 50f multicolored   .80   .80
329 A67 150f multicolored   2.25 2.25

1988 Summer Olympics, Seoul — A68

1988, Sept. 17   Litho.   Perf. 14½
330 A68 50f Running   .50   .50
331 A68 80f Equestrian   .90   .90
332 A68 150f Fencing   1.75 1.75
333 A68 200f Soccer   3.00 3.00
        Nos. 330-333 (4)   6.15 6.15

Gulf Cooperation Council Supreme Council 9th Regular Session, Bahrain — A69

1988, Dec. 19   Litho.   Perf. 14½
334 A69 50f multicolored   .80   .80
335 A69 150f multicolored   2.25 2.25

Miniature Sheets

Camels — A70

No. 336: a, Close-up of head, rider in background. b, Camel kneeling at rest. c, Two adults, calf. d, Three adults. e, Camel facing right. f, Mount and rider (facing left).

No. 337, vert.: a, Man walking in front of camel, oil well. b, Man walking in front of camel. c, Oil well, camel's head. d, Mount and rider (facing forward). e, Mount and rider (facing right). f, Two dromedaries at a run.

Perf. 13½x14, 14x13½
1989, June 15
336	A70	Sheet of 6	11.00	11.00
a.-f.		150f any single	1.40	1.40
337	A70	Sheet of 6	11.00	11.00
a.-f.		150f any single	1.40	1.40

Sheik Isa — A71

1989, Dec. 16   Litho.   Perf. 13½x14
338	A71	25f multicolored	.40	.25
339	A71	40f multicolored	.45	.25
340	A71	50f multicolored	.50	.25
341	A71	60f multicolored	.55	.25
342	A71	75f multicolored	.65	.30
343	A71	80f multicolored	.65	.30
344	A71	100f multicolored	.85	.40
345	A71	120f multicolored	1.00	.45
346	A71	150f multicolored	1.30	.60
347	A71	200f multicolored	1.50	.85
a.		Souv. sheet of 10, #338-347	9.00	9.00
		Nos. 338-347 (10)	7.85	3.90

Houbara (Bustard) — A72

No. 348: a, Two birds facing right. b, Two birds facing each other. c, Chicks. d, Adult, chick. e, Adult, facing right, vert. f, In flight. g, Adult facing right. h, Chick, facing left, vert. i, Adult facing left. j, Adult male, close-up. k, Courtship display. l, Two birds facing left.

1990, Feb. 17   Photo.   Perf. 14
348		Sheet of 12	18.00	18.00
a.-l.	A72	150f any single	1.30	1.30

Gulf Air, 40th Anniv. A73

1990, Mar. 24   Litho.   Perf. 14½
360	A73	50f multicolored	.50	.50
361	A73	80f multicolored	.80	.80
362	A73	150f multicolored	1.60	1.60
363	A73	200f multicolored	2.40	2.40
		Nos. 360-363 (4)	5.30	5.30

Chamber of Commerce, 50th Anniv. — A74

1990, May 26
364	A74	50f multicolored	.50	.50
365	A74	80f multicolored	.75	.75
366	A74	150f multicolored	1.50	1.50
367	A74	200f multicolored	1.90	1.90
		Nos. 364-367 (4)	4.65	4.65

Intl. Literacy Year A75

1990, Sept. 8   Litho.   Perf. 14½
368	A75	50f multicolored	.45	.45
369	A75	80f multicolored	.70	.70
370	A75	150f multicolored	1.35	1.35
371	A75	200f multicolored	1.75	1.75
		Nos. 368-371 (4)	4.25	4.25

Miniature Sheet

Indigenous Birds — A76

No. 372: a, Galerida cristata. b, Upupa epops. c, Pycnonotus leucogenys. d, Streptopelia turtur. e, Streptopelia decaocto. f, Falco tinnunculus. g, Passer domesticus, horiz. h, Lanius excubitor, horiz. i, Psittacula krameri.

1991, Sept. 15   Litho.   Perf. 14½
372	A76	Sheet of 9	20.00	20.00
a.-i.		150f any single	1.80	1.80

See Nos. 382, 407.

A77

Coronation of Sheik Isa, 30th Anniv. — A77a

Litho. & Embossed
1991, Dec. 16   Perf. 14½
373	A77	50f multicolored	.45	.45
374	A77a	50f multicolored	.45	.45
375	A77	80f multicolored	.70	.70
376	A77a	80f multicolored	.70	.70
377	A77	150f multicolored	1.50	1.50
378	A77a	150f multicolored	1.50	1.50
379	A77	200f multicolored	2.10	2.10
380	A77a	200f multicolored	2.10	2.10
		Nos. 373-380 (8)	9.50	9.50

Souvenir Sheet
Perf. 14x14½
381		Sheet of 2	11.00	11.00
a.		A77a 500f multicolored	5.25	5.25
b.		A77 500f multicolored	5.25	5.25

No. 381 contains 41x31mm stamps.

Indigenous Birds Type of 1991
Miniature Sheet

No. 382: a, Ciconia ciconia. b, Merops apiaster. c, Sturnus vulgaris. d, Hypocolius ampelinus. e, Cuculus canorus. f, Turdus viscivorus. g, Coracias garrulus. h, Carduelis carduelis. i, Lanius collurio. j, Turdus iliacus, horiz. k, Motacilla alba, horiz. l, Oriolus oriolus, horiz. m, Erithacus rubecula. n, Luscinia luscinia. o, Muscicapa striata. p, Hirundo rustica.

1992, Mar. 21   Litho.   Perf. 14½
382		Sheet of 16	25.00	25.00
a.-p.		A76 150f any single	1.25	1.25

Miniature Sheet

Horse Racing — A78

No. 383: a, Horses leaving starting gate. b, Trainers leading horses. c, Horses racing around turn. d, Horses in stretch racing by flags. e, Two horses racing by grandstand. f, Five horses galloping. g, Two brown horses racing. h, Black horse, gray horse racing.

1992, May 22
383	A78	Sheet of 8	12.50	12.50
a.-h.		150f any single	1.20	1.20

1992 Summer Olympics, Barcelona — A79

1992, July 25   Litho.   Perf. 14½
384	A79	50f Equestrian	.50	.50
385	A79	80f Running	.90	.90
386	A79	150f Judo	1.50	1.50
387	A79	200f Cycling	2.10	2.10
		Nos. 384-387 (4)	5.00	5.00

Bahrain Intl. Airport, 60th Anniv. A80

1992, Oct. 27   Litho.   Perf. 14½
388	A80	50f multicolored	.40	.40
389	A80	80f multicolored	.60	.60
390	A80	150f multicolored	1.50	1.50
391	A80	200f multicolored	2.00	2.00
		Nos. 388-391 (4)	4.50	4.50

Children's Art — A81

Designs: 50f, Girl jumping rope, vert. 80f, Women in traditional dress, vert. 150f, Women stirring kettle. 200f, Fishermen.

1992, Nov. 28   Litho.   Perf. 14½
392	A81	50f multicolored	.35	.35
393	A81	80f multicolored	.55	.55
394	A81	150f multicolored	1.10	1.10
395	A81	200f multicolored	1.75	1.75
		Nos. 392-395 (4)	3.75	3.75

Inauguration of Expansion of Aluminum Bahrain — A82

50f, Ore funicular. 80f, Smelting pot. 150f, Mill. 200f, Cylindrical aluminum ingots.

1992, Dec. 16
396	A82	50f multicolored	.45	.45
397	A82	80f multicolored	.80	.80
398	A82	150f multicolored	1.50	1.50
399	A82	200f multicolored	2.00	2.00
		Nos. 396-399 (4)	4.75	4.75

Bahrain Defense Force, 25th Anniv. A83

Designs: 50f, Artillery forces, vert. 80f, Fighters, tanks, and ship, vert. 150f, Frigate. 200f, Jet fighter.

Perf. 13½x13, 13x13½
1993, Feb. 5   Litho.
400	A83	50f multicolored	.45	.45
401	A83	80f multicolored	.65	.65
402	A83	150f multicolored	1.35	1.35
403	A83	200f multicolored	1.75	1.75
		Nos. 400-403 (4)	4.20	4.20

World Meteorology Day — A84

Designs: 50f, Satellite image of Bahrain, vert. 150f, Infrared satellite map of world. 200f, Earth, seen from space, vert.

1993, Mar. 23   Litho.   Perf. 14½
404	A84	50f multicolored	.65	.65
405	A84	150f multicolored	1.75	1.75
406	A84	200f multicolored	2.60	2.60
		Nos. 404-406 (3)	5.00	5.00

Bird Type of 1991
Miniature Sheet

No. 407: a, Ardea purpurea. b, Gallinula chloropus. c, Phalacrocorax nigrogularis. d, Dromas ardeola. e, Alcedo atthis. f, Vanellus vanellus. g, Haematopus ostralegus, horiz. h, Nycticorax nycticorax. i, Sterna caspia, horiz. j, Arenaria interpres, horiz. k, Rallus aquaticus, horiz. l, Anas platyrhychos, horia. m, Larus fuscus, horiz.

1993, May 22   Litho.   Perf. 14½
407   Sheet of 13 + 2 labels 24.00 24.00
  a.-m. A76 150f any single 1.75 1.75

Gazella Subgutturosa Marica — A85

1993, July 24   Litho.   Perf. 14½
408 A85 25f Calf 1.20 1.20
409 A85 50f Female standing 2.25 2.25
410 A85 50f Female walking 2.25 2.25
411 A85 150f Male 6.25 6.25
  Nos. 408-411 (4) 11.95 11.95

World Wildlife Federation.

Wild Flowers — A86

Designs: a, Lycium shawii. b, Alhagi maurorum. c, Caparis spinosa. d, Cistanche phelypae. e, Asphodelus tenuifolius. f, Limonium axillare. g, Cynomorium coccineum. h, Calligonum polygonoides.

1993, Oct. 16   Litho.   Perf. 13½x13
412 A86 150f Sheet of 8,
  #a.-h. 9.00 9.00

A87

1994, Jan. 22   Litho.   Perf. 14½
Background Color
413 A87 50f yellow .50 .50
414 A87 80f blue green .75 .75
415 A87 150f purple 1.50 1.50
416 A87 200f blue 2.25 2.25
  Nos. 413-416 (4) 5.00 5.00

Intl. Year of the Family.

Butterflies — A88

No. 417: a, Lepidochrysops arabicus. b, Ypthima bolanica. c, Eurema brigitta. d, Precis limnoria. e, Aglais urticae. f, Colotis protomedia. g, Salamis anacardii. h, Byblia ilithyia.

No. 418: a, Papilio machaon. b, Agrodiaetus loewii. c, Vanessa cardui. d, Papilio demoleus. e, Hamanumida daedalus. f, Funonia orithya. g, Funonia chorimine. h, Colias croceus.

Perf. 13½x13, 13x13½
1994, Mar. 21   Litho.
417 A88 50f Sheet of 8, #a.-
  h. 3.75 3.75
418 A88 150f Sheet of 8, #a.-
  h. 11.00 11.00

No. 418 is horiz.

A89

1994, May 8   Litho.   Perf. 14½
419 A89 50f lilac & multi .50 .50
420 A89 80f yellow & multi .80 .80
421 A89 150f salmon & multi 1.50 1.50
422 A89 200f green blue & multi 2.00 2.00
  Nos. 419-422 (4) 4.80 4.80

Intl. Red Cross & Red Crescent Societies, 75th anniv.

1994 World Cup Soccer
Championships, US — A90

Designs: 50f, Goalkeeper. 80f, Heading ball. 150f, Dribbling ball. 200f, Slide tackle.

1994, June 17   Litho.   Perf. 14
423 A90 50f multicolored .55 .55
424 A90 80f multicolored .75 .75
425 A90 150f multicolored 1.40 1.40
426 A90 200f multicolored 2.10 2.10
  Nos. 423-426 (4) 4.80 4.80

Bahrain's First Satellite Earth Station,
25th Anniv. — A91

1994, July 14
427 A91 50f blue & multi .75 .75
428 A91 80f yellow & multi 1.00 1.00
429 A91 150f violet & multi 1.75 1.75
430 A91 200f pink, yellow & multi 2.25 2.25
  Nos. 427-430 (4) 5.75 5.75

Education in
Bahrain, 75th
Anniv. — A92

1994, Nov. 19   Litho.   Perf. 14½
431 A92 50f yellow & multi .55 .55
432 A92 80f buff & multi .85 .85
433 A92 150f salmon & multi 1.60 1.60
434 A92 200f pink & multi 2.25 2.25
  Nos. 431-434 (4) 5.25 5.25

Gulf Cooperation Council Supreme Council, 15th Regular Session, Bahrain — A93

1994, Dec. 19   Perf. 14
435 A93 50f blue green & multi .50 .50
436 A93 80f brown & multi .80 .80
437 A93 150f lilac rose & multi 1.50 1.50
438 A93 200f blue & multi 2.25 2.25
  Nos. 435-438 (4) 5.05 5.05

Date Palm
A94

Designs: 80f, Flowering stage. 100f, Dates beginning to ripen. 200f, Dates up close. 250f, Trees from distance. 500f, Pitcher, basket of dates.

1995, Mar. 21   Litho.   Perf. 14
439 A94 80f multicolored .75 .75
440 A94 100f multicolored .80 .80
441 A94 200f multicolored 1.75 1.75
442 A94 250f multicolored 2.00 2.00
  Nos. 439-442 (4) 5.30 5.30
Souvenir Sheet
443 A94 500f multicolored 4.25 4.25

No. 443 contains one 65x48mm stamp.

Fight
Against
Polio
A95

1995, Apr. 22   Litho.   Perf. 13x13½
444 A95 80f pink & multi .55 .55
445 A95 200f blue & multi 1.50 1.50
446 A95 250f lt brown & multi 2.10 2.10
  Nos. 444-446 (3) 4.15 4.15

World Health Day.

1st Natl.
Industries
Exhibition
A96

1995, May 15
447 A96 80f blue green & multi .60 .60
448 A96 200f lilac & multi 1.75 1.75
449 A96 250f lt brown & multi 2.25 2.25
  Nos. 447-449 (3) 4.60 4.60

FAO,
50th
Anniv.
A97

Fields of various crops.

1995, June 17   Litho.   Perf. 14
450 A97 80f lilac & multi .60 .60
451 A97 200f blue & multi 1.90 1.90
452 A97 250f lt pink & multi 2.50 2.50
  Nos. 450-452 (3) 5.00 5.00

Arab League, 50th
Anniv. — A98

1995, Sept. 14   Litho.   Perf. 14½
453 A98 80f pink & multi .60 .60
454 A98 200f blue & multi 1.75 1.75
455 A98 250f yellow & multi 2.50 2.50
  Nos. 453-455 (3) 4.85 4.85

UN,
50th
Anniv.
A99

1995, Oct. 24   Litho.   Perf. 14½
456 A99 80f yellow & multi .55 .55
457 A99 100f green & multi .90 .90
458 A99 200f pink & multi 1.75 1.75
459 A99 250f blue & multi 2.40 2.40
  Nos. 456-459 (4) 5.60 5.60

Miniature Sheet

Traditional Architecture — A100

No. 460 — Example of architecture, detail: a, Tower with balcony. b, Arched windows behind balcony. c, Double doors under arch. d, Four rows of square windows above row of arched windows. e, Door flanked by two windows. f, Three windows.

1995, Nov. 20   Litho.   Perf. 14½
460 A100 200f Sheet of 6,
  #a.-f. 9.00 9.00

National
Day — A101

1995, Dec. 16   Litho.   Perf. 14½
461 A101 80f blue & multi .60 .60
462 A101 100f green & multi .90 .90
463 A101 200f violet & multi 2.00 2.00
464 A101 250f blue grn & multi 2.25 2.25
  Nos. 461-464 (4) 5.75 5.75

Public Library, 50th
Anniv. — A102

1996, Mar. 23   Litho.   Perf. 14
465 A102   80f pink & multi   .70   .70
466 A102 200f green & multi   2.00 2.00
467 A102 250f blue & multi   2.40 2.40
      Nos. 465-467 (3)   5.10 5.10

Pearl Diving — A103

Designs: 80f, Group of divers on ship, three
in water. 100f, Five divers in water, ship. 200f,
Diver underneath water. 250f, Diver being pulled up, underwater scene.
500f, Lantern, weight, scales, pearls, knife.

1996, May 8   Litho.   Perf. 14
468 A103   80f multicolored   .65   .65
469 A103 100f multicolored   .90   .90
470 A103 200f multicolored   1.90 1.90
471 A103 250f multicolored   2.10 2.10
      Nos. 468-471 (4)   5.55 5.55
Souvenir Sheet
Perf. 14½
472 A103 500f multicolored   6.00 6.00
No. 472 contains one 70x70mm stamp.

1996 Summer Olympics,
Atlanta — A104

1996, July 19   Litho.   Perf. 14
473 A104   80f olive & multi   .70   .70
474 A104 100f pink & multi   .90   .90
475 A104 200f blue grn & multi   2.00 2.00
476 A104 250f orange & multi   2.40 2.40
      Nos. 473-476 (4)   6.00 6.00

Interpol, Intl. Criminal Police
Organization — A105

1996, Sept. 25   Litho.   Perf. 14
477 A105   80f blue & multi   .75   .75
478 A105 100f yellow & multi   1.00 1.00
479 A105 200f pink & multi   2.00 2.00
480 A105 250f green & multi   2.75 2.75
      Nos. 477-480 (4)   6.50 6.50

Aluminum Production in Bahrain, 25th
Anniv. — A106

1996, Nov. 20   Litho.   Perf. 14
481 A106   80f bister & multi   .65   .65
482 A106 100f orange & multi   .80   .80
483 A106 200f blue & multi   2.00 2.00
484 A106 250f green & multi   2.50 2.50
      Nos. 481-484 (4)   5.95 5.95

Accession to the Throne by Sheik Isa
Bin Salman Al Khalifa, 35th
Anniv. — A107

1996, Dec. 16
485 A107   80f gray & multi   .55   .55
486 A107 100f green & multi   .80   .80
487 A107 200f pink & multi   1.75 1.75
488 A107 250f blue & multi   2.25 2.25
      Nos. 485-488 (4)   5.35 5.35

Bahrain Refinery, 60th Anniv. — A108

1997, Jan. 15   Litho.   Perf. 14
489 A108   80f red & multi   .80   .80
490 A108 200f blue & multi   2.25 2.25
491 A108 250f yellow & multi   2.50 2.50
      Nos. 489-491 (3)   5.55 5.55

Pure Strains of Arabian Horses, Amiri
Stud — A109

No. 492: a, Musannaan, Al-Jellabieh,
Rabdaan. b, Kuheilaan weld umm zorayr. c,
Al-Jellaby. d, Musannaan. e, Kuheilaan
aladiyat. f, Kuheilaan aafas. g, Al-Dhahma. h,
Mlolshaan. i, Al-Kray. j, Krush. k, Al
Hamdaany. l, Hadhfaan. m, Rabda. n, Al-
Suwaitieh. o, Al-Obeyah. p, Al-Shuwaimeh. q,
Al-Ma'anaghieh. r, Al-Tuwaisah. s, Wadhna. t,
Al-Saqlawieh. u, Al-Shawafah.

1997, Apr. 23   Perf. 14x14½
492 A109 200f Sheet of 21,
           #a.-u.   32.50 32.50

9th Men's Junior World Volleyball
Championship — A110

1997, Aug. 21   Litho.   Perf. 14x14½
493 A110   80f brown & multi   .70   .70
494 A110 100f green & multi   .90   .90
495 A110 200f gray brn & multi   1.75 1.75
496 A110 250f blue & multi   1.90 1.90
      Nos. 493-496 (4)   5.25 5.25

Montreal Protocol
on Substances
that Deplete
Ozone Layer, 10th
Anniv. — A111

1997, Sept. 16   Litho.   Perf. 14½
497 A111   80f yellow & multi   .60   .60
498 A111 100f purple & multi   .80   .80
499 A111 200f red & multi   1.60 1.60
500 A111 250f green & multi   2.00 2.00
      Nos. 497-500 (4)   5.00 5.00

Sheikh Isa
Bin Salman
Bridge
A112

Designs: 80f, Pylon, supports. 200f, Center
of bridge. 250f, 500f, Entire span.

1997, Dec. 28   Litho.   Perf. 13x13½
501 A112   80f multicolored   .75   .75
502 A112 200f multicolored   2.00 2.00
Size: 76x26mm
503 A112 250f multicolored   2.25 2.25
      Nos. 501-503 (3)   5.00 5.00
Souvenir Sheet
504 A112 500f multicolored   4.50 4.50

Inuaguration of Urea Plant, GPIC
(Refinery) Complex — A113

Designs: 80f, View of plant from Persian
Gulf. 200f, Plant facilities. 250f, Aerial view.

1998, Mar. 3   Litho.   Perf. 13x13½
505 A113   80f multicolored   .60   .60
506 A113 200f multicolored   1.90 1.90
507 A113 250f multicolored   2.50 2.50
      Nos. 505-507 (3)   5.00 5.00

World Health Organization, 50th
Anniv. — A114

1998, May 11   Litho.   Perf. 14
508 A114   80f orange & multi   .55   .55
509 A114 200f green & multi   1.75 1.75
510 A114 250f gray & multi   2.50 2.50
      Nos. 508-510 (3)   4.80 4.80

1998 World Cup Soccer
Championships, France — A115

Designs: 200f, Soccer balls, world maps,
vert. 250f, Players, globe, vert.

1998, June 10
511 A115   80f multicolored   .60   .60
512 A115 200f multicolored   1.90 1.90
513 A115 250f multicolored   2.50 2.50
      Nos. 511-513 (3)   5.00 5.00

14th
Arabian
Gulf
Soccer
Cup,
Bahrain
A116

Design: 200f, 250f, Soccer ball.

1998, Oct. 30   Litho.   Perf. 14
514 A116   80f shown   .60   .60
515 A116 200f pale violet & multi 1.90 1.90
516 A116 250f bister & multi   2.50 2.50
      Nos. 514-516 (3)   5.00 5.00

Grand
Competition
for Holy Koran
Recitation
A117

1999, Jan. 9   Litho.   Perf. 14
517 A117 100f gray olive & multi   1.00 1.00
518 A117 200f yellow & multi   2.00 2.00
519 A117 250f green & multi   2.25 2.25
      Nos. 517-519 (3)   5.25 5.25

Isa Bin Salman Al-Khalifa (1933-99),
Emir of Bahrain — A118

Natl. flag, map and: 100f, 500f, Emir holding
sword, vert. 250f, Portrait up close, vert.

Perf. 13¼ (#520, 522), 14¼ (#521)
1999, June 5   Litho.
520 A118 100f multicolored   1.10 1.10
521 A118 200f multicolored   2.00 2.00
522 A118 250f multicolored   2.25 2.25
      Nos. 520-522 (3)   5.35 5.35
Souvenir Sheet
Perf. 14½x13
523 A118 500f multicolored   4.75 4.75
Nos. 520, 522 are 31x50mm. No. 523 contains one 67x102mm stamp.

Intl. Year of
Older
Persons
A119

1999, Oct. 9 Litho. Perf. 13x13½
524 A119 100f multi   1.00 1.00
525 A119 200f multi, diff.   2.00 2.00
526 A119 250f multi, diff.   2.25 2.25
   Nos. 524-526 (3)   5.25 5.25

Bahrain Stock Exchange, 10th
Anniv. — A120

Design: 200f, Pearl Monument, bridge. 250f,
Globe.

1999, Nov. 24 Litho. Perf. 14¼
527 A120 100f shown   .80 .80
528 A120 200f multicolored   1.60 1.60
529 A120 250f multicolored   1.75 1.75
   Nos. 527-529 (3)   4.15 4.15

Hamad Bin Isa Al-
Khalifa, Emir of
Bahrain — A121

Emir Hamad: 100f, 500f, Receiving flag
from late Emir. 200f, And flag. 250f, And map.

1999, Dec. 16 Litho. Perf. 14½
531 A121 100f multi   .90 .90
532 A121 200f multi   2.00 2.00
533 A121 250f multi   2.10 2.10
   Nos. 531-533 (3)   5.00 5.00
Souvenir Sheet
Perf. 13¼x12¾
534 A121 500f multi   4.50 4.50

Dilmun
Culture
Exhibition
A122

Map of Bahrain and: 100f, Bull's head, seal.
200f, Bull's head. 250f, Seal.

2000, Feb. 26 Litho. Perf. 14¼
535 A122 100f multi   .80 .80
536 A122 200f multi   1.75 1.75
537 A122 250f multi   2.00 2.00
   Nos. 535-537 (3)   4.55 4.55

Gulf Air,
50th
Anniv.
A123

Map of Bahrain and: 100f, Emblem, world
map. 200f, Emblem. 250f, Birds.

2000, Mar. 24
538 A123 100f multi   1.25 1.25
539 A123 200f multi   2.50 2.50
540 A123 250f multi   2.75 2.75
   Nos. 538-540 (3)   6.50 6.50

Made in Bahrain Exhibition — A124

2000, May 9 Perf. 14½
541 A124 100f shown   1.35 1.35
542 A124 200f Emblem, diff. 2.75 2.75
543 A124 250f Oil refinery 3.50 3.50
   Nos. 541-543 (3)   7.60 7.60

Souvenir Sheet

Passage Through Time — A125

No. 544: a, Minarets, fort, flag on dhow's
stern. b, Dhows, oil refinery. c, Minaret, date
picker. d, Satellite dishes, fort, flag. e, Bridge,
pool. f, Woman, jar, dhows. g, Dhows, coffee
pot. h, Man with falcon, horse and rider. i,
Pearl divers. j, Oyster shuckers. k, Men casting nets. l, Men repairing nets.

Litho. with Foil Application
2000, Oct. 9 Perf. 14¼
544 A125 Sheet of 12   24.00 24.00
 a.-d. 100f Any single   1.00 1.00
 e.-h. 200f Any single   2.00 2.00
 i.-l. 250f Any single   2.50 2.50

21st Supreme Council Session of the
Gulf Co-operation Council — A126

Designs: 100f, Emblem. 200f, Flags.

2000, Dec. 30 Litho. Perf. 14¼
545-546 A126 Set of 2   3.75 3.75

Beit al-Quran, Manama — A127

Designs: 100f, Stained-glass window. 200f,
Building illuminated at dusk. 250f, Building
during day.
500f, Building during day, stained-glass window, building illuminated at dusk.

2001, Feb. 18 Litho. Perf. 14¼
547-549 A127 Set of 3   5.00 5.00
Size: 170x80mm
Imperf
550 A127 500f multi   5.00 5.00

Housing and Agriculture Ministry, 25th
Anniv. — A128

Various buildings: 100f, 150f, 200f, 250f.

2001, Apr. 28 Perf. 14¼
551-554 A128 Set of 4   6.00 6.00

Intl. Volunteers Year — A129

Emblem and: 100f, Stylized people with
arms raised, vert. 150f, Clasped hands. 200f,
Stars. 250f, Stylized people holding hands.

2001, Sept. 29 Litho. Perf. 14¼
555-558 A129 Set of 4   7.25 7.25

Day of the
Arab Woman
A130

Designs: 100f, Emblem. 200f, Emblem and
rings. 250f, Women, horiz.

2002, Feb. 1 Litho. Perf. 14¼
559-561 A130 Set of 3   5.75 5.75

Souvenir Sheet

2002 World Cup Soccer
Championships, Japan and
Korea — A131

No. 562: a, 100f. b, 200f, c, 250f.

2002, May 31
562 A131 Sheet of 3, #a-c   6.50 6.50

King Hamad — A132

2002, July 15 Litho. Perf. 13½x13¾
Background Color
563 A132 25f gray   .25 .25
564 A132 40f brt purple   .25 .25
565 A132 50f dark gray   .30 .30
566 A132 60f dk bl green   .50 .50
567 A132 80f blue   .60 .60
568 A132 100f orange brown .85 .85
569 A132 125f cerise   .95 .95
570 A132 150f pinkish orange 1.25 1.25
571 A132 200f olive green   1.75 1.75
572 A132 250f rose pink   2.10 2.10
573 A132 300f tan   2.40 2.40
574 A132 400f dull green   3.00 3.00

Size: 26x36mm
Perf. 13¼x13
575 A132 500f rose violet   4.00 4.00
 a. Perf. 13¼x13x13¼x14   4.00 4.00
576 A132   1d dull orange   7.75 7.75
577 A132   2d gray blue   16.00 16.00
578 A132   3d brown violet   24.00 24.00
 a. Souvenir sheet, #563-574,
     575a, 576-578   67.50 67.50
   Nos. 563-578 (16)   65.95 65.95

World Teachers'
Day — A133

Background color: 100f, Gray green. 200f,
Gray.

2002, Oct. 5 Litho. Perf. 13¼x13
579-580 A133 Set of 2   2.25 2.25

Parliamentary Elections — A134

Designs: 100f, Flag. 200f, Hand placing ballot in box, vert.

2002, Oct. 24 Perf. 13x13¼, 13¼x13
581-582 A134 Set of 2   2.25 2.25

National
Day — A135

King Hamad, flag and background color of:
100f, Gray. 200f, Brown violet, vert. 250f, Dark
red, vert.

Perf. 13x13¼, 13¼x13
2002, Dec. 16 Litho.
583-585 A135 Set of 3   4.50 4.50

Arab
Summit
Conference
2003
A136

No. 586: a, Bahrain. b, Sudan. c, Saudi Ara-
bia. d, Djibouti. e, Algeria. f, Tunisia. g, United
Arab Emirates. h, Jordan. i, Comoro Islands. j,
Qatar. k, Palestine. l, Oman. m, Iraq. n,
Somalia. o, Syria. p, Yemen. q, Mauritania. r,
Morocco. s, Egypt. t, Libya. u, Lebanon. v,
Kuwait.
500f, Montage of scenes.

Litho. With Foil Application
2003, Mar. 1 Perf. 13
586   Sheet of 22   32.50 32.50
 a.-h. A136 100f Any single   .65 .65
 i.-o. A136 200f Any single 1.30 1.30
 p.-v. A136 250f Any single 1.60 1.60
Size: 120x103mm
Imperf
587 A136 500f multi   3.75 3.75

World Health Day A137

UN and Healthy Environments for Children Emblems and: 100f, Children, flowers. 200f, Stylized children.

2003, Apr. 7   **Litho.**   **Perf. 14¼**
588-589   A137   Set of 2   2.75 2.75

World Environment Day — A138

No. 590: a, Swan. b, Peacock. c, Flamingo. d, Ostrich. e, Rumex vesicarius. f, Arnebia hispidissima. g, Capparis spinosa. h, Cassia italica. i, Crab. j, Turtle. k, Sting ray. l, Shark.

2003, June 5   **Perf. 13**
590   A138   Sheet of 12   20.00 20.00
a.-d.   100f Any single   .75   .75
e.-h.   200f Any single   1.50 1.50
i.-l.   250f Any single   2.00 2.00

Intl. Children's Day — A139

No. 591, vert.: a, 100f, Child reading book. b, 150f, Child looking at flowers.
No. 592: a, 200f, Children in field. b, 250f, Children in classroom.

2003, Nov. 20   **Litho.**   **Perf. 14¼**
     Vert. Pairs, #a-b
591-592   A139   Set of 2   6.00 6.00
   Printed in sheets containing four of each pair.

National Day — A140

King Hamad on horse with panel color of: 100f, Bronze. 200f, Gold. 250f, Silver. 500f, No panel.

   Litho. with Foil Application
2003, Dec. 16   **Perf. 14½**
593-595   A140   Set of 3   4.00 4.00
     Souvenir Sheet
596   A140   500f multi   3.75 3.75
   No. 596 contains one 55x95mm stamp.

Mother's Day A141

Designs: 100f, Mother and infant. 200f, Mother reading to child.

2004, Mar. 21   **Litho.**   **Perf. 13x13¼**
597-598   A141   Set of 2   2.25 2.25

Bahrain Formula 1 Grand Prix — A142

No. 599: a, 100f, Race car, red background (76x36mm). b, 150f, Race car, green background (76x36mm). c, 200f, Race car, blue background (76x36mm). d, 250f, Race car, orange background (76x36mm). e, 500f, Race tower (51x51mm).

2004, Apr. 4   **Litho.**   **Perf. 13**
599   A142   Sheet of 5, #a-e   9.00 9.00

Intl. Day Against Drugs A143

UN emblem and: 100f, People reaching out to addict. 150f, Addict's arm. 200f, Addict and snake-like needles. 250f, Arms reaching out.

2004, June 24   **Perf. 14¼**
600-603   A143   Set of 4   4.75 4.75

2004 Summer Olympics, Athens — A144

No. 604: a, 100f, Track. b, 150f, Swimming. c, 200f, Sailboarding. d, 250f, Shooting.

2004, Aug. 13
604   A144   Sheet of 4, #a-d   4.25 4.25

Gulf Cooperation Council, 25th Regular Session A145

Emblem and: 100f, Hands. 200f, Draped flags. 250f, Circle of flags. 500f, Bridge, boats and buildings.

2004, Dec. 20   **Litho.**   **Perf. 14¼**
605-607   A145   Set of 3   3.00 3.00
     Souvenir Sheet
     Perf. 13¼
608   A145   500f multi   2.75 2.75
   No. 608 contains one 175x54mm stamp.

Bahrain Garden Fair A146

Emblem and various flowers: 100f, 200f, 250f.

2005, Mar. 3   **Perf. 13x13¼**
609-611   A146   Set of 3   3.00 3.00

Inauguration of Constitutional Court — A147

Background colors: 100f, Brown black. 200f, Orange brown. 250f, Blue.

2005, Apr. 18   **Perf. 14½**
612-614   A147   Set of 3   3.75 3.75

Discovery of Artifacts of Dilmon Civilization, 50th Anniv. — A148

Designs: No. 615, 100f, Figurine of human. No. 616, 100f, Sculpted discs. No. 617, 100f, Equestrian statue. No. 618, 200f, Overturned jar and artifacts. No. 619, 200f, Two jars. No. 620, 200f, Jar and lidded jar. No. 621, 250f, Wall, horiz. No. 622, 250f, Steps, horiz. No. 623, 250f, Aerial view of archaeological site, horiz.
   500f, Wall, Arab and Western men, horiz.

2005, Apr. 27   **Litho.**   **Perf. 14¼**
615-623   A148   Set of 9   7.75 7.75
623a   Miniature sheet, #615-623   12.00 12.00
     Souvenir Sheet
     Perf. 14½
624   A148   500f multi   3.75 3.75
   No. 624 contains one 88x58mm stamp.

National Day A149

King Hamad and various buildings: 100f, 200f, 250f. 200f is vert.

2005, Dec. 16   **Litho.**   **Perf. 14¼**
625-627   A149   Set of 3   3.00 3.00

A150

Gulf Cooperation Council, 25th Anniv. — A151

   Litho. With Foil Application
2006, May 25   **Perf. 14**
628   A150   100f multi   2.25 2.25
     Imperf
     Size: 165x105mm
629   A151   500f multi   7.50 7.50
   See Kuwait Nos. 1646-1647, Oman Nos. 477-478, Qatar Nos. 1107-1108, Saudi Arabia No. 1378, and United Arab Emirates Nos. 831-832.

2006 World Cup Soccer Championships, Germany — A152

Emir Hamad and: 100f, Emblem. 200f, Emblem, globe, soccer ball, spheres. 250f, Emblem, globe.

2006, June 9   **Litho.**   **Perf. 14¼**
630-632   A152   Set of 3   3.50 3.50

National Day — A153

King Hamad: 100f, Holding flag and book. 200f, With crown above head. 250f, With crown above head, profile portrait. 500f, Like 100f (36x50mm).

     Perf. 14¼, 14 (500f)
2006, Dec. 16   **Litho.**
633-636   A153   Set of 4   5.75 5.75

Gulf Cooperation Council Consumer Protection Day — A154

Designs: 100f, Gulf Cooperation Council emblem, people under umbrella. 200f, People under umbrella of Gulf Cooperation Council flags.

2007, Mar. 1   **Perf. 13x13¼**
637-638 A154   Set of 2   1.75 1.75
Each stamp printed in sheet of 20 + 5 labels.

National Day — A155

King Hamad: 100f, And crown. 200f, Waving, horiz. 250f, With men, boats, horsemen, horiz.

2007, Dec. 16   Litho.   **Perf. 14¼**
639-641 A155   Set of 3   3.00 3.00
640a   Souvenir sheet, 2 each
    #639-640, perf. 13¼   3.25 3.25

Arab Productive Families Day — A156

Hands of: 100f, Wood carver and basket weaver. 200f, Decoration nailer and seamstress.

2008, Mar. 15   **Perf. 13¼**
642-643 A156   Set of 2   1.90 1.90

Intl. Nurses Day A157

Designs: 100f, Operating room. 200f, Nurses and child.

2008, May 12   **Perf. 14¼**
644-645 A157   Set of 2   1.75 1.75

Third Session of Ministerial Meeting of Arab-Chinese Cooperation Forum, Manama — A158

Emblem, Great Wall of China and: 100f, Arch. 200f, Building.

2008, May 21   **Perf. 13**
646-647 A158   Set of 2   1.75 1.75

"Business Friendly" Advertising Campaign — A159

Text "Business Friendly" in various styles: 100f, 200f.

2008, Aug. 1   Litho.   **Perf. 13¼x13**
648-649 A159   Set of 2   2.10 2.10

Souvenir Sheet

2008 Summer Olympics, Beijing — A160

No. 650: a, 100f, Runner crossing finish line. b, 200f, Equestrian.

2008, Aug. 8   **Perf. 14x13**
650 A160   Sheet of 2, #a-b   2.10 2.10

Miniature Sheets

A161

Bahraini Ardha — A162

No. 651 — Color of sky: a, Purple. b, Red brown. c, Blue gray. d, Red violet. e, Gray. f, Yellow orange. g, Blue green. h, Dull brown.
No. 652 — Man in foreground: a, Carrying flag. b, In white robes. c, In red orange robes holding sword.

2008, Dec. 16   **Perf. 13¼x13**
651 A161   100f Sheet of 8, #a-h   6.50 6.50

        Perf. 14
652 A162   200f Sheet of 3, #a-c   3.50 3.50

First Gulf Cooperation Council and Association of South East Asian Nations Ministerial Meeting, Manama A163

Emblems and: 100f, Dhow. 200f, Dhow, diff.

2009, June 29   Litho.   **Perf. 14¼**
653-654 A163   Set of 2   2.00 2.00

Souvenir Sheet

Arab Postal Day — A164

No. 655 — Emblem and: a, World map, pigeon. b, Camel caravan.

Litho. With Foil Application
2009, Aug. 3   **Perf. 13¼**
655 A164   500f Sheet of 2, #a-b   6.50 6.50

Palm Tree Symposium — A165

2009, Nov. 10   Litho.   **Perf. 14¼**
656 A165   100f multi   .75 .75

A166

Bahraini Women's Day A167

2009, Dec. 1   **Perf. 13x13¼**
657 A166   100f multi   .75 .75
658 A167   200f multi   1.25 1.25

Miniature Sheet

Education in Bahrain, 90th Anniv. — A168

No. 659: a, 100f, Boys outside of school building. b, 100f, Students in math class. c, 200f, Student holding soldering iron. d, 200f, Graduates. e, 250f, Teacher pointing to diagram. f, 250f, Students seated in class.

2009, Dec. 14   **Perf. 13¼x14¼**
659 A168   Sheet of 6, #a-f   6.75 6.75

National Day A169

Designs: 100f, Flag, map, King Hamad with crown above head, brown background at UL. 200f, As 100f, with blue background at UL. 250f, King Hamad with other sheikhs, buildings, map, horsemen, and flag. 500f, As 250f.

Litho. With Foil Application
2009, Dec. 16   **Perf. 14¼**
660-662 A169   Set of 3   3.75 3.75
    Size: 126x101mm
       Imperf
663 A169   500f multi   5.75 5.75

Bahrain Intl. Airshow A170

Airshow emblem and: 100f, King Hamad, airplanes. 200f, Curved red lines.

2010, Jan. 21   Litho.   **Perf. 13¼x13**
664-665 A170   Set of 2   1.90 1.90

2010 World Cup Soccer Championships, South Africa — A171

2010 World Cup: 100f, Emblem. 200f, Mascot. 250f, Soccer ball, globe, horiz. (36x26mm).

    Perf. 13, 13x13¼ (250f)
2010, June 11   **Litho.**
666-668 A171   Set of 3   3.50 3.50

World Post Day — A172

2010, Oct. 9   **Perf. 13**
669 A172   250f multi   1.75 1.75

National Day — A173

King Hamad and stylized dove: 100f, Holding ballot above ballot box. 200f, Holding scales of justice. 250f, Writing, vert.

2010, Dec. 16   **Perf. 14¼**
670-672 A173   Set of 3   3.00 3.00

Bahraini Women's Day — A174

King Hamad and: 100f, Round Supreme Council for Women 10th anniversary emblem. 200f, Rectangular emblem with circles. 500f, King Hamad and buildings.

2011, Dec. 1   **Perf. 14¼**
673-674 A174   Set of 2   1.60 1.60
    Souvenir Sheet
      Perf. 13¼x13
675 A174   500f multi   2.75 2.75
No. 675 contains one 90x35mm stamp.

National Day — A175

King Hamad and: 100f, People, heart with Arabic inscription. 200f, Stylized bird over map of Bahrain. 250f, Stylized boat on water, vert.

2011, Dec. 16   **Perf. 14¼**
676-678 A175 Set of 3   3.00 3.00

Discovery of Oil in Bahrain, 80th Anniv. — A176

Designs: 100f, Airplane over Bahrain Petroleum Company building. 150f, Bahrain Petroleum Company Center of Excellence. 200f, Bridge, man, boy, dhow. 250f, Oil tanks, solar energy facility.

2012, June 17
679-682 A176 Set of 4   3.75 3.75

Royal Charity Organization, 10th Anniv. — A177

2012, July 31
683 A177 250f multi   1.40 1.40

Arab Postal Day — A178

2012, Aug. 3   **Perf. 12¾x13¼**
684 A178 250f multi   1.40 1.40

6th World Urban Forum, Naples, Italy A179

Emblem and: No. 685, 200f, United Nations Secretary-General Ban Ki-Moon giving award to King Hamad. No. 686, 200f, Bridge, city skyline. No. 687, 200f, Building with wind turbines.

2012, Sept. 1
685-687 A179 Set of 3   3.25 3.25
687a   Souvenir sheet of 3, #685-687, perf. 13½x13   4.75 4.75
No. 687a sold for 900f.

Manama, 2012 Capital of Arab Culture A180

2012, Sept. 27   **Perf. 14¼**
688 A180 200f multi   1.10 1.10

World Habitat Day A181

Designs: No. 689, 100f, Building, denomination in black. No. 690, 100f, Building, diff., denomination in white. No. 691, 100f, Buildings around pond.

2012, Oct. 1   **Perf. 14¼**
689-691 A181 Set of 3   1.60 1.60
A souvenir sheet containing perf. 13½x13 examples of Nos. 689-691 sold for 900f.

Opening of National Theater, Manama A182

2012, Nov. 12
692 A182 250f multi   1.40 1.40

A183

33rd Supreme Council Summit of the Gulf Cooperation Council A184

Litho. With Foil Application
2012, Dec. 24
693 A183 200f multi   1.10 1.10
694 A184 200f multi   1.10 1.10

Miniature Sheet

33rd Supreme Council Summit of the Gulf Cooperation Council — A185

No. 695 — Various buildings, flag of: a, United Arab Emirates, Sheikh Khalifa. b, Saudi Arabia, King Abdullah. c, Bahrain, King Hamad. d, Kuwait, Sheikh Sabah. e, Qatar, Sheikh Hamad. f, Oman, Sultan Qaboos.

Litho. With Foil Application
2012, Dec. 24   **Perf. 13½x13**
695 A185 100f Sheet of 6, #a-f   5.50 5.50
No. 695 sold for 1d.

Annual Fine Arts Exhibition, 40th Anniv. — A190

2014, Jan. 15   **Litho.**   **Perf. 14¼**
704 A190 200f multi   1.10 1.10

King Hamad, 1¼-Anna Local Stamp of 1953 — A186

Designs: 200f, With decorative border and white frame. 500f, Without decorative border and white frame.

2013, Feb. 15   **Litho.**   **Perf. 14¼**
Granite Paper
696 A186 200f multi   1.10 1.10
Souvenir Sheet
Perf. 13¼
697 A186 500f multi   2.75 2.75
First postage stamps of Bahrain, 60th anniv.

Insurance Day — A187

Bahrain Insurance Association emblem and: 100f, Dhows and stylized city skyline. 200f, House, automobile, airplane, medical bag, stethoscope. 250f, Insurance Day emblem.

2013, Mar. 26   **Litho.**   **Perf. 14¼**
698-700 A187 Set of 3   3.00 3.00

Sheikh Isa Award for Service to Humanity A188

Color of geometric pattern in background: 100f, Red brown. 200f, Olive brown.

2013, May 26   **Litho.**   **Perf. 13**
701-702 A188 Set of 2   1.60 1.60

Miniature Sheet

National Day — A189

No. 703 — King Hamad and people carrying flag of Bahrain: a, 200f, Woman wearing headdress and glasses. b, 250f, Woman with stethoscope. c, 300f, Man wearing headdress. d, 400f, Man wearing hard hat.

2013, Dec. 16   **Litho.**   **Perf. 14½**
703 A189 Sheet of 4, #a-d   6.25 6.25

Third Bahrain International Airshow — A191

Various airshow performers: 200f, 300f, 400f.

2014, Jan. 16   **Litho.**   **Perf. 14¼**
705-707 A191 Set of 3   4.75 4.75

Bahrain Grand Prix, 10th Anniv. A192

Victorious drivers and their cars: 100f, Michael Schumacher, 2004. 150f, Fernando Alonso, 2005, 2006, 2010. 200f, Felipe Massa, 2007, 2008. 250f, Jenson Button, 2009. 500f, Sebastian Vettel, 2012, 2013.

2014, Apr. 6   **Litho.**   **Perf. 14¼**
708-712 A192 Set of 5   6.50 6.50

All Civilizations in Service to Humanity International Interfaith Dialogue — A193

Designs: 200f, Entire tree in green, with world map in white. 250f, Close-up of green tree. 300f, White tree and silhouette of face.

2014, May 5   **Litho.**   **Perf. 13**
713-715 A193 Set of 3   4.00 4.00

Bahrain Bourse, 25th Anniv. — A194

2014, June 16   **Litho.**   **Perf. 14¼**
716 A194 200f multi   1.10 1.10

2014 World Cup Soccer Championships. Brazil — A195

Silhouettes of various people, arm extended on person in: 200f, Orange. 250f, Green and blue, vert. 300f, Red violet.

2014, June 12   **Litho.**   **Perf. 14¼**
717-719 A195 Set of 3   4.00 4.00

National
Day — A196

Designs: 200f, Man and woman holding rope on flagpole with Bahrain flag. 300f, Clasped hands on map of Bahrain. 400f, Doves and map of Bahrain.

2014, Dec. 16	Litho.		Perf. 14¼
720-722 A196	Set of 3		4.75 4.75

Souvenir Sheet

National Initiative for Agricultural
Development — A197

No. 723: a, Sheikhs and children. b, Sheikh, army officer, crowd of people, sign.

Perf. 12¾x13¼

2015, Feb. 26		Litho.
723 A197	500f Sheet of 2, #a-b	5.50 5.50

Miniature Sheet

Bahrain Garden Club, 50th
Anniv. — A198

No. 724 — Photographs from Garden Club events dated: a, 200f, 1967 (50x60mm). b, 200f, 1989 (50x30mm). c, 200f, 1990 (50x60mm). d, 200f, 1978 (50x60mm). e, 200f, 1992 (50x30mm). f, 300f, 1990 (50x60mm). g, 300f, 1993 (50x30mm). h, 300f, 1994 (50x30mm). i, 400f, 1996 (50x30mm). j, 400f, 2004 (50x60mm). k, 400f, 1997 (50x30mm). l, 400f, 1998 (Sheikhs, women, vegetables, 50x30mm). m, 400f, 2014 (50x60mm). n, 400f, 1998 (Sheikh and children, 50x30mm). o, 500f, 1988 (100x60mm).

Perf. 12¾x13¼

2015, Feb. 26		Litho.
724 A198	Sheet of 15, #a-o	25.50 25.50

Manama, 2015 Capital of Arab
Youth — A199

King Hamad, emblems and: 200f, Manama 2015 emblem. 300f, Young men holding flag with Manama 2015 emblem.

2015, Dec. 3	Litho.		Perf. 14¼
725-726 A199	Set of 2		2.75 2.75

National
Day
A200

King Hamad, various buildings and people: 200f, 300f, 400f, 1d.

2015, Dec. 16		Litho.	Perf. 14¼
727-729 A200	Set of 3		4.75 4.75

Size: 202x92mm

Imperf

730 A200	1d multi	5.50 5.50

Bahraini Currency, 50th
Anniv. — A201

No. 731 — Obverse and reverse of: a, Half-dinar banknote, 10-fils coin. b, Quarter-dinar banknote, 5-fils coin. c, 100-fils banknote, 1-fils coin. d, 10-dinar banknote, 100-fils coin. e, 5-dinar banknote, 50-fils coin. f, 1-dinar banknote, 25-fils coin.

2015, Dec. 30	Litho.		Perf. 14¼
731 A201	300f Block of 6, #a-f		9.50 9.50
g.	Souvenir sheet of 6, #731a-731f, perf, 13¼		13.50 13.50

No. 731g sold for 2.50d.

Arab Postal Day — A202

No. 732 — Globe at: a, 200f, Left. b, 300f, Right.

2016, Aug. 3	Litho.	Perf. 14
732 A202	Horiz. pair, #a-b	2.75 2.75

Relationship Between Bahrain and
United Kingdom, 200th Anniv. — A203

200th anniv. emblem and various Bahraini and British buildings: 200f, 500f.

2016, Nov. 10	Litho.		Perf. 14¼
733-734 A203	Set of 2		3.75 3.75

Supreme Council for Women, 15th
Anniv. — A204

2016, Dec. 1	Litho.	Perf. 13
735 A204	500f multi	2.75 2.75

Gulf Cooperation Council Summit 37th
Regular Session — A205

Color behind denomination: 250f, White. 500f, Gold.

2016, Dec. 6	Litho.		Perf. 13
736-737 A205	Set of 2		4.00 4.00

Miniature Sheet

University of Bahrain, 30th
Anniv. — A206

No. 738: a, Building and tower. b, Aerial view of campus. c, Aerial view of courtyard with palm trees, curved building at right. d, Aerial view of building, two buses in foreground. e, Aerial view of plaza with covered walkways. f, Building and large 30th anniv. emblem.

2016, Dec. 29	Litho.		Perf. 14¼
738 A206	500f Sheet of 6, #a-f		16.00 16.00

POSTAL TAX STAMPS

PT1

1973, Oct. 21	Litho.	Perf. 14½
RA1 PT1	5f sky blue	225.00 125.00

PT2

1974		Litho.	Perf. 14½
RA2 PT2	5f light blue		7.50 .40
a.		Perf. 14½x13½	7.50 .40

No. RA2a was issued around 1988.

PT3

No. RA3 is inscribed "STATE OF BAHRAIN".

2000-02		Litho.	Perf. 14½x14
RA3 PT3	10f green & black		3.00 .40
RA4 PT3	10f green & black ('02)		3.00 .40

No gum examples of RA1-RA4 are considered used.

BANGKOK

'baŋ,käk

LOCATION — Capital of Siam (Thailand)

Stamps were issued by Great Britain under rights obtained in the treaty of 1855. These were in use until July 1, 1885, when the stamps of Siam were designated as the only official postage stamps to be used in the kingdom.

100 Cents = 1 Dollar

Excellent counterfeits of Nos. 1-22 are plentiful.

Stamps of Straits Settlements Overprinted in Black

1882		Wmk. 1	Perf. 14	
1	A2	2c brown	4,500.	1,950.
2	A2	4c rose	4,250.	1,650.
b.		Double overprint		9,750.
3	A6	5c brown violet	475.	550.
4	A2	6c violet	325.	150.
5	A3	8c yel orange	3,750.	290.
6	A7	10c slate	750.	200.
7	A3	12c blue	1,500.	600.
8	A3	24c green	900.	190.
9	A4	30c claret	57,500.	39,000.
10	A5	96c olive gray	9,750.	4,000.

See note after No. 20.

1882-83		Wmk. 2		
11	A2	2c brown	750.00	450.00
12	A2	2c rose ('83)	75.00	57.50
a.		Inverted overprint	19,000.	16,500.
b.		Double overprint	3,500.	3,500.
c.		Triple overprint	13,000.	
13	A2	4c rose	900.00	400.00
14	A2	4c brown ('83)	100.00	90.00
a.		Double overprint	4,500.	
15	A6	5c ultra ('83)	425.00	210.00
16	A2	6c violet ('83)	325.00	170.00
a.		Double overprint	9,000.	
17	A3	8c yel orange	250.00	82.50
a.		Inverted overprint	30,000.	16,000.
18	A7	10c slate	260.00	110.00
19	A3	12c violet brn ('83)	450.00	190.00
20	A3	24c green	8,000.	3,750.

Double overprints must have two clear impressions. Partial double overprints exist on a number of values of these issues. They sell for a modest premium over catalogue value depending on how much of the impression is present.

1883		Wmk. 1		
21	A5	2c on 32c pale red	3,500.	3,500.

On Straits Settlements No. 9

1885		Wmk. 38		
22	A7	32c on 2a yel (B+B)	45,000.	

BANGLADESH

,bäŋ-glə-'desh

LOCATION — In southern, central Asia, touching India, Burma, and the Bay of Bengal
GOVT. — Republic in the British Commonwealth
AREA — 55,598 sq. mi.
POP. — 127,117,967 (1999 est.)
CAPITAL — Dhaka (Dacca)

Bangladesh, formerly East Pakistan, broke away from Pakistan in April 1971, proclaiming its independence. It consists of 14 former eastern districts of Bengal and the former Sylhet district of Assam province of India.

100 Paisas = 1 Rupee

100 Paisas (Poishas) = 1 Taka (1972)

Catalogue values for all unused stamps in this country are for Never Hinged items.

Various stamps of Pakistan were handstamped locally for use in Bangladesh from March 26, 1971 until April 30, 1973. Thousands of varieties exist.

Map of Bangladesh
A1

Sheik Mujibur Rahman
A2

Designs: 20p, "Dacca University Massacre." 50p, "A Nation of 75 Million People." 1r, Flag of Independence (showing map). 2r, Ballot box. 3r, Broken chain. 10r, "Support Bangladesh" and map.

		Perf. 14x14½		
1971, July 29		Litho.		Unwmk.
1	A1	10p red, dk pur & lt bl	.25	.25
2	A1	20p bl, grn, red & yel	.25	.25
3	A1	50p dp org, gray & brn	.25	.25
4	A1	1r red, emer & yel	.25	.25
5	A1	2r lil rose, lt & dk bl	.40	.40
6	A1	3r blue, emer & grn	.50	.50
7	A2	5r dp org, tan & blk	1.00	1.00
8	A1	10r gold, dk bl & lil rose	1.75	1.75
		Nos. 1-8 (8)	4.65	4.65

A set of 15 stamps of types A1 and A2 in new paisa-taka values and colors was rejected by Bangladesh officials and not issued. Bangladesh representatives in England released these stamps, which were not valid, on Feb. 1, 1972. Value, set $8.
Imperfs of Nos. 1-8 were in the Format International liquidation. They are not errors.

Nos. 1-8 Overprinted in Black or Red

1971, Dec. 20				
9	A1	10p multicolored	.25	.25
10	A1	20p multicolored	.20	
11	A1	50p multicolored	.35	
12	A1	1r multicolored	.75	
13	A1	2r multicolored	1.10	
14	A1	3r multicolored	1.50	
15	A2	5r multicolored (R)	4.00	4.00
16	A1	10r multicolored	5.00	5.00
		Nos. 9-16 (8)	13.15	

Liberation of Bangladesh.
The 10p, 5r and 10r were issued in Dacca, but Nos. 10-14 were not put on sale in Bangladesh.

Monument — A3

1972, Feb. 21		Litho.	Perf. 13	
32	A3	20p green & rose	.35	.35

Language Movement Martyrs.

"Independence"
A4

1972, Mar. 26		Photo.	Perf. 13	
33	A4	20p maroon & red	.30	.25
34	A4	60p dark blue & red	.50	.45
35	A4	75p purple & red	.55	.55
		Nos. 33-35 (3)	1.35	1.25

First anniversary of independence.

Doves of Peace — A5

1972, Dec. 16		Litho.	Perf. 13	
36	A5	20p ocher & multi	.25	.25
37	A5	60p lilac & multi	.30	.30
38	A5	75p yellow green & multi	.30	.30
		Nos. 36-38 (3)	.85	.85

Victory Day, Dec. 16.

Flower Growing from Ruin — A6

1973, Mar. 25		Litho.	Perf. 13	
39	A6	20p ocher & multi	.25	.25
40	A6	60p brown & multi	.30	.30
41	A6	1.35t violet blue & multi	.65	.65
		Nos. 39-41 (3)	1.20	1.20

Martyrs of the war of liberation.

Embroidered Quilt — A7

Hilsa — A8

Court of Justice — A9

Designs: 3p, Jute field. 5p, Jack fruit. 10p, Farmer plowing with ox team. 20p, Hibiscus rosenensis. 25p, Tiger. 60p, Bamboo and water lilies. 75p, Women picking tea. 90p, Handicrafts. 2t, Collecting date palm juice, vert. 5t, Net fishing. 10t, Sixty-dome Mosque.

		Perf. 14x14½, 14½x14		
1973, Apr. 30			Litho.	
		Size: 21x28mm, 28x21mm		
42	A7	2p black	.25	.25
43	A7	3p bright green	.50	.50
44	A7	5p light brown	.50	.25
45	A7	10p black	.30	.25
46	A7	20p olive	.50	.25
47	A7	25p red lilac	3.25	.25
48	A8	50p rose lilac	2.25	.30
49	A7	60p gray	2.25	1.25
50	A7	75p orange	1.25	1.25
51	A7	90p red brown	1.50	2.00

Taka Expressed as "TA"
Size: 35x22mm, 22x35mm

52	A9	1t violet	6.00	.25
53	A9	2t greenish gray	6.00	1.25
54	A9	5t grayish blue	7.50	2.75
55	A9	10t rose	12.00	6.00
		Nos. 42-55 (14)	44.05	16.80

See Nos. 82-85, 95-106, 165-176, 356. For overprints see Nos. O1-O10, O13.

Human Rights Flame — A10

1973, Dec. 10		Litho.	Perf. 13x13½	
56	A10	10p blue & multi	.25	.25
57	A10	1.25t violet & multi	.25	.25

25th anniversary of the Universal Declaration of Human Rights.

Family, Chart, Map of Bangladesh — A11

1974, Feb. 10		Litho.	Perf. 13½	
58	A11	20p blue grn & multi	.25	.25
59	A11	25p brt blue & multi	.25	.25
60	A11	75p red & multi	.25	.25
		Nos. 58-60 (3)	.75	.75

First census in Bangladesh.
For overprints see Nos. 194-196.

Copernicus, Heliocentric System — A12

1974, July 22		Litho.	Perf. 13½	
61	A12	25p violet, blk & org	.25	.25
62	A12	75p emerald, blk & org	.25	.25

Nicolaus Copernicus (1473-1543), Polish astronomer.

Flag and UN Headquarters A13

1974, Sept. 25		Litho.	Perf. 13½	
63	A13	25p lilac & multi	.25	.25
64	A13	1t blue & multi	.25	.25

Admission of Bangladesh to the UN.

Designs: 25p, 1.75t, UPU emblem. 1.25t, 5t, Mail runner. 25p, 1.25t, country and denomination appear on a yellow background, 1.75t, 5t, blue background.

1974, Oct. 9   **Perf. 13½**
65	A14	25p multicolored	.25	.25
66	A14	1.25t multicolored	.25	.25
67	A14	1.75t multicolored	.25	.25
68	A14	5t multicolored	.80	.80
a.		Souv. sheet of 4, #65-68, imperf.		80.00
		Nos. 65-68 (4)	1.55	1.55

A15

1974, Nov. 4   **Litho.**
69	A15	25p Royal bengal tiger	.85	.25
70	A15	50p Tiger cub	1.10	.75
71	A15	2t Swimming tiger	2.00	2.00
		Nos. 69-71 (3)	3.95	3.95

"Save the Tiger," World Wildlife Fund.

Type of 1973
Taka Expressed in Bengali
1974-75   Perf. 14½x14, 14x14½
Size: 35x22mm, 22x35mm
82	A9	1t violet	1.50	.25
83	A9	2t grayish green	3.00	2.00
84	A9	5t grayish blue ('75)	7.00	.75
85	A9	10t rose ('75)	25.00	15.00
		Nos. 82-85 (4)	36.50	18.00

See Nos. 350-356. For overprints see Nos. O11-O12, O14.

Family — A16   Children — A17

Family A18

1974, Dec. 30   Litho.   Perf. 14
86	A16	25p ocher & multi	.25	.25
87	A17	70p claret & multi	.25	.25
88	A18	1.25t multicolored	.50	.50
		Nos. 86-88 (3)	1.00	1.00

Family planning. The numerals on No. 87 look like "90" but mean "70."

Betbunia Satellite Earth Station — A19

1975, June 14   Litho.   Perf. 14
89	A19	25p red, black & silver	.25	.25
90	A19	1t vio blue, blk & silver	.25	.25

Opening of Betbunia Satellite Earth Station.

Allegory, IWY Emblem A20

1975, Dec. 31   Litho.   Perf. 15
91	A20	50p rose & multi	.25	.25
92	A20	2t lt lilac & multi	.25	.25

International Women's Year.

Types of 1973 Redrawn
1976-77   Litho.   Perf. 15x14½
Size: 18x23mm, 23x18mm
95	A7	5p green	.25	.25
96	A7	10p black	.25	.25
97	A7	20p olive green	2.00	.25
98	A7	25p rose lilac	7.00	.25
99	A8	50p rose lilac	4.25	.25
100	A7	60p gray	.50	.50
101	A7	75p olive	2.00	2.00
102	A7	90p red brown	.50	.50

Taka Expressed in Bengali
Size: 32x20mm, 20x32mm
103	A9	1t violet	2.50	.25
104	A9	2t greenish gray	2.50	.25
105	A9	5t grayish blue	4.00	3.00
106	A9	10t rose ('77)	15.00	6.00
		Nos. 95-106 (12)	40.75	13.75

For overprints see Nos. O16-O25.

Telephones, 1876 and 1976 — A21   Alexander Graham Bell — A22

1976, Mar. 10   Litho.   Perf. 15
107	A21	2.25t multicolored	.25	.25
108	A22	5t multicolored	.60	.60

Centenary of first telephone call by Alexander Graham Bell, Mar. 10, 1876.

Eye and Healthful Food A23

1976, Apr. 7   Litho.   Perf. 15
109	A23	30p yellow & multi	.50	.25
110	A23	2.25t orange & multi	1.25	1.25

World Health Day: Foresight prevents blindness.

Liberty Bell A24

Designs: 2.25t, Statue of Liberty, New York Skyline. 5t, Mayflower. 10t, Mt. Rushmore, presidents' heads.

1976, May 29   Photo.   Perf. 13½x14
111	A24	30p multicolored	.25	.25
112	A24	2.25t multicolored	.25	.25
113	A24	5t multicolored	.50	.50
114	A24	10t multicolored	.50	.50
a.		Souv. sheet, #111-114, perf 13	3.50	3.50
		Nos. 111-114 (4)	1.50	1.50

American Bicentennial. Sheet exists imperf. Value, $90.

Weaver, Chemist, Farmer, Student and Emblem — A25

1976, July 29   Litho.   Perf. 15
115	A25	30p multicolored	.25	.25
116	A25	2.25t multicolored	.40	.40

25th anniversary of Colombo Plan.
For overprint see No. 252.

Hurdles — A26

Montreal Olympic Emblem and: 30p, Running, horiz. 1t, High jump. 2.25t, Swimming, horiz. 3.50t, Gymnastics. 5t, Soccer.

1976, Nov. 29   Litho.   Perf. 15
117	A26	25p multicolored	.25	.25
118	A26	30p multicolored	.25	.25
119	A26	1t multicolored	.25	.25
120	A26	2.25t multicolored	.45	.45
121	A26	3.50t multicolored	.75	.75
122	A26	5t multicolored	1.40	1.40
		Nos. 117-122 (6)	3.35	3.35

21st Olympic Games, Montreal, Canada, July 17-Aug. 1.

Coronation Ceremony — A27

Designs: 2.25t, Queen Elizabeth II. 10t, Queen and Prince Philip.

1977, Feb. 7   Perf. 14x15
123	A27	30p multicolored	.25	.25
124	A27	2.25t multicolored	.25	.25
125	A27	10t multicolored	.75	.75
a.		Souv. sheet, #123-125, perf 14½	1.25	1.25
		Nos. 123-125 (3)	1.25	1.25

25th anniv. of the reign of Elizabeth II.
For overprint see No. 228B.

Qazi Nazrul Islam — A28

Nazrul A29

1977, Aug. 29   Litho.   Perf. 14
126	A28	40p lt green & black	.25	.25
127	A29	2.25t multicolored	.45	.45

Qazi Nazrul Islam (1899-1976), natl. poet.

Pigeon Carrying Letter A30

1977, Sept. 29   Litho.   Perf. 14
128	A30	30p multicolored	.25	.25
129	A30	2.25t multicolored	.25	.25

Asian-Oceanic Postal Union (AOPU), 15th anniversary.

Leopard A31

40p and 1t are vert.

1977, Nov. 9   Litho.   Perf. 13
130	A31	40p Asiatic black bear	.25	.25
131	A31	1t Axis deer	.25	.25
132	A31	2.25t shown	.30	.30
133	A31	3.50t Gayal	.30	.30
134	A31	4t Elephant	1.00	1.00
135	A31	5t Bengal tiger	1.25	1.25
		Nos. 130-135 (6)	3.35	3.35

Campfire, Tent, Scout Emblem — A32

Designs: 3.50t, Emblem, first aid, signaling, horiz. 5t, Scout emblem and oath.

1978, Jan. 22   Litho.   Perf. 13
136	A32	40p multicolored	.25	.25
137	A32	3.50t multicolored	.75	.75
138	A32	5t multicolored	1.50	1.50
		Nos. 136-138 (3)	2.50	2.50

1st National Boy Scout Jamboree, Jan. 22.
For overprint see No. 269.

Champac — A33

Flowers and Flowering Trees: 1t, Pudding pipe tree. 2.25t, Flamboyant tree. 3.50t, Water lilies. 4t, Butea. 5t, Anthocephalus indicus.

1978, Mar. 31   Litho.   Perf. 13
139	A33	40p multicolored	.25	.25
140	A33	1t multicolored	.30	.30
141	A33	2.25t multicolored	.35	.35
142	A33	3.50t multicolored	.50	.50
143	A33	4t multicolored	.50	.50
144	A33	5t multicolored	.50	.50
		Nos. 139-144 (6)	2.40	2.40

For overprints see Nos. 259A-259F.

Crown, Scepter and Staff of State — A34

Designs: 3.50t, Royal family on balcony. 5t, Queen Elizabeth II and Prince Philip. 10t, Queen in coronation regalia, Westminster Abbey.

1978, May 20   Perf. 14
145	A34	40p multicolored	.25	.25
146	A34	3.50t multicolored	.25	.25
147	A34	5t multicolored	.25	.25
148	A34	10t multicolored	.45	.45
a.		Souv. sheet, #145-148, perf 14½	1.25	1.25
		Nos. 145-148 (4)	1.20	1.20

Coronation of Queen Elizabeth II, 25th anniv.

Alan Cobham's DH50, 1926 — A35

Planes: 2.25t, Capt. Hans Bertram's Junkers W33 Atlantis, 1932-33. 3.50t, Wright brothers' plane. 5t, Concorde.

1978, June 15   Litho.   Perf. 13
149	A35	40p multicolored	.25	.25
150	A35	2.25t multicolored	.25	.25
151	A35	3.50t multicolored	.50	.50
152	A35	5t multicolored	3.75	3.75
		Nos. 149-152 (4)	4.75	4.75

75th anniversary of powered flight.

Holy Kaaba, Mecca — A37

Design: 3.50t, Pilgrims at Mt. Arafat, horiz.

1978, Nov. 9   Litho.   Perf. 13
154	A37	40p multicolored	.25	.25
155	A37	3.50t multicolored	.75	.75

Pilgrimage to Mecca.

Jasim Uddin, Poet A38

1979, Mar. 14   Litho.   Perf. 14
156	A38	40p multicolored	.25	.25

Rowland Hill — A39

Hill and Stamps of Bangladesh: 3.50t, No. 1, horiz. 10t, No. 66, horiz.

1979, Nov. 26   Litho.   Perf. 14
157	A39	40p multicolored	.25	.25
158	A39	3.50t multicolored	.35	.35
159	A39	10t multicolored	.80	.80
a.		Souvenir sheet of 3, #157-159	3.50	3.50
		Nos. 157-159 (3)	1.40	1.40

Sir Rowland Hill (1795-1879), originator of penny postage.

Moulana Bhashani — A40

1979, Nov. 17   Perf. 12½
160	A40	40p multicolored	.45	.45

Moulana Abdul Hamid Khan Bhashani (1880-1976), philosopher and statesman.

A41

IYC Emblem and: 40p, Boys and Hoops. 3.50t, Boys flying kites. 5t, Children jumping.

1979, Dec. 17   Perf. 14x14½
161	A41	40p multicolored	.25	.25
162	A41	3.50t multicolored	.35	.35
163	A41	5t multicolored	.50	.50
a.		Souv. sheet, #161-163, perf 14½	2.00	2.00
		Nos. 161-163 (3)	1.10	1.10

International Year of the Child.

Type of 1973

Designs: 5p, Lalbag Fort. 10p, Fenchungan Fertilizer Factory, vert. 15p, Pineapple. 20p, Gas well. 25p, Jute on boat. 30p, Banana tree. 40p, Baitul Mukarram Mosque. 50p, Baitul Mukarram Mosque. 80p, Garh excavations. 1ta, Dotara (musical instrument.) 2t, Karnaphuli Dam.

1979-82   Photo.   Perf. 14½
Size: 18x23mm, 23x18mm
165	A7	5p brown ('79)	.25	.25
166	A7	10p Prus blue	.25	.25
167	A7	15p yellow org ('81)	.25	.25
168	A7	20p dk carmine ('79)	.25	.25
169	A7	25p dk blue ('82)	.30	.30
170	A7	30p lt olive grn ('80)	3.50	3.50
171	A9	40p rose magenta ('79)	.65	.65
172	A9	50p black & gray ('81)	6.50	6.50
173	A7	80p dk brown ('80)	.50	.50

174	A7	1t red lilac ('81)	8.50	8.50
175	A7	2t brt ultra ('81)	4.25	4.25
		Nos. 165-175 (11)	25.20	25.20

For overprints see Nos. O27-O36.

A42

Rotary Intl., 75th Anniv.: 40p, Rotary emblem, diff.

1980, Feb. 23   Litho.   Perf. 14
179	A42	40p multicolored	.25	.25
180	A42	5t ultra & gold	.65	.65

For overprints see Nos. 285-286.

Canal Digging A43

1980, Mar. 27   Litho.   Perf. 14
181	A43	40p multicolored	.45	.45

Sher-e-Bangla A.K. Fazlul Huq (1873-1962), Natl. Leader — A44

1980, Apr. 27   Litho.   Perf. 14
182	A44	40p multicolored	.45	.45

Early Mail Transport, London 1980 Emblem — A45

10t, Modern mail transport.

1980, May 5
183	A45	1t shown	.25	.25
184	A45	10t multicolored	1.25	1.25
a.		Souvenir sheet of 2, #183-184	2.25	2.25

London 80 Intl. Stamp Exhib., May 6-14.

Dome of the Rock — A46

1980, Aug. 21   Litho.   Perf. 14½
185	A46	50p violet rose	1.00	.30

For the families of Palestinians.
A 50p stamp for the Palestinian liberation struggle was prepared for issue on the same day as No. 185, but was not issued because of errors in the Arabic inscription in the design. Value, $10.

Adult Education A47

1980, Aug. 23   Perf. 13½
186	A47	50p multicolored	.40	.25

Beach Scene A48

1980, Sept. 27   Litho.   Perf. 14
187	A48	50p shown	.35	.35
188	A48	5t Beach scene, diff.	.65	.65
a.		Souvenir sheet of 2, #187-188	1.50	1.50
b.		Pair, #187-188	1.00	1.00

World Tourism Conference, Manila, Sept. 27. No. 188b has continuous design.
For overprints see Nos. 243-244.

Hegira (Pilgrimage Year) — A49

1980, Nov. 11   Photo.   Perf. 14
189	A49	50p multicolored	.40	.25

A50

Design: Deer and Boy Scout emblem.

1981, Jan. 1   Litho.   Perf. 14
190	A50	50p multicolored	.25	.25
191	A50	5t multicolored	1.25	1.25

5th Asia-Pacific and 2nd Bangladesh Scout Jamboree, 1980-1981.
For overprint, see No. 321.

A51

1980, Dec. 9   Litho.   Perf. 14
192	A51	50p multicolored	.25	.25
193	A51	2t multicolored	.35	.35

Begum Roquiah (1880-1932), educator.

Nos. 58-60
Overprinted

1981, Mar. 6   **Perf. 13½**
194	A11	20p multicolored	.25	.25
195	A11	25p multicolored	.25	.25
196	A11	75p multicolored	.25	.25
	Nos. 194-196 (3)		.75	.75

A52

1981, Mar. 16   **Litho.**   **Perf. 14**
197	A52	1t multicolored	.25	.25
198	A52	15t multicolored	1.75	1.75
	a.	Souvenir sheet of 2, #197-198	2.75	2.75

Queen Mother Elizabeth, 80th birthday (1980).

A53

50p, Citizen Holding Rifle & Flag. 2t, People, map.

1981, Mar. 26
199	A53	50p multicolored	.25	.25
200	A53	2t multicolored	.25	.25

10th anniversary of independence.
For overprint on 199, see No. 210A.

UN Conference on Least-developed
Countries, Paris — A54

1981, Sept. 1   **Litho.**   **Perf. 14x13½**
201	A54	50p multicolored	.50	.25

Birth Centenary
of Kemal
Ataturk (First
President of
Turkey) — A55

1981, Nov. 10   **Litho.**   **Perf. 14**
202	A55	50p Portrait	.50	.50
203	A55	1t Portrait, diff.	1.00	1.00

Intl. Year
of the
Disabled
A56

50p, Sign language, vert. 2t, Amputee.

1981, Dec. 26   **Litho.**   **Perf. 14**
204	A56	50p multicolored	.50	.25
205	A56	2t multicolored	1.00	1.00

World Food
Day, Oct.
16 — A57

1981, Dec. 31   **Litho.**   **Perf. 13½x14**
206	A57	50p multicolored	.60	.60

Boat Hauling
Rice
Straw — A58

1982, May 22   **Litho.**   **Perf. 13½x14**
207	A58	50p multicolored	.60	.60

10th Anniv. of UN Conf. on Human Environment.
For overprint see No. 281.

A59

1982, Oct. 9
208	A59	50p multicolored	.55	.55

Dr. Kazi Motahar Hossain, educator and statistician.

Scouting
Year
A60

1982, Oct. 21   **Litho.**   **Perf. 14**
209	A60	50p Emblem, knots	.80	.30
210	A60	2t Baden-Powell, vert.	2.50	2.50

No. 199
Overprinted

1982, Nov. 21   **Litho.**   **Perf. 14**
210A	A53	50p multi	4.50	4.50

Armed Forces Day.

Capt.
Mohiuddin
Jahangir
A61

No. 211 — Liberation heroes (tablet color): b, Sepoy Hamidur Rahman (pale green). c, Sepoy Mohammed Mustafa Kamal (rose claret). d, Mohammad Ruhul Amin (yellow). e, M. Matiur Rahman (olive bister). f, Lance-Naik Munshi Abdur Rouf (brown orange). g, Lance-Naik Nur Mouhammad (bright yellow green).

1982, Dec. 16   **Litho.**   **Perf. 14**
211		Strip of 7	2.25	2.25
	a.-g.	A61 50p multicolored	.30	.30

Metric
System
A62

1983, Jan. 10   **Litho.**   **Perf. 14**
212	A62	50p Mail scale, vert.	.60	.60
213	A62	2t Weights, measures	2.00	2.00

TB Bacillus
Centenary
A63

1983, Feb. 20   **Litho.**   **Perf. 14**
214	A63	50p Koch	1.40	1.40
215	A63	1t Slides, microscope	2.40	2.40

A64

1983, Mar. 14   **Litho.**   **Perf. 14**
216	A64	1t Open stage theater	.25	.25
217	A64	3t Boat race	.25	.25
218	A64	10t Snake dance	.55	.55
219	A64	15t Tea garden	.90	.90
	Nos. 216-219 (4)		1.95	1.95

Commonwealth Day.

Jnantapash
Shahidullah
(1885-1969),
Educator and
Linguist — A65

1983, July 10   **Litho.**   **Perf. 14**
220	A65	50p multicolored	.85	.85

Birds
A66

Designs: 50p, Copsychus saularis. 2t, Halcyon smyrnensis, vert. 3.75t, Dinopium benghalense, vert. 5t, Carina scutulota.

1983, Aug. 17   **Litho.**   **Perf. 14**
221	A66	50p multi	.85	.40
222	A66	2t multi	1.00	1.00
223	A66	3.75t multi	1.40	1.40
224	A66	5t multi	1.60	1.60
	a.	Souvenir sheet of 4, #221-224	6.50	6.50
	Nos. 221-224 (4)		4.85	4.40

No. 224a sold for 13t.

Local Fish
A67

50p, Macrobrachium rosengergii. 2t, Stromateus cinereus. 3.75t, Labeo rohita. 5t, Anabas testudineus.

1983, Oct. 31   **Litho.**   **Perf. 14**
225	A67	50p multicolored	.75	.75
226	A67	2t multicolored	.80	.80
227	A67	3.75t multicolored	1.00	1.00
228	A67	5t multicolored	1.25	1.25
	a.	Souv. sheet of 4, #225-228, imperf.	6.00	6.00
	Nos. 225-228 (4)		3.80	3.80

No. 228a sold for 13t.

No. 125
Overprinted in
Red

1983, Nov. 14   **Litho.**   **Perf. 14**
228B	A27	10t multicolored	15.00	15.00

No. 228B also exists with the overprint reading "Nov. '33" instead of "Nov. '83." Value, $15.

World Communications Year — A68

50p, Messenger, vert. 5t, Jet, train, ship, vert. 10t, Dish antenna, messenger.

1983, Dec. 21   **Litho.**   **Perf. 14**
229	A68	50p multicolored	.35	.35
230	A68	5t multicolored	1.50	1.50
231	A68	10t multicolored	2.00	2.00
	Nos. 229-231 (3)		3.85	3.85

Hall
A69

50p, Sangsad Bhaban. 5t, Shait Gumbaz.

1983, Dec. 5   Litho.   Perf. 14
232	A69	50p multicolored	.25	.25
233	A69	5t multicolored	1.75	1.75

14th Islamic Foreign Ministers Conference.

A70

5p, Mailboat. 10p, Dacca P.O. counter. 15p, IWTA Terminal. 20p, Sorting mail. 25p, Mail delivery. 30p, Postman at mailbox. 50p, Mobile post office. 1t, Kamalapur Railway Station. 2t, Zia Intl. Airport. 5t, Khulna P.O.

Perf. 11½x12½, 12½x11½
1983, Dec. 21
234	A70	5p multicolored	.40	.40
235	A70	10p multicolored	.40	.30
236	A70	15p multicolored	.50	.30
237	A70	20p multicolored	1.50	.30
238	A70	25p multicolored	.75	.30
239	A70	30p multicolored	.75	.30
240	A70	50p multicolored	1.50	.30

Size: 30½x18½mm
Perf. 12x11½
241	A70	1t multicolored	1.50	.40
242	A70	2t multicolored	2.25	1.75
242A	A70	5t multicolored	4.00	4.00
		Nos. 234-242A (10)	13.55	8.35

Nos. 235-237, 239-242A horiz.
Nos. 234-240 reprinted on cream paper.
See Nos. 270-271. For overprints see Nos. O37-O46, O48, O51-O52.

No. 188b Overprinted in Red in English

or Bengali

1984, Feb. 1   Litho.   Perf. 14
243	A48	50p Beach Scene	1.25	1.25
244	A48	5t Beach Scene, diff.	2.00	2.00
a.		Pair, #243-244	5.75	5.75

1st Bangladesh Natl. Philatelic Exhibition, 1984. No. 244a has continuous design.

A71

50p, Girl examining stamp album. 7.50t, Boy updating collection.

1984, May 17   Perf. 14½
245		50p multicolored	.75	.75
246		7.50t multicolored	2.50	2.50
a.		Souvenir sheet of 2, #245-246	6.00	6.00
b.		A71 Pair, #245-246	3.50	3.50
c.		As "a," overprinted	10.00	10.00

No. 246a sold for 10t.
Overprint in sheet margin of No. 246c reads: "SILVER JUBILEE / BANGLADESH POSTAGE STAMPS 1971-96."

Dacca
Zoo — A72

1t, Sarus crane, gavial. 2t, Peafowl, royal Bengal tiger.

1984, July 17   Litho.   Perf. 14
247	A72	1t multicolored	1.75	1.00
248	A72	2t multicolored	3.00	3.00

Postal Life
Insurance,
Cent. — A73

1984, Dec. 3
249	A73	1t Chicken hawk, hen	.75	.25
250	A73	5t Beneficiaries	2.00	2.00

Abbasudin
Ahmad, Bengali
Singer — A74

1984, Dec. 24
251	A74	3t multicolored	1.00	1.00

No. 116 Ovptd. for
KHULNAPEX '84
Stamp Exhibition

1984, Dec. 29   Perf. 15
252	A25	2.25t multicolored	1.75	1.75

1984
Summer
Olympics,
Los
Angeles
A75

1984, Dec. 31   Perf. 14
253	A75	1t Bicycling	1.50	.30
254	A75	5t Field hockey	2.00	2.00
255	A75	10t Volleyball	2.50	2.50
		Nos. 253-255 (3)	6.00	4.80

Islamic Development Bank, 9th Annual
Congress, Dacca — A76

1985, Feb. 2
256	A76	1t Farmer	.35	.25
257	A76	5t Four Asian races	1.50	1.50

UN Child
Survival
Campaign
A77

1985, Mar. 14
258	A77	1t Breastfeeding	.40	.30
259	A77	10t Growth monitoring	2.25	2.25

**Nos. 139-144 Ovptd. in Bengali for
Local Elections**

1985, May 16   Litho.   Perf. 14x14½
259A	A33	40p multicolored	1.25	.50
259B	A33	1t multicolored	1.00	.40
259C	A33	2.25t multicolored	1.00	.85
259D	A33	3.50t multicolored	2.00	1.00
259E	A33	4t multicolored	2.00	1.00
259F	A33	5t multicolored	4.50	1.10
		Nos. 259A-259F (6)	11.75	4.85

UN Decade for
Women — A78

1985, July 18   Perf. 14
260	A78	1t shown	.25	.25
261	A78	10t Technology	1.75	1.75

UN, 40th
Anniv.
A79

1985, Sept. 15
262	A79	1t UN building	.25	.25
263	A79	10t World map, natl. flag	1.40	1.40

11th anniv. of UN admission.

Intl. Youth
Year — A80

1985, Nov. 2   Litho.   Perf. 14
264	A80	1t Scissors, pencil	.25	.25
265	A80	5t Hammer, wrenches	.40	.40

Seven Doves,
Council
Emblem — A81

1985, Dec. 8   Litho.   Perf. 14
266	A81	1t shown	.40	.40
267	A81	5t Flags, lotus blossom	1.00	1.00

1st South Asian Regional Council Summit, SARC, Dacca.

Shilpacharya
Zainul Abedin
(1914-1976),
Founder, Dacca
College of
Art — A82

1985, Dec. 28
268	A82	3t multicolored	1.00	.50

No. 138
Overprinted
Reading Up

1985, Dec. 29   Perf. 13
269	A32	5t multicolored	3.50	3.50

3rd Natl. Scout Jamboree.
The overprint comes in two types.

Postal Services Type of 1983-84
1986-93   Litho.   Perf. 12x11½
Size: 30½x19mm
270	A70	3t Sorting machine	3.50	1.25

Perf. 12x12½
Size: 33½x22½mm
271	A70	4t Chittagong Port	1.25	.75

Issued: 3t, Jan. 11, 1986; 4t, Apr. 22, 1993.
For overprint see No. O46.

Fishing
Net, by
Safiuddin
Ahmed
A83

Paintings by Bengali artists: 5t, Happy Return, by Quamrul Hassan. 10t, Levelling the Plowed Field, by Zainul Abedin.

1986, Apr. 6   Litho.   Perf. 14
275 A83 1t multicolored   .25   .25
276 A83 5t multicolored   .60   .60
277 A83 10t multicolored   .75   .75
  Nos. 275-277 (3)   1.60   1.60
  For overprint see No. 322.

1986 World Cup Soccer
Championships, Mexico — A84

1986, June 29   Perf. 15x14
278 A84 1t Stealing the ball   .50   .25
279 A84 10t Goal   3.50   3.50
Souvenir Sheet
Imperf
279A A84 20t multicolored   8.00   8.00
  No. 279A contains one stamp 62x45mm
  with simulated perfs.

Gen. M.A.G. Osmani (1918-1984),
Liberation Forces Commander-in-
Chief — A85

1986, Sept. 10   Litho.   Perf. 14
280 A85 3t multicolored   2.00   1.00

No. 207 Ovptd.

1986, Dec. 3   Litho.   Perf. 13½x14
281 A58 50p on #207   4.00   4.00

Intl. Peace
Year — A86

A87

1986, Dec. 25   Litho.   Perf. 12x12½
282 A86 1t shown   .65   .65
283 A86 10t City ruins, flower   2.50   2.50
Souvenir Sheet
284 A87 20t shown   2.00   2.00

Nos. 179-180
Overprinted or
Surcharged

1987, Jan. 12   Perf. 14
285 A42 1t on 40p multicolored   .25   .25
286 A42 5t multicolored   .75   .75

Language Movement, 35th
Anniv. — A88

1987, Feb. 21   Perf. 12½x12
287 3t Protestors   1.50   1.50
288 3t Memorial   1.50   1.50
  a. A88 Pair, Nos. 287-288   3.50   3.50

World Health
Day — A89

1987, Apr. 7   Perf. 11½x12
289 A89 1t Child immunization   2.50   2.50
  See No. 318.

Bengali New
Year — A90

1t, Bengali script, embroidery.

1987, Apr. 16   Perf. 12x12½
290 A90 1t multicolored   .25   .25
291 A90 10t shown   .75   .75

Jute
Carpet
A91

Exports: 1t, Jute shika (wall hanging, bowl-
holder and mats), vert. 10t, Table lamp and
shade, vert.

Perf. 12x12½, 12½x12
1987, May 18   Litho.
292 A91 1t multicolored   .25   .25
293 A91 5t shown   .35   .35
294 A91 10t multicolored   .50   .50
  Nos. 292-294 (3)   1.10   1.10

Ustad Ayet
Ali Khan
(1884-1967),
Composer,
and Surbahar
A92

1987, Sept. 8   Perf. 12x12½
295 A92 5t multicolored   1.50   1.00

Transportation — A93

1987, Oct. 24   Litho.   Perf. 12½x12
296 A93 2t Palanquin   .40   .40
297 A93 3t Bicycle rickshaw   1.50   .50
298 A93 5t Paddle steamer   1.75   .75
299 A93 7t Train   4.25   1.75
300 A93 10t Ox cart   1.00   1.00
  Nos. 296-300 (5)   8.90   4.40
  For overprint see No. 424.

Hossain Shahid
Suhrawardy
(1893-1963),
Politician — A94

1987, Dec. 5   Litho.   Perf. 12x12½
301 A94 3t multicolored   .45   .45

Intl. Year of Shelter for the
Homeless — A95

1987, Dec. 15   Perf. 12½x12
302 5t Homeless people   .60   .60
303 5t Prosperous community   .60   .60
  a. A95 Pair, Nos. 302-303   2.75   2.75

Natl. Democracy, 1st Anniv. — A96

Design: Pres. Hossain Mohammed Ershad
addressing parliament.

1987, Dec. 31
304 A96 10t multicolored   1.50   1.00

Woman
Tending
Crop
A97

1988, Jan. 26
305 A97 3t shown   .25   .25
306 A97 5t Milking cow, village   .50   .50
  Intl. Fund for Agricultural Development
(IFAD) Seminar on Loans for Women in Rural
Areas.

1988 Summer Olympics, Seoul — A98

  No. 307 — Seoul Olympics emblem and: a,
Basketball. b, Weight lifting. c, Women's tennis. d, Shooting. e, Boxing.

1988, Sept. 29   Litho.   Perf. 11½
307   Strip of 5   7.50   7.50
  a.-e. A98 5t any single   1.50   1.50

Historical
Sites
A99

  Designs: 1t, Shait Gumbaz Mosque (inte-
rior), Bagerhat. 4t, Paharpur Monastery. 5t,
Kantanagar Temple, Dinajpur. 10t, Lalbag
Fort, Dacca.

1988, Oct. 9   Perf. 12½x12
308 A99 1t multicolored   .65   .65
309 A99 4t multicolored   1.25   1.25
310 A99 5t multicolored   1.25   1.25
311 A99 10t multicolored   2.00   2.00
  Nos. 308-311 (4)   5.15   5.15

Qudrat-i-Khuda
(1900-1977),
Scientist — A100

1988, Nov. 3   Perf. 12x12½
312 A100 5t multicolored   .75   .40

Asia Cup
Cricket — A101

1988, Nov. 27
313   Strip of 3   4.00   4.00
  a. A101 1t Wicketkeeper   .75   .75
  b. A101 5t Batsman   1.50   1.50
  c. A101 10t Bowler   2.25   2.25

Intl. Red Cross and Red Crescent Organizations, 125th Annivs. — A102

1988, Oct. 26   Litho.   Perf. 12x12½
314 A102 5t Emblems, Dunant   2.00 .30
315 A102 10t Blood donation   2.75 1.25

Dacca G.P.O., 25th Anniv. — A103

1988, Dec. 6   Perf. 12
316 A103 1t Exterior   .25 .25
317 A103 5t Sales counter   .60 .40

World Health Day Type of 1987
1988, Jan. 16   Litho.   Perf. 11½x12
318 A89 25p Oral rehydration   .60 .60

32nd Meeting of the Colombo Plan Consultative Committee, Dacca — A104

1988, Nov. 29   Perf. 12x12½
319 A104 3t multicolored   .25 .25
320 A104 10t multicolored   .65 .65

No. 191 Ovptd.

1988, Dec. 29   Litho.   Perf. 14
321 A50 5t multicolored   5.25 4.00
5th Natl. Rover Moot (Scouting).

No. 277 Overprinted

1989, Mar. 1
322 A83 10t multicolored   1.00 1.00
4th Asiatic Exposition.

A106

1989, Mar. 13   Litho.   Perf. 12x12½
324 A106 10t multicolored   1.00 1.00
Police academy, Sardah, 75th anniv.

A107

Modernizing water supply services.

1989, Mar. 7   Litho.   Perf. 12x12½
325 A107 10t multicolored   .75 .75
12th Natl. Science & Technology Week.

A108

French Revolution, Bicent. — A109

Scenes from the revolution: 5t, Close-up of revolutionaries destroying the Bastille, vert. No. 326b, Liberty guiding the people. No. 326c, Women's march on Versailles, vert. No. 327a, Celebration of the Federation on the Champ de Mars. No. 327b, Storming of the Bastille. 25t, Montage of scenes, #326a-326c.

1989, July 12   Perf. 14
326   Sheet of 3 + label   2.75 2.75
 a.   A108 5t multicolored   .50 .50
 b.-c.   A108 10t any single   1.10 1.10
Perf. 14x15
327   Strip of 2 + label   3.00 3.00
 a.-b.   A109 17t any single   1.25 1.25
Size: 152x88mm
Imperf
328 A108 25t multicolored   3.00 3.00
 Nos. 326-328 (3)   8.75 8.75
Labels picture the revolution anniv. emblem.

Rural Development in Asia and the Pacific (CIRDAP), 10th Anniv. — A110

1989, Aug. 10   Litho.   Perf. 12½x12
329   5t multi   .75 .75
330   10t multi   .75 .75
 a.   Pair, Nos. 329-330   1.75 1.75

Child Survival A111

10t, Women and children, diff.
1989, Aug. 22
331 A111 1t shown   .25 .25
332 A111 10t multicolored   .75 .75
SOS Children's Village, 40th anniv.

Involvement of the Bangladesh Army in UN Peace-keeping Operations, 1st Anniv. — A112

1989, Sept. 12   Perf. 12x12½
333 A112 4t shown   .75 .75
334 A112 10t Camp, two soldiers   1.50 1.50

2nd Asian Poetry Festival, Dacca — A113

1989, Nov. 17   Litho.   Perf. 12x12½
335 A113 2t multicolored   .25 .25
336 A113 10t multicolored   1.00 1.00

State Printing Office A114

1989, Dec. 7   Perf. 13½
337 A114 10t multicolored   .85 .85

Bangladesh Television, 25th Anniv. — A115

10t, Emblem, flowers, diff.
1989, Dec. 25   Litho.   Perf. 12½x12
338 A115 5t shown   .50 .50
339 A115 10t multicolored   1.25 1.25

World Wildlife Fund A116

Gavialis gangeticus: 50p, In water. 2p, Gavial's jaws. 4t, Four gavials. 10t, Two gavials resting.

1990, Jan. 31   Litho.   Perf. 14
340 A116 50p multi   .90 .45
341 A116 2t multi   1.15 1.05
342 A116 4t multi   1.75 1.75
343 A116 10t multi   2.25 2.25
 a.   Block of 4, #340-343   7.00 7.00
 Nos. 340-343 (4)   6.05 5.50

Natl. Population Day — A117

1990, Feb. 2   Perf. 14
344 A117 6t multicolored   1.00 .55

Penny Black, 150th Anniv. — A118

10t, Penny Black, No. 230.

1990, May 6   Perf. 14
345 A118 7t shown   2.00 2.00
346 A118 10t multicolored   2.50 2.50

Justice Syed Mahbub Murshed, (1911-1979) — A119

1990, Apr. 3   Litho.   Perf. 12½x12
347 A119 5t multicolored   3.00 3.00

Intl. Literacy Year — A120

Design: 10t, Boy teaching girl to write.

1990, Apr. 10   Perf. 12x12½
348 A120 6t multicolored   1.25 .50
349 A120 10t multicolored   2.25 1.50

Type of 1973 Redrawn and

Loading Cargo Plane — A121

Curzon Hall — A122

Fertilizer Plant — A123

Postal Academy, Rajshahi
A124

Salimullah Hall — A125

Bangla Academy — A126

Designs: No. 356, Sixty-dome Mosque (English inscription at LR).

1989-99 ***Perf. 12x11½, 12, 12x12½***

350 A121 3t multicolored .35 .35
a. Perf. 14¼x14 .60 .25
351 A122 5t gray blk & red brn .60 .25
a. Perf. 14¼ .60 .25
352 A123 10t carmine 1.00 1.00
353 A124 20t multicolored 2.25 2.25

Perf. 14½x14

354 A125 6t blue gray & yel 1.00 1.00

Perf. 14x14½

355 A126 2t brown & green .75 .35

Perf. 14¼

Size: 35x22 mm

Taka Expressed in Bengali

356 A9 10t rose 1.00 .75
Nos. 350-356 (7) 6.95 5.95

Issued: 5t, 3/31; 3t, 4/30; 10t, 20t, 7/8; 6t, 1/30/91; 2t, 12/3/93; No. 356, 3/18/99; No. 351a, 8/31/99.

No. 356 is very similar to No. 85 but differs in several ways: the inscription "Sixty-Dome Mosque" has been enlarged and moved from the upper left of the vignette to the lower right; a Bengali inscription has been added in its place at upper left; and the entire design has been lightened considerably, especially in the skyline of the mosque.

For overprints see Nos. O47A-O47B, O50.

World Cup Soccer Championships, Italy — A133

10t, Soccer player, diff. 25t, Colosseum, soccer ball.

1990, June 12 **Litho.** ***Perf. 14***

362 A133 8t shown 2.50 2.50
363 A133 10t multicolored 3.00 3.00

Size: 115x79mm

Imperf

364 A133 25t multicolored 15.00 15.00
Nos. 362-364 (3) 20.50 20.50

Fruits — A134

1t, Mangifera indica. 2t, Psidium guayava. 3t, Citrullus vulgaris. 4t, Carica papaya. 5t, Artocarpus heterophyllus. 10t, Averrhoa carambola.

1990, July 16 ***Perf. 12x12½***

365 A134 1t multicolored .50 .25
366 A134 2t multicolored .50 .25
367 A134 3t multicolored .60 .25
368 A134 4t multicolored .70 .30
369 A134 5t multicolored 1.10 .65
370 A134 10t multicolored 2.10 1.50
Nos. 365-370 (6) 5.50 3.20

UN Conference on Least Developed Nations, Paris — A135

1990, Sept. 3 **Litho.** ***Perf. 14***

371 A135 10t multicolored 2.10 2.10

Asia-Pacific Postal Training Center, 20th Anniv. — A136

1990, Sept. 10 ***Perf. 13½x14***

372 2t multicolored 1.00 1.00
373 6t multicolored 1.75 1.75
a. A136 Pair, #372-373 3.00 3.00

No. 373a has continuous design.

11th Asian Games, Beijing
A137

1990, Sept. 22 ***Perf. 14***

374 A137 2t Rowing 1.10 .30
375 A137 4t Kabaddi 1.40 .30
376 A137 8t Wrestling 2.00 1.50
377 A137 10t Badminton 3.50 2.00
Nos. 374-377 (4) 8.00 4.10

Lalon Shah, Poet — A138

1990, Oct. 17 **Litho.** ***Perf. 14***

378 A138 6t multicolored 1.50 1.00

UN Development Program, 40th Anniv. — A139

1990, Oct. 24 **Litho.** ***Perf. 14***

379 A139 6t multicolored 1.00 .70

A139a

1990, Nov. 29 **Litho.** ***Perf. 14½x14***

379A A139a 2t brown .30 .30

Immunization program. See No. 560.
For surcharge see O47.

A140

Butterflies: No. 380, Danaus chrysippus. No. 381, Precis almana. No. 382, Ixias pyrene. No. 383, Danaus plexippus.

1990, Dec. 24 **Litho.** ***Perf. 13½x12***

380 A140 6t multicolored 2.00 2.00
381 A140 6t multicolored 2.00 2.00
382 A140 10t multicolored 2.25 2.25
383 A140 10t multicolored 2.25 2.25
a. Block of 4, #380-383 10.00 10.00
Nos. 380-383 (4) 8.50 8.50

UN Decade Against Drugs
A141

1991, Jan 1 **Litho.** ***Perf. 14x13½***

384 A141 2t Drugs, map 1.25 .50
385 A141 4t shown 2.00 1.25

Third National Census — A142

1991, Mar. 12 **Litho.** ***Perf. 14***

386 A142 4t multicolored 1.75 1.75

Independence, 20th Anniv. — A143

No. 387: a, Invincible Bangla statue. b, Freedom Fighter statue. c, Mujibnagar Memorial. d, Eternal flame. e, National Martyrs' Memorial.

1991, Mar. 26 ***Perf. 13½***

387 A143 4t Strip of 5, #a.-e. 6.00 6.00
a.-e. Any single 1.00 1.00

No. 387 printed in continuous design.

A144

Pres. Ziaur Rahman, 10th Death Anniv. — A145

1991, May 30 ***Perf. 14***

388 A144 50p multicolored .30 .30
389 A145 2t multicolored 1.50 1.50
a. Souvenir sheet of 2, #388-389 2.75 2.75

No. 389a sold for 10t.

Endangered Animals — A146

2t, Petaurista petaurista. 4t, Presbytis entellus, vert. 6t, Buceros bicornis, vert. 10t, Manis crassicaudata.

1991, June 16 ***Perf. 12***

390 A146 2t multicolored 2.50 2.50
391 A146 4t multicolored 2.50 2.50
392 A146 6t multicolored 2.50 2.50
a. Pair, #391-392 6.00 6.00
393 A146 10t multicolored 2.50 2.50
a. Pair, #390, 393 5.00 5.00
Nos. 390-393 (4) 10.00 10.00

Kaikobad (1857-1951), Poet — A147

1991, July 21 **Litho.** ***Perf. 14***

394 A147 6t multicolored 1.75 1.75

Rabindranath Tagore, Poet, 50th Anniv. of Death — A148

1991, Aug. 7

395 A148 4t multicolored 1.75 1.75

Blood and Eye Donations
A149

1991, Sept. 19

396 A149 3t shown 1.25 1.25
397 A149 5t Blind man and eye 2.00 2.00

Sandhani, Medical Students Association, 14th anniversary.

Shahid Naziruddin, Leader of Democratic Movement, 1st Anniv. of Death — A150

1991, Oct. 10
398 A150 2t multicolored 1.00 .60

Shaheed Noor Hossain, 4th Death Anniv. — A151

1991, Nov. 10 Litho. Perf. 14
399 A151 2t multicolored 1.00 .60

Archaeological Treasures of Mainamati — A152

No. 400: a, Bronze Stupa with images of Buddha. b, Bowl and pitcher. c, Ruins of Salban Vihara Monastery. d, Gold coins. e, Terra-cotta plaque.

1991, Nov. 26 Litho. Perf. 13½
400 A152 4t Strip of 5, #a.-e. 8.00 8.00
a.-e. Any single 1.50 1.50

Mass Uprising, First Anniv. A153

1991, Dec. 6 Perf. 14
401 A153 4t multicolored 1.50 1.25

Miniature Sheets

Martyred Intellectuals Who Died in 1971 — A154

No. 402: a, A.N.M. Munier Chowdhury. b, Ghyasuddin Ahmad. c, S.M.A. Rashidul Hasan. d, Muhammad Anwar Pasha. e, Dr. Md. Mortaza. f, Shahid Saber. g, Fazlur Rahman Khan. h, Ranada Prasad Saha. i, Adhyaksha Joges Chandra Ghose. j, Santosh Chandra Bhattacharyya.
No. 403: a, Dr. Gobinda Chandra Deb. b, A.N.M. Muniruzzaman. c, Mufazzal Haider Chaudhury. d, Dr. Abdul Alim Choudhury. e, Sirajuddin Hossain. f, Shahidulla Kaiser. g, Altaf Mahmud. h, Dr. Jyotirmay Guha Thakurta. i, Dr. Md. Abul Khair. j, Dr. Serajul Haque Khan.
No. 404: a, Dr. Mohammad Fazle Rabbi. b, Mir Abdul Quyyum. c, A.N.M. Golam Mostafa. d, Dhirendranath Dutta. e, S.A. Mannan (Ladu Bhai). f, Nizamuddin Ahmad. g, Abul Bashar Chowdhury. h, Selina Parveen. i, Dr. Abul Kalam Azad. j, Saidul Hassan.
No. 404K: l, LCDR. Moazzam Hussain. m, Muhammad Habibur Rahman. n, Khandoker Abu Taleb. o, Moshiur Rahman. p, Md. Abdul Muktadir. q, Nutan Chandra Sinha. r, Syed

Nazmul Haque. s, Dr. Mohammed Amin Uddin. t, Dr. N.A.M. Faizul Mohee. u, Sukha Ranjan Somaddar.

1991-93 Litho. Perf. 13½
402 A154 2t Sheet of 10, #a-j + 5 labels 22.00 15.00
a.-j. Any single .80 .60
403 A154 2t Sheet of 10, #a-j + 5 labels 22.00 15.00
a.-j. Any single .80 .60
404 A154 2t Sheet of 10, #a-j + 5 labels 22.00 15.00
a.-j. Any single .80 .60

Perf. 14½
404K A154 2t Sheet of 10, #l-u + 5 labels 15.00 10.00
l.-u. Any single .60 .40

Independence, 20th anniv. Issued: Nos. 402-404, 12/14/91; No. 404K, 12/14/93. See Nos. 470-471, 499-500, 534-535, 558-559, 568-569, 595-596, 627-628.

Shrimp — A155

No. 405, Penaeus monodon. No. 406, Metapenaeus monoceros.

1991, Dec. 31 Perf. 14
405 6t multicolored 3.00 3.00
406 6t multicolored 3.00 3.00
a. A155 Pair, #405-406 6.50 6.50

Shaheed Mirze Abu Raihan Jaglu, 5th Death Anniv. A156

1992, Feb. 8 Litho. Perf. 14x13½
407 A156 2t multicolored 1.75 1.50

World Environment Day — A157

Design: 4t, Scenes of environmental protection and pollution control, vert.

1992, June 5 Litho. Perf. 14
408 A157 4t multicolored 1.25 1.25
409 A157 10t multicolored 2.50 2.50

Nawab Sirajuddaulah of Bengal (1733-1757) A158

1992, July 2 Litho. Perf. 14
410 A158 10t multicolored 2.00 1.25

Syed Ismail Hossain Sirajee (1880-1931), Writer & Poet — A159

1992, July 17
411 A159 4t multicolored 1.50 1.50

Tree Week — A160

2t, Couple planting tree, horiz. 4t, Birds, trees.

1992, July 17 Litho. Perf. 14
412 A160 2t multicolored 1.50 .80
413 A160 4t multicolored 2.00 1.25

1992 Summer Olympics, Barcelona — A161

No. 414 — Olympic rings and: a, 4t, Rowing. b, 6t, Hands holding Olympic torch. c, 10t, Peace doves. d, 10t, Clasped hands.

1992, July 25 Litho. Perf. 14
414 A161 Block of 4, #a.-d. 7.50 7.50
a.-d. Any single 1.60 1.60

The Star Mosque, 18th Cent. A162

1992, Oct. 29 Litho. Perf. 14½x14
415 A162 10t multicolored 3.25 3.00

Masnad-E-Ala Isa Khan, 393rd Anniv. of Death — A163

1992, Sept. 15 Perf. 14x14½
416 A163 4t multicolored 1.25 .60

7th SAARC Summit, Dacca — A164

1992, Dec. 5
417 A164 6t Flags of members 1.60 1.60
418 A164 10t Emblem 2.00 2.00

1992 Bangladesh Natl. Philatelic Exhibition — A165

No. 419: a, Elephant and mahout, ivory work, 19th cent. b, Post rider, mail box and postman delivering mail to villager.

1992, Sept. 26 Perf. 14½x14
419 A165 10t Pair, #a.-b. + label 3.00 3.00
a.-b. Either single 1.50 1.50
c. Souv. sheet, imperf. 6.00 6.00

No. 419c contains one strip of No. 419 with simulated perforations and sold for 25t.

1992 Intl. Conference on Nutrition, Rome — A166

1992, Dec. 5
420 A166 4t multicolored 1.25 .55

Meer Nisar Ali Titumeer (1782-1831) — A167

1992, Nov. 19 Litho. Perf. 14½x14
421 A167 10t multicolored 1.75 1.75

Archaeological Relics, Mahasthan — A168

No. 422 — Relics from 3rd century B.C.-15th century A.D.: a, Terracotta seal and head. b, Terracotta hamsa. c, Terracotta Surya image. d, Gupta stone columns.

1992, Nov. 30 Litho. Perf. 14½x14
422 A168 10t Strip of 4, #a.-d. 8.00 8.00
a.-d. Any single 2.00 2.00

Canal Digging — A169

No. 423: a, Workers digging canal. b, Completed project.

1993, Mar. 31 Litho. Perf. 14½x14
423 A169 2t Pair, #a.-b. 2.10 2.10
a.-b. Either single .80 .80

No. 300 Overprinted

1992, Aug. 18   Litho.   Perf. 12½x12
424 A93 10t multicolored   3.25 3.25

Syed Abdus
Samad (1895-
1964), Soccer
Player — A170

1993, Feb. 2   Perf. 14x14½
425 A170 2t multicolored   2.00 1.00

A171

1993, Apr. 14
426 A171 2t multicolored   1.00 .50
Completion of 14th cent. Bengali era.

Haji Shariat
Ullah (1770-
1839), Social
Reformer,
Religious and
Political
Leader — A172

1993, Mar. 10   Litho.   Perf. 14x14½
427 A172 2t multicolored   2.00 1.25

World
Health
Day
A173

6t, Prevent accidents. 10t, Prevent violence, vert.

1993, Apr. 7   Perf. 14½x14, 14x14½
428 A173 6t multicolored   2.50 2.50
429 A173 10t multicolored   3.00 3.00

Compulsory Primary
Education — A174

No. 430, Slate, chalk, books. No. 431, Hand writing, children, vert.

1993, May 26
430 A174 2t multicolored   1.25 .80
431 A174 2t multicolored   1.25 .80

Nawab Sir Salimullah (1871-1915),
Social Reformer — A175

1993, June 7   Litho.   Perf. 14½x14
432 A175 4t multicolored   1.40 1.00

Fishing
Industry
A176

1993, Aug. 15   Litho.   Perf. 14½x14
433 A176 2t multicolored   .60 .40

Tomb of Sultan Ghiyasuddin Azam
Shah — A177

1993, Dec. 30   Litho.   Perf. 14½x14
434 A177 10t multicolored   .90 .90

Scenic
Views
A178

Designs: No. 435, Sunderban. No. 436, Madhabkunda Waterfall, vert. No. 437, River, mountains, vert. No. 438, Beach, Kuakata.

1993, Oct. 30   Perf. 14½x14, 14x14½
435 A178 10t multicolored   1.50 1.50
436 A178 10t multicolored   1.50 1.50
437 A178 10t multicolored   1.50 1.50
438 A178 10t multicolored   1.50 1.50
  a.   Souv. sheet, #435-438, im-
          perf   6.00 6.00
        Nos. 435-438 (4)   6.00 6.00

No. 438a sold for 50t and has simulated perfs.

6th Asian Art
Biennial,
Bangladesh
A179

1993, Nov. 7   Litho.   Perf. 14x14½
439 A179 10t multicolored   .90 .90

Foy's
Lake
A180

1993, Nov. 6   Perf. 14½x14
440 A180 10t multicolored   1.40 1.40
Tourism month.

14th Asian
Pacific, 5th
Bangladesh Natl.
Scout Jamboree
A181

1994, Jan. 5   Perf. 14x14½
441 A181 2t multicolored   .50 .30

Oral Rehydration
Solution, 25th
Anniv. — A182

1994, Feb. 5   Litho.   Perf. 13½x14
442 A182 2t multicolored   .75 .75

6th SAF
Games,
Dhaka
A183

1993, Dec. 6   Perf. 14x13½, 13½x14
443 A183 2t Shot put   .40 .25
444 A183 4t Runners, vert.   .50 .35

Mosques
A184

Mosques: 4t, Interior, Chhota Sona, Nawabgonj. No. 446, Exterior, Chhota Sona. No. 447, Exterior, Baba Adam's, Munshigonj.

1994, Mar. 30   Litho.   Perf. 14x13½
445 A184 4t multicolored   .65 .25
446 A184 6t multicolored   .65 .65
447 A184 6t multicolored   .65 .65
        Nos. 445-447 (3)   1.95 1.55
For overprint see No. 509.

ILO, 75th
Anniv.
A185

Designs: 4t, People, oxen working in fields. 10t, Man rotating gearwheel, vert.

Perf. 14x13½, 13½x14
1994, Apr. 11   Litho.
448 A185 4t multicolored   .30 .25
449 A185 10t multicolored   1.10 1.00

Bangla Era, 15th
Cent. — A186

1994, Apr. 14   Perf. 13½x14
450 A186 2t multicolored   .65 .30

Traditional
Festivals
A187

1994, May 12   Perf. 14x13½
451 A187 4t Folk Festival   .50 .50
452 A187 4t Baishakhi Festival   .50 .50

Intl. Year of the
Family — A188

1994, May 15   Perf. 13½x14
453 A188 10t multicolored   1.40 1.40

Tree Planting
Campaign
A189

4t, Family planting trees. 6t, Hands, seedlings.

1994, June 15   Litho.   Perf. 13½x14
454 A189 4t multicolored   .55 .25
455 A189 6t multicolored   .85 .65

1994 World Cup
Soccer
Championships,
US — A190

Soccer player's uniform colors: a, Red, yellow & blue. b, Yellow, green, & red.

1994, June 17   Litho.   Perf. 14½
456 A190 20t Pair, #a.-b. + la-
            bel   5.00 5.00
  a.-b. Either single   2.50 2.50
          Complete booklet, #456   40.00

No. 456 was printed in panes of 15 (3x5), with each horizontal row containing Nos. 456a and 456b with a connecting label depicting the championship mascot. The booklet contains two No. 456, attached to the booklet cover by sheet selvage.

Jamuna Multi-Purpose Bridge — A191

1994, July 24   *Perf. 14½x14*
457 A191 4t multicolored   3.50 1.25

Birds — A192

Designs: 4t, Oriolus xanthornus. No. 459, Gallus gallus. No. 460, Dicrurus paradiseus. No. 461, Dendrocitta vagabunda.

1994, Aug. 31   *Perf. 14x14½*
458 A192 4t multicolored   .50 .50
459 A192 6t multicolored   .75 .75
460 A192 6t multicolored   .75 .75
461 A192 6t multicolored   .75 .75
   a.   Souvenir sheet, #458-461   4.00 4.00
     Nos. 458-461 (4)   2.75 2.75

No. 461a sold for 25t.

Dr. Mohammad Ibrahim (1911-89), Pioneer in Treatment of Diabetes — A193

1994, Sept. 6   **Litho.**   *Perf. 14½x14*
462 A193 2t multicolored   .75 .25

Nawab Faizunnessa Chowdhurani (1834-1903), Social Reformer A194

1994, Sept. 23   *Perf. 14x14½*
463 A194 2t multicolored   .50 .25

12th Asian Games, Hiroshima, Japan A195

1994, Oct. 2   *Perf. 14½x14*
464 A195 4t multicolored   2.00 .60

Shells A196

Designs: No. 465, White, pink pearls, oysters. No. 466, Snail, three other shells. No.

467, Scallop, other shells. No. 468, Spiral shaped shells, vert.

Perf. 14½x14, 14x14½
1994, Oct. 30   **Litho.**
465 A196 6t multicolored   1.60 1.60
466 A196 6t multicolored   1.60 1.60
467 A196 6t multicolored   1.60 1.60
468 A196 6t multicolored   1.60 1.60
     Nos. 465-468 (4)   6.40 6.40

Democracy Demonstration, Death of Dr. Shamsul Alam Khan Milon, 4th Anniv. — A197

1994, Nov. 27   *Perf. 14½x14*
469 A197 2t multicolored   .35 .25

Martyred Intellectual Type of 1991

No. 470: a, Dr. Harinath Dey. b, Dr. Lt. Col. A.F. Ziaur Rahman. c, Mamum Mahmud. d, Mohsin Ali Dewan. e, Dr. Lt. Col. N.A.M. Jahangir. f, Shah Abdul Majid. g, Muhammad Akhter. h, Meherunnesa.
No. 471: a, Dr. Kasiruddin Talukder. b, Fazlul Haque Choudhury. c, Md. Shamsuzzaman. d, A.K.M. Shamsuddin. e, Lt. Mohammad Anwarul Azim. f, Nurul Amin Khan. g, Mohammad Sadeque. h, Md. Araz Ali.

1994, Dec. 14   *Perf. 14½*
470 A154 2t Sheet of 8, #a-h + 4 labels   5.00 3.75
   a.-h.   Any single   .40 .35
471 A154 2t Sheet of 8, #a-h + 4 lables   5.00 3.75
   a.-h.   Any single   .40 .35

Vegetables A199

No. 472, Diplazium esculentum. No. 473, Momordica charantia. No. 474, Lagenaria siceraria. No. 475, Trichosanthes dioica. No. 476, Solanum melongena. No. 477, Cucurbita maxima.

1994, Dec. 24   *Perf. 14x14½, 14½x14*
472 A199   4t multicolored   1.00 .75
473 A199   4t multicolored   1.00 .75
474 A199   6t multicolored   1.25 1.00
475 A199   6t multicolored   1.25 1.00
476 A199 10t multicolored   1.90 1.90
477 A199 10t multicolored   1.90 1.90
     Nos. 472-477 (6)   8.30 7.30

Nos. 472-476 are vert.

World Tourism Organization, 20th Anniv. — A200

1995, Jan. 2   *Perf. 14½x14*
478 A200 10t multicolored   2.50 2.50

Intl. Trade Fair, Dhaka A201

Designs: 4t, Trade products. 6t, Factories, emblems of industry.

1995, Jan. 7   **Litho.**   *Perf. 14x14½*
479 A201 4t multicolored   .30 .25
480 A201 6t multicolored   .70 .60

Bangladesh Rifles, Bicent. — A202

1995, Jan. 10   **Litho.**   *Perf. 14½x14*
481 A202 2t shown   .85 .85
482 A202 4t Building, battalion   2.25 2.25

Fight Against Cancer — A203

1995, Apr. 7   **Litho.**   *Perf. 14x14½*
483 A203 2t multicolored   .45 .25

Natl. Diabetes Awareness Day — A204

1995, Feb. 28   *Perf. 14*
484 A204 2t multicolored   1.50 .80

For overprint see No. O49.

Munshi Mohammad Meherullah (1861-1907), Educator A205

1995, June 7   **Litho.**   *Perf. 14x14½*
485 A205 2t multicolored   .45 .25

FAO, 50th Anniv. — A206

1995, Oct. 16   **Litho.**   *Perf. 14*
486 A206 10t multicolored   .75 .75

UN, 50th Anniv. A207

UN emblem, "50," and: 2t, Dove of peace, UN headquarters. No. 488, "1945," earth from space, "1995." No. 489, Hands of different nationalities clasping, UN headquarters.

1995, Oct. 24   *Perf. 14½x14*
487 A207   2t multicolored   .35 .25
488 A207 10t multicolored   .95 .95
489 A207 10t multicolored   .95 .95
     Nos. 487-489 (3)   2.25 2.15

Flowers — A208

Designs: No. 490, Bombax ceiba. No. 491, Lagerstroemia speciosa. No. 492, Gloriosa superba. No. 493, Canna indica. No. 494, Bauhinia purpurea. No. 495, Passiflora incarnata.

1995, Oct. 9   *Perf. 14½x14, 14x14½*
490 A208   6t multicolored   1.20 .90
491 A208   6t multi, vert.   1.20 .90
492 A208 10t multi, vert.   1.60 1.60
493 A208 10t multi, vert.   1.60 1.60
494 A208 10t multi, vert.   1.60 1.60
495 A208 10t multi, vert.   1.60 1.60
     Nos. 490-495 (6)   8.80 8.20

Shaheed Khandaker Mosharraf Hossain A208a

1995, Oct. 16   **Litho.**   *Perf. 13¾x14¼*
496 A208a 2t multi   110.00 —

No. 496 was removed from sale shortly after release.

18th Eastern Regional Conference on Tuberculosis and Respiratory Diseases, Dhaka — A209

1995, Oct. 29   **Litho.**   *Perf. 14½x14*
497 A209 6t multicolored   2.00 .75

South Asian Assoc. for Regional Cooperation (SAARC), 10th Anniv. — A210

1995, Dec. 8   **Litho.**   *Perf. 14x14½*
498 A210 2t multicolored   1.75 .75

Martyred Intellectual Type of 1991

No. 499: a, Shaikh Habibur Rahman. b, Dr. Major Naimul Islam. c, Md. Shahidullah. d, Ataur Rahman Khan Khadim. e, A.B.M. Ashraful Islam Bhuiyan. f, Dr. Md. Sadat Ali. g, Sarafat Ali. h, M.A. Sayeed.
No. 500: a, Abdul Ahad. b, Lt. Col. Mohammad Abdul Qadir. c, Mozammel Hoque Chowdhury. d, Rafiqul Haider Chowdhury. e, Dr. Azharul Haque. f, A.K. Shamsuddin. g, Anudwaipayan Bhattacharjee. h, Lutfunnahar Helena.

1995, Dec. 14   **Litho.**   *Perf. 14½x14*
499 A154 2t Sheet of 8, #a-h + 4 labels   6.00 6.00
   a.-h.   Any single   .60 .60
500 A154 2t Sheet of 8, #a-h + 4 labels   6.00 6.00
   a.-h.   Any single   .60 .60

Second Asian Pacific Community Development Scout Camp — A211

1995, Dec. 18   Litho.   Perf. 14x14½
501 A211 2t multicolored   .90   .35

Volleyball, Cent. — A212

1995, Dec. 25
502 A212 6t multicolored   1.00   .75

Traditional Costumes — A213

Designs: No. 503, Man in punjabi and lungi, vert. No. 504, Woman in sari, vert. No. 505, Christian bride and groom, vert. No. 506, Muslim bridal couple, vert. No. 507, Hindu bridal couple. No. 508, Buddhist bridal couple.

1995, Dec. 25   Perf. 14x14½, 14½x14
503 A213 6t multicolored   1.10 1.10
504 A213 6t multicolored   1.10 1.10
505 A213 10t multicolored   1.50 1.50
506 A213 10t multicolored   1.50 1.50
507 A213 10t multicolored   1.50 1.50
508 A213 10t multicolored   1.50 1.50
        Nos. 503-508 (6)   8.20 8.20

No. 446 Ovptd. in Red

1995, Aug. 23   Litho.   Perf. 14x13½
509 A184 6t multicolored   2.75 2.75

Shaheed Amanullah Mohammad Asaduzzaman (1942-69) A214

1996, Jan. 20   Perf. 14x14½
510 A214 2t multicolored   .45   .25

1996 World Cup Cricket Championships — A215

1996, Feb. 14   Perf. 14x14½, 14½x14
511 A215 4t Pitching, vert.   1.40   .60
512 A215 6t At bat, vert.   1.75   .90
513 A215 10t shown   2.50 2.50
        Nos. 511-513 (3)   5.65 4.00

Independence, 25th Anniv. — A216

Designs: No. 514, Natl. Martrys' Memorial. No. 515, Industrial development. No. 516, 1971 Destruction of war. No. 517, Educational development. No. 518, Development in communication. No. 519, Development in health.

1996, Mar. 26   Litho.   Perf. 14x14½
514 A216 4t multicolored   .85   .85
515 A216 4t multicolored   .85   .85
516 A216 4t multicolored   .85   .85
517 A216 4t multicolored   .85   .85
518 A216 4t multicolored   .85   .85
519 A216 4t multicolored   .85   .85
        Nos. 514-519 (6)   5.10 5.10

Michael Madhusudan Dutt (1824-73), Writer — A217

1996, June 29   Litho.   Perf. 14x14½
520 A217 4t multicolored   .60   .25
    No. 520 exists imperf. Value, $37.50

1996 Summer Olympic Games, Atlanta A218

1996, July 19   Litho.   Perf. 14
521 A218 4t Gymnast, vert.   .35   .25
522 A218 6t Judo, vert.   .45   .35
523 A218 10t High jumper   .50   .50
524 A218 10t Runners   .50   .50
  a.   Souvenir sheet, #521-524 2.25 2.25
        Nos. 521-524 (4)   1.80 1.60

No. 524a sold for 50t. Exists imperf. Value, $125.

Sheikh Mujibur Rahman (1920-75), Prime Minister — A219

Design: No. 527, Maulana Mohammad Akrum Khan (1868-1968).

1996   Litho.   Perf. 14x14½
526 A219 4t multicolored   .60   .25
527 A219 4t multicolored   .55   .25
  Issued: No. 526, 8/15/96, No. 527, 8/18/96.
  No. 526 exists imperf. Value, $37.50

Ustad Alauddin Khan (1862-1972), Musician A220

1996, Sept. 6   Litho.   Perf. 14x14½
528 A220 4t multicolored   .75   .25

Children's Paintings A221

Perf. 14x14½, 14½x14
1996, Oct. 9   Litho.
529 A221 2t Kingfisher, vert.   .60   .45
530 A221 4t River Crossing   .80   .45

Jailed, 21st Death Anniv. — A222

No. 531: a, Syed Nazrul Islam. b, Tajuddin Ahmad. c, M. Monsoor Ali. d, A.H.M. Quamaruzzaman.

1996, Nov. 3   Litho.   Perf. 14x14½
531 A222 4t Block of 4, #a.-d.   2.00 2.00

UNICEF, 50th Anniv. — A223

Designs: 4t, Children receiving food, medicine, aid. 10t, Mother holding infant.

1996, Dec. 11
532 A223 4t multicolored   .50   .25
533 A223 10t multicolored   1.10 1.10

Martyred Intellectual Type of 1991

No. 534: a, Dr. Jekrul Haque. b, Munshi Kabiruddin Ahmed. c, Md. Abdul Jabbar. d, Mohammad Amir. e, A.K.M. Shamsul Huq Khan. f, Dr. Siddique Ahmed. g, Dr. Soleman Khan. h, S.B.M. Mizanur Rahman.
No. 535: a, Aminuddin. b, Md. Nazrul Islam. c, Zahirul Islam. d, A.K. Lutfor Rahman. e, Afsar Hossain. f, Abul Hashem Mian. g, A.T.M. Alamgir. h, Baser Ali.

1996, Dec. 14   Litho.   Perf. 14½x14
534 A154 2t Sheet of 8, #a-h + 4
        labels   4.75 4.75
535 A154 2t Sheet of 8, #a-h + 4
        labels   4.75 4.75

Victory Day, 25th Anniv. A224

Designs: 4t, People celebrating, natl. flag. 6t, Soldiers, monument, vert.

1996, Dec. 16   Perf. 14½x14, 14x14½
536 A224 4t multicolored   .35   .35
537 A224 6t multicolored   .75   .75

Paul Harris (1868-1947), Founder of Rotary Intl. — A225

1997, Feb. 18   Litho.   Perf. 14x14½
538 A225 4t multicolored   .50   .25

Sheikh Mujibur Rahman's Mar. 7 Speech, 26th Anniv. — A226

1997, Mar. 7   Perf. 12½
539 A226 4t multicolored   .50   .25

Sheikh Mujibur Rahman (1920-75) A227

1997, Mar. 17   Perf. 14x14½
540 A227 4t multicolored   .50   .25

Independence, 25th Anniv. (in 1996) — A228

1997, Mar. 26   Litho.   Perf. 12½
541 A228 4t multicolored   .50   .25

Heinrich von Stephan (1831-97) A229

1997, Apr. 8 Litho. Perf. 14x14½
542 A229 4t multicolored   .50 .25

Livestock A230

1997, Apr. 10 Litho. Perf. 14½x14
543 A230 4t Goat   1.00 .90
544 A230 4t Sheep   1.00 .90
545 A230 6t Cow   1.25 1.00
546 A230 6t Buffalo   1.25 1.00
    Nos. 543-546 (4)   4.50 3.80

Paintings — A231

Designs: 6t, "Tilling the Field-2," by S.M. Sultan (1923-94). 10t, "Three Women," by Quamrul Hassan (1921-88).

1997, June 26 Litho. Perf. 12½
547 A231 6t multicolored   .60 .30
548 A231 10t multicolored 1.00 1.00

6th Intl. Cricket Council Trophy Championship, Malaysia — A232

1997, Sept. 4
549 A232 10t multicolored   4.25 4.25

Ancient Mosques A233

Designs: 4t, Kusumba Mosque, Naogaon, 1558. 6t, Atiya Mosque, Tangail, 1609. 10t, Bagha Mosque, Rajshahi, 1523.

1997, Sept. 4 Litho. Perf. 14½x14
550 A233 4t multicolored   .75 .40
551 A233 6t multicolored   1.00 .55
552 A233 10t multicolored 1.75 2.00
    Nos. 550-552 (3)   3.50 2.95

Abdul Karim Sahitya Visharad (1871-1953), Scholar — A234

1997, Oct. 11 Perf. 14x14½
553 A234 4t multicolored   .60 .25

9th Asia-Pacific, 7th Bangladesh Rover Moot '97 — A235

1997, Oct. 25 Perf. 14x14½
554 A235 2t multicolored   .60 .25

Armed Forces, 25th Anniv. A236

1997, Nov. 11 Perf. 14½x14
555 A236 2t multicolored   2.00 .70

East Bengal Regiment, 50th Anniv. A237

1998, Feb. 15
556 A237 2t multicolored   1.25 .60

Mohammad Mansooruddin (1904-87) A238

1998, Feb. 4 Perf. 14x14½
557 A238 4t multicolored   1.75 1.00

Martyred Intellectual Type of 1991
No. 558: a, Dr. Shamsuddin Ahmed. b, Mohammad Salimullah. c, Mohiuddin Haider. d, A.B.M. Abdur Rahim. e, Nitya Nanda Paul. f, Abdul Jabber. g, Dr. A.B.M. Humayun Kabir. h, Khaja Nizamuddin Bhuiyan.
No. 559: a, Gulam Hossain. b, Ali Karim. c, Md. Moazzem Hossain. d, Rafiqul Islam. e, M. Nur Hussain. f, Captain Mahmood Hossain Akonda. g, Abdul Wahab Talukder. h, Dr. Hasimoy Hazra.

1997, Dec. 14
558 A154 2t Sheet of 8, #a-h, + 4 labels   6.00 6.00
559 A154 2t Sheet of 8, #a-h, + 4 labels   6.00 6.00

Immunization Type of 1990
1998, Jan. 22 Perf. 14½x14
560 A139a 1t green   .25 .25
For overprint see No. O53.

Bulbul Chowdhury (1919-54), Dancer — A239

1998, May 17 Perf. 14x14½
561 A239 4t multicolored   .60 .25

Opening of the Bangabandhu Bridge — A240

Designs: 4t, East approach road. 6t, West approach road. 8t, River training works. 10t, Bangabandhu Bridge.

1998, June 23 Perf. 14
562 A240 4t multicolored   .80 .80
563 A240 6t multicolored   .95 .95
564 A240 8t multicolored   1.25 1.25
565 A240 10t multicolored 1.60 1.60
    Nos. 562-565 (4)   4.60 4.60

1998 World Cup Soccer Championships, France — A241

1998, June 10
566 A241 6t Trophy   .90 .30
567 A241 18t Player, trophy 2.10 2.10

Martyred Intellectual Type of 1991
No. 568: a, Md. Khorshed Ali Sarker. b, Abu Yakub Mahfuz. c, S.M. Nurul Huda. d, Nazmul Hoque Sarker. e, Md. Taslim Uddin. f, Gulam Mostafa. g, A. H. Nurul Alam. h, Timir Kanti Dev.
No. 569: a, Altaf Hossain. b, Aminul Hoque. c, S.M. Fazlul Hoque. d, Mozammel Ali. e, Syed Akbar Hossain. f, Sk. Abdus Salam. g, Abdur Rahman. h, Dr. Shyamal Kanti Lala.

1998, Dec. 14 Litho. Perf. 14½x14
Sheets of 8, #a-h, + 4 labels
568-569 A154 2t Set of 2   11.50 11.50

Princess Diana (1961-97) — A242

No. 570 — Diana in: a, 8t, Hat. b, 18t, Black dress. c, 22t, Blue dress.

1998, June 6 Litho. Perf. 14¼
570 A242 Horiz. strip of 3, #a-c   6.50 6.50

World Solar Program, 1996-2005 A243

1998, Sept. 24 Litho.
571 A243 10t multicolored   1.50 1.50

World Habitat Day — A244

1998, Oct. 5
572 A244 4t multicolored   1.50 .75

Intl. Fund for Agricultural Development, 20th Anniv. — A245

Sunflower and: 6t, Farmers, "20." 10t, Vegetables, pickers.

1998, Oct. 17
573 A245 6t multicolored   .65 .35
574 A245 10t multicolored 1.10 1.10
For overprint see No. 668.

Wills Intl. Cup Cricket Matches A246

1998, Oct. 28
575 A246 6t multicolored   2.25 1.50

Begum Rokeya (1880-1932), Author, Educator — A247

1998, Dec. 9 Litho. Perf. 14¼x13¾
576 A247 4t multicolored   1.40 .60

Universal Declaration of Human Rights, 50th Anniv. — A248

1998, Dec. 10 Perf. 13¾x14¼
577 A248 10t multi   1.40 1.40

UN Peacekeeping, 50th Anniv. — A249

1998, Dec. 30   *Perf. 13¾x14¼*
578 A249 10t multi   1.40 1.40

Qazi Nazrul Islam (1899-1976), Poet — A250

1998, Dec. 31   *Perf. 14¼*
579 A250 6t multi   1.40 .70

Sixth National Scout Jamboree A251

1999, Feb. 6   *Perf. 13¾x14¼*
580 A251 2t multi   1.10 .50

Surjya Sen (1894-1934), Anti-Colonial Leader — A252

1999, Mar. 22   *Perf. 14¼x13¾*
581 A252 4t multi   1.40 .55

Dr. Fazlur Rahman Khan (1929-82), Architect of Sears Tower, Chicago — A253

1999, Apr. 13   *Perf. 13¾x14¼*
582 A253 4t multi   1.10 .65

ICC Cricket World Cup, England — A254

Designs: 8t, Emblems. 10t, Bangladesh flag, cricket ball, tiger.

1999, May 11   *Perf. 13¾x14¼*
583 A254 8t multi   1.75 1.75
584 A254 10t multi   2.50 2.50
 a.   Souv. sheet, #583-584, perf 14¼ 6.25 6.25
        No. 584a sold for 30t.

Mother Teresa (1910-97) A255

1999, Sept. 5   *Perf. 13¾x14¼*
585 A255 4t multi   1.75 .90

Admission to UN, 25th Anniv. — A256

1999, Sept. 13
586 A256 8t multi   1.25 .60

Shaheed Mohammad Maizuddin (1930-84) A257

1999, Sept. 27
587 A257 2t multi   .60 .30
        No. 587 exists imperf. Value, $37.50.

Intl. Year of Older Persons — A258

1999, Oct. 1
588 A258 6t multi   1.25 .70

World Habitat Day A259

1999, Oct. 4   *Perf. 14¼x13¾*
589 A259 4t multi   1.25 .55

UPU, 125th Anniv. A260

1999, Oct. 9   *Perf. 14¼x13¾*
590 A260 4t Truck   .85 .60
591 A260 4t Motorcycle   .85 .60
592 A260 6t Boat   1.25 1.25
593 A260 6t Airplanes   1.25 1.25
 a.   Souv. sheet, #590-593, perf 14¼ 4.50 4.50
      Nos. 590-593 (4)   4.20 3.70
  No. 593a sold for 25t. No. 593a exists imperf. Value, $15.

Sir Jagadis Chandra Bose (1858-1937), Physicist A261

1999, Nov. 5   *Perf. 13¾x14¼*
594 A261 4t multi   1.60 .50

Martyred Intellectuals Type of 1991

   No. 595: a, Dr. Mohammad Shafi. b, Maulana Kasimuddin Ahmed. c, Quazi Ali Imam. d, Sultanuddin Ahmed. e, A.S.M. Ershadullah. f, Mohammad Fazlur Rahman. g, Dr. Capt. A. K. M. Farooq. h, Md. Latafot Hossain Joarder.
   No. 596 — Martyred intellectuals who died in 1971: a, Ram Ranjan Bhattacharjya. b, Abani Mohan Dutta. c, Sunawar Ali. d, Abdul Kader Miah. e, Dr. Major Rezaur Rahman. f, Md. Shafiqul Anowar. g, A.A.M. Mozammel Hoque. h, Khandkar Abul Kashem.

1999, Dec. 14   **Litho.**   *Perf. 14¼*
595 A154 2t Sheet of 8, #a-h, +
         4 labels   5.50 5.50
596 A154 2r Sheet of 8, #a-h, +
         4 labels   5.50 5.50

Millennium — A262

   Designs: 4t, Natl. Martyr's Memorial, flag. 6t, Satellite, computer, satellite dish, Bangabandhu Bridge, vert.

       Perf. 14¼x13¾, 13¾x14¼
2000, Jan. 1   **Litho.**
597-598 A262 Set of 2   2.50 1.75

Fifth Cub Camporee A263

2000, Feb. 13   *Perf. 13¾x14¼*
599 A263 2t multi   .95 .40

Jibanananda Das (1899-1954), Poet — A264

1999, Nov. 22
600 A264 4t multi   .95 .40

Dr. Muhammad Shamsuzzoha (1934-69), Educator A265

2000, Feb. 18
601 A265 4t multi   .95 .40

Intl. Mother Language Day — A266

   Martyrs: No. 602, 4t, Abul Barkat (1927-52). No. 603, 4t, Abdul Jabbar (1919-52). No. 604, 4t, Shafiur Rahman (1918-52). No. 605, 4t, Rafiq Uddin Ahmad (1926-52).

2000, Feb. 21
602-605 A266 Set of 4   3.00 2.40

World Meteorological Organization, 50th Anniv. — A267

2000, Mar. 23
606 A267 10t multi   2.00 1.50

ICC Cricketnext.com Cricket Week — A268

2000, Apr. 8
607 A268 6t multi   2.25 1.25

Insects — A269

   Designs: 2t, Wasp. 4t, Grasshopper. 6t, Apis indica. 10t, Bombyx mori.

2000, May 18   *Perf. 14¼*
608-611 A269 Set of 4   4.25 4.25

Fauna A270

Designs: No. 612, 4t, Gekko gecko. No. 613, 4t, Hystrix indica. No. 614, 6t, Python molurus. No. 615, 6t, Varanus bengalensis.

2000, May 18   *Perf. 14¼x13¾*
612-615 A270 Set of 4   4.00 4.00

7th Pepsi Asia Cricket Cup — A271

2000, May 28   *Perf. 13¾x14¼*
616 A271 6t multi   2.25 1.10

Birds A272

Designs: No. 617, 4t, Amaurornis phoenicurus. No. 618, 4t, Gallicrex cinerea. No. 619, 6t, Phalacrocorax niger, vert. No. 620, 6t, Ardeola grayii, vert.

Perf. 14¼x13¾, 13¾x14¼
2000, July 15
617-620 A272 Set of 4   4.25 4.25

For overprint, see No. 723.

2000 Summer Olympics, Sydney — A273

Shot putters: 6t, Woman. 10t, Man.

2000, Sept. 18   *Perf. 13¾x14¼*
621-622 A273 Set of 2   3.00 2.00

Bangladesh — People's Republic of China Diplomatic Relations, 25th Anniv. — A274

2000, Oct. 4   Litho.   *Perf. 12½*
623 A274 6t multi   2.00 .75

Idrakpur Fort, Munshigonj — A275

Vajrasattva Bhojavihara Mainamati, Comilla — A276

Perf. 14¼x13¾, 13¾x14¼
2000, Nov. 5   Litho.
624 A275 4t multi   1.00 .40
625 A276 6t multi   1.50 1.00

Intl. Volunteers Year (in 2001) — A277

2000, Dec. 5   Litho.   *Perf. 13¾x14¼*
626 A277 6t multi   1.40 .65

Martyred Intellectuals Type of 1991

No. 627, 2t: a, M. A. Gofur. b, Faizur Rahman Ahmed. c, Muslimuddin Miah. d, Sgt. Shamsul Karim Khan. e, Bhikku Zinananda. f, Abdul Jabber. g, Sekander Hayat Chowdhury. h, Chishty Shah Helalur Rahman.

No. 628, 2t: a, Birendra Nath Sarker. b, A. K. M. Nurul Haque. c, Sibendra Nath Mukherjee. d, Zahir Raihan. e, Ferdous Dowla Bablu. f, Capt. A. K. M. Nurul Absur. g, Mizanur Rahman Miju. h, Dr. Shamshad Ali.

2000   Litho.   *Perf. 12½*
Sheets of 8, #a-h, + 4 labels
627-628 A154 Set of 2   16.00 16.00

Hason Raza (1854-1922) A278

2000 ?   *Perf. 13¾x14¼*
629 A278 6t multi   1.60 .75

2001 Census — A279

2001, Jan. 23   Litho.   *Perf. 13¾x14¼*
630 A279 4t multi   1.50 .75

UN High Commissioner for Refugees, 50th Anniv. (in 2001) — A280

Perf. 13¾x14¼
2000, Dec. 14   Litho.
631 A280 10t multi   1.50 1.50

Hunger-Free Bangladesh — A281

Perf. 14¼x13¾
2001, Mar. 17   Litho.
632 A281 6t multi   1.50 1.00

Peasant Women, by Rashid Chowdhury A282

2001, Apr. 1   Litho.   *Perf. 13¾x14¼*
633 A282 10t multi   2.75 2.25

Houses of Worship — A283

No. 634: a, Lalbagh Kella Mosque. b, Uttara Ganabhavan, Natore. c, Armenian Church, Armanitola. d, Panam Nagar, Sonargaon.

2001, Apr. 30   *Perf. 14¼x13¾*
634 A283 6t Block of 4, #a-d   4.50 4.50

World No Tobacco Day A284

2001, May 31   Litho.   *Perf. 14¼x13¾*
635 A284 10t multi   2.25 2.25

Artists — A285

No. 636: a, Ustad Gul Mohammad Khan (1876-1979). b, Ustad Khadem Hossain Khan (1923-91). c, Gouhar Jamil (1928-80). d, Abdul Alim (1931-74).

2001, May 31   *Perf. 13¾x14¼*
636 A285 6t Block of 4, #a-d   4.00 4.00

Begum Sufia Kamal (1911-99), Poet — A286

2001, June 20
637 A286 4t multi   .75 .30

Fish — A287

No. 638: a, Hilsa. b, Tengra. c, Punti. d, Khalisa.

2001, July 9   *Perf. 14¼x13¾*
638 A287 10t Block of 4, #a-d   5.00 4.00

First Completion of Parliamentary Term — A288

2001, July 13
639 A288 10t multi   3.25 2.40

8th Parliamentary Elections — A289

2001, Sept. 30
640 A289 2t multi   .75 .45

Year of Dialogue Among Civilizations A290

2001, Oct. 24   *Perf. 14¼*
641 A290 10t multi   1.75 1.75
   a.   Souvenir sheet of 1   4.50 4.50

No. 641a sold for 30t.

Meer Mosharraf Hossain (1847-1912) A291

2001, Nov. 13   *Perf. 13¾x14¼*
642 A291 4t multi   .90 .40

World AIDS
Day — A292

2001, Dec. 1
643 A292 10t multi   2.25 1.75

Victory in War of Independence, 30th
Anniv. — A293

Medals: a, Bir Bikram. b, Bir Protik. c, Bir
Sreshto. d, Bir Uttom.

2001, Dec. 16
644 A293 Horiz. strip of 4   6.00 6.00
a.-d.   10t Any single   1.50 1.50

10th Asian Art
Biennale — A294

2002, Jan. 9 Litho. Perf. 13¾x14¼
645 A294 10t multi   1.75 1.10

Great Language Movement, 50th
Anniv. — A295

No. 646: a, 38 symbols. b, Monument. c, 30
symbols.
30t, Emblem, vert.

2002, Feb. 21   Perf. 14¼x13¾
646 A295 Horiz. strip of 3   3.00 3.00
a.-c.   10t Any single   1.00 1.00
         Souvenir Sheet
         Perf. 14¼
647 A295 30t multi   3.00 3.00

Rokuon-ji
Temple,
Japan — A296

2002, Apr. 11 Litho. Perf. 13¾x14¼
648 A296 10t multi   1.25 1.25
Bangladesh-Japan diplomatic relations,
30th anniv.

Poverty
Alleviation
Through
Goat
Production
A297

2002, Apr. 27   Perf. 14¼x13¾
649 A297 2t multi   .45   .25

United Nations
Special Session
on
Children — A298

2002, Apr. 28   Perf. 13¾x14¼
650 A298 10t multi   1.25 1.25

Mohammad
Nasiruddin
(1888-1994),
Journalist
A299

2002, May 21
651 A299 4t multi   .90   .35

A300

Tree
Planting
Campaign
A301

Perf. 14¼x13¾, 13¾x14¼
2002, June 15
652 A300 10t shown   1.00 1.00
653 A300 10t Tree, vert.   1.00 1.00
654 A301 10t shown   1.00 1.00
         Nos. 652-654 (3)   3.00 3.00

2002 World Cup Soccer
Championships, Japan and
Korea — A303

No. 656: a, Flags of participants, trophy in
UR. b, World map, soccer field, trophy. c,
Flags, trophy in UL.

2002, May 31 Litho. Perf. 14¼x13¾
656 A303 Horiz. strip of 3   4.25 4.25
a.-c.   10t Any single   1.25 1.25

SOS Children's
Village, 30th
Anniv. — A304

2002, July 9 Litho.   Perf. 13¾x14¼
657 A304 6t multi   1.20   .40

World Population
Day — A305

2002, July 11
658 A305 6t multi   1.20   .40

Fish
A306

Designs: No. 659, 4t, Labeo gonius. No.
660, 4t, Ompook pabda.

2002, Aug. 10   Perf. 14¼x13¾
659-660 A306 Set of 2   1.60 1.60

Bangladesh - United Kingdom
Friendship Bridge — A307

2002, Sept. 10
661 A307 4t multi   1.20   .35

World Habitat
Day — A308

2002, Oct. 7   Perf. 13¾x14¼
662 A308 4t multi   1.20   .35

Children's
Games
A309

Designs: No. 663, 4t, Dariabandha. No.
664, 4t, Kanamachee.

2002, Nov. 10   Perf. 14¼x13¾
663-664 A309 Set of 2   1.50 1.50
25th Anniversary of Bangladesh National
Philatelic Association
For overprint see No. 686.

National Book
Year (in
2002) — A310

2003, Jan. 1 Litho. Perf. 13¾x14¼
665 A310 6t multi   .65   .35

Jasimuddin
(1903-76),
Poet — A311

2003, Jan. 1
666 A311 5t multi   .65   .35

South Asian
Soccer
Federation
Championships
A312

2003, Jan. 10
667 A312 10t multi   2.25 1.50

No. 574
Overprinted

Perf. 13¾x14¼
2003, Feb. 19   Litho.
668 A245 10t multi   2.25 2.00

Shefa-ul-mulk Hakim Habib-ur-
Rahman — A313

Perf. 13¾x14¼
2003, Feb. 23   Litho.
669 A313 8t multi   .75   .75

Pres. Ziaur
Rahman (1936-
81)
A314

2003, May 29
670 A314 4t multi   .75   .35

Tree
Planting
Campaigns
A315

Designs: 6t, Fruit, woman and child planting tree. 8t, Family, hands with seedling, vert. 12t, Tree, fruit, family, vert.

2003 Perf. 14¼x13¾, 13¾x14¼
671-673 A315 Set of 3   4.50 2.75

Issued: 6t, 6/12; 8t, 12t, 6/1.
Fruit tree planting fortnight (No. 671); National tree plantation campaign (Nos. 672-673).

Labeo Calbasu A316

Perf. 14¼x13¾
2003, Aug. 12   Litho.
674 A316 2t multi   .85 .65

Inauguration of Rajshahi-Dhaka Rail Link — A317

2003, Aug. 14   Perf. 13¾x14¼
675 A317 10t multi   1.75 1.75

49th Commonwealth Parliamentary Conference — A318

2003, Oct. 7   Perf. 14¼x13¾
676 A318 10t multi   1.50 .80

Eid Mubarak A319

2003, Nov. 25   Perf. 13¾x14¼
677 A319 4t multi   1.10 .60

Intl. Center for Diarrheal Disease Research, Bangladesh, 25th Anniv. — A320

2003, Dec. 7
678 A320 10t multi   1.10 .55

Rajshahi University, 50th Anniv. — A321

2003, Dec. 21   Perf. 14¼x13¾
679 A321 4t multi   1.10 .55

National Library Year (in 2003) A322

2004, Jan. 1   Litho.   Perf. 14¼x13¾
680 A322 6t multi   1.00 .75

Seventh Bangladesh and Eighth SAARC Scout Jamboree — A323

2004, Jan. 6
681 A323 2t multi   1.25 .75

Sport and the Environment — A324

2004, Jan. 10
682 A324 10t multi   1.50 1.50

11th Asian Art Biennale A325

2004, Jan. 15
683 A325 5t multi   .65 .25

National Day A326

2004, Mar. 24
684 A326 5t multi   .60 .25

World Health Day A327

2004, Apr. 7
685 A327 6t multi   .60 .25

No. 663 Overprinted

Silver Jubilee Bangladesh National Philatelic Association

2004, May 31
686 A309 4t multi   1.00 .75

National Tree Plantation Campaign — A328

No. 687: a, Fruit, stylized tree. b, Trees and other plants.

2004, June 1   Litho.   Perf. 13¾x14¼
687 A328 10t Horiz. pair, #a-b   1.50 1.50

Bangladesh - Iran Friendship — A329

No. 688: a, Tower, Iranian flag, poet Hafez Shirazi. b, Tower, Bangladesh flag, poet Nazrul Islam.

2004, June 3   Litho.   Perf. 14¼x13¾
688 A329 10t Horiz. pair, #a-b   2.75 2.75

Fruit Tree Planting Fortnight A330

2004, June 6   Perf. 13¾x14¼
689 A330 10t multi   1.00 .75

Intl. Year of Rice A331

2004, June 21   Perf. 14¼x13¾
690 A331 5t multi   .60 .60

World Population Day — A332

2004, July 11   Litho.   Perf. 13¾x14¼
691 A332 6t multi   .60 .30

Bangladesh Partnership With United Nations, 30th Anniv. — A333

2004, Sept. 16   Perf. 14¼x13¾
692 A333 4t multi   .50 .25

Bhasani Novo Theater, Dhaka A334

2004, Sept. 25
693 A334 4t multi   .50 .25

Rotary International, Cent. (in 2005) — A335

2004, Oct. 22   Litho.   Perf. 13¾x14¼
694 A335 4t multi   .50 .25

Miniature Sheet

Flowers — A336

No. 695: a, Argemone mexicana. b, Cyanotis axillaris. c, Thevetia peruvians. d, Pentapetes phoenicea. e, Aegle marmelos. f, Datura stramonium.

2004, Dec. 1   Litho.   Perf. 14¼x12½
695 A336 5t Sheet of 6, #a-f   4.25 4.25

13th South Asian Association for Regional Cooperation Summit, Dhaka — A337

2004, Dec. 8   Perf. 13¾x14¼
696 A337 6t multi   .50 .25

Fish — A338

No. 697: a, Sperata aor. b, Notopterus notepterus.

Perf. 14¼x13¾

2004, Dec. 20   Litho.
697 A338 10t Horiz. pair, #a-b   2.25 2.25

6th National Cub Scout Camporee A339

Perf. 13¾x14¼

2004, Dec. 26   Litho.
698 A339 6t multi   .75 .75

Intl. Year of Microcredit — A340

No. 699: a, 4t, Woman with bowl, globe on cart with coin wheels. b, 10t, Woman pushing handle on coin and globe pulley system.

2005, Jan. 15   **Perf. 14¼x13¾**
699 A340 Horiz. pair, #a-b   1.75 1.75

South Asia Tourism Year A341

2005, Feb. 1
700 A341 4t multi   .75 .40

Independence Day — A342

2005, Mar. 24
701 A342 10t multi   1.25 .75

Cooperative Movement, Cent. — A343

2005, Mar. 31   **Perf. 13¾x14¼**
702 A343 5t multi   .75 .40

National Tree Planting Campaign — A344

No. 703: a, Family planting tree. b, Three trees.

2005, June 1   **Perf. 14¼x13¾**
703 A344 6t Horiz. pair, #a-b   1.50 1.50

Famous Men — A345

No. 704: a, G. A. Mannan (1933-92), choreographer. b, Ustad Phuljhuri Khan (1920-82), musician. c, Usted Abed Hossain Khan (1928-96), musician. d, Ustad Munshi Raisuddin (1901-73), musician.

2005, June 5   **Perf. 13¾x14¼**
704 A345 6t Block of 4, #a-d   2.50 2.50

Nandus Nandus A346

2005, Aug. 7   **Perf. 14¼x13¾**
705 A346 10t multi   1.25 1.25

Dr. Nawab Ali (1902-77), Physician A347

2005, Dec. 4 Litho. **Perf. 13¾x14¼**
706 A347 8t multi   1.00 .75

Science Book Year (in 2005) A348

2006, Jan. 1   **Perf. 14¼x13¾**
707 A348 10t multi   1.10 .75

World Summit on the Information Society, Tunis (in 2005) — A349

2006, Jan. 22
708 A349 10t multi   1.10 .75

OPEC Intl. Development Fund, 30th Anniv. — A350

2006, Jan. 28
709 A350 10t multi   1.10 .75

Diplomatic Relations Between Bangladesh and People's Republic of China, 30th Anniv. — A351

No. 710: a, Tienanmen Square, Beijing. b, National Assembly Building, Dhaka. c, Gabkhan River Bridge, Bangladesh. d, Great Wall of China.

2006, Mar. 6   **Perf. 12**
710 A351 Horiz. strip of 4   3.50 3.50
  a.-d.   10t Any single   .35 .30
  e.   Souvenir sheet, #710a-710d   5.00 5.00

National Day A352

2006, Mar. 26   **Perf. 14¼x13¾**
711 A352 10t multi   1.10 .75

World Health Day — A353

2006, July 19 Litho. **Perf. 13¾x14¼**
712 A353 6t multi   1.00 .50

ICC Under 19 World Cricket Cup (in 2004) — A354

2006, July 19
713 A354 10t multi   1.25 .75

Tree Planting Campaign and Tree Fair — A355

2006, June 5   **Perf. 14¼x13¾**
714 A355 10t multi   1.10 .75

Five Years of Peace and Development A356

2006, Oct. 25 Litho. **Perf. 13¾x14¼**
715 A356 10t multi   1.25 .75

World AIDS Day — A357

2006, Dec. 6
716 A357 10t multi   1.10 .75

Mohamed Habibullah Bahar Choudhury (1906-66), Writer — A358

2007, June 25
717 A358 10t multi   1.10 .75

Intl. Women's Day — A359

2007, Mar. 8
718 A359 10t multi   1.10 .75

World Health Day — A360

2007, Apr. 7
719 A360 6t multi   1.10 .75

BANGLADESH

173

Natl. Tree
Planting
Campaign
A361

2007, June 3
720 A361 10t multi   1.10 .75

Scouting, Cent. — A362

No. 721 — Scouting Centenary emblem
and: a, Scouts. b, Lord Robert Baden-Powell.

2007, July 9   *Perf. 14¼x13¾*
721 A362 10t Horiz. pair, #a-b   2.25 2.25

2007 ICC Cricket World Cup, West
Indies — A363

No. 722: a, Cricket World Cup, bowler, tiger,
horiz. b, Batsman, Cricket World cup, horiz. c,
Cricket players, bails, wickets, glove and balls.
d, Players, Cricket World Cup.

*Perf. 14¼x13¾ (horiz. stamps),
13¾x14¼*
2007, Apr. 19
722 A363 10t Block of 4, #a-d   4.50 4.50

No. 617 Overprinted

Methods and Perfs. As Before
2007, July 29
723 A272 4t multicolored   1.75 1.25

Dr. Muhammad
Yunus, 2006
Nobel Peace
Prize
Winner — A364

Perf. 13¾x14¼
2007, Aug. 29   Litho.
724 A364 10t multi   30.00 30.00
On Sept. 2, 2007 No. 724 was withdrawn
from sale because "Muhammad" was abbreviated rather than spelled out, and the Nobel
medal shown was for Medicine and not Peace,

Dr. Muhammad
Yunus, 2006
Nobel Peace
Prize
Winner — A365

2007, Sept. 7 Litho. *Perf. 13¾x14¼*
725 A365 10t multi   1.50 1.50

Bangladesh Flood Relief — A366

No. 726: a, Three children standing in flood
water. b, People and goats in flood water. c,
People on corrugated metal roof. d, Line of
people standing in flood water. e, People with
food bowls, inundated buildings.

2007, Sept. 13   *Perf. 13½x12½*
726   Sheet of 5   5.00 5.00
a.-e.   A366 2t Any single   1.00 .35
No. 726 was printed as a sheet of six
stamps. The upper left stamp, showing Prime
Minister Fakhruddin Ahmed, was removed
from all sheets prior to sale, because he did
not give permission for his image to be used
on the stamp.

2007 ICC World Twenty20 Cricket
Tournament, South Africa — A367

No. 727: a, Batsman, map of South Africa.
b, Cricket match.

2007, Sept. 24   *Perf. 14¼x13¾*
727 A367 4t Horiz. pair, #a-b   3.00 3.00

Intl.
Migrants
Day
A368

2007, Dec. 18
728 A368 10t multi   1.50 .75

Independence
Day — A369

2008, Mar. 25   *Perf. 13¾x14¼*
729 A369 10t multi   1.50 .75

World
Health
Day
A370

2008, Apr. 7 Litho. *Perf. 14½x13¾*
730 A370 10t multi   1.50 .75

Sundarbans UNESCO World Heritage
Site — A371

No. 731: a, Deer. b, River. c, Man in jungle.
d, Tiger.

2008, Apr. 18   *Perf. 14½x13¾*
731 A371 10t Block of 4, #a-d   8.00 8.00
e.   Souvenir sheet, #731a-731d,
     perf. 13¾   9.00 9.00
f.   As "e," imperf.   9.00 9.00
Nos. 731e and 731f each sold for 50t.

Reign of Aga
Khan, 50th
Anniv. — A372

Text "Celebrating 50 Years": No. 732, 3t,
Against green background. No. 733, 3t,
Against red background. No. 734, 6t, In circle,
denomination in white. No. 735, 6t, In circle,
denomination in gold.

2008, May 19   *Perf. 13¾x14½*
732-735 A372 Set of 4   2.25 1.50

2008 Summer Olympics,
Beijing — A373

No. 736: a, 10t, Runners. b, 15t, Shooting.
c, 20t, Mascots of 2008 Summer Olympics. d,
25t, Greece #117, Bangladesh #122, Pierre
de Coubertin.

2008, July 6   *Perf. 14½x13¾*
736 A373 Block of 4, #a-d   5.00 2.50

Stamp Day — A374

2008, July 29   Imperf.
737 A374 50t multi   4.00 2.00

Miniature Sheet

Japan International Cooperation
Agency — A375

No. 738: a, 3t, Khepupara Radar Station,
Patuakhali. b, 7t, Vocational training program.
c, 10t, Jamuna Multi-purpose Bridge. d, 10t,
Polio vaccination program.

2008, Sept. 23   *Perf. 12½x12*
738 A375 Sheet of 4, #a-d   2.50 2.50

Dhaka Chamber
of Commerce
and Industry,
50th
Anniv. — A376

2008, Oct. 23 Litho. *Perf. 13¾x14½*
739 A376 10t multi   1.50 .75

Agriculture
Day — A377

2008, Nov. 15
740 A377 4t multi   .75 .35

Nimtali
Deuri,
Dhaka
A378

2008, Nov. 28   *Perf. 14½x13¾*
741 A378 6t multi   .80 .35
Dhaka as capital city, 400th anniv.

Beach, Cox's Bazar — A379

2008, Nov. 30   *Perf. 12½*
742 A379 10t multi   1.25 .60

Intl. Day
of
Persons
with
Disabilities
A380

2008, Dec. 3   *Perf. 14½x13¾*
743 A380 3t multi   .75 .35

Intl. Year of Sanitation A381

2008, Dec. 24   *Perf. 13¾x14½*
744 A381 3t multi   .75   .35

Souvenir Sheet

Bangladesh No. 32 — A382

2009, Feb. 20   *Perf. 12½x14½*
745 A382 50t multi   6.00   3.00

Intl. Mother Language Day.

Sheikh Mujibur Rahman (1920-75), President, and Children — A383

2009, Mar. 16   *Perf. 12½*
746 A383 10t multi   1.25   .60

Children's Day.

National Day — A384

2009, Mar. 25
747 A384 3t multi   1.00   .35

World Health Day — A385

2009, Apr. 7 Litho.   *Perf. 13¾x14½*
748 A385 3t multi   1.25   .50

Souvenir Sheet

China 2009 World Stamp Exhibition, Luoyang — A386

No. 749: a, 10t, Exhibition emblem. b, 10t, Exhibition mascot. c, 20t, Ox.

2009, Apr. 10   *Perf. 14½x12½*
749 A386   Sheet of 3, #a-c, + label   5.00   5.00

No. 749 also was issued in a quantity of 750 with serial numbers. Value, $35.

Shamsun Nahar Mahmud (1908-64), Educator A387

2009, May 26   *Perf. 13¾x14½*
750 A387 4t multi   .75   .40

Natl. Tree Plantation Campaign and Tree Fair — A388

2009, May 31
751 A388 3t multi   .50   .30

Daylight Savings Time — A389

2009, June 19   *Perf. 12x13¾*
752 A389 5t multi   .65   .30

World Population Day A390

2009, July 11   *Perf. 14½x13¾*
753 A390 6t multi   .75   .40

Intl. Year of Astronomy — A391

No. 754: a, Telescope of Galileo Galilei, 1609. b, Andromeda Galaxy.

2009, July 19   *Perf. 12*
754 A391 10t Pair, #a-b   3.00   3.00

Miniature Sheet

National Mourning Day — A392

No. 755: a, 3t, Begum Fazilatunnessa Mujib. b, 3t, Sheikh Kamal. c, 3t, Sheikh Jamal. d, 3t, Sheikh Russel. e, 3t, Sheikh Abu Naser. f, 3t, Sultana Kamal Khuku. g, 3t, Parveen Jamal Rosy. h, 3t, Abdur Rab Serniabat. i, 3t, Sheikh Fazlul Haque Moni. j, 3t, Begum Arju Moni. k, 3t, Colonel Jamiluddin Ahmed. l, 3t, Baby Serniabat. m, 3t, Arif Serniabat. n, 3t, Sukanto Abullah Babu. o, 3t, Shahid Serniabat. p, 3t, Abdul Nayeem Khan Rintu. q, 15t, Sheikh Mujibur Rahman, President of Bangladesh.

2009, Aug. 12
755 A392   Sheet of 17, #a-q, + label   6.00   6.00

Stamps depict members of family of Sheikh Mujibur Rahman killed in Aug. 15, 1975, army coup.

World Food Day — A393

No. 756: a, Medal. b, Various foods. c, Boat carrying crops. d, Fishing boat, net full of fish.

2009, Oct. 16 Litho.   *Perf. 14¼x13¾*
756 A393 3t Block of 4, #a-d   1.75   1.75

Center for the Rehabilitation of the Paralyzed, 30th Anniv. — A394

No. 757: a, Entrance to Center, two women. b, Patients and staff.

2009, Nov. 12   *Perf. 12¼x12½*
757 A394 7t Horiz. pair, #a-b   1.75   1.75

Prof. Abdul Moktader (1909-93), Educator A395

2009, Dec. 27   *Perf. 14¼x13¾*
758 A395 4t multi   .50   .25

Eighth National Scout Jamboree A396

2010, Jan. 16
759 A396 10t multi   3.25   1.50

Miniature Sheet

Rose Varieties Cultivated in Bangladesh — A397

No. 760: a, Alec's Red. b, Royal Highness. c, Queen Elizabeth. d, Ballerina. e, Alexander. f, Blue Moon. g, Papa Meilland. h, Double Delight. i, Iceberg. j, Sonia. k, Sunblest. l, Picadilly. m, Pascali.

2010, Feb. 11   *Perf. 12*
760 A397 10t Sheet of 13, #a-m, + label   25.00   25.00

Opening of Intl. Mother Language Institute, Dhaka — A398

2010. Feb. 21
761 A398 15t multi   4.50   3.00

Intl. Women's Day A399

2010, Mar. 3   *Perf. 14¼x13¾*
762 A399 5t multi   2.00   1.00

A souvenir sheet containing one 10t stamp commemorating National Children's Day sold for 25t. Value, $9.

Miniature Sheet

National Day — A400

No. 763 — Liberation War Monuments at: a, Public Library Campus, Brahman Baria. b, Shafipur, Gazipur. c, Jagannath Hall, Dhaka University. d, Vocational Training Institute, Rangpur.

2010, Mar. 26   **Perf. 14¾x14¼**
763 A400 5t Sheet of 4, #a-d   7.00 7.00

2010 Intl. Cricket Council World Twenty 20 Tournament, West Indies A401

2010, Apr. 22   **Litho.**   **Perf. 13¼**
764 A401 15t multi   4.50 3.00

Souvenir Sheet

Bangabandhu Sheikh Mujib Medical University, 12th Anniv. — A402

2010, May 2   **Perf. 13¾x12**
765 A402 20t multi   7.50 5.00

Natl. Tree Planting Campaign and Tree Fair A403

2010, June 1   **Perf. 14¼x14**
766 A403 6t multi   1.50 .75

Dhaka as Capital City, 400th Anniv. — A404

No. 767: a, The Great Katra, Mughal era. b, Buckland Bund on Buriganga River, British era. c, Kamlapur Railway Station, Pakistan era. d, Dhaka in 2008.

2010, June 16   **Perf. 12x14¼**
767 A404 10t Block of 4, #a-d   12.00 12.00

Intl. Center for Diarrheal Disease Research in Bangladesh, 50th Anniv. A405

2010, June 20   **Perf. 13½**
768 A405 5t gold & black   1.75 1.00

2010 World Cup Soccer Championships, South Africa — A406

No. 769: a, Two players. b, Three players. c, Mascot.

2010, July 11   **Perf. 14¼x13¾**
769   Horiz. strip of 3   6.00 6.00
a.-b.   A406 10t Either single   1.50 1.50
c.   A406 20t multi   1.50 1.50

Souvenir Sheet

Bangkok 2010 Intl. Stamp Exhibition — A407

No. 770: a, Raj Banbihar (Buddhist Monastery), Rangamati, Bangladesh. b, Buddha Dhatu Jadi (Buddhist temple), Bandarban, Bangladesh.

2010, Aug. 2   **Perf. 12**
770 A407 20t Sheet of 2, #a-b   6.00 6.00

No. 770 also was issued in a quantity of 2,000 with serial numbers. Value, $25.

Miniature Sheet

Indigenous People — A408

No. 771: a, Chakma woman with blue and red clothes. b, Chakma woman with sash. c, Chakma woman weaving. d, Two Chakma women. e, Marma woman with flower above ear. f, Marma woman holding bouquet of flowers. g, Marma women picking crops. h, Marma women dancing. i, Mru woman with red blouse. j, Mru woman with bracelets on arms. k, Mru women pounding grain. l, Mru man spearing animal in pen. m, Tripura woman with red clothes. n, Tripura woman with pale pink clothes. o, Tripura women carrying wood. p, Tripura woman dancing. q, Pangkhua woman. r, Pangkhua woman and man. s, Pangkhua man with basket. t, Pangkhua man with bull's skull.

2010, Aug. 2   **Litho.**   **Perf. 12**
771 A408 5t Sheet of 20, #a-t   12.00 12.00

No. 771 also was issued in a quantity of 1,000 inscribed "Bangkok 2010 - 25th Asian International Stamp Exhibition Bangladesh Participation" in the left and right margins. Value, $45.

Birds — A409

No. 772: a, House sparrow. b, Red munia. c, Spotted dove. d, Common myna.

2010, Sept. 27
772 A409 10t Block of 4, #a-d   6.00 6.00

A souvenir sheet containing No. 772 sold for 100t; value, $8. An imperf. souvenir sheet of No. 772 inscribed "Portugal 2010 World Philatelic Exhibition Bangladesh Participation" exists; value, $20. A pane of four No. 772 (16 stamps) inscribed "Portugal 2010 World Philatelic Exhibition Bangladesh Participation" exists; value, $35.

Year of the Tiger — A410

2010, Sept. 28   **Perf. 13¼x13**
773 A410 50t multi   7.00 7.00

A souvenir sheet containing No. 773 exists. Value, $15.

Abu Nayem Mohammed Nazibudding Khan (1954-71), Fredom Fighter — A411

2010, Dec. 14   **Perf. 13½**
774 A411 3t multi   .40 .30

Population and Housing Census — A412

2011, Jan. 27   **Perf. 13¾x14¼**
775 A412 3t multi   .40 .30

Seventh National Cub Scout Camporee — A413

2011, Feb. 9   **Perf. 14¼x13¾**
776 A413 10t multi   1.50 .75

1972 Return to Bangladesh of Sheikh Mujibur Rahman (1920-75) — A414

No. 777: a, Rahman and followers. b, Rahman waving to crowd. c, Rahman.

2011, Feb. 10   **Perf. 13½**
777   Horiz. strip of 3   2.50 2.50
a.-b.   5t Either single   .70 .70
c.   10t multi   1.10 1.10

Mahatma Gandhi (1869-1948) — A415

No. 778 — Gandhi: a, At Laksham Railway Station on way to Noakhali. b, With others at Noakhali. c, Alone at Noakhali.

2011, Feb. 10   **Litho.**
778   Horiz. strip of 3   6.00 6.00
a.   A415 10t multi   1.50 1.50
b.   A415 15t multi   2.00 2.00
c.   A415 20t multi   2.25 2.25
d.   Sheet of 6, 2 each #778a-778c   3.00 3.00

Indipex 2011 World Philatelic Exhibition, New Delhi

2011 ICC Cricket World Cup Championships, Bangladesh A416

No. 779: a, Bowler. b, Batsman. c, Wicketkeeper. d, Fielder.
50t, Players and umpire, horiz.

2011, Feb. 23   **Perf. 12½**
779   Horiz. strip of 4   12.00 12.00
a.-d.   A416 20t Any single   2.50 2.50

Size: 127x91mm
Imperf
780 A416 50t multi   7.50 7.50

Intl. Anti-Corruption Day (in 2010) — A417

2011, Feb. 24   **Perf. 12½**
781 A417 5t multi   .70 .40

Miniature Sheet

Independence, 40th Anniv. — A418

No. 782: a, 10t, Bangabandhu Square Fountain, Dhaka (32x41mm). b, 10t, Victory of Bangla Monument, Chittagong (32x41mm). c, 10t, Memorial of Liberation War, Rajarbagh Police Line, Dhaka (32x43mm). d, 10t, Invincible Bhoirab, Kishoreganj (32x43mm). e, 20t, Sheikh Mujibur Rahman (1920-75), First President of Bangladesh (32x84mm).

Perf. 12x12x14¼x12 (#782a-782b), 14¼x12x12x12 (#782c-782d), 12
2011, Mar. 26
782   A418   Sheet of 5, #a-e   7.50 7.50

Probashi Kallyan Bank — A419

2011, Apr. 20   *Perf. 12½*
783   A419 10t multi   1.50   .75

Sir Rabindranath Tagore (1861-1941), Poet — A420

No. 784 — Tagore and: a, Shilaidaha, Kushtia. b, Shahjadpur, Siraganj. c, Dakkhindihi, Khulna. d, Patishar, Naogaon.

2011, May 6   *Perf. 13½*
784   A420 10t Block of 4, #a-d   6.00 6.00
   A souvenir sheet containing a perf. 14¼x13½ example of No. 784 sold for 100t. Value, $10.

National Tree Planting Campaign — A421

2011, June 1   *Perf. 14¼x13¾*
785   A421 10t multi   1.50   .75

Qazi Nazrul Islam (1899-1976), National Poet — A422

No. 786 — Nazrul Islam and: a, House with red roof. b, House, pond and sign. c, Building with arches. d, Sculpture, Nazrul Museum.

Perf. 13¾x14¼
2011, June 24   Litho.
786   A422 10t Block of 4, #a-d   6.00 6.00
   Imperforate and Perf. 14¼x13¾ examples of souvenir sheets containing Nos. 786a-786d each sold for 100t. Value, $15.

Rare Turtles — A423

No. 787: a, Hardella thurjii. b, Geoclemys hamiltonii.

2011, July 17   *Perf. 14¼x13¼*
787   A423 10t Horiz. pair, #a-b   4.00 4.00

   A miniature sheet containing four 10t stamps depicting rare animals of Bangladesh sold for 100t. Value, $7.50.

Miniature Sheet

Birds of the Sundarbans World Heritage Site — A424

No. 788: a, Heliopais personata. b, Leptoptilos javanicus. c, Haliaeetus leucogaster. d, Bubo coromandus. e, Pelargopsis amauroptera. f, Halcyon coromanda. g, Alcedo meninting. h, Halcyon pileata. i, Todiramphus chloris. j, Treron bicincta. k, Gorsachius melanolophus. l, Pitta megarhyncha.

2011, July 17   Litho.   *Perf. 13¾x12*
788   A424 10t Sheet of 12, #a-l 10.00 10.00
   No. 788 exists in a quantity of 3,600 with serial number and inscription for Phila Nippon '11 exhibition; value, $20.

Stringed Instruments — A425

No. 789: a, Dotara (orange background). b, Ektara (green background). c, Sarinda (pale lilac background). d, Sarangi (blue background).

2011, July 21   *Perf. 14¼x13¾*
789   A425 5t Block of 4, #a-d   1.50 1.50

Miniature Sheet

Silver Coins — A426

No. 790 — Silver coins from reign of: a, Sultan Fakhr al-Din Mubarak Shah, 1334-49. b, Sultan Shams al-Din Ilyas Shah, 1342-57. c, Sultan Ghiyath al-Din A'zam Shah, 1389-1410. d, Sultan Jalal al-Din Muhammad Shah, 1415-32.

2011, July 21   *Perf. 13¾x12*
790   A426 10t Sheet of 4, #a-d   3.00 3.00

Miniature Sheet

PhilaNippon '11 Intl. Philatelic Exhibition, Yokohama — A427

No. 791: a, Imperial Palace, Tokyo. b, Cherry blossoms. c, Mt. Fuji. d, Kiyomizu Temple, Kyoto. e, Sumo wrestling.

2011, July 21   *Perf. 12x13¾*
791   A427 10t Sheet of 5, #a-d   6.00 6.00
   No. 791 sold for 100t.

Dhaka Club, Cent. A428

2011, Aug. 19   *Perf. 14¼x13¾*
792   A428 3t multi   .40   .25

E-Asia 2011 Conference, Dhaka — A429

2011, Dec. 1   Litho.
793   A429 10t multi   1.00   .50

Victory in War of Independence, 40th Anniv. — A430

2011, Dec. 16
794   A430 10t multi   1.00   .50

Bangladesh College of Physicians and Surgeons, 40th Anniv. — A431

2011, Dec. 28   *Perf. 12½*
795   A431 10t multi   1.00   .50

Language Movement, 60th Anniv. — A432

2012, Feb. 28   *Perf. 13¼x13½*
796   A432 21t multi   1.50   .75

National Day — A433

2012, Mar. 26   *Perf. 13¾x14¼*
797   A433 26t multi   1.75 1.00

National Plantation Day A434

2012, June 5   *Perf. 14¼x13¾*
798   A434 10t multi   .75   .40

Endangered Animals — A435

No. 799: a, 15t, Gyps bengalensis. b, 25t, Semnopithecus entellus.

2012, June 14
799   A435 Horiz. pair, #a-b   3.00 3.00
   A souvenir sheet containing imperforate examples of Nos. 799a and 799b sold for 100t.

Birds — A436

No. 800: a, Ichthyophaga ichthyaetus. b, Centropus bengalensis.

2012, June 14   **Perf. 13¼**
800 A436   Horiz. pair + central label   3.00 3.00
a.-b.   20t Either single   1.25 1.25

Indonesia 2012 World Stamp Championship, Jakarta. Perf. 12x13½ and imperforate sheets containing four 10t stamps depicting different birds each sold for 100t.

Butterflies — A437

No. 801: a, Leopard lacewing. b, Striped tiger. c, Lemon pansy. d, Knight.

2012, June 14   **Perf. 12x13¼**
801 A437   10t Block of 4, #a-d   4.75 4.75
e.   Block of 4, #801a-801d, perf. 12¾   3.00 3.00

Birds and Their Nests — A438

No. 802: a, Ploceus philippinus. b, Pycnonotus cafer. c, Orthotomus sutorius. d, Dinopium benghalense. e, Hypothymis azurea. f, Psittacula krameri.

2012, June 14   **Perf. 13**
802 A438   20t Block of 6, #a-f   8.00 8.00
g.   Souvenir sheet of 6, #802a-802f, imperf.   10.00 10.00

No. 802g sold for 150t.

Rotary International in Bangladesh, 75th Anniv. — A439

2012, July 1   **Perf. 14¼x13¾**
803 A439   10t multi   .90 .40

Open Heart Surgery in Bangladesh, 30th Anniv. (in 2011) — A440

2012, Sept. 12   **Perf. 13½**
804 A440   10t multi   .85 .40

Intl. Ozone Day A441

2012, Sept. 16   **Perf. 14¼x13¾**
805 A441   10t multi   .95 .40

Montreal Protocol, 25th anniv.

24th Asia Pacific Regional Scout Conference A442

2012, Nov. 24   **Perf. 13¾x14¼**
806 A442   20t multi   1.40 .60

Bangladesh Police Academy, Cent. — A443

2012, Dec. 6   **Perf. 14¼x13¾**
807 A443   12t multi   1.00 .50

Asia-Pacific Postal Union, 50th Anniv. (in 2012) — A444

2013, Jan. 13
808 A444   3t multi   1.75 .30

Birds — A445

No. 809: a, Anser indicus. b, Netta rufina. c, Numenius arquata. d, Clamator coromandus. e, Falco tinnunculus. f, Luscinia calliope. g, Motacilla citreola. h, Ciconia nigra,

2013, Jan. 13   **Litho.**   **Perf. 12¾**
809 A445   10t Block of 8, #a-h   8.00 8.00
i.   Souvenir sheet of 8, #809a-809h, perf. 13¼x12   8.00 8.00

SOS Children's Villages in Bangladesh, 40th Anniv. — A446

2013, Jan. 30   **Litho.**   **Perf. 13¾x14¼**
810 A446   10t multi   1.25 .50

Audit Day A447

2013, Feb. 7   **Perf. 14¼x13¾**
811 A447   5t multi   .75 .30

Sheikh Mujibur Rahman (1920-75), Prime Minister — A448

2013, Mar. 26   **Perf. 13¾x14¼**
812 A448   10t multi   .75 .30

Independence, 42nd anniv.

National Tree Planting Campaign A449

2013, June 5   **Perf. 14¼x13¾**
813 A449   10t multi   .75 .30

Bangladesh National Museum, Cent. — A450

2013, July 8   **Perf. 12¾**
814 A450   10t multi   .75 .30

Statue of Buddha, Dharmarajika Maha Vihara, Dhaka — A451

2013, July 30   **Perf. 13¾x14¼**
815 A451   10t multi   1.50 .75

A souvenir sheet with one perf. 13¼ example of No. 815 sold for 40t. Value, $6.

Flowers — A452

No. 816: a, Mimosa pudica. b, Mesua nagassarium. c, Dillenia indica. d, Wrightia coccinea.

2013, July 30   **Perf. 12x13½**
816 A452   10t Block of 4, #a-d   3.00 3.00
e.   Souvenir sheet of 4, #816a-816d, imperf.   4.00 4.00

No. 816e sold for 60t.

Tiger Protection — A453

No. 817: a, Tiger with grass showing above head, Bengali text on top line. b, Two tigers, English text on top line. c, Tiger, English text on top line. d, Tiger with trees and sky above head, Bengali text on top line.

2013, July 30   **Perf. 13¼**
817 A453   10t Block of 4, #a-d   8.50 8.50
e.   Souvenir sheet of 4, #817a-817d, perf. 12x13½   7.50 7.50

No. 817e sold for 80t. An imperforate sheet similar to No. 817e, but with the Bangladesh flag and Thailand 2013 World Stamp Exhibition emblem in the sheet margin, sold for 100t.

Miniature Sheet

Endangered Animals — A454

No. 818: a, 6t, Lutra lutra. b, 8t, Naja naja. c, 10t, Nycticebus bengalensis. d, 12t, Hoolock hoolock.

2013, July 30   **Perf. 13½x13¼**
818 A454   Sheet of 4, #a-d   5.50 5.50
e.   Like No. 818, imperf.   5.50 5.50

No. 818 sold for 60t. No. 818e sold for 70t, and has the emblem for the Thailand 2013 World Stamp Exhibition in sheet margin. Value, $9.50.

International Ozone Day — A455

       Perf. 14¼x13¾
2013, Sept. 16   **Litho.**
819 A455   10t multi   1.75 .50

Victory Day,
42nd
Anniv. — A456

Perf. 13¾x14¼

2013, Dec. 16   Litho.
820 A456 10t multi   1.50 .75

National
Day
A457

Perf. 14¼x13¾

2014, Mar. 26   Litho.
821 A457 10t multi   1.50 .50

National Tree
Planting
Campaign
A458

2014, June 5 Litho. **Perf. 13¾x14¼**
822 A458 10t multi   1.50 .50

World
Population
Day
A459

Perf. 14¼x14x13¾

2014, July 11   Litho.
823 A459 10t multi   1.50 .50

Flowers — A460

No. 824: a, Dendrobium aphyllum. b,
Rhyncostylis refusa. c, Nymphaea nouchali. d,
Ochna obtusata.

2014, Aug. 4 Litho. **Perf. 13¼x14¼**
824 A460 10t Block of 4, #a-d   5.00 5.00
     e. Souvenir sheet of 4, #824a-
         824d, perf. 12x13¾
Philakorea 2014 World Stamp Exhibition
(No. 824e). No. 824e sold for 60t and exists
imperforate.

Bay of Bengal
Initiative for
Multi-Sectoral
Technical and
Economic
Cooperation
Secretariat,
Dhaka — A461

Perf. 13¾x14¼

2014, Sept. 13   Litho.
825 A461 4t multi   .50 .25

Admission of
Bangladesh into
United Nations,
40th
Anniv. — A462

Perf. 13¾x14¼

2014, Sept. 17   Litho.
826 A462 5t multi   .50 .25

16th Asian Art Biennale,
Bangladesh — A463

2014, Dec. 1 Litho. **Perf. 14¼x13¾**
827 A463 10t multi   .50 .25

Bangladesh Betar, 75th Anniv. — A464

Perf. 14¼x13¾

2014, Dec. 15   Litho.
828 A464 10t multi   .50 .25
Bangladesh Betar, state-run radio broadcasting organization.

Victory
Day, 43rd
Anniv.
A465

Perf. 14¼x13¾

2014, Dec. 16   Litho.
829 A465 10t multi   .50 .25

Bangladesh
Television, 50th
Anniv. — A466

Perf. 13¾x14¼

2014, Dec. 25   Litho.
830 A466 10t multi   .50 .25

International
Customs
Day — A467

2015, Jan. 26 Litho. **Perf. 13¾x14¼**
831 A467 10t multi   .50 .25

ICC Cricket World Cup, Australia and
New Zealand — A468

2015, Mar. 15 Litho. **Perf. 12x11¼**
832 A468 10t multi   .50 .25

National Day — A469

Perf. 13½x13¼

2015, Mar. 26   Litho.
833 A469 10t multi   .50 .25

International Telecommunication
Union, 150th Anniv. — A470

2015, May 18 Litho. **Perf. 14¼x13¾**
834 A470 10t multi   .50 .25

Stamp
Day — A471

2015, July 29 Litho. **Perf. 13¾x14¼**
835 A471 10t multi   .50 .25

Diplomatic Relations Between
Bangladesh and People's Republic of
China, 40th Anniv. — A472

2015, Oct. 17 Litho. **Perf. 13¼x13½**
836 A472 10t multi   .25 .25

Victory
Day — A473

Perf. 13¾x14¼

2015, Dec. 16   Litho.
837 A473 10t multi   .25 .25

Traditional Boats — A474

No. 838, 10t: a, Saudagari. b, Dingi.
No. 839, 10t, horiz.: a, Kunda. b, Ghasi.

Perf. 13¾x14¼, 14¼x13¾

2015, Dec. 16   Litho.
         Horiz. Pairs, #a-b
838-839 A474   Set of 2   1.10 1.10

Souvenir Sheet

Traditional Boats — A475

2015, Dec. 16   Litho.   **Imperf.**
840 A475 100t multi   2.60 2.60

Souvenir Sheet

Concert for Bangladesh, 44th
Anniv. — A476

Perf. 14¼x13¼

2015, Dec. 16   Litho.
841 A476 40t multi   1.60 1.60
     a.   Imperf.   1.60 1.60
Nos. 841and 841a each sold for 60t.

Indian Ocean Naval Symposium,
Dhaka — A477

2016, Jan. 11 Litho. **Perf. 14¼x13¾**
842 A477 10t multi   .25 .25

Scouting in Bangladesh, Cent. — A478

Scouting trefoil and: 10t, Scouts hiking. 20t, Ring of stylized scouts.

2016, Jan. 23 Litho. *Perf. 13¾x14¼*
843-844 A478 Set of 2 .80 .80

International Customs Day — A479

2016, Jan. 25 Litho. *Perf. 13¾x14¼*
845 A479 10t multi .25 .25

A480

Muslim Festival A481

2016, Feb. 5 Litho. *Perf. 13¾x14¼*
846 A480 5t multi .25 .25
Perf. 14¼x13¾
847 A481 10t multi .25 .25

Radharaman Dutta (1833-1915), Poet — A482

Perf. 13¾x14¼
2016, Mar. 14 Litho.
848 A482 10t multi .25 .25

National Day A483

Perf. 14¼x13¾
2016, Mar. 26 Litho.
849 A483 10t multi .25 .25

World Telecommunication and Information Society Day — A484

2016, May 18 Litho. *Perf. 14¼x13¾*
850 A484 10t multi .25 .25

Miniature Sheet

Birds — A485

No. 851: a, Lonchura punctulata. b, Megalaima haemacephala. c, Merops orientalis. d, Aethopyga siparaja. e, Dicaeum cruentatum. f, Chalcophaps indica. g, Pericrocotus flammeus. h, Oriolus xanthornus.

2016, May 28 Litho. *Perf. 13¼x13*
851 A485 10t Sheet of 8, #a-h 2.10 2.10
2016 World Stamp Show, New York.

Stamp Day — A486

2016, July 29 Litho. *Perf. 13x13¼*
852 A486 10t multi .25 .25

This sheet of four 10t stamps, released Aug. 10, 2016, sold for 100t.

National Mourning Day A487

Perf. 14¼x13¾
2016, Aug. 16 Litho.
853 A487 10t multi .25 .25

A souvenir sheet containing an imperforate example of No. 853 with simulated perforations sold for 40t.

This souvenir sheet containing one 20t stamp, released Aug. 21, 2016, sold for 80t. It also exists imperforate with simulated perforations.

University of Chittagong, 50th Anniv. — A488

Perf. 13¾x14¼
2016, Nov. 19 Litho.
854 A488 10t multi .25 .25

Victory Day — A489

Perf. 13¾x14¼
2016, Nov. 19 Litho.
855 A489 16t multi .40 .40

Paintings by Hashem Khan — A490

No. 856 — Various paintings with denomination of: a, 3t. b, 7t. c, 10t, vert. d, 12t.

Perf. 13¼x14¼
2016, Dec. 16 Litho.
856 A490 Block of 4, #a-d .85 .85
  e. Sheet of 4, #856a-856d, imperf. 1.25 1.25

No. 856e sold for 45t.

11th National Rover Moot — A491

2017, Jan. 26 Litho. *Perf. 13¾x14¼*
857 A491 10t multi .25 .25

International Customs Day — A492

2017, Jan. 30 Litho. *Perf. 13¾x14¼*
858 A492 10t multi .25 .25

Children's Day — A493

Perf. 12¾x12½
2017, Mar. 17 Litho.
859 A493 10t multi .25 .25

National Day and Independence Day — A494

2017, Mar. 26 Litho. *Perf. 13¾*
860 A494 10t multi .25 .25

136th Assembly of the Inter-Parliamentrary Union, Dhaka — A495

No. 861: a, Sheikh Mujibur Rahman (1920-75) in boat. b, Shaheed Minar Monument, Dhaka. c, National Assembly Building. d, Royal Bengal tiger.

2017, Apr. 1 Litho. *Perf. 14¼x13¾*
861 A495 10t Block of 4, #a-d 1.00 1.00
  e. Souvenir sheet of 4, #861a-
       861d, perf. 14¼x13½ 1.00 1.00

Hardinge Bridge, Cent. (in 2015) — A496

No. 862: a, Train on bridge. b, Bridge and Padma River.

2017, Apr. 27 Litho. *Perf. 14¼x13¾*
862 A496 25t Horiz. pair, #a-b 1.25 1.25
  c. Souvenir sheet of 2, #862a-
       862b, imperf. 1.25 1.25

No. 862c has simulated perforations.

Rotary
Club of
Dhaka,
80th
Anniv.
A497

2017, May 8   Litho.   Perf. 14¼x13¾
863 A497 15t multi   .40 .40

World Telecommunication and
Information Society Day — A498

2017, May 17   Litho.   Perf. 14¼x13¾
864 A498 10t multi   .25 .25

Floating Markets and
Agriculture — A499

No. 865 — Various photographs and
inscriptions: a, 5t, Floating Market. b, 5t,
Floating Agriculture. c, 7t, Floating Agriculture. d,
7t, Floating Market.

2017, June 16   Litho.   Perf. 13¼
865 A499 Block of 4, #a-d   .60 .60
  e. Souvenir sheet of 4, #865a-865d .75 .75
No. 865e sold for 30t.

Photographs of 1971 War
Crimes — A500

No. 866 — Various photographs of war
crimes numbered at UR: a, 1. b, 2. c, 3. d, 4. e,
5. f, 6. g, 7. h, 8. i, 9. j, 10. k, 11. l, 12. m, 13. n,
14. o, 15. p, 15. q, 17. r, 18. s, 19. t, 20. u, 21.
v, 22. w, 23. x, 24. y, 25. z, 26. aa, 27. ab, 28.
ac, 29. ad, 30. ae, 31. af, 32. ag, 33. ah, 34. ai,
35. aj, 36. ak, 37. al, 38. am, 39. an, 40. ao,
41. ap, 42. aq, 43. ar, 44. as, 45. at, 46. au,
47. av, 48. aw, 49. ax, 50. ay, 51. az, 52. ba,
53. bb, 54. bc, 55. bd, 56. be, 57. bf, 58. bg,
59. bh, 60. bi, 61. bj, 62. bk, 63. bl, 64. bm, 65.
bn, 66. bo, 67. bp, 68. bq, 69. br, 70. bs, 71.

2017, July 9   Litho.   Perf. 12½
866   Sheet of 71 + label   18.00 18.00
  a.-bs. A500 10t Any single   .25 .25
  bt. Sheet of 3, #866a-866c (1-
       3), + label, imperf.   1.00 1.00
  bu. Sheet of 4, #866d-866g (4-
       7), imperf.   1.00 1.00
  bv. Sheet of 4, #866h-866k (8-
       11), imperf.   1.00 1.00
  bw. Sheet of 4, #866l-866o (12-
       15), imperf.   1.00 1.00
  bx. Sheet of 4, #866p-866s (16-
       19), imperf.   1.00 1.00
  by. Sheet of 4, #866t-866w (20-
       23), imperf.   1.00 1.00
  bz. Sheet of 4, #866x-866aa
       (24-27), imperf.   1.00 1.00
  ca. Sheet of 4, #866ab-866ae
       (28-31), imperf.   1.00 1.00
  cb. Sheet of 4, #866af-866ai
       (32-35), imperf.   1.00 1.00
  cc. Sheet of 4, #866aj-866am
       (36-39), imperf.   1.00 1.00
  cd. Sheet of 4, #866an-866aq
       (40-43), imperf.   1.00 1.00
  ce. Sheet of 4, #866ar-866au
       (44-47), imperf.   1.00 1.00
  cf. Sheet of 4, #866av-866ay
       (48-51), imperf.   1.00 1.00
  cg. Sheet of 4, #866az-866bc
       (52-55), imperf.   1.00 1.00
  ch. Sheet of 4, #866bd-866bg
       (56-59), imperf.   1.00 1.00

  ci. Sheet of 4, #866bh-866bk
       (60-63), imperf.   1.00 1.00
  cj. Sheet of 4, #866bl-866bo
       (64-67), imperf.   1.00 1.00
  ck. Sheet of 4, #866bp-866bs
       (68-71), imperf.   1.00 1.00
Nos. 866bt-866ck each have simulated perforations. No. 866bt sold for 40t.

A501

Bengali New Year — A502

No. 867 — Parade with: a, Tiger float at left.
b, Mother and child float at center.

2017, Apr. 13   Litho.   Perf. 12½
867 A501 10t Horiz. pair, #a-b   .50 .50
Imperf
868 A502 50t multi   1.25 1.25

Flowers — A503

No. 869: a, Thunbergia grandiflora. b,
Eichhornia crassipes.
No. 870: a, Hiptage benghalensis. b, Lippia
alba.

2017, Aug. 3   Litho.   Perf. 13½14¼
869 A503 5t Horiz. pair, #a-b   .25 .25
870 A503 7t Horiz. pair, #a-b   .35 .35

Stamp
Day
A504

Perf. 14¼x13½
2017, Aug. 10   Litho.
871 A504 7t multi   .25 .25

OFFICIAL STAMPS

Nos. 42-47, 49-50,
52, 82-84 and 54
Overprinted in Black
or Red

Perf. 14x14½, 14½x14
1973-75   **Litho.**
O1   A7   2p black (R)   .25 2.10
O2   A7   3p brt green   .25 2.10
O3   A7   5p lt brown   .30   .25
O4   A7   10p black (R)   .30   .25
O5   A7   20p olive   2.75   .25
O6   A7   25p red lilac   6.00   .25
O8   A7   60p gray (R)   6.00 3.25
O9   A7   75p orange ('74) 2.25   .40
O10 A9   1t violet (#52) 19.00 8.25
O11 A9   1t violet (#82) 7.50   .70

O12 A9   2t grayish grn ('74) 10.50 3.25
O13 A9   5t gray blue (#54)   7.50 13.50
O14 A9   5t grysh bl (#84)
          ('75)   17.50 17.50
Nos. O1-O14 (13)   80.10 52.05
Issue date: Apr. 30, 1973.

**Nos. 95-101, 103-105 Overprinted
"SERVICE" in Black or Red**
1976   Litho.   Perf. 15x14½, 14½x15
O16 A7   5p green   2.50 1.50
O17 A7   10p black (R)   3.50 1.50
O18 A7   20p olive   4.00 1.50
O19 A7   25p rose   5.50 1.50
O20 A8   50p rose lilac   6.25   .90
O21 A7   60p gray (R)   .65 3.75
O22 A7   75p olive   .65 5.00
Perf. 15
O23 A9   1t violet   5.00   .70
O24 A9   2t greenish gray   .80 3.25
O25 A9   5t grayish blue   .65 3.25
Nos. O16-O25 (10)   29.50 22.85

Nos. 165-175 Ovptd. "SERVICE"
1979-82   Photo.   Perf. 14½
O27 A7   5p brown   2.40 3.25
O28 A7   10p Prussian blue 2.40 3.50
O29 A7   15p yellow orange 2.40 3.25
O30 A7   20p dk carmine   2.10 3.25
O31 A7   25p dk blue ('82) 1.25 3.25
O31A A7   30p lt ol grn ('80) 4.50 3.75
O32 A9   40p rose magenta 3.75 3.25
O33 A7   50p gray ('81)   .60   .25
O34 A7   80p dark brown   3.25   .65
O35 A7   1t red lilac ('81) .60   .25
O36 A7   2t brt ultra ('81) .70 3.50
Nos. O27-O36 (11)   23.95 28.15

**#234-242, 242A, 271 Ovptd.
"Service" in Red, Diagonally Up on
#O43A, 1t, 2t, 4t, 5t**
1983-93   Perf. 11½x12½, 12½x11½
O37 A70 5p bluish green   .25   .25
O38 A70 10p deep magenta   .25   .25
O39 A70 15p blue   .25   .25
O40 A70 20p dark gray   .25   .25
O41 A70 25p slate   .25   .25
O42 A70 30p gray brown   .25   .25
O43 A70 50p yellow brown   .25   .25
O43A A70 50p yellow brown   .25   .25
Size: 30½x28½mm
Perf. 12x11½
O44 A70 1t ultramarine   1.50   .25
O45 A70 2t Prussian blue   .25   .25
O45A A70 5t red violet
Size: 33½x22½mm
Perf. 12
O46 A70 4t blue   2.50 1.00
Nos. O37-O46 (12)   6.25 3.50
Issued: 4t, 6/28/90; No. O43A, 1993(?);
others, 12/21/83. 5t, 7/27/92.

No. 379A Ovptd. in
Red

1990   Litho.   Perf. 14½x14
O47 A139a 2t brown   .75   .75

**No. 350 Ovptd. "Service" Diagonally
in Red**
1994, July 16   Litho.   Perf. 12x11½
O47A A122 3t multicolored 11.50 11.50

No. 354
Ovptd. in Red

1992, Nov. 22   Litho.   Perf. 14½x14
O47B A125 6t blue gray & yel 1.00 1.00

No. 241
Ovptd. in Red

1992, Sept. 16   Litho.   Perf. 12x11½
O48 A70 1t ultramarine   1.00 1.00

No. 484 Ovptd.
in Red

1996   Litho.   Perf. 14
O49 A204 2t multicolored 2.75 2.75

No. 351 Ovptd. in
Blue

1997?   Litho.   Perf. 12
O50 A122 5t multicolored   .30   .30
Bengali overprint reads from top to bottom.

Nos. 235, 237
Ovptd. in Black or
Red

1997?   Perf. 12½x11½
O51 A70 10p on #235   .75   .75
O52 A70 20p on #237 (R)   1.50 1.50

No. 560 Ovptd. in Red

1998   Litho.   Perf. 14½x14
O53 A139a 1t green   .25   .25

BARBADOS

bär-'bä-ₔdōs

LOCATION — A West Indies island east of the Windwards
GOVT. — Independent state in the British Commonwealth
AREA — 166 sq. mi.
POP. — 266,100 (1997 est.)
CAPITAL — Bridgetown

The British colony of Barbados became an independent state on November 30, 1966.

4 Farthings = 1 Penny
12 Pence = 1 Shilling
20 Shillings = 1 Pound
100 Cents = 1 Dollar (1950)

> Catalogue values for unused stamps in this country are for Never Hinged items, beginning with Scott 207 in the regular postage section, Scott B2 in the semipostal section and Scott J1 in the postage due section.

Watermarks

Wmk. 5 — Small Star   Wmk. 6 — Large Star

Values for unused stamps are for examples with original gum as defined in the catalogue introduction. Very fine examples of Nos. 10-42a, 44-59a will have perforations touching the design on at least one side due to the narrow spacing of the stamps on the plates and imperfect perforation methods. Stamps with perfs clear of the design on all four sides are extremely scarce and will command higher prices.

Britannia — A1

		1852-55 Unwmk. Engr. Imperf. Blued Paper		
1	A1	(½p) deep green	165.00	375.00
a.		(½p) yellow green	9,000.	800.00
2	A1	(1p) dark blue	45.00	80.00
		Pair, on cover		500.00
a.		(1p) blue	65.00	225.00
3	A1	(2p) slate blue	30.00	
a.		(2p) grayish slate	325.00	1,400.
b.		As "a," vert. half used as 1p on cover		9,350.
4	A1	(4p) brn red ('55)	130.00	325.00
		Nos. 1-4 (4)	370.00	

No. 3 was not placed in use. Beware of color changelings of Nos. 2-3 that may resemble No. 3a. Certificates of authenticity are required for Nos. 3a and 3b.
Use of No. 3b was authorized from Aug. 4 to Sept. 21, 1854.

		1855-58 White Paper		
5	A1	(½p) dp grn ('58)	210.00	230.00
a.		(½p) yellow green ('57)	600.00	125.00
6	A1	(1p) blue	110.00	70.00
a.		(1p) pale blue	185.00	80.00

It is believed that the (4p) brownish red on white paper exists only as No. 17b.

Britannia — A2

		1859		
8	A2	6p rose red	850.00	140.00
9	A2	1sh black	260.00	85.00
		Pin-perf. 14		
10	A1	(½p) pale yel grn	3,000.	500.00
11	A1	(1p) blue	2,500.	175.00
		Pin-perf. 12½		
12	A1	(½p) pale yel grn	10,000.	800.00
12A	A1	(1p) blue		1,750.
		Pin-perf. 14x12½		
12B	A1	(½p) pale yel grn		8,500.
		1861 *Clean-Cut Perf. 14 to 16*		
13	A1	(½p) dark blue grn	200.00	23.00
14	A1	(1p) pale blue	825.00	92.50
a.		(1p) blue	925.00	100.00
b.		Half used as ½p on cover		—
		Rough Perf. 14 to 16		
15	A1	(½p) green	35.00	47.50
a.		(½p) blue green	62.50	85.00
b.		Imperf., pair	825.00	
16	A1	(1p) blue	87.50	4.25
a.		Diagonal half used as ½p on cover		—
b.		Imperf., pair	875.00	650.00
c.		(1p) deep blue	82.50	4.50
17	A1	(4p) rose red	175.00	77.50
a.		(4p) brown red	210.00	87.50
b.		As "a," imperf., pair	1,750.	
c.		(4p) rose red, imperf., pair		1,200.
18	A1	(4p) vermilion	350.00	120.00
a.		Imperf., pair	1,650.	
19	A2	6p rose red	400.00	26.00
20	A2	6p orange ver	175.00	37.50
a.		6p vermilion	200.00	32.00
b.		Imperf., pair	825.00	1,100.
21	A2	1sh brnsh blk	82.50	12.00
b.		Horiz. pair, imperf. btwn.	10,000.	
c.		1sh blue (error)	20,000.	

No. 21c was never placed in use. All examples are pen-marked (some have been removed) and have clipped perfs on one or more sides.
Use of No. 14b, 16a was authorized from 4/63-11/66. Only two full covers are known with bisected 1p stamps. The bisected stamps (Nos. 14b, 16a, 33a, 51b) are typically found on fragments or partial covers.

		Perf. 11 to 13		
22	A1	(½p) deep green	16,500.	
23	A1	(1p) blue	2,500.	

Nos. 22 and 23 were never placed in use.

		1870 Wmk. 6 *Rough Perf. 14 to 16*		
24	A1	(½p) green	180.00	11.00
a.		Imperf., pair (#24)	1,400.	
b.		(½p) yellow green	240.00	55.00
25	A1	(1p) blue	2,750.	77.50
a.		Imperf., pair	3,000.	
26	A1	(4p) dull red	1,750.	130.00
27	A2	6p vermilion	1,100.	100.00
28	A2	1sh black	500.00	21.00
		1871 Wmk. 5		
29	A1	(1p) blue	200.00	4.50
30	A1	(4p) rose red	1,425.	77.50
31	A2	6p vermilion	775.00	28.00
32	A2	1sh black	275.00	18.00
		1872 *Clean-Cut Perf. 14½ to 16*		
33	A1	(1p) blue	350.00	3.25
a.		Diagonal half used as ½p on cover		—
34	A2	6p vermilion	1,050.	92.50
35	A2	1sh black	210.00	19.00
		Perf. 11 to 13x14½ to 16		
36	A1	(½p) blue green	400.00	70.00
37	A1	(4p) vermilion	875.00	125.00
		1873 *Perf. 14*		
38	A2	3p claret	375.00	140.00
		Wmk. 6		
		Clean-Cut Perf. 14½ to 16		
39	A1	(½p) blue green	500.00	30.00
40	A1	(4p) rose red	1,550.	275.00
41	A2	6p vermilion	1,000.	105.00
a.		Imperf., pair	110.00	1,750.
b.		Horiz. pair, imperf. btwn.	11,000.	
42	A2	1sh black	170.00	24.00
a.		Horiz. pair, imperf. btwn.	10,000.	

Britannia — A3

		1873 Wmk. 5 *Perf. 15½x15*		
43	A3	5sh dull rose	1,200.	375.00

For surcharged bisects see Nos. 57-59.

		1874 Wmk. 6 *Perf. 14*		
44	A2	½p blue green	65.00	17.50
45	A2	1p blue	150.00	5.50
		Clean-Cut Perf. 14½ to 16		
45A	A2	1p blue		24,000.
		1875 Wmk. 1 *Perf. 12½*		
46	A2	½p yellow green	100.00	9.25
47	A2	4p scarlet	375.00	29.00
48	A2	6p orange	750.00	80.00
49	A2	1sh purple	575.00	5.00
		Nos. 46-49 (4)	1,800.	123.25
		1875-79 *Perf. 14*		
50	A2	½p yel grn ('76)	27.50	1.00
51	A2	1p ultramarine	150.00	2.25
a.		Half used as ½p on cover		1,350.
b.		1p gray blue	150.00	1.60
		Watermarked sideways		1,000.
52	A2	3p violet ('78)	185.00	16.50
53	A2	4p rose red	160.00	15.00
a.		4p scarlet	250.00	5.00
b.		As "a," perf. 14x12½	9,000.	
54	A2	4p lake	575.00	4.50
55	A2	6p chrome yel	160.00	2.40
a.		6p yellow, wmkd. sideways	400.00	15.00
56	A2	1sh purple ('78)	185.00	9.25
a.		1sh violet ('76)	7,750.	45.00
b.		1sh dull mauve ('79)	575.00	6.00
c.		Half used as 6p on cover		—

Nos. 48, 49, 55, 56 have the watermark sideways.
No. 53b was never placed in use.

A4   A5

Large Surcharge, ("1" 7mm High, "D" 2¾mm High)

		1878 Wmk. 5 *Perf. 15½x15*		
		Slanting Serif		
57	A4	1p on half of 5sh	6,250.	850.00
a.		Unsevered pair	28,500.	2,750.
b.		Unsevered horiz. pair, #57 + 58		5,500.
d.		Unsevered horiz. pair, #57 + 58, imperf. between		44,000.
e.		Unsevered horiz. pair, #57 + 59	46,000.	9,350.
		Straight Serif		
58	A4	1p on half of 5sh	8,250.	1,050.
a.		Unsevered pair		4,750.
		Small Surcharge, ("1" 6mm, "D" 2½mm High)		
59	A5	1p on half of 5sh	10,000.	1,175.
a.		Unsevered pair	42,000.	5,500.

On Nos. 57, 58 and 59 the surcharge is found reading upwards or downwards.
The perforation, which divides the stamp into halves, measures 11½ to 13.
The old denomination has been cut off the bottom of the stamps.

Queen Victoria — A6

		1882-85 Typo. Wmk. 2 *Perf. 14*		
60	A6	½p green	35.00	2.25
61	A6	1p carmine rose	60.00	1.35
a.		1p rose	90.00	2.75
b.		Half used as ½p on cover		1,800.
62	A6	2½p dull blue	145.00	1.70
a.		2½p ultramarine	125.00	1.70
63	A6	3p magenta	10.00	35.00
a.		3p lilac ('85)	125.00	50.00
64	A6	4p slate	375.00	4.75
65	A6	4p brown ('85)	17.50	2.25
66	A6	6p olive gray	85.00	52.50

67	A6	1sh orange brown	32.50	24.00
68	A6	5sh bister	180.00	215.00
		Nos. 60-68 (9)	940.00	338.80

No. 65 Surcharged in Black

		1892		
69	A6	½p on 4p brown	2.75	6.50
a.		Without hyphen	21.00	40.00
b.		Double surcharge, one albino	—	
c.		Double surch., red & black	950.00	1,275.
d.		As "c," without hyphen	3,750.	4,250.

A8

		1892-1903 Wmk. 2		
70	A8	1f sl & car ('96)	2.75	.25
71	A8	½p green	2.75	.25
72	A8	1p carmine rose	5.50	.25
73	A8	2p sl & org ('99)	15.00	1.25
74	A8	2½p ultramarine	20.00	.25
75	A8	5p olive brn	8.00	5.25
76	A8	6p vio & car	18.50	3.00
77	A8	8p org & ultra	5.00	32.50
78	A8	10p bl grn & car	13.00	10.00
79	A8	2sh6p slate & org	55.00	70.00
80	A8	2sh6p pur & grn ('03)	160.00	325.00
		Nos. 70-80 (11)	305.50	448.00

See Nos. 90-101. For surcharge see No B1.

Victoria Jubilee Issue

Badge of Colony — A9

		1897 Wmk. 1		
81	A9	1f gray & car	11.00	.75
82	A9	½p gray green	11.00	.75
83	A9	1p carmine rose	15.00	.75
84	A9	2½p ultra	17.50	1.00
85	A9	5p dk olive brn	42.50	21.50
86	A9	6p vio & car	50.00	27.50
87	A9	8p org & ultra	24.00	28.50
88	A9	10p bl grn & car	75.00	62.50
89	A9	2sh6p slate & org	115.00	65.00
		Nos. 81-89 (9)	361.00	208.50
		Bluish Paper		
81a	A9	1f gray & car	32.50	35.00
82a	A9	½p gray green	32.50	35.00
83a	A9	1p carmine rose	44.00	47.50
84a	A9	2½p ultra	45.00	52.50
85a	A9	5p dk olive brn	260.00	300.00
86a	A9	6p vio & car	150.00	165.00
87a	A9	8p org & ultra	160.00	175.00
88a	A9	10p bl grn & car	215.00	275.00
89a	A9	2sh6p slate & org	150.00	150.00
		Nos. 81a-89a (9)	1,089.	1,235.
		Badge Type of 1892-1903		
		1904-10 Wmk. 3		
90	A8	1f gray & car	14.00	3.25
91	A8	1f brown ('09)	11.00	.35
92	A8	½p green	27.50	.25
93	A8	1p carmine rose	30.00	.25
94	A8	1p carmine ('09)	32.50	.25
95	A8	2p gray ('10)	13.00	25.00
96	A8	2½p ultramarine	32.50	.35
97	A8	6p vio & car	29.00	40.00
98	A8	6p dl vio & vio ('10)	22.50	35.00
99	A8	8p org & ultra	90.00	135.00
100	A8	1sh blk, grn ('10)	20.00	21.00
101	A8	2sh6p pur & green	70.00	160.00
		Nos. 90-101 (12)	372.00	420.70

Nelson Centenary Issue

Lord Nelson
Monument — A10

1906		Engr.	Wmk. 1
102	A10	1f gray & black	18.00	2.50
103	A10	½p green & black	12.00	.40
104	A10	1p car & black	15.00	.25
105	A10	2p org & black	4.00	5.50
106	A10	2½p ultra & black	4.50	1.50
107	A10	6p lilac & black	22.50	30.00
108	A10	1sh rose & black	26.00	62.50
		Nos. 102-108 (7)	102.00	102.65

See Nos. 110-112.

The "Olive
Blossom"
A11

1906, Aug. 15			Wmk. 3
109	A11	1p blk, green & blue	20.00	.30

Tercentenary of the 1st British landing.

Nelson Type of 1906

1907, July 6			Wmk. 3
110	A10	1f gray & black	6.25	14.00
111	A10	2p org & black	32.50	47.50
112	A10	2½p ultra & black	10.00	50.00
a.		2½p indigo & black	825.00	1,000.
		Nos. 110-112 (3)	48.75	111.50

A12

A13

King
George V — A14

1912			Typo.
116	A12	¼p brown	2.50	1.90
117	A12	½p green	4.75	.25
a.		Booklet pane of 6		
118	A12	1p carmine	12.00	.25
a.		1p scarlet	45.00	4.25
b.		Booklet pane of 6		
119	A12	2p gray	8.00	25.00
120	A12	2½p ultramarine	1.90	1.50
121	A13	3p violet, yel	2.25	17.50
122	A13	4p blk & scar, yel	5.50	27.50
123	A13	6p vio & red vio	15.00	15.00
124	A14	1sh black, green	17.50	29.00
125	A14	2sh vio & ultra, bl	65.00	70.00
126	A14	3sh grn & violet	125.00	130.00
		Nos. 116-126 (11)	259.40	317.90

Seal of the
Colony — A15

1916-18			Engr.
127	A15	¼p brown	.90	.50
128	A15	½p green	4.50	.25
129	A15	1p red	3.00	.25
130	A15	2p gray	16.00	42.50
131	A15	2½p ultramarine	8.50	3.75
132	A15	3p violet, yel	15.00	20.00
133	A15	4p red, yel	1.50	17.50
134	A15	4p red & blk ('18)	2.50	4.50
135	A15	6p claret	15.00	10.00
136	A15	1sh black, green	17.50	13.50

137	A15	2sh violet, blue	22.50	9.25
138	A15	3sh dark violet	75.00	180.00
139	A15	3sh dk vio & grn ('18)	30.00	115.00
a.		3sh bright violet & green ('18)	300.00	450.00
		Nos. 127-139 (13)	211.90	417.00

Nos. 134 and 139 are from a re-engraved die. The central medallion is not surrounded by a line and there are various other small alterations.

Victory Issue

Victory

A16   A17

1920, Sept. 9			Wmk. 3
140	A16	¼p bister & black	.35	.85
141	A16	½p yel grn & blk	2.25	.25
a.		Booklet pane of 2		
142	A16	1p org red & blk	5.00	.25
a.		Booklet pane of 2		
143	A16	2p gray & black	3.25	19.00
144	A16	2½p ultra & dk bl	3.50	28.50
145	A16	3p red lilac & blk	4.50	8.00
146	A16	4p gray grn & blk	4.50	8.75
147	A16	6p orange & blk	6.50	27.50
148	A17	1sh yel grn & blk	22.50	57.50
149	A17	2sh brown & blk	52.50	80.00
150	A17	3sh orange & blk	57.50	100.00

1921, Aug. 22			Wmk. 4
151	A16	1p org red & blk	21.00	.35
		Nos. 140-151 (12)	183.35	330.95

A18

1921-24			Wmk. 4
152	A18	¼p brown	.30	.25
153	A18	½p green	1.90	.50
154	A18	1p carmine	1.00	.25
155	A18	2p gray	2.00	.25
156	A18	2½p ultramarine	1.90	10.00
158	A18	6p claret	4.25	9.00
159	A18	1sh blk, emer ('24)	60.00	160.00
160	A18	2sh dk vio, blue	12.50	26.00
161	A18	3sh dark violet	30.00	90.00

			Wmk. 3	
162	A18	3p violet, yel	2.50	14.00
163	A18	4p red, yel	2.25	27.50
164	A18	1sh black, green	7.50	25.00
		Nos. 152-164 (12)	126.10	362.75

A19

1925-35		Wmk. 4	Perf. 14
165	A19	¼p brown	.30	.25
166	A19	½p green	.65	.25
a.		Perf. 13½x12½ ('32)	11.50	.25
b.		Booklet pane of 10		
167	A19	1p carmine	.65	.25
a.		Perf. 13½x12½ ('32)	14.50	.60
b.		Booklet pane of 10		
168	A19	1½p org, perf. 13½x12½ ('32)	9.00	1.25
a.		Booklet pane of 6		
b.		Perf. 14	17.50	4.00
169	A19	2p gray	.80	4.00
170	A19	2½p ultramarine	.60	1.00
a.		Perf. 13½x12½ ('32)	22.50	11.00
171	A19	3p vio brn, yel	1.25	.55
172	A19	3p red brn, yel ('35)	7.50	7.50
173	A19	4p red, yel	.95	1.25
174	A19	6p claret	1.25	1.10
175	A19	1sh blk, emerald	3.50	8.75
a.		Perf. 13½x12½ ('32)	75.00	50.00
176	A19	1sh brn blk, yel grn ('32)	9.00	12.50
177	A19	2sh violet, bl	8.75	10.00
178	A19	2sh6p car, blue ('32)	32.50	52.50
179	A19	3sh dark violet	14.00	24.00
		Nos. 165-179 (15)	90.70	125.15

Charles I
and
George
V — A20

1927, Feb. 17			Perf. 12½
180	A20	1p carmine lake	1.25	.90
a.		Perf. 12x12½	5.00	4.00

Tercentenary of the settlement of Barbados.

Common Design Types pictured following the introduction.

Silver Jubilee Issue
Common Design Type

1935, May 6			Perf. 11x12
186	CD301	1p car & dk bl	2.10	.30
187	CD301	1½p blk & ultra	4.50	8.00
188	CD301	2½p ultra & brn	2.40	6.00
189	CD301	1sh brn vio & ind	21.00	32.50
		Nos. 186-189 (4)	30.00	46.80
		Set, never hinged	45.00	

Coronation Issue
Common Design Type

1937, May 14			Perf. 13½x14
190	CD302	1p carmine	.25	.25
191	CD302	1½p brown	.40	.80
192	CD302	2½p bright ultra	.45	.90
		Nos. 190-192 (3)	1.10	1.95
		Set, never hinged	2.50	

A21

1938-47		Perf. 13-14 & Compound	
193	A21	½p green	5.00	.25
b.		Perf. 14	55.00	1.50
c.		Booklet pane of 10		
193A	A21	½p bister ('42)	.25	.45
194	A21	1p carmine	14.00	.25
b.		Perf. 13½x13	195.00	5.00
c.		Booklet pane of 10		
194A	A21	1p green ('42)	.25	.25
d.		Perf. 13½x13	3.50	1.00
195	A21	1½p red orange	.25	.65
c.		Perf. 14	4.75	.80
d.		Booklet pane of 6		
195A	A21	2p rose lake ('41)	.90	3.75
195B	A21	2p brt rose red ('43)	.50	1.00
e.		Perf. 14	.50	2.10
196	A21	2½p ultramarine	.65	.95
197	A21	3p brown	.65	3.50
b.		Perf. 14	.25	.75
197A	A21	3p deep bl ('47)	.65	2.50
198	A21	4p black	.25	.25
a.		Perf. 14	.65	6.50
199	A21	6p violet	.65	.65
199A	A21	8p red vio ('46)	.45	3.25
200	A21	1sh brn olive	1.40	.25
a.		1sh olive green	12.50	3.00
201	A21	2sh6p brown vio	7.00	2.25
201A	A21	5sh indigo ('41)	6.50	11.00
		Nos. 193-201A (16)	39.35	31.20
		Set, never hinged	57.50	

For surcharge see No. 209.

Kings
Charles I,
George VI
Assembly
Chamber
and Mace
A22

1939, June 27		Engr.	Wmk. 4
202	A22	½p deep green	2.15	2.00
203	A22	1p scarlet	2.15	1.35
204	A22	1½p deep orange	2.25	.65

205	A22	2½p ultramarine	3.25	9.00
206	A22	3p yellow brown	3.25	6.00
		Nos. 202-206 (5)	13.05	19.00
		Set, never hinged	21.00	

Tercentenary of the General Assembly.

> Catalogue values for unused stamps in this section, from this point to the end of the section, are for Never Hinged items.

Peace Issue
Common Design Type

1946, Sept. 18			
207	CD303	1½p deep orange	.25	.55
208	CD303	3p brown	.25	.55

Nos. 195e, 195B,
Surcharged in Black

1947, Apr. 21			Perf. 14
209	A21	1p on 2p brt rose red	2.40	5.25
b.		Perf. 13½x13	3.25	6.50
c.		As "b.," double surcharge	3,250.	

Silver Wedding Issue
Common Design Types
Perf. 14x14½

1948, Nov. 24	Photo.		Wmk. 4
210	CD304	1½p orange	.35	.55

Engraved; Name Typographed
Perf. 11½x11

211	CD305	5sh dark blue	18.00	12.50

UPU Issue
Common Design Types

1949, Oct. 10	Perf. 13½, 11x11½		
212	CD306	1½p red orange	.55	2.15
213	CD307	3p indigo	2.75	7.50
214	CD308	4p gray	.55	3.50
215	CD309	1sh olive	.55	1.00
		Nos. 212-215 (4)	4.40	14.15

Dover
Fort — A23

Admiral Nelson
Statue — A24

Designs: 2c, Sugar cane breeding. 3c, Public buildings. 6c, Casting net. 8c, Intercolonial schooner. 12c, Flying Fish. 24c, Old Main Guard Garrison. 48c, Cathedral, vert. 60c, Careenage. $1.20, Map, vert. $2.40, Great Seal, 1660.

Perf. 11x11½ (A23), 13x13½ (A24)			
1950, May 1		Engr.	Wmk. 4
216	A23	1c slate	.35	4.75
217	A23	2c emerald	.25	3.25
218	A23	3c slate & brown	1.25	4.25
219	A24	4c carmine	.30	.40
220	A23	6c blue	.35	2.50
221	A23	8c choc & blue	1.60	4.00
222	A23	12c olive & aqua	1.25	1.85
223	A23	24c gray & red	1.25	1.25
224	A24	48c violet	11.00	9.00
225	A24	60c brn car & bl grn	14.00	13.75
226	A24	$1.20 olive & car	14.00	5.50
227	A23	$2.40 gray	27.50	45.00
		Nos. 216-227 (12)	73.10	94.80

University Issue
Common Design Types

1951, Feb. 16			Perf. 14x14½
228	CD310	3c turq bl & choc	.60	.30
229	CD311	12c ol brn & turq bl	1.25	1.25

Stamp of
1852
A25

Perf. 13½

1952, Apr. 15		**Wmk. 4**	**Engr.**	
230	A25	3c slate bl & dp grn	.40	.30
231	A25	4c rose pink & bl	.50	1.00
232	A25	12c emer & slate bl	.50	1.00
233	A25	24c gray blk & red brn	1.00	.80
		Nos. 230-233 (4)	2.40	3.10

Centenary of Barbados postage stamps.

Coronation Issue
Common Design Type

1953, June 4		**Perf. 13½x13**		
234	CD312	4c red orange & black	1.00	.25

Harbor
Police
A26

Designs: 1c Dover Fort. 2c, Sugar cane breeding. 3c, Public buildings. 4c, Admiral Nelson Statue, vert. 6c, Casting net. 8c, Intercolonial schooner. 12c, Flying Fish. 24c, Old Main Guard Garrison. 48c, Cathedral, vert. 60c, Careenage. $1.20, Map, vert. $2.40, Great Seal, 1660 ("E II R").

Perf. 11x11½ (horiz.), 13x13½ (vert.)

1953-57			**Engr.**	
235	A23	1c slate ('53)	.25	1.00
236	A23	2c grnsh blue & deep org	.25	.75
237	A23	3c emerald & blk	1.75	1.10
238	A24	4c orange & gray	.25	.25
239	A26	5c dp car & dp bl	1.75	.75
240	A23	6c red brown	.75	.75
241	A23	8c brt blue & blk	1.05	.40
242	A23	12c brn ol & aqua	1.75	.25
243	A23	24c gray & red ('56)	1.05	.25
244	A24	48c violet ('56)	11.00	1.25
245	A23	60c brown car & blue grn ('56)	17.50	5.25
246	A24	$1.20 ol & car ('56)	32.50	4.50
247	A23	$2.40 gray ('57)	2.40	2.25
		Nos. 235-247 (13)	72.25	18.75

See Nos. 257-264.

West Indies Federation
Common Design Type

1958, Apr. 23		**Perf. 11½x11**	**Wmk. 314**	
248	CD313	3c green	.40	.25
249	CD313	6c blue	.60	2.25
250	CD313	12c carmine rose	.60	.40
		Nos. 248-250 (3)	1.60	2.90

Deep
Water
Harbor,
Bridgetown
A27

1961, May 6		**Engr.**	**Perf. 11x11½**	
251	A27	4c orange & black	.25	.50
252	A27	8c ultra & black	.30	.60
253	A27	24c black & pink	.45	.60
		Nos. 251-253 (3)	1.00	1.70

Deep Water Harbor at Bridgetown opening.

Scout Emblem
and Map of
Barbados — A28

Perf. 11½x11

1962, Mar. 9			**Wmk. 314**	
254	A28	4c orange & black	.60	.25
255	A28	12c gray & blue	1.75	.25
256	A28	$1.20 grnsh gray & car rose	1.75	3.75
		Nos. 254-256 (3)	4.10	4.25

50th anniv. of the founding of the Boy Scouts of Barbados.

Queen Types of 1953-57
Perf. 11x11½, 13x13½

1964-65			**Engr.**	**Wmk. 314**
257	A23	1c slate	.70	4.50
258	A24	4c orange & gray	.40	.60
259	A23	8c brt bl & blk ('65)	.60	.40
260	A23	12c brn ol & aqua ('65)	.75	
261	A23	24c gray & red	.75	.85
262	A24	48c violet	3.75	1.50
263	A23	60c brn car & bl grn	13.00	4.00
264	A23	$2.40 gray ('65)	1.75	1.75
		Nos. 257-264 (8)	21.70	
		Nos. 257-259,261-264 (7)		13.60

The 12c was never put on sale in Barbados.

ITU Issue
Common Design Type
Perf. 11x11½

1965, May 17		**Litho.**	**Wmk. 314**	
265	CD317	2c lilac & ver	.25	.25
266	CD317	48c yellow & gray	1.25	1.00

Sea Horse
A29

Designs: 1c, Deep sea coral. 2c, Lobster. 4c, Sea urchin. 5c, Staghorn coral. 6c, Butterflyfish. 8c, File shell. 12c, Balloonfish. 15c, Angelfish. 25c, Brain coral. 35c, Brittle star. 50c, Flyingfish. $1, Queen conch shell. $2.50, Fiddler crab.

Wmk. 314 Upright

1965, July 15		**Photo.**	**Perf. 14x13½**	
267	A29	1c dk blue, pink & black	.35	.35
268	A29	2c car rose, sepia & org	.30	.25
269	A29	3c org, brn & sep ("Hippocanpus")	.60	.60
270	A29	4c ol grn & dk bl	.30	.35
a.		Imperf., pair	325.00	250.00
271	A29	5c lil, brn & pink	.45	.60
272	A29	6c grnsh bl, yel & blk	.55	.50
273	A29	8c ultra, org, red & blk	.45	.35
274	A29	12c rose lil, yel & blk	.50	.35
275	A29	15c red, yel & blk	1.10	.80
276	A29	25c yel brn & ultra	1.40	1.10
277	A29	35c orn, rose brn & blk	2.00	.35
278	A29	50c yel grn & ultra	2.75	.95
279	A29	$1 gray & multi	3.75	2.00
280	A29	$2.50 lt bl & multi	4.00	5.25
		Nos. 267-280 (14)	18.50	13.80

1966-69 | | | **Wmk. 314 Sideways** |

$5, "Dolphin" (coryphaena hippurus).

267a	A29	1c	.25	.25
268a	A29	2c ('67)	.30	1.40
269A	A29	3c ("Hippocampus") ('67)	.30	2.75
270b	A29	4c	.55	.25
271a	A29	5c	.45	.25
272a	A29	6c ('67)	.70	.25
273a	A29	8c ('67)	.70	.25
274a	A29	12c ('67)	.50	.25
275a	A29	15c	2.10	.25
276a	A29	25c	2.10	.40
277a	A29	35c	2.40	.65
278a	A29	50c	2.10	4.25
279a	A29	$1	6.00	1.00
280a	A29	$2.50	7.50	3.00
280B	A29	$5 dk ol & multi ('69)	17.50	12.00
		Nos. 267a-280B (15)	43.45	27.20

For surcharge see No. 327.

Churchill Memorial Issue
Common Design Type

1966, Jan. 24		**Wmk. 314**	**Perf. 14**	
281	CD319	1c multicolored	.30	3.00
282	CD319	4c multicolored	.45	.25
283	CD319	25c multicolored	1.00	.50
284	CD319	35c multicolored	1.25	.70
		Nos. 281-284 (4)	3.00	4.45

Royal Visit Issue
Common Design Type

1966, Feb. 4		**Litho.**	**Perf. 11x12**	
285	CD320	3c violet blue	.50	.25
286	CD320	35c dark car rose	2.50	1.75

UNESCO Anniversary Issue
Common Design Type

1967, Jan. 6		**Litho.**	**Perf. 14**	
287	CD323	4c "Education"	.25	.25
288	CD323	12c "Science"	.90	.55
289	CD323	25c "Culture"	1.35	1.35
		Nos. 287-289 (3)	2.50	2.15

Arms of
Barbados — A30

Designs: 25c, Hilton Hotel, horiz. 35c, Garfield Sobers, captain of Barbados and West Indies Cricket Team. 50c, Pine Hill Dairy, horiz.

1966, Dec. 2		**Unwmk.**	**Photo.**	
290	A30	4c multicolored	.25	.25
291	A30	25c multicolored	.25	.25
292	A30	35c multicolored	2.00	.80
293	A30	50c multicolored	.85	.85
		Nos. 290-293 (4)	3.35	2.15

Barbados' independence, Nov. 30, 1966.

Policeman and
Anchor
Monument — A31

Designs: 25c, Policeman with telescope. 35c, Police motor launch, horiz. 50c, Policemen at Harbor Gate.

1967, Oct. 16		**Litho.**	**Perf. 13½x14**	
294	A31	4c multicolored	.25	.25
295	A31	25c multicolored	.40	.25
296	A31	35c multicolored	.45	.25
297	A31	50c multicolored	.70	.70
		Nos. 294-297 (4)	1.80	1.45

Centenary of Bridgetown Harbor Police.
For surcharge see No. 322.

Independence Arch — A32

1st Anniv. of Independence: 4c, Sir Winston Scott, Governor-General, vert. 35c, Treasury Building. 50c, Parliament Building.

Perf. 14½x14, 14x14½

1967, Dec. 4		**Photo.**	**Unwmk.**	
298	A32	4c multicolored	.25	.25
299	A32	25c multicolored	.25	.25
300	A32	35c multicolored	.30	.30
301	A32	50c multicolored	.40	.40
		Nos. 298-301 (4)	1.20	1.20

UN Building, — A33

1968, Feb. 27			**Perf. 14½x14**	
302	A33	15c multicolored	.40	.40

20th anniv. of the UN Economic Commission for Latin America.

Radar Antenna on
Top of Old — A34

Designs: 25c, Caribbean Meteorological Institute, Barbados, horiz. 50c, HARP gun used in High Altitude Research Program, at Paragon in Christ Church, Barbados.

Perf. 14x14½, 14½x14

1968, June 4		**Photo.**	**Unwmk.**	
303	A34	3c violet & multi	.25	.25
304	A34	25c vermilion & multi	.25	.25
305	A34	50c orange & multi	.40	.40
		Nos. 303-305 (3)	.90	.90

World Meteorological Day.

Girl Scout at Campfire, — A35

Lady Baden-Powell, Queen Elizabeth II and: 25c, Pax Hill Headquarters. 35c, Girl Scout badge.

Perf. 14x14½

1968, Aug. 29		**Photo.**	**Unwmk.**	
306	A35	3c dp ultra, blk & gold	.25	.25
307	A35	25c bluish green, black & gold	.35	.35
308	A35	35c org yel, blk & gold	.65	.65
		Nos. 306-308 (3)	1.25	1.25

Barbados Girl Scouts' 50th anniv.

Human
Rights
Flame
and
Escape
A36

Designs: 4c, Human Rights flame, hands, and broken chain. 25c, Human Rights flame, family and broken chain.

Perf. 11x11½

1968, Dec. 10		**Litho.**	**Unwmk.**	
309	A36	4c violet, gray grn & red brown	.25	.25
310	A36	25c org, blk & blue	.25	.25
311	A36	35c grnsh blue, blue, blk & org	.25	.25
		Nos. 309-311 (3)	.75	.75

International Human Rights Year.

In the
Paddock
A37

Horse Racing: 25c, "They're off!" 35c, On the flat. 50c, The Finish.

1969, Mar. 15   Litho.   Perf. 14½
312	A37	4c multicolored	.25	.25
313	A37	25c multicolored	.25	.25
314	A37	35c multicolored	.30	.30
315	A37	50c multicolored	.40	.40
a.		Souvenir sheet of 4, #312-315	3.50	3.50
		Nos. 312-315 (4)	1.20	1.20

Map of Caribbean — A38

Design: 12c, 50c, "Strength in Unity," horiz.

Perf. 14x14½, 14½x14

1969, May 6   Photo.   Wmk. 314
316	A38	5c brown & multi	.25	.25
317	A38	12c ultra & multi	.25	.25
318	A38	25c green & multi	.25	.25
319	A38	50c magenta & multi	.25	.25
		Nos. 316-319 (4)	1.00	1.00

1st anniv. of CARIFTA (Caribbean Free Trade Area).

ILO Emblem A39

Perf. 14x13

1969, Aug. 5   Litho.   Unwmk.
320	A39	4c bl grn, brt grn & blk	.25	.25
321	A39	25c red brn, brt mag & red	.25	.25

50th anniv. of the ILO.

No. 294 Surcharged

1969, Aug. 30   Perf. 13½x14
322	A31	1c on 4c multicolored	.45	.45

Barbados Boy Scout Emblem — A40

Designs: 25c, Sea Scouts rowing in Bridgetown harbor. 35c, Campfire. 50c, Various Scouts in front of National Headquarters and Training Center, Hazelwood.

Perf. 13½x13

1969, Dec. 16   Litho.   Unwmk.
323	A40	5c multicolored	.25	.25
324	A40	25c multicolored	.65	.25
325	A40	35c multicolored	.85	.25
326	A40	50c multicolored	1.25	1.25
a.		Souvenir sheet of 4, #323-326	16.50	16.50
		Nos. 323-326 (4)	3.00	2.00

Attainment of independence by the Barbados Boy Scout Assoc.

No. 271a Surcharged

Wmk. 314 Sideways
1970, Mar. 11   Photo.   Perf. 14x13½
327	A29	4c on 5c multicolored	.50	.50

This locally applied surcharge exists in several variations: double, triple, on back, in pair with one missing, etc.

Lion at Gun Hill — A41

Barbados Museum A42

2c, Trafalgar Fountain. 3c, Montefiore Drinking Fountain. 4c, St. James' Monument. 5c, St. Ann's Fort. 6c, Old Sugar Mill, Morgan Lewis. 8c, Cenotaph. 10c, South Point Lighthouse. 15c, Sharon Moravian Church. 25c, George Washington House. 35c, St. Nicholas Abbey. 50c, Bowmanston Pumping Station. $1, Queen Elizabeth Hospital. $2.50, Modern sugar factory. $5, Seawell Intl. Airport.

Wmk. 314 Upright (A41), Sideways (A42)

Perf. 12½x13, 13x12½

1970, May 4   Photo.
328	A41	1c bl grn & multi	.25	.80
329	A41	2c crimson & multi	.25	.80
330	A41	3c blue & multi	.25	.80
331	A41	4c yellow & multi	.85	.25
332	A41	5c dp org & multi	.25	.25
333	A41	6c dull yel & multi	.30	.30
334	A41	8c dp blue & multi	.25	.25
335	A41	10c red & multi	2.75	.50
336	A42	12c ultra & multi	1.25	.25
337	A42	15c yellow & multi	.25	.70
338	A42	25c orange & multi	.25	.25
339	A42	35c pink & multi	.25	.70
340	A42	50c bl grn & multi	.40	1.00
341	A42	$1 emerald & multi	.55	2.50
342	A42	$2.50 ver & multi	1.75	4.00
343	A42	$5 yellow & multi	6.00	11.00
		Nos. 328-343 (16)	15.85	24.35

Nos. 328-332, 334-343 were reissued in 1971 on glazed paper.

Wmk. 314 Sideways (A41), Upright (A42)

1972-74
331a	A41	4c	2.40	1.75
332a	A41	5c	2.10	1.75
333a	A41	6c	6.00	11.50
334a	A41	8c	2.40	1.50
335a	A41	10c ('74)	4.75	6.75
336a	A42	12c	2.40	4.00
337a	A42	15c	1.25	1.50
338a	A42	25c	4.00	3.00
339a	A42	35c	3.50	.80
340a	A42	50c	4.75	1.75
341a	A42	$1	8.75	3.25
342a	A42	$2.50 ('73)	6.00	8.25
343a	A42	$5 ('73)	6.25	5.25
		Nos. 331a-343a (13)	54.55	51.05

For surcharge, see No. 391.

Primary Education, UN and — A43

UN and Education Year Emblems and: 5c, Secondary education (student with microscope). 25c, Technical education (men working with power drill). 50c, University building.

1970, June 26   Litho.   Perf. 14
344	A43	4c multicolored	.25	.25
345	A43	5c multicolored	.25	.25
346	A43	25c multicolored	.25	.25
347	A43	50c multicolored	.30	.30
		Nos. 344-347 (4)	1.05	1.05

UN, 25th anniv., and Intl. Education Year.

Minnie Root A44

Flowers: 1c, Barbados Easter lily, vert. 10c, Eyelash orchid. 25c, Pride of Barbados, vert. 35c, Christmas hope.

1970, Aug. 24   Litho.   Wmk. 314
348	A44	1c green	.25	.25
349	A44	5c deep magenta	.60	.25
350	A44	10c dark blue	2.10	.40
351	A44	25c brt orange brown	1.60	.95
352	A44	35c blue	1.60	1.10
a.		Souvenir sheet of 5	4.00	4.00
		Nos. 348-352 (5)	6.15	2.95

No. 352a contains 5 imperf. stamps similar to Nos. 348-352 with simulated perforations.

Christ Carrying Cross — A45

Easter: 10c, 50c, Resurrection, by Benjamin West, St. George's Anglican Church. 35c like 4c, Window from St. Margaret's Anglican Church, St. John.

1971, Apr. 7   Wmk. 314   Perf. 14
353	A45	4c purple & multi	.25	.25
354	A45	10c silver & multi	.25	.25
355	A45	35c brt blue & multi	.25	.25
356	A45	50c gold & multi	.25	.25
		Nos. 353-356 (4)	1.00	1.00

Sailfish Craft A46

Tourism: 5c, Tennis. 12c, Horseback riding. 25c, Water-skiing. 50c, Scuba diving.

1971, Aug. 17   Perf. 14x14½
357	A46	1c multicolored	.25	.25
358	A46	5c multicolored	.40	.25
359	A46	12c multicolored	.65	.25
360	A46	25c multicolored	.40	.25
361	A46	50c multicolored	.55	.55
		Nos. 357-361 (5)	2.25	1.55

Samuel Jackman Prescod — A47

1971, Sept. 26   Perf. 14
362	A47	3c orange & multi	.25	.25
363	A47	35c ultra & multi	.30	.25

Samuel Jackman Prescod (1806-1871), 1st black member of Barbados Assembly.

Coat of Arms A48

15c, 50c, Flag and map of Barbados.

1971, Nov. 23
364	A48	4c light blue & multi	.30	.25
365	A48	15c multicolored	.60	.25
366	A48	25c yel green & multi	.60	.25
367	A48	50c blue & multi	1.25	1.25
		Nos. 364-367 (4)	2.75	2.00

5th anniv. of independence.

Telegraphy, 1872 and 1972 — A49

Designs: 10c, "Stanley Angwin" off St. Lawrence Coast. 35c, Earth station and Intelsat 4. 50c, Mt. Misery tropospheric scatter station.

1972, Mar. 28   Perf. 14
368	A49	4c purple & multi	.25	.25
369	A49	10c emerald & multi	.25	.25
370	A49	35c red & multi	.50	.25
371	A49	50c orange & multi	.75	.75
		Nos. 368-371 (4)	1.75	1.50

Centenary of telecommunications to and from Barbados.

Lord Baden-Powell, Charles — A50

5c, Map of Barbados and Combermere School, vert. 25c, Photograph of 1922 troop. 50c, Flags of various Boy Scout troops.

1972, Aug. 1
372	A50	5c ultra & multi	.25	.25
373	A50	15c ultra & multi	.25	.25
374	A50	25c ultra & multi	.55	.25
375	A50	50c ultra & multi	1.00	1.00
		Nos. 372-375 (4)	2.05	1.75

60th anniv. of Barbados Boy Scouts and 4th Caribbean Jamboree.

Bookmobile, Open Book — A51

Intl. Book Year: 15c, Visual aids truck. 25c, Central Library, Bridgetown. $1, Codrington College.

1972, Oct. 31   Litho.   Wmk. 314
376	A51	4c brt pink & multi	.30	.25
377	A51	15c dull org & multi	.35	.25
378	A51	25c buff & multi	.35	.25
379	A51	$1 lt violet & multi	1.50	1.50
		Nos. 376-379 (4)	2.50	2.25

Pottery Wheels A52

Barbados pottery industry: 15c, Kiln. 25c, Finished pottery, Chalky Mount. $1, Pottery on sale at market.

1973, Mar. 1   Wmk. 314   Perf. 14
380	A52	5c dull red & multi	.25	.25
381	A52	15c olive grn & multi	.25	.25
382	A52	25c gray & multi	.40	.25
383	A52	$1 yellow & multi	1.50	1.50
		Nos. 380-383 (4)	2.40	2.25

First Flight in Barbados, — A53

Aircraft: 15c, First flight to Barbados, De Havilland biplane, 1928. 25c, Passenger plane, 1939. 50c, Vickers VC-10 over control tower, 1973.

1973, July 25   Perf. 12½x12
384	A53	5c blue & multi	.40	.25
385	A53	15c vio blue & multi	1.35	.25
386	A53	25c multicolored	1.60	.90
387	A53	50c blue & multi	2.75	2.50
		Nos. 384-387 (4)	6.10	3.30

Chancellor Sir Hugh Wooding — A54

Designs: 25c, Sherlock Hall. 35c, Cave Hill Campus. 35c, Cave Hill Campus.

1973, Dec. 11   Perf. 13x14
388	A54	5c dp orange & multi	.25	.25
389	A54	25c red brown & multi	.25	.25
390	A54	35c multicolored	.30	.30
		Nos. 388-390 (3)	.80	.80

25th anniv. of the Univ. of the West Indies.

No. 338a Surcharged

1974, Apr. 30 Photo. Perf. 13x12½
391	A42	4c on 25c multi	.45	.45
a.		"4c." omitted		17.00

Old Sailboat A55

Designs: 35c, Rowboat. 50c, Motor-powered fishing boat. $1, Trawler "Calamar."

1974, June 11   Wmk. 314   Perf. 14
392	A55	15c blue & multi	.25	.25
393	A55	35c multicolored	.30	.25
394	A55	50c vio blue & multi	.35	.35
395	A55	$1 blue & multi	2.75	2.75
a.		Souvenir sheet of 4, #392-395	6.25	6.25
		Nos. 392-395 (4)	3.65	3.60

Fishing boats of Barbados.

Fire Orchid — A56

Orchids: 1c, Cattleya gaskelliana alba. 3c, Rose Marie. 4c, Fiery red orchid. 5c, Schomburgkia humboltii. 8c, Dancing dolls. 10c, Spider orchids. 12c, Dendrobium aggregatum. 15c, Lady slippers. 20c, Spathoglottis. 25c, Eyelash. 35c, Bletia patula. 45c, Sunset Glow. 50c, Sunset Glow. $1, Ascocenda red gem. $2.50, Brassolaeliocattleya nugget. $5, Caularthron bicornutum. $10, Moon orchid. 1c, 20c, 25c, $2.50, $5 horizontal.

Wmk. 314 Sideways; Upright (1c, 20c, 25c, $1, $10)

1974-77   Photo.   Perf. 14
396	A56	1c multi	.30	1.50
397	A56	2c shown	.30	1.50
398	A56	3c multi	.50	1.00
399	A56	4c multi	2.00	1.10
400	A56	5c multi	.55	.30
401	A56	8c multi	1.75	1.10
402	A56	10c multi	.90	.30
403	A56	12c multi	.75	3.25
404	A56	15c multi	.75	.75
404C	A56	20c multi	5.75	5.75
405	A56	25c multi	.90	.90
406B	A56	45c multi	7.50	5.50
407	A56	50c multi	7.50	5.25

Perf. 14½x14, 14x14½
408	A56	$1 multi	11.00	4.00
409	A56	$2.50 multi	3.00	2.50
410	A56	$5 multi	3.00	7.25
411	A56	$10 multi	3.00	16.00
		Nos. 396-411 (18)	51.70	60.20

Issued: 20c, 45c, 5/3/77; others, 9/16/74. For surcharge see No. B2.

Wmk. 314 Upright; Sideways (1c, 25c, $1)

1976   Perf. 14
396a	A56	1c multicolored	.90	4.00
397a	A56	2c multicolored	1.10	4.00
398a	A56	3c multicolored	1.25	4.50
399a	A56	4c multicolored	.90	4.50
402a	A56	10c multicolored	1.75	4.50
404a	A56	15c multicolored	1.50	1.50
405a	A56	25c multicolored	3.00	1.50
406a	A56	35c multicolored	3.25	2.00

Perf. 14½x14
408a	A56	$1 multicolored	9.50	7.00
		Nos. 396a-408a (9)	23.15	33.50

1975   Wmk. 373   Perf. 14
396b	A56	1c multicolored	.25	1.60
397b	A56	2c multicolored	.25	1.60
398b	A56	3c multicolored	.25	1.60
399b	A56	4c multicolored	.70	3.50
400b	A56	5c multicolored	.45	.25
402b	A56	10c multicolored	.45	.25
403b	A56	12c multicolored	10.00	.25
404b	A56	15c multicolored	.95	.25
405b	A56	25c multicolored	.95	.25
406c	A56	45c multicolored	.80	.25
407b	A56	50c multicolored	8.00	7.25

Perf. 14½x14, 14x14½
408b	A56	$1 multicolored	12.50	16.00
409b	A56	$2.50 multicolored	12.50	5.75
410b	A56	$5 multicolored	12.50	9.25
411b	A56	$10 multicolored	5.00	16.00
		Nos. 396b-411b (15)	75.55	64.05

UPU Emblem, Barbados No. 64 — A57

Cent. of the UPU: 35c, Letters encircling globe. 50c, Barbados coat of arms. $1, Map of Barbados, sailing ship and jet.

1974, Oct. 9   Litho.   Perf. 14½
412	A57	8c brt rose, org & gray	.25	.25
413	A57	35c red, blk, & ocher	.25	.25
414	A57	50c vio blue, bl & sil	.25	.25
415	A57	$1 ultra, blk & brn	.60	.60
a.		Souvenir sheet of 4, #412-415	2.25	2.25
		Nos. 412-415 (4)	1.35	1.35

Yacht Britannia off Barbados — A58

Royal Visit, Feb. 1975: 35c, $1, Palms and sunset.

1975, Feb. 18
416	A58	8c brown & multi	1.00	.35
417	A58	25c blue & multi	1.75	.35
418	A58	35c purple & multi	.80	.40
419	A58	$1 violet & multi	2.00	4.75
		Nos. 416-419 (4)	5.55	5.85

St. Michael's Cathedral — A59

Designs: 15c, Bishop Coleridge. 50c, All Saints' Church. $1, St. Michael, stained glass window, St. Michael's Cathedral.

Wmk. 314

1975, July 29   Litho.   Perf. 14
420	A59	5c blue & multi	.25	.25
421	A59	15c lilac & multi	.25	.25
422	A59	50c green & multi	.50	.50
423	A59	$1 multicolored	.80	.80
a.		Souvenir sheet of 4, #420-423	2.00	2.25
		Nos. 420-423 (4)	1.80	1.80

Anglican Diocese in Barbados, sesquicentennial.

Pony Float A60

Designs: 25c, Stiltsman (band and masqueraders). 35c, Maypole dancing. 50c, Cuban dancers.

1975, Nov. 18   Litho.   Wmk. 373
424	A60	8c yellow & multi	.25	.25
425	A60	25c buff & multi	.25	.25
426	A60	35c ultra & multi	.25	.25
427	A60	50c orange & multi	.30	.30
a.		Souvenir sheet of 4, #424-427	1.25	1.25
		Nos. 424-427 (4)	1.05	1.05

Crop-over (harvest) festival.

Sailing Ship, 17th Cent. — A61

350th Anniv. of 1st Settlement: 10c, Bearded fig tree and fruit. 25c, Ogilvy's 17th cent. map. $1, Capt. John Powell.

1975, Dec. 17   Wmk. 373   Perf. 13½
428	A61	4c lt blue & multi	.55	.25
429	A61	10c lt blue & multi	.35	.25
430	A61	25c yellow & multi	1.05	.40
431	A61	$1 dk red & multi	1.05	1.05
a.		Souvenir sheet of 4, #428-431	3.75	3.75
		Nos. 428-431 (4)	3.00	1.95

Coat of Arms — A62

Coil Stamps

1975, Dec.   Unwmk.   Perf. 15x14
432	A62	5c light blue	.30	.75
433	A62	25c violet	.40	1.00

Map of West Indies, Bats, A63

Prudential Cup — A64

1976, July 7   Litho.   Perf. 14
438	A63	25c lt blue & multi	1.35	1.35
439	A64	45c lilac rose & black	1.35	1.35

World Cricket Cup, won by West Indies Team, 1975.

Map of South Carolina settled — A65

American Bicentennial: 25c, George Washington and map of Bridge Town area. 50c, Declaration of Independence. $1, Masonic emblem and Prince Hall, founder and Grand Master of African Grand Lodge, Boston, 1790-1807.

1976, Aug. 17 Wmk. 373 Perf. 13½
440	A65	15c multicolored	.65	.25
441	A65	25c multicolored	.65	.25
442	A65	50c multicolored	1.00	1.00
443	A65	$1 multicolored	1.40	1.40
		Nos. 440-443 (4)	3.70	2.90

Mailman with Bicycle A66

PO Act, 125th anniv.: 35c, Mailman on motor scooter. 50c, Cover with Barbados No. 2. $1, Mail truck.

1976, Oct. 19   Litho.   Perf. 14
444	A66	8c rose red, blk & bis	.25	.25
445	A66	35c multicolored	.25	.25
446	A66	50c vio blue & multi	.35	.35
447	A66	$1 red & multi	.60	1.00
		Nos. 444-447 (4)	1.45	1.85

Coast Guard Vessels A67

Designs: 15c, Bank note, reverse, showing Barbados Parliament. 25c, National anthem by Van Roland Edwards (music) and Irvine Burgie (lyrics). $1, Independence Day parade.

1976, Nov. 30   Perf. 13x13½
448	A67	5c multicolored	.30	.25
449	A67	15c multicolored	.30	.25
450	A67	25c yel, brown & blk	.30	.25
451	A67	$1 multicolored	1.25	1.25
a.		Souvenir sheet of 4, #448-451	2.75	2.75
		Nos. 448-451 (4)	2.15	2.00

10th anniv. of independence.

Queen Knighting
Garfield — A68

Designs: 50c, Queen arriving at Westminster Abbey. $1, Queen leaving coach.

1977, Feb. 7   **Perf. 14x13½**
452 A68 15c silver & multi   .25   .25
453 A68 50c silver & multi   .45   .45
454 A68 $1 silver & multi   .85   .85
    Nos. 452-454 (3)   1.55 1.55

25th anniv. of the reign of Queen Elizabeth II. See Nos. 467-469.

Underwater Park — A69

Beauty of Barbados: 35c, Royal palms, vert. 50c, Underwater caves. $1, Stalagmite in Harrison's Cave, vert.

1977, May 3   **Wmk. 373**   **Perf. 14**
455 A69 5c multicolored   .25   .25
456 A69 35c multicolored   .50   .25
457 A69 50c multicolored   .65   .75
458 A69 $1 multicolored   1.25 1.25
  a.   Souvenir sheet of 4, #455-458   4.25 4.25
    Nos. 455-458 (4)   2.65 2.50

House of
Commons
Maces — A70

Designs: 25c, Speaker's chair. 50c, Senate Chamber. $1, Sam Lord's Castle, horiz.

1977, Aug. 2   **Litho.**   **Perf. 13½**
459 A70 10c red brown & yel   .25   .25
460 A70 25c slate grn & org   .25   .25
461 A70 50c dk green, grn & yel   .25   .25
462 A70 $1 dk & lt blue & org   .35   .35
    Nos. 459-462 (4)   1.10 1.10

13th Regional Conference of Commonwealth Parliamentary Association.

Charles I Handing
Charter — A71

Designs: 12c, Charter scroll. 45c, Charles I and Earl of Carlisle, horiz. $1, Map of Barbados, by Richard Ligon, 1657, horiz.

Perf. 13½x13, 13x13½
1977, Oct. 11   **Litho.**   **Wmk. 373**
463 A71 12c buff & multi   .25   .25
464 A71 25c buff & multi   .25   .25
465 A71 45c buff & multi   .25   .25
466 A71 $1 buff & multi   .55   .55
    Nos. 463-466 (4)   1.30 1.30

350th anniv. of charter granting Barbados to the Earl of Carlisle.

Silver Jubilee Type, 1977, Inscribed: "ROYAL VISIT"

1977, Oct. 31   **Unwmk.**   **Roulette 5**
467 A68 15c silver & multi   .35   .35
468 A68 50c silver & multi   .25   .25
469 A68 $1 silver & multi   .50   .50
    Nos. 467-469 (3)   1.10 1.10

Caribbean visit of Queen Elizabeth II. Printed on peelable paper backing inscribed in ultramarine multiple rows: "SILVER JUBILEE ROYAL VISIT BARBADOS." Printed with die-cut label inscribed in black "BEND & PEEL" attached at left of stamp. Sheets of 50 stamps and 50 labels.

Gibson's Map of Bridgetown, — A72

25c, Bridgetown, engraving by S. Copens, 1695. 45c, Trafalgar Square, Bridgetown, drawing by J. M. Carter, 1835. $1, The Bridges, 1978.

Wmk. 373
1978, Mar. 1   **Litho.**   **Perf. 14½**
470 A72 12c gold & multi   .25   .25
471 A72 25c gold & multi   .25   .25
472 A72 45c gold & multi   .25   .25
473 A72 $1 gold & multi   .25   .25
    Nos. 470-473 (4)   1.00 1.00

350th anniv. of founding of Bridgetown.

Elizabeth II Coronation Anniv. Issue
Souvenir Sheet
Common Design Types

1978, Apr. 21   **Unwmk.**   **Perf. 15**
474   Sheet of 6   1.35 1.35
  a.   CD326 50c Griffin of Edward III   .25
  b.   CD327 50c Elizabeth II   .25   .25
  c.   CD328 50c Pelican   .25   .25

No. 474 contains 2 se-tenant strips of Nos. 474a-474c, separated by horizontal gutter with commemorative and descriptive inscriptions and showing central part of coronation with coach.

Freak
Bridge
Hand
A73

10c, World Bridge Fed. emblem. 45c, Central American and Caribbean Bridge Fed. emblem. $1, Map of Caribbean, cards.

Wmk. 373
1978, June 6   **Litho.**   **Perf. 14½**
475 A73 5c multicolored   .25   .25
476 A73 10c multicolored   .25   .25
477 A73 45c multicolored   .25   .25
478 A73 $1 multicolored   .70   .70
  a.   Souvenir sheet of 4, #475-478   2.40 2.40
    Nos. 475-478 (4)   1.45 1.45

7th Regional Bridge Tournament, Dover Centre, Barbados, June 5-14.

Girl Guides' Camp — A74

Designs: 28c, Girl Guides helping children and handicapped. 50c, Badge with "60," vert. $1, Badge with initials, vert.

1978, Aug. 1   **Litho.**   **Perf. 13½**
479 A74 12c multicolored   .25   .25
480 A74 28c multicolored   .50   .25
481 A74 50c multicolored   .75   .40
482 A74 $1 multicolored   1.00 1.00
    Nos. 479-482 (4)   2.50 1.90

Girl Guides of Barbados, 60th anniv.

Garment
Industry
A75

Industries of Barbados: 28c, Cooper, vert. 45c, Blacksmith, vert. 50c, Wrought iron industry.

1978, Nov. 14   **Litho.**   **Perf. 14**
483 A75 12c multicolored   .25   .25
484 A75 28c multicolored   .25   .25
485 A75 45c multicolored   .35   .35
486 A75 50c multicolored   .40   .40
    Nos. 483-486 (4)   1.25 1.25

Early Mail
Steamer
A76

Ships: 25c, Q.E.II in Deep Water Harbour. 50c, Ra II (raft) nearing Barbados. $1, Early mail steamer.

1979, Feb. 8   **Litho.**   **Perf. 13x13½**
487 A76 12c multicolored   .45   .25
488 A76 25c multicolored   .65   .25
489 A76 50c multicolored   1.00 1.00
490 A76 $1 multicolored   1.35 1.35
    Nos. 487-490 (4)   3.45 2.85

Barbados
No. 235
A77

28c, Barbados #430, vert. 45c, Penny Black and Maltese postmark, vert. 50c, Barbados #21b.

Wmk. 373
1979, May 8   **Litho.**   **Perf. 14**
491 A77 12c multicolored   .25   .25
492 A77 28c multicolored   .30   .30
493 A77 45c multicolored   .40   .40
    Nos. 491-493 (3)   .95   .95

Souvenir Sheet
494 A77 50c multicolored   1.10 1.10

Sir Rowland Hill (1795-1879), originator of penny postage.

Birds — A78

1c, Grass canaries. 2c, Rain birds. 5c, Sparrows. 8c, Frigate birds. 10c, Cattle egrets. 12c, Green gaulins. 20c, Hummingbirds. 25c, Ground doves. 28c, Blackbirds. 35c, Green-throated caribs. 45c, Wood doves. 50c, Ramiers. 55c, Black-breasted plover. 70c, Yellow breasts. $1, Pee whistlers. $2.50, Christmas birds. $5, Kingfishers. $10, Red-seal coot.

1979-81   **Photo.**   **Wmk. 373**   **Perf. 14**
495 A78 1c multicolored   .25 1.25
496 A78 2c multicolored   .25 1.25
497 A78 5c multicolored   .25   .70
498 A78 8c multicolored   1.25 2.25
499 A78 10c multicolored   .25   .40
500 A78 12c multicolored   .75 1.50
501 A78 20c multicolored   .30   .55
502 A78 25c multicolored   .30   .60
503 A78 28c multicolored   3.00 2.00
504 A78 35c multicolored   1.10   .70
505 A78 45c multicolored   2.25 1.50
506 A78 50c multicolored   2.25 1.50
506A A78 55c multi ('81)   6.00 3.50
507 A78 70c multicolored   3.25 3.25
508 A78 $1 multicolored   3.25 1.50
509 A78 $2.50 multicolored   3.25 6.00

---

510 A78 $5 multicolored   4.75   9.00
511 A78 $10 multicolored   7.00 14.00
    Nos. 495-511 (18)   39.70 52.20

Issue dates: 55c, Sept. 1; others, Aug. 7. See Nos. 570-572. For surcharges see No. 563-565

Launcher
Transported
through — A79

Designs: 10c, Gun on landing craft, Foul Bay, horiz. 20c, Firing of 16-inch launcher by day. 28c, Bath Earth Station and Intelsat IV-A, horiz. 45c, ITOS/NOAA over Caribbean, horiz. 50c, Intelsat IV-A over Atlantic, and globe. $1, Lunar landing module, horiz.

1979, Oct. 9   **Photo.**
512 A79 10c multicolored   .35   .25
513 A79 12c multicolored   .35   .25
514 A79 20c multicolored   .40   .25
515 A79 28c multicolored   .40   .30
516 A79 45c multicolored   .65   .55
517 A79 50c multicolored   .65   .65
    Nos. 512-517 (6)   2.80 2.25

Souvenir Sheet
518 A79 $1 multicolored   2.00 2.00

Space exploration. No. 518 commemorates 10th anniversary of first moon landing. No. 516 is incorrectly inscribed "Intelsat."

Family, IYC
Emblem — A80

IYC Emblem and: 28c, Children holding hands and map of Barbados. 45c, Boy and teacher. 50c, Children playing. $1, Boy and girl flying kite.

1979, Nov. 27   **Litho.**   **Perf. 14**
519 A80 12c multicolored   .25   .25
520 A80 28c multicolored   .25   .25
521 A80 45c multicolored   .25   .25
522 A80 50c multicolored   .25   .25
523 A80 $1 multicolored   .25   .25
    Nos. 519-523 (5)   1.25 1.25

Map of Barbados, Anniversary — A81

Rotary Intl., 75th Anniv.: 28c, Map of district 404. 50c, 75th anniv. emblem. $1, Paul P. Harris, founder.

1980, Feb. 19   **Litho.**   **Perf. 13½**
524 A81 12c multicolored   .25   .25
525 A81 28c multicolored   .25   .25
526 A81 50c multicolored   .25   .25
527 A81 $1 multicolored   .30   .30
    Nos. 524-527 (4)   1.05 1.05

A82

12c, Regiment volunteer, artillery company, 1909. 35c, Drum major. 50c, Sovereign's, regimental flags. $1, Women's corps.

Wmk. 373

1980, Apr. 8		**Litho.**		**Perf. 14½**
528	A82	12c multicolored	.35	.25
529	A82	35c multicolored	.45	.35
530	A82	50c multicolored	.55	.45
531	A82	$1 multicolored	.65	.65
		Nos. 528-531 (4)	2.00	1.70

Barbados Regiment, 75th anniv.

Souvenir Sheets

A83

Early mailman, London 1980 emblem. The vignette is a different color for each stamp.

Wmk. 373

1980, May 6		**Litho.**		**Perf. 14**
532	A83	Sheet of 6	1.05	1.05
a.-f.		28c any single	.25	.25
533	A83	Sheet of 6	1.20	1.20
a.-f.		50c any single	.25	.25

London 80 Intl. Stamp Exhib., May 6-14.

Underwater Scenes — A84

1980, Sept. 30		**Litho.**		**Perf. 13½**
534	A84	12c multicolored	.25	.25
535	A84	28c multicolored	.60	.35
536	A84	50c multicolored	.80	.45
537	A84	$1 multicolored	1.35	1.35
a.		Souvenir sheet of 4, #534-537	4.00	4.00
		Nos. 534-537 (4)	3.00	2.40

Bathsheba Railroad Station — A85

28c, Cab stand, The Green. 45c, Muledrawn tram. 70c, Horse-drawn bus. $1, Fairchild St. railroad station.

1981, Jan. 13		**Litho.**		**Perf. 14½**
538	A85	12c shown	.25	.25
539	A85	28c multicolored	.25	.25
540	A85	45c multicolored	.30	.30
541	A85	70c multicolored	.50	.50
542	A85	$1 multicolored	.75	.75
		Nos. 538-542 (5)	2.05	2.05

See Nos. 577-580.

Visually Handicapped Girl — A86

25c, Sign language alphabet, vert. 45c, Blind people crossing street, vert. $2.50, Baseball game.

1981, May 19		**Litho.**		**Perf. 14**
543	A86	10c shown	.25	.25
544	A86	25c multicolored	.25	.25
545	A86	45c multicolored	.45	.35
546	A86	$2.50 multicolored	.90	.90
		Nos. 543-546 (4)	1.85	1.75

International Year of the Disabled.

Royal Wedding Issue
Common Design Type

Wmk. 373

1981, July 22		**Litho.**		**Perf. 13½**
547	CD331	28c Bouquet	.25	.25
548	CD331	50c Charles	.25	.25
549	CD331	$2.50 Couple	.40	.40
		Nos. 547-549 (3)	.90	.90

4th Caribbean Arts Festival (CARIFESTA), A87

15c, Landship maneuver. 20c, Yoruba dancer. 40c, Tuk band. 55c, Frank Collymore (sculpture). $1, Barbados Harbor (painting).

1981, Aug. 11		**Litho.**		**Perf. 14½**
550	A87	15c multicolored	.25	.25
551	A87	20c multicolored	.25	.25
552	A87	40c multicolored	.30	.30
553	A87	55c multicolored	.45	.45
554	A87	$1 multicolored	.70	.70
		Nos. 550-554 (5)	1.95	1.95

Hurricane Gladys, View from A88

35c, Satellite view over Barbados. 60c, Police watch. $1, Spotter plane.

1981, Sept. 29		**Litho.**		**Perf. 14**
555	A88	35c multicolored	.50	.25
556	A88	50c shown	.65	.45
557	A88	60c multicolored	1.00	.65
558	A88	$1 multicolored	1.35	1.35
		Nos. 555-558 (4)	3.50	2.70

Harrison's Cave — A89

10c, Twin Falls. 20c, Rotunda Room Stream. 55c, Rotunda Room formation. $2.50, Cascade Pool.

			Perf. 14x14½	
1981, Dec. 1		**Litho.**		**Wmk. 373**
559	A89	10c multicolored	.25	.25
560	A89	20c multicolored	.25	.25
561	A89	55c multicolored	.40	.40
562	A89	$2.50 multicolored	1.60	1.60
		Nos. 559-562 (4)	2.50	2.50

Nos. 503, 505, 507 Surcharged

1981, Sept. 1		**Photo.**		**Perf. 14**
563	A78	15c on 28c multi	.35	.35
564	A78	40c on 45c multi	.40	.40
565	A78	60c on 70c multi	.65	.65
		Nos. 563-565 (3)	1.40	1.40

Black Belly Sheep A90

1982, Feb. 9				**Litho.**
566	A90	40c Ram	.30	.30
567	A90	50c Ewe	.40	.40
568	A90	60c Ewe, lambs	.50	.50
569	A90	$1 Pair, map	.80	.80
		Nos. 566-569 (4)	2.00	2.00

Bird Type of 1979

Wmk. 373

1982, Mar. 1		**Photo.**		**Perf. 14**
570	A78	15c like #503	6.50	5.50
571	A78	40c like #506	6.50	6.00
572	A78	60c like #507	6.50	6.50
		Nos. 570-572 (3)	19.50	18.00

Transportation Type of 1981

20c, Lighter. 35c, Rowboat. 55c, Speightstown schooner. $2.50, Inter-colonial schooner.

1982, Apr. 6		**Litho.**		**Perf. 14½**
577	A85	20c multicolored	.25	.25
578	A85	35c multicolored	.40	.40
579	A85	55c multicolored	.60	.60
580	A85	$2.50 multicolored	2.75	2.75
		Nos. 577-580 (4)	4.00	4.00

Early marine transport.

Visit of Pres. Ronald Reagan — A92

No. 581, Barbados Flag, arms. No. 582, US Flag, arms.

1982, Apr. 8		**Litho.**		**Perf. 14**
581		20c multicolored	.55	.55
582		20c multicolored	.55	.55
a.		A92 Pair, Nos. 581-582	1.10	1.10
583		55c like #581	.70	.70
584		55c like #582	.70	.70
a.		A92 Pair, Nos. 583-584	1.40	1.40
		Nos. 581-584 (4)	2.50	2.50

Printed in sheets of 8 with gutter showing Pres. Reagan and Prime Minister Tom Adams.

Princess Diana Issue
Common Design Type

1982, July 1		**Litho.**		**Perf. 14½**
585	CD333	20c Arms	.25	.25
586	CD333	60c Diana	.55	.40
587	CD333	$1.20 Wedding	1.00	1.00
588	CD333	$2.50 Portrait	1.60	1.60
		Nos. 585-588 (4)	3.40	3.25

Scouting Year — A93

15c, Helping woman. 40c, Sign, emblem, flag, horiz. 55c, Religious service, horiz. $1, Flags. $1.50, Laws.

1982, Sept. 7		**Wmk. 373**		**Perf. 14**
589	A93	15c multicolored	.60	.40
590	A93	40c multicolored	1.90	.40
591	A93	55c multicolored	1.10	.75
592	A93	$1 multicolored	1.70	1.70
		Nos. 589-592 (4)	5.30	3.10

Souvenir Sheet

593	A93	$1.50 multicolored	5.25	5.25

Washington's 250th Birth — A94

10c, Arms. 55c, Washington's house, Barbados. 60c, Taking command. $2.50, Taking oath.

1982, Nov. 2				**Perf. 13½x13**
594	A94	10c multicolored	.25	.25
595	A94	55c multicolored	.40	.40
596	A94	60c multicolored	.40	.40
597	A94	$2.50 multicolored	1.20	1.20
		Nos. 594-597 (4)	2.25	2.25

A95

1983, Mar. 14		**Litho.**		**Perf. 14**
598	A95	15c Map, globe	.25	.25
599	A95	40c Beach	.35	.25
600	A95	60c Sugar cane harvest	.45	.45
601	A95	$1 Cricket game	1.70	1.70
		Nos. 598-601 (4)	2.75	2.65

Commonwealth Day.

Gulf Fritillary A96

		Perf. 13½x13		
1983, Feb. 8		**Litho.**		**Wmk. 373**
602	A96	20c shown	1.75	.50
603	A96	40c Monarch	2.75	.50
604	A96	55c Mimic	2.75	.70
605	A96	$2.50 Hanno Blue	5.75	5.50
		Nos. 602-605 (4)	13.00	7.20

Manned Flight Bicentenary — A97

20c, US Navy dirigible. 40c, Douglas DC-3. 55c, Vickers Viscount. $1, Lockheed TriStar.

1983, June 14		**Litho.**		**Perf. 14**
606	A97	20c multi	.45	.25
607	A97	40c multi	1.20	.55
608	A97	55c multi	1.30	.70
609	A97	$1 multi	1.75	1.75
		Nos. 606-609 (4)	4.70	3.25

Nash 600, 1941 A98

45c, Dodge, 1938. 75c, Ford Model AA, 1930. $2.50, Dodge Four, 1918.

1983, Aug. 9		**Litho.**		**Perf. 14**
610	A98	25c shown	.70	.70
611	A98	45c multicolored	.80	.45
612	A98	75c multicolored	1.25	1.25
613	A98	$2.50 multicolored	2.60	2.60
		Nos. 610-613 (4)	5.35	4.60

A99

20c, Players. 65c, Emblem, map. $1, Cup.

1983, Aug. 30 Litho. Perf. 14

614	A99	20c multicolored	.45	.30
615	A99	65c multicolored	.85	.55
616	A99	$1 multicolored	1.20	1.20
		Nos. 614-616 (3)	2.50	2.05

World Cup Table Tennis Championship.

A100

Christmas: 10c, 25c, Angel with lute, painting details. $2, The Virgin and Child, by Masaccio.

1983, Nov. 1 Perf. 14

617	A100	10c multicolored	.60	.40
618	A100	25c multicolored	1.40	.40

Souvenir Sheet

619	A100	$2 multicolored	3.50	3.50

Barbados Museum, Golden A101

Museum Paintings: 45c, by Richard Day. 75c, St. Ann's Garrison in Barbados by W.S. Hedges. $2.50, Needham's Point, Carlisle Bay.

1983, Nov. 1 Perf. 14

620	A101	45c multicolored	1.10	.50
621	A101	75c multicolored	1.70	1.70
622	A101	$2.50 multicolored	5.50	5.50
		Nos. 620-622 (3)	8.30	7.70

1984 Olympics, Los Angeles A102

1984, Apr. 3 Litho. Perf. 14

623	A102	50c Track & field	.80	.60
624	A102	65c Shooting	1.00	.75
625	A102	75c Sailing	1.10	1.10
626	A102	$1 Bicycling	3.50	3.50
a.		Souvenir sheet of 4, #623-626	8.75	8.75
		Nos. 623-626 (4)	6.40	5.95

Lloyd's List Issue
Common Design Type

45c, World map. 50c, Bridgetown Harbor. 75c, Philosopher. $1, Sea Princess.

1984, Apr. 25 Litho. Perf. 14½

627	CD335	45c multicolored	1.05	.60
628	CD335	50c multicolored	1.25	.70
629	CD335	75c multicolored	1.90	1.90
630	CD335	$1 multicolored	1.90	1.90
		Nos. 627-630 (4)	6.10	5.15

Souvenir Sheet

1984 UPU Congress — A103

1984, June 6 Litho. Perf. 13½

631	A103	$2 #213, UPU emblem	4.50	4.50

World Chess Fed., 60th Anniv. A104

1984, Aug. 8 Perf. 14x14½

632	A104	25c Junior match	1.75	.45
633	A104	45c Knights	2.00	.75
634	A104	65c Queens	2.25	2.00
635	A104	$2 Rooks	5.25	5.25
		Nos. 632-635 (4)	11.25	8.45

Christmas — A105

50c, Poinsettia. 65c, Snow-on-the-mountain. 75c, Christmas candle. $1, Christmas hope.

1984, Oct. 24 Litho. Perf. 14

636	A105	50c multicolored	1.80	1.00
637	A105	65c multicolored	2.00	1.80
638	A105	75c multicolored	2.25	2.25
639	A105	$1 multicolored	2.50	2.50
		Nos. 636-639 (4)	8.55	7.55

Marine Life A106

1c, Bristle worm. 2c, Spotted trunk fish. 5c, Coney fish. 10c, Pink-tipped anemone. 20c, Christmas tree worm. 25c, Hermit crab. 35c, Animal flower. 40c, Vase sponge. 45c, Spotted moray. 50c, Ghost crab. 65c, Flamingo tongue snail. 75c, Sergeant major fish. $1, Caribbean warty anemone. $2.50, Green turtle. $5, Rock beauty. $10, Elkhorn coral.

1985 Litho. Wmk. 373 Perf. 14

640	A106	1c multi	.90	.90
641	A106	2c multi	.90	.90
642	A106	5c multi	3.00	3.00
643	A106	10c multi	1.00	1.00
645	A106	20c multi	2.75	2.75
646	A106	25c multi	1.90	1.90
648	A106	35c multi	4.50	4.50
649	A106	40c multi	4.50	4.50
650	A106	45c multi	1.90	1.90
651	A106	50c multi	3.25	3.25
653	A106	65c multi	3.25	3.25
654	A106	75c multi	3.25	3.25
656	A106	$1 multi	3.50	3.50
657	A106	$2.50 multi	9.00	9.00
658	A106	$5 multi	10.50	10.50
659	A106	$10 multi	11.50	11.50
		Nos. 640-659 (16)	65.60	65.60

Issued: 10c, 20c, 25c, 50c, $2.50, $5, 2/26; 5c, 35c, 40c, 65c, $10, 4/9; 1c, 2c, 45c, 75c, $1, 5/7.

1987, Sep. 15 Inscribed "1987"

640a	A106	1c	4.00	4.00
641a	A106	2c	4.00	4.00
645a	A106	20c	7.00	7.00
651a	A106	50c	9.00	9.00
654a	A106	75c	15.00	15.00
658a	A106	$5	20.00	20.00
		Nos. 640a-658a (6)	59.00	59.00

Without Imprint

1986, Jan. 6 Wmk. 384

642b	A106	5c	1.25	1.25
643b	A106	10c	1.25	1.25
645b	A106	20c	1.25	1.25
646b	A106	25c	3.00	1.75
648b	A106	35c	1.75	1.75
651b	A106	50c	2.50	2.50
657b	A106	$2.50	4.75	4.75
658b	A106	$5	8.25	8.25
659b	A106	$10	10.50	10.50
		Nos. 642b-659b (9)	34.50	33.25

1986 Inscribed "1986"

640c	A106	1c	.40	3.00
641c	A106	2c	.40	3.00
643c	A106	10c	.40	.40
645c	A106	20c	.40	.40
646c	A106	25c	.50	.50
649c	A106	40c	.60	.60

650c	A106	45c	.80	.60
651c	A106	50c	.80	.80
653c	A106	65c	.85	.85
654c	A106	75c	.90	.90
656c	A106	$1	1.10	1.10
657c	A106	$2.50	2.50	7.50
658c	A106	$5	5.00	10.00
659c	A106	$10	10.00	10.00
		Nos. 640c-659c (14)	24.65	39.65

Issued: 1c, 2c, 40c, 45c, 7/23. 10c, 25c, 50c-$10, 8/18.

1987 Inscribed "1987"

642d	A106	5c	20.00	10.00
643d	A106	10c	.40	.40
646d	A106	25c	.50	.50
648d	A106	35c	20.00	10.00
649d	A106	40c	.60	.60
650d	A106	45c	.80	.60
653d	A106	65c	.85	.85
654d	A106	75c	.90	.90
656d	A106	$1	1.10	1.10
659d	A106	$10	10.00	10.00
		Nos. 642d-659d (10)	55.15	34.95

1988 Inscribed "1988"

643e	A106	10c	.40	.40

Queen Mother 85th Birthday
Common Design Type

25c, At Buckingham Palace, 1930. 65c, With Lady Diana, 1981. 75c, At the docks. $1, Holding Prince Henry. $2, Opening the Garden Center, Syon House.

Perf. 14½x14

1985, June 7 Litho. Wmk. 384

660	CD336	25c multi	.35	.30
661	CD336	65c multi	2.50	1.25
662	CD336	75c multi	.80	.80
663	CD336	$1 multi	.85	.85
		Nos. 660-663 (4)	4.50	3.20

Souvenir Sheet

664	CD336	$2 multi	3.50	3.50

Audubon Birth Bicentenary — A107

Illustrations of North American bird species: 45c, Falco peregrinus. 65c, Dendroica discolor. 75c, Ardea herodias. $1, Dendroica petechia.
Nos. 666-668 vert.

Wmk. 373

1985, Aug. 6 Litho. Perf. 14

665	A107	45c multicolored	2.50	1.10
666	A107	65c multicolored	2.60	2.50
667	A107	75c multicolored	3.00	2.75
668	A107	$1 multicolored	3.25	3.25
		Nos. 665-668 (4)	11.35	9.60

Satellite Orbiting Earth A108

1985, Sept. 10

669	A108	75c multicolored	1.00	1.00

INTELSAT, Intl. Telecommunications Satellite Consortium, 20th anniv.

Royal Barbados Police, 150th Anniv. — A109

25c, Traffic Department. 50c, Police Band. 65c, Dog Force. $1, Mounted Police. $2, Band on parade, horiz.

1985, Nov. 19

670	A109	25c multi	2.25	.75
671	A109	50c multi	1.60	1.10
672	A109	65c multi	1.80	1.60
673	A109	$1 multi	2.00	2.00
		Nos. 670-673 (4)	7.65	5.45

Souvenir Sheet

674	A109	$2 multi	3.75	3.75

Queen Elizabeth II 60th Birthday
Common Design Type

Designs: 25c, Age 2. 50c, Senate House opening, University College of the West Indies, Jamaica, 1953. 65c, With Prince Philip, Caribbean Tour, 1985. 75c, Banquet, state visit to Sao Paulo, Brazil, 1968. $2, Visiting Crown Agents, 1983.

Perf. 14x14½

1986, Apr. 21 Wmk. 384

675	CD337	25c scar, blk & sil	.30	.25
676	CD337	50c ultra & multi	.50	.45
677	CD337	65c green & multi	.60	.55
678	CD337	75c violet & multi	.60	.60
679	CD337	$2 rose vio & multi	1.35	1.35
		Nos. 675-679 (5)	3.35	3.20

EXPO '86, Vancouver — A110

50c, Trans-Canada North Star. $2.50, Lady Nelson.

1986, May 2 Perf. 14

680	A110	50c multicolored	1.25	.80
681	A110	$2.50 multicolored	2.75	2.75

AMERIPEX '86 — A111

$2, Statue of Liberty, NY Harbor.

1986, May 22 Wmk. 373

682	A111	45c No. 441	.95	.50
683	A111	50c No. 442	1.05	.65
684	A111	65c No. 558	1.20	1.20
685	A111	$1 Nos. 583-584	1.50	1.50
		Nos. 682-685 (4)	4.70	3.85

Souvenir Sheet

686	A111	$2 multicolored	12.50	12.50

Statue of Liberty, cent.

Royal Wedding Issue, 1986
Common Design Type

Designs: 45c, Informal portrait. $1, Andrew in navy uniform.

Perf. 14½x14

1986, July 23 Litho. Wmk. 384

687	CD338	45c multicolored	.85	.50
688	CD338	$1 multicolored	1.40	.75

Electrification of Barbados, A112

10c, Transporting utility poles, 1923. 25c, Heathfield ladder, 1935. 65c, Transport fleet, 1941. $2, Bucket truck, 1986.

Wmk. 384

1986, Sept. 16 Litho. Perf. 14

689	A112	10c multi	.25	.25
690	A112	25c multi, vert.	.35	.30
691	A112	65c multi	1.00	.85
692	A112	$2 multi, vert.	2.40	2.40
		Nos. 689-692 (4)	4.00	3.80

Christmas — A113

Church windows and flowers: 25c, Alpinia purpurata. 50c, Anthurium andraeanum. 75c, Heliconia rostrata. $2, Heliconia psittacorum.

1986, Oct. 28   **Wmk. 373**
693	A113	25c multicolored	.35	.25
694	A113	50c multicolored	.55	.55
695	A113	75c multicolored	1.00	1.00
696	A113	$2 multicolored	2.00	2.00
		Nos. 693-696 (4)	3.90	3.80

Natl. Special Olympics, 10th Anniv. A114

1987, Mar. 27   **Wmk. 373**   *Perf. 14*
697	A114	15c Shot put	.25	.25
698	A114	45c Wheelchair race	.50	.50
699	A114	65c Girl's long jump	.75	.75
700	A114	$2 Emblem, creed	2.25	2.25
		Nos. 697-700 (4)	3.75	3.75

CAPEX '87 — A115

25c, Barn swallow. 50c, Yellow warbler. 65c, Audubon's shearwater. 75c, Black-whiskered vireo. $1, Scarlet tanager.

1987, June 12
701	A115	25c multicolored	2.75	.65
702	A115	50c multicolored	3.25	1.75
703	A115	65c multicolored	3.25	1.75
704	A115	75c multicolored	3.50	3.50
705	A115	$1 multicolored	3.75	3.75
		Nos. 701-705 (5)	16.50	11.40

Natl. Scouting Movement, 75th Anniv. — A116

1987, July 24   *Perf. 14x14½*
706	A116	10c Scout sign	.25	.25
707	A116	25c Campfire	.65	.30
708	A116	65c Merit badges, etc.	1.40	.70
709	A116	$2 Marching band	3.50	3.50
		Nos. 706-709 (4)	5.80	4.75

Bridgetown Synagogue Restoration A117

50c, Exterior. 65c, Interior. 75c, Ten Commandments, vert. $1, Marble laver, vert.

1987, Oct. 6   **Wmk. 384**   *Perf. 14½*
710	A117	50c multicolored	3.25	2.40
711	A117	65c multicolored	3.50	3.50
712	A117	75c multicolored	3.75	3.75
713	A117	$1 multicolored	4.50	4.50
		Nos. 710-713 (4)	15.00	14.15

Natl. Independence, 21st Anniv. — A118

E.W. Barrow (1920-87), Father of Independence — A119

25c, Coat of arms, seal of the colony. 45c, Natl. flag, Union Jack. 65c, Silver dollar, penny. $2, Old and new regimental flags, Queen Elizabeth's colors.

1987, Nov. 24   **Litho.**   *Perf. 14½*
714	A118	25c multicolored	.55	.25
715	A118	45c multicolored	1.35	.45
716	A118	65c multicolored	1.35	.65
717	A118	$2 multicolored	4.50	3.25
		Nos. 714-717 (4)	7.75	4.60

Souvenir Sheet
718	A119	$1.50 multicolored	2.40	2.40

Cricket A120

Bat, wicket posts, ball, 18th cent. belt buckle and batters: 15c, E.A. "Manny" Martindale. 45c, George Challenor. 50c, Herman C. Griffith. 75c, Harold Austin. $2, Frank Worrell.

1988   **Litho.**   **Wmk. 373**   *Perf. 14*
719	A120	15c multicolored	3.75	1.25
720	A120	45c multicolored	4.50	1.25
720A	A120	50c multicolored	5.25	3.00
721	A120	75c multicolored	5.50	4.50
722	A120	$2 multicolored	6.25	6.25
		Nos. 719-722 (5)	25.25	16.25

The 50c was originally printed with the wrong photograph but was not issued. Examples of the error have appeared on the market. Issued: No. 720A, July 11; others, June 6.

Lizards — A121

10c, Kentropyx borckianus. 50c, Hemidactylus mabouia. 65c, Anolis extremus. $2, Gymnophthalmus underwoodii.

1988, June 13
723	A121	10c multicolored	2.50	.75
724	A121	50c multicolored	3.50	1.25
725	A121	65c multicolored	4.00	1.75
726	A121	$2 multicolored	8.50	8.00
		Nos. 723-726 (4)	18.50	11.75

1988 Summer Olympics, Seoul — A122

Wmk. 373
1988, Aug. 2   **Litho.**   *Perf. 14½*
727	A122	25c Cycling	2.25	.60
728	A122	45c Running	.95	.50
729	A122	75c Swimming	1.15	.95
730	A122	$2 Yachting	2.60	2.40
a.		Souvenir sheet of 4, #727-730	7.50	7.50
		Nos. 727-730 (4)	6.95	4.45

Lloyds of London, 300th Anniv.
Common Design Type

40c, Royal Exchange, 1774. 50c, Sugar mill (windmill), horiz. 65c, Container ship Author, horiz. $2, Sinking of the Titanic, 1912.

1988, Oct. 18   **Litho.**   *Perf. 14*
731	CD341	40c multicolored	1.10	.50
732	CD341	50c multicolored	1.40	.60
733	CD341	65c multicolored	2.75	.75
734	CD341	$2 multicolored	7.25	6.50
		Nos. 731-734 (4)	12.50	8.35

Harry Bayley Observatory, 25th Anniv. A123

Designs: 25c, Observatory, crescent Moon, Venus and Harry Bayley. 65c, Observatory and constellations. 75c, Andromeda Galaxy and telescope. $2, Orion Constellation.

1988, Nov. 28   **Wmk. 384**   *Perf. 14½*
735	A123	25c multicolored	.90	.35
736	A123	65c multicolored	2.00	.95
737	A123	75c multicolored	2.25	1.25
738	A123	$2 multicolored	4.25	4.25
		Nos. 735-738 (4)	9.40	6.80

Commercial Aviation, 50th Anniv. — A124

Designs: 25c, Caribbean Airline Liat BAe748. 65c, Pan American DC-8. 75c, Two British Airways Concordes, Grantley Adams Intl. Airport. $2, Two Caribbean Air Cargo Boeing 707-351c.

1989, Mar. 20   **Litho.**   *Perf. 14*
739	A124	25c multicolored	3.25	.70
740	A124	65c multicolored	4.75	1.75
741	A124	75c multicolored	4.75	1.75
742	A124	$2 multicolored	7.50	6.75
		Nos. 739-742 (4)	20.25	10.95

Parliament, 350th Anniv. A125

25c, Assembly chamber. 50c, The Speaker. 75c, Parliament, c. 1882. $2.50, Queen in Parliament.

1989, July 19   **Litho.**   *Perf. 13½*
743	A125	25c multicolored	.55	.30
744	A125	50c multicolored	.85	.55
745	A125	75c multicolored	1.50	.80
746	A125	$2.50 multicolored	3.50	3.00
		Nos. 743-746 (4)	6.40	4.65

See No. 752.

Wildlife Preservation — A126

10c, Wild hare, vert. 50c, Red-footed tortoise. 65c, Green monkey, vert. $2, Toad. $1, Mongoose, vert.

1989, Aug. 1   *Perf. 14x13½*
747	A126	10c multicolored	1.00	.50
748	A126	50c multicolored	2.00	1.00
749	A126	65c multicolored	3.00	1.75
750	A126	$2 multicolored	4.75	4.75
		Nos. 747-750 (4)	10.75	8.00

Souvenir Sheet
751	A126	$1 multicolored	2.75	2.75

Parliament Anniv. Type of 1989
Souvenir Sheet

1989, Oct. 9   **Wmk. 373**   *Perf. 13½*
752	A125	$1 The Mace	2.00	2.00

35th Commonwealth Parliamentary Conf.

Wild Plants — A127

Inscribed "1989"

2c, Bread'n cheese. 5c, Scarlet cordia. 10c, Columnar cactus. 20c, Spiderlily. 25c, Rock balsam. 30c, Hollyhock. 45c, Yellow shakshak. 50c, Whitewood. 55c, Bluebell. 65c, Prickly sage. 70c, Seaside samphire. 80c, Flat-hand dildo. $1.10, Lent tree. $2.50, Rodwood. $5, Cowitch. $10, Maypole.

1989, Nov. 1   **Wmk. 373**   *Perf. 14½*
753	A127	2c multi	.80	1.20
754	A127	5c multi	1.30	1.50
755	A127	10c multi	1.30	.75
756	A127	20c multi	1.30	.75
757	A127	25c multi	1.30	.45
758	A127	30c multi	1.90	.60
759	A127	45c multi	1.60	.85
760	A127	50c multi	1.90	.90
761	A127	55c multi	2.60	1.50
762	A127	65c multi	2.00	1.50
763	A127	70c multi	3.25	3.75
764	A127	80c multi	4.50	4.00
765	A127	$1.10 multi	3.75	4.50
766	A127	$2.50 multi	5.25	5.25
767	A127	$5 multi	8.50	10.00
768	A127	$10 multi	16.50	18.50
		Nos. 753-768 (16)	57.75	56.00

35c, Red sage. 90c, Herringbone.

1991-92   **Inscribed "1991"**
754a	A127	5c	.50	.50
755a	A127	10c	.50	.40
756a	A127	20c	.50	.40
758A	A127	35c multi	1.25	1.00
763a	A127	70c	1.25	1.25
764A	A127	90c multi	1.75	1.75
765a	A127	$1.10	1.75	1.75
		Nos. 754a-765a (7)	7.50	7.05

Nos. 758A and 764A issued June 9, 1992 (inscribed 1991).
For overprints see Nos. 788-790.

Inscribed "1990"
1990   **Litho.**   **Wmk. 384**
753b	A127	2c	.40	.35
754b	A127	5c	.40	.35
755b	A127	10c	.40	.35
756b	A127	20c	.40	.35
757b	A127	25c	.55	.45
759b	A127	45c	.85	.75
760b	A127	50c	1.00	1.00
762b	A127	65c	1.25	1.25
766b	A127	$2.50	4.50	4.50
767b	A127	$5	9.00	8.75
768b	A127	$10	18.00	17.50
		Nos. 753b-768b (11)	36.75	35.60

World Stamp Expo '89, Washington, DC — A128

Water sports.

1989, Nov. 17   Wmk. 384   Perf. 14

769	A128	25c Water skiing	1.75	.55
770	A128	50c Yachting	3.00	1.40
771	A128	65c Scuba diving	3.00	2.00
772	A128	$2.50 Surfing	7.25	7.25
		Nos. 769-772 (4)	15.00	11.20

Horse Racing A129

Wmk. 373

1990, May 3   Litho.   Perf. 14

773	A129	25c Bugler, jockeys	.70	.40
774	A129	45c Parade ring	1.05	.65
775	A129	75c In the straight	1.50	1.05
776	A129	$2 Winner, vert.	3.75	3.75
		Nos. 773-776 (4)	7.00	5.85

Barbados No. 2 — A130

Stamps on stamps: No. 778, Barbados #61. 65c, Barbados #73. $2.50, Barbados #121. No. 781a, Great Britain #1. No. 781b, Barbados #108.

1990, May 3

777	A130	25c shown	1.75	.55
778	A130	50c multicolored	2.60	1.25
779	A130	65c multicolored	2.75	1.75
780	A130	$2.50 multicolored	6.00	6.00
		Nos. 777-780 (4)	13.10	9.55

Souvenir Sheet

781		Sheet of 2	4.25	4.25
a.-b.		A130 50c any single	1.50	1.50

Stamp World London '90.

Queen Mother, 90th Birthday
Common Design Types

75c, At age 23. $2.50, Engagement portrait, 1923.

1990, Aug. 8   Wmk. 384   Perf. 14x15

782	CD343	75c multi	1.00	.70

Perf. 14½

783	CD344	$2.50 gray grn	3.00	3.00

Insects A131

50c, Dragonfly. 65c, Black hardback beetle. 75c, Green grasshopper. $2, God-horse.

Wmk. 373

1990, Oct. 16   Perf. 14

784	A131	50c multicolored	2.25	1.10
785	A131	65c multicolored	2.60	1.25
786	A131	75c multicolored	3.00	1.75
787	A131	$2 multicolored	5.50	5.50
		Nos. 784-787 (4)	13.35	9.60

Nos. 757, 764 and 766 Overprinted

1990, Nov. 21   Perf. 14½

788	A127	25c on No. 757	2.40	.75
789	A127	80c on No. 764	4.25	3.00
790	A127	$2.50 on No. 766	10.00	10.00
		Nos. 788-790 (3)	16.65	13.75

Christmas — A132

20c, Christmas star. 50c, Nativity scene. $1, Stained glass window. $2, Angel.

1990, Dec. 4   Perf. 14

791	A132	20c multicolored	1.05	.30
792	A132	50c multicolored	1.50	.65
793	A132	$1 multicolored	2.75	1.90
794	A132	$2 multicolored	4.50	4.50
		Nos. 791-794 (4)	9.80	7.35

Yellow Warbler A133

20c, Male, female, nest. 45c, Female, chicks. $1, Male, fledgling.

1991, Mar. 4

795	A133	10c shown	1.75	1.25
796	A133	20c multicolored	3.25	1.25
797	A133	45c multicolored	4.00	1.25
798	A133	$1 multicolored	6.50	6.00
		Nos. 795-798 (4)	15.50	9.75

World Wildlife Fund.

Fishing A134

5c, Daily catch, vert. 50c, Line fishing. 75c, Cleaning fish. $2.50, Game fishing, vert.

Perf. 13½x14, 14x13½

1991, June 18   Litho.   Wmk. 373

799	A134	5c multicolored	.65	.55
800	A134	50c multicolored	2.10	1.00
801	A134	75c multicolored	2.75	1.40
802	A134	$2.50 multicolored	5.50	5.50
		Nos. 799-802 (4)	11.00	8.45

Freemasonry in Barbados, 250th Anniv. — A135

Designs: 25c, Masonic Building, Bridgetown. 65c, Compass and square. 75c, Royal arch jewel. $2.50, Columns, apron and centenary badge.

1991, Sept. 17   Perf. 14

803	A135	25c multicolored	2.10	.75
804	A135	65c multicolored	3.25	1.50
805	A135	75c multicolored	3.25	1.50
806	A135	$2.50 multicolored	7.50	7.50
		Nos. 803-806 (4)	16.10	11.25

Butterflies A136

20c, Polydamus swallowtail. 50c, Long-tailed skipper, vert. 65c, Cloudless sulphur. $2.50, Caribbean buckeye, vert. $4, Painted lady.

1991, Nov. 15   Wmk. 384

807	A136	20c multicolored	1.50	.55
808	A136	50c multicolored	2.00	.85
809	A136	65c multicolored	2.40	1.25
810	A136	$2.50 multicolored	5.50	5.50
		Nos. 807-810 (4)	11.40	8.15

Souvenir Sheet

811	A136	$4 multicolored	13.00	13.00

Phila Nippon '91.

Independence, 25th Anniv. — A137

Governor-General Dame Nita Barrow and: 10c, Students in classroom. 25c, Barbados Workers Union headquarters. 65c, Building industry. 75c, Agriculture. $1, Inoculations given at health clinic. $2.50, Gordon Greenidge, Desmond Haynes, cricket players (no portrait).

1991, Nov. 20   Wmk. 373

812	A137	10c multicolored	.35	.35
813	A137	25c multicolored	.55	.55
814	A137	65c multicolored	1.25	1.25
815	A137	75c multicolored	1.50	1.50
816	A137	$1 multicolored	1.75	1.75
		Nos. 812-816 (4)	5.40	5.40

Souvenir Sheet

817	A137	$2.50 multi, vert.	16.00	16.00

Easter — A138

35c, Christ carrying cross. 70c, Christ on cross. 90c, Christ taken down from cross. $3, Christ risen.

Wmk. 384

1992, Apr. 7   Litho.   Perf. 14

818	A138	35c multicolored	.70	.35
819	A138	70c multicolored	1.25	.85
820	A138	90c multicolored	1.50	1.25
821	A138	$3 multicolored	4.00	4.00
		Nos. 818-821 (4)	7.45	6.45

Flowering Trees — A139

10c, Cannon ball. 30c, Golden shower. 80c, Frangipani. $1.10, Flamboyant.

Perf. 14x13½

1992, June 9   Litho.   Wmk. 373

822	A139	10c multicolored	.85	.55
823	A139	30c multicolored	1.50	.65
824	A139	80c multicolored	3.00	3.00
825	A139	$1.10 multicolored	3.75	3.75
		Nos. 822-825 (4)	9.10	7.95

Orchids A140

Designs: 55c, Epidendrum "Costa Rica." 65c, Cattleya guttaca. 70c, Laeliacattleya "Splashing Around." $1.40, Phalaenopsis "Kathy Saegert."

1992, Sept. 8   Perf. 13½x14

826	A140	55c multicolored	1.35	.80
827	A140	65c multicolored	1.90	1.35
828	A140	70c multicolored	1.90	1.35
829	A140	$1.40 multicolored	3.00	3.00
		Nos. 826-829 (4)	8.15	6.50

For overprints see Nos. 838-841.

Transport and Tourism A141

Designs: 5c, Mini Moke, Gun Hill Signal Station, St. George. 35c, Tour bus, Bathsheba Beach, St. Joseph. 90c, BWIA McDonnell Douglas MD 83, Grantley Adams Airport. $2, Cruise ship Festivale, deep water harbor, Bridgetown.

Wmk. 373

1992, Dec. 15   Litho.   Perf. 14½

830	A141	5c multicolored	.80	.75
831	A141	35c multicolored	1.75	.45
832	A141	90c multicolored	3.50	3.25
833	A141	$2 multicolored	5.75	5.75
		Nos. 830-833 (4)	11.80	10.20

Cacti and Succulents A142

10c, Barbados gooseberry. 35c, Night-blooming cereus. $1.40, Aloe. $2, Scrunchineel.

Wmk. 373

1993, Feb. 9   Litho.   Perf. 14

834	A142	10c multicolored	.75	.40
835	A142	35c multicolored	1.80	.50
836	A142	$1.40 multicolored	4.25	4.25
837	A142	$2 multicolored	4.75	4.75
		Nos. 834-837 (4)	11.55	9.90

Nos. 826-829 Ovptd. on 2 or 4 lines

Perf. 13½x14

1993, Apr. 1   Litho.   Wmk. 373

838	A140	55c on #826 multi	1.90	1.90
839	A140	65c on #827 multi	2.25	2.25
840	A140	70c on #828 multi	2.25	2.25
841	A140	$1.40 on #829 multi	3.25	3.25
		Nos. 838-841 (4)	9.65	9.65

Royal Air Force, 75th Anniv.
Common Design Type

Designs: 10c, Hawker Hunter. 30c, Handley Page Victor. 70c, Hawker Typhoon. $3, Hawker Hurricane.

No. 846a, Armstrong Whitworth Siskin 3a. b, Supermarine S.6B. c, Supermarine Walrus. d, Hawker Hart.

1993, Apr. 1   Perf. 14

842	CD350	10c multicolored	1.00	.55
843	CD350	30c multicolored	1.40	.55
844	CD350	70c multicolored	2.25	2.25
845	CD350	$3 multicolored	5.00	5.00
		Nos. 842-845 (4)	9.65	8.35

Souvenir Sheet

846	CD350	50c Sheet of 4, #a.-d.	4.00	4.00

Cannon A143

Designs: 5c, 18-pounder Culverin, 1625, Denmark Fort. 45c, 6-pounder Commonwealth gun, 1649-1660, St. Ann's Fort. $1, 9-pounder Demi-culverin, 1691, The Main Guard. $2.50, 32-pounder Demi-cannon, 1693-94, Charles Fort.

Wmk. 373

1993, June 8   Litho.   Perf. 13

847	A143	5c multicolored	.45	.45
848	A143	45c multicolored	1.30	.65
849	A143	$1 multicolored	2.60	2.60
850	A143	$2.50 multicolored	4.00	4.00
		Nos. 847-850 (4)	8.35	7.70

Barbados Museum, 60th Anniv. — A144

Designs: 10c, Shell box, carved figure. 75c, Map, print of three people. 90c, Silver cup, print of soldier. $1.10, Map.

Wmk. 373

1993, Sept. 14   Litho.   Perf. 14

851	A144	10c multicolored	.55	.55
852	A144	75c multicolored	1.80	1.80
853	A144	90c multicolored	2.40	2.40
854	A144	$1.10 multicolored	2.75	2.75
		Nos. 851-854 (4)	7.50	7.50

Prehistoric Aquatic Reptiles — A145

a, Plesiosaurus. b, Ichthyosaurus. c, Elasmosaurus. d, Mosasaurus. e, Archelon. Continuous design.

Wmk. 373

1993, Oct. 28   Litho.   Perf. 13

855 A145 90c Strip of 5, #a.-e. 14.00 14.00

A146

10c, Cricket. 35c, Motor racing. 50c, Golf. 70c, Run Barbados 10k. $1.40, Swimming.

Wmk. 384

1994, Jan. 11   Litho.   Perf. 14

856	A146	10c multi	1.40	.75
857	A146	35c multi	1.50	.55
858	A146	50c multi	2.60	1.80
859	A146	70c multi	2.00	2.00
860	A146	$1.40 multi	2.40	2.40
		Nos. 856-860 (5)	9.90	7.50

Sports & tourism.

Migratory Birds A147

10c, Whimbrel. 35c, American golden plover. 70c, Ruddy turnstone. $3, Tricolored heron.

Wmk. 373

1994, Feb. 18   Litho.   Perf. 14

861	A147	10c multicolored	.70	.70
862	A147	35c multicolored	1.40	.70
863	A147	70c multicolored	2.25	2.25
864	A147	$3 multicolored	5.25	5.25
		Nos. 861-864 (4)	9.60	8.90

Hong Kong '94.

1st UN Conference of Small Island Developing States — A148

10c, Bathsheba. 65c, Pico Tenneriffe. 90c, Ragged Point Lighthouse. $2.50, Consett Bay.

1994, Apr. 25   Perf. 14x14½

865	A148	10c multicolored	.50	.30
866	A148	65c multicolored	1.75	1.00
867	A148	90c multicolored	4.75	2.25
868	A148	$2.50 multicolored	4.50	4.50
		Nos. 865-868 (4)	11.50	8.05

Order of the Caribbean Community A149

First award recipients: No. 869, Sir Shridath Ramphal, statesman, Guyana. No. 870, Derek Walcott, writer, Nobel Laureate, St. Lucia. No. 871, William Demas, economist, Trinidad and Tobago.

Wmk. 373

1994, July 4   Litho.   Perf. 14

869	A149	70c multicolored	1.00	1.00
870	A149	70c multicolored	1.00	1.00
871	A149	70c multicolored	1.00	1.00
		Nos. 869-871 (3)	3.00	3.00

Ships A150

Designs: 5c, Dutch Flyut, 1695. 10c, Geestport, 1994. 25c, HMS Victory, 1805. 30c, Royal Viking Queen, 1994. 35c, HMS Barbados, 1945. 45c, Faraday, 1924. 50c, USCG Hamilton, 1974. 65c, HMCS Saguenay, 1939. 70c, Inanda, 1928. 80c, HMS Rodney, 1944. 90c, USS John F. Kennedy, 1982. $1.10, William & John, 1627. $5, USCG Champlain, 1931. $10, Artist, 1877.

Wmk. 373

1994, Aug. 16   Litho.   Perf. 14

872	A150	5c multicolored	.50	.50
873	A150	10c multicolored	.50	.50
874	A150	25c multicolored	.50	.50
875	A150	30c multicolored	.80	.80
876	A150	35c multicolored	.95	.95
877	A150	45c multicolored	1.05	1.05
878	A150	50c multicolored	1.20	1.20
879	A150	65c multicolored	1.60	1.60
880	A150	70c multicolored	1.80	1.80
881	A150	80c multicolored	2.40	2.40
882	A150	90c multicolored	2.60	2.60
883	A150	$1.10 multicolored	3.00	3.00
884	A150	$5 multicolored	11.50	11.50
885	A150	$10 multicolored	23.00	23.00
		Nos. 872-885 (14)	51.40	51.40

1997   Inscribed "1997"

872a	A150	5c multicolored	.95	.95
873a	A150	10c multicolored	.95	.95
874a	A150	25c multicolored	1.15	.70
875a	A150	30c multicolored	1.90	.70
876a	A150	35c multicolored	1.90	.95
877a	A150	45c multicolored	1.90	.95
880a	A150	70c multicolored	3.50	.70
882a	A150	90c multicolored	4.00	2.75
885a	A150	$10 multicolored	13.50	13.50
		Nos. 872a-885a (9)	29.75	22.15

1998   Inscribed "1998"

872b	A150	5c multicolored	.50	.50
873b	A150	10c multicolored	.50	.50
877b	A150	45c multicolored	1.10	.95
880b	A150	70c multicolored	2.60	2.60
		Nos. 872b-880b (4)	4.70	4.35

1999   Inscribed "1999"

873c	A150	10c multicolored	1.80	.85
877c	A150	45c multicolored	2.60	.65
885c	A150	$10 multicolored	20.00	20.00
		Nos. 873c-885c (3)	24.40	21.50

1996   Wmk. 384

872d	A150	5c	.45	.45
873d	A150	10c	.45	.45
875d	A150	30c	.55	.55
876d	A150	35c	.70	.70
877d	A150	45c	1.00	1.00
878d	A150	50c	1.15	1.15
879d	A150	65c	1.30	1.30
880d	A150	70c	1.60	1.60
881d	A150	80c	1.80	1.80
882d	A150	90c	2.25	2.25
883d	A150	$1.10	2.50	2.50
884d	A150	$5	10.50	10.50
		Nos. 872d-884d (12)	24.25	24.25

Inscribed "1996."
Issued: Nos. 875d-877d, 879d-882d, 9/1; others, May 1.

West India Regiment, Bicent. — A151

Designs: 30c, 2nd Regiment, 1860. 50c, 4th Regiment, Light Company, 1795. 70c, 3rd Regiment, drum major, 1860. $1, 5th Regiment, undress, working dress, 1815. $1.10, 1st, 2nd Regiments, Review Order, 1874.

Perf. 15x14

1995, Feb. 21   Litho.   Wmk. 373

886	A151	30c multicolored	.80	.45
887	A151	50c multicolored	1.10	.70
888	A151	70c multicolored	1.50	1.50
889	A151	$1 multicolored	1.75	1.75
890	A151	$1.10 multicolored	2.10	2.10
		Nos. 886-890 (5)	7.25	6.50

End of World War II
Common Design Type

10c, Barbadians serving in the Middle East. 35c, Lancaster bomber. 55c, Spitfire fighter. $2.50, SS Davisian sunk off Barbados, July 10, 1940.
$2, Reverse of War Medal 1939-45.

Wmk. 373

1995, May 8   Litho.   Perf. 14

891	CD351	10c multicolored	1.10	.70
892	CD351	35c multicolored	1.60	.70
893	CD351	55c multicolored	2.00	1.00
894	CD351	$2.50 multicolored	5.50	5.50
		Nos. 891-894 (4)	10.20	7.90

Souvenir Sheet

895 CD352 $2 multicolored 4.00 4.00

Combermere School, 300th Anniv. — A152

Designs: 5c, Scouting, Combermere 1st Barbados, 1912. 20c, Violin, sheet music. 35c, Cricket, Sir Frank Worrell, vert. 90c, Frank Collymore, #553. $3, Landscape.

Wmk. 373

1995, July 25   Litho.   Perf. 14

896	A152	5c multicolored	.45	.45
897	A152	20c multicolored	.65	.65
898	A152	35c multicolored	1.90	.65
899	A152	$3 multicolored	2.75	2.75
		Nos. 896-899 (4)	5.75	4.50

Souvenir Sheet

900	Sheet of 5, #896-899, 900a	6.75	6.75
a.	A152 90c multicolored	1.00	1.00

UN, 50th Anniv.
Common Design Type

Designs: 30c, Douglas C-124 Globemaster, Korea 1950-53. 45c, Royal Navy Sea King helicopter. $1.40, Wessex helicopter, UNFI-CYP, Cyprus 1964. $2, Gazelle helicopter, UNFICYP, Cyprus 1964.

Wmk. 373

1995, Oct. 24   Litho.   Perf. 14

901	CD353	30c multicolored	1.00	.55
902	CD353	45c multicolored	1.50	.70
903	CD353	$1.40 multicolored	2.25	2.25
904	CD353	$2 multicolored	2.25	2.25
		Nos. 901-904 (4)	7.00	5.75

Water Lilies — A153

Wmk. 373

1995, Dec. 19   Litho.   Perf. 14

905	A153	10c Blue beauty	.60	.45
906	A153	65c White water lily	1.45	1.45
907	A153	70c Sacred lotus	1.45	1.45
908	A153	$3 Water hyacinth	4.50	4.50
		Nos. 905-908 (4)	8.00	7.85

Barbados Philatelic Society, Cent. A154

Magnifiying glass, tongs, and: 10c, #70. 55c, #109. $1.10, #148. $1.40, #192.

Wmk. 373

1996, Jan. 30   Litho.   Perf. 14

909	A154	10c multicolored	.40	.35
910	A154	55c multicolored	.75	.55
911	A154	$1.10 multicolored	1.75	1.75
912	A154	$1.40 multicolored	1.90	1.90
		Nos. 909-912 (4)	4.80	4.55

A155

Modern Olympic Games, Cent. — A156

20c, Soccer. 30c, Relay race. 55c, Basketball. $3, Rhythmic gymnastics. $2.50, Discus thrower.

1996, Apr. 2   Litho.   Perf. 14

913	A155	20c multicolored	.60	.40
914	A155	30c multicolored	.65	.40
915	A155	55c multicolored	2.25	.85
916	A155	$3 multicolored	3.25	3.25
		Nos. 913-916 (4)	6.75	4.90

Souvenir Sheet

917 A156 $2.50 multicolored 3.50 3.50

Olymphilex '96 (No. 917).

CAPEX '96
A157

Transportation links with Canada: 10c, Canadian Airlines DC10. 90c, Air Canada Boeing 767. $1, Air Canada 320 Airbus. $1.40, Canadian Airlines Boeing 767.

Wmk. 373

			1996, June 7	Litho.	Perf. 14
918	A157	10c multicolored	.50	.45
919	A157	90c multicolored	1.75	1.25
920	A157	$1 multicolored	1.75	1.75
921	A157	$1.40 multicolored	2.25	2.25
		Nos. 918-921 (4)	6.25	5.70

Chattel Houses
A158

House features: 35c, Shed roof, lattice work. 70c, Pedimented porch, carved wooden trim. $1.10, Decorative, elegant porch. $2, Hip roof, bell pelmet window hoods.

1996, June 7

922	A158	35c multicolored	.55	.35
923	A158	70c multicolored	1.05	.75
924	A158	$1.10 multicolored	1.30	1.30
925	A158	$2 multicolored	2.10	2.10
		Nos. 922-925 (4)	5.00	4.50

Christmas
A159

Children's paintings: 10c, Going to Church on Christmas morning. 30c, The Tuk Band. 55c, Caroling on Christmas. $2.50, Decorated houses.

Wmk. 373

			1996, Nov. 12	Litho.	Perf. 14½
926	A159	10c multicolored	.50	.25
927	A159	30c multicolored	.75	.45
928	A159	55c multicolored	1.05	.70
929	A159	$2.50 multicolored	2.50	2.50
		Nos. 926-929 (4)	4.80	3.90

UNICEF, 50th anniv.

Hong Kong '97 — A160

Dogs: 10c, Doberman pinscher. 30c, German shepherd. 90c, Japanese akita. $3, Irish red setter.

Perf. 14x14½

			1997, Feb. 12	Litho.	Wmk. 373
930	A160	10c multicolored	.90	.50
931	A160	30c multicolored	1.70	.50
932	A160	90c multicolored	2.50	1.45
933	A160	$3 multicolored	5.25	5.25
		Nos. 930-933 (4)	10.35	7.70

Visit of US Pres. Clinton to Barbados, May 1997
A161

35c, Barbados flag, arms. 90c, US flag, arms.

			1997, May 9	Litho.	Perf. 14
934	A161	35c multicolored	1.00	1.00
935	A161	90c multicolored	1.50	1.50
a.		Pair, #934-935	2.75	2.75

Issued in sheets of 8 stamps + 2 labels. Sheets exist both with and without a "Pacific '97" overprint in the margin.

Shells — A162

5c, Measled cowry. 35c, Trumpet triton. 90c, Scotch bonnet. $2, West Indian murex. $2.50, Sea bottom with miscellaneous shells.

			1997, July 29	Litho.	Perf. 14
936	A162	5c multicolored	.40	.40
937	A162	35c multicolored	1.00	.35
938	A162	90c multicolored	1.90	.95
939	A162	$2 multicolored	2.75	2.75
		Nos. 936-939 (4)	6.05	4.45

Souvenir Sheet

940	A162	$2.50 multicolored	4.00	4.00

Public Library, 150th Anniv.
A163

Designs: 10c, Lucas manuscripts. 30c, Storytelling to children. 70c, Bookmobile. $3, Information technology.

			1997, Oct. 1	Litho.	Perf. 14
941	A163	10c multicolored	.30	.25
942	A163	30c multicolored	.65	.35
943	A163	70c multicolored	1.50	.70
944	A163	$3 multicolored	3.25	3.25
		Nos. 941-944 (4)	5.70	4.55

Fruit — A164

			1997, Dec. 16	Litho.	Perf. 14½
945	A164	35c Barbados cherry	.65	.40
946	A164	40c Sugar apple	.75	.40
947	A164	$1.15 Soursop	1.75	1.75
948	A164	$1.70 Papaya	2.40	2.40
		Nos. 945-948 (4)	5.55	4.95

Souvenir Sheet

Sir Grantley Adams, Birth Cent. — A165

a, Natl. Arms. b, Grantley Adams. c, Natl. flag.

			1998, Apr. 27	Litho.	Perf. 13
949	A165	$1 Sheet of 3, #a.-c.	9.00	9.00

Diana, Princess of Wales (1961-97)
Common Design Type of 1998

Portraits wearing: a, Blue hat. b, Red suit jacket. c, Tiara. d, Black and white.

1998, May   **Perf. 14½x14**

950	CD355	$1.15 Sheet of 4, #a.-d.	5.00	5.00

Organization of American States, 50th Anniv. — A166

Designs: 15c, Beach during storm, beach during sunny day. $1, Dancers in native costumes. $2.50, Judge reading at podium, statue of justice.

			1998, June 30	Litho.	Perf. 14
951	A166	15c multicolored	.25	.25
952	A166	$1 multicolored	1.00	1.00
953	A166	$2.50 multicolored	2.60	2.60
		Nos. 951-953 (3)	3.85	3.85

University of West Indies, 50th Anniv.
A167

40c, Frank Worrell Hall. $1.15, Graduation. $1.40, Plaque, hummingbird. $1.75, Quadrangle.

			1998, July 20		Perf. 14½
954	A167	40c multicolored	.60	.35
955	A167	$1.15 multicolored	1.60	1.60
956	A167	$1.40 multicolored	2.00	2.00
957	A167	$1.75 multicolored	3.50	3.50
		Nos. 954-957 (4)	7.70	7.45

Tourism
A168

10c, Catamaran, vert. 45c, Jolly Roger. 70c, Atlantis submarine. $2, MV Harbor Master, vert.

			1998, Dec. 1	Litho.	Perf. 14
958	A168	10c multicolored	.35	.35
959	A168	45c multicolored	1.15	.45
960	A168	70c multicolored	1.75	1.25
961	A168	$2 multicolored	3.75	3.75
		Nos. 958-961 (4)	7.00	5.80

Australia '99, World Stamp Expo — A169

			1999, Mar. 19	Litho.	Perf. 14
962	A169	$4 Sailboat	5.50	5.50

Piping Plover
A170

World Wildlife Fund: 10c, Juvenile in shallow water. 45c, Female with eggs. 50c, Fledglings in nest, male, female. 70c, Male.

			1999, Apr. 27	Litho.	Perf. 14
963	A170	10c multicolored	.25	.25
964	A170	45c multicolored	1.00	.75
965	A170	50c multicolored	1.00	1.00
966	A170	70c multicolored	1.30	1.30
		Nos. 963-966 (4)	3.55	3.30

1st Manned Moon Landing, 30th Anniv.
Common Design Type

Designs: 40c, Astronaut training. 45c, First stage separation. $1.15, Lunar module. $1.40, Docking with service module. $2.50, Looking at earth from moon.

Perf. 14x13¾

			1999, July 20	Litho.	Wmk. 384
967	CD357	40c multicolored	.75	.50
968	CD357	45c multicolored	.75	.50
969	CD357	$1.15 multicolored	1.90	1.50
970	CD357	$1.40 multicolored	2.00	2.00
		Nos. 967-970 (4)	5.40	4.50

Souvenir Sheet
Perf. 14

971	CD357	$2.50 multicolored	3.25	3.25

No. 971 contains one 40mm circular stamp.

Rabbits
A171

Designs: a, Rabbit running. b, Rabbit profile. c, Rabbit nursing young. d, Two rabbits leaping. e, Two rabbits at rest.

Perf. 14x14½

			1999, Aug. 21	Litho.	Wmk. 373
972	A171	70c Strip of 5, #a.-e.	9.00	9.00

China 1999 World Philatelic Exhibition.

UPU, 125th Anniv.
A172

			1999, Oct. 11	Litho.	Perf. 14
973	A172	10c Mail coach	1.10	.45
974	A172	45c Mail van	1.60	.55
975	A172	$1.75 Airplane	2.25	2.25
976	A172	$2 Computers	2.50	2.50
		Nos. 973-976 (4)	7.45	5.75

Souvenir Sheet

Millennium — A173

Wmk. 373

			2000, Feb. 8	Litho.	Perf. 14
977	A173	$3 multicolored	6.25	6.25

100th Test Cricket Match at Lord's Ground — A174

Designs: 45c, Sir Conrad Hunte. 90c, Malcolm Marshall. $2, Sir Garfield St. A. Sobers. $2.50, Lord's Ground, horiz.

Wmk. 373
2000, May 22   Litho.   Perf. 14
978 A174 45c multi 1.20 .55
979 A174 90c multi 2.40 1.10
980 A174 $2 multi   4.25 4.25
   Nos. 978-980 (3) 7.85 5.90
Souvenir Sheet
981 A174 $2.50 multi 4.50 4.50
The Stamp Show 2000, London (No. 981).

Sites in Barbados A175

5c, Drax Hall House. 10c, Reaping sugar cane. 40c, Needham's Point Lighthouse. 45c, Port St. Charles. 65c, Synagogue. 70c, Bridgetown port (boats point right). No. 987A, 70c, Bridgetown port (boats point left). 90c, Harrison's Cave. $1.15, Villa Nova. $1.40, Cricket at Kensington Oval. $1.75, Sunbury House. $2, Bethel Methodist Church. $3, Barbados Wildlife Reserve. $5, Royal Westmoreland golf course. $10, Grantley Adams Intl. Airport.

Wmk. 373
2000, May 22   Litho.   Perf. 14
982 A175 5c multi   .25 .25
983 A175 10c multi, vert. .25 .25
  a. Inscribed "2002" 1.25 1.25
  b. Inscribed "2004" 2.40 2.40
984 A175 40c multi, vert. .50 .50
985 A175 45c multi .60 .60
986 A175 65c multi .90 .90
987 A175 70c multi 1.10 1.10
987A A175 70c multi 1.10 1.10
988 A175 90c multi 1.35 1.35
989 A175 $1.15 multi 1.75 1.75
990 A175 $1.40 multi 1.90 1.90
991 A175 $1.75 multi 2.50 2.50
992 A175 $2 multi   3.00 3.00
993 A175 $3 multi, vert. 4.25 4.25
994 A175 $5 multi, vert. 7.75 7.75
995 A175 $10 multi 14.50 14.50
  Nos. 982-995 (15) 41.70 41.70
Nos. 982-987, 988-995 issued 5/22.

World Stamp Expo 2000, Anaheim — A176

25c, Golf equipment. 40c, Golfer on golf ball. $1.40, Golfer at tee. $2, Golfer putting.

Perf. 14½x14¼
2000, July 7   Litho.   Wmk. 373
996-999 A176 Set of 4 7.75 7.75

Vintage Cars A177

Designs: 10c, 1947 Bentley Mk VI. 30c, Vanden Plas Princess. 90c, 1952 Austin Atlantic. $3, 1950 Bentley Special.

Perf. 14¼x14½
2000, Nov. 7   Wmk. 373
1000-1003 A177 Set of 4 7.50 7.50

Souvenir Sheet

Hong Kong 2001 Stamp Exhibition — A178

Wmk. 373
2001, Feb. 1   Litho.   Perf. 13¼
1004 A178 $3 Thread snake 5.50 5.50

Deep Sea Creatures — A179

No. 1005: a, Lizard fish. b, Goldentail moray. c, Blackbar soldierfish. d, Golden zoanthid. e, Sponge brittle star. f, Magnificent feather duster. g, Bearded fireworm. h, Lima shell. i, Yellow tube sponge.

Wmk. 373
2001, May 31   Litho.   Perf. 13½
1005 A179 45c Sheet of 9, #a-i 7.50 7.50

Phila Nippon '01, Japan A180

Various kites: 10c, 65c, $1.40, $1.75.

2001, Aug. 1   Perf. 14
1006-1009 A180 Set of 4 4.75 4.75

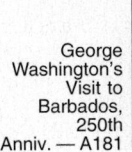

George Washington's Visit to Barbados, 250th Anniv. — A181

Designs: 45c, Washington, ship, trunk, dockworker. 50c, Washington, ship, palm trees. $1.15, Washington, Declaration of Independence. $2.50, Fort at Needham's Point. $3, Portrait of Washington.

Wmk. 373
2001, Nov. 2   Litho.   Perf. 13¼
1010-1013 A181 Set of 4 7.25 7.25
Souvenir Sheet
1014 A181 $3 multi 4.00 4.00

Independence, 35th Anniv. — A182

Designs: 25c, Bank Holiday Bear. 45c, Tuk band. $1, Landship Movement Maypole

dance. $2, National anthem, saxophone and guitar.

2001, Nov. 29   Litho.   Perf. 14
1015-1018 A182 Set of 4 6.75 6.75

Reign Of Queen Elizabeth II, 50th Anniv. Issue
Common Design Type

Designs: Nos. 1019, 1023a, 10c, Princess Elizabeth. Nos. 1020, 1023b, 70c, Wearing red hat. Nos. 1021, 1023c, $1, Wearing crown. Nos. 1022, 1023d, $1.40, Wearing purple hat. No. 1023e, $3, 1955 portrait by Annigoni (38x50mm).

Perf. 14¼x14½, 13¾ (#1023e)
2002, Feb. 6   Wmk. 373
With Gold Frames
1019 CD360 10c multicolored .40 .40
1020 CD360 70c multicolored 1.40 1.40
1021 CD360 $1 multicolored 1.60 1.60
1022 CD360 $1.40 multicolored 2.25 2.25
  Nos. 1019-1022 (4) 5.65 5.65
Souvenir Sheet
Without Gold Frames
1023 CD360 Sheet of 5, #a-e 7.50 7.50

Inland Post, 150th Anniv. A183

Map of Barbados and: 10c, #1. 45c, Early postman. $1.15, Steam packet R.M.S. Esk. $2, BWIA Tristar.

2002, Apr. 15   Perf. 14
1024-1027 A183 Set of 4 5.75 5.75

Flowers — A184

Designs: 10c, Red ginger, vert. 40c, Heliconia caribaea, vert. $1.40, Tube rose. $2.50, Anthurium.

Perf. 14¾x14, 14x14¾
2002, May 30   Litho.
1028-1031 A184 Set of 4 5.50 5.50

First Settlement, 375th Anniv. — A185

Designs: 10c, Drax Hall, St. George. 45c, Donkey cart truck. $1.15, Remains of cattle mill, Gibbons. $3, Morgan Lewis, St. Andrew.

Wmk. 373
2002, Sept. 6   Litho.   Perf. 14
1032-1035 A185 Set of 4 9.00 9.00

Christmas A186

Designs: 45c, Traditional Christmas fare. $1.15, Christmas morning in the park. $1.40, Nativity scene.

2002, Nov. 11
1036-1038 A186 Set of 3 4.00 4.00

Pan-American Health Organization, Cent. — A187

Designs: 10c, AIDS awareness. 70c, Health and longevity. $1.15, Director General Sir George Alleyne. $2, Women's health.

Wmk. 373
2002, Dec. 2   Litho.   Perf. 14
1039-1042 A187 Set of 4 6.00 6.00

Royal Navy Ships A188

Designs: 10c, HMS Tartar, 1764. 70c, HMS Barbadoes, 1803. $1.15, HMS Valerian, 1926. $2.50, HMS Victorious, 1941.

Wmk. 373
2003, May 26   Litho.   Perf. 14
1043-1046 A188 Set of 4 8.50 8.50

Settlement Of Bridgetown, 375th Anniv. — A189

Designs: 10c, Broad Street, c. 1900. $1.15, Swan Street, 1900. $1.40, Roebuck Street, c. 1880. $2, Chamberlain Bridge.

Wmk. 373
2003, July 7   Litho.   Perf. 14
1047-1050 A189 Set of 4 8.00 8.00
1050a Souvenir sheet, #1047-1050 8.25 8.25

Powered Flight, Cent. — A190

Designs: 10c, McDonnell F2H-2 Banshee. 45c, Vickers Viscount 700. 50c, Douglas DC-9-30. $1.15, Short Sunderland MK II. $1.40, North American P-51D Mustang. $2.50, Concorde.

Stamps + Labels
Perf. 13¼x13¾
2003, Sept. 22   Litho.   Wmk. 373
1051-1056 A190 Set of 6 10.00 10.00

Festivals — A191

No. 1057: a, Fishermen hauling in catch, Oistins Fish Festival. b, Saxophonist, Barbados Jazz Festival. c, Costumed man and woman, Crop Over Festival. d, Dancers, National Independence Festival of Creative

Arts. e, Choir, National Independence Festival of Creative Arts. f, Three people in costume, Crop Over Festival. g, Bassist, Barbados Jazz Festival. h, Fish boning, Oistins Fish Festival.

Wmk. 373
2003, Nov. 24   Litho.   Perf. 13¾
1057 A191 45c Sheet of 8, #a-
        h, + central
        label   10.50 10.50

Cadet Corps, Cent. A192

Designs: 10c, Cadet Corps Flag. 25c, Regular Band marching. 50c, Toy Soldier Band. $1, Sea Cadets. $3, Map reading.

Wmk. 373
2004, July 19   Litho.   Perf. 14
1058-1062 A192 Set of 5   8.00 8.00

2004 Summer Olympics, Athens — A193

Designs: 10, Swimming. 70c, Shooting. $1.15, Running. $2, Judo.

Wmk. 373
2004, Aug. 16   Litho.   Perf. 14
1063-1066 A193 Set of 4   7.00 7.00

FIFA (Fédération Internationale de Football Association), Cent. — A194

Various soccer players: 5c, 90c, $1.40, $2.50.

Perf. 14x14¾
2004, Oct. 20   Litho.   Wmk. 373
1067-1070 A194 Set of 4   7.00 7.00

Corals — A195

No. 1071: a, Brain coral. b, Pillar coral (yellow). c, Pillar coral (tan). d, Fan coral. e, Yellow pencil coral. $3.50, Maze coral.

2004, Nov. 15   Perf. 14x14¼
1071   Horiz. strip of 5   13.50 13.50
  a.-e.   A195 $1 Any single   2.50 2.50
Souvenir Sheet
Perf. 13¼
1072 A195 $3.50 multi   6.50 6.50
No. 1072 contains one 36x36mm stamp.

Butterflies A196

Designs: 50c, White peacock. $1, Great southern white. $1.40, Orion. $2.50, Mimic. $8, Monarch.

Wmk. 373
2005, Apr. 21   Litho.   Perf. 14
1073-1076 A196 Set of 4   13.00 13.00
Souvenir Sheet
1077 A196 $8 multi   11.50 11.50
Pacific Explorer 2005 World Stamp Expo, Sydney.

Trees A197

Designs: 5c, Baobab, 10c, African tulip tree. 25c, Rose of Sharon. 45c, Black willow. 50c, Black pearl tree. 75c, Seaside mahoe. 90c, Quickstick. $1, Jerusalem thorn. $1.15, Pink cassia. $1.40, Orchid tree. $1.75, Yellow poui. $2.10, Lignum vitae. $3, Wild cinnamon. $5, Pride of India. $10, Immortelle.

Wmk. 373
2005, July 20   Litho.   Perf. 13¾
1078 A197 5c multi   .25   .25
1079 A197 10c multi   .25   .25
1080 A197 25c multi   .35   .35
1081 A197 45c multi   .60   .60
1082 A197 50c multi   .65   .65
1083 A197 75c multi   .85   .85
1084 A197 90c multi   1.00 1.00
1085 A197 $1 multi   1.10 1.10
1086 A197 $1.15 multi   1.60 1.60
1087 A197 $1.40 multi   1.75 1.75
1088 A197 $1.75 multi   2.25 2.25
1089 A197 $2.10 multi   2.75 2.75
1090 A197 $3 multi   3.75 3.75
1091 A197 $5 multi   6.00 6.00
1092 A197 $10 multi   11.50 11.50
     Nos. 1078-1092 (15)   34.65 34.65

Dated "2010"
2010   Wmk. 406   Litho.   Perf. 13¾
1078a   5c multi   .25   .25
1079a   10c multi   .25   .25
1082a   50c multi   .50   .50
1086a $1.15 multi   1.25 1.25
1087a $1.40 multi   1.40 1.40
1088a $1.75 multi   1.75 1.75
    Nos. 1078a-1088a (6)   5.40 5.40

Barbados Fire Service, 50th Anniv. A198

Designs: 5c, Three firefighters. 10c, Parade at firehouse. 90c, Yellow fire truck. $1.15, Old fire trucks. $2.50, Red fire truck.

Wmk. 373
2005, Sept. 26   Litho.   Perf. 14
1093-1097 A198 Set of 5   14.00 14.00

Extreme Anoles A199

Designs: 10c, Three anoles. 50c, Two anoles. $1.75, One anole. $2, Hatchling and eggs.

Wmk. 373
2005, Nov. 28   Litho.   Perf. 14
1098-1101 A199 Set of 4   9.50 9.50

Worldwide Fund for Nature (WWF) A200

Queen angelfish and: 10c, Diver. $1.15, Coral. $1.40, Sea floor. $2.10, Coral, diff.

Wmk. 373
2006, Jan. 30   Litho.   Perf. 14
1102-1105 A200 Set of 4   6.50 6.50
1105a   Sheet, 2 each #1102-1105 13.00 13.00

Washington 2006 World Philatelic Exhibition — A201

Children: 10c, Reading. 50c, Playing wheelchair basketball. $2, At computer. $2.50, Playing violins.

Perf. 13¼x13½
2006, May 26   Litho.   Wmk. 373
1106-1109 A201 Set of 4   8.50 8.50

Cave Shepherd Store, Cent. A202

Store facades from around: 10c, 1911. 50c, 2000. $1.75, 1975. $2, 1920.

Wmk. 373
2006, Nov. 1   Litho.   Perf. 13¾
1110-1113 A202 Set of 4   8.50 8.50

Enfranchisement of Free Colored and Black Barbadians, 175th Anniv. — A203

Designs: 10c, Old Town Hall, Coleridge Street. 50c, Samuel Jackman Prescod (1806-71). $1.40, Introduction of ballot box, 1885. $2.50, Sir James Lyon, Governor from 1829-33.

2006, Nov. 27
1114-1117 A203 Set of 4   6.75 6.75

2007 ICC Cricket World Cup — A204

Designs: $1.75, Joel "Big Bird" Garner. $2.10, Old Kensington Oval, horiz. $3, New Kensington Oval, horiz. $10, ICC Cricket World Cup.

Wmk. 373
2007, Mar. 19   Litho.   Perf. 14
1118-1120 A204 Set of 3   7.00 7.00
Souvenir Sheet
Litho. & Embossed
1121 A204 $10 multi   10.00 10.00

Abolition of Slavery, Bicent. — A205

Designs: 10c, Sculpture of Bussa, slave revolt leader. $1, William Wilberforce, British abolitionist. $1.75, Slave hut, horiz. $2, Freedom celebration, 1838, horiz. $3, Slave ship.

Perf. 14¾x14¼, 14¼x14¾
2007, Mar. 26   Litho.   Wmk. 373
1122-1125 A205 Set of 4   5.00 5.00
Souvenir Sheet
1126 A205 $3 multi   3.00 3.00

Opening of Jewish Synagogue Museum, Bridgetown A206

Designs: 5c, Interior of synagogue. 10c, Museum building. $1.40, Hanukiah. $2.50, Stained-glass window.

2007, May 15   Perf. 12½x13
1127-1130 A206 Set of 4   4.25 4.25

Turtles A207

Turtles: 10c, Green. 50c, Loggerhead. $1, Hawksbill. $2.50, Leatherback.

Perf. 12½x13
2007, Oct. 29   Litho.   Unwmk.
1131-1134 A207 Set of 4   4.25 4.25

Algae — A208

Designs: 10c, Padina gymnospora. 50c, Ulva lactuca. $1.75, Sargassum platycarpum. $2, Udotea conglutinata.

Wmk. 373
2008, July 14   Litho.   Perf. 13¾
1135-1138 A208 Set of 4   4.50 4.50

Barbadians and Aircraft — A209

Designs: 10c, Second Barbados Contingent. 50c, Warren Alleyne, Supermarine Spitfire Mk IX. $1.75, Wing Commander Aubrey Inniss, Bristol Beaufighter Mk VIC. $2, Flying Officer Errol Barrow, Avro Lancaster B Mk 1. $6, Concorde over Barbados.

Wmk. 373
2008, July 30   Litho.   *Perf. 14*
1139-1142 A209   Set of 4   4.50 4.50
Souvenir Sheet
1143 A209 $6 multi   6.00 6.00

Christmas
A210

Paintings: 10c, Christmas Moon, by Alison Chapman-Andrews. 50c, Preparing for Christmas, by Virgil Broodhagen. $1.40, Christmas Candles, by Darla Trotman. $3, Poinsettia and Snow on the Mountain, by Trotman.

2008, Nov. 11   Wmk. 406   *Perf. 13½*
1144-1147 A210   Set of 4   5.00 5.00

Louis Braille (1809-52), Educator of the Blind — A211

Braille and: 50c, Hands of worker using pliers. $1.40, Worker caning chair. $1.75, Student reading Braille text at Braille typewriter. $2, "Louis Braille" in Braille text.

2009, July 6   Perf. 14
1148-1151 A211   Set of 4   5.75 5.75

Restructured Criminal Court, 300th Anniv. — A212

Designs: 10c, New Court House. 50c, Handcuffs, seal of the court. $1.40, Judge's robe, wig and gavel. $2.50, Old Court House.

Wmk. 406
2009, Nov. 10   Litho.   *Perf. 12½*
1152-1155 A212   Set of 4   4.50 4.50

Queen's Park, Bridgetown, Cent. (in 2009) A213

Designs: 90c, Queen's Park Fountain. $1, Baobab tree. $1.40, Queen's Park House. $2, Band stand.
$4, Band stand at park's opening.

Perf. 12½x13
2010, Jan. 11   Unwmk.
1156-1159 A213   Set of 4   5.50 5.50
Souvenir Sheet
1160 A213 $4 multi   4.00 4.00

Fireball World Championships Regatta — A214

Various racing sailboats: 10c, 50c, 90c, $1.75, $2.

2010, Apr. 23   Wmk. 406   *Perf. 14*
1161-1165 A214   Set of 5   5.25 5.25

Girl Guides, Cent. A215

Girl Guides: 10c, At camp. 50c, Giving salute. $1, In various uniforms. $2.50, On parade.
$3.50, Centenary emblem, emblems of Girl Guides and Barbados Girl Guides.

Perf. 14¼x14
2010, Sept. 22   Litho.   Wmk. 406
1166-1169 A215   Set of 4   4.25 4.25
Souvenir Sheet
1170 A215 $3.50 multi   3.50 3.50

Fruits — A216

Designs: 5c, Golden apples. 10c Coconuts. 35c, Cashews. 40c, Mammy apples. 60c, Barbados cherries. 65c, Sugar apples. 80c, Sea grapes. $1, Tamarinds. $1.25, Carambolas. $1.50, Mangos. $1.80, Bananas. $2.20, Guavas. $2.75, Avocados. $3, Gooseberries. $5, Soursops. $10, Pomegranates.

Unwmk.
2011, Feb. 7   Litho.   *Perf. 13*
1171 A216   5c multi   .25 .25
1172 A216   10c multi   .25 .25
1173 A216   35c multi   .35 .35
1174 A216   40c multi   .40 .40
1175 A216   60c multi   .60 .60
1176 A216   65c multi   .65 .65
1177 A216   80c multi   .80 .80
1178 A216 $1 multi   1.00 1.00
1179 A216 $1.25 multi   1.25 1.25
1180 A216 $1.50 multi   1.50 1.50
1181 A216 $1.80 multi   1.90 1.90
1182 A216 $2.20 multi   2.25 2.25
1183 A216 $2.75 multi   2.75 2.75
1184 A216 $3 multi   3.00 3.00
1185 A216 $5 multi   5.00 5.00
1186 A216 $10 multi   10.00 10.00
Nos. 1171-1186 (16)   31.95 31.95

Sailor's Valentines (Shell Art) — A217

Designs: 10c, Valentine from 1800s. 65c, "With My Love." $2.20, "Live Today, Hope Tomorrow." $2.75, "Evermore."

Perf. 12½x13
2011, Feb. 14   Wmk. 406
1187-1190 A217   Set of 4   5.75 5.75

Wedding of Prince William and Catherine Middleton — A218

Designs: 15c, Middleton in wedding dress with attendant. 65c, Couple in carriage. $1.80, Couple holding hands, vert. $2.20, Couple waving, vert.

Wmk. 406
2011, Aug. 3   Litho.   *Perf. 14*
1191-1194 A218   Set of 4   5.00 5.00

Reign of Queen Elizabeth II, 60th Anniv. A219

Queen Elizabeth II: 10c, Exiting Barbados Parliament, 1989. $1.40, Wearing tiara, 1952. $2.10, Inspecting Barbados soldiers, 1977. $2.50, At Goddard Space Flight Center, Maryland, 2007.
$4, Queen Elizabeth II and Prince Philip at opening of Barbados Parliament, 1987.

2012, Mar. 12   Wmk. 406   *Perf. 13*
1195-1198 A219   Set of 4   6.25 6.25
Souvenir Sheet
Perf. 13½x13
1199 A219 $4 multi   4.00 4.00
No. 1199 contains one 60x40mm stamp.

Bridgetown Landmarks A220

Designs: 10c, Gun Hill Signal Station. 65c, Clock tower, Main Guardhouse, Bridgetown Garrison. $2, St. Mary's Church, horiz. $2.75, Public Library, horiz.

2012, July 18   *Perf. 14*
1200-1203 A220   Set of 4   5.50 5.50
National Trust, 50th anniv.

Bridgetown Port, 50th Anniv. (in 2011) — A221

Designs: 10c, Pelican Island. 65c, Lightermen delivering cargo. $1.75, Tugboat Barbados II. $2.80, Aerial view of Bridgetown Port.

2012, Oct. 1
1204-1207 A221   Set of 4   5.50 5.50

Lighthouses A222

Designs: 65c, Harrison Point Lighthouse. $1.50, South Point Lighthouse. $1.80, Needham's Point Lighthouse. $2.20, East Point Lighthouse.

2013, June 13
1208-1211 A222   Set of 4   6.25 6.25

Churches A223

Designs: 10c, Holetown Methodist Church. 65c, Mt. Tabor Moravian Church. $1.80, St. Patrick's Roman Catholic Church. $3, St. John's Anglican Church.

Wmk. 406
2013, Sept. 30   Litho.   *Perf. 13¼*
1212-1215 A223   Set of 4   5.75 5.75

Seven Wonders of Barbados — A224

Designs: No. 1216, 65c, Morgan Lewis Windmill. No. 1217, 65c, St. Nicholas Abbey. No. 1218, 65c, Dry Dock, horiz. No. 1219, 65c, Music Rocks, horiz. No. 1220, 65c, Cove Bay, horiz. No. 1221, 65c, Harrison's Cave, horiz. No. 1222, 65c, Lion of Gun Hill, yellow frame, horiz. No. 1223a, Like No. 1222, pale green frame (48x48mm).

Wmk. 406
2014, Feb. 21   Litho.   *Perf. 13¼*
1216-1222 A224   Set of 7   4.75 4.75
Miniature Sheet
1223   Sheet of 7, #1216-1221, 1223a   4.75 4.75
a.   A224 65c multi   .65 .65

Barbados Parliament, 375th Anniv. A225

Designs: 10c, Bust of Sir Conrad Reeves (1821-1902), Chief Justice of Barbados. 65c, Speaker's chair. $1.40, Sir Kenmore Husbands (1905-91), House of Assembly Speaker. $2, House of Assembly stained-glass window depicting King Charles I.
$5, Mace.

Wmk. 406
2014, June 26   Litho.   *Perf. 13¾*
1224-1227 A225   Set of 4   4.25 4.25
Souvenir Sheet
1228 A225 $5 multi   5.00 5.00

Panama Canal, Cent. — A226

Designs: 10c, SS Ancon arrives at Cristobal, 1909. 65c, Track shifting gang, 1911, horiz. $1, Rock slide at Gold Hill, 1911, horiz. $2, Workers moving building, 1914, horiz. $3, Floor slab on rock, 1915, horiz.

Wmk. 406
2014, Aug. 15   Litho.   *Perf. 14*
1229-1233 A226   Set of 5   6.75 6.75

University of West Indies Branch at
Cave Hill, Barbados, 50th Anniv.
A227

Designs: 10c, Clock Tower. 65c, Student
receiving scroll. $1.40, Golden Stool. $2.50,
Standard bearer.

Wmk. 406

2014, Sept. 15		**Litho.**		***Perf. 14***	
1234-1237	A227	Set of 4		4.75	4.75

A228

Gardens — A229

Designs: 10c, Gardenia Gardens. 65c,
Hunte's Garden. $1.80, Glendale Gardens.
$2.20, Eusteen's Gardens.
No. 1242: Various arrangements, as shown.

	Perf. 12½x13¼			
2014, Dec. 18	**Litho.**	**Wmk. 406**		
1238-1241	A228	Set of 4	4.75	4.75
Miniature Sheet				
	Perf. 13¼			
1242	A229	$1 Sheet of 4, #a-d	4.00	4.00

Windmills — A230

Designs: 10c, Graeme Hall Windmill. 65c,
Balls Windmill. $2.20, St. Nicholas Abbey
Windmill. $2.50, Morgan Lewis Windmill.

Wmk. 406

2015, June 23		**Litho.**		***Perf. 14***	
1243-1246	A230	Set of 4		5.50	5.50

Famous
Barbadians
A231

Designs: 5c, Bussa (d. 1816), leader of
slave rebellion. 10c, Sir Grantley Adams
(1898-1971), first Premier of Barbados. 25c,
Sir Frank Walcott (1916-99), ambassador to
the United Nations. 60c, Sir Hugh Springer

(1913-94), Governor-General. 65c, Daphne
Joseph-Hackett (1915-88), actress. $1, Dr.
Charles Duncan O'Neal (1879-1936), physician, founder of Democratic League. $1.50,
Samuel Jackman Prescod (1806-71), member
of Parliament. $1.80, Clement Osbourne
Payne (1904-41), trade union leader. $2,
Arlington DaCosta Edwards (1933-96), governmental minister, educator. $2.20, Sarah
Ann Gill (1795-1866), anti-slavery religious
leader. $2.50, Eunice Gibson (1895-1974),
founder of Barbados Registered Nurses Association. $3, Errol Walton Barrow (1920-87),
first Prime Minister of Barbados. $5, James
Arthur Tudor (1892-1985), business leader
and politician. $10, Sir Garfield Sobers, cricket
player.

Wmk. 406

2016, Jan. 18	**Litho.**		***Perf. 12½***	
1247	A231	5c multi	.25	.25
1248	A231	10c multi	.25	.25
1249	A231	25c multi	.25	.25
1250	A231	60c multi	.60	.60
1251	A231	65c multi	.65	.65
1252	A231	$1 multi	1.00	1.00
1253	A231	$1.50 multi	1.50	1.50
1254	A231	$1.80 multi	1.80	1.80
1255	A231	$2 multi	2.00	2.00
1256	A231	$2.20 multi	2.20	2.20
1257	A231	$2.50 multi	2.50	2.50
1258	A231	$3 multi	3.00	3.00
1259	A231	$5 multi	5.00	5.00
1260	A231	$10 multi	10.00	10.00
	Nos. 1247-1260 (14)		31.00	31.00

Landships
A232

Designs: 10c, Landship Tuk band, 1970s.
65c, Maypole. $1.80, Landship performance at
Crop Over Heritage Gala, 2009. $2.20, Com-
mander Leon Marshall (1906-73).
$5, Lord High Commander Vernon Nathan-
iel Watson, vert.

Wmk. 406

2016, Aug. 17		**Litho.**		***Perf. 14***	
1261-1264	A232	Set of 4		4.75	4.75
Souvenir Sheet					
1265	A232	$5 multi		5.00	5.00

Independence, 50th Anniv. — A233

Designs: 10c, Bus. 65c, Samuel Jackman
Prescod Polytechnic. $1, Pine Hill Dairy.
$1.50, Blenheim Cricket Ground. $1.80, Barbados blackbelly sheep. $2.20, Hilton Barba-
dos Resort.
$8, Prime Minister Errol Walton Barrow on
Independence Night, 1966, vert.

Wmk. 406

2016, Nov. 18		**Litho.**		***Perf. 14***	
1266-1271	A233	Set of 6		7.25	7.25
Souvenir Sheet					
1272	A233	$8 multi		8.00	8.00

Centenarians of
Barbados — A234

Designs: No. 1273, 65c, Rev. C. Vincent S.
Belle (1915-2016). No. 1274, 65c, Vivian
Ursula Blenman (1913-2014). No. 1275, 65c,
Beatrice Gertrude Carrington (1912-2012).
No. 1276, 65c, Winston Cameron Catline
(1915-2015). No. 1277, 65c, Olive Augusta
Licorish (1914-2015). No. 1278, 65c, Alma
Geraldine Rae (1911-2014). No. 1279, 65c,
Rose Adeline Wiltshire (1914-2015). No.
1280, 65c, Aldora Odessa Yearwood (1915-
2015). No. 1281, 65c, Francis Medford Clarke.

No. 1282, 65c, Vera Elaine Gibbs. No. 1283,
65c, Doris Elese Greaves. No. 1284, 65c, Iona
Viola Griffith. No. 1285, 65c, Helen Lizetta
Hutchinson. No. 1286, 65c, Constance L.
Inniss. No. 1287, 65c, Christopher McDonald
Smith. No. 1288, 65c, Rupert Sydney
Springer. No. 1289, 65c, Carlotta Elise Strick-
land. No. 1290, 65c, Alicia Waithe. No. 1291,
65c, Elaine Ometa Walkes. No. 1292, 65c,
Edithe Vimetta St. Clair Wilkinson.
No. 1293: a, James Emmanuel Sisnett
(1900-2013). b, Emily Clarke (1902-2013). c,
Marie Millicent Trotman (1905-2013). d, Milli-
cent Alberta Yearwood. e, Melville Williams. f,
Eleise Hortense Rock. g, Sylvia Maughan.

Wmk. 406

2016, Dec. 8		**Litho.**		***Perf. 14***	
1273-1292	A234	Set of 20		13.00	13.00
Miniature Sheet					
1293	A234	65c Sheet of 7, #a- g, + 2 labels		4.75	4.75

No. 1293b is not inscribed with country
name.

Motor
Sports
A235

Cars, checkered flag and inscriptions: 10c,
Triumph TR4, June Rally, 1970. 65c, Mitsub-
ishi Shogun, Mud Dogs, 2011. $1.80, Toyota
Starlet, Sprint Event, 1988. $2.20, Subaru
Impreza, Sol Rally, 2012.
No. 1298 — Cars, checkered flag and
inscriptions: a, Williams Digicel International
Race meet, 2011. b, Radical SR3S. c, Big
saloons leave the line. d, Bushy Park start,
1994. e, Karting.

Wmk. 406

2017, June 12		**Litho.**		***Perf. 12¾***	
1294-1297	A235	Set of 4		4.75	4.75
Miniature Sheet					
1298	A235	$1 Sheet of 5, #a-e		5.00	5.00

SEMI-POSTAL STAMPS

No. 73 Surcharged in
Red

	Perf. 14			
1907, Jan. 25	**Typo.**	**Wmk. 2**		
B1	A8	1p on 2p sl & org	7.00	13.00
a.	No period after 1d		70.00	110.00
b.	Inverted surcharge		2.00	7.50
c.	Inverted surcharge, no period after 1d		47.50	105.00
d.	Double surcharge		925.00	1,000.
e.	Dbl. surch., both invtd.		925.00	
f.	Dbl. surch., one invtd.		1,200.	
g.	Vert. pair, one normal, one surcharge double			1,200.
h.	Pair with surcharges tête-bêche		1,800.	

No. 406
Surcharged

1979, May 29	**Photo.**	**Wmk. 314**		
B2	A56	28c + 4c on 35c multi	.70	.70

The surtax was for victims of the eruption of
Mt. Soufrière.

POSTAGE DUE STAMPS

D1

1934-47	**Typo.**	**Wmk. 4**	***Perf. 14***	
J1	D1	½p green ('35)	1.60	8.50
J2	D1	1p black	2.25	1.75
a.	Half used as ½p on cover			2,500.
J3	D1	3p dk car rose ('47)	26.00	23.00
	Nos. J1-J3 (3)		29.85	33.25

A 2nd die of the 1p was introduced in 1947.
Use of #J2a was authorized from Mar. 1934
through Feb. 1935. Some examples have "½d"
written on the bisect in black or red ink.

1950

J4	D1	1c green	.30	3.00
J5	D1	2c black	1.00	6.50
J6	D1	6c carmine rose	1.00	8.50
	Nos. J4-J6 (3)		2.30	18.00

Values are for 1953 chalky paper printing.
Values on ordinary paper, unused $32, used
$85.

Wmk. 4a (error)

J4a	D1	1c green	450.00	650.00
J5a	D1	2c black	800.00	
J6a	D1	6c carmine rose	180.00	
	Nos. J4a-J6a (3)		1,430.	

1965, Aug. 3		**Wmk. 314**		***Perf. 14***	
J7	D1	1c green		.50	4.50
J8	D1	2c black		.60	5.50
J9	D1	6c carmine rose		1.50	13.00
a.	Wmk. sideways, perf 14x13½			10.50	20.00
	Nos. J7-J9 (3)			2.60	23.00

Issued: No. J9a, 2/4/74.

Wmk. 314 Sideways

1974, Dec. 4			***Perf. 13x13½***	
J8b	D1	2c	8.00	20.00
J9b	D1	6c	8.00	20.00

D2

Designs: Each stamp shows different stylized flower in background.

	Perf. 13½x14			
1976, May 12	**Litho.**		**Wmk. 373**	
J10	D2	1c brt pink & mag	.35	.80
J11	D2	2c lt & dk vio blue	.35	.80
J12	D2	5c yellow & brown	.35	.80
J13	D2	10c lilac & purple	.45	1.05
J14	D2	25c yel green & dk grn	1.10	3.00
J15	D2	$1 rose & red	1.10	3.00
	Nos. J10-J15 (6)		3.70	9.45

1985, July			***Perf. 15x14***	
J10a	D2	1c	.50	.50
J11a	D2	2c	.50	.50
J12a	D2	5c	.50	.50
J13a	D2	10c	.50	.50
J14a	D2	25c	.50	.50
	Nos. J10a-J14a (5)		2.50	2.50

WAR TAX STAMP

No. 118 Overprinted

1917		**Wmk. 3**	***Perf. 14***	
MR1	A12	1p carmine	.55	.25
a.	Imperf., pair		2,500.	

BARBUDA

bär-'büd-ə

LOCATION — In northern Leeward Islands, West Indies
GOVT. — Dependency of Antigua
AREA — 63 sq. mi.
POP. — 1,500 (1995 est.)
See Antigua.

12 Pence = 1 Shilling
100 Cents = 1 Dollar (1951)

Catalogue values for unused stamps in this country are for Never Hinged items, beginning with Scott 12 in the regular postage section, and Scott B1 in the semi-postal section.

Watermark

Wmk. 380 — "POST OFFICE"

Leeward Islands Stamps of 1912-22 Ovptd. in Black or Red

Die II

For description of dies I and II, see Dies of British Colonial Stamps in the catalogue introduction.

1922, July 13 **Wmk. 4** **Perf. 14**

1	A5	½p green	1.75	12.00
2	A5	1p rose red	1.75	12.00
3	A5	2p gray	1.75	7.50
4	A5	2½p ultramarine	1.75	9.00
5	A5	6p vio & red vio	2.25	19.00
6	A5	2sh vio & ultra, *bl*	13.50	55.00
7	A5	3sh green & violet	32.50	75.00
8	A5	4sh blk & scar (R)	40.00	75.00

Wmk. 3

9	A5	3p violet, *yel*	2.00	15.00
10	A5	1sh blk, *emer* (R)	1.75	9.00
11	A5	5sh grn & red, *yel*	65.00	125.00
		Nos. 1-11 (11)	164.00	413.50
		Set, never hinged	300.00	

Beware of forgeries, especially used examples dated June 1, 1923.

Catalogue values for unused stamps in this section, from this point to the end of the section, are for Never Hinged items.

Map — B1

Fish — B2

20c, Great barracuda. 25c, Great amberjack. 35c, French angelfish. 50c, Porkfish. 75c, Striped parrotfish. $1, Long-spine squirrelfish. $2.50, Catalufa. $5, Blue chromis.

1968-70 **Litho.** **Unwmk.** **Perf. 14**

12	B1	½c blk, salmon pink & red brn	.45	2.75
13	B1	1c blk, org & brt org	1.25	.30
14	B1	2c blk, brt pink & brt rose	1.60	1.25
15	B1	3c blk, yel & org yel	1.40	.40
16	B1	4c blk, lt grn & brt grn	2.00	2.75
17	B1	5c blk, bl grn & brt bl grn	1.60	.25
18	B1	6c blk, lt lil & red lil	1.00	2.25
19	B1	10c blk, lt bl & dk bl	1.40	1.00
20	B1	15c blk, dl grn & grn	1.60	3.00
21	B2	20c multicolored	1.40	1.40
22	B2	25c multicolored	1.10	.30
23	B2	35c multicolored	1.40	.35
24	B2	50c multicolored	.70	.55
25	B2	75c multicolored	.70	.60
26	B2	$1 multicolored	.60	1.10
27	B2	$2.50 multicolored	1.00	.75
28	B2	$5 multicolored	1.25	1.60
		Nos. 12-28 (17)	20.45	20.60

Issued: ½c-15c, 11/19/68; 20c, 7/22/70; 25c-75c, 2/5/69; others, 3/6/69.
For surcharge see No. 80.

1968 Summer Olympics, Mexico City — B3

Designs: 25c, Running, Aztec calendar stone. 35c, High jumping, Aztec statue. 75c, Yachting, Aztec lion mask. $1, Soccer, Aztec carved stone.

1968, Dec. 20

29	B3	25c multicolored	.40	.25
30	B3	35c multicolored	.50	.30
31	B3	75c multicolored	.85	.45
		Nos. 29-31 (3)	1.75	1.00

Souvenir Sheet

32	B3	$1 multicolored	3.00	3.75

The Ascension, by Orcagna — B4

1969, Mar. 24

33	B4	25c blue & black	.25	.45
34	B4	35c dp carmine & blk	.25	.50
35	B4	75c violet & black	.25	.55
		Nos. 33-35 (3)	.75	1.50

Easter.

3rd Caribbean Boy Scout Jamboree — B5

1969, Aug. 7

36	B5	25c Flag ceremony	.50	.55
37	B5	35c Campfire	.60	.70
38	B5	75c Rowing	.80	.95
		Nos. 36-38 (3)	1.90	2.20

The Sistine Madonna, by Raphael — B6

1969, Oct. 20

39	B6	½c multicolored	.25	.30
40	B6	25c multicolored	.25	.25
41	B6	35c multicolored	.25	.25
42	B6	75c multicolored	.25	.40
		Nos. 39-42 (4)	1.00	1.20

Christmas.

English Monarchs — B7

No. 43, William I. No. 44, William II. No. 45, Henry I. No. 46, Stephen. No. 47, Henry II. No. 48, Richard I. No. 49, John. No. 50, Henry III. No. 51, Edward I. No. 52, Edward II. No. 53, Edward III. No. 54, Richard II. No. 55, Henry IV. No. 56, Henry V. No. 57, Henry VI. No. 58, Edward IV. No. 59, Edward V. No. 60, Richard III. No. 61, Henry VII. No. 62, Henry VIII. No. 63, Edward VI. No. 64, Lady Jane Grey. No. 65, Mary I. No. 66, Elizabeth I. No. 67, James I. No. 68, Charles I. No. 69, Charles II. No. 70, James II. No. 71, William III. No. 72, Mary II. No. 73, Anne. No. 74, George I. No. 75, George II. No. 76, George III. No. 77, George IV. No. 78, William IV. No. 79, Victoria.

1970-71 **Perf. 14½x14**

43-79	B7	35c Set of 37	8.00	13.00

Issued: 1970, No. 43, 2/16; No. 44, 3/2; No. 45, 3/16; No. 46, 4/4; No. 47, 4/15; No. 48, 5/1; No. 49, 5/15; No. 50, 6/1; No. 51, 6/15; No. 52, 7/1; No. 53, 7/15; No. 54, 8/1; No. 55, 8/15; No. 56, 9/1; No. 57, 9/15; No. 58, 10/1; No. 59, 10/15; No. 60, 11/2; No. 61, 11/16; No. 62, 12/1; No. 63, 12/15.
1971: No. 64, 1/2; No. 65, 1/15; No. 66, 2/1; No. 67, 2/15; No. 68, 3/1; No. 69, 3/15; No. 70, 4/1; No. 71, 4/15; No. 72, 5/1; No. 73, 5/15; No. 74, 6/1; No. 75, 6/15; No. 76, 7/1; No. 77, 7/15; No. 78, 8/2; No. 79, 8/16.
See Nos. 622-627 for other Monarchs.

No. 12 Surcharged

1970, Feb. 26 **Perf. 14**

80	B1	20c on ½c multicolored	.40	.40

Easter — B8

1970, Mar. 16

81	B8	25c Carrying Cross	.25	.30
82	B8	35c Descent from cross	.25	.30
83	B8	75c Crucifixion	.25	.35
a.		Strip of 3, #81-83	.70	.70

Charles Dickens B9

1970, July 10

84	B9	20c Oliver Twist	.30	.30
85	B9	75c Old Curiosity Shop	.65	.65

Christmas — B10

Designs: 20c, Madonna of the Meadow, by Giovanni Bellini. 50c, Madonna, Child and Angels from Wilton Diptych. 75c, Nativity, by Piero della Francesca.

1970, Oct. 15

86	B10	20c multicolored	.25	.25
87	B10	50c multicolored	.25	.30
88	B10	75c multicolored	.25	.35
		Nos. 86-88 (3)	.75	.90

British Red Cross, Cent. B11

20c, Patient in wheelchair, vert. 75c, Child care.

1970, Dec. 21

89	B11	20c multicolored	.25	.40
90	B11	35c shown	.25	.50
91	B11	75c multicolored	.40	.85
		Nos. 89-91 (3)	.90	1.75

Easter — B12

Details from the Mond Crucifixion, by Raphael.

1971, Apr. 7

92	B12	35c Angel	.25	.95
93	B12	50c Crucifixion	.25	1.10
94	B12	75c Angel, diff.	.30	1.25
a.		Strip of 3, #92-94	.85	3.50

Martello Tower B13

25c, Sailboats. 50c, Hotel bungalows. 75c, Government House, mystery stone.

1971, May 10

95	B13	20c shown	.25	.40
96	B13	25c multicolored	.25	.45
97	B13	50c multicolored	.25	.50
98	B13	75c multicolored	.40	.70
		Nos. 95-98 (4)	1.15	2.05

Christmas — B14

Paintings: ½c, The Granduca Madonna, by
Raphael. 35c, The Ansidei Madonna, by
Raphael. 50c, The Virgin and Child, by Botti-
celli. 75c, The Madonna of the Trees, by
Bellini.

1971, Oct. 4
99	B14	½c multicolored	.25	.25
100	B14	35c multicolored	.25	.25
101	B14	50c multicolored	.25	.25
102	B14	75c multicolored	.25	.30
		Nos. 99-102 (4)	1.00	1.05

A set of four stamps for Durer (20c,
35c, 50c, 75c) was not authorized.
Value $12.

All stamps are types of Antigua or
overprinted on stamps of Antigua
unless otherwise specified. Many of the
"BARBUDA" overprints are vertical.

**Antigua Nos. 321-322 (Wedding of
Princess Anne and Mark Phillips)
Ovptd. "BARBUDA"**

1973, Nov. 14   Perf. 13½
103	A65	35c multicolored	6.00	5.00
104	A65	$2 multicolored	1.50	2.00

**Antigua Nos. 313-315a (Butterfly
costumes) Ovptd. in Red
"BARBUDA"**

1973, Nov. 26   Perf. 13½x14
105	A63	20c multicolored	.25	.25
106	A63	35c multicolored	.50	.60
107	A63	75c multicolored	.85	.85
		Nos. 105-107 (3)	1.60	1.70

Souvenir Sheet
108		Sheet of 4, #105-107, 108a	1.75	2.50
a.		A63 5c multicolored		

Carnival, 1973.

**Antigua Nos. 307, 309, 311, 311a
(Uniforms) Ovptd. "BARBUDA"**

**   Perf. 14x13½**

1973, Nov. 26   Wmk. 314
109	A53	½c multicolored	.25	.25
110	A53	20c multicolored	.25	.25
111	A53	75c multicolored	.55	.35
		Nos. 109-111 (3)	1.05	.85

Souvenir Sheet
112		Sheet of 5, #109-111, 112a-112b + label	3.50	3.50
a.		A53 10c multicolored		
b.		A53 35c multicolored		

**Antigua Nos. 241a, 242-243, 244a,
245-248, 249a, 250-254, 255a, 256,
256a, 257 Ovptd. "BARBUDA"**

Wmk. 314 Sideways, Upright

1973-74   Perf. 14
113	A51	½c multicolored	.30	.45
114	A51	1c multicolored	.30	.45
115	A51	2c multicolored	.45	.50
116	A51	3c multicolored	.45	.45
117	A51	4c multicolored	.60	.50
118	A51	5c multicolored	.80	.80
119	A51	6c multicolored	.80	.80
120	A51	10c multicolored	1.00	1.00
121	A51	15c multicolored	1.00	1.20
122	A51	20c multicolored	1.00	1.20
123	A51	25c multicolored	1.00	1.20
124	A51	35c multicolored	1.00	1.20
125	A51	50c multicolored	1.00	1.20
126	A51	75c multicolored	1.00	1.20
127	A51	$1 multicolored	1.00	1.20
128	A51	$2.50 multicolored	2.40	4.25
a.		Wmk. upright	8.50	9.25
129	A51	$5 multicolored	3.00	5.50
		Nos. 113-129 (17)	17.10	22.90

Issue dates: ½c, 3c, 15c, $1, $2.50, Feb. 18,
1974. Others, Nov. 26.

**Antigua Nos. 316-320a (Christmas)
Ovptd. in Silver or Red "BARBUDA"**

**   Perf. 14½**

1973, Dec. 11   Photo.   Unwmk.
130	A64	3c multicolored	.25	.25
131	A64	5c multicolored	.25	.25
132	A64	20c multicolored	.25	.25
133	A64	35c multicolored (R)	.25	.25
134	A64	$1 multicolored (R)	.25	.25
		Nos. 130-134 (5)	1.25	1.25

Souvenir Sheet
135		Sheet of 5 + label	5.00	7.00
a.		A64 35c multicolored (S)		
b.		A64 $1 multicolored (S)		

No. 135 contains Nos. 130-132, 135a-135b.

**Antigua Nos. 323-324a (Visit of
Princess Anne and Mark Phillips to
Antigua) Ovptd. "BARBUDA"**

1973, Dec. 16   Litho.   Perf. 13½
136	A65	35c multicolored	.25	.25
137	A65	$2 multicolored	1.25	1.25
a.		Souvenir sheet of 2, #136-137	6.00	7.00

**Antigua Nos. 325-328 (University of
West Indies) Ovptd. "BARBUDA"**

1974, Feb. 18   Wmk. 314
138	A66	5c multicolored	.25	.25
139	A66	20c multicolored	.25	.25
140	A66	35c multicolored	.25	.25
141	A66	75c multicolored	.25	.25
		Nos. 138-141 (4)	1.00	1.00

**Antigua Nos. 329-333 (Uniforms)
Ovptd. "BARBUDA"**

1974, May 1   Perf. 14x13½
142	A53	½c multicolored	.25	.25
143	A53	10c multicolored	.25	.25
144	A53	20c multicolored	.25	.25
145	A53	35c multicolored	.35	.25
146	A53	75c multicolored	.50	.40
		Nos. 142-146 (5)	1.60	1.40

No. 333a exists with overprint.

**Antigua Nos. 334-340 Ovptd. Type
"a" or "b" in Red**

a & b

**1974, July 15   Unwmk.   Perf. 14½
Se-tenant Pairs Overprinted Type
"a" on Left Stamp, Type "b" on
Right Stamp**
148	A67	½c multicolored	.25	.25
149	A67	1c multicolored	.25	.25
150	A67	2c multicolored	.40	.25
151	A67	5c multicolored	1.00	1.00
152	A67	20c multicolored	.95	1.50
153	A67	35c multicolored	3.00	4.50
154	A67	$1 multicolored	6.50	12.00
		Nos. 148-154 (7)	12.35	19.25

Souvenir Sheet

**   Perf. 13**
155		Sheet of 7 + label	7.50	11.50
a.		A67 ½c multicolored	.25	.35
b.		A67 1c multicolored	.25	.35
c.		A67 2c multicolored	.25	.35
d.		A67 5c multicolored	.25	.35
e.		A67 20c multicolored	1.00	1.60
f.		A67 35c multicolored	1.25	3.25
g.		A67 $1 multicolored	4.00	4.75

UPU, cent.

**Antigua Nos. 341-344a (Steel bands
- Carnival 1974) Ovptd. "BARBUDA"**

1974, Aug. 14   Wmk. 314   Perf. 14
156	A68	5c multicolored	.25	.25
157	A68	20c multicolored	.25	.25
158	A68	35c multicolored	.25	.25
159	A68	75c multicolored	.25	.25
a.		Souvenir sheet of 4, #156-159	1.00	1.00
		Nos. 156-159 (4)	1.00	1.00

Antigua Nos. 345-
348a Overprinted

and

World Cup Soccer
Championships — B16

Various soccer plays.

1974, Sept. 2   Unwmk.   Perf. 15, 14
160	A69	5c multicolored	.25	.25
161	A69	35c multicolored	.25	.25
162	B16	35c multicolored	.25	.25
163	A69	75c multicolored	.25	.25
164	A69	$1 multicolored	.25	.25
a.		Souv. sheet of 4, #160-161, 163-164 + 2 labels, perf. 13½	1.25	1.25
165	B16	$1.20 multicolored	.40	.40
166	B16	$2.50 multicolored	.60	.70
a.		Souv. sheet of 3, #162, 165-166	1.40	1.40
		Nos. 160-166 (7)	2.25	2.35

UPU,
Cent. — B17

1974, Sept. 30   Perf. 14x13½
167	B17	35c Ship letter, 1833	.25	.25
168	B17	$1.20 #1, 2 on FDC	.25	.30
169	B17	$2.50 Airplane, map	.40	.50
a.		Souvenir sheet of 3, #167-169	1.90	1.90
		Nos. 167-169 (3)	.90	1.05

Greater
Amberjack
B18

½c, Oleander, rose bay. 1c, Blue petrea. 2c,
Poinsettia. 3c, Cassia tree. 5c, Holy Trinity
School. 6c, Snorkeling. 10c, Pilgrim Holiness
Church. 15c, New Cottage Hospital. 20c, Post
Office & Treasury. 25c, Island jetty & boats.
35c, Martello Tower. 50c, Warden's House.
75c, Inter-island air service. $1, Tortoise.
$2.50, Spiny lobster. $5, Frigate birds. $10,
Hibiscus.

1974-75   Perf. 14x14½, 14½x14
170	B18	½c multi	.25	.50
171	B18	1c multi	.30	.50
172	B18	2c multi	.30	.50
173	B18	3c multi	.30	.50
174	B18	4c shown	2.75	.50
175	B18	5c multi	.35	.50
176	B18	6c multi	.35	.50
177	B18	10c multi	.35	.30
178	B18	15c multi	.35	.30
179	B18	20c multi	.35	.30
180	B18	25c multi	.70	.55
181	B18	35c multi	.70	.55

Size: 39x25mm

Perf. 14
182	B18	50c multi	.70	.55
183	B18	75c multi	2.25	1.75
184	B18	$1 multi	1.50	1.40

Size: 45x29mm

Perf. 13½x14
185	B18	$2.50 multi	1.75	3.50
186	B18	$5 multi	6.25	5.50
a.		Perf. 14x15	13.50	17.50

Size: 34x47mm
187	B18	$10 multi	4.00	6.75
		Nos. 170-187 (18)	23.50	24.70

Nos. 170-173, 180, 187 vert.

Issued: 4c, 5c, 6c, 10c, 15c, 20c, 25c, 35c,
75c, 10/15/74; ½c, 1c, 2c, 3c, 50c, $1, $2.50,
No. 186, 1/6/75; No. 186a, 7/24/75; $10,
9/19/75.

For overprints see Nos. 213-214.

**Antigua Nos. 349-352a Ovptd. in
Red**

and

Winston Churchill, Birth Cent. — B19

1974   Perf. 14½, 13½x14
188	A70	5c multicolored	.25	.25
189	B19	5c Making broadcast	.25	.25
190	A70	35c multicolored	.30	.25
191	B19	35c Portrait	.25	.25
192	A70	75c multicolored	.50	.50
193	B19	75c Painting	.25	.25
194	A70	$1 multicolored	.85	.80
a.		Souv. sheet of 4, #188, 190, 192, 194	10.50	20.00
195	B19	$1 Victory sign	.35	.30
a.		Souv. sheet of 4, #189, 191, 193, 195	1.50	2.00
		Nos. 188-195 (8)	3.00	2.85

Issue dates: Nos. 188, 190, 192, 194, Oct.
15, others, Nov. 20. For overprints see Nos.
213-214.

**Antigua Nos. 353-360a (Christmas
paintings) Ovptd. "BARBUDA"**

1974, Nov. 25   Perf. 14½
196	A71	½c multicolored	.25	.25
197	A71	1c multicolored	.25	.25
198	A71	2c multicolored	.25	.25
199	A71	3c multicolored	.25	.25
200	A71	5c multicolored	.25	.25
201	A71	20c multicolored	.25	.25
202	A71	35c multicolored	.25	.25
203	A71	75c multicolored	.25	.25
a.		Souv. sheet, #200-203, perf 13½	1.10	1.40
		Nos. 196-203 (8)	2.00	2.00

**Antigua Nos. 369-373a (Nelson's
Dockyard) Ovptd. "BARBUDA"**

1975, Mar. 17
204	A72	5c multicolored	.25	.25
205	A72	15c multicolored	.45	.35
206	A72	35c multicolored	.55	.45
207	A72	50c multicolored	.65	.65
208	A72	$1 multicolored	.75	.75
a.		Souv. sheet of 5, #204-208 + label, perf. 13½x14	3.00	4.25
		Nos. 204-208 (5)	2.65	2.45

Stamps from No. 208a are 43x28mm.

Battle
of the
Saints
B20

1975, May 30   Perf. 13½x14
209	B20	35c shown	.75	.75
210	B20	50c Two ships	1.00	1.00
211	B20	75c Ships firing	1.25	1.25
212	B20	95c Sailors abandoning ship	1.50	1.50
		Nos. 209-212 (4)	4.50	4.50

Barbuda No. 186a Ovptd.

a

1975, July 2 — Perf. 14x15
213 B18 (a) $5 multicolored 5.50 6.50
214 B18 (b) $5 multicolored 5.50 6.50

Overprint "a" is in 1st and 3rd vertical rows, "b" 2nd and 4th. The 5th row has no overprint. This can be collected se-tenant either as Nos. 213, 214 or 213, 214 and 186a. Value, strip of three, $22.50.

Military Uniforms — B21

Designs: 35c, Officer of 65th Foot, 1763. 50c, Grenadier, 27th Foot, 1701-1710. 75c, Officer of 21st Foot, 1793-1796. 95c, Officer, Royal Regiment of Artillery, 1800.

1975, Sept. 17 — Perf. 14
215 B21 35c multicolored .50 .50
216 B21 50c multicolored .75 .75
217 B21 75c multicolored 1.25 1.25
218 B21 95c multicolored 1.50 1.50
Nos. 215-218 (4) 4.00 4.00

Barbuda Nos. 189, 191, 193, 195 Ovptd.

1975, Oct. 24 — Perf. 13½x14
219 B19 5c multicolored .25 .25
220 B19 35c multicolored .25 .25
221 B19 75c multicolored .25 .25
222 B19 $1 multicolored .30 .25
Nos. 219-222 (4) 1.05 1.00

Antigua Nos. 394-401a (Christmas) Ovptd. "BARBUDA"

1975, Nov. 17 — Perf. 14
223 A77 ½c multicolored .25 .25
224 A77 1c multicolored .25 .25
225 A77 2c multicolored .25 .25
226 A77 3c multicolored .25 .25
227 A77 5c multicolored .25 .25
228 A77 10c multicolored .25 .25
229 A77 35c multicolored .25 .25
230 A77 $2 multicolored .25 .25
a. Souvenir sheet of 4, #227-230 2.00 2.25
Nos. 223-230 (8) 2.00 2.00

Antigua Nos. 402-404 (World Cup Cricket) Ovptd. "BARBUDA"

1975, Dec. 15 — Perf. 14
231 A78 5c multicolored 1.10 1.10
232 A78 35c multicolored 2.10 2.10
233 A78 $2 multicolored 3.75 3.75
Nos. 231-233 (3) 6.95 6.95

American Revolution, Bicent. — B22

Details from Surrender of Cornwallis at Yorktown, by Trumbull: No. 234a, British officers. b, Gen. Benjamin Lincoln. c, Washington, Allied officers.
The Battle of Princeton: No. 235a, Infantry. b, Battle. c, Cannon fire.
Surrender of Burgoyne at Saratoga by Trumbull: No. 236a, Mounted officer. b, Washington, Burgoyne. c, American officers.

Signing the Declaration of Independence, by Trumbull: No. 237a, Delegates to Continental Congress. b, Adams, Sherman, Livingston, Jefferson and Franklin. c, Hancock, Thomson, Read, Dickinson, and Rutledge. Strips of 3 have continuous designs.

1976, Mar. 8 — Perf. 13½x13
234 B22 15c Strip of 3, #a.-c. .25 .25
235 B22 35c Strip of 3, #a.-c. .80 .80
d. Souvenir sheet, #234-235 1.20 1.20
236 B22 $1 Strip of 3, #a.-c. 1.00 1.00
237 B22 $2 Strip of 3, #a.-c. 1.75 1.75
d. Souvenir sheet, #236-237 3.00 3.00

See Nos. 244-247.

Birds B23

35c, Bananaquits. 50c, Blue-hooded euphonia. 75c, Royal tern. 95c, Killdeer. $1.25, Glossy cowbird. $2, Purple gallinule.

1976, June 30 — Perf. 13½x14
238 B23 35c multicolored 1.00 .65
239 B23 50c multicolored 1.00 .75
240 B23 75c multicolored 1.25 1.00
241 B23 95c multicolored 1.50 1.10
242 B23 $1.25 multicolored 1.50 1.10
243 B23 $2 multicolored 1.50 1.40
Nos. 238-243 (6) 7.75 6.00

Barbuda #234-237 With Inscription Added at Top Across the Three Stamps in Blue

1976, Aug. 12 — Perf. 13½x14
Size: 38x31mm
244 B22 15c Strip of 3, #a.-c. .30 .30
245 B22 35c Strip of 3, #a.-c. .50 .50
d. Souvenir sheet of 2, #244-245 1.00 1.00
246 B22 $1 Strip of 3, #a.-c. .75 .75
247 B22 $2 Strip of 3, #a.-c. 1.25 1.25
d. Souvenir sheet, #246-247 2.75 2.75

Nos. 244-247 are perforated on outside edges; imperf. vertically within.

Antigua Nos. 448-452 (Christmas) Ovptd. "BARBUDA"

1976, Dec. 2 — Perf. 14
248 A85 8c multicolored .25 .25
249 A85 10c multicolored .25 .25
250 A85 15c multicolored .25 .25
251 A85 50c multicolored .25 .25
252 A85 $1 multicolored .25 .25
Nos. 248-252 (5) 1.25 1.25

Antigua Nos. 431-437 (Olympic Games) Ovptd. "BARBUDA"

1976, Dec. 28 — Perf. 15
253 A82 ½c yellow & multi .25 .25
254 A82 1c purple & multi .25 .25
255 A82 2c emerald & multi .25 .25
256 A82 15c brt blue & multi .25 .25
257 A82 30c olive & multi .25 .25
258 A82 $1 orange & multi .25 .25
259 A82 $2 red & multi .25 .25
a. Souv. sheet, #256-259, perf 13½ 2.25 2.25
Nos. 253-259 (7) 1.75 1.75

Telephone, Cent. — B24

$1.25, Satellite dish, television. $2, Satellites in earth orbit.

1977, Jan. 31 — Perf. 14
260 B24 75c shown .25 .25
261 B24 $1.25 multicolored .25 .35
262 B24 $2 multicolored .50 .60
a. Souv. sheet, #260-262, perf 15 1.25 1.25
Nos. 260-262 (3) 1.00 1.20

Coronation of Queen Elizabeth II, 25th Anniv. — B25

Designs: Nos. 263a, St. Margaret's Church, Westminster. b, Westminster Abbey entrance. c, Westminster Abbey.
Nos. 264a, Riders on horseback. b, Coronation coach. c, Team of horses. Strips of 3 have continuous designs.

1977, Feb. 7 — Perf. 13½x13
263 B25 75c Strip of 3, #a.-c. .35 .35
264 B25 $1.25 Strip of 3, #a.-c. .55 .55

Souvenir Sheet
265 B25 Sheet of 6 1.25 1.25

Nos. 263a-264c se-tenant with labels. No. 265 contains Nos. 263a-264c with silver borders.

Antigua Nos. 405-422 (1976 Definitives) Ovptd. "BARBUDA"

1977, Apr. 4 — Perf. 15
266 A79 ½c multicolored .25 .25
267 A79 1c multicolored .25 .25
268 A79 2c multicolored .25 .25
269 A79 3c multicolored .25 .25
270 A79 4c multicolored .25 .25
271 A79 5c multicolored .25 .25
272 A79 6c multicolored .25 .25
273 A79 10c multicolored .25 .25
274 A79 15c multicolored .25 .25
275 A79 20c multicolored .25 .25
276 A79 25c multicolored .25 .25
277 A79 35c multicolored .30 .25
278 A79 50c multicolored .35 .35
279 A79 75c multicolored .35 .35
280 A79 $1 multicolored .65 .65
Perf. 13½x14
281 A80 $2.50 multicolored 1.80 2.10
282 A80 $5 multicolored 3.50 4.00
283 A80 $10 multicolored 6.75 7.75
Nos. 266-283 (18) 16.45 18.20

For overprints see Nos. 506-516.

Antigua Nos. 459-464 (Royal Family) Ovptd. "BARBUDA"

1977, Apr. 4 — Perf. 13½x14, 12
284 A87 10c multicolored .25 .25
285 A87 30c multicolored .25 .25
286 A87 50c multicolored .25 .25
287 A87 90c multicolored .25 .35
288 A87 $2.50 multicolored .50 1.00
Nos. 284-288 (5) 1.50 2.10

Souvenir Sheet
289 A87 $5 multicolored 1.50 1.50

A booklet of self-adhesive stamps contains one pane of six rouletted and die cut 50c stamps in design of 90c (silver overprint), and one pane of one die cut $5 (gold overprint) in changed colors. Panes have marginal inscriptions.
For overprints see Nos. 312-317.

Antigua Nos. 465-471a (Boy Scouts) Ovptd. "BARBUDA"

1977, June 13 — Perf. 14
290 A88 ½c multicolored .25 .25
291 A88 1c multicolored .25 .25
292 A88 2c multicolored .25 .25
293 A88 10c multicolored .25 .25
294 A88 30c multicolroed .50 .50
295 A88 90c multicolored .70 .70
296 A88 $2 multicolored 1.40 1.40
a. Souvenir sheet of 3, #294-296 3.60 3.60
Nos. 290-296 (7) 3.60 3.60

Overprint is slightly smaller on No. 296a.

Antigua Nos. 472-476a (Carnival) Ovptd. "BARBUDA"

1977, Aug. 12
297 A89 10c multicolored .25 .25
298 A89 30c multicolored .25 .25
299 A89 50c multicolored .25 .25
300 A89 90c multicolored .25 .25
301 A89 $1 multicolored .25 .30
a. Souvenir sheet of 4, #298-301 1.90 1.90
Nos. 297-301 (5) 1.25 1.30

Royal Visit B26

50c, Royal yacht Britannia. $1.50, Jubliee emblem. $2.50, Flags.

1977, Oct. 27 — Perf. 14½
302 B26 50c multicolored .25 .25
303 B26 $1.50 multicolored .25 .25
304 B26 $2.50 multicolored .40 .50
a. Souvenir sheet of 3, #302-304 1.50 1.50
Nos. 302-304 (3) .90 1.00

Antigua Nos. 483-489 (Christmas) Ovptd. "BARBUDA"

1977, Nov. 15 — Perf. 14
305 A90 ½c multicolored .25 .25
306 A90 1c multicolored .25 .25
307 A90 2c multicolored .25 .25
308 A90 8c multicolored .25 .25
309 A90 10c multicolored .25 .25
310 A90 25c multicolored .25 .25
311 A90 $2 multicolored .25 .25
a. Souvenir sheet of 4, #308-311 1.60 1.60
Nos. 305-311 (7) 1.75 1.75

Antigua Nos. 477-482 (Royal Visit overprints) Ovptd. "BARBUDA" in Black

1977, Dec. 20 — Perf. 12
312 A87 10c multicolored .25 .25
313 A87 30c multicolored .25 .25
314 A87 50c multicolored .25 .25
315 A87 90c multicolored .25 .25
316 A87 $2.50 multicolored .40 .40
Nos. 312-316 (5) 1.40 1.40

Nos. 312-316 exist with blue overprint.

1977, Nov. 28 — Perf. 13½x14
312a A87 10c multicolored .25 .25
313a A87 30c multicolored .25 .25
314a A87 50c multicolored .25 .25
315a A87 90c multicolored .25 .25
316a A87 $2.50 multicolored .40 .40
Nos. 312a-316a (5) 1.40 1.40

Souvenir Sheet
317 A87 $5 multicolored 1.75 1.75

Overprint of Nos. 312-316a differs from that on Nos. 312-316.

Anniversaries — B27

First navigable airships, 75th anniv: No. 318a, Zeppelin LZ1. b, German Naval airship L31. c, Graf Zeppelin. d, Gondola on military airship.
Soviet space program, 20th anniv: No. 319a, Sputnik, 1957. b, Vostok rocket, 1961. c, Voskhod rocket, 1964. d, Space walk, 1965.
Lindbergh's Atlantic crossing, 50th anniv: No. 320a, Fueling for flight. b, New York take-off. c, Spirit of St. Louis. d, Welcome in England.
Coronation of Queen Elizabeth II, 25th anniv: No. 321a, Lion of England. b, Unicorn of Scotland. c, Yale of Beaufort. d, Falcon of Plantagenets.
Rubens, 400th birth anniv: No. 322a, Two lions. b, Daniel in the Lion's Den. c, Two lions lying down. d, Lion at Daniel's feet. Block of 4 has continuous design.

1977, Dec. 29 — Perf. 14½x14
Blocks of 4
318 B27 75c #a.-d. 1.75 1.75
319 B27 95c #a.-d. 2.10 2.10
320 B27 $1.25 #a.-d. 2.40 2.40
321 B27 $2 #a.-d. 3.00 3.00
322 B27 $5 #a.-d. 3.00 4.00
e. Min. sheet, #318-322 + 4 labels 11.00 18.00
Nos. 318-322 (5) 12.25 13.25

Antigua Nos. 490-494a (10th Anniversary of Statehood) Ovptd. "BARBUDA"

1978, Feb. 15 — Perf. 13x13½
323 A91 10c multicolored .25 .25
324 A91 15c multicolored .25 .25
325 A91 50c multicolored 1.25 .80
326 A91 90c multicolored .40 .40
327 A91 $2 multicolored .55 .90
a. Souv. sheet, #324-327, perf 14 5.00 4.00
Nos. 323-327 (5) 2.70 2.60

Pieta, by Michelangelo — B28

Works by Michelangelo: 95c, Holy Family. $1.25, Libyan Sibyl. $2, The Flood.

1978, Mar. 23   *Perf. 13½x14*

328	B28	75c multicolored	.25	.25
329	B28	95c multicolored	.25	.25
330	B28	$1.25 multicolored	.25	.25
331	B28	$2 multicolored	.25	.25
a.		Souvenir sheet of 4, #328-331	2.25	2.25
		Nos. 328-331 (4)	1.00	1.00

Antigua Nos. 495-502 (Wright Brothers) Ovptd. "BARBUDA"

1978, Mar. 23   *Perf. 14*

332	A92	½c multicolored	.25	.25
333	A92	1c multicolored	.25	.25
334	A92	2c multicolored	.25	.25
335	A92	10c multicolored	.25	.25
336	A92	50c multicolored	.35	.35
337	A92	90c multicolored	.45	.45
338	A92	$2 multicolored	1.10	1.10
		Nos. 332-338 (7)	2.90	2.90

Souvenir Sheet

339	A92	$2.50 multicolored	2.10	3.25

Antigua Nos. 503-507 (Sailing Week) Ovptd. "BARBUDA"

1978, May 22   *Perf. 14½*

340	A93	10c multicolored	.25	.25
341	A93	50c multicolored	.45	.45
342	A93	90c multicolored	.75	.75
343	A93	$2 multicolored	1.40	1.40
		Nos. 340-343 (4)	2.85	2.85

Souvenir Sheet

344	A93	$2.50 multicolored	2.25	3.00

Coronation of Queen Elizabeth II, 25th Anniv. — B29

Crowns: No. 345a, St. Edward's. b, Imperial State. No. 346a, Queen Mary's. b, Queen Mother's. No. 347a, Queen Consort's. b, Queen Victoria's.

1978, June 2   *Perf. 15*
Miniature Sheets of Two Each Plus Two Labels

345	B29	75c Sheet of 4	.75	.75
346	B29	$1.50 Sheet of 4	1.25	1.25
347	B29	$2.50 Sheet of 4	2.00	2.00

Souvenir Sheet
Perf. 14½

348	B29	Sheet of 6, #345a-347b	1.50	2.50

Antigua Nos. 508-514 (QEII Coronation Anniversary) Ovptd. in Black or Deep Rose Lilac "BARBUDA"

1978   *Perf. 14*

349	A94	10c multicolored	.25	.25
350	A94	30c multicolored	.25	.25
351	A94	50c multicolored	.25	.25
352	A94	90c multicolored	.40	.40
353	A94	$2 multicolored	.75	.75
		Nos. 349-353 (5)	1.90	1.90

Souvenir Sheet

354	A94	$5 multicolored	1.60	1.60

Self-adhesive

355		Souvenir booklet	6.50	6.50
a.		A95 Bklt. pane, 3 each 25c and 50c, die cut, rouletted (DRL)	1.50	1.50
b.		A95 $5 Bklt. pane of 1, die cut	5.00	5.00

Issued: Nos. 349-354, June 2; #355, Oct. 12.

Antigua Nos. 515-518 (World Cup Soccer) Ovptd. "BARBUDA"

1978, Sept. 12   *Perf. 15*

356	A96	10c multicolored	.25	.25
357	A96	15c multicolored	.25	.25
358	A96	$3 multicolored	1.00	1.00
		Nos. 356-358 (3)	1.50	1.50

Souvenir Sheet

359		Sheet of 4	1.50	1.50
a.		A96 25c multicolored	.25	.25
b.		A96 30c multicolored	.25	.25
c.		A96 50c multicolored	.25	.25
d.		A96 $2 multicolored	.75	.75

Antigua Nos. 519-523 (Flowers) Ovptd. "BARBUDA"

1978, Nov. 20   *Perf. 14*

360	A97	25c multicolored	.40	.40
361	A97	50c multicolored	.60	.60
362	A97	90c multicolored	.80	.90
363	A97	$2 multicolored	1.75	2.25
		Nos. 360-363 (4)	3.55	4.15

Souvenir Sheet

364	A97	$2.50 multicolored	3.50	3.50

Flora and Fauna B30

25c, Blackbar soldierfish. 50c, Painted lady. 75c, Dwarf poinciana. 95c, Zebra butterfly. $1.25, Bougainvillea.

1978, Nov. 20   *Perf. 15*

365	B30	25c multicolored	2.10	2.10
366	B30	50c multicolored	3.25	3.25
367	B30	75c multicolored	2.50	3.50
368	B30	95c multicolored	3.25	3.50
369	B30	$1.25 multicolored	2.25	3.50
		Nos. 365-369 (5)	13.35	15.85

Antigua Nos. 524-527 (Christmas) Ovptd. in Silver "BARBUDA"

1978, Nov. 20   *Perf. 14*

370	A98	8c multicolored	.25	.25
371	A98	25c multicolored	.25	.25
372	A98	$2 multicolored	.75	.75
		Nos. 370-372 (3)	1.25	1.25

Souvenir Sheet

373	A98	$4 multicolored	2.25	2.25

Events and Annivs. B31

Designs: 75c, 1978 World Cup Soccer Championships, vert. 95c, Wright Brothers 1st powered flight, 75th anniv. $1.25, First Trans-Atlantic balloon flight, Aug. 1978. $2, Coronation of Elizabeth II, 25th anniv., vert.

1978, Dec. 20   *Perf. 14*

374	B31	75c multicolored	.55	.55
375	B31	95c multicolored	.65	.65
376	B31	$1.25 multicolored	.95	.95
377	B31	$2 multicolored	1.10	1.10
a.		Souv. sheet, #374-377, imperf	6.50	7.00
		Nos. 374-377 (4)	3.25	3.25

No. 377a has simulated perfs.

Nos. 528-532 Overprinted in Bright Blue

and

Sir Rowland Hill, Death Cent. — B32

75c, Sir Rowland Hill, vert. 95c, Mail coach, 1840. $1.25, London's first pillar box, 1855. No. 384, $2, St. Martin's Post Office, London, vert.

1979, Apr. 4

378	A99	25c multicolored	.25	.25
379	A99	50c multicolored	.25	.25
380	B32	75c multicolored	.30	.30
381	B32	95c multicolored	.35	.35
382	A99	$1 multicolored	.45	.45
383	B32	$1.25 multicolored	.50	.50
384	B32	$2 multicolored	.80	.80
a.		Souvenir sheet of 4, #380-381, 383-384, imperf.	2.00	2.00
385	A99	$2 multicolored	1.00	1.00
		Nos. 378-385 (8)	3.90	3.90

Souvenir Sheet

386	A99	$2.50 multicolored	2.00	2.00

No. 384a has simulated perfs.

Antigua Nos. 533-536 (Easter) Ovptd. "BARBUDA"

1979, Apr. 16

387	A100	10c multicolored	.40	.40
388	A100	50c multicolored	.60	.60
389	A100	$4 multicolored	1.50	1.50
		Nos. 387-389 (3)	2.50	2.50

Souvenir Sheet

390	A100	$2.50 multicolored	1.25	1.50

Intl. Civil Aviation Organization, 30th Anniv. — B33

75c, Passengers leaving 747. 95c, Air traffic controllers. $1.25, Plane on runway.

1979, May 24   *Perf. 13½x14*

391	B33	75c multicolored	.30	.40
392	B33	95c multicolored	.40	.50
393	B33	$1.25 multicolored	.50	.60
a.		Block of 3, #391-393 + label	1.50	1.50

Antigua Nos. 537-541 (Int'l Year of the Child) Ovptd. "BARBUDA"

1979, May 24   *Perf. 14*

394	A101	25c multicolored	.30	.30
395	A101	50c multicolored	.45	.45
396	A101	90c multicolored	1.00	1.00
397	A101	$2 multicolored	1.25	1.25
		Nos. 394-397 (4)	3.00	3.00

Souvenir Sheet

398	A101	$5 multicolored	2.25	2.25

Antigua Nos. 542-546 (Sport Fish) Ovptd. "BARBUDA"

1979, Aug. 1   *Perf. 14½*

399	A102	30c multicolored	.40	.30
400	A102	50c multicolored	.55	.50
401	A102	90c multicolored	.70	.70
402	A102	$3 multicolored	1.50	2.00
		Nos. 399-402 (4)	3.15	3.50

Souvenir Sheet

403	A102	$2.50 multicolored	1.75	2.25

Antigua Nos. 547-551 (Capt. Cook) Ovptd. "BARBUDA"

1979, Aug. 1   *Perf. 14*

404	A103	25c multicolored	.50	.45
405	A103	50c multicolored	1.25	.60
406	A103	90c multicolored	1.25	.75
407	A103	$3 multicolored	2.40	2.10
		Nos. 404-407 (4)	5.40	3.90

Souvenir Sheet

408	A103	$2.50 multicolored	2.50	2.50

Intl. Year of the Child — B34

Details of the Christ Child from various paintings by Durer: 25c, 1512. 50c, 1516. 75c, 1526. $1.25, 1502.

1979, Sept. 24   *Perf. 14x13½*

409	B34	25c multicolored	.25	.25
410	B34	50c multicolored	.25	.25
411	B34	75c multicolored	.25	.25
412	B34	$1.25 multicolored	.30	.30
a.		Souvenir sheet of 4, #409-412	1.25	1.25
		Nos. 409-412 (4)	1.05	1.05

Antigua Nos. 552-556 (Christmas) Ovptd. "BARBUDA"

1979, Nov. 21   *Perf. 14*

413	A104	8c multicolored	.25	.25
414	A104	25c multicolored	.25	.25
415	A104	50c multicolored	.40	.25
416	A104	$4 multicolored	1.25	1.25
		Nos. 413-416 (4)	2.15	2.00

Souvenir Sheet
Perf. 12x12½

417	A104	$3 multicolored	1.40	1.40

Antigua Nos. 557-561 (Moscow Olympics) Ovptd. "BARBUDA"

1980, Mar. 18

418	A105	10c multicolored	.25	.25
419	A105	25c multicolroed	.25	.25
420	A105	$1 multicolored	.30	.30
421	A105	$2 multicolored	.40	.40
		Nos. 418-421 (4)	1.20	1.20

Souvenir Sheet

422	A105	$3 multicolored	1.75	2.25

Antigua Nos. 571A-571D (London '80 Ovpts.) Overprinted "BARBUDA" in Dark Blue

1980, May 6   *Perf. 12*

423	A99	25c multicolored	.35	.25
424	A99	50c multicolored	.45	.50
425	A99	$1 multicolored	.75	.85
426	A99	$2 multicolored	2.50	1.90
		Nos. 423-426 (4)	4.05	3.50

Nos. 423-426 exist without the "London 1980" overprint.

First Moon Landing, 10th Anniv. — B35

75c, Crew badge. 95c, Plaque left on moon. $1.25, Lunar, command modules. $2, Lunar module.

1980, May 21   *Perf. 13½x14*

427	B35	75c multicolored	.40	.40
428	B35	95c multicolored	.45	.45
429	B35	$1.25 multicolored	.55	.55
430	B35	$2 multicolored	.85	.85
a.		Souvenir sheet of 4, #427-430	2.50	2.50
		Nos. 427-430 (4)	2.25	2.25

American Widgeon B36

2c, Snowy plover. 4c, Rose-breasted grosbeak. 6c, Mangrove cuckoo. 10c, Adelaide's warbler. 15c, Scaly-breasted thrasher. 20c, Yellow-crowned night heron. 25c, Bridled quail dove. 35c, Carib grackle. 50c, Northern pintail. 75c, Black-whiskered vireo. $1, Blue-winged teal. $1.50, Green-throated carib. $2, Red-necked pigeon. $2.50, Stolid flycatcher. $5,

Yellow-bellied sapsucker. $7.50, Caribbean elaenia. $10, Great egret.

1980, June 16   *Perf. 14½x14*

431	B36	1c shown	.70	.45
432	B36	2c multicolored	.70	.45
433	B36	4c multicolored	.80	.45
434	B36	6c multicolored	.80	.45
435	B36	10c multicolored	.80	.45
436	B36	15c multicolored	.80	.45
437	B36	20c multicolored	1.00	.45
438	B36	25c multicolored	1.00	.45
439	B36	35c multicolored	1.00	1.60
440	B36	50c multicolored	1.10	.45
441	B36	75c multicolored	1.25	.50
442	B36	$1 multicolored	1.40	.85

Perf. 14x14½

443	B36	$1.50 multicolored	2.00	1.10
444	B36	$2 multicolored	3.25	1.60
445	B36	$2.50 multicolored	4.00	1.90
446	B36	$5 multicolored	4.50	3.75
447	B36	$7.50 multicolored	6.25	6.50
448	B36	$10 multicolored	8.50	7.75
		Nos. 431-448 (18)	39.85	29.60

Nos. 443-448 vert.

Antigua Nos. 572-578 (Paintings) Ovptd. "BARBUDA"

1980, July 29   *Perf. 13½x14, 14x13½*

449	A106a	10c multicolored	.25	.25
450	A106a	30c multicolored	.25	.25
451	A106a	50c multicolored	.40	.40
452	A106a	90c multicolored	.50	.50
453	A106a	$1 multicolored	.50	.50
454	A106a	$4 multicolored	2.25	2.25
		Nos. 449-454 (6)	4.15	4.15

Souvenir Sheet
Perf. 14

455	A106a	$5 multicolored	3.50	3.50

Antigua Nos. 579-583 (Rotary Int'l) Ovptd. "BARBUDA"

1980, Sept. 8   *Perf. 14*

456	A107	30c multicolored	.25	.25
457	A107	50c multicolored	.25	.25
458	A107	90c multicolored	.35	.35
459	A107	$3 multicolored	1.00	1.00
		Nos. 456-459 (4)	1.85	1.85

Souvenir Sheet

460	A107	$5 multicolored	2.25	2.50

Antigua Nos. 584-586 (Queen Mother) Optd. "BARBUDA"

1980, Oct. 6

461	A108	10c multicolored	.50	.30
462	A108	$2.50 multicolored	2.50	2.50

Souvenir Sheet
Perf. 12

463	A108	$3 multicolored	3.50	3.50

Antigua Nos. 587-591 (Birds) Ovptd. "BARBUDA"

1980, Dec. 8   *Perf. 14*

464	A109	10c multicolored	3.25	1.25
465	A109	30c multicolored	4.00	1.60
466	A109	$1 multicolored	5.00	3.50
467	A109	$2 multicolored	6.00	6.25
		Nos. 464-467 (4)	18.25	12.60

Souvenir Sheet

468	A109	$2.50 multicolored	9.00	7.75

Antigua Nos. 602-606 (Locomotives) Ovptd. "BARBUDA"

1981, Jan. 26

469	A111	25c multicolored	1.50	.45
470	A111	50c multicolored	1.75	.55
471	A111	90c multicolored	2.40	.80
472	A111	$3 multicolored	3.50	1.90
		Nos. 469-472 (4)	9.15	3.70

Souvenir Sheet

473	A111	$2.50 multicolored	3.00	3.00

Famous Women — B37

50c, Florence Nightingale. 90c, Marie Curie. $1, Amy Johnson. $4, Eleanor Roosevelt.

1981, Mar. 9   *Perf. 14x13½*

474	B37	50c multicolored	.25	.25
475	B37	90c multicolored	.55	.55
476	B37	$1 multicolored	.50	.50
477	B37	$4 multicolored	.70	.70
		Nos. 474-477 (4)	2.00	2.00

Walt Disney Characters at Sea — B38

10c, Goofy. 20c, Donald Duck. 25c, Mickey Mouse. 30c, Goofy fishing. 35c, Goofy sailing. 40c, Mickey fishing. 75c, Donald Duck boating. $1, Minnie Mouse. $2, Chip 'n Dale.

$2.50, Donald Duck, diff.

1981, May 15   *Perf. 13½x14*

478	B38	10c multi	1.60	.40
479	B38	20c multi	1.75	.70
480	B38	25c multi	2.40	.75
481	B38	30c multi	2.40	1.00
482	B38	35c multi	2.40	1.00
483	B38	40c multi	2.75	1.40
484	B38	75c multi	3.00	1.75
485	B38	$1 multi	3.75	2.25
486	B38	$2 multi	4.75	3.50
		Nos. 478-486 (9)	24.80	12.55

Souvenir Sheet

487	B38	$2.50 multi	14.00	14.00

Antigua Nos. 618-622 (Picasso) Ovptd. "BARBUDA"

1981, June 9   *Perf. 14*

488	A112	10c multicolored	.25	.25
489	A112	50c multicolored	.50	.50
490	A112	90c multicolored	1.00	1.00
491	A112	$4 multicolored	2.50	2.50
		Nos. 488-491 (4)	4.25	4.25

Souvenir Sheet
Perf. 14x14½

492	A112	$5 multicolored	4.50	4.50

Miniature Sheets

Royal Wedding — B39

a-b, $1, L & R sides of Buckingham Palace. c-d, $1.50, L & R sides of Caernarvon Castle. e-f, $4, L & R sides of Highgrove House. No. 496, St. Paul's Cathedral, vert.

Sheets of 6, #a-f

1981, July 27   *Perf. 11x11½*

493	B39	blk & salmon	3.00	3.00
494	B39	blk & purple	3.00	3.00
495	B39	blk & gray grn	3.00	3.00

Souvenir Sheet
Perf. 11½x11

496	B39	$5 multicolored	1.25	1.25

Stamps of same denomination have continuous design. For surcharges see Nos. 592-594.

Common Design Types pictured following the introduction.

Antigua Nos. 623-627 (Royal Wedding) Ovptd. in Black or Silver "BARBUDA"

1981, Aug. 14   *Perf. 14*

497	CD331a	25c multicolored	.25	.25
498	CD331a	50c multicolored	.25	.25
499	CD331a	$4 multicolored	.70	.70
		Nos. 497-499 (3)	1.20	1.20

Souvenir Sheet

500	CD331	$5 multicolored	1.25	1.25

Self-adhesive

501	CD331	Booklet	8.50	8.50
a.		Pane of 6 (2x25c, 2x$1, 2x$2), Charles, die cut, rouletted (S)	4.00	4.00
b.		Pane of 1, $5 Couple, die cut (S)	4.00	4.00

Issued: Nos. 497-500, Aug. 24; No. 501, Oct. 12.
For surcharge see No. B1.

Intl. Year of the Disabled B40

50c, Travel. 90c, Braille, sign language. $1, Helping hands. $4, Mobility aids.

1981, Sept. 14   *Perf. 14*

502	B40	50c multicolored	.50	.50
503	B40	90c multicolored	.50	.50
504	B40	$1 multicolored	.50	.50
505	B40	$4 multicolored	.75	.75
		Nos. 502-505 (4)	2.25	2.25

Antigua Nos. 607-617 (Independence Ovpts.) Ovptd. "BARBUDA"

1981, Nov. 1   *Perf. 15*

506	A79	6c multicolored	.25	.25
507	A79	10c multicolored	.25	.25
508	A79	20c multicolored	.25	.25
509	A79	25c multicolored	.30	.25
510	A79	35c multicolored	.40	.30
511	A79	50c multicolored	.55	.40
512	A79	75c multicolored	.75	.60
513	A79	$1 multicolored	1.10	.75

Perf. 13½x14

514	A80	$2.50 multicolored	2.75	1.90
515	A80	$5 multicolored	5.00	3.75
516	A80	$10 multicolored	10.00	7.00
		Nos. 506-516 (11)	21.60	16.20

Antigua Nos. 628-632 (Girl Guides) Ovptd. "BARBUDA"

1981, Dec. 14   *Perf. 15*

517	A113	10c multicolored	.90	.25
518	A113	50c multicolored	1.50	.55
519	A113	90c multicolored	2.25	1.00
520	A113	$2.50 multicolored	3.50	2.75
		Nos. 517-520 (4)	8.15	4.55

Souvenir Sheet

521	A113	$5 multicolored	6.00	6.00

Antigua Nos. 643-647 (Int'l Year of the Disabled) Ovptd. "BARBUDA"

1981, Dec. 14

522	A116	10c multicolored	.25	.25
523	A116	50c multicolored	.50	.50
524	A116	90c multicolored	1.00	1.00
525	A116	$2 multicolored	2.00	2.00
		Nos. 522-525 (4)	3.75	3.75

Souvenir Sheet

526	A116	$4 multicolored	3.00	3.00

Antigua Nos. 638-642 (Christmas) Ovptd. in Black or Silver "BARBUDA"

1981, Dec. 22

527	A115	8c multi	.25	.25
528	A115	30c multi	.40	.40
529	A115	$1 multi (S)	.50	.50
530	A115	$3 multi	1.60	1.60
		Nos. 527-530 (4)	2.75	2.75

Souvenir Sheet

531	A115	$5 multi	2.25	2.50

Birth of Prince William — B41

Various portraits.

1982, June 21   Wmk. 380   *Perf. 14*

532	B41	$1 buff & multi	.65	.65
533	B41	$2.50 lt pink & multi	1.25	1.25
534	B41	$5 lt lilac & multi	2.75	2.75
		Nos. 532-534 (3)	4.65	4.65

Souvenir Sheet

535	B41	$4 Couple	4.75	4.75

See Nos. 540-543.

The overprint on stamps of Antigua, from here on, read "BARBUDA MAIL" in one or two lines.

Antigua Nos. 672-675 (Royal Baby) Ovptd. in Black or Silver
Perf. 14½x14

1982, Oct. 12   *Unwmk.*

536	CD332	90c multi	.60	.60
537	CD332	$1 multi (S)	.65	.65
538	CD332	$4 multi	2.75	2.75
		Nos. 536-538 (3)	4.00	4.00

Souvenir Sheet

539	CD332	$5 multi	4.00	4.00

Barbuda Nos. 532-535 Inscribed at Top

Various portraits.

Perf. 14x14½

1982, July 1   *Wmk. 380*

540	B41	$1 lt grn & multi	1.40	.60
541	B41	$2.50 pale sal & multi	2.25	1.50
542	B41	$5 lt bl & multi	3.25	3.00
		Nos. 540-542 (3)	6.90	5.10

Souvenir Sheet

543	B41	$4 Couple	5.00	5.00

Antigua Nos. 663-666 (Diana) Ovptd. in Black or Silver
Perf. 14½x14

1982, Aug. 30   *Unwmk.*

544	CD332	90c multi	.70	.50
545	CD332	$1 multi (S)	.80	.60
546	CD332	$4 multi	3.25	1.60
		Nos. 544-546 (3)	4.75	2.70

Souvenir Sheet

547	CD332	$5 multi	5.00	5.00

Antigua Nos. 676-683 (Washington/FDR) Overprinted

1982, Dec. 6   *Perf. 15*

551	A121	10c multicolored	.25	.25
552	A121	25c multicolored	.40	.25
553	A121	45c multicolored	1.75	.50
554	A121	60c multicolored	.50	.50
555	A121	$1 multicolored	2.25	.75
556	A121	$3 multicolored	1.75	1.25
		Nos. 551-556 (6)	6.90	3.50

Souvenir Sheets

557	A121	$4 on #682	3.50	5.00
558	A121	$4 on #683	3.50	5.00

Antigua Nos. 684-688 (Christmas) Overprinted

1982, Dec. 6   *Perf. 14*

559	A122	10c multicolored	.25	.25
560	A122	30c multicolored	.35	.35
561	A122	$1 multicolored	.85	.85
562	A122	$4 multicolored	2.10	2.10
		Nos. 559-562 (4)	3.55	3.55

Souvenir Sheet

563	A122	$5 multicolored	3.00	4.00

Antigua Nos. 689-693 (Raphael) Overprinted

1983, Mar. 14		Perf. 14½	
564 A123	45c multicolored	.25	.25
565 A123	50c multicolored	.35	.35
566 A123	60c multicolored	.35	.35
567 A123	$3 multicolored	2.25	2.25
Nos. 564-567 (4)		3.20	3.20

Souvenir Sheet

568 A123	$5 multicolored	2.50	2.50

Antigua Nos. 694-697 (Commonwealth Day) Overprinted

1983, Mar. 14		Perf. 14	
569 A124	25c multicolored	.60	.60
570 A124	45c multicolored	.85	.85
571 A124	60c multicolored	1.40	*1.50*
572 A124	$3 multicolored	3.50	*4.00*
Nos. 569-572 (4)		6.35	*6.95*

Antigua Nos. 698-702 (WCY) Overprinted

1983, Apr. 12			
573 A125	15c multicolored	2.50	.30
574 A125	50c multicolored	4.50	1.40
575 A125	60c multicolored	4.00	1.40
576 A125	$3 multicolored	6.25	4.00
Nos. 573-576 (4)		17.25	7.10

Souvenir Sheet

577 A125	$5 multicolored	4.50	*5.75*

First Manned Balloon Flight, Bicent. — B43

$1, Vincenzo Lunardi, 1785. $1.50, Montgolfier brothers, 1783. $2.50, Blanchard & Jeffries, 1785. $5, Graf Zeppelin, 1928.

1983, June 13			
578 B43	$1 multicolored	.50	.50
579 B43	$1.50 multicolored	.75	.75
580 B43	$2.50 multicolored	1.25	1.25
Nos. 578-580 (3)		2.50	2.50

Souvenir Sheet

581 B43	$5 multicolored	4.50	4.75

No. 581 exists imperf. Value, $12.50.

Antigua Nos. 703-707 (Marine Mammals) Overprinted

1983, July 4		Perf. 15	
582 A126	15c multicolored	2.50	.75
583 A126	50c multicolored	9.00	3.75
584 A126	60c multicolored	10.50	4.00
585 A126	$3 multicolored	14.50	7.00
Nos. 582-585 (4)		36.50	15.50

Souvenir Sheet

586 A126	$5 multicolored	12.50	12.50

Antigua Nos. 726-730 (Flight) Overprinted

1983, Sept. 12			
587 A128	30c multicolored	1.75	1.10
588 A128	50c multicolored	2.00	1.40
589 A128	60c multicolored	2.50	1.75
590 A128	$4 multicolored	7.25	7.25
Nos. 587-590 (4)		13.50	11.50

Souvenir Sheet

591 A128	$5 multicolored	6.75	*7.75*

Barbuda Nos. 493-495 Surcharged 45c on $1, 50c on $1.50 & 60c on $4

1983, Oct. 21		Perf. 11½x11	
592 B39	Sheet of 6, #493	3.50	3.50
593 B39	Sheet of 6, #494	3.50	3.50
594 B39	Sheet of 6, #495	3.50	3.50

Antigua Nos. 708-725 (Definitives) Overprinted

1983, Oct. 28		Perf. 14	
595 A127	1c multicolored	.25	.25
596 A127	2c multicolored	.25	.25
597 A127	3c multicolored	.25	.25
598 A127	5c multicolored	.25	.25
599 A127	10c multicolored	.45	.30
600 A127	15c multicolored	.80	.30
601 A127	20c multicolored	.80	.30
602 A127	25c multicolored	.85	.30
603 A127	30c multicolored	1.10	.50
604 A127	40c multicolored	1.25	.70
605 A127	45c multicolored	1.41	.70
606 A127	50c multicolored	1.60	.70
607 A127	60c multicolored	1.90	.90
608 A127	$1 multicolored	2.50	1.75
609 A127	$2 multicolored	3.00	3.50
610 A127	$2.50 multicolored	5.25	5.75
611 A127	$5 multicolored	5.50	6.25
612 A127	$10 multicolored	8.50	16.00
Nos. 595-612 (18)		35.91	38.95

Antigua Nos. 731-735 (Christmas) Overprinted

1983, Oct. 28		Perf. 14	
613 A129	10c multicolored	.25	.25
614 A129	30c multicolored	.25	.25
615 A129	$1 multicolored	.85	*.90*
616 A129	$4 multicolored	3.75	*4.00*
Nos. 613-616 (4)		5.10	*5.40*

Souvenir Sheet

617 A129	$5 multicolored	6.00	6.00

Antigua Nos. 736-739 (Methodists) Ovptd. in Black or Silver

1983, Dec. 14		Perf. 14	
618 A130	15c multicolored (S)	.45	.25
619 A130	50c multicolored (S)	.75	.50
620 A130	60c multicolored	.75	.60
621 A130	$3 multicolored	3.25	3.25
Nos. 618-621 (4)		5.20	4.60

Members of Royal Family — B44

1984, Feb. 14		Perf. 14½x14	
622 B44	$1 Edward VII	.75	1.50
623 B44	$1 George V	.75	1.50
624 B44	$1 George VI	.75	1.50
625 B44	$1 Elizabeth II	.75	1.50
626 B44	$1 Prince Charles	.75	1.50
627 B44	$1 Prince William	.75	1.50
Nos. 622-627 (6)		4.50	9.00

Nos. 740-744 Overprinted

and

1984 Summer Olympics, Los Angeles — B45

$1.50, Olympic Stadium, Athens. $2.50, Olympic Stadium, Los Angeles. $5, Torch bearer.

1984		Perf. 15, 13½ (B45)	
628 A131	25c multicolored	.35	.25
629 A131	50c multicolored	.50	.40
630 A131	90c multicolored	.60	.45
631 B45	$1.50 multicolored	.75	.75
632 B45	$2.50 multicolored	1.50	1.50
633 A131	$3 multicolored	3.00	*2.50*
634 B45	$5 multicolored	3.00	*4.00*
a.	Souv. sheet of 1, perf. 15	3.25	*4.00*
Nos. 628-634 (7)		9.70	9.85

Souvenir Sheet

635 A131	$5 multicolored	6.50	*7.25*

Issue dates: A131, Apr. 26, B45, July 27.

Antigua Nos. 755-759 (Flowers) Overprinted

1984, July 12		Perf. 15	
636 A133	15c multicolored	1.10	.90
637 A133	50c multicolored	1.40	1.60
638 A133	60c multicolored	1.75	1.90
639 A133	$3 multicolored	2.90	*4.00*
Nos. 636-639 (4)		7.15	*8.40*

Souvenir Sheet

640 A133	$5 multicolored	5.50	5.50

Antigua Nos. 745-749 (Ships) Overprinted

1984, July 12			
641 A132	45c multicolored	3.25	.85
642 A132	50c multicolored	3.25	1.00
643 A132	60c multicolored	4.25	1.25
644 A132	$4 multicolored	10.00	9.25
Nos. 641-644 (4)		20.75	12.35

Souvenir Sheet

645 A132	$5 multicolored	11.50	10.75

Antigua Nos. 760-767 (U.S. Presidents) Ovptd. in Black or Silver

1984, Oct. 1		Perf. 14	
646 A134	10c multicolored (S)	.25	.25
647 A134	20c multicolored (S)	.30	.30
648 A134	30c multicolored	.40	.40
649 A134	40c multicolored	.65	.65
650 A134	90c multicolored (S)	1.10	1.10
651 A134	$1.10 multicolored (S)	1.10	*1.25*
652 A134	$1.50 multicolored (S)	1.50	*2.00*
653 A134	$2 multicolored	2.00	*2.75*
Nos. 646-653 (8)		7.30	8.70

Antigua Nos. 768-772 (Slavery) Overprinted

1984, Oct. 1			
654 A135	40c multicolored	.65	.65
655 A135	50c multicolored	.80	.80
656 A135	60c multicolored	1.10	1.10
657 A135	$3 multicolored	3.25	3.25
Nos. 654-657 (4)		5.80	5.80

Souvenir Sheet

658 A135	$5 multicolored	6.25	6.25

Antigua Nos. 773-778 (Birds) Overprinted

1984, Nov. 21		Perf. 15	
659 A136	40c multicolored	3.75	1.00
660 A136	50c multicolored	4.25	1.10
661 A136	60c multicolored	4.50	1.75
662 A136	$2 multicolored	6.25	3.00
663 A136	$3 multicolored	6.25	5.00
Nos. 659-663 (5)		25.00	11.35

Souvenir Sheet

664 A136	$5 multicolored	22.50	22.50

Antigua Nos. 782-791 (Paintings) Overprinted in Silver

1984		Perf. 15	
665 A137a	15c multicolored	.25	.25
666 A137a	25c multicolored	.40	.40
667 A137a	50c multicolored	.80	.50
668 A137a	60c multicolored	1.00	1.00
669 A137a	70c multicolored	1.25	1.25
670 A137a	90c multicolored	1.40	1.40
671 A137a	$3 multicolored	2.50	2.50
672 A137a	$4 multicolored	3.50	3.50
Nos. 665-672 (8)		11.10	10.80

Souvenir Sheets

673 A137a	$5 #790	4.00	*5.00*
674 A137a	$5 #791, horiz.	4.00	*5.00*

Issued: Correggio, 11/21; Degas, 11/30.

Antigua Nos. 779-781 (AUSIPEX '84) Overprinted

1984, Nov. 30			
675 A137	$1 multicolored	1.00	1.00
676 A137	$5 multicolored	4.00	*5.00*

Souvenir Sheet

677 A137	$5 multicolored	5.00	*6.00*

Antigua Nos. 819-827 (20th Century Leaders) Overprinted

1985, Feb. 18			
678 A139	60c multicolored	6.00	6.00
679 A139	60c multicolored	6.00	6.00
680 A139	60c multicolored	6.00	6.00
681 A139	60c multicolored	6.00	6.00
682 A139	$1 multicolored	6.50	6.75
683 A139	$1 multicolored	6.50	6.75
684 A139	$1 multicolored	6.50	6.75
685 A139	$1 multicolored	6.50	6.75
Nos. 678-685 (8)		50.00	51.00

Souvenir Sheet

686 A139	$5 multicolored	13.00	13.00

Queen Mother (Lady Elizabeth Bowes-Lyon), 1907 — B46

45c, Duchess of York, 1926. 50c, Coronation, 1937. 60c, Queen Mother. 90c, Wearing tiara. $2, Wearing blue hat. $3, With children.

1985, Feb. 26		Perf. 14x14½	
687 B46	15c shown	.35	.35
688 B46	45c multicolored	.45	.45
689 B46	50c multicolored	.45	.45
690 B46	60c multicolored	.45	.45
691 B46	90c multicolored	.55	.55
692 B46	$2 multicolored	.90	.90
693 B46	$3 multicolored	1.25	1.25
Nos. 687-693 (7)		4.40	4.40

For overprints see Nos. 724-728, 733, 735.

Antigua Nos. 828-834 (Statue of Liberty) Overprinted

1985, May 10		Perf. 15	
694 A140	25c multicolored	.40	.40
695 A140	30c multicolored	.55	.55
696 A140	50c multicolored	.55	.55
697 A140	90c multicolored	1.00	1.00
698 A140	$1 multicolored	1.10	1.10
699 A140	$3 multicolored	3.00	3.00
Nos. 694-699 (6)		6.60	6.60

Souvenir Sheet

700 A140	$5 multicolored	5.50	5.50

Audubon, Birth Bicentenary — B47

45c, Roseate tern. 50c, Mangrove cuckoo. 60c, Yellow-crowned night heron. $5, Brown pelican.

1985, Apr. 4   *Perf. 14*
701	B47	45c multicolored	.35	.35
702	B47	50c multicolored	.40	.40
703	B47	60c multicolored	.45	.45
704	B47	$5 multicolored	3.75	3.75
		Nos. 701-704 (4)	4.95	4.95

**Antigua Nos. 845-849, 910-913
(Audubon) Ovptd. in Black or Silver**

1985-86   *Perf. 15, 12½x12*
705	A143	60c on #910 (S)	9.00	7.00
706	A143	90c on #845	11.00	8.25
707	A143	90c on #911 (S)	11.00	8.25
708	A143	$1 on #846	11.00	8.25
709	A143	$1.50 on #847	11.00	11.00
710	A143	$1.50 on #912 (S)	13.50	13.00
711	A143	$3 on #848	22.50	22.50
712	A143	$3 on #913	25.00	25.00
		Nos. 705-712 (8)	114.00	103.25

Souvenir Sheet
713	A143	$5 on #849	40.00	40.00

Issue dates: Nos. 706, 708-709, 711, 713,
July 18, 1985. Others, Dec. 1986.

**Antigua Nos. 850-854 (Butterflies)
Overprinted**

1985, July 18   *Perf. 14*
714	A144	25c multicolored	9.50	9.00
715	A144	60c multicolored	11.00	10.00
716	A144	95c multicolored	14.00	13.50
717	A144	$4 multicolored	25.00	25.00
		Nos. 714-717 (4)	59.50	57.50

Souvenir Sheet
718	A144		42.50	42.50

**Antigua Nos. 840-844 (Motorcycles)
Overprinted**

1985, Aug. 2
719	A142	10c multicolored	1.75	1.50
720	A142	30c multicolored	2.75	2.25
721	A142	60c multicolored	3.75	3.50
722	A142	$4 multicolored	12.00	12.00
		Nos. 719-722 (4)	20.25	19.25

Souvenir Sheet
723	A142	$5 multicolored	15.00	15.00

Barbuda Nos.
687-693
Overprinted in
Silver or Black

Antigua Nos.
866A-870 (Queen
Mother) Ovptd. in
Silver or Black

Perf. 14, 12x12½ (#729, 731, 736)

1985-86
724	B46	15c multi	.40	.40
725	B46	45c multi	.55	.55
726	B46	50c multi	.70	.70
727	B46	60c multi	.90	.90
728	B46	90c multi	1.20	1.20
729	A148	90c multi	1.20	1.20
730	A148	$1 multi (S)	1.40	1.40
731	A148	$1 like #730	1.40	1.40
732	A148	$1.50 multi (S)	2.25	2.25
733	B46	$2 multi	2.60	2.60
734	A148	$2.50 multi	3.50	3.50
735	B46	$3 multi	4.50	4.50
736	A148	$3 multi	4.50	4.50
		Nos. 724-736 (13)	25.10	25.10

Souvenir Sheet
737	A148	$5 multi	15.00	15.00

Queen Mother's 85th birthday.
Issue dates: 15c, 45c, 50c, 60c, No. 728,
$2, No. 735, Aug. 2. No. 730, $1.50, $2.50,
Nov. 8. Others, Dec. 1986. Nos. 729, 731, 736
issued in sheets of 5 plus label.

**Antigua Nos. 835-839 (Scenes)
Overprinted**

1985, Aug. 30   *Perf. 15*
738	A141	15c multicolored	.40	.40
739	A141	50c multicolored	.65	.65
740	A141	60c multicolored	.75	.75
741	A141	$3 multicolored	4.00	4.00
		Nos. 738-741 (4)	5.80	5.80

Souvenir Sheet
742	A141	$5 multicolored	6.75	6.75

**Antigua Nos. 855-859 (Airplanes)
Overprinted**

1985, Aug. 30   *Perf. 14*
743	A145	30c multicolored	1.90	1.90
744	A145	90c multicolored	3.25	3.25
745	A145	$1.50 multicolored	4.00	4.00
746	A145	$3 multicolored	5.50	5.50
		Nos. 743-746 (4)	14.65	14.65

Souvenir Sheet
747	A145	$5 multicolored	8.50	8.50

**Antigua Nos. 860-861 (Maimonides)
Overprinted**

1985, Nov. 25   *Perf. 14*
748	A146	$2 yellow green	11.50	11.50

Souvenir Sheet
749	A146	$5 deep brown	11.00	11.00

**Antigua Nos. 871-875 (Marine Life)
Ovptd. in Black or Silver**

1985, Nov. 25
750	A149	15c multi (S)	7.50	2.25
751	A149	45c multi	7.50	1.10
752	A149	60c multi	7.50	2.25
753	A149	$3 multi (S)	17.00	8.75
		Nos. 750-753 (4)	39.50	14.35

Souvenir Sheet
754	A149	$5 multi	21.00	21.00

**Antigua Nos. 862-866 (Youth Year)
Overprinted**

1986, Feb. 17
755	A147	25c multicolored	.30	.30
756	A147	50c multicolored	.60	.60
757	A147	60c multicolored	.65	.65
758	A147	$3 multicolored	3.25	3.25
		Nos. 755-758 (4)	4.80	4.80

Souvenir Sheet
759	A147	$5 multicolored	6.50	6.50

**Antigua Nos. 886-889 (Royal Visit)
Overprinted**

1986, Feb. 17   *Perf. 14½*
760	A152	60c multicolored	3.50	1.10
761	A152	$1 multicolored	3.50	2.40
762	A152	$4 multicolored	9.50	9.75
		Nos. 760-762 (3)	16.50	13.25

Souvenir Sheet
763	A152	$5 multicolored	16.00	16.00

**Antigua Nos. 876-880 (Bach)
Overprinted**

1986, Mar. 10   *Perf. 14*
764	A150	25c multicolored	4.00	1.10
765	A150	50c multicolored	4.00	3.00
766	A150	$1 multicolored	5.50	5.75
767	A140	$3 multicolored	10.00	9.50
		Nos. 764-767 (4)	23.50	19.35

Souvenir Sheet
768	A150	$5 multicolored	35.00	35.00

**Antigua Nos. 881-885 (Girl Guides)
Overprinted**

1986, Mar. 10   *Perf. 14*
769	A151	15c multicolored	3.00	2.25
770	A151	45c multicolored	5.00	5.00
771	A151	60c multicolored	5.00	5.00
772	A151	$3 multicolored	14.00	14.00
		Nos. 769-772 (4)	27.00	26.25

Souvenir Sheet
773	A151	$5 multicolored	45.00	40.00

**Antigua Nos. 905-909 (Christmas)
Overprinted**

1986, Apr. 4   *Perf. 15*
774	A156	10c multicolored	.65	.65
775	A156	25c multicolored	1.40	1.40
776	A156	60c multicolored	2.40	2.40
777	A156	$4 multicolored	7.00	7.00
		Nos. 774-777 (4)	11.45	11.45

Souvenir Sheet
778	A156	$5 multicolored	8.00	8.00

Queen
Elizabeth
II, 60th
Birthday
B48

$1, Shaking hands. $2, Talking with woman.
$2.50, With officer.
$5, Portraits.

1986, Apr. 21
779	B48	$1 multi	.90	.90
780	B48	$2 multi	.90	.90
781	B48	$2.50 multi	.90	.90
		Nos. 779-781 (3)	2.70	2.70

Souvenir Sheet
Perf. 13½x14
782	B48	$5 multi	7.50	7.50

No. 782 contains one 34x27mm stamp.

**Antigua Nos. 925-928 (Queen's
Birthday) Overprinted in Silver or
Black**

1986, Aug. 12
783	CD339	60c multi	1.40	1.40
784	CD339	$1 multi	2.25	2.25
785	CD339	$4 multi	9.00	9.00
		Nos. 783-785 (3)	12.65	12.65

Souvenir Sheet
786	CD339	$5 multi (Bk)	10.50	10.50

Nos. 920-924 Overprinted and

Halley's
Comet
B49

$2.50, Early telescope, dish antenna, vert.
$5, World map, comet.

1986   *Perf. 14, 15 (B49)*
787	A158	5c multicolored	2.25	2.25
788	A158	10c multicolored	2.25	2.25
789	A158	60c multicolored	6.25	5.50
790	B49	$1 shown	1.10	1.10
791	B49	$2.50 multicolored	1.60	1.60
792	B49	$4 multicolored	17.00	15.00
793	B49	$5 multicolored	2.75	2.75
		Nos. 787-793 (7)	33.20	30.45

Souvenir Sheet
794	A159	$5 multicolored	10.50	10.50

Issued: Nos. 790-791, 793, 7/10; others,
9/22.

**Antigua Nos. 901-904 (UN)
Overprinted**

1986, Aug. 12   *Perf. 13½x14*
795	A155	40c multicolored	3.25	3.25
796	A155	$1 multicolored	4.75	4.75
797	A155	$3 multicolored	8.25	8.25
		Nos. 795-797 (3)	16.25	16.25

Souvenir Sheet
Perf. 14x13½
798	A155	$5 multicolored	25.00	25.00

**Antigua Nos. 915-919 (World Cup
Soccer) Overprinted**

1986, Aug. 28   *Perf. 14*
799	A157	30c multicolored	4.25	1.10
800	A157	60c multicolored	6.25	6.00
801	A157	$1 multicolored	6.75	6.50
802	A157	$4 multicolored	12.50	12.50
		Nos. 799-802 (4)	29.75	26.10

Souvenir Sheet
803	A157	$5 multicolored	30.00	30.00

See Nos. 848-851.

**Antigua Nos. 934-938 (AMERIPEX
'86) Overprinted**

1986, Aug. 28   Litho.   *Perf. 15*
804	A161	25c multicolored	5.00	5.00
805	A161	50c multicolored	6.00	6.00
806	A161	$1 multicolored	8.50	8.50
807	A161	$3 multicolored	14.50	14.50
		Nos. 804-807 (4)	34.00	34.00

Souvenir Sheet
808	A161	$5 multicolored	20.00	20.00

**Antigua Nos. 939-942 (Royal
Wedding) Ovptd. in Silver**

1986, Sept. 22   *Perf. 14*
809	CD340	45c multicolored	.55	.55
810	CD340	60c multicolored	.75	.75
811	CD340	$4 multicolored	5.25	5.25
		Nos. 809-811 (3)	6.55	6.55

Souvenir Sheet
812	CD340	$5 multicolored	8.00	8.00

**Antigua Nos. 943-947 (Conch
Shells) Overprinted in Silver or
Black**

1986, Nov. 10   *Perf. 15*
813	A162	15c multicolored	6.25	6.25
814	A162	45c multicolored	6.50	6.50
815	A162	60c multicolored	9.50	9.50
816	A162	$3 multicolored	20.00	24.00
		Nos. 813-816 (4)	42.25	46.25

Souvenir Sheet
817	A162	$5 multi (Bk)	35.00	35.00

**Antigua Nos. 948-957 (Flowers)
Overprinted**

1986, Nov. 10
818	A163	10c multicolored	.45	.45
819	A163	15c multicolored	.45	.45
820	A163	50c multicolored	.90	.90
821	A163	60c multicolored	1.10	1.10
822	A163	70c multicolored	1.25	1.25
823	A163	$1 multicolored	1.75	1.75
824	A163	$3 multicolored	5.50	5.50
825	A163	$4 multicolored	6.25	6.25
		Nos. 818-825 (8)	17.65	17.65

Souvenir Sheets
826	A163	$4 multicolored	22.50	22.50
827	A163	$5 multicolored	22.50	22.50

**Antigua Nos. 958-962 (Fungi)
Overprinted**

1986, Nov. 28
828	A164	10c multicolored	2.25	2.25
829	A164	50c multicolored	8.50	8.50
830	A164	$1 multicolored	13.00	13.00
831	A164	$4 multicolored	24.00	24.00
		Nos. 828-831 (4)	47.75	47.75

Souvenir Sheet
832	A164	$5 multicolored	47.50	47.50

**Antigua Nos. 929-933 (Boats)
Overprinted**

1987, Jan. 12   *Perf. 14*
833	A160	30c multicolored	2.10	1.00
834	A160	60c multicolored	3.75	1.75
835	A160	$1 multicolored	5.00	3.00
836	A160	$3 multicolored	9.50	9.50
		Nos. 833-836 (4)	20.35	15.25

Souvenir Sheet
837	A160	$5 multicolored	40.00	40.00

**Antigua Nos. 968-972A (Classic
Cars) Overprinted**

1987, Jan. 12
838	A165	10c multicolored	.75	.55
839	A165	15c multicolored	1.10	.50
840	A165	50c multicolored	1.25	1.10
841	A165	60c multicolored	1.50	1.40
842	A165	70c multicolored	1.75	1.60
843	A165	$1 multicolored	2.40	2.40
844	A165	$3 multicolored	6.50	6.50
845	A165	$4 multicolored	8.00	8.00
		Nos. 838-845 (8)	23.25	22.05

Souvenir Sheets
846	A165	$5 multi (#972)	20.00	20.00
847	A165	$5 multi (#972A)	20.00	20.00

Automobile, cent.

**Antigua Nos. 963-966 (World Cup
Winners Ovpts.) Overprinted**

1987, Mar. 10
848	A157	30c multicolored	3.25	1.60
849	A157	60c multicolored	4.25	2.90
850	A157	$1 multicolored	5.50	4.50
851	A157	$4 multicolored	19.00	19.00
		Nos. 848-851 (4)	32.00	28.00

See Nos. 799-802.

**Antigua Nos. 1000-1004 (America's
Cup) Overprinted**

1987, Apr. 23   *Perf. 15*
852	A170	30c multicolored	1.25	.65
853	A170	60c multicolored	1.75	.70
854	A170	$1 multicolored	2.75	1.25
855	A170	$3 multicolored	3.75	3.00
		Nos. 852-855 (4)	9.50	5.60

Souvenir Sheet
856	A171	$5 multicolored	9.00	9.00

Antigua Nos. 1005-1014 (WWF) Overprinted

1987, July 1   *Perf. 14*

857	A172	15c multicolored	42.50	20.00
858	A173	30c multicolored	5.75	4.00
859	A172	40c multicolored	55.00	24.00
860	A173	50c multicolored	7.50	6.50
861	A172	60c multicolored	77.50	40.00
862	A173	$1 multicolored	80.00	40.00
863	A173	$2 multicolored	15.00	15.00
864	A173	$3 multicolored	15.00	15.00
		Nos. 857-864 (8)	298.25	164.50

Souvenir Sheets

865	A172	$5 multicolored	110.00	80.00
866	A173	$5 multicolored	110.00	80.00

Antigua Nos. 1025-1034 (Transportation) Overprinted

1987, July 28   *Perf. 15*

867	A175	10c multicolored	3.25	3.25
868	A175	15c multicolored	3.50	2.50
869	A175	30c multicolored	3.75	1.60
870	A175	50c multicolored	4.25	1.60
871	A175	60c multicolored	5.00	2.25
872	A175	70c multicolored	5.50	5.00
873	A175	90c multicolored	6.50	6.25
874	A175	$1.50 multicolored	11.00	11.00
875	A175	$2 multicolored	13.00	14.50
876	A175	$3 multicolored	21.00	21.00
		Nos. 867-876 (10)	76.75	68.95

Marine Life B50

5c, Shore crab. 10c, Sea cucumber. 15c, Stop light parrotfish. 25c, Banded coral shrimp. 35c, Spotted drum. 60c, Thorny starfish. 75c, Atlantic trumpet triton. 90c, Featherstar, yellow beaker sponge. $1, Blue gorgonian, vert. $1.25, Slender filefish, vert. $5, Barred hamlet, vert. $7.50, Fairy basslet, vert. $10, Fire coral, butterfly fish, vert.

1987, July 28

877	B50	5c multicolored	.25	.25
878	B50	10c multicolored	.25	.25
879	B50	15c multicolored	.25	.25
880	B50	25c multicolored	.25	.30
881	B50	35c multicolored	.30	.40
882	B50	60c multicolored	.35	.45
883	B50	75c multicolored	.40	.90
884	B50	90c multicolored	.50	1.10
885	B50	$1 multicolored	.60	1.10
886	B50	$1.25 multicolored	.70	1.25
887	B50	$5 multicolored	1.50	8.00
888	B50	$7.50 multicolored	2.75	9.25
889	B50	$10 multicolored	5.00	11.50
		Nos. 877-889 (13)	13.10	35.00

For surcharges see Nos. 1133-1134.

Antigua Nos. 1048-1052 (Seoul Olympics) Ovptd. in Silver or Black

1987, Oct. 12   *Perf. 14*

890	A178	10c multicolored	.75	.75
891	A178	60c multicolored	1.90	1.90
892	A178	$1 multicolored	2.90	2.90
893	A178	$3 multicolored	9.00	9.00
		Nos. 890-893 (4)	14.55	14.55

Souvenir Sheet

894	A178	$5 multi (Bk)	16.00	16.00

1988 Summer Olympics, Seoul.

Antigua Nos. 990-999 (Chagall) Ovptd. in Black or Silver

1987, Oct. 12   *Perf. 13½x14*

895	A169	10c multicolored	.90	1.10
896	A169	30c multicolored	1.10	.90
897	A169	40c multicolored	1.40	1.10
898	A169	60c multicolored	2.00	1.75
899	A169	90c multicolored	3.25	2.75
900	A169	$1 multicolored (S)	3.50	3.25
901	A169	$3 multicolored	8.50	8.50
902	A169	$4 multicolored	11.00	11.00
		Nos. 895-902 (8)	31.65	30.35

Size: 110x95mm
Imperf

903	A169	$5 multicolored	16.00	16.00
904	A169	$5 multicolored (S)	16.00	16.00

Antigua Nos. 1015-1024 (Statue of Liberty) Ovptd. in Silver or Black

1987, Nov. 5   *Perf. 14*

905	A174	15c multicolored	.65	.65
906	A174	30c multicolored	.80	.80
907	A174	45c multicolored	1.10	1.10
908	A174	50c multicolored		
		(Bk)	1.25	1.25
909	A174	60c multicolored	1.60	1.60
910	A174	90c multicolored	2.25	2.25

911	A174	$1 multicolored	2.75	2.75
912	A174	$2 multicolored	5.50	5.50
913	A174	$3 multicolored		
		(Bk)	7.50	7.50
914	A174	$5 multicolored	12.50	12.50
		Nos. 905-914 (10)	35.90	35.90

Antigua Nos. 1040-1047 (Entertainers) Ovptd. in Black or Silver

1987, Nov. 5

915	A177	15c multicolored	4.25	1.75
916	A177	30c multicolored	9.00	3.25
917	A177	45c multicolored	4.25	1.75
918	A177	50c multicolored	4.25	2.00
919	A177	60c multicolored	14.50	3.50
920	A177	$1 multicolored	6.75	3.50
921	A177	$2 multicolored	9.50	6.25
922	A177	$3 multicolored (S)	29.00	12.50
		Nos. 915-922 (8)	81.50	34.50

Antigua Nos. 1035-1039 (Reptiles & Amphibians) Overprinted

1987, Dec. 8

923	A176	30c multicolored	3.75	2.50
924	A176	60c multicolored	7.75	4.75
925	A176	$1 multicolored	12.00	7.50
926	A176	$3 multicolored	36.00	36.00
		Nos. 923-926 (4)	59.50	50.75

Souvenir Sheet

927	A176	$5 multicolored	40.00	40.00

Antigua Nos. 1063-1067 (Christmas) Overprinted

1988, Jan. 12

928	A181	45c multicolored	.90	.90
929	A181	60c multicolored	1.40	1.40
930	A181	$1 multicolored	2.25	2.25
931	A181	$4 multicolored	8.50	8.50
		Nos. 928-931 (4)	13.05	13.05

Souvenir Sheet

932	A181	$5 multicolored	13.00	13.00

Antigua Nos. 1083-1091 (Salvation Army) Overprinted

1988, Mar. 25

933	A184	25c multicolored	1.40	1.10
934	A184	30c multicolored	1.60	1.10
935	A184	40c multicolored	1.75	1.40
936	A184	45c multicolored	1.75	1.60
937	A184	50c multicolored	1.90	1.75
938	A184	60c multicolored	2.50	2.25
939	A184	$1 multicolored	3.50	3.50
940	A184	$2 multicolored	7.25	7.25
		Nos. 933-940 (8)	21.65	19.95

Souvenir Sheet

941	A184	$5 multicolored	39.00	39.00

Antigua Nos. 1058-1062 (U.S. Constitution) Ovptd. in Silver

1988, May 6

942	A180	15c multicolored	.40	.40
943	A180	45c multicolored	.70	.70
944	A180	60c multicolored	1.00	1.00
945	A180	$4 multicolored	6.00	6.00
		Nos. 942-945 (4)	8.10	8.10

Souvenir Sheet

946	A180	$5 multicolored	7.00	7.00

Antigua Nos. 1068-1072 (Royal Wedding Anniv.) Overprinted

1988, July 4

947	A182	25c multicolored	2.90	1.40
948	A182	60c multicolored	4.25	1.75
949	A182	$2 multicolored	6.00	5.75
950	A182	$3 multicolored	8.50	8.50
		Nos. 947-950 (4)	21.65	17.40

Souvenir Sheet

951	A182	$5 multicolored	20.00	16.00

Antigua Nos. 1073-1082 (Birds) Overprinted

1988, July 4

952	A183	10c multicolored	3.25	2.10
953	A183	15c multicolored	4.00	2.10
954	A183	50c multicolored	4.25	3.50
955	A183	60c multicolored	5.00	4.50
956	A183	70c multicolored	6.25	4.75
957	A183	$1 multicolored	8.00	6.50
958	A183	$3 multicolored	18.00	18.00
959	A183	$4 multicolored	27.50	27.50
		Nos. 952-959 (8)	76.25	68.95

Souvenir Sheets

960	A183	$5 multi (#1081)	27.50	24.00
961	A183	$5 multi (#1082)	27.50	24.00

Antigua Nos. 1092-1101 (Columbus) Overprinted

1988, July 25

962	A185	10c multicolored	3.25	1.10
963	A185	15c multicolored	3.50	1.40
964	A185	45c multicolored	4.25	2.00
965	A185	60c multicolored	4.00	2.90
966	A185	90c multicolored	4.50	3.75

967	A185	$1 multicolored	5.50	4.50
968	A185	$3 multicolored	12.50	12.50
969	A185	$4 multicolored	16.00	16.00
		Nos. 962-969 (8)	53.50	44.15

Souvenir Sheets

970	A185	$5 multi (#1100)	19.00	19.00
971	A185	$5 multi (#1101)	19.00	19.00

Antigua Nos. 1102-1111 (Titian Paintings) Overprinted

1988, July 25   *Perf. 13½x14*

972	A187	30c multicolored	.90	.70
973	A187	40c multicolored	1.00	.80
974	A187	45c multicolored	1.10	.90
975	A187	50c multicolored	1.25	1.10
976	A187	$1 multicolored	2.00	2.00
977	A187	$2 multicolored	4.75	4.75
978	A187	$3 multicolored	6.00	6.00
979	A187	$4 multicolored	9.00	9.00
		Nos. 972-979 (8)	26.00	25.25

Souvenir Sheets

980	A187	$5 multi (#1110)	13.50	13.50
981	A187	$5 multi (#1111)	13.50	13.50

Antigua Nos. 1053-1057 (Scout Jamboree) Overprinted

1988, Aug. 25   *Perf. 15*

982	A179	10c multicolored	3.50	2.00
983	A179	60c multicolored	9.00	3.50
984	A179	$1 multicolored	4.50	3.75
985	A179	$3 multicolored	9.00	9.00
		Nos. 982-985 (4)	26.00	18.25

Souvenir Sheet

986	A179	$5 multicolored	24.00	24.00

Antigua Nos. 1112-1116 (Sailboats) Overprinted

1988, Aug. 25

987	A188	30c multicolored	1.60	1.25
988	A188	60c multicolored	2.25	2.25
989	A188	$1 multicolored	3.00	3.00
990	A188	$3 multicolored	8.50	8.50
		Nos. 987-990 (4)	15.35	15.00

Souvenir Sheet

991	A188	$5 multicolored	20.00	17.50

Antigua Nos. 1127-1136 (Flowering Trees) Overprinted

1988, Sept. 16   *Perf. 14*

992	A190	10c multicolored	.45	.50
993	A190	30c multicolored	.60	.60
994	A190	50c multicolored	.75	.75
995	A190	90c multicolored	1.10	1.10
996	A190	$1 multicolored	1.60	1.60
997	A190	$2 multicolored	3.00	3.00
998	A190	$3 multicolored	4.25	4.25
999	A190	$4 multicolored	5.25	5.25
		Nos. 992-999 (8)	17.00	17.05

Souvenir Sheets

1000	A191	$5 multi (#1135)	9.00	9.00
1001	A191	$5 multi (#1136)	9.00	9.00

Antigua Nos. 1140-1144 (Seoul Olympics) Overprinted

1988, Sept. 16

1002	A192	40c multicolored	2.00	1.10
1003	A192	60c multicolored	2.75	1.75
1004	A192	$1 multicolored	4.00	3.00
1005	A192	$3 multicolored	6.50	6.50
		Nos. 1002-1005 (4)	15.25	12.35

Souvenir Sheet

1006	A192	$5 multicolored	15.00	15.00

Antigua Nos. 1145-1162 (Butterflies) Overprinted

1988-90

1007	A193	1c multicolored	.55	.55
1008	A193	2c multicolored	.55	.55
1009	A193	3c multicolored	.55	.55
1010	A193	5c multicolored	.55	.55
1011	A193	10c multicolored	.55	.55
1012	A193	15c multicolored	.55	.55
1013	A193	20c multicolored	.55	.55
1014	A193	25c multicolored	.55	.55
1015	A193	30c multicolored	.65	.65
1016	A193	40c multicolored	.70	.70
1017	A193	45c multicolored	.90	.90
1018	A193	50c multicolored	1.00	1.00
1019	A193	60c multicolored	1.25	1.25
1020	A193	$1 multicolored	1.90	1.90
1021	A193	$2 multicolored	4.00	4.00
1022	A193	$2.50 multicolored	4.75	4.75
1023	A193	$5 multicolored	10.00	10.00
1024	A193	$10 multicolored	20.00	20.00
1025	A193	$20 multi ('90)	27.50	27.50
		Nos. 1007-1025 (19)	77.05	77.05

Issue dates: $20, May 4, others Dec. 8.
The overprint on No. 1025 is in a thin sans-serif typeface, while Nos. 1007-1024 are overprinted with a thick serif typeface.

Antigua Nos. 1162A-1167 (Kennedy) Overprinted

1989, Apr. 28

1026	A194	1c multicolored	.65	1.10
1027	A194	2c multicolored	.65	1.10
1028	A194	3c multicolored	.65	1.10
1029	A194	4c multicolored	.65	1.10
1030	A194	30c multicolored	1.40	.80
1031	A194	60c multicolored	3.50	1.60
1032	A194	$1 multicolored	4.00	2.75
1033	A194	$4 multicolored	10.00	10.00
		Nos. 1026-1033 (8)	21.50	19.55

Souvenir Sheet

1034	A194	$5 multicolored	16.00	16.00

Antigua Nos. 1175-1176 (Arawaks) Overprinted

1989, May 24

1035	A196	$1.50 Strip of 4, #a.-d.	25.00	25.00

Souvenir Sheet

1036	A196	$6 multicolored	15.00	18.00

Antigua Nos. 1177-1186 (Jets) Overprinted

1989, May 29

1037	A197	10c multicolored	2.00	1.75
1038	A197	30c multicolored	2.40	1.75
1039	A197	40c multicolored	2.90	2.50
1040	A197	60c multicolored	3.50	3.50
1041	A197	$1 multicolored	4.75	4.75
1042	A197	$2 multicolored	7.50	7.50
1043	A197	$3 multicolored	12.00	12.00
1044	A197	$4 multicolored	18.00	18.00
		Nos. 1037-1044 (8)	53.05	51.75

Souvenir Sheets

1045	A197	$7 multi (#1185)	35.00	27.50
1046	A197	$7 multi (#1186)	35.00	27.50

Antigua Nos. 1187-1196 (Cruise Ships) Overprinted

1989, Sept. 18

1047	A198	25c multicolored	3.50	1.60
1048	A198	45c multicolored	4.25	2.10
1049	A198	50c multicolored	4.25	3.00
1050	A198	60c multicolored	5.50	3.25
1051	A198	75c multicolored	5.50	4.50
1052	A198	90c multicolored	7.25	6.25
1053	A198	$3 multicolored	13.00	13.00
1054	A198	$4 multicolored	17.00	17.00
		Nos. 1047-1054 (8)	60.25	50.70

Souvenir Sheets

1055	A198	$6 multi (#1195)	40.00	35.00
1056	A198	$6 multi (#1196)	40.00	35.00

Antigua Nos. 1197-1206 (Hiroshige Paintings) Overprinted

1989, Dec. 14   *Perf. 14x13½*

1057	A199	25c multicolored	2.75	1.25
1058	A199	45c multicolored	3.25	1.90
1059	A199	50c multicolored	3.75	2.75
1060	A199	60c multicolored	4.00	3.25
1061	A199	$1 multicolored	4.75	5.00
1062	A199	$2 multicolored	8.00	8.00
1063	A199	$3 multicolored	11.50	11.50
1064	A199	$4 multicolored	16.00	16.00
		Nos. 1057-1064 (8)	54.00	49.65

Souvenir Sheets

1065	A199	$5 multi (#1205)	30.00	27.50
1066	A199	$5 multi (#1206)	30.00	27.50

Antigua Nos. 1217-1222 (World Cup Soccer) Overprinted

1989, Dec. 20   *Perf. 14*

1067	A201	15c multicolored	1.90	.90
1068	A201	25c multicolored	1.90	.90
1069	A201	$1 multicolored	3.00	3.00
1070	A201	$5 multicolored	11.00	11.00
		Nos. 1067-1070 (4)	17.80	15.80

Souvenir Sheets

1071	A201	$5 multi (#1221)	22.50	22.50
1072	A201	$5 multi (#1222)	22.50	22.50

Antigua Nos. 1264-1273 (Christmas) Overprinted

1989, Dec. 20

1073	A208	10c multicolored	.60	.60
1074	A208	25c multicolored	.60	.60
1075	A208	30c multicolored	.70	.70
1076	A208	50c multicolored	.90	.90
1077	A208	60c multicolored	1.10	1.10
1078	A208	70c multicolored	1.50	1.25
1079	A208	$4 multicolored	5.50	5.50
1080	A208	$5 multicolored	7.00	7.00
		Nos. 1073-1080 (8)	17.90	17.55

Souvenir Sheets

1081	A208	$5 multi (#1272)	15.00	15.00
1082	A208	$5 multi (#1273)	15.00	15.00

Antigua Nos. 1223-1232 (Mushrooms) Overprinted

1990, Feb. 21

1083	A202	10c multicolored	2.50	1.60
1084	A202	25c multicolored	2.50	1.60
1085	A202	50c multicolored	4.00	3.25
1086	A202	60c multicolored	4.25	3.50
1087	A202	75c multicolored	5.50	4.50
1088	A202	$1 multicolored	6.50	6.00
1089	A202	$2 multicolored	18.00	18.00
1090	A202	$4 multicolored	25.00	25.00
		Nos. 1083-1090 (8)	68.25	63.45

Souvenir Sheets

1091	A202	$6 multi (#1231)	40.00	35.00
1092	A202	$6 multi (#1232)	40.00	35.00

Antigua Nos. 1233-1237 (Wildlife) Overprinted

1990, Mar. 30

1093	A203	25c multicolored	1.25	.80
1094	A203	45c multicolored	3.25	1.25
1095	A203	60c multicolored	3.00	1.90
1096	A203	$4 multicolored	12.50	12.50
		Nos. 1093-1096 (4)	20.00	16.45

Souvenir Sheet

1097	A203	$5 multicolored	30.00	30.00

Antigua Nos. 1258-1262 (Moon Landing) Overprinted

1990, Mar. 30

1098	A206	10c multicolored	1.25	1.25
1099	A206	45c multicolored	1.75	1.75
1100	A206	$1 multicolored	4.50	4.50
1101	A206	$4 multicolored	19.00	19.00
		Nos. 1098-1101 (4)	26.50	26.50

Souvenir Sheet

1102	A206	$5 multicolored	29.00	29.00

Antigua Nos. 1275-1284 (America) Overprinted

1990, June 6

1103	A210	10c multicolored	1.60	.65
1104	A210	20c multicolored	1.60	.65
1105	A210	25c multicolored	2.00	.65
1106	A210	45c multicolored	2.25	1.00
1107	A210	60c multicolored	2.50	1.40
1108	A210	$2 multicolored	5.25	5.25
1109	A210	$3 multicolored	7.50	7.50
1110	A210	$4 multicolored	10.00	10.00
		Nos. 1103-1110 (8)	32.70	27.10

Souvenir Sheets

1111	A210	$5 multi (#1283)	19.00	19.00
1112	A210	$5 multi (#1284)	19.00	19.00

Antigua Nos. 1285-1294 (Orchids) Overprinted

1990, July 12

1113	A211	15c multicolored	3.25	1.40
1114	A211	45c multicolored	2.50	2.00
1115	A211	50c multicolored	2.75	2.75
1116	A211	60c multicolored	2.90	2.90
1117	A211	$1 multicolored	5.25	5.25
1118	A211	$2 multicolored	10.00	10.00
1119	A211	$3 multicolored	15.00	15.00
1120	A211	$4 multicolored	27.00	27.00
		Nos. 1113-1120 (8)	68.65	66.30

Souvenir Sheets

1121	A211	$6 multi (#1293)	27.00	24.00
1122	A211	$6 multi (#1294)	27.00	24.00

Antigua Nos. 1295-1304 (Fish) Overprinted

1990, Aug. 14

1123	A212	10c multicolored	2.75	1.60
1124	A212	15c multicolored	2.75	1.60
1125	A212	50c multicolored	3.00	2.10
1126	A212	60c multicolored	3.75	2.75
1127	A212	$1 multicolored	5.00	4.50
1128	A212	$2 multicolored	8.00	8.00
1129	A212	$3 multicolored	12.50	12.50
1130	A212	$4 multicolored	17.00	17.00
		Nos. 1123-1130 (8)	54.75	50.05

Souvenir Sheets

1131	A212	$5 multi (#1303)	27.00	24.00
1132	A212	$5 multi (#1304)	27.00	24.00

Barbuda Nos. 888-889 Surcharged "1st Anniversary / Hurricane Hugo / 16th September, 1989-1990"

1990, Sept. 17   *Perf. 15*

1133	B50	$5 on $7.50	14.00	14.00
1134	B50	$7.50 on $10	21.00	21.00

Antigua Nos. 1324-1328 (Queen Mother) Overprinted

1990, Oct. 12   *Perf. 14*

1135	A217	15c multicolored	11.50	2.75
1136	A217	35c multicolored	15.00	2.25
1137	A217	75c multicolored	23.00	4.00
1138	A217	$3 multicolored	40.00	23.00
		Nos. 1135-1138 (4)	89.50	33.00

Souvenir Sheet

1139	A217	$6 multicolored	85.00	42.50

Antigua No. 1313 Ovptd. in Silver
Miniature Sheet

1990, Dec. 14

1140	A215	45c Sheet of 20,		
		#a.-t.	85.00	85.00

Antigua Nos. 1360-1369 (Christmas) Overprinted

1990, Dec. 14   *Perf. 14x13½, 13½x14*

1141	A221	25c multicolored	.75	.75
1142	A221	30c multicolored	.95	.95
1143	A221	40c multicolored	1.00	1.00
1144	A221	60c multicolored	1.50	1.50
1145	A221	$1 multicolored	2.75	2.75
1146	A221	$2 multicolored	5.25	5.25
1147	A221	$4 multicolored	12.50	12.50
1148	A221	$5 multicolored	12.50	12.50
		Nos. 1141-1148 (8)	37.20	37.20

Souvenir Sheets

1149	A221	$6 multi (#1368)	19.00	19.00
1150	A221	$6 multi (#1369)	19.00	19.00

Antigua Nos. 1305-1308 (Penny Black) Overprinted

1991, Feb. 4   *Perf. 15x14*

1151	A213	45c green	5.00	2.00
1152	A213	60c bright rose	6.00	2.75
1153	A213	$5 bright ultra	24.00	21.00
		Nos. 1151-1153 (3)	35.00	25.75

Souvenir Sheet

1154	A213	$6 black	35.00	35.00

Antigua Nos. 1309-1312 (Stamp World London '90) Overprinted

1991, Feb. 4   *Perf. 13½*

1155	A214	50c red & deep grn	5.25	2.75
1156	A214	75c red & vio brn	6.50	4.00
1157	A214	$4 red & brt ultra	20.00	20.00
		Nos. 1155-1157 (3)	31.75	26.75

Souvenir Sheet

1158	A214	$6 red & black	35.00	35.00

Birds — B52

1991, Mar. 25   Litho.   *Perf. 14*

1164	B52	60c Troupial	2.40	.95
1168	B52	$2 Christmas bird	3.75	3.25
1169	B52	$4 Rose-breasted grosbeak	6.50	6.50
1171	B52	$7 Stolid flycatcher	10.50	*12.50*
		Nos. 1164-1171 (4)	23.15	*23.20*

Antigua Nos. 1329-1333 (Barcelona '92) Overprinted

1991, Apr. 23   Litho.   *Perf. 14*

1173	A218	50c multicolored	3.00	1.40
1174	A218	75c multicolored	3.50	2.00
1175	A218	$1 multicolored	4.50	2.50
1176	A218	$5 multicolored	13.50	13.50
		Nos. 1173-1176 (4)	24.50	19.40

Souvenir Sheet

1177	A218	$6 multicolored	24.00	24.00

Antigua Nos. 1350-1359 (Birds) Overprinted

1991, Apr. 23

1178	A220	10c multicolored	2.50	1.75
1179	A220	25c multicolored	3.25	1.00
1180	A220	50c multicolored	3.50	2.00
1181	A220	60c multicolored	3.75	2.40
1182	A220	$1 multicolored	4.50	4.25
1183	A220	$2 multicolored	7.75	7.75
1184	A220	$3 multicolored	12.00	12.00
1185	A220	$4 multicolored	13.50	*15.00*
		Nos. 1178-1185 (8)	50.75	46.15

Souvenir Sheets

1186	A220	$6 multi (#1358)	25.00	22.00
1187	A220	$6 multi (#1359)	25.00	22.00

Antigua Nos. 1370-1379 (Rubens Paintings) Overprinted

1991, June 21   *Perf. 14x13½*

1188	A222	25c multicolored	.95	.95
1189	A222	45c multicolored	1.60	1.60
1190	A222	50c multicolored	1.75	1.75
1191	A222	60c multicolored	2.00	2.00
1192	A222	$1 multicolored	3.50	3.50
1193	A222	$2 multicolored	6.75	6.75
1194	A222	$3 multicolored	10.00	10.00
1195	A222	$4 multicolored	13.50	13.50
		Nos. 1188-1195 (8)	40.05	40.05

1196	A222	$6 multi (#1378)	20.00	20.00
1197	A222	$6 multi (#1379)	20.00	20.00

Antigua Nos. 1380-1390 (World War II) Overprinted

1991, July 25   Litho.   *Perf. 14*

1198	A223	10c multicolored	4.75	1.75
1199	A223	15c multicolored	6.00	1.75
1200	A223	25c multicolored	6.75	1.75
1201	A223	45c multicolored	12.00	3.25
1202	A223	50c multicolored	6.75	3.50
1203	A223	$1 multicolored	15.00	6.75
1204	A223	$2 multicolored	15.00	13.50
1205	A223	$4 multicolored	19.00	19.00
1206	A223	$5 multicolored	19.00	19.00
		Nos. 1198-1206 (9)	104.25	70.25

Souvenir Sheets

1207	A223	$6 multi (#1389)	45.00	35.00
1208	A223	$6 multi (#1390)	45.00	35.00

Antigua Nos. 1411-1420 (Voyages) Overprinted

1991, Aug. 26   Litho.   *Perf. 14*

1209	A226	10c multicolored	1.75	1.20
1210	A226	15c multicolored	2.00	1.20
1211	A226	45c multicolored	2.40	.80
1212	A226	60c multicolored	2.50	1.75
1213	A226	$1 multicolored	3.25	2.75
1214	A226	$2 multicolored	6.00	5.75
1215	A226	$4 multicolored	15.00	15.00
1216	A226	$5 multicolored	17.00	17.00
		Nos. 1209-1216 (8)	49.90	45.45

Souvenir Sheets

1217	A226	$6 multi (#1419)	23.00	21.00
1218	A226	$6 multi (#1420)	23.00	21.00

Antigua Nos. 1401-1410 (Butterflies) Overprinted

1991, Oct. 18

1219	A225	10c multicolored	3.75	1.75
1220	A225	35c multicolored	4.00	2.40
1221	A225	50c multicolored	4.75	2.50
1222	A225	75c multicolored	5.75	2.75
1223	A225	$1 multicolored	6.00	3.50
1224	A225	$2 multicolored	7.50	7.50
1225	A225	$4 multicolored	12.00	12.00
1226	A225	$5 multicolored	13.50	13.50
		Nos. 1219-1226 (8)	57.25	45.90

Souvenir Sheets

1227	A225	$6 multi (#1409)	32.50	25.00
1228	A225	$6 multi (#1410)	32.50	25.00

Antigua Nos. 1446-1455 (Royal Family) Overprinted

1991, Nov. 18

1229	CD347	10c multicolored	3.75	2.00
1230	CD347	15c multicolored	4.75	1.50
1231	CD347	20c multicolored	4.75	1.50
1232	CD347	40c multicolored	5.75	1.50
1233	CD347	$1 multicolored	6.00	4.75
1234	CD347	$2 multicolored	7.50	8.25
1235	CD347	$4 multicolored	12.50	17.50
1236	CD347	$5 multicolored	15.00	17.50
		Nos. 1229-1236 (8)	60.00	54.50

Souvenir Sheets

1237	CD347	$4 multi (#1454)	32.50	32.50
1238	CD347	$4 multi (#1455)	32.50	32.50

Antigua Nos. 1503-1510 (Christmas) Overprinted

1991, Dec. 24   *Perf. 12*

1239	A238	10c multicolored	2.50	1.50
1240	A238	30c multicolored	2.75	.80
1241	A238	40c multicolored	3.00	.95
1242	A238	60c multicolored	3.25	1.50
1243	A238	$1 multicolored	3.50	2.25
1244	A238	$3 multicolored	6.00	6.00
1245	A238	$4 multicolored	9.00	9.00
1246	A238	$5 multicolored	11.00	11.00
		Nos. 1239-1246 (8)	41.00	33.00

Antigua Nos. 1421-1435 (Van Gogh Paintings) Overprinted

1992, Feb. 20   *Perf. 13½*

1249	A227	5c multicolored	1.75	1.75
1250	A227	10c multicolored	1.90	1.75
1251	A227	15c multicolored	1.90	.95
1252	A227	25c multicolored	1.90	.95
1253	A227	30c multicolored	2.00	.95
1254	A227	40c multicolored	2.10	.95
1255	A227	50c multicolored	2.10	1.50
1256	A227	75c multicolored	3.50	2.00
1257	A227	$1 multicolored	6.00	2.75
1258	A227	$3 multicolored	7.25	7.25
1259	A227	$4 multicolored	9.00	9.00
1260	A227	$5 multicolored	11.00	11.00
		Nos. 1249-1260 (12)	50.40	40.80

Size: 102x76mm
Imperf

1261	A227	$5 multi (#1433)	16.00	16.00
1262	A227	$5 multi (#1434)	16.00	16.00
1263	A227	$6 multi	19.00	19.00

Antigua Nos. 1476-1485 (De Gaulle) Overprinted

1992, Apr. 7   Litho.   *Perf. 14*

1264	A231	10c multi	2.75	1.75
1265	A231	15c multi, vert.	3.00	1.75
1266	A231	45c multi, vert.	4.00	1.00
1267	A231	60c multi, vert.	4.50	1.50
1268	A231	$1 multi	5.00	2.75
1269	A231	$2 multi	7.50	7.50
1270	A231	$4 multi	13.50	13.50
1271	A231	$5 multi, vert.	14.50	14.50
		Nos. 1264-1271 (8)	54.75	44.25

Souvenir Sheets

1272	A231	$6 multi (#1484)	27.50	25.00
1273	A231	$6 multi (#1485)	27.50	25.00

Antigua Nos. 1551-1560 (Easter) Overprinted

1992, Apr. 16   Litho.   *Perf. 14x13½*

1274	A242	10c multicolored	1.90	1.20
1275	A242	15c multicolored	2.10	1.20
1276	A242	30c multicolored	2.25	.85
1277	A242	40c multicolored	2.50	1.20
1278	A242	$1 multicolored	4.00	2.75
1279	A242	$2 multicolored	7.50	7.50
1280	A242	$4 multicolored	10.50	10.50
1281	A242	$5 multicolored	13.50	13.50
		Nos. 1274-1281 (8)	44.25	38.70

Souvenir Sheets

1282	A242	$6 multi (#1559)	22.00	22.00
1283	A242	$6 multi (#1560)	22.00	22.00

Antigua Nos. 1489-1492 (Scouts) Overprinted

1992, June 19   Litho.   *Perf. 14*

1284	A234	75c multi	3.50	2.10
1285	A234	$2 multi, vert.	3.50	3.50
1286	A234	$3.50 multi	5.00	5.00
		Nos. 1284-1286 (3)	12.00	10.60

Souvenir Sheet

1287	A234	$5 multi, vert.	25.00	25.00

Antigua Nos. 1493-1494 (Mozart) Overprinted

1992, June 19

1288	A235	$1.50 multi	10.50	5.75
1289	A235	$4 multi	12.50	12.50

Antigua Nos. 1495-1496 (Glider, Locomotive) Overprinted

1992, June 19

1290	A236	$2 multi	3.50	3.50
1291	A236	$2.50 multi, vert.	10.50	5.75

Antigua Nos. 1499-1502 (Brandenburg Gate) Overprinted

1992, June 19

1292	A237	25c multicolored	1.20	.85
1293	A237	$2 multicolored	3.50	3.50
1294	A237	$3 multicolored	4.00	4.00

Souvenir Sheet

1295	A237	$4 multicolored	27.50	27.50
		Nos. 1292-1295 (4)	36.20	35.85

Antigua No. 1488 (Pearl Harbor) Overprinted

1992, Aug. 12   Litho.   *Perf. 14½x15*

1295A	A233	$1 Sheet of 10, #b-k	105.00	80.00

Antigua Nos. 1571-1578 (America) Overprinted

1992, Oct. 12   Litho.   *Perf. 14*

1296	A244	15c multicolored	2.25	1.00
1297	A244	30c multicolored	2.50	1.50
1298	A244	40c multicolored	3.00	1.60
1299	A244	$1 multicolored	4.75	4.25
1300	A244	$2 multicolored	11.00	8.25
1301	A244	$4 multicolored	17.00	17.00
		Nos. 1296-1301 (6)	40.50	33.60

Souvenir Sheets

1302	A244	$6 multicolored	21.00	19.00
1303	A244	$6 multicolored	21.00	19.00

Antigua Nos. 1599-1600 (America) Overprinted

1992, Oct. 12   *Perf. 14½*

1304	A247	$1 multicolored	5.25	4.75
1305	A247	$2 multicolored	9.75	9.00

Antigua Nos. 1513-1518 (QEII Accession) Overprinted

1992, Nov. 3   *Perf. 14*

1306	CD348	10c multicolored	8.00	2.75
1307	CD348	30c multicolored	9.75	1.90
1308	CD348	$1 multicolored	13.50	1.50
1309	CD348	$5 multicolored	24.00	19.00
		Nos. 1306-1309 (4)	55.25	28.65

Souvenir Sheets

1310	CD348	$6 multi (#1517)	35.00	27.50
1311	CD348	$6 multi (#1518)	35.00	27.50

Antigua Nos. 1541-1550 (Dinosaurs) Ovptd. "BARBUDA / MAIL"

1992, Dec. 8

1312	A241	10c multicolored	4.00	2.50
1313	A241	15c multicolored	4.75	2.25
1314	A241	30c multicolored	5.75	1.50
1315	A241	50c multicolored	5.75	2.75
1316	A241	$1 multicolored	7.00	4.75
1317	A241	$2 multicolored	11.00	9.75
1318	A241	$4 multicolored	13.50	13.50
1319	A241	$5 multicolored	16.00	16.00
Nos. 1312-1319 (8)			*67.75*	*53.00*

Souvenir Sheets

1320	A241	$6 multi (#1549)	35.00	25.00
1321	A241	$6 multi (#1550)	35.00	25.00

Antigua Nos. 1609-1618 (Christmas) Ovptd. "BARBUDA MAIL"

1992, Dec. 8   Litho.   Perf. 13½x14

1322	A251	10c multicolored	3.50	1.00
1323	A251	25c multicolored	3.50	1.00
1324	A251	30c multicolored	3.50	1.40
1325	A251	40c multicolored	3.75	1.60
1326	A251	60c multicolored	5.00	2.25
1327	A251	$1 multicolored	6.00	2.75
1328	A251	$4 multicolored	14.50	15.00
1329	A251	$5 multicolored	18.00	18.00
Nos. 1322-1329 (8)			*57.75*	*43.00*

Souvenir Sheets

1330	A251	$6 multi (#1616)	30.00	30.00
1331	A251	$6 multi (#1617)	30.00	30.00

Antigua No. 1601 (Mega-Event Stamp Show) Ovptd. "BARBUDA MAIL"

1992   Litho.   Perf. 14

Souvenir Sheet

1332	A248	$6 multicolored	25.00	25.00

Antigua Nos. 1519-1528 (Mushrooms) Ovptd.

1993, Jan. 25   Litho.   Perf. 14

1333	A239	10c multicolored	2.10	.95
1334	A239	15c multicolored	2.75	.95
1335	A239	30c multicolored	3.50	1.50
1336	A239	40c multicolored	5.00	2.75
1337	A239	$1 multicolored	6.75	4.50
1338	A239	$2 multicolored	12.00	12.00
1339	A239	$4 multicolored	15.00	15.00
1340	A239	$5 multicolored	19.00	19.00
Nos. 1332-1339 (8)			*72.10*	*62.65*

Souvenir Sheets

1341	A239	$6 multi (#1527)	35.00	32.50
1342	A239	$6 multi (#1528)	35.00	32.50

Antigua Nos. 1561-1570 (Spanish Art) Ovptd.

1993, Mar. 22   Litho.   Perf. 13

1343	A243	10c multicolored	2.75	1.75
1344	A243	15c multicolored	3.25	1.75
1345	A243	30c multicolored	3.75	1.75
1346	A243	40c multicolored	4.50	1.75
1347	A243	$1 multicolored	6.00	3.75
1348	A243	$2 multicolored	8.00	8.00
1349	A243	$4 multicolored	12.50	12.50
1350	A243	$5 multicolored	14.50	14.50
Nos. 1343-1350 (8)			*55.25*	*45.75*

Imperf
Size: 120x95mm

1351	A243	$6 multi (#1569)	27.50	27.50
1352	A243	$6 multi (#1570)	27.50	27.50

Antigua Nos. 1589-1598 (Nature) Ovptd.

1993, May 10   Litho.   Perf. 14

1353	A246	10c multicolored	3.25	1.75
1354	A246	25c multicolored	3.50	1.75
1355	A246	45c multicolored	4.00	1.75
1356	A246	60c multicolored	4.25	1.90
1357	A246	$1 multicolored	5.50	3.25
1358	A246	$2 multicolored	7.50	7.50
1359	A246	$4 multicolored	12.50	12.50
1360	A246	$5 multicolored	14.50	14.50
Nos. 1353-1360 (8)			*55.00*	*44.90*

Souvenir Sheets

1361	A246	$6 multi (#1597)	25.00	23.00
1362	A246	$6 multi (#1598)	25.00	23.00

Antigua Nos. 1603-1608 (Inventors/Pioneers) Ovptd.

1993, June 29   Litho.   Perf. 14

1363	A250	10c multicolored	1.00	*1.25*
1364	A250	25c multicolored	3.75	1.20
1365	A250	30c multicolored	2.25	1.20
1366	A250	40c multicolored	3.75	1.20
1367	A250	60c multicolored	6.75	2.25
1368	A250	$1 multicolored	4.75	3.50
1369	A250	$4 multicolored	10.50	10.50
1370	A250	$5 multicolored	12.50	12.50
Nos. 1363-1370 (8)			*45.25*	*33.60*

Souvenir Sheets

1371	A250	$6 multi (#1607)	22.00	22.00
1372	A250	$6 multi (#1608)	22.00	22.00

Antigua Nos. 1619-1632 (Anniversaries/Events) Ovptd.

1993, Aug. 16   Litho.   Perf. 14

1373	A252	10c multi	3.25	1.75
1374	A252	40c multi	5.50	1.50
1375	A253	45c multi	1.20	.85
1376	A252	75c multi	1.75	1.50
1377	A252	$1 multi	3.75	2.50
1378	A252	$1.50 multi	4.75	3.75
1379	A252	$2 multi	17.00	7.75
1380	A253	$2 multi (#1626)	9.75	6.75
1381	A253	$2 multi (#1627)	4.75	4.75
1382	A252	$2.25 multi	4.75	4.75
1383	A252	$3 multi	7.00	7.00
1384	A252	$4 multi (#1630)	9.00	9.00
1385	A252	$4 multi (#1631)	9.00	9.00
1386	A252	$6 multi	10.50	10.50
Nos. 1373-1386 (14)			*91.95*	*71.35*

Souvenir Sheets

1387	A252	$6 multi (#1633)	*19.00*	*19.00*
1388	A252	$6 multi (#1634)	*19.00*	*19.00*
1389	A252	$6 multi (#1635)	*19.00*	*19.00*
1390	A252	$6 multi (#1636)	*19.00*	*19.00*
Nos. 1387-1390 (4)			*76.00*	*76.00*

Antigua Nos. 1650-1659 (Flowers) Ovptd.

1993, Sept. 21   Litho.   Perf. 14

1391	A256	15c multicolored	2.50	1.75
1392	A256	25c multicolored	3.25	1.20
1393	A256	30c multicolored	3.50	1.50
1394	A256	40c multicolored	4.00	1.75
1395	A256	$1 multicolored	4.50	3.50
1396	A256	$2 multicolored	5.50	5.50
1397	A256	$4 multicolored	10.50	10.50
1398	A256	$5 multicolored	12.50	12.50
Nos. 1391-1398 (8)			*46.25*	*38.20*

Souvenir Sheets

1399	A256	$6 multi (#1658)	21.00	21.00
1400	A256	$6 multi (#1659)	21.00	21.00

Barbuda Nos. 1164-1171 Overprinted

1993, Oct. 9   Litho.   Perf. 14

1400A	B52	60c multi (#1164)	2.25	2.25
1400B	B52	$2 multi (#1168)	7.50	7.50
1400C	B52	$4 multi (#1169)	15.00	15.00
1400D	B52	$7 multi (#1171)	25.00	25.00
Nos. 1400A-1400D (4)			*49.75*	*49.75*

Antigua No. 1660-1662 (Endangered Species) Ovptd.

1993, Nov. 11   Litho.   Perf. 14

1401	A257	$1 Sheet of 12, #a.-l.	85.00	85.00

Souvenir Sheets

1401M	A257	$6 multi (#1661)	17.50	17.50
1401N	A257	$6 multi (#1662)	17.50	17.50

Antigua Nos. 1647, 1649 (Louvre) Overprinted

1994, Jan. 6   Litho.   Perf. 12

1401O	A255	$1 Sheet of 8, #p-w, + label	45.00	45.00

Souvenir Sheet

1994, Jan. 6   Litho.   Perf. 14½

1401X	A255	$6 multi (#1649)	37.50	37.50

Antigua Nos. 1697-1710 (Soccer) Ovptd.

1994, Mar. 3   Litho.   Perf. 14

1404-1415	A267	$2 Set of 12	65.00	65.00

Souvenir Sheets

1416	A267	$6 multi (#1709)	24.00	24.00
1417	A267	$6 multi (#1710)	24.00	24.00

Antigua Nos. 1676-1678 (Japanese Royal Wedding) Ovptd.

1994, Apr. 21   Litho.   Perf. 14

1418	A260	40c multicolored	2.10	1.00
1419	A260	$3 multicolored	4.75	4.75

Souvenir Sheet

1420	A260	$6 multicolored	17.00	17.00

Antigua Nos. 1679-1682 (Picasso) Ovptd.

1994, Apr. 21

1421-1423	A261	Set of 3	10.00	8.50

Souvenir Sheet

1424	A261	$6 multicolored	17.00	17.00

Antigua Nos. 1683-1685 (Copernicus) Ovptd.

1994, Apr. 21

1425	A262	40c multicolored	2.10	1.00
1426	A262	$4 multicolored	6.25	6.25

Souvenir Sheet

1427	A262	$5 multicolored	17.00	17.00

Antigua Nos. 1686-1688 (Willy Brandt) Ovptd.

1994, Apr. 21

1428	A263	30c multicolored	2.10	1.00
1429	A263	$4 multicolored	6.25	6.25

Souvenir Sheet

1430	A263	$6 multicolored	15.00	15.00

Antigua Nos. 1692-1693 (Clinton) Ovptd.

1994, Apr. 21

1431	A265	$5 multicolored	6.50	6.50

Souvenir Sheet

1432	A265	$6 multicolored	17.00	17.00

Antigua Nos. 1694-1696 (Lillehammer Olympics) Ovptd.

1994, Apr. 21

1433	A266	15c multicolored	2.25	1.75
1434	A266	$5 multicolored	6.50	6.50

Souvenir Sheet

1435	A266	$6 multicolored	15.00	15.00

Antigua Nos. 1732-1735 (Masons) Ovptd.

1994, Apr. 21

1436-1439	A270	Set of 4	25.00	8.00

Antigua Nos. 1711-1720 (Aviation) Ovptd.

1994, June 15

1440-1446	A268	Set of 7	45.00	45.00

Souvenir Sheets

1447	A268	$6 multi (#1718)	20.00	20.00
1448	A268	$6 multi (#1719)	20.00	20.00
1449	A268	$6 multi (#1720)	20.00	20.00

Antigua Nos. 1736-1741 (Cars) Ovptd.

1994, June 15

1450-1453	A271	30c Set of 4	35.00	35.00

Souvenir Sheets

1454	A271	$6 multi (#1740)	19.00	19.00
1455	A271	$6 multi (#1741)	19.00	19.00

Antigua Nos. 1753-1762 (Fine Art) Overprinted

1994, Aug. 18   Litho.   Perf. 13½x14

1455A-1455H	A273	Set of 8	40.00	40.00

Souvenir Sheets

1455I	A273	$6 multi (#1761)	*19.00*	*19.00*
1455J	A273	$6 multi (#1762)	*19.00*	*19.00*

Antigua Nos. 1689-1691 (Polska '93) Ovptd.

1994, Sept. 21   Litho.   Perf. 14

1456	A264	$1 multicolored	7.25	5.75
1457	A264	$3 multicolored	17.50	17.50

Souvenir Sheet

1458	A264	$6 multicolored	20.00	20.00

Antigua Nos. 1786-1795 (Orchids) Ovptd.

1994, Sept. 21   Litho.   Perf. 14

1459-1466	A279	Set of 8	50.00	50.00

Souvenir Sheets

1467	A279	$6 multi (#1794)	25.00	25.00
1468	A279	$6 multi (#1795)	25.00	25.00

Antigua Nos. 1776-1781 (Sierra Club) Ovptd.

1994, Nov. 3   Litho.   Perf. 14

1469	A277	$1.50 multi (#1776)	40.00	40.00
1470	A277	$1.50 multi (#1777)	40.00	40.00

Souvenir Sheets

1471	A277	$1.50 multi (#1778)	7.00	7.00
1472	A277	$1.50 multi (#1779)	7.00	7.00
1472A	A277	$1.50 multi (#1780)	7.00	7.00
1472B	A277	$1.50 multi (#1781)	7.00	7.00

Antigua Nos. 1835-1842 (Soccer) Ovptd.

1995, Jan. 12   Litho.   Perf. 14

1473-1478	A291	Set of 6	30.00	30.00

Souvenir Sheets

1479	A291	$6 multi (#1841)	15.00	15.00
1480	A291	$6 multi (#1842)	15.00	15.00

Antigua Nos. 1857-1866 (Christmas) Ovptd.

1995, Jan. 12   Litho.   Perf. 14

1481-1488	A295	Set of 8	30.00	30.00

Souvenir Sheets
Perf. 13½x14

1489	A295	$6 multi (#1865)	15.00	15.00
1490	A295	$6 multi (#1866)	15.00	15.00

Antigua Nos. 1829-1834 (Country Music) Ovptd.

1996, Feb. 14   Litho.   Perf. 14

1491	A290	75c multi (#1829)	12.50	12.50
1492	A290	75c multi (#1830)	12.50	12.50
1493	A290	75c multi (#1831)	12.50	12.50

Souvenir Sheets

1494	A290	$6 multi (#1832)	14.50	14.50
1495	A290	$6 multi (#1833)	14.50	14.50
1496	A290	$6 multi (#1834)	14.50	14.50

Antigua Nos. 1867-1881 (Birds) Ovptd.

1996   Litho.   Perf. 14½x14

1497	A296	15c multi (#1867)	1.00	.80
1498	A296	25c multi (#1868)	1.10	.90
1499	A296	35c multi (#1869)	1.25	.90
1500	A296	40c multi (#1870)	1.40	.90
1501	A296	45c multi (#1871)	1.60	.90
1502	A296	60c multi (#1872)	1.60	1.25
1503	A296	65c multi (#1873)	1.60	1.25
1504	A296	70c multi (#1873)	1.75	1.40
1505	A296	75c multi (#1874)	1.90	1.60
1506	A296	90c multi (#1875)	2.00	*3.25*
1507	A296	$1.20 multi (#1876)	2.25	*5.25*
1508	A296	$2 multi (#1877)	3.00	*7.25*
1509	A296	$5 multi (#1878)	6.25	*9.00*
1510	A296	$10 multi (#1879)	12.50	*12.00*
1511	A296	$20 multi (#1880)	19.00	*26.00*
Nos. 1497-1511 (15)			*58.20*	*72.65*

Antigua Nos. 1806-1808 (Marine Life) Ovptd.

1996, Jan. 22   Litho.   Perf. 14

1512	A281	50c Sheet of 9, #a.-i.	13.50	13.50

Souvenir Sheets

1513	A281	$6 multi (#1807)	12.50	12.50
1514	A281	$6 multi (#1808)	12.50	12.50

Antigua Nos. 1949-1956 (Christmas) Ovptd.

1996, Jan. 22   Perf. 13½x14

1515-1520	A314	Set of 6	19.00	19.00

Souvenir Sheets

1521	A314	$5 multi (#1955)	12.00	12.00
1522	A314	$6 multi (#1956)	13.50	13.50

Antigua Nos. 1763-1765 (Hong Kong '94) Overprinted

1995, Feb. 24   Litho.   Perf. 14

1523	A274	40c multi (#1763)	7.50	5.75
1524	A274	40c multi (#1764)	7.50	5.75
a.		Horiz. pair, #1523-1524	16.00	16.00

Miniature Sheet

1525	A274	40c Sheet of 6, #a-f (#1765)	*16.00*	*16.00*

Antigua Nos. 1814-1815 (Olympics) Overprinted

1995, Feb. 24   Litho.   Perf. 14

1526-1527	A284	Set of 2	12.50	12.50

An additional item was released in this set. The editors would like to examine it.

Antigua Nos. 1782-1785 (Year of the Dog) Overprinted

1995, Apr. 4   Litho.   Perf. 14

1529	A278	50c Sheet of 12, #a-l	19.00	19.00
1530	A278	75c Sheet of 12, #a-l	*23.00*	*20.00*

Souvenir Sheets

1531	A278	$6 multi (#1784)	22.00	17.50
1532	A278	$6 multi (#1785)	22.00	17.50

Antigua Nos. 1817-1820 (Cricket) Overprinted

1995, May 18   Litho.   Perf. 14

1533-1535	A286	Set of 3	20.00	17.00

Souvenir Sheet

1535A	A286	$3 multi (#1820)	16.00	13.50

Antigua Nos. 1824-1828 (Philakorea '94) Overprinted

Perf. 14, 13½ (#1494H)

1995, July 12   Litho.

1536-1538	A288	Set of 3	35.00	35.00

Miniature Sheet

1539	A289	75c Sheet of 8, #a-h (#1827)	17.00	17.00

Souvenir Sheet

1540	A288	$4 multi (#1828)	45.00	45.00

Antigua Nos. 1843-1845 (Caribbean) Overprinted

1995, May 18   Litho.   Perf. 14

1541-1543	A292	Set of 3	9.00	9.00

Antigua No. 1809 (Year Family) Overprinted

1995, July 12   Litho.   Perf. 14

1543A	A282	90c multi	5.25	5.25

Antigua Nos. 1821-1823 (Moon Landing) Overprinted

1995, July 12   Litho.   Perf. 14

1544	A287	$1.50 Sheet of 6, #a-f (#1821)	23.00	17.00
1545	A287	$1.50 Sheet of 6, #a-f (#1822)	23.00	17.00

Souvenir Sheet

1545G	A287	$6 multi (#1823)	30.00	25.00

Antigua Nos. 1810-1813 (D-Day) Ovptd.

1995, Sept. 29   Litho.   Perf. 14

1546-1548	A283	Set of 3	35.00	27.50

Souvenir Sheet

1549	A283	$6 multi (#1813)	30.00	30.00

End of World War II, 50th
Anniv. — B53

Design: German bombers over St. Paul's
Cathedral, London.

1995, Nov. 13   Litho.   Perf. 13

1550	B53	$8 multicolored	35.00	32.50

For overprints and surcharges see Nos.
1639, B3.

Queen
Elizabeth,
the Queen
Mother, 95th
Birthday
B54

1995, Nov. 20

1551	B54	$7.50 multicolored	27.50	27.50

For overprints and surcharges see Nos.
1638, B2.

United Nations, 50th Anniv. — B55

1995, Nov. 27

1552	B55	$8 New York City	19.00	19.00

For surcharge see No. B4.

Antigua Nos. 1955-1956 (Christmas) Overprinted

1996, Jan. 22   Litho.   Perf. 13½x14

Souvenir Sheets

1552G	A314	$5 multi (#1955)	11.00	10.00
1552H	A314	$6 multi (#1956)	12.50	11.00

Six additional items were issued in this set.
The editors would like to examine any
examples.

Antigua Nos. 1848, 1850-1851, 1854-1856 (Birds) Ovptd.

1996, Feb. 14   Litho.   Perf. 14

1553	A294	15c multi (#1848)	.75	.75
1553A	A294	40c multi (#1850)	2.00	2.00
1554	A294	$1 multi (#1851)	2.75	2.75
1555	A294	$4 multi (#1854)	10.50	10.50
		Nos. 1553-1555 (4)	16.00	16.00

Souvenir Sheets

1556	A294	$6 multi (#1855)	15.00	15.00
1557	A294	$6 multi (#1856)	15.00	15.00

Antigua Nos. 1882-1890 (Prehistoric Animals) Ovptd.

1996, June 13   Litho.   Perf. 14

1558-1563	A297	Set of 6	25.00	25.00
1564	A297	75c Sheet of 12, #a-l	27.50	27.50

Souvenir Sheets

1565	A297	$6 multi (#1889)	19.00	19.00
1566	A297	$6 multi (#1890)	19.00	19.00

Antigua Nos. 1891-1898 (Atlanta Olympics) Ovptd.

1996, July 16   Litho.   Perf. 14

1567-1572	A298	Set of 6	20.00	20.00

Souvenir Sheets

1573	A298	$6 multi (#1897)	13.50	13.50
1574	A298	$6 multi (#1898)	13.50	13.50

Antigua Nos. 1930-1933 (Boy Scouts) Ovptd.

1996, Sept. 10

1575	A310	$1.20 Strip of 3, #a.-c. (#1930)	12.50	12.50
1576	A310	$1.20 Strip of 3, #a.-c. (#1931)	12.50	12.50

Souvenir Sheets

1577	A310	$6 multi (#1932)	9.50	9.50
1578	A310	$6 multi (#1933)	9.50	9.50

Antigua Nos. 1945-1948 (Nobel Prize) Ovptd.

1996, Oct. 25   Litho.   Perf. 14

1579	A313	$1 Sheet of 9, #a.-i. (#1945)	13.50	13.50
1580	A313	$1 Sheet of 9, #a.-i. (#1946)	13.50	13.50

Souvenir Sheets

1581	A313	$6 multi (#1947)	12.50	12.50
1582	A313	$6 multi (#1948)	12.50	12.50

Antigua Nos. 2001-2002 (QEII Birthday) Ovptd.

1996, Nov. 14   Perf. 13½x14

1583	A323	$2 Strip of 3, #a.-c.	13.50	13.50

Souvenir Sheet

1584	A323	$6 multicolored	15.00	15.00

Antigua Nos. 2018-2025 (Christmas) Ovptd.

1997, Jan. 28   Litho.   Perf. 13½x14

1585-1590	A328	Set of 6	12.50	12.50

Souvenir Sheets

1591	A328	$6 multi (#2024)	12.50	12.50
1592	A328	$6 multi (#2025)	12.50	12.50

Antigua Nos. 1905-1906 (FAO) Ovptd.

1997, Feb. 24   Perf. 14

1593	A301	Strip of 3, #a.-c.	10.50	10.50

Souvenir Sheet

1594	A301	$6 multicolored	13.50	13.50

Antigua Nos. 1907-1908 (Rotary) Ovptd.

1997, Feb. 24

1595	A302	$5 multicolored	13.50	13.50

Souvenir Sheet

1596	A302	$6 multicolored	15.00	15.00

Antigua Nos. 1899-1902 (World War II) Ovptd.

1997, Apr. 4   Litho.   Perf. 14

1597	A299	$1.20 Sheet of 6, #a.-f.	27.50	27.50
1598	A299	$1.20 Sheet of 8, #a.-h.	20.00	20.00

Souvenir Sheets

1599	A299	$3 multi (#1901)	19.00	19.00
1600	A299	$6 multi (#1902)	20.00	20.00

Antigua Nos. 1903-1904 (UN) Ovptd.

1997   Litho.   Perf. 14

1601	A300	Strip of 3, #a.-c.	9.00	9.00

Souvenir Sheet

1602	A300	$6 multicolored	12.50	12.50

Antigua Nos. 1909-1910 (Queen Mother) Ovptd.

1997   Perf. 13½x14

1603	A303	$1.50 Strip or block of 4, #a.-d.	17.50	17.50

Souvenir Sheet

1604	A303	$6 multicolored	19.00	19.00

Antigua Nos. 1913-1917 (Bees) Ovptd.

1997   Litho.   Perf. 14

1605-1608	A305	Set of 4	15.00	15.00

Souvenir Sheet

1609	A305	$6 multicolored	15.00	15.00

Antigua Nos. 1918-1919 (Cats) Ovptd.

1997

1610	A306	45c Sheet of 12, #a-l	20.00	20.00

Souvenir Sheet

1611	A306	$6 multicolored	15.00	15.00

Antigua Nos. 1928-1929 (Flowers) Ovptd.

1997

1612	A309	75c Sheet of 12, #a-l	17.00	17.00

Souvenir Sheet

1613	A309	$6 multicolored	15.00	15.00

Antigua Nos. 1934-1942 (Trains) Ovptd.

1997, May 30   Litho.   Perf. 14

1614-1619	A311	Set of 6	12.00	12.00
1620	A311	$1.20 Sheet of 9, #a.-i.	13.50	13.50

Souvenir Sheets

1621	A311	$6 multi (#1941)	13.50	13.50
1621A	A311	$6 multi (#1942)	13.50	13.50

Antigua Nos. 1911-1912 (Ducks) Ovptd.

1997   Litho.   Perf. 14

1622	A304	75c Sheet of 12, #a-l	21.00	21.00

Souvenir Sheet

1623	A304	$6 multicolored	21.00	21.00

Antigua Nos. 1943-1944 (Birds) Ovptd.

1997

1624	A312	75c Sheet of 12, #a-l	7.50	7.50

Souvenir Sheet

1625	A312	$6 multicolored	8.50	8.50

Antigua Nos. 1967-1970 (Mushrooms) Ovptd.

1997

1626	A317	75c Strips of 4, #a.-d. (#1967)	8.50	8.50
1627	A317	75c Strips of 4, #a.-d. (#1968)	8.50	8.50

Souvenir Sheets

1628	A317	$6 multi (#1969)	12.50	12.50
1629	A317	$6 multi (#1970)	12.50	12.50

Antigua Nos. 1970A-1974 (Ships) Ovptd.

1997, Nov. 3   Litho.   Perf. 14

1629A-1629F	A318	Set of 6	6.00	6.00
1629G	A318	$1.20 Sheet of 6, #k-p (#1971)	12.50	12.50
1629H	A318	$1.50 Sheet of 6, #q-v (#1972)	12.50	12.50

Souvenir Sheets

1629I	A318	$6 multi (#1973)	10.50	10.50
1629J	A318	$6 multi (#1974)	10.50	10.50

Antigua Nos. 2111-2118 (Christmas) Ovptd.

1997   Litho.   Perf. 14

1630-1635	A345	Set of 6	11.50	11.50

Souvenir Sheets

1636	A345	$6 multi (#2117)	9.50	9.50
1637	A345	$6 multi (#2118)	9.50	9.50

Antigua Nos. 2069-2070 (Royal Anniv.) Ovptd.

1997, Nov. 3   Litho.   Perf. 14

1637A	A337	$1 Sheet of 6, #c-h (#2069)	15.00	15.00

Souvenir Sheet

1637B	A337	$6 multi (#2070)	20.00	20.00

Nos. 1550-
1551 Ovptd.
in Gold

1997, July 25   Litho.   Perf. 13

1638	B54	$7.50 on #1551	15.00	15.00
1639	B53	$8 on #1550	15.00	15.00

Antigua Nos. 1983-1986 (Sea Birds) Ovptd.

1998   Litho.   Perf. 14

1640	A320	75c Vert. strip, #a.-d. (#1983)	7.25	7.25
1641	A320	75c Vert. strip, #a.-d. (#1984)	7.25	7.25

Souvenir Sheets

1643	A320	$5 multi (#1985)	9.00	9.00
1644	A320	$6 multi (#1986)	9.75	9.75

Antigua Nos. 1975-1982 (Atlanta Olympics) Overprinted

1998, Mar. 25   Litho.   Perf. 14

1644A-1644D	A319	Set of 4	10.50	10.50
1644E	A319	90c Sheet of 9, #f-n (#1979)	12.50	12.50
1644O	A319	90c Sheet of 9, #p-x (#1980)	12.50	12.50

Souvenir Sheets

1644Y	A319	$5 multi (#1981)	9.50	9.50
1644Z	A319	$6 multi (#1982)	9.50	9.50

Antigua Nos. 2003-2004 (Cavalry) Ovptd.

1998   Litho.   Perf. 14

1645	A324	60c Block of 4, #a.-d.	11.50	11.50

Souvenir Sheet

1646	A324	$6 multi	12.50	12.50

Antigua Nos. 2013-2017 (Radio) Overprinted

1998, Mar. 25   Litho.   Perf. 14

1646A-1646D	A327	Set of 4	12.50	12.50

Souvenir Sheet

1646E	A327	$6 multi	16.00	16.00

Antigua Nos. 2094-2102 (Soccer) Ovptd.

1998
1647-1652 A342 Set of 6   11.50 11.50
1653 A342 $1 Sheet of 8 + label   19.00 19.00
      Souvenir Sheets
1654 A342 $6 multi (#2101)   10.00 10.00
1655 A342 $6 multi (#2102)   10.00 10.00

Antigua Nos. 2005-2008 (UNICEF) Ovptd.

1998   *Litho.*   *Perf. 14*
1656-1658 A325 Set of 3   10.50 10.50
      Souvenir Sheet
1659 A325 $6 multicolored   12.50 12.50

Antigua Nos. 2009-2012 (Jerusalem) Ovptd.

1998
1660-1662 A326 Set of 3   11.50 11.50
      Souvenir Sheet
1663 A326 $6 multicolored   12.50 12.50

Antigua Nos. 2119-2122 (Diana) Ovptd.

1998   *Litho.*   *Perf. 14*
1664 A346 $1.65 Sheet of 6, #a-f (#2119)   12.50 12.50
1665 A346 $1.65 Sheet of 6, #a-f (#2120)   12.50 12.50
      Souvenir Sheets
1666 A346 $6 multi (#2121)   8.50 8.50
1667 A346 $6 multi (#2122)   8.50 8.50

Antigua Nos. 2037-2038 (Broadway) Ovptd.

1998   *Litho.*   *Perf. 14*
1668 A330 $1 Sheet of 9, #a.-i. (#2037)   22.00 22.00
      Souvenir Sheet
1669 A330 $6 multi (#2038)   19.00 19.00

Antigua Nos. 2063-2064 (Chaplin) Ovtpd.

1998
1670 A334 $1 Sheet of 9, #a.-i. (#2063)   22.00 22.00
      Souvenir Sheet
1671 A334 $6 multi (#2064)   19.00 19.00

Antigua Nos. 2039-2047 (Butterflies) Ovptd.

1998   *Litho.*   *Perf. 14*
1672-1675 A331 Set of 4   12.50 12.50
1676 A331 $1.10 Sheet of 9, #a.-i. (#2043)   17.50 17.50
1677 A331 $1.10 Sheet of 9, #a.-i. (#2044)   17.50 17.50
      Souvenir Sheets
1678 A331 $6 multi (#2045)   12.50 12.50
1679 A331 $6 multi (#2046)   12.50 12.50
1680 A331 $6 multi (#2047)   12.50 12.50

Antigua Nos. 2140-2148 (Lighthouses) Ovptd.

1998
1681-1688 A349 Set of 8   23.00 23.00
      Souvenir Sheet
1689 A349 $6 multi (#2148)   23.00 23.00

Antigua Nos. 2211-2219 (Christmas) Ovptd.

1998
1690-1696 A366 Set of 7   15.00 15.00
      Souvenir Sheets
1697 A366 $6 multi (#2218)   10.00 10.00
1698 A366 $6 multi (#2219)   10.00 10.00

Antigua Nos. 2058-2062 (Animals) Ovptd.

1998   *Litho.*   *Perf. 14*
1699 A333 $1.20 Sheet of 6, #a.-f. (#2058)   13.50 13.50
1700 A333 $1.65 Sheet of 6, #a.-f. (#2059)   16.00 16.00
      Souvenir Sheets
1701 A333 $6 multi (#2060)   11.00 11.00
1702 A333 $6 multi (#2061)   11.00 11.00
1703 A333 $6 multi (#2062)   11.00 11.00

Antigua Nos. 2067-2068 (Von Stephan) Ovptd.

1999   *Litho.*   *Perf. 14*
1704 A336 $1.75 Sheet of 3, #a.-c.   15.00 15.00
      Souvenir Sheet
1705 A336 $6 multi (#2068)   12.50 12.50

Antigua Nos. 2071-2072 (Fairy Tales) Ovptd.

1999   *Perf. 13½x14*
1706 A338 $1.75 Sheet of 3, #a.-c.   15.00 15.00
      Souvenir Sheet
1707 A338 $6 multi (#2072)   12.50 12.50

Antigua Nos. 2084-2093 (Orchids) Ovptd.

1999   *Litho.*   *Perf. 14*
1708-1713 A341 Set of 6   15.00 15.00
1714 A341 $1.65 Sheet of 8, #a.-h. (#2090)   23.00 23.00
1715 A341 $1.65 Sheet of 8, #a.-h. (#2091)   23.00 23.00
      Souvenir Sheets
1716 A341 $6 multi (#2092)   14.50 14.50
1717 A341 $6 multi (#2093)   14.50 14.50

Antigua Nos. 2065-2066 (Rotary) Ovptd.

1999   *Litho.*   *Perf. 14*
1718 A335 $1.75 multicolored   11.50 11.50
      Souvenir Sheet
1719 A335 $6 multicolored   12.50 12.50

Antigua Nos. 2075-2083 (Mushrooms) Ovptd.

1999
1720-1725 A340 Set of 6   19.00 19.00
1726 A340 $1.75 Sheet of 6, #a.-f.   22.00 22.00
      Souvenir Sheets
1727 A340 $6 multi (#2082)   14.50 14.50
1728 A340 $6 multi (#2083)   14.50 14.50

Antigua No. 2184 (Diana) Ovptd.

1999
1729 A358 $1.20 multicolored   5.50 5.50

Antigua Nos. 2268, 2269 (Royal Wedding) Overprinted "BARBOUDA MAIL"

1999, Aug. 12   *Litho.*   *Perf. 13½*
1729A A378 $3 Sheet of 3, #b-d   — —
1729E A378 $6 multi   12.50 12.50

   An additional sheet was released in this set. The editors would like to examine it.

Antigua Nos. 2107-2110 (Trains) Ovptd.

1999   *Litho.*   *Perf. 14*
1730 A344 $1.65 Sheet of 6, #a.-f. (#2107)   11.50 11.50
1731 A344 $1.65 Sheet of 6, #a.-f. (#2108)   11.50 11.50
      Souvenir Sheets
1732 A344 $6 brown (#2109)   8.50 8.50
1733 A344 $6 brown (#2110)   8.50 8.50

Antigua Nos. 2133-2139 (Church) Ovptd.

1999
1734-1739 A348 Set of 6   8.00 8.00
      Souvenir Sheet
1740 A348 $6 multi (#2139)   9.00 9.00

Antigua Nos. 2155-2161 (High School) Ovptd.

1999
1741-1746 A351 Set of 6   11.00 11.00
      Souvenir Sheet
1747 A351 $6 multi (#2161)   10.00 10.00

Antigua Nos. 2295-2301 (Christmas) Ovptd.

1999   *Perf. 13¾*
1748-1753 A383 Set of 6   13.50 13.50
      Souvenir Sheet
1754 A383 $6 multi (#2301)   11.50 11.50

Antigua Nos. 2103-2106 (Animals) Ovptd.

2000   *Litho.*   *Perf. 14*
1755 A343 $1.65 Sheet of 6, #a-f (#2103)   19.00 19.00
1756 A343 $1.65 Sheet of 6, #a-f (#2104)   19.00 19.00
      Souvenir Sheets
1757 A343 $6 multi (#2105)   16.00 16.00
1758 A343 $6 multi (#2106)   16.00 16.00

Antigua Nos. 2123-2132 (Fish) Ovptd.

2000
1759-1764 A347 Set of 6   13.50 13.50
1765 A347 $1.65 Sheet of 6, #a-f (#2129)   18.00 18.00
1766 A347 $1.65 Sheet of 6, #a-f (#2130)   18.00 18.00
      Souvenir Sheets
1767 A347 $6 multi (#2131)   17.00 17.00
1768 A347 $6 multi (#2132)   17.00 17.00

Antigua Nos. 2166-2170 (Ships) Ovptd.

2000   *Litho.*   *Perf. 14x14½*
1769 A353 $1.75 Sheet of 3, #a-c (#2166)   12.50 12.50
1770 A353 $1.75 Sheet of 3, #a-c (#2167)   12.50 12.50
      Souvenir Sheets
1771 A353 $6 multi (#2168)   8.50 8.50
1772 A353 $6 multi (#2169)   8.50 8.50
1773 A353 $6 multi (#2170)   8.50 8.50

Antigua Nos. 2172-2175 (Antique Autos) Ovptd.

2000   *Perf. 14*
1774 A355 $1.65 Sheet of 6, #a-f (#2172)   15.00 15.00
1775 A355 $1.65 Sheet of 6, #a-f (#2173)   15.00 15.00
      Souvenir Sheets
1776 A355 $6 multi (#2174)   10.00 10.00
1777 A355 $6 multi (#2175)   10.00 10.00

Antigua Nos. 2194-2197 (Scouts) Ovptd.

2000
1778-1780 A361 Set of 3   10.50 10.50
      Souvenir Sheet
1781 A361 $6 multi   13.50 13.50

Antigua No. 2198 (OAS) Ovptd.

2000   *Perf. 13½*
1782 A362 $1 multi   6.25 6.25

Antigua Nos. 2176-2179 (Aircraft) Overprinted

2000, Apr. 4   *Litho.*   *Perf. 14*
1783 A356 $1.65 Sheet of 6, #a-f (#2176)   17.00 17.00
1784 A356 $1.65 Sheet of 6, #a-f (#2177)   17.00 17.00
      Souvenir Sheets
1785 A356 $6 multi (#2178)   12.50 12.50
1786 A356 $6 multi (#2179)   12.50 12.50

Antigua Nos. 2373-2374 (Queen Mother) Overprinted Litho., Margin Embossed

2000, Aug. 4   *Perf. 14*
1787 A404 $2 Sheet of 4, #a-d + label   19.00 19.00
      Souvenir Sheet
      Perf. 13¾
1788 A404 $6 multi   15.00 15.00

Antigua No. 2242 (John Glenn) Overprinted

2000, Nov. 30   *Litho.*   *Perf. 14*
1789 A371 $1.75 Sheet of 4, #a-d   25.00 25.00

Antigua Nos. 2243-2246 (Space) Overprinted

2000, Nov. 30   *Litho.*   *Perf. 14*
1790 A372 $1.65 Sheet of 6, #a-f (#2243)   12.50 12.50
1791 A372 $1.65 Sheet of 6, #a-f (#2244)   12.50 12.50
      Souvenir Sheets
1792 A372 $6 multi (#2245)   12.50 12.50
1793 A372 $6 multi (#2246)   12.50 12.50

Antigua Nos. 2386-2389 (Battle of Britain) Overprinted

2000, Nov. 30   *Litho.*   *Perf. 14*
1794 A409 $1.20 Sheet of 8, #a-h (#2386)   25.00 25.00
1795 A409 $1.20 Sheet of 8, #a-h (#2387)   25.00 25.00
      Souvenir Sheets
1796 A409 $6 multi (#2388)   17.00 17.00
1797 A409 $6 multi (#2389)   17.00 17.00

Antigua No. 2186, 2189 (Gandhi) Overprinted

2000, Oct.   *Litho.*   *Perf. 14*
1810 A359 $1 multi (#2186)   — —
      Souvenir Sheet
1812 A359 $6 multi (#2189)   — —

   Three additional stamps exist in this set. The editors would like to examine any examples.

SEMI-POSTAL STAMPS

   Catalogue values for unused stamps in this section are for Never Hinged items.

Barbuda No. 501 Crudely Surcharged

1982, June 28   **Self-Adhesive**
B1 CD331 Booklet   13.50

Nos. 1550-1552 Surcharged in Silver

1995, Nov.   *Litho.*   *Perf. 13*
B2 B54 $7.50 +$1 on #1551   6.75 *9.50*
B3 B53 $8 +$1 on #1550   15.00 13.50
B4 B55 $8 +$1 on #1552   6.75 *9.50*
   Nos. B2-B4 (3)   28.50 32.50

BASUTOLAND

bə-'sü-tə-ˌland

LOCATION — An enclave in the state of South Africa
GOVT. — British Crown Colony
AREA — 11,716 sq. mi.
POP. — 733,000 (est. 1964)
CAPITAL — Maseru

The Colony, a former independent native state, was annexed to the Cape Colony in 1871. In 1883 control was transferred directly to the British Crown. Stamps of the Cape of Good Hope were used from 1871 to 1910 and those of the Union of South Africa from 1910 to 1933. Basutoland became the independent state of Lesotho on Oct. 4, 1966.

12 Pence = 1 Shilling
100 Cents = 1 Rand (1961)

Catalogue values for unused stamps in this country are for Never Hinged items, beginning with Scott 29 in the regular postage section and Scott J1 in the postage due section.

George V — A1

Crocodile and River Scene

Perf. 12½
1933, Dec. 1   Engr.   Wmk. 4

1	A1	½p emerald	1.50	2.40
2	A1	1p carmine	1.25	1.75
3	A1	2p red violet	1.50	1.10
4	A1	3p ultra	1.25	1.40
5	A1	4p slate	2.75	9.50
6	A1	6p yellow	3.00	2.40
7	A1	1sh red orange	4.25	5.00
8	A1	2sh6p dk brown	45.00	57.50
9	A1	5sh violet	82.50	92.50
10	A1	10sh olive green	225.00	240.00
		Nos. 1-10 (10)	368.00	413.55
		Set, never hinged	750.00	

Common Design Types pictured following the introduction.

Silver Jubilee Issue
Common Design Type
1935, May 4   Perf. 13½x14

11	CD301	1p car & blue	1.00	3.00
12	CD301	2p gray blk & ultra	1.10	3.25
13	CD301	3p blue & brown	4.50	7.50
14	CD301	6p brt vio & indigo	5.00	7.50
		Nos. 11-14 (4)	11.60	21.25
		Set, never hinged	20.00	

Coronation Issue
Common Design Type
1937, May 12   Perf. 13½x14

15	CD302	1p carmine	.25	1.00
16	CD302	2p rose violet	.40	1.00
17	CD302	3p bright ultra	.50	1.00
		Nos. 15-17 (3)	1.15	3.00
		Set, never hinged	1.75	

George VI — A2

1938, Apr. 1   Perf. 12½

18	A2	½p emerald	.25	1.25
19	A2	1p rose car	1.25	.85
20	A2	1½p light blue	.45	.65
21	A2	2p rose lilac	.45	.80
22	A2	3p ultra	.50	1.50
23	A2	4p gray	1.60	4.25

24	A2	6p yel ocher	2.00	1.75
25	A2	1sh red orange	3.00	1.40
26	A2	2sh6p black brown	14.00	9.00
27	A2	5sh violet	30.00	10.00
28	A2	10sh olive green	32.50	24.00
		Nos. 18-28 (11)	86.00	55.45
		Set, never hinged	130.00	

Catalogue values for unused stamps in this section, from this point to the end of the section, are for Never Hinged items.

Peace Issue

South Africa Nos. 100-102 Overprinted

Basic stamps inscribed alternately in English and Afrikaans.

1945, Dec. 3   Wmk. 201   Perf. 14

29	A42	1p rose pink & choc, pair	.70	.90
a.		Single, English	.25	.25
b.		Single, Afrikaans	.25	.25
30	A43	2p vio & slate blue, pair	.70	.75
a.		Single, English	.25	.25
b.		Single, Afrikaans	.25	.25
31	A43	3p ultra & dp ultra, pair	.70	.95
a.		Single, English	.25	.25
b.		Single, Afrikaans	.25	.25
		Nos. 29-31 (3)	2.10	2.60

King George VI — A3

King George VI and Queen Elizabeth A4

Princess Margaret Rose and Princess Elizabeth A5

Royal British Family A6

Perf. 12½
1947, Feb. 17   Wmk. 4   Engr.

35	A3	1p red	.25	.25
36	A4	2p green	.25	.25
37	A5	3p ultra	.25	.25
38	A6	1sh dark violet	.25	.25
		Nos. 35-38 (4)	1.00	1.00

Visit of the British Royal Family, Mar. 11-12, 1947.

Silver Wedding Issue
Common Design Types
1948, Dec. 1   Photo.   Perf. 14x14½

39	CD304	1½p brt ultra	.30	.25

Engr.; Name Typo.
Perf. 11½

40	CD305	10sh dk brn ol	52.50	55.00

UPU Issue
Common Design Types
Engr.; Name Typo. on 3p, 6p
Perf. 13½, 11x11½
1949, Oct. 10   Wmk. 4

41	CD306	1½p blue	.50	1.50
42	CD307	3p indigo	2.25	2.00
43	CD308	6p orange yel	1.25	5.00
44	CD309	1sh red brown	.75	1.00
		Nos. 41-44 (4)	4.75	10.00

Coronation Issue
Common Design Type
1953, June 3   Engr.   Perf. 13½x13

45	CD312	2p red violet & black	.50	.60

Qiloane Hill — A7

Shearing Angora Goats — A8

Designs: 1p, Orange River. 2p, Mosotho horseman. 3p, Basuto household. 4½p, Maletsunyane falls. 6p, Herdboy with lesiba. 1sh, Pastoral scene. 1sh3p, Plane at Lancers Gap. 2sh6p, Old Fort Leribe. 5sh, Mission cave house.

Perf. 13½, 11½ (#56)
1954, Oct. 18   Wmk. 4

46	A7	½p dk brown & gray	.55	.25
47	A7	1p dp grn & gray blk	.50	.25
48	A7	2p org & dp blue	1.00	.25
49	A7	3p car & ol green	2.00	.40
50	A7	4½p dp blue & ind	1.50	.25
51	A7	6p dk grn & org brn	2.50	.25
52	A7	1sh rose vio & dk ol green	2.25	.40
53	A7	1sh3p aqua & brown	27.50	9.00
54	A7	2sh6p lilac rose & dp ultra	29.00	14.00
55	A7	5sh dp car & black	14.00	12.00
56	A8	10sh dp cl & black	40.00	27.50
		Nos. 46-56 (11)	120.80	64.55

See Nos. 72-82, 87-91. For surcharges see Nos. 57, 61-71.

No. 48 Surcharged

1959, Aug. 1

57	A7	½p on 2p org & dp blue	.30	.25

Chief Moshoeshoe (Moshesh) — A9

Designs: 1sh, Council chamber. 1sh3p, Mosotho on horseback.

Perf. 13x13½
1959, Dec. 15   Wmk. 314

58	A9	3p lt yel, grn & blk	.60	.25
59	A9	1sh green & pink	.60	.25
60	A9	1sh3p orange & ultra	.80	.50
		Nos. 58-60 (3)	2.00	1.00

Institution of the Basutoland National Council.

Nos. 46-56 Surcharged with New Value

2½c I   2½c II   3½c I   3½c II
5c I   5c II   10c I   10c II
12½c I   12½c II
25c I   25c II   25c III
50c I   50c II   R1 I   R1 II   R1 III

Perf. 13½, 11½ (#71)
1961, Feb. 14   Wmk. 4

61	A7	½c on ½p	.25	.25
a.		Double surcharge	750.00	
62	A7	1c on 1p	.25	.25
63	A7	2c on 2p	1.25	1.50
a.		Inverted surcharge	225.00	
64	A7	2½c on 3p (II)	.25	.25
b.		Inverted surcharge (II)	8,000.	8,000.
65	A7	3½c on 4½p (II)	.35	.25
a.		Type I	4.00	8.50
66	A7	5c on 6p (II)	.80	.25
a.		Type I	.40	
67	A7	10c on 1sh (I)	.50	.25
a.		Type II	175.00	180.00
68	A7	12½c on 1sh3p (II)	13.00	4.75
a.		Type I	6.00	2.25
69	A7	25c on 2sh6p (I)	1.90	.75
a.		Type II	57.50	15.00
b.		Type III	1.90	2.50
70	A7	50c on 5sh (II)	4.50	6.00
a.		Type I	8.50	5.50
71	A8	1r on 10sh (III)	32.50	27.50
a.		Type I	67.50	27.50
b.		Type II	32.50	67.50
		Nos. 61-71 (11)	55.55	42.00

Surcharge types on Nos. 64-71 are numbered chronologically.

Types of 1954
Value in Cents and Rands

Designs: ½c, Qiloane Hill. 1c, Orange River. 2c, Mosotho horseman. 2½c, Basuto household. 3½c, Maletsunyane Falls. 5c, Herdboy with lesiba. 10c, Pastoral scene. 12½c, Plane at Lancers Gap. 25c, Old Fort Leribe. 50c, Mission cave house. 1r, Shearing Angora goats.

1961-63   Wmk. 4   Engr.   Perf. 13½

72	A7	½c dk brn & gray ('62)	.25	.30
73	A7	1c dp grn & gray blk ('62)	.30	.40
74	A7	2c org & dp bl ('62)	3.00	1.50
75	A7	2½c car & ol grn	2.00	.85
76	A7	3½c dp bl & ind ('62)	.80	1.50
77	A7	5c dk grn & org brn ('62)	.65	.70
78	A7	10c rose vio & dk ol ('62)	.40	.50
79	A7	12½c aqua & brn ('62)	25.00	12.00
80	A7	25c lilac rose & dp ultra ('62)	6.50	6.50
81	A7	50c dp car & blk ('62)	20.00	25.00

Perf. 11½

82	A8	1r dp cl & blk ('63)	52.50	27.50
		Nos. 72-82 (11)	111.40	76.75

See Nos. 87-91. For overprints on stamps and types see Lesotho Nos. 5-14, 20a.

Freedom from Hunger Issue
Common Design Type
Perf. 14x14½
1963, June 4   Photo.   Wmk. 314

83	CD314	12½c lilac	.50	.25

Red Cross Centenary Issue
Common Design Type
1963, Sept. 2   Litho.   Perf. 13

84	CD315	2½c black & red	.30	.25
85	CD315	12½c ultra & red	.90	.65

Queen Type of 1961-63
1964   Engr.   Perf. 13½

87	A7	1c grn & gray blk	.25	.35
88	A7	2½c car & ol green	.25	.30
89	A7	5c dk green & org brn	.45	.60

90	A7	12½c aqua & brown	12.00 2.50
91	A7	50c dp car & black	7.00 15.00
		Nos. 87-91 (5)	19.95 18.75

Mosotho
Woman and
Child — A10

Designs: 3½c, Maseru border post. 5c,
Mountains. 12½c, Legislative Building.

Perf. 14x13½

1965, May 10 Photo. Wmk. 314

97	A10	2½c ultra & multi	.25 .25
98	A10	3½c blue & bister	.50 .30
99	A10	5c blue & ocher	.50 .30
100	A10	12½c lt blue, blk & buff	.60 .70
		Nos. 97-100 (4)	1.85 1.55

Attainment of self-government.

ITU Issue
Common Design Type

1965, May 17 Litho. Perf. 11x11½

101	CD317	1c ver & red lilac	.25 .25
102	CD317	20c grnsh bl & org brn	.60 .40

Intl. Cooperation Year Issue
Common Design Type

1965, Oct. 25 Wmk. 314 Perf. 14½

103	CD318	½c blue grn & cl	.25 .50
104	CD318	12½c lt vio & green	.50 .35

Churchill Memorial Issue
Common Design Type

1966, Jan. 24 Photo. Perf. 14
Design in Black, Gold and Carmine Rose

105	CD319	1c bright blue	.25 1.00
106	CD319	2½c green	.55 .25
107	CD319	10c brown	.75 .50
108	CD319	22½c violet	1.25 1.50
		Nos. 105-108 (4)	2.80 3.25

POSTAGE DUE STAMPS

Catalogue values for all unused
stamps in this section are for
Never Hinged items.

D1

1933-52 Wmk. 4 Typo. Perf. 14
Chalky Paper

J1	D1	1p dark red ('51)	2.00 8.50
a.		1p carmine, ordinary paper	3.50 14.50
b.		1p dk car, ordinary paper ('38)	50.00 60.00
c.		Wmk. 4a (error)	160.00
d.		Wmk. 4, crown missing (error)	400.00
J2	D1	2p lt violet ('52)	.40 25.00
a.		2p lt violet, ordinary paper	10.00 24.00
b.		Wmk. 4a (error)	160.00
c.		Wmk. 4, crown missing (error)	400.00

For surcharge see No. J7.

Coat of Arms — D2

1956, Dec. 1

J3	D2	1p carmine	.50 3.00
J4	D2	2p dark purple	.50 6.00

Nos. J2-J4
Surcharged

1961

J5	D2	1c on 1p carmine	.25 .40
J6	D2	1c on 2p dk purple	.25 1.25
J7	D1	5c on 2p lt violet	1.50 7.00
a.		Wmk. 4a (error)	375.00
b.		Wmk. 4, crown missing (error)	2,000.
J8	D2	5c on 2p dark pur ("5" 7½mm high)	.25 .45
a.		"5" 3½mm high	17.50 55.00
		Nos. J5-J8 (4)	2.25 9.10

Value in Cents

1964 Wmk. 314 Perf. 14

J9	D2	1c carmine	4.50 26.00
J10	D2	5c dark purple	4.50 26.00

For overprints see Lesotho Nos. J1-J2.

OFFICIAL STAMPS

Nos. 1-3 and 6 Overprinted
"OFFICIAL"

1934 Wmk. 4 Engr. Perf. 12½

O1	A1	½p emerald	15,000. 7,500.
O2	A1	1p carmine	5,500. 3,750.
O3	A1	2p red violet	6,000. 1,250.
O4	A1	6p yellow	15,000. 5,000.

Counterfeits exist.

BATUM

bä-'tūm

LOCATION — A seaport on the Black
Sea

Batum is the capital of Adzhar, a territory which, in 1921, became an autonomous republic of the Georgian Soviet
Socialist Republic.

Stamps of Batum were issued under
the administration of British forces
which occupied Batum and environs
between December, 1918, and July,
1920, following the Treaty of Versailles.

100 Kopecks = 1 Ruble

Counterfeits of Nos. 1-65 abound.

A1

1919 Unwmk. Litho. Imperf.

1	A1	5k green	7.00 27.50
2	A1	10k ultramarine	4.00 12.50
3	A1	50k yellow	7.50 14.00
4	A1	1r red brown	12.00 9.50
5	A1	3r violet	11.50 20.00
6	A1	5r brown	11.00 42.50
		Nos. 1-6 (6)	53.00 126.00

For overprints and surcharges see Nos. 13-
20, 51-65.

Nos. 7-12, 21-50: numbers in
parentheses are those of the basic
Russian stamps.

Russian Stamps of
1909-17 Surcharged

1919 On Stamps of 1917

7	10r on 1k orange (#119)		75.00 75.00
8	10r on 3k red (#121)		22.50 32.50

On Stamp of 1909-12
Perf. 14x14½

9	10r on 5k claret (#77)		950.00 950.00

On Stamp of 1917

10	10r on 10k on 7k light blue (#117)		975.00 900.00
	Nos. 7-10 (4)		2,023. 1,958.

Russian Stamps of
1909-13 Surcharged

1919

11	35k on 4k carmine (#76)		4,000. 6,000.
12	35k on 4k dull red (#91)		10,000. 13,000.

This surcharge was intended for postal
cards. A few cards which bore adhesive
stamps were also surcharged.

Values are for stamps off card and without
gum.

Type of 1919 Issue
Overprinted

1919 Unwmk. Imperf.

13	A1	5k green	22.50 15.00
14	A1	10k dark blue	12.00 18.00
15	A1	25k orange	21.00 18.00
16	A1	1r pale blue	6.00 18.00
17	A1	2r salmon pink	1.75 9.00
18	A1	3r violet	1.75 10.00
19	A1	5r brown	2.00 10.00
a.		"CCUPATION"	475.00 475.00
20	A1	7r dull red	5.00 11.00
		Nos. 13-20 (8)	72.00 109.00

Russian Stamps of 1909-17
Surcharged in Various Colors

10r & 50r   15r

On Stamps of 1917

1919-20 Imperf.

21	10r on 3k red (#121)		25.00 27.50
a.	Inverted overprint		500.00
22	15r on 1k org (R) (#119)		50.00 100.00
23	15r on 1k org (Bk) (#119)		100.00 150.00
a.	Inverted overprint		750.00 750.00
24	15r on 1k org (V) (#119)		75.00 110.00
25	50r on 1k org (#119)		975.00 800.00
26	50r on 2k green (#120)		975.00 1,100.

On Stamps of 1909-17
Perf. 14x14½

27	50r on 2k green (#74)		1,000. 850.00
28	50r on 3k red (#75)		1,700. 2,500.
29	50r on 4k car (#76)		1,500. 1,500.
30	50r on 5k claret (#77)		975.00 975.00
31	50r on 10k dk blue (R) (#79)		3,000. 3,500.
32	50r on 15k red brn & blue (#81)		700.00 850.00

Surcharged

On Stamps of 1909-17

33	25r on 5k cl (Bk) (#77)		100.00 150.00
34	25r on 5k cl (Bl) (#77)		100.00 150.00
a.	Inverted overprint		300.00
35	25r on 10k on 7k lt blue (Bk) (#117)		150.00 175.00
36	25r on 10k on 7k lt blue (Bl) (#117)		100.00 110.00
37	25r on 20k on 14k bl & rose (Bk) (#118)		100.00 150.00

38	25r on 20k on 14k bl & rose (Bl) (#118)		200.00 200.00
39	25r on 25k grn & gray vio (Bk) (#83)		160.00 175.00
a.	Inverted overprint		250.00
40	25r on 25k grn & gray vio (Bl) (#83)		100.00 135.00
41	25r on 50k vio & green (Bk) (#85a)		110.00
a.	Inverted overprint		250.00
42	25r on 50k vio & green (Bl) (#85a)		100.00 150.00
43	50r on 2k green (#74)		250.00 175.00
44	50r on 3k red (#75)		200.00 175.00
45	50r on 4k car (#76)		200.00 250.00
46	50r on 5k claret (#77)		200.00 100.00

On Stamps of 1917
Imperf

47	50r on 2k green (#120)		975.00 650.00
48	50r on 3k red (#121)		975.00 675.00
49	50r on 5k claret (#123)		1,600. 1,700.

On Stamp of 1913
Perf. 13½

50	50r on 4k dull red (Bl) (#91)		100.00 120.00

Nos. 3, 13 and 15 Surcharged in
Black or Blue

No. 51   No. 55

1920 Imperf.

51	A1	25r on 5k green	75.00 100.00
52	A1	25r on 5k grn (Bl)	250.00 100.00
53	A1	25r on 25k orange	35.00 45.00
54	A1	25r on 25k org (Bl)	100.00 140.00
55	A1	50r on 50k yellow	30.00 40.00
56	A1	50r on 50k yel (Bl)	100.00 125.00
		Nos. 51-56 (6)	590.00 550.00

The surcharges on Nos. 21-56 inclusive are
handstamped and are known double, inverted,
etc.

Tree Type of 1919 Overprinted Like
Nos. 13-20

1920

57	A1	1r orange brown	2.25 12.00
58	A1	2r gray blue	2.25 12.00
59	A1	3r rose	2.25 12.00
60	A1	5r black brown	2.25 12.00
61	A1	7r yellow	2.25 12.00
62	A1	10r dark green	2.25 12.00
63	A1	15r violet	2.75 17.50
64	A1	25r vermilion	2.50 16.00
65	A1	50r dark blue	2.75 20.00
		Nos. 57-65 (9)	21.50 125.50

The variety "BPITISH" occurs on Nos. 57-
65. Value, about $150 each.

BECHUANALAND

ˌbech-ˈwä-nə-ˌland

(British Bechuanaland)

LOCATION — Southern Africa
GOVT. — A British Crown Colony, which included the area of the former Stellaland, annexed in 1895 to the Cape of Good Hope Colony.
AREA — 51,424 sq. mi.
POP. — 72,700 (1891)
CAPITAL — Vryburg

British Bechuanaland stamps were also used in Bechuanaland Protectorate until 1897.

12 Pence = 1 Shilling
20 Shillings = 1 Pound

Watermarks

Wmk. 29 — Orb   Wmk. 14 — VR in Italics

Cape of Good Hope Stamps of 1871-85 Overprinted

1885-87		**Wmk. 1**		**Perf. 14**
Black Overprint				
1	A6	4p blue ('86)	95.00	85.00
		Wmk. 2		
		Black Overprint		
3	A6	3p claret	60.00	70.00
		Red Overprint		
4	A6	½p black	35.00	47.50
a.		Overprint in lake	5,500.	10,000.
b.		Double overprint in lake & blk	900.00	1,100.
		Wmk. Anchor (16)		
		Black Overprint		
5	A6	½p black ('87)	17.50	30.00
a.		"ritish"	2,750.	2,600.
b.		Double overprint	4,250.	
6	A6	1p rose	27.50	11.00
a.		"ritish"	7,500.	4,250.
b.		Double overprint		2,300.
7	A6	2p bister	55.00	11.00
a.		"ritish"	9,000.	5,500.
b.		Double overprint		2,500.
8	A3	6p violet	220.00	47.50
9	A3	1sh green ('86)	375.00	190.00
a.		"ritish"	24,000.	18,000.

There is no period after Bechuanaland on the genuine stamps.

Great Britain No. 111 Overprinted in Black

1887			**Wmk. 30**	
10	A54	½p vermilion	2.75	1.50
a.		Double overprint	2,700.	

For overprints see Bechuanaland Protectorate Nos. 51-53.

A1   A2

A3

1887		**Typo.**		**Wmk. 29**
Country Name in Black				
11	A1	1p lilac	29.00	4.75
12	A1	2p lilac	125.00	2.75
13	A1	3p lilac	8.50	8.75
14	A1	4p lilac	65.00	2.75
15	A1	6p lilac	80.00	3.00
		Wmk. 14		
16	A2	1sh green	37.50	12.00
17	A2	2sh green	70.00	60.00
18	A2	2sh6p green	80.00	80.00
19	A2	5sh green	135.00	180.00
		Pen cancellation		15.00
20	A2	10sh green	275.00	400.00
		Pen cancellation		45.00
		Wmk. 29		
21	A3	£1 lilac	1,100.	900.00
		Pen cancellation		65.00
22	A3	£5 lilac	4,000.	1,900.
		Pen cancellation		200.00

The corner designs and central oval differs on No. 22.
For overprints see Bechuanaland Protectorate Nos. 54-58, 60-66. For surcharges see Nos. 23-28, 30, AR2, Cape of Good Hope No. 171.
Fiscal cancels can be pen cancellations or ink stampings.
Beware of cleaned pen (fiscal) cancellations and forged postmarks on Nos. 21-22.

1d.

Nos. 11-12, 14-16 Surcharged

Black Surcharge

1888		**Country Name in Black**		
23	A1	1p on 1p lilac	9.25	8.00
a.		Double surcharge		
24	A1	6p on 6p lilac	165.00	20.00
		Red Surcharge		
25	A1	2p on 2p lilac	65.00	4.00
a.		"2" with curved tail	350.00	180.00
26	A1	4p on 4p lilac	450.00	600.00
		Green Surcharge		
27	A1	2p on 2p lilac		4,000.
a.		"2" with curved tail		20,000.
		Blue Surcharge		
27A	A1	6p on 6p lilac		25,000.
		Wmk. 14		
		Black Surcharge		
28	A2	1sh on 1sh green	300.00	100.00

British

Cape of Good Hope No.41 Overprinted in Green

1889			**Wmk. 16**	
29	A4	½p black	5.00	40.00
a.		Double ovpt., one inverted	3,500.	
b.		Double ovpt., one vertical	1,200.	
c.		Pair, one stamp without ovpt.	10,000.	

Exists with "British" missing from shifted overprint.

One Half-Penny

No. 13 Surcharged in Black

1888			**Wmk. 29**	
30	A1	½p on 3p lilac & blk	275.00	325.00

Stamps with errors of spelling in the surcharge are fakes.

Cape of Good Hope Nos. 43-44 Overprinted in Black, Reading Up

1891			**Wmk. 16**	
31	A4	1p rose	14.00	18.50
a.		Horiz. pair, one without overprint	26,000.	
b.		"British" omitted	4,250.	—
c.		"Bechuanaland" omitted	3,500.	
32	A4	2p bister	8.00	2.75
a.		Without period	325.00	390.00

See Nos. 38-39. Only one example of No. 31b exists. It is in the Royal Collection in London.

BRITISH BECHUANALAND

Stamps of Great Britain Overprinted in Black

1891-94			**Wmk. 30**	
33	A40	1p lilac	7.25	2.00
34	A56	2p green & car	24.00	5.00
35	A59	4p brown & green	4.50	.80
a.		Half used as 2p on cover		3,000.
36	A62	6p violet, *rose*	9.00	2.50
37	A65	1sh green ('94)	16.00	19.50
a.		Half used as 6p on cover		
		Nos. 33-37 (5)	60.75	29.80

For surcharges, see Cape of Good Hope Nos. 172, 176-177.

Cape of Good Hope Nos. 43-44 Overprinted, Reading Down

1893-95			**Wmk. 16**	
38	A6	1p rose	4.25	3.00
a.		No dots over both "i" of "British"	160.00	160.00
c.		As "a," reading up	4,500.	
d.		Pair, one without overprint		
39	A6	2p bister ('95)	11.00	3.50
a.		Double overprint	1,700.	850.00
b.		No dots over both "i" of "British"	275.00	175.00
d.		As "b," reading up	4,750.	

The missing dot-over-i variety exists only on this issue. Nos. 38c and 39d resulted from the sheets being fed into the press upside down. Nos. 38-39 exist with "British" missing (from shifted overprint).

BRITISH BECHUANALAND

Cape of Good Hope No. 42 Overprinted

"BECHUANALAND" 16mm Long Overprint Lines 13mm Apart

1897				
40	A6	½p light green	3.25	20.00

"BECHUANALAND" 15mm Long Overprint Lines 10½mm Apart

41	A6	½p light green	22.50	75.00

"BECHUANALAND" 15mm Long Overprint Lines 13½mm Apart

42	A6	½p light green	47.50	150.00
		Nos. 40-42 (3)	73.25	245.00

Nos. 40-42 actually are issues of Bechuanaland Protectorate.

BECHUANALAND PROTECTORATE

ˌbech-ˈwä-nə-ˌland prə-ˈtek-tˌə-ˌrət

LOCATION — In central South Africa, north of the Republic of South Africa, east of South West Africa and bounded on the north by the Caprivi Strip of South West Africa and on the east by Southern Rhodesia
GOVT. — British Protectorate
AREA — 222,000 sq. mi.
POP. — 540,400 (1964)
CAPITAL — Vryburg (to 1895), Mafeking (to 1965), Gaberones

Bechuanaland Protectorate became self-governing in 1965 and achieved indepenence as the republic of Botswana, Sept. 30, 1966.

12 Pence = 1 Shilling
20 Shillings = 1 Pound
100 Cents = 1 Rand (1961)

> Catalogue values for unused stamps in this country are for Never Hinged items, beginning with Scott 137 in the regular postage section and Scott J7 in the postage due section.

Additional Overprint in Black on Bechuanaland No. 10

a   b

c

1888-90		**Wmk. 30**		**Perf. 14**
51	A54(a)	½p ver ('90)	275.00	450.00
a.		Double overprint	1,800.	
b.		"Protectorte"		2,200.
c.		As "b," double overprint	20,000.	
52	A54(b)	½p ver ('88)	13.00	55.00
a.		Double overprint	375.00	
53	A54(c)	½p ver ('90)	225.00	250.00
a.		Inverted overprint	100.00	130.00
b.		Double overprint	150.00	200.00
c.		As "a," double	750.00	850.00
d.		"Portectorate"	—	—
e.		As "a," "Portectorate"	20,000.	

For surcharge see No. 68.

Bechuanaland Nos. 16-20 Overprinted Type "b" in Black

		Wmk. 14		
Country Name in Black				
54	A2	1sh green	150.00	65.00
a.		First "o" omitted	6,750.	3,750.
55	A2	2sh green	800.00	1,200.
a.		First "o" omitted	20,000.	
56	A2	2sh6p green	650.00	1,100.
a.		First "o" omitted	20,000.	
57	A2	5sh green	1,400.	2,750.
a.		First "o" omitted	25,000.	
58	A2	10sh green	5,250.	7,500.
a.		First "o" omitted	25,000.	

Bechuanaland Nos. 11-15 Ovptd. Type "b" and Srchd. in Black

1888 — Wmk. 29
Country Name in Black

60	A1	1p on 1p lilac	20.00	16.00
a.		Short "1"	475.00	550.00
61	A1	2p on 2p lilac	45.00	20.00
a.		"2" with curved tail	950.00	550.00
63	A1	3p on 3p reddish lil	225.00	290.00
64	A1	4p on 4p lilac	475.00	550.00
a.		Small "4"	6,000.	6,000.
65	A1	6p on 6p lilac	125.00	55.00

In #60 the "1" is 2½mm high; in #60a, 2mm.

Value Surcharged in Red

66	A1	4p on 4p lilac	160.00	60.00
a.		Double overprint		2,750.

Cape of Good Hope
Type of 1886
Overprinted in Green

1889 — Wmk. 16

67	A6	½p black	6.50	55.00
a.		Double overprint	600.00	800.00

No. 67 exists with "Bechuanaland" missing and with ovpt. words reversed (from shifted overprint).

Bechuanaland Protectorate No. 52 Surcharged in Black

Wmk. 30

68	A54	4p on ½p ver	47.50	6.00
a.		Inverted surcharge		4,500.
b.		"rpence" omitted		7,000.

Stamps of Great Britain 1881-87, Overprinted in Black

1897, Oct.

69	A54	½p vermilion	3.00	2.50
70	A40	1p lilac	4.50	.85
71	A56	2p green & car	16.00	4.50
72	A58	3p violet, yel	6.25	15.00
73	A59	4p brown & green	29.00	25.00
74	A62	6p violet, rose	225.00	16.00
		Nos. 69-74 (6)	83.75	63.85

For surcharges see Cape of Good Hope Nos. 167-170, 173-175.

Same on Great Britain No. 125
1902, Feb. 25

75	A54	½p blue green	1.75	4.00

Stamps of Great Britain, 1902, Overprinted in Black

1904-12

76	A66	½p gray grn ('06)	2.75	4.50
77	A66	1p car ('05)	12.00	.65
78	A66	2½p ultra	12.50	9.00
79	A74	1sh scar & grn ('12)	60.00	170.00
		Nos. 76-79 (4)	87.25	184.15

Same on Great Britain No. 143
1908

80	A66	½p pale yel green	4.25	4.00

Transvaal No. 274 overprinted "Bechuanaland Protectorate," formerly listed as No. 81, now appears as No. AR1 in the Postal-Fiscal Stamps section.

Great Britain No. 154 Overprinted Like Nos. 76-79
1912, Sept. — Wmk. 30 — Perf. 15x14

82	A81	1p scarlet	4.00	.90

Great Britain Stamps of 1912-13 Overprinted Like Nos. 76-79
Wmk. Crown and GvR (33)
1913-24

83	A82	½p green	1.40	2.00
84	A83	1p scarlet ('15)	3.25	.85
85	A84	1½p red brn ('20)	7.00	3.50
86	A85	2p redsh org (I)	13.00	4.25
b.		2p orange (II) ('24)	47.50	4.00
87	A86	2½p ultra	4.00	27.50
88	A87	3p bluish violet	6.75	16.00
89	A88	4p slate green	7.25	40.00
90	A89	6p dull violet	10.00	27.50
91	A90	1sh bister	22.50	45.00
		Nos. 83-91 (9)	75.15	166.60

The dies of No. 86 are the same as in Great Britain 1912-13 issue.

Wmk. 34 — Perf. 11x12

92	A91	2sh6p dk brn ('15)	150.00	300.00
a.		2sh6p light brown ('16)	125.00	300.00
93	A91	5sh rose car ('14)	180.00	450.00
a.		5sh carmine ('19)	350.00	500.00

Nos. 92, 93 were printed by Waterlow Bros. & Layton; Nos. 92a, 93a were printed by Thomas De La Rue & Co.

Same Overprint On Retouched Seahorses Stamps of 1919 (Great Britain Nos. 179, 180)
1920-23

94	A91	2sh6p gray brown	100.00	200.00
95	A91	5sh car rose	140.00	325.00

Nos. 94-95 measure 22.5-23mm vertically. Most examples have a small dot of color at top center, outside of frameline. Perforation holes are larger and usually are evenly spaced.

Great Britain Stamps of 1924 Overprinted like Nos. 76-79
Wmk. Crown and Block GvR Multiple (35)
1925-27 — Perf. 15x14

96	A82	½p green ('27)	1.65	2.00
97	A83	1p scarlet	2.25	1.00
99	A85	2p deep org (II)	2.50	1.25
101	A87	3p violet ('26)	5.50	30.00
102	A88	4p sl grn ('26)	8.00	55.00
103	A89	6p dl vio, chalky paper	75.00	110.00
104	A90	1sh bister ('26)	11.00	30.00
		Nos. 96-104 (7)	105.90	229.25

George V — A11

Perf. 12½
1932, Dec. 12 — Engr. — Wmk. 4

105	A11	½p green	2.75	.35
a.		Horiz. pair, imperf between	32,500.	
106	A11	1p carmine	2.00	.40
107	A11	2p red brown	2.00	.45
108	A11	3p ultra	5.25	6.00
109	A11	4p orange	5.25	15.00
110	A11	6p red violet	8.00	9.50
111	A11	1sh blk & ol grn	7.00	10.00
112	A11	2sh blk & org	27.50	75.00
113	A11	2sh6p blk & car	29.00	55.00
114	A11	3sh blk & red vio	50.00	65.00
115	A11	5sh blk & ultra	135.00	135.00
116	A11	10sh blk & red brown	350.00	350.00
		Nos. 105-116 (12)	623.75	721.70

Common Design Types pictured following the introduction.

Silver Jubilee Issue
Common Design Type
1935, May 4 — Perf. 11x12

117	CD301	1p car & blue	1.75	6.75
118	CD301	2p black & ultra	2.50	6.25
119	CD301	3p ultra & brown	3.50	11.00
120	CD301	6p brown vio & ind	8.00	12.00
		Nos. 117-120 (4)	15.75	36.00
		Set, never hinged	24.00	

Coronation Issue
Common Design Type
1937, May 12 — Perf. 13½x14

121	CD302	1p carmine	.25	.50
122	CD302	2p brown	.30	1.25
123	CD302	3p bright ultra	.40	1.60
		Nos. 121-123 (3)	.95	3.35
		Set, never hinged	1.75	

George VI, Cattle and Baobab Tree — A12

1938, Apr. 1 — Perf. 12½

124	A12	½p green	3.00	3.75
125	A12	1p rose car	.60	.65
126	A12	1½p light blue	.75	1.25
127	A12	2p brown	.60	.75
128	A12	3p ultra	.75	3.00
129	A12	4p orange	1.50	4.25
130	A12	6p rose violet	3.25	3.00
131	A12	1sh blk & ol grn	3.50	9.50
133	A12	2sh6p black & car	9.00	20.00
135	A12	5sh black & ultra	27.50	32.50
136	A12	10sh black & brn	19.00	37.50
		Nos. 124-136 (11)	69.45	116.15
		Set, never hinged	110.00	

> Catalogue values for unused stamps in this section, from this point to the end of the section, are for Never Hinged items.

Peace Issue

South Africa Nos. 100-102 Overprinted

Basic stamps inscribed alternately in English and Afrikaans.

1945, Dec. 3 — Wmk. 201 — Perf. 14

137	A42	1p rose pink & choc, pair	.75	1.50
a.		Single, English	.25	.25
b.		Single, Afrikaans	.25	.25
138	A43	2p vio & slate blue, pair	.55	1.50
a.		Single, English	.25	.25
b.		Single, Afrikaans	.25	.25
139	A43	3p ultra & dp ultra, pair	.75	1.75
a.		Single, English	.25	.25
b.		Single, Afrikaans	.25	.25
c.		Vert. pair, one with overprint omitted	17,000.	
		Nos. 137-139 (3)	2.05	4.75

World War II victory of the Allies.

Royal Visit Issue
Types of Basutoland, 1947
Perf. 12½
1947, Feb. 17 — Wmk. 4 — Engr.

143	A3	1p red	.25	.25
144	A4	2p green	.25	.25
145	A5	3p ultra	.25	.25
146	A6	1sh dark violet	.25	.25
		Nos. 143-146 (4)	1.00	1.00

Visit of the British Royal Family, 4/17/47.

Silver Wedding Issue
Common Design Types
1948, Dec. 1 — Photo. — Perf. 14x14½

147	CD304	1½p brt ultra	.35	.25

Engr.; Name Typo.
Perf. 11½x11

148	CD305	10sh gray black	42.50	47.50

UPU Issue
Common Design Types
Engr.; Name Typo. on 3p and 6p
1949, Oct. 10 — Perf. 13½, 11x11½

149	CD306	1½p blue	.30	1.00
150	CD307	3p indigo	1.50	1.50
151	CD308	6p red lilac	.80	2.75
152	CD309	1sh olive	.75	2.00
		Nos. 149-152 (4)	3.35	7.25

Coronation Issue
Common Design Type
1953, June 3 — Engr. — Perf. 13½x13

153	CD312	2p brown & black	.75	.35

Elizabeth II — A13

1955-58 — Perf. 13x13½

154	A13	½p green	.60	.35
155	A13	1p rose car	1.00	.25
156	A13	2p brown	1.50	.35
157	A13	3p ultra	3.50	2.50
158	A13	4p orange ('58)	13.00	13.00
159	A13	4½p indigo	1.75	1.25
160	A13	6p rose violet	1.50	.90
161	A13	1sh blk & ol grn	1.50	1.50
162	A13	1sh3p blk & rose vio	16.00	10.00
163	A13	2sh6p black & car	13.50	10.50
164	A13	5sh black & ultra	20.00	17.50
165	A13	10sh black & brn	42.50	20.00
		Nos. 154-165 (12)	116.35	78.10

For surcharges see Nos. 169-179.

Victoria, Elizabeth II and Water Hole — A14

Perf. 14½x14
1960, Jan. 21 — Photo. — Wmk. 314

166	A14	1p brown & black	.50	.50
167	A14	3p car rose & black	.50	.50
168	A14	6p ultra & black	.50	.50
		Nos. 166-168 (3)	1.50	1.50

Proclamation of the Protectorate, 75th anniv.

Nos. 155-165 Surcharged

Elizabeth II, Type I

(surcharge types: 1c I, 1c II; 3½c I, 3½c II, 3½c III; 5c I, 5c II; R1 I, R1 II)

Perf. 13x13½
1961, Feb. 14 — Wmk. 4 — Engr.

169		1c on 1p (I)	.35	.25
a.		Type II	.45	.25
170		2c on 2p	.25	.25
171		2½c on 3p	.35	.25
a.		Pair, one without surcharge	16,000.	
b.		Type II	1.75	3.00
172		2½c on 3p	4.50	8.00
173		3½c on 4p (III)	.25	.25
a.		Type I	.60	.60
b.		Type II	3.00	12.00

174	5c on 6p (II)		.25	.25
a.	Type I		2.25	3.25
175	10c on 1sh		.30	.30
a.	Pair, one without surcharge		20,000.	
176	12½c on 1sh3p ("12½c" 11¼mm wide)		.65	.35
a.	"12½c" 12½mm wide		.85	.75
177	25c on 2sh6p		1.75	1.00
178	50c on 5sh		2.25	3.00
179	1r on 10sh (II, "R1" at lower center)		26.00	20.00
a.	Type II, "R1" at lower left		27.50	30.00
b.	Type I		375.00	175.00
	Nos. 169-179 (11)		36.90	33.90

Nos. 173a and 173b are found in the same sheet; each comes with "3½c" in both wide and narrow settings.

Surch. types are numbered chronologically. These and other minor varieties of these overprints are collected by specialists.

African Golden Oriole — A15 Baobab Tree — A16

Designs: 2c, African hoopoe. 2½c, Scarlet-chested sunbird. 3½c, Cape widow bird (Yellow bishop). 5c, Swallow-tailed bee-eater. 7½c, Gray hornbill. 10c, Red-headed weaver. 12½c, Brown-hooded kingfisher. 20c, Woman musician. 35c, Woman grinding corn. 50c, Bechuana ox. 1r, Lion. 2r, Police camel patrol.

Perf. 14x14½, 14½x14

1961, Oct. 2	**Photo.**		**Wmk. 314**	
180	A15	1c lilac, blk & yel	1.75	.55
181	A15	2c pale ol, blk & org	2.25	4.25
182	A15	2½c bis, blk, grn & dp car	1.75	.25
183	A15	3½c pink, blk & yel	2.75	4.75
184	A15	5c dl org, blk, grn & bl	3.50	1.25
185	A15	7½c yel grn, blk, red & brn	2.25	2.75
186	A15	10c aqua & multi	2.25	.75
187	A15	12½c gray, yel, red & blue	19.00	6.00
188	A15	20c gray & brn	4.00	4.75
189	A16	25c yel & dk brn	5.00	2.75
190	A16	35c dp org & ultra	4.50	6.00
191	A16	50c lt ol grn & sep	2.75	2.75
192	A15	1r ocher & black	10.00	3.00
193	A15	2r blue & brn	30.00	12.50
	Nos. 180-193 (14)		91.75	52.30

For overprints see Botswana Nos. 5-18.

Freedom from Hunger Issue
Common Design Type

1963, June 4			**Perf. 14x14½**	
194	CD314	12½c green	.50	.50

Red Cross Centenary Issue
Common Design Type

1963, Sept. 2	**Litho.**		**Perf. 13**	
195	CD315	2½c black & red	.25	.25
196	CD315	12½c ultra & red	.70	.60

Shakespeare Issue
Common Design Type

1964, Apr. 23	**Photo.**		**Perf. 14x14½**	
197	CD316	12½c red brown	.35	.35

Notwani River Dam, Gaberones Water Supply — A17

	Wmk. 314			
1965, Mar. 1	**Photo.**		**Perf. 14½**	
198	A17	2½c dark red & gold	.25	.25
199	A17	5c deep ultra & gold	.30	.25
200	A17	12½c brown & gold	.40	.40
201	A17	25c emerald & gold	.50	.50
	Nos. 198-201 (4)		1.45	1.40

Internal self-government, Mar. 1, 1965.

ITU Issue
Common Design Type

		Perf. 11x11½		
1965, May 17	**Litho.**		**Wmk. 314**	
202	CD317	2½c ver & dl yel	.35	.25
203	CD317	12½c red lil & pale brn	.75	.50

Intl. Cooperation Year Issue
Common Design Type

1965, Oct. 25			**Perf. 14½**	
204	CD318	1c bl grn & claret	.25	.50
205	CD318	12½c lt vio & grn	.60	.50

Churchill Memorial Issue
Common Design Type

1966, Jan. 24	**Photo.**		**Perf. 14**	

Design in Black, Gold and Carmine Rose

206	CD319	1c bright blue	.25	1.20
207	CD319	2½c green	.45	.25
208	CD319	12½c brown	.85	.40
209	CD319	20c violet	.95	.65
	Nos. 206-209 (4)		2.50	2.50

Haslar Smoke Generator — A18

	Wmk. 314			
1966, June 1	**Photo.**		**Perf. 14½**	
210	A18	2½c shown	.35	.25
211	A18	5c Bugler	.35	.25
212	A18	15c Gun site	1.00	.35
213	A18	35c Regimental cap badge	.40	.95
	Nos. 210-213 (4)		2.10	1.80

25th anniv. of the Bechuanaland Pioneers and Gunners of World War II.

POSTAL-FISCAL STAMPS

Transvaal No. 274
Overprinted

1910, July			**Wmk. 3**	
AR1	A27	12sh6p brn org & blk	190.00	375.00

This stamp was issued for fiscal use in January 1907, but the "POSTAGE" inscription was not obliterated, and examples were accepted for postal use during 1910-11.

Bechuanaland No. 16
surcharged "£5"

1918			**Wmk. 29**	
AR2	A2	£5 on 1sh green	92,000.	—

Examples without full gum or with no gum sell for much less than the values for examples with full gum.

The known used examples of AR2 are all fiscally used. Value, $1,400.

South Africa No. 3
Overprinted in two lines

1922			**Wmk. 177**	
AR3	A2	1p rose red	50.00	155.00

POSTAGE DUE STAMPS

Postage Due Stamps
of Great Britain
Overprinted

On Stamp of 1914-22

1926		**Wmk. 33**	**Perf. 14x14½**	
J1	D1	1p carmine	11.00	125.00

On Stamps of 1924-30
Wmk. 35

J2	D1	½p emerald	11.00	75.00

Overprinted

J3	D1	2p black brown	11.00	100.00
	Nos. J1-J3 (3)		33.00	300.00
	Set, never hinged		52.50	

D2

1932		**Wmk. 4** **Typo.**	**Perf. 14½**	
J4	D2	½p olive green	6.75	60.00
J5	D2	1p carmine rose	8.00	10.00
a.		1p carmine ('58)	1.50	27.50
J6	D2	2p dull violet	10.00	57.50
a.	2p violet ('58)		1.75	22.00
c.	As "a," thick "d"		47.50	
b.	As No. J6, thick "d"		120.00	
	Nos. J4-J6 (3)		24.75	127.50
	Set, never hinged		40.00	

Nos. J5a, J6a and J6b are on chalky paper. For detailed listings, see the Scott Classic Specialized catalogue.

> **Catalogue values for unused stamps in this section, from this point to the end of the section, are for Never Hinged items.**

Nos. J4-J6 Surcharged

Type I Type II

1961, Feb. 14			**Chalky Paper**	
J7	D2	1c on 1p car rose, II	.25	1.75
a.	Type I		.30	.60
b.	Double surcharge, II		375.00	
c.	Ordinary paper, II		20.00	65.00
J8	D2	2c on 2p dull vio, II	.25	2.00
a.	Thick "d," II		4.75	
b.	Ordinary paper, II		170.00	180.00
c.	As "b," thick "d"		800.00	
d.	Type I		.35	1.75
e.	As "d," thick "d"		7.50	

Ordinary Paper

J9	D2	5c on ½p ol green, I	.50	.75
	Nos. J7-J9 (3)		1.00	4.50

Denominations in Cents

1961		**Wmk. 4**	**Perf. 14**	
J10	D2	1c carmine rose	.30	2.25
J11	D2	2c dull violet	.30	2.00
J12	D2	5c olive green	.50	2.00
	Nos. J10-J12 (3)		1.10	6.25

BELARUS

ˌbē-lə-ˈrüs

(Byelorussia)

(White Russia)

LOCATION — Eastern Europe, bounded by Russia, Latvia, Lithuania and Poland
GOVT. — Independent republic, member of the Commonwealth of Independent States
AREA — 80,134 sq. mi.
POP. — 10,401,784 (1999 est.)
CAPITAL — Minsk

With the breakup of the Soviet Union on Dec. 26, 1991, Belarus and ten former Soviet republics established the Commonwealth of Independent States.

100 Kopecks = 1 Ruble

> **Catalogue values for all unused stamps in this country are for Never Hinged items.**

Five denominations, perf and imperf, of this design produced in 1920 were not put in use. Value $5. Forgeries abound.

Cross of Ephrosinia of Polotsk — A1

1992, Mar. 20	**Litho.**		**Perf. 12x12½**	
1	A1	1r multicolored	.45	.45

For overprint and surcharge see Nos. 17, 230.

R.R. Schurma (1892-1978), Composer — A2

1992, Apr. 10	**Photo.**		**Perf. 12x11½**	
2	A2	20k blue & black	.45	.45

For surcharge see No. 203.

Arms of Polotsk — A3

Designs: No. 13, Stag jumping fence. No. 14, Man's head, sword.

1992-94	**Photo.**		**Perf. 12x11½**	
11	A3	2r shown	.45	.45

Perf. 12x12½

12	A3	25r Minsk	.35	.35
13	A3	700r Grodno	.45	.45
14	A3	700r Vitebsk	.45	.45
		Nos. 11-14 (4)	1.70	1.70

Issued: 2r, 6/9/92; 25r, 11/11/93; Nos. 13, 14, 10/17/94.

National
Symbols
A4

Designs: No. 15, Natl. arms. No. 16, Map, flag.

1992, Aug. 31   Litho.   Perf. 12x12½

15	A4	5r black, red & yellow	.65	.65
16	A4	5r multicolored	.65	.65

For surcharges see Nos. 55-58, 61-64.

No. 1
Overprinted

Cross of Ephrosinia of Polotsk — A5

1992, Sept. 25   Litho.   Perf. 12x12½

17	A1	1r on #1 multi	.45	.45

Souvenir Sheet
Perf. 12

18	A5	5r multicolored	.80	.80

Orthodox Church in Belarus, 1000th anniv.
No. 18, imperf, was issued Feb. 15, 1993.
Value $1.75.
For surcharges see Nos. 59-60, 65-66.

Buildings
A6

Designs: No. 19, Church of Boris Gleb, Grodno, 12th cent. No. 20, Mir Castle, 16th cent. No. 21, Nesvizh Castle, 16th-19th cent. No. 22, Kamyanets Tower, 12th-13th cent, vert. No. 23, Church of Ephrosinia of Polotsk, 12th cent., vert. No. 24, Calvinist Church, Zaslaw, 16th cent., vert.

1992, Oct. 15   Litho.   Perf. 12

19	A6	2r multicolored	.25	.25
20	A6	2r multicolored	.25	.25
21	A6	2r multicolored	.25	.25
22	A6	2r multicolored	.25	.25
23	A6	2r multicolored	.25	.25
24	A6	2r multicolored	.25	.25
		Nos. 19-24 (6)	1.50	1.50

Centuries of construction are in Roman numerals.

Natl. Arms — A7

1992-94   Litho.   Perf. 12x12½

25	A7	30k light blue	.25	.25
26	A7	45k olive green	.25	.25
27	A7	50k green	.25	.25
28	A7	1r brown	.25	.25
29	A7	2r red brown	.25	.25
30	A7	3r org yellow	.30	.25
31	A7	5r blue	.30	.25
32	A7	10r red	.60	.40
33	A7	15r violet	.45	.30
34	A7	25r yellow green	.60	.45
35	A7	50r bright pink	.50	.40
36	A7	100r henna brown	.55	.35
37	A7	150r plum	.80	.45
38	A7	200r blue green	.80	.40
39	A7	300r salmon pink	.80	.40
40	A7	600r light lilac	.80	.40
40A	A7	1000r rose carmine	1.30	.40
40B	A7	3000r gray blue	3.00	1.25
		Nos. 25-40B (18)	11.80	6.80

Issued: 30k, 45k, 50k, 11/10; 1r-3r, 10r, 1/4/93; 5r, 15r, 25r, 2/9/93; 50r, 100r, 150r, 6/16/93; 200r-3,000r, 12/28/94; others, 1992.
For surcharges see Nos. 72-74, 141-142, 211A-212.

Ceramics
A8

Designs: No. 41, Pitcher and bowl. No. 42, Four pieces on tree branches. No. 43, Two large pitchers. No. 44, One large pitcher.

1992, Dec. 24   Litho.   Perf. 11½

41	A8	1r multicolored	.25	.25
42	A8	1r multicolored	.25	.25
43	A8	1r multicolored	.25	.25
44	A8	1r multicolored	.25	.25
		Nos. 41-44 (4)	1.00	1.00

M. I.
Garetzky
(1893-1938),
Writer — A9

1993, June 22   Photo.   Perf. 12x11½

45	A9	50r magenta	.40	.40

Straw
Figures
A10

Designs: 5r, Chickens. 10r, Child, mother, vert. 15r, Woman, vert. 25r, Man with scythe, woman with rake, vert.

Perf. 12x11½, 11½x12

1993, Apr. 22   Litho.

47	A10	5r multicolored	.30	.30
48	A10	10r multicolored	.30	.30
49	A10	15r multicolored	.30	.30
50	A10	25r multicolored	.50	.50
		Nos. 47-50 (4)	1.40	1.40

First World
Congress of White
Russians — A11

1993, July 8   Litho.   Perf. 12

51	A11	50r multicolored	.80	.80

Europa — A12

Paintings by Chagall: No. 52, Promenade, vert. No. 53, Man Over Vitebsk. 2500r, Allegory.

1993, Oct. 12   Litho.   Perf. 14

52	A12	1500r multicolored	5.00	6.00
53	A12	1500r multicolored	5.00	6.00
a.		Pair, #52-53	10.00	12.00

Souvenir Sheet

54	A12	2500r multicolored	40.00	45.00

Nos. 15-16, 18 Surcharged

a   b

c   d

Size and location of surcharge varies.

1993, Oct. 15   Litho.   Perf. 12x12½

55	A4(a)	1500r on 5r #15	4.50	4.50
56	A4(b)	1500r on 5r #15	4.50	4.50
a.		Pair, #55-56	11.50	11.50
57	A4(c)	1500r on 5r #16	4.50	4.50
58	A4(d)	1500r on 5r #16	4.50	4.50
a.		Pair, #57-58	11.50	11.50
		Nos. 55-58 (4)	18.00	18.00

Souvenir Sheets
Perf. 12

Overprints "e" & "f" on No. 18 are slightly different and have the wording at right reading down and Olympic Rings in upper left corner. No. 59 in Belarusian and No. 60 in English.

59	A5(e)	1500r on 5r #18	10.00	10.00
60	A5(f)	1500r on 5r #18	10.00	10.00

Nos. 59 and 60 exist imperf. Value, each $15. The status of No. 60 is in question.

Nos. 15-16, 18 Surcharged

g   h

i   j

Size and location of surcharge varies.

1993, Oct. 15   Litho.   Perf. 12x12½

61	A4(g)	1500r on 5r #15	4.50	4.50
62	A4(h)	1500r on 5r #15	4.50	4.50
a.		Pair, #61-62	11.50	11.50
63	A4(i)	1500r on 5r #16	4.50	4.50
64	A4(j)	1500r on 5r #16	4.50	4.50
a.		Pair, #63-64	11.50	11.50
		Nos. 61-64 (4)	18.00	18.00

Souvenir Sheets
Perf. 12

Overprints "k" & "l" on No. 18 are slightly different and have the wording at right reading down. No. 65 in Belarusian and No. 66 in English.

65	A5(k)	1500r on 5r #18	10.00	10.00
66	A5(l)	1500r on 5r #18	10.00	10.00

The status of Nos. 65-66 are in question. They exist imperf. Value, each $15.

Stansilavski
Church
A13

1993, Nov. 24   Litho.   Perf. 12

67	A13	150r multicolored	.50	.50

For surcharge see No. 242.

Famous
People
A14

Designs: 50r, Kastus Kalinovsky, led 1863 independence movement. No. 69, Prince Rogvold of Polotsk, map of Polotsk. No. 70, Princess Rogneda, daughter of Rogvold, fortress. 100r, Statue of Simon Budny (1530-93), writer and printer, vert.

1993   Perf. 12x12½, 12½x12

68	A14	50r multicolored	.30	.30
69	A14	75r multicolored	.30	.30
70	A14	75r multicolored	.30	.30
71	A14	100r multicolored	.30	.30
		Nos. 68-71 (4)	1.20	1.20

Issued: 50r, 12/29; 75r, 12/30; 100r, 12/31.

Nos. 27, 29, 30
Surcharged

1994, Feb. 1 Photo. Perf. 12x12½
72 A7 15r on 30k light green .30 .30
73 A7 25r on 45k olive green .30 .30
74 A7 50r on 50k green .30 .30
Nos. 72-74 (3) .90 .90

Birds — A15

1994, Jan. 19 Litho. Perf. 11½
75 A15 20r Aguila chrysaetos .25 .25
76 A15 40r Cygnus olor .25 .25
77 A15 40r Alcedo atthis .25 .25
a. Block of 3, #75-77 + label .55 .55
See Nos. 87-89. For surcharge see No. 303.

Six World Wildlife Fund labels with 1000r denominations depicting 3 different animals and 3 different birds exist. They were not valid for postage.

Liberation of Soviet Areas, 50th Anniv. A16

No. 78 — Battle maps and: a, Katyusha rockets, liberation of Russia. b, Fighter planes, liberation of Ukraine. c, Combined offensive, liberation of Belarus.

1994, July 3 Litho. Perf. 12
78 A16 500r Block of 3 #a.-c. + label .85 .85
See Russia No. 6213, Ukraine No. 195.

1994 Winter Olympics, Lillehammer A17

No. 79, Speed skating. No. 80, Women's figure skating. No. 81, Hockey. No. 82, Cross-country skiing. No. 83, Biathlon.

1994, Aug. 30 Litho. Perf. 12x12½
79 A17 1000r multicolored .25 .25
80 A17 1000r multicolored .25 .25
81 A17 1000r multicolored .25 .25
82 A17 1000r multicolored .25 .25
83 A17 1000r multicolored .25 .25
Nos. 79-83 (5) 1.25 1.25

Painters — A18

Designs: No. 84, Farmer, oxen in field, by Ferdinand Rushchyts. No. 85, Knight on horseback, by Jasev Drazdovich. No. 86, Couple walking up path, by Petra Sergievich.

1994, July 18 Litho. Perf. 12
84 A18 300r multicolored .25 .25
85 A18 300r multicolored .25 .25
86 A18 300r multicolored .25 .25
Nos. 84-86 (3) .75 .75
For overprint see No. 127.

Bird Type of 1994
1994, Sept. 30 Perf. 11½
87 A15 300r like #75 .25 .25
88 A15 400r like #76 .25 .25
89 A15 400r like #77 .25 .25
Nos. 87-89 (3) .75 .75

Ilya Yefimovich Repin (1844-1930), Ukrainian Painter — A19

Designs: No. 90, Self-portrait. No. 91, Repin Museum.

1994, Oct. 31 Litho. Perf. 12x12½
90 1000r multicolored .40 .40
91 1000r multicolored .40 .40
a. A19 Pair, #90-91 .80 .80

Churches A20

Designs: No. 92, Sacred Consolidated Church, Sinkavitsch, 16th cent. No. 93, Sts. Peter and Paul Cathedral, Gomel, 19th cent.

1994, Oct. 20 Litho. Perf. 12
92 A20 700r multicolored .25 .25
93 A20 700r multicolored .25 .25

Kosciuszko Uprising, Bicent. (in 1994) — A21

Battle scene and: No. 94, Tomasz Vaishetcki (1754-1816). No. 95, Jakov Jasinski (1761-94). No. 96, Tadeusz Kosziuszko (1746-1817). No. 97, Mikhail K. Aginski (1765-1833).

1995, Jan. 11 Perf. 12½x12
94 A21 600r multicolored .30 .30
95 A21 600r multicolored .30 .30
96 A21 1000r multicolored .30 .30
97 A21 1000r multicolored .30 .30
Nos. 94-97 (4) 1.20 1.20

End of World War II, 50th Anniv. — A22

1995, May 4 Litho. Perf. 13½
98 A22 180r multicolored .25 .25
99 A22 600r multicolored .25 .25
Nos. 98-99 exist imperf. Value, set $125.

Alexander Stepanovich Popov — A23

1995, May 7 Perf. 14
100 A23 600r multicolored .40 .40
Radio, cent. Exists imperf. Value, $35.

A24

1995-96 Litho. Perf. 13x14
102 A24 180r olive brown & red .25 .25
103 A24 200r gray green & bister .25 .25
105 A24 280r green & blue .25 .25
109 A24 600r plum & bister .35 .35
Nos. 102-109 (4) 1.10 1.10
No. 102 exists imperf. Value, $30.
Issued: 180r, 5/10/95; 280r, 5/18/95; 600r, 8/29/95; 200r, 1/30/96.
For surcharges see Nos. 401-402.

Ivan Chersky (1845-92), Geographer A25

1995, May 15 Litho. Perf. 13½x14
113 A25 600r multicolored .40 .40
Exists imperf. Value, $45.

Traditional Costumes — A26

Designs: 600r, Woman wearing shawl, coat, ankle length skirt, man with long coat. 1200r, Woman wearing shawl & apron holding child, man wearing vest, knickers.

1995, July 13 Litho. Perf. 14½x14
114 A26 180r multicolored .25 .25
115 A26 600r multicolored .25 .25
116 A26 1200r multicolored .35 .35
Nos. 114-116 (3) .85 .85
See Nos. 164-167, 214-216.

World Wildlife Fund — A27

Various depictions of beaver.

1995, July 20 Perf. 12
117 A27 300r multi .30 .30
118 A27 450r multi .30 .30
119 A27 450r multi, horiz. .30 .30
120 A27 800r multi, horiz. .30 .30
Nos. 117-120 (4) 1.20 1.20

Book Fair — A28

1995, Aug. 29 Litho. Perf. 14
121 A28 600r multicolored .30 .30
Exists imperf. Value, $50.

A29

1995, Oct. 3 Litho. Perf. 14
122 A29 600r Natl. arms .25 .25
123 A29 600r Flag .25 .25
New national symbols. Nos. 122-123 exist imperf. Value, set $100.

UN, 50th Anniv. — A30

1995, Oct. 24 Litho. Perf. 13½x14
124 A30 600r bister, black & blue .30 .30
Exists imperf. Value, $40.

Churches A31

Designs: No. 125, Mstislav, 17th-19th cent. No. 126, Kamai, 17th cent.

1995, Nov. 21 Perf. 14
125 A31 600r multicolored .25 .25
126 A31 600r multicolored .25 .25

No. 84 Overprinted

1995, Dec. 27 Litho. Perf. 12
127 A18 300r multicolored .40 .40

P. V. Sukhi (1895-1975), Airplane Designer A32

1995, Dec. 27 Perf. 13½
128 A32 600r multicolored .40 .40
Exists imperf. Value, $45.

Designs: 1000r, Lynx lynx. No. 130, Capreolus capreolus. No. 131, Ursus arctos. 3000r, Alces alces. 5000r, Bison bonasus. 10,000r, Cervus elaphus, vert.

1995-96　　　Litho.　　　Perf. 14

129	A33	1000r multi	.30	.30
130	A33	2000r multi, vert.	.35	.35
131	A33	2000r multi	.35	.35
132	A33	3000r multi, vert.	.40	.40
133	A33	5000r multi	.55	.55
		Nos. 129-133 (5)	1.95	1.95

Souvenir Sheet
Imperf

134	A33	10,000r multicolored	2.25	2.25

Issued: Nos. 129-133, 2/6/96; No. 134, 12/29/95.
For surcharge, see No. 607.

Famous People — A34

Designs: 600r, L. Sapega (1557-1633), statesman. 1200r, K. Semyanovitch (1600-51), military scholar. 1800r, S. Polotzki (1629-80), writer.

1995, Dec. 30　　　Litho.　　　Perf. 12

135	A34	600r multicolored	.30	.30
136	A34	1200r multicolored	.30	.30
137	A34	1800r multicolored	.30	.30
		Nos. 135-137 (3)	.90	.90

Miniature Sheet

Butterflies — A35

No. 138: a, Apatura iris. b, Lopinga achine. c, Callimorpha dominula. d, Catocala fraxini. e, Papilio machaon. f, Parnassius apollo. g, Ammobiota hebe. h, Colias palaeno.
No. 139, Proserpinus proserpina. No. 140, Vacciniina optilete.

1996, Mar. 29　　　Litho.　　　Perf. 14

138	A35	300r Sheet of 8, #a.-h.	6.00	6.00

Souvenir Sheets

139-140	A35	1000r Set of 2	13.50	13.50

Inscribed 1995.

Nos. 28, 34 Surcharged
in Green or Red

1996　　　Litho.　　　Perf. 12x12½

141	A7	(B) on 1r #28 (G)	.30	.30
142	A7	(A) on 25r #34 (R)	.30	.30

Nos. 141-142 were valued at 200r and 400r, respectively, on day of issue.
Issued: No. 141, 2/28; No. 142, 3/13.

Souvenir Sheet

Beaver — A36

1996, Mar. 26　　　Litho.　　　Perf. 12½x12

143	A36	1200r multicolored	.45	.45

Kondrat Krapiva (1896-1991),
Writer — A37

1996, Mar. 5　　　Litho.　　　Perf. 14x14½

144	A37	1000r multicolored	.40	.40

Chernobyl Disaster, 10th Anniv. — A38

No. 145 — Radiation symbol and: a, Eye. b, Leaf showing contamination. c, Boarded-up window.

1996, Apr. 10　　　Litho.　　　Perf. 14

145	A38	1000r Block of 3, #a.-c. + label	.55	.55

Coat of Arms — A39

1996, May 6　　　Litho.　　　Perf. 13½

146	A39	100r blue & black	.25	.25
147	A39	500r green & black	.25	.25
148	A39	600r ver & black	.25	.25
149	A39	1000r org & black	.25	.25
150	A39	1500r dp lil rose & blk	.25	.25
151	A39	1800r violet & black	.25	.25
152	A39	2200r rose vio & blk	.25	.25
153	A39	3300r yellow & blk	.30	.30
154	A39	5000r grn bl & blk	.40	.55
155	A39	10,000r ap grn & blk	.90	1.10
156	A39	30,000r brn & black	2.75	3.00
157	A39	50,000r red brn & blk	4.50	5.25
		Nos. 146-157 (12)	10.60	11.95

See Nos. 182, 196-201. For surcharges see Nos. 395-399.

Agreement
with Russia
A40

1996, June 14　　　　　Perf. 13½x14

158	A40	1500r multicolored	.40	.40

Exists imperf. Value, $40.

1996
Summer
Olympic
Games,
Atlanta
A41

No. 159, Rhythmic gymnastics. No. 160, Discus. No. 161, Wrestling. No. 162, Weight lifting.
5000r, Shooting, vert.

1996, July 15　　　Litho.　　　Perf. 14

159	A41	3000r multicolored	.55	.55
160	A41	3000r multicolored	.55	.55
161	A41	3000r multicolored	.55	.55
162	A41	3000r multicolored	.55	.55
		Nos. 159-162 (4)	2.20	2.20

Nos. 159-162 exist imperf. Value, set $300.

Souvenir Sheet
Imperf

163	A41	5000r multicolored	1.00	1.00

No. 163 has simulated perforations.

Regional Costume Type of 1995

Couples in traditional 19th cent. costumes: 1800r, Kapilska-Kletzky region. 2200r, David-Gorodok-Turai region. 3300r, Kobrin region. 5000r, Naralyan region.

1996, Aug. 13　　　Litho.　　　Perf. 14

164	A26	1800r multicolored	.30	.30
165	A26	2200r multicolored	.35	.35
166	A26	3300r multicolored	.40	.40
		Nos. 164-166 (3)	1.05	1.05

Souvenir Sheet
Imperf

167	A26	5000r multicolored	1.00	1.00

Medicinal
Plants — A42

No. 168, Sanguisorba officinaus. No. 169, Acorus calamus. 2200r, Potentilla erecta. 3300r, Frangula alnus. 5000r, Menyanthes trifoliata.

1996, Aug. 15　　　　　Perf. 14x13½

168	A42	1500r multicolored	.25	.25
169	A42	1500r multicolored	.25	.25
170	A42	2200r multicolored	.25	.25
171	A42	3300r multicolored	.35	.35
		Nos. 168-171 (4)	1.10	1.10

Souvenir Sheet
Imperf

172	A42	5000r multicolored	.90	.90

Birds — A44

No. 173: a, Ardea cinerea. b, Ciconia nigra. c, Phalacrocorax caroo. d, Ciconia ciconia. e, Larus ridibundus. f, Gallinago gallinago. g, Chlidonias leucopterus. h, Remiz pendulinus. i, Botaurus stellaris. j, Fulica atra. k, Ixobrychus minutus. l, Alcedo atthts.

No. 174: a, Anas crecca. b, Anas strepera. c, Anas acuta. d, Anas platyrhynchos. e, Aythya marila. f, Clangula hyemalis. g, Anas clypeata. h, Anas querquedula. i, Anas penelope. j, Arthya nyroca. k, Bucephala clangula. l, Mergus merganser. m, Mergus albellus. n, Aythya fuligula. o, Mergus serrator. p, Aythya ferina.
Each 1000r: No. 175, Aythya ferina, diff. No. 176, Gallinago gallinago, diff.

1996, Sept. 10　　　Litho.　　　Perf. 14

173	A44	400r Sheet of 12, #a.-l.	6.75	6.75
174	A44	400r Sheet of 16, #a.-p.	6.75	6.75

Souvenir Sheets

175-176	A44	Set of 2	9.00	9.00

Grammar Book,
1596 — A45

1996, Sept. 19　　Litho.　　Perf. 14x13½

177	A45	1500r multicolored	.45	.45

Exists imperf. Value, $30.

Churches
A46

No. 178, Pinsk. No. 179, Mogilev, 17th cent.

1996, Sept. 24　　　　　Perf. 14x14½

178	A46	3300r multicolored	.40	.40
179	A46	3300r multicolored	.40	.40

Nos. 178-179 exist imperf.

Mikola Shchakatskin (1896-1940), Art
Critic — A47

1996, Oct. 16

180	A47	2000r multicolored	.40	.40

Minsk
Telephone
Station,
Cent.
A48

1996, Nov. 14

181	A48	2000r multicolored	.40	.40

Natl. Arms Type of 1996

1996, Nov. 21　　Litho.　　Perf. 13½x14

182	A39	200r gray green & black	.40	.40

Pres. Aleksandr G. Lukashenko, Natl.
Flag — A49

1996, Dec. 6　　　Litho.　　　Perf. 13½

183	A49	2500r multicolored	.45	.45

БЕЛАРУСЬ BELARUS 1996 3000
Famous Men — A50

Designs: No. 184, Kyril Turovski (1130-81), Bishop of Turov. No. 185, Mikola Gusovski (1470-1533), writer. No. 186, Mikolaj Radziwil (1515-65), chancellor of Lithuania.

1996, Dec. 17   *Perf. 13½*
184 A50 3000r multicolored   .40 .40
185 A50 3000r multicolored   .40 .40
186 A50 3000r multicolored   .40 .40
     Nos. 184-186 (3)   1.20 1.20

New Year — A51

Designs: 1500r, Christmas tree, buildings in Minsk.

1996, Dec. 21   *Perf. 14*
187 A51 1500r multicolored, vert.   .25 .25
188 A51 2000r multicolored   .30 .30
Nos. 187-188 exist imperf. Value, set $50.

БЕЛАРУСЬ 1996 3500
Natl. Museum of Art, Minsk — A52

Icons: No. 189, Madonna and Child, Smolensk, 16th cent. No. 190, Paraskeva, 16th cent. No. 191, Ilya, 17th cent. No. 192, Three saints, 18th cent.
5000r, Birth of Christ, by Peter Yacijevitsch, 1649.

1996, Dec. 26   *Perf. 13½*
189 A52 3500r multicolored   .40 .40
190 A52 3500r multicolored   .40 .40
191 A52 3500r multicolored   .40 .40
192 A52 3500r multicolored   .40 .40
     Nos. 189-192 (4)   1.60 1.60
Souvenir Sheet
Imperf
193 A52 5000r multicolored   .95 .95

Georgi K. Zhukov (1896-1974), Soviet Marshal A53

1997, Jan. 3   *Perf. 13½*
194 A53 2000r multicolored   .40 .40

БЕЛАРУСЬ 3500
Kupala Natl. Theater, Minsk — A54

1997, Jan. 3   *Perf. 13½x14*
195 A54 3500r multicolored   .50 .50
     Exists imperf.

Coat of Arms Type of 1996
1997   *Litho.*   *Perf. 13½x14*
196 A39 400r lt brown & black   .30 .30
197 A39 800r dull blue & black   .30 .30
198 A39 1500r brt blue & black   .55 .55
199 A39 2000r apple green &
           black   .70 .70
200 A39 2500r dk blue & black   .60 .60
201 A39 3000r brown & black   .55 .55
     Nos. 196-201 (6)   3.00 3.00

Issued: 400r, 2000r, 1/9; 1500r, 1/16; 800r, 2500r, 3000r, 9/22.
For surcharge see No. 398.

БЕЛАРУСЬ 1997 BELARUS 2000
V.K. Byalynitsky-Birulya (1872-1957), Painter — A55

1997, Feb. 26   *Perf. 14*
202 A55 2000r multicolored   .40 .40

No. 2 Surcharged in Gray

1997, Mar. 10 Photo. *Perf. 12x11½*
203 A2 3500r on 20k bl & blk   .50 .50

Fish — A56

Designs: 2000r, Salmo trutta. 3000r, Vimba vimba. No. 206, Thymallus thymallus. No. 207, Barbus barbus.
5000r, Acipenser ruthenus.

1997, Apr. 10 Litho. *Perf. 13½x14*
204 A56 2000r multicolored   .30 .30
205 A56 3000r multicolored   .40 .40
206 A56 4500r multicolored   .50 .50
207 A56 4500r multicolored   .50 .50
     Nos. 204-207 (4)   1.70 1.70
Souvenir Sheet
208 A56 5000r multicolored   1.00 1.00

Intl. Conference on Sustainable Development of Countries with Economies in Transition — A57

Designs: 3000r, Earth with "SOS" formed in atmosphere. 4500r, Hand above flora and fauna.

1997, Apr. 16   *Perf. 14x14½*
209 A57 3000r multicolored   .40 .40
210 A57 4500r multicolored   .60 .60
  a.   Pair, #209-210 + label   1.00 1.00

50
БЕЛАРУСЬ BELARUS 1997 3000
Entry into UPU, 50th Anniv. — A58

1997, May 13   *Perf. 14½x14*
211 A58 3000r multicolored   .50 .50

БЕЛАРУСЬ 100
Nos. 28-29 Surcharged in Violet Blue

1997   *Litho.*   *Perf. 12x12½*
211A A7 100r on 1r brown   8.00 8.00
212   A7 100r on 2r red brn   .25   .25
     Issued: 2r, 5/22. No. 211A, surcharged in error, was not regularly issued.

БЕЛАРУСЬ BELARUS 1997 3000
Independence Day, July 3 — A59

1997, June 26   *Perf. 14½x14*
213 A59 3000r multicolored   .50 .50

Traditional Costume Type
Men and women in 19th cent. costumes, regions: 2000r, Dzisna. 3000r, Navagrudak. 4500r, Byhau.

1997, July 10
214 A26 2000r multicolored   .25 .25
215 A26 3000r multicolored   .40 .40
216 A26 4500r multicolored   .55 .55
     Nos. 214-216 (3)   1.20 1.20

БЕЛАРУСЬ BELARUS 1997 3000 480
Book Printing in Belarus, 480th Anniv. — A60

Designs: No. 217, Text, Vilnius period. No. 218, Text, Prague period. 4000r, F. Skorina (1488-1535), Polotsk period. 7500r, F. Skorina, Krakow period.

1997, Sept. 7   *Perf. 13½*
217 A60 3000r shown   .40 .40
218 A60 3000r gray, black & red   .40 .40
219 A60 4000r gray, black & red   .40 .40
220 A60 7500r gray, black & red   .80 .80
     Nos. 217-220 (4)   2.00 2.00

БЕЛАРУСЬ 3000 1997
Pinsk Jesuit College A61

1997, Sept. 13   *Perf. 14x14½*
221 A61 3000r multicolored   .45 .45

National Library, 75th Anniv. A62

1997, Sept. 15
222 A62 3000r multicolored   .45 .45

3000 1997
Belarus School for the Blind, Cent. A63

1997, Sept. 28 Litho. *Perf. 14x14¼*
223 A63 3000r multicolored   .45 .45

БЕЛАРУСЬ 3000
Intl. Children's Day — A64

1997, Sept. 28 Litho. *Perf. 14x14½*
224 A64 3000r multicolored   .45 .45

4000 БЕЛАРУСЬ BELARUS
Fight Against AIDS — A65

1997, Oct. 14   *Perf. 14½x14*
225 A65 4000r multicolored   .50 .50

БЕЛАРУСЬ BELARUS 1997 3300
Farm Tractors A66

Designs: 3300r, Belarus "1221." 4400r, First wheel tractor, 1953. No. 228, Belarus "952." No. 229, Belarus "680."

1997, Oct. 16   *Perf. 14x14½*
226 A66 3300r multicolored   .35 .35
227 A66 4400r multicolored   .40 .40
228 A66 7500r multicolored   .65 .65
229 A66 7500r multicolored   .65 .65
  a.   Sheet, 2 ea #226-229 + label   4.25 4.25
     Nos. 226-229 (4)   2.05 2.05

1992 3000 БЕЛАРУСЬ BELARUS
No. 1 Surcharged

1997, Dec. 8 Litho. *Perf. 12x12½*
230 A1 3000r on 1r multi   .45 .45

Holiday Greetings A68

1997, Dec. 23 Litho. Perf. 14x14¼
231	A68	1400r New Year	.25	.25
232	A68	4400r Christmas	.45	.45

1998 Winter Olympic Games, Nagano — A69

Designs: a, 2000r, Cross country skiing. b, 3300r, Ice hockey. c, 4400r, Biathlon. d, 7500r, Freestyle skiing.

1998, Feb. 3 Litho. Perf. 13½
233	A69	Block of 4, #a.-d.	1.40	1.40

P.M. Masherov (1918-80), Politician A70

1998, Feb. 12 Litho. Perf. 13½
234	A70	2500r multicolored	.45	.45

Minsk Automobile Plant — A71

Dump trucks: 1400r, 1947 MAZ-205. 2000r, 1968 MAZ-503B. 3000r, 1977 MAZ-5549. 4400r, 1985 MAZ-5551. 7500r, 1994 MAZ-5516.

1998, Apr. 23 Litho. Perf. 13½
235	A71	1400r multicolored	.40	.40
236	A71	2000r multicolored	.40	.40
237	A71	3000r multicolored	.50	.50
238	A71	4400r multicolored	.70	.70
239	A71	7500r multicolored	1.10	1.10
a.		Souvenir sheet, #235-239 + label	2.40	2.40
		Nos. 235-239 (5)	3.10	3.10

Europa — A72

1998, May 5 Litho. Perf. 14
240	A72	15,000r multicolored	.80	.80

Town of Nesvizh, 775th Anniv.

A73

1998, May 20 Litho. Perf. 14
241	A73	8600r multicolored	1.40	1.40

Adam Mickiewicz (1798-1855), poet.

No. 67 Surcharged in Silver with Post Horn, New Value and Cyrillic Text

1998, May 22 Perf. 12
242	A13	8600r on 150r multi	.45	.45

St. Petersburt-Mahilyou Post Route, 225th anniv.

A74

Songbirds from Red Book of Belarus: 1500r, Luscinia svecica. 3200r, Remiz pendulinus. 3800r, Acrocephalus paludicola. 5300r, Locustella luscinioides. 8600r, Parus cyanus.

1998, May 29 Perf. 14
243	A74	1500r multicolored	.30	.30
244	A74	3200r multicolored	.35	.35
245	A74	3800r multicolored	.35	.35
246	A74	5300r multicolored	.50	.50
247	A74	8600r multicolored	.65	.65
a.		Sheet, 2 each #243-247	4.00	4.00
		Nos. 243-247 (5)	2.15	2.15

A75

Designs: 100r, Water-powered mill. 200r, Windmill. 500r, Stork. 1000r, Bison. 2000r, Christmas Star. 3200r, Dulcimer. 5000r, Church, Synkovichy. 5300r, Hurdy-gurdy. 10,000r, Flaming wheel.

1998 Perf. 13½x14
248	A75	100r green & black	.25	.25
249	A75	200r brown & black	.25	.25
250	A75	500r bl, lt blu & blk	.25	.25
251	A75	1000r grn, lt grn & blk	.25	.25
252	A75	2000r bl, lt bl & blk	.25	.25
253	A75	3200r ap grn & blk	.50	.50
254	A75	5000r bl, lt bl & blk	.25	.25
255	A75	5300r bis, blk & buff	.75	.75
256	A75	10,000r org, lt org & blk	.30	.30
		Nos. 248-256 (9)	3.05	3.05

Issued: 100r, 200r, 7/1; 3200r, 5300r, 6/23; 2000r, 10,000r, 8/5;
See Nos. 282-288, 331-335, 338-339, 361, 363, 409-413. For surcharge see No. 400.

Belarussian Auto Works (BelAZ), 50th Anniv. — A76

Designs: 1500r, Front end loader.
Large quarry truck models: 3200r, #75131. 3800r, #75303. 5300r, #75483. 8600r, #755.

1998, Aug. 12 Perf. 14x14½
259	A76	1500r multicolored	.25	.25
260	A76	3200r multicolored	.25	.25
261	A76	3800r multicolored	.25	.25
262	A76	5300r multicolored	.25	.25
263	A76	8600r multicolored	.25	.25
a.		Sheet of 5, #259-263 + label	2.00	2.00
		Nos. 259-263 (5)	1.25	1.25

A77

Mushrooms: 2500r, Morchella esculenta. 3800r, Morchella conica. 4600r, Macrolepiota rhacodes. 5800r, Marcrolepiota procera. 9400r, Coprinus comatus.

1998, Sept. 10 Litho. Perf. 14¼x14
264	A77	2500r multicolored	.25	.25
265	A77	3800r multicolored	.25	.25
266	A77	4600r multicolored	.25	.25
267	A77	5800r multicolored	.25	.25
268	A77	9400r multicolored	.25	.25
		Nos. 264-268 (5)	1.25	1.25

Tête-bêche pair
264a	A77	2500r	.45	.45
265a	A77	3800r	.45	.45
266a	A77	4600r	.55	.55
267a	A77	5800r	.65	.65
268a	A77	9400r	1.00	1.00

See Nos. 316-320.

Wooden Sculptures — A78

Designs: 3400r, Naversha, 12-13th cent. 3800r, Archangel Michael, 1470-1480. 5800r, Prophet Zacharias, 1642-1646. 9400r, Madonna and Child, 16th cent.

1998, Oct. 6 Perf. 13½
269	A78	3400r multicolored	.25	.25
270	A78	3800r multicolored	.25	.25
271	A78	5800r multicolored	.25	.25
272	A78	9400r multicolored	.25	.25
		Nos. 269-272 (4)	1.00	1.00

World Stamp Day — A79

1998, Oct. 9 Perf. 14x14½
273	A79	5500r multicolored	.35	.35

Paintings from Natl. Art Museum — A80

3000r, "Kalozha" (church), by V.K. Tsvirko (1913-93). 3500r, "Corner Living Room," by S.U. Zhukovsky (1875-1944). 5000r, "Winter Dream," by V.K. Byalynitsky-Birula (1872-1957). 5500r, "Portrait of a Girl," by I.I. Aly-ashkevich (1777-1830). 10,000r, "Woman with a Bowl of Fruit," by I.F. Hrutski (1810-85).

1998, Oct. 20 Perf. 13½
274	A80	3000r multi	.30	.30
275	A80	3500r multi	.30	.30
276	A80	5000r multi	.30	.30
277	A80	5500r multi, vert.	.30	.30
278	A80	10,000r multi, vert.	.30	.30
		Nos. 274-278 (5)	1.50	1.50

A81

1998, Nov. 25 Perf. 14½x14
279	A81	7100r multicolored	.35	.35

Universal Declaration of Human Rights, 50th anniv.

Christmas and New Year — A82

No. 280, Girl wearing short yellow coat, rabbit, log cabin. No. 281, Rabbit, girl wearing long fur-trimmed pink coat, hat.

1998, Nov. 30
280	A82	5500r multicolored	.25	.25
281	A82	5500r multicolored	.25	.25
a.		Pair, #280-281	.40	.40

Type of 1998

Designs: 800r, Church. 1500r, Dulcimer. 3000r, Hurdy-gurdy. 30,000r, Water-powered mill. 50,000r, Windmill. 100,000r, Exhibition center, Minsk, horiz. 500,000r, Dancers.

Perf. 13½x14, 14x13½
1998-99 Litho.
282	A75	800r red lil, pale lil & blk	.25	.25
283	A75	1500r golden brn, buff & blk	.25	.25
284	A75	3000r yel, pale yel & blk	.25	.25
285	A75	30,000r Prus bl, lt bl & blk	.30	.30
286	A75	50,000r org, pale org & blk	.45	.45
287	A75	100,000r brt pink & blk	.70	.70
288	A75	500,000r brn & blk	2.40	2.40
		Nos. 282-288 (7)	4.60	4.60

Issued: 800r, 2/5/99; 1500r, 3000r, 12/22/98; 30,000r, 50,000r, 4/14/99; 100,000r, 4/22/99; 500,000r, 6/25/99.

Statues of Aleksander Pushkin and Adam Mickiewicz, St. Petersburg — A95

1999, Jan. 20 Litho. Perf. 13½
294	A95	15,300r multi	.35	.35

Trucks Made In Minsk — A96

10,000r, Model 8007. 15,000r, Model 543M rocket launcher. No. 297, Model 7907. No. 298, Model 543m with radar.
No. 299: a, 50,000r, Model 7917. b, 150,000r, Model 74135.

1999, Feb. 23
295 A96 10,000r multi .30 .30
296 A96 15,000r multi .30 .30
297 A96 30,000r multi .40 .40
298 A96 30,000r multi .40 .40
Nos. 295-298 (4) 1.40 1.40

Souvenir Sheet
299 A96 Sheet of 6, #295-298, 299a, 299b + 3 labels 2.50 2.50

No. 295 printed in sheets of 8.
See Nos. 322-323.

Glassware in National History and Culture Museum — A97

1999, Mar. 4
300 A97 30,000r Goblet .25 .25
301 A97 30,000r Three pieces .25 .25
302 A97 100,000r Lamp .50 .50
Nos. 300-302 (3) 1.00 1.00

No. 77a Surcharged in Red

1999, Apr. 26   Litho.   Perf. 11½
303 A15 150,000r on No. 77a 1.10 1.10

Europa — A98

Nature Reserves: No. 304, Berezina, 1925. No. 305, Belovezhskaya Forest, 1939.

1999, Apr. 27   Litho.   Perf. 13½
304 A98 150,000r multicolored 1.10 1.10
305 A98 150,000r multicolored 1.10 1.10

Regional Architecture — A99

1999, June 10   Litho.   Perf. 13½
306 A99 50,000r Well .35 .35
307 A99 50,000r House .35 .35
308 A99 100,000r Windmill .80 .80
Nos. 306-308 (3) 1.50 1.50

No. 306 printed in sheets of 8.

Paintings A100

Designs; 30,000r, Portrait of Y. M. Pen, by A. M. Brazer. 60,000r, St. Anthony's Church, Vitebsk, by S. B. Yudovin. No. 311, Street in Vitebsk, by Y. M. Pen. No. 312, House in Vitebsk, by M. P. Michalap, horiz.
200,000r, Etching by Marc Chagall.

1999, July 2
309 A100 30,000r multi .25 .25
310 A100 60,000r multi .35 .35
311 A100 100,000r multi .50 .50
312 A100 100,000r multi .50 .50
Nos. 309-312 (4) 1.60 1.60

Souvenir Sheet
313 A100 200,000r multi 1.60 1.60

V. M. Karvat (1958-96), Hero — A101

1999, Aug. 12
314 A101 25,000r multi .35 .35

UPU, 125th Anniv. — A102

No. 315: a, Minsk post office, 1954. b, First Minsk post office, 1800.

1999, Aug. 20
315 A102 150,000r Pair, #a.-b. 1.60 1.60

Mushroom Type of 1998

Designs: 30,000r, Flammulina velutipes. 50,000r, Kuehneromyces mutabilis. 75,000r, Lyophyllum connatum. 100,000r, Lyophyllum decastes.
150,000r, Armillariella mellea.

1999, Aug. 21   Perf. 14¼x14
316 A77 30,000r multi .25 .25
a. Tete beche pair .50 .50
317 A77 50,000r multi .40 .40
a. Tete beche pair .80 .80
318 A77 75,000r multi .55 .55
a. Tete beche pair 1.10 1.10
319 A77 100,000r multi .80 .80
a. Tete beche pair 1.60 1.60
Nos. 316-319 (4) 2.00 2.00

Souvenir Sheet
320 A77 150,000r multi 1.40 1.40
a. Tete beche pair 2.75 2.75

Left margin of No. 320 is perforated, and sheet contains two labels.

Re-annexation of Western Belarus from Poland, 60th Anniv. — A103

1999, Sept. 17   Litho.   Perf. 13½x14
321 A103 29,000r multi .30 .30

Truck Type of 1999

51,000r, MAZ-6430. 86,000r, MAZ-4370.

1999, Nov. 15   Litho.   Perf. 13½
322 A96 51,000r multi .25 .25
323 A96 86,000r multi .35 .35

Children's Art — A104

1999, Nov. 25
324 A104 32,000r shown .25 .25
325 A104 59,000r Girl, vert. .35 .35

New Year — A105

No. 326: a, Bear, snow-covered trees. b, People, snowman.

1999, Nov. 30   Perf. 14x14¼
326 A105 30,000r Pair, #a-b, + central label .35 .35

Christianity, 2000th Anniv. — A106

Designs: 50r, Spaso-Preobrazhenskaya Church, Polotsk. 75r, St. Atistratig Cathedral, Slutsk. 100r, Rev, Serafim Sorovsky Church, Beloozersk.

2000, Jan. 1   Perf. 14¼x14
327 A106 50r multi .35 .35
328 A106 75r multi .60 .60
329 A106 100r multi .90 .90
Nos. 327-329 (3) 1.85 1.85

Souvenir Sheet

Christianity, 2000th Anniversary — A107

No. 330: a, Mother of God mosaic, St. Sofia, Cathedral, Kiev, 11th cent. b, Christ Pantocrator fresco, Church of the Savoior's Transfiguration, Polotsk, 12th cent. c, Volodymyr Madonna, Tretiakov Gallery, Moscow, 12th cent.

2000, Jan. 5   Perf. 12x12¼
330 A107 100r Sheet of 3, #a-c 1.75 1.75

See Ukraine No. 370, Russia No. 6568.

Type of 1998 and

Kryzhachok Dancers — A108

1r, Bison. 2r, Christmas star. 3r, Hurdygurdy. 5r, Church, Synkovichy. 10r, Flaming wheel. A, Kupala folk holiday. 20r, Kryzhachok dancers. 30r, Water-powered mill. 50r, Windmill.

2000-02   Litho.   Perf. 13¼x13¾
Inscribed "2000"
331 A75 1r multi .25 .25
332 A75 2r multi .25 .25
333 A75 3r multi .25 .25
334 A75 5r multi .25 .25
335 A75 10r multi .25 .25
336 A108 A multi .25 .25
337 A108 20r multi .25 .25
338 A75 30r multi .25 .25
339 A75 50r orange frame .40 .40
Nos. 331-339 (9) 2.40 2.40

Inscribed "2002"
333a A75 3r multi .25 .25
336a A108 A multi .25 .25
337a A108 20r multi .25 .25
339a A75 50r bister brn frame .30 .30
Nos. 333a-339a (4) 1.05 1.05

Booklet Stamp
Self-Adhesive
Serpentine Die Cut 5¾
340 A108 20r red & black .30 .30
a. Booklet pane of 18 3.00
Booklet, #340a 3.00

No. 336 sold for 19r on day of issue. No. 340 has a line below the country name. Nos. 337 and 364 have lines of microprinting below the country name.
Issued: 1r, 5r, 10r, 1/6; No. 340, 1/14; 2r, 30r, 1/29; 3r, A, No. 337, 3/10; 50r, 4/6; Nos. 333a, 337a, 2/12/02; No. 336a, 4/24/02; No. 339a, 8/8/02.
See Nos. 362, 364-370, 414.

Sukhoi Fighter Aircraft A109

Designs: Nos. 341, 344a, Su-24. Nos. 342, 344b, Su-25. Nos. 343, 344c, Su-27.

2000, Feb. 23   Litho.   Perf. 14x14¼
341 A109 50r multicolored .35 .35
342 A109 50r multicolored .35 .35
343 A109 50r multicolored .35 .35
Nos. 341-343 (3) 1.05 1.05

Souvenir Sheet
344 Sheet of 3 + label 1.60 1.60
a.-c. A109 150r Any single .50 .50

See Nos. 383-384.

Birds — A110

Designs: No. 345, Mergellus albelius. No. 346, Burhinus oedicnemus. 75r, Lagopus lagopus. 100r, Aquila pomarina, vert.

Perf. 13½x13¾, 13¾x13½
2000, Mar. 22
345 A110 50r multi .40 .40
346 A110 50r multi .40 .40
347 A110 75r multi .50 .50
348 A110 100r multi .70 .70
Nos. 345-348 (4) 2.00 2.00

Partisan Madonna of Minsk, by M. Savitsky — A111

2000, Apr. 27   Perf. 13½
349 A111 100r multi .50 .50

End of World War II, 55th anniv.

Europa, 2000
Common Design Type
2000, May 9   Perf. 14x13½
350 CD17 250r multi 1.75 1.75
a. Tete beche pair 4.25 4.25

Ballet — A112

Designs: 100r, Male dancer lifting female dancer. 150r, Dancer with crown.

2000, May 25 Litho. Perf. 13¾x13½
351 A112 100r multi   .60 .60

Souvenir Sheet
352 A112 150r multi + label   1.10 1.10

UN High Commissioner for Refugees, 50th Anniv. — A113

2000, Aug. 23 Litho. Perf. 13½x14
353 A113 50r multi   .30 .30

Worldwide Fund for Nature (WWF) — A114

Lynx lynx: No. 354, 100r, Close-up of head. No. 355, 100r, On tree. No. 356, 150r, On snow. No. 357, 150r, Adult and young.

2000, Aug. 25 Perf. 14x13½
354-357 A114 Set of 4   3.00 3.00
357a   Sheet, 2 each #354-357   6.25 6.25

Intl. Year of Culture of Peace A115

2000, Sept. 5 Litho. Perf. 13½x14
358 A115 100r multi   .50 .50

2000 Summer Olympics, Sydney — A116

No. 359: a, Gymnast on rings. b, Kayak. c, Rhythmic gymnastics.

2000, Sept. 10 Litho. Perf. 14x13½
359 A116 100r Strip of 3, #a-c   1.40 1.40

Souvenir Sheet
360 A116 400r Runner + label   2.50 2.50
Compare Nos. 360 and 382.

Types of 1998 and 2000

Designs: 20r, Kryzhachok dancers. 30r, Water-powered mill. B, Dazhynki Crop Festival. A, Kupala folk holiday. 50r, Windmill. 100r, Exhibition center, Minsk, horiz. 200r, Vitebsk Town Hall. 500r, Dancers.

13¼x14, 14x13¼ (#361), Serpentine Die Cut 5¾ (#364-370)

2000-01 Litho.
361 A75 100r brt pink & blk   .45 .45
  a.   Inscribed "2002"   .30 .30
362 A108 200r yel grn & blk ('01)   .60 .60
  a.   Inscribed "2003"

363 A75 500r brn & blk ('01)   1.25 1.25
  a.   Inscribed "2003"   1.50 1.50

Self-Adhesive
364 A108 20r red & black   .25 .25
365 A108 30r green & black   .25 .25
366 A108 B yel & black   .25 .25
367 A108 A blue & black   .25 .25
368 A108 50r brown & black   .25 .25
369 A108 100r brt pink & blk   .25 .25
370 A108 200r yel grn & blk ('01)   .50 .50
     Nos. 361-370 (10)   4.30 4.30

Issued: 20r, 30r, B, A, 50r, 11/8/00. No. 362, 500r, 3/19/01; No. 361, 10/18/00; No. 370, 3/29/01.

No. 364 has a line of microprinting below country name, No. 340 has hairline. Nos. 366-367 sold for 34r and 39r respectively on day of issue. Nos. 364-368 each issued in sheets of 24.

Amber — A117

Halite — A118

Flint — A119

Sylvite — A120

2000, Nov. 22 Litho. Perf. 14x14¼
371 A117 200r multi   .75 .75
372 A118 200r multi   .75 .75
373 A119 200r multi   .75 .75
374 A120 200r multi   .75 .75
     Nos. 371-374 (4)   3.00 3.00

New Year 2001 — A121

2000, Nov. 28 Litho. Perf. 14x13½
375 A121 200r multi   1.00 1.00

Christmas — A122

2000, Dec. 5
376 A122 100r multi   .60 .60

A123

Children's Art Contest Winners A124

2000, Dec. 26 Perf. 13½
377 A123 100r multi   .35 .35
378 A124 100r multi   .35 .35

St. Euphrosyne of Polotsk, 900th Anniv. of Birth — A125

2001, Jan. 5 Litho. Imperf.
379 A125 500r multi   1.50 1.50

Brest Arms — A126   Gomel Arms — A127

2001, Jan. 10 Perf. 14¼x14
380 A126 200r multi   .70 .70
381 A127 200r multi   .70 .70

Souvenir Sheet

Medal Count From 2000 Summer Olympics, Sydney — A128

Perf. 13¾x13½
2001, Feb. 22 Litho.
382 A128 1000r multi + label   4.50 4.50

Sukhoi Airplane Type of 2000

Designs: No. 383, 250r, RD (ANT-25), 1933. No. 384, 250r, Rodina (ANT-37), 1936.

2001, Feb. 23 Litho. Perf. 14x14¼
383-384 A109 Set of 2   1.75 1.75

Beetles — A130

No. 385: a, Lucanus cervus. b, Oryctes nasicornis.

Perf. 13½x13¾
2001, Mar. 22 Litho.
385 A130 300r Pair, #a-b   1.75 1.75

Flowers — A131

Designs: 200r, Nymphaea alba. 400r, Cypripedium calceolus.

2001, Apr. 25 Litho. Perf. 14x14¼
386-387 A131 Set of 2   2.00 2.00
  a.   Booklet pane of 12, 6 each
       #386-387   22.50   —
       Booklet, #387a   22.50

The two center vertical pairs in No. 387a are Tête-bêche.

Europa — A132

National Parks: 400r, Prypyatski. 1000r, Narachanski.

2001, May 4 Perf. 13¾x13½
388-389 A132 Set of 2   5.50 5.50

Chernobyl Nuclear Disaster, 15th Anniv. — A133

2001, June 9
390 A133 50r multi   .30 .30

Native Costumes — A134

Designs: 200r, Woman and children, Slutsk, 19th cent. 1000r, Man, woman and child, Pinsk, 19th cent.

2001, June 15 Perf. 14¼x14
391-392 A134 Set of 2   3.00 3.00
  a.   Booklet pane of 6, 3 each #391-
       392   10.00   —
       Booklet, #392a   10.00

Independence, 10th
Anniv. — A135

Litho. with Hologram Affixed
2001, July 3 *Perf. 14¼x14*
393 A135 500r multi 1.25 1.25

Commonwealth of
Independent States,
10th Anniv. — A136

2001, July 12 Litho. *Perf. 14x13½*
394 A136 195r multi .50 .50

Nos. 102, 105, 146, 148,
150, 153, 198 and 248
Surcharged in Black, Red
or Blue

Methods and Perfs as Before
2001
395 A39 400r on 100r #146 .65 .65
396 A39 400r on 600r #148 .65 .65
397 A39 400r on 1500r #150 .65 .65
398 A39 400r on 1500r #198 .65 .65
399 A39 400r on 3300r #153 .65 .65
400 A75 1000r on 100r #248
(R) 2.10 2.10
401 A24 1000r on 180r #102
(Bl) 2.10 2.10
402 A24 1000r on 280r #105 2.10 2.10
Nos. 395-402 (8) 9.55 9.55
Issued: No. 397, 8/10; others 10/8.

Folktales — A137

Designs: 100r, The Blue Suit Made Inside
Out. 200r, Okh and the Golden Snuffbox.

2001, Aug. 24 Litho. *Perf. 13½*
403-404 A137 Set of 2 1.00 1.00

Year of Dialogue
Among Civilizations
A138

2001, Sept. 5 *Perf. 14¼x14*
405 A138 400r multi 1.00 1.00
a. Tête-bêche pair 2.75 2.75

Souvenir Sheet

Otto Y. Shmidt (1891-1956), Arctic
Explorer — A139

2001, Sept. 30 *Perf. 14x13½*
406 A139 3000r multi 8.00 8.00

Water
Sports — A140

Designs: 200r, Sailboarding. 1000r,
Waterskiing.

2001, Oct. 25 *Perf. 13¾x13½*
407 A140 200r multi .50 .50
408 A140 1000r multi 2.00 2.00
a. Booklet pane, 2 each #407-408 5.00 5.00
Booklet, #408a 5.00
b. Souvenir sheet, #408 + 2 labels 2.00 2.00

**Types of 1998-2000 Redrawn, Type
of 2000 and**

A141

Designs: 1r, Bison, with microprinting added
in tree branch. 2r, Christmas star, with
microprinting replacing line below country
name. 5r, Church, Synkovichy, with microprinting replacing lower line in church window. 10r,
Flaming wheel, with microprinting replacing
line in fire. 30r, Water-powered mill, with
microprinting in vertical posts to right of water
wheel. B, Dazhynki Crop Festival. H, Church,
Polotsk. C, Railway station, Brest. 1000r, Arms
of Francis Skaryna, first Belarussian printer.
2000r, City Hall, Minsk. 3000r, City Hall, Nesvizh. 5000r, City Hall, Chechersk.

2001-02 Litho. *Perf. 13¼x14*
409 A75 1r grn, lt grn &
blk .25 .25
410 A75 2r bl, lt bl & blk .25 .25
411 A75 5r dk bl, lt bl &
blk .25 .25
412 A75 10r org, lt org &
blk .25 .25
413 A75 30r bl grn, lt bl &
blk .25 .25
414 A108 B bister & blk .25 .25
415 A141 H lt yel, bis &
blk .50 .50
416 A141 C lt yel, ol grn &
blk .60 .60
417 A141 1000r pink, rose &
blk 2.00 2.00
418 A141 2000r lt bl, bl & blk 3.25 3.25
a. Inscribed "2007" 1.60 1.60
419 A141 3000r lt org, org &
blk 4.75 4.75
420 A141 5000r lt grn, grn &
blk 8.00 8.00
Nos. 409-420 (12) 20.60 20.60

Nos. 414-416 sold for 55r, 236r and 314r
respectively on day of issue. Issued: 1r, 2r,
1/28/02; 5r, 2/1/02; 10r, 2/12/02; 30r, 7/10/02;
B, 3/22/02; H, C, 7/16/02; 1000r, 2000r, 3000r,
5000r, 11/16.
See No. 612.

House of
Mercy,
Minsk
A142

2001, Nov. 30 *Perf. 13¾x14¼*
421 A142 200r multi .50 .50

Christmas New Year's Day
A143 A144

2001, Dec. 3 *Perf. 14¼x14*
422 A143 100r multi .40 .40
423 A144 100r multi .40 .40

Yevgeniy V.
Klumov
(1876-1944),
Surgeon
A145

2001, Dec. 16 *Perf. 13½x14*
424 A145 100r multi .40 .40

Arms of
Borisov — A146

2002, Jan. 25 *Perf. 14¼x14*
425 A146 200r multi .50 .50

2002 Winter
Olympics,
Salt Lake
City — A147

Designs: No. 426, 300r, Slalom. No. 427,
300r, Figure skating. No. 428, 500r, Biathlon.
No. 429, 500r, Ski jumping.

2002, Feb. 1 *Perf. 13½x14*
426-429 A147 Set of 4 3.25 3.25

Formica
Rufa — A148

2002, Mar. 20
430 A148 200r shown .50 .50
431 A148 1000r Colony, vert. 2.00 2.00
a. Booklet pane, 2 #430-431 + 2
labels 7.25 —
Complete booklet, #431a 7.25
b. Souvenir sheet, #431 + 2 labels 2.00 2.00

Souvenir Sheet

Accomplishments of Belarus Winter
Olympics Athletes — A149

2002, Apr. 10 *Perf. 14x13½*
432 A149 2000r multi + 2 labels 3.00 3.00

Europa — A150

Designs: 400r, Clown. 500r, Horse.

2002, Apr. 30
433-434 A150 Set of 2 2.40 2.40

Janka Kupala Jakub Kolas
(1882-1942), (1882-1956),
Poet — A151 Poet — A152

2002
435 A151 100r multi .45 .45
436 A152 100r multi .45 .45

Souvenir Sheet
437 Sheet of 2 + central label 2.00 2.00
a. A151 500r red & multi .90 .90
b. A152 500r red & multi .90 .90

Issued: No. 435, 7/6; No. 436, 9/21; No.
437, 6/27.

Flowers — A153

Designs: 30r, Trifolium. 50r, Matricaria.
100r, Pulsatilla patens. 200r, Nuphar lutea.
500r, Chamaenerion angustifolium.
B, Linum. A, Centaurea cyanus. H, Campanula. C, Rhododendron.

2002 Litho. *Serpentine Die Cut 9*
Self-Adhesive
438 A153 30r multi .25 .25
439 A153 50r multi .25 .25
440 A153 100r multi .25 .25
441 A153 200r multi .35 .35
442 A153 500r multi .90 .90

Booklet Stamps
443 A153 B multi .25 .25
a. Booklet pane of 6 1.75
Complete booklet, 4 #443a 10.00
444 A153 A multi .30 .30
a. Booklet pane of 6 2.50
Complete booklet, 4 #444a 14.00
445 A153 H multi .50 .50
a. Booklet pane of 6 2.50
Complete booklet, 4 #445a 10.00
446 A153 C multi .60 .60
a. Booklet pane of 6 3.50
Complete booklet, 4 #446a 14.00
Nos. 438-446 (9) 3.65 3.65

Nos. 443-446 sold for 75r, 90r, 236r and
314r respectively on day of issue.
Issued: 200r, 500r, 9/12; B, H, 7/24; A, C,
8/6. 30r, 50r, 100r, 8/28.

222

BELARUS

Children's
Activities
A154

Designs: 90r, Go-carting. 230r, Model airplane flying.

2002, July 25   Litho.   Perf. 13½x14
447-448 A154   Set of 2   .75 .75

Souvenir Sheet

Bird Life International — A155

No. 449: a, Ciconia ciconia. b, Oriolus oriolus. c, Motacilla alba.

2002, July 30
449 A155 200r Sheet of 3, #a-c,
+ label   1.75 1.75

Bridges — A156

Designs: 200r, Svisloch River Bridge,
Minsk. 300r, Sozh River Bridge, Gomel. 500r,
Western Dvina River Bridge, Vitebsk.

2002, Aug. 20   Perf. 13½
450-452 A156   Set of 3   2.50 2.50

Intl. Year of
Ecotourism
A157

2002, Sept. 10   Perf. 13½x14
453 A157 300r multi   1.00 1.00
 a.   Booklet pane of 4 + 4 labels   14.00
      Complete booklet, #453a   14.00

No. 453 printed in sheets of 12 + 8 labels.

Souvenir Sheet

Space Exploration, 45th
Anniv. — A158

2002, Nov. 28   Litho.   Perf. 13½
454 A158 3000r multi   4.50 4.50

Paintings in National Art
Museum — A159

Designs: No. 455, 300r, Battle of Nyemize,
by M. Filipovich, 1922. No. 456, 300r, By the
Church, by F. Rushchits, 1899, vert.

2002, Nov. 28   Litho.   Perf. 13½
455-456 A159   Set of 2   1.25 1.25

Christmas and New
Year's Day — A160

Designs: No. 457, 300r, Santa Claus. No.
458, 300r, Angel with bell.

2002, Dec. 5   Litho.   Perf. 14x13½
457-458 A160   Set of 2   1.25 1.25

Arms — A161

Designs: No. 459, 300r, Minsk (shown). No.
460, 300r, David-Gorodok.

2003, Jan. 24   Perf. 14¼x14
459-460 A161   Set of 2   1.00 1.00

See Nos. 490-491, 543-545.

Souvenir Sheet

Kasimir S. Malevich (1878-1935),
Artist — A162

2003, Feb. 21
461 A162 3000r multi + label   3.50 3.50

Reptiles
A163

Designs: 300r, Coronella austriaca. 600r,
Emys orbicularis.

2003, Mar. 12   Perf. 13½x14
462-463 A163   Set of 2   1.00 1.00
463a   Miniature sheet, 4 each
         #462-463   5.00 5.00

Intl. Year of Fresh
Water — A164

2003, Mar. 25   Perf. 14¼x14
464 A164 370r multi   .50 .50

Passer
Domesticus — A165

2003, Mar. 31   Perf. 14x13½
465 A165 630r multi   .90 .90

Printed in sheets of 7 + label.
See No. 520.

Children's
Activities
A166

Designs: No. 466, 300r, Rollerblading. No.
467, 300r, Scooter riding, vert.

2003, Apr. 22   Perf. 13½x14, 14x13½
466-467 A166   Set of 2   .80 .80

A167

Europa — A168

2003, Apr. 24
468 A167 400r multi   .50 .50
 a.   Booklet pane of 8   5.00   —
      Complete booklet, #468a   7.00
469 A168 700r multi   1.25 1.25
 a.   Booklet pane of 8   10.00 —
      Complete booklet, #469a   12.00

Endangered
Flowers — A169

Designs: 270r, Trollius europaeus. 740r, Iris
sibirica.

2003, June 30   Perf. 14x13½
470-471 A169   Set of 2   1.60 1.60
471a   Miniature sheet, 4 each
         #470-471   6.50 6.50

Traditional
Clothing — A170

Clothing of: 380r, West Polesye region.
430r, Mogilyov region.

2003, July 10   Litho.   Perf. 14¼x14
472-473 A170   Set of 2   1.50 1.50
473a   Sheet, 4 each #472-473 +
         central label   4.50   —

See Nos. 564-565.

Souvenir Sheet

Yachting — A171

No. 474: a, Boat with blue sails. b, Boat with
red and white sail, vert.

2003, July 22   Litho.   Perf. 13½
474 A171 1000r Sheet of 2, #a-b 2.50 2.50

Souvenir Sheets

A172

Exhibits at Natl. Museum of History
and Culture — A173

Designs: 1000r, Stone ax head, early
Bronze Age. No. 476, Ceramic bowl, early
Bronze Age. No. 477, Weapon, 14th cent.

2003, Aug. 20
475 A172 1000r multi   .90 .90
476 A173 1500r multi + label   1.75 1.75
477 A173 1500r multi + label   1.75 1.75

Wooden Buildings — A174

Designs: 270r, Horse stable, Povitie, 19th
cent. 430r, St. George's Church, Sinkevichi,
1724. 740r, Water mill, Volma, 19th-20th cent.

2003, Sept. 18
478-480 A174   Set of 3   1.35 1.35
480a   Souvenir sheet, #478-480 1.75 1.75

Dogs — A175

Designs: 270r, Golden retriever. 380r, Mastiff. 430r, German shepherd.

2003, Oct. 14   Perf. 14x13½
481-483 A175   Set of 3   1.50 1.50
483a   Souvenir sheet, 2 each #481-
         483, + 2 labels   3.00 3.00

FIFA (Fédération Internationale de Football Association), Cent. (in 2004) — A176

Designs: No. 484, 380r, Player dribbling ball. No. 485, 380r, Goalie holding ball, vert. 460r, Players, diff. 780r, Goalie holding ball, diff., vert.

Perf. 14x14¼, 14¼x14
2003, Nov. 14   Litho.
484-487 A176   Set of 4   2.50 2.50

Christmas and New Year's Day — A177

2003, Nov. 15   **Perf. 14x13½**
488 A177 380r Angel   .45   .45
  a.   Miniature sheet of 6   2.75 2.75
489 A177 780r Santa Claus   1.00 1.00
  a.   Miniature sheet of 6   6.00 6.00
  b.   Booklet pane, 4 each #488-489 5.75 —
       Complete booklet, #489b   5.75

Arms Type of 2003

Designs: 460r, Slonim. 780r, Zaslavl.

2004, Jan. 20   **Perf. 14¼x14**
490-491 A161   Set of 2   1.40 1.40

There Came Spring, by Pavel Maslennikov — A178

2004, Feb. 1   **Perf. 13½**
492 A178 290r multi   .50   .50

Fruit — A179

Designs: 5r, Prunus spinosa. 10r, Vaccinium vitis-idaea. 20r, Vaccinium myrtillus. 30r, Oxycoccus palustris. 50r, Vaccinium uliginosum. 100r, Rubus idaeus. B, Fragaria ananassa. A, Ribes rubrum. 200r, Rubus caesius. H, Ribes nigrum. 300r, Rubus saxatilis. C, Grossularia reclinata. 500r, Fragaria. P, Hippophae rhamnoides. 1000r, Cerasus vulgaris.

2004   **Perf. 13¼x13¾**
493 A179   5r multi   .25   .25
494 A179   10r multi   .25   .25
495 A179   20r multi   .25   .25
496 A179   30r multi   .25   .25
497 A179   50r multi   .25   .25
498 A179   100r multi   .25   .25
499 A179   B multi   .25   .25
500 A179   A multi   .25   .25
501 A179   200r multi   .25   .25
502 A179   H multi   .35   .35
503 A179   300r multi   .35   .35
504 A179   C multi   .45   .45
505 A179   500r multi   .45   .45
506 A179   P multi   .70   .70
507 A179   1000r multi   .80   .80
  a.   Miniature sheet, #493-507 6.00 6.00
       Nos. 493-507 (15)   5.35 5.35

Issued: 5r, 10r, 20r, 30r, A, P, 2/9; 50r, 100r, B, 200r, H, 300r, C, 500r, 1000r, 2/13. Nos. 499, 500, 502, 504 and 506 each sold for 100r, 120r, 290r, 420r and 780r respectively on day of issue.

St. Valentine's Day — A180

2004, Feb. 14   **Perf. 13½x13¾**
508 A180 H multi   .55   .55
  a.   Miniature sheet of 7 + label 4.50 4.50
No. 508 sold for 290r on day of issue.

Trees — A181

Designs: 100r, Alnus incana. B, Betula pendula. A, Pinus sylvsetris. 200r, Viburnum opulus. H, Fraxinus excelsior. 300r, Tilia cordata. 400r, Corylus avellana. C, Sorbus aucuparia. 500r, Quercus robur. P, Carpinus betulus. 1000r, Ulmus laevis.

2004, Mar. 23   *Serpentine Die Cut 9*
Self-Adhesive
509 A181   100r multi   .25   .25
510 A181   B multi   .25   .25
511 A181   A multi   .25   .25
512 A181   200r multi   .25   .25
513 A181   H multi   .35   .35
514 A181   300r multi   .35   .35
515 A181   400r multi   .50   .50
516 A181   C multi   .55   .55
517 A181   500r multi   .65   .65
518 A181   P multi   1.00 1.00
519 A181   1000r multi   1.00 1.00
  a.   Miniature sheet, #509-519, + label 5.50 5.50
       Nos. 509-519 (11)   5.40 5.40

Nos. 510, 511, 513, 516 and 518 each sold for 100r, 120r, 290r, 420r and 780r respectively on day of issue.

Bird Type of 2003
2004, Mar. 31   **Perf. 13¾x13½**
520 A165 870r Delichon urbica   1.10 1.10
Printed in sheets of 7 + label.

World Under-18 Ice Hockey Championships, Minsk — A182

2004, Apr. 16   Litho.
521 A182 320r multi   .60   .60
Printed in sheets of 18 + 2 labels.

Europa A183

Designs: 320r, Mushroom picker. 870r, Fisherman.

2004, May 4   **Perf. 13½x13¾**
522 A183 320r multi   .40   .40
  a.   Booklet pane of 7 + label 2.75 —
       Complete booklet, #522a   4.00
523 A183 870r multi   1.10 1.10
  a.   Booklet pane of 7 + label 7.50 —
       Complete booklet, #523a   8.75

Souvenir Sheet

Liberation of Belarus, 60th Anniv. — A184

No. 524: a, 500r, Monument to Soviet Army (30x40mm). b, 1000r, The Parade of Partisans in Minsk, by Y. Zaitsev.

2004, May 4   **Perf. 13½**
524 A184   Sheet of 2, #a-b   1.75 1.75

Locomotives and Railroad Stations — A185

Designs: 320r, Series D 1-3-0, Mosty Station. 870r, Series A 2-3-0, Vitebsk Station.

2004, May 31   Litho.   **Perf. 14x14¼**
525-526 A185   Set of 2   1.50 1.50
526a   Sheet of 12, 6 each #525-526 17.00 17.00

Insects A186

Designs: 320r, Polistes gallicus. 505r, Bombus lucorum. 2000r, Apis mellifera.

2004, June 3   **Perf. 13½x13¾**
527-528 A186   Set of 2   1.00 1.00
Souvenir Sheet
Perf. 13½x13¼
529 A186 2000r multi   2.00 2.00
No. 529 contains one 40x30mm stamp.

Souvenir Sheet

Paintings by Yehuda Pen (1854-1937) — A187

No. 530: a, Self-portrait. b, Watchmaker, horiz.

Perf. 13¼x13½, 13½x13¼ (#530b)
2004, June 5
530 A187 1000r Sheet of 2, #a-b 2.00 2.00

2004 Summer Olympics, Athens A188

Designs: 320r, Cycling. 505r, Hammer throw. 870r, Tennis.

2004, July 13   **Perf. 14x14¼**
531-533 A188   Set of 3   2.00 2.00

Butterflies — A189

Designs: 300r, Euphydryas maturna. 500r, Pericallia matronula. 800r, Zerynthia polyxena. 1200r, Eudia pavonia.

2004, Sept. 10   **Perf. 14¼x14**
534-537 A189   Set of 4   3.25 3.25
  a.   Miniature sheet, 3 each #534-537 + 4 labels 13.00 13.00

Souvenir Sheet

Gold Medalists at 2004 Summer Olympics — A190

No. 538: a, Yuliya Nesterenko. b, Igor Makarov.

2004, Oct. 7   Litho.   **Perf. 14x13½**
538 A190 500r Sheet of 2, #a-b, + central label 1.40 1.40

Horses — A191

No. 539: a, Byelorussian harness horse (UL stamp). b, Andalusian horse (UR stamp). c, Head of Byelorussian harness horse (LL stamp). d, Head of Andalusian horse (LR stamp).

2004, Oct. 27   **Perf. 12½x12**
539 A191   500r Sheet of 4, #a-d 2.00 2.00

Cats — A192

No. 540: a, 300r, Persian. b, 500r, Thai (denomination at UL). c, 500r, Red Persian (denomination at LR). d, 800r, Mixed breed (denomination at UL). e, 800r, British Shorthair (denomination at LL).

2004, Oct. 29   **Perf. 13½x14**
540 A192   Sheet of 5, #a-e, + label 2.75 2.75

Happy New Year — A193

2004, Dec. 8 **Litho.** **Perf. 13¾x13½**
541 A193 320r multi .45 .45

Minsk Metro Stations — A194

No. 542: a, Victory Square Station (gray panel). b, Yakub Kolas Square Station (yellow orange panel).

2004, Dec. 22 **Perf. 13½**
542 Horiz. pair 1.50 1.50
a.-b. A194 560r Either single .75 .75

Arms Type of 2003

Designs: 160r, Dubrovno. 350r, Kamenets. 900r, Mogilyov.

2005, Jan. 25 **Perf. 14¼x14**
543-545 A161 Set of 3 1.50 1.50

Gerasim Bogomolov (1905-81), Hydrologist — A195

2005, Feb. 18 **Perf. 13¾x13½**
546 A195 350r multi .45 .45

Souvenir Sheet

Icons — A196

No. 547: a, Virgin of Vladimir, by Fyodor Povny. b, Nativity, by Georgi Sutulin and Olga Belaya. c, Archangel Michael, by Andrei Kosikov.

Litho. with Foil Application
2005, Mar. 22 **Perf. 11½**
547 A196 1500r Sheet of 3, #a-c 4.25 4.25

Strix Nebulosa A197

Perf. 13½x13¾
2005, Mar. 31 **Litho.**
548 A197 900r multi 1.00 1.00

Comes in sheets of 7 + label.

A198

A199

A200

End of World War II, 60th Anniv. A201

No. 553: a, Signing of surrender documents. b, Victory parade (52x30mm).

2005, Apr. 12 **Perf. 13½x13¾**
549 A198 A multi .30 .30
550 A199 H multi .35 .35
551 A200 H multi .35 .35
552 A201 P multi .90 .90
Nos. 549-552 (4) 1.90 1.90

Souvenir Sheet
Perf. 13½x13¼, 13½ (#553b)
553 A201 1000r Sheet of 2, #a-b 2.00 2.00

No. 549 sold for 160r, Nos. 550 and 551 each sold for 360r, and No. 552 sold for 930r on day of issue.

Souvenir Sheet

Fauna — A202

No. 554: a, 500r, Aquila danga. b, 500r, Catocala sponsa. c, 1000r, Castor fiber. d, 1000r, Meles meles.

2005, Apr. 15 **Perf. 12**
554 A202 Sheet of 4, #a-d, + label 3.00 3.00

See Russia No. 6906.

Europa A203

Designs: 500r, Scallions, carrot, onion, peppers and tomato. 1000r, Bread and hat.

2005, May 4 **Perf. 13½x13¾**
555-556 A203 Set of 2 1.50 1.50
555a Booklet pane of 7 + label 3.50 —
Complete booklet, #555a 3.50
556a Booklet pane of 7 + label 8.50 —
Complete booklet, #556a 8.50

Stefaniya Stanyuta (1905-2000), Actress — A204

2005, May 13 **Litho.** **Perf. 13¾x13½**
557 A204 160r multi .40 .40
Printed in sheets of 16 + 4 labels.

Souvenir Sheet

Hans Christian Andersen (1805-75), Author — A205

2005, May 20 **Perf. 13¼x13½**
558 A205 2000r multi 2.00 2.00

Worldwide Fund for Nature (WWF) A206

Ciconia nigra: No. 559, In flight. No. 560, Standing on one leg.
No. 561: a, Head. b, Legs and chicks.

2005, June 2 **Perf. 13½x13¾**
559 A206 500r multi .50 .50
560 A206 500r multi .50 .50
561 A206 1000r Vert. pair, #a-b 2.00 2.00
c. Block of 4, #559, 560, 561a, 561b 3.50 3.50

Harvesting, by Mikhail Sevruk — A207

2005, July 14 **Perf. 13½**
562 A207 170r multi .30 .30

World Summit on the Information Society, Tunis — A208

2005, July 20
563 A208 360r multi .45 .45

Traditional Clothing Type of 2003

Women wearing clothing of: 360r, Mosty region. 570r, Lepel region.

2005, Aug. 18 **Perf. 14¼x14**
564-565 A170 Set of 2 1.00 1.00
565a Sheet of 8, 4 each #564-565, + central label 4.00 4.00

Intl. Year of Sport and Physical Education A209

2005, Aug. 30 **Perf. 13½x13¾**
566 A209 570r multi .60 .60

Volkovysk, 1000th Anniv. — A210

2005, Sept. 2 **Perf. 13½**
567 A210 360r multi .40 .40

Turov Eparchy, 1000th Anniv. — A211

2005, Sept. 17 **Perf. 13¾x13½**
568 A211 360r multi .40 .40

Chess — A212

No. 569 — Background color: a, Dark red. b, Orange brown.

2005, Sept. 23 **Perf. 14x14¼**
569 A212 500r Pair, #a-b 1.00 1.00
c. Booklet pane, 3 #569a, 4 #569b + label 6.00 —
Complete booklet, #569c 6.00
d. Booklet pane, 3 #569a, 4 #569b + label, imperf. 6.00 —
Complete booklet, #569d 6.00

Souvenir Sheet

Castles — A213

No. 570: a, 500r, Vytautas Castle, Grodno. b, 1000r, Lida Castle, Lida.

2005, Nov. 15 **Perf. 13½x14**
570 A213 Sheet of 2, #a-b 2.00 2.00

New Year's
Day &
Christmas
A214

2005, Dec. 5   **Litho.**   *Perf. 14x14¼*
571   A214 360r multi   .80   .80

Printed in sheets of 9 and in sheets of 8 + label.

2006 Winter
Olympics,
Turin
A215

2006, Jan. 16   *Perf. 13½x14*
572   A215 500r Snowboarding   1.25 1.25

Souvenir Sheet
Perf. 14x13½
573   A215 2000r Freestyle skiing,
            vert.   2.50 2.50

No. 573 contains one 30x40mm stamp.

Arms of
Turov — A216

Arms of
Novogrudok
A217

2006, Jan. 30   *Perf. 14¼x14*
574   A216 500r multi   .80   .80
575   A217 500r multi   .80   .80

Vanellus
Vanellus
A218

2006, Apr. 18   *Perf. 13½x14*
576   A218 930r multi   .90   .90

Printed in sheets of 7 + label.

Chernobyl
Nuclear
Accident,
20th Anniv.
A219

2006, Apr. 19
577   A219 360r multi   .60   .60

Europa — A220

Children's drawings: 500r, Penguins, by Lina Filippoch. 1000r, Pegasus, by Daria Buneeva, horiz.

2006, May 4   *Perf. 14x13½, 13½x14*
578-579 A220 Set of 2   1.50 1.50
578a   Booklet pane of 7 + label   3.75   —
        Complete booklet, #578a   3.75
579a   Booklet pane of 7 + label   7.25   —
        Complete booklet, #579a   7.25

Ivan Shamyakin (1921-2004),
Writer — A221

2006, June 2   *Perf. 14x14¼*
580   A221 360r multi   .45   .45

Birds — A222

Designs: 10r, Oenanthe oenanthe. 20r, Parus caeruleus. 30r, Ficedula hypoleuca. 50r, Carduelis cannabina. 100r, Sylvia curruca. (160r), Erithacus rubecula. (190r), Phoenicurus ochruros. 200r, Fringilla coelebs. 300r, Passer montanus. (360r), Parus major. 500r, Carduelis chloris. 1000r, Coccothraustes coccothraustes.

2006, June 16   *Perf. 13½x14*
581   A222 10r multi   .25   .25
582   A222 20r multi   .25   .25
583   A222 30r multi   .25   .25
584   A222 50r multi   .25   .25
585   A222 100r multi   .25   .25
586   A222 (160r) multi   .25   .25
587   A222 (190r) multi   .25   .25
588   A222 200r multi   .25   .25
589   A222 300r multi   .25   .25
590   A222 (360r) multi   .35   .35
591   A222 500r multi   .50   .50
592   A222 1000r multi   .85   .85
      a.   Souvenir sheet, #581-592 4.00 4.00
           Nos. 581-592 (12)   3.95 3.95

Bats
A223

Designs: No. 593, 500r, No. 596a, 1000r, Myotis dascyneme. No. 594, 500r, No. 596b, 1000r, Vespertilio murinus. No. 595, 500r, No. 596c, 1000r, Barbastella barbastellus.

2006, June 19   *Perf. 14x14¼*
593-595 A223 Set of 3   1.50 1.50
Souvenir Sheet
Perf. 13½x13¼
596   A223 1000r Sheet of 3, #a-c 3.50 3.50

Souvenir Sheet

Belarus Medals at 2006 Winter
Olympics — A224

Perf. 13¾x13½
2006, June 22   **Litho.**
597   A224 2000r multi + 2 labels 2.25 2.25

Souvenir Sheet

Augustow Canal — A225

2006, Aug. 11   *Perf. 14x14¼*
598   A225 2000r multi   2.25 2.25

Locomotives and Railroad
Stations — A226

Designs: No. 599, 1000r, Ov class locomotive, Brest Station (shown). No. 600, 1000r, E class locomotive, Molodechno Station.

2006, Sept. 8
599-600 A226 Set of 2   2.00 2.00
600a   Miniature sheet, 4 each #599-
        600, + central label   7.25 7.25

Orchids
A227

Designs: No. 601, 1000r, Dachylorhiza majalis and insect. No. 602, 1000r, Cephalanthera rubra and dragonfly facing right. No. 603, 1000r, Cephalanthera rubra and dragonfly facing left.

Perf. 13½x13¾
2006, Sept. 16   **Litho.**
601-603 A227 Set of 3   3.00 3.00
602a   Miniature sheet, 4 each
        #601-602   8.00 8.00

Renewable
Energy
A228

Designs: 210r, Wind turbines. 970d, Hydroelectric power station.

2006, Oct. 10   **Litho.**   *Perf. 14x14¼*
604-605 A228 Set of 2   1.25 1.25
605a   Miniature sheet, 3 each #604-
        605   3.75 3.75

Regional Communications
Commonwealth, 15th Anniv. — A229

2006, Oct. 13   *Perf. 13½x13¾*
606   A229 410r multi   1.25 1.25

No. 134 Surcharged in Silver and
Black

2006, Nov. 10   **Litho.**   *Imperf.*
607   A33 3500r on 10,000r #134   3.75 3.75

Belfila 2006 National Philatelic Exhibition.

Discus
Fish — A230

Various discus fish with denominations in: No. 608, 500r, White (shown). No. 609, 500r, White, diff. No. 610, 500r, Blue. No. 611, 500r, Yellow.

2006, Nov. 16   *Perf. 13½x14*
608-611 A230 Set of 4   2.00 2.00
611a   Sheet of 8, 2 each #608-611 5.00 5.00

Buildings Type of 2001-02
Perf. 13½x13¾
2006, Dec. 20   **Litho.**
612   A141 3000r Shklov City Hall 2.50 2.50

New Year
2007 — A231

No. 613 — Tree and stars in: a, Dark blue. b, White.

2006, Dec. 22   *Perf. 13¾x13½*
613   A231 500r Pair, #a-b   1.10 1.10

Printed in sheets containing three of each stamp.

Arms of
Krugloe — A232

Arms of
Pinsk — A233

2007, Jan. 22   *Perf. 14¼x14*
614   A232 600r multi   .85   .85
615   A233 600r multi   .85   .85

Napoleon Orda (1807-83), Artist and Musician — A234

Perf. 13¾x13½
2007, Feb. 14   **Litho.**
616 A234 2000r multi + label   3.75 3.75
   Printed in sheets of 2 stamps + 2 labels.

Luscinia Luscinia A235

2007, Mar. 26   **Perf. 13½x13¾**
617 A235 1000r multi   2.75 2.75
   Printed in sheets of 7 stamps + label.

Europa — A236

Scouting emblem, "100," and: 500r, Knot. 1000r, Emblem of Natl. Scout Association.

2007, May 4   **Litho.**   **Perf. 14¼x14**
618-619 A236   Set of 2   2.50 2.50
619a   Booklet pane, 4 #618, 3
     #619, + label   9.25 9.25
     Complete booklet, #619a   9.25
   Scouting, cent.

Wildlife A237

Designs: No. 620, Vulpes vulpes. No. 621, Mustela putorius. No. 622, Dryomys nitedula. No. 623, Sciurus vulgaris.

Serpentine Die Cut 9¼
2007, June 19   **Self-Adhesive**
620 A237 B multi   .30 .30
621 A237 B multi   .30 .30
622 A237 A multi   .30 .30
623 A237 A multi   .30 .30
a.   Miniature sheet, 2 each #620-
     623, + central label   2.50 2.50
     Nos. 620-623 (4)   1.20 1.20

On day of issue, Nos. 620 and 621 each sold for 190r, and Nos. 622 and 623 each sold for 220r.

Souvenir Sheet

Struve Geodetic Arc — A238

2007, Sept. 20   **Perf. 14¼x14**
624 A238 5000r multi + 2 labels   5.00 5.00

Birds A239

No. 625 — Birds of the Cepkeliai Nature Reserve, Lithuania, and Katra Sanctuary, Belarus: a, Gallinago media. b, Crex crex.

2007, Oct. 3   **Litho.**   **Perf. 13½x13¾**
625   Horiz. pair + central la-
     bel   2.00 2.00
a.-b.   A239 1000r Either single   1.00 1.00
   Printed in sheets of 3 pairs. See Lithuania No. 848.

BirdLife International A240

Birds: No. 626, 500r, Surnia ululu. No. 627, 500r, Nyctea scandiaca. No. 628, 1000r, Glaucidium passerinum. No. 629, 1000r, Asio flammeus.

2007, Nov. 23   **Perf. 13¾x13½**
626-629 A240   Set of 4   3.50 3.50
629a   Miniature sheet, 2 each
     #626-629   7.00 7.00
   Nos. 626-629 each printed in sheets of 7 + label.

Portraits by Unknown Artists in National Museum A241

Designs: Nos. 630a, 631a, Kshishtof Veselovsky, 1636. Nos. 630b, 631b, Griesel Sapega, 1632. Nos. 630c, 631c, Alexandra Marianna Veselovskaya, 1640.

2007, Nov. 28   **Perf. 13½**
630   Horiz. strip of 3   3.75 3.75
a.-c.   A241 1050r Any single   1.20 1.20
     Souvenir Sheet
631   Sheet of 3   6.00 6.00
a.-c.   A241 1500r Any single   2.00 2.00
   No. 630 printed in sheets of 2 strips.

Christmas and New Year's Day — A242

Designs: No. 632, 240r, Children making snowman. No. 633, 240r, Child giving present to another child.
No. 634: a, Boy holding sack. b, Girl holding snowflake.

2007, Dec. 7   **Perf. 13¾x13½**
632-633 A242   Set of 2   1.25 1.25
     Souvenir Sheet
634   Sheet, #632-633, 634a-
     634b + 2 labels   4.50 4.50
a.-b.   A242 1500r Either single   1.90 1.90
   Nos. 632-633 were each printed in sheets of 7 + label.

Christmas and New Year's Day — A243

No. 635: a, Christmas tree. b, Candle.

2007, Dec. 7
635 A243 1050r Pair, #a-b   2.40 2.40
c.   Souvenir sheet, #635a-635b   3.00 3.00
   No. 635 was printed in sheets containing 4 each Nos. 635a-635b.

Church Bells — A244

Various bells from: 600r, 1937. 1000r, 19th cent. 1200r, 1928. 2500r, 18th cent.

2007, Dec. 7   **Perf. 13½**
636-638 A244   Set of 3   3.00 3.00
     Souvenir Sheet
     Perf. 14x14¼
639 A244 2500r multi   2.75 2.75
   No. 639 contains one 40x28mm stamp.

Weaver — A245

Blacksmith — A246

2007, Dec. 21   **Perf. 13½**
640 A245 600r multi   .70 .70
641 A246 600r multi   .70 .70
   Nos. 640-641 each printed in sheets of 6.

Farm Animals — A247

Designs: 240r, Sheep. 440r, Ram. 500r, Pig. 1050r, Cows. 1500r, Goats.

2007, Dec. 29   **Litho.**
642-646 A247   Set of 5   4.25 4.25
   Nos. 642-646 each printed in sheets of 6.

Hunting — A248

Designs: 440r, Falconry. 1050r, Deer hunt, horiz.

Perf. 13¾x13½, 13½x13¾
2008, Jan. 30
647-648 A248   Set of 2   1.40 1.40
   Nos. 647-648 each printed in sheets of 8.

Vincent Dunin-Marcinkevich (1808-84), Writer — A249

2008, Feb. 4   **Perf. 14¼x14**
649 A249 440r multi   .80 .80
   Printed in sheets of 8.

Souvenir Sheet

Prince Konstantin Ostrozhsky (1526-1608) — A250

2008, Feb. 17
650 A250 2500r multi + label   2.75 2.75

Egretta Alba — A251

2008, Mar. 13   **Perf. 13¾x13½**
651 A251 1050r multi   2.00 2.00
   Printed in sheets of 7 + label.

Intl. Telecommunications, Information and Bank Technologies Exhibition — A252

2008, Apr. 4   **Perf. 14x14¼**
652 A252 (440r) multi   1.40 1.40
   Printed in sheets of 8.

Europa
A253

Designs: No. 653, 1000r, Letter on birch bark. No. 654, 1000r, Computer keyboard, envelopes, "@" symbol.

2008, May 28   Litho.   Perf. 13½x14
653-654 A253   Set of 2   2.00 2.00
654a   Booklet pane, 3 each #653-
654 + 2 labels   6.75   —
Complete booklet, #654a   6.75

Mammals — A254

Designs: 10r, Nyctereutes procyonoides. 200r, Mustela lutreola. 300r, Lepus europaeus. 400r, Canis lupus. 1000r, Martes martes.

2008, June 10   Perf. 13½x14
655 A254   10r multi   .25 .25
656 A254   200r multi   .25 .25
657 A254   300r multi   .35 .35
658 A254   400r multi   .45 .45
659 A254   1000r multi   .90 .90
a.   Miniature sheet, 3 each #655-
659   6.25 6.25
Nos. 655-659 (5)   2.20 2.20

See No. 681.

Flowers — A255

Designs: 20r, Paeonia lactiflora. 30r, Petunia hybrida. 50r, Narcissus hybridus. 100r, Tulipa gesneriana. (200r), Dahlia cultorum. (240r), Rosa hybrida. (440r), Zinnia elegans. 500r, Lilium hybrida.

2008, June 10
660 A255   20r multi   .25 .25
661 A255   30r multi   .25 .25
662 A255   50r multi   .25 .25
663 A255   100r multi   .25 .25
664 A255   (200r) multi   .25 .25
665 A255   (240r) multi   .30 .30
666 A255   (440r) multi   .40 .40
667 A255   500r multi   .50 .50
a.   Miniature sheet, 3 each #660-
667   6.00 6.00
Nos. 660-667 (8)   2.45 2.45

Mushrooms — A256

Designs: 1000r, Cantharellus cibarius. 1500r, Boletus edulis.

2008, July 8   Litho.   Perf. 14x13½
668-669 A256   Set of 2   3.50 3.50

2008
Summer
Olympics,
Beijing
A257

2008, Aug. 15   Perf. 14x14¼
670 A257   1000r multi   2.25 2.25

Miniature Sheets

Orders of Belarus — A258

Medals of Belarus — A259

No. 671: a, Order of Exceptional Courage (star in white circle). b, Order of Military Glory (two soldiers in blue laureated circle). c, First, second and third class Orders of the Motherland (three orders with ribbons). d, First, second and third class Orders for Service to the Motherland (three orders without ribbons). e, Order of Friendship of Peoples (Blue violet ribbon). f, Order of Honor (two people in circle within a diamond). g, Order of Francysk Skaryna (red ribbon). h, Order of Mother (light and dark blue ribbon).

No. 672: a, Medal of Note for Military Service (round medal with star, torch, red and green banner). b, Medal of Hero of Belarus (star-shaped medal). c, Medal for Bravery (round medal with airplanes, tank and text). d, Medal for Labor Achievements (round medal with gray and red ribbon). e, First, second and third class medals for Perfect Service (three round medals with green and red ribbons). f, Medal of Note in Guarding the Civil Order (round medal with blue ribbon with red stripes). g, Medal of Note for Guarding the State Border (round medal with border guard and boundary marker). h, Medal of Francysk Skaryna (green and white ribbon).

2008, Aug. 28   Perf. 13½
671 A258   1000r Sheet of 8,
#a-h, + 2 labels   8.00 8.00
672 A259   1000r Sheet of 8,
#a-h, + 2 labels   8.00 8.00

Arms of
Orsha — A260

Arms of
Vitsebsk — A261

Arms of
Nesvizh — A262

2008   Perf. 14¼x14
673 A260   500r multi   .65 .65
674 A261   600r multi   .80 .80
675 A262   1000r multi   1.20 1.20
Nos. 673-675 (3)   2.65 2.65

Issued: 600r, 9/15; 500r, 1000r, 9/19.

Remembrance of the
Holocaust — A263

2008, Oct. 21   Perf. 13½x13¾
676 A263   500r multi   1.50 1.50
Printed in sheets of 8 + label.

Souvenir Sheet

Baptism of Vladimir I (Christianization of Kievan Rus), 1020th Anniv. — A264

No. 677: a, Holy Virgin of Iljinsk and Chernigov. b, Christ Pantocrator. c, Grand Prince Vladimir.

2008, Oct. 25   Perf. 13½
677 A264   1500r Sheet of 3, #a-c   4.50 4.50

Souvenir Sheet

Nesvizh Castle, 425th Anniv. — A265

2008, Dec. 8   Litho.   Perf. 13½x14
678 A265   3000r multi + label   3.00 3.00

Christmas and New
Year's Day — A266

New Year's Day — A267

2008, Dec. 9   Perf. 14x13½
679 A266   500r multi   .50 .50
Perf. 13½
680 A267   1000r multi   .90 .90

Mammals Type of 2008
2008, Dec. 10   Perf. 13½x14
681 A254   5000r Bison bonasus   3.50 3.50

BirdLife
International
A268

Owls: No. 682, 500r, Bubo bubo. No. 683, 500r, Athene noctua. No. 684, 1000r, Otus scops. No. 685, 1000r, Strix uralensis.

2008, Dec. 22   Perf. 14x13½
682-685 A268   Set of 4   3.00 3.00
685a   Sheet of 8, 2 each #682-685   6.50 6.50

Nos. 682-685 each were printed in sheets of 7 + label.

Louis Braille
(1809-52),
Educator of
the
Blind — A269

2009, Jan. 4   Perf. 13½x14
686 A269   700r multi   .65 .65

Vladimir Muliavin (1941-2003), Folk
Singer — A270

2009, Jan. 12   Litho.
687 A270   1000r multi + label   .90 .90

Withdrawal of
Soviet Troops
From
Afghanistan,
20th Anniv.
A271

2009, Jan. 20
688 A271   400r multi   .45 .45
Printed in sheets of 8 + central label.

Commonwealth of Independent States
Executive Committee Building,
Minsk — A272

2009, Feb. 18   Perf. 14x14¼
689 A272   500r multi   .55 .55

Miniature Sheet

Folk Holidays — A273

No. 690: a, Kaliady (people walking in snow carrying torches). b, Spring greetings (child in white robe). c, Dazhynki (woman in field of rye). d, Kupalle (woman holding flower).

2009, Mar. 1   **Perf. 14x13½**
690 A273 500r Sheet of 4, #a-d,
+ 4 labels   1.75 1.75

Anser Anser
A274

2009, Mar. 31   **Perf. 13½x14**
691 A274 1000r multi   .85 .85

Printed in sheets of 7 + label.

Europa
A275

Designs: No. 692, 1000r, Armillary sphere, telescope of Galileo. No. 693, 1000r, Moon, dish antenna, satellite.

2009, Apr. 15   **Perf. 13½x14**
692-693 A275   Set of 2   1.75 1.75
693a   Booklet pane of 6, 3 each
    #692-693, + 2 labels   5.25 —
    Complete booklet, #693a   5.25

Intl. Year of Astronomy. Nos. 692-693 each were printed in sheets of 7 + label.

Souvenir Sheet

Year of Native Land — A276

2009, Apr. 21   **Litho.**   **Perf. 13½x14**
694 A276 2500r multi   2.25 2.25

Poultry — A277

Designs: No. 695, 1000r, Geese. No. 696, 1000r, Ducks.
3000r, Rooster and hen, horiz.

2009, May 5   **Perf. 14¼x14**
695-696   A277   Set of 2   1.60 1.60
Souvenir Sheet
Perf. 13½x13¾
697 A277 3000r multi + 2 labels   2.75 2.75

Endangered
Flora — A278

Designs: No. 698, 1500r, Anemone sylvestris. No. 699, 1500r, Scorzonera glabra.

2009, June 8   **Perf. 14¼x14**
698-699 A278   Set of 2   2.50 2.50

Nos. 698-699 each were printed in sheets of 5 + label.

Souvenir Sheet

Liberation From Nazi Control, 65th
Anniv. — A279

No. 700: a, Victory Square, Minsk. b, Women in Minsk, 1944.

2009, June 26   **Perf. 14x13½**
700 A279 500r Sheet of 2, #a-b   1.50 1.50

Air Sports
A280

Designs: No. 701, 1500r, Two Yak-52 airplanes. No. 702, 1500r, An-2 airplane and skydiver.

2009, July 4   **Perf. 13½x14**
701-702 A280   Set of 2   2.50 2.50

Nos. 701-702 each were printed in sheets of 5 + label.

Andrei A. Gromyko
(1909-89), Foreign
Affairs Minister of
Soviet
Union — A281

2009, July 18   **Perf. 14x13½**
703 A281 800r multi   .65 .65

Holy Virgin of
Borkolabovo, 350th
Anniv. — A282

2009, July 24   **Perf. 14¼x14**
704 A282 1380r multi   1.10 1.10

Arms of
Smorgon — A283

Arms of
Kobrin — A284

2009   **Litho.**
705 A283 1000r multi   .85 .85
706 A284 1000r multi   .85 .85

Issued: No. 705, 9/6; No. 706, 9/19. Nos. 705-706 each were printed in sheets of 8 + label.

Souvenir Sheet

Belovezhskaya Puscha National
Park — A285

No. 707: a, Deer. b, Aurochs. c, Wild boars.

2009, Oct. 3   **Perf. 14x14¼**
707 A285 1500r Sheet of 3, #a-c   4.50 4.50

A286

2009, Oct. 16   **Perf. 13½x14**
708 A286 1380r multi   1.10 1.10

First Telegraph Line Between Minsk and Bobruisk, 150th Anniv.
Printed in sheets of 7 + 2 labels.

Galina K.
Makarova
(1919-93),
Actress
A287

2009, Oct. 23
709 A287 800r multi   .65 .65

Printed in sheets of 5 + label.

Paintings in Natl. Art Museum — A288

Designs: No. 710, 1000r, Sky Blue Day, by Vitaly K. Tsvirko, 1980. No. 711, 1000r, Evening in Minsk Province, by Apollinary G. Goravsky, 1870s.

2009, Nov. 5   **Litho.**   **Perf. 13½**
710-711 A288   Set of 2   1.75 1.75

Souvenir Sheet

Christmas and New Year's
Day — A289

No. 712: a, Decorated tree. b, Angel.

2009, Nov. 12   **Perf. 13¼x13½**
712 A289 1500r Sheet of 2, #a-b,
+ central label   2.50 2.50

Souvenir Sheet

Russian Blue Cats — A290

No. 713: a, Head of adult cat. b, Two kittens. c, Three kittens.

2009, Nov. 23   **Perf. 13½**
713 A290 2500r Sheet of 3, #a-c,
+ label   5.75 5.75

Sports Facilities in Minsk — A291

No. 714: a, Soccer Stadium (with arched roof). b, Minsk Arena (circular building).

2009, Nov. 30
714 A291 1500r Vert. pair, #a-b   2.50 2.50

Printed in sheets containing 2 pairs and 2 labels.

Souvenir Sheet

Foundation Treaty of the Union State (Economic and Political Confederation With Russia), 10th Anniv. — A292

Litho. With Foil Application
2009, Dec. 8   **Perf. 14¼x14**
715 A292 4500r multi + 2 labels   4.00 4.00

Souvenir Sheet

2010 Winter Olympics,
Vancouver — A293

2010, Jan. 25   **Litho.**   **Perf. 13½x14**
716 A293 3000r multi + 5 labels   2.50 2.50

Souvenir Sheet

Paintings by Ivan Khrutski (1810-85) — A294

No. 717: a, Self-portrait, 1884. b, Still Life with Dead Game, Vegetables and Mushrooms, 1854.

2010, Feb. 8 *Perf. 14x14¼*
717 A294 1500r Sheet of 2, #a-b 2.75 2.75

Ivan Naumenko (1925-2006), Writer — A295

2010, Feb. 16 *Perf. 13½*
718 A295 800r multi .60 .60
Printed in sheets of 5 + label.

Falco Tinnunculus A296

2010, Mar. 19 *Perf. 13½x13¾*
719 A296 1000r multi .85 .85
Printed in sheets of 7 + label.

Souvenir Sheet

Slutsk Sashes — A297

No. 720: a, Iosif Zhagel wearing sash. b, Slutsk Gate, Nesvizh. c, Detail of Slutsk sash.

2010, Mar. 26 *Perf. 14x14¼*
720 A297 1000r Sheet of 3, #a-c 2.50 2.50

Europa A298

Designs: No. 721, 1000r, Boy reading book, book characters. No. 722, 1000r, Girl reading book, butterfly.

2010, Mar. 30 *Perf. 13½x14*
721-722 A298 Set of 2 1.75 1.75
722a Booklet pane of 6, 3 each #721-722, + 2 labels 5.25 —
  Complete booklet, #722a 5.25

A299

End of World War II, 65th Anniv. — A300

No. 724: a, 500r, Soldiers at liberation of Minsk. b, 1500r, Berlin Liberation Monument.

2010, Apr. 16 *Perf. 14x13½*
723 A299 500r multi .40 .40
Souvenir Sheet
724 A300 Sheet of 2, #a-b, + label 1.75 1.75
No. 723 was printed in sheets of 5 + label.

Souvenir Sheet

Intl. Year of Biodiversity — A301

No. 725: a, 300r, Bears. b, 300r, Fish. c, 2400r, Birds, "2010," waves, man, child, tree.

2010, Apr. 23 *Perf. 13½x14*
725 A301 Sheet of 3, #a-c 2.50 2.50

Expo 2010, Shanghai — A302

2010, May 1 *Perf. 14x13½*
726 A302 500r multi .40 .40

Postal Agreement With Sovereign Military Order of Malta — A303

2010, June 21 Litho. *Perf. 13½*
727 A303 (920r) multi 1.25 1.25

Sailboats — A304

Designs: 920r, Optimist class. 1420r, Luch class.

2010, June 28 *Perf. 14¼x14*
728-729 A304 Set of 2 2.00 2.00
Nos. 728-729 each were printed in sheets of 7 + label.

Battle of Grunwald, 600th Anniv. A305

2010, July 15 *Perf. 14x14¼*
730 A305 1500r multi 1.25 1.25
Printed in sheets of 4.

Darya Domracheva, Bronze Medalist in Biathlon — A306

Sergei Novikov, Silver Medalist in Biathlon — A307

Aleksei Grishin, Gold Medalist in Freestyle Skiing — A308

2010, July 23 *Perf. 14x13½*
731 A306 (290r) multi .40 .40
732 A307 (920r) multi 1.00 1.00
733 A308 (1420r) multi 1.60 1.60
a. Sheet of 6, 2 each #731-733 + 3 labels 6.00 6.00
  Nos. 731-733 (3) 3.00 3.00

Belarussian medalists at 2010 Winter Olympics, Vancouver. Nos. 731-732 each were printed in sheets of 8 + label.

Miniature Sheet

Belarussian Gold Medalists at 2008 Summer Olympics, Beijing — A309

No. 734: a, Men's canoe doubles team. b, Aksana Miankova, women's hammer throw. c, Andrei Aramnau, weightlifting. d, Men's kayak fours team.

2010, July 24 *Perf. 14¼x14*
734 A309 1000r Sheet of 4, #a-d 3.75 3.75

S Class Locomotive, Vilenski Railroad Station, Minsk — A310

Shch Class Locomotive, Mogilyov Railroad Station — A311

2010, Aug. 2 *Perf. 12x12¼*
735 A310 1000r multi 1.10 1.10
736 A311 1000r multi 1.10 1.10
a. Sheet of 10, 5 each #735-736, + 2 labels 11.00 11.00
Nos. 735-736 each were printed in sheets of 11 + label.

Worldwide Fund for Nature (WWF) A312

Various depictions of Ophiogomphus cecilia: 900r, 1000r, 1400r, 1500r.

2010, Aug. 10 *Perf. 13½x14*
737-740 A312 Set of 4 4.00 4.00
740a Sheet of 8, 2 each #737-740 8.00 8.00

Mushrooms — A313

Designs: No. 741, 500r, Clavaridelphus pistillaris and bird. No. 742, 500r, Langermannia gigantea and bird. No. 743, 500r, Hericium coralloides and bird. No. 744, 1000r, Sparassis laminosa and butterfly. No. 745, 1000r, Polyporus umbellatus and rodent.

2010, Aug. 18 *Perf. 14x13½*
741-745 A313 Set of 5 4.00 4.00
Nos. 741-745 each were printed in sheets of 9 + label.

Arms of Khoiniki — A314

Arms of Lida — A315

2010 Litho. *Perf. 14¼x14*
746 A314 900r multi .75 .75
747 A315 1400r multi 1.25 1.25
Issued: 900r, 9/5; 1400r, 9/24.

Souvenir Sheet

Republican Trade Union Palace of Culture — A316

2010, Sept. 15 *Perf. 13½*
748 A316 2000r multi + label 1.60 1.60

United Nations, 65th Anniv. A317

2010, Oct. 24   Litho.   Perf. 13½x13
749   A317   1000r multi   .85   .85
Printed in sheets of 5 + label.

Russian Spaniel — A318

Irish Setter — A319

Russo-European Laika — A320

2010, Nov. 10   Perf. 13x13½
750   A318   1000r multi   .75   .75
751   A319   1000r multi   .75   .75
752   A320   1000r multi   .75   .75
a.   Souvenir sheet of 6, 2 each #750-752, + 3 labels   4.50   4.50
Nos. 750-752 (3)   2.25   2.25

New Year 2011 — A321

Christmas — A322

2010, Nov. 12   Perf. 13½
753   A321   1000r multi   .85   .85
754   A322   1000r multi   .85   .85
a.   Souvenir sheet of 4, 2 each #753-754, + 4 labels   3.50   3.50

Nos. 753-754 each were printed in sheets of 7 + label.

2010 Junior Eurovision Song Contest, Minsk A323

2010, Nov. 20   Perf. 13½x14
755   A323   (1010r) multi   1.40   1.40
Printed in sheets of 10 + 2 labels.

Arms of Gantsevichi A324

2010, Nov. 20   Perf. 14¼x14
756   A324   900r multi   .70   .70

Souvenir Sheet

Mir Castle — A325

Litho. & Embossed
2010, Dec. 16   Perf. 13x13½
757   A325   5000r multi   4.00   4.00

Primula Elatior — A326

Orchis Ustulata — A327

2011, Jan. 10   Litho.   Perf. 12¼x12
758   A326   (1160r) multi   1.25   1.25
759   A327   (1790r) multi   1.90   1.90
a.   Souvenir sheet of 4, 2 each #758-759, + 2 labels   6.50   6.50

Endangered flowers.

Preservation of Polar Regions and Glaciers — A328

Designs: 1500r, Map of Antarctica, penguins. 2500r, Map of Arctic region, polar bear.

2011, Feb. 11
760-761   A328   Set of 2   4.50   4.50
761a   Tête-bêche pair, #760-761   4.50   4.50
761b   Souvenir sheet, 3 #761a   10.50   10.50

Nos. 760-761 each were printed in sheets of 5 + label.

Numenius Arquata A329

Perf. 13½x13¾
2011, Mar. 14   Litho.
762   A329   1500r multi   1.10   1.10
Printed in sheets of 7 + label.

Souvenir Sheets

Cross of St. Euphrosyne of Polotsk, 850th Anniv. — A330

Cross with denomination in: 5000r, Red. 10,000r, Gold.

Litho. & Embossed
2011, Mar. 21   Perf. 13x13½
763   A330   5000r multi   4.50   4.50
Litho. & Embossed With Foil Application
764   A330   10,000r multi   8.50   8.50

First Man in Space, 50th Anniv. — A331

2011, Apr. 12   Litho.   Perf. 13x13½
765   A331   (1160r) multi   1.25   1.25

Europa — A332

Forest and: 2000r, Buck. 2500r, Bison.

2011, Apr. 14   Perf. 12½x12
766-767   A332   Set of 2   3.00   3.00
767a   Sheet of 6, 3 each #766-767   13.00   13.00

Intl. Year of Forests.

Chernobyl Nuclear Disaster, 25th Anniv. A333

2011, Apr. 26   Perf. 13½x13
768   A333   (1330r) multi   1.40   1.40

AIDS Prevention, 30th Anniv. — A334

2011, May 12   Perf. 13¾x13½
769   A334   (1330r) multi   1.40   1.40
Printed in sheets of 8 + central label.

Musical Instruments — A335

No. 770: a, Tar, Azerbaijan. b, Hurdy-gurdy, Belarus.

2011, May 25   Perf. 14x14¼
770   A335   (1330r) Pair, #a-b   2.75   2.75
See Azerbaijan No. 950.

Capitals of Belarus and Armenia — A336

No. 771 — Buildings and arms of: a, Minsk, Belarus ("Belarus" at left). b, Yerevan, Armenia ("Belarus" at right).

2011, June 1   Perf. 13½
771   A336   (1330r) Horiz. pair, #a-b   2.75   2.75
See Armenia No. 875.

Commonweath of Independent States, 20th Anniv. — A337

2011, June 28   Perf. 13½x13¾
772   A337   (1330r) multi   1.25   1.25

Souvenir Sheet

Diplomatic Relations Between Belarus and Venezuela, 15th Anniv. — A338

2011, July 5   Perf. 12¼x12
773   A338   3000r multi   1.75   1.75

Slavianski Bazaar Intl. Arts Festival, Vitebsk — A339

No. 774: a, (360r), Stage, Vitebsk coat of arms. b, (1400r), Slavianski Bazaar emblem, Vitebsk Town Hall.

2011, July 8   Perf. 13½x13
774   A339   Horiz. pair, #a-b   1.50   1.50

A340

Equestrian Sports — A341

Designs: No. 775, (1400r), Horse racing. No. 776, (1400r), Dressage. No. 777, (1400r), Jumping. No. 778, Dressage half-pass, vert.

2011, July 12   *Perf. 12x12¼*
775-777   A340   Set of 3   4.25   4.25
Souvenir Sheet
Perf. 12¼x12
778   A341   (2160r) multi   1.90   1.90

Non-Aligned Movement, 50th Anniv. — A342

2011, Aug. 2   *Perf. 14x13½*
779   A342   (1400r) multi   1.25   1.25

Lota Lota
A343

Esox Lucius
A344

2011, Aug. 18   *Perf. 14x14¼*
780   A343   (1400r) multi   1.10   1.10
781   A344   (2160r) multi   1.75   1.75
  a.   Souvenir sheet of 6, 3 each
          #780-781   10.00 10.00

Regional Communications Commonwealth, 20th Anniv. — A345

2011, Sept. 20   *Perf. 13½x13*
782   A345   (1540r) multi   1.25   1.25

Souvenir Sheet

Buildings in Belarus and Iran — A346

No. 783: a, Mir Castle (building with steeples), Mir, Belarus. b, Arg of Karim Khan (building with round turrets), Shiraz, Iran.

2011, Sept. 28   *Perf. 12x12¼*
783   A346   (2380r) Sheet of 2,
              #a-b   4.00   4.00
See Iran No. 3046.

Arms of Molodechno
A347

2011, Sept. 30   *Perf. 12*
784   A347   (1620r) multi   1.25   1.25

Costumes of Malorita Region — A348   Costumes of Kalinkovichi Region — A349

2011, Oct. 11   *Perf. 14x13½*
785   A348   (1620r) multi   1.25   1.25
786   A349   (2500r) multi   2.25   2.25
  a.   Souvenir sheet of 8, 4 each
          #785-786   14.00 14.00

New Year 2012 — A350

Christmas — A351

Litho. & Embossed With Foil Application
2011, Nov. 11   *Perf. 12*
787   A350   (2450r) multi   1.10   1.10
788   A351   (3750r) multi   1.75   1.75

Poster Pigeons A352

Starominsk Stately Piegons A353

Strasser Pigeons A354

2011, Nov. 28   **Litho.**   *Perf. 12x12¼*
789   A352   5000r multi   1.75   1.75
790   A353   5000r multi   1.75   1.75
791   A354   5000r multi   1.75   1.75
  a.   Souvenir sheet of 6, 2 each
          #789-791   10.50 10.50
      Nos. 789-791 (3)   5.25   5.25

Souvenir Sheet

Diplomatic Relations Between Belarus and People's Republic of China, 20th Anniv. — A355

Litho. & Embossed
2012, Jan. 20   *Perf. 12¼x12*
792   A355   15,000r multi   4.75   4.75

Geometric Designs
A356   A357

2012, Jan. 27   **Litho.**   *Perf. 13½x13*
793   A356   (1100r) gray & red   .60   .60
794   A357   (1650r) multi   .90   .90

Souvenir Sheet

Orthodox Churches — A358

No. 795: a, St. Sophia Cathedral, Polotsk, and trees. b, All Saints Monument Church, Minsk, and lamp post.

2012, Feb. 22   *Perf. 12¼x12*
795   A358   10,000r Sheet of 2,
              #a-b   7.00   7.00

A359   A360

Architecture
A361   A362

Designs: 50r, Mahiliou Town Hall. 100r, Kamianets Tower. 200r, Nesvizh Castle, Nesvizh. 500r, Epiphany Church, Polatsk. (500r), Kosava Palace, Kosava. 1000r, Rumyantsev-Paskevich Palace, Homel. 2000r, Mir Castle, Mir. (2450r), Red Church, Minsk. (3750r), Church-fortress, Murovanka. 5000r, Main Post Office, Minsk. 10,000r, Lida Castle, Lida. 20,000r, Bernardine Monastery, Budslau.

2012, Mar. 2   **Litho.**   *Perf. 13½x13*
796   A359   50r multi   .25   .25
797   A359   100r multi   .25   .25
798   A359   200r multi   .25   .25
799   A359   500r multi   .25   .25
800   A360   (500r) multi   .25   .25
801   A359   1000r multi   .40   .40
802   A359   2000r multi   .75   .75
803   A361   (2450r) multi   .95   .95
804   A362   (3750r) multi   1.50   1.50
805   A359   5000r multi   1.90   1.90
806   A359   10,000r multi   3.75   3.75
807   A359   20,000r multi   7.75   7.75
      Nos. 796-807 (12)   18.25 18.25

Self-Adhesive
Die Cut
808   A359   50r multi   .25   .25
809   A359   100r multi   .25   .25
810   A359   200r multi   .25   .25
811   A359   500r multi   .25   .25
812   A360   (500r) multi   .25   .25
813   A359   1000r multi   .40   .40
814   A359   2000r multi   .75   .75
815   A361   (2450r) multi   .95   .95
816   A362   (3750r) multi   1.50   1.50
817   A359   5000r multi   1.90   1.90
818   A359   10,000r multi   3.75   3.75
819   A359   20,000r multi   7.75   7.75
      Nos. 808-819 (12)   18.25 18.25

Europa — A363

No. 820 — People facing: a, Right. b, Left.

2012, Mar. 12   *Perf. 13x13½*
820   A363   5000r Horiz. pair,
              #a-b   3.00   3.00
  c.   Souvenir sheet of 6, 3 each
          #820a-820b   9.00   9.00

Apus Apus — A364

2012, Mar. 22   *Perf. 14x13½*
821   A364   (3750r) multi   2.00   2.00
Printed in sheets of 7 + label.

Costumes From Turov and Mozyr Regions — A365

Costumes From Liahovichi Region — A366

2012, Apr. 12   *Perf. 14¼x14*
822   A365   (2750r) multi   1.25   1.25
823   A366   (4250r) multi   1.75   1.75
  a.   Souvenir sheet of 8, 4 each
          #822-823 + label   12.00 12.00

Polypodium Vulgare and Silhouette of Butterfly A367

Salvinia Natans and Silhouette of Fish A368

Litho. & Embossed
2012, May 3   *Perf. 12x12¼*
824 A367 (2750r) multi   1.25   1.25
825 A368 (4250r) multi   1.75   1.75
  a.   Souvenir sheet of 8, 4 each #824-825   12.00   12.00

Endangered plants.

Souvenir Sheet

Diplomatic Relations Between Belarus and Cuba, 20th Anniv. — A369

Litho. (Margin Litho. & Embossed)
2012, May 25   *Perf. 12¼x12*
826 A369 15,000r multi   6.00   6.00

Hemiechinus Auritus — A370

Erinaceus Concolor A371

2012, June 20   **Litho.**   *Perf. 12x12¼*
827 A370 (3300r) multi   1.25   1.25
828 A371 (5100r) multi   1.75   1.75
  a.   Souvenir sheet of 4, 2 each #827-828   6.00   6.00

See Kazakhstan No. 669.

Triturus Cristatus A372

Lissotriton Vulgaris A373

2012, June 25   *Perf. 13*
829 A372 (3300r) multi   1.25   1.25
830 A373 (5100r) multi   1.75   1.75
  a.   Souvenir sheet of 4, 2 each #829-830   6.00   6.00

See Russia No. 7367.

Souvenir Sheet

Portrait of Marc Chagall, by Yuri Pen — A374

2012, July 7   *Perf. 13½x13*
831 A374 15,000r multi   5.00   5.00

Marc Chagall (1887-1985), painter.

French Invasion, Bicent. A375

2012, July 10   *Perf. 13½x14*
832 A375 (5100r) multi   2.00   2.00

Printed in sheets of 8 + central label.

Eurasian Economic Community — A376

Litho. & Embossed
2012, July 26   *Perf. 13x13½*
833 A376 (3300r) multi   1.50   1.50

Printed in sheets of 10 + 5 labels.

Belarussian Railway, 150th Anniv. — A377

2012, Aug. 1   **Litho.**
834 A377 (5100r) multi   2.00   2.00

Arms of Glubokoe — A378

Arms of Gorki — A379

2012, Aug. 21   *Perf. 12*
835 A378 (4800r) multi   1.75   1.75
836 A379 (5800r) multi   2.00   2.00

Fire and Rescue Sports in Belarus, 75th Anniv. A380

2012, Sept. 8   *Perf. 13½x14*
837 A380 5000r multi   1.75   1.75

Maxim Tank (1912-95), Poet — A381

2012, Sept. 15   *Perf. 13x13½*
838 A381 (4800r) multi   1.60   1.60

Christmas — A382   New Year's Day — A383

Litho. & Embossed With Foil Application
2012, Nov. 20   *Perf. 12¼x12*
839 A382 (3000r) blue & gold   1.00   1.00
840 A383 (4500r) sil & grn   1.50   1.50

Souvenir Sheet

Diplomatic Relations Between Belarus and Israel, 20th Anniv. — A384

2012, Dec. 18   **Litho.**
841 A384 15,000r multi   5.75   5.75

A385

A386

2013 World Track Cycling Championships, Minsk — A388

2013, Jan. 28   *Perf. 12*
845 A388 (5500r) multi   2.00   2.00

Botrychium Matricariifolium A389

Coracias Garrulus A390

2013, Jan. 31   *Perf. 12¼x12, 12x12¼*
846 A389 (5500r) multi   2.40   2.40
847 A390 (5800r) multi   2.50   2.50
  a.   Souvenir sheet of 2, #846-847   5.00   5.00

Endangered flora and fauna.

A391   A392

Embroidery A393

2013, Feb. 12   *Perf. 12*
848 A391 (3000r) multi   1.25   1.25
849 A392 (4500r) multi   1.90   1.90
850 A393 (5500r) multi   2.40   2.40
     Nos. 848-850 (3)   5.55   5.55

2012 Summer Olympics, London A387

2012, Dec. 21   *Perf. 12x12¼*
842 A385 (4500r) bronze & blk   1.75   1.75
843 A386 (5500r) sil & blk   2.10   2.10
844 A387 (5800r) gold & blk   2.25   2.25
     Nos. 842-844 (3)   6.10   6.10

Upupa Epops A394

2013, Mar. 12   *Perf. 13½x13*
851 A394 (5800r) multi   2.25   2.25

Khatyn Massacre, 70th Anniv. — A395

2013, Mar. 22
852 A395 (4500r) multi   2.00   2.00

Souvenir Sheet

Belarussian Landscape - Drecheluki Country Estate, by Yuliy Klever — A396

2013, Apr. 10   **Perf. 13x13½**
853 A396 15,000r multi   5.00 5.00

20th Intl. Telecommunications, Information and Banking Technologies Exhibition, Minsk — A397

2013, Apr. 23   **Perf. 12x12¼**
854 A397 (3000r) multi   1.40 1.40

Souvenir Sheet

Dancers — A398

No. 855: a, Kryzhachok dancers, Belarus (man without hat). b, Terekeme dancers, Azerbaijan (man with hat).

2013, Apr. 24   **Perf. 13½x13¼**
855 A398 5000r Sheet of 2, #a-b 3.50 3.50
See Azerbaijan No. 1020.

Peugeot Partner Mail Van A399

MAZ 437143-340 Mail Truck A400

2013, Apr. 29   **Perf. 12x12¼**
856 A399 (5500r) multi   2.25 2.25
857 A400 (5800r) multi   2.25 2.25
   a.   Souvenir sheet of 4, 2 each #856-857, + label   9.00 9.00
Europa.

Souvenir Sheet

St. Cyril of Turov (1130-82) — A401

Litho. With Foil Application
2013, May 11
858 A401 15,000r multi   5.00 5.00

National Academic Bolshoi Opera and Ballet Theater — A402

2013, May 22   **Litho.**   **Perf. 13x13½**
859 A402 (5500r) multi   2.25 2.25

Souvenir Sheet

Slavonic Alphabet of Saints Cyril and Methodius, 1150th Anniv. — A403

Litho. With Foil Application
2013, May 24   **Perf. 13½x13**
860 A403 15,000r multi   5.25 5.25

2013 Belarussian Presidency of the Commonwealth of Independent States — A404

2013, May 30   **Litho.**
861 A404 (4500r) multi   2.00 2.00

Souvenir Sheet

Diplomatic Relations Between Azerbaijan and Belarus, 20th Anniv. — A405

Litho. (Sheet Margin Litho. With Foil Application)
2013, June 11   **Perf. 12¼x12**
862 A405 15,000r multi   5.25 5.25
See Azerbaijan No. 1027.

Defense of Brest Fortress, 1941 — A406

2013, June 21   **Litho.**   **Perf. 13x13½**
863 A406 (5500r) multi   2.00 2.00

Souvenir Sheet

Madonna and Child Icon, National Sanctuary, Budslau, 400th Anniv. — A407

Litho. & Embossed (Sheet Margin Litho. With Foil Application)
2013, July 6   **Perf. 12x12¼**
864 A407 15,000r multi   5.25 5.25

Panthera Pardis Orientalis A408

Ovis Musimon A409

Haliaeetus Pelagicus A410

Panthera Tigris Altaica A411

2013, July 9   **Litho.**   **Perf. 12x12¼**
865 A408 (4000r) multi   1.50 1.50
866 A409 (5500r) multi   2.00 2.00
867 A410 (6500r) multi   2.50 2.50
868 A411 (7000r) multi   2.75 2.75
   a.   Souvenir sheet of 4, #865-868, + 2 labels   8.75 8.75
    Nos. 865-868 (4)   8.75 8.75
Animals in Belarusian zoos.

Belarussian State Puppet Theater, Minsk, 75th Anniv. A412

2013, July 10
869 A412 (5500r) multi   2.00 2.00

Souvenir Sheet

Christianization of Russia, 1025th Anniv. — A413

No. 870 — Icons depicting: a, The Lamentation of Christ, 19th cent. b, Old Testament Trinity, 18th cent. c, Christ Pantocrator, 18th cent.

Litho., Margin Litho. With Foil Application
2013, July 28   **Perf. 13½x13**
870 A413 5000r Sheet of 3, #a-c 5.25 5.25
See Russia No. 7466, Ukraine No. 930.

Tennis Players — A414

No. 871: a, Victoria Azarenka serving. b, Maxim Mirnyi chasing ball.

2013, Aug. 14   **Litho.**   **Perf. 13½x13**
871 A414 (7000r) Pair, #a-b   5.25 5.25

Arms of Bykhov — A415   Arms of Zhlobin — A416

2013   **Litho.**   **Perf. 14¼x14**
872 A415 (6500r) multi   2.25 2.25
873 A416 (6500r) multi   2.25 2.25
   Issued: No. 872, 8/20; No. 873, 9/4.

Mushrooms
A417   A418

Designs: No. 874, Hydnum repandum and spider. No. 875, Lactarius torminosus and beetle. No. 876, Cantharellus cinereus and ladybug. No. 877, Rozites caperatus, bird and pine cone.

2013, Sept. 10   **Litho.**   **Perf. 13x13½**
874 A417 (4000r) multi   1.40 1.40
875 A417 (4000r) multi   1.40 1.40
876 A418 (5500r) multi   1.90 1.90
877 A418 (5500r) multi   1.90 1.90
   a.   Souvenir sheet of 8, 2 each #874-877   13.50 13.50
    Nos. 874-877 (4)   6.60 6.60

234 BELARUS

Historical Means of Communication and Emblem of Regional Communications Commonwealth A419

2013, Oct. 9   Litho.   Perf. 13½x13
878 A419 (4000r) multi   1.60 1.60

Souvenir Sheet

Diplomatic Relations Between Belarus and Armenia, 20th Anniv. — A420

2013, Oct. 24   Litho.   Perf. 12¼x12
879 A420 15,000r multi   5.00 5.00

See Armenia No. 952.

Miniature Sheet

Israeli Leaders Born in Belarus — A421

No. 880: a, Yitzhak Shamir (1915-2012), prime minister. b, Chaim Weizmann (1874-1952), president. c, Shimon Peres (born 1923), president. d, Zalman Shazar (1889-1974), president. e, Menachem Begin (1913-92), prime minister.

Litho. With Foil Application
2013, Oct. 30   Perf. 12x12¼
880 A421 Sheet of 5 + la-
           bel   11.00 11.00
a.-b.   (4000r) Either single   1.60 1.60
c.-d.   (5500r) Either single   2.40 2.40
e.   (7000r) multi   3.00 3.00

Miniature Sheet

Animated Cartoons — A422

No. 881: a, The Wolf and the Ram (wolf and ram wearing stocking hats. b, Adventures of Nesterka (family in front of cabin). c, About the Girl Zhenya (girl and gate). d, A Small Fish Named Impossible (three fish). e, Pilipka (boy and witch with broom). f, Snow White and Rose Red (Snow White, dwarf and cat). g, Adventures of the Reactive Piglet (piglet and bird looking at book). h, The Centipede (centipede with ribbon).

2013, Nov. 1   Litho.   Perf. 13¼x13½
881 A422 (4000r) Sheet of 8,
          #a-h   12.50 12.50

Christmas — A423

New Year 2014 — A424

2013, Nov. 5   Litho.   Perf. 13
882 A423 (4000r) multi   1.50 1.50
883 A424 (6500r) multi   2.50 2.50
a.   Pair, #882-883   4.00 4.00

Nos. 882-883 were printed in sheets of 6 (3 of each stamp) + 2 labels.

Happy Postcrossing A425

2014, Jan. 2   Litho.   Perf. 12¼x12
884 A425 (5000r) multi   1.90 1.90

Hoarfrost, Tapestry by G. H. Stasevich A426

Horses, Tapestry by L. N. Gustova A427

2014, Jan. 4   Litho.   Perf. 14x14¼
885 A426 (1600r) multi   .60 .60
886 A427 (6500r) multi   2.40 2.40

Souvenir Sheet

Belarus Saints, Icon in Memorial Church of All Saints, Minsk — A428

No. 887: a, 30 saints facing right. b, 16 saints and church. c, 30 saints facing left.

Litho. With Foil Application
2014, Jan. 7   Perf. 13½x13
887 A428 (8000r) Sheet of 3,
          #a-c   8.75 8.75

Arkadi Kuleshov (1914-78), Poet — A429

2014, Feb. 6   Litho.   Perf. 13x13½
888 A429 (1600r) multi   .65 .65

Souvenir Sheet

2014 Winter Olympics, Sochi, Russia — A430

2014, Feb. 7   Litho.   Perf. 13x13½
889 A430 20,000r multi   6.00 6.00

2014 Ice Hockey World Championships, Minsk — A431

2014, Feb. 8   Litho.   Perf. 13x13½
890 A431 (6500r) multi   2.40 2.40

Surmas and Surma Player A432

Horum and Horum Player A433

2014, Mar. 6   Litho.   Perf. 13½x13
891 A432 (7500r) multi   2.75 2.75
892 A433 (8000r) multi   3.00 3.00
a.   Souvenir sheet of 6, 3 each
     #891-892, + 2 labels   17.50 17.50

Europa.

Cuculus Canorus A434

2014, Mar. 11   Litho.   Perf. 13½x13
893 A434 (5000r) multi   1.90 1.90

Floral Design From Sash Made in Slutsk A435

Litho. & Embossed
2014, Mar. 14   Perf. 13¼
894 A435 (5000r) multi   1.90 1.90

Intl. Year of Family Farming A436

2014, Mar. 18   Litho.   Perf. 12
895 A436 (7500r) multi   2.75 2.75

Miniature Sheet

Space Exploration — A437

No. 896: a, Pyotr Klimuk, first Belarussian cosmonaut in space, space station at left. b, Vladimir Kovalyonok, cosmonaut, space station at right. c, Belarussian satellite over earth. d, Oleg Novitskiy, cosmonaut, rocket launch at left.

2014, Apr. 12   Litho.   Perf. 13½x13
896 A437 (5000r) Sheet of 4, #a-
          d   7.25 7.25

Belarus in UNESCO, 60th Anniv. — A438

2014, Apr. 14   Litho.   Perf. 13x13½
897 A438 (5000r) multi   1.90 1.90

Souvenir Sheet

Liberation of Belarus, Russia and Ukraine From Nazi Occupation, 70th Anniv. — A439

2014, Apr. 18   Litho.   Perf. 13¼x13
898 A439 15,000r multi   4.75 4.75

See Russia No. 7520.

Trade Unions in Belarus, 110th Anniv. — A440

2014, Apr. 24   Litho.   Perf. 12x12¼
899 A440 (1600r) multi   .65   .65

No. 899 was printed in sheets of 8 + 4 central labels.

Nadezhda Skardino, Biathlon Bronze Medalist A441

Alla Tsuper, Gold Medalist in Women's Aerial Freestyle Skiing A442

Anton Kushnir, Gold Medalist in Men's Aerial Freestyle Skiing A443

Darya Domracheva, Biathlon Gold Medalist — A444

Litho. & Embossed
2014, May 2   Perf. 13½x13
900 A441 (6500r) multi   2.40 2.40
901 A442 (6500r) multi   2.40 2.40
902 A443 (6500r) multi   2.40 2.40
    Nos. 900-902 (3)   7.20 7.20
Souvenir Sheet
Perf.
903 A444 (8000r) multi   3.00 3.00

Souvenir Sheet

Flora and Fauna of Bogs — A445

No. 904: a, Tetrao tetrix. b, Pinus sylvestris, vert.

2014, May 14   Litho.   Perf. 12
904 A445 (8000r) Sheet of 2, #a-b   6.00 6.00

Grodno Regional Drama Theater — A446

2014, June 5   Litho.   Perf. 13x13½
905 A446 (5000r) multi   1.75 1.75

Yakub Kolas National Academic Drama Theater A447

2014, June 20   Litho.   Perf. 12x12¼
906 A447 (5000r) multi   1.75 1.75

Solidago Canadensis A448   Heracleum Sosnowskyi A449

Litho. & Embossed
2014, July 25   Perf. 12¼x12
907 A448 (1600r) multi   .60   .60
908 A449 (5000r) multi   1.75 1.75

Flowers in National Academy of Sciences Central Botanical Garden A450

Designs: No. 909, (6500r), Dahlia "Diadema." No. 910, (6500r), Paeonia "Pamyati Gagarina," vert. No. 911, (6500r), Rosa "Gloria Dei," vert. No. 912, (6500r), Lilium "Zorenka."

Perf. 12x12¼, 12¼x12
2014, Aug. 22   Litho.
909-912 A450 Set of 4   8.75 8.75
912a   Souvenir sheet of 4, #909-912, + central label   8.75 8.75

Nos. 909-912 were each issued in sheets of 4 + central label.

Arms and Tourist Attractions of Zaslawye — A451

2014, Sept. 5   Litho.   Perf. 13x13½
913 A451 (6500r) multi   2.25 2.25

Arms of Gorodok — A452

2014, Sept. 19   Litho.   Perf. 12
914 A452 (5000r) multi   1.75 1.75

New Year 2015 — A453

Christmas A454

2014, Oct. 2   Litho.   Perf. 13½x13¼
915 A453 (1600r) multi   .60   .60
916 A454 (7500r) multi   2.75 2.75

Souvenir Sheet

World Post Day — A455

2014, Oct. 9   Litho.   Perf. 12¼x12
917 A455 20,000r multi   5.00 5.00

Belarussian Exarchate, 25th Anniv. A456

Litho. With Foil Application
2014, Oct. 11   Perf. 13½x13
918 A456 (7500r) multi   2.75 2.75

National Art Museum, 75th Anniv. — A457

Litho. & Embossed With Foil Application
2014, Nov. 10   Perf. 13x13½
919 A457 (5000r) multi   1.75 1.75

Diplomatic Relations Between Belarus and Serbia, 20th Anniv. — A458

Litho., Margin Litho. With Foil Application
2014, Nov. 15   Perf. 12
920 A458 20,000r multi   6.00 6.00

Biathlon A459

2014, Nov. 20   Litho.   Perf. 12x12¼
921 A459 (6500r) multi   2.25 2.25

A460   A461

A462   Wildlife of Naliboki Forest — A463

2014, Nov. 27   Litho.   Perf. 12¼x12
922   Horiz. strip of 4   7.75 7.75
a. A460 (1600r) multi   .60   .60
b. A461 (5000r) multi   1.90 1.90
c. A462 (6500r) multi   2.40 2.40
d. A463 (7500r) multi   2.75 2.75
e. Booklet pane of 4, #922a-922d   7.75
    Complete booklet, #922e   7.75

Nyctereutes Procyonoides A464   Mustela Lutreola A465

Lepus Europaeus A466   Canis Lupus A467

Martes Martes — A468

2014, Dec. 10 Litho. *Die Cut*
Self-Adhesive

923	A464	(1600r) multi	.60	.60
924	A465	(5000r) multi	1.90	1.90
925	A466	(6500r) multi	2.40	2.40
926	A467	(7500r) multi	2.75	2.75
927	A468	(8000r) multi	3.00	3.00
	Nos. 923-927 (5)		10.65	10.65

Church of
Saints Simon
and Helena,
Minsk
A469

2015, Jan. 23 Litho. *Perf. 13½x13*

928	A469	(5000r) multi	1.90	1.90

MAZ-6440RA Truck — A470

BELAZ-75710 Dump Truck — A471

MZKT-600100 Truck — A472

AMKADOR
732
Backhoe
A473

Belarus
2422
Tractor
A474

2015, Jan. 30 Litho. *Perf. 14x14¼*

929		Vert. strip of 5	11.50	11.50
a.	A470	(6500r) multi	2.25	2.25
b.	A471	(6500r) multi	2.25	2.25
c.	A472	(6500r) multi	2.25	2.25
d.	A473	(6500r) multi	2.25	2.25
e.	A474	(6500r) multi	2.25	2.25

Souvenir Sheet

New Year 2015 (Year of the
Goat) — A475

**Litho. & Embossed With Foil
Application**
2015, Feb. 19 *Perf.*

930	A475	30,000r multi	7.25	7.25

A476

Victory in World War II, 70th
Anniv. — A477

Designs: No. 931, Soldiers with captured
Nazi flags.
No. 932: a, Soldiers with guns raised in victory. b, Soldiers celebrating in Berlin.

2015, Mar. 10 Litho. *Perf. 12x12¼*

931	A476	(7500r) multi	2.50	2.50

Souvenir Sheet
**Litho., Margin Litho. With Foil
Application**

932	A477	Sheet of 2	5.25	5.25
a.		(7500r) multi	2.50	2.50
b.		(8000r) multi	2.75	2.75

No. 931 was printed in sheets of 8 + label.

Francishak Bahushevich (1840-1900),
Poet — A478

2015, Mar. 21 Litho. *Perf. 12x12¼*

933	A478	(5000r) multi	1.90	1.90

Souvenir Sheet

Metropolitan Philaret of
Belarus — A479

**Litho., Margin Litho. With Foil
Application**
2015, Mar. 21 *Perf.*

934	A479	30,000r multi	7.00	7.00

20th
Belarussian
Energy and
Ecology
Congress,
Minsk
A480

2015, Mar. 26 Litho. *Perf. 12x12¼*

935	A480	(5000r) multi	1.90	1.90

Asio Otus — A481

2015, Apr. 1 Litho. *Perf. 13x13½*

936	A481	(8000r) multi	2.75	2.75

Rag
Dolls — A482

Wooden
Toys — A483

2015, Apr. 13 Litho. *Perf. 12¼x12*

937		Horiz. pair	5.25	5.25
a.	A482	(10,500r) multi	2.50	2.50
b.	A483	(12,000r) multi	2.75	2.75
c.		Souvenir sheet of 2, #937a-937b	5.25	5.25

Europa.

Souvenir Sheet

Francysk Skaryna (c. 1490-c.1551),
Book Printer — A484

**Litho., Margin Litho. With Foil
Application**
2015, Apr. 16 *Perf. 13x13½*

938	A484	20,000r blk & silver	4.75	4.75

Eurasian
Economic
Union
A485

2015, May 13 Litho. *Perf. 12x12¼*

939	A485	(10,500r) multi	2.50	2.50

Flowers of Central Botanical Garden of
the National Academy of Sciences,
Minsk
A486

Designs: No. 940, (7800r), Philadelphus
"Elbrus." No. 941, (7800r), Syringa "Vera
Horuzhaya." No. 942, (7800r), Paeonia suffruticosa. No. 943, (7800r), Rhododendron
"Akademik Smolskiy."

2015, May 29 Litho. *Perf. 12x12¼*

940-943	A486	Set of 4	7.50	7.50
943a		Souvenir sheet of 4, #940-943	7.50	7.50

Souvenir Sheet

St. Vladimir (c. 958-1015) — A487

Litho. With Foil Application
2015, June 20 *Perf.*

944	A487	30,000r gold & red	7.00	7.00

Arms of
Shchuchyn — A488

2015, Aug. 4 Litho. *Perf. 12*

945	A488	(7800r) multi	1.60	1.60

United Nations, 70th Anniv. — A489

Litho. & Embossed
2015, Aug. 11 *Perf. 13x13½*

946	A489	(10,500r) multi	2.10	2.10

Coccinella
Septempunctata
A490

Psyllobora Vigintiduopunctata — A491

Propylea
Quatuordecimpunctata — A492

Calvia Quatuordecimguttata — A493

Litho. & Embossed

2015, Aug. 26			Perf. 12	
947	A490	(3600r) multi	.70	.70
948	A491	(7800r) multi	1.60	1.60
948	A492	(9600r) multi	1.90	1.90
950	A493	(10,500r) multi	2.10	2.10
a.		Souvenir sheet of 4, #947-950	6.50	6.50
		Nos. 947-950 (4)	6.30	6.30

A494   A495

A496   Spermophilus Suslicus — A497

2015, Sept. 1		Litho.	Perf. 12	
951	A494	(3600r) multi	.70	.70
952	A495	(7800r) multi	1.60	1.60
953	A496	(9600r) multi	1.90	1.90
954	A497	(10,500r) multi	2.10	2.10
a.		Souvenir sheet of 4, #951-954	6.50	6.50
		Nos. 951-954 (4)	6.30	6.30

Worldwide Fund for Nature (WWF).

Brest Academic Drama Theater — A498

2015, Sept. 11	Litho.	Perf. 13x13½		
955	A498	(3600r) multi	.70	.70

Yanka Kupala National Academic Theater — A499

Litho. With Foil Application

2015, Sept. 14		Perf. 13½x13		
956	A499	(9600r) multi	1.90	1.90

The Lake, by Ossip Zadkine — A500

Landscape with a Red Roof, by Ossip Lubitch — A501

Designs: No. 958, Eva, by Chaim Soutine, vert. No. 960, Lovers, by Marc Chagall, vert.

Perf. 13x13½, 13½x13				
2015, Sept. 29			Litho.	
957	A500	(7800r) multi	1.60	1.60
958	A500	(7800r) multi	1.60	1.60
959	A501	(9600r) multi	1.90	1.90
960	A501	(9600r) multi	1.90	1.90
a.		Souvenir sheet of 4, #957-960	7.00	7.00
		Nos. 957-960 (4)	7.00	7.00

Hyla Arborea A502

Rana Temporaria A503

Rana Lessonae A504

Bombina Bombina A505

2015, Oct. 16		Litho.	Perf. 12	
961	A502	(3600r) multi	.70	.70
962	A503	(7800r) multi	1.60	1.60
963	A504	(9600r) multi	1.90	1.90
964	A505	(10,500r) multi	2.10	2.10
a.		Souvenir sheet of 4, #961-964	6.50	6.50
		Nos. 961-964 (4)	6.30	6.30

New Year 2016 A506

Christmas A507

2015, Nov. 3		Litho.	Perf. 12	
965	A506	(9600r) multi	1.90	1.90
966	A507	(10,500r) multi	2.10	2.10
a.		Souvenir sheet of 4, 2 each #965-966	8.00	8.00

Souvenir Sheet

Satellites — A508

No. 967: a, DZZ satellite, Belarus. b, Azerspace-1 satellite, Azerbaijan.

Litho., Sheet Margin Litho. With Foil Application

2015, Dec. 3			Perf.	
967	A508	20,000r Sheet of 2, #a-b	7.75	7.75

See Azerbaijan No. 1099.

Souvenir Sheet

Paintings by Belarussian and Chinese Artists — A509

No. 968: a, Summer (flowers and pots), by Valeriana Zholtok, 1977. b, Flash of Summer Lightning, the Song of Polesye (four birds in flight), by Gavriil Vashchenko, 1968-96. c, Aurochs, by Gennady Loyko, 1968. d, Bull, by Lui Da Wei, 2015. e, Peonies, by Guo Yi Cong, 1984. f, Crane, by Zhan Geng Xi, 2008.

2015, Dec. 15		Litho.	Perf. 12	
968	A509	Sheet of 6	10.50	10.50
a.		(3600r) multi	.60	.60
b.		(9300r) multi	1.60	1.60
c.-d.		(11,700r) Either single	1.90	1.90
e.		(12,600r) multi	2.10	2.10
f.		(14,400r) multi	2.40	2.40

Kalduny (Stuffed Dumplings) A510

2016, Jan. 18	Litho.	Perf. 13½x13		
969	A510	(12,600r) multi	2.10	2.10

Sarcochilus Sp. — A511

Zygopetalum Maculatum — A512

Dendrobium Unicum A513

Bulbophyllum Ornatissimum — A514

2016, Jan. 28		Litho.	Perf. 12	
970	A511	(3600r) multi	.60	.60
971	A512	(9300r) multi	1.60	1.60
972	A513	(11,700r) multi	1.90	1.90
973	A514	(12,600r) multi	2.10	2.10
a.		Souvenir sheet of 4, #970-973	6.25	6.25
		Nos. 970-973 (4)	6.20	6.20

Regional Commmunications Commonwealth, 25th Anniv. — A515

Litho. With Foil Application

2016, Feb. 2		Perf. 13x13½		
974	A515	(12,600r) multi	2.10	2.10

Carabus Cancellatus A516

Carabus Nitens A517

Carabus Intricatus A518

Carabus Clathratus A519

2016, Feb. 16		Litho.	Perf. 13½x13	
975	A516	(3600r) multi	.60	.60
976	A517	(9300r) multi	1.60	1.60
977	A518	(11,700r) multi	1.90	1.90
978	A519	(12,600r) multi	2.10	2.10
a.		Souvenir sheet of 4, #975-978	6.25	6.25
		Nos. 975-978 (4)	6.20	6.20

Endangered insects.

Bucephala Clangula A520

2016, Mar. 17	Litho.	Perf. 13½x13		
979	A520	(12,600r) multi	2.10	2.10

A521

Europa
A522

2016, Apr. 5   Litho.   Perf. 12
980   A521 (12,600r) multi   2.25 2.25
981   A522 (14,400r) multi   2.50 2.50
  a. Souvenir sheet of 4, 2 each
         #980-981   9.50 9.50
        Think Green Issue.

Belintersat-1 — A523

2016, Apr. 12   Litho.   Perf. 13¼
982   A523 (12,600r) multi   2.25 2.25

Souvenir Sheet

View With Cypress Trees, by Leon
Bakst (1866-1924) — A524

2016, May 11   Litho.   Perf. 13½x13
983   A524 (14,400r) multi   2.60 2.60

Eagles — A525

No. 984: a, Aquila nipalensis. b, Aquila
chrysaetos.

2016, May 12   Litho.   Perf. 12
984   A525 (12,600r) Pair, #a-b   4.50 4.50
        See Azerbaijan No. 1112.

Souvenir Sheet

2016 Summer Olympics, Rio de
Janeiro — A526

2016, June 7   Litho.   Perf.
985   A526 (14,400r) multi   2.60 2.60

Soldiers Defending Brest
Fortress — A527

Heroes of the Defense of Brest
Fortress — A528

No. 987: a, Ivan M. Zubachov (bald man). b,
Piotr M. Gavrilov (wearing medal). c, Andrey
M. Kizhevatov (wearing green collar insignia).

**Litho. & Embossed With Foil
Application**
2016, June 22   Perf. 13x13½
986   A527 (12,600r) multi   2.25 2.25
Souvenir Sheet
Litho. With Foil Application
Perf. 12
987   A528   Sheet of 3   4.50 4.50
  a. (3600r) multi   .65   .65
  b. (9300r) multi   1.75 1.75
  c. (11,700r) multi   2.10 2.10
        See Russia No. 7734.

Flag of
Belarus
A529

Belarus Coat of
Arms — A530

Design: (1.44r), Belarus coat of arms, diff.

Litho. With Foil Application
2016, July 3   Perf. 13½x13
988   A529 (36k) multi   .65   .65
Perf. 13x13½
989   A530 (1.26r) multi   2.25 2.25
Souvenir Sheet
Perf.
990   A530 (1.44r) multi   2.60 2.60
No. 990 contains one 40mm diameter stamp.

Souvenir Sheet

St. Sophia Cathedral, Polotsk — A531

**Litho., Sheet Margin Litho &
Embossed With Foil Application**
2016, July 4   Perf. 13x13½
991   A531 (1.44r) multi   2.60 2.60

Belarus Coat of
Arms — A532

2016, July 6   Litho.   Die Cut
Self-Adhesive
Frame Color
992   A532   1k light blue   .25   .25
993   A532   2k brown   .25   .25
994   A532   5k green   .25   .25
995   A532 10k yellow   .25   .25
996   A532 20k turquoise   .35   .35
997   A532 30k rose lilac   .55   .55
998   A532 50k gray   .90   .90
999   A532   1r blue   1.75 1.75
1000   A532   2r red   3.50 3.50
1001   A532   5r apple green   8.75 8.75
1002   A532 10r beige   17.50 17.50
1003   A532 20r violet   35.00 35.00
       Nos. 992-1003 (12)   69.30 69.30

Circus Venues and
Performers — A533

No. 1004: a, (36k), Clown juggling balls,
Gomel State Circus. b, (1.26r), Horses,
Belarusian State Circus.

2016, July 8   Litho.   Perf. 13x13½
1004   A533   Pair, #a-b   3.00 3.00

Souvenir Sheet

Beekeeping — A534

No. 1005: a, Apiarist and hives. b, Bee and
flower.

2016, Aug. 12   Litho.   Perf. 13¼
1005   A534 (1.44r) Sheet of 2, #a-
         b   5.25 5.25

Arms of
Rahachow — A535

2016, Aug. 16   Litho.   Perf. 14¼x14
1006   A535 (93k) multi   1.75 1.75

Commonwealth of Independent States,
25th Anniv. — A536

2016, Aug. 30   Litho.   Perf. 12
1007   A536 (1.44r) multi   2.60 2.60

Day of the
Preliminary
Investigation
Officer — A537

Litho. With Foil Application
2016, Sept. 6   Perf. 12
1008   A537 (1.26r) multi   2.10 2.10
No. 1008 was printed in sheets of 8 + central label.

26th Meeting of the Coordination
Council of Attorneys General of the
Commonwealth of Independent
States — A538

No. 1009 — Flag of Belarus and: a, Emblem
and office of Belarus Attorney General, date in
black. b, Emblem and office of Coordination
Council of Commonwealth of Independent
States, date in white.

2016, Sept. 7   Litho.   Perf. 12x12¼
1009   A538   Horiz. pair   2.75 2.75
  a. (36k) multi   .65   .65
  b. (1.26r) multi   2.10 2.10

Woodworking — A539

No. 1010 — Woodworker with mallet and: a,
Carving of a bull. b, Wooden flasks.

2016, Sept. 8   Litho.   Perf. 13x13½
1010   A539   Horiz. pair   2.75 2.75
  a. (36k) multi   .65   .65
  b. (1.26r) multi   2.10 2.10
Joint issue of the Republic of Belarus and
the Republic of Moldova.
See Moldova No. 922.

Belarus Customs
Service, 25th
Anniv. — A540

Litho. & Embossed
2016, Sept. 15   Perf. 12
1011   A540 (1.26r) multi   2.10 2.10

Statue of St. Sofia, Buildings and Coat of Arms of Slutsk — A541

2016, Sept. 16   Litho.   Perf. 13x13½
1012 A541 (1.17r) multi   2.00 2.00
First mention in writing of Slutsk, 900th anniv.

Souvenir Sheet

Icons — A542

No. 1013: a, Hodegetria from Peter and Paul Church, Halynka, 17th cent. b, St. Anthony of Padua and Jesus, Archangel Michael Church, Miratsichy, 1744.

Litho. & Embossed With Foil Application
2016, Sept. 29   Perf. 13½x13
1013 A542 (1.44r) Horiz. pair, #a-b   5.00 5.00

National Parks of Belarus and Pakistan — A543

No. 1014: a, Narachanski National Park, flag and arms of Belarus. b, Saiful Muluk National Park, flag and arms of Pakistan.

2016, Oct. 5   Litho.   Perf. 13x13½
1014 A543 Horiz. pair   2.75 2.75
 a.   (36k) multi   .65 .65
 b.   (1.26r) multi   2.10 2.10
See Pakistan No. 1238.

Arctia Caja A544

Nymphalis Antiopa A545

Zygaena Filipendulae A546

Smerinthus Ocellata A547

2016, Oct. 19   Litho.   Perf. 12
1015 A544 (36k) multi   .65 .65
1016 A545 (93k) multi   1.60 1.60
1017 A546 (1.17r) multi   2.00 2.00

1018 A547 (1.26r) multi   2.10 2.10
 a. Souvenir sheet of 4, #1015-1018   6.50 6.50
 Nos. 1015-1018 (4)   6.35 6.35

Snowflake — A548

Star of Bethlehem, Angels and Church — A549

Litho. With Foil Application
2016, Oct. 27   Perf. 13
1019 A548 (36k) multi   .80 .80
1020 A549 (1.26r) multi   3.00 3.00
 a. Souvenir sheet of 4, 2 each #1019-1020   7.75 7.75
New Year's Day and Christmas.

Souvenir Sheet

Medalists at 2016 Summer Olympics — A550

No. 1021: a, Seven bronze medalists and bronze medal. b, Four silver medalists and silver medal. c, Uladzislau Hancharou and trampolining gold medal, vert.

Perf. 13½x13, 13x13½
2016, Nov. 30   Litho.
1021 A550 Sheet of 3   8.00 8.00
 a.   (93k) multi   2.00 2.00
 b.   (1.26r) multi   2.75 2.75
 c.   (1.44r) multi   3.25 3.25

Miniature Sheet

Medalists at 2016 Summer Paralympics — A551

No. 1022: a, Aliaksandr Tryputs, javelin bronze medalist (26x30mm). b, Andrei Pranevich, fencing gold medalist holding épée (26x30mm). c, Uladzimir Izotau, swimming gold medalist, holding stuffed mascot (26x30mm). d, Ihar Boki, winner of 6 gold and 1 bronze swimming medals (26x37mm).

UNICEF, 70th Anniv. — A552

2016, Nov. 30   Litho.   Perf. 13x13½
1022 A551 Sheet of 4   10.00 10.00
 a.   (93k) multi   2.00 2.00
 b.-c. (1.17r) Either single 2.60 2.60
 d.   (1.26r) multi   2.75 2.75

2016, Dec. 8   Litho.   Perf. 13x13½
1023 A552 (1.26r) multi   2.75 2.75

Maksim Bahdanovich (1891-1917), Writer — A553

2016, Dec. 9   Litho.   Perf. 13x13½
1024 A553 (36k) multi   .85 .85

Postcrossing A554

2017, Jan. 3   Litho.   Die Cut
Self-Adhesive
1025 A554 (1.17r) multi   2.75 2.75

Bengal Cat — A555

Maine Coon Cat — A556

Scottish Fold Cat — A557

British Shorthair Cat — A558

2017, Jan. 18   Litho.   Perf. 12
1026 A555 (36k) multi   .80 .80
1027 A556 (36k) multi   .80 .80
1028 A557 (93k) multi   2.10 2.10
1029 A558 (93k) multi   2.10 2.10
 a. Souvenir sheet of 8, 2 each #1026-1029   12.00 12.00
 Nos. 1026-1029 (4)   5.80 5.80

Diplomatic Relations Between Belarus and People's Republic of China, 25th Anniv. A559

Litho. With Foil Application
2017, Jan. 20   Perf. 12
1030 A559 (1.26r) multi   2.75 2.75

French Bulldog — A560

Dachshund A561

Chihuahua A562

American Cocker Spaniel — A563

2017, Jan. 26   Litho.   Perf. 12
1031 A560 (36k) multi   .80 .80
1032 A561 (36k) multi   .80 .80
1033 A562 (93k) multi   2.10 2.10
1034 A563 (93k) multi   2.10 2.10
 a. Souvenir sheet of 8, 2 each #1031-1034   12.00 12.00
 Nos. 1031-1034 (4)   5.80 5.80

Crafts — A564

No. 1035: a, Woven straw horse. b, Pottery.

2017, Feb. 17   Litho.   Perf. 12
1035 A564 Pair + 2 labels   5.00 5.00
 a.   (93k) multi + label   2.25 2.25
 b.   (1.26r) multi + label   2.75 2.75

Souvenir Sheet

Belarusian Militia, Cent. — A565

No. 1036: a, Emblem of the Ministry of Internal Affairs (40mm diameter). b, Ministry of Internal Affairs Building (52x37mm).

Perf. (#1036a), Perf. 13x13½
Litho. with Foil Application
2017, Feb. 24
1036 A565 (1.44r) Sheet of 2, #a-
            b   6.50 6.50

Maskouskaya Metro Station,
Minsk — A566

Piatroushchyna Metro Station,
Minsk — A567

2017, Feb. 27   Litho.   **Perf. 13x13½**
1037 A566 (1.17r) multi   2.60 2.60
1038 A567 (1.17r) multi   2.60 2.60
  a.   Souvenir sheet of 4, 2 each
       #1037-1038   10.50 10.50

Souvenir Sheet

First Written Mention of Minsk, 950th
Anniv. — A568

Litho. With Foil Application
2017, Mar. 3   **Perf. 13x13½**
1039 A568 5r multi   10.00 10.00

Diplomatic
Relations
Between
Belarus
and Poland,
25th Anniv.
A569

Litho. With Foil Application
2017, Mar. 15   **Perf. 12**
1040 A569 (1.26r) multi   2.75 2.75

Galerida
Cristata
A570

2017, Mar. 22   Litho.   **Perf. 13½x13**
1041 A570 (1.26r) multi   2.75 2.75

Reconstructed Gate of Ruzhany
Palace — A571

Gomel
Palace
A572

2017, Apr. 20   Litho.   **Perf. 12**
1042 A571 (1.38r) multi   3.00 3.00
1043 A572 (1.56r) multi   3.25 3.25
  a.   Souvenir sheet of 4, 2 each
       #1042-1043   12.50 12.50

Europa.

Cricetus
Cricetus
A573

Mustela
Erminea
A574

Meles Meles
A575

Ursus Arctos
A576

2017, Apr. 27   Litho.   **Perf. 13½x13**
1044   Horiz. strip of 4   8.50 8.50
  a.   A573 (42k) multi   .85   .85
  b.   A574 (1.02r) multi   2.10 2.10
  c.   A575 (1.26r) multi   2.60 2.60
  d.   A576 (1.38r) multi   2.75 2.75
Endangered animals from Red Book of
Belarus.

Narcissus   Tulipa
"Holiday   "Armani" — A578
Sun" — A577

2017, May 3   Litho.   **Perf. 12**
1045 A577 (1.02r) multi   2.10 2.10
1046 A578 (1.38r) multi   2.75 2.75
  a.   Souvenir sheet of 4, 2 each
       #1045-1046   9.75 9.75
Flowers of Central Botanical Garden.

Minsk Horse-Drawn Rail Car in
Sabornaya Square — A579

Minsk Horse-Drawn Rail Car — A580

Conductor
and Empty
Car
A581

Minsk Horse-Drawn Rail Car on
Zaharyeuskaya Street — A582

2017, May 10   Litho.   **Perf. 12**
1047 A579   (42k) multi   .75   .75
1048 A580 (1.02r) multi   1.75 1.75
1049 A581 (1.26r) multi   2.10 2.10
1050 A582 (1.38r) multi   2.40 2.40
  a.   Souvenir sheet of 4, #1047-
       1050   7.00 7.00
   Nos. 1047-1050 (4)   7.00 7.00
Minsk Horse-Drawn Railway, 125th anniv.

Prosecutor's Office,
95th Anniv. — A583

Litho. With Foil Application
2017, June 22   **Perf. 12**
1051 A583 (1.38r) vio bl & gold 2.40 2.40

Horses — A584

No. 1052: a, New Kirgiz horse facing left. b,
Trakehner horse facing right.

2017, June 30   Litho.   **Perf. 12**
1052 A584 (1.38r) Pair, #a-b   4.75 4.75

World War II Memorial, Lion Statue,
Town Hall and Coat of Arms of
Mogilev — A585

2017, July 3   Litho.   **Perf. 12**
1053 A585 (1.26r) multi   2.25 2.25

Yanka Kupala
(1882-1942),
Writer
A586

**Litho. & Embossed With Foil
Application**
2017, July 7   **Perf. 13½x13**
1054 A586 (1.02r) multi   1.90 1.90

Diplomatic
Relations
Between
Belarus
and Latvia,
25th Anniv.
A587

**Litho. & Embossed With Foil
Application**
2017, July 19   **Perf. 12**
1055 A587 (1.38r) multi   2.50 2.50

Arms of
Polotsk — A588

2017, Aug. 24   Litho.   **Perf. 14¼x14**
1056 A588 (1.02r) multi   1.90 1.90

Souvenir Sheet

Book Printing in Belarus, 500th
Anniv. — A589

Litho. With Foil Application
2017, Sept. 1   **Perf. 12**
1057 A589 (1.56r) multi   2.75 2.75

Diplomatic
Relations
Between
Belarus and
India, 25th
Anniv.
A590

Litho. & Embossed With Foil Application
2017, Sept. 12   **Perf. 12**
1058 A590 (1.38r) multi   2.50 2.50
See India No.

Souvenir Sheet

Marker for Struve Geodetic Arc, Map of Triangulation in Belarus, and Józef Chodzko (1800-81), Surveyor — A591

2017, Sept. 14   **Litho.**   *Perf. 12*
1059 A591 3r multi   5.50 5.50

Coat of Arms and Tourist Attractions of Gomel — A592

2017, Sept. 16   **Litho.**   *Perf. 13*
1060 A592 (1.26r) multi   2.40 2.40

Diplomatic Relations Between Belarus and Kazakhstan, 25th Anniv. — A593

2017, Sept. 16   **Litho.**   *Perf. 12*
1061 A593 (1.38r) multi   2.60 2.60
See Kazakhstan No.

Christmas — A594

New Year's Day — A595

2017, Oct. 12   **Litho.**   *Perf. 13¼x13*
1062 A594 (42k) multi   .70 .70
1063 A595 (1.26r) multi   2.00 2.00
a.   Souvenir sheet of 4, 2 each #1062-1063   5.50 5.50

Souvenir Sheet

Diocese of Polotsk, 1025th Anniv. — A596

No. 1064: a, Annunciation Church, Vitebsk ("P" at LL). b, St. Sophia Cathedral, Polotsk ("P" at LR). c, Transfiguration Church, Polotsk ("P" atUR).

Litho. & Embossed, Sheet Margin Litho. & Embossed With Foil Application
2017, Oct. 26   **Perf. 12**
1064 A596 (1.56r) Sheet of 3, #a-c   8.75 8.75

Mir Interstate Television and Radio Company, 25th Anniv. A597

Litho. & Embossed
2017, Oct. 31   **Perf. 13½x13**
1065 A597 (42k) multi   .80 .80

Joint Issue of Belarus, Kazakhstan & Russia. See Kazakhstan No. , Russia No.

BELGIAN CONGO
'bel-jən 'käŋ,gō

LOCATION — Central Africa
GOVT. — Belgian colony
AREA — 902,082 sq. mi. (estimated)
POP. — 12,660,000 (1956)
CAPITAL — Léopoldville

Congo was an independent state, founded by Leopold II of Belgium, until 1908 when it was annexed to Belgium as a colony. In 1960 it became the independent Republic of the Congo. See Congo Democratic Republic and Zaire.

100 Centimes = 1 Franc

Catalogue values for unused stamps in this country are for Never Hinged items, beginning with Scott 187 in the regular postage section, Scott B32 in the semipostal section, Scott C17 in the airpost section, and Scott J8 in the postage due section.

Independent State
 A1   A2
King Leopold II — A3

1886   Unwmk.   Typo.   Perf. 15
1 A1 5c green   15.00 26.00
2 A1 10c rose   5.50 6.00
3 A2 25c blue   60.00 47.50
4 A3 50c olive green   9.00 9.00

5 A1 5fr lilac   400.00 350.00
a.   Perf. 14   1,100. 650.00
b.   5fr deep lilac   850.00 525.00
Nos. 1-5 (5)   489.50 438.50
Set, never hinged   1,100.
Counterfeits exist.
For surcharge see No. Q1.

King Leopold II — A4

1887-94
6 A4 5c grn ('89)   1.00 1.25
7 A4 10c rose ('89)   1.75 1.75
8 A4 25c blue ('89)   1.75 1.75
9 A4 50c reddish brn   67.50 32.50
10 A4 50c gray ('94)   4.00 22.50
11 A4 5fr violet   1,350. 550.00
12 A4 5fr gray ('92)   165.00 130.00
On portion of parcel wrapper   1,250.
13 A4 10fr buff ('91)   625.00 400.00
Nos. 6-13 (8)   2,216. 1,140.
Set, never hinged   3,500.

The 25fr amd 50fr in gray were not issued. Values, each $35.
Counterfeits exist of Nos. 10-13, 25fr and 50fr unused, used, genuine stamps with faked cancels and counterfeit stamps with genuine cancels.
For surcharges, see Nos. Q3-Q6.

Port Matadi — A5

River Scene on the Congo, Stanley Falls — A6

Inkissi Falls — A7

Railroad Bridge on M'pozo River — A8

Hunting Elephants A9

Bangala Chief and Wife — A10

1894-1901   **Engr.**   *Perf. 12½ to 15*
14 A5 5c pale bl & blk   19.00 19.00
15 A5 5c red brn & blk ('95)   4.50 1.75
16 A5 5c grn & blk ('00)   2.25 .60
17 A6 10c red brn & blk   19.00 19.00
18 A6 10c grnsh bl & blk ('95)   4.50 2.00
a.   Center inverted   3,000. 3,000.
19 A6 10c car & blk ('00)   4.75 1.10
20 A7 25c yel org & blk   5.25 3.75
21 A7 25c lt bl & blk ('00)   5.50 2.50
22 A8 50c grn & blk   2.00 2.00
23 A8 50c ol & blk ('00)   5.50 1.25

24 A9 1fr lilac & blk   32.50 17.50
a.   1fr rose lilac & black   475.00 37.50
25 A9 1fr car & blk ('01)   425.00 9.50
26 A10 5fr lake & blk   57.50 40.00
a.   5fr carmine rose & black   130.00 62.50
Nos. 14-26 (13)   587.25 119.95
Set, never hinged   1,100.

For overprintes see Nos. 31-32, 34, 36-37, 39.

Climbing Oil Palms — A11

Congo Canoe A12

1896
27 A11 15c ocher & blk   5.25 1.25
28 A12 40c bluish grn & blk   5.25 4.00
Set, never hinged   18.50

For overprints see Nos. 33, 35.

Congo Village A13

River Steamer on the Congo A14

1898
29 A13 3.50fr red & blk   200.00 145.00
a.   Perf. 14x12   575.00 350.00
30 A14 10fr yel grn & blk   160.00 50.00
a.   Center inverted   25,000.
b.   Perf. 12   800.00 52.50
c.   Perf. 12x14   500.00 —
As "c," pen canceled   21.00
Set, never hinged   550.00

Nos. 29-30 exist imperf. Value, set $850.
For overprints see Nos. 38, 40.

Belgian Congo

Overprinted

1908
31 A5 5c green & blk   8.75 8.00
a.   Handstamped   5.50 3.00
32 A6 10c car & blk   16.00 14.00
a.   Handstamped   5.50 3.00
33 A11 15c ocher & blk   9.25 8.00
a.   Handstamped   8.00 5.00
34 A7 25c lt blue & blk   5.75 3.00
a.   Handstamped   15.00 5.00
c.   Double overprint (#34)   300.00
35 A12 40c bluish grn & blk   3.25 3.00
a.   Handstamped   16.00 8.75
36 A8 50c olive & blk   6.25 3.00
a.   Handstamped   8.00 5.50
b.   As #36, inverted overprint   775.00
37 A9 1fr car & blk   27.50 8.50
a.   Handstamped   75.00 17.50
38 A13 3.50fr red & blk   42.50 30.00
a.   Handstamped   450.00 200.00
b.   As #38, inverted overprint   750.00
c.   As #38, double overprint   —
39 A10 5fr car & blk   75.00 37.50
a.   Handstamped   150.00 77.50
40 A14 10fr yel grn & blk   140.00 35.00
a.   Perf. 14½   375.00
b.   Handstamped   275.00 90.00
c.   Handstamped, perf. 14½   575.00 325.00
Nos. 31-40 (10)   334.25 150.00
Set, never hinged   800.00

Most of the above handstamps are also found inverted and double.

There are two types of handstamped overprints, those applied in Brussels and those applied locally. There are eight types of each overprint. Values listed are the lowest for each stamp.

Counterfeits of the handstamped overprints exist.

Imperf examples of No. 37 are proofs.

Port Matadi
A15

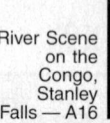

River Scene on the Congo, Stanley Falls — A16

Climbing Oil Palms — A17

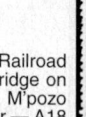

Railroad Bridge on M'pozo River — A18

1909   Perf. 14

41	A15	5c green & blk	1.00	1.00
42	A16	10c carmine & blk	1.00	.65
43	A17	15c ocher & blk	37.50	20.00
44	A18	50c olive & blk	4.25	2.75
		Nos. 41-44 (4)	43.75	24.40
		Set, never hinged	200.00	

Port Matadi
A19

River Scene on the Congo, Stanley Falls — A20

Climbing Oil Palms — A21

Inkissi Falls — A22

Congo Canoe
A23

Railroad Bridge on M'pozo River — A24

Hunting Elephants
A25

Congo Village
A26

Bangala Chief and Wife — A27

River Steamer on the Congo
A28

1910-15   Engr.   Perf. 14, 15

45	A19	5c green & blk	.75	.30
46	A20	10c carmine & blk	.75	.30
47	A21	15c ocher & blk	.70	.30
48	A21	15c grn & blk ('15)	.60	.25
a.		Booklet pane of 10	25.00	
49	A22	25c blue & blk	2.25	.60
50	A23	40c bluish grn & blk	3.25	2.50
51	A23	40c brn red & blk ('15)	5.50	3.00
52	A24	50c olive & blk	5.00	2.50
53	A24	50c brn lake & blk ('15)	9.50	3.00
54	A25	1fr carmine & blk	4.50	3.75
55	A25	1fr ol bis & blk ('15)	3.50	1.10
56	A26	3fr red & blk	23.00	14.50
57	A27	5fr carmine & blk	35.00	32.50
58	A27	5fr ocher & blk ('15)	2.50	1.25
59	A28	10fr green & blk	29.00	26.00
		Nos. 45-59 (15)	125.80	91.85
		Set, never hinged	370.00	

Nos. 48, 51, 53, 55 and 58 exist imperforate. Value, set $150.

For overprints and surcharges see Nos. 64-76, 81-86, B5-B9.

Port Matadi
A29

Stanley Falls, Congo River — A30

Inkissi Falls — A31

TEN CENTIMES.
Type I — Large white space at top of picture and two small white spots at lower edge. Vignette does not fill frame.
Type II — Vignette completely fills frame.

1915

60	A29	5c green & blk	.30	.25
a.		Booklet pane of 10	19.00	
61	A30	10c car & blk (II)	.30	.25
a.		10c carmine & black (I)	.30	.25
d.		Booklet pane of 10 (II)	25.00	
62	A31	25c blue & blk	1.50	.50
a.		Booklet pane of 10	125.00	
		Nos. 60-62 (3)	2.10	1.00
		Set, never hinged	8.00	

Nos. 60-62 exist imperforate. Value, set $15.

For surcharges see Nos. 77-80, 87, B1-B4.

For stamps of Belgian Congo overprinted "RUANDA", "URUNDI" or "EST AFRICAIN ALLEMAND OCCUPATION BELGE", see German East Africa.

Stamps of 1910 Issue Surcharged in Red or Black

1921

64	A23	5c on 40c bluish grn & blk (R)	.40	.40
65	A19	10c on 5c grn & blk (R)	.40	.40
66	A24	15c on 50c ol & blk (R)	.40	.40
a.		Inverted surcharge	275.00	
67	A21	25c on 15c ocher & blk (R)	2.75	1.40
68	A20	30c on 10c car & blk (R)	.75	.70
69	A22	50c on 25c bl & blk (R)	2.75	1.50
		Nos. 64-69 (6)	7.45	4.80
		Set, never hinged	13.00	

The position of the new value and the bars varies on Nos. 64 to 69.

No. 54 Overprinted

1921

70	A25	1fr carmine & blk	1.60	1.60
a.		Double overprint	125.00	
71	A26	3fr red & blk	4.00	3.50
72	A27	5fr carmine & blk	12.00	11.00
73	A28	10fr green & blk (R)	8.50	5.75
		Nos. 70-73 (4)	26.10	21.85
		Set, never hinged	67.50	

Belgian Surcharges

Nos. 51, 53, 60-62 Surcharged in Black or Red

1922

74	A24	5c on 50c	.65	.55
a.		Inverted surcharge	120.00	120.00
75	A29	10c on 5c (R)	.65	.50
76	A23	25c on 40c (R)	3.75	.60
77	A30	30c on 10c (II)	.40	.40
a.		30c on 10c (I)	.65	.35
b.		Double surcharge	7.50	7.50
c.		Inverted surcharge	190.00	190.00
78	A31	50c on 25c (R)	1.25	.45
a.		Inverted surcharge	190.00	190.00
		Nos. 74-78 (5)	6.70	2.50
		Set, never hinged	16.00	

No. 74 has the surcharge at each side.

Congo Surcharges
Nos. 60, 51 Surcharged in Red or Black

a

b

1922

80	A29	10c on 5c (R)	.70	.70
		Never hinged	2.25	
a.		Inverted surcharge	47.50	37.50
b.		Double surcharge	6.00	
c.		Double surch., one invtd.	50.00	
d.		Pair, one without surcharge	52.50	
e.		On No. 45	325.00	325.00
81	A23	25c on 40c	1.25	.65
		Never hinged	4.00	
a.		Inverted surcharge	47.50	37.50
b.		Double surcharge	6.75	
c.		"25c" double		
d.		25c on 5c, No. 60	225.00	225.00

Nos. 55, 58 Surcharged in Red

1922

84	A25	10c on 1fr (R)	.75	.60
		Never hinged	2.25	
a.		Double surcharge	17.50	
b.		Inverted surcharge	47.50	37.50
85	A27	25c on 5fr	2.50	2.50
		Never hinged	7.00	

Nos. 68, 77 Handstamped

86	A20	25c on 30c on 10c	25.00	22.50
		Never hinged	45.00	
87	A30	25c on 30c on 10c (II)	22.50	22.50
		Never hinged	42.50	

Nos. 86-87 exist with handstamp surcharge inverted.

Counterfeit handstamped surcharges exist.

Headdress — A32

Ubangi Man — A33

Watusi Cattle — A34

Basket Making — A35

Designs: No. 88, Ubangi woman. No. 89, Baluba woman. No. 90, Babuende woman. Nos. 91, 97, 106-108, Ubangi man. Nos. 92, 100-101, Weaving on loom. No. 93, Basket making. Nos. 94-96, 102, Wood carving. Nos. 98-99, Archer. Nos. 103-105, Making pottery. No. 109, Working rubber. No. 110, Making palm oil. No. 111, African elephant. Nos. 112-113, Watussi cattle.

1923-27 Engr. Perf. 12

88	A32	5c yellow	.35	.25
89	A33	10c green	.25	.25
90	A33	15c olive brown	.25	.25
91	A33	20c olive grn ('24)	.25	.25
92	A34	20c green ('26)	.50	.25
93	A35	25c red brown	.30	.25
94	A34	30c rose red ('24)	.65	.65
95	A34	30c olive grn ('25)	.30	.25
96	A34	35c green ('27)	.75	.45
97	A33	40c violet ('25)	.30	.25
98	A35	50c gray blue	.30	.25
99	A35	50c buff ('25)	.65	.25
100	A34	75c red orange	.30	.25
101	A34	75c gray bl ('25)	.65	.35
102	A34	75c salmon red ('26)	.30	.25
103	A35	1fr bister brown	.85	.40
104	A35	1fr dl blue ('25)	.65	.25
105	A35	1fr rose red ('27)	1.25	.25
106	A33	1.25fr dl blue ('26)	.95	.40
107	A33	1.50fr dl blue ('26)	.95	.30
108	A33	1.75fr dl blue ('27)	7.50	5.50
109	A35	3fr gray brn ('24)	6.00	3.25
110	A35	5fr gray ('24)	15.00	8.00
111	A35	10fr gray blk ('24)	27.50	15.00

1925-26

112	A34	45c dk vio ('26)	.70	.40
113	A34	60c carmine rose	.70	.30
		Nos. 88-113 (26)	68.15	38.50
		Set, never hinged	250.00	

For surcharges see Nos. 114, 136-138, 157.

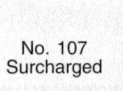

No. 107 Surcharged

1927, June 14

114	A32	1.75fr on 1.50fr dl bl	1.00	1.00
		Never hinged	2.00	

Sir Henry Morton Stanley — A45

1928, June 30 Perf. 14

115	A45	5c gray blk	.25	.25
116	A45	10c dp violet	.25	.25
117	A45	20c orange red	.50	.30
118	A45	35c green	1.25	.75
119	A45	40c red brown	.60	.25
120	A45	60c black brn	1.00	.50
121	A45	1fr carmine	.40	.25
122	A45	1.60fr dk gray	9.00	8.00
123	A45	1.75fr dp blue	2.00	1.00
124	A45	2fr dk brown	1.60	.95
125	A45	2.75fr red violet	9.00	.45
126	A45	3.50fr rose lake	1.60	1.10
127	A45	5fr slate grn	1.50	1.10
128	A45	10fr violet blue	2.00	1.10
129	A45	20fr claret	9.00	7.00
		Nos. 115-129 (15)	39.95	23.25
		Set, never hinged	130.00	

Sir Henry M. Stanley (1841-1904), explorer.
Nos. 115-129 exist in two sizes: 36mm and 37mm high.

Nos. 118, 121-123, 125-126 Surcharged in Red, Blue or Black

1931, Jan. 15

130	A45	40c on 35c	1.50	.65
131	A45	1.25fr on 1fr (Bl)	1.00	.25
132	A45	2fr on 1.60fr	1.50	.50
133	A45	2fr on 1.75fr	1.50	.40
134	A45	3.25fr on 2.75fr (Bk)	4.00	3.00
135	A45	3.25fr on 3.50fr (Bk)	8.75	7.50

Nos. 96, 108, 112 Surcharged in Red

Perf. 12½, 12

136	A44	40c on 35c grn	6.00	5.00
137	A44	50c on 45c dk vio	3.75	2.00

No. 108 Surcharged

138	A32	2(fr) on 1.75fr dl bl	18.50	16.00
		Nos. 130-138 (9)	46.50	35.30
		Set, never hinged	160.00	

View of Sankuru River — A46

Flute Players — A50

Designs: 15c, Kivu Kraal. 20c, Sankuru River rapids. 25c, Uele hut. 50c, Musicians of Lake Leopold II. 60c, Batetelas drummers. 75c, Mangbetu woman. 1fr, Domesticated elephant of Api. 1.25fr, Mangbetu chief. 1.50fr, 2fr, Village of Mondimbi. 2.50fr, 3.25fr, Okapi. 4fr, Canoes at Stanleyville. 5fr, Woman preparing cassava. 10fr, Baluba chief. 20fr, Young woman of Irumu.

1931-37 Engr. Perf. 11½

139	A46	10c gray brn ('32)	.25	.25
140	A46	15c gray ('32)	.25	.25
141	A46	20c brn lil ('32)	.25	.25
142	A46	25c dp blue ('32)	.25	.25
143	A50	25c dp grn ('32)	.30	.30
144	A46	50c violet ('32)	.25	.25
b.		Booklet pane of 8	7.00	
145	A50	60c vio brn ('32)	.30	.30
146	A50	75c rose ('32)	.30	.30
b.		Booklet pane of 8	5.50	
147	A50	1fr rose red ('32)	.30	.30
148	A50	1.25fr red brown	.30	.30
b.		Booklet pane of 8	5.50	
149	A46	1.50fr dk ol gray ('37)	.30	.30
b.		Booklet pane of 8	9.00	
150	A46	2fr ultra ('32)	.35	.30
151	A46	2.50fr dp blue ('37)	.50	.30
b.		Booklet pane of 8	15.00	
152	A46	3.25fr gray blk ('32)	.80	.50
153	A46	4fr dl vio ('32)	.50	.30
154	A50	5fr dp vio ('32)	1.00	.40
155	A50	10fr red ('32)	1.25	1.00
156	A50	20fr blk brn ('32)	2.50	1.50
		Nos. 139-156 (18)	9.95	7.35
		Set, never hinged	27.50	

No. 109 Surcharged in Red

1932, Mar. 15 Perf. 12

157	A44	3.25fr on 3fr gray brn	9.00	6.00
		Never hinged	27.00	

King Albert Memorial Issue

King Albert — A62

1934, May 7 Photo. Perf. 11½

158	A62	1.50fr black	1.25	.90
		Never hinged	3.00	

No. 158 exists imperf. Value, $67.50.

Leopold I, Leopold II, Albert I, Leopold III — A63

1935, Aug. 15 Engr. Perf. 12½x12

159	A63	50c green	1.75	1.00
160	A63	1.25fr dk carmine	1.75	.35
161	A63	1.50fr brown vio	1.75	.35
162	A63	2.40fr brown org	5.75	5.75
163	A63	2.50fr lt blue	5.75	2.00
164	A63	4fr brt violet	5.75	2.75
165	A63	5fr black brn	5.75	3.00
		Nos. 159-165 (7)	28.25	15.20
		Set, never hinged	80.00	

Founding of Congo Free State, 50th anniv. Nos. 159-165 exist imperf. Value set, $3,500.
For surcharges see Nos. B21-B22.

Molindi River — A64   Bamboos — A65

Suza River — A66   Rutshuru River — A67

Karisimbi A68

Mitumba Forest A69

1937-38 Photo. Perf. 11½

166	A64	5c purple & blk	.30	.25
167	A65	90c car & brn	.50	.35
168	A66	1.50fr dp red brn & blk	.40	.35
169	A67	2.40fr ol blk & brn	.35	.30
170	A68	2.50fr dp ultra & blk	.50	.50
171	A69	4.50fr dk grn & brn	.55	.45
172	A69	4.50fr car & sep	.50	.50
		Nos. 166-172 (7)	3.10	2.50
		Set, never hinged	7.50	

National Parks.

Nos. 166-171 were issued Mar. 1, 1938. Exist imperf. Value, set $100.

No. 172 was issued in sheets of four measuring 140x111mm. It was sold by subscription, the subscription closing Dec. 31, 1938. Value: unused $3.75. Exists imperf. Value, $1,250.

See No. B26. For surcharges see Nos. 184, 186.

King Albert Memorial, Leopoldville — A70

1941, Feb. 7 Litho. Perf. 11

173	A70	10c lt gray	.45	.30
174	A70	15c brown vio	.50	.30
175	A70	25c lt blue	.60	.45
176	A70	50c lt violet	.60	.30
177	A70	75c rose pink	2.00	.65
178	A70	1.25fr gray	.60	.50
179	A70	1.75fr orange	1.50	.65
180	A70	2.50fr carmine	1.10	.35
181	A70	2.75fr vio blue	1.50	1.10
182	A70	5fr lt olive grn	7.75	7.75
183	A70	10fr rose red	6.00	4.75
		Nos. 173-183 (11)	22.60	17.10
		Set, never hinged	90.00	

Exist imperforate. Value, set hinged, $120.00, used $62.50.
For surcharge see No. 185.

Nos. 168, 179, 169 Surcharged in Blue or Black

Nos. 184, 186   No. 185

1941-42 Perf. 11½, 11

184	A66	5c on 1.50fr (Bl)	.25	.25
a.		Inverted surcharge	27.50	27.50
185	A70	75c on 1.75fr ('42)	.50	.40
a.		Inverted surcharge	27.50	27.50
186	A67	2.50(fr) on 2.40fr ('42)	1.25	1.00
a.		Double surcharge	27.50	27.50
b.		Inverted surcharge	27.50	27.50
		Nos. 184-186 (3)	2.00	1.65
		Set, never hinged	5.00	

Catalogue values for unused stamps in this section, from this point to the end of the section, are for Never Hinged items.

A71

Oil Palms — A72

Congo Woman — A73

Leopard
A74

Askari — A75

Okapi
A76

Inscribed "Congo Belge Belgisch Congo"

1942, May 23   Engr.   Perf. 12½
187	A71	5c red	.25	.25
188	A72	10c olive grn	.25	.25
189	A72	15c brown car	.25	.25
190	A72	20c dp ultra	.25	.25
191	A72	25c brown vio	.25	.25
192	A72	30c blue	.25	.25
193	A72	50c dp green	.25	.25
194	A72	60c chestnut	.25	.25
195	A73	75c dl lil & blk	.35	.35
196	A73	1fr dk brn & blk	.35	.35
197	A73	1.25fr rose red & blk	.35	.35
198	A74	1.75fr dk gray brn	1.25	.90
199	A74	2fr ocher	1.25	.25
200	A74	2.50fr carmine	1.25	.25
201	A75	3.50fr dk ol grn	.75	.25
202	A75	5fr orange	1.25	.25
203	A75	6fr brt ultra	.75	.25
204	A75	7fr black	1.25	.25
205	A75	10fr dp brown	1.25	.25
206	A76	20fr plum & blk	14.50	1.25
		Nos. 187-206 (20)	26.55	6.65

Same Inscribed "Belgisch Congo Congo Belge"
207	A72	10c olive grn	.25	.25
208	A72	15c brown car	.25	.25
209	A72	20c dp ultra	.25	.25
210	A72	25c brown vio	.25	.25
211	A72	30c blue	.25	.25
212	A72	50c dp green	.25	.25
213	A72	60c chestnut	.25	.25
214	A73	75c dl lil & blk	.25	.25
215	A73	1fr dk brn & blk	.35	.35
216	A73	1.25fr rose red & blk	.35	.35
217	A74	1.75fr dk gray brn	1.00	.55
218	A74	2fr ocher	1.00	.25
219	A74	2.50fr carmine	1.00	.25
220	A75	3.50fr dk ol grn	.90	.25
221	A75	5fr orange	1.00	.25
222	A75	6fr brt ultra	.90	.25
223	A75	7fr black	1.00	.25
224	A75	10fr dp brown	1.00	.25
225	A76	20fr plum & blk	14.00	1.25
		Nos. 207-225 (19)	24.50	6.05

Miniature sheets of Nos. 193, 194, 197, 200, 211, 214, 217 and 219 were printed in 1944 by the Belgian Government in London and given to the Belgian political review, Message, which distributed them to its subscribers, one a month. Values per sheet: with selvage at left, about $100; without selvage at left, $35.

Remainders of these eight miniature sheets received marginal overprints in various colors in 1950, specifying a surtax of 100fr per sheet and paying tribute to the UPU. These sheets, together with four of Ruanda-Urundi, were sold by the Committee of Cultural Works (and not at post offices) in sets of 12 for 1,217.15 francs. Set value, $1,750.

Nos. 187-227 imperforate had no franking value. Value, set $275.

For surcharges see Nos. B34-B37.

Congo Woman — A77

Askari — A78

1943, Jan. 1
226	A77	50fr ultra & blk	11.00	1.60
227	A78	100fr car & blk	16.00	2.75

Slaves and Arab Guards
A79

Auguste Lambermont
A80

Design: 10fr, Leopold II.

Perf. 13x11½, 12½x12
1947   Engr.   Unwmk.
228	A79	1.25fr black brown	.35	.25
229	A80	3.50fr dark blue	.50	.25
230	A80	10fr red orange	1.50	.25
		Nos. 228-230 (3)	2.35	.75

50th anniv. of the abolition of slavery in Belgian Congo. See Nos. 261-262.

Baluba Carving of Former King — A82

Carved figures and masks of Baluba tribe: 10c, 50c, 2fr, "Ndoha," figure of tribal king. 15c, 70c, 1.20fr, 2.50fr, "Tshimanyi," an idol. 20c, 75c, 1.60fr, 3.50fr, "Buangakokoma," statue of kneeling beggar. 25c, 1fr, 2.40fr, 5fr, "Mbuta," sacred double cup, carved with two faces, Man and Woman. 40c, 1.25fr, 6fr, 8fr, "Ngadimuashi," female mask. 1.50fr, 3fr, 10fr, 50fr, "Buadi-Muadi," mask with squared features. 6.50fr, 20fr, 100fr, "Mbowa," executioner's mask with buffalo horns.

1947-50   Perf. 12½
231	A82	10c dp org ('48)	.30	.25
232	A82	15c ultra ('48)	.30	.25
233	A82	20c brt bl ('48)	.30	.25
234	A82	25c rose car ('48)	.30	.25
235	A82	40c violet ('48)	.30	.25
236	A82	50c olive brn	.30	.25
237	A82	70c yel grn ('48)	.30	.25
238	A82	75c magenta ('48)	.30	.25
239	A82	1fr yel org & dk vio	2.75	.25
240	A82	1.20fr gray & brn ('50)	.30	.25
241	A82	1.25fr lt bl grn & mag ('48)	.40	.25
242	A82	1.50fr ol & mag ('50)	18.00	5.00
243	A82	1.60fr bl gray & brt bl ('50)	.60	.25
244	A82	2fr org & mag ('48)	.40	.25
245	A82	2.40fr bl grn & dk grn ('50)	.50	.25
246	A82	2.50fr brn red & bl grn	.60	.25
247	A82	3fr lt ultra & ind ('49)	7.00	.25
248	A82	3.50fr lt bl & blk ('48)	6.00	.30
249	A82	5fr bis & mag ('48)	2.25	.25
250	A82	6fr brn org & ind ('48)	2.50	.25
251	A82	6.50fr red org & red brn ('49)	3.00	.40
252	A82	8fr gray bl & dk grn ('50)	3.25	.35
253	A82	10fr pale vio & red brn ('48)	42.50	.30
254	A82	20fr red org & vio brn ('48)	5.00	.40
255	A82	50fr dp org & blk ('48)	7.50	.40
256	A82	100fr crim & blk brn ('48)	10.00	.75
		Nos. 231-256 (26)	114.95	12.40

Railroad Train and Map — A83

1948, July 1   Unwmk.   Perf. 13½
| 257 | A83 | 2.50fr dp bl & grn | 1.40 | .50 |

50th anniv. of railway service in the Congo.

Globe and Ship
A84

1949, Nov. 21   Perf. 11½
Granite Paper
| 258 | A84 | 4fr violet blue | 1.25 | .60 |

75th anniv. of the UPU.

Allegorical Figure and Map — A85

1950, Aug. 12   Perf. 12x12½
259	A85	3fr blue & indigo	3.00	.35
260	A85	6.50fr car rose & blk brn	3.00	.35

Establishment of Katanga Province, 50th anniv.

Portrait Type of 1947

Designs: 1.50fr, Cardinal Lavigerie. 3fr, Baron Dhanis.

Perf. 12½x12
1951, June 25   Unwmk.
261	A80	1.50fr purple	2.75	.35
262	A80	3fr black brown	2.75	.35

Littonia — A86

10c, Dissotis. 15c, Protea. 20c, Vellozia. 40c, Ipomoea. 50c, Angraecum. 60c, Euphorbia. 75c, Ochna. 1fr, Hibiscus. 1.25fr, Protea. 1.50fr, Schrizoglossum. 2fr, Ansellia. 3fr, Costus. 4fr, Nymphaea. 5fr, Thunbergia. 6.50fr, Thonningia. 7fr, Gerbera. 8fr, Gloriosa. 10fr, Silene. 20fr, Aristolochia. 50fr, Eulophia. 100fr, Crytosepalum.

Granite Paper

1952-53   Photo.   Perf. 11½
Flowers in Natural Colors
Size: 21x25½mm
263	A86	10c multi	.35	.25
264	A86	15c multi	.25	.25
265	A86	20c multi	.30	.25
266	A86	25c shown	.35	.25
267	A86	40c multi	.35	.25
268	A86	50c multi	.70	.25
269	A86	60c multi	.60	.25
270	A86	75c multi	.80	.25
271	A86	1fr multi	.80	.25
272	A86	1.25fr multi ('53)	2.00	.50
273	A86	1.50fr multi	1.50	.25
274	A86	2fr multi	2.00	.25
275	A86	3fr multi	1.75	.25
276	A86	4fr multi	1.75	.25
277	A86	5fr multi	2.00	.25
278	A86	6.50fr multi	2.00	.25
279	A86	7fr multi	3.50	.25
280	A86	8fr multi ('53)	4.25	.35
281	A86	10fr multi ('53)	6.00	.50
282	A86	20fr multi	9.00	.50

Size: 22x32mm
283	A86	50fr multi ('53)	20.00	1.25
284	A86	100fr multi ('53)	27.50	2.00
		Nos. 263-284 (22)	87.75	9.10

Nos. 264, 269 and 270 with additional surcharges are varieties of Congo Democratic Republic Nos. 324, 327 and 328.

St. Francis Xavier — A86a

1953, Jan. 5   Engr.   Perf. 12½x13
| 285 | A86a | 1.50fr ultra & gray blk | .85 | .50 |

400th death anniv. of St. Francis Xavier.

Canoe on Lake Kivu — A87

1953, Jan. 5   Perf. 14
286	A87	3fr car & blk	3.25	.45
287	A87	7fr dp bl & brn org	3.25	.25

Issued to publicize the Kivu Festival, 1953.

Royal Colonial Institute Jubilee Medal
A88

Design: 6.50fr, Same with altered background and transposed inscriptions.

1954, Dec. 27   Photo.   Perf. 13½
288	A88	4.50fr indigo & gray	2.25	.75
289	A88	6.50fr dk grn & brn	1.75	.30

25th anniv. of the founding of the Belgian Royal Colonial Institute. Exist imperf. Value, set $45.

King Baudouin and Tropical Scene
A89

Designs: King and various views.

Inscribed "Congo Belge-Belgisch Congo"
Engr.; Portrait Photo.
1955, Feb. 15   Unwmk.   Perf. 11½
Portrait in Black
290	A89	1.50fr rose car	15.00	2.25
291	A89	3fr green	9.00	1.75
292	A89	4.50fr ultra	9.00	1.25
293	A89	6.50fr dp claret	14.00	.60

Inscribed "Belgisch Congo-Congo Belge"
294	A89	1.50fr rose car	15.00	2.25
295	A89	3fr green	9.00	1.75
296	A89	4.50fr ultra	9.00	1.25
297	A89	6.50fr deep claret	14.00	.60
		Nos. 290-297 (8)	94.00	11.70

Exist imperf. Value, set $325.

Map of Africa and Emblem of Royal Touring Club — A90

1955, July 26   Engr.   Perf. 11½
Inscription in French
298 A90 6.50fr vio blue   3.25   .50
Inscription in Flemish
299 A90 6.50fr vio blue   3.25   .50

5th International Congress of African Tourism, Elisabethville, July 26-Aug. 4. Nos. 298-299 printed in alternate rows.
Exist imperf. Value, set $40.

Kings of Belgium A91

1958, July 1   Unwmk.   Perf. 12½
300 A91 1fr rose vio   1.00   .25
301 A91 1.50fr ultra   1.00   .25
302 A91 3fr rose car   1.00   .25
303 A91 5fr green   1.75   .25
304 A91 6.50fr brn red   1.40   .25
305 A91 10fr dl vio   1.60   .25
   Nos. 300-305 (6)   7.75 1.80

Belgium's annexation of Congo, 50th anniv. Exist imperf. Value, set $80.

Roan Antelope — A92

Black Buffaloes A93

Designs: 20c, White rhinoceros. 40c, Giraffe. 50c, Thick-tailed bushbaby. 1fr, Gorilla. 2fr, Black-and-white colobus (monkey). 3fr, Elephants. 5fr, Okapis. 6.50fr, Impala. 8fr, Giant pangolin. 10fr, Eland and zebras.

1959, Oct. 15   Photo.   Perf. 11½
Granite Paper
306 A92 10c bl & brn   .30   .25
307 A93 20c red org & slate   .30   .25
308 A92 40c brn & bl   .30   .25
309 A93 50c brt ultra, red &
             sep   .30   .25
310 A92 1fr brn, grn & blk   .30   .25
311 A93 1.50fr blk & org yel   .40   .25
312 A92 2fr crim, blk & brn   .40   .25
313 A93 3fr blk, gray & lil rose   1.00   .25
314 A92 5fr brn, dk brn & brt
             grn   1.10   .25
315 A93 6.50fr bl, brn & org yel   1.25   .25
316 A92 8fr org brn, ol bis &
             lil   1.40   .40
317 A93 10fr multi   1.50   .25
   Nos. 306-317 (12)   8.55 3.15

Exist imperf. Value, set $100.

Madonna and Child — A94

1959, Dec. 1   Unwmk.   Perf. 11½
318 A94 50c golden brn, ocher &
             red brn   .25   .25
319 A94 1fr dk bl, pur & red brn   .25   .25
320 A94 2fr gray, brt bl & red
             brn   .40   .25
   Nos. 318-320 (3)   .90   .75

Exist imperf. Value, set $30.

Map of Africa and Symbolic Honeycomb A95

1960, Feb. 19   Unwmk.   Perf. 11½
Inscription in French
321 A95 3fr gray & red   .35   .25
Inscription in Flemish
322 A95 3fr gray & red   .35   .25

Commission for Technical Co-operation in Africa South of the Sahara (C. C. T. A.), 10th anniv. Exists imperf. Value, set $20.

SEMI-POSTAL STAMPS

Types of 1910-15 Issues Surcharged in Red

1918, May 15   Unwmk.   Perf. 14, 15
B1 A29 5c + 10c grn & bl   .50   .50
B2 A30 10c + 15c car & bl
            (I)   .50   .50
B3 A21 15c + 20c bl grn &
            bl   .50   .50
B4 A31 25c + 25c dp bl &
            pale bl   .50   .50
B5 A23 40c + 40c brn red
            & bl   .75   .75
B6 A24 50c + 50c brn lake
            & bl   .75   .75
B7 A25 1fr + 1fr ol bis &
            bl   3.00 3.00
B8 A27 5fr + 5fr ocher &
            bl   15.00 15.00
B9 A28 10fr + 10fr grn & bl 160.00 160.00
   Nos. B1-B9 (9)   181.50 181.50
   Set, never hinged   525.00

The position of the cross and the added value varies on the different stamps.
Nos. B1-B9 exist imperforate without gum. Value, set $600.
Perf 15 examples of Nos. B1-B6 are worth approximately twice the values shown.
For overprints, see German East Africa Nos. NB1-NB9.

SP1

Design: No. B11, Inscribed "Belgisch Congo."

1925, July 8   Perf. 12½
B10 SP1 25c + 25c car & blk   .40   .40
B11 SP1 25c + 25c car & blk   .40   .40
   a. Pair, Nos. B10-B11   1.00 1.00
        Never hinged   1.60

Colonial campaigns in 1914-1918. The surtax helped erect at Kinshasa a monument to those who died in World War I.

Nurse Weighing Child — SP3

First Aid Station SP5

Designs: 20c+10c, Missionary & Child. 60c+30c, Congo hospital. 1fr+50c, Dispensary service. 1.75fr+75c, Convalescent area. 3.50fr+1.50fr, Instruction on bathing infant. 5fr+2.50fr, Operating room. 10fr+5fr, Students.

1930, Jan. 16   Engr.   Perf. 11½
B12 SP3 10c + 5c ver   1.00 1.00
B13 SP3 20c + 10c dp brn   1.25 1.25
B14 SP3 35c + 15c dp grn   1.90 1.90
B15 SP5 60c + 30c dl vio   2.25 2.25
B16 SP3 1fr + 50c dk car   3.75 3.75
B17 SP5 1.75fr + 75c dp bl   8.75 8.75
B18 SP5 3.50fr + 1.50fr rose
            lake   11.00 11.00
B19 SP5 5fr + 2.50fr red
            brn   15.00 15.00
B20 SP5 10fr + 5fr gray blk   17.50 17.50
   Nos. B12-B20 (9)   62.40 62.40
   Set, never hinged   160.00

The surtax was intended to aid welfare work among the natives, especially the children.

Nos. 161, 163 Surcharged "+50c" in Blue or Red

1936, May 15   Perf. 12½x12
B21 A63 1.50fr + 50c (Bl)   8.75 5.75
B22 A63 2.50fr + 50c (R)   4.50 3.00
   Set, never hinged   25.00

Surtax was for the King Albert Memorial Fund.

Queen Astrid with Congolese Children — SP12

1936, Aug. 29   Photo.   Perf. 12½
B23 SP12 1.25fr + 5c dk brn   .65   .65
B24 SP12 1.50fr + 10c dull
             rose   .65   .65
B25 SP12 2.50fr + 25c dk blue 1.25 1.25
   Nos. B23-B25 (3)   2.55 2.55
   Set, never hinged   7.00

Issued in memory of Queen Astrid. The surtax was for the aid of the National League for Protection of Native Children.

Souvenir Sheet

National Parks — SP13

1938, Oct. 3   Perf. 11½
Star in Yellow
B26 SP13 Sheet of 6   67.50 67.50
             Never hinged   130.00
             On first day cover   80.00
   a. 5c ultra & light brown   6.00 6.00
   b. 90c ultra & light brown 6.00 6.00
   c. 1.50fr ultra & light brown 6.00 6.00
   d. 2.40fr ultra & light brown 6.00 6.00
   e. 2.50fr ultra & light brown 6.00 6.00
   f. 4.50fr ultra & light brown 6.00 6.00

Intl. Tourist Cong. A surtax of 3.15fr was for the benefit of the Congo Tourist Service. Exists imperf. Value $1,350.

Marabou Storks and Vultures — SP14

Buffon's Kob — SP15

Designs: 1.50fr+1.50fr, Pygmy chimpanzees. 4.50fr+4.50fr, Dwarf crocodiles. 5fr+5fr, Lioness.

1939, June 6   Photo.   Perf. 14
B27 SP14 1fr + 1fr dp claret 10.00 *12.00*
B28 SP15 1.25fr + 1.25fr car 10.00 *12.00*
B29 SP15 1.50fr + 1.50fr brt
             pur   10.00 *12.00*
B30 SP14 4.50fr + 4.50fr sl grn 10.00 *12.00*
B31 SP15 5fr + 5fr brown   10.00 *12.00*
   Nos. B27-B31 (5)   50.00 *60.00*
   Set, never hinged   95.00

Surtax for the Leopoldville Zoological Gardens. Exists imperf. Value, set $225.
Sold in full sets by subscription.

> **Catalogue values for unused stamps in this section, from this point to the end of the section, are for Never Hinged items.**

Lion of Belgium and Inscription "Belgium Shall Rise Again" — SP19

1942, Feb. 17   Engr.   Perf. 12½
B32 SP19 10fr + 40fr brt grn   3.00 3.00
B33 SP19 10fr + 40fr vio bl   3.00 3.00

Nos. 193, 216, 198 and 220 Surcharged in Red

a

b

c

1945
B34 A72 (a) 50c + 50fr   6.00 3.50
B35 A73 (b) 1.25fr + 100fr   6.00 3.50
B36 A74 (c) 1.75fr + 100fr   6.00 3.50
B37 A75 (b) 3.50fr + 100fr   6.00 3.50
   Nos. B34-B37 (4)   24.00 *14.00*

The surtax was for the Red Cross. Sold in full sets by subscription.

Mozart at Age
7 — SP20

Queen Elisabeth and Sonata by
Mozart — SP21

Perf. 11½

1956, Oct. 10   Unwmk.   Engr.

B38	SP20	4.50fr + 1.50fr brt lil	6.50	2.75
B39	SP21	6.50fr + 2.50fr ultra	9.00	3.75

200th anniv. of the birth of Wolfgang
Amadeus Mozart. Exist imperf.
The surtax was for the Pro-Mozart
Committee.
Exist imperf. Value, set $110.

Nurse and
Children
SP22

Designs: 4.50fr+50c, Patient receiving injection. 6.50fr+40c, Patient being bandaged.

1957, Dec. 10   Photo.   Perf. 13x10½
Cross in Carmine

B40	SP22	3fr + 50c dk bl	1.25	.55
B41	SP22	4.50fr + 50c dk grn	1.40	.55
B42	SP22	6.50fr + 50c red brn	1.60	.75
		Nos. B40-B42 (3)	4.25	1.85

The surtax was for the Red Cross.
Exist imperf. Value, set $100.

High Jump
SP23

1960, May 2   Unwmk.   Perf. 13½

B43	SP23	50c + 25c shown	.60	.35
B44	SP23	1.50fr + 50c Hurdles	.85	.35
B45	SP23	2fr + 1fr Soccer	1.00	.35
B46	SP23	3fr + 1.25fr Javelin	1.40	.95
B47	SP23	6.50fr + 3.50fr Discus	1.60	1.00
		Nos. B43-B47 (5)	5.45	3.00

17th Olympic Games, Rome, Aug. 25-Sept.
11. The surtax was for the youth of Congo.
Exist imperf. Value, set $140.

AIR POST STAMPS

Wharf on
Congo
River
AP1

Congo
"Country
Store"
AP2

View of
Congo
River
AP3

Stronghold in the
Interior — AP4

Unwmk.
1920, July 1   Engr.   Perf. 12

C1	AP1	50c orange & blk	.70	.25
C2	AP2	1fr dull vio & blk	.75	.25
C3	AP3	2fr blue & blk	1.10	.50
C4	AP4	5fr green & blk	2.00	.90
		Nos. C1-C4 (4)	4.55	1.90
		Set, never hinged	14.00	

Kraal
AP5

Porters
on Safari
AP6

1930, Apr. 2

C5	AP5	15fr dk brn & blk	3.25	1.10
C6	AP6	30fr brn vio & blk	3.50	1.75
		Set, never hinged	22.50	

Fokker F VII
over Congo
AP7

1934, Jan. 22   Perf. 13½x14

C7	AP7	50c gray black	.30	.25
C8	AP7	1fr dk carmine	.50	.25
a.		Booklet pane of 8	8.00	
C9	AP7	1.50fr green	.50	.25
C10	AP7	3fr brown	.35	.25
C11	AP7	4.50fr brt ultra	.60	.25
a.		Booklet pane of 8	14.00	
C12	AP7	5fr red brown	.45	.25
C13	AP7	15fr brown vio	1.00	.50
C14	AP7	30fr red orange	2.00	1.75
C15	AP7	50fr violet	5.50	3.00
		Nos. C7-C15 (9)	11.20	6.85
		Set, never hinged	27.50	

The 1fr, 3fr, 4.50fr, 5fr, 15fr exist imperf.
Values: 3fr, $37.50; 5fr, $60; 15fr, $32.50.

**No. C10 Surcharged in Blue with
New Value and Bars**

1936, Mar. 25

C16	AP7	3.50fr on 3fr brown	.60	.25
		Never hinged	1.25	

> Catalogue values for unused
> stamps in this section, from this
> point to the end of the section, are
> for Never Hinged items.

No. C9
Surcharged
in Black

1942, Apr. 27

C17	AP7	50c on 1.50fr green	1.25	.40
a.		Inverted surcharge	50.00	19.00

POSTAGE DUE STAMPS

In 1908-23 regular postage stamps
handstamped "TAXES" or "TAXE," usually boxed, were used in lieu of postage
due stamps.

D1

1923   Typo.   Unwmk.   Perf. 14

J1	D1	5c black brown	.25	.25
J2	D1	10c rose red	.25	.25
J3	D1	15c violet	.25	.25
J4	D1	30c green	.30	.25
J5	D1	50c ultramarine	.40	.35
J6	D1	50c blue ('29)	.45	.35
J7	D1	1fr gray	.55	.40
		Nos. J1-J7 (7)	2.45	2.10
		Set, never hinged	6.00	

Nos. J1-J7 exist imperf. Value, set $37.50.

> Catalogue values for unused
> stamps in this section, from this
> point to the end of the section, are
> for Never Hinged items.

D2

1943   Perf. 14x14½

J8	D2	10c olive green	.30	.25
J9	D2	20c dark ultramarine	.30	.25
J10	D2	50c green	.30	.25
J11	D2	1fr dark brown	.30	.25
J12	D2	2fr yellow orange	.30	.25
		Nos. J8-J12 (5)	1.50	1.25

1943   Perf. 12½

J8a	D2	10c olive green	.90	.30
J9a	D2	20c dark ultramarine	.90	.30
J10a	D2	50c green	.90	.30
J11a	D2	1fr dark brown	.95	.50
J12a	D2	2fr yellow orange	1.60	.50
		Nos. J8a-J12a (5)	5.25	1.90

D3

1957   Engr.   Perf. 11½

J13	D3	10c olive brown	.35	.25
J14	D3	20c claret	.55	.25
J15	D3	50c green	.55	.25
J16	D3	1fr light blue	.55	.30
J17	D3	2fr vermilion	.65	.45
J18	D3	4fr	.80	.60
J19	D3	6fr violet blue	1.10	.60
		Nos. J13-J19 (7)	4.55	2.70

Exist imperf. Value, set $20.

PARCEL POST STAMPS

Nos. 5, 11-12 Handstamped
Surcharges in Black or Blue

No. Q1

No. Q3

No. Q4

1887-93   Unwmk.   Perf. 15

Q1	A1	3.50fr on 5fr lil	1,400.	1,000.
Q3	A4	3.50fr on 5fr vio	1,200.	675.00
Q4	A4	3.50fr on 5fr vio		
		('88)	950.00	550.00
Q6	A4	3.50fr on 5fr gray		
		('93)	190.00	190.00
		Never hinged	300.00	

Nos. Q1, Q3-Q4, and Q6 are known with
inverted surcharge and double surcharge, and
No. Q6 in pair with unsurcharged stamp.
These varieties sell for somewhat more than
the normal surcharges.

Genuine stamps with counterfeit
surcharges, counterfeit stamps with counterfeit surcharges, and both with counterfeit
cancels exist.

BELGIUM
ˈbel-jəm

LOCATION — Western Europe, border-
ing the North Sea
GOVT. — Constitutional Monarchy
AREA — 11,778 sq. mi.
POP. — 10,396,421 (2004)
CAPITAL — Brussels

100 Centimes = 1 Franc
100 Cents = 1 Euro (2002)

Catalogue values for unused
stamps in this country are for
Never Hinged items, beginning
with Scott 322 in the regular postage section, Scott B370 in the
semi-postal section, Scott C8 in
the airpost section, Scott CB1 in
the airpost semi-postal section,
Scott F1 in the registration stamp
section, Scott J40 in the postage
due section, Scott M1 in the military stamp section, Scott O36 in
the officials section, and Scott
Q267 in the parcel post section.

Watermarks

Wmk. 96
(With Frame)

Wmk. 96a
(No Frame)

King Leopold I — A1

Wmk. Two "L's" Framed (96)

1849	Engr.		Imperf.
1	A1	10c brown	2,600.	100.00
a.		10c red brown	4,300.	425.00
b.		10c bister brown	2,900.	140.00
c.		10c dark brown	2,650.	85.00
2	A1	20c blue	2,650.	57.50
a.		20c milky blue	3,700.	160.00
b.		20c greenish blue	3,900.	290.00

The reprints are on thick and thin wove and
thick laid paper unwatermarked.
A pale blue shade exists that is often confused with the milky blue.
A souvenir sheet containing reproductions
of the 10c, 20c and 40c of 1849-51 with black
burelage on back was issued Oct. 17, 1949,
for the cent. of the 1st Belgian stamps. It was
sold at BEPITEC 1949, an intl. stamp exhib. at
Brussels, and was not valid. Value, $15.

King Leopold I — A2

1849-50		Thin Paper
3	A2 10c brown ('50)	2,500.	100.00
4	A2 20c blue ('50)	2,200.	62.50
5	A2 40c carmine rose	2,000.	525.00

Nos. 3-5 were printed on both thick and thin
paper. See *Scott Classic Specialized Catalog
of Stamps & Covers* for detailed listings.

Wmk. Two "L's" Without Frame (96a)

1851-54			
6	A2 10c brown	625.00	8.50
a.	Ribbed paper ('54)	1,000.	62.50

7	A2 20c blue	800.00	8.00
a.	Ribbed paper ('54)	1,000.	62.50
8	A2 40c car rose	4,250.	110.00
a.	Ribbed paper ('54)	5,000.	260.00

Nos. 6-8 were printed on both thin and thick
paper. See *Scott Classic Specialized Catalogue of Stamps & Covers* for detailed listings.
Nos. 6a, 7a, 8a must have regular and parallel ribs covering the whole stamp.

1858-61		Unwmk.
Stamps 17½x22mm; Oval 17¼high		
9	A2 1c green ('61)	225.00	125.00
10	A2 10c brown	475.00	9.00
11	A2 20c blue	500.00	9.00
12	A2 40c vermilion	3,750.	150.00

Nos. 9 and 13 were valid for postage on
newspapers and printed matter only.
Nos. 10-12 were printed in two sizes: 21mm
high (with a 16½mm high oval) and 22mm
high (with a 17¼mm high oval). The 22mm
high stamps were issued in 1861. See *Scott
Classic Specialized Catalogue of Stamps &
Covers* for detailed listings.
*Reprints of Nos. 9 to 12 are on thin wove
paper. The colors are brighter than those of
the originals. They were made from the dies
and show lines outside the stamps.*

Values for Nos. 13-16 are for
stamps with perfs cutting into the
design. Values for perforated stamps
from Nos. 17 through 107 are for
examples with perforations touching
the design on one or two sides.
Stamps with all perforations clear are
exceptional and command substantial premiums.

1863-65		Perf. 14½
13	A2 1c green	62.50	26.00
14	A2 10c brown	80.00	3.75
15	A2 20c blue	80.00	3.50
16	A2 40c carmine rose	450.00	25.00
	Nos. 13-16 (4)	672.50	58.25

Nos. 13-16 also come perf 12½ and
12½x13½, which were issued in 1863. Values
differ. See the *Scott Classic Specialized Catalogue* for detailed listings.

King Leopold I — A3a
A3

A4   A4a

A5

London Print

1865	Typo.	Perf. 14
17	A5 1fr pale violet	1,750.	110.00

Brussels Print
Thick or Thin Paper

1865-67		Perf. 15, 14½x14
18	A3 10c slate ('67)	185.00	2.25
b.	Pair, imperf. between		
19	A3a 20c blue ('67)	290.00	2.00
20	A4 30c brown ('67)	625.00	11.00
b.	Pair, imperf. between	2,000.	
21	A4a 40c rose ('67)	775.00	20.00
22	A5 1fr violet	2,000.	97.50

Nos. 18-22 are valued as perf. 15. Nos. 18-
22 also come perf. 14½x14, issued in 1865-
66. Values differ. See the *Scott Classic Specialized Catalogue.* Nos. 18b and 20b are from
the earlier printings.
*The reprints are on thin paper, imperforate
and ungummed.*

Coat of Arms — A6

1866-67		Imperf.
23	A6 1c gray	250.00	150.00
	Perf. 15, 14½x14		
24a	A6 1c gray	45.00	16.00
25b	A6 2c blue ('67)	140.00	90.00
26b	A6 5c brown	175.00	90.00
	Nos. 23-26b (4)	610.00	346.00

Nos. 23-26b were valid for postage on
newspapers and printed matter only.
Values are for perf. 15 stamps. Values for
14½x14 differ. See the *Scott Classic Specialized Catalogue* for detailed listings.
Counterfeits exist.
*Reprints of Nos. 24-26 are on thin paper,
imperforate and without gum.*

Imperf. varieties of 1869-1912
(between Nos. 28-105) are without
gum.

A7   A8

A9   A10

A11   King Leopold
II — A12

1869-70		Perf. 15
28	A7 1c green	8.25	.40
29	A7 2c ultra ('70)	25.00	1.65
30	A7 5c buff ('70)	62.50	.75
31	A7 8c lilac ('70)	67.50	50.00
32	A8 10c green	27.50	.40
33	A9 20c lt ultra ('70)	125.00	.90
34	A10 30c buff ('70)	80.00	4.00
35	A11 40c brt rose ('70)	135.00	6.50
36	A12 1fr dull lilac ('70)	400.00	17.00
	1fr rose lilac	500.00	20.00
	Never hinged	850.00	
	Nos. 28-36 (9)	930.75	81.60

The frames and inscriptions of Nos. 30, 31
and 42 differ slightly from the illustration.
Minor "broken letter" varieties exist on several values.
Nos. 28-30, 32-33, 35-38 also were printed
in aniline colors. These are not valued
separately.
Nos. 28-36 exist imperforate, without gum.
The 1c and 2c are valued from $55 to $85.
The 40c and 1fr stamps are scarcer, valued
from $500 to $675. Some denominations exist
with gum. Pairs command premiums. Large
multiples are scarce.
See Nos. 40-43, 49-51, 55.

A13   A14

King Leopold II — A15

1875-78			
37	A13 25c olive bister	165.00	1.45
a.	25c ocher	185.00	1.55
38	A14 50c gray	275.00	11.00
	Roller cancel		12.50
a.	50c gray black	325.00	50.00
b.	50c deep black	1,750.	250.00
39	A15 5fr dp red brown	1,700.	1,450.
	Roller cancel		700.00
a.	5fr pale brown ('78)	3,750.	1,450.
	Roller cancel		700.00

No. 37 exists imperforate, without gum.
Value, $250.
Dangerous counterfeits of No. 39 exist.

Printed in Aniline Colors

1881		Perf. 14
40	A7 1c gray green	18.00	.85
41	A7 2c lt ultra	19.00	3.00
42	A7 5c orange buff	55.00	1.25
a.	5c red orange	55.00	1.25
43	A8 10c gray green	27.50	1.10
44	A13 25c olive bister	95.00	3.00
	Nos. 40-44 (5)	214.50	9.20

See note following No. 36.

A16   A17

A18   A19

1883			
45	A16 10c carmine	27.50	2.50
46	A17 20c gray	175.00	10.00
47	A18 25c blue	360.00	35.00
	Roller cancel		15.00
48	A19 50c violet	325.00	35.00
	Roller cancel		15.00
	Nos. 45-48 (4)	887.50	82.50

A20

A21

A22

1884-85   **Perf. 14**

49	A7	1c olive green	16.00	.75
50	A7	1c gray	4.25	.40
51	A7	5c green	37.50	.40
52	A20	10c rose, *bluish*	12.50	.40
a.		Grayish paper	13.50	.50
c.		Yellowish paper	225.00	22.50
53	A21	25c blue, *pink* ('85)	15.00	.75
54	A22	1fr brown, *grnsh*	750.00	17.50

The frame and inscription of No. 51 differ slightly from the illustration.
See note after No. 36.
Nos. 50-54 exist imperforate, without gum. The 1c and 10c stamps are valued from $32.50 to $55. The 5c, 25c and 1fr stamps are valued from $160 to $375.

A23

A24

A25   A26

1886-91

55	A7	2c purple brn ('88)	13.50	1.65
56	A23	20c olive, *grnsh*	200.00	1.65
b.		20c deep olive, grnsh	210.00	1.90
57	A24	35c vio brn, *brnsh* ('91)	18.00	3.00
58	A25	50c bister, *yelsh*	12.50	2.25
59	A26	2fr violet, *pale lil*	72.50	35.00
		Roller cancel		7.50
		Nos. 55-59 (5)	316.50	43.55

Nos. 56 and 57 exist imperforate, without gum. No. 56 is valued at $275. No. 57 is valued at $55.

Values quoted for Nos. 60-107 are for stamps with label attached. Stamps without label sell for much less.

Coat of Arms   King Leopold
A27   A28

Type A27 has two 1mm high ornamental bands across the top and bottom of the label. These bands do not appear on Type A32.

1893-1900

60	A27	1c gray	1.00	.25
61	A27	2c yellow	1.00	1.10
a.		Wmkd. coat of arms in sheet ('95)	—	—
62	A27	2c violet brn ('94)	1.65	.40
63	A27	2c red brown ('98)	3.00	.90
64	A27	5c yellow grn	9.00	.30
65	A28	10c orange brn	4.00	.30
66	A28	10c brt rose ('00)	3.25	.40
67	A28	20c olive green	15.00	.60
68	A28	25c ultra	10.00	.50
a.		No ball to "5" in upper left corner	32.50	12.50
69	A28	35c violet brn	22.50	1.50
a.		35c red brown	35.00	2.40
70	A28	50c bister	57.50	20.00
71	A28	50c gray ('97)	62.50	2.50

72	A28	1fr car, *lt grn*	80.00	20.00
73	A28	1fr orange ('00)	100.00	5.00
74	A28	2fr lilac, *rose*	80.00	70.00
75	A28	2fr lilac ('00)	160.00	13.50
		Nos. 60-75 (16)	610.40	137.25
		Set, never hinged	1,700.	

Antwerp Exhibition Issue

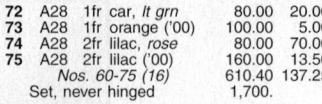

Arms of Antwerp — A29

1894

76	A29	5c green, *rose*	4.75	3.25
77	A29	10c carmine, *bluish*	3.75	2.50
78	A29	25c blue, *rose*	1.00	1.00
		Nos. 76-78 (3)	9.50	6.75
		Set, never hinged	22.00	

Brussels Exhibition Issue

St. Michael and Satan
A30   A31

1896-97   **Perf. 14x14**

79	A30	5c dp violet	1.00	.60
80	A31	10c orange brown	8.50	3.50
81	A31	10c lilac brown	.50	.35
		Nos. 79-81 (3)	10.00	4.45
		Set, never hinged	25.00	

A32   A33

A34

A35

A36

A37

A38

A39

Two types of 1c:
I — Periods after "Dimanche" and "Zondag" in label.
II — No period after "Dimanche." Period often missing after "Zondag."

1905-11   **Perf. 14**

82	A32	1c gray (I) ('07)	1.50	.25
a.		Type II ('08)	2.00	.60

83	A32	2c red brown ('07)	14.50	5.75
84	A32	5c green ('07)	11.50	.60
85	A33	10c dull rose	1.75	.60
86	A34	20c olive grn	26.00	1.00
87	A35	25c ultra	12.00	.85
a.		25c deep blue ('11)	13.50	2.00
88	A36	35c red brn	27.50	2.40
89	A37	50c bluish gray	95.00	4.00
90	A38	1fr yellow orange	110.00	8.00
91	A39	2fr violet	75.00	22.50
		Bar cancellation		5.00
		Nos. 82-91 (10)	374.75	45.95
		Set, never hinged	800.00	

A40

A41

Lion of Belgium — A42

A43

King
Albert I — A44

1912

92	A40	1c orange	.25	.25
93	A41	2c orange brn	.25	.45
94	A42	5c green	.25	.25
95	A43	10c red	.75	.40
96	A43	20c olive grn	16.00	4.00
97	A43	35c bister brn	1.00	.70
98	A43	40c green	16.00	14.50
99	A43	50c gray	1.00	.80
100	A43	1fr orange	4.00	3.00
101	A43	2fr violet	17.50	17.50
102	A44	5fr plum	80.00	25.00
		Nos. 92-102 (11)	137.00	66.85

Counterfeits exist of Nos. 97-102. Those of No. 102 are common.
For overprints see Nos. Q49-Q50, Q52, Q55-Q55A, Q57-Q60.

A45

1912-13   **Larger Head**

103	A45	10c red	.40	.25
a.		Without engraver's name	.25	.25
104	A45	20c olive green ('13)	.40	.40
a.		Without engraver's name	2.00	2.00
105	A45	25c ultramarine	4.25	.30
a.		Without engraver's name	.25	.40
107	A45	40c green ('13)	.50	.60
		Nos. 103-107 (4)	5.55	1.55
		Set, never hinged	9.50	

For overprints see Nos. Q51, Q53-Q54, Q56.

Albert I
A46

Cloth Hall of Ypres
A47

Bridge of
Dinant — A48

Library of
Louvain — A49

Scheldt River
at Antwerp
A50

Anti-slavery
Campaign in
the Congo
A51

King Albert I
at Furnes
A52

Kings of
Belgium
Leopold I,
Albert I,
Leopold II
A53

1915-20   **Typo.**   **Perf. 14**

108	A46	1c orange	.25	.25
109	A46	2c chocolate	.25	.25
110	A46	3c gray blk ('20)	.30	.25
111	A46	5c green	1.00	.25
112	A46	10c carmine	.90	.25
113	A46	15c purple	1.50	.25
114	A46	20c red violet	3.00	.25
115	A46	25c blue	.50	.40

Engr.

116	A47	35c brown org & blk	.50	.30
117	A48	40c green & black	1.00	.30
a.		Vert. pair, imperf. btwn.		
118	A49	50c car rose & blk	4.50	.30
119	A50	1fr violet	32.50	1.00
120	A51	2fr slate	21.00	2.00
121	A52	5fr dp blue	275.00	125.00
		Telegraph or railroad cancel		55.00
122	A53	10fr brown	20.00	20.00
		Nos. 108-122 (15)	362.20	151.05
		Set, never hinged	1,250.	

Two types each of the 1c, 10c and 20c; three of the 2c and 15c; four of the 5c, differing in the top left corner.
See No. 138. For surcharges see Nos. B34-B47.
Nos. 111-119 were handstamped "T" for local provisional use. For detailed listings see *Scott Classic Specialized Catalogue 1840-1940.*

Perron of Liege
(Fountain) — A54

Size: 18¼x28½mm

1919, July 25   **Perf. 11½**

123	A54	25c blue	2.40	.35
a.		25c deep blue	3.00	.45

Size: 18½x28mm

1919, July 19
123B A54 25c blue 400.00 400.00
   c. Sheet of 10 .... 6,000. 6,000.

No. 123B is the first printing, which was issued in sheets of 10. Nos. 123 and 123a were later printings, issued in sheets of 100.

King Albert in Trench Helmet — A55

Perf. 11, 11½, 11½x11, 11x11½

1919   **Size: 18½x22mm**
124 A55 1c lilac brn .... .25 .25
125 A55 2c olive .... .25 .25

Size: 22x26
126 A55 5c green .... .25 .25
127 A55 10c carmine,
      22x26¾mm .... .25 .25
   a. Size: 22½x26mm .... 1.00 .60
128 A55 15c gray vio,
      22x26¾mm .... .30 .30
   a. Size: 22½x26mm .... 2.40 .60
129 A55 20c olive blk 1.10 1.10
130 A55 25c deep blue 1.60 1.60
131 A55 35c bister brn 3.00 3.00
132 A55 40c red 5.00 5.00
133 A55 50c red brn 9.50 10.00
134 A55 1fr lt orange 40.00 40.00
135 A55 2fr violet 375.00 375.00

Size: 28x33½mm
136 A55 5fr car lake 100.00 100.00
137 A55 10fr claret 110.00 110.00
   Nos. 124-137 (14) 646.50 647.00
Set, never hinged .... 1,150.

Type of 1915 Inscribed: "FRANK" instead of "FRANKEN"

1919, Dec.   **Perf. 14, 15**
138 A52 5fr deep blue 1.75 1.25
   Never hinged 3.00

Town Hall at Termonde — A56

1920   **Perf. 11½**
139 A56 65c claret & black,
      27x22mm .... .75 .25
   Never hinged 1.50
   a. Center inverted .... 67,500.
   b. Size: 26¼x22½mm 5.75 2.40
   Never hinged 13.50

For surcharge see No. 143.

Nos. B48-B50 Surcharged in Red or Black

1921   **Perf. 12**
140 SP6 20c on 5c + 5c
      (R) .... .60 .25
   a. Inverted surcharge 625.00 625.00
   Never hinged .... 1,100.
141 SP7 20c on 10c + 5c .... .40 .25
142 SP8 20c on 15c + 15c
      (R) .... .60 .25
   a. Inverted surcharge 625.00 625.00
   Never hinged .... 1,100.

No. 139 Surcharged in Red

143 A56 55c on 65c claret &
      blk .... 1.50 .35
   a. Pair, one without surcharge .... 2.25 .85
   Nos. 140-143 (4) 3.10 1.10
Set, never hinged 8.50

A58

1922-27   **Typo.**   **Perf. 14**
144 A58 1c orange .... .25 .25
145 A58 2c olive ('26) .... .25 .25
146 A58 3c fawn .... .25 .25
147 A58 5c gray .... .25 .25
148 A58 10c blue grn .... .25 .25
149 A58 15c plum ('23) .... .25 .25
150 A58 20c black brn .... .25 .25
151 A58 25c magenta .... .25 .25
   a. 25c dull violet ('23) .... .50 .50
152 A58 30c vermilion .... .40 .25
153 A58 30c rose ('25) .... .35 .25
154 A58 35c red brown .... .35 .30
155 A58 35c blue grn ('27) .... .80 .35
156 A58 40c rose .... .50 .25
157 A58 50c bister ('25) .... .50 .25
158 A58 60c olive brn ('27) .... 3.75 .25
159 A58 1.25fr dp blue ('26) 1.50 1.25
160 A58 1.50fr brt blue ('26) .... 2.50 .50
   b. 1.50fr intense bright blue ('30) 15.00 4.00
161 A58 1.75fr ultra ('27) .... 1.75 .25
   a. Tete beche pair 11.00 5.00
   c. Bklt. pane of 4 + 2 labels 40.00
   Nos. 144-161 (18) 14.40 5.90
Set, never hinged 32.50

See Nos. 185-190. For overprints and surcharges see Nos. 191-195, 197, B56, O1-O6.

A59

1921-25   **Engr.**
Perf. 11, 11x11½, 11½, 11½x11, 11½x12, 11½x12½, 12½
162 A59 50c dull blue .... .30 .25
163 A59 75c scarlet ('22) .... .25 .25
164 A59 75c ultra ('24) .... .45 .25
165 A59 1fr black brn ('22) .... .80 .25
166 A59 1fr dk blue ('25) .... .60 .25
167 A59 2fr dk green ('22) .... .90 .25
168 A59 5fr brown vio ('23) 13.50 15.00
169 A59 10fr magenta ('22) 9.00 6.50
   Nos. 162-169 (8) 25.80 23.00
Set, never hinged 52.50

No. 162 measures 18x20¾mm and was printed in sheets of 100.

Philatelic Exhibition Issues

1921, May 26   **Perf. 11½**
170 A59 50c dark blue 3.50 3.50
   Never hinged 4.75
   a. Sheet of 25 .... 200.00 175.00
   Never hinged 225.00

No. 170 measures 17½x21¼mm, was printed in sheets of 25 and sold at the Philatelic Exhibition at Brussels.
The sheet normally has pin holes and a cancellation-like marking in the margin. These are considered unused and the condition valued here.

Souvenir Sheet

1924, May 24   **Perf. 11½**
171   Sheet of 4 .... 225.00 200.00
   Never hinged 400.00
   a. A59 5fr red brown 10.00 10.00
   Never hinged 14.00

Sold only at the Intl. Phil. Exhib., Brussels. Sheet size: 130x145mm.
The sheet normally has pin holes and a cancellation-like marking in the margin. These are considered unused and the condition valued here. Sheets with wrinkles, toning or significant gum skips sell for much less.

Kings Leopold I and Albert I — A60

1925   **Perf. 14**
172 A60 10c dp green 8.25 8.25
173 A60 15c dull vio 3.75 4.50
174 A60 20c red brown 3.75 4.50
175 A60 25c grnsh black 3.75 4.50
176 A60 30c vermilion 3.75 4.50

---

177 A60 35c lt blue 3.75 4.50
178 A60 40c brnsh blk 3.75 4.50
179 A60 50c yellow brn 3.75 4.50
180 A60 75c dk blue 3.75 4.50
181 A60 1fr dk violet 7.00 7.50
182 A60 2fr ultra 4.00 4.00
183 A60 5fr blue blk 3.75 4.50
184 A60 10fr dp rose 6.75 8.00
   Nos. 172-184 (13) 59.75 68.25
Set, never hinged 126.00

75th anniv. of Belgian postage stamps.
Nos. 172-184 were sold only in sets and only by The Administration of Posts, not at post offices.

A61

1926-27   **Typo.**
185 A61 75c dk violet .... .75 .70
186 A61 1fr pale yellow .... .60 .35
187 A61 1fr rose red ('27) .... 1.50 .25
   a. Tete beche pair 7.50 4.50
   c. Bklt. pane 4 + 2 labels 25.00
188 A61 2fr Prus blue .... 3.25 .45
189 A61 5fr emerald ('27) 32.50 1.60
190 A61 10fr dk brown ('27) 70.00 7.75
   Nos. 185-190 (6) 108.60 11.10
Set, never hinged 249.00

For overprints and surcharge see Nos. 196, Q174-Q175.

Stamps of 1921-27 Surcharged in Carmine, Red or Blue

1927
191 A58 3c on 2c olive (C) .... .25 .25
192 A58 10c on 15c plum (R) .... .25 .25
193 A58 35c on 40c rose (Bl) .... .40 .25
194 A58 1.75fr on 1.50fr brt bl
      (C) .... 1.75 .80
   Nos. 191-194 (4) 2.65 1.55
Set, never hinged 3.75

Nos. 153, 185 and 159 Surcharged in Black

1929, Jan. 1
195 A58 5c on 30c rose .... .25 .25
196 A61 5c on 75c dk violet .... .25 .25
197 A58 5c on 1.25fr dp blue .... .25 .25
   Nos. 195-197 (3) .... .75 .75
Set, never hinged .... .85

The surcharge on Nos. 195-197 is a precancelation which alters the value of the stamp to which it is applied.
Values for precanceled stamps in unused column are for those which have not been through the post and have original gum. Values in second column are for postally used, gumless stamps.

A63

1929-32   **Typo.**   **Perf. 14**
198 A63 1c orange .... .25 .25
199 A63 2c emerald ('31) .... .45 .45
200 A63 3c red brown .... .25 .25
201 A63 5c slate .... .25 .25
   c. Bklt. pane of 4 + 2 labels 8.25
202 A63 10c olive grn .... .25 .25
   c. Bklt. pane of 4 + 2 labels 4.50
203 A63 20c brt violet .... 1.00 .25
204 A63 25c rose red .... .45 .25
   c. Bklt. pane of 4 + 2 labels 8.25
205 A63 35c green .... .50 .25
   c. Bklt. pane of 4 + 2 labels 9.75
206 A63 40c red vio ('30) .... .35 .25
   c. Bklt. pane of 4 + 2 labels 9.75
207 A63 50c dp blue .... .45 .25
   c. Bklt. pane of 4 + 2 labels 8.25
208 A63 60c rose ('30) .... 2.25 .25
   c. Bklt. pane of 4 + 2 labels 30.00
209 A63 70c org brn ('30) .... 1.10 .25
   c. Bklt. pane of 4 + 2 labels 22.50

---

210 A63 75c dk blue ('30) .... 2.25 .25
   b. 75c blue violet .... 2.40 .25
211 A63 75c dp brown ('32) .... 6.50 .25
   b. Bklt. pane of 4 + 2 labels 16.30 3.70
   Nos. 198-211 (14) 62.50

For overprints and surcharges see Nos. 225-226, 240-241, 254-256, 309, O7-O15.

Tete Beche Pairs
201a A63 5c .... .60 .60
202a A63 10c .... .30 .30
204a A63 25c 1.75 1.75
205a A63 35c 2.75 2.75
206a A63 40c 2.75 2.75
207a A63 50c 2.25 2.25
208a A63 60c 8.00 7.50
209a A63 70c 6.00 5.00
210a A63 75c 9.00 8.50
211a A63 75c 30.00 30.00
   Nos. 201a-211a (10) 63.40 61.40
Set, never hinged 160.00

Tete-beche gutter pairs also exist.

A64

1929, Jan. 25   **Engr.**   **Perf. 14½, 14**
212 A64 10fr dk brown 17.50 4.50
213 A64 20fr dk green 100.00 25.00
214 A64 50fr red violet 17.50 17.50
   a. Perf. 14½ 55.00 45.00
215 A64 100fr brownish lake 17.50 17.50
   a. Perf. 14½ 50.00 40.00
   Nos. 212-215 (4) 152.50 64.50
Set, never hinged 276.50

Peter Paul Rubens — A65   Zenobe Gramme — A66

1930, Apr. 26   **Photo.**   **Perf. 12½x12**
216 A65 35c blue green .... .40 .25
217 A66 35c blue green .... .40 .25
Set, never hinged 2.10

No. 216 issued for the Antwerp Exhibition, No. 217 the Liege Exhibition.

Leopold I, by Lievin de Winne — A67   Leopold II, by Joseph Leempoels — A68

Design: 1.75fr, Albert I.

1930, July 1   **Engr.**   **Perf. 11½**
218 A67 60c brown violet .... .25 .25
219 A68 1fr carmine .... .90 .80
220 A68 1.75fr dk blue 2.25 1.25
   Nos. 218-220 (3) 3.40 2.30
Set, never hinged 9.60

Centenary of Belgian independence. For overprints see Nos. 222-224.

Antwerp Exhibition Issue
Souvenir Sheet

Arms of Antwerp A70

1930, Aug. 9 — *Perf. 11½*
221 A70 4fr Sheet of 1   300.00 250.00
    Never hinged   600.00
    a.   Single stamp   100.00 85.00

Size: 142x141mm. Inscription in lower margin "ATELIER DU TIMBRE-1930-ZEGELFABRIEK." Each purchaser of a ticket to the Antwerp Phil. Exhib., Aug. 9-15, was allowed to purchase one stamp. The ticket cost 6 francs.

The sheet normally has pin holes and a cancellation-like marking in the margin. These are considered unused and the condition valued here. Sheets with wrinkles or toning sell for much less.

Nos. 218-220
Overprinted in Blue
or Red

1930, Oct.
222 A67 60c brown vio (Bl)   2.00 2.00
223 A68 1fr carmine (Bl)   8.25 7.75
224 A68 1.75fr dk blue (R)   14.50 14.50
    Nos. 222-224 (3)   24.75 24.25
    Set, never hinged   55.00

50th meeting of the administrative council of the Intl. Labor Bureau at Brussels.
The names of the painters and the initials of the engraver have been added at the foot of these stamps.

Stamps of 1929-30 Surcharged in Blue or Black

1931, Feb. 20 — *Perf. 14*
225 A63 2c on 3c red brown (Bl)   .25 .25
226 A63 10c on 60c rose (Bk)   .25 .25
    Set, never hinged   3.75

The surcharge on No. 226 is a precancelation which alters the denomination. See note after No. 197.

King Albert — A71

1931, June 15 — *Photo.*
227 A71 1fr brown carmine   .50 .25
    Never hinged   1.00

King Albert — A71a

1932, June 1
228 A71a 75c bister brown   1.25 .25
    Never hinged   5.00
    a.   Tete beche pair   6.75 6.75
    Never hinged   17.50
    c.   Bklt. pane 4 + 2 labels   18.00

See No. 257. For overprint see No. O18.

A72

1931-32 — *Engr.*
229 A72 1.25fr gray black   .75 .50
230 A72 1.50fr brown vio   1.50 .50
231 A72 1.75fr dp blue   .80 .25
232 A72 2fr red brown   1.10 .25
233 A72 2.45fr dp violet   3.00 .40
234 A72 2.50fr black brn ('32)   12.00 .50
235 A72 5fr dp green   25.00 1.10
236 A72 10fr claret   55.00 12.50
    Nos. 229-236 (8)   99.15 16.00
    Set, never hinged   275.00

Nos. 206 and 209 Surcharged as No. 226, but dated "1932"
1932, Jan. 1
240 A63 10c on 40c red vio   2.75 .35
241 A63 10c on 70c org brn   2.50 .25
    Set, never hinged   22.50

See note after No. 197.

Gleaner A73   Mercury A74

1932, June 1   *Typo.*   *Perf. 13½x14*
245 A73 2c pale green   .35 .35
246 A74 5c dp orange   .25 .25
247 A73 10c olive grn   .25 .25
    a.   Tete beche pair   4.00 4.00
    Never hinged   7.50
    c.   Bklt. pane 4 + 2 labels   15.00
248 A74 20c brt violet   1.10 .25
249 A73 25c deep red   .70 .25
    a.   Tete beche pair   3.50 3.50
    Never hinged   6.50
    c.   Bklt. pane 4 + 2 labels   15.00
250 A74 35c dp green   2.75 .25
    Nos. 245-250 (6)   5.40 1.60
    Set, never hinged   14.50

For overprints see Nos. O16-O17.

Auguste Piccard's Balloon — A75

1932, Nov. 26   *Engr.*   *Perf. 11½*
251 A75 75c red brown   3.50 .30
252 A75 1.75fr dk blue   17.50 2.50
253 A75 2.50fr dk violet   20.00 13.50
    Nos. 251-253 (3)   41.00 16.30
    Set, never hinged   112.50

Issued in commemoration of Prof. Auguste Piccard's two ascents to the stratosphere.

Nos. 206 and 209 Surcharged as No. 226, but dated "1933"
1933, Nov. — *Perf. 14*
254 A63 10c on 40c red vio   17.50 3.50
255 A63 10c on 70c org brn   16.00 1.50
    Set, never hinged   100.00

No. 206 Surcharged as No. 226, but dated "1934"
1934, Feb.
256 A63 10c on 40c red vio   16.00 1.50
    Never hinged   52.50

For Nos. 254 to 256 see note after No. 197. Regummed examples of Nos. 254-256 are plentiful.

King Albert Memorial Issue
Type of 1932 with Black Margins
1934, Mar. 10 — *Photo.*
257 A71a 75c black   .30 .25
    Never hinged   1.00

Congo Pavilion — A76

Designs: 1fr, Brussels pavilion. 1.50fr, "Old Brussels." 1.75fr, Belgian pavilion.

1934, July 1 — *Perf. 14x13½*
258 A76 35c green   .75 .40
259 A76 1fr dk carmine   1.25 .40
260 A76 1.50fr maroon   5.50 .90
261 A76 1.75fr blue   5.50 .40
    Nos. 258-261 (4)   13.00 2.10
    Set, never hinged   50.00

Brussels Intl. Exhib. of 1935.

King Leopold III A80   A81

1934-35 — *Perf. 13½x14*
262 A80 70c olive blk ('35)   .35 .25
    a.   Tete beche pair   1.50 1.50
    c.   Bklt. pane 4 + 2 labels   6.25
263 A80 75c brown   .65 .25
Perf. 14x13½
264 A81 1fr rose car ('35)   3.00 .35
    Nos. 262-264 (3)   4.00 .85
    Set, never hinged   11.00

For overprint see No. O19.

Coat of Arms — A82

1935-48   *Typo.*   *Perf. 14*
265 A82 2c green ('37)   .25 .25
266 A82 5c orange   .25 .25
267 A82 10c olive bister   .25 .25
    a.   Tete beche pair   .30 .25
    Never hinged   .50
    b.   Bklt. pane 4 + 2 labels   4.50
268 A82 15c dk violet   .25 .25
269 A82 20c lilac   .25 .25
270 A82 25c carmine rose   .25 .25
    a.   Tete beche pair   .30 .40
    Never hinged   .55
    c.   Bklt. pane 4 + 2 labels   4.50
271 A82 25c yel org ('46)   .25 .25
272 A82 30c brown   .25 .25
273 A82 35c green   .25 .25
    a.   Tete beche pair   .30 .30
    Never hinged   .50
    c.   Bklt. pane 4 + 2 labels   3.00
274 A82 40c red vio ('38)   .25 .25
275 A82 50c blue   .40 .25
276 A82 60c slate ('41)   .25 .25
277 A82 65c red lilac ('46)   .25 .25
278 A82 70c lt blue grn ('45)   .25 .25
279 A82 75c lilac rose ('45)   .25 .25
280 A82 80c green ('48)   4.00 .40
281 A82 90c dull vio ('46)   .25 .25
282 A82 1fr red brown ('45)   .25 .25
    Nos. 265-282 (18)   8.40 4.65
    Set, never hinged   17.00

Several stamps of type A82 exist in various shades.
Nos. 265, 361 were privately overprinted and surcharged "+10FR." by the Association Belgo-Americaine for the dedication of the Bastogne Memorial, July 16, 1950. The overprint is in six types. Value $1.50 per set.
See design O1. For overprints and surcharges see Nos. 312-313, 361-364, 390-394, O20-O22, O24, O26-O28, O33.

A83   A83a

Perf. 14, 14x13½, 11½
1936-56 — *Photo.*
Size: 17½x21¾mm
283 A83 70c brown   .30 .25
    a.   Tete beche pair   .80 .80
    Never hinged   1.40
    c.   Bklt. pane 4 + 2 labels   7.50
Size: 20¾x24mm
284 A83a 1fr rose car   .30 .25
285 A83a 1.20fr dk brown ('51)   .80 .25
    a.   Perf. 11½ ('56)   1.20 .25
    Never hinged   2.75
286 A83a 1.50fr brt red vio ('43)   .40 .30

287 A83a 1.75fr dp ultra ('43)   .25 .25
288 A83a 1.75fr dk car ('50)   .25 .25
289 A83a 2fr dk pur ('43)   1.50 1.50
290 A83a 2.25fr grnsh blk ('43)   .25 .25
291 A83a 2.50fr org red ('51)   1.75 .30
    a.   Perf. 11½ ('56)   20.00 .25
    Never hinged   60.00
292 A83a 3.25fr chestnut ('43)   .25 .25
293 A83a 5fr dp green ('43)   1.50 .50
    Nos. 283-293 (11)   7.55 4.35
    Set, never hinged   18.00

Nos. 287-288, 290-291, 293 inscribed "Belgie-Belgique."
See designs A85, A91. For overprints and surcharges see Nos. 314, O23, O25, O29, O31, O34.

A84

1936-51   *Engr.*   *Perf. 14x13½*
294 A84 1.50fr rose lilac ('41)   .60 .35
295 A84 1.75fr dull blue   .25 .25
296 A84 2fr dull vio   .40 .30
297 A84 2.25fr gray vio ('41)   .25 .25
298 A84 2.45fr black   45.00 .70
299 A84 2.50fr ol blk ('39)   2.00 .25
300 A84 3.25fr org brn ('41)   .30 .25
301 A84 5fr dull green   2.40 .50
302 A84 10fr vio brn   .60 .25
    a.   10fr light brown ('46)   10.00 .25
    Never hinged   35.00
303 A84 20fr vermilion   1.00 .30
    a.   20fr rose orange ('36)   1.15 .40
    Never hinged   4.00
Perf. 11½
304 A84 3fr yel brn ('51)   .55 .25
305 A84 4fr bl, *bluish* ('50)   4.75 .25
    a.   White paper   9.00 .25
    Never hinged   14.50
306 A84 6fr brt rose car ('51)   2.75 .25
307 A84 10fr brn vio ('51)   .55 .25
308 A84 20fr red ('51)   1.10 .25
    Nos. 294-308 (15)   62.50 4.65
    Set, never hinged   150.00

See No. 1159. For overprint and surcharges see Nos. 316-317, O32.

No. 206 Surcharged as No. 226, but dated "1937"
1937   *Unwmk.*   *Perf. 14*
309 A63 10c on 40c red vio   .25 .25
    Never hinged   .30

See note after No. 197.

A85

1938-41   *Photo.*   *Perf. 13½x14*
310 A85 75c olive gray   .25 .25
    a.   Tete beche pair   .75 .80
    Never hinged   1.50
    c.   Bklt. pane 4 + 2 labels   6.75
311 A85 1fr rose pink ('41)   .25 .25
    a.   Tete beche pair   .25 .25
    Never hinged   .40
    b.   Booklet pane of 6   2.25
    c.   Bklt. pane 4 + 2 labels   2.25
    Set, never hinged   .80

For overprints and surcharges see Nos. 315, O25, O30, O35.

Nos. 272, 274, 283, 310, 299, 298 Srchd. in Blue, Black, Carmine or Red

a   b

c

1938-42

312	A82 (a)	10c on 30c (Bl)	.25	.25
313	A82 (a)	10c on 40c (Bl)	.25	.25
314	A83 (b)	10c on 70c (Bk)	.25	.25
315	A85 (b)	50c on 75c (C)	.25	.25
316	A84 (c)	2.25fr on 2.50fr (C)	.45	.45
317	A84 (c)	2.50fr on 2.45fr (R)	11.00	

Nos. 312-317 (6) 12.45 1.70
Set, never hinged 26.00

Issue date: No. 317, Oct. 31, 1938.

Basilica and Bell Tower — A86

Water Exhibition Buildings — A87

Designs: 1.50fr, Albert Canal and Park. 1.75fr, Eygenbilsen Cut in Albert Canal.

1938, Oct. 31   Perf. 14x13½, 13½x14

318	A86	35c dk blue grn	.25	.25
319	A87	1fr rose red	.45	.30
320	A87	1.50fr vio brn	1.10	.60
321	A87	1.75fr ultra	1.25	.25

Nos. 318-321 (4) 3.05 1.40
Set, never hinged 11.00

Intl. Water Exhibition, Liège, 1939.

> **Catalogue values for unused stamps in this section, from this point to the end of the section, are for Never Hinged items.**

Lion Rampant — A90

1944   Unwmk.   Photo.   Perf. 12½
Inscribed: "Belgique-Belgie"

322	A90	5c chocolate	.25	.25
323	A90	10c green	.25	.25
324	A90	25c lt blue	.25	.25
325	A90	35c brown	.25	.25
326	A90	50c lt bl grn	.25	.25
327	A90	75c purple	.25	.25
328	A90	1fr vermilion	.25	.25
329	A90	1.25fr chestnut	.25	.25
330	A90	1.50fr orange	1.10	.40
331	A90	1.75fr brt ultra	.25	.25
332	A90	2fr aqua	6.25	2.00
333	A90	2.75fr dp mag	.25	.25
334	A90	3fr claret	.50	.40
335	A90	3.50fr sl blk	.50	.40
336	A90	5fr dk olive	13.50	5.00
337	A90	10fr black	.90	.60

Nos. 322-337 (16) 25.25 11.30

Inscribed: "Belgie-Belgique"

338	A90	5c chocolate	.25	.25
339	A90	10c green	.25	.25
340	A90	25c lt bl	.25	.25
341	A90	35c brown	.25	.25
342	A90	50c lt bl grn	.25	.25
343	A90	75c purple	.25	.25
344	A90	1fr vermilion	.25	.25
345	A90	1.25fr chestnut	.25	.25
346	A90	1.50fr orange	.30	.45
347	A90	1.75fr brt ultra	.25	.25
348	A90	2fr aqua	2.50	1.25
349	A90	2.75fr dp magenta	.25	.25
350	A90	3fr claret	.50	.40
351	A90	3.50fr slate blk	.50	.40
352	A90	5fr dark olive	5.25	3.00
353	A90	10fr black	.75	1.00

Nos. 338-353 (16) 12.30 9.00

Leopold III, Crown and V — A91

1944-57   Perf. 14x13½

354	A91	1fr brt rose red	.50	.25
355	A91	1.50fr magenta	.45	.25
356	A91	1.75fr dp ultra	.65	.45
357	A91	2fr dp vio	2.50	.30
358	A91	2.25fr grnsh blk	.75	.40
359	A91	3.25fr chnt brn	.75	.25
360	A91	5fr dk bl grn	5.00	.25
a.		Perf. 11½ ('57)	200.00	.30

Nos. 354-360 (7) 10.60 2.15

Nos. 355, 357, 359 inscribed "Belgique-Belgie."

For surcharges see Nos. 365-367 and footnote following No. 367.

Stamps of 1935-41 Overprinted in Red

1944   Perf. 14

361	A82	2c pale green	.25	.25
362	A82	15c indigo	.25	.25
363	A82	20c brt violet	.25	.25
364	A82	60c slate	.25	.25

Nos. 361-364 (4) 1.00 1.00

See note following No. 282.

Nos. 355, 357, and 360 Srchd. Typographically in Black or Carmine

1946   Perf. 14x13½

365	A91	On 1.50fr magenta	.70	.25
366	A91	On 2fr dp vio (C)	2.00	.70
367	A91	On 5fr dk bl grn (C)	1.75	.30

Nos. 365-367 (3) 4.45 1.25

To provide denominations created by a reduction in postal rates, the Government produced Nos. 365-367 by typographed surcharge. Also, each post office was authorized on May 20, 1946, to surcharge its stock of 1.50fr, 2fr and 5fr stamps "-10 percent." Hundreds of types and sizes of this surcharge exist, both hand-stamped and typographed. These include the "1,35," "1,80" and "4,50" applied at Ghislenghien.

M. S. Prince Baudouin — A92

2.25fr, S.S. Marie Henriette. 3.15fr, S.S. Diamant.

Perf. 14x13½, 13½x14
1946, June 15   Photo.   Unwmk.

368	A92	1.35fr brt bluish grn	.25	.25
369	A92	2.25fr slate green	.45	.25
370	A92	3.15fr slate black	.50	.25

Nos. 368-370 (3) 1.20 .75

Centenary of the steamship line between Ostend and Dover.

No. 368 exists in two sizes: 21¼x18¼mm and 21x17mm. Nos. 369-370 are 24½x20mm.

Capt. Adrien de Gerlache — A95

Belgica and Explorers A96

1947, June   Perf. 14x13½, 11½

371	A95	1.35fr crimson rose	.45	.25
372	A96	2.25fr gray black	3.50	1.00

50th anniv. of Capt. Adrien de Gerlache's Antarctic Expedition.

Joseph A. F. Plateau — A97

1947, June   Perf. 14x13½

373 A97 3.15fr deep blue 1.10 .25

Issued to mark the World Film and Fine Arts Festival, Brussels, June, 1947.

Chemical Industry — A98

Industrial Arts — A99

Agriculture A100

Textile Industry A102

Communications Center — A101

Iron Manufacture A103

Photogravure (#374-376, 378),
Typographed (#377, 380), Engraved
1948   Unwmk.   Perf. 11½

374	A98	60c blue grn	.30	.25
375	A98	1.20fr brown	2.25	.25
376	A99	1.35fr red brown	.30	.25
377	A100	1.75fr brt red	.35	.25
378	A99	1.75fr dk gray grn	.60	.25
379	A101	2.25fr gray blue	1.00	.50
380	A100	2.50fr dk car rose	7.00	.60
381	A101	3fr brt red vio	12.00	.55
382	A102	3.15fr deep blue	1.00	.65
383	A102	4fr brt ultra	10.00	.40
384	A103	6fr blue green	23.00	.60
385	A103	6.30fr brt red vio	2.75	2.00

Nos. 374-385 (12) 60.55 6.55

See Nos. O42-O46.

Leopold I — A104

1949, July 1   Engr.   Perf. 14x13½

386	A104	90c dk green	.65	.35
387	A104	1.75fr brown	.45	.25
388	A104	3fr red	9.25	3.00
389	A104	4fr deep blue	7.75	1.00

Nos. 386-389 (4) 18.10 4.60

Cent. of Belgium's 1st postage stamps. See note on souvenir sheet below No. 2.

Stamps of 1935-45 Precanceled and Surcharged in Black

1949   Perf. 14

390	A82	5c on 15c dk vio	.25	.25
391	A82	5c on 30c brown	.25	.25
392	A82	5c on 40c red vio	.25	.25
393	A82	20c on 70c lt bl grn	.30	.35
394	A82	20c on 75c lil rose	.25	.25

Similar Surcharge and Precancellation in Black on Nos. B455-B458
Perf. 14x13½

395	SP251	10c on #B455	2.50	2.50
396	SP251	40c on #B456	1.25	1.25
397	SP251	80c on #B457	.65	.65
398	SP251	1.20fr on #B458	1.50	1.50

Nos. 390-398 (9) 7.20 7.25

See note after No. 197.

St. Mary Magdalene, from Painting by Gerard David — A105

1949, July 15   Photo.   Perf. 11

399 A105 1.75fr dark brown .70 .30

Gerard David Exhibition at Bruges, 1949.

Allegory of UPU A106

1949, Oct. 1   Engr.   Perf. 11½

400 A106 4fr deep blue 4.25 2.25

75th anniv. of the UPU.

Symbolical of Pension Fund — A107

Perf. 11½
1950, May 1   Unwmk.   Photo.

401 A107 1.75fr dark brown .50 .25

General Pension Fund founding, cent.

Lion Rampant — A108

1951, Feb. 15   Engr.   Perf. 11½
402 A108 20c blue   .25   .25

1951-75   Typo.   Perf. 13½x14
Size: 17½x21mm
403 A108 2c org brn ('60)   .25   .25
404 A108 3c brt lil ('60)   .25   .25
405 A108 5c pale violet   .25   .25
406 A108 5c brt pink ('74)   .25   .25
407 A108 10c red orange   .25   .25
408 A108 15c brt pink ('59)   .25   .25
409 A108 20c claret   .25   .25
410 A108 25c green   1.50   .25
411 A108 25c lt bl grn ('66)   .25   .25
412 A108 30c gray grn ('57)   .25   .25
413 A108 40c brown olive   .25   .25
414 A108 50c ultra   .25   .25
   a.   50c light blue   .25   .25
415 A108 60c lilac rose   .25   .25
416 A108 65c violet brn   11.50   .50
417 A108 75c bluish lilac   .25   .25
418 A108 80c emerald   .75   .25
419 A108 90c deep blue   .75   .25
420 A108 1fr rose   .25   .25
421 A108 2fr emerald ('73)   .25   .25
422 A108 2.50fr brown ('70)   .25   .25
423 A108 3fr brt pink ('70)   .25   .25
424 A108 4fr brt rose lil ('74)   .25   .25
425 A108 4.50fr blue ('74)   .30   .25
426 A108 5fr brt lilac ('75)   .30   .25
Size: 17x20½mm
427 A108 1.50fr dk sl grn ('69)   .25   .25

Perf. 13½x13
428 A108 2fr emerald ('68)   .25   .25

Photo.   Perf. 11½
Size: 20½x24mm
429 A108 50c light blue ('61)   .45   .25
430 A108 60c lilac rose ('66)   1.10   .70
431 A108 1fr carmine rose
             ('59)   .25   .25

Perf. 13½x12½
Size: 17½x22mm
432 A108 50c lt blue ('75)   .25   .25
   a.   Booklet pane of 4 (#432, 784
        and 2 #785) + labels   1.00
   b.   Booklet pane of 4 (#432 and 3
        #787) + labels   1.50
433 A108 1fr rose ('69)   2.00   .90
434 A108 2fr emerald ('72)   .50   .30
   e.   Booklet pane of 6 (4 #434 + 2
        #475)   5.50
   f.   Booklet pane of 5 (#434, 4
        #476 + label)   8.00
       Nos. 403-434 (32)   24.65   9.40

Counterfeits exist of No. 416. Nos. 429, 431
also issued in coils with black control number on
back of every fifth stamp. Nos. 432-434 issued
in booklet panes only. No. 432 has one
straightedge, and stamps in the pane are tete-
beche. Each pane has 2 labels showing Belgian postal emblem and a large selvage with
postal code instructions.
    Nos. 433-434 have 1 or 2 straight-edges.
Panes have a large selvage with inscription or
map of Belgium showing postal zones.
    See designs A386, O5. For surcharges see
Nos. 477-478, 563-567.

Francois de Tassis
(Franz von
Taxis) — A109

Portraits: 1.75fr, Jean-Baptiste of Thurn &
Taxis. 2fr, Baron Leonard I. 2.50fr, Count
Lamoral I. 3fr, Count Leonard II. 4fr, Count
Lamoral II. 5fr, Prince Eugene Alexander.
5.75fr, Prince Anselme Francois. 8fr, Prince
Alexander Ferdinand. 10fr, Prince Charles
Anselme. 20fr, Prince Charles Alexander.

1952, May 14   Engr.   Perf. 11½
Laid Paper
435 A109 80c olive grn   .40   .35
436 A109 1.75fr red org   .40   .35
437 A109 2fr violet brn   .75   .45
438 A109 2.50fr carmine   1.25   .55
439 A109 3fr olive bis   1.25   .55
440 A109 4fr ultra   1.25   .75
441 A109 5fr red brn   3.25   1.00
442 A109 5.75fr blue vio   4.00   2.00

443 A109 8fr gray   14.00   3.50
444 A109 10fr rose vio   18.00   4.50
445 A109 20fr brown   80.00 24.50
       Nos. 435-445,B514 (12)   264.55 138.50
       13th UPU Cong., Brussels, 1952.

King
Baudouin — A110

1952-58   Engr.   Perf. 11½
Size: 21x24mm
446 A110 1.50fr gray green   1.25   .25
447 A110 2fr crimson   .45   .25
448 A110 4fr ultra   3.75   .25
Size: 24½x35mm
449 A110 50fr gray brn   24.00   .25
   a.   50fr violet brown   100.00   .60
450 A110 100fr rose red
             ('58)   16.00   .25

King
Baudouin — A111

1953-72   Photo.   Perf. 11½
451 A111 1.50fr gray   .25   .25
452 A111 2fr rose carmine   7.25   .25
453 A111 2fr green   .25   .25
454 A111 2.50fr red brn ('57)   .50   .25
   a.   2.50fr orange brown ('70)   .25   .25
455 A111 3fr rose lil ('58)   .40   .25
456 A111 3.50fr brt yel grn
             ('58)   .75   .25
457 A111 4fr brt ultra   .50   .25
458 A111 4.50fr dk red brn
             ('62)   3.00   .25
459 A111 5fr violet ('57)   1.25   .25
460 A111 6fr dp pink ('58)   .75   .25
461 A111 6.50fr gray ('60)   95.00 15.00
462 A111 7fr blue ('60)   .90   .25
463 A111 7.50fr grysh brn
             ('58)   87.50 16.00
464 A111 8fr bluish gray
             ('58)   1.00   .25
465 A111 8.50fr claret ('58)   20.00   .45
466 A111 9fr gray ('58)   95.00   1.90
467 A111 12fr lt bl grn ('66)   13.50   .45
468 A111 30fr red org ('58)   10.00   .25
Redrawn
469 A111 2.50fr org brn ('71)   .35   .25
470 A111 4.50fr brown ('72)   2.25   .60
471 A111 7fr blue ('71)   .60   .25

Perf. 13½x12½
Size: 17½x22mm
472 A111 1.50fr gray ('70)   .60   .30
   b.   Bklt. pane of 10   6.50
   c.   Bklt. pane, 3 #472, 3 #475   15.00
473 A111 2.50fr org brn ('70)   6.00   5.00
   h.   Bklt. pane, 1 #473, 5 #475   16.00
474 A111 3fr lilac rose
             ('69)   .60   .25
   a.   Bklt. pane of 5 + label   25.00
   b.   Bklt. pane, 2 #433, 6 #474   18.00
475 A111 3.50fr brt yel grn
             ('70)   .60   .25
476 A111 4.50fr dull red brn
             ('72)   .60   .35
       Nos. 446-476 (31)   394.85 45.55

Nos. 451, 453, 454a, 455, 456, 458 also
issued in coils with black control number on
back of every fifth stamp. These coils, except
for No. 451, are on luminescent paper.
    On Nos. 469-471, the 2, 4 and 7 are 3mm
high. The background around the head is
white. On Nos. 454, 458, 462 the 2, 4 and 7
are 2½mm high and the background is tinted.
    Nos. 472-476 issued in booklets only and
have 1 or 2 straight-edges. All panes have a
large selvage with inscription or map.
    See designs M1, O3.

Luminescent Paper
    Stamps issued on both ordinary and
luminescent paper include: Nos. 307-
308, 430-431, 449-451, 453-460, 462,
464, 467-468, 472, 643-644, 650-651,
837, Q385, Q410.
    Stamps issued only on luminescent
paper include: Nos. 433, 454a, 472b,
473-474, 649, 652-658, 664-670, 679-
682, 688-690, 694-696, 698-703, 705-
711, 713-726, 729-747, 751-754, 756-
757, 759, 761-762, 764, 766, 769, 772,
774, 778, 789, 791-793, 795, 797-799,
801-807, 809-811, 814-818, 820-834,
836, 838-848.
    See note after No. 857.

Nos. 416 and 419
Surcharged and
Precanceled in Black

1954, Jan. 1   Unwmk.   Perf. 13½x14
477 A108 20c on 65c vio brn   1.50   .30
478 A108 20c on 90c dp blue   1.50   .25
       See note after No. 197.

Map and
Rotary
Emblem
A112

80c, Mermaid and Mercury holding emblem.
4fr, Rotary emblem and two globes.

1954, Sept. 10   Engr.   Perf. 11½
479 A112 20c red   .25   .25
480 A112 80c dark green   .40   .30
481 A112 4fr ultra   1.40   .40
       Nos. 479-481 (3)   2.05   .95

5th regional conf. of Rotary Intl. at Ostend.
No. 481 for Rotary 50th Anniv. (in 1955).
    A souv. sheet containing one each, imperf.,
was sold for 500 francs. It was not valid for
postage. Value, $200.

The Rabot and
Begonia — A113

Designs: 2.50fr, The Oudeburg and azalea.
4fr, "Three Towers" and orchid.

1955, Feb. 15   Photo.
482 A113 80c brt carmine   .40   .40
483 A113 2.50fr black brn   8.50   2.50
484 A113 4fr dk rose brn   5.00   .70
       Nos. 482-484 (3)   13.90   3.60
       Ghent Intl. Flower Exhibition, 1955.

Homage to
Charles V as
a Child, by
Albrecht de
Vriendt
A114

Charles V, by
Titian — A115

4fr, Abdication of Charles V, by Louis
Gallait.

Emile Verhaeren,
by Montald
Constant — A116

1955, May 11   Engr.
488 A116 20c dark gray   .25   .25
       Birth cent. of Verhaeren, poet.

Allegory of
Textile
Manufacture
A117

1955, May 11
489 A117 2fr violet brown   1.00   .25

2nd Intl. Textile Exhibition, Brussels, June
1955.

"The Foolish Virgin"
by Rik
Wouters — A118

1955, June 10
490 A118 1.20fr olive green   1.10   1.10
491 A118 2fr violet   1.60   .25

3rd biennial exhibition of sculpture, Antwerp,
June 11-Sept. 10, 1955.

"Departure of
Volunteers from
Liege, 1830" by
Charles
Soubre — A119

1955, Sept. 10   Photo.
492 A119 20c grnsh slate   .25   .25
493 A119 2fr chocolate   .75   .25

Exhibition "The Romantic Movement in
Liege Province," Sept. 10-Oct. 31, 1955; and
125th anniv. of Belgium's independence from
the Netherlands.

Pelican Giving
Blood to
Young — A120

1956, Jan. 14   Engr.
494 A120 2fr brt carmine   .35   .25

Blood donor service of the Belgian Red
Cross.

1955, Mar. 25   Unwmk.   Perf. 11½
485 A114 20c rose red   .25   .25
486 A115 2fr dk gray green   .80   .25
487 A114 4fr blue   5.00   1.25
       Nos. 485-487 (3)   6.05   1.75
       Charles V Exhibition, Ghent, 1955.

Buildings of Tournai, Ghent and Antwerp — A121

1956, July 14 **Photo.**
495 A121 2fr brt ultra .30 .25
The Scheldt exhibition (Scaldis) at Tournai, Ghent and Antwerp, July-Sept. 1956.

Europa Issue

"Rebuilding Europe" — A122

1956, Sept. 15 **Engr.**
496 A122 2fr lt green 1.25 .25
497 A122 4fr purple 7.75 .45
Issued to symbolize the cooperation among the six countries comprising the Coal and Steel Community.

Train on Map of Belgium and Luxembourg A123

1956, Sept. 29
498 A123 2fr dark blue .35 .25
Issued to mark the electrification of the Brussels-Luxembourg railroad.

Edouard Anseele — A124

1956, Oct. 27
499 A124 20c violet brown .25 .25
Cent. of the birth of Edouard Anseele, statesman, and in connection with an exhibition held in his honor at Ghent.

"The Atom" and Exposition Emblem — A125

1957-58 **Unwmk.**
500 A125 2fr carmine rose .25 .25
501 A125 2.50fr green ('58) .35 .25
502 A125 4fr brt violet blue .50 .25
503 A125 5fr claret ('58) 1.25 .55
Nos. 500-503 (4) 2.35 1.30
1958 World's Fair at Brussels.

Emperor Maximilian I Receiving Letter — A126

1957, May 19
504 A126 2fr claret .35 .25
Day of the Stamp, May 19, 1957.

Sikorsky S-58 Helicopter A127

1957, June 15
505 A127 4fr gray grn & brt bl .80 .45
100,000th passenger carried by Sabena helicopter service, June 15, 1957.

Zeebrugge Harbor A128

1957, July 6
506 A128 2fr dark blue .35 .25
50th anniv. of the completion of the port of Zeebrugge-Bruges.

Leopold I Entering Brussels, 1831 — A129

Leopold I Arriving at Belgian Border A130

1957, July 17 **Photo.**
507 A129 20c dk gray grn .25 .25
508 A130 2fr lilac .55 .25
126th anniv. of the arrival in Belgium of King Leopold I.

Boy Scout and Girl Scout Emblems A131

Design: 4fr, Robert Lord Baden-Powell, painted by David Jaggers, vert.

Perf. 11½
1957, July 29 **Unwmk.** **Engr.**
509 A131 80c gray .25 .25
510 A131 4fr light green 1.10 .45
Cent. of the birth of Lord Baden-Powell, founder of the Boy Scout movement.

"Kneeling Woman" by Lehmbruck — A132

1957, Aug. 20 **Photo.**
511 A132 2.50fr dk blue grn 1.00 .85
4th Biennial Exposition of Sculpture, Antwerp, May 25-Sept. 15.

"United Europe" — A133

1957, Sept. 16 **Engr.** **Perf. 11½**
512 A133 2fr dk violet brn .50 .25
513 A133 4fr dark blue 1.50 .35
Europa: United Europe for peace and prosperity.

Queen Elisabeth Assisting at Operation, by Allard L'Olivier A134

Perf. 11½
1957, Nov. 23 **Unwmk.** **Engr.**
514 A134 30c rose lilac .25 .25
50th anniv. of the founding of the Edith Cavell-Marie Depage and St. Camille schools of nursing.

Post Horn and Historic Postal Insignia A135

1958, Mar. 16 **Photo.** **Perf. 11½**
515 A135 2.50fr gray .25 .25
Postal Museum Day.

United Nations Issue

International Labor Organization A136

Allegory of UN — A137

Designs: 1fr, FAO. 2fr, World Bank. 2.50fr, UNESCO. 3fr, UN Pavilion. 5fr, ITU. 8fr, Intl. Monetary Fund. 11fr, WHO. 20fr, UPU.

Perf. 11½
1958, Apr. 17 **Unwmk.** **Engr.**
516 A136 50c gray 2.00 2.00
517 A136 1fr claret .30 .35
518 A137 1.50fr dp ultra .30 .35
519 A137 2fr gray brown .45 .50
520 A136 2.50fr olive grn .30 .45

521 A136 3fr grnsh blue .50 .55
522 A137 5fr rose lilac .35 .40
523 A136 8fr red brown .65 .70
524 A136 11fr dull lilac 1.25 1.40
525 A136 20fr car rose 2.00 2.25
Nos. 516-525,C15-C20 (16) 10.60 11.40
World's Fair, Brussels, Apr. 17-Oct. 19.
Postally valid only from the UN pavilion at the Brussels Fair. Proceeds went toward financing the UN exhibits.

Eugène Ysaye A138

1958, Sept. 1
526 A138 30c dk blue & plum .25 .25
Ysaye (1858-1931), violinist, composer.

Common Design Types pictured in section at front of book.

Europa Issue, 1958
Common Design Type
1958, Sept. 13 **Photo.**
Size: 24½x35mm
527 CD1 2.50fr brt red & blue 1.00 .25
528 CD1 5fr brt blue & red 3.25 .35
Issued to show the European Postal Union at the service of European integration.

Universal Declaration of Human Rights, 10th Anniv. — A140

Infant and UN Emblem.

1958, Dec. 10 **Engr.**
529 A140 2.50fr blue gray .30 .25

Charles V , Jean-Baptiste of Thurn and Taxis — A141

1959, Mar. 15 **Unwmk.**
530 A141 2.50fr green .40 .25
Issued for the Day of the Stamp. Design from painting by J.-E. van den Bussche.

NATO Emblem — A142

1959, Apr. 3 **Photo.** **Perf. 11½**
531 A142 2.50fr dp red & dk bl .40 .25
532 A142 5fr emerald & dk bl 1.10 .75
10th anniv. of NATO. See No. 720.

City Hall,
Audenarde — A143

1959, Aug. 17　　　　　　Engr.
533　A143　2.50fr deep claret　　　.30　.25

Pope Adrian VI, by
Jan van
Scorel — A144

1959, Aug. 31　　　　　Perf. 11½
534　A144　2.50fr dark red　　　.25　.25
535　A144　5fr Prus blue　　　.40　.40

500th anniv. of the birth of Pope Adrian VI.

Europa Issue, 1959
Common Design Type
1959, Sept. 19　　　　　Photo.
Size: 24x35½mm
536　CD2　2.50fr dark red　　　.30　.25
537　CD2　5fr brt grnsh blue　　1.25　.35

Boeing 707
A146

Engraved and Photogravure
1959, Dec. 1　　　　　Perf. 11½
538　A146　6fr dk bl gray & car　1.90　.80

Inauguration of jet flights by Sabena Airlines.

Countess of
Taxis — A147

1960, Mar. 21　Engr.　Perf. 11½
539　A147　3fr dark blue　　　.85　.25

Alexandrine de Rye, Countess of Taxis, Grand Mistress of the Netherlands Posts, 1628-1645, and day of the stamp, Mar. 21, 1960. The painting of the Countess is by Nicholas van der Eggermans.

24th Ghent Intl.
Flower
Exhibition — A148

40c, Indian azalea. 3fr, Begonia. 6fr, Anthurium, bromelia.

1960, Mar. 28　　　　　Unwmk.
540　A148　40c multicolored　　.25　.25
541　A148　3fr multicolored　　.50　.25
542　A148　6fr multicolored　　1.25　.50
　　　Nos. 540-542 (3)　　2.00　1.00

Steel Workers, by
Constantin
Meunier — A149

Design: 3fr, The sower, field and dock workers, from "Monument to Labor," Brussels, by Constantin Meunier, horiz.

Engraved and Photogravure
1960, Apr. 30　　　　　Perf. 11½
543　A149　40c claret & brt red　.25　.25
544　A149　3fr brown & brt red　.50　.25

Socialist Party of Belgium, 75th anniv.

Congo River
Boat
Pilot — A150

Designs: 40c, Medical team. 1fr, Planting tree. 2fr, Sculptors. 2.50fr, Shot put. 3fr, Congolese officials. 6fr, Congolese and Belgian girls playing with doll. 8fr, Boy pointing on globe to independent Congo.

1960, June 30　Photo.　Perf. 11½
Size: 35x24mm
545　A150　10c bright red　　.25　.25
546　A150　40c rose claret　　.25　.25
547　A150　1fr brt lilac　　.60　.30
548　A150　2fr gray green　　.60　.30
549　A150　2.50fr blue　　1.00　.35
550　A150　3fr dk bl gray　　1.00　.30
Size: 51x35mm
551　A150　6fr violet bl　　2.50　.75
552　A150　8fr dk brown　　8.00　5.00
　　　Nos. 545-552 (8)　　14.20　7.50

Independence of Congo.

Europa Issue, 1960
Common Design Type
1960, Sept. 17
Size: 35x24½mm
553　CD3　3fr claret　　.40　.25
554　CD3　6fr gray　　.85　.30
　　　Nos. 553-554 (2)　　1.25　.55

Children Examining Stamp and
Globe — A152

1960, Oct. 1　Photo.　Perf. 11½
555　A152　40c bis & blk + label　.25　.25

Promoting stamp collecting among children.

H. J. W. Frère-
Orban
A153

Engraved and Photogravure
1960, Oct. 17　　　　　Unwmk.
Portrait in Brown
556　A153　10c orange yel　　.25　.25
557　A153　40c blue grn　　.25　.25
558　A153　1.50fr brt violet　　.70　.60
559　A153　3fr red　　.90　.25
　　　Nos. 556-559 (4)　　2.10　1.35

Centenary of Communal Credit Society.

King
Baudouin
and Queen
Fabiola
A154

1960, Dec. 13　Photo.　Perf. 11½
Portraits in Dark Brown
560　A154　40c green　　.35　.25
561　A154　3fr red lilac　　.90　.25
562　A154　6fr dull blue　　2.25　.45
　　　Nos. 560-562 (3)　　3.50　.95

Wedding of King Baudouin and Dona Fabiola de Mora y Aragon, Dec. 15, 1960.

Nos. 412, 414
Surcharged

1961-68　Typo.　Perf. 13½x14
563　A108　15c on 30c gray grn　.25　.25
564　A108　15c on 50c blue ('68)　.25　.25
565　A108　20c on 30c gray grn　.25　.25
　　　Nos. 563-565 (3)　　.75　.75

No. 412 Surcharged
and Precanceled

1961
566　A108　15c on 30c gray grn　.90　.25
567　A108　20c on 30c gray grn　1.90　1.00

See note after No. 197.

Nicolaus Rockox,
by Anthony Van
Dyck — A155

Engraved and Photogravure
1961, Mar. 18　　　　　Perf. 11½
568　A155　3fr bister, blk & brn　.35　.25

400th anniv. of the birth of Nicolaus Rockox, mayor of Antwerp.

Seal of Jan Bode,
Alderman of
Antwerp,
1264 — A156

1961, Apr. 16　　　　　Photo.
569　A156　3fr buff & brown　.35　.25

Issued for Stamp Day, April 16.

Senate
Building,
Brussels,
Laurel and
Sword
A157

Engraved and Photogravure
1961, Sept. 14　Unwmk.　Perf. 11½
570　A157　3fr brn & Prus grn　.55　.25
571　A157　6fr dk brn & dk car　1.00　.45

50th Conference of the Interparliamentary Union, Brussels, Sept. 14-22.

Europa Issue, 1961
Common Design Type
1961, Sept. 16　　　　　Photo.
572　CD4　3fr yel grn & dk grn　.25　.25
573　CD4　6fr org brn & blk　.50　.25

Atomic
Reactor
Plant, BR2,
Mol — A159

Designs: 3fr, Atomic Reactor BR3, vert. 6fr, Atomic Reactor plant BR3.

1961, Nov. 8　Unwmk.　Perf. 11½
574　A159　40c dk blue grn　.25　.25
575　A159　3fr red lilac　　.25　.25
576　A159　6fr bright blue　.45　.35
　　　Nos. 574-576 (3)　　.95　.85

Atomic nuclear research center at Mol.

Horta
Museum — A160

1962, Feb. 15　　　　　Engr.
577　A160　3fr red brown　.30　.25

Baron Victor Horta (1861-1947), architect.

Postrider,
16th
Century
A161

Engraved and Photogravure
1962, Mar. 25　　　　　Perf. 11½
Chalky Paper
578　A161　3fr brn & slate grn　.30　.25

Stamp Day. See No. 677.

Gerard Mercator
(Gerhard Kremer,
1512-1594),
Cartographer
A162

Engraved and Photogravure
1962, Apr. 14　　　　　Unwmk.
579　A162　3fr sepia & gray　.30　.25

Bro. Alexis-Marie
Gochet (1835-
1910), Geographer,
Educator — A163

Portrait: 3fr, Canon Pierre-Joseph Triest (1760-1836), educator and founder of hospitals and orphanages.

1962, May 19　Engr.　Perf. 11½
580　A163　2fr dark blue　　.30　.25
581　A163　3fr golden brown　.30　.25

Europa Issue, 1962
Common Design Type
1962, Sept. 15   Photo.
582 CD5 3fr dp car, citron & blk   .25 .25
583 CD5 6fr olive, citron & blk   .40 .40

Hand with Barbed Wire and Freed Hand — A165

1962, Sept. 16   Engr. & Photo.
584 A165 40c lt blue & blk   .25 .25

Issued in memory of concentration camp victims.

Adam, by Michelangelo, Broken Chain and UN Emblem — A166

1962, Nov. 24   Perf. 11½
585 A166 3fr gray & blk   .25 .25
586 A166 6fr lt redsh brn & dk brn   .45 .30

UN Declaration of Human Rights.

Henri Pirenne (1862-1935), Historian — A167

1963, Jan. 15   Engr.
587 A167 3fr ultramarine   .35 .25

Swordsmen and Ghent Belfry A168

3fr, Modern fencers. 6fr, Arms of the Royal and Knightly Guild of St. Michael, vert.

Engraved and Photogravure
1963, Mar. 23   Unwmk.   Perf. 11½
588 A168 1fr brn red & pale bl   .25 .25
589 A168 3fr dk vio & yel grn   .25 .25
590 A168 6fr gray, blk, red, bl & gold   .65 .35
   Nos. 588-590 (3)   1.15 .85

350th anniv. of the granting of a charter to the Ghent guild of fencers.

Stagecoach A169

1963, Apr. 7
591 A169 3fr gray & ocher   .25 .25

Stamp Day. See No. 678.

Hotel des Postes, Paris, Stagecoach and Stamp, 1863 A170

Perf. 11½
1963, May 7   Unwmk.   Engr.
592 A170 6fr dk brn, gray & yel grn   .55 .35

Cent. of the 1st Intl. Postal Conf., Paris, 1863.

"Peace," Child in Rye Field — A171

1963, May 8   Engr. & Photo.
593 A171 3fr grn, blk, yel & brn   .30 .25
594 A171 6fr buff, blk, brn & org   .75 .30

May 8th Movement for Peace. (On May 8, 1945, World War II ended in Europe).

Allegory and Shields of 17 Member Nations A172

1963, June 13   Unwmk.   Perf. 11½
595 A172 6fr blue & black   .55 .30

10th anniversary of the Conference of European Transport Ministers.

Seal of Union of Belgian Towns — A173

1963, June 17
596 A173 6fr grn, red, blk & gold   .55 .35

Intl. Union of Municipalities, 50th anniv.

Caravelle over Brussels National Airport A174

Photogravure and Engraved
1963, Sept. 1   Unwmk.   Perf. 11½
597 A174 3fr green & gray   .30 .25

40th anniversary of SABENA airline.

Europa Issue, 1963
Common Design Type
1963, Sept. 14   Photo.
Size: 35x24mm
598 CD6 3fr blk, dl red & lt brn   .70 .25
599 CD6 6fr blk, lt bl & lt brn   .90 .30
   Nos. 598-599 (2)   1.60 .55

Jules Destrée A176

Design: No. 601, Henry Van de Velde.

Perf. 11½
1963, Nov. 16   Unwmk.   Engr.
600 A176 1fr rose lilac   .25 .25
601 A176 1fr green   .25 .25

Jules Destrée (1863-1936), statesman and founder of the Royal Academy of French Language and Literature, and of Henry Van de Velde (1863-1957), architect.
No. 600 incorrectly inscribed "1864."

Development of the Mail, Bas-relief — A177

1963, Nov. 23   Engr. & Photo.
602 A177 50c dl red, slate & blk   .25 .25

Postal checking service, 50th anniv.

Dr. Armauer G. Hansen A178

Fight Against Leprosy: 2fr, Leprosarium. 5fr, Father Joseph Damien.

1964, Jan. 25   Unwmk.   Perf. 11½
603 A178 1fr brown org & blk   .25 .25
604 A178 2fr brown org & blk   .25 .25
605 A178 5fr brown org & blk   .45 .35
  a.   Souvenir sheet of 3, #603-605   3.00 2.75
   Nos. 603-605 (3)   .95 .85

No. 605a sold for 12fr.

Andreas Vesalius (1514-64), Anatomist — A179

Jules Boulvin (1855-1920), Mechanical Engineer A180

Design: 2fr, Henri Jaspar (1870-1939), statesman and lawyer.

Engraved and Photogravure
1964, Mar. 2   Unwmk.   Perf. 11½
606 A179 50c pale grn & blk   .25 .25
607 A180 1fr pale grn & blk   .25 .25
608 A180 2fr pale grn & blk   .25 .25
   Nos. 606-608 (3)   .75 .75

Postilion of Liege, 1830-40 — A181

1964, Apr. 5   Engr.   Perf. 11½
609 A181 3fr gray black   .25 .25

Issued for Stamp Day 1964.

Arms of Ostend A182

1964, May 16   Photo.
610 A182 3fr ultra, ver, gold & blk   .25 .25

Millennium of Ostend.

Flame, Hammer and Globe — A183

1fr, "SI" and globe. 2fr, Flame over wavy lines.

1964, July 18   Unwmk.   Perf. 11½
611 A183 50c dark blue & red   .25 .25
612 A183 1fr dark blue & red   .25 .25
613 A183 2fr dark blue & red   .25 .25
   Nos. 611-613 (3)   .75 .75

Centenary of the First Socialist International, founded in London, Sept. 28, 1864.

Europa Issue, 1964
Common Design Type
1964, Sept. 12   Photo.   Perf. 11½
Size: 24x35½mm
614 CD7 3fr yel grn, dk car & gray   .50 .25
615 CD7 6fr car rose, yel grn & bl   .90 .35

Benelux Issue

King Baudouin, Queen Juliana and Grand Duchess Charlotte — A185

1964, Oct. 12
616 A185 3fr olive, lt grn & mar   .40 .25

20th anniv. of the customs union of Belgium, Netherlands and Luxembourg.

Hand, Round & Pear-shaped Diamonds — A186

1965, Jan. 23   Unwmk.   Perf. 11½
617 A186 2fr ultra, dp car & blk   .25 .25

Diamond Exhibition "Diamantexpo," Antwerp, July 10-28, 1965.

Symbols of Textile Industry — A187

1965, Jan. 25   Photo.
618 A187 1fr blue, red & blk   .25 .25

Eighth textile industry exhibition "Textirama," Ghent, Jan. 29-Feb. 2, 1965.

Vriesia — A188

Designs: 2fr, Echinocactus. 3fr, Stapelia.

1965, Feb. 13　　Engr. & Photo.
619　A188　1fr multicolored　　.25　.25
620　A188　2fr multicolored　　.25　.25
621　A188　3fr multicolored　　.25　.25
　a.　Souvenir sheet of 3, #619-621　1.75　1.75
　　Nos. 619-621 (3)　　.75　.75

25th Ghent International Flower Exhibition, Apr. 24-May 3, 1965.
No. 621a was issued Apr. 26 and sold for 20fr.

Paul Hymans (1865-1941), Belgian Foreign Minister, First President of the League of Nations — A189

1965, Feb. 24　　Engr.　　Perf. 11½
622　A189　1fr dull purple　　.25　.25

Peter Paul Rubens — A190

2fr, Frans Snyders. 3fr, Adam van Noort. 6fr, Anthony Van Dyck. 8fr, Jacob Jordaens.

1965, Mar. 15　　Photo. & Engr.
Portraits in Sepia
623　A190　1fr carmine rose　　.25　.25
624　A190　2fr blue green　　.25　.25
625　A190　3fr plum　　.25　.25
626　A190　6fr deep carmine　　.50　.25
627　A190　8fr dark blue　　.65　.40
　　Nos. 623-627 (5)　　1.90　1.40

Issued to commemorate the founding of the General Savings and Pensions Bank.

Sir Rowland Hill as Philatelist — A191

1965, Mar. 27　　Engr.　　Perf. 11½
628　A191　50c blue green　　.25　.25

Issued to publicize youth philately. The design is from a mural by J. E. Van den Bussche in the General Post Office, Brussels.

Postmaster, c. 1833 — A192

1965, Apr. 26　　Unwmk.　　Perf. 11½
629　A192　3fr emerald　　.25　.25

Issued for Stamp Day.

Telephone, Globe and Teletype Paper — A193

1965, May 8　　Photo.
630　A193　2fr dull purple & blk　　.25　.25

Cent. of the ITU.

Staircase, Affligem Abbey — A194

1965, May 27　　Engr.
631　A194　1fr gray blue　　.25　.25

St. Jean Berchmans and his Birthplace A195

1965, May 27　　Engr. & Photo.
632　A195　2fr dk brn & red brn　　.25　.25

Issued to honor St. Jean Berchmans (1599-1621), Jesuit "Saint of the Daily Life."

TOC H Lamp and Arms of Poperinge — A196

1965, June 19　　Photo.　　Perf. 11½
633　A196　3fr ol bis, blk & car　　.25　.25

50th anniv. of the founding of Talbot House in Poperinge, which served British soldiers in World War I, and where the TOC H Movement began (Christian Social Service; TOC H is army code for Poperinge Center).

Belgian Farmers' Association (Boerenbond), 75th Anniv. — A197

50c, Farmer with tractor. 3fr, Farmer with horse-drawn roller.

Engraved and Photogravure
1965, July 17　　Unwmk.　　Perf. 11½
634　A197　50c bl, ol, bis brn & blk　　.25　.25
635　A197　3fr bl, ol grn, ol & blk　　.25　.25

Europa Issue, 1965
Common Design Type
1965, Sept. 25　　　　Perf. 11½
Size: 35½x24mm
636　CD8　1fr dl rose & blk　　.25　.25
637　CD8　3fr grnsh gray & blk　　.25　.25

Leopold I (1790-1865) A199

1965, Nov. 13　　Engr.
638　A199　3fr sepia　　.25　.25
639　A199　6fr bright violet　　.55　.40

The designs of the vignettes are similar to A4 and A5.

Joseph Lebeau (1794-1865), Foreign Minister — A200

1965, Nov. 13　　Photo.
640　A200　1fr multicolored　　.25　.25

Tourist Issue

Grapes and Houses, Hoeilaart A201　　Bridge and Castle, Huy A202

No. 643, British War Memorial, Ypres. No. 644, Castle Spontin. No. 645, City Hall, Louvain. No. 646, Ourthe Valley. No. 647, Romanesque Cathedral, gothic fountain, Nivalles. No. 648, Water mill, Kasterlee. No. 649, City Hall, Cloth Guild and Statue of Margarethe of Austria, Malines. No. 650, Town Hall, Lier. No. 651, Castle Bouillon. No. 652, Fountain and Kursaal Spa. No. 653, Windmill, Bokrijk. No. 654, Mountain road, Vielsalm. No. 655, View of Furnes. No. 656, City Hall and Belfry, Mons. No. 657, St. Martin's Church, Aalst. No. 658, Abbey and fountain, St. Hubert.

1965-71　　Engr.　　Perf. 11½
641　A201　50c vio bl, lt bl & yel grn　　.25　.25
642　A202　50c sl grn, lt bl & red brn　　.25　.25
643　A202　1fr grn, lt bl, sal & brn　　.25　.25
644　A202　1fr ind, lt bl & ol　　.25　.25
645　A201　1fr brt rose lil, lt bl & blk　　.25　.25
646　A202　1fr blk, grnsh bl & ol　　.25　.25
647　A201　1.50fr sl, sky bl & bis　　.25　.25
648　A202　1.50fr blk, bl & ol　　.25　.25
649　A201　1.50fr dk bl & buff　　.25　.25
650　A201　2fr brn, lt bl & ind　　.25　.25
651　A202　2fr dk brn, grn & ocher　　.25　.25
652　A202　2fr bl, brt grn & blk　　.25　.25
653　A202　2fr bl, lt bl & yel　　.25　.25
654　A202　2fr blk, lt bl & yel grn　　.25　.25
655　A202　2fr car, lt bl & dk brn　　.25　.25
656　A201　2.50fr vio, buff & blk　　.25　.25
657　A201　2.50fr vio, lt bl, blk & ol　　.25　.25
658　A201　2.50fr vio bl & yel　　.25　.25
　　Nos. 641-658 (18)　　4.50　4.50

Issued: Nos. 641-642, 11/13/65; Nos. 643-644, 7/15/67; Nos. 645-646, 12/16/68; Nos. 647-648, 7/6/70; Nos. 649, 656, 12/11/71; Nos. 650-651, 11/11/66; Nos. 652-653, 6/24/68; Nos. 654-655, 9/6/69; Nos. 657-658, 9/11/71.

Queen Elisabeth Type of Semi-Postal Issue, 1956
1965, Dec. 23　　Photo.　　Perf. 11½
659　SP305　3fr dark gray　　.25　.25

Queen Elisabeth (1876-1965).
A dark frame has been added in design of No. 659; 1956 date has been changed to

1965; inscription in bottom panel is Koningin Elisabeth Reine Elisabeth 3F.

"Peace on Earth" A203

Arms of Pope Paul VI — A204

1fr, "Looking toward a Better Future" (family, new buildings, sun & landscape).

1966, Feb. 12　　Photo.　　Perf. 11½
660　A203　50c multicolored　　.25　.25
661　A203　1fr ocher, blk & bl　　.25　.25
662　A204　3fr gray, gold, car & blk　　.25　.25
　　Nos. 660-662 (3)　　.75　.75

75th anniv. of the encyclical by Pope Leo XIII "Rerum Novarum," which proclaimed the general principles for the organization of modern industrial society.

Rural Mailman, 19th Century — A205

1966, Apr. 17　　Photo.　　Unwmk.
663　A205　3fr blk, dl yel & pale lil　　.25　.25

Stamp Day. For overprint see No. 673.

Iguanodon, Natural Science Institute A206

Arend-Roland Comet, Observatory A207

Designs: No. 665, Ancestral head and spiral pattern, Kasai; Central Africa Museum. No. 666, Snowflakes, Meteorological Institute. No. 667, Seal of Charles V, Royal Archives. No. 668, Medieval scholar, Royal Library. 8fr, Satellite and rocket, Space Aeronautics Institute.

1966, May 28　　Engr. & Photo.
664　A206　1fr green & blk　　.25　.25
665　A206　2fr gray, blk & brn org　　.25　.25
666　A206　2fr blue, blk & yel　　.25　.25
667　A207　3fr dp rose, blk & gold　　.25　.25
668　A207　3fr multicolored　　.25　.25
669　A207　6fr ultra, yel & blk　　.40　.25
670　A207　8fr multicolored　　.55　.40
　　Nos. 664-670 (7)　　2.20　1.90

National scientific heritage.

Atom Symbol and Retort — A208

Engraved and Photogravure
1966, July 9   Unwmk.   *Perf. 11½*
671 A208 6fr gray, blk & red   .40 .25

Issued to publicize the European chemical plant, EUROCHEMIC, at Mol.

August Kekulé, Benzene Ring — A209

1966, July 9
672 A209 3fr brt blue & blk   .25 .25

August Friedrich Kekule (1829-96), chemistry professor at University of Ghent (1858-67).

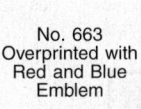

No. 663 Overprinted with Red and Blue Emblem

1966, July 11   Photo.
673 A205 3fr multicolored   .25 .25

19th Intl. P.T.T. Cong., Brussels, July 11-15.

Rik Wouters (1882-1916), Self-portrait A210

1966, Sept. 6   Photo.   *Perf. 11½*
674 A210 60c multicolored   .25 .25

Europa Issue, 1966
Common Design Type
1966, Sept. 24   Engr.   *Perf. 11½*
Size: 24x34mm
675 CD9 3fr brt green   .25 .25
676 CD9 6fr brt rose lilac   .55 .25

Types of 1962-1963 Overprinted in Black and Red

1966, Nov. 11   Engr. & Photo.
677 A161 60c sepia & grnsh gray .25 .25
678 A169 3fr sepia & pale bister .25 .25

75th anniv., Royal Fed. of Phil. Circles of Belgium. Overprint shows emblem of F.I.P.

Lions Emblem — A214

1967, Jan. 14   *Perf. 11½*
679 A214 3fr gray, blk & bl   .25 .25
680 A214 6fr lt green, blk & vio .40 .25

Lions Club Intl., 50th anniv.

Pistol by Leonhard Cleuter A215

1967, Feb. 11   Photo.
681 A215 2fr dp car, blk & cream .25 .25

Fire Arms Museum in Liege.

International Tourist Year Emblem A216

1967, Feb. 11
682 A216 6fr ver, ultra & blk   .50 .25

International Tourist Year, 1967.

Birches and Trientalis A217

Design: No. 684, Dunes, beach grass, privet and blue thistles.

1967, Mar. 11   Photo.   *Perf. 11½*
683 A217 1fr multicolored   .25 .25
684 A217 1fr multicolored   .25 .25

Issued to publicize the nature preserves at Hautes Fagnes and Westhoek.

Paul Emile Janson(1872-1944), Lawyer, Statesman — A218

1967, Apr. 15   Engr.   *Perf. 11½*
685 A218 10fr blue   .80 .25

Postilion A219

1967, Apr. 16   Photo. & Engr.
686 A219 3fr rose red & claret   .25 .25

Issued for Stamp Day, 1967.

Inscribed: "FITCE"
1967, June 24   *Perf. 11½*
687 A219 10fr ultra, sep & emer .80 .45

Issued to commemorate the meeting of the Federation of Common Market Telecommunications Engineers, Brussels, July 3-8.

Europa Issue, 1967
Common Design Type
1967, May 2   Photo.
Size: 24x35mm
688 CD10 3fr blk, lt bl & red   .25 .25
689 CD10 6fr blk, grnsh gray &
           yel   .80 .30

Flax, Shuttle and Mills — A221

1967, June 3   Photo.   *Perf. 11½*
690 A221 6fr tan & multi   .40 .25

Belgian linen industry.

Old Kursaal, Ostend — A222

1967, June 3   Engr. & Photo.
691 A222 2fr dk brn, lt bl & yel .25 .25

700th anniversary of Ostend as a city.

Charles Plisnier and Lodewijk de Raet Foundations A223

Designs: No. 692, Caesar Crossing Rubicon, 15th Century Tapestry. No. 693, Emperor Maximilian Killing a Boar, 16th cent. tapestry.

1967, Sept. 2   Photo.   *Perf. 11½*
692 A223 1fr multicolored   .25 .25
693 A223 1fr multicolored   .25 .25

Universities of Ghent and Liège, 150th Anniv. — A224

Arms of Universities: No. 694, Ghent. No. 695, Liege.

Engraved and Photogravure
1967, Sept. 30   *Perf. 11½*
694 A224 3fr gray & multi   .25 .25
695 A224 3fr gray & multi   .25 .25

Princess Margaret of York — A225

1967, Sept. 30   Photo.
696 A225 6fr multicolored   .45 .30

British Week, Sept. 28-Oct. 2.

"Virga Jesse," Hasselt — A226

1967, Nov. 11   Engr.   *Perf. 11½*
697 A226 1fr slate blue   .25 .25

Christmas, 1967.

Hand Guarding Worker — A227

1968, Feb. 3   Photo.   *Perf. 11½*
698 A227 3fr multicolored   .25 .25

Issued to publicize industrial safety.

Military Mailman, 1916, by James Thiriar — A228

Engraved and Photogravure
1968, Mar. 17   *Perf. 11½*
699 A228 3fr sepia, lt bl & brn .25 .25

Issued for Stamp Day, 1968.

View of Grammont and Seal of Baudouin VI — A229

Historic Sites: 3fr, Theux-Franchimont fortress, sword and seal. 6fr, Neolithic cave and artifacts, Spiennes. 10fr, Roman oil lamp and St. Medard's Church, Wervik.

1968, Apr. 13   Photo.   *Perf. 11½*
700 A229 2fr bl, blk, lil & rose .25 .25
701 A229 3fr orange, blk & car .25 .25
702 A229 6fr ultra, ind & bis   .45 .25
703 A229 10fr tan, blk, yel & gray .75 .30
    Nos. 700-703 (4)   1.70 1.05

Stamp of 1866, No. 23 — A230

1968, Apr. 13   Engr.   Perf. 13
704 A230 1fr black   .25 .25
Centenary of the Malines Stamp Printery.

Europa Issue, 1968
Common Design Type
1968, Apr. 27   Photo.   Perf. 11½
Size: 35x24mm
705 CD11 3fr dl grn, gold & blk   *.30* .25
706 CD11 6fr carmine, sil & blk   *.95* .25

St. Laurent Abbey, Liège — A232

Designs: 3fr, Gothic Church, Lisseweghe. No. 709. Barges in Zandvliet locks. No. 710, Ship in Neuzen lock, Ghent Canal. 10fr, Ronquieres canal ship lift.

Engraved and Photogravure
1968, Sept. 7   Perf. 11½
707 A232 2fr ultra, gray ol &
                   sep   .25 .25
708 A232 3fr ol bis, gray & sep   .30 .25
709 A232 6fr ind, brt bl & sep   .55 .25
710 A232 6fr black, grnsh bl &
                   ol   .45 .25
711 A232 10fr bister, brt bl & sep .80 .30
            Nos. 707-711 (5)   2.35 1.30
No. 710 issued Dec. 14 for opening of lock at Neuzen, Netherlands.

Christmas Candle — A233

1968, Dec. 7   Perf. 11½
712 A233 1fr multicolored   .25 .25
Christmas, 1968.

St. Albertus Magnus — A234

1969, Feb. 15   Engr.   Perf. 11½
713 A234 2fr sepia   .25 .25
The Church of St. Paul in Antwerp (16th century) was destroyed by fire in Apr. 1968.

Ruins of Aulne Abbey, Gozee — A235

1969, Feb. 15   Engr. & Photo.
714 A235 3fr brt pink & blk   .25 .25
Aulne Abbey was destroyed in 1794 during the French Revolution.

The Travelers, Roman Sculpture — A236

1969, Mar. 15   Engr.   Perf. 11½
715 A236 2fr violet brown   .25 .25
2,000th anniversary of city of Arlon.

Broodjes Chapel, Antwerp — A237

1969, Mar. 15   Engr. & Photo.
716 A237 3fr gray & blk   .25 .25
150th anniv. of public education in Antwerp.

Post Office Train — A238

1969, Apr. 13   Photo.   Perf. 11½
717 A238 3fr multicolored   .25 .25
Issued for Stamp Day.

Europa Issue, 1969
Common Design Type
1969, Apr. 26   Size: 35x24mm
718 CD12 3fr lt grn, brn & blk   *.25* .25
719 CD12 6fr sal, rose car & blk *.50* .25

NATO Type of 1959 Redrawn and Dated "1949-1969"
1969, May 31   Photo.   Perf. 11½
720 A142 6fr org brn & ultra   .45 .35
20th anniv. of NATO. No. 720 inscribed Belgique-Belgie and OTAN-NAVO.

Construction Workers, by F. Leger — A240

1969, May 31
721 A240 3fr multicolored   .25 .25
50th anniversary of the ILO.

World Bicycling Road Championships, Terlaemen to Zolder, Aug. 10. — A241

1969, July 5   Photo.   Perf. 11½
722 A241 6fr Bicyclist   .50 .30

Ribbon in Benelux Colors — A242

1969, Sept. 6   Photo.   Perf. 11½
723 A242 3fr blk, red, ultra & yel .25 .25
Signing of the customs union of Belgium, Netherlands & Luxembourg, 25th anniv.

Annevoie Garden and Pascali Rose A243

No. 725, Lochristi Garden and begonia.

1969, Sept. 6
724 A243 2fr multicolored   .25 .25
725 A243 2fr multicolored   .25 .25

Armstrong, Collins, Aldrin and Map Showing Tranquillity Base — A245

1969, Sept. 20   Photo.
726 A245 6fr black   .45 .30
See note after Algeria No. 427. See No. B846.

Wounded Veteran — A246

1969, Oct. 11   Engr.   Perf. 11½
727 A246 1fr blue gray   .25 .25
Natl. war veterans' aid organization (O.N.I.G.). The design is similar to type SP10.

Mailman — A247

1969, Oct. 18   Photo.
728 A247 1fr deep rose & multi   .25 .25
Issued to publicize youth philately. Design by Danielle Saintenoy, 14.

Kennedy Tunnel Under the Schelde, Antwerp A248

6fr, Three highways crossing near Loncin.

1969, Nov. 8   Engr.   Perf. 11½
729 A248 3fr multicolored   .25 .25
730 A248 6fr multicolored   .40 .35
Issued to publicize the John F. Kennedy Tunnel under the Schelde and the Walloon auto route and interchange near Loncin.

Henry Carton de Wiart, by Gaston Geleyn — A249

1969, Nov. 8
731 A249 6fr sepia   .50 .35
Count de Wiart (1869-1951), statesman.

The Census at Bethlehem (detail), by Peter Brueghel A250

1969, Dec. 13   Photo.
732 A250 1.50fr multicolored   .25 .25
Christmas, 1969.

Symbols of Bank's Activity, 100fr Coin A251

1969, Dec. 13   Engr. & Photo.
733 A251 3.50fr lt ultra, blk & sil .25 .25
50th anniv. of the Industrial Credit Bank (Societe nationale de credit a l'industrie).

Camellia — A252

1970, Jan. 31   Photo.   Perf. 11½
734 A252 1.50fr shown   .25 .25
735 A252 2.50fr Water lily   .25 .25
736 A252 3.50fr Azalea   .30 .25
   a.   Souvenir sheet of 3, #734-736   2.00 1.75
            Nos. 734-736 (3)   .80 .75
Ghent Int'l Flower Exhibition. No. 736a was issued Apr. 25 and sold for 25fr.

Beeches in Botanical Garden — A253

1970, Mar. 7   Engr. & Photo.
737 A253 3.50fr shown   .30 .25
738 A253 7fr Birches   .55 .45
European Nature Conservation Year.

Youth Stamp
Day — A254

1970, Apr. 4   **Photo.**
739 A254 1.50fr Mailman   .25 .25

New UPU Headquarters and
Monument, Bern — A255

1970, Apr. 12   **Engr. & Photo.**
740 A255 3.50fr grn & lt grn   .30 .25
Opening of the new UPU Headquarters,
Bern.

Europa Issue, 1970
Common Design Type
1970, May 1   **Photo.**   *Perf. 11½*
    Size: 35x24mm
741 CD13 3.50fr rose cl, yel &
      blk   .30 .25
742 CD13 7fr ultra, pink & blk   .80 .30

Cooperative Alliance Emblem — A257

1970, June 27   **Photo.**   *Perf. 11½*
743 A257 7fr black & org   .55 .25
Intl. Cooperative Alliance, 75th anniv.

Ship in
Ghent
Terneuzen
Lock,
Zelzate
A258

Design: No. 745, Clock Tower, Virton, vert.

1970, June 27   **Engr. & Photo.**
744 A258 2.50fr indigo & lt bl   .25 .25
745 A258 2.50fr dk pur & ocher   .25 .25

King
Baudouin — A259

1970-80   **Engr.**   *Perf. 11½*
746 A259 1.75fr green ('71)   .25 .25
747 A259 2.25fr gray grn ('72)   .35 .25
748 A259 2.50fr gray grn ('74)   .25 .25
749 A259 3fr emerald ('73)   .25 .25
750 A259 3.25fr violet brn ('75)   .25 .25
751 A259 3.50fr orange brn   .25 .25
752 A259 3.50fr brown ('71)   .40 .25
753 A259 4fr blue ('72)   .35 .25
754 A259 4.50fr brown ('72)   .30 .25
755 A259 4.50fr grnsh bl ('74)   .35 .25
756 A259 5fr lilac ('72)   .40 .25
757 A259 6fr rose car ('72)   .50 .25
758 A259 6.50fr vio blk ('74)   .45 .25
759 A259 7fr ver ('71)   .55 .25
760 A259 7.50fr brt pink ('75)   .55 .25
761 A259 8fr black ('72)   .60 .25
762 A259 9fr ol bis ('71)   .80 .25
763 A259 9fr red brn ('80)   .75 .25
764 A259 10fr rose car ('71)   .80 .25
765 A259 11fr gray ('76)   .85 .25
766 A259 12fr Prus bl ('72)   .90 .25
767 A259 13fr slate ('75)   1.00 .25
768 A259 14fr gray grn ('76)   1.10 .25
769 A259 15fr lt vio ('71)   1.00 .25
770 A259 16fr green ('77)   1.75 .25
771 A259 17fr dull mag ('75)   1.25 .25
772 A259 18fr steel bl ('71)   1.25 .25

773 A259 18fr grnsh bl ('80)   1.75 .25
774 A259 20fr vio bl ('71)   1.25 .25
775 A259 22fr black ('74)   1.75 1.50
776 A259 22fr lt grn ('79)   1.60 .40
777 A259 25fr lilac ('75)   1.75 .25
778 A259 30fr ocher ('72)   2.00 .25
779 A259 35fr emer ('80)   3.25 .30
780 A259 40fr dk blue ('77)   4.00 .30
781 A259 45fr brown ('80)   4.75 .45

   Perf. 12½x13½
    Photo.
   Size: 22x17mm
782 A259 3fr emerald ('73)   1.10 .75
   a. Booklet pane of 4 (#782 and
      3 #783) + labels   10.00
783 A259 4fr blue ('73)   .50 .50
784 A259 4.50fr grnsh bl ('75)   .40 .30
785 A259 5fr lilac ('73)   .35 .25
   a. Booklet pane of 4 + labels   2.75
786 A259 6fr carmine ('78)   .40 .25
787 A259 6.50fr dull pur ('75)   .45 .25
788 A259 8fr gray ('78)   .55 .25
   Nos. 746-788 (43)   43.35 13.25

No. 751 issued Sept. 7, 1970, King
Baudouin's 40th birthday, and is inscribed
"1930-1970." Dates are omitted on other
stamps of type A259.
Nos. 754, 756 also issued in coils in 1973
and Nos. 757, 761 in 1978, with black control
number on back of every fifth stamp.
Nos. 782-788 issued in booklets only. Nos.
782, 784 have one straight-edge, Nos. 786,
788 have two. The rest have one or two.
Stamps in the panes are tete-beche. Each
pane has two labels showing Belgian Postal
emblem with a large selvage with postal code
instructions. Nos. 786, 788 not luminescent.
See designs M2, O4. See Nos. 432a, 432b,
977a, 977b.

UN Headquarters,
NY — A260

1970, Sept. 12   **Engr. & Photo.**
789 A260 7fr dk brn & Prus bl   .55 .25
25th anniversary of the United Nations.

25th International
Fair at Ghent, Sept.
12-27 — A261

1970, Sept. 19
790 A261 1.50fr Fair emblem   .25 .25

Queen
Fabiola — A262

1970, Sept. 19
791 A262 3.50fr lt blue & blk   .30 .25
Issued to publicize the Queen Fabiola Foundation for Mental Health.

The Mason, by
Georges
Minne — A263

1970, Oct. 17   *Perf. 11½*
792 A263 3.50fr dull yel & sep   .30 .25
50th anniv. of the National Housing Society.

Man, Woman and City — A264

1970, Oct. 17   **Photo.**
793 A264 2.50fr black & multi   .25 .25
Social Security System, 25th anniv.

Madonna with the
Grapes, by Jean
Gossaert — A265

1970, Nov. 14   **Engr.**   *Perf. 11½*
794 A265 1.50fr dark brown   .25 .25
Christmas 1970.

Arms of
Eupen,
Malmédy
and Saint-
Vith
A266

Engraved and Photogravure
1970, Dec. 12   *Perf. 11½*
795 A266 7fr sepia & dk brn   .55 .25
The 50th anniversary of the return of the
districts of Eupen, Malmédy and Saint-Vith.

Automatic
Telephone — A267

1971, Jan. 16   **Photo.**   *Perf. 11½*
796 A267 1.50fr multicolored   .25 .25
Automatization of Belgian telephone system.

50th
Automobile
Show,
Brussels,
Jan. 19-31
A268

1971, Jan. 16
797 A268 2.50fr "Auto"   .25 .25

Belgian Touring
Club, 75th
Anniv. — A269

1971, Feb. 13
798 A269 3.50fr Club emblem   .30 .25

Tournai
Cathedral
A270

1971, Feb. 13   **Engr.**
799 A270 7fr bright blue   .45 .35
Cathedral of Tournal, 8th centenary.

"The Letter Box,"
by T.
Lobrichon — A271

1971, Mar. 13   **Engr.**   *Perf. 11½*
800 A271 1.50fr dark brown   .25 .25
Youth philately.

Albert I, Jules Destrée and
Academy — A272

Engraved and Photogravure
1971, Apr. 17   *Perf. 11½*
801 A272 7fr gray & blk   .55 .35
Founding of the Royal Academy of Language and French Literature, 50th anniv.

Stamp Day — A273

1971, Apr. 25
802 A273 3.50fr Mailman   .30 .25

Europa Issue, 1971
Common Design Type
1971, May 1   **Photo.**
   Size: 35x24mm
803 CD14 3.50fr olive & blk   .55 .25
804 CD14 7fr dk ol grn & blk   .75 .30

Radar Ground Station A275

1971, May 15   **Photo.**   **Perf. 11½**
805 A275 7fr multicolored   .55   .35
   3rd World Telecommunications Day.

Antarctic Explorer, Ship and Penguins — A276

1971, June 19   **Photo.**   **Perf. 11½**
806 A276 10fr multicolored   .50   .45
   Tenth anniversary of the Antarctic Treaty pledging peaceful uses of and scientific cooperation in Antarctica.

Abbey of Notre Dame, Orval, 900th Anniv. — A277

1971, June 26   **Engr.**   **Perf. 11½**
807 A277 2.50fr Orval Abbey   .25   .25

Georges Hubin (1863-1947), Socialist Leader, Minister of State — A278

1971, June 26   **Engr. & Photo.**
808 A278 1.50fr vio bl & blk   .25   .25

Mr. and Mrs. Goliath, the Giants of Ath — A279

View of Ghent A280

1971, Aug. 7   **Photo.**
809 A279 2.50fr multicolored   .25   .25

Engr.
810 A280 2.50fr gray brown   .25   .25

Test Tubes and Insulin Molecular Diagram — A281

1971, Aug. 7   **Photo.**
811 A281 10fr lt gray & multi   .70   .45
   50th anniversary of the discovery of insulin.

Family and "50" — A283

1971, Sept. 11   **Photo.**
812 A283 1.50fr green & multi   .25   .25
   Belgian Large Families League, 50th anniv.

Achaemenidaen Tomb, Buzpar, and Persian Coat of Arms — A284

Engraved and Photogravure
1971, Oct. 2   **Perf. 11½**
813 A284 7fr multicolored   .55   .35
   2500th anniversary of the founding of the Persian empire by Cyrus the Great.

Dr. Jules Bordet (1870-1945), Serologist, Immunologist A285

Portrait: No. 815, Stijn Streuvels(1871-1945), Novelist (pen name Frank Lateur).

1971, Oct. 2   **Engr.**
814 A285 3.50fr slate green   .25   .25
815 A285 3.50fr dark brown   .25   .25

Flight into Egypt, Anonymous A286

1971, Nov. 13   **Photo.**
816 A286 1.50fr multicolored   .25   .25
   Christmas 1971.

Federation of Belgian Industries (FIB), 25th Anniv. — A287

1971, Nov. 13
817 A287 3.50fr black, ultra & gold   .30   .25

International Book Year 1972 — A288

1972, Feb. 19
818 A288 7fr bister, blk & bl   .55   .30

Coins of Belgium and Luxembourg A289

1972, Feb. 19   **Engr. & Photo.**
819 A289 1.50fr orange, blk & sil   .25   .25
   Economic Union of Belgium and Luxembourg, 50th anniversary.

Traffic Signal and Road Signs — A290

1972, Feb. 19   **Photo.**
820 A290 3.50fr blue & multi   .25   .25
   Via Secura (road safety), 25th anniversary.

Belgica '72 Emblem A291

1972, Mar. 27
821 A291 3.50fr choc, bl & lil   .30   .25
   International Philatelic Exhibition, Brussels, June 24-July 9.

"Your Heart is your Health" — A292

1972, Mar. 27
822 A292 7fr blk, gray, red & bl   .50   .30
   World Health Day.

Auguste Vermeylen (1872-1945), Flemish Writer, Educator — A293

Portrait, by Isidore Opsomer.
1972, Mar. 27
823 A293 2.50fr multicolored   .25   .25

Stamp Day 1972 — A294

1972, Apr. 23
824 A294 3.50fr Astronaut on Moon   .30   .25

Europa Issue 1972
Common Design Type
1972, Apr. 29   **Size: 24x35mm**
825 CD15 3.50fr lt blue & multi   *.35*   .25
826 CD15   7fr rose & multi   *.60*   .30

"Freedom of the Press" — A296

1972, May 13   **Photo.**   **Perf. 11½**
827 A296 2.50fr multicolored   .25   .25
   50th anniv. of the BELGA news information agency and 25th Congress of the Intl. Federation of Newspaper Editors (F.I.E.J.), Brussels, May 15-19.

Freight Cars with Automatic Coupling A297

1972, June 3
828 A297 7fr blue & multi   .50   .30
   Intl. Railroad Union, 50th anniv.

View of Couvin — A298

No. 830, Aldeneik Church, Maaseik, vert.

1972, June 24   **Engr.**   **Perf. 13½x14**
829 A298 2.50fr bl, vio brn & sl grn   .25   .25
830 A298 2.50fr dk brown & bl   .25   .25

Beatrice, by Gustave de Smet — A299

1972, Sept. 9   **Photo.**   **Perf. 11½**
831 A299 3fr multicolored   .30   .25
   Youth philately.

Radar Station, Intelsat 4 — A300

1972, Sept. 16
832 A300 3.50fr lt bl, sil & blk   .30 .25
Opening of the Lessive satellite earth station.

Frans Masereel(1889-1972), Wood Engraver — A301

1972, Oct. 21
833 A301 4.50fr Self-portrait   .35 .25

Adoration of the Kings, by Felix Timmermans A302

1972, Nov. 11   Photo.   Perf. 11½
834 A302 3.50fr black & multi   .30 .25
Christmas 1972.

Maria Theresa, Anonymous A303

1972, Dec. 16   Photo.   Perf. 11½
835 A303 2fr multicolored   .25 .25
200th anniversary of the Belgian Academy of Science, Literature and Art, founded by Empress Maria Theresa.

WMO Emblem, Meteorological Institute, Ukkel — A304

1973, Mar. 24   Photo.   Perf. 11½
836 A304 9fr blue & multi   .70 .35
Cent. of intl. meteorological cooperation.

Natl. Industrial Fire Prevention Campaign — A305

1973, Mar. 24
837 A305 2fr "Fire"   .25 .25

Man and WHO Emblem — A306

1973, Apr. 7
838 A306 8fr dk red, ocher & blk   .50 .35
25th anniv. of WHO.

Europa Issue 1973
Common Design Type

1973, Apr. 28   Size: 35x24mm
839 CD16 4.50fr org brn, vio bl & yel   .35 .25
840 CD16 8fr olive, dk bl & yel   .65 .40

Thurn and Taxis Courier — A308

Engraved and Photogravure
1973, Apr. 28   Perf. 11½
841 A308 4.50fr black & red brn   .35 .25
Stamp Day.

Arrows Circling Globe — A309

1973, May 12   Photo.
842 A309 3.50fr dp ocher & multi   .30 .25
5th International Telecommunications Day.

Workers' Sports Exhibition Poster, Ghent, 1913 A310

1973, May 12
843 A310 4.50fr multicolored   .35 .25
60th anniversary of the International Workers' Sports Movement.

Fair Emblem A311

1973, May 12   Photo.   Perf. 11½
844 A311 4.50fr multicolored   .35 .25
25th International Fair, Liege, May 12-27.

DC-10 and 1923 Biplane over Brussels Airport — A312

Design: 10fr, Tips biplane, 1908.

1973, May 19   Engr. & Photo.
845 A312 8fr gray bl, blk & ultra   .65 .40
846 A312 10fr grn, lt bl & blk   .80 .45
50th anniv. of SABENA, Belgian airline (8fr) and 25th anniv. of the "Vieilles Tiges" Belgian flying pioneers' society (10fr).

Adolphe Sax and Tenor Saxophone A313

1973, Sept. 15   Photo.
847 A313 9fr green, blk & bl   .60 .30
Adolphe Sax (1814-1894), inventor of saxophone.

Fresco from Bathhouse, Ostend — A314

1973, Sept. 15
848 A314 4.50fr multicolored   .35 .25
Year of the Spa.

St. Nicholas Church, Eupen — A315

No. 850, Town Hall, Leau. No. 851, Aarshot Church. No. 852, Chimay Castle. No. 853, Gemmenich Border: Belgium, Germany, Netherlands. No. 854, St. Monan and church, Nassogne. No. 855, Church tower, Dottignes. No. 856, Grand-Place, Sint-Truiden.

1973-75   Engr.   Perf. 13
849 A315   2fr plum, sep & lt vio   .25 .25
850 A315   3fr black, lt bl & mar   .50 .25
851 A315   3fr brn blk & yel   .30 .25
852 A315   4fr grnsh blk & grnsh bl   .35 .25
853 A315   4fr grnsh blk & bl   .40 .25
854 A315   4fr grnsh blk & bl   .40 .25

855 A315   4.50fr multicolored   .50 .25
856 A315   5fr multicolored   .50 .25
    Nos. 849-856 (8)   3.20 2.00
Nos. 851, 855 not luminescent. Nos. 850, 852-854, 856 horiz.

Charley, by Henri Evenepoel — A316

1973, Oct. 13   Photo.   Perf. 11½
857 A316 3fr multicolored   .25 .25
Youth philately.

Luminescent Paper
Starting with No. 858, all stamps are on luminescent paper unless otherwise noted.

Jean-Baptiste Moens — A317

1973, Oct. 13   Engr. & Photo.
858 A317 10fr multi + label   .80 .45
50th anniversary of the Belgian Stamp Dealers' Association. Printed in sheets of 12 stamps and 12 labels showing association emblem.

Adoration of the Shepherds, by Hugo van der Goes — A318

1973, Nov. 17   Engr.   Perf. 11½
859 A318 4fr blue   .30 .25
Christmas 1973.

Louis Pierard, by M. I. Ianchelevici A319

1973, Nov. 17   Engr. & Photo.
860 A319 4fr vermilion & buff   .30 .25
Louis Pierard (1886-1952), journalist, member of Parliament.

Highway, Automobile Club Emblem A320

1973, Nov. 17   **Photo.**
861 A320 5fr yellow & multi   .40   .25
   Flemish Automobile Club, 50th anniv.

Early Microphone, Emblem of Radio Belgium — A321

1973, Nov. 24   **Engr. & Photo.**
862 A321 4fr blue & black   .35   .25
   50th anniversary of Radio Belgium.

Felicien Rops (1833-1898), Painter, Engraver A323

Engraved and Photogravure
1973, Dec. 8   **Perf. 11½**
863 A323 7fr Self-portrait   .55   .25

King Albert, (1875-1934) A324

1974, Feb. 16   **Photo.**   **Perf. 11½**
864 A324 4fr Prus green & blk   .30   .25

Sun, Bird, Flowers and Girl — A325

1974, Mar. 25   **Photo.**   **Perf. 11½**
865 A325 3fr violet & multi   .25   .25
   Protection of the environment.

NATO Emblem A326

1974, Apr. 20   **Photo.**   **Perf. 11½**
866 A326 10fr dp to lt blue   .75   .40
   25th anniversary of the signing of the North Atlantic Treaty.

Hubert Krains — A327

1974, Apr. 27   **Engr. & Photo.**
867 A327 5fr black & gray   .40   .25
   Stamp Day.

Europa Issue

"Destroyed City," by Ossip Zadkine — A328

Design: 10fr, Solidarity, by Georges Minne.

1974, May 4
868 A328 5fr black & red   .65   .25
869 A328 10fr black & ultra   .80   .40

Children A329

1974, May 18   **Photo.**   **Perf. 11½**
870 A329 4fr lt blue & multi   .30   .25
   10th Lay Youth Festival.

Planetarium, Brussels A330

Soleilmont Abbey Ruins — A331

4fr, Pillory, Braine-le-Chateau. 7fr, Fountain, Ghent (procession symbolic of Chamber of Rhetoric). 10fr, Belfry, Bruges, vert.

Engr. and Photo.
1974, June 22   **Perf. 11½**
871 A330 3fr sky blue & blk   .30   .25
872 A330 4fr lilac rose & blk   .40   .25
873 A331 5fr lt green & blk   .45   .25
874 A331 7fr dull yellow & blk   .55   .25
875 A330 10fr black, blue & brn   .70   .45
     Nos. 871-875 (5)   2.40   1.45
   Historic buildings and monuments.

"BENELUX" A332

1974, Sept. 7   **Photo.**   **Perf. 11½**
876 A332 5fr bl grn, dk grn & lt bl   .35   .25
   30th anniversary of the signing of the customs union of Belgium, Netherlands and Luxembourg.

Jan Vekemans, by Cornelis de Vos — A333

1974, Sept. 14
877 A333 3fr multicolored   .25   .25
   Youth philately.

Leon Tresignies, Willebroek Canal Bridge A334

1974, Sept. 28   **Engr. & Photo.**
878 A334 4fr brn & ol grn   .35   .25
   60th death anniversary of Corporal Leon Tresignies (1886-1914), hero of World War I.

Montgomery Blair, UPU Emblem A335

10fr, Heinrich von Stephan, UPU emblem.

1974, Oct. 5   **Perf. 11½**
879 A335 5fr green & blk   .40   .25
880 A335 10fr brick red & blk   .80   .40
   Centenary of Universal Postal Union.

Symbolic Chart — A336

1974, Oct. 12   **Photo.**   **Perf. 11½**
881 A336 7fr multicolored   .55   .30
   Central Economic Council, 25th anniv.

Rotary Emblem A337

1974, Oct. 19
882 A337 10fr multicolored   .75   .35
   Rotary International of Belgium, 50th Anniv.

Wild Boar (Regimental Emblem) — A338

1974, Oct. 26
883 A338 3fr multicolored   .25   .25
   Granting of the colors to the Ardennes Chasseurs Regiment, 40th anniversary.

Angel, by Van Eyck Brothers — A341

1974, Nov. 16   **Perf. 11½**
884 A341 4fr rose lilac   .30   .25
   Christmas 1974. The Angel shown is from the triptyque "The Mystical Lamb" in the Saint-Bavon Cathedral, Ghent.

Adolphe Quetelet, by J. Odevaere — A342

1974, Dec. 14   **Engr. & Photo.**
885 A342 10fr black & buff   .75   .45
   Death centenary of Adolphe Quetelet (1796-1874), statistician, astronomer and Secretary of Royal Academy of Brussels.

Themabelga, International Thematic Stamp Exhibition, Brussels, Dec. 13-21, 1975 — A343

6.50fr, Themabelga emblem.

1975, Feb. 15   **Photo.**   **Perf. 11½**
912 A343 6.50fr multi   .50   .25

Ghent Intl. Flower Exhib., Apr. 26-May 5 — A344

4.50fr, Neoregelia carolinae. 5fr, Coltsfoot. 6.50fr, Azalea.

1975, Feb. 22
913 A344 4.50fr multi   .35   .25
Photogravure and Engraved
914 A344 5fr multi   .40   .25
915 A344 6.50fr multi   .50   .25
     Nos. 913-915 (3)   1.25   .75

Charles Buls Normal School for Boys, Brussels, Cent. — A345

School emblem, man Leading boy.

1975, Mar. 15   **Perf. 11½**
916 A345 4.50fr black & multi   .35   .25

Davids Foundation Emblem A346

1975, Mar. 22   **Photo.**
917 A346 5fr yellow & multi   .40   .25
   Centenary of the Davids Foundation, a Catholic organization for the promotion of Flemish through education and books.

King Albert (1875-1934) A347

1975, Apr. 5   **Engr. & Photo.**
918 A347 10fr black & maroon   .70   .35

Mailman, 1840, by James Thiriar — A348

1975, Apr. 19   **Engr.**   **Perf. 11½**
919 A348 6.50fr dull magenta   .50   .25
   Stamp Day 1975.

St. John, from Last Supper, by Bouts — A349

   Europa: 10fr, Woman's Head, detail from "Trial by Fire," by Dirk Bouts.

1975, Apr. 26   **Engr. & Photo.**
920 A349 6.50fr black, grn & blue   .65   .25
921 A349 10fr black, ocher & red   .90   .45

Liberation of Concentration Camps, 30th Anniv. — A350

   Concentration Camp Symbols: "B" denoted political prisoners, "KG" prisoners of war.

1975, May 3   **Photo.**
922 A350 4.50fr multicolored   .35   .25

Hospice of St. John, Bruges A351

Church of St. Loup, Namur — A352

   Design: 10fr, Martyrs' Square, Brussels.

1975, May 12   **Engr.**   **Perf. 11½**
926 A351 4.50fr deep rose lilac   .40   .25
927 A352   5fr slate green   .45   .25
928 A351 10fr bright blue   .85   .40
       Nos. 926-928 (3)   1.70   .90
   European Architectural Heritage Year.

Library, Louvain University, Ryckmans and Cerfaux A355

1975, June 7   **Photo.**   **Perf. 11½**
931 A355 10fr dull blue & sepia   .75   .35
   25th anniversary of Louvain Bible Colloquium, founded by Professors Gonzague Ryckmans (1887-1969) and Lucien Cerfaux (1883-1968).

"Metamorphose" by Pol Mara — A356

1975, June 14
932 A356 7fr multicolored   .50   .30
   Queen Fabiola Mental Health Foundation.

Marie Popelin, Palace of Justice, Brussels — A357

1975, June 21   **Engr. & Photo.**
933 A357 6.50fr green & claret   .55   .25
   International Women's Year 1975. Marie Popelin (1846-1913), first Belgian woman doctor of law.

Assia, by Charles Despiau — A358

1975, Sept. 6   **Perf. 11½**
934 A358 5fr yellow grn & blk   .35   .25
   Middelheim Outdoor Museum, 25th anniv.

Cornelia Vekemans, by Cornelis de Vos — A359

1975, Sept. 20   **Photo.**
935 A359 4.50fr multicolored   .40   .25
   Youth philately.

Map of Schelde-Rhine Canal — A360

1975, Sept. 20
936 A360 10fr multicolored   .75   .35
   Opening of connection between the Schelde and Rhine, Sept. 23, 1975.

National Bank, W. F. Orban, Founder A361

Photogravure and Engraved
1975, Oct. 11   **Perf. 12½x13**
937 A361 25fr multicolored   2.00   .50
   Natl. Bank of Belgium, 125th anniv.

Edmond Thieffry and Plane, 1925 A362

1975, Oct. 18   **Perf. 11½**
938 A362 7fr black & lilac   .55   .30
   First flight Brussels to Kinshasa, Congo, 50th anniversary.

"Seat of Wisdom" St. Peter's, Louvain — A363

1975, Nov. 8   **Perf. 11½**
939 A363 6.50fr blue, blk & grn   .50   .25
   University of Louvain, 550th anniversary.

Angels, by Rogier van der Weyden A364

1975, Nov. 15
940 A364 5fr multicolored   .40   .25
   Christmas 1975.

Willemsfonds Emblem — A365

1976, Feb. 21   **Photo.**   **Perf. 11½**
941 A365 5fr multicolored   .35   .25
   Willems Foundation, which supports Flemish language and literature, 125th anniv.

American Bicentennial Emblem — A366

1976, Mar. 13   **Photo.**   **Perf. 11½**
942 A366 14fr multi + label   1.00   .55
   American Bicentennial. Black engraved inscription on labels commemorates arrival of first Walloon settlers in Nieu Nederland.

Cardinal Mercier — A367

1976, Mar. 20   **Engr.**
943 A367 4.50fr brt rose lilac   .35   .25
   Desire Joseph Cardinal Mercier (1851-1926), professor at Louvain University, spiritual and patriotic leader during World War I.

Flemish Economic Organization (Vlaams Ekonomisch Verbond), 50th Anniv. — A368

1976, Apr. 3   **Photo.**   **Perf. 11½**
944 A368 6.50fr multicolored   .50   .25

General Post Office, Brussels A369

1976, Apr. 24   **Engr.**   **Perf. 11½**
945 A369 6.50fr sepia   .50   .25
   Stamp Day.

Potter's Hands A370

   Europa: 6.50fr, Basket maker, vert.

1976, May 8 Photo.
946 A370 6.50fr multicolored .70 .25
947 A370 14fr multicolored 1.60 .40

Truck on Road A371

1976, May 8
948 A371 14fr black, yel & red 1.00 .45

15th Intl. Road Union Cong., Brussels, May 9-13.

Queen Elisabeth (1876-1965) A372

1976, May 24 Perf. 11½
949 A372 14fr green 1.00 .45

Ardennes Draft Horses A373

1976, June 19
950 A373 5fr multicolored .40 .30

Ardennes Draft Horses Assoc., 50th anniv.

Souvenir Sheets

King Baudouin — A374

1976, June 26
951 A374 Sheet of 3 2.75 2.75
a. 4.50fr gray .75 .75
b. 6.50fr ocher .75 .75
c. 10fr brick red .80 .80
952 A374 Sheet of 2 4.25 4.25
a. 20fr yellow green 1.60 1.60
b. 30fr Prussian blue 2.40 2.40

25th anniv. of the reign of King Baudouin. No. 951 sold for 30fr, No. 952 for 70fr. The surtax went to a new foundation for the improvement of living conditions in honor of the King.

Electric Train and Society Emblem — A375

1976, Sept. 11 Photo. Perf. 11½
953 A375 6.50fr multi .55 .25

Natl. Belgian Railroad Soc., 50th anniv.

William of Nassau, Prince of Orange — A376

1976, Sept. 11 Engr.
954 A376 10fr slate green .75 .35

400th anniv. of the pacification of Ghent.

New Subway Train A377

1976, Sept. 18 Photo.
955 A377 6.50fr multi .55 .25

Opening of first line of Brussels subway.

Young Musician, by W. C. Duyster — A378

1976, Oct. 2 Photo. Perf. 11½
956 A378 4.50fr multi .35 .25

Young musicians and youth philately.

Charles Bernard — A379

St. Jerome in the Mountains, by Le Patinier — A380

Blind Leading the Blind, by Bruegel the Elder A381

No. 958, Fernand Victor Toussaint van Boelaere.

1976, Oct. 16 Engr.
957 A379 5fr violet .40 .25
958 A379 5fr red brn & sepia .40 .25
959 A380 6.50fr dark brown .55 .25
960 A381 6.50fr slate green .55 .25
Nos. 957-960 (4) 1.90 1.00

Charles Bernard (1875-1961), French-speaking journalist; Toussaint van Boelaere (1875-1947), Flemish journalist; No. 959, Charles Plisnier Belgian-French Cultural Society. No. 960, Assoc. for Language Promotion.

Remouchamps Caves — A382

Hunnegem Priory, Gramont, and Madonna A383

Designs: No. 963, River Lys and St. Martin's Church. No. 964, Ham-sur-Heure Castle.

1976, Oct. 23 Engr. Perf. 13
961 A382 4.50fr multi .40 .25
962 A383 4.50fr multi .40 .25
963 A383 5fr multi .40 .25
964 A383 5fr multi .40 .25
Nos. 961-964 (4) 1.60 1.00

Tourism. Nos. 961-962 are not luminescent.

Nativity, by Master of Flemalle — A384

1976, Nov. 20 Perf. 11½
965 A384 5fr violet .40 .25

Christmas 1976.

Rubens' Monogram — A385

1977, Feb. 12 Photo. & Engr.
966 A385 6.50fr lilac & blk .50 .25

Peter Paul Rubens (1577-1640), painter.

Heraldic Lion — A386

1977-85 Typo. Perf. 13½x14
Size: 17x20mm
967 A386 50c brn ('80) .25 .25
a. 50c orange brown ('85) .25 .25
968 A386 1fr brt lil .25 .25
a. 1fr bright rose lilac ('84) .25 .25
969 A386 1.50fr gray ('78) .25 .25
970 A386 2fr orange ('78) .25 .25
970A A386 2.50fr yel grn ('81) .30 .25
971 A386 2.75fr Prus bl ('80) .30 .25
972 A386 3fr vio ('78) .30 .25
a. 3fr dull violet ('84) .25 .25
973 A386 4fr red brn ('80) .35 .25
a. 4fr rose brown ('85) .90 .25
974 A386 4.50fr lt ultra .40 .25
975 A386 5fr grn ('80) .40 .25
a. 5fr emerald green ('84) .40 .25
976 A386 6fr dl red brn .50 .25
a. 6fr light red brown ('85) .50 .25
Nos. 967-976 (11) 3.55 2.75

Nos. 967-976 were printed on various papers.

1978, Aug. Photo. Perf. 13½x12½
Size: 17x22mm
Booklet Stamps
977 A386 1fr brt lilac .25 .25
a. Bklt. pane, #977-978, 2 #786 1.50
b. Bklt. pane, #977, 979, 2 #788 2.00
978 A386 2fr yellow .30 .30
979 A386 3fr violet .50 .50
Nos. 977-979 (3) 1.05 1.05

Each pane has 2 labels showing Belgian Postal emblem, also a large selvage with zip code instructions. No. 977-979 not luminescent.
See Nos. 1084-1088, design O5.

Anniversary Emblem A387

1977, Mar. 14 Photo. Perf. 11½
982 A387 6.50fr sil & multi .50 .25

Royal Belgian Association of Civil and Agricultural Engineers, 50th anniversary.

Birds and Lions Emblem A388

1977, Mar. 28
983 A388 14fr multi 1.00 .30

Belgian District #112 of Lions Intl., 25th anniv.

Pillar Box, 1852 — A389

1977, Apr. 23 Engr.
984 A389 6.50fr slate green .55 .25

Stamp Day 1977.

Gileppe Dam, Jalhay A390

Europa: 14fr, War Memorial, Yser at Nieuport.

1977, May 7 Photo. Perf. 11½
985 A390 6.50fr multi .60 .25
986 A390 14fr multi .80 .40

Mars and Mercury Association Emblem — A391

1977, May 14
987 A391 5fr multi .35 .25

Mars and Mercury Association of Reserve and Retired Officers, 50th anniversary.

Prince de Hornes Coat of Arms — A392

Conversion of St. Hubertus — A394

Battle of the Golden Spur, from Oxford Chest — A393

Designs: 6.50fr, Froissart writing book, vert.

1977, June 11   Engr.   Perf. 11½
988	A392	4.50fr violet	.35	.25
989	A393	5fr red	.40	.25
990	A393	6.50fr dark brown	.45	.25
991	A394	14fr slate green	1.00	.50
		Nos. 988-991 (4)	2.20	1.25

300th anniv. of the Principality of Overijse (4.50fr); 675th anniv. of the Battle of the Golden Spur (5f); 600th anniv. of publication of 1st volume of the Chronicles of Jehan Froissart (6.50fr); 1250th anniv. of the death of St. Hubertus (14fr).

Rubens, Self-portrait
A395

1977, June 25   Photo.
992	A395	5fr multi	.40	.25
a.		Souvenir sheet of 3	1.25	1.00

Peter Paul Rubens (1577-1640), painter. Stamps in No. 992a are 37¼mm high, No. 992, 35¼mm. No. 992a sold for 20fr.

Open Book, from The Lamb of God, by Van Eyck Brothers — A396

1977, Sept. 3   Photo.   Perf. 11½
993	A396	10fr multi	.70	.35

Intl. Federation of Library Associations (IFLA), 50th Anniv. Cong., Brussels, Sept. 5-10.

Gymnast and Soccer Player — A397

6.50fr, Fencers in wheelchairs, horiz. 10fr, Basketball players. 14fr, Hockey players.

1977, Sept. 10
994	A397	4.50fr multi	.40	.25
995	A397	6.50fr multi	.50	.25
996	A397	10fr multi	.75	.40
997	A397	14fr multi	1.10	.50
		Nos. 994-997 (4)	2.75	1.40

Workers' Gymnastics and Sports Center, 50th anniversary (4.50fr); sport for the Handicapped (6.50fr); 20th European Basketball Championships (10fr); First World Hockey Cup (14fr).

Europalia 77 Emblem — A398

1977, Sept. 17
998	A398	5fr gray & multi	.40	.25

5th Europalia Arts Festival, featuring German Federal Republic, Belgium, Oct.-Nov. 1977.

The Egg Farmer, by Gustave De Smet — A399

1977, Oct. 8   Engr. & Photo.
999	A399	4.50fr bister & blk	.35	.25

Publicity for Belgian eggs.

Mother and Daughter with Album, by Constant Cap A400

1977, Oct. 15   Engr.
1000	A400	4.50fr dark brown	.35	.25

Youth Philately.
No. 1000 exists in red in a deluxe souvenir sheet. Value, $100.

Bailiff's House, Gembloux — A401

Market Square, St. Nicholas A402

No. 1002, St. Aldegonde Church & Cultural Center. No. 1004, Statue and bridge, Liège.

1977, Oct. 22
1001	A401	4.50fr multi	.35	.25
1002	A401	4.50fr multi	.35	.25
1003	A402	5fr multi	.40	.25
1004	A402	5fr multi	.40	.25
		Nos. 1001-1004 (4)	1.50	1.00

Tourism. Nos. 1001-1004 not luminescent. See Nos. 1017-1018, 1037-1040.

Nativity, by Rogier van der Weyden — A403

1977, Nov. 11   Engr.
1005	A403	5fr rose red	.40	.25

Christmas 1977.

Symbols of Transportation and Map — A404

Campidoglio Palace, Rome, and Map — A406

Designs: No. 1007, European Parliament, Strasbourg, Emblem, vert. No. 1009, Paul-Henri Spaak and map of 19 European member countries.

1978, Mar. 18   Photo.   Perf. 11½
1006	A404	10fr blue & multi	.80	.30
1007	A404	10fr blue & multi	.80	.30
1008	A406	14fr blue & multi	1.00	.50
1009	A406	14fr blue & multi	1.00	.50
		Nos. 1006-1009 (4)	3.60	1.60

European Action: 25th anniversary of the European Transport Ministers' Conference; 1st general elections for European Parliament; 20th anniversary of the signing of the Treaty of Rome; Paul Henri Spaak (1899-1972), Belgian statesman who worked for the establishment of European Community.

Grimbergen Abbey — A407

1978, Apr. 1   Engr.
1010	A407	4.50fr red brown	.35	.25

850th anniversary of the Premonstratensian Abbey at Grimbergen.

Ostend Chamber of Commerce and Industry, 175th Anniv. — A408

1978, Apr. 8   Photo.
1011	A408	8fr Emblem	.50	.30

No. 39 with First Day Cancel — A409

1978, Apr. 15
1012	A409	8fr multicolored	.55	.25

Stamp Day.

Europa Issue

Pont des Trous, Tournai A410

8fr, Antwerp Cathedral, by Vaclav Hollar.

Photogravure and Engraved
1978, May 6   Perf. 11½
1013	A410	8fr multi, vert.	.85	.25
1014	A410	14fr multi	1.10	.40

Virgin of Ghent, Porcelain Plaque — A411

Paul Pastur Workers' University, Charleroi — A412

1978, Sept. 16   Photo.   Perf. 11½
1015	A411	6fr multicolored	.45	.30
1016	A412	8fr multicolored	.60	.30

Municipal education in Ghent, 150th anniversary; Paul Pastur Workers' University, Charleroi, 75th anniv. Nos. 1015-1016 are not luminescent.

Types of 1977 and

Tourist Guide, Brussels A413

No. 1017, Jonathas House, Enghien. No. 1018, View of Wetteren and couple in local costume. No. 1020, Prince Carnival, Eupen-St. Vith.

1978, Sept. 25   Photo. & Engr.
1017	A401	4.50fr multi	.35	.30
1018	A402	4.50fr multi	.35	.30
1019	A413	6fr multi	.45	.30
1020	A413	6fr multi	.45	.30
		Nos. 1017-1020 (4)	1.60	1.20

Tourism. Nos. 1017-1020 are not luminescent.

Royal Flemish Engineer's Organization, 50th Anniv. — A414

1978, Oct. 7   Photo.
1021	A414	8fr Emblem	.50	.25

Young Philatelist A415

1978, Oct. 14   Engr.   Perf. 11½
1022	A415	4.50fr dk violet	.35	.30

Youth philately.

Nativity, Notre Dame, Huy — A416

1978, Nov. 18   Engr.   Perf. 11½
1023	A416	6fr black	.45	.30

Christmas 1978.

Tyll Eulenspiegel, Lay Action Emblem — A417

1979, Mar. 3　　Photo.　　Perf. 11½
1024　A417　4.50fr multi　　　　.35　.25
　　10th anniversary of Lay Action Centers.

European Parliament Emblem — A418

1979, Mar. 3
1025　A418　8fr multicolored　　.60　.25
　　European Parliament, first direct elections, June 7-10.

St. Michael Banishing Lucifer — A419

1979, Mar. 17　　Photo. & Engr.
1026　A419　4.50fr rose red & blk　.35　.30
1027　A419　8fr brt green & blk　　.70　.30
　　Millennium of Brussels.

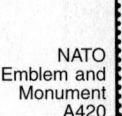

NATO Emblem and Monument A420

1979, Mar. 31　　　　　　　Photo.
1028　A420　3fr multicolored　　2.00　.50
　　NATO, 30th anniv.

Prisoner's Head — A421

1979, Apr. 7　　Photo. & Engr.
1029　A421　6fr orange & blk　　.40　.25
　　25th anniversary of the National Political Prisoners' Monument at Breendonk.

Belgium No. Q2 — A422

1979, Apr. 21　　Photo.　　Perf. 11½
1030　A422　8fr multicolored　　.55　.30
　　Stamp Day 1979.

Mail Coach and Truck A423

　　Europa: 14fr, Chappe's heliograph, Intelsat satellite and dish antenna.

1979, Apr. 28　　　　　Photo. & Engr.
1031　A423　8fr multicolored　　.85　.25
1032　A423　14fr multicolored　1.60　.35

Chamber of Commerce Emblem — A424

1979, May 19　　Photo.　　Perf. 11½
1033　A424　8fr multicolored　　.50　.25
　　Verviers Chamber of Commerce and Industry, 175th anniversary.

"50" Emblem A425

1979, June 9　　Photo.　　Perf. 11½
1034　A425　4.50fr gold & ultra　.35　.25
　　Natl. Fund for Professional Credit, 50th anniv.

Merchants, Roman Bas-relief A426

1979, June 9
1035　A426　10fr multicolored　　.65　.30
　　Belgian Chamber of Trade and Commerce, 50th anniversary.

"Tintin" as Philatelist A427

1979, Sept. 29　　Photo.　　Perf. 11½
1036　A427　8fr multicolored　　2.25　.70
　　Youth philately.

Tourism Types of 1977

　　Designs: No. 1037, Belfry, Thuin. No. 1038, Royal Museum of Central Africa, Tervuren. No. 1039, St. Nicholas Church and cattle, Ciney. No. 1040, St. John's Church and statue of Our Lady, Poperinge.

Perf. 11½ (A401), 13 (A402)
1979, Oct. 22　　　　　Photo. & Engr.
1037　A401　5fr multicolored　　.40　.30
1038　A402　5fr multicolored　　.40　.30
1039　A401　6fr multicolored　　.50　.30
1040　A402　6fr multicolored　　.50　.30
　　Nos. 1037-1040 (4)　　　1.80　1.20

Francois Auguste Gevaert A429　　Piano, String Instruments A430

　　Design: 6fr, Emmanuel Durlet.

1979, Nov. 3　　　　　　Perf. 11½
1041　A429　5fr brown　　　　.40　.30
1042　A429　6fr brown　　　　.55　.30
1043　A430　14fr brown　　　1.00　.45
　　Nos. 1041-1043 (3)　　1.95　1.05
　　Francois Auguste Gevaert (1828-1908), musicologist and composer; Emmanuel Durlet (1893-1977), pianist; Queen Elisabeth Musical Chapel Foundation, 40th anniv.

Virgin and Child, Notre Dame, Foy — A431

1979, Nov. 24　　　　Photo. & Engr.
1044　A431　6fr lt grnsh blue　　.40　.25
　　Christmas 1979.

Independence, 150th Anniversary — A432

1980, Jan. 26　　Photo.　　Perf. 11½
1045　A432　9fr purple　　　　.60　.25

Frans van Cauwelaert (1880-1961), Minister of State — A433

1980, Feb. 25　　　　　　　Engr.
1046　A433　5fr gray　　　　　.40　.25

Ghent Flower Show, Apr. 19-27 — A434

　　5fr, Spring flowers. 6.50fr, Summer flowers. 9fr, Autumn flowers.

1980, Mar. 10　　　　　　Photo.
1047　A434　5fr multi　　　　.40　.30
1048　A434　6.50fr multi　　　.50　.30
1049　A434　9fr multi　　　　.60　.30
　　Nos. 1047-1049 (3)　　1.50　.90

P.T.T., 50th Anniv. A435

1980, Apr. 14　　Photo.　　Perf. 11½
1050　A435　10fr multicolored　　.70　.30

Belgium No. C4 — A436

1980, Apr. 21
1051　A436　9fr multicolored　　.65　.30
　　Stamp Day.

Europa — A437

　　9fr, St. Benedict, by Hans Memling. 14fr, Margaret of Austria (1480-1530).

1980, Apr. 28
1052　A437　9fr multicolored　　.70　.25
1053　A437　14fr multicolored　1.10　.35

4th Interparliamentary Conf. for European Cooperation & Security, Brussels, May 12-18 — A438

　　5fr, Palais des Nations, Brussels.

1980, May 10　　Photo.　　Perf. 11½
1054　A438　5fr multicolored　　.35　.25

Golden Carriage, 1780, Mons A439

　　Tourism: No. 1056, Canal landscape, Damme.

1980, May 17
1055　A439　6.50fr multi　　　.45　.30
1056　A439　6.50fr multi　　　.45　.30

Souvenir Sheet

Royal Mint Theater, Brussels — A440

Photo. & Engr.

1980, May 31   **Perf. 11½**
1057 A440 50fr black   4.50   4.50

150th anniv. of independence. Sold for 75fr.

King Baudouin, 50th Birthday — A441

1980, Sept. 6   **Photo.**   **Perf. 11½**
1058 A441 9fr rose claret   .65   .25

View of Chiny A442

Portal and Court, Diest — A443

1980   **Engr.**   **Perf. 13**
1059 A442 5fr multicolored   .40   .30
1060 A443 5fr multicolored   .40   .30

Tourism. Nos. 1059-1060 are not luminescent.
Issued: No. 1059, 9/27; No. 1060, 12/13.
See Nos. 1072-1075, 1120-1125.

Emblem of Belgian Heart League A444

1980, Oct. 4   **Photo.**   **Perf. 11½**
1061 A444 14fr blue & magenta   1.00   .50

Heart Week, Oct. 20-25.

Rodenbach Statue, Roulers — A445

1980, Oct. 11
1062 A445 9fr multicolored   .65   .30

Albrecht Rodenbach (1856-1880), poet.

Youth Philately — A446

1980, Oct. 27   **Photo.**   **Perf. 11½**
1063 A446 5fr multicolored   .40   .25

National Broadcasting Service, 50th Anniversary A447

1980, Nov. 10
1064 A447 10fr gray & blk   .70   .40

Garland and Nativity, by Daniel Seghers, 17th Century A448

1980, Nov. 17
1065 A448 6.50fr multicolored   .45   .30

Christmas 1980.

Baron de Gerlache, by F.J. Navez — A449

Leopold I, By Geefs A450

9fr, Baron de Stassart, by F.J. Navez.

1981, Mar. 16   **Photo.**   **Perf. 11½**
1066 A449 6fr multicolored   .40   .30
1067 A449 9fr multicolored   .60   .30

Photogravure and Engraved
1068 A450 50fr multicolored   3.25   .60

Sesquicentennial of Chamber of Deputies, Senate and Dynasty.

Tchantchès and Op-Signoorke, Puppets — A451

Photogravure and Engraved
1981, May 4   **Perf. 11½**
1069 A451 9fr shown   .80   .25
1070 A451 14fr d'Artagnan and Woltje   1.10   .45

Europa.

Impression of M.A. de Cock (Founder of Post Museum) — A452

1981, May 18   **Photo.**
1071 A452 9fr multicolored   .65   .30

Stamp Day.

Tourism Types of 1980

No. 1072, Virgin and Child statue, Our Lady's Church, Tongre-Notre Dame. No. 1073, Egmont Castle, Zottegem. No. 1074, Eau d'Heure River. No. 1075, Tongerlo Abbey, Antwerp.

1981, June 15   **Engr.**   **Perf. 11½**
1072 A442   6fr multi   .50   .30
1073 A442   6fr multi   .50   .30
1074 A443   6.50fr multi   .50   .30
1075 A443   6.50fr multi   .50   .30
   Nos. 1072-1075 (4)   2.00   1.20

Soccer Player — A453

1981, Sept. 5   **Photo.**   **Perf. 11½**
1076 A453 6fr multicolored   .50   .30

Soccer in Belgium centenary; Royal Antwerp Soccer Club.

E. Remouchamps, Founder — A454

1981, Sept. 5   **Photo. & Engr.**
1077 A454 6.50fr cream & dk brn   .45   .30

Walloon Language and Literature Club 125th anniv.

Audit Office Sesquicentennial — A455

1981, Sept. 12   **Engr.**
1078 A455 10fr dp claret   .70   .30

French Horn A456

1981, Sept. 12   **Photo.**
1079 A456 6.50fr multi   .45   .30

Vredekring (Peace Circle) Band of Antwerp centenary.

Souvenir Sheet

Pieta, by Ben Genaux — A457

1981, Sept. 19   **Photo.**   **Perf. 11½**
1080 A457 20fr multicolored   2.00   2.00

Mining disaster at Marcinelle, 25th anniv. Sold for 30fr.

Mausoleum of Marie of Burgundy and Charles the Bold, Bruges — A458

1981, Oct. 10   **Photo. & Engr.**
1081 A458 50fr multi   3.25   .75

Youth Philately — A459

1981, Oct. 24   **Photo.**
1082 A459 6fr multi   .40   .30

Type of 1977 and

A459a

A460

King Baudouin — A460a

Photo. and Engr.; Photo.

1980-86 Perf. 13½x14, 11½

1084	A386	65c brt rose	.25	.25
1085	A386	1fr on 5fr grn	.25	.25
1086	A386	7fr brt rose	.55	.25
1087	A386	8fr grnsh bl	.65	.25
1088	A386	9fr dl org	.70	.25
1089	A459a	10fr blue	.70	.25
1090	A459a	11fr dl red	.80	.25
1091	A459a	12fr grn	1.00	.25
1092	A459a	13fr scar	1.00	.25
1093	A459a	15fr red org	1.75	.30
1094	A459a	20fr dk bl	1.75	.25
1095	A459a	22fr lilac	2.50	.60
1096	A459a	23fr gray grn	2.60	.60
1097	A459a	30fr brown	2.10	.25
1098	A459a	40fr red org	3.50	.25
1099	A460	50fr lt grnsh bl & bl	4.75	.30
1100	A460a	50fr tan & dk brn	5.00	.25
1101	A460	65fr pale lil & blk	6.00	.80
1102	A460	100fr lt bis brn & dk bl	9.75	.50
1103	A460a	100fr lt bl & dk bl	13.50	.25
	Nos. 1084-1103 (20)		59.10	6.60

Issued: 65c, 4/14/80; 1fr, 5/3/82; 7fr, 5/17/82; 8fr, 5/9/83; 9fr, 2/11/85; 65fr, No. 1099, 1102, 11/5/81; 10fr, 11/15/82; 11fr, 4/5/83; 12fr, 1/23/84; 15fr, 22fr, 30fr, No. 1100, 3/26/84; 20fr, 40fr, No. 1103, 6/12/84; 23fr, 2/25/85; 13fr, 3/10/86. See Nos. 1231-1234. Printed on various papers.

Max Waller, Movement Founder — A461

Designs: 6.50fr, The Spirit Drinkers, by Gustave van de Woestyne. 9fr, Fernand Severin, poet, 50th death anniv. 10fr, Jan van Ruusbroec, Flemish mystic, 500th birth anniv. 14fr, Thought and Man TV series, 25th anniv.

1981, Nov. 7

1104	A461	6fr multi	.45	.30
1105	A461	6.50fr multi	.50	.30
1106	A461	9fr multi	.60	.30
1107	A461	10fr multi	.70	.40
1108	A461	14fr multi	1.10	.50
	Nos. 1104-1108 (5)		3.35	1.80

La Jeune Belgique cultural movement cent. (6fr).

Nativity, 16th Cent. Engraving — A466

1981, Nov. 21

1109	A466	6.50fr multi	.40	.30

Christmas 1981.

Royal Conservatory of Music Sesquicentennial — A467

Design: 9fr, Judiciary sesquicentennial.

1982, Jan. 25 Photo. Perf. 11½

1110	A467	6.50fr multi	.40	.30
1111	A467	9fr multi	.60	.30

A468

6fr, Cyclotron. 14fr, Galaxy, telescope. 50fr, Koch.

1982, Mar. 1

1112	A468	6fr multicolored	.40	.30
1113	A468	14fr multicolored	.85	.40
1114	A468	50fr multicolored	3.00	.70
	Nos. 1112-1114 (3)		4.25	1.40

Radio-isotope production, Natl. Radio-elements Institute, Fleurus (6fr); Royal Belgian Observatory (14fr); centenary of TB bacillus discovery (50fr).

Joseph Lemaire (1882-1966), Minister of State — A469

1982, Apr. 17 Photo. Perf. 11½

1115	A469	6.50fr multi	.45	.30

Europa 1982 A470

10fr, Universal suffrage. 17fr, Edict of Tolerance, 1781.

1982, May 1

1116	A470	10fr multicolored	1.00	.25
1117	A470	17fr multicolored	1.75	.35

Stamp Day — A471

1982, May 22 Photo. & Engr.

1118	A471	10fr multi	.70	.30

67th World Esperanto Congress, Anvers A472

1982, June 7 Photo. Perf. 11½

1119	A472	12fr Tower of Babel	.95	.35

Tourism Type of 1980

Designs: No. 1120, Tower of Gosselies. No. 1121, Zwijveke Abbey, Dendermonde. No. 1122, Stavelot Abbey. No. 1123, Villers-la-Ville Abbey ruins. No. 1124, Geraardsbergen Abbey entrance. No. 1125, Beveren Pillory.

1982, June 21 Photo. & Engr.

1120	A443	7fr lt bl & blk	.55	.30
1121	A443	7fr lt grn & blk	.55	.30
1122	A442	7.50fr tan & dk brn	.55	.30
1123	A442	7.50fr lt vio & pur	.55	.30
1124	A443	7.50fr slate & blk	.55	.30
1125	A443	7.50fr beige & blk	.55	.30
	Nos. 1120-1125 (6)		3.30	1.80

Self Portrait, by L.P. Boon (b. 1912) — A473

Designs: 10fr, Adoration of the Shepherds, by Hugo van der Goes (1440-1482). 12fr, The King on His Throne, carving by M. de Ghelderode (1898-1962). 17fr, Madonna and Child, by Pieter Paulus (1881-1959).

1982, Sept. 13 Photo. Perf. 11½

1126	A473	7fr multicolored	.55	.30
1127	A473	10fr multicolored	.70	.40
1128	A473	12fr multicolored	.80	.40
1129	A473	17fr multicolored	1.45	.40
	Nos. 1126-1129 (4)		3.50	1.50

Abraham Hans, Writer (1882-1932) A474

1982, Sept. 27

1130	A474	17fr multicolored	1.25	.40

Youth Philately and Scouting A475

1982, Oct. 2 Photo. Perf. 11½

1131	A475	7fr multicolored	.55	.30

Grand Orient Lodge of Belgium Sesquicentennial A476

1982, Oct. 16 Photo. & Engr.

1132	A476	10fr Man taking oath	.80	.25

Cardinal Joseph Cardijn (1882-1967) A477

1982, Nov. 13 Photo.

1133	A477	10fr multicolored	.70	.30

St. Francis of Assisi (1182-1226) A478

1982, Nov. 27

1134	A478	20fr multicolored	1.25	.50

Horse-drawn Trolley A479

1983, Feb. 12 Photo. Perf. 11½

1135	A479	7.50fr shown	.70	.35
1136	A479	10fr Electric trolley	1.00	.30
1137	A479	50fr Trolley, diff.	4.00	.60
	Nos. 1135-1137 (3)		5.70	1.25

Intl. Fed. for Periodical Press, 24th World Congress, Brussels, May 11-13 A480

1983, Mar. 19 Photo. Perf. 11½

1138	A480	20fr multicolored	1.30	.50

Homage to Women A481

1983, Apr. 16

1139	A481	8fr Operator	.70	.30
1140	A481	11fr Homemaker	.80	.30
1141	A481	20fr Executive	1.50	.50
	Nos. 1139-1141 (3)		3.00	1.10

Stamp Day — A482

1983, Apr. 23

1142	A482	11fr multicolored	.80	.30

Procession of the Precious Blood, Bruges A483

1983, Apr. 30 Photo. Perf. 11½

1143	A483	8fr multicolored	.55	.25

The design of No. 1143 is continuous, and collectors often prefer pairs to demonstrate this feature. Value, unused or used, $2.

Europa 1983 — A484

Paintings by P. Delvaux. 11fr vert.

1983, May 14

1144	A484	11fr Common Man	.90	.25
1145	A484	20fr Night Train	1.60	.45

Manned Flight Bicentenary A485

1983, June 11 Photo. Perf. 11½

1146	A485	11fr Balloon over city	.75	.30
1147	A485	22fr Country	1.50	.40

Our Lady's Church, Hastiere A486

No. 1149, Landen. No. 1150, Park, Mouscron. No. 1151, Wijnendale Castle, Torhout.

1983, June 25
1148 A486 8fr shown .65 .30
1149 A486 8fr multicolored .65 .30
1150 A486 8fr multicolored .65 .30
1151 A486 8fr multicolored .65 .30
Nos. 1148-1151 (4) 2.60 1.20

Tineke Festival, Heule — A487

1983, Sept. 10 Photo.
1152 A487 8fr multi .55 .30

Enterprise Year Emblem A488

1983, Sept. 24
1153 A488 11fr multicolored .75 .30
European year for small and medium-sized enterprises and craft industry.

Youth Philately — A489

1983, Oct. 10 Photo. *Perf. 11½*
1154 A489 8fr multicolored .55 .30

Belgian Exports A490

No. 1155, Diamond industry. No. 1156, Metallurgy. No. 1157, Textile industry.

1983, Oct. 24 *Perf. 11½*
1155 A490 10fr multicolored .80 .30
1156 A490 10fr multicolored .80 .30
1157 A490 10fr multicolored .80 .30
Nos. 1155-1157 (3) 2.40 .90

See Nos. 1161-1164.

Hendrik Conscience (1812-1883), Novelist — A491

1983, Nov. 7
1158 A491 20fr multicolored 1.40 .40

Leopold III Type of 1936
1983, Dec. 12 Engr. *Perf. 12x11½*
1159 A84 11fr black .75 .25
Leopold III memorial (1901-1983), King 1934-1951.

Free University of Brussels, Sesqui. — A492

Photogravure and Engraved
1984, Jan. 14 *Perf. 11½*
1160 A492 11fr multicolored .80 .25

Exports Type of 1983
No. 1161, Chemicals. No. 1162, Food. No. 1163, Transportation equipment. No. 1164, Technology.

1984, Jan. 28 Photo.
1161 A490 11fr multicolored .80 .30
1162 A490 11fr multicolored .80 .30
1163 A490 11fr multicolored .80 .30
1164 A490 11fr multicolored .80 .30
Nos. 1161-1164 (4) 3.20 1.20

King Albert I, 50th Death Anniv. — A494

1984, Feb. 11 Photo. & Engr.
1165 A494 8fr tan & dk brn .60 .30

1984 Summer Olympic Games — A495

Souvenir Sheet
1984, Mar. 3 Photo.
1166 Sheet of 2 2.50 2.50
a. A495 10fr Archery .75 .75
b. A495 24fr Dressage 1.40 1.40
See Nos. B1029-B1030.

Family, Globe, Birds — A496

1984, Mar. 24 Photo. *Perf. 11½*
1167 A496 12fr multicolored .90 .30
"Movement without a Name" peace org.

St. John Bosco Canonization A497

1984, Apr. 7
1168 A497 8fr multicolored .60 .30

Europa (1959-84) A498

1984, May 5 Photo. *Perf. 11½*
1169 A498 12fr black & red .95 .25
1170 A498 22fr black & ultra 1.75 .30

Stamp Day — A499

1984, May 19
1171 A499 12fr No. 52 .90 .30

2nd European Parliament Elections A500

1984, May 26
1172 A500 12fr multicolored .90 .30

Royal Military School, 150th Anniv. — A501

1984, June 9 Photo. *Perf. 11½*
1173 A501 22fr Hat 1.50 .45

Notre-Dame de la Chappelle, Brussels A502

Churches: No. 1175, St. Martin's, Montignyle-Tilleul. No. 1176, Tielt, vert.

Perf. 11½x12, 12x11½
1984, June 23 Photo. & Engr.
1174 A502 10fr multicolored .75 .35
1175 A502 10fr multicolored .75 .35
1176 A502 10fr multicolored .75 .35
Nos. 1174-1176 (3) 2.25 1.05

50th Anniv. of Chirojeugd (Christian Youth Movement) A503

1984, Sept. 15 Photo. *Perf. 11½*
1177 A503 10fr Emblem .75 .35

Affligem Abbey A504

8fr, Averbode, vert. 22fr, Chimay, vert. 24fr, Rochefort, vert.

1984, Oct. 6 Photo. & Engr.
1178 A504 8fr tan & black .55 .35
1179 A504 22fr dull mauve & lake brn 1.50 .55
1180 A504 24fr pale blue & indigo 1.75 .55
1181 A504 50fr shown 4.00 .75
Nos. 1178-1181 (4) 7.80 2.20

Youth Philately A505

1984, Oct. 20 Photo.
1182 A505 8fr Postman smurf 1.25 .60

Arthur Meulemans (1884-1966), Composer — A506

1984, Nov. 17 Photo. & Engr.
1183 A506 12fr multicolored .85 .65

St. Norbert, 850th Death Anniv. — A507

1985, Jan. 14 Photo. & Engr.
1184 A507 22fr sepia & beige 1.60 .50

Europalia '85 — A508

1985, Jan. 21 Photo.
1185 A508 12fr Virgin of Louvain .85 .30

Belgian Assoc. of Professional Journalists, Cent. A509

1985, Feb. 11 Photo.
1186 A509 9fr multicolored .65 .30

Ghent Flower Festival, Orchids — A510

No. 1187, Vanda coerules. No. 1188, Phalaenopsis. No. 1189, Suphrolaelio cattleo riffe.

Photogravure and Engraved

1985, Mar. 18			**Perf. 11½**	
1187	A510	12fr multi	.80	.30
1188	A510	12fr multi	.80	.30
1189	A510	12fr multi	.80	.30
		Nos. 1187-1189 (3)	2.40	.90

Visit of Pope John Paul II
A511

1985, Apr. 1			**Photo.**	
1190	A511	12fr multicolored	.80	.30

Belgian Worker's Party Cent.
A512

9fr, Chained factory gate. 12fr, Broken wall, red flag.

1985, Apr. 15			**Photo.**	
1191	A512	9fr multicolored	.60	.40
1192	A512	12fr multicolored	.80	.30

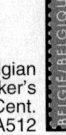

Jean de Bast (1883-1975), Engraver
A513

1985, Apr. 22			**Engr.**	
1193	A513	12fr blue black	.80	.30

Stamp Day.

Public Transportation Year — A514

Design: 9fr, Steam tram locomotive Type 18, 1896. 12fr, Locomotive Elephant and tender, 1835. 23fr, Type 23 tank engine, 1904. 24fr, Type I Pacific locomotive, 1935. 50fr, Type 27 electric locomotive, 1975.

1985, May 6			**Photo.**	
1194	A514	9fr multicolored	.70	.30
1195	A514	12fr multicolored	.80	.30
1196	A514	23fr multicolored	1.60	.60
1197	A514	24fr multicolored	1.75	.60
		Nos. 1194-1197 (4)	4.85	1.80

Souvenir Sheet

1198	A514	50fr multicolored	4.00	4.00

Europa 1985
A515

12fr, Cesar Franck at organ, 1887. 23fr, Folk figures.

1985, May 13			**Photo.**	
1199	A515	12fr multicolored	.95	.25
1200	A515	23fr multicolored	1.90	.40

26th Navigation Congress, Brussels
A516

No. 1201, Zeebruge Harbor. No. 1202, Projected lock at Strepy-Thieu.

1985, June 10		**Photo.**	**Perf. 11½**	
1201	A516	23fr multicolored	1.60	.60
1202	A516	23fr multicolored	1.60	.60

St. Martin's Church, Marcinelle
A517

Tourism: No. 1203, Church of the Assumption of Our Lady, Avernas-le-Baudouin, vert. No. 1204, Church of the Old Beguinage, Tongres, vert. No. 1206, Private residence, Puyenbroeck.

1985, June 24			**Perf. 11½**	
1203	A517	12fr multicolored	.80	.30
1204	A517	12fr multicolored	.80	.30
1205	A517	12fr multicolored	.80	.30
1206	A517	12fr multicolored	.80	.30
		Nos. 1203-1206 (4)	3.20	1.20

Queen Astrid (1905-1935)
A518

1985, Sept. 2			**Perf. 11½**	
1207	A518	12fr brown	.90	.30

Baking Pies for the Mattetart of Geraardsbergen
A519

Folk events: 24fr, Children dancing, centenary of the St. Lambert de Hermalle-Argenteau Les Rouges youth organization.

1985, Sept. 16				
1208	A519	12fr multicolored	.85	.30
1209	A519	24fr multicolored	1.75	.50

Liberation from German Occupation, 40th Anniv. — A520

Allegories: 9fr, Dove, liberation of concentration camps. 23fr, Battle of Ardennes. 24fr, Destroyer, liberation of the River Scheldt estuary.

1985, Sept. 30		**Photo.**	**Perf. 11½**	
1210	A520	9fr multicolored	.70	.30
1211	A520	23fr multicolored	1.60	.60
1212	A520	24fr multicolored	1.75	.60
		Nos. 1210-1212 (3)	4.05	1.50

Ernest Claes (1885-1968), Author
A521

9fr, Portrait, book character.

1985, Oct. 7				
1213	A521	9fr multicolored	.65	.30

Intl. Youth Year — A522

9fr, Nude in repose, angel.

1985, Oct. 21				
1214	A522	9fr multicolored	.65	.30

King Baudouin & Queen Fabiola, 25th Wedding Anniv. — A523

1985, Dec. 9				
1215	A523	12fr multicolored	1.00	.35

Birds — A524

No. 1216, Roitelet huppe. No. 1217, Pic epeichette. No. 1218, Moineau friquet. No. 1219, Gros bec. No. 1220, Bruant des roseaux. No. 1221, Rouge gorge. No. 1222, Gorge bleue. No. 1223, Traquet Patre. No. 1224, Sittele torchepot. No. 1225, Bouvreuil. No. 1226, Mesange bleue. No. 1227, Martinpecheur. No. 1228, Chardonneret. No. 1229, Grive musicienne. No. 1230, Pinson.

Photo. (50c-2fr, No. 1220, 4.50fr-6fr, No. 1229, 10fr), Typo. (Others)

1985-91			**Perf. 11½**	
1216	A524	50c multicolored	.25	.25
1217	A524	1fr multicolored	.30	.25
1218	A524	2fr multicolored	.25	.25
1219	A524	3fr multicolored	.50	.25
1220	A524	3fr multicolored	.35	.25
1221	A524	3.50fr multicolored	.30	.25
1222	A524	4fr multicolored	.40	.25
1223	A524	4.50fr multicolored	.45	.25
1224	A524	5fr multicolored	.40	.25
1225	A524	6fr multicolored	.60	.25
1226	A524	7fr multicolored	.60	.25
1227	A524	8fr multicolored	.70	.25
1228	A524	9fr multicolored	1.00	.25
1229	A524	9fr multicolored	.70	.25
1230	A524	10fr multicolored	.75	.25
		Nos. 1216-1230 (15)	7.55	3.75

Issued: 7fr, 9/7/87; 5fr, 6fr, 9/12/88; 4fr, 4/17/89; 2fr, 12/4/89; 1fr, 1/8/90; 10fr, 1/15/90; 50c, Nos. 1220, 1229, 9/30/91; others, 9/30/85.
Printed on various papers.
See Nos. 1432-1447, 1627, 1641, 1645, 1651, 1660, 1676, 1696, 1700, 1702-1703, 1714-1715. For stamps denominated in francs

and euros, see Nos. 1785-1790A, 1836-1840. For stamps denominated in euros only, see Nos. 1912-1916, 1970-1979, 2071-2076, 2123-2127, 2218-2222, 2278-2280, 2346-2347, 2402-2403, 2409-2411, 2481.

King Type of 1981

1986-90		**Photo.**	**Perf. 11½**	
1231	A459a	14fr dark gray	1.00	.25
1232	A459a	24fr dk grysh green	2.00	.40
1233	A459a	25fr blue black	2.10	.25
1234	A460a	200fr sage grn & dl gray grn	29.00	.75
		Nos. 1231-1234 (4)	34.10	1.65

Issued: 24fr, 4/7/86; 200fr, 11/3/86; 14fr, 1/15/90; 25fr, 2/19/90.
Printed on various papers.

Congo Stamp Cent. — A525

10fr, Belgian Congo #3.

1986, Jan. 27		**Photo.**	**Perf. 11½**	
1236	A525	10fr multicolored	1.40	.25

No. 1236 is most often collected as a pair. Value never hinged, $8.
See Zaire No. 1230.

Carnival Cities of Aalst and Binche
A526

Folklore: masks, giants.

1986, Feb. 3				
1237	A526	9fr Aalst Belfry	.60	.35
1238	A526	12fr Binche Gilles	.90	.30

Intl. Peace Year — A527

1986, Mar. 10				
1239	A527	23fr Emblem, dove	1.75	.50

Stamp Day — A528

1986, Apr. 21		**Photo.**	**Perf. 11½**	
1240	A528	13fr Artifacts	.90	.30

Europa 1986
A529

1986, May 5				
1241	A529	13fr Fish	1.00	.25
1242	A529	24fr Flora	2.25	.45

Dogs — A530

9fr, Malines sheepdog. 13fr, Tervueren sheepdog. 24fr, Groenendael sheepdog. 26fr, Flemish cattle dog.

1986, May 26		Photo.	Perf. 11½	
1243	A530	9fr multicolored	.70	.30
1244	A530	13fr multicolored	1.10	.45
1245	A530	24fr multicolored	1.75	.80
1246	A530	26fr multicolored	1.90	.85
	Nos. 1243-1246 (4)		5.45	2.40

St. Ludger's Church, Zele — A531

No. 1248, Waver Town Hall. No. 1249, Nederzwalm Canal. No. 1250, Chapel of Our Lady of the Dunes, Bredene. No. 1251, Licot Castle, Viroinval. No. 1252, Eynenbourg Castle, La Calamine.

1986, June 30		Photo. & Engr.		
1247	A531	9fr multi	.60	.30
1248	A531	9fr multi	.60	.30
1249	A531	13fr multi, horiz.	.95	.30
1250	A531	13fr multi	.95	.30
1251	A531	13fr multi, horiz.	.95	.30
1252	A531	13fr multi, horiz.	.95	.30
	Nos. 1247-1252 (6)		5.00	1.80

Youth Philately A532

1986, Sept. 1		Photo.	Perf. 11½	
1253	A532	9fr dl ol grn, blk & dk red	.60	.40

Cartoon Exhibition, Knokke.

Famous Men — A533

Designs: 9fr, Constant Permeke, painter, sculptor. 13fr, Baron Michel-Edmond de Selys Longchamps, scientist. 24fr, Felix Timmermans, writer. 26fr, Maurice Careme, poet.

1986, Sept. 29				
1254	A533	9fr multicolored	.60	.30
1255	A533	13fr multicolored	1.00	.40
1256	A533	24fr multicolored	1.75	.60
1257	A533	26fr multicolored	1.90	.55
	Nos. 1254-1257 (4)		5.25	1.75

Royal Academy for Dutch Language and Literature, Cent. A534

1986, Oct. 6		Engr.		
1258	A534	9fr dark blue	.60	.30

Natl. Beer Industry A535

13fr, Glass, barley, hops.

		Perf. 12½x11½		
1986, Oct. 13		Photo.		
1259	A535	13fr multicolored	1.00	.40

Provincial Law and Councils, 150th Anniv. A536

1986, Oct. 27		Perf. 11½		
1260	A536	13fr Stylized map	1.00	.30

Christian Trade Union, Cent. A537

1986, Dec. 13		Photo.	Perf. 11½	
1261	A537	9fr shown	.60	.40
1262	A537	13fr design reversed	.90	.30

Flanders Technology Intl. — A538

1987, Mar. 2		Photo.		
1263	A538	13fr multi	.90	.30

EUROPALIA '87, Austrian Cultural Events — A539

Design: Woman, detail of a fresco by Gustav Klimt, Palais Stoclet, Brussels.

1987, Apr. 4		Photo.	Perf. 11½	
1264	A539	13fr multicolored	.90	.25

Stamp Day 1987 — A540

Portrait: Jakob Wiener (1815-1899), 1st engraver of Belgian stamps.

1987, Apr. 11		Photo. & Engr.		
1265	A540	13fr grnsh blue & blk grn	.90	.30

Folklore A541

9fr, Penitents procession, Veurne. 13fr, Play of John and Alice, Wavre.

1987, Apr. 25		Photo.		
1266	A541	9fr multicolored	.60	.40
1267	A541	13fr multicolored	.90	.30

Europa 1987 — A542

Modern architecture: 13fr, Louvain-la-Neuve Church. 24fr, Regional Housing Assoc. Tower, St. Maartensdal at Louvain.

1987, May 9		Photo.		
1268	A542	13fr multicolored	1.00	.25
1269	A542	24fr multicolored	2.10	.40

Statue of Andre-Ernest Gretry (1741-1813), French Composer A543

1987, May 23				
1270	A543	24fr multicolored	1.75	.75

Wallonie Royal Opera, Liege, 20th anniv.

Tourism — A544

No. 1271, Statues of Jan Breydel and Pieter de Conin, Bruges. No. 1272, Boondael Chapel, Brussels. No. 1273, Windmill, Keerbergen. No. 1274, St. Christopher's Church, Racour. No. 1275, Virelles Lake, Chimay.

1987, June 13				
1271	A544	13fr multicolored	.90	.30
1272	A544	13fr multicolored	.90	.30
1273	A544	13fr multicolored	.90	.30
1274	A544	13fr multicolored	.90	.30
1275	A544	13fr multicolored	.90	.30
	Nos. 1271-1275 (5)		4.50	1.50

Royal Belgian Rowing Assoc., Cent. — A545

European Volleyball Championships A546

1987, Sept. 5				
1276	A545	9fr multicolored	.60	.40
1277	A546	13fr multicolored	.90	.30

Foreign Trade Year — A547

1987, Sept. 12				
1278	A547	13fr multi	.90	.30

Belgian Social Reform, Cent. A548

1987, Sept. 19				
1279	A548	26fr Leisure, by P. Paulus	1.75	.75

Youth Philately A549

1987, Oct. 3				
1280	A549	9fr multicolored	1.75	.50

Newspaper Centennials A550

No. 1281, Le Soir. No. 1282, Hett Lattste Nieuws, vert.

1987, Dec. 12				
1281	A550	9fr multicolored	.70	.30
1282	A550	9fr multicolored	.70	.30

The Sea — A551

Designs: a, Lighthouse, trawler, rider and mount. b, Trawler, youths playing volleyball on beach. c, Cruise ship, sailboat, beach and cabana. d, Shore, birds.

1988, Feb. 6　Photo.　Perf. 11½
1283　Strip of 4 + label　3.25　3.25
a.-d. A551 10fr any single　.70　.55
No. 1283 has a continuous design.

Dynamism of the Regions A552

No. 1284, Operation Athena. No. 1285, Flanders Alive Campaign.

1988, Mar. 5　Photo.　Perf. 11½
1284　A552 13fr multicolored　.90　.35
1285　A552 13fr multicolored　.90　.35

Stamp Day — A553

Painting: 19th Cent. Postman, by James Thiriar.

1988, Apr. 16　Photo. & Engr.
1286　A553 13fr buff & sepia　.95　.30

Europa 1988 — A554

Transport and communication: 13fr, Satellite dish. 24fr, Non-polluting combustion engine.

1988, May 9　Photo.　Perf. 11½
1287　A554 13fr multicolored　1.10　.25
1288　A554 24fr multicolored　1.90　.75

Tourism — A555

Designs: No. 1289, Romanesque watchtower, ca. 12th-13th cent., Amay, vert. No. 1290, Our Lady of Hanswijk Basilica, 988, Mechelen, vert. No. 1291, St. Sernin's Church, 16th cent., Waimes. No. 1292, Old Town Hall, 1637, and village water pump, 1761, Peer, vert. No. 1293, Our Lady of Bon-Secours Basilica, 1892, Peruwelz.

Photo. & Engr.
1988, June 20　Perf. 11½
1289　A555 9fr beige & blk　.70　.40
1290　A555 9fr lt blue & blk　.70　.40
1291　A555 9fr pale blue grn & blk　.70　.40
1292　A555 13fr pale pink & blk　.90　.30
1293　A555 13fr pale bluish gray & blk　.90　.30
Nos. 1289-1293 (5)　3.90　1.80
Our Lady of Hanswijk Basilica millennium (No. 1290); Waimes village, 1100th anniv. (No. 1291).

Jean Monnet (1888-1979), French Economist — A556

1988, Sept. 12　Perf. 11½
1294　A556 13fr black　.95　.35

Tapestry in the Hall of the Royal Academy of Medicine — A557

Academies building and: No. 1296, Lyre, quill pen, open book and atomic symbols.

1988, Sept. 17　Photo.
1295　A557 9fr shown　.55　.30
1296　A557 9fr multi　.55　.30
Royal Academy of Medicine (No. 1295); Royal Academy of Science, Literature and Fine Arts (No. 1296).

Cultural Heritage A558

Artifacts: 9fr, Statue and mask in the Antwerp Ethnographical Museum. 13fr, Sarcophagus, St. Martin's Church, Trazegnies. 24fr, Church organ, Geraardsbergen. 26fr, Shrine, St. Hadelin's Church, Vise.

1988, Sept. 24
1297　A558 9fr multi　.70　.30
1298　A558 13fr multi　.90　.25
1299　A558 24fr multi　1.75　.60
1300　A558 26fr multi　1.90　.60
Nos. 1297-1300 (4)　5.25　1.75

Youth Philately A559

1988, Oct. 10
1301　A559 9fr multi　1.60　.50

Natl. Postal Savings Bank, 75th Anniv. A560

1988, Nov. 7
1302　A560 13fr multi　1.00　.50

Christmas 1988 and New Year 1989 A561

1988, Nov. 21
1303　A561 9fr Winter landscape　.65　.30

Royal Mounted Guard, 50th Anniv. A562

1988, Dec. 12
1304　A562 13fr multi　.95　.35

Printing Presses A563

9fr, J. Moretus I, Antwerp Museum, vert. 24fr, Stanhope, Printing Museum, Brussels, vert. 26fr, Litho Krause, Royal Museum, Mariemont.

1988, Dec. 19　Engr.
1305　A563 9fr bl blk & blk　.70　.30
1306　A563 24fr dark red brn　1.60　.55
1307　A563 26fr grn & slate grn　1.75　.50
Nos. 1305-1307 (3)　4.05　1.35

Lace A564

No. 1308, Marche-en-Famenne. No. 1309, Brussels. No. 1310, Brugge.

1989, Mar. 20　Photo.
1308　A564 9fr multi　.70　.35
1309　A564 13fr multi　.90　.25
1310　A564 13fr multi　.90　.25
Nos. 1308-1310 (3)　2.50　.85

Stamp Day A565

13fr, Mail coach, post chaise.

1989, Apr. 24　Photo. & Engr.
1311　A565 13fr multicolored　.95　.35

Europa 1989 — A566

Children's toys.

1989, May 8　Photo.
1312　A566 13fr Marbles, horiz.　1.25　.30
1313　A566 24fr Jumping-jack　1.90　.70

Royal Academy of Fine Arts, Antwerp, 325th Anniv. — A567

1989, May 22　Perf. 11½
1314　A567 13fr multi　.85　.30

European Parliament 3rd Elections — A568

1989, June 5　Photo.
1315　A568 13fr Brussels　.85　.30

Declaration of Rights of Man and the Citizen, Bicent. — A569

1989, June 12　Perf. 11½
1316　A569 13fr multi + label　1.00　.50

Tourism A570

No. 1317, St. Tillo's Church, Izegem. No. 1318, Logne Castle, Ferrieres. No. 1319, St. Laurentius's Church, Lokeren. No. 1320, Antoing Castle, Antoing.

1989, June 26　Photo. & Engr.
1317　A570 9fr multi　.70　.30
1318　A570 9fr multi, vert.　.70　.30
1319　A570 13fr multi, vert.　1.00　.30
1320　A570 13fr multi, vert.　1.00　.30
Nos. 1317-1320 (4)　3.40　1.20

Ducks — A571

1989, Sept. 4　Photo.　Perf. 12
Booklet Stamps
1321　A571 13fr Mallard (8a)　1.25　.50
1322　A571 13fr Winter teal (8b)　1.25　.50
1323　A571 13fr Shoveller (8c)　1.25　.50
1324　A571 13fr Pintail (8d)　1.25　.50
a.　Bklt. pane of 4, #1321-1324　5.00
　　Complete booklet, #1324a　5.00

Shigefusa Uesugi, a Seated Japanese Warrior, 13th Cent. A572

1989, Sept. 18   **Perf. 11½**
1325 A572 24fr multicolored   1.60 .60
Europalia.

Education League, 125th Anniv. — A573

1989, Sept. 25
1326 A573 13fr multicolored   .85 .30

Treaty of London, 150th Anniv. — A574

13fr, Map of Limburg Provinces.

1989, Oct. 2   **Photo.**
1327 A574 13fr multicolored   .85 .30
See Netherlands No. 750.

Mr. Nibbs — A575

1989, Oct. 9   **Perf. 11½**
1328 A575 9fr multicolored   1.25 .40
Youth philately promotion.

Christmas, New Year 1990 A576

9fr, Salvation Army band.

1989, Nov. 20   **Photo.**
1329 A576 9fr multicolored   .65 .30

Fr. Damien (1840-89), Missionary, Molokai Is. Leper Colony, Hawaii A577

1989, Nov. 27   **Photo.**
1330 A577 24fr multicolored   1.75 .60

Father Adolf Daens — A578

1989, Dec. 11   **Photo. & Engr.**
1331 A578 9fr pale & dk grn   .60 .30

The Young Post Rider, an Engraving by Albrecht Durer — A579

1990, Jan. 12   **Photo. & Engr.**
1332 A579 14fr buff & red blk   1.10 .55
Postal communications in Europe, 500th anniv.
See Austria No. 1486, Germany No. 1592, Berlin No. 9N584 and German Democratic Republic No. 2791.

Ghent Flower Festival — A580

No. 1333, Iris florentina. No. 1334, Cattleya harrisoniana. No. 1335, Lilium bulbiferum.

1990, Mar. 3   **Photo.**
1333 A580 10fr multicolored   .70 .40
1334 A580 14fr multicolored   1.00 .35
1335 A580 14fr multicolored   1.00 .35
    Nos. 1333-1335 (3)   2.70 1.10

Intl. Women's Day — A581

25fr, Emilienne Brunfaut.

1990, Mar. 12   **Photo.**   **Perf. 11½**
1336 A581 25fr multicolored   1.75 .75

Wheelchair Basketball — A582

Sports.

1990, Mar. 19
1337 A582 10fr multicolored   .65 .40
1338 A582 14fr multicolored   1.00 .30
1339 A582 25fr shown   1.60 .60
    Nos. 1337-1339 (3)   3.25 1.30
Special Olympics (10fr); and 1990 World Cup Soccer Championships, Italy (14fr).

Natl. Water Supply Soc., 75th Anniv. A583

1990, Apr. 2
1340 A583 14fr Water means life   .95 .35

Postman Roulin, by Van Gogh — A584

1990, Apr. 9
1341 A584 14fr multicolored   .95 .35
Stamp Day.

Labor Day, Cent. A585

1990, Apr. 30
1342 A585 25fr multicolored   1.75 .75

Europa 1990 A586

Post offices.

1990, May 7   **Photo. & Engr.**
1343 A586 14fr Ostend 1   *1.10* .25
1344 A586 25fr Liege 1, vert.   *2.50* .70

18-Day Campaign, 1940 — A587

14fr, Lys Monument, Courtrai.

1990, May 14   **Photo.**   **Perf. 11½**
1345 A587 14fr multicolored   1.10 .60
Resistance of German occupation.

Stamp Collecting Promotion Type of 1988
Souvenir Sheet

Various flowers from *Sixty Roses for a Queen*, by P.J. Redoute (1759-1840): a, Rose tricolore. b, Belle Rubaree. c, Mycrophylla. d, Amelie rose. e, Adelaide rose. f, Helene rose.

1990, June 2   **Photo. & Engr.**
1346   Sheet of 6   36.00 36.00
  a.-c. SP487 14fr any single   2.50 2.50
  d.-f. SP487 25fr any single   3.00 3.00
BELGICA '90, Brussels, June 2-10. sold for 220fr.

Battle of Waterloo, 1815 — A588

Design: Marshal Ney leading the French cavalry.

1990, June 18   **Photo.**
1352 A588 25fr multi + label   2.00 1.40

Tourism A589

1990, July 9
1353 A589 10fr Antwerp   .80 .45
1354 A589 10fr Dendermonde   .80 .45
1355 A589 14fr Gerpinnes, vert.   .95 .30
1356 A589 14fr Lommel   .95 .30
1357 A589 14fr Watermael   .95 .30
    Nos. 1353-1357 (5)   4.45 1.80

A590   A590a

King Baudouin A590b

1990-92   **Photo.**   **Perf. 11½**
1364 A590 14fr multicolored   1.10 .25
1365 A590a 15fr rose car   1.25 .25
1366 A590a 28fr blue green   2.00 .55
1367 A590b 100fr slate green   7.50 .50
    Nos. 1364-1367 (4)   11.85 1.55
Issue dates: 14fr, Sept. 7; 15fr, Apr. 1; 28fr, Aug. 3, 1992; 100fr, Sept. 14, 1992.

Fish A591

Designs: No. 1383, Perch (Perche). No. 1384, Minnow (Vairon). No. 1385, Bitterling (Bouviere). No. 1386, Stickleback (Epinoche).

1990, Sept. 8   **Perf. 12**
1383 A591 14fr multicolored   1.75 .60
1384 A591 14fr multicolored   1.75 .60
1385 A591 14fr multicolored   1.75 .60
1386 A591 14fr multicolored   1.75 .60
  a.   Bklt. pane of 4, #1383-1386   7.00 *7.00*
    Complete booklet, #1386a   7.25

Youth Philately A592

1990, Oct. 13   **Perf. 11½**
1387 A592 10fr multicolored   1.50 .50

St. Bernard, 900th Birth Anniv. — A593

1990, Nov. 5 **Photo & Engr.**
1388 A593 25fr black & buff 1.75 .60

Winter Scene by Jozef Lucas A594

1990, Nov. 12 **Photo.**
1389 A594 10fr multi .70 .30

Christmas.

Self-Portrait A595

Paintings by David Teniers (1610-1690).

1990, Dec. 3
1390 A595 10fr shown .70 .30
1391 A595 14fr Dancers 1.00 .30
1392 A595 25fr Bowlers 1.90 .60
  Nos. 1390-1392 (3) 3.60 1.20

A596

Designs: 14fr, The Sower by Constantin Meunier (1831-1905). 25fr, Brabo Fountain by Jef Lambeaux (1852-1908).

Photo. & Engr.
1991, Mar. 18 **Perf. 11½**
1393 A596 14fr buff & blk 1.00 .30
1394 A596 25fr lt bl & dk bl 1.60 .60

A597

No. 1395, Rhythmic gymnastics. No. 1396, Korfball.

1991, Apr. 8 **Photo.** **Perf. 11½**
1395 A597 10fr multicolored .65 .35
1396 A597 10fr multicolored .65 .35

No. 1395, European Youth Olympics. No. 1396, Korfball World Championships.

Stamp Printing Office, Mechlin — A598

1991, Apr. 22
1397 A598 14fr multicolored .95 .40

Stamp Day.

Liberal Trade Union, Cent. A599

1991, Apr. 29
1398 A599 25fr blue & lt blue 1.60 .75

Europa A600

14fr, Olympus-1 satellite. 25fr, Hermes space shuttle.

1991, May 6
1399 A600 14fr multicolored 1.25 .25
1400 A600 25fr multicolored 2.50 .75

Rerum Novarum Encyclical, Cent. A601

1991, May 13 **Photo.** **Perf. 11½**
1401 A601 14fr multicolored .90 .30

Princess Isabel & Philip le Bon — A602

1991, May 27 **Photo.** **Perf. 11½**
1402 A602 14fr multicolored .90 .35

Europalia '91. See Portugal No. 1861.

Tourism A603

Designs: No. 1403, Neptune's Grotto, Couvin. No. 1404, Dieleghem Abbey, Jette. No. 1405, Town Hall, Niel, vert. No. 1406, Nature Reserve, Hautes Fagnes. No. 1407, Legend of giant Rolarius, Roeselare, vert.

1991, June 17 **Photo. & Engr.**
1403 A603 14fr multicolored 1.00 .30
1404 A603 14fr multicolored 1.00 .30
1405 A603 14fr multicolored 1.00 .30
1406 A603 14fr multicolored 1.00 .30
1407 A603 14fr multicolored 1.00 .30
  Nos. 1403-1407 (5) 5.00 1.50

King Baudouin, Coronation, 40th Anniv. and 60th Birthday A604

1991, June 24 **Photo.**
1408 A604 14fr multicolored 1.90 .30

Royal Academy of Medicine, 150th Anniv. — A605

Photo. & Engr.
1991, Sept. 2 **Perf. 11½**
1409 A605 10fr multicolored .70 .30

The English Coast at Dover by Alfred W. Finch (1854-1930) A606

1991, Sept. 9 **Photo.**
1410 A606 25fr multicolored 1.75 .75

See Finland Nos. 868-869.

Mushrooms — A607

No. 1411, Amanita phalloides (13A). No. 1412, Amanita rubescens (13B). No. 1413, Boletus erythropus (13C). No. 1414, Hygrocybe persistens (13D).

1991, Sept. 16 **Photo.** **Perf. 12**
Booklet Stamps
1411 A607 14fr multicolored 1.60 .70
1412 A607 14fr multicolored 1.60 .70
1413 A607 14fr multicolored 1.60 .70
1414 A607 14fr multicolored 1.60 .70
  a. Bklt. pane of 4, #1411-1414 7.00 7.00
    Complete booklet, #1414a 7.25

Doctors Without Borders A608

Design: No. 1415, Amnesty Intl.

1991, Sept. 23 **Perf. 11½**
1415 A608 25fr multicolored 1.60 .60
1416 A608 25fr multicolored 1.60 .60

Telecom '91 — A609

1991, Oct. 7 **Photo.** **Perf. 11½**
1417 A609 14fr multicolored .90 .35

6th World Forum and Exposition on Telecommunications, Geneva, Switzerland.

Youth Philately — A610

Cartoon characters: No. 1418, Blake and Mortimer, by Edgar P. Jacobs (16a). No. 1419, Cori the ship boy, by Bob De Moor (16b). No. 1420, Cities of the Fantastic, by Francois Schuiten (16c). No. 1421, Boule and Bill, by Jean Roba (16d).

1991, Oct. 14 **Perf. 12**
Booklet Stamps
1418 A610 14fr multicolored 1.60 1.00
1419 A610 14fr multicolored 1.60 1.00
1420 A610 14fr multicolored 1.60 1.00
1421 A610 14fr multicolored 1.60 1.00
  a. Bklt. pane of 4, #1418-1421 7.00 7.00
    Complete booklet, #1421a 7.25

Belgian Newspapers, Cent. — A611

No. 1422, Gazet Van Antwerpen. No. 1423, Het Volk.

1991, Nov. 4 **Photo.** **Perf. 11½**
1422 A611 14fr multicolored .65 .30
1423 A611 10fr multicolored .65 .30

Icon of Madonna and Child, Chevetogne Abbey A612

1991, Nov. 25 **Photo.** **Perf. 11½**
1424 A612 10fr multicolored .60 .30

Christmas.

Wolfgang Amadeus Mozart, Death Bicent. — A613

1991, Dec. 2 **Photo.** **Perf. 11½**
1425 A613 25fr multicolored 1.75 .75

Fire
Fighting — A614

1992, Feb. 10   Photo.   Perf. 11½
1426 A614 14fr multicolored   .85   .30

Belgian Resistance
in WWII — A615

1992, Feb. 24
1427 A615 14fr multicolored   .85   .35

Belgian Carpet
Industry — A616

Antwerp
Diamond
Club, Cent.
A617

Design: 14fr, Chef's hat, cutlery.

1992, Mar. 9
1428 A616 10fr multicolored   .65   .35
1429 A616 14fr multicolored   .90   .30
1430 A617 27fr multicolored   1.75   .60
      Nos. 1428-1430 (3)   3.30   1.25

Belgian Association of Master Chefs.

Expo '92,
Seville
A618

1992, Mar. 23
1431 A618 14fr multicolored   .90   .35

Bird Type of 1985

No. 1432, Sizerin flamme. No. 1433, Merle noir. No. 1434, Grive mauvis. No. 1435, Gobe mouche noir. No. 1436, Bergeronette grise. No. 1437, Etourneau sansonnet. No. 1438, Hirondelle de cheminee. No. 1439, Geai des chenes. No. 1440, Cincle plongeur. No. 1441, Phragmite des joncs. No. 1442, Loriot. No. 1443, Mesange charbonniere. No. 1444, Verdier. No. 1445, Troglodyte mignon. No. 1446, Moineau domestique. No. 1446A, Pouillot fitis. No. 1447, Jaseur boreal.

1992-96   Photo.   Perf. 11½
1432 A524 1fr multicolored   .25   .25
1433 A524 2fr multicolored   .25   .25
1434 A524 2fr multicolored   .25   .25
1435 A524 4fr multicolored   .35   .25
1436 A524 4fr multicolored   .35   .25
1437 A524 5fr multicolored   .35   .25
1438 A524 5fr multicolored   .35   .25
1439 A524 5.50fr multicolored   .50   .25
1440 A524 6fr multicolored   .50   .25
1441 A524 6.50fr multicolored   .50   .30
1442 A524 7fr multicolored   .60   .25
1443 A524 8fr multicolored   .60   .25
1444 A524 10fr multicolored   .75   .25
1445 A524 11fr multicolored   .80   .25
1446 A524 13fr multicolored   1.00   .25

1446A A524 14fr multicolored   1.00   .25
1447 A524 16fr multicolored   1.25   .25
      Nos. 1432-1447 (17)   9.65   4.30

Issued: 11fr, 4/1/92; 1fr, 2fr, 6fr, 8fr, 10fr, 6/92; 4fr, 5fr, 7fr, 9/7/92; 5.50fr, 9/27/93; 13fr, 16fr, 1/3/94; 6.50fr, 10/3/94; 14fr, 12/18/95; No. 1435A, 5/6/96; No. 1433A, 1434, 7/1/96.
Printed on various papers.
See No. 1838 for similar stamp with additional Euro denomination.

Jean Van Noten
(1903-1982),
Stamp
Designer — A619

Photo. & Engr.
1992, Apr. 13   Perf. 11½
1448 A619 15fr ver & black   .85   .35

Stamp Day.

Abstract Painting by Jo
Delahaut — A620

No. 1449, Witte Magie No. 6, by Roger Raveel.

1992, Apr. 27   Photo.   Perf. 11½
1449 A620 15fr multi, vert.   .90   .30
1450 A620 15fr multi   .90   .30

European Discovery of America, 500th
Anniv. — A621

28fr, 500 with globe and astrolabe inside "00" of 500.

1992, May 2
1451 A621 15fr shown   *1.25*   *.30*
1452 A621 28fr multicolored   *2.25*   *.90*

Europa.

Fight
Racism — A622

1992, May 18   Photo.   Perf. 11½
1453 A622 15fr black, gray & pink   .85   .30

Paintings from Orsay Museum,
Paris — A623

Paintings by Belgian artists: 11fr, The Hamlet, by Jacob Smits. 15fr, The Bath, by Alfred Stevens. 30fr, The Man at the Helm, by Theo Van Rysselberghe.

1992, June 15   Photo.   Perf. 11½
1454 A623 11fr multicolored   .75   .40
1455 A623 15fr multicolored   1.10   .35
1456 A623 30fr multicolored   2.00   .80
      Nos. 1454-1456 (3)   3.85   1.55

Tourism — A624

Designs: No. 1457, Manneken Pis Fountain, Brussels. No. 1458, Landcommander Castle Alden Biesen, Bilzen, horiz. No. 1459, Building facade, Andenne. No. 1460, Fools' Monday Carnival, Renaix, horiz. No. 1461, Great Procession, Tournai, horiz.

Photo. & Engr.
1992, July 6   Perf. 11½
1457 A624 15fr multicolored   .95   .40
1458 A624 15fr multicolored   .95   .40
1459 A624 15fr multicolored   .95   .40
1460 A624 15fr multicolored   .95   .40
1461 A624 15fr multicolored   .95   .40
      Nos. 1457-1461 (5)   4.75   2.00

Village of Andenne, 1300th anniv. (No. 1459). Grand Procession of Tournai, 900th anniv. (No. 1461).

Animals — A625

1992, Sept. 7   Photo.   Perf. 12
Booklet Stamps
1462 A625 15fr Polecat (13a)   1.50   .65
1463 A625 15fr Squirrel (13b)   1.50   .65
1464 A625 15fr Hedgehog (13c)   1.50   .65
1465 A625 15fr Dormouse (13d)   1.50   .65
  a.   Bklt. pane of 4, #1462-1465   6.00   *6.00*
          Complete booklet, #1465a   6.00

Brabant Revolution — A626

Design: 15fr, Troops fighting and Henri Van der Noot, Jean Andre Van der Meersch, and Jean Francois Vonck, rebel leaders.

Photo. & Engr.
1992, Sept. 21   Perf. 11½
1466 A626 15fr multicolored   .85   .30

Arms of Thurn and
Taxis — A627

1992, Oct. 5   Photo.   Perf. 11½
1467 A627 15fr multicolored   .90   .35

Gaston
Lagaffe, by
Andre
Franquin
A628

1992, Oct. 12
1468 A628 15fr multicolored   1.25   .35

Youth philately.

Single European Market — A629

1992, Oct. 26
1469 A629 15fr multicolored   .85   .30

Antwerp Zoo, 150th
Anniv. — A630

1992, Nov. 16
1470 A630 15fr Okapi   .85   .30
1471 A630 30fr Tamarin   2.00   1.00

The
Brussels
Place
Royale in
Winter, by
Luc De
Decker
A631

1992, Nov. 23
1472 A631 11fr multicolored   .70   .30

Christmas.

History
A632

Designs: 11fr, Council of Leptines, 1250th anniv. 15fr, 28fr, Missale Romanum of Matthias Corvinus (Matyas Hunyadi, King of Hungary) (diff. details). 30fr, Battles of Neerwinden (1693, 1793).

1993, Mar. 15　Photo.　Perf. 11½
1473　A632　11fr multicolored　.75　.30
1474　A632　15fr multicolored　1.00　.40
1475　A632　30fr multicolored　2.00　.75
　　　Nos. 1473-1475 (3)　3.75　1.45
Souvenir Sheet
1476　A632　28fr multicolored　2.00　2.00
　　Size of No. 1474, 80x28mm. No. 1476 contains one 55x40mm stamp.
　　See Hungary No. 3385-3386.

A633

A634

Antwerp, Cultural City of Europe
A635

　　Designs: No. 1477, Panoramic view of Antwerp. No. 1478, Antwerp Town Hall, designed by Cornelis Floris. No. 1479, Woman's Head and Warrior's Torso, by Jacob Jordaens. No. 1480, St. Job's Altar (detail), Schoonbroek. No. 1481, Angels on stained glass window, Mater Dei Chapel of Institut Marie-Josee, by Eugeen Yoors, vert.

1993, Mar. 22
1477　A633　15fr multicolored　1.00　.55
1478　A634　15fr multicolored　1.00　.55
1479　A635　15fr gray & multi　1.00　.55
1480　A635　15fr green & multi　1.00　.55
1481　A635　15fr blue & multi　1.00　.55
　　　Nos. 1477-1481 (5)　5.00　2.75
Antwerp '93.

Stamp Day — A636

1993, Apr. 5
1482　A636　15fr No. 74　　.95　.35

Contemporary Paintings — A637

　　Europa: 15fr, Florence 1960, by Gaston Bertrand. 28fr, De Sjees, by Constant Permeke.

1993, Apr. 26　Photo.　Perf. 11½
1483　A637　15fr multicolored　1.00　.25
1484　A637　28fr multicolored　2.00　.60

Butterflies — A638

1993, May 10
1485　A638　15fr Vanessa atalanta　.95　.40
1486　A638　15fr Apatura iris　.95　.40
1487　A638　15fr Inachis io　.95　.40
1488　A638　15fr Aglais urticae　.95　.40
　　　Nos. 1485-1488 (4)　3.80　1.60

Alumni Assoc. (UAE), Free University of Brussels, 150th Anniv.
A639

1993, May 17
1489　A639　15fr blue & black　.85　.30
　　No. 1489 is usually collected as a horizontal pair. Value, $5 never-hinged.

Europalia '93 — A640

1993, May 24
1490　A640　15fr Mayan statuette　.85　.35

Folklore A641

　　Designs: 11fr, Ommegang Procession, Brussels. 15fr, Royal Moncrabeau Folk Group, Namur. 28fr, Stilt walkers of Merchtem, vert.

1993, June 7　Photo.　Perf. 11½
1491　A641　11fr multicolored　.75　.40
1492　A641　15fr multicolored　.95　.30
1493　A641　28fr multicolored　1.50　.75
　　　Nos. 1491-1493 (3)　3.20　1.45

Tourism A642

　　Castles: No. 1494, La Hulpe. No. 1495, Cortewalle (Beveren). No. 1496, Jehay. No. 1497, Arenberg (Heverlee), vert. No. 1498, Raeren.

Photo. & Engr.
　　　　　　　　　　Perf. 11½
1494　A642　15fr pale green & blk　.95　.40
1495　A642　15fr pale lilac & black　.95　.40
1496　A642　15fr pale blue & black　.95　.40
1497　A642　15fr pale brn & black　.95　.40
1498　A642　15fr pale olive & blk　.95　.40
　　　Nos. 1494-1498 (5)　4.75　2.00

Intl. Triennial Exhibition of Tournai
A643

1993, July 5　Photo.　Perf. 11½
1499　A643　15fr black, blue & red　.85　.30

Belgian Presidency of European Community Council
A644

1993, Aug. 9　Photo.　Perf. 11½
1500　A644　15fr multicolored　.85　.30

Rene Magritte (1898-1967), Artist — A645

1993, Aug. 9
1501　A645　30fr multicolored　1.90　.75

King Baudouin (1930-1993) — A646

1993, Aug. 17　Photo.　Perf. 11½
1502　A646　15fr black & gray　1.00　.25

European House Cats — A647

1993, Sept. 6　Photo.　Perf. 12
Booklet Stamps
1503　A647　15fr Brown & white
　　　　　　　(10a)　　　1.25　.60
1504　A647　15fr Black & white
　　　　　　　(10b)　　　1.25　.60
1505　A647　15fr Gray tabby (10c)　1.25　.60
1506　A647　15fr Calico (10d)　1.25　.60
　a.　Booklet pane of 4, #1503-1506　5.00　5.00
　　　Complete booklet, #1506a　5.00

Publication of De Humani Corporis Fabrica, by Andreas Vesalius, 1543 — A648

1993, Oct. 4　Photo.　Perf. 11½
1507　A648　15fr multicolored　.85　.30

Air Hostess Natacha, by Francois Walthery — A649

1993, Oct. 18
1508　A649　15fr multicolored　1.10　.45
　　Youth philately.

Publication of "Faux Soir," 50th Anniv. — A650

1993, Nov. 8　Photo.　Perf. 11½
1509　A650　11fr multicolored　.75　.40

Notre-Dame de la Chapelle, Brussels
A651

1993, Nov. 22　Photo.　Perf. 11½
1510　A651　11fr multicolored　.60　.30

Christmas, New Year.

Children, Future Decisionmakers — A652

1993, Dec. 13　Photo.　Perf. 11½
1511　A652　15fr multicolored　.85　.30

A653

A654

A655

A655a

King Albert II
1993-98　Photo.　Perf. 11½
1512　A653　16fr lt gray &
　　　　　　multi　　1.40　.25
1513　A653　16fr lt & dk bl
　　　　　　grn　　1.00　.25
1514　A655　16fr multi　1.40　.25

1515	A655	16fr blue	.90	.25
1516	A655	17fr blue	1.10	.25
1517	A655	18fr olive black	1.00	.25
1518	A655	19fr dp gray vio	1.20	.30
1519	A653	20fr cream &		
		brn	1.40	.40
1520	A655	20fr brown	1.20	.25
1521	A655	25fr sepia	1.30	.30
1522	A655	28fr claret	1.90	.30
1523	A653	30fr red lilac	1.50	.25
1524	A653	32fr violet blue	1.75	.25
1525	A653	32fr cream &		
		org brn	1.75	.25
1526	A655	34fr dk bl gray	1.50	.50
1527	A655	36fr dk sl bl	1.75	.25
1528	A653	40fr pink & car	2.40	.30
1529	A655	50fr green	4.00	.35
1530	A655	50fr green	3.00	.40
1531	A654	100fr multi	6.00	.35
1532	A654	200fr multi	12.50	2.50
		Nos. 1512-1532 (21)	49.95	8.45

Coil Stamp

1536	A655a	19fr deep gray		
		vio	1.50	1.25

Issued: No. 1512, 12/15/93; No. 1513, 1/17/94; 30fr, 2/4/94; No. 1525, 3/7/94; 50fr, 4/18/94; No. 1519, 6/6/94; 40fr, 6/20/94; 100fr, 10/3/94; 200fr, 5/2/95; No. 1514, 6/6/96; No. 1515, 1530, 28fr, 9/2/96; 17fr, 12/16/96; 34fr, 36fr, 2/10/97; 18fr, 4/7/97; No. 1518, 7/7/97; 25fr, 4/20/98; No. 1536, 8/10/98; No. 1520, 10/19/98; No. 1524, 11/9/98.

Paintings
A656

Designs: No. 1537, The Malleable Darkness, by Octave Landuyt. No. 1538, Ma Toute Belle, by Serge Vandercam. vert.

1994, Jan. 31   Photo.   Perf. 11½

1537	A656	16fr multicolored	1.00	.35
1538	A656	16fr multicolored	1.00	.35

Airplanes
A657

13fr, Hanriot-Dupont HD-1. 15fr, Spad XIII. 30fr, Schreck FBA-H. 32fr, Stampe-Vertongen SV-4B.

1994, Feb. 28

1539	A657	13fr multicolored	.90	.50
1540	A657	15fr multicolored	1.10	.50
1541	A657	30fr multicolored	2.00	1.00
1542	A657	32fr multicolored	2.25	1.00
		Nos. 1539-1542 (4)	6.25	3.00

Daily Newspapers — A658

No. 1543, "Le Jour-Le Courier," cent., vert. No. 1544, "La Wallonie," 75th anniv.

1994, Mar. 21   Photo.   Perf. 11½

1543	A658	16fr multicolored	1.00	.35
1544	A658	16fr multicolored	1.00	.35

Fall of the Golden Calf (Detail), by
Fernand Allard l'Olivier — A659

1994, Mar. 28

1545	A659	16fr multicolored	1.00	.40

Charter of Quaregnon, cent.

Stamp Day — A660

1994, Apr. 11   Photo.   Perf. 11½

1546	A660	16fr No. 102	1.00	.35

History
A661

Scenes from Brabantse Yeesten, 15th cent. illuminated manuscript: 13fr, Reconciliation between John I and Arnold, squire of Wezemaal. 16fr, Tournament at wedding of Charles the Bold and Margaret of York. 30fr, Battle of Woeringen.

1994, Apr. 25

1547	A661	13fr multicolored	.85	.40
1548	A661	16fr multicolored	1.00	.30
1549	A661	30fr multicolored	2.00	.90
		Nos. 1547-1549 (3)	3.85	1.60

No. 1549 is 81x28mm.

Europa — A662

Designs: 16fr, Abbe Georges Lemaitre (1894-1966), proposed "big-bang" theory of origins of universe. 30fr, Gerardus Mercator (1512-94), cartographer, astronomer.

1994, May 9   Photo.   Perf. 11½

1550	A662	16fr multicolored	*1.10*	*.25*
1551	A662	30fr multicolored	*2.40*	*.90*

Papal Visit
A663

No. 1552, Father Damien (1840-89). No. 1553, St. Mutien-Marie (1841-1917), Christian educator.

1994, May 16   Perf. 11½x12

1552	A663	16fr multicolored	1.00	.35
1553	A663	16fr multicolored	1.00	.35

Tourism
A664

Churches: No. 1554, St. Peter's, Bertem. No. 1555, St. Bavo's, Kanegem, vert. No. 1556, Royal St. Mary's, Schaarbeek. No. 1557, St. Gery's, Aubechies. No. 1558, Sts. Peter and Paul, Saint-Severin, Condroz, vert.

1994, June 13   Photo.   Perf. 11½

1554	A664	16fr multicolored	1.00	.35
1555	A664	16fr multicolored	1.00	.35
1556	A664	16fr multicolored	1.00	.35
1557	A664	16fr multicolored	1.00	.35
1558	A664	16fr multicolored	1.00	.35
		Nos. 1554-1558 (5)	5.00	1.75

Guillaume
Lekeu
(1870-94),
Composer
A665

Design: No. 1560, Detail of painting by Hans Memling (c.1430-94).

1994, Aug. 16   Photo.   Perf. 11½

1559	A665	16fr multicolored	1.00	.35
1560	A665	16fr multicolored	1.00	.35

Liberation of Belgium, 50th
Anniv. — A666

Design: 16fr, General Crerar, Field Marshal Montgomery, Gen. Bradley, Belgium landscape.

1994, Sept. 5   Photo.   Perf. 11x11½

1561	A666	16fr multicolored	1.10	.60

Wildflowers — A667

Designs: No. 1562, Caltha palustris. No. 1563, Cephalanthera damasonium. No. 1564, Calystegia soldanella. No. 1565, Epipactis helleborine.

**1994, Sept. 26   Photo.   Perf. 12
Booklet Stamps**

1562	A667	16fr multi (14a)	1.10	.75
1563	A667	16fr multi (14b)	1.10	.75
1564	A667	16fr multi (14c)	1.10	.75
1565	A667	16fr multi (14d)	1.10	.75
a.		Booklet pane of 4, #1562-1565	5.00	*5.00*
		Complete booklet, #1565a	5.00	
		Nos. 1562-1565 (4)	4.40	3.00

Cubitus the Dog,
by Luc
Dupanloup — A668

1994, Oct. 10   Perf. 11½

1566	A668	16fr multicolored	1.25	.45

Youth philately.

Georges
Simenon
(1903-89),
Writer
A669

Photo. & Engr.

1994, Oct. 17   Perf. 11½

1567	A669	16fr multicolored	1.00	.30

See France No. 2443, Switzerland No. 948.

Christmas
A670

1994, Dec. 5   Photo.   Perf. 11½

1568	A670	13fr multicolored	.90	.30

Anniversaries and Events — A671

No. 1569, August Vermeylen Fund, 50th anniv. No. 1570, Belgian Touring Club, cent. No. 1571, Assoc. of Belgian Enterprises, cent. No. 1572, Dept. of Social Security, 50th anniv.

1995, Feb. 13   Photo.   Perf. 11½

1569	A671	16fr multicolored	1.00	.30
1570	A671	16fr multicolored	1.00	.30
1571	A671	16fr multicolored	1.00	.30
1572	A671	16fr multicolored	1.00	.30
		Nos. 1569-1572 (4)	4.00	1.20

Flowers of
Ghent
A672

13fr, Hibiscus rosa-sinensis. 16fr, Rhododendron simsii. 30fr, Fuchsia hybrida.

1995, Mar. 6

1573	A672	13fr multicolored	.75	.65
1574	A672	16fr multicolored	1.00	.75
1575	A672	30fr multicolored	2.00	1.60
		Nos. 1573-1575 (3)	3.75	3.00

Games — A673

13fr, Crossword puzzles. 16fr, Chess. 30fr, Scrabble. 34fr, Cards.

1995, Mar. 20

1576	A673	13fr multicolored	.75	.40
1577	A673	16fr multicolored	.95	.60
1578	A673	30fr multicolored	1.90	1.00
1579	A673	34fr multicolored	2.25	1.25
		Nos. 1576-1579 (4)	5.85	3.25

Stamp Day — A674

1995, Apr. 10   Photo. & Engr.

1580	A674	16fr Frans de Troyer	1.00	.35

Peace &
Freedom
A675

Europa: 16fr, Broken barbed wire, prison guard tower. 30fr, Mushroom cloud, "Never again."

1995, Apr. 24   Photo.   Perf. 11½
1581 A675 16fr multicolored   1.25   .25
1582 A675 30fr multicolored   2.40   1.00

Liberation of concentration camps, 50th anniv. (No. 1581). Nuclear Non-Proliferation Treaty, 25th anniv. (No. 1582).

Battle of Fontenoy, 250th Anniv. — A676

16fr, Irish soldiers, Cross of Fontenoy.

1995, May 15   Photo.   Perf. 11½
1583 A676 16fr multicolored   1.00   .30

See Ireland No. 967.

UN, 50th Anniv. A677

1995, May 22   Photo.   Perf. 11½
1584 A677 16fr multicolored   1.00   .35

"Sauvagemont, Maransart," by Pierre Alechinsky — A678

No. 1586: "Telegram-style," by Pol Mara.

1995, June 6
1585 A678 16fr multicolored   1.00   .30
1586 A678 16fr multicolored   1.00   .30

Tourism A679

Architectural designs: No. 1587, Cauchie house, Brussels, by Paul Cauchie (1875-1952). No. 1588, De Viif Werelddelen, corner building, Antwerp, by Frans Smet-Verhas (1851-1925). No. 1589, House, Liege, by Paul Jaspar (1859-1945).

1995, June 26
1587 A679 16fr multicolored   1.00   .40
1588 A679 16fr multicolored   1.00   .40
1589 A679 16fr multicolored   1.00   .40
     Nos. 1587-1589 (3)   3.00   1.20

Sailing Ships — A680

No. 1590, Mercator. No. 1591, Kruzenstern. No. 1592, Sagres II. No. 1593, Amerigo Vespucci.

Booklet Stamps

1995, Aug. 21   Photo.   Perf. 12
1590 A680 16fr multicolored   1.10   .60
1591 A680 16fr multicolored   1.10   .60
1592 A680 16fr multicolored   1.10   .60
1593 A680 16fr multicolored   1.10   .60
  a. Booklet pane of 4, #1590-1593   5.00   5.00
      Complete booklet, #1593a   5.00
      Nos. 1590-1593 (4)   4.40   2.40

Classic Motorcycles A681

13fr, 1908 Minerva. 16fr, 1913 FN, vert. 30fr, 1929 La Mondiale. 32fr, 1937 Gillet, vert.

1995, Sept. 25   Photo.   Perf. 11½
1594 A681 13fr multi   .75   .50
1595 A681 16fr multi   .90   .60
1596 A681 30fr multi   1.75   1.50
1597 A681 32fr multi   2.00   1.60
     Nos. 1594-1597 (4)   5.40   4.20

Comic Character, Sammy, by Arthur Berckmans A682

1995, Oct. 9   Photo.   Perf. 11½
1598 A682 16fr multicolored   1.00   .45

Youth philately.

King's Day A683

16fr, King Albert II and Queen Paola.

1995, Nov. 15   Photo.   Perf. 11½
1599 A683 16fr multicolored   1.00   .35

Christmas — A684

13fr, Nativity scene from "Breviary," book of devotions, c. 1500.

1995, Nov. 20
1600 A684 13fr multicolored   .85   .30

Liberal Party, 150th Anniv. — A685

1996, Mar. 4   Photo.   Perf. 11½
1601 A685 16fr multicolored   1.00   .80

Portrait of Emile Mayrisch (1862-1928), by Théo Van Rysselberghe (1862-1926) — A686

1996, Mar. 2
1602 A686 (A) multicolored   2.00   .80

No. 1602 was valued at 16fr on day of issue. See Luxembourg No. 939.

Oscar Bonnevalle, Stamp Designer — A687

1996, Apr. 1
1603 A687 16fr multicolored   1.00   .60

Stamp Day.

Insects A688

No. 1604, Sympetrum sanguineum. No. 1605, Bombus terrestris. No. 1606, Lucanus cervus. No. 1607, Melolontha melolontha. No. 1608, Gryllus campestris. No. 1609, Coccinella septempunctata.

1996, Apr. 1   Photo.   Perf. 12
Booklet Stamps
1604 A688 16fr multicolored   1.00   .75
1605 A688 16fr multicolored   1.00   .75
1606 A688 16fr multicolored   1.00   .75
1607 A688 16fr multicolored   1.00   .75
1608 A688 16fr multicolored   1.00   .75
1609 A688 16fr multicolored   1.00   .75
  a. Booklet pane, #1604-1609   7.50   7.50
      Complete booklet, #1609a   7.50
      Nos. 1604-1609 (6)   6.00   4.50

Famous Women A689

Europa: 16fr, Yvonne Nevejean (1900-87), saved Jewish children during World War II. 30fr, Marie Gevers (1883-1975), poet.

1996, May 6   Photo.   Perf. 11½
1610 A689 16fr multicolored   1.00   .25
1611 A689 30fr multicolored   2.00   1.00

Tourism — A690

Designs: No. 1612, Grotto of Han-Sur-Lesse, horiz. No. 1613, Village of Begijnendijk as separate community, bicent.

1996, June 10   Photo.   Perf. 11½
1612 A690 16fr multicolored   1.00   .35
1613 A690 16fr multicolored   1.00   .35

Architecture in Brussels — A691

No. 1614, La Maison du Roi (Grand Place). No. 1615, Galeries Royales Saint-Hubert. No. 1616, Le Palais d'Egmont, Le Petit Sablon, horiz. No. 1617, Le Cinquantenaire, horiz.

1996, June 10
1614 A691 16fr multi (7a)   1.10   .40
1615 A691 16fr multi (7b)   1.10   .40
1616 A691 16fr multi (7c)   1.10   .40
1617 A691 16fr multi (7d)   1.10   .40
     Nos. 1614-1617 (4)   4.40   1.60

Auto Races at Spa, Cent. A692

No. 1618, 1900 German 6CV. No. 1619, 1925 Alfa Romeo P2. No. 1620, 1939 Mercedes Benz W154. No. 1621, 1967 Ferrari 330P.

1996, July 1
1618 A692 16fr multicolored   1.00   .40
1619 A692 16fr multicolored   1.00   .40
1620 A692 16fr multicolored   1.00   .40
1621 A692 16fr multicolored   1.00   .40
     Nos. 1618-1621 (4)   4.00   1.60

Paintings of Historical Figures — A693

Portraits from town hall triptych, Zierikzee, Netherlands: No. 1622, Philip I, the Handsome (1478-1506). No. 1623, Juana of Castile, the Mad (1479-1555).

1996, Sept. 2   Photo.   Perf. 11½
1622 A693 16fr multicolored   1.00   .45
1623 A693 16fr multicolored   1.00   .45

Paintings from National Gallery, London — A694

14fr, Reading Man, by Rogier Van Der Weyden (1399-1464). 16fr, Susanna Fourment, by Peter Paul Rubens (1577-1640). 30fr, A Man in a Turban, by Jan Van Eyck (1390-1441).

1996, Sept. 2
1624 A694 14fr multicolored   .90   .50
1625 A694 16fr multicolored   1.10   .60
1626 A694 30fr multicolored   2.25   1.25
     Nos. 1624-1626 (3)   4.25   2.35

Bird Type of 1985

1996, Oct. 7   Photo.   Perf. 11½
1627 A524 6fr Tarin des aulnes   .50   .25

Comic Character, Cloro, by Raymond Macherot — A695

1996, Oct. 7
1628 A695 16fr multicolored   1.10   .60
Youth Philately.

Almanac of Mons, by Fr. Charles Letellier, 150th Anniv. A696

1996, Oct. 7
1629 A696 16fr multicolored   1.00   .40

Music and Literature A697

No. 1630, Arthur Grumiaux (1921-86), violinist. No. 1631, Flor Peeters (1903-86), organist. No. 1632, Christian Dotremont (1922-79), poet, artist. No. 1633, Paul Van Ostaijen (1896-1928), writer.

Photo. & Engr.   **Perf. 11½**
1996, Oct. 28
1630 A697 16fr multicolored   1.00   .40
1631 A697 16fr multicolored   1.00   .40
1632 A697 16fr multicolored   1.00   .40
1633 A697 16fr multicolored   1.00   .40
   Nos. 1630-1633 (4)   4.00 1.60

Christmas and New Year — A698

Scenes from Christmas Market: a, Decorated trees, rooftops. b, Lighted greeting signs. c, Church. d, Selling desert items. e, Selling Nativity scenes. f, Selling meat. g, Santa ringing bell. h, Man smoking pipe, people with presents. i, People shopping.

1996, Nov. 18   **Photo.**   **Perf. 11½**
1634 A698 Sheet of 9, #a.-i.   7.50 7.50
  a.-i.   14fr Any single   .75   .60

Catholic Faculty University, Mons, Cent. A699

1997, Jan. 20   **Photo.**   **Perf. 11½**
1635 A699 17fr multicolored   1.00   .30

Opera at Theatre Royal de la Monnaie, Brussels — A700

No. 1636, Marie Sasse (1834-1907), soprano. No. 1637, Ernest Van Dijck (1861-1923), tenor. No. 1638, Hector Dufranne (1870-1951), baritone. No. 1639, Clara Clairbert (1899-1970), soprano.

1997, Feb. 10
1636 A700 17fr multicolored   1.10   .45
1637 A700 17fr multicolored   1.10   .45
1638 A700 17fr multicolored   1.10   .45
1639 A700 17fr multicolored   1.10   .45
   Nos. 1636-1639 (4)   4.40 1.80

Eastern Cantons — A701

1997, Feb. 10   **Photo.**   **Perf. 11½**
1640 A701 17fr multicolored   1.10   .45

Bird Type of 1985
1997, Mar. 10
1641 A524 15fr Mesange boreale   .95   .25

UN Peace-Keeping Forces — A702

1997, Mar. 10
1642 A702 17fr multicolored   1.00   .35

Stories and Legends A703

Europa: 17fr, "De Bokkenrijders" (The Goat Riders). 30fr, Jean de Berneau.

1997, Mar. 10   **Photo.**   **Perf. 11½**
1643 A703 17fr multicolored   1.25   .25
1644 A703 30fr multicolored   2.00 1.00

Bird Type of 1985
150fr, Pie bavarde, horiz.

1997, Apr. 7   **Size: 35x25mm**
1645 A524 150fr multicolored   8.00 1.50
See No. 1840 for similar stamp with additional Euro denomination.

Constant Spinoy (1924-93), Stamp Engraver — A704

1997, Apr. 7   **Photo. & Engr.**
1646 A704 17fr multicolored   1.10   .40
Stamp Day.

Intl. Flower Show, Liege — A705

1997, Apr. 21   **Photo.**
1647 A705 17fr multicolored   1.00   .35

Paintings by Paul Delvaux (1897-1994) A706

Details or entire paintings: 15fr, Woman with garland of leaves in hair. 17fr, Nude, horiz. 32fr, Woman wearing hat, trolley.

1997, Apr. 21
1648 A706 15fr multicolored   .95   .50
1649 A706 17fr multicolored   1.10   .60
1650 A706 32fr multicolored   2.10   .95
   Nos. 1648-1650 (3)   4.15 2.05

Bird Type of 1985
3fr, Alouette des champs.

1997, May 7   **Photo.**   **Perf. 11½**
1651 A524 3fr multicolored   .25   .25

Queen Paola, 60th Birthday A707

1997, May 26
1652 A707 17fr Belvedere Castle 1.10   .50
See Italy No. 2147.

Cartoon Character, "Jommeke," by Jef Nys — A708

1997, May 26
1653 A708 17fr multicolored   1.30   .65

World Congress of Rose Societies — A709

Roses: No. 1654, Rosa damascena coccinea. No. 1655, Rosa sulfurea. No. 1656, Rosa centifolia.

1997, July 7   **Photo.**   **Perf. 11½**
1654 A709 17fr multicolored   1.10   .55
1655 A709 17fr multicolored   1.10   .55
1656 A709 17fr multicolored   1.10   .55
   Nos. 1654-1656 (3)   3.30 1.65

Churches — A710

No. 1657, Basilica of St. Martin, Halle. No. 1658, Notre Dame Church, Laeken, horiz. No. 1659, Basilica of St. Martin, Liège.

1997, July 7   **Photo. & Engr.**
1657 A710 17fr multicolored   1.10   .45
1658 A710 17fr multicolored   1.10   .45
1659 A710 17fr multicolored   1.10   .45
   Nos. 1657-1659 (3)   3.30 1.35

Bird Type of 1985
7fr, Bergeronnette printaniere.

1997, Sept. 1   **Photo.**   **Perf. 11½**
1660 A524 7fr multicolored   .55   .30

Bees and Apiculture — A711

No. 1661, Queen, workers. No. 1662, Development of the larvae. No. 1663, Bee exiting cell. No. 1664, Bee collecting nectar. No. 1665, Two bees. No. 1666, Two bees on honeycomb.

1997, Sept. 1   **Photo.**   **Perf. 12**
     Booklet Stamps
1661 A711 17fr multi (15a)   1.25   .60
1662 A711 17fr multi (15b)   1.25   .60
1663 A711 17fr multi (15c)   1.25   .60
1664 A711 17fr multi (15d)   1.25   .60
1665 A711 17fr multi (15e)   1.25   .60
1666 A711 17fr multi (15f)   1.25   .60
  a.   Booklet pane of 6, #1661-1666   8.50 8.50
    Complete booklet, #1666a   8.50
   Nos. 1661-1666 (6)   7.50 3.60

Craftsmen A712

1997, Sept. 1   **Perf. 11½**
1667 A712 17fr Stone cutter   1.25   .40
1668 A712 17fr Mason   1.25   .40
1669 A712 17fr Carpenter   1.25   .40
1670 A712 17fr Blacksmith   1.25   .40
   Nos. 1667-1670 (4)   5.00 1.60

Antarctic Expedition by the Belgica, Cent. — A713

1997, Sept. 22   **Photo.**   **Perf. 11½**
1671 A713 17fr multicolored   1.10   .50

Royal Museum of Central Africa, Cent. — A714

No. 1672, Mask, Shaba, Congo. No. 1673, Outside view of museum, horiz. 34fr, Dish Bearer sculpture, Buli area, Congo.

1997, Sept. 22   **Photo.**   **Perf. 11½**
1672 A714 17fr multicolored   1.10   .50
1673 A714 17fr multicolored   1.10   .60
1674 A714 34fr multicolored   2.25 1.25
   Nos. 1672-1674 (3)   4.45 2.35

No. 1673 is 25x73mm.

"Fairon," by Pierre Grahame — A715

Christmas.

1997, Oct. 25   Photo.   Perf. 11½
1675 A715 15fr multicolored   1.00   .35

Bird Type of 1985

15fr, Mesange boreale, horiz.

1997, Dec. 1   Photo.   Perf. 11½
1676 A524 15fr multicolored   1.15 1.00

No. 1676 issued in coil rolls with every fifth stamp numbered on reverse. Vert. pairs of No. 1676 exist. Value, $650.

Rhododendron
A716

Booklet Stamp
Serpentine Die Cut 13½ on 2 or 3 Sides

1997, Dec. 1   Self-Adhesive
1677 A716 (17fr) multicolored   1.60   .25
 a.   Booklet pane of 10   16.00

By its nature, No. 1677a is a complete booklet. The peelable backing serves as a booklet cover.
Compare with design A757.

"Thalys" High Speed Train — A717

1998, Jan. 19   Photo.   Perf. 11½
1678 A717 17fr multicolored   1.10   .45

Woman Suffrage in Belgium, 50th Anniv. — A718

1998, Jan. 19
1679 A718 17fr multicolored   1.10   .30

Gerard Walschap (1898-1989), Poet, Playwright — A719

No. 1681, Norge (1898-1990), writer

1998, Feb. 16   Photo.   Perf. 11½
1680 A719 17fr multicolored   1.10   .30
1681 A719 17fr multicolored   1.10   .30

Paintings, by René Magritte (1898-1967) — A720

No. 1682, "La Magie Noire (Black Magic)," nude woman. No. 1683, "La Corde Sensible (Heartstring)," cloud over champagne glass. No. 1684, "Le Chateau des Pyrenees (Castle of the Pyranees)," castle atop floating rock.

1998, Mar. 9   Photo.   Perf. 11½
1682 A720 17fr multi, vert.   1.10   .40
1683 A720 17fr multi   1.10   .40
1684 A720 17fr multi, vert.   1.10   .40
    Nos. 1682-1684 (3)   3.30 1.20

Belgian Artists — A721

Details or entire paintings: No. 1685, "La Foire aux Amours," by Félicien Rops (1833-98). No. 1686, "Hospitality for the Strangers," by Gustave van de Woestijne (1881-1947). No. 1687, Self-portrait, "The Man with the Beard," by Felix de Boeck (1898-1995). No. 1688, "Black Writing Mixed with Colors," by Karel Appel & Christian Cotremont of COBRA.

1998, Mar. 9   Perf. 12
Booklet Stamps
1685 A721 17fr multicolored   1.10   .75
1686 A721 17fr multicolored   1.10   .75
1687 A721 17fr multicolored   1.10   .75
1688 A721 17fr multicolored   1.10   .75
 a.   Booklet pane, #1685-1688   5.75 5.75
       Complete booklet, #1688a   5.75
    Nos. 1685-1688 (4)   4.40 3.00

Museum of Fine Arts, Ghent, bicent. (No. 1686). COBRA art movement of painters and poets, 50th anniv. (No. 1688).

Sabena Airlines, 75th Anniv. — A722

1998, Apr. 20   Photo.   Perf. 11½
1689 A722 17fr multicolored   1.10   .50

Belgian Stamp Dealers' Assoc., 75th Anniv. A723

1998, Apr. 20   Photo.   Perf. 11½
1690 A723 17fr multicolored   1.10   .40

"The Return," by René Magritte (1898-1967) — A724

1998, Apr. 20
1691 A724 17fr multicolored   1.10   .50
    See France No. 2637.

Wildlife
A725

No. 1692, Vulpes vulpes. No. 1693, Cervus elaphus. No. 1694, Sus scrofa. No. 1695, Capreolus capreolus.

1998, Apr. 20
1692 A725 17fr multi   1.10   .50
1693 A725 17fr multi   1.10   .50
1694 A725 17fr multi   1.10   .50
1695 A725 17fr multi   1.10   .50
    Nos. 1692-1695 (4)   4.40 2.00

"Souvenir Sheets"
Starting in 1998, items looking like souvenir sheets have appeared in the market. The 1998 item is similar to No. 1695. The 1999 item is similar to No. 1725. The 2000 item is similar to No. 1811. These have no postal value.

Bird Type of 1985

1fr, Mesange huppee.

1998, May 4   Photo.   Perf. 11½
1696 A524 1fr multicolored   .25   .25

Edmund Struyf (1911-96), Founder of Pro-Post, Assoc. for Promotion of Philately — A726

1998, May 4   Photo. & Engr.
1697 A726 17fr multicolored   1.10   .35
    Stamp Day.

Natl. Festivals A727

No. 1698, Torhout & Werchter Rock Festival. No. 1699, Wallonia Festival.

1998, May 4   Photo.   Perf. 11½
1698 A727 17fr multicolored   1.10   .30
1699 A727 17fr multicolored   1.10   .30
    Europa.

Bird Type of 1985

7.50fr, Pie-grieche grise.

1998, July 6   Photo.   Perf. 11½
1700 A524 7.50fr multicolored   .45   .25
    See No. 1837 for similar stamp with additional Euro denomination.

European Heritage Days — A728

a, Logo. b, Bourla Theatre, Antwerp. c, La Halle, Durbuy. d, Halletoren, Kortrijk. e, Louvain Town Hall. f, Perron, Liège. g, Royal Theatre, Namur. h, Aspremont-Lynden Castle, Rekem. i, Neo-Gothic kiosk, Sint-Niklaas. j, Chapelle Saint Vincent, Tournai. k, Villers-la-Ville Abbey. l, Saint Gilles Town Hall, Brussels.

1998, July 6
1701 A728 Sheet of 12   14.00 12.00
 a.-l.   17fr Any single   1.10   .50

Bird Type of 1985

1998   Photo.   Perf. 11½
1702 A524 9fr Pic vert   .60   .50
1703 A524 10fr Turtle dove   .60   .50
    Issued: 9fr, 8/10; 10fr, 9/28/98.

Free Thinking A729

1998, Aug. 10   Photo.   Perf. 11½
1704 A729 17fr multicolored   1.10   .30

Philips van Marnix van Sint-Aldegonde (1540-98), Author — A730

1998, Aug. 10
1705 A730 17fr multicolored   1.10   .35

Mniszech Palace (Belgian Embassy), Warsaw, Bicent. A731

Photo. & Engr.

1998, Sept. 28   Perf. 11½
1706 A731 17fr multicolored   1.10   .35
    See Poland No. 3420.

Contemporary Belgium Films — A732

No. 1707, "Le Huitieme Jour". No. 1708, "Daens".

1998, Sept. 28   Photo.
1707 A732 17fr multicolored   1.10   .35
1708 A732 17fr multicolored   1.10   .35

Cartoon Characters, "Chick Bill" and "Ric Hochet" — A733

1998, Oct. 19   Photo.   Perf. 11½
1709 A733 17fr multicolored   1.25   .45
    Youth philately.

Assoc. of Space Explorers, 14th World Congress, Brussels — A734

1998, Oct. 19
1710 A734 17fr multicolored   1.25 .40

World Post Day A735

1998, Oct. 19   Photo.   Perf. 11½
1711 A735 34fr blue & dark blue 2.25 1.25
World Assoc. for the Development of Philately.

FGTB-ABVV Trade Union, Cent. — A736

Center panel of triptych by Constant Draz (1875-)

1998, Nov. 9   Photo.   Perf. 11½
1712 A736 17fr multicolored   1.10 .35

Christmas and New Year — A737

1998, Nov. 9
1713 A737 (17fr) multicolored   1.50 .40

Bird Type of 1985

16fr, Mesange noire. 21fr, Grive litorne, horiz.

1998-99   Photo.   Perf. 11½
1714 A524 16fr multicolored   1.00 .30
1715 A524 21fr multicolored   1.40 .65

No. 1715 also issued in coils with number on reverse of every 5th stamp.
Issued: 16fr, 1/25/99; 21fr, 12/14/98.
See No. 1839 for similar stamp with additional Euro denomination.

A738

Greetings Stamps: No. 1716, Burning candle. No. 1717, Stork carrying a heart. No. 1718, Wristwatch. No. 1719, Four leaf clover with one leaf a heart. No. 1720, Two doves. No. 1721, Heart with arrow through it. No. 1722, Heart-shaped head on woman. No. 1723, Heart-shaped head on man.

1999, Jan. 25   Photo.   Perf. 12
Booklet Stamps
1716 A738 (17fr) multicolored   1.50 .50
1717 A738 (17fr) multicolored   1.50 .50
1718 A738 (17fr) multicolored   1.50 .50
1719 A738 (17fr) multicolored   1.50 .50
1720 A738 (17fr) multicolored   1.50 .50
1721 A738 (17fr) multicolored   1.50 .50
1722 A738 (17fr) multicolored   1.50 .50
1723 A738 (17fr) multicolored   1.50 .50
  a. Booklet pane, #1716-1723 12.00 12.00
      Complete booklet, #1723a 12.00
      Nos. 1716-1723 (8)   12.00 4.00

Nos. 1716-1717, 1719-1720 each also issued in sheets of 20 on July 1. Value, each sheet, $30.

Owls — A739

1999, Feb. 22   Photo.   Perf. 11½
1724 A739 17fr Tyto alba   1.10 .45
1725 A739 17fr Athene noctua   1.10 .45
1726 A739 17fr Strix aluco   1.10 .45
1727 A739 17fr Asio otus   1.10 .45
    Nos. 1724-1727 (4)   4.40 1.80

NATO, 50th Anniv. A740

No. 1728, Leopard tank. No. 1729, F16 fighter. No. 1730, Frigate Wandelaar. No. 1731, Hospital tent. No. 1732, General staff.

1999, Mar. 15
1728 A740 17fr multicolored   1.10 .60
1729 A740 17fr multicolored   1.10 .60
1730 A740 17fr multicolored   1.10 .60
1731 A740 17fr multicolored   1.10 .60
1732 A740 17fr multicolored   1.10 .60
    Nos. 1728-1732 (5)   5.50 3.00

UPU, 125th Anniv. A741

1999, Mar. 15
1733 A741 34fr multicolored   2.25 .90

No. 1733 is usually collected as a horizontal pair. Value, $5 never-hinged or used.

National Parks and Nature Reserves A742

Europa: No. 1734, De Bunt, near town of Hamme. No. 1735, Harchies-Hensies-Pommeroeul.

1999, Apr. 12
1734 A742 17fr multicolored   *1.25 .55*
1735 A742 17fr multicolored   *1.25 .55*

First Belgian Postage Stamps, 150th Anniv. A743

Photo. & Engr.
1999, Apr. 26   Perf. 11½
1736 A743 17fr No. 1   1.10 .70
1737 A743 17fr No. 2   1.10 .70
  a. Pair, #1736-1737   3.00 2.50

Painting, "My Favorite Room," by James Ensor (1860-1949) — A744

Designs: No. 1739, Woman Eating Oysters, vert. 30fr, Triumph Over Death, vert. 32fr, Old Lady With Masks, vert.

1999, May 17   Photo.   Perf. 11½
1738 A744 17fr multicolored   1.10 .40
1739 A744 17fr multicolored   1.10 .40
1740 A744 30fr multicolored   2.00 1.25
1741 A744 32fr multicolored   2.25 1.25
    Nos. 1738-1741 (4)   6.45 3.30

See Israel No. 1365A.
Issued: No. 1738, 5/17; Nos. 1739-1741, 9/11.

Tourism — A745

No. 1742, Giants at Geraardsbergen Fair, vert. No. 1743, Cart d'Or procession of the Confrérie de la Miséracordie, Mons.

1999, June 7   Photo.   Perf. 11½
1742 A745 17fr multi (10a)   1.10 .40
1743 A745 17fr multi (10b)   1.10 .40

Belgian Chocolate A746

1999, June 7
1744 A746 17fr Bean picker   1.10 .35
1745 A746 17fr Candy maker   1.10 .35
1746 A746 17fr Consumer   1.10 .35
    Nos. 1744-1746 (3)   3.30 1.05

King Albert and Queen Paola, 40th Wedding Anniv. — A747

1999, July 2   Photo.   Perf. 11½
1747 A747 17fr multicolored   1.25 .50

Royalty Type of Semi-Postal Stamps
Souvenir Sheet

Kings: a, 50fr, Leopold I. b, 32fr, Leopold II. c, 17fr, Albert I. d, 17fr, Leopold III. e, 32fr, Baudouin. f, 50fr, Albert II.

Photo. & Engr.
1999, Sept. 29   Perf. 11½
1748 SP514 Sheet of 6, #a.-f. 20.00 20.00

Bruphila '99. No. 1748 sold for 300fr.

Nobel Laureates in Peace — A750

Designs: 17fr, Henri La Fontaine (1854-1943). 21fr, Auguste Beernaert (1829-1912).

Photo. & Engr.
1999, Sept. 30   Perf. 11½
1749 A750 17fr red & gold   1.10 .45
1750 A750 21fr blue & gold   1.40 .85

See Sweden Nos. 2357-2358.

A751   A752

A753

A754

King Albert II
1999-2001   Photo.   Perf. 11¾x11½
1752 A751 17fr multicolored   1.10 .25
1753 A751 17fr prus blue   1.10 .25
1754 A751 19fr blue   1.25 .25
1755 A751 20fr yel brown   1.40 .30
1756 A751 23fr violet   3.50 3.00
1757 A751 25fr brown   1.75 .40
1758 A751 30fr vio black   1.90 .35
1759 A751 32fr green   2.00 .30
1760 A751 34fr gray blue   2.10 1.75
1761 A751 36fr brown   2.25 .40
    Nos. 1752-1761 (10)   18.35 7.25

Engr.
Perf. 11½
1766 A753 50fr blue   3.25 .55

Photo.   Perf. 11½
1768 A754 100fr multi   6.75 .75

Engr.
1769 A753 200fr claret   13.50 2.75
    Nos. 1752-1769 (13)   41.85 11.30

No. 1756 issued in coils. Vert. coil pairs of No. 1756 exist. Value, $600.
Issued: 17fr, 10/4; 19fr, 1/24/00; 30fr, 4/3/00; 32fr, 6/19/00; 23fr, 9/4/00; 50fr, 9/11/00; No. 1753, 11/18/00; 36fr, 12/4/00; 20fr, 25fr, 34fr, 100fr, 200fr, 3/26/01.

Youth Philately — A756

Comic strips: a, Corentin, by Paul Cuvelier (16a). b, Jerry Spring, by Jijé (16b). c, Gil Jourdan, by Maurice Tillieux (16c). d, La Patrouille des Castors, by Mitacq (16d). e, Entrance hall of Belgian Comic Strip Museum (16e). f, Hassan & Kadour, by Jacques Laudy (16f). g, Buck Danny, by Victor Hubinon (16g).

h, Tif et Tondu, by Fernand Dineur (16h). i, Les Timour, by Sirius (16i).

1999, Oct. 2	Photo.		Perf. 11½	
1771	A756	Sheet of 9, #a.-i.	12.50	12.50
a.-d.		17fr Any single	1.10	.80
e.		17f	2.00	1.50
f.-i.		17fr Any single	1.10	.80

Geranium — A757   Tulip — A758

Die Cut 10x9¾ on 2 or 3 sides

1999-2000		Self-Adhesive	Photo.	
		Booklet Stamps		
1772	A757	(17fr) multi	1.50	.25
a.		Complete booklet, 10 #1772	16.00	
1773	A758	(21fr) multi	2.25	.35
a.		Booklet, 10 #1773	24.00	

Die Cut Perf. 11¼

Coil Stamps

Litho.

1774	A757	(17fr) multi	9.00	.35

Photo.

Serpentine Die Cut 13¾

1774A	A757	(17fr) multi	12.50	.35
1775	A758	(21fr) multi	6.00	.75

Nos. 1774-1775 are on a waxed backing paper larger than the stamp.

Issued: No. 1773, 4/17/00; No. 1774A, 2/01. others, 11/22/99.

No. 1774A is dated 2000.

Christmas — A762

1999, Nov. 8		Photo.		Perf. 11½
1776	A762	17fr multi	1.10	.35

Wedding of Prince Philippe and Mathilde d'Udekem d'Acoz, Dec. 4 — A763

1999, Nov. 29				
1777	A763	17fr shown	1.25	.65

Souvenir Sheet

1778	A763	21fr Couple, diff.	1.75	1.75

The 20th Century

A764

A764a

A764b

A764c

No. 1779: a, Pope John XXIII. b, King Baudouin. c, Willy Brandt. d, John F. Kennedy. e, Mahatma Gandhi. f, Dr. Martin Luther King, Jr. g, Lenin. h, Che Guevara. i, Golda Meir. j, Nelson Mandela. k, Jesse Owens, Modern Olympic Games. l, Soccer. m, Tour de France. n, Edith Piaf. o, The Beatles. p, Charlie Chaplin. q, Tourism. r, Youth movements. s, Tintin comic strips. t, Philately.

No. 1780: a, Yser front, World War I. b, Concentration camps. c, First atomic bomb. d, Yalta Conference. e, United Nations. f, Decolonization. g, Vietnam War. h, Collapse of the Berlin Wall. i, Peace movements. j, Middle East conflict. k, Rene Magritte, artist. l, Le Corbusier, architect. m, Bertolt Brecht, dramatist. n, James Joyce, novelist. o, Anne Teresa de Keersmaeker, choreographer. p, Bela Bartók, composer. q, Andy Warhol, artist. r, Maria Callas, opera singer. s, Henry Moore, sculptor. t, Toots Thielemans, Charlie Parker, jazz musicians.

No. 1781: a, Ovide Decroly, pedagogue. b, Alternative energy. c, Aviation. d, Sigmund Freud, psychologist. e, Space travel. f, Claude Lévi-Strauss, anthropologist. g, Genetics. h, Pierre Teilhard de Chardin, theologist. i, Max Weber, sociologist. j, Albert Einstein, physicist. k, Penicillin. l, Ilya Prigogine, chemist. m, Roland Barthes, semiotician. n, Simone de Beauvoir, feminist. o, Information. p, John Maynard Keynes, economist. q, Marc Bloch, historian. r, Atomic energy, J. Robert Oppenheimer, physicist. s, Pierre and Marie Curie, physicists. t, Ludwig Josef Wittgenstein, philosopher.

No. 1782: a, Social housing policy. b, May 1968 student protests. c, Telecommunications. d, Wealth and poverty. e, Secularization (laicisation). f, Urbanization. g, Universal suffrage. h, Social security. i, Education (enseignement). j, Aging of the population (vieillissement de la population). k, European Union. l, Universal Declaration of Human Rights. m, Consumer society. n, Women's liberation. o, Deindustrialization. p, Oil crises. q, Mobility. r, Contraception. s, Radio and television. t, Home appliances (appareils menagers).

1999-2002		Photo.		Perf. 11½
1779		Sheet of 20	25.00	25.00
a.-d.	A764	17fr Any single	1.10	.80
e.	A764	17fr	2.00	1.00
f.-r.	A764	17fr Any single	1.10	.80
s.	A764	17fr	3.00	1.75
t.	A764	17fr	1.10	.80
1780		Sheet of 20	22.00	22.00
a.-t.	A764a	17fr Any single	1.10	.80
1781		Sheet of 20	22.00	22.00
a.-t.	A764b	17fr Any single	1.10	.80
1782		Sheet of 20	22.00	22.00
a.-t.	A764c	41c Any single	1.10	.80
		Nos. 1779-1782 (4)	91.00	91.00

Issued: No. 1779, 12/6/99. No. 1780, 11/20/00. No. 1781, 10/22/01. No. 1782, 10/28/02.

Denominations on No. 1782 are in euros.

Year 2000 A765

2000, Jan. 3		Photo.	Perf. 11¾x11½
1783	A765	17fr multi	1.10	.30

Brussels, 2000 European City of Culture — A766

Brussels skyline and: a, Seven people. b, Harmonica player, dancer. c, Airplane, train, ships.

2000, Jan. 24		Photo.	Perf. 11½
1784		Strip of 3 + 2 labels	3.50	3.50
a.-c.	A766	17fr any single	1.10	.45

Bird Type of 1985

1fr, Beccroisé des sapins. 2fr, Grimpereau des jardins. 3fr, Pipit parlouse. 5fr, Pinson du nord. 10fr, Pouillot siffleur. No. 1790, 16fr, Pie grièche écorcheur. No. 1790A, 16fr, Pie grièche écoucheur, horiz.

Without "F" and With Euro Denomination

2000		Photo.		Perf. 11¾
1785	A524	1fr multicolored	.90	.45
1786	A524	2fr multicolored	.25	.25
1787	A524	3fr multicolored	.25	.25
1788	A524	5fr multicolored	.30	.25
1789	A524	10fr multicolored	.65	.30
1790	A524	16fr multicolored	1.00	.45
1790A	A524	16fr multicolored	2.50	2.00
		Nos. 1785-1790A (7)	5.85	3.95

No. 1790A issued in coils.

Issued: No. 1790, 1/24; 1fr, 2fr, 3fr, 5fr, 5/8; 10fr, 9/11; No. 1790A, 9/4.

Holy Roman Emperor Charles V (1500-58) A767

2000, Feb. 21		Photo.	Perf. 11½
1791	A767	17fr shown	1.10	.60
1792	A767	21fr At age 40	1.25	.75

Souvenir Sheet

1793	A767	34fr In armor	2.25	2.25
a.		Ovptd. in margin	2.25	2.25

No. 1793a was issued 10/6/00 and overprint in margin reads "ESPANA 2000 / Exposición Mundial de Filatelia / Madrid 6-14/X/2000." See Spain Nos. 3026-3028.

World Mathematics Year — A768

2000, Feb. 21				
1794	A768	17fr multi	1.10	.30

Stampin' The Future Children's Stamp Design Contest Winner — A769

2000, Feb. 21				
1795	A769	17fr multi	1.25	.35

European Soccer Championships, Belgium and Netherlands — A770

2000, Mar. 27				
1796	A770	Pair + label	2.75	2.50
a.		17fr Players	1.40	.60
b.		21fr Ball	1.75	.65

Serpentine Die Cut 10x9¾ on 3 sides

Booklet Stamp

Self-Adhesive

Size: 21x27mm

1797	A770	(17fr) Players, diff.	1.25	.40
a.		Booklet, 10 #1797	14.50	

See Netherlands Nos. 1045-1046.

Worldwide Fund for Nature — A771

Endangered amphibians and reptiles: No. 1798, Vipera berus. No. 1799, Lacerta agilis, vert. No. 1800, Hyla arborea, vert. No. 1801, Salamandra salamandra.

Perf. 11¾x11½, 11½x11¾

2000, Mar. 27				Photo.
1798	A771	17fr multi	1.25	.50
1799	A771	17fr multi	1.25	.50
1800	A771	17fr multi	1.25	.50
1801	A771	17fr multi	1.25	.50
		Nos. 1798-1801 (4)	5.00	2.00

Stamp Day — A772

2000, Apr. 3		Photo.	Perf. 11½
1802	A772	17fr multi	1.25	.40

Franz von Taxis — A773

2000, Apr. 3				
1803	A773	17fr multi + label	1.40	1.40

Postal system in Europe, 500th anniv., Belgica 2001 Stamp Exhibition.

Ghent Flower Show A774

Designs: 16fr, Iris spuria. 17fr, Rhododendron, horiz. 21fr, Begonia.

2000, Apr. 17				
1804	A774	16fr multi	1.10	.50
1805	A774	17fr multi	1.25	.55
1806	A774	21fr multi	1.50	.75
		Nos. 1804-1806 (3)	3.85	1.80

Prince Philippe's Fund A775

2000, Apr. 17
1807 A775 17fr multi 1.25 .30

2000 Summer Olympics and Paralympics, Sydney A776

Designs: 17fr, Belgian Olympic team emblem. No. 1809, Taekwondo. No. 1810, Wheelchair racer, horiz.
30fr+7fr, Swimmer in triathlon, horiz.

2000, May 8
1808 A776 17fr multi 1.25 .50
1809 A776 17fr +4fr multi 1.50 1.50
1810 A776 17fr +4fr multi 1.50 1.50
Nos. 1808-1810 (3) 4.25 3.50

Souvenir Sheet
1811 A776 30fr +7fr multi 2.75 2.75

Olymphilex 2000 (No. 1811).

Opening of Musical Instrument Museum, Brussels — A777

No. 1812, Harpsichord (15a). No. 1813, Violin (15b). No. 1814, Lutes (15c). No. 1815, Treble viol (15d). No. 1816, Trumpets (15e). No. 1817, Johann Sebastian Bach (15f).

2000, May 8 **Photo.** **Perf. 11¾**
Booklet Stamps
1812 A777 (17fr) multi 1.50 1.00
1813 A777 (17fr) multi 1.50 1.00
1814 A777 (17fr) multi 1.50 1.00
1815 A777 (17fr) multi 1.50 1.00
1816 A777 (17fr) multi 1.50 1.00
1817 A777 (17fr) multi 1.50 1.00
a. Booklet pane, #1812-1817 8.50 9.00
Booklet, #1817a 8.50
Nos. 1812-1817 (6) 9.00 6.00

Europa, 2000
Common Design Type
2000, May 9 **Perf. 11½**
1818 CD17 (21fr) multi 1.40 .60

UNESCO World Heritage Sites A778

Designs: No. 1819, Flemish Béguinages. No. 1820, Grand-Place, Brussels. No. 1821, Boat lifts, Canal du Centre.

2000, June 19 **Perf. 11½x11¾**
1819 A778 17fr multi 1.40 .60
1820 A778 17fr multi 1.40 .60
1821 A778 17fr multi 1.40 .60
Nos. 1819-1821 (3) 4.20 1.80

Tourism A779

Churches and their organs: No. 1822, Norbertine Abbey Church, Grimbergen. No. 1823, Collégiale Sainte Waudru, Mons. No. 1824, O.-L.-V. Hemelvaartkerk, Ninove. No. 1825, St. Peter's Church, Bastogne.

2000, June 19 **Perf. 11½**
1822 A779 17fr multi 1.10 .40
1823 A779 17fr multi 1.10 .40
1824 A779 17fr multi 1.10 .40
1825 A779 17fr multi 1.10 .40
Nos. 1822-1825 (4) 4.40 1.60

A780

2000, Sept. 4 **Photo.** **Perf. 11¾**
1826 A780 17fr multi 4.50 4.50

European Postal Services, 500th Anniv., Belgica 2001 Stamp Exhibition.
No. 1826 issued in coils. Vert. coil pairs of No. 1826 exist. Value, $600.

Youth Philately — A781

2000, Sept. 11 **Perf. 11¾x11½**
1827 A781 17fr multi 1.20 .60

Hainault Flower Show A782

2000, Sept. 11 **Perf. 11½x11¾**
1828 A782 17fr multi 1.20 .40

Violets — A783

Die Cut Perf. 10x9¾ on 2 or 3 Sides
2000, Sept. 11 **Photo.**
Booklet Stamp
Self-Adhesive
1829 A783 (17fr) multi 1.50 .30
a. Booklet, 10 #1829 16.00

Contemporary Art — A784

No. 1831, Bing of the Ferro Lusto X, by Panamarenko. No. 1832, Construction, by Anne-Mie Van Kerckhoven. No. 1833, Belgique Eternelle, by J. & L. Charlier. No. 1834, Roses from series "Les Belles de Nuit," by Marie-Jo Lafontaine.

Perf. 11½x11¾, 11¾x11½
2000, Oct. 16 **Photo.**
1831 A784 17fr multi (21a) 1.15 .60
1832 A784 17fr multi (21b), vert. 1.15 .60
1833 A784 17fr multi (21c) 1.15 .60
1834 A784 17fr multi (21d) 1.15 .60
Nos. 1831-1834 (4) 4.60 2.40

Christmas — A785

2000, Nov. 20 **Photo.** **Perf. 11½**
1835 A785 17fr multi 1.20 .40

Bird Type of 1985
50c, Roitelet huppe. 7.50fr, Pie-grieche grise. 8fr, Mesange charbonniere. 16fr, Sterne pierregarin. 21fr, Grive litorne, horiz. 150fr, Pie bavarde, horiz.

Without F and With Euro Denomination
2000-01 **Photo.** **Perf. 11¾**
1836 A524 50c multi .25 .25
1837 A524 7.50fr multi .50 .30
1838 A524 8fr multi .60 .70
1838A A524 16fr multi 1.25 .25
1839 A524 21fr multi 1.50 .25

Perf. 11½x11¾
Size: 35x25mm
1840 A524 150fr multi 10.00 2.00
Nos. 1836-1840 (6) 14.10 3.75

Issued: 8fr, 12/4/00. 50c, 7.50fr, 21fr, 150fr, 3/26/01; 16fr, 6/9/01. Numbers have been reserved for additional stamps in this set.

Holy Year 2000 — A786

Photo. & Engr.
2000, Dec. 27 **Perf. 11½**
1841 A786 17fr multicolored 1.10 .30
With tab 1.50

Royalty Type of Semi-Postal Stamps
Souvenir Sheet
Queens: a, 50fr, Louise-Marie. b, 32fr, Marie-Henriette. c, 17fr, Elisabeth. d, 17fr, Astrid. e, 32fr, Fabiola. f, 50fr, Paola.

Photo. & Engr.
2001, Feb. 12 **Perf. 11½**
1842 SP514 Sheet of 6, #a-f 18.00 18.00

No. 1842 sold for 300fr.

Zénobe Gramme (1826-1901), Electrical Engineer — A787

2001, Mar. 19 **Photo.**
1843 A787 17fr multi 1.25 .40

Catholic University of Louvain, 575th Anniv. — A788

2001, Mar. 19
1844 A788 17fr multi 1.25 .40

Europa — A789

2001, Apr. 23 **Photo.** **Perf. 11½**
1845 A789 21fr multi 1.50 .60

Musical and Literary Personalities A790

Designs: No. 1846, Willem Elsschot (1882-1960), writer. No. 1847, Albert Ayguesparse (1900-96), writer.
21fr, Queen Elisabeth (1876-1965), patron of Queen Elisabeth Intl. Music Competition, horiz.

2001, Apr. 23 **Photo.** **Perf. 11½**
1846 A790 17fr multi 1.25 .35
1847 A790 17fr multi 1.25 .35

Souvenir Sheet
1848 A790 21fr multi 1.75 1.75

Queen Elisabeth Intl. Music Competition, 50th anniv. (No. 1848).

Belgian Natl. Railway Company, 75th Anniv. — A790A

No. 1848A: b, 1938 Type 12 locomotive No. 12004. c, 1971 Series 06 dual engine No. 671. d, 1991 Series 03 threefold engine No. 328.

2001, May 7 **Photo.** **Perf. 11¾x11½**
1848A Horiz. strip of 3 + 2 labels 4.25 4.25
b.-d. A790A 17fr Any single 1.25 .60

A791

European Posts, 500th Anniv. — A792

Designs: No. 1849, Franz von Taxis, 16th cent. postrider. No. 1850, 17th cent. postman on road near Brussels. No. 1851, 18th cent. postman, quill pen, postal notice. No. 1852, 19th cent. postman, train, Belgium #2 on cover. No. 1853, 20th cent. postman, motorcycle, airplanes, mailboxes.
No. 1854: 150fr, 21st cent. postwoman, Belgica 2001 emblem.

Perf. 11¾x11½

2001, June 9   Photo.

Stamp + label

1849	A791	17fr multi	1.25	1.00
1850	A792	17fr multi	1.25	1.00
1851	A792	17fr multi	1.25	1.00
1852	A792	17fr multi	1.25	1.00
1853	A792	17fr multi	1.25	1.00
	Nos. 1849-1853 (5)		6.25	5.00

Souvenir Sheet

1854	A792	150fr multi	16.00	16.00

Nos. 1849 printed in sheets of 10 stamps + 10 labels. For Nos. 1850-1853, each is printed in sheets of 12 stamps + 12 labels.
No. 1854 contains one 38x48mm stamp without an attached label, and sold for 300fr, with the surtax going to Pro Post for the promotion of philately.

Houses of Worship — A793

Designs: 17fr, Hassan II Mosque, Casablanca, Morocco. 34fr, Koekelberg Basilica.

2001, June 10   Photo.   Perf. 11½

1855	A793	17fr multi	1.25	.50
1856	A793	34fr multi	2.50	1.25

See Morocco Nos. 897-898.

Musées Royaux des Beaux Arts, Brussels, 200th Anniv. — A794

No. 1857: a, Winter Landscape With Skaters, by Pieter Breughel the Elder. b, Study of a Negro's Head, by Peter Paul Rubens. c, Sunday, by Frits Van den Berghe. d, Mussel Triumph II, by Marcel Broodthaers.

2001, June 11   Photo.   Perf. 12

1857		Booklet pane of 4	5.00	5.00
a.-d.		A794 17fr Any single	1.25	.90
		Booklet, #1857	5.25	

Ancient Chinese Receptacles A795

Designs: 17fr, Earthenware vase. 34fr, Porcelain coffee pot.

2001, June 12   Photo.   Perf. 11½

1858	A795	17fr multi	1.25	.30
1859	A795	34fr multi	2.50	1.25

See People's Republic of China Nos. 3108-3109.

Youth Philately — A796

2001, June 13

1860	A796	17fr multi	1.25	.65

Belgian Chairmanship of European Union A797

2001, June 15

1861	A797	17fr multi	1.25	.50

Tourism — A798

Town hall belfries: No. 1862, Binche. No. 1863, Dixmude.

2001, Aug. 6   Perf. 11½x11¾

1862	A798	17fr multi	1.25	.35
1863	A798	17fr multi	1.25	.35

Farmsteads — A799

2001, Aug. 6   Perf. 11¾x11½

1864	A799	17fr Damme	1.25	.40
1865	A799	17fr Beauvechain	1.25	.40
1866	A799	17fr Leuven	1.25	.40
1867	A799	17fr Honnelles	1.25	.40
1868	A799	17fr Hasselt	1.25	.40
	Nos. 1864-1868 (5)		6.25	2.00

Stam and Pilou, Mascots of Stampilou Youth Philatelic Club — A800

2001, Oct. 8   Photo.   Die Cut

Self-Adhesive Booklet Stamp

1869	A800	(17fr) multi	1.50	.50
a.		Booklet of 5 + 5 labels	8.00	8.00

Stamp Day.

Christmas A801

2001, Nov. 12   Photo.   Perf. 11½

1870	A801	15fr multi	1.10	.40

Violets A802

Belgian Post Emblem A802a

Narcissus — A803

Tulips — A804

2001, Dec. 10   Photo.   Perf. 11½

1871	A802	(17fr) multi	1.75	1.40
1871A	A802a	(17fr) red	1.75	1.40

Self-Adhesive Booklet Stamps

Die Cut Perf. 10 on 2 or 3 Sides

1872	A803	(17fr) multi	1.50	.35
a.		Booklet pane of 10	15.00	15.00

Die Cut Perf. 9¾ on 3 Sides

1873	A804	(21fr) multi	2.25	.45
a.		Booklet pane of 10	24.00	24.00
	Nos. 1871-1873 (4)		7.25	3.60

Issued: No. 1871, 10/17; No. 1871A, 12/1. Nos. 1872, 1873, 12/10.
Nos. 1871 and 1871A were each issued in sheets of 15 stamps + 15 labels that could be personalized. The sheets sold for 605fr.

Death Announcement Stamp — A805

2001, Dec. 10   Photo.   Perf. 11½

1874	A805	(17fr) multi	1.50	.40

See Nos. 1936 and 2035.

Tintin in Africa — A806

Tintin: 17fr, In jungle. 34fr, In automobile.

2001, Dec. 31

1875	A806	17fr multi	1.25	.70

Souvenir Sheet

1876	A806	34fr multi	3.25	3.25

No. 1876 contains one 48x37mm stamp. See Democratic Republic of Congo (Zaire) Nos. 1613-1614.

100 Cents = 1 Euro (€)

King Albert II — A807

King Albert II — A808

King Albert II — A809   King Albert II — A810

2002-06   Photo.   Perf. 11½

1877	A808	7c red & gray bl	.25	.25
1879	A807	42c red	1.00	.30
1881	A807	47c dark green	1.25	1.00
1882	A808	49c red	1.00	.25
1882A	A809	49c red	1.25	1.25
1882B	A809	50c red	1.40	.30
1882C	A810	50c multi	1.50	.30
1883	A807	52c blue	1.25	.85
1884	A810	52c red & car	1.25	.35
1885	A807	59c dk blue	1.50	1.25
1886	A807	60c blue	1.60	.70
1887	A807	60c brt blue + etiquette	1.75	.40
1888	A807	70c brt blue + etiquette	2.00	.45
1888A	A810	70c blue	2.00	.45
1889	A808	79c red & ultra	2.00	.60
1890	A809	79c red & ultra	2.25	.50
1891	A809	80c red & ultra	2.25	.45
1892	A807	80c ultra + etiquette	2.00	.80
1893	A810	83c red & bl vio	2.25	.50
1895	A808	€4.21 red & pur	11.50	2.00
	Nos. 1877-1895 (20)		41.25	12.95

Issued: 42c, 52c, 1/1/02. 47c. 5/6/02. 7c, 49c, 59c, No. 1889, 11/4/02. €4.21, 8/11/03. No. 1890, 10/6/03. No. 1882A, 10/27/03; 50c, 60c, 80c, 4/19/04. Nos. 1887, 1892, 9/27/04. 70c, 3/21/05. Nos. 1882C, 1888A, 7/21/05. No. 1884, 1/23/06. No. 1893, 3/20/06.
No. 1888A is inscribed "A Prior" at left.

World Cyclo-Cross and Road Bicycling Championships A811

Royal Belgian Tennis Federation, Cent. — A812

No. 1897: a, Rider looking back. b, Rider with fist in air.
No. 1898: a, Women's tennis. b, Men's tennis.

2002, Jan. 21   Photo.   Perf. 11½

1897	A811	Vert. pair	2.50	1.10
a.-b.		42c Any single	1.25	.55
1898	A812	Horiz. pair	2.50	1.10
a.-b.		42c Any single	1.25	.55

University of
Antwerp,
150th Anniv.
A813

2002, Feb. 11   Photo. & Engr.
1899 A813 42c multi   1.25 .45

Bruges,
2002
European
Capital of
Culture
A814

Designs: No. 1900, Restorations and new
architecture (4a). No. 1901, Classical and contemporary music (4b). No. 1902, Classical
exhibitions and contemporary art (4c).

2002, Mar. 4   Photo.
1900 A814 42c multi   1.25 .50
1901 A814 42c multi   1.25 .50
1902 A814 42c multi   1.25 .50
   Nos. 1900-1902 (3)   3.75 1.50

Anna Bijns (1494-1575), Poet — A815

Anna Boch (1848-
1936),
Painter — A816

2002, Mar. 4
1903 A815 42c multi   1.10 .50
1904 A816 84c multi   2.40 1.00

Stamp
Day — A817

2002, Apr. 22   Photo.   Perf. 11½
1905 A817 47c multi   1.25 .60

Belgian Dog Breeds — A818

Designs: No. 1906, Schipperke. No. 1907,
Bouvier des Ardennes. No. 1908, Saint-
Hubert. No. 1909, Brussels griffon. No. 1910,
Papillon.

2002, Apr. 22   Photo.   Perf. 11½
Stamp + Label
1906 A818 42c multi   1.25 .90
1907 A818 42c multi   1.25 .90
1908 A818 42c multi   1.25 .90
1909 A818 42c multi   1.25 .90
1910 A818 42c multi   1.25 .90
 a. Vert. strip of 5, #1906-1910, +
     5 labels   6.50 6.50
   Nos. 1906-1910 (5)   6.25 4.50

Europa
A819

2002, May 6
1911 A819 52c multi   1.50 .70

**Bird Type of 1985 With Euro
Denominations Only**

7c, Pigeon colombin. 25c, Huitrier pie. 35c,
Pic epeiche. 41c, Tourterelle Turque. 57c,
Guifette noire. 70c, Chevalier gambette. €1,
Traquet motteux, horiz. €2, Grand gravelot,
horiz. €5, Combattant varie, horiz.

2002-03   Photo.   Perf. 11½
1912 A524 7c multicolored   .25 .25
1913 A524 25c multicolored   .60 .50
1913A A524 35c multicolored 1.00 .25
1913B A524 41c multicolored 1.00 .30
1913C A524 57c multicolored 1.75 .65
1913D A524 70c multicolored 1.90 .80
Size:38x27mm
1914 A524 €1 multicolored 3.00 .65
1915 A524 €2 multicolored 6.00 1.00
1916 A524 €5 multicolored 14.50 3.50
   Nos. 1912-1916 (9)   30.00 7.90
   Issued: 7c, 5/6. 25c, 7/15. 35c, 3/31/03. 41c,
57c, 70c, €1, €2, €5, 11/4/02. This is an
expanding set.

Leffe Abbey, 850th Anniv. — A820

2002, June 10   Photo.   Perf. 11½
1917 A820 42c multi + label 1.25 .60

Castles — A821

No. 1918: a, Chimay. b, Alden Biesen. c,
Wissekerke. d, Corroy-le-Château. e,
Reinhardstein. f, Loppem. g, Horst. h, Ecaus-
sinnes-Lalaing. i, Ooidonk. j, Modave. Nos.
1918a-1918f are 45x24mm; Nos. 1918g-1918j
are 52x21mm.

2002, June 10
1918 A821 Sheet of 10   12.50 12.50
 a.-j. 42c Any single   1.10 .50

Belgian Post Emblem
— A821a

2002, June 15   Photo.   Perf. 11½
1918K A821a (42c) red   2.10 2.10
   Issued in sheets of 15 stamps + 15 labels
that could be personalized. The sheets sold for
€16.

Horses
A822

Designs: 40c, Jumping. 42c, Driving, vert.
52c, St. Paul's Horse Procession, Opwijk,
cent., vert.

2002, July 1   Photo.   Perf. 11½
1919 A822 40c multi   1.10 .60
1920 A822 42c multi   1.25 .65
   Souvenir Sheet
1921 A822 52c multi   1.50 1.50
   No. 1921 contains one 38x49mm stamp.

Battle of the
Courtrai, 700th
Anniv. — A823

Designs: 42c, Golden spurs of defeated
French knights. 52c, Castle.
57c, Battle scene, horiz.

2002, July 15
1922 A823 42c multi   1.10 .50
1923 A823 52c multi   1.40 1.50
   Souvenir Sheet
1924 A823 57c multi   2.00 2.00
   No. 1924 contains one 49x38mm stamp.

Windmills — A824

Designs: 42c, Onze-Lieve-Vrouw-Lombeek
windmill, Belgium. 52c, Ilha do Faial windmill,
Azores.

2002, July 15   Photo.   Perf. 11½
1925 A824 42c multi   1.10 .70
1926 A824 52c multi   1.40 1.20
   See Portugal Azores Nos. 471-472.

Lace — A825

Lace from: 42c, Liederkerke, Belgium. 74c,
Pag Island, Croatia.

2002, July 15
1927 A825 42c multi   1.10 .65
1928 A825 74c multi   2.10 1.10
   See Croatia Nos. 497-498.

Youth
Philately
A826

2002, July 15   Photo.   Perf. 11½
1929 A826 42c multi   1.25 .75

Rights of the
Child — A827

2002, Sept. 30   Photo.   Perf. 11½
1930 A827 42c multi   1.25 .40

Jean Rey (1902-83),
Politician — A828

2002, Sept. 30   Photo. & Engr.
1931 A828 52c dk bl & lt bl 1.50 1.25

Christmas — A829

No. 1932: a, Family at ice cream truck. b,
Ski jumper in Christmas tree. c, Sledder in air,
skier in snow. d, Skier on hillside. e, Skiers
with torches. f, Boy with ice cream cone. g,
Children in snowball fight. h, Children, man
and snowman. i, People at snack stand. j,
Cow, policeman and burglars.

2002, Oct. 28   Photo.
1932 A829 Sheet of 10   12.50 12.50
 a.-j. 41c Any single   1.10 .50

Princess
Elizabeth,
1st
Birthday
A830

Designs: 49c, Princess Elizabeth, vert. 59c,
Princesses Elizabeth and Mathilde, Prince
Philippe.
84c, Princess Elizabeth, diff.

2002, Nov. 4   Photo.   Perf. 11½
1933 A830 49c multi   1.25 .40
1934 A830 59c multi   1.60 1.40
   Souvenir Sheet
1935 A830 84c multi   2.75 2.75
   No. 1935 contains one 48x37mm stamp.
Margins on sheets of No. 1933, inscribed
"Prior," served as etiquettes.

Death Announcement Stamp — A831

2002, Nov. 4
1936 A831 (49c) multi   1.40 .30
   Compare with type A882.

Crocuses — A832

Booklet Stamp
Die Cut Perf. 10 on 2 or 3 Sides
2002, Nov. 4   **Self-Adhesive**
1937 A832 (49c) multi   1.50   .30
  a.   Booklet pane of 10   16.00

Coil Stamp
Serpentine Die Cut
13¼x13½x13¾x14
1938 A832 (49c) multi   1.50   .30
Compare illustration A832 with A859.

80th Birthday of
Cartoonist Marc
Sleen — A833

Designs: 49c, Nero and Adhemar. 82c,
Sleen with cartoon characters.

2002, Dec. 30   **Perf. 11½**
1939 A833 49c multi   1.25   .50
Souvenir Sheet
1940 A833 82c multi   3.00 3.00
No. 1940 contains one 48x37mm stamp.
Margins on sheets of No. 1939, inscribed
"Prior," served as etiquettes.

Henry van de Velde (1863-1957),
Architect — A834

Designs: 49c, New House, Tervuren, 1927-
28 (1a). No. 1942, Paris World's Fair Pavilion,
1937 (1b), vert. No. 1943, Book Tower, Ghent
(1c), vert.
84c, Marie Sèthe, wife of van de Velde, on
Art Nouveau staircase, vert.

2003, Jan. 27
1941 A834 49c multi   1.25   .40
1942 A834 59c multi   1.60 1.10
1943 A834 59c multi   1.60 1.10
    Nos. 1941-1943 (3)   4.45 2.60
Souvenir Sheet
1944 A834 84c multi   2.50 2.50
No. 1944 contains one 37x48mm stamp.
Margins on sheets of No. 1941, inscribed
"Prior," served as etiquettes.

Love for
Service
Occupations
A835

No. 1945: a, Firefighters. b, Police. c, Civil
defense workers. d, Nurses. e, Postal workers.
f, Birdcage and hearts.

2003, Jan. 27
1945   Sheet of 10, #1945e-
             1945f, 2 each
             #1945a-1945d   13.00 13.00
  a.-f.   A835 49c Any single   1.25   .65
Margins on sheets, inscribed "Prior," served
as etiquettes.

Hector
Berlioz
(1803-69),
Composer
A836

2003, Feb. 24
1946 A836 59c multi   1.40 1.25

Traditional
Sports
A837

Designs: No. 1947, Lawn bowling (4a). No.
1948, Archery (4b).
82c, Pigeon racing, vert.

2003, Feb. 24
1947 A837 49c multi   1.25   .50
1948 A837 49c multi   1.25   .50
Souvenir Sheet
1949 A837 82c multi   2.50 2.50
No. 1949 contains one 37x48mm stamp.
Margins on sheets of Nos. 1947-1948,
inscribed "Prior," served as etiquettes.

Organization
Anniversaries
A838

Designs: No. 1950, Association of Engineers of Mons sesquicentennial (5a). No.
1951, Solvay Business School centennial (5b).

2003, Mar. 17
1950 A838 49c multi   1.25   .50
1951 A838 49c multi   1.25   .50
Margins on sheets of Nos. 1950-1951,
inscribed "Prior," served as etiquettes.

Liège International
Flower
Show — A839

2003, Apr. 28   **Photo.** **Perf. 11½**
1952 A839 49c multi   1.25   .40
Margins on sheets, inscribed "Prior," served
as etiquettes.

Georges Simenon
(1903-89),
Writer — A840

Designs: 49c, Poster for "Maigret Sets a
Trap." 59c, Poster for "The Cat."
84c, Simenon at typewriter.

2003, Apr. 28
1953 A840 49c multi   1.25   .60
1954 A840 59c multi   1.60   .90
Souvenir Sheet
1955 A840 84c multi   2.50 2.50
No. 1955 contains one 38x48mm stamp.
Margins on sheets of No. 1953, inscribed
"Prior," served as etiquettes.

Carillons — A841

No. 1956: a, St. Rombout's Cathedral,
Mechelen (denomination at left). b, Sts. Peter
and Paul Cathedral, St. Petersburg, Russia
(denomination at right).

Photo. & Engr.
2003, May 12   **Perf. 11½**
1956 A841   Horiz. pair   3.25 3.25
  a.-b.   59c Either single   1.25 1.00
See Russia No. 6767.

Stamp
Day — A842

2003, May 19   **Photo.** **Perf. 11½**
1957 A842 49c multi   1.25   .50
Margins on sheets, inscribed "Prior," served
as etiquettes.

Youth
Philately — A843

2003, May 19
1958 A843 49c multi   1.35   .50
Margins on sheets, inscribed "Prior," served
as etiquettes.

Belgian Post
Emblem — A844

2003   **Photo.** **Perf. 11½**
1959 A844 49c red   2.50 1.25
Issued in sheets of 15 stamps + 15 labels
that could be personalized. The sheets sold for
€16.

Minerals
A845

No. 1960: a, Calcite (11a). b, Quartz (11b).
c, Barite (11c). d, Galena (11d). e, Turquoise
(11e).

2003, June 30   **Photo.** **Perf. 11½**
1960   Vert. strip of 5   6.50 6.50
  a.-e.   A845 49c Any single   1.25   .60
Issued in sheets of 2 strips. Margins on
sheets, inscribed "Prior," served as etiquettes.

Europa — A846

2003, June 30
1961 A846 59c multi   1.60 1.00

Tourism — A847

No. 1962: a, La Robe de Mariée, by Paul
Delvaux (Koksijde, 13a). b, Tapestry
(Oudenaarde, 13b). c, Fist sculpture by Rik
Poot, City Hall (Vilvoorde, 13c). d, Royal Cas-
tle, playing card suits (Turnhout, 13d). e,
Statue of Ambiorix, Gallo-Roman Museum
(Tongeren, 13e). f, Fountain by Pol Bury,
mineshaft frame (La Louvière, 13f). g, City
Hall, lion statue (Braine l'Alleud, 13g). h, For-
est, Mardasson Memorial (Bastogne, 13i). i,
Büchtelturm, snow-covered tree (Sankt Vith,
13j). j, Saxophone, Citadel (Dinant, 13h).

2003, July 7
1962 A847   Sheet of 10   13.00 13.00
  a.-g. 41c Any single   1.10   .65
  h.-i. 52c Either single   1.25   .85
  j.   57c multi   1.50   .95

Statues and
Fountains — A848

Designs: No. 1963, Monument to the Sea-
sonal Worker, Rillaar (14a). No. 1964, La
Toinade, Treignes (14b). No. 1965, Hamont
Textile Teut, Hamont-Achel (14c). No. 1966,
Vaartkapoen, Brussels (14d). No. 1967, Maca
Wavre (14e).

2003, July 7
1963 A848 49c multi   1.40   .60
1964 A848 49c multi   1.40   .60
1965 A848 49c multi   1.40   .60
1966 A848 49c multi   1.40   .60
1967 A848 49c multi   1.40   .60
    Nos. 1963-1967 (5)   7.00 3.00
Margins on sheets, inscribed "Prior," served
as etiquettes.

A849

Kings Baudouin and Albert II — A850

2003, Aug. 11
1968 A849 49c multi   1.35   .50
Souvenir Sheet
1969 A850 Sheet of 2   4.50 4.50
  a. 59c King Baudouin   1.75 1.25
  b. 84c King Albert II   2.50 2.00
Reign of King Albert II, 10th anniv.

**Bird Type of 1985 with Euro
Denominations Only**

1c, Rossignol philoméle. 2c, Becassine des Marais. 40c, Gobemouche gris. 44c, Hirondelle de fenetre. 52c, Huppe fasciée. 55c, Petit gravelot. 65c, Mouette rieuse. 75c, Pluvier doré. €3.72, Poule d'Eau. €4, Hibou grand-duc.

2003-04	**Photo.**	***Perf. 11½***	
1970 A524	1c multicolored	.25	.25
1971 A524	2c multicolored	.50	.60
1972 A524	40c multicolored	.90	.25
1973 A524	44c multicolored	1.10	1.00
1974 A524	52c multicolored	1.25	1.00
1975 A524	55c multicolored	1.25	1.00
1976 A524	65c multicolored	2.00	1.00
1977 A524	75c multicolored	2.10	1.00

Size: 38x27mm
1978 A524 €3.72 multicolored 10.00 1.75
1979 A524 €4 multicolored   11.50 2.25
  Nos. 1970-1979 (10)   30.85 10.10

Issued: 2c, 52c, 8/11. 1c, 40c, 44c, 55c, 65c, 75c, €4, 4/19/04. €3.72, 10/27. This is an expanding set. Numbers may change.

Europalia
Italia
Festival,
Belgium
A851

Designs: 49c, Still Life, by Giorgio Morandi. 59c, 1947 Cisitalia 202, designed by Battista Pininfarina.

2003, Sept. 15	**Photo.**	***Perf. 11½***	
1980 A851	49c multicolored	1.30	.45
1981 A851	59c multicolored	1.60	.95

See Italy Nos. 2568-2569. Margins on sheets of No. 1980, inscribed "Prior," served as etiquettes.

Saint
Nicholas — A852

2003, Oct. 27
1982 A852 49c multicolored   1.30   .50
Margins on sheets, inscribed "Prior," served as etiquettes.

Social
Cohesion
A853

2003, Oct. 27
1983 A853 49c multicolored   1.30   .50
Margins on sheets, inscribed "Prior," served as etiquettes.

Miniature Sheet

Belgian Television, 50th Anniv. — A854

No. 1984: a, Jardin Extraordinaire (yellow panel, 18a). b, Old camera (blue panel, 18b). c, Broadcasting tower (green panel, 18c). d, Cassiers and Jef Burm (red violet panel, 18d). e, Schipper Naast Mathilde (red panel, 18e).

2003, Nov. 3
1984 A854 Sheet of 5   6.00 6.00
  a.-e. 41c Any single   1.10   .80

Books — A855

Books and: No. 1985, Man with apple (19a). No. 1986, Duplicating machine (19b), horiz. No. 1987, Woman reader, cat (19c).

2003, Nov. 12
1985 A855 49c multi   1.25   .50
1986 A855 49c multi   1.25   .50
1987 A855 49c multi   1.25   .50
  Nos. 1985-1987 (3)   3.75 1.50
Margins on sheets, inscribed "Prior," served as etiquettes.

Authors — A856

Designs: 49c, Maurice Gilliams (1900-82). 59c, Marguerite Yourcenar (1903-87).

2003, Nov. 12
1988 A856 49c brown   1.25   .50
1989 A856 59c org brn & org 1.50   .90
Margins on sheets of No. 1988, inscribed "Prior," served as etiquettes.

Christmas — A857

2003, Nov. 17
1990 A857 41c multi + label   1.25   .50

Yellow
Tulips — A858

Crocuses — A859

Booklet Stamp
Die Cut Perf. 9¾ on 2 or 3 Sides
2003   **Photo.**   **Self-Adhesive**
1991 A858 (59c) multi   2.00   .50
  a. Booklet pane of 10   22.50

Coil Stamp
***Serpentine Die Cut
13¾x14x13¼x13½***
1992 A859 (49c) multi   1.50   .30
Issued: No. 1991, 11/12. Compare illustration A859 with A832.

Tennis
Players — A860

Designs: No. 1993, Justine Henin-Hardenne. No. 1994, Kim Clijsters, horiz.

2003, Nov. 24   ***Perf. 11½***
1993 A860 49c multi   1.10   .50
1994 A860 49c multi   1.10   .50
Margins on sheets, inscribed "Prior," served as etiquettes.

Red Carnations
A861

Booklet Stamp
Die Cut Perf. 9¾ on 2 or 3 Sides
2004, Jan. 19   **Self-Adhesive**
1995 A861 (49c) multi   1.40   .30
  a. Booklet pane of 10   14.00

Miniature Sheet

Art by Fernand Khnopff (1858-1921) — A862

No. 1996: a, Portrait of Marguerite Khnopff (1a, 27x48mm). b, Caresses (1b, 55x24mm). c, Brown Eyes and a Blue Flower (1c, 55x24mm). d, An Abandoned City (1d, 27x48mm).

2004, Jan. 19   ***Perf. 11½***
1996 A862 Sheet of 4   4.50 4.50
  a.-d. 41c Any single   1.25   .50

Youth
Philately
A863

2004, Jan. 19
1997 A863 41c multi   1.10   .60

Miniature Sheet

Famous Belgians — A864

No. 1998: a, Peter Piot, director of UN Program on AIDS (3a). b, Nicole Van Goethem, film director (3b). c, Dirk Frimout and Frank de Winne, astronauts (3c). d, Jacques Rogge, Intl. Olympic Committee President (3d). e, Christian de Duve, 1974 Nobel laureate in Physiology or Medicine (3e). f, Gabrielle Petit, World War II heroine (3f). g, Catherine Verfaille and Christine Van Broeckhoven, medical researchers (3g). h, Jacques Stibbe, philatelist (3h). i, Queen Fabiola (3i). j, Adrien van der Burch, patron of 1935 Brussels Intl. Exhibition (3j).

2004, Feb. 16
1998 A864 Sheet of 10   15.00 15.00
  a.-j. 57c Any single   1.40 1.00

Stamp Day
A865

2004, Feb. 16
1999 A865 41c multi   1.10   .50

Sugar
Industry
A866

Designs: No. 2000, Sugar beet (5a). No. 2001, Refinery (5b). No. 2002, Street in Tienen (5c).

2004, Mar. 15
2000 A866 49c multi   1.25   .50
2001 A866 49c multi   1.25   .50
2002 A866 49c multi   1.25   .50
  Nos. 2000-2002 (3)   3.75 1.50

Miniature Sheet

Tintin and the Moon — A867

No. 2003: a, Model of Tintin and rocket (6a). b, Technical sketch of rockets for "Destination Moon" (6b). c, Tintin on spacecraft mattress, from "Destination Moon" (6c). d, Tintin on spacecraft ladder, from "Explorers on the Moon" (6d). e, Tintin on Moon, from "Explorers on the Moon" (6e).

2004, Mar. 15
| 2003 | 41c | Sheet of 5 | 7.00 | 7.00 |
| a.-e. | | 41c Any single | 1.25 | .80 |

European Parliament Elections A868

2004, Apr. 19
| 2004 | A868 | 22c multi | | .50 | .50 |

Miniature Sheet

Expansion of the European Union — A869

No. 2005: a, Flags of newly-added countries, "Prior" at right (8bis b). b, As "a," "Prior" at left (8bis c). c, European Parliament, Brussels (8bis a). d, #2004 (8bis d).

2004, Apr. 19　　　　　Perf. 11½
2005	A869	Sheet of 4, #a-d	6.50	6.50
a.-b.		50c Either single	1.25	.90
c.-d.		60c Either single	1.50	1.00

Religious Buildings — A870

Designs: No. 2006, Chapel in the Woods, Buggenhout (9a). No. 2007, Sanctuary, Banneaux. (9b). No. 2008, Scherpenheuvel Basilica, Montaigu (9c). No. 2009, Sanctuary, Beauraing, horiz. (9d).

2004, Apr. 19　　　　　　　Engr.
2006	A870	49c green	1.25	.50
2007	A870	49c brown	1.25	.50
2008	A870	49c purple	1.25	.50
2009	A870	49c blue	1.25	.50
		Nos. 2006-2009 (4)	5.00	2.00

Margins on sheets, inscribed "Prior," served as etiquettes.

A871

Belgian Post Emblem — A872

2004, Apr. 19　　　　　　Photo.
| 2010 | A871 | 49c red | 1.60 | 1.00 |
| 2011 | A872 | (49c) red | 1.60 | .60 |

Compare illustration A871 with A844.

Liège A873

Designs: No. 2012, Museum of Modern and Contemporary Art, sculpture, by Jef Lambeaux (10a). No. 2013, Bridge designed by Santiago Calatrava (10b). 75c, Steel foundry equipment, vert. (10c).

2004, May 17　　Photo.　　Perf. 11½
| 2012 | A873 | 44c multi | 1.25 | .45 |
| 2013 | A873 | 44c multi | 1.25 | .45 |

Souvenir Sheet
| 2014 | A873 | 75c multi | 2.25 | 2.25 |

No. 2014 contains one 38x49mm stamp.

Climatology A874

Designs: 50c, Climate and carbon dioxide (11a). 65c, Relations between Sun and Earth (11b). No. 2017, Earth (11c). No. 2018, Sun (11d).

2004, May 17
2015	A874	50c multi	1.25	.50
2016	A874	65c multi	1.50	.65
2017	A874	80c multi	2.00	.85
2018	A874	80c multi	2.00	.85
		Nos. 2015-2018 (4)	6.75	2.85

Margins on sheets of Nos. 2015 and 2017, inscribed "Prior," served as etiquettes.

Edgar P. Jacobs (1904-87), Cartoonist A875

Blake and Mortimer, by Jacobs — A876

2004, May 24
| 2019 | A875 | 60c multi | 1.60 | .75 |

Souvenir Sheet
| 2020 | A876 | €1.20 multi | 4.00 | 4.00 |

See France No. 3027.

Jazz Musicians A877

Designs: No. 2021, Django Reinhardt (1910-53), guitarist (13a). No. 2022, Fud Candrix (1908-74), saxophonist (13b). No. 2023, René Thomas (1927-75), guitarist (13c). No. 2024, Jack Sels (1922-70), saxophonist (13d). No. 2025, Bobby Jaspar (1926-63), saxophonist (13e).

2004, May 24
2021	A877	50c multi	1.40	.50
2022	A877	50c multi	1.40	.50
2023	A877	50c multi	1.40	.50
2024	A877	50c multi	1.40	.50
2025	A877	50c multi	1.40	.50
		Nos. 2021-2025 (5)	7.00	2.50

Expansion of European Union — A878

No. 2026 — Flags of newly-admitted countries: a, Cyprus. b, Estonia. c, Hungary. d, Latvia. e, Lithuania. f, Malta. g, Poland. h, Czech Republic. i, Slovakia. j, Slovenia.

Die Cut Perf. 10 on 2 or 3 Sides
2004, June 7　　　　　　Photo.
Self-Adhesive
| 2026 | | Booklet pane of 10 | 12.00 | 12.00 |
| a.-j. | A878 | 44c Any single | 1.10 | .80 |

King Albert II, 70th Birthday A879

2004, June 7　　　　　Perf. 11½
| 2027 | A879 | 50c shown | 1.25 | .40 |

Souvenir Sheet
| 2028 | A879 | 80c Close-up | 2.50 | 2.50 |

Margins on sheets of No. 2027, inscribed "Prior," served as etiquettes. No. 2028 contains one 38x49mm stamp.

Europa A880

Photography contest winners: No. 2029, The Belgian Coast, by Muriel Vekemans (15a). No. 2030, The Belgian Ardennes, by Freddy Deburghgraeve (15b).

2004, June 7
| 2029 | A880 | 55c multi | 1.40 | .60 |
| 2030 | A880 | 55c multi | 1.40 | .60 |

2004 Summer Olympics, Athens A881

Designs: 50c, Women's basketball, vert. 55c, Mountain biking. 60c, Pole vault. 80c, Olympic torch.

2004, July 12
2031	A881	50c multi	1.25	.55
2032	A881	55c multi	1.40	.60
2033	A881	60c multi	1.50	.70
		Nos. 2031-2033 (3)	4.15	1.85

Souvenir Sheet
| 2034 | A881 | 80c multi | 2.40 | 2.40 |

Margins on sheets of No. 2031, inscribed "Prior," served as etiquettes. No. 2034 contains one 49x38mm stamp.

Death Announcement Stamp — A882

2004, Sept. 20
| 2035 | A882 | (50c) multi | 1.50 | .50 |

Compare with type A831.

Sculptures by Idel Ianchelevici (1909-94) — A883

Designs: 50c, L'appel (18a). 55c, Perennis Perdurat Poeta (18b).

2004, Sept. 20
| 2036 | A883 | 50c multi | 1.25 | .50 |
| 2037 | A883 | 55c multi | 1.50 | .90 |

Margins on sheets of No. 2036, inscribed "Prior," served as etiquettes. See Romania Nos. 4666-4667.

Impatiens — A884

Booklet Stamp
Die Cut Perf. 10x9¾ on 2 or 3 Sides
2004　　　Photo.　　Self-Adhesive
| 2038 | A884 | (50c) multi | 1.40 | .30 |
| a. | | Booklet pane of 10 | 15.00 | |

Coil Stamp
Serpentine Die Cut 13¾x14
| 2039 | A884 | (50c) multi | 1.40 | .30 |

Issued: No. 2038, 9/27; No. 2039, 12/15.

Belgian World War II Volunteers Medal A885

2004, Sept. 27　　Photo.　　Perf. 11½
| 2040 | A885 | 50c multi | 1.40 | .50 |

Miniature Sheet

Forest Week — A886

No. 2041: a, Squirrel and blackcap. b, Nightingale, robin and red admiral butterfly. c, Bumblebee, vole, flowers, mushrooms, head of weasel. d, Jay, flowers, rear of weasel, left wing of peacock butterfly.

2004, Sept. 27
| 2041 | A886 | Sheet of 4 | 5.00 | 5.00 |
| a.-d. | | 44c Any single | 1.10 | .80 |

Miniature Sheet

Belgica 2006 World Youth Philatelic
Exhibition — A887

No. 2042: a, Pony. b, Robin. c, Kitten. d,
Puppy. e, Fish.

2004, Oct. 18
| 2042 | A887 | Sheet of 5 | 14.00 | 14.00 |
| a.-e. | | 44c Any single | 2.50 | 2.50 |

No. 2042 sold for €5, with €2.80 of this
going to fund the exhibition.

Halloween — A888

Designs: No. 2043, Witch, bats and black
cat. No. 2044, Jack o'lantern and bats.

Booklet Stamp
Die Cut Perf. 10x9¾ on 2 or 3 Sides
2004, Oct. 18		**Self-Adhesive**		
2043	A888	44c multi	1.00	.30
2044	A888	44c multi	1.00	.30
a.		Booklet pane, 5 each		
		#2043-2044	12.50	12.50

Writers
A889

Designs: 50c, Raymond Jean de Kremer
(pen names Jean Ray and John Flanders)
(1887-1964). 75c, Johan Daisne (1912-78).
80c, Gérald Bertot (pen name Thomas Owen)
(1910-2002), vert.

2004, Nov. 3 **Perf. 11½**
2045	A889	50c multi	1.25	.50
2046	A889	75c multi	2.00	.75
2047	A889	80c multi	2.10	1.00
		Nos. 2045-2047 (3)	5.35	2.25

Margins on sheets of Nos. 2045 and 2047,
inscribed "Prior," served as etiquettes.

Battle of
the Bulge,
60th Anniv.
A890

Designs: 44c, Urban warfare. 55c, Tank, war
victims, vert. 65c, Soldiers in forest.

2004, Nov. 3
2048	A890	44c multi	1.10	.55
2049	A890	55c multi	1.40	.75
2050	A890	65c multi	1.75	.95
		Nos. 2048-2050 (3)	4.25	2.25

Christmas
A891

Paintings by Peter Paul Rubens: No. 2051,
The Flight Into Egypt. Nos. 2052, 2053, Adoration of the Magi.

2004, Nov. 22 **Perf. 11½**
| 2051 | A891 | 44c tan & multi | 1.25 | .35 |
| 2052 | A891 | 44c blue & multi | 1.25 | .35 |

Self-Adhesive
Booklet Stamp
Size: 22x22mm
Die Cut Perf. 10x9¾ on 2 or 3 Sides
| 2053 | A891 | 44c blue & multi | 1.25 | .60 |
| a. | | Booklet pane of 10 | 25.00 | 25.00 |

See Germany Nos. B946-B947.

Miniature Sheet

Champion Motocross Riders — A892

No. 2054: a, René Baeten. b, Jacky Martens. c, Georges Jobe. d, Joel Robert. e, Eric
Geboers. f, Roger De Coster. g, Stefan Everts.
h, Gaston Rahier. i, Joel Smets. j, Harry
Everts. k, André Malherbe. l, Steve Ramon.

2004, Nov. 22 **Perf. 11½**
2054	A892	Sheet of 12 +		
		central label and		
		12 etiquettes	16.50	16.50
a.-l.		50c Any single	1.25	.80

Belgian Post
Emblem — A893

2005, Jan. 17
| 2055 | A893 | 6c red | .25 | .25 |

Women's
Council,
Cent. — A894

2005, Jan. 17 **Photo.** **Perf. 11½**
| 2056 | A894 | 50c multi | 1.50 | .65 |

Margins on sheets, inscribed "Prior," served
as etiquettes.

Michel
Vaillant,
Comic Strip
by Jean
Graton
A895

2005, Jan. 17 **Photo.** **Perf. 11½**
| 2057 | A895 | 50c multi | 1.50 | .65 |

Website for
Belgium's 175th
Anniversary
Celebrations
A896

Die Cut Perf. 10 on 3 Sides
2005, Feb. 14 **Photo.**
Self-Adhesive
Booklet Stamp
| 2058 | A896 | (50c) multi | 1.50 | .30 |
| a. | | Booklet pane of 10 | 15.00 | |

Rotary
International,
Cent. — A897

2005, Feb. 14 **Perf. 11½**
| 2059 | A897 | 80c multi | 2.40 | 1.10 |

Linguists
A898

Designs: No. 2060, Maurice Grevisse
(1895-1980), French language grammarian
(5a). No. 2061, Johan Hendrik van Dale
(1828-72), Dutch language lexicographer (5b).

2004, Feb. 12
| 2060 | A898 | 55c multi | 1.60 | .75 |
| 2061 | A898 | 55c multi | 1.60 | .75 |

Souvenir Sheet

King Albert II and Queen
Paola — A899

2005, Feb. 28
| 2062 | A899 | 75c multi | 2.25 | 2.25 |

Belgian Independence, 175th anniv.
No. 2062 was later sold in a presentation
folder that additionally contained a €4 silver
stamp depicting Kings Leopold I and Albert I.
This folder sold for €10.

Miniature Sheet

Belgian Independence, 175th
Anniv. — A900

No. 2063 — History of Belgium: a, First train
(6bis a). b, Bakuba dancer, Belgian Congo
(6bis b). c, Teacher in classroom (6bis c). d,
Industrialization (6bis d). e, Family (Social progress) (6bis e). f, War (6bis f). g, 1958 World's
Fair (6bis g). h, Street sign (Federalism) (6bis
h). i, Berlaymont Building (Europe) (6bis i). j,
L'Ombre et son Ombre, by René Magritte (Art)
(6bis j).

2005, Feb. 28
| 2063 | A900 | Sheet of 10 | 12.50 | 12.50 |
| a.-j. | | 44c Any single | 1.25 | .60 |

A901

Belgica 2006
World Youth
Philatelic
Exhibition — A902

Designs: Nos. 2064a, 2065, Space Shuttle
(8a). Nos. 2064b, 2067, Airplane (8b). Nos.
2064c, 2066, Train (8c). Nos. 2064d, 2068
Race car (8d). Nos. 2064e, 2069, Motorboat
(8e).

2005, Mar. 21 **Perf. 11½**
| 2064 | A901 | Sheet of 5 | 13.00 | 13.00 |
| a.-e. | | 44c Any single | 2.60 | 2.60 |

Booklet Stamps
Self-Adhesive
Die Cut Perf. 10 on 3 Sides
2065	A902	44c multi	1.25	.30
2066	A902	44c multi	1.25	.30
2067	A902	44c multi	1.25	.30
2068	A902	44c multi	1.25	.30
2069	A902	44c multi	1.25	.30
a.		Booklet pane, 2 each		
		#2065-2069	12.50	

No. 2064 sold for €5, with €2.80 of this
going to fund the exhibition.

Belgian Post
Emblem — A903

2005, Mar. 21 **Perf. 11½**
| 2070 | A903 | 10c bright blue | .50 | .25 |

Bird Type of 1985 With Euro
Denominations Only

3c, Mesange nonnette. 5c, Bruant zizi. 20c,
Mouette melanocephale. 44c, Pigeon ramier.
60c, Perdrix grise. 75c, Roitelet triple-
bandeau.

2005 **Photo.** **Perf. 11½**
2071	A524	3c multicolored	.25	.25
2072	A524	5c multicolored	.25	.25
2073	A524	20c multicolored	.60	.25
2074	A524	44c multicolored	1.25	.30
2075	A524	60c multicolored	1.75	.40
2076	A524	75c multicolored	2.25	.50
		Nos. 2072-2076 (5)	6.10	1.70

Issued: 5c, 20c, 60c, 3/21. 3c, 44c, 75c, 4/4.

Rose
Varieties
A904

Designs: 44c, Belinda (9a). 70c, Pink Iceberg, vert. (9b). 80c, Old Master (9c).

2005, Apr. 4 **Photo.** **Perf. 11½**
2077	A904	44c multi	1.25	.55
2078	A904	70c multi	2.00	.95
2079	A904	80c multi	2.40	1.10
		Nos. 2077-2079 (3)	5.65	2.60

2005 Ghent Flower Show. Nos. 2077-2079
are impregnated with a rose scent. Margins on
sheets of No. 2079, inscribed "Prior," served
as etiquettes.

Europa — A905

No. 2080: a, The Children's Table, by Gustave van de Woestijne (10a). b, Still Life With Oysters, Fruit and Pastry, by Clara Peeters (10b).

2005, Apr. 4
2080	A905	Horiz. pair	3.75 1.50
a.-b.		60c Either single	1.75 .70

Black Stork A906

2005, Apr. 4　　　**Photo. & Engr.**
2081	A906	€4 multi	12.00 5.25

Stamp Day.

End of World War II, 60th Anniv. A907

Designs: No. 2082, Soldiers and civilians celebrating (12a). No. 2083, Drawing of concentration camp internee, by Wilchar (12b). No. 2084, Photograph of liberated concentration camp internees (12c).

2005, May 9　　　**Photo.**
2082	A907	44c multi	1.25 .55
2083	A907	44c multi	1.25 .55
2084	A907	44c multi	1.25 .55
		Nos. 2082-2084 (3)	3.75 1.65

Return of Last Belgian Battalion from Korean War, 50th Anniv. — A908

2005, May 9　　　**Perf. 11½**
2085	A908	44c multi	1.25 .55

Clocks — A909

Designs: No. 2086, Zimmer Tower clock, Lier (14a). No. 2087, Belfry of Mons clock (14b). No. 2088, Mont des Arts clock, Brussels (14c).

2005, May 9　　　**Engr.**
2086	A909	44c deep blue	1.25 .55
2087	A909	44c dark brown	1.25 .55
2088	A909	44c reddish brown	1.25 .55
		Nos. 2086-2088 (3)	3.75 1.65

Vacations A910

Designs: No. 2089, Woman on beach, bird (14bis a). No. 2090, Man in Ardennes Forest, deer (14bis b).

2005, May 9　　　**Photo.**
2089	A910	50c multi + etiquette	1.50 .60
2090	A910	50c multi + etiquette	1.50 .60

Hearts — A911

Darwinhybrid Tulips — A912

Baby Boy — A913

Baby Girl — A914

Doves and Wedding Rings — A915

Wedding Rings — A916

Die Cut Perf. 9¾ on 2 or 3 Sides
2005, May 9　　　**Photo.**
Booklet Stamps
Self-Adhesive
2091	A911	(50c) multi	1.50 .30
a.		Booklet pane of 10	15.00
2092	A912	A multi	2.00 .45
a.		Booklet pane of 10	20.00
2093	A913	80c multi	2.40 .50
a.		Booklet pane of 10	24.00
2094	A914	80c multi	2.40 .50
a.		Booklet pane of 10	24.00
2095	A915	80c multi	2.40 .50
2096	A916	80c multi	2.40 .50
a.		Booklet pane of 10, 5 each #2095-2096	24.00
		Nos. 2091-2096 (6)	13.10 2.75

No. 2092 sold for 70c on day of issue.

Miniature Sheet

International Judo Champions From Belgium — A917

No. 2097: a, Robert Van de Walle (15a). b, Ingrid Berghmans (15b). c, Ulla Werbrouck (15c). d, Gella Vandecaveye (15d). e, Christel Deliège (15e). f, Johan Laats (15f).

2005, June 20　　　**Perf. 11½**
2097	A917	Sheet of 6	9.00 9.00
a.-f.		50c Any single	1.50 .60

Tapestries and Carpets — A918

Designs: 44c, L'humanité Assaillie par les Sept Péchés Capitaux tapestry, Belgium (16a). 60c, Carpet from Hereke region, Turkey (16b).

2005, June 20
2098	A918	44c multi	1.25 .55
2099	A918	60c multi	1.75 .70

See Turkey Nos. 2943-2944.

National Radio Broadcasting Institute, 75th Anniv. — A919

2005, June 20
2100	A919	50c multi	1.50 .60

Margins on sheets, inscribed "Prior," served as etiquettes.

Souvenir Sheet

Shells and Snails — A920

No. 2101: a, Buccinum undatum (31x46mm, 17a). b, Donax vittatus (29x38mm, 17b). c, Epitonium clathrus (25x33mm, 17c). d, Interior of Anodonta cygnea (42x48mm, 17d). e, Cepaea nemoralis, Arion rufus (33x40mm, 17e). f, Exterior of Anodonta cygnea (32x34mm, 17f).

2005, July 25　　　**Photo.**　　　***Die Cut***
Self-Adhesive
2101	A920	Sheet of 6	7.50
a.-f.		44c Any single	1.25 .55

Chrysanthemums A921

Die Cut Perf. 10 on 2 or 3 Sides
2005, Sept. 12　　　**Photo.**
Self-Adhesive
Booklet Stamp
2102	A921	(50c) multi	1.50 .35
a.		Booklet pane of 10	15.00

Shrine of Our Lady, by Nicolas of Verdun, 800th Anniv. A922

2005, Sept. 12　　　**Photo.**　　　**Perf. 11½**
2103	A922	75c multi	2.25 .95

Buildings in Belgium and Singapore — A923

Designs: No. 2104, Belgian Center for Comic Strip Art, Brussels (19a). No. 2105, Museum of Musical Instruments, Brussels (19b). No. 2106, Shops on Bukit Pasoh Road, Singapore (19c). No. 2107, Shop on Kandahar Street, Singapore (19d).

2005, Sept. 12
2104	A923	44c multi	1.25 .55
2105	A923	44c multi	1.25 .55
2106	A923	65c multi	1.90 .80
2107	A923	65c multi	1.90 .80
		Nos. 2104-2107 (4)	6.30 2.70

See Singapore Nos. 1160-1163.

Europalia Festival A924

Paintings by Russian artists: 50c, The Reaper, by Kasimir Malevitch (19bis a). 70c, Allegorical Scene, by Sergei Sudeikin (19bis b).

2005, Sept. 12
2108	A924	50c multi	1.50 .60
2109	A924	70c multi	2.00 .85

Margins on sheets of No. 2108, inscribed "Prior," served as etiquettes.

Miniature Sheet

Asterix in Belgium — A925

No. 2110: a, Asterix (27x27mm, 19 ter a). b, Cacofonix (27x40mm, 19 ter b). c, Getafix (38x28mm, 19 ter c) d, Obelix (38x28mm, 19 ter d). e, Vitalstatistix (27x40mm, 19 ter e). f, Asterix at banquet (38x32mm, 19 ter f).

2005, Sept. 24		**Photo.**	**Perf. 11½**	
2110	A925	Sheet of 6	10.50	10.50
a.-f.		60c Any single	1.75	.70

Miniature Sheet

Contemporary Art — A926

No. 2111: a, La Traviata, by Lili Dujourie (20b). b, Donderwalk, by Panamarenko (20h). c, Jeu de Mains, by Michel François (20a). d, OBJET Noir, by Joelle Tuerlinckx (20c). e, Représentation d'un Corps Rond, by Ann Veronica Janssens (20g). f, Tournus, by Marthe Wéry (20e). g, Mur de Montée des Anges, by Jan Fabre (20d). h, ABC Ecole d Paris, by Jef Geys (20f). i, Portrait of an Artist by Himself (XII), by Jan Vercruysse, vert. (20i). j, Figuur op de Rug Gezien, by Luc Tuymans, vert. (20j).

2005, Oct. 10				
2111	A926	Sheet of 10	12.50	12.50
a.-j.		44c multi	1.25	.55

Miniature Sheet

Hans Christian Andersen (1805-75), Author — A927

No. 2112 — Stories by Andersen: a, The Princess and the Pea (21a). b, The Ugly Duckling (21b). c, Thumbelina (21c). d, The Little Mermaid (21d). e, The Emperor's New Clothes (21e).

2005, Oct. 10		**Photo.**	**Perf. 11½**	
2112	A927	Sheet of 5	7.50	7.50
a.-e.		50c Any single	1.50	.60

Left margins on No. 2112, inscribed "Prior" served as etiquettes.

Hans Christian Andersen (1805-75), Author — A927a

Nos. 2113: a, The Princess and the Pea, "Prior" at L (21a). b, As "a," "Prior" at R. c, The Ugly Duckling, "Prior" at L (21b). d, As "c," "Prior" at R. e, Thumbelina, "Prior" at L (21c). f, As "e," "Prior" at R. g, The Little Mermaid, "Prior" at L (21d). h, As "g," "Prior" at R. i, The Emperor's New Clothes, "Prior" at L (21d). j, As "i," "Prior" at R.

Die Cut 9¾ on 2 or 3 Sides

2005, Oct. 10			**Photo.**	
Self-Adhesive				
2113		Booklet pane of 10	15.00	
a.-j.		A927a 50c Any single	1.50	.60

Brass Band Musicians — A928

No. 2114: a, Bass drum (22a). b, Trumpet (22b). c, Sousaphone (22c). d, Clarinet (22d). e, Tuba (22e).

2005, Oct. 31			**Perf. 11½**	
2114		Booklet pane of 5+5 etiquettes	7.50	—
a.-e.		A928 50c Any single	1.50	.60
		Complete booklet, #2114	7.50	

Writers — A929

No. 2118: a, Maurits Sabbe (1873-1938) (23a). b, Arthur Masson (1896-1970) (23b).

2005, Oct. 31		**Photo.**	**Perf. 11½**	
2118	A929	Horiz. pair	2.50	2.50
a.-b.		44c Either single	1.25	.55

Christmas — A930

2005, Oct. 31		**Photo.**	**Perf. 11½**	
2119	A930	44c multi	1.25	.55

Christmas Type of 2005
Die Cut Perf. 9¾ on 2 or 3 Sides

2005, Oct. 31		**Photo.**	
Booklet Stamp			
Self-Adhesive			
Size: 18x26mm			
2120	A930	44c multi	1.25 .55
a.		Booklet pane of 10	12.50

Queen Astrid (1905-35) — A931

Queen Astrid: 44c, Wearing tiara (25a). 80c, Holding son (25b).

2005, Oct. 31		**Photo.**	**Perf. 11½**	
2121	A931	44c multi	1.25	.55

Souvenir Sheet

2122	A931	80c multi	2.40	.95

No. 2122 contains one 38x49mm stamp.

Bird Type of 1985 With Euro Denominations Only

2006		**Photo.**	**Perf. 11½**	
2123	A524	23c Grebe à cou noir	.65	.25
2124	A524	30c Râle des genêts	.90	.25
2125	A524	46c Avocette	1.40	.30
2126	A524	78c Barge à queue noire	2.25	.45
		Size: 38x27mm		
2127	A524	€4.30 Grebe huppé	12.50	3.00
		Nos. 2123-2127 (5)	17.70	4.25

Issued: 30c, 46c, 1/23; 78c, 3/20; €4.30, 5/15. 23c, 6/6.

Wolfgang Amadeus Mozart (1756-91), Composer A932

2006, Jan. 23		**Photo.**	**Perf. 11½**	
2128	A932	70c multi	2.00	.85

Playwrights A933

Designs: 52c, Michel de Ghelderode (1898-1962). 78c, Herman Teirlinck (1879-1967).

2006, Jan. 23				
2129	A933	52c blk & blue	1.50	.65
2130	A933	78c blk & red vio	2.25	.95

Margins on sheets of No. 2129, inscribed "Prior," served as etiquettes.

Composers of Polyphonic Music — A934

No. 2131: a, Guillaume Dufay (c. 1400-74) and Gilles Binchois (c. 1400-60). b, Johannes Ockeghem (c. 1410-97). c, Jacob Obrecht (c. 1457-1505). d, Adriaan Willaert (c. 1490-1562). e, Orlandus Lassus (1532-94).

2006, Jan. 23				
2131		Booklet pane of 5	8.75	—
a.-e.		A934 60c Any single	1.75	.70
		Complete booklet, #2131	8.75	

Farm Animals — A935

No. 2132: a, Donkey. b, Chicken and rooster. c, Two ducks. d, Pig and piglets. e, Cow. f, Goat. g, Two rabbits. h, Two horses. i, Sheep. j, Three geese.

2006, Jan. 23		**Die Cut Perf. 10x9¾**	
Self-Adhesive			
2132		Booklet pane of 10	14.00
a.-j.		A935 46c Any single	1.40 .55

A936   A937

Designs: 46c, (52c), Crossbowmen.

2006, Feb. 20			**Perf. 11½**	
2133	A936	46c multi	1.40	.55

Booklet Stamp
Self-Adhesive

2134	A937	(52c) multi	1.50	.60
a.		Booklet pane of 10	15.00	

Souvenir Sheet

Democracy in Belgium, 175th Anniv. — A938

No. 938: a, Senate chambers (red brown floor). b, King Leopold I, vert. c, Chamber of Representatives (green floor).

2006, Feb. 20				
2135	A938	Sheet of 3 + 2 labels	4.25	2.50
a.-c.		46c Any single	1.40	.50

Souvenir Sheet

Freedom of the Press — A939

No. 2136: a, Face with open mouth. b, Stylized birds and building, horiz.

2006, Feb. 20
2136	A939	Sheet, 3 #2136a, 2 #2136b + 5 etiquettes	7.50	4.50
a.-b.		52c Either single	1.50	.65

A940

Stamp
Festival — A941

2006, Mar. 20   Photo.   Perf. 11½
2137	A940	46c multi	1.40	.55

Booklet Stamps
Self-Adhesive
2138	A941	(52c) "Prior" at L	1.50	.60
2139	A941	(52c) "Prior" at R	1.50	.60
a.		Booklet pane, 5 each #2138-2139	15.00	

Justus Lipsius
(1547-1606),
Philologist — A942

Photo. & Engr.
2006, Mar. 20   Perf. 11½
2140	A942	70c buff & brown	2.00	.85

Start of Giro d'Italia
Cycling Race in
Wallonia — A943

2006, Apr. 24   Photo.
2141	A943	52c multi	1.40	.65

Printed in sheets of 5. Margins on sheets, inscribed "Prior," served as etiquettes.

Painting
Details — A944

No. 2142 — Paintings by Lambert Lombard (1506-66): a, L'Offrande de Joachim Refusée (six men). b, Auguste et la Sybile de Tibur (four men).

No. 2143 — Paintings by Léon Spilliaert (1881-1946): a, Duizeling (figure on staircase). b, De Dame met de Hoed (woman in hat).

2006, Apr. 24
2142	A944	Vert. pair	4.00	1.60
a.-b.		65c Either single	1.90	.80
2143	A944	Vert. pair	4.00	1.60
a.-b.		65c Either single	1.90	.80

Souvenir Sheet

Memorial Van Damme Track and Field
Competition — A945

No. 2144 — Runners of the 1970s and 1980s: a, John Walker. b, Alberto Juantorena. c, Ivo Van Damme. d, Sebastian Coe. e, Steve Ovett.

2006, Apr. 24   Perf. 11½
2144	A945	Sheet of 5 + 5 etiquettes	7.50	3.25
a.-e.		52c Any single	1.50	.65

Miniature Sheet

International Billiards Champions From
Belgium — A946

No. 2145: a, Clément Van Hassel. b, Tony Schrauwen. c, Léo Corin. d, Emile Wafflard. e, Ludo Dielis. f, Jos Vervest. g, Frédéric Caudron. h, Laurent Boulanger. i, Paul Stroobants, Eddy Leppens, and Peter De Backer. j, Raymond Ceulemans. k, Raymond Steylaerts. l, Jozef Philipoom.

2006, Apr. 26
2145	A946	Sheet of 12 + label + 12 etiquettes	18.00	7.50
a.-l.		52c Any single	1.50	.60

Belgica 2006 Intl. Philatelic
Exhibition, Brussels
A947　　　　A948

2006, May 15   Perf. 11½
Size:21x25mm
2146	A947	46c multi	1.40	.60
		Size:22x26mm		
2146A	A947	46c multi	12.00	9.50

Booklet Stamp
Self-Adhesive
Die Cut Perf. 9¾x10 on 2 or 3 Sides
2147	A948	(52c) multi	1.50	.70
a.		Booklet pane of 10	15.00	

No. 2146A was available in sheets with personalizable labels in November and December 2006, and afterwards available without labels.

Red
Cross — A949

Booklet Stamp
Die Cut Perf. 10x9¾ on 2 or 3 Sides
2006, May 15   Self-Adhesive
Location of "Prior"
2148	A949	(52c) At left	1.50	.70
2149	A949	(52c) At right	1.50	.70
a.		Booklet pane, 5 each #2148-2149	15.00	

See No. B1172.

Lighthouses
A950

Photo. & Engr.
2006, May 15   Perf. 11½
2150	A950	46c Blankenberge	1.40	.60
2151	A950	46c Heist	1.40	.60
2152	A950	46c Nieuwpoort	1.40	.60
2153	A950	46c Ostend	1.40	.60
		Nos. 2150-2153 (4)	5.60	2.40

Souvenir Sheet

Fish of the North Sea — A951

No. 2154: a, Petite roussette (dogfish, 50x26mm). b, Cabillaud (cod, 47x26mm). c, Raie bouclée (thornback ray, 50x26mm). d, Hareng (herring, 33x25mm). e, Plie (flounder, 33x25mm).

2006, May 15   Photo.
2154	A951	Sheet of 5	7.00	3.25
a.-e.		46c Any single	1.40	.65

Belgian
Olympic
and
Interfederal
Committee,
Cent.
A952

2006, June 6   Photo.   Perf. 11½
2155	A952	52c multi	1.50	.70

Souvenir Sheet

2006 World Cup Soccer
Championships, Germany — A953

2006, June 6
2156	A953	€1.30 multi	3.75	2.10

Miniature Sheet

Scenes of Wallonian Villages — A954

No. 2157: a, House and flowers, Deigné. b, Arch, Mélin. c, Statue, Saint-Hadelin Church, Celles. d, Bridge, Lompret. e, Fountain, Ny.

2006, June 6
2157	A954	Sheet of 5	7.50	3.50
a.-e.		52c Any single	1.50	.70

Centaurea — A955

Booklet Stamp
Die Cut Perf. 9¾ on 2 or 3 Sides
2006, Aug. 7   Self-Adhesive
2158	A955	(52c) multi	1.50	.35
a.		Booklet pane of 10	15.00	

Marcinelle
Coal Mine
Disaster,
50th Anniv.
A956

2006, Aug. 7   Perf. 11½
2159	A956	70c multi	2.00	.95

Rembrandt
Tulips — A957

Die Cut Perf. 9¾ on 2 or 3 Sides
2006, Sept. 25   Photo.
Self-Adhesive
Booklet Stamp
2160	A957	A multi	2.00	.45
a.		Booklet pane of 10	20.00	

No. 2160 sold for 70c on day of issue.

Institute of Tropical Medicine, Antwerp, Cent. — A958

2006, Sept. 25   *Perf. 11½*
2161   A958   80c multi   2.40   1.00

Oosterlingenhuis, Bruges — A959   Oosters Huis, Antwerp — A960

2006, Sept. 25
2162   A959   70c multi   2.00   .90
2163   A960   80c multi   2.40   1.00

Hanseatic League, 650th anniv.

Belgian Philatelic Academy — A961

2006, Oct. 23   **Photo.**   *Perf. 11½*
2164   A961   52c multi   1.40   .70

Printed in sheets of 10. Margins on sheets, inscribed "Prior," served as etiquettes.

Souvenir Sheet

Belgica 2006 Intl. Philatelic Exhibition, Brussels — A962

No. 2165: a, Tennis ball. b, Tulips as stemware. c, Butterflies as four-leaf clover. d, Illuminated tent. e, Vignettes of Nos. 2165a-2165d with speech balloons.

2006, Nov. 16
2165   A962   Sheet of 5   13.50   13.50
a.-e.   46c Any single   2.60   2.60

No. 2165 sold for €5.

Souvenir Sheet

Belgica 2006 Emblem — A963

2006, Nov. 16
2166   A963   €1.95 multi   13.50   13.50

No. 2166 sold for €5.

Europa — A964

No. 2167 — Children's drawings: a, Zebra and cows, by Nassira Tadmiri. b, People and rainbow, by Lize-Maria Verhaeghe.

2006, Nov. 17
2167   A964   Horiz. pair   2.80   2.80
a.-b.   52c Either single   1.40   .70

Printed in sheets of 5 pairs. Margins on sheets, inscibed "Prior," served as etiquettes.

A965

Paintings by COBRA Group Artists — A966

No. 2168: a, New Skin, by Pierre Alechinsky. b, Untitled by Asger Jorn.

2006, Nov. 17   *Perf. 11½*
Souvenir Sheet
2168   A965   Sheet of 2   3.25   3.25
a.   46c multi   1.25   1.25
b.   70c multi   2.00   2.00

Booklet Stamp
Self-Adhesive
Die Cut Perf. 9¾ on 2 or 3 Sides
2169   A966   (52c) Like #2168a   1.40   .70
a.   Booklet pane of 10   14.00

See Denmark Nos. 1367-1370.

A967

Dance — A968

Designs: Nos. 2170a, 2173, Rock and roll. Nos. 2170b, 2172, Waltz. Nos. 2170c, 2171, Tango. Nos. 2170d, 2174, Cha cha cha. Nos. 2170e, 2175, Samba.

2006, Nov. 18   *Perf. 11½*
2170   A967   Sheet of 5   8.00   8.00
a.-e.   60c Any single   1.60   .80
Booklet Stamps
Self-Adhesive
Die Cut Perf. 9¾ on 2 or 3 Sides
2171   A968   (52c) multi   1.40   .70
2172   A968   (52c) multi   1.40   .70
2173   A968   (52c) multi   1.40   .70
2174   A968   (52c) multi   1.40   .70
2175   A968   (52c) multi   1.40   .70
a.   Booklet pane of 10, 2 each
     #2171-2175   14.00

Kramikske, Comic Strip by Jean-Pol Vandenbroeck A969

2006, Nov. 19   *Perf. 11½*
2176   A969   46c multi   1.25   .60

Youth philately.

Miniature Sheet

Belgian Foods and Beverages — A970

No. 2177: a, Shrimps and tomato. b, Witloof chicory (Belgian endive). c, Eel in green sauce. d, Chocolate. e, Orval beer, vert. f, Gin, vert. g, Ham, sausages, bread and condiments, vert. h, Waffles, vert. i, Mussels, vert. j, Geuze (doubly-fermented beer), vert.

2006, Nov. 19   *Perf. 11½*
2177   A970   Sheet of 10   12.50   12.50
a.-j.   46c Any single   1.25   .60

Angel Playing Psaltery — A971   Angel Playing Trumpet Marine — A972

Angel Playing Lute — A973   Angel Playing Trumpet — A974

Angel Playing Shawm — A975   Head of Angel — A976

Angels painted by Hans Memling: No. 2179, Head of angel on #2178a. No. 2180, Head of angel on #2178b. No. 2181, Head of angel on #2178c. No. 2182, Head of angel on #2178d. No. 2183, Head of angel on #2178e.

2006, Nov. 20   *Perf. 12x11¾*
2178   Horiz. strip of 5   6.25   6.25
a.   A971   46c multi   1.25   .60
b.   A972   46c multi   1.25   .60
c.   A973   46c multi   1.25   .60
d.   A974   46c multi   1.25   .60
e.   A975   46c multi   1.25   .60
Booklet Stamps
Self-Adhesive
Die Cut Perf. 9¾ on 2 or 3 Sides
2179   A976   46c multi   1.25   .60
2180   A976   46c multi   1.25   .60
2181   A976   46c multi   1.25   .60
2182   A976   46c multi   1.25   .60
2183   A976   46c multi   1.25   .60
a.   Booklet pane of 10, 2 each
     #2179-2183   12.50
    Nos. 2179-2183 (5)   6.25   3.00

Christmas.

"Happy Birthday to You" — A977

Birthday Cake — A978

Booklet Stamp
Die Cut Perf. 9¾ on 2 or 3 Sides
2006, Nov. 20   **Self-Adhesive**
2184   A977   (52c) "Prior" at left   1.40   .70
2185   A978   (52c) "Prior" at right   1.40   .70
2186   A978   (52c) "Prior" at left   1.40   .70
2187   A977   (52c) "Prior" at right   1.40   .70
a.   Booklet pane of 10, 3 each
     #2184-2185, 2 each #2186-
     2187   14.00
    Nos. 2184-2187 (4)   5.60   2.80

Christmas — A979

2006, Nov. 20   **Photo.**   *Perf. 11½*
2188   A979   46c multi   12.00   9.50

No. 2188 was available in sheets with personalizable labels in November and December 2006, and afterwards available without labels. Compare types A979 and A930.

Bicycle — A980   Bowling Ball and Pins — A981

Golf Club and Ball — A982   Bicycle — A983

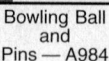

Bowling Ball and Pins — A984

Golf Club and Ball — A985

2007, Jan. 8   Photo.   Perf. 11½
2189	A980	46c multi	1.25	.60
2190	A981	60c multi	1.60	.80
2191	A982	65c multi	1.75	.85
		Nos. 2189-2191 (3)	4.60	2.25

Booklet Stamps
Self-Adhesive
Die Cut Perf. 9¾ on 2 or 3 Sides
2192	A983	(52c) "Prior" at left	1.40	1.40
2193	A983	(52c) "Prior" at right	1.40	1.40
a.		Booklet pane, 5 each #2192-2193	14.00	
2194	A984	(52c) "Prior" at left	1.40	1.40
2195	A984	(52c) "Prior" at right	1.40	1.40
a.		Booklet pane, 5 each #2194-2195	14.00	
2196	A985	(52c) "Prior" at left	1.40	1.40
2197	A985	(52c) "Prior" at right	1.40	1.40
a.		Booklet pane, 5 each #2196-2197	14.00	
		Nos. 2192-2197 (6)	8.40	8.40

World Cross-country Cycling Championships, Hooglede-Gits.

King Albert II Type of 2005 and

King Albert II — A986

King Albert II, Numeral on European Union Flag — A987

King Albert II, Numeral on Globe — A988

2007-09   Photo.   Perf. 11½
2200	A986	1 red & gray	1.50	.40
2202	A810	80c bl, bl gray & blk	2.10	.55
2203	A987	1 blue & multi	2.25	1.10
2204	A810	90c bl, brn gray & blk	2.40	.60
2205	A988	1 brn org & multi	2.50	1.25
2206	A986	2 grn & gray	3.00	.75
2210	A986	3 dk bl & gray	4.50	1.10
2211	A987	3 bl grn & multi	6.75	3.50
2213	A986	5 vio & gray	7.50	1.90
2214	A986	3 red vio & multi	7.50	3.75
2216	A986	7 brn & gray	10.50	2.60
		Nos. 2200-2216 (11)	50.50	17.50

Issued: Nos. 2202, 2204, 1/29; Nos. 2200, 2206, 2210, 2213, 2216, 10/1; Nos. 2203, 2205, 2211, 2214, 1/2/09.
Nos. 2202 and 2204 are inscribed "A Prior" at left.
Stamps of type A987 were intended for usee to destinations within Europe, and type A988 for use to destinations outside of Europe.
On day of issue, No. 2200 sold for 52c, No. 2203, for 80c, No. 2205, for 90c, No. 2206, for €1.04, No. 2210, for €1.56, No. 2211, for €2.40, No. 2213, for €2.60, No. 2214, for €2.70, and No. 2216, for €3.64.

Bird Type of 1985 With Euro Denominations Only

5c, Sarcelle d'hiver. 6c, Chouette cheveche. 10c, Chouette de Tengmalm. 23c, Choucas des Tours. 40c, Hibou moyen-duc. 70c, Martinet noir. 75c, Faucon crecerelle.

2007   Perf. 11½
2218	A524	5c multicolored	.25	.25
2218A	A524	6c multicolored	.25	.25
2219	A524	10c multicolored	.25	.25
2220	A524	23c multicolored	.60	.25
2220A	A524	40c multicolored	1.25	.30
2221	A524	70c multicolored	1.90	.50
2222	A524	75c multicolored	2.00	.50
		Nos. 2218-2222 (7)	6.50	2.30

Issued: 5c, 10c, 2/26; 23c, 3/26; 70c, 75c, 1/29; 6c, 7/9; 40c, 11/12.

Alix, Comic Strip by Jacques Martin A990

2007, Jan. 29
2223	A990	52c multi	1.40	.70

Youth philately. Printed in sheets of 5. Margins on sheets, inscribed "Prior," served as etiquettes.

Miniature Sheet

Accordions — A991

No. 2224: a, Accordion with piano-like keyboard at left. b, Concertina with hexagonal ends. c, Bohemians accordion. d, Accordion with brown and black trim. e, Accordion with red trim.

2007, Jan. 29
2224	A991	Sheet of 5 + 5 etiquettes	7.00	7.00
a.-e.		52c Any single	1.40	.70

Red Cross Mobile Library for Hospitals — A992

Booklet Stamps
Die Cut Perf. 9¾ on 2 or 3 Sides
2007, Feb. 26   Self-Adhesive
2225	A992	(52c) "Prior" at left	1.40	.70
2226	A992	(52c) "Prior" ar right	1.40	.70
a.		Booklet pane, 5 each #2225-2226	14.00	

See No. B1175.

Miniature Sheet

Female Writers — A993

No. 2227: a, Julia Tulkens (1902-95), poet. b, Madeleine Bourdouxhe (1906-96), novelist. c, Christine D'haen, poet. d, Jacqueline Harpman, novelist. e, Maria Rosseels (1916-2005), novelist.

2007, Feb. 26   Perf. 11½
2227	A993	Sheet of 5 + 5 etiquettes	7.00	7.00
a.-e.		52c Any single	1.40	.70

Stoclet House, Brussels, Designed by Josef Hoffmann — A994

Designs: 52c, Building interior. 80c, Building exterior.

2007, Mar. 26
2228	A994	52c multi	1.40	.70
2229	A994	80c multi	2.25	1.10

Margins of sheets of No. 2228, inscribed "Prior," served as etiquettes. See Czech Republic Nos. 3338-3339.

Souvenir Sheet

Popular Theater — A995

No. 2230: a, Scene from "Tati l'Pèriki." b, Romain Deconinck, actor and impresario, vert. c, Scene from "Le Mariage de Mademoiselle Beulemans."

2007, Mar. 26   Photo.   Perf. 11¾
2230	A995	Sheet of 3 + 2 labels	3.75	3.75
a.-c.		46c Any single	1.25	.60

European Union, 50th Anniv. — A996

2007, Apr. 30   Perf. 11¼x11½
2231	A996	80c multi	2.25	1.10

Europa — A997

Designs: 46c, Lord Robert Baden-Powell, founder of Scouting movement. 75c, Scouts.

2007, Apr. 30   Perf. 11½x11¼
2232	A997	46c multi	1.25	.65

Souvenir Sheet
Perf. 11½
2233	A997	75c multi	2.10	2.10

Scouting, cent. No. 2233 contains one 38x49mm stamp.

The Adventures of Tintin — A998

No. 2234 — Tintin book covers translated in: a, French (Tintin au Pays des Soviets). b, Danish (Tintin i Congo). c, English (Tintin in America). d, Luxemburgian (Dem Pharao seng Zigaren). e, Chinese (dragon on cover). f, Portuguese (O Idolo Roubado). g, Bengali (Tintin in boat on cover). h, Slovak (Zezlo Král'a Otakara). i, Russian (Tintin and camels on cover). j, Icelandic (Dularfulla Stjarnan). k, Polish (Tajemnica Jednorozca). l, Afrikaans (Die Skat van Rackham die Rooie). m, Tintin

author, Hergé. n, Arabic (Tintin and men with man in chair above table on cover). o, Spanish (El Templo del Sol). p, German (Im Reiche des Schwarzend Goldes). q, Finnish (Päämääränä Kuu). r, Swedish (Manen Tur Och Retur). s, Japanese (Tintin and men behind rocks on cover). t, Turkish (Ambardaki Kömür). u, Tibetan (Tintin on snowy mountain). v, Italian (I Gioielli della Castafiore). w, Indonesian (Penerbangan 714). x, Greek (Tintin and Mayan temple on cover). y, Dutch (Kuifje en de Alfa-Kunst).

2007, May 22   Perf. 11½
2234	A998	Sheet of 25	32.00	32.00
a.-y.		46c Any single	1.25	.65

Museums — A999

Designs: 46c, Museum of Fashion, Hasselt. 75c, Notre Dame à la Rose Hospital Museum, Lessines. 92c, Jewish Museum of Belgium, Brussels.

2007, June 18   Photo.   Perf. 11½
2235	A999	46c multi	1.25	.60
2236	A999	75c multi	2.10	1.10
2237	A999	92c multi	2.50	1.25
		Nos. 2235-2237 (3)	5.85	2.95

Souvenir Sheet

Opening of Princess Elisabeth Base, Antarctica — A1000

2007, June 18
2238	A1000	75c multi	2.10	2.10

A1001

Vacations A1002

Designs: Nos. 2239, 2241, 2242, Woman, man with kite. Nos. 2240, 2243, 2244, People carrying canoe and woman.

2007   Photo.   Perf. 11½
2239	A1001	52c multi	1.50	.75
2240	A1001	52c multi	1.50	.75

Booklet Stamps
Self-Adhesive
Die Cut Perf. 9¾ on 2 or 3 Sides

2241	A1002	(52c) "Prior" at left	1.50	.75
2242	A1002	(52c) "Prior" at right	1.50	.75
a.		Booklet pane of 10, 5 each	15.00	
		#2241-2242		
2243	A1002	(52c) "Prior" at left	1.50	.75
2244	A1002	(52c) "Prior" at right	1.50	.75
a.		Booklet pane of 10, 5 each	15.00	
		#2243-2244		
		Nos. 2239-2244 (6)	9.00	4.50

Issued: Nos. 2239-2240, 7/9; Nos. 2241-2244, 6/18. Margins on sheets of Nos. 2239-2240, inscribed "Prior," served as etiquettes.

Tour de France in Belgium — A1003

2007, July 9   **Perf. 11½**
2245 A1003 52c multi   1.50 .75

Printed in sheets of 5. Margins on sheets, inscribed "Prior," served as etiquettes.

A1004

Port of Zeebrugge, Cent. — A1005

2007, July 9   **Perf. 11½**
2246 A1004 €1.04 multi   3.00 1.50

Booklet Stamps
Self-Adhesive
Die Cut Perf. 9¾ on 2 or 3 Sides

2247	A1005	(52c) "Prior" at left	1.50	.75
2248	A1005	(52c) "Prior" at right	1.50	.75
a.		Booklet pane of 10, 5 each	15.00	
		#2247-2248		
		Nos. 2246-2248 (3)	6.00	3.00

Margins on sheets of No. 2246, inscribed "Prior," served as etiquettes.

Tourism — A1006

Designs: No. 2249, Athénée François Bovesse, Namur. No. 2250, Collège Saint-Michel, Brussels. No. 2251, Heilig Hart College, Maasmechelen.

Photo. & Engr.
2007, Sept. 3   **Perf. 11½**

2249	A1006	52c multi	1.50	.75
2250	A1006	52c multi	1.50	.75
2251	A1006	52c multi	1.50	.75
		Nos. 2249-2251 (3)	4.50	2.25

Tombeau du Géant, Botassart A1007

2007, Sept. 3   **Photo.**
2252 A1007 52c multi   1.50 .75

Rotunda of Luxembourg Train Station, Luxembourg A1008

2007, Sept. 3   **Photo. & Engr.**
2253 A1008 80c multi   2.25 1.10

See Luxembourg No. 1221.

Miniature Sheet

Scenes From Films By Belgian Directors — A1009

No. 2254: a, Misère au Borinage, by Henri Storck. b, Le Fils, by Jean-Pierre and Luc Dardenne. c, The Man Who Had His Hair Cut Short, by André Delvaux. d, Malpertuis, by Harry Kümel. e, Dust, by Marion Hansel.

2007, Sept. 3   **Photo.**
2254 A1009   Sheet of 5   7.50 7.50
a.-e.   52c Any single   1.50 .75

Souvenir Sheet

Queen Paola, 70th Birthday — A1010

2007, Sept. 3
2255 A1010 €1.04 multi   3.00 1.50

Belgian Post Emblem — A1011

2007, Oct. 1   **Photo.**   **Perf. 11½**
2256 A1011 1 red & black   1.50 .40

Sold for 52c on day of issue.

Fruit — A1012

No. 2257: a, Pears. b, Strawberries. c, Red currants. d, Apples. e, Grapes. f, Cherries. g, Raspberries. h, Peaches. i, Plums. j, Blackberries.

Die Cut Perf. 9¾ on 2 or 3 Sides
2007, Oct. 1   **Photo.**
Self-Adhesive
2257   Booklet pane of 10   15.00
a.-j.   A1012 1 Any single   1.50 .40

Nos. 2257a-2257j each sold for 52c on day of issue.

Mourning Stamp A1013

2007, Oct. 15   **Perf. 11½**
2258 A1013 1 multi   1.50 .75

Sold for 52c on day of issue.

Miniature Sheet

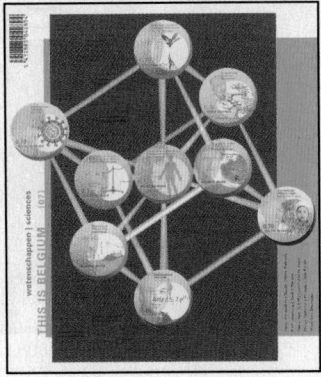

Scientists — A1014

No. 2259 — Scientist and field: a, Marc Van Montagu, molecular genetics. b, Paul Janssen, pharmaceutical entrepreneur. c, Lise Thiry, microbiology. d, Chris Van den Wyngaert, international criminal law. e, Peter Carmeliet, molecular medicine. f, Philippe Van Parijs, social philosophy. g, Marie-Claire Foblets, anthropology. h, André Berger, climatology. i, Pierre Deligne, mathematics.

2007, Oct. 15   **Die Cut**
Self-Adhesive
2259 A1014   Sheet of 9   18.00 18.00
a.-i.   70c Any single   2.00 1.00

Postage Stamp Festival A1015

Designs: Nos. 2260a, 2261, Man with pipe, book, typewriter. Nos. 2260b, 2262, Woman, hearts, vase, picture frame, typewriter. Nos.

2260c, 2263, Man, musical symbols, typewriter. Nos. 2260d, 2264, Woman in cat costume, typewriter. Nos. 2260e, 2265, Boy at computer.

2007, Oct. 15   **Perf. 11½**
2260 A1015   Sheet of 5   7.50 7.50
a.-e.   1 Any single   1.50 .75

Booklet Stamps
Self-Adhesive
Size: 28x20mm
Die Cut Perf. 9¾ on 2 or 3 Sides

2261	A1015	1 multi	1.50	.40
2262	A1015	1 multi	1.50	.40
2263	A1015	1 multi	1.50	.40
2264	A1015	1 multi	1.50	.40
2265	A1015	1 multi	1.50	.40
a.		Booklet pane of 10, 2 each	15.00	
		#2261-2265		
		Nos. 2261-2265 (5)	7.50	2.00

On day of issue, Nos. 2260a-2260e, 2261-2265 each sold for 52c.

Dahlias — A1016   Tulips — A1017

Petunias A1018

Coil Stamp
Serpentine Die Cut 13¾x14
2007, Oct. 15   **Self-Adhesive**
2266 A1016 1 multi   1.50 .40

Booklet Stamps
Die Cut Perf. 9¾ on 2 or 3 Sides

2267	A1016	1 multi	1.50	.40
a.		Booklet pane of 10	15.00	
2268	A1017	A multi	2.40	.60
a.		Booklet pane of 10	24.00	
2269	A1018	2 multi	3.00	.75
a.		Booklet pane of 10	30.00	
		Nos. 2266-2269 (4)	8.40	2.15

On day of issue, Nos. 2266-2267 each sold for 52c; No. 2268, for 80c; No. 2269, for €1.04.

Les Chemins de la Liberté (Le Voyage), by Thierry Merget A1019

2007, Nov. 12   **Photo.**   **Perf. 11½**
2270 A1019 1 multi   1.60 .80

Miniature Sheet

International Billiards Champions From Belgium — A1020

No. 2271: a, Piet J. Van Duppen. b, Albert Collette. c, Gustaaf Van Belle. d, Piet Sels. e, Gaston De Doncker. f, Théo Moons. g, René Gabriels. h, Victor Luypaerts. i, René Vingerhoedt.

2007, Nov. 12
2271 A1020   Sheet of 9   14.50 14.50
a.-i.   1 Any single   1.60   .80

On day of issue, Nos. 2271a-2271i each sold for 52c.

Bride and Groom A1021   Father and Infant Son A1022

Mother and Infant Daughter — A1023

Booklet Stamps
Die Cut 9¾ on 2 or 3 Sides
2007, Nov. 12   Self-Adhesive
2272 A1021 1 multi   1.60   .40
a.   Booklet pane of 10   16.00
2273 A1022 1 multi   1.60   .40
a.   Booklet pane of 10   16.00
2274 A1023 1 multi   1.60   .40
a.   Booklet pane of 10   16.00
  Nos. 2272-2274 (3)   4.80 1.20

On day of issue, Nos. 2272-2274 each sold for 52c.

Christmas
A1024   A1025

2007, Nov. 12   Perf. 11½
2275 A1024 1 multi   1.60   .80

Booklet Stamps
Self-Adhesive
Size: 24x29mm
Die Cut Perf. 9¾ on 2 or 3 Sides
2276 A1024 1 multi   1.40   .40
a.   Booklet pane of 10   14.00
2277 A1025 A multi   2.10 1.10
a.   Booklet pane of 10   21.00

On day of issue, Nos. 2275 and 2276 each had a franking value of 52c, and No. 2277 had a franking value of 80c. On day of issue, No. 2276a sold for €4.68, and No. 2277a sold for €7.20.

Bird Type of 1985 With Euro Denominations Only

10c, Accenteur mouchet. 15c, Cassenoix moucheté. €4.40, Faucon pélerin.

2008, Jan. 21   Photo.   Perf. 11½
2278 A524 10c multi + etiquette   .30   .25
2279 A524 15c multi + etiquette   .45   .25
Size: 38x27mm
2280 A524 €4.40 multicolored 13.00 3.25
  Nos. 2278-2280 (3)   13.75 3.75

Red Cross Blood Donation — A1026

Die Cut Perf. 9¾ on 2 or 3 Sides
2008, Jan. 21   Photo.
Booklet Stamp
Self-Adhesive
2281 A1026 1 multi   1.60   .80
a.   Booklet pane of 10   16.00

See No. B1176. No. 2281 sold for 52c on day of issue.

Miniature Sheet

Paintings by René Magritte (1898-1967) — A1027

No. 2282: a, The Man from the Sea, 1927 (30x40mm). b, Scheherazade, 1950 (30x40mm). c, Midnight Marriage, 1926 (30x40mm). d, Georgette, 1935 (33x40mm). e, The Ignorant Fairy, 1956 (49x37mm).

Perf. 11½, 11¼x11½ (#2282b)
2008, Jan. 21
2282 A1027 Sheet of 5 + 2 labels   8.00 8.00
a.-e.   1 Any single   1.60   .80

Nos. 2282a-2282e each sold for 52c on day of issue. Ungummed imperforate examples of No. 2282 were given as gifts to some standing order subscribers, and were not sold.

Toys — A1028

No. 2283: a, Automobile. b, Baby carriage. c, Doll. d, Airplane. e, Horse. f, Tram. g, Diabolo. h, Teddy bear. i, Top. j, Scooter.

Die Cut Perf. 9¾ on 2 or 3 Sides
2008, Feb. 11   Self-Adhesive
2283   Booklet pane of 10   16.50
a.-j. A1028 1 Any single   1.60   .80

Nos. 2283a-2283j each sold for 54c on day of issue.

Jeremiah, Comic Book Character by Hermann Huppen A1029

2008, Feb. 11   Perf. 11½
2284 A1029 1 multi   1.60   .80

No. 2284 sold for 54c on day of issue.

Souvenir Sheet

Floralies of Ghent Flower Show, Bicent. — A1030

2008, Feb. 11
2285 A1030 80c multi   2.50 1.25

Jewish Community in Belgium, Bicent. A1031

2008, Mar. 17   Photo. & Engr.
2286 A1031 90c multi   3.00 1.50

Detective Novels — A1032

No. 2287: a, L'Assassin Habite au 21, by Stanislas-André Steeman. b, De Zaak Alzheimer, by Jef Geeraerts.

2008, Mar. 17   Photo.
2287 A1032 Horiz. pair, #a-b   3.50 1.75
a.-b.   1 Either single   1.75   .85

Nos. 2287a-2287b each sold for 54c on day of issue.

2008, Apr. 14
2288 A1033 1 multi   1.75   .85
2289 A1033 80c multi   2.50 1.25
2290 A1033 90c multi   2.75 1.40
  Nos. 2288-2290 (3)   7.00 3.50

No. 2289 sold for 54c on day of issue.

Miniature Sheet

Antverpia 2010 Intl. Philatelic Exhibition — A1034

No. 2291: a, Train, building. b, Buildings, statue. c, Port, cargo containers. d, Models, Flanders Fashion Institute Building. e, Woman wearing necklace, diamonds.

2008, Apr. 14   Perf. 11½
2291 A1034 Sheet of 5   15.50 15.50
a.-e.   1 Any single   3.00   3.00

On day of issue, No. 2291 sold for €5 but Nos. 2291a-2291e each had a 54c franking value.

Miniature Sheet

Spirou, Comic Strip by André Franquin — A1035

No. 2292: a, Count of Champignac (with magnifying glass). b, Fantasio. c, Spirou. d, Seccotine (girl). e, Zorglub (bearded man).

2008, Apr. 14
2292 A1035 Sheet of 5   8.75 8.75
a.-e.   1 Any single   1.75   .85

Nos. 2292a-2292e each sold for 54c on day of issue.

Mickey Mouse, 80th Anniv. — A1036

2008, May 19   Photo.   Perf. 11½
2293 A1036 1 multi   1.75   .85

Sold for 54c on day of issue. Printed in sheets of 5.

Diversity at Work — A1037

2008, May 19
2294 A1037 2 multi   3.50 1.75

Sold for €1.08 on day of issue.

Designs: 1, Coastal tram. 80c, Charleroi tram. 90c, Brussels tram.

Trams A1033

Souvenir Sheet

La Constance and Les Elèves de Thémis Masonic Lodges, Bicent. — A1038

2008, May 19			Litho.	
2295	A1038	3 multi	5.25	5.25

Sold for €1.62 on day of issue.

Europa A1039

2008, May 19		Photo.	Perf. 11½	
2296	A1039	80c multi	2.60	1.25

Booklet Stamp
Self-Adhesive
Size: 30x24mm
Die Cut Perf. 9¾ on 2 or 3 Sides

2008, May 19				
2297	A1039	1 multi	1.75	.85
a.	Booklet pane of 10		17.50	

No. 2297 sold for 54c on day of issue.

Tagetes Patula — A1040 Orange Favorite Tulips — A1041

Booklet Stamps
Die Cut Perf. 9¾ on 2 or 3 Sides

2008, May 19			Self-Adhesive	
2298	A1040	1 multi	1.75	.85
a.	Booklet pane of 10		17.50	
2299	A1041	A multi	2.60	1.25
a.	Booklet pane of 10		26.00	

On day of issue, No. 2298 sold for 54c, and No. 2299 sold for 80c. See No. 2316.

Souvenir Sheet

Queen Fabiola, 80th Birthday — A1042

No. 2300: a, Queen Fabiola and King Baudouin, black and white photo. b, Drawing of Queen Fabiola. c, Queen Fabiola and King Baudouin, color photo.

2008, June 11			Perf. 11½	
2300	A1042	Sheet of 3	5.25	5.25
a.-c.	1 Any single		1.75	.85

Nos. 2300a-2300c each sold for 54c on day of issue.

Sculptures A1043

Designs: 1, La Mer, by George Grard. 80c, Sculpture from Imago series, by Emile Desmedt. 90c, Autoportrait, by Gérald Dederen.

2008, June 11			Litho.	
2301	A1043	1 multi	1.75	.85
2302	A1043	80c multi	2.50	1.25
2303	A1043	90c multi	2.75	1.40
	Nos. 2301-2303 (3)		7.00	3.50

No. 2301 sold for 54c on day of issue.

A1044

Outdoor Activities A1045

Family: Nos. 2304, 2306, Cycling. Nos. 2305, 2307, Walking.

2008, June 11			Perf. 11½	
2304	A1044	1 multi	1.75	.85
2305	A1044	1 multi	1.75	.85

Booklet Stamps
Self-Adhesive
Die Cut Perf. 9¾ on 2 or 3 Sides

2306	A1045	1 multi	1.75	.85
a.	Booklet pane of 10		17.50	
2307	A1045	1 multi	1.75	.85
a.	Booklet pane of 10		17.50	

On day of issue, Nos. 2304-2307 each sold for 54c.

Folklore and Traditions A1046

Designs: No. 2308, Hopduvelfeesten, Asse. No. 2309, Planting of the Meyboom, Brussels, 700th anniv., vert. No. 2310, Eupen Carnival, vert. No. 2311, Royal Walloon Cabaret Company, Tournai, cent., vert.

Photo. & Engr.

2008 July 14			Perf. 11½	
2308	A1046	1 multi	1.75	.85
2309	A1046	1 multi	1.75	.85
2310	A1046	1 multi	1.75	.85
2311	A1046	1 multi	1.75	.85
	Nos. 2308-2311 (4)		7.00	3.40

On day of issue Nos. 2308-2311 each sold for 54c.

2008 Summer Olympics, Beijing — A1047

Designs: 1, BMX racer. 90c, Women's relay race, horiz. 2, Tennis, horiz.

2008, July 14			Photo.	
2312	A1047	1 multi	1.75	.85
2313	A1047	90c multi	3.00	1.50

Souvenir Sheet

2314	A1047	2 multi	3.50	1.75

No. 2314 contains one 48x38mm stamp. On day of issue, Nos. 2312 and 2314 sold for 54c and €1.08, respectively.

Miniature Sheet

Brussels World's Fair, 50th Anniv. — A1048

No. 2315: a, Soviet Union Pavilion and plaza (red panel). b, Thailand Pavilion (yellow panel). c, Hostesses carrying flags (green panel). d, Fair's star emblems (blue panel). e, Atomium (red violet panel).

Perf. 11½ on 3 or 4 Sides

2008, July 14				
2315	A1048	Sheet of 5 + 4 labels	8.75	8.75
a.-e.	1 Any single		1.75	.85

On day of issue, Nos. 2315a-2315e each sold for 54c.

Tagetes Patula Type of 2008
Serpentine Die Cut 13¼x13½

2008, Sept. 29			Photo.	

Coil Stamp
Self-Adhesive

2316	A1040	1 multi	1.50	.40

On day of issue No. 2316 sold for 54c.

St. Gabriel Guild (Religion on Stamps Society), 50th Anniv. A1049

Photo. & Engr.

2008, Sept. 29			Perf. 11½	
2317	A1049	1 multi	1.50	.75

Sold for 54c on day of issue.

Miniature Sheet

Photography — A1050

No. 2318 — Photography by: a, Tim Dirven. b, Paul Ausloos. c, Léonard Missone. d, Harry Gruyaert. e, Stephan Vanfleteren.

2008, Sept. 29			Photo.	
2318	A1050	Sheet of 5	7.50	7.50
a.-e.	80c Any single		1.50	.75

A1051

Smurfs — A1052

No. 2319: a, Smurf and Smurfette kissing. b, Smurfs shaking hands. c, Smurf blowing noisemaker. d, Smurf carrying dessert. e, Smurf eating cake, vert.

No. 2320, Smurf waving, orange background. No. 2321, Smurfette. No. 2322, Papa Smurf. No. 2323, Smurf with drum, horiz. No. 2324, Smurf writing letter. No. 2325, Smurf giggling. No. 2326, Smurf carrying mail bag and letter. No. 2327, Brainy Smurf (with glasses). No. 2328, Gargamel. No. 2329, Smurf with mail bag, letter and posthorn, horiz.

Perf. 11¾x11¼, 11¼(#2319e)

2008, Sept. 29				
2319	A1051	Sheet of 5	7.50	7.50
a.-e.	1 Any single		1.50	.75

Booklet Stamps
Self-Adhesive
Die Cut Per. 10 on 2 or 3 Sides

2320	A1052	1 multi	1.50	.75
2321	A1052	1 multi	1.50	.75
2322	A1052	1 multi	1.50	.75
2323	A1052	1 multi	1.50	.75
2324	A1052	1 multi	1.50	.75
2325	A1052	1 multi	1.50	.75
2326	A1052	1 multi	1.50	.75
2327	A1052	1 multi	1.50	.75
2328	A1052	1 multi	1.50	.75
2329	A1052	1 multi	1.50	.75
a.	Booklet pane of 10, #2320-2329		15.00	
	Nos. 2320-2329 (10)		15.00	7.50

On day of issue, Nos. 2319a-2319e and 2320-2329 each sold for 54c.

A1053

Mustelids A1054

No. 2330: a, Ermine, vert. (hermine, 38x42mm). b, Sable (martre, 48x38mm). c, Marten (fouine, 48x38mm). d, Polecat, vert. (putois, 38x42mm). e, Otter, vert. (38x48mm). f, Badger (blaireau, 48x38mm).

No. 2331, Marten (martre). No. 2332, Marten (fouine). No. 2333, Polecat. No. 2334, Otter. No. 2335, Badger.

Perf. 11½x11¼, 11½ (#2330e, 2330f)

2008, Sept. 29				
2330	A1053	Sheet of 6	9.00	9.00
a.-f.	1 Any single		1.50	.75

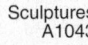

Booklet Stamps
Self-Adhesive
Die Cut Perf. 10 on 2 or 3 Sides

2331	A1054	1 multi	1.50	.75
2332	A1054	1 multi	1.50	.75
2333	A1054	1 multi	1.50	.75
2334	A1054	1 multi	1.50	.75
2335	A1054	1 multi	1.50	.75
a.	Booklet pane of 10, 2 each			
	#2331-2335		15.00	
	Nos. 2331-2335 (5)		7.50	3.75

On day of issue, Nos. 2330a-2330f and 2331-2335 each sold for 54c.

Belgian Congo, Cent. A1055

Photo. & Engr.
2008, Oct. 20   Perf. 11½

2336	A1055	1 Belgian Congo #37	1.40	.70

On day of issue, No. 2336 sold for 54c.

Museums A1056

Designs: 1, National Footwear Museum, Izegem. No. 2338, Musée en Piconrue, Bastogne. No. 2339, David and Alice van Buuren Museum, Brussels.

2008, Oct. 20   Litho.

2337	A1056	1 multi	1.40	.70
2338	A1056	80c multi	2.10	1.10
2339	A1056	80c multi	2.10	1.10
	Nos. 2337-2339 (3)		5.60	2.90

On day of issue, No. 2337 sold for 54c.

Souvenir Sheet

End of World War I, 90th Anniv. — A1057

No. 2340: a, Soldiers at Menin Gate, Ypres. b, Statue of King Albert I, Nieuwpoort. c, Poppies.

Perf. 11½x11¼
2008, Oct. 20   Photo.

2340	A1057	Sheet of 3	7.00	7.00
a.-c.	90c Any single		2.25	1.10

Universal Declaration of Human Rights, 60th Anniv. — A1058

2008, Nov. 12   Perf. 11½
2341	A1058	90c multi	2.25	1.10

Miniature Sheet

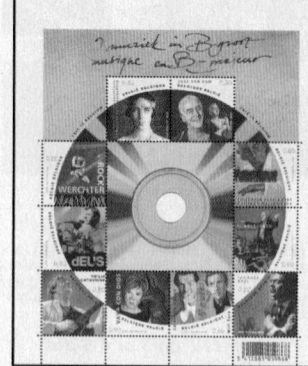

Belgian Music — A1059

No. 2342: a, Queen Elisabeth Competition. b, José Van Dam. c, Rock Werchter. d, Philippe Herreweghe and Collegium Vocale Gent. e, dEUS. f, Conductor Robert Groslot and orchestra. g, Philip Catherine. h, Vaya Con Dios. i, Salvatore Adamo and Will Tura. j, Jacques Brel.

2008, Nov. 12   Perf. 11¾x11¼
2342	A1059	Sheet of 10 + label	21.00	21.00
a.-j.	80c Any single		2.10	1.10

A1060

Christmas
A1061   A1062

No. 2343 — Stained-glass window: a, Désiré Cardinal Mercier. b, St. Francis holding Cross. c, Mary, Joseph and Holy Spirit. d, Franciscan monk. e, Infant Jesus.

2008, Nov. 12   Perf. 11¼
2343	A1060	Sheet of 5	7.00	7.00
a.-e.	1 Any single		1.40	.70

Booklet Stamps
Self-Adhesive
Die Cut Perf. 9¾ on 2 or 3 Sides

2344	A1061	1 multi	1.40	.70
a.	Booklet pane of 10		14.00	
2345	A1062	(80c) multi	2.10	1.10
a.	Booklet pane of 10		21.00	

On day of issue, Nos. 2343a-2343e and 2344 each sold for 54c.

Bird Type of 1985 With Euro Denominations Only

27c, Bécasse des bois. €4.60, Pygargue a queue blanche.

2009   Photo.   Perf. 11½
2346	A524	27c multicolored	.75	.35

Size: 31x27mm
2347	A524	€4.60 multicolored	13.00	6.50

Issued: 27c, 4/6; €4.60, 1/2.

Tulipa Bakeri — A1063

Booklet Stamps
Die Cut Perf. 9¾ on 2 or 3 Sides
2009, Jan. 2   Self-Adhesive
2348	A1063	1 multi	2.25	1.10
a.	Booklet pane of 10		22.50	

On day of issue, No. 2348 sold for 80c.

Miniature Sheet

German-speaking Community in Belgium — A1064

No. 2349: a, Marker at border of Belgium, Germany and Netherlands, near Kelmis (30x40mm). b, Jug from Raeren (30x40mm). c, Bütgenbach Lake (30x40mm). d, Eupen Sanitorium (33x40mm). e, Marksman, horiz. (49x37mm).

2009, Jan. 19   Perf. 11½
2349	A1064	Sheet of 5	10.50	10.50
a.-e.	1 Any single		2.10	2.10

On day of issue, Nos. 2349a-2349e each sold for 80c.

Introduction of the Euro, 10th Anniv. — A1065

Booklet Stamps
Die Cut Perf. 9¾ on 2 or 3 Sides
2009, Jan. 19   Self-Adhesive
2350	A1065	1 dk blue & blue	1.40	.70
a.	Booklet pane of 10		14.00	

No. 2350 sold for 54c on day of issue.

Louis Braille (1809-52), Educator of the Blind — A1066

Photo., Engr. & Embossed
2009, Feb. 23   Perf. 11½
2351	A1066	1 multi	1.50	.75

Sold for 59c on day of issue.

River and Canal Barge A1067

2009, Feb. 23   Photo.
2352	A1067	2 multi	3.00	1.50

Sold for €1.18 on day of issue.

Postage Stamp Festival — A1068

2009, Mar. 9
2353	A1068	1 multi	1.60	.80

Sold for 59c on day of issue.

Famous Women — A1069

No. 2354: a, Marthe Boel (1877-1956), President of Intl. Council of Women. b, Lily Boeykens (1930-2005), Belgian representative to U.N. Commission on the Status of Women.

2009, Mar. 9   Litho.
2354	A1069	Horiz. pair	3.25	1.60
a.-b.	1 Either single		1.60	.80

On day of issue, Nos. 2354a-2354b each sold for 59c.

Souvenir Sheet

Preservation of Polar Regions and Glaciers — A1070

No. 2355: a, Penguins. b, Polar bear.

2009, Mar. 9   Perf. 11½
2355	A1070	Sheet of 2	5.75	5.75
a.-b.	1 Either single		2.75	1.40

On day of issue, Nos. 2355a-2355b each sold for €1.05.

Souvenir Sheet

Europa — A1071

2009, Apr. 6
2356	A1071	1 multi	2.40	1.25

Intl. Year of Astronomy. Sold for 90c on day of issue.

Miniature Sheet

UNESCO World Heritage
Sites — A1072

No. 2357: a, Neolithic Flint Mines, Spiennes. b, Notre-Dame Cathedral, Tournai. c, Plantin-Moretus Museum, Antwerp. d, Historic Center of Bruges. e, Town Houses of Architect Victor Horta, Brussels.

2009, Apr. 6		Photo. & Engr.	
2357 A1072	Sheet of 5	14.00	14.00
a.-e.	1 Any single	2.75	1.40

On day of issue, Nos. 2357a-2357e each sold for €1.05.

A1073   A1074

A1075   A1076

Characters From Animated Movie "Suske en Wiske - De Texas Rakkers" — A1077

Die Cut Perf. 9¾ on 2 or 3 Sides
2009, Apr. 6   **Photo.**
Booklet Stamps
Self-Adhesive

2358 A1073	1 multi	1.60	.80
2359 A1074	1 multi	1.60	.80
2360 A1075	1 multi	1.60	.80
2361 A1076	1 multi	1.60	.80
2362 A1077	1 multi	1.60	.80
a.	Booklet pane of 10, 2 each #2358-2362	16.00	
	Nos. 2358-2362 (5)	8.00	4.00

On day of issue, Nos. 2358-2362 each sold for 59c.

Miniature Sheet

Antverpia 2010 European Philatelic Championships, Antwerp — A1078

No. 2363: a, Antwerp Museum of Contemporary Art, Flemish Village, by Luc Tuymans. b, Orbino, sculpture by Luc Deleu, Middelheim Museum. c, Actors, Toneelhuis Theater. d, Poster for movie, "Hollywood on the Scheldt," Roma Cinema. e, Writings of Willem Elsschot, sculpture of Elsschot by Wilfried Pas.

2009, May 11		Photo.	Perf. 11½
2363 A1078	Sheet of 5	15.50	15.50
a.-e.	1 Any single	3.00	3.00

No. 2363 sold for €5.50. Nos. 2363a-2363e each had a franking value of 59c on day of issue.

Composers — A1079

Designs: No. 2364, Henry Purcell (1659-95). No. 2365, Georg Friedrich Handel (1685-1759). No. 2366, Joseph Haydn (1732-1809). No. 2367, Felix Mendelssohn-Bartholdy (1809-47). No. 2368, Clara Schumann (1819-96).

2009, May 11		Perf. 11¾x11½
	Booklet Stamps	

2364 A1079	1 multi	2.50	1.25
2365 A1079	1 multi	2.50	1.25
2366 A1079	1 multi	2.50	1.25
2367 A1079	1 multi	2.50	1.25
2368 A1079	1 multi	2.50	1.25
a.	Booklet pane of 5, #2364-2368	12.50	—
	Complete booklet, #2368a	12.50	
	Nos. 2364-2368 (5)	12.50	6.25

On day of issue Nos. 2364-2368 each sold for 90c.

Vacations — A1080

Designs: No. 2369, Man with camera. No. 2370, Woman with camera.

Booklet Stamps
Die Cut Perf. 9¾ on 2 or 3 Sides
2009, May 11   **Self-Adhesive**

2369 A1080	1 multi	1.75	.45
2370 A1080	1 multi	1.75	.45
a.	Booklet pane of 10, 5 each #2369-2370	17.50	

On day of issue Nos. 2369-2370 each sold for 59c.

Aviation and Space Exploration Milestones A1081

No. 2371: a, First command of International Space Station by European, 2009. b, Apollo 11 moon landing, 1969. c, First flight of Concorde, 1969. d, Circumnavigational flight of Graf Zeppelin, 1929. e, Flight by Louis Blériot across English Channel, 1909.

Photo. (#2371a), Photo. & Engr.
2009, June 8			Perf. 11½
2371	Vert. strip of 5	8.75	8.75
a.-e.	A1081 1 Any single	1.75	.85

Nos. 2371a-2371e each sold for 59c on day of issue. No. 2371 was printed in sheets containing two strips.

Energy Conservation A1082

Designs: No. 2372, Fluorescent light bulb. No. 2373, Windmill. No. 2374, Bus. No. 2375, Solar energy. No. 2376, Insulated house.

Booklet Stamps
Die Cut Perf. 9¾ on 2 or 3 Sides
2009, June 8   **Self-Adhesive**

2372 A1082	1 multi	1.75	.45
2373 A1082	1 multi	1.75	.45
2374 A1082	1 multi	1.75	.45
2375 A1082	1 multi	1.75	.45
2376 A1082	1 multi	1.75	.45
a.	Booklet pane of 10, 2 each #2372-2376	17.50	
	Nos. 2372-2376 (5)	8.75	2.25

On day of issue Nos. 2372-2376 each sold for 59c.

Yoko Tsuno, Comic Strip by Roger Leloup — A1083

2009, June 29		Photo.	Perf. 11½
2377 A1083	1 multi	1.75	.85

Sold for 59c on day of issue.

Souvenir Sheet

50th Wedding Anniv. of King Albert II and Queen Paola — A1084

2009, June 29			Litho.
2378 A1084	3 multi	5.00	2.50

Sold for €1.77 on day of issue.

Maurice Béjart (1927-2007), Choreographer A1085

2009, Aug. 31			Litho.
2379 A1085	1 multi	2.60	1.40

Sold for 90c on day of issue.

1950s Citroen Mail Van A1086

1960s Bedford Mail Van A1087

1970s Renault Mail Van A1088

1980s Renault Mail Van A1089

2009 Citroen Mail Van A1090

2009, Aug. 31		Photo. & Engr.	
2380 A1086	1 multi	1.75	.85
2381 A1087	1 multi	1.75	.85
2382 A1088	1 multi	1.75	.85
2383 A1089	1 multi	1.75	.85
2384 A1090	1 multi	1.75	.85
a.	Vert. strip of 5, #2380-2384	8.75	4.25
	Nos. 2380-2384 (5)	8.75	4.25

On day of issue, Nos. 2380-2384 each sold for 59c.

Circus Performers — A1091

Designs: No. 2385, Musicians. No. 2386, Bicyclist on tightrope. No. 2387, Magician levitating woman. No. 2388, Human pyramid. No. 2389, Trapeze artists. No. 2390, Clown on ball and acrobat. No. 2391, Acrobats with ball. No. 2392, Magician with doves and rabbit. No. 2393, Acrobat on horseback. No. 2394, Juggler on unicycle.

Die Cut Perf. 10 on 2 or 3 Sides
2009, Aug. 31   **Photo.**
Booklet Stamps
Self-Adhesive

2385 A1091	1 multi	1.75	.45
2386 A1091	1 multi	1.75	.45
2387 A1091	1 multi	1.75	.45
2388 A1091	1 multi	1.75	.45
2389 A1091	1 multi	1.75	.45
2390 A1091	1 multi	1.75	.45
2391 A1091	1 multi	1.75	.45
2392 A1091	1 multi	1.75	.45
2393 A1091	1 multi	1.75	.45
2394 A1091	1 multi	1.75	.45
a.	Booklet pane of 10, #2385-2394	17.50	
	Nos. 2385-2394 (10)	17.50	4.50

On day of issue, Nos. 2385-2394 each sold for 59c.

The Triptych of the Seven Sacraments, Detail of Painting by Rogier van der Weyden — A1092

2009, Sept. 21		Litho.	Perf. 11½
2395 A1092	2 multi	3.50	1.75

Opening of Leuven Museum exhibition of works by Rogier van der Weyden. Sold for €1.18 on day of issue.

Miniature Sheet

Mont des Arts District, Brussels — A1093

No. 2396: a, General State Archives (40x33mm). b, Royal Museum of Fine Arts of Belgium (40x33mm). c, Royal Library of Belgium (40x33mm). d, Brussels Meeting Center (40x33mm). e, Old Palace of Brussels (38x49mm). f, Saint Jacques-sur-Coudenberg Church, Protestant Chapel (49x38mm). g,

Palace of Fine Arts (40x33mm). h, Royal Belgian Film Archive (40x33mm). i, Belvue Museum (40x33mm). j, Musical Instruments Museum (40x33mm).

Perf. 11½ on 2, 3 or 4 Sides

2009, Sept. 21		Photo.
2396 A1093	Sheet of 10	17.50 8.75
a.-j.	1 Any single	1.75 .85

Nos. 2396a-2396j each sold for 59c on day of issue.

Chinese Dragon — A1094

Booklet Stamps
Die Cut Perf. 10 on 2 or 3 Sides

2009, Oct. 5		Self-Adhesive
2397 A1094	1 multi	1.75 .85
a.	Booklet pane of 10	17.50

Europalia China Cultural Festival. No. 2397 sold for 59c on day of issue.

Canonization of Father Damien (1840-89) — A1095

2009, Oct. 5		Perf. 11½
2398 A1095	1 multi	2.75 1.40

Sold for 90c on day of issue.

Souvenir Sheet

Comic Strip Museum Festival — A1096

2009, Oct. 5		Photo.
2399 A1096	1 multi	3.25 1.60

Sold for €1.05 on day of issue. Imperforate examples were gifts to standing order customers.

Miniature Sheet

Toy Trains — A1097

No. 2400: a, Streamline Mettoy train (blue locomotive and cars). b, Märklin Bavarian locomotive "Aloisus" (locomotive with gold-trimmed window and smokestack). c, Märklin SNCB locomotive tender (locomotive facing left with red trim). d, Märklin Haine-St. Pierre SNCB Diesel locomotive (locomotive with green and yellow trim). e, Märklin Storchenbein locomotive tender replica (locomotive with front wheel in red). f, Märklin Type 16 SNCB locomotives (gray locomotives with yellow and red trim). g, French tin toy train and cars (red locomotive and cars). h, Märklin ICE Deutsches Bahn locomotives (white locomotives with red trim). i, Unpainted French wooden toy train and cars. j, Blue and red Belgian wooden locomotive with pull string.

2009, Oct. 5		Perf. 11¾x11¼
2400 A1097	Sheet of 10	17.50 8.75
a.-j.	1 Any single	1.75 .85

Nos. 2400a-2400j each sold for 59c on day of issue.

Miniature Sheet

Trees — A1098

No. 2401: a, Scotch pine (pin sylvestre). b, Beech (hêtre). c, Birch (bouleau). d, Larch (mélèze). e, Oak (chêne).

2009, Oct. 5	Litho.	Perf. 11½
2401 A1098	Sheet of 5	17.50 8.75
a.-e.	2 Any single	3.50 1.75

Nos. 2401a-2401e each sold for €1.18 on day of issue.

Bird Type of 1985 With Euro Denominations Only

2009, Sept. 21	Litho.	Perf. 11½
2402 A524	1c Pic noir	.25 .25
2403 A524	10c Chouette hulotte	.30 .25

Miniature Sheet

Literature — A1099

No. 2404: a, Tom Lanoye, writer. b, Hugo Claus (1929-2008), writer. c, Anne Provoost, writer. d, Poetry Summers, Watou, vert. e, Redu, town with 22 book stores, vert. f, Boekenbeurs Antwerpen, vert. g, Brussels Book Fair, vert. h, Pierre Mertens, writer. i, Amélie Nothomb, writer. j, Henri Vernes, writer.

2009, Nov. 3	Photo.	Perf. 11½
2404 A1099	Sheet of 10	17.50 17.50
a.-j.	1 Any single	1.75 .85

Nos. 2404a-2404j each sold for 59c on day of issue.

A1100

Christmas A1101

Yellow panel at: No. 2406, Left. No. 2407, Right.

Booklet Stamps
Die Cut Perf. 9¾ on 2, 3 or 4 Sides

2009, Nov. 3		Self-Adhesive
2405 A1100	1 multi	1.75 .45
a.	Booklet pane of 10	17.50
2406 A1101	1 multi	2.75 1.40
2407 A1101	1 multi	2.75 1.40
a.	Booklet pane of 10, 5 each #2406-2407	27.50
	Nos. 2405-2407 (3)	7.25 3.25

On day of issue, No. 2405 sold for 59c and Nos. 2406-2407 each sold for 90c.

Mourning Stamp — A1102

Die Cut Perf. 10 on 2 or 3 Sides

2010, Jan. 4		Photo.

Booklet Stamp
Self-Adhesive

2408 A1102	1 multi	1.75 .85
a.	Booklet pane of 10	17.50

No. 2408 sold for 59c on day of issue.

Bird Type of 1985 With Euro Denominations Only

5c, Grèbe castagneux. €4.09, Faisan de colchide. €4.60, Chouette effraie.

2010	Photo.	Perf. 11½
2409 A524	5c multicolored	.25 .25
	Size: 32x23mm	
2410 A524	€4.09 multicolored	10.50 5.25
	Size: 27x32mm	
2411 A524	€4.60 multicolored	13.00 6.50
	Nos. 2409-2411 (3)	23.75 12.00

Issued: 5c, 1/18; €4.09, 6/14; €4.60, 1/4.

Organ Donation A1103

Booklet Stamps
Die Cut Perf. 10 on 2 or 3 Sides

2010, Jan. 18		Self-Adhesive
2412 A1103	1 multi	1.75 .85
a.	Booklet pane of 10	17.50

No. 2412 sold for 59c on day of issue.

Souvenir Sheet

Paul Otlet (1868-1944), Information Scientist — A1104

2010, Jan. 18	Litho.	Perf. 11½
2413 A1104	€4.60 multi	13.00 6.50

Miniature Sheet

Antverpia 2010 European Philatelic Championship, Antwerp — A1105

No. 2414: a, Magnifying glass, #2414e, 2414f, emblem of Royal National Association of Belgian Postage Stamp Circles. b, Shopping center, Antwerp. c, Antwerp Zoo. d, Museum aan de Stroom, Antwerp. e, House and self-portrait of Peter Paul Rubens, Antwerp. f, Antwerp City Hall and Cathedral.

2010, Jan. 18		
2414 A1105	Sheet of 6	18.00 18.00
a.-f.	1 Any single	3.00 3.00

Royal National Association of Belgian Postage Stamp Circles, 120th anniv. Nos. 2414a-2414f each had a franking value of 59c on the day of issue. No. 2414 sold for €6.50, with the remaining €2.96 going to Antverpia 2010.

Largo Winch, Comic Strip by Philippe Francq A1106

2010, Feb. 22		Perf. 11½
2415 A1106	1 multi	1.60 .80

Sold for 59c on day of issue.

Authors Who Lived in Brussels — A1107

Designs: No. 2416, Paul Verlaine, Arthur Rimbaud. No. 2417, Charles Baudelaire. No. 2418, Multatuli. No. 2419, Charlotte & Emily Bronte. No. 2420, Victor Hugo.

2010, Feb. 22   *Perf. 11½*
Booklet Stamps

2416	A1107	2 multi	3.25	1.60
2417	A1107	2 multi	3.25	1.60
2418	A1107	2 multi	3.25	1.60
2419	A1107	2 multi	3.25	1.60
2420	A1107	2 multi	3.25	1.60
a.		Booklet pane of 5, #2416-2420	16.50	—
		Complete booklet, #2420a	16.50	
		Nos. 2416-2420 (5)	16.25	8.00

On day of issue, Nos. 2416-2420 each sold for €1.18.

Ghent Floralies — A1108

No. 2421: a, Nicotiana alata. b, Lychnis coronaria.

2010, Mar. 15   **Photo. & Engr.**

2421	A1108	Vert. pair	3.25	1.60
a.-b.		1 Either single	1.60	.80

On day of issue, Nos. 2421a-2421b each sold for 59c.

Souvenir Sheet

Europa — A1109

No. 2422: a, Boy on books, dog reading book. b, Girl on mushroom, cat reading book.

2010, Mar. 15   **Litho.**

2422	A1109	Sheet of 2	14.50	7.25
a.-b.		3 Either single	7.25	3.50

On day of issue, Nos. 2422a-2422b each sold for €2.70.

Baby Animals
A1110

Die Cut Perf. 10 on 2 or 3 Sides
2010, Mar. 15   **Photo.**
Booklet Stamps
Self-Adhesive

2423	A1110	1 Two chicks	1.60	.80
2424	A1110	1 Two rabbits	1.60	.80
2425	A1110	1 Kitten	1.60	.80

2426	A1110	1 Two ducklings	1.60	.80
2427	A1110	1 Colt	1.60	.80
2428	A1110	1 Puppy sitting	1.60	.80
2429	A1110	1 Puppy lying	1.60	.80
2430	A1110	1 Two kittens	1.60	.80
2431	A1110	1 Head of colt	1.60	.80
2432	A1110	1 Two lambs	1.60	.80
a.		Booklet pane of 10, #2423-2432	16.00	
		Nos. 2423-2432 (10)	16.00	8.00

On day of issue, Nos. 2423-2432 each sold for 59c.

Prince Philippe, 50th Birthday A1111

2010, Apr. 15   **Litho.**   *Perf. 11½*

2433	A1111	2 multi	3.25	1.60

Sold for €1.18 on day of issue.

A1112

No. 2434 — Category and artist: a, Oceans and Seas, by Igor Volt. b, Forests, by Lander Keyaerts. c, Endangered Species, by Eva Sterkens. d, Climate, by Lucie Octave. e, Energy, by Louise Van Goylen.

2010, Apr. 15

2434		Vert. strip of 5	8.00	4.00
a.-e.	A1112	1 Any single	1.60	.80

Winning Designs in "Save the Earth" Children's Stamp Design Contest.
Nos. 2434a-2434e each sold for 59c on day of issue.

Souvenir Sheet

Antverpia 2010 European Philatelic Championship, Antwerp — A1113

2010, Apr. 15

2435	A1113	3 multi	13.50	13.50

No. 2435 sold for €5. The stamp had a franking value of €1.77 on the day of issue, with the remaining €3.23 of the sale price going to Antverpia 2010.

Miniature Sheet

Bird Paintings by André Buzin — A1114

No. 2436: a, Buse variable. b, Faucon hobereau. c, Epervier d'Europe. d, Milan royal. e, Autour des palombes.

2010, Apr. 15

2436	A1114	Sheet of 5	12.00	12.00
a.-e.		1 Any single	2.40	1.25

Use of Buzin's bird paintings on Belgium's definitive stamps, 25th anniv. Nos. 2436a-2436e each sold for 90c on day of issue.

Miniature Sheet

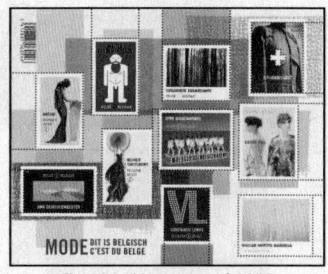

Fashion Houses — A1115

No. 2437: a, Natan (30x48mm). b, Walter Van Beirendonck (30x48mm). c, Veronique Branquinho, horiz. (43x35mm). d, A. F. Vandevorst (33x44mm). e, Olivier Theyskens (32x48mm). f, Dirk Bikkembergs, horiz. (48x38mm). g, Cathy Pill (38x48mm). h, Ann Demeulemeester, horiz. (44x27mm). i, Veronique Leroy (29x33mm). j, Maison Martin Margiela, horiz. (48x38mm).

2010, Apr. 15   **Photo.**

2437	A1115	Sheet of 10	16.00	16.00
a.-j.		1 Any single	1.60	.80

Nos. 2437a-2437j each sold for 59c on day of issue. No. 2437d has a perforated cross in the vignette.

Belgian Railways, 175th Anniv. A1116

Photo. & Engr.
2010, May 10   *Perf. 11½*

2438	A1116	2 multi	3.00	1.50

Sold for €1.18 on day of issue.

Parties — A1117

Designs: No. 2439, Man and woman with noisemakers. No. 2440, Hands holding gift and bouquet of roses. No. 2441, Man's hand holding Chinese lantern, woman wearing mask. No. 2442, Hands of servers holding trays with birthday cake and drinks. No. 2443, Girl sipping drink, boy holding balloon.

Die Cut Perf. 10 on 2 or 3 Sides
2010, May 10   **Photo.**
Booklet Stamps
Self-Adhesive
Background Color

2439	A1117	1 green	1.50	.75
2440	A1117	1 red	1.50	.75
2441	A1117	1 violet	1.50	.75
2442	A1117	1 blue	1.50	.75
2443	A1117	1 orange	1.50	.75
a.		Booklet pane of 10, 2 each #2439-2443	15.00	
		Nos. 2439-2443 (5)	7.50	3.75

Nos. 2439-2443 each sold for 59c on day of issue.

2010 World Cup Soccer Championships, South Africa — A1118

2010 Youth Olympics, Singapore A1119

Eddy Merckx, Professional Cyclist — A1120

2010, June 14   **Litho.**   *Perf. 11½*

2444	A1118	1 multi	2.25	1.10
2445	A1119	1 multi	2.75	1.40
2446	A1120	2 multi	3.00	1.50
		Nos. 2444-2446 (3)	8.00	4.00

On day of issue, No. 2444 sold for 90c, No. 2445 sold for €1.05, and No. 2446 sold for €1.18.

Independence of Belgian Congo, 50th Anniv. — A1121

2010, June 14

2447	A1121	1 multi	2.75	1.40

Sold for €1.05 on day of issue.

National Elections — A1122

2010, May 12   **Photo.**   *Perf. 11½*

2448	A1122	1 multi	.70	.35

Sold for 28c on day of issue.

Belgian Presidency of the European Union Council A1123

2010, July 1   **Litho.**   *Perf. 11½*

2449	A1123	1 multi	2.25	1.10

Sold for 90c on day of issue.

Miniature Sheet

High-rise Buildings — A1124

No. 2450: a, Le Tonneau, Brussels. b, Sint-Maartensdal, Louvain. c, Le Fer à Cheval, Brussels. d, Boerentoren, Antwerp. e, La Cité de Droixhe, Liège.

2010, Aug. 30
2450 A1124 Sheet of 5   12.00 6.25
a.-e.   1 Any single   2.40 1.25

Nos. 2450a-2450e each sold for 90c on day of issue. Imperforate sheets were gifts to standing order customers.

Fletsknooppunten A1125

Le Ravel — A1126

Die Cut Perf. 10 on 2 or 3 Sides
2010, Aug. 30   **Photo.**
Booklet Stamps
Self-Adhesive
2451 A1125 1 multi   1.60 .80
2452 A1126 1 multi   1.60 .80
a.   Booklet pane of 10, 5 each #2451-2452   16.00

Bicycle paths. Nos. 2451-2452 each sold for 59c on day of issue.

1953 Ford Mail Bus A1127

1931 Mail Train Car A1128

1979 Bedford Mail Truck A1129

1968 Mail Train Car A1130

2009 Volvo Mail Truck A1131

Photo. & Engr.
2010, Aug. 30   ***Perf. 11½***
2453 A1127 1 multi   1.60 .80
2454 A1128 1 multi   1.60 .80
2455 A1129 1 multi   1.60 .80
2456 A1130 1 multi   1.60 .80
2457 A1131 1 multi   1.60 .80
a.   Vert. strip of 5, #2453-2457   8.00 4.00
Nos. 2453-2457 (5)   8.00 4.00

On day of issue, Nos. 2453-2457 each sold for 59c.

De Mena Recreation Center, Rotselaar A1132

Telematics Center, Marche-en-Famenne — A1133

Wiels Center for Contemporary Art, Brussels — A1134

2010, Sept. 20   **Litho.**
2458 A1132 1 multi   2.50 1.25
2459 A1133 1 multi   3.00 1.50
2460 A1134 2 multi   3.25 1.60
Nos. 2458-2460 (3)   8.75 4.35

Repurposed brewery buildings. On day of issue, No. 2458 sold for 90c; No. 2459, for €1.05; No. 2460, for €1.18.

Miniature Sheet

Hesbaye Region — A1135

No. 2461: a, Blossoming orchard, Sint-Truiden (30x40mm). b, Fruit blossoms (30x40mm). c, Fruit, wine and beer (30x40mm). d, Hélécine (33x40mm). e, Farm, Perwez (49x37mm).

Perf. 11¼x11½ (#a-c), 11½ (#d-e)
2010, Sept. 20   **Photo.**
2461 A1135 Sheet of 5 + 2 labels   12.50 6.25
a.-e.   1 Any single   2.50 1.25

On day of issue, Nos. 2461a-2461e each sold for 90c.

Bpost Emblem — A1136

2010, Oct. 18   **Photo.**   ***Perf. 11½***
2462 A1136 1 multi   1.75 .85

Sold for 59c on day of issue.

Tools A1137

Tools of: No. 2463, Cordonnier (shoemaker). No. 2464, Sabotier (clog maker). No. 2465, Maréchal-ferrant (farrier). No. 2466, Blanchisseuse (washerwoman). No. 2467, Fileuse (spinner).

2010, Oct. 18   **Litho.**
2463 A1137 1 multi   1.75 .85
2464 A1137 1 multi   1.75 .85
2465 A1137 1 multi   1.75 .85
2466 A1137 1 multi   1.75 .85
2467 A1137 1 multi   1.75 .85
a.   Vert. strip of 5, #2463-2467   8.75 4.25
Nos. 2463-2467 (5)   8.75 4.25

Nos. 2463-2467 each sold for 59c on day of issue.

Pays de Connaisance A1138   Voyage Dans la Lune A1139

Un Cri — A1140

L'Etranger A1141

La Mer ce Grand Sculpteur A1142

Oiseau A1143

Waha Church Window — A1144   Pluie — A1145

Un Monde — A1146   L'Aube — A1147

Serpentine Die Cut 8
2010, Oct. 18   **Litho.**
Booklet Stamps
Self-Adhesive
2468 A1138 1 multi   1.75 .85
2469 A1139 1 multi   1.75 .85
2470 A1140 1 multi   1.75 .85
2471 A1141 1 multi   1.75 .85
2472 A1142 1 multi   1.75 .85
2473 A1143 1 multi   1.75 .85
2474 A1144 1 multi   1.75 .85
2475 A1145 1 multi   1.75 .85
2476 A1146 1 multi   1.75 .85
2477 A1147 1 multi   1.75 .85
a.   Booklet pane of 10, #2468-2477   17.50
Nos. 2468-2477 (10)   17.50 8.50

Art of Jean-Michel Folon (1934-2005). Nos. 2468-2477 each sold for 59c on day of issue.

Souvenir Sheet

Primitive Flemish Paintings — A1148

No. 2478: a, Madonna and Child, by Roger de la Pasture. b, Portrait of Laurent Froimont, by Rogier van der Weyden.

2010, Nov. 8   ***Perf. 11½***
2478 A1148 Sheet of 2   15.00 15.00
a.-b.   3 Either single   7.50 3.75

Nos. 2478a-2478b each sold for €2.70 on day of issue. See France No. 3924.

Christmas A1149

Santa Claus, reindeer and sleigh facing: No. 2479, Left. No. 2480, Right.

Die Cut Perf. 9¾ on 2 or 3 Sides
2010, Nov. 8   **Photo.**
Booklet Stamps
Self-Adhesive
2479 A1149 1 multi   1.60 .80
a.   Booklet pane of 10   16.00
2480 A1149 1 multi   2.50 1.25
a.   Booklet pane of 10   25.00

On day of issue, No. 2479 sold for 59c and No. 2480 sold for 90c.

Bird Type of 1985 With Euro Denominations Only
2011, Jan. 3   **Litho.**   ***Perf. 11½***
2481 A524 8c Canard pilet   .25 .25

Liberaliztion of Postal Market — A1150

2011, Jan. 3   Litho.   **Perf. 11½**
2482 A1150 1 multi   1.75   .85
Sold for 61c on day of issue.

Intl. Year of Chemistry A1151

2011, Jan. 17
2483 A1151 1 multi   1.75   .85
Sold for 61c on day of issue.

Signs of the Zodiac — A1152

Serpentine Die Cut 7½
2011, Jan. 17   **Self-Adhesive**
2484 A1152 1 multi   1.75   .85
Sold for 61c on day of issue. Printed in sheets of 10 + 12 stickers depicting the Zodiac signs, which could be placed on the stamp.

Homes of Authors A1153

Designs: No. 2485, La Maison Blanche, home of Maurice Carême, Anderlecht. No. 2486, Domus Erasmi, home of Desiderius Erasmus, Anderlecht. No. 2487, Het Lijsternest, home of Stijn Streuvels, Ingooigem.

2011, Jan. 17
2485 A1153 1 multi   2.60   1.25
2486 A1153 1 multi   3.00   1.50
2487 A1153 2 multi   3.50   1.75
   Nos. 2485-2487 (3)   9.10   4.50
On day of issue, No. 2485 sold for 93c; No. 2486, for €1.10; and No. 2487, for €1.22.

G. Dam, Painting by Luc Tuymans A1154

2011, Feb. 14
2488 A1154 1 multi   1.75   .85
Sold for 61c on day of issue.

European Year of the Volunteer A1155

Die Cut Perf. 9¾ on 2 or 3 Sides
2011, Feb. 14   Photo.
Booklet Stamp
Self-Adhesive
2489 A1155 1 multi   1.75   .85
  a.   Booklet pane of 10   17.50
No. 2489 sold for 61c on day of issue.

Belgian Art Masterpieces — A1156

Belgian Architecture A1157

Atomium and Manneken Pis, Brussels A1158

Tank and Mardasson Memorial, Bastogne A1159

Lion's Mound, Waterloo A1160

Serpentine Die Cut 8
2011, Feb. 14   Litho.
Booklet Stamps
Self-Adhesive
2490 A1156 1 multi   3.25   1.60
2491 A1157 1 multi   3.25   1.60
2492 A1158 1 multi   3.25   1.60
2493 A1159 1 multi   3.25   1.60
2494 A1160 1 multi   3.25   1.60
  a.   Booklet pane of 5, #2490-2494   16.50
   Nos. 2490-2494 (5)   16.25   8.00
On day of issue, Nos. 2490-2494 each sold for €1.10.

Bal du Rat Mort, Drawing by James Ensor — A1161

2011, Mar. 7   **Perf. 11½**
2495 A1161 1 multi   1.75   .85
Cercle Coecilia, 150th anniv. Sold for 61c on day of issue.

Miniature Sheet

Vegetables — A1162

No. 2496: a, Vitellote (purple potato) and topinambour (Jerusalem artichoke). b, Pâtisson (patty pan squash). c, Carotte violette (purple carrot) and panais (parsnip). d, Bette (chard). e, Cardon (cardoon).

2011, Mar. 7   Photo.
2496 A1162   Sheet of 5   15.00   15.00
  a.-e.   1 Any single   3.00   1.50
On day of issue, Nos. 2496a-2496e each sold for €1.10.

Miniature Sheet

Mining Heritage of the Campine Region — A1163

No. 2497: a, Miner's housing, Beringen (31x40mm). b, Coal (31x40mm). c, Shaft tower, railway car, As (31x40mm). d, Slagheap and countryside, Zolder (33x40mm). e, People on slagheap, Eisden (49x37mm).

2011, Apr. 4   Photo.
2497 A1163   Sheet of 5   14.00   14.00
  a.-e.   1 Any single   2.75   1.40
On day of issue, Nos. 2497a-2497e each sold for 93c.

Fair Scenes — A1164

Designs: No. 2498, Flying swings. No. 2499, Fortune-teller. No. 2500, Man and woman on carousel horses. No. 2501, Roller coaster. No. 2502, Ferris wheel. No. 2503, Shooting gallery. No. 2504, Cotton candy vendor. No. 2505, Bumper cars. No. 2506, Boy and carousel. No. 2507, Haunted house.

Die Cut Perf. 9¾ on 2 or 3 Sides
2011, Apr. 4   Photo.
Booklet Stamps
Self-Adhesive
2498 A1164 1 multi   1.75   .90
2499 A1164 1 multi   1.75   .90
2500 A1164 1 multi   1.75   .90
2501 A1164 1 multi   1.75   .90
2502 A1164 1 multi   1.75   .90
2503 A1164 1 multi   1.75   .90
2504 A1164 1 multi   1.75   .90
2505 A1164 1 multi   1.75   .90
2506 A1164 1 multi   1.75   .90
2507 A1164 1 multi   1.75   .90
  a.   Booklet pane of 10, #2498-2507   17.50
   Nos. 2498-2507 (10)   17.50   9.00
On day of issue Nos. 2498-2507 each sold for 61c.

A1165

A1166

A1167

A1168

Mailboxes A1169

Photo. & Engr.
2011, May 16   **Perf. 11½**
2508 A1165 1 multi   1.75   .90
2509 A1166 1 multi   1.75   .90
2510 A1167 1 multi   1.75   .90
2511 A1168 1 multi   1.75   .90
2512 A1169 1 multi   1.75   .90
  a.   Horiz. strip of 5, #2508-2512   8.75   4.50
   Nos. 2508-2512 (5)   8.75   4.50
On day of issue, Nos. 2518-2512 each sold for 61c.

A1170

A1171

A1172

A1173

A1174

Graffiti on De
Wand Tram
Station Walls,
Laeken — A1174

2011, May 16   **Litho.**
2513   Sheet of 5   14.00   7.00
   a.   A1170 1 multi   2.75   1.40
   b.   A1171 1 multi   2.75   1.40
   c.   A1172 1 multi   2.75   1.40
   d.   A1173 1 multi   2.75   1.40
   e.   A1174 1 multi   2.75   1.40
     On day of issue, Nos. 2513a-2513e each
sold for 93c.

Miniature Sheet

Cartoon Art — A1175

No. 2514: a, Head with crown and emoticon
face, by Marec (Marc de Cloedt) (27x38mm).
b, Laughing baby being held by ankles, by Zak
(Jacques Moeraert) (38x33mm). c, Map of
Belgium with face and arms, by Kamagurka
(Luc Zeebroek) (38x38mm). d, Large man with
club and small man sticking out tongue, by
Frédéric du Bus (38x38mm). e, Man with pencil for mouth flexing muscles by Clou (Christian Louis) (38x38mm). f, Pencil as gun, by Gal
(Gerard Alsteens) (38x33mm). g, Small jester
flipping large man off see-saw, by Pierre Kroll
(38x38mm). h, Green creature drawing happy
face on paper on soldier's back, by Nicolas
Vadot (38x38mm). i, Man in superhero costume with dog on leash, by Zaza (Klaas

Storme) (38x38mm). j, Clown lifting barbell, by
Cécile Bertrand (38x38mm).

2011, June 27   **Photo.**
2514   A1175   Sheet of 10   17.50   8.50
   a.-j.   1 Any single   1.75   .85
     On day of issue, Nos. 2514a-2514j each
sold for 61c.

Miniature Sheet

Women's Sports — A1176

No. 2515: a, Field hockey. b, Soccer. c, Basketball. d, Volleyball. e, Handball.

2011, June 27   **Litho.**
2515   A1176   Sheet of 5   16.50   8.00
   a.-e.   1 Any single   3.25   1.60
     On day of issue, Nos. 2515a-2515e each
sold for €1.10.

Posters by Henri
de Toulouse-
Lautrec (1864-
1901)
A1177

Designs: No. 2516, Confetti. No. 2517, Aris-
tide Bruant Dans son Cabaret. No. 2518, May
Milton. No. 2519, Divan Japonais. No. 2520,
Reine de Joie. No. 2521, Le Salon des Cent
(La Passagère du 54). No. 2522, Caudieux.
No. 2523, Jane Avril. No. 2524, Eldorado-Aris-
tide Bruant Dans son Cabaret. No. 2525, Mou-
lin Rouge, La Goulue.

2011, June 27   *Serpentine Die Cut 8*
Booklet Stamps
Self-Adhesive
2516   A1177   1 multi   1.75   .85
2517   A1177   1 multi   1.75   .85
2518   A1177   1 multi   1.75   .85
2519   A1177   1 multi   1.75   .85
2520   A1177   1 multi   1.75   .85
2521   A1177   1 multi   1.75   .85
2522   A1177   1 multi   1.75   .85
2523   A1177   1 multi   1.75   .85
2524   A1177   1 multi   1.75   .85
2525   A1177   1 multi   1.75   .85
   a.   Booklet pane of 10, #2516-
       2525   17.50
     Nos. 2516-2525 (10)   17.50   8.50
     On day of issue, Nos. 2516-2525 each sold
for 61c.

Miniature Sheet

Courthouses — A1178

No. 2526 — Courthouse in: a, Arlon. b,
Ghent. c, Mons. d, Antwerp. e, Charleroi.

2011, Aug. 29   **Litho.**   **Perf. 11½**
2526   A1178   Sheet of 5   17.50   8.75
   a.-e.   2 Any single   3.50   1.75
     On day of issue, Nos. 2526a-2526e each
sold for €1.22.

Miniature Sheet

Tintin — A1179

No. 2527, Scenes from Tintin cartoons,
animated and live-action films: a, Tintin and
the Crab with the Golden Claws, 1947. b, Tintin and the Crab with the Golden Claws, 1941.
c, Black Island (animated), 1961. d, Black
Island, 1938. e, Tintin and the Golden Fleece
(live-action), 1961. f, Tintin and the Blue
Oranges, 1964. g, Tintin and the Sun Temple,
1969. h, Tintin and the Sun Temple, 1949. i,
Tintin and the Blue Lotus, 1991. j, Tintin and
the Blue Lotus, 1936.

2011, Aug. 29
2527   A1179   Sheet of 10   17.50   8.75
   a.-j.   1 Any single   1.75   .85
     On day of issue, Nos. 2527a-2527j each
sold for 61c. Imperforate sheets were gifts to
standing order customers.

Souvenir Sheet

Europa — A1180

No. 2528: a, Eurasian jay. b, Fawn.

2011, Sept. 19
2528   A1180   Sheet of 2   15.50   7.50
   a.-b.   3 Either single   7.75   3.75
     Intl. Year of Forests. On day of issue, Nos.
2528a-2528b each sold for €2.79.

Bpost Emblem — A1181

2011-12   **Photo.**   **Perf. 11¾x11½**
2529   A1181   1 multi   1.75   .85
2530   A1181   2 multi   3.50   1.75
Self-Adhesive
Die Cut Perf. 11¾x11½
2531   A1181   1 multi   1.75   .85
2532   A1181   2 multi   3.50   1.75
     Issued: Nos. 2529, 2531, 9/19. Nos. 2530,
2532, 3/12/12. On day of issue, Nos. 2529 and
2531 each sold for 61c, and Nos. 2530 and
2532 each sold for €1.30.

Queen Paola and
Child — A1182

2011, Oct. 17   **Litho.**   **Perf. 11½**
2533   A1182   1 multi   1.75   .85
     No. 2533 sold for 61c on day of issue.

Miniature Sheet

Candies — A1183

No. 2534: a, Babeluttes (wrapped caramel
pieces) (25x33mm). b, Cuberdons (chocolate-
covered jellies) (26x47mm). c, Caramels
(25x33mm). d, Guimauves (marshmallows)
(26x50mm). e, Gommes (gummy bears)
(26x50mm).

2011, Oct. 17   **Photo.**
2534   A1183   Sheet of 5   13.00   13.00
   a.-e.   1 Any single   2.60   1.25
     Nos. 2534a-2534e each sold for 93c on day
of issue.

Souvenir Sheet

Europalia Intl. Arts Festival,
Brazil — A1184

No. 2535 — Brazilian Indians wearing: a,
Headdress of feathers. b, Earrings.

2011, Nov. 2   **Litho.**
2535   A1184   Sheet of 2   10.00   10.00
   a.-b.   3 Either single   5.00   2.50
     Nos. 2535a-2535b each sold for €1.83 on
day of issue.

Snowman
A1185

Angel — A1186

Die Cut Perf. 9¾ on 2 or 3 Sides
2011, Nov. 2   Photo.
Booklet Stamps
Self-Adhesive

2536	A1185	1 multi	1.75	.85
a.	Booklet pane of 10		17.50	
2537	A1186	1 multi	2.60	1.25
a.	Booklet pane of 10		26.00	

Christmas. On day of issue, Nos. 2536 and 2537 sold for 61c and 93c, respectively.

Detail From Mayan Calendar — A1187

2012, Jan. 16   Litho.   Perf. 11½

2538	A1187	1 multi	3.25	1.60

No. 2538 sold for €1.19 on day of issue.

Miniature Sheet

Trappist Beer Brands — A1188

No. 2539 — Bottle, cap and goblet of: a, Achel. b, Chimay. c, Orval. d, Rochefort. e, Westmalle. f, Westvleteren.

Perf. 11½ on 3 or 4 Sides
2012, Jan. 16

2539	A1188	Sheet of 6	16.00	16.00
a.-f.	1 Any single		2.60	1.25

Nos. 2539a-2539f each sold for 99c on day of issue.

Mythical Creatures A1189

Designs: No. 2540, Mermaid (sirène). No. 2541, Werewolf (loup-garou). No. 2542, Unicorn (licorne). No. 2543, Dragon. No. 2544, Winged serpent (amphiptère). No. 2545, Pegasus. No. 2546, Griffin (griffon). No. 2547, Centaur. No. 2548, Sphinx. No. 2549, Harpy (harpie).

Die Cut Perf. 9¾ on 2 or 3 Sides
2012, Jan. 16   Photo.
Booklet Stamps
Self-Adhesive

2540	A1189	1 multi	1.75	.85
2541	A1189	1 multi	1.75	.85
2542	A1189	1 multi	1.75	.85
2543	A1189	1 multi	1.75	.85
2544	A1189	1 multi	1.75	.85
2545	A1189	1 multi	1.75	.85
2546	A1189	1 multi	1.75	.85
2547	A1189	1 multi	1.75	.85
2548	A1189	1 multi	1.75	.85
2549	A1189	1 multi	1.75	.85
a.	Booklet pane of 10, #2540-2549		17.50	
	Nos. 2540-2549 (10)		17.50	8.50

Nos. 2540-2549 each sold for 65c on day of issue. See Nos. 2608-2617.

Souvenir Sheet

Europa — A1190

No. 2550 — Various Belgian tourist attractions with country name at: a, LL. b, UR.

2012, Feb. 13   Litho.   Perf. 11½

2550	A1190	Sheet of 2	16.00	16.00
a.-b.	3 Either single		8.00	4.00

Nos. 2550a-2550b each sold for €2.97 on day of issue.

Calligraphy — A1191

Designs: No. 2551, Latin calligraphy. No. 2552, Arabic calligraphy. No. 2553, Chinese calligraphy. No. 2554, Hindi calligraphy. No. 2555, Greek calligraphy.

Perf. 11¼x11¾
2012, Feb. 13   Photo.
Booklet Stamps

2551	A1191	1 multi	3.25	1.60
2552	A1191	1 multi	3.25	1.60
2553	A1191	1 multi	3.25	1.60
2554	A1191	1 multi	3.25	1.60
2555	A1191	1 multi	3.25	1.60
a.	Booklet pane of 5, #2551-2555		16.50	—
	Complete booklet, #2555a		16.50	
	Nos. 2551-2555 (5)		16.25	8.00

Nos. 2551-2555 each sold for €1.19 on day of issue.

Souvenir Sheet

Cartographers — A1192

No. 2556: a, Gerardus Mercator (1512-94). b, Jodocus Hondius (1563-1612).

Photo. & Engr.
2012, Mar. 12   Perf. 11½

2556	A1192	Sheet of 2	19.00	19.00
a.-b.	3 Either single		9.50	4.75

Nos. 2556a-2556b each sold for €3.57 on day of issue.

Cirque du Soleil Performers A1193

Décrocher La Lune A1194

A New Day — A1195

La Rêve A1196

The House of Dancing Water A1197

Serpentine Die Cut 8
2012, Mar. 12   Litho.
Booklet Stamps
Self-Adhesive

2557	A1193	1 multi	2.60	1.25
2558	A1194	1 multi	2.60	1.25
2559	A1195	1 multi	2.60	1.25
2560	A1196	1 multi	2.60	1.25
2561	A1197	1 multi	2.60	1.25
a.	Booklet pane of 5, #2557-2561		13.00	
	Nos. 2557-2561 (5)		13.00	6.25

Scenes from theater productions of director Franco Dragone. Nos. 2557-2561 each sold for 99c on day of issue.

Souvenir Sheet

Sinking of the Titanic, Cent. — A1198

No. 2562 — Stereoptic images of the sinking of the Titanic with top line of smoke from smokestack touching white square around "3": a, At LL corner of square. b, Directly below "3."

2012, Apr. 16   Perf. 11½

2562	A1198	Sheet of 2	19.00	19.00
a.-b.	3 Either single		9.50	4.75

Nos. 2562a-2562b each sold for €3.57 on day of issue. See Finland (Aland Islands) No. 328.

Pets — A1199

Designs: No. 2563, Canaries. No. 2564, Guinea pig. No. 2565, Cat. No. 2566, Goldfish. No. 2567, Parakeets. No. 2568, Shetland pony. No. 2569, Chihuahua. No. 2570, Hamsters. No. 2571, Rabbits. No. 2572, Dog with tongue visible.

Die Cut Perf. 9¾ on 2 or 3 Sides
2012, Apr. 16   Photo.
Booklet Stamps
Self-Adhesive

2563	A1199	1 multi	1.75	.85
2564	A1199	1 multi	1.75	.85
2565	A1199	1 multi	1.75	.85
2566	A1199	1 multi	1.75	.85
2567	A1199	1 multi	1.75	.85
2568	A1199	1 multi	1.75	.85
2569	A1199	1 multi	1.75	.85
2570	A1199	1 multi	1.75	.85
2571	A1199	1 multi	1.75	.85
2572	A1199	1 multi	1.75	.85
a.	Booklet pane of 10, #2563-2572		17.50	
	Nos. 2563-2572 (10)		17.50	8.50

Nos. 2563-2572 each sold for 65c on day of issue.

Jef Geys

Floristan Sunflower, by Jef Geys — A1200

2012, May 21   Litho.   Perf. 11½

2573	A1200	1 multi	1.75	.85

Exhibition of art by Jef Geys, Royal Museum of Fine Arts, Brussels. No. 2573 sold for 65c on day of issue.

2012 Summer Olympics, London A1201

2012, May 21

2574	A1201	1 multi	3.00	1.50

No. 2574 sold for €1.19 on day of issue.

Independence of Rwanda and Burundi, 50th Anniv. — A1202

Designs: No. 2575, Rwandan basket with lid. No. 2576, Burundian drum.

2012, May 21

2575	A1202	1 yel & multi	3.00	1.50
2576	A1202	1 red & multi	3.00	1.50

Nos. 2575-2576 each sold for €1.19 on day of issue.

Cabaret on the Banks of the River, by Jan Breughel — A1203

2012, June 25

2577	A1203	1 multi	1.60	.80

Exhibition of philatelic collection of Prince Albert II of Monaco, Bruges. No. 2577 sold for 65c on day of issue. See Monaco No. 2681.

Pieris Brassicae A1204

Papilion Machaon A1205

Die Cut Perf. 10 on 2 or 3 Sides
2012, June 25   Photo.
Booklet Stamps
Self-Adhesive

2578	A1204	1 multi	1.60	.40
a.	Booklet pane of 10		16.00	

Die Cut Perf. 10 on 3 Sides

2579	A1205	1 multi	2.50	.65
a.	Booklet pane of 5		12.50	

On day of issue No. 2578 sold for 65c and No. 2579 sold for 99c.

Volcan
Ensorcelé
A1206

A Propos de
Binche
A1207

Sans Espoir
de Bâtiment
Pour Anvers
ni Même
Pour l'Escaut
A1208

Parfois, C'est
l'Inverse
A1209

A la Ligne
A1210

Aquarelle
Estampillée
A1211

Labyrinthe
d'Apparat
A1212

Encreur
A1213

Nuages en
Pantalon
A1214

Le Dernier
Jour
A1215

2012, June 25 *Sawtooth Die Cut 8¼*
Booklet Stamps
Self-Adhesive

2580	A1206	1 multi	1.60	.80
2581	A1207	1 multi	1.60	.80
2582	A1208	1 multi	1.60	.80
2583	A1209	1 multi	1.60	.80
2584	A1210	1 multi	1.60	.80
2585	A1211	1 multi	1.60	.80
2586	A1212	1 multi	1.60	.80
2587	A1213	1 multi	1.60	.80
2588	A1214	1 multi	1.60	.80
2589	A1215	1 multi	1.60	.80
a.	Booklet pane of 10, #2580-2589		16.00	
Nos. 2580-2589 (10)			16.00	8.00

Paintings by Pierre Alechinsky. Nos. 2580-2589 each sold for 65c on day of issue.

Zenobe
Gramme,
by William
Vance
A1216

2012, Sept. 17   Litho.   Perf. 11½
2590 A1216 1 multi   1.75   .85
No. 2590 sold for 65c on day of issue.

Miniature Sheet

Comic Strip Characters — A1217

No. 2591: a, Gil and Jo (boy and parrot, yellow green background), by Jef Nys (36x24mm). b, Gaston Lagaffe (light blue background), by André Franquin (27x40mm). c, Bob and Bobette (country name in red), by Willy Vandersteen (38x24mm). d, Jerry Spring (cowboy holding hat), by Jijé (40x27mm). e, Cori le Moussaillon (boy climbing rope ladder on ship's mast), by Bob de Moor (27x40mm). f, Tintin (with dog Snowy), by Hergé (32x36mm). g, Blake and Mortimer (two men, yellow green background), by Edgar P. Jacobs (40x27mm). h, Néro (man walking), by Marc Sleen (27x40mm). i, Lucky Luke (cowboy wearing hat), by Morris (27x40mm). j, The Smurfs, by Peyo (40x27mm).

Perf. 11½, 11¾ (#2591f)
2012, Sept. 17   Photo.
2591 A1217   Sheet of 10   17.50 17.50
  a.-j.   1 Any single   1.75   .85
Nos. 2591a-2591j each sold for 65c on day of issue. Imperforate examples of No. 2591 were gifts to standing order customers.

Tree Leaves — A1218

Designs: No. 2592, Acer macrophyllum. No. 2593, Acer palmatum. No. 2594, Morus nigra. No. 2595, Sorbus alnifolia. No. 2596, Ginkgo biloba. No. 2597, Betula pendula. No. 2598, Fagus sylvatica. No. 2599, Aesculus hippocastanum. No. 2600, Euonymus europaeus. No. 2601, Quercus pondaim.

Die Cut Perf. 9¾ on 2 or 3 Sides
2012, Sept. 17   Self-Adhesive
Booklet Stamps

2592	A1218	1 multi	1.75	.85
2593	A1218	1 multi	1.75	.85
2594	A1218	1 multi	1.75	.85
2595	A1218	1 multi	1.75	.85
2596	A1218	1 multi	1.75	.85
2597	A1218	1 multi	1.75	.85
2598	A1218	1 multi	1.75	.85
2599	A1218	1 multi	1.75	.85
2600	A1218	1 multi	1.75	.85
2601	A1218	1 multi	1.75	.85
a.	Booklet pane of 10, #2592-2601		17.50	
Nos. 2592-2601 (10)			17.50	8.50

Nos. 2592-2601 each sold for 65c on day of issue.

An Offering to
Ceres, by Jacob
Jordaens — A1219

2012, Oct. 8   Litho.   Perf. 11½
2602 A1219 1 multi   1.75   .85
No. 2602 sold for 65c on day of issue.

St. Martin
Festival — A1220

2012, Oct. 8
2603 A1220 1 multi   1.75   .85
No. 2603 sold for 65c on day of issue.

Miniature Sheet

Condroz Region — A1221

No. 2604: a, Hay rolls in field (30x40mm). b, Fontaine Castle (30x40mm). c, Glasses of regional beers (30x40mm). d, Belgian blue-white cattle grazing (33x40mm). e, Dinant (49x37mm). .

Perf. 11¼x11½, 11½ (#2604d, 2604e)
2012, Oct. 8   Photo.
2604 A1221   Sheet of 5 +2 labels   13.00 13.00
  a.-e.   1 Any single   2.60   1.25
Nos. 2604a-2604e each sold for 99c on day of issue.

Apatura
Ilia — A1222

Serpentine Die Cut 13¼x14
2012, Oct. 29   Self-Adhesive
Coil Stamp
2605 A1222 1 multi   1.75   .85
No. 2605 sold for 65c on day of sale.

Christmas

A1223   A1224

Die Cut Perf. 9¾ on 2 or 3 Sides
2012, Oct. 29   Self-Adhesive
Booklet Stamps

2606	A1223	1 multi	1.75	.85
a.	Booklet pane of 10		17.50	
2607	A1224	1 multi	2.60	1.25
a.	Booklet pane of 10		26.00	

On day of issue, No. 2606 sold for 65c; No. 2607, for 99c.

Mythical Creatures Type of 2012

Designs: No. 2608, Devil (diable). No. 2609, Troll. No. 2610, Ghost (fantôme). No. 2611, Magician (magicien). No. 2612, Witch (sorcière). No. 2613, Dwarf (nain). No. 2614, Fairy (fée). No. 2615, Giant (géant). No. 2616, Prince. No. 2617, Elf.

2013, Jan. 21   Self-Adhesive
Booklet Stamps

2608	A1189	1 multi	1.90	.95
2609	A1189	1 multi	1.90	.95
2610	A1189	1 multi	1.90	.95
2611	A1189	1 multi	1.90	.95
2612	A1189	1 multi	1.90	.95
2613	A1189	1 multi	1.90	.95
2614	A1189	1 multi	1.90	.95
2615	A1189	1 multi	1.90	.95
2616	A1189	1 multi	1.90	.95
2617	A1189	1 multi	1.90	.95
a.	Booklet pane of 10, #2608-2617		19.00	
Nos. 2608-2617 (10)			19.00	9.50

Nos. 2608-2617 each sold for 67c on day of issue.

Black Grouse
A1225

2013, Jan. 21   Litho.   Perf. 11¾x11½
2618 A1225 (40c) multi   1.10   .55

Princess Mathilde,
40th
Birthday — A1226

2013, Jan. 21   Perf. 11½
2619 A1226 1 multi   1.90   .95
No. 2619 sold for 67c on day of issue.

Kid Paddle,
Animated
Cartoon by
Midam
A1227

2013, Jan. 21
2620 A1227 1 multi   1.90   .95
No. 2620 sold for 67c on day of issue.

Miniature Sheet

Road Safety — A1228

No. 2621 — Winning designs in stamp design contest: a, Road and sign with smile, by Jean-Louis Rondia. b, Automobile, traffic light, cyclist, flowers, by Ellen Labey. c, Child and woman in crosswalk, by Kiattisak Nulong. d, Snail on road at night, by Jean-Louis Verbaert. e, Cyclist and traffic light, by Antoine Buscemi.

Litho. & Silk-screened

2013, Feb. 11		Perf. 13¼x13½
2621 A1228	Sheet of 5	17.50 8.75
a.-e.	2 Any single	3.50 1.75

Nos. 2621a-2621e each sold for €1.34 on day of issue.

Souvenir Sheet

Europa — A1229

No. 2622 — Postal van facing: a, Right. b, Left.

2013, Feb. 11	Litho.	Perf. 11½
2622 A1229	Sheet of 2	16.00 8.00
a.-b.	3 Either single	8.00 4.00

Nos. 2622a-2622b each sold for €3.09 on day of issue.

Tour des Flandres Bicycle Race, Cent. — A1230

2013, Mar. 25		
2623 A1230	1 multi	1.75 .85

No. 2623 sold for 67c on day of issue.

Miniature Sheet

Chocolates — A1231

No. 2624: a, Spiral in chocolate granules. b, Stack of chocolate pieces. c, Heart-shaped candy. d, Cookie with chocolate frosting, horiz. e, Squares of chocolate and piece of candy, horiz.

2013, Mar. 25		Perf. 12
2624 A1231	Sheet of 5	16.50 8.00
a.-e.	1 Any single	3.25 1.60

Nos. 2624a-2624e each sold for €1.24 on day of issue. No. 2624 is impregnated with a chocolate scent.

Bpost Emblem — A1232

Perf. 11¾x11½

2013, Mar. 25		Photo.
Self-Adhesive		
2625 A1232	1 multi + label	2.75 1.40

No. 2625 sold for €1.03. The label shown is generic, and labels could be personalized for an additional charge. Compare with Type A1181.

Vanessa Atalanta — A1233   Aglais Urticae — A1234

Die Cut Perf. 10 on 3 Sides

2013, Mar. 25	Self-Adhesive
Booklet Stamps	
2626 A1233	1 multi	3.25 1.60
a.	Booklet pane of 5	16.50
2627 A1234	2 multi	3.50 1.75
a.	Booklet pane of 5	17.50

On day of issue No. 2626 sold for €1.24, and No. 2627 sold for €1.34.

Souvenir Sheet

First Airmail Flight in Deperdussin Monoplane, Cent. — A1235

No. 2628 — Monoplane: a, On ground at Saint-Denis-Westrem. b, In air at Berchem-Sainte-Agathe.

Photo. & Engr.

2013, Apr. 15		Perf. 11½
2628 A1235	Sheet of 2	16.50 8.25
a.-b.	3 Either single	8.25 4.00

On day of issue, Nos. 2628a-2628b each sold for €3.09.

The Valley of the Sambre A1236

The Promenade A1237

Summer Afternoon (Tea in the Garden) A1238

Arab Fantasy A1239

Portrait of Marguerite Van Mons A1240

Marie Sèthe at the Harmonium A1241

Bathing Woman A1242

Sisters of the Painter Schlobach A1243

A Reading by Emile Verhaeren A1244

The Artist's Wife and Daughter A1245

Sawtooth Die Cut 8¼

2013, Apr. 15		Litho.
Booklet Stamps		
Self-Adhesive		
2629 A1236	1 multi	1.75 .85
2630 A1237	1 multi	1.75 .85
2631 A1238	1 multi	1.75 .85
2632 A1239	1 multi	1.75 .85
2633 A1240	1 multi	1.75 .85
2634 A1241	1 multi	1.75 .85
2635 A1242	1 multi	1.75 .85
2636 A1243	1 multi	1.75 .85
2637 A1244	1 multi	1.75 .85
2638 A1245	1 multi	1.75 .85
a.	Booklet pane of 10, #2629-2638	17.50
	Nos. 2629-2638 (10)	17.50 8.50

Paintings by Théo van Rysselberghe (1862-1926). On day of issue, Nos. 2629-2638 each sold for 67c.

Opera Houses and Scenes from Operas by Richard Wagner (1813-83) and Giuseppe Verdi (1813-1901) A1246

Designs: No. 2639, Ghent Opera House, scene from Das Rheingold, by Wagner. No. 2640, Antwerp Opera House, scene from Don Carlos, by Verdi. No. 2641, Brussels Opera House (at UR), scene from Macbeth, by Verdi. No. 2642, Brussels Opera House (at UL), scene from Parsifal, by Wagner. No. 2643, Liège Opera House, scene from Otello, by Verdi

Photo. & Engr.

2013, May 13		Perf. 11½
Booklet Stamps		
2639 A1246	1 multi	2.75 1.40
2640 A1246	1 multi	2.75 1.40
2641 A1246	1 multi	2.75 1.40
2642 A1246	1 multi	2.75 1.40
2643 A1246	1 multi	2.75 1.40
a.	Booklet pane of 5, #2639-2643	14.00 —
	Complete booklet, #2643a	14.00
	Nos. 2639-2643 (5)	13.75 7.00

On day of issue, Nos. 2639-2643 each sold for €1.03.

Animals in Antwerp Zoo — A1247

Designs: No. 2644, Eyes of owl. No. 2645, Trunk of elephant. No. 2646, Nose and mouth of lion. No. 2647, Heads of two penguins. No. 2648, Head of seal. No. 2649, Head of zebra. No. 2650, Eye of tiger. No. 2651, Eyes of lion tamarin. No. 2652, Head and hindquarters of okapi. No. 2653, Necks of giraffes.

Die Cut Perf. 10 on 2 or 3 Sides

2013, May 13		Photo.
Booklet Stamps		
Self-Adhesive		
2644 A1247	1 multi	1.90 .95
2645 A1247	1 multi	1.90 .95
2646 A1247	1 multi	1.90 .95
2647 A1247	1 multi	1.90 .95
2648 A1247	1 multi	1.90 .95
2649 A1247	1 multi	1.90 .95
2650 A1247	1 multi	1.90 .95
2651 A1247	1 multi	1.90 .95
2652 A1247	1 multi	1.90 .95
2653 A1247	1 multi	1.90 .95
a.	Booklet pane of 10, #2644-2653	19.00
	Nos. 2644-2653 (10)	19.00 9.50

On day of issue, Nos. 2644-2653 each sold for 67c.

Music Festivals A1248

2013, June 24		Litho.	Perf. 11½
2654 A1248	1 multi	1.75 .85

No. 2654 sold for 67c on day of issue.

Arab Fantasy A1239 section — A1240 Portrait... A Reading by Emile Verhaeren A1244

Miniature Sheet

Royal Meteorological Institue,
Cent. — A1249

No. 2655: a, Royal Meteorological Institute
Building (60x30mm). b, Cloud over Sun, tree
in spring (40x30mm). c, Sun over tree in summer (40x30mm). d, Rain cloud over tree in
autumn (40x30mm). e, Snow cloud over tree
in winter (40x30mm).

Perf. 13¼ (#2655a), 13x13¼

2013, June 24
2655   A1249   Sheet of 5   14.00 7.00
  a.-e.   1 Any single   2.75 1.40

On day of issue, Nos. 2655a-2655e each
sold for €1.03. The leaves on the trees on
Nos. 2655b-2655e are printed in
thermochromic ink and change colors when
the stamp is warmed.

Souvenir Sheet

Twenty Year Reign of King Albert
II — A1250

No. 2656 — King Albert II wearing: a, Uniform and sash. b, Overcoat and scarf.

2013, June 24   **Perf. 11½**
2656   A1250   Sheet of 2   16.50 8.25
  a.-b.   3 Either single   8.25 4.00

On day of issue, Nos. 2656a-2656b each
sold for €3.09.

Souvenir Sheet

Belgian Kings — A1251

No. 2657: a, King Philippe (crown at UL). b,
King Albert II (crown at UR).

2013, Sept. 2   Litho.   Perf. 11½
2657   A1251   Sheet of 2   16.50 8.50
  a.-b.   3 Either single   8.25 4.25

Abdication of King Albert II and ascension to
throne of King Philippe. Nos. 2657a-2657b
each sold for €3.09 on day of issue.

Lily — A1252

Die Cut Perf. 9¾ on 2 or 3 Sides
2013, Sept. 13   Photo.
Booklet Stamp
Self-Adhesive
2658   A1252   1 multi   1.90 .95
  a.   Booklet pane of 10   19.00

No. 2658 sold for 67c on day of issue.

Good Luck
Symbols — A1253

Designs: No. 2659, Hand with crossed fingers. No. 2660, Numeral "7." No. 2661, Horseshoe. No. 2662, Four-leaf clover. No. 2663,
Ladybug.

Die Cut Perf. 9¾ on 2 or 3 Sides
2013, Sept. 13   Litho.
Booklet Stamps
Self-Adhesive
2659   A1253   1 multi   1.90 .95
2660   A1253   1 multi   1.90 .95
2661   A1253   1 multi   1.90 .95
2662   A1253   1 multi   1.90 .95
2663   A1253   1 multi   1.90 .95
  a.   Booklet pane of 10, 2 each
           #2659-2663   19.00
  Nos. 2659-2663 (5)   9.50 4.75

Nos. 2659-2663 each sold for 67c on day of
issue.

Souvenir Sheet

Household Items Created by Henry
Van de Velde (1863-1957), Interior
Designer — A1254

No. 2664: a, Candelabra. b, Chair.

2013, Sept. 13   Litho.   Perf. 13½x14
2664   A1254   Sheet of 2   16.50 8.50
  a.-b.   3 Either single   8.25 4.25

Nos. 2664a-2664b each sold for €3.09 on
day of issue.

International Red Cross, 150th
Anniv. — A1255

2013, Oct. 28   Litho.   Perf. 11½
2665   A1255   1 multi   3.50 1.75

No. 2665 sold for €1.24 on day of issue.
See Spain No. 3939.

Photograph
From Red
Star Line
Museum,
Antwerp
A1256

Photograph
From War
Museum,
Bastogne
A1257

Photographs From Dossin Barracks
Museum of Deportation and
Resistance, Mechlin — A1258

2013, Oct. 28   Litho.   Perf. 11½
2666   A1256   1 multi   1.90   .95
2667   A1257   1 multi   1.90   .95
2668   A1258   1 multi   1.90   .95
  Nos. 2666-2668 (3)   5.70 2.85

Nos. 2666-2668 each sold for 67c on day of
issue.

Christmas
A1259   A1260

Die Cut Perf. 9¾ on 2 or 3 Sides
2013, Oct. 28   Photo.
Booklet Stamps
Self-Adhesive
2669   A1259   1 multi   1.90   .95
  a.   Booklet pane of 10   19.00
2670   A1260   1 multi   2.75 1.40
  a.   Booklet pane of 10   27.50

On day of issue No. 2669 sold for 67c and
No. 2670 sold for €1.03.

A1261   A1262

King Philippe
A1263

Perf. 11¾x11½
2013, Oct. 28   Photo.
2671   A1261   1 multi   2.10   .55
2672   A1262   1 Europe multi   3.00   .75
2673   A1263   1 World multi   3.75   .95
  Nos. 2671-2673 (3)   8.85 2.25

On day of issue, Nos. 2671-2673 sold for
77c, €1.13, and €1.34, respectively, but each
stamp sold for 10c less if purchased in quantities of 10.
Compare types A1262-A1263 with types
A1361-A1362.

French Bulldog
A1264

Bichon Maltese
Mix
A1265

Belgian
Malinois
A1266

Golden
Retriever
A1267

Yorkshire
Terrier
A1268

Border Collie
A1269

Poodle
A1270

Cocker Spaniel
A1271

Chihuahua
A1272

Jack Russell
Terrier
A1273

Die Cut Perf. 10 on 2 or 3 Sides
2014, Jan. 27   Litho.
Booklet Stamps
Self-Adhesive
2674   A1264   1 multi   1.90   .95
2675   A1265   1 multi   1.90   .95
2676   A1266   1 multi   1.90   .95
2677   A1267   1 multi   1.90   .95
2678   A1268   1 multi   1.90   .95
2679   A1269   1 multi   1.90   .95
2680   A1270   1 multi   1.90   .95
2681   A1271   1 multi   1.90   .95
2682   A1272   1 multi   1.90   .95
2683   A1273   1 multi   1.90   .95
  a.   Booklet pane of 10, #2674-
           2683   19.00
  Nos. 2674-2683 (10)   19.00 9.50

Nos. 2674-2683 each sold for 70c on day of
issue.

Miniature Sheet

Flora in Meise Botanical
Garden — A1274

No. 2684: a, Amorphophallus. b, Lithops. c,
Nepenthes. d, Myrmecodia. e, Strongylodon.

2014, Jan. 27   Perf. 11½
2684   A1274   Sheet of 5   19.00 9.50
  a.-e.   2 Any single   3.75 1.90

Nos. 2684a-2684e each sold for €1.40 on
day of issue.

The Son,
Painting by
Michael
Borremans
A1275

2014, Feb. 17   Litho.   Perf. 11½
2685   A1275   1 multi   2.00 1.00

No. 2685 sold for 70c on day of issue.

Miniature Sheet

Paintings of Mammals by André Buzin — A1276

No. 2686: a, Lapin de garenne (European rabbits). b, Renard (foxes). c, Lynx. d, Chevreuil (roe deer). e, Sanglier (wild pigs).

2014, Feb. 17   Litho.   Perf. 11½
2686 A1276   Sheet of 5   20.00 10.00
a.-e.   2 Any single   4.00   2.00

Nos. 2686a-2686e each sold for €1.40 on day of issue.

International Women's Day — A1277

2014, Mar. 10   Litho.   Perf. 11½
2687 A1277 1 World black   3.50 1.75
No. 2687 sold for €1.29 on day of issue.

Earth Hour — A1278

Litho. & Silk-Screened
2014, Mar. 10   Perf. 12
2688 A1278 1 World multi   3.50 1.75
No. 2688 sold for €1.29 on day of issue.

Miniature Sheet

Anatomical Drawings by Andreas Vesalius (1514-64) — A1279

No. 2689: a, Nude man. b, Skeleton. c, Nervous system. d, Muscular system. e, Circulatory system.

Photo. & Engr.
2014, Apr. 22   Perf. 11½
2689 A1279   Sheet of 5   20.00 10.00
a.-e.   2 Any single   4.00   2.00

Nos. 2689a-2689e each sold for €1.40 on day of issue. See Portugal No. 3592.

Tintin — A1280

Bianca Castafiore A1281

Thomson and Thompson A1282

Snowy — A1283

Professor Calculus — A1284

Captain Haddock — A1285

Abdullah — A1286

Chang Chong-Chen A1287

General Alcazar — A1288

Nestor — A1289

Die Cut Perf. 10 on 2 or 3 Sides
2014, Apr. 22   Photo.
Booklet Stamps
Self-Adhesive
2690	A1280	1 multi	2.00	1.00
2691	A1281	1 multi	2.00	1.00
2692	A1282	1 multi	2.00	1.00
2693	A1283	1 multi	2.00	1.00
2694	A1284	1 multi	2.00	1.00
2695	A1285	1 multi	2.00	1.00
2696	A1286	1 multi	2.00	1.00
2697	A1287	1 multi	2.00	1.00
2698	A1288	1 multi	2.00	1.00
2699	A1289	1 multi	2.00	1.00
a.		Booklet pane of 10, #2690-2699	20.00	
	Nos. 2690-2699 (10)		20.00	10.00

Nos. 2690-2699 each sold for 70c on day of issue.

2014 World Cup Soccer Championships, Brazil — A1290

2014, June 10   Litho.   Perf. 12
2700 A1290 1 Europa multi   3.00 1.50
No. 2700 sold for €1.07 on day of issue.

2014 Men's Field Hockey World Cup, The Hague, Netherlands A1291

2014, June 10   Litho.   Perf. 11½
2701 A1291 1 World multi   3.50 1.75
No. 2701 sold for €1.29 on day of issue.

Souvenir Sheet

International Year of Crystallography — A1292

No. 2702 — Snowflake and molecular diagrams for ice with: a, 10 red atoms. b, 20 red atoms in cube.

Serpentine Die Cut 8½x9
2014, June 10   Silk-Screened
On Polyester Film
Self-Adhesive
2702 A1292   Sheet of 2   17.00
a.-b.   3 World Either single   8.50   4.25

Nos. 2702a-2702b each sold for €3.07 on day of issue. See Slovenia No. 1050.

Wallonia Mines UNESCO World Heritage Sites — A1293

Photo. & Engr.
2014, July 7   Perf. 11½
2703 A1293 1 World black   3.50 1.75
No. 2703 sold for €1.29 on day of issue. Printed in sheets of 5.

Souvenir Sheet

Europa — A1294

No. 2704: a, Saxophone. b, Musician playing saxophone.

Litho. & Embossed (#2704a), Litho. (#2704b)
2014, July 7   Perf. 11½
2704 A1294   Sheet of 2   17.50 8.75
a.-b.   3 Europe Either single   8.75   4.25

Nos. 2704a-2704b each sold for €3.21 on day of issue.

Souvenir Sheet

Panama Canal, Cent. — A1295

No. 2705: a, Construction of Panama Canal. b, Ship passing through Panama Canal.

2014, July 7   Litho.   Perf. 11½
2705 A1295   Sheet of 2   21.00 10.50
a.-b.   3 World Either single   10.50   5.25

Nos. 2705a-2705b each sold for €3.87 on day of issue.

Blood Will Tell — A1296

Portrait of Adrienne Crowet A1297

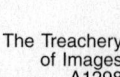

The Treachery
of Images
A1298

Golconda
A1299

The Great Family
A1300

Discovery
A1301

The Domain of
Arnheim
A1302

The Empire of
Lights
A1303

Personal
Values
A1304

The Breast
A1305

Sawtooth Die Cut 8¼x8¾, 8¾x8¼
2014, Sept. 8   Litho.
Booklet Stamps
Self-Adhesive

2706	A1296 1 multi	1.90	.95
2707	A1297 1 multi	1.90	.95
2708	A1298 1 multi	1.90	.95
2709	A1299 1 multi	1.90	.95
2710	A1300 1 multi	1.90	.95
2711	A1301 1 multi	1.90	.95
2712	A1302 1 multi	1.90	.95
2713	A1303 1 multi	1.90	.95
2714	A1304 1 multi	1.90	.95
2715	A1305 1 multi	1.90	.95
a.	Booklet pane of 10, #2706-2715	19.00	
	Nos. 2706-2715 (10)	19.00	9.50

Paintings by René Magritte (1898-1967).
Nos. 2706-2715 each sold for 70c on day of
issue.

Le Petit
Spirou,
Comic Strip
by Tome
and Janry
A1306

2014, Oct. 6   Litho.   Perf. 11½
2716 A1306 1 multi   1.75   .85
No. 2716 sold for 70c on day of issue.

Locomotives
A1307

2014, Oct. 6   Litho.   Perf. 11½
2717 A1307 2 multi   3.50   1.75
No. 2717 sold for €1.40 on day of issue and
was issued in sheets of 5.

Miniature Sheet

World War I, Cent. — A1308

No. 2718 — War events of 1914: a, Execution of civilians of Dinant (40x30mm). b, Refugees (37x49mm). c, Withdrawal of Belgian
forces along the Meuse River (40x30mm). d,
Attack of Belgians along Yser Front
(40x33mm). e, Destruction of Leuven University Library (40x30mm).

2014, Oct. 16   Photo.   Perf. 11½
2718 A1308 Sheet of 5 + 2
            labels   17.50   8.75
a.-e.   2 Any single   3.50   1.75
On day of issue, Nos. 2718a-2718e each
sold for €1.40.

A1309

A1310

A1311

A1312

A1313

A1314

A1315

A1316

A1317

Butterflies
A1318

Serpentine Die Cut 14
2014, Oct. 6   Self-Adhesive   Litho.
Coil Stamps

2719	A1309 1 multi	1.75	.85
2720	A1310 1 multi	1.75	.85
2721	A1311 1 multi	1.75	.85
2722	A1312 1 multi	1.75	.85
2723	A1313 1 multi	1.75	.85
2724	A1314 1 multi	1.75	.85
2725	A1315 1 multi	1.75	.85
2726	A1316 1 multi	1.75	.85
2727	A1317 1 multi	1.75	.85
2728	A1318 1 multi	1.75	.85
a.	Horiz. strip of 10, #2719-2728	17.50	
	Nos. 2719-2728 (10)	17.50	8.50

On day of issue, Nos. 2719-2728 each sold
for 70c.

Miniature Sheet

Optical Illusions — A1319

No. 2729: a, Clown's face in tea set and
fruit. b, Pencils. c, Cubes. d, Key and silhouette of man. e, "2" hidden in lines.

2014, Oct. 27   Litho.   Perf. 11½
2729 A1319 Sheet of 5   17.50   8.75
a.-e.   2 Any single   3.50   1.75
Nos. 2729a-2729e each sold for €1.40 on
day of issue.

A1320

Christmas
A1321

Die Cut Perf. 9¾ on 2 or 3 Sides
2014, Oct. 27   Photo.
Booklet Stamps
Self-Adhesive

2730	A1320 1 multi	1.75	.85
a.	Booklet pane of 10	17.50	
2731	A1321 1 Europe multi	2.75	1.40
a.	Booklet pane of 10	27.50	

On day of issue, No. 2730 sold for 70c and
No. 2731 sold for €1.07.

Thorgal,
Comic
Book
Character
Drawn by
Grzegorz
Rosinski
A1322

2015, Jan. 26   Litho.   Perf. 11½
2732 A1322 2 multi   3.25   1.60
No. 2732 sold for €1.44 on day of issue.

King
Philippe — A1323

Die Cut Perf. 10 on 2 or 3 Sides
2015, Jan. 26   Litho.
Booklet Stamps
Self-Adhesive
Background Color

2733	A1323 1 red	1.75	.45
a.	Booklet pane of 10	17.50	
2734	A1323 2 yel orange	3.25	.80
a.	Booklet pane of 5	16.50	

On day of issue, Nos. 2733-2734 sold for
72c and €1.44, respectively. Compare with
type A1261.

A1324

A1325

A1326

A1327

A1328

A1329

A1330

A1331

A1332

A1333

Die Cut Perf. 10x10¼
2015, Jan. 26   Litho.
Booklet Stamps
Self-Adhesive

2735	A1324 1 multi	1.75	.85
2736	A1325 1 multi	1.75	.85
2737	A1326 1 multi	1.75	.85
2738	A1327 1 multi	1.75	.85
2739	A1328 1 multi	1.75	.85
2740	A1329 1 multi	1.75	.85
2741	A1330 1 multi	1.75	.85
2742	A1331 1 multi	1.75	.85
2743	A1332 1 multi	1.75	.85

2744	A1333	1 multi	1.75	.85
a.	Booklet pane of 10, #2735-2744		17.50	
	Nos. 2735-2744 (10)		17.50	8.50

On day of issue, Nos. 2735-2744 each sold for 72c.

Miniature Sheet

Queen Fabiola (1928-2014) — A1334

No. 2795 — Queen Fabiola: a, Wearing tiara (image used for #B729). b, Wearing scarf, with King Baudoin (image used for #2300a). c, Wearing tiara and necklace (image ussed for #B1125). d, With King Baudoin (image used for #B1095). e, Without tiara (image used for #2300b).

2015, Jan. 26	Litho.	Perf. 11½
2745 A1334	Sheet of 5	16.50 16.50
a.-e.	2 Any single	3.25 1.60

Nos. 2745a-2745e each sold for €1.44 on day of issue.

Miniature Sheet

Tapestries — A1335

No. 2746: a, The Storm, by Liliane Badin, 1963. b, Tantra on Yellow, by Jan Yoors, 1977. c, The Picking, by Edmond Dubrunfaut, 1962. d, History of Jacob: Sharing of the Livestock, by Bernard van Orley and Willem de Kempeneere, 1525-50. e, History of Hercules: Conquest of the Island of Sheep, by unknown creator, 15th cent.

2015, Jan. 26	Litho.	Perf. 11½
2746 A1335	Sheet of 5	16.50 16.50
a.-e.	2 Any single	3.25 1.60

Nos. 2746a-2746e each sold for €1.44 on day of issue.

Miniature Sheet

Birds and Mammals — A1336

No. 2747: a, Oie cendrée (graylag goose). b, Cygne tuberculé (mute swan). c, Héron cendré (gray heron). d, Grand-duc (Eurasian eagle-owl). e, Foulque macroule (Eurasian coot). f, Cerf rouge (red deer). g, Hermine (ermine). h, Loutre d'Europe (European otter). i, Lièvre brun (brown hare). j, Ecureuil roux (red squirrel).

2015, Mar. 23	Litho.	Perf. 12½
2747 A1336	Sheet of 10	16.00 16.00
a.-j.	1 Any single	1.60 .80

Nos. 2747a-2747j each sold for 72c on day of issue.

Miniature Sheet

World War I, Cent. — A1337

No. 2748 — Events of 1915: a, Prime Minister Henri Jaspar, health examination of child (40x30mm). b, Red Cross worker serving food to soldiers (37x49mm). c, Food distribution, bag of flour (40x30mm). d, Bread ration ticket, soldier sharing food with child (40x33mm). e, Belgian government officials in exile in Saint-Adresse, France, Ministerial residence, mail box (40x30mm).

2015, Mar. 23	Litho.	Perf. 11½
2748 A1337	Sheet of 5	12.50 12.50
a.-e.	1 Europe Any single	2.50 1.25

Nos. 2748a-2748e each sold for €1.10 on day of issue. See France No. 4778-4779.

Bpost Emblem — A1338

2015, Apr. 13	Self-Adhesive	Perf. 11¾x11½ Photo.
2749 A1338	1 World multi	3.00 1.50

No. 2749 sold for €1.32 on day of issue.

Souvenir Sheet

Europa — A1339

No. 2750: a, Girls playing with hoop. b, Boys with soccer ball.

2015, Apr. 13	Litho.	Perf. 11½
2750 A1339	Sheet of 2	15.00 15.00
a.-b.	3 Europe Either single	7.50 3.75

Nos. 2750a-2750b each sold for €3.30 on day of issue.

Lucky Luke — A1340

Jolly Jumper — A1341

Rantanplan A1342

Joe Dalton A1343

Ma Dalton — A1344

Hank Bully — A1345

Jesse James — A1346

Indian — A1347

Billy the Kid — A1348

Calamity Jane — A1349

Die Cut Perf. 10 on 2 or 3 Sides
2015, Apr. 13				Litho.

Booklet Stamps
Self-Adhesive

2751	A1340	1 multi	1.75	.85
2752	A1341	1 multi	1.75	.85
2753	A1342	1 multi	1.75	.85
2754	A1343	1 multi	1.75	.85
2755	A1344	1 multi	1.75	.85
2756	A1345	1 multi	1.75	.85
2757	A1346	1 multi	1.75	.85
2758	A1347	1 multi	1.75	.85
2759	A1348	1 multi	1.75	.85
2760	A1349	1 multi	1.75	.85
a.	Booklet pane of 10, #2751-2760		17.50	
	Nos. 2751-2760 (10)		17.50	8.50

Lucky Luke cartoon characters, drawn by Morris. Nos. 2751-2760 each sold for 72c on day of issue.

Queen Elisabeth (1876-1965) A1350

Queen Elisabeth: No. 2761, Wearing tiara, 1923. No. 2762, Playing violin, c. 1908.

2015, May 11	Photo. & Engr.	Perf. 11½
2761 A1350	1 multi	1.60 .80
2762 A1350	1 multi	1.60 .80

Nos. 2761-2762 were printed in sheets of 10 containing five of each stamp. Each sold for 72c on day of issue. Imperforate sheets of 10 were given as gifts to standing order customers.

Miniature Sheet

Camouflaged Insects — A1351

No. 2763: a, Phromnia rosea on plant stem). b, Gastropacha quercifolia (brown insect on leaf). c, Phyllium giganteum. d, Haaniella dehaanii on stem with thorns. e, Hymenopus coronatus on flower.

2015, May 11	Litho.	Perf. 11½
2763 A1351	Sheet of 5	16.50 16.50
a.-e.	2 Any single	3.25 1.60

Nos. 2763a-2763e each sold for €1.44 on day of issue.

Miniature Sheet

Battle of Waterloo, 200th Anniv. — A1352

No. 2764: a, Arthur Wellesley, first Duke of Wellington (1769-1852). b, Gebhard Leberecht von Blücher (1742-1819). c, William, Prince of Orange (1792-1849). d, Michel Ney (17691-1815). e, Napoleon Bonaparte (1769-1821).

2015, June 1	Photo. & Engr.	Perf. 11½
2764 A1352	Sheet of 5	12.50 12.50
a.-e.	1 Europe Any single	2.50 1.25

Nos. 2764a-2764e each sold for €1.10 on day of issue.

Shrimp Fisherman on Horseback of Oostduinkerke — A1353

2015, June 29	Litho.	Perf. 11½
2765 A1353	1 World blk & gray	3.00 1.50

No. 2765 sold for €1.32 on day of issue.

Miniature Sheet

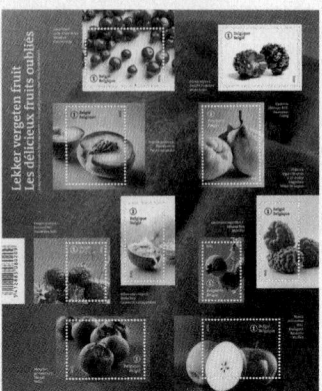

Fruit — A1354

No. 2766: a, Vaccinium oxycoccus (cranberries, 40x30mm). b, Morus nigra (black mulberries, 40x30mm). c, Prunus persica (peaches, 30x40mm). d, Cydonia oblonga (quinces, 30x40mm). e, Ribes uva-crispa (gooseberry, 20x40mm). f, Rubus x loganobacus (loganberries, 20x40mm). g, Fragaria vesca (wild strawberries, 20x30mm). h, Vaccinium myrtillus (European blueberries, 20x30mm). i, Mespilus germanica (medlars, 40x30mm). j, Malus domestica (apples, 40x30mm).

2015, June 29   Litho.   Perf. 12

| 2766 | A1354 | Sheet of 10 | 16.00 | 16.00 |
| a.-j. | | 1 Any single | 1.60 | .80 |

Nos. 2766a-2766j each sold for 72c on day of issue.

European Women's Volleyball Championships, Belgium and the Netherlands A1355

2015, Sept. 7   Litho.   Perf. 12

| 2767 | A1355 | 1 Europe multi | 2.50 | 1.25 |

No. 2767 sold for €1.10 on day of issue.

Dinosaurs A1356

Die Cut Perf. 10 on 2 or 3 Sides

2015, Sept. 7   Litho.

Booklet Stamps
Self-Adhesive

2768	A1356	1 Giraffatitan	1.60	.80
2769	A1356	1 Torvosaurus	1.60	.80
2770	A1356	1 Olorotitan	1.60	.80
2771	A1356	1 Deinonychus	1.60	.80
2772	A1356	1 Aurornis	1.60	.80
2773	A1356	1 Ankylosaurus	1.60	.80
2774	A1356	1 Finiosaurus	1.60	.80
2775	A1356	1 Pteranodon	1.60	.80
2776	A1356	1 Iguanodon	1.60	.80
2777	A1356	1 Kentrosaurus	1.60	.80
a.		Booklet pane of 10, #2768-2777	16.00	
		Nos. 2768-2777 (10)	16.00	8.00

On day of issue, Nos. 2768-2777 each sold for 72c.

No. 2774 description is spelled wrong (Finiosaurus), it should be Einiosaurus.

Miniature Sheet

Hot Air Balloons — A1357

No. 2778: a, Orange and red OO-SWF balloon. b, Belgica balloon. c, Le Flesselles balloon. d, Burner firing in gondola under blue balloon. e, Funny Bunny balloon, ballons in background.

Photo. & Engr., Photo. (#2778a, 2778d, 2778e)

2015, Sept. 7   Perf. 11½

| 2778 | A1357 | Sheet of 5 | 16.50 | 8.25 |
| a.-e. | | 2 Any single | 3.25 | 1.60 |

On day of issue, Nos. 2778a-2778e each sold for €1.44.

Souvenir Sheet

Manuscript Illuminations Depicting Nativity — A1358

No. 2779 — Illustration from: a, Bible with Raphael d'Urbino illustrations (Mary at right). b, Breviary of Philippe le Bon (Mary at left).

2015, Oct. 26   Litho.   Perf. 11½

| 2779 | A1358 | Sheet of 2 | 14.50 | 7.25 |
| a.-b. | | 3 Europe Either single | 7.25 | 3.50 |

On day of issue, Nos. 2779a-2779b both sold for €3.30.

Christmas
A1359   A1360

Die Cut Perf. 10 on 2 or 3 Sides

2015, Oct. 26   Litho.

Booklet Stamps
Self-Adhesive

2780	A1359	1 red & multi	1.60	.80
a.		Booklet pane of 10	16.00	
2781	A1360	1 Europe green	2.50	1.25
a.		Booklet pane of 10	25.00	

A1361   King Philippe — A1362

Die Cut Perf. 10 on 3 Sides

2016, Mar. 14   Litho.

Booklet Stamps
Self-Adhesive

2782	A1361	1 Europe multi	2.60	.65
a.		Booklet pane of 5	13.00	
2783	A1362	1 World multi	3.25	.80
a.		Booklet pane of 5	16.50	

On day of issue, No. 2782 sold for €1.13 and No. 2783 sold for €1.35. Compare types A1361-A1362 with types A1262-A1263.

Cédric, Comic Strip by Raoul Cauvin and B. D. Laudec, 30th Anniv. A1363

2016, Mar. 14   Litho.   Perf. 11½

| 2784 | A1363 | 2 multi | 3.50 | 1.75 |

No. 2784 sold for €1.48 on day of issue.

Emile Verhaeren (1855-1916), Poet — A1364

2016, Mar. 14   Litho.   Perf. 12½

| 2785 | A1364 | 2 multi | 3.50 | 1.75 |

No. 2785 sold for €1.48 on day of issue.

Princess Elisabeth A1365

Prince Gabriel — A1366

Prince Emmanuel A1367

Princess Eléonore A1368

Royal Family — A1369

2016, Mar. 14   Litho.   Perf. 12

2786	A1365	1 multi	1.75	.85
2787	A1366	1 multi	1.75	.85
2788	A1367	1 multi	1.75	.85
2789	A1368	1 multi	1.75	.85
2790	A1369	1 multi	1.75	.85
a.		Horiz. strip of 5, #2786-2790	8.75	4.25
		Nos. 2786-2790 (5)	8.75	4.25

On day of issue, Nos. 2786-2790 each sold for 74c.

Miniature Sheet

Job Training — A1370

No. 2791: a, Dredge near island, Abu Dhabi (30x40mm). b, Person playing carillon (40x30mm). c, Building under construction and completed building (40x40mm). d, Item made by 3-d printer (40x30mm). e, People painting airplane wing (30x40mm).

2016, Mar. 14   Litho.   Perf. 12

| 2791 | A1370 | Sheet of 5 | 13.00 | 13.00 |
| a.-e. | | 1 Europe Any single | 2.60 | 1.40 |

On day of issue, Nos. 2791a-2791e each sold for €1.13.

Europa A1371

2016, June 13   Litho.   Perf. 11½

| 2792 | A1371 | 1 Europe multi | 2.60 | 1.40 |

Think Green Issue.
No. 2792 sold for €1.13 on day of issue.

Miniature Sheet

Birds and Flowers of Zwin Nature Park — A1372

No. 2793: a, Tadorna tadorna flying right (30x40mm). b, Sterna hirundo flying right (40x30mm). c, Hirundo rustica flying left (30x30mm). d, Recurvirostra avosetta flying left (30x40mm). e, Platalea leucorodia standing (30x40mm). f, Salicornia pusilla (green & brown rose plant, 30x40mm). g, Spergularia media (purple flower, 40x30mm). h, Limonium vulgare (purple flower, 30x30mm). i, Glaux maritima (pink flower, 30x40mm). j, Atriplex pedunculata (green and brown plant, 30x40mm).

2016, June 13   Litho.   *Perf. 12*
2793 A1372   Sheet of 10   17.50 17.50
a.-j.   1 Any single   1.75   .85
On day of issue, Nos. 2793a-2793j each sold for 74c.

Miniature Sheet

Airplanes — A1373

No. 2794: a, Tipsy Nipper, 1959 (48x28mm). b, Sabca S.40, 1939 (73x28mm). c, Renard R.35 (73x28mm). d, César Bataille, 1911 (73x28mm). e, De Brousckère, 1911 (97x28mm).

Photo., Photo. & Engr. (#2794e)
2016, June 13   ***Perf. 11½***
2794 A1373   Sheet of 5   17.50 17.50
a.   1 multi   1.75   .85
b.-d.   2 Any single   3.50   1.75
e.   3 multi   5.25   2.60
On day of issue, No. 2794a sold for 74c, Nos. 2794b-2794d each sold for €1.48, and No. 2794e sold for €2.22.

Miniature Sheet

World War I, Cent. — A1374

No. 2795 — Events of 2016: a, Clandestine publications (40x30mm). b, Gabrielle Petit (1893-1916), spy for Britain executed by Germans, and prison cell (38x49mm). c, Henri Pirenne (1862-1935), historian and arrested resistance leader (40x30mm). d, Commandant Albert De Bueger (1885-1940), Belgian seaplane at Battle of Tabora, German East Africa (40x33mm). e, Belgians forced to work for Germans and political cartoon denouncing forced labor (40x30mm).

2016, June 13   Photo.   *Perf. 11½*
2795 A1374   Sheet of 5   13.00 13.00
a.-e.   1 Europe Any single   2.60   1.40
On day of issue, Nos. 2795a-2795e each sold for €1.13.

Souvenir Sheet

Postal Agreement of 1516, 500th Anniv. — A1375

No. 2796: a, Coat of arms of Jean-Baptiste de Taxis. b, Franz von Taxis (1459-1517), operator of early European postal system.

Litho., Sheet Margin Litho. & Embossed
2016, June 13   ***Perf. 11½***
2796 A1375   Sheet of 2   15.50 15.50
a.-b.   3 Europe Either single   7.75   4.00
On day of issue, Nos. 2796a-2796b each sold for €3.39.

Miniature Sheet

Belgium at Night — A1376

No. 2797: a, Liège-Guillemins Railway Station, Liège. b, Port of Antwerp. c, Atomium, Brussels. d, St. Rombold's Cathedral, Mechelen. e, Notre Dame Cathedral, Tournai.

2016, Aug. 22   Litho.   *Perf. 12½*
2797 A1376   Sheet of 5   13.00 13.00
a.-e.   1 Europe Any single   2.60   1.40
Nos. 2797a-2797e each sold for €1.13 on day of issue.

Miniature Sheet

Endangered Animals — A1377

No. 2798: a, White rhinoceros (30x40mm). b, Mountain gorillas (30x40mm). c, African elephants (60x40mm). d, Polar bear (30x40mm). e, Siberian tiger (30x40mm).

2016, Aug. 22   Litho.   *Perf. 12*
2798 A1377   Sheet of 5   13.00 13.00
a.-e.   1 Europe Any single   2.60   1.40
Nos. 2798a-2798e each sold for €1.13 on day of issue.

Miniature Sheet

2016 Summer Olympics and Paralympics, Rio de Janeiro — A1378

No. 2799: a, Sailing. b, Rowing. c, Para-cycling. d, Wheelchair racing. e, Para-equestrian.

2016, Aug. 22   Litho.   *Perf. 12*
2799 A1378   Sheet of 5   15.00 15.00
a.-e.   1 World Any single   3.00   1.50
Nos. 2799a-2799e each sold for €1.35 on day of issue.

Miniature Sheet

Tintin Magazine, 70th Anniv. — A1379

No. 2800 — Magazine cover of: a, French edition, Sept. 26, 1946 (Le Temple du Soleil). b, French edition, Oct. 3, 1946 (Corentin at police call box). c, French edition, Oct. 17, 1946 (Blake and Mortimer on ship). d, Dutch edition, Sept. 20, 1951 (sailing ship). e, Dutch edition, Mar. 24, 1949 (people and house).

2016, Aug. 22   Litho.   *Perf. 12*
2800 A1379   Sheet of 5   17.50 17.50
a.-e.   2 Any single   3.50   1.75
Nos. 2800a-2800e each sold for €1.48 on day of issue.

Miniature Sheet

Paintings by Rik Wouters (1882-1916) — A1380

No. 2801: a, Tulips, 1913. b, Woman Reading (Femme lisant), 1913, vert. c, Self-portrait with Cigar, 1913, vert. d, The Ravine, 1913. e, The Ironer, 1912..

2016, Aug. 22   Litho.   *Perf. 12*
2801 A1380   Sheet of 5   17.50 17.50
a.-e.   2 Any single   3.50   1.75
Nos. 2801a-2801e each sold for €1.48 on day of issue.

Brussels Chief Rabbi Albert Guigui, Antwerp Bishop Johan Bonny, and Imam Khalid Benhaddou — A1381

2016, Oct. 24   Litho.   *Perf. 11½*
2802 A1381 1 multi   1.75   .85
Campaign for religious tolerance. No. 2802 sold for 74c on day of issue.

New NATO Headquarters Building, Brussels — A1382

2016, Oct. 24   Litho.   *Perf. 12*
2803 A1382 1 Europe multi   2.50   1.25
No. 2803 sold for €1.13 on day of issue and was printed in sheets of 5.

Begonia
A1383

Dahlia
A1384

Narcissus
A1385

Greek Anemone
A1386

Tulip — A1387

Iris — A1388

Amaryllis
A1389

Crocus
A1390

Lily
A1391

Hyacinth
A1392

Serpentine Die Cut 14¼x14

2016, Oct. 24   **Photo.**

Coil Stamps
Self-Adhesive

2804	A1383	1 multi	1.75	.45
2805	A1384	1 multi	1.75	.45
2806	A1385	1 multi	1.75	.45
2807	A1386	1 multi	1.75	.45
2808	A1387	1 multi	1.75	.45
2809	A1388	1 multi	1.75	.45
2810	A1389	1 multi	1.75	.45
2811	A1390	1 multi	1.75	.45
2812	A1391	1 multi	1.75	.45
2813	A1392	1 multi	1.75	.45
a.	Vert. strip of 10, #2804-2813		17.50	
	Nos. 2804-2813 (10)		*17.50*	*4.50*

Nos. 2804-2813 each sold for 74c on day of
issue.

Miniature Sheet

Belgian Nobel Laureates — A1393

No. 2814: a, Jules Bordet, 1919 Physiology
or Medicine laureate. b, Corneille Heymans,
1938 Physiology or Medicine laureate. c, Maurice Maeterlinck, 1911 Literature laureate. d,
Albert Claude and Christian de Duve, 1974
Physiology or Medicine laureates. e, François
Englert, 2013 Physics laureate, and Robert
Brout, physicist. f, Ilya Prigogine, 1977 Chemistry laureate. g, Gustave Rolin-Jaequemyns,
honorary president of Institute of International
Law, 1904 Peace laureate. h, Auguste Beernaert, 1909 Peace laureate. i, Dominique Pire,
1958 Peace laureate. j, Henri La Fontaine,
1913 Peace laureate.

Photo. & Engr.

2016, Oct. 24   ***Perf. 11½***

2814	A1393	Sheet of 10	17.50	17.50
a.-j.	1 Any single		1.75	.85

On day of issue, Nos. 2814a-2814j sold
for 74c.

Miniature Sheet

Super Moon of November 14,
2016 — A1394

No. 2815: a, Comparison of normal appear-
ance of Moon with increased apparent size of
Super Moon (80x30mm). b, Moon and couple
(40x30mm). c, Moon and trees (40x30mm). d,
Moon and church steeple (40x30mm). e,
Moon and airplane (40x30mm).

2016, Oct. 24   **Litho.**   ***Perf. 12***

2815	A1394	Sheet of 5	12.50	12.50
a.-e.	1 Europe Any single		2.50	1.25

On day of issue, Nos. 2815a-2815e each
sold for €1.13.

Santa Claus
A1395

Reindeer
A1396

Die Cut Perf. 10 on 2 or 3 Sides

2016, Oct. 24   **Litho.**

Booklet Stamps
Self-Adhesive

2816	A1395	1 multi	1.75	.85
a.	Booklet pane of 10		17.50	
2817	A1396	1 Europe multi	2.50	1.25
a.	Booklet pane of 10		2.50	

On day of issue, No. 2816 sold for 74c and
No. 2817 sold for €1.13.

Mother and
Child
A1397

2017, Jan. 30   **Litho.**   ***Perf. 11½***

2818	A1397	1 multi	1.60	.80

No. 2818 sold for 74c on day of issue.

Miniature Sheet

Gaston Lagaffe Comic Strip, by André
Franquin, 60th Anniv. — A1398

No. 2819: a, Gaston Lagaffe (40x50mm). b,
Aimé De Mesmaeker (30x40mm). c, Léon
Prunelle (30x40mm). d, M'oiselle Jeanne
(30x40mm). e, Joseph Longtarin (30x40mm).

2017, Jan. 30   **Litho.**   ***Perf. 12***

2819	A1398	Sheet of 5	16.50	16.50
a.-e.	2 Any single		3.25	1.60

On day of issue, Nos. 2819a-2819e each
sold for €1.48. Black and white imperforate
sheets with simulated perforations were given
as gifts to standing order customers.

Bpost Emblem — A1399

2017, Mar. 6   **Photo.**   ***Perf. 11½***

Self-Adhesive

2820	A1399	1 Europe multi	2.40	1.25

No. 2820 sold for €1.13 on day of issue and
could be personalized.

Miniature Sheet

Bluebells in Blue Forest,
Halle — A1400

No. 2821: a, Open bluebell and buds
(30x30mm). b, Close-up of flower (30x30mm).
c, Buds (30x30mm). d, Open flowers
(30x30mm). e, Flowers on forest floor, tree
trunks (40x30mm).

2017, Mar. 6   **Litho.**   ***Perf. 12***

2821	A1400	Sheet of 5	16.50	16.50
a.-e.	2 Any single		3.25	1.60

On day of issue, Nos. 2821a-2821e each
sold for €1.48.

Miniature Sheet

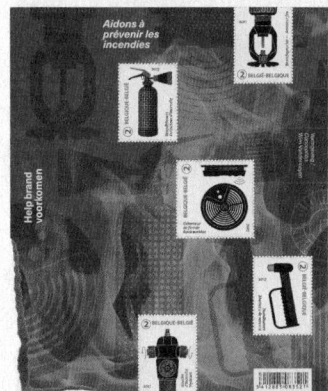

Fire Prevention Equipment — A1401

No. 2822: a, Fire sprinkler head (30x40mm).
b, Fire extinguisher (30x40mm). c, Smoke
detector (40x40mm). d, Emergency hammer
(30x40mm). e, Hydrant (30x40mm).

Perf. 12 on 3 or 4 Sides

2017, Mar. 6   **Litho.**

2822	A1401	Sheet of 5	16.50	16.50
a.-e.	2 Any single		3.25	1.60

On day of issue, Nos. 2822a-2822e each
sold for €1.48.

World Temperature Maps From 1950
and 2017 — A1402

Climate Change Goal of Temperature
Decrease of 2 Degrees — A1403

Die Cut Perf. 11½

2017, Mar. 6   **Litho.**

Booklet Stamps
Self-Adhesive

2823	A1402	1 multi	1.60	.80
2824	A1403	1 multi	1.60	.80
a.	Booklet pane of 10, 5 each #2823-2824		16.00	

On day of issue, Nos. 2823-2824 each sold
for 74c.

Sand
Castle
A1404

2017, June 12   **Litho.**   ***Perf. 12***

2825	A1404	1 Europe multi	2.60	1.40

Europa. No. 2825 sold for €1.13 on day of
issue and portions of the design are coated
with sand grains.

Miniature Sheet

Belgian Winners of the Tour de France
Bicycle Race — A1405

No. 2826: a, Odiel Defraeye, 1912. b, Philippe Thys, 1913, 1914, 1920. c, Firmin
Lambot, 1919, 1922. d, Léon Scieur, 1921. e,
Lucien Buyze, 1926. f, Maurice De Waele,
1929. g, Romain Maes, 1935. h, Sylvère
Maes, 1936, 1939. i, Eddy Merckx, 1969,
1970, 1971, 1972, 1974. j, Lucien Van Impe,
1976.

2017, June 12   **Litho.**   ***Perf. 12½***

2826	A1405	Sheet of 10	17.50	17.50
a.-j.	1 Any single		1.75	.85

On day of issue, Nos. 2826a-2826j each
sold for 74c. Imperforate sheets of 10 were
given as gifts to standing order customers.

Miniature Sheet

Medical Advances — A1406

No. 2827: a, Adolphe Quetelet (1796-1874),
developer of body-mass index (40x30mm). b,
Albin Lambotte (1866-1955), developer of surgical treatment of open bone fractures

(37x49mm). c, Alfons Vandoninck, developer of mosquito repellent (40x30mm). d, Albert Hustin (1882-1967), developer of blood storage anti-coagulant (37x33mm). e, Ferdinand Peeters (1918-98), developer of birth control pills (40x30mm).

2017, June 12 **Photo.** **Perf. 11½**
2827 A1406 Sheet of 5 13.00 13.00
a.-e. 1 Europe Any single 2.60 1.40

On day of issue, Nos. 2827a-2827e each sold for €1.13.

Souvenir Sheet

Protestant Reformation, 500th Anniv. — A1407

No. 2828: a, Door of All Saints' Church, Wittenberg, Germany. b, Martin Luther (1483-1546), religious reformer.

Photo. & Engr.
2017, June 12 **Perf. 11½**
2828 A1407 Sheet of 2 15.50 15.50
a.-b. 3 Europe Either single 7.75 4.00

On day of issue, Nos. 2828a-2828b each sold for €3.39.

White Rose — A1408

Die Cut Perf. 10 on 2 or 3 Sides
2017, Aug. 21 **Litho.**
Booklet Stamp
Self-Adhesive
2829 A1408 1 multi 1.75 .90
a. Booklet pane of 10 17.50

No. 2829 sold for 74c on day of issue.

Kinky and Cosy, Comic Strip Characters by Marnix Verduyn A1409

2017, Aug. 21 **Litho.** **Perf. 11½**
2830 A1409 2 multi 3.50 1.75

No. 2830 sold for €1.48 on day of issue and was printed in sheets of 5.

Souvenir Sheet

University Bicentennials — A1410

No. 2831: a, University of Liège lecture hall, satellite. b, University of Ghent building, colored chemical reaction in flower.

Photo. & Engr.
2017, Aug. 21 **Perf. 11½**
2831 A1410 Sheet of 2 9.50 10.00
a.-b. 3 World Either single 9.75 5.00

Nos. 2831a-2831b each sold for €4.05 on day of issue.

Miniature Sheet

Belgian Trains — A1411

No. 2832: a, Type 1935 electric train without identification number, 1935 (40x28mm). b, Type 653 Diesel locomotive 65304, 1936 (40x28mm). c, Type 12 Atlantic steam locomotive and tender (80x28mm). d, Series 54 Diesel locomotive 5404, 1955-57 (40x28mm). e, Desiro electric train 08079, 2008 (40x28mm).

Photo., Photo. & Engr. Sheet Margin
2017, Aug. 21 **Perf. 11½**
2832 A1411 Sheet of 5 17.50 8.75
a.-e. 2 Any single 3.50 1.75

Nos. 2832a-2832e each sold for €1.48 on day of issue.

Miniature Sheet

Marine Mammals — A1412

No. 2833: a, Dauphin souffleur (bottlenose dolphin) (40x30mm). b, Dauphin à bec blanc (white-beaked dolphin) (40x30mm). c, Baleine à bosse (humpback whale) (40x60mm). d, Phoque gris et veau marin (gray seal and harbor seal) (40x30mm). e, Marsouin (harbor porpoise) (40x30mm).

2017, Aug. 21 **Litho.** **Perf. 12**
2833 A1412 Sheet of 5 14.00 7.00
a.-e. 1 Europe Any single 2.75 1.40

Nos. 2833a-2833e each sold for €1.13 on day of issue. Animal names are not found on the stamps, but on frames that surround each stamp.

SEMI-POSTAL STAMPS

Values quoted for Nos. B1-B24 are for stamps with label attached. Stamps without label sell for one-tenth or less.

St. Martin of Tours Dividing His Cloak with a Beggar
SP1   SP2

Unwmk.
1910, June 1 **Typo.** **Perf. 14**
B1 SP1 1c gray .75 .75
B2 SP1 2c purple brn 8.00 8.00
B3 SP1 5c peacock blue 1.90 1.90
B4 SP1 10c brown red 1.90 1.90
B5 SP2 1c gray green 1.90 1.90
B6 SP2 2c violet brn 5.00 5.00
B7 SP2 5c peacock blue 2.25 2.25
B8 SP2 10c carmine 2.25 2.25
Nos. B1-B8 (8) 23.95 23.95
Set, never hinged 65.00

Overprinted "1911" in Black
1911, Apr. 1
B9 SP1 1c gray 27.50 16.00
a. Inverted overprint
B10 SP1 2c purple brn 125.00 72.50
B11 SP1 5c peacock blue 8.00 5.25
B12 SP1 10c brown red 8.00 5.25
B13 SP2 1c gray green 42.50 27.50
B14 SP2 2c violet brn 60.00 32.50
B15 SP2 5c peacock blue 8.00 5.25
B16 SP2 10c carmine 8.00 5.25
Nos. B9-B16 (8) 287.00 169.50
Set, never hinged 600.00

Overprinted "CHARLEROI-1911"
1911, June
B17 SP1 1c gray 4.00 2.50
B18 SP1 2c purple brn 16.00 10.00
B19 SP1 5c peacock blue 9.00 6.50
B20 SP1 10c brown red 9.00 6.50
B21 SP2 1c gray green 4.00 2.50
B22 SP2 2c violet brn 11.00 9.00
B23 SP2 5c peacock blue 9.00 6.50
B24 SP2 10c carmine 9.00 6.50
Nos. B17-B24 (8) 71.00 50.00
Set, never hinged 175.00

Nos. B1-B24 were sold at double face value, except the 10c denominations which were sold for 15c. The surtax benefited the national anti-tuberculosis organization.

King Albert I — SP3

1914, Oct. 3 **Litho.**
B25 SP3 5c green & red 5.00 5.00
B26 SP3 10c red 1.00 1.00
B27 SP3 20c violet & red 15.00 15.00
Nos. B25-B27 (3) 21.00 21.00
Set, never hinged 90.00

Counterfeits of Nos. B25-B27 abound. Probably as many as 90% of the stamps on the market are counterfeits. Values are for genuine examples.

Merode Monument — SP4

1914, Oct. 3
B28 SP4 5c green & red 4.50 3.00
B29 SP4 10c red 7.50 7.50
B30 SP4 20c violet & red 75.00 75.00
Nos. B28-B30 (3) 87.00 85.50
Set, never hinged 175.00

Counterfeits of Nos. B28-B30 abound. Probably as many as 90% of the stamps on the market are counterfeits. Genuine stamps have a tail on the "Q" of "BELGIQUE" at the top of the stamp, counterfeits don't have a tail. Values are for genuine examples.

King Albert I — SP5

1915, Jan. 1 **Perf. 12, 14**
B31 SP5 5c green & red 5.00 3.00
a. Perf. 12x14 16.00 12.00
B32 SP5 10c rose & red 20.00 6.00
B33 SP5 20c violet & red 25.00 14.00
a. Perf. 14x12 500.00 250.00
b. Perf. 12 50.00 32.50
Nos. B31-B33 (3) 50.00 23.00
Set, never hinged 150.00

Nos. B25-B33 were sold at double face value. The surtax benefited the Red Cross.

Types of Regular Issue of 1915 Surcharged in Red

Nos. B34-B40   Nos. B41-B43

Nos. B44-B47

1918, Jan. 15 **Typo.** **Perf. 14**
B34 A46 1c + 1c dp orange .50 .50
B35 A46 2c + 2c brown .60 .60
B36 A46 5c + 5c blue grn 1.40 1.40
B37 A46 10c + 10c red 2.25 2.25
B38 A46 15c + 15c brt violet 3.25 3.25
B39 A46 20c + 20c plum 7.50 7.50
B40 A46 25c + 25c ultra 7.50 7.50
Engr.
B41 A47 35c + 35c lt vio & blk 10.00 10.00
B42 A48 40c + 40c dull red & blk 10.00 10.00
B43 A49 50c + 50c turq blue & blk 12.00 12.00
B44 A50 1fr + 1fr bluish slate 35.00 35.00
B45 A51 2fr + 2fr dp gray grn 100.00 100.00
B46 A52 5fr + 5fr brown 250.00 250.00
B47 A53 10fr + 10fr dp blue 550.00 500.00
Nos. B34-B47 (14) 990.00 940.00
Set, never hinged 2,000.

Discus Thrower — SP6   Racing Chariot — SP7

Runner — SP8

1920, May 20 **Engr.** **Perf. 12**
B48 SP6 5c + 5c dp green 1.40 1.40
B49 SP7 10c + 5c carmine 1.40 1.40
B50 SP8 15c + 15c dk brown 3.00 3.00
Nos. B48-B50 (3) 5.80 5.80
Set, never hinged 17.00

7th Olympic Games, 1920. Surtax benefited wounded soldiers. Exists imperf.
For surcharges see Nos. 140-142.

Allegory: Asking Alms from the Crown — SP9

1922, May 20
B51 SP9 20c + 20c brown 1.40 1.40
    Never hinged 2.75

Wounded Veteran — SP10

1923, July 5
B52 SP10 20c + 20c slate gray 2.50 2.50
    Never hinged 7.50

Surtax on Nos. B51-B52 was to aid wounded veterans.

SP11

1925, Dec. 15 Typo. Perf. 14
B53 SP11 15c + 5c dull vio & red .50 .25
B54 SP11 30c + 5c gray & red .25 .25
B55 SP11 1fr + 10c chalky blue
       & red 1.25 1.40
    Nos. B53-B55 (3) 2.00 1.90
    Set, never hinged 3.00

Surtax for the Natl. Anti-Tuberculosis League.

SP12

St. Martin, by Van Dyck
SP13   SP14

1926, Feb. 10
B56 SP12 30c + 30c bluish grn
      (red surch.) .50 .50
B57 SP13 1fr + 1fr lt blue 7.25 7.25
B58 SP14 1fr + 1fr lt blue 1.10 1.25
    Nos. B56-B58 (3) 8.85 9.00
    Set, never hinged 20.00

The surtax aided victims of the Meuse flood.

Lion and Cross of Lorraine — SP15

Queen Elisabeth and King Albert SP16

1926, Dec. 6 Typo. Perf. 14
B59 SP15 5c + 5c dk brown .25 .25
B60 SP15 20c + 5c red brown .45 .40
B61 SP15 50c + 5c dull violet .30 .25

Perf. 11½
Engr.
B62 SP16 1.50fr + 25c dk blue .75 .70
B63 SP16 5fr + 1fr rose red 6.50 6.00
    Nos. B59-B63 (5) 8.25 7.60
    Set, never hinged 16.00

Surtax was used to benefit tubercular war veterans.

Boat Adrift SP17

1927, Dec. 15 Engr. Perf. 11½, 14
B64 SP17 25c + 10c dk brn .70 .70
B65 SP17 35c + 10c yel grn .70 .70
B66 SP17 60c + 10c dp vio .60 .40
B67 SP17 1.75fr + 25c dk blue 1.50 2.00
B68 SP17 5fr + 1fr plum 4.50 4.75
    Nos. B64-B68 (5) 8.00 8.55
    Set, never hinged 16.00

The surtax on these stamps was divided among several charitable associations.

Ogives of Orval Abbey — SP18

Monk Carving Capital of Column — SP19

Ruins of Orval Abbey SP20

Design: 60c+15c, 1.75fr+25c, 3fr+1fr, Countess Matilda recovering her ring.

1928, Sept. 15 Photo. Perf. 11½
B69 SP18 5c + 5c red & gold .25 .25
B70 SP18 25c + 5c dk vio & gold .45 .45
Engr.
B71 SP19 35c + 10c dp grn 1.25 1.25
B72 SP19 60c + 15c red brn .75 .25
B73 SP19 1.75fr + 25c dk blue 3.25 2.10
B74 SP19 2fr + 40c dp vio 25.00 21.00
B75 SP19 3fr + 1fr red 22.50 20.00
Perf. 14
B76 SP20 5fr + 5fr rose lake 15.50 15.50
B77 SP20 10fr + 10fr ol green 15.50 15.50
    Nos. B69-B77 (9) 84.45 76.30
    Set, never hinged 150.00

Surtax for the restoration of the ruined Orval Abbey.

St. Waudru, Mons — SP22

St. Rombaut, Malines — SP23

Designs: 25c + 15c, Cathedral of Tournal. 60c + 15c, St. Bavon, Ghent. 1.75fr + 25c, St. Gudule, Brussels. 5fr + 5fr, Louvain Library.

1928, Dec. 1 Photo. Perf. 14, 11½
B78 SP22 5c + 5c carmine .25 .25
B79 SP22 25c + 15c ol brn .25 .25
Engr.
B80 SP23 35c + 10c dp grn 1.50 1.50
B81 SP23 60c + 15c red brn .45 .45
B82 SP23 1.75fr + 25c vio bl 10.50 10.50
B83 SP23 5fr + 5fr red vio 21.00 21.00
    Nos. B78-B83 (6) 33.95 33.95
    Set, never hinged 65.00

The surtax was for anti-tuberculosis work.

Nos. B69-B77 with this overprint in blue or red were privately produced. They were for the laying of the 1st stone toward the restoration of the ruined Abbey of Orval. Value, set, $650.
Forgeries of the overprint exist.

Waterfall at Coo — SP28

Bayard Rock, Dinant — SP29

Designs: 35c+10c, Menin Gate, Ypres. 60c+15c, Promenade d'Orleans, Spa. 1.75fr+25c, Antwerp Harbor. 5fr+5fr, Quai Vert, Bruges.

1929, Dec. 2 Engr. Perf. 11½
B93 SP28 5c + 5c red brn .25 .25
B94 SP29 25c + 15c gray
       blk .95 .90
B95 SP28 35c + 10c green 1.25 1.40
B96 SP28 60c + 15c rose
       lake .85 .75
B97 SP28 1.75fr + 25c dp blue 6.75 6.75
Perf. 14
B98 SP29 5fr + 5fr dl vio 40.00 40.00
    Nos. B93-B98 (6) 50.05 50.05
    Set, never hinged 70.00

Bornhem — SP34

Beloeil — SP35

Gaesbeek SP36

25c + 15c, Wynendaele. 70c + 15c, Oydonck. 1fr + 25c, Ghent. 1.75fr + 25c, Bouillon.

1930, Dec. 1 Photo. Perf. 14
B99 SP34 10c + 5c violet .25 .30
B100 SP34 25c + 15c olive brn .60 .60
Engr.
B101 SP35 40c + 10c brn
       vio .80 1.00
B102 SP35 70c + 15c gray
       blk .55 .55
B103 SP35 1fr + 25c rose
       lake 5.50 5.50
B104 SP35 1.75fr + 25c dp bl 7.25 4.50

B105 SP36 5fr + 5fr gray 45.00 52.50
    Nos. B99-B105 (7) 59.95 64.95
    Set, never hinged 80.00

Philatelic Exhibition Issue
Souvenir Sheet

Prince Leopold — SP41

1931, July 18 Photo. Perf. 14
B106 SP41 2.45fr + 55c car
       brn 225.00 225.00
    Never hinged 650.00
 a. Single stamp 100.00

Sold exclusively at the Brussels Phil. Exhib., July 18-21, 1931. Size: 122x159mm. Surtax for the Veterans' Relief Fund.

The sheet normally has pin holes and a cancellation-like marking in the margin. These are considered unused and the condition valued here.

Queen Elisabeth — SP42

1931, Dec. 1 Engr.
B107 SP42 10c + 5c red
       brn .30 .50
B108 SP42 25c + 15c dk
       vio 1.40 1.50
B109 SP42 50c + 10c dk
       grn 1.10 1.25
B110 SP42 75c + 15c blk
       brn .95 .85
B111 SP42 1fr + 25c rose
       lake 8.00 7.25
B112 SP42 1.75fr + 25c ultra 5.75 4.75
B113 SP42 5fr + 5fr brn
       vio 65.00 65.00
    Nos. B107-B113 (7) 82.50 81.10
    Set, never hinged 150.00

The surtax was for the National Anti-Tuberculosis League.

Désiré Cardinal Mercier — SP43

Mercier Protecting Children and Aged at Malines — SP44

Mercier as Professor at Louvain University — SP45

Mercier in Full Canonicals, Giving His Blessing SP46

1932, June 10 Photo. Perf. 14½x14
B114	SP43	10c + 10c dk violet	1.10	.70
B115	SP43	50c + 30c brt violet	2.75	3.00
B116	SP43	75c + 25c olive brn	2.75	2.75
B117	SP43	1fr + 2fr brown red	7.25	7.25

Engr. Perf. 11½
B118	SP44	1.75fr + 75c dp blue	85.00	100.00
B119	SP45	2.50fr + 2.50fr dk brn	85.00	85.00
B120	SP44	3fr + 4.50fr dull grn	85.00	85.00
B121	SP45	5fr + 20fr vio brn	95.00	100.00
B122	SP46	10fr + 40fr brn lake	210.00	250.00
		Nos. B114-B122 (9)	573.85	633.70
		Set, never hinged	950.00	

Honoring Cardinal Mercier and to obtain funds to erect a monument to his memory.

Belgian Infantryman — SP47

1932, Aug. 4 Perf. 14½x14
B123	SP47	75c + 3.25fr red brn	80.00	80.00
		Never hinged	125.00	
B124	SP47	1.75fr + 4.25fr dk blue	80.00	80.00
		Never hinged	125.00	

Honoring Belgian soldiers who fought in WWI and to obtain funds to erect a natl. monument to their glory.

Sanatorium at Waterloo SP48

1932, Dec. 1 Photo. Perf. 13½x14
B125	SP48	10c + 5c dk vio	.30	.90
B126	SP48	25c + 15c red vio	1.00	1.25
B127	SP48	50c + 10c red brn	1.00	1.25
B128	SP48	75c + 15c ol brn	1.00	.80
B129	SP48	1fr + 25c dp red	15.00	12.50
B130	SP48	1.75fr + 25c dp blue	12.00	11.00
B131	SP48	5fr + 5fr gray grn	100.00	110.00
		Nos. B125-B131 (7)	130.30	137.70
		Set, never hinged	250.00	

Surtax for the assistance of the Natl. Anti-Tuberculosis Society at Waterloo.

View of Old Abbey SP49

Ruins of Old Abbey — SP50

Count de Chiny Presenting First Abbey to Countess Matilda SP56

Restoration of Abbey in XVI and XVII Centuries SP57

Abbey in XVIII Century, Maria Theresa and Charles V — SP58

Madonna and Arms of Seven Abbeys SP60

Designs: 25c+15c, Guests, courtyard, 50c+25c, Transept. 75c+50c, Bell Tower. 1fr+1.25fr, Fountain. 1.25fr+1.75fr, Cloisters. 5fr+20fr, Duke of Brabant placing 1st stone of new abbey.

1933, Oct. 15 Perf. 14
B132	SP49	5c + 5c dull grn	57.50	65.00
B133	SP50	10c + 15c ol grn	52.50	57.50
B134	SP49	25c + 15c dk brn	52.50	57.50
B135	SP50	50c + 25c red brn	52.50	57.50
B136	SP50	75c + 50c dp grn	52.50	57.50
B137	SP50	1fr + 1.25fr cop red	52.50	57.50
B138	SP49	1.25fr + 1.75fr gray blk	52.50	57.50
B139	SP56	1.75fr + 2.75fr blue	60.00	65.00
B140	SP57	2fr + 3fr mag	60.00	65.00
B141	SP58	2.50fr + 5fr dull brn	60.00	65.00
B142	SP56	5fr + 20fr vio	65.00	65.00

Perf. 11½
B143	SP60	10fr + 40fr bl	375.00	375.00
		Nos. B132-B143 (12)	992.50	1,045.
		Set, never hinged	1,500.	

The surtax was for a fund to aid in the restoration of Orval Abbey. Counterfeits exist.

"Tuberculosis Society" — SP61

1933, Dec. 1 Engr. Perf. 14x13½
B144	SP61	10c + 5c blk	1.50	1.50
B145	SP61	25c + 15c vio	5.00	5.00
B146	SP61	50c + 10c red brn	3.75	3.75
B147	SP61	75c + 15c blk	16.00	15.00
B148	SP61	1fr + 25c cl	18.00	18.00
B149	SP61	1.75fr + 25c vio bl	21.00	21.00
B150	SP61	5fr + 5fr lilac	175.00	140.00
		Nos. B144-B150 (7)	240.25	204.25
		Set, never hinged	350.00	

The surtax was for anti-tuberculosis work.

Peter Benoit — SP62

1934, June 1 Photo.
B151	SP62	75c + 25c olive brn	6.00	6.00
		Never hinged	12.50	

The surtax was to raise funds for the Peter Benoit Memorial.

SP63

King Leopold III — SP64

1934, Sept. 15
B152	SP63	75c + 25c ol blk	18.00	17.00
		Never hinged	37.50	
a.		Sheet of 20	925.00	925.00
		Never hinged	1,100.	
B153	SP64	1fr + 25c red vio	17.00	16.00
		Never hinged	37.50	
a.		Sheet of 20	925.00	925.00
		Never hinged	1,100.	

The surtax aided the National War Veterans' Fund. Sold for 4.50fr a set at the Exhibition of War Postmarks 1914-18, held at Brussels by the Royal Philatelic Club of Veterans. The price included an exhibition ticket. Sold at Brussels post office Sept. 18-22. No. B152 printed in sheets of 20 (4x5) and 100 (10x10). No. B153 printed in sheets of 20 (4x5) and 150 (10x15).

1934, Sept. 24
B154	SP63	75c + 25c violet	1.50	1.50
		Never hinged	2.50	
B155	SP64	1fr + 25c red brn	10.50	10.50
		Never hinged		

The surtax aided the National War Veterans' Fund. No. B154 printed in sheets of 100 (10x10); No. B155 in sheets of 150 (10x15). These stamps remained in use one year.

Crusader SP65

1934, Nov. 17 Engr. Perf. 13½x14
Cross in Red
B156	SP65	10c + 5c blk	1.50	1.50
B157	SP65	25c + 15c brn	2.10	2.00
B158	SP65	50c + 10c dull grn	2.10	2.10
B159	SP65	75c + 15c vio brn	1.00	1.00
B160	SP65	1fr + 25c rose	10.50	10.50
B161	SP65	1.75fr + 25c ultra	9.00	9.00

B162	SP65	5fr + 5fr brn vio	125.00	125.00
		Nos. B156-B162 (7)	151.20	151.10
		Set, never hinged	550.00	

The surtax was for anti-tuberculosis work.

Prince Baudouin, Princess Josephine and Prince Albert SP66

1935, Apr. 10 Photo.
B163	SP66	35c + 15c dk grn	1.25	1.10
B164	SP66	70c + 30c red brn	1.25	.90
B165	SP66	1.75fr + 50c dk blue	4.50	5.25
		Nos. B163-B165 (3)	7.00	7.25
		Set, never hinged	20.00	

Surtax was for Child Welfare Society.

Stagecoach — SP67

1935, Apr. 27
B166	SP67	10c + 10c ol blk	.75	.80
B167	SP67	25c + 25c bis brn	2.25	2.10
B168	SP67	35c + 25c dk green	3.00	2.75
		Nos. B166-B168 (3)	6.00	5.65
		Set, never hinged	15.00	

Printed in sheets of 10. Value, set of 3, $175.

Souvenir Sheet

Franz von Taxis — SP68

1935, May 25 Engr. Perf. 14
B169	SP68	5fr + 5fr grnsh blk	150.00	150.00
		Never hinged	450.00	
a.		Single stamp	115.00	
		Never hinged	140.00	

Sheets measure 91½x117mm.
Nos. B166-B169 were issued for the Brussels Philatelic Exhibition (SITEB).
The sheet normally has pin holes and a cancellation-like marking in the margin. These are considered unused and the condition valued here.

Queen Astrid — SP69

1935 Photo. Perf. 11½
Borders in Black
B170	SP69	10c + 5c ol blk	.25	.25
B171	SP69	25c + 15c brown	.25	.30
B172	SP69	35c + 5c dk green	.25	.25

B173	SP69	50c + 10c rose lil	.80 .65
B174	SP69	70c + 5c gray blk	.25 .25
B175	SP69	1fr + 25c red	1.00 .85
B176	SP69	1.75fr + 25c blue	2.40 1.75
B177	SP69	2.45fr + 55c dk vio	3.00 3.25

Nos. B170-B177 (8)   8.20 7.55
Set, never hinged   25.00

Queen Astrid Memorial issue. The surtax was divided among several charitable organizations.
Issued: No. B174, 10/31; others, 12/1.

Borgerhout Philatelic Exhibition Issue
Souvenir Sheet

Town Hall, Borgerhout SP70

1936, Oct. 3
B178 SP70 70c + 30c pur brn 90.00 62.50
    Never hinged 275.00
a.   Single stamp 45.00
    Never hinged 60.00

Sheet measures 115x126mm.
The sheet normally has pin holes and a cancellation-like marking in the margin. These are considered unused and the condition valued here.

Town Hall and Belfry of Charleroi SP71

Charleroi Youth Exhibition
Souvenir Sheet

1936, Oct. 18   **Engr.**
B179 SP71 2.45fr + 55c gray blue 65.00 60.00
    Never hinged 150.00
a.   Single stamp 45.00
    Never hinged 60.00

Sheet measures 95x120mm.
The sheet normally has pin holes and a cancellation-like marking in the margin. These are considered unused and the condition valued here.

Prince Baudouin — SP72

1936, Dec. 1 Photo. Perf. 14x13½
B180	SP72	10c + 5c dk brn	.25 .25
B181	SP72	25c + 5c violet	.25 .25
B182	SP72	35c + 5c dk green	.25 .25
B183	SP72	50c + 5c vio brn	.50 .60
B184	SP72	70c + 5c ol grn	.25 .25
B185	SP72	1fr + 25c cerise	1.10 .45
B186	SP72	1.75fr + 25c ultra	1.90 1.10
B187	SP72	2.45fr + 2.55fr vio rose	5.25 6.75

Nos. B180-B187 (8)   9.75 9.90
Set, never hinged   30.00

The surtax was for the assistance of the National Anti-Tuberculosis Society.

1937, Jan. 10
B188 SP72 2.45fr + 2.55fr slate 2.50 2.50
    Never hinged 6.50

Intl. Stamp Day. Surtax for the benefit of the Brussels Postal Museum, the Royal Belgian Phil. Fed. and the Anti-Tuberculosis Soc.

Queen Astrid and Prince Baudouin — SP73

1937, Apr. 15   **Perf. 11½**
B189	SP73	10c + 5c mag	.25 .25
B190	SP73	25c + 5c ol blk	.25 .25
B191	SP73	35c + 5c dk grn	.25 .25
B192	SP73	50c + 5c violet	1.25 1.25
B193	SP73	70c + 5c slate	.25 .30
B194	SP73	1fr + 25c dk car	1.60 1.40
B195	SP73	1.75fr + 25c dp ultra	2.75 2.75
B196	SP73	2.45fr + 1.55fr dk brn	6.75 6.50

Nos. B189-B196 (8)   13.35 12.95
Set, never hinged   45.00

The surtax was to raise funds for Public Utility Works.

Queen Mother Elisabeth — SP74

1937, Sept. 15   **Perf. 14x13½**
B197 SP74 70c + 5c int black .30 .30
B198 SP74 1.75fr + 25c brt ultra .70 .70
Set, never hinged   2.00

Souvenir Sheet
Perf. 11½
B199   Sheet of 4 45.00 25.00
    Never hinged 125.00
a.   SP74 1.50fr+2.50fr red brn 4.25 3.75
b.   SP74 2.45fr+3.55fr red vio 3.75 2.25

Issued for the benefit of the Queen Elisabeth Music Foundation in connection with the Eugene Ysaye intl. competition.
No. B199 contains two se-tenant pairs of Nos. B199a and B199b. Size: 111x145mm. On sale one day, Sept. 15, at Brussels.
The sheet normally has pin holes and a cancellation-like marking in the margin. These are considered unused and the condition valued here.

Princess Josephine-Charlotte SP75

1937, Dec. 1   **Perf. 14x13½**
B200	SP75	10c + 5c sl grn	.25 .25
B201	SP75	25c + 5c lt brn	.25 .25
B202	SP75	35c + 5c yel grn	.25 .25
B203	SP75	50c + 5c ol gray	.70 .60
B204	SP75	70c + 5c brn red	.25 .25
B205	SP75	1fr + 25c red	1.25 .90
B206	SP75	1.75fr + 25c vio bl	1.50 1.25
B207	SP75	2.45fr + 2.55fr mag	5.75 6.00

Nos. B200-B207 (8)   10.20 9.75
Set, never hinged   30.00

King Albert Memorial Issue
Souvenir Sheet

King Albert Memorial — SP76

1938, Feb. 17   **Perf. 11½**
B208 SP76 2.45fr + 7.55fr brn vio 20.00 16.50
    Never hinged 62.50
a.   Single stamp 15.00
    Never hinged 20.00

Dedication of the monument to King Albert.
The sheet normally has pin holes and a cancellation-like marking in the margin. These are considered unused and the condition valued here. Sheets without the "cancellation" are extremely scarce. Values: unused, $525; never hinged, $1,000.

King Leopold III in Military Plane SP77

1938, Mar. 15
B209	SP77	10c + 5c car brn	.25 .30
B210	SP77	35c + 5c dp grn	.35 .90
B211	SP77	70c + 5c gray blk	.95 .75
B212	SP77	1.75fr + 25c ultra	2.25 2.10
B213	SP77	2.45fr + 2.55fr pur	5.25 4.50

Nos. B209-B213 (5)   9.05 8.55
Set, never hinged   22.50

The surtax was for the benefit of the National Fund for Aeronautical Propaganda.

Basilica of Koekelberg SP78

Interior View of the Basilica of Koekelberg SP79

1938, June 1   **Photo.**
B214	SP78	10c + 5c lt brn	.25 .25
B215	SP78	35c + 5c grn	.25 .25
B216	SP78	70c + 5c gray grn	.25 .25
B217	SP78	1fr + 25c car	.70 .60
B218	SP78	1.75fr + 25c ultra	.70 .70
B219	SP78	2.45fr + 2.55fr brn vio	3.25 3.75

Engr.
B220 SP79 5fr + 5fr dl brn 12.25 11.50
Nos. B214-B220 (7)   17.65 17.30
Set, never hinged   35.00

Souvenir Sheet

1938, July 21 Engr. Perf. 14
B221 SP79 5fr + 5fr lt vio 16.00 16.00
    Never hinged 25.00
a.   Single stamp 14.00
    Never hinged 16.00

The surtax was for a fund to aid in completing the National Basilica of the Sacred Heart at Koekelberg.
Nos. B214, B216 and B218 are different views of the exterior of the Basilica.
The sheet normally has pin holes and a cancellation-like marking in the margin. These are considered unused and the condition valued here.

Stamps of 1938 Surcharged in Black

Nos. B222-B223

No. B224

1938, Nov. 10   **Perf. 11½**
B222 SP78 40c on 35c+5c grn .50 .60
B223 SP78 75c on 70c+5c gray grn .75 .90
B224 SP78 2.50 +2.50fr on 2.45+2.55fr 6.75 7.50

Nos. B222-B224 (3)   8.00 9.00
Set, never hinged   19.00

Prince Albert of Liege — SP81

1938, Dec. 10 Photo. Perf. 14x13½
B225	SP81	10c + 5c brown	.25 .25
B226	SP81	30c + 5c mag	.25 .30
B227	SP81	40c + 5c olive gray	.25 .30
B228	SP81	75c + 5c slate grn	.25 .25
B229	SP81	1fr + 25c dk car	.75 1.10
B230	SP81	1.75fr + 25c ultra	.75 1.10
B231	SP81	2.50fr + 2.50fr dp grn	5.25 8.25
B232	SP81	5fr + 5fr brn lake	16.00 12.50

Nos. B225-B232 (8)   23.75 24.05
Set, never hinged   70.00

Henri Dunant SP82

Florence Nightingale SP83

Queen Mother Elisabeth and Royal Children — SP84

Queen Astrid — SP86

King Leopold and Royal Children SP85

Queen Mother Elisabeth and Wounded Soldier — SP87

1939, Apr. 1   Photo.   Perf. 11½
Cross in Carmine

B233	SP82	10c + 5c brn	.25	.25
B234	SP83	30c + 5c brn car	.45	.45
B235	SP84	40c + 5c ol gray	.25	.30
B236	SP85	75c + 5c slate blk	.60	.25
B237	SP84	1fr + 25c brt rose	3.00	1.60
B238	SP85	1.75fr + 25c brt ultra	.90	1.25
B239	SP86	2.50fr + 2.50fr dl vio	1.90	2.40
B240	SP87	5fr + 5fr gray grn	6.50	8.25
	Nos. B233-B240 (8)		13.85	14.75
	Set, never hinged		42.50	

75th anniversary of the founding of the International Red Cross Society.

In 1941, No. B240 was privately overprinted with a circular red cross overprint and 1941 date. Value, $105.

Rubens' House, Antwerp
SP88

"Albert and Nicolas Rubens" — SP89

Arcade, Rubens' House
SP90

"Helena Fourment and Her Children" — SP91

Rubens and Isabelle Brandt — SP92

Peter Paul Rubens — SP93

"The Velvet Hat" — SP94

"Descent from the Cross"
SP95

1939, July 1

B241	SP88	10c + 5c brn	.25	.25
B242	SP89	40c + 5c brn car	.25	.25
B243	SP90	75c + 5c ol blk	.65	.65
B244	SP91	1fr + 25c rose	2.50	2.50

B245	SP92	1.50fr + 25c sep	2.75	2.75
B246	SP93	1.75fr + 25c dp ultra	4.50	4.50
B247	SP94	2.50fr + 2.50fr brt red vio	15.00	15.00
B248	SP95	5fr + 5fr slate gray	19.00	19.00
	Nos. B241-B248 (8)		44.90	44.90
	Set, never hinged		140.00	

Issued to honor Peter Paul Rubens. The surtax was used to restore Rubens' home in Antwerp.

"Martin van Nieuwenhove" by Hans Memling (1430?-1495), Flemish Painter — SP96

1939, July 1

B249	SP96	75c + 75c olive blk	2.75	2.75
	Never hinged		4.50	

Twelfth Century Monks at Work — SP97

Reconstructed Tower Seen through Cloister — SP98

Monks Laboring in the Fields
SP99

Orval Abbey, Aerial View
SP100

Bishop Heylen of Namur, Madonna and Abbot General Smets of the Trappists — SP101

King Albert I and King Leopold III and Shrine — SP102

1939, July 20

B250	SP97	75c + 75c ol blk	3.50	3.75
B251	SP98	1fr + 1fr rose red	2.25	2.25
B252	SP99	1.50fr + 1.50fr dl brn	2.25	2.25
B253	SP100	1.75fr + 1.75fr saph	2.25	2.25

B254	SP101	2.50fr + 2.50fr brt red vio	10.00	9.00
B255	SP102	5fr + 5fr brn car	10.00	10.00
	Nos. B250-B255 (6)		30.25	29.50
	Set, never hinged		82.50	

The surtax was used for the restoration of the Abbey of Orval.

Bruges
SP103

Furnes
SP104

Belfries: 30c+5c, Thuin. 40c+5c, Lierre. 75c+5c, Mons. 1.75fr+25c, Namur. 2.50fr+2.50fr, Alost. 5fr+5fr, Tournai.

1939, Dec. 1   Photo.   Perf. 14x13½

B256	SP103	10c + 5c ol gray	.25	.25
B257	SP103	30c + 5c brn org	.30	.40
B258	SP103	40c + 5c brt red vio	.50	.50
B259	SP103	75c + 5c olive blk	.25	.25

Engr.

B260	SP104	1fr + 25c rose car	1.25	1.50
B261	SP104	1.75fr + 25c dk blue	1.25	1.50
B262	SP104	2.50fr + 2.50fr dp red brn	8.75	9.50
B263	SP104	5fr + 5fr pur	12.00	13.25
	Nos. B256-B263 (8)		24.55	27.15
	Set, never hinged		65.00	

Mons
SP111

Ghent
SP112

Coats of Arms: 40c+10c, Arel. 50c+10c, Bruges. 75c+15c, Namur. 1fr+25c, Hasselt. 1.75fr+50c, Brussels. 2.50fr+2.50fr, Antwerp. 5fr+5fr, Liege.

1940-41   Typo.   Perf. 14x13½

B264	SP111	10c + 5c multi	.25	.25
B265	SP112	30c + 5c multi	.25	.25
B266	SP111	40c + 10c multi	.25	.25
B267	SP112	50c + 10c multi	.25	.25
B268	SP111	75c + 15c multi	.25	.25
B269	SP112	1fr + 25c multi	.30	.30
B270	SP111	1.75fr + 50c multi	.45	.40
B271	SP112	2.50fr + 2.50fr multi	1.25	1.25
B272	SP111	5fr + 5fr multi	1.50	1.50
	Nos. B264-B272 (9)		4.75	4.70
	Set, never hinged		8.50	

Nos. B264, B269-B272 issued in 1941. Surtax for winter relief. See No. B279.

Queen Elisabeth Music Chapel
SP120

Bust of Prince Albert of Liege — SP121

1940, Nov.   Photo.   Perf. 11½

B273	SP120	75c + 75c slate	3.50	3.50
B274	SP120	1fr + 1fr rose red	1.25	1.25
B275	SP121	1.50fr + 1.50fr Prus grn	1.25	1.25

B276	SP121	1.75fr + 1.75fr ultra	1.25	1.25
B277	SP120	2.50fr + 2.50fr brn org	3.50	3.50
B278	SP121	5fr + 5fr red vio	3.50	3.50
	Nos. B273-B278 (6)		14.25	14.25
	Set, never hinged		55.00	

The surtax was for the Queen Elisabeth Music Foundation. Nos. B273-B278 were not authorized for postal use, but were sold to advance subscribers either mint or canceled to order. See Nos. B317-B318.

Arms Types of 1940-41
Souvenir Sheets
Cross and City Name in Carmine
Arms in Color of Stamp
Perf. 14x13½, Imperf.

1941, May				Typo.
B279		Sheet of 9	16.00	16.00
		Never hinged	18.00	
a.	SP111	10c + 5c slate	1.10	1.25
b.	SP112	30c + 5c emerald	1.10	1.25
c.	SP111	40c + 10c chocolate	1.10	1.25
d.	SP112	50c + 10c light violet	1.10	1.25
e.	SP111	75c + 15c dull purple	1.10	1.25
f.	SP112	1fr + 25c carmine	1.10	1.25
g.	SP111	1.75fr + 50c dull blue	1.10	1.25
h.	SP112	2.50fr + 2.50fr ol gray	1.10	1.25
i.	SP111	5fr + 5fr dull violet	4.00	4.25

The sheets measure 106x148mm. The surtax was used for relief work.

Painting
SP123

Sculpture
SP124

Monks Studying Plans of Orval Abbey — SP128

Designs: 40c+60c, 2fr+3.50fr, Monk carrying candle. 50c+65c, 1.75fr+2.50fr, Monk praying. 75c+1fr, 3fr+5fr, Two monks singing.

1941, June   Photo.   Perf. 11½

B281	SP123	10c + 15c brn org	.40	.40
B282	SP124	30c + 30c ol gray	.40	.40
B283	SP124	40c + 60c dp brn	.40	.40
B284	SP124	50c + 65c vio	.40	.40
B285	SP124	75c + 1fr brt red vio	.40	.40
B286	SP124	1fr + 1.50fr rose red	.40	.40
B287	SP123	1.25fr + 1.75fr dp yel grn	.40	.40
B288	SP123	1.75fr + 2.50fr dp ultra	.40	.40
B289	SP123	2fr + 3.50fr red vio	.40	.40
B290	SP124	2.50fr + 4.50fr dl red brn	.40	.40
B291	SP124	3fr + 5fr dk ol grn	.40	.40
B292	SP128	5fr + 10fr grnsh blk	1.40	1.40
	Nos. B281-B292 (12)		5.80	5.80
	Set, never hinged		11.50	

The surtax was used for the restoration of the Abbey of Orval.

Maria Theresa
SP129

Charles the Bold
SP130

Portraits (in various frames): 35c+5c, Charles of Lorraine. 50c+10c, Margaret of Parma. 60c+10c, Charles V. 1fr+15c, Johanna of Castile. 1.50fr+1fr, Philip the Good. 1.75fr+1.75fr, Margaret of Austria. 3.25fr+3.25fr, Archduke Albert. 5fr+5fr, Archduchess Isabella.

1941-42			**Photo.**	
B293	SP129	10c + 5c ol blk	.25	.25
B294	SP129	35c + 5c dl grn	.25	.25
B295	SP129	50c + 10c brn	.25	.25
B296	SP129	60c + 10c pur	.25	.25
B297	SP129	1fr + 15c brt car rose	.25	.25
B298	SP129	1.50fr + 1fr red vio	.25	.25
B299	SP129	1.75fr + 1.75fr ryl bl	.25	.25
B300	SP130	2.25fr + 2.25fr dl red brn	.30	.30
B301	SP129	3.25fr + 3.25fr lt brn	.40	.40
B302	SP129	5fr + 5fr sl grn	.80	.80
	Nos. B293-B302 (10)		3.25	3.25
	Set, never hinged		5.00	

Souvenir Sheet

Archduke Albert and Archduchess Isabella — SP139

B302A	SP139	Sheet of 2 ('42)	11.00	11.00
		Never hinged	14.50	
b.		3.25fr+6.75fr turquoise blue	4.50	4.50
c.		5fr+10fr dark carmine	4.50	4.50

The surtax was for the benefit of National Social Service Work among soldiers' families.

Souvenir Sheets

Monks Studying Plans of Orval Abbey — SP140

1941, Oct.   Photo.   Perf. 11½
Inscribed "Belgie-Belgique"

B303	SP140	5fr + 15fr ultra	10.00	10.00
		Never hinged	22.50	

Inscribed "Belgique-Belgie"
Imperf

B304	SP140	5fr + 15fr ultra	10.00	10.00
		Never hinged	22.50	

Surtax for the restoration of Orval Abbey. No. B304 exists perforated.
In 1942 these sheets were privately trimmed and overprinted "1142 1942" and ornament.

St. Martin Statue, Church of Dinant
SP141

Lennik, Saint-Quentin
SP142

St. Martin's Church, Saint-Trond
SP146

Statues of St. Martin: 50c+10c, 3.25fr+3.25fr, Beck, Limburg. 60c+10c, 2.25fr+2.25fr, Dave on the Meuse. 1.75fr+50c, Hal, Brabant.

1941-42			**Photo.**	**Perf. 11½**
B305	SP141	10c + 5c chest	.25	.25
B306	SP142	35c + 5c dk bl grn	.25	.25
B307	SP142	50c + 10c vio	.25	.25
B308	SP142	60c + 10c dp brn	.25	.25
B309	SP141	1fr + 15c car	.25	.25
B310	SP141	1.50fr + 25c sl grn	.25	.25
B311	SP142	1.75fr + 50c dk ultra	.30	.30
B312	SP142	2.25fr + 2.25fr red vio	.30	.30
B313	SP142	3.25fr + 3.25fr brn vio	.35	.35
B314	SP146	5fr + 5fr dk ol grn	.70	.70
	Nos. B305-B314 (10)		3.15	3.15
	Set, never hinged		5.00	

Souvenir Sheets
Inscribed "Belgie-Belgique"

B315	SP146	5fr + 20fr vio brn ('42)	22.50	22.50
		Never hinged	32.50	

Inscribed "Belgique-Belgie"
Imperf

B316	SP146	5fr + 20fr vio brn ('42)	22.50	22.50
		Never hinged	32.50	

In 1956, the Bureau Europeen de la Jeunesse et de l'Enfance privately overprinted Nos. B315-B316: "Congres Europeen de l'education 7-12 Mai 1956," in dark red and dark green respectively. A black bar obliterates "Winterhulp-Secours d'Hiver."

Souvenir Sheets

Queen Elisabeth Music Chapel — SP147

1941, Dec. 1   Photo.   Perf. 11½
Inscribed "Belgique-Belgie"

B317	SP147	10fr + 15fr ol blk	6.50	6.00
		Never hinged	9.50	

Inscribed "Belgie-Belgique"
Imperf

B318	SP147	10fr + 15fr ol blk	6.50	6.00
		Never hinged	9.50	

The surtax was for the Queen Elisabeth Music Foundation. These sheets were perforated with the monogram of Queen Elisabeth in 1942. Value, $3 each.
In 1954 Nos. B317-B318 were overprinted for the birth cent. of Edgar Tinel, composer. These overprinted sheets were not postally valid. Value, $4 each.

Jean Bollandus
SP148

Christophe Plantin
SP156

Designs: 35c+5c, Andreas Vesalius. 50c+10c, Simon Stevinus. 60c+10c, Jean Van Helmont. 1fr+15c, Rembert Dodoens. 1.75fr+50c, Gerardus Mercator. 3.25fr+3.25fr, Abraham Ortelius. 5fr+5fr, Justus Lipsius.

1942, May 15			**Photo.**	**Perf. 14x13½**
B319	SP148	10c + 5c dl brn	.25	.25
B320	SP148	35c + 5c gray grn	.25	.25
B321	SP148	50c + 10c fawn	.25	.25
B322	SP148	60c + 10c grnsh blk	.25	.25

Engr.

B323	SP148	1fr + 15c brt rose	.25	.25
B324	SP148	1.75fr + 50c dl bl	.25	.25
B325	SP148	3.25fr + 3.25fr lil rose	.25	.25
B326	SP148	5fr + 5fr vio	.25	.25

Perf. 13½x14

B327	SP156	10fr + 30fr red org	1.40	1.40
	Nos. B319-B327 (9)		3.40	3.40
	Set, never hinged		3.50	

The surtax was used to help fight tuberculosis.
No. B327 was sold by subscription at the Brussels Post Office, July 1-10, 1942.

Belgian Prisoner — SP158

1942, Oct. 1   Perf. 11½

B331	SP158	5fr + 45fr olive gray	7.00	7.00
		Never hinged	16.00	

The surtax was for prisoners of war. Value includes a brown inscribed label which alternates with the stamps in the sheet.

SP159

SP164

SP162

SP168

Various Statues of St. Martin.

1942-43				
B332	SP159	10c + 5c org	.25	.25
B333	SP159	35c + 5c dk bl grn	.25	.25
B334	SP159	50c + 10c dp brn	.25	.25
B335	SP162	60c + 10c blk	.25	.25
B336	SP159	1fr + 15c brt rose	.25	.25
B337	SP164	1.50fr + 25c grnsh blk	.25	.25
B338	SP164	1.75fr + 50c dk bl	.25	.25
B339	SP162	2.25fr + 2.25fr brn	.30	.30
B340	SP162	3.25fr + 3.25fr brt red vio	.45	.45
B341	SP168	5fr + 10fr hn brn	1.25	1.25
B342	SP168	10fr + 20fr rose brn & vio brn ('43)	1.10	1.10

Inscribed "Belgique-Belgie"

B343	SP168	10fr + 20fr gldn brn & vio brn ('43)	1.40	1.40
	Nos. B332-B343 (12)		6.25	6.25
	Set, never hinged		12.50	

The surtax was for winter relief.
Issue dates: Nos. B332-B341, Nov. 12, 1942; Nos. B342-B343, Apr. 3, 1943.

Prisoners of War — SP170

No. B345, 2 prisoners with package from home.

1943, May   Photo.   Perf. 11½

B344	SP170	1fr + 30fr ver	2.75	2.75
B345	SP170	1fr + 30fr brn rose	2.50	2.50
	Set, never hinged		9.50	

The surtax was used for prisoners of war.

Roof Tiler
SP172

Coppersmith
SP173

Statues in Petit Sablon Park, Brussels: 35c+5c, Blacksmith. 60c+10c, Gunsmith. 1fr+15c, Armsmith. 1.75fr+75c, Goldsmith. 3.25fr+3.25fr, Fishdealer. 5fr+25fr, Watchmaker.

1943, June 1				
B346	SP172	10c + 5c chnt brn	.25	.25
B347	SP172	35c + 5c grn	.25	.25
B348	SP173	50c + 10c dk brn	.25	.25
B349	SP173	60c + 10c slate	.25	.25
B350	SP173	1fr + 15c dl rose brn	.25	.25
B351	SP173	1.75fr + 75c ultra	.25	.25
B352	SP173	3.25fr + 3.25fr brt red vio	.40	.40
B353	SP173	5fr + 25fr dk pur	.90	.90
	Nos. B346-B353 (8)		2.80	2.80
	Set, never hinged		3.75	

Surtax for the control of tuberculosis.

"O" SP180

"ORVAL" — SP185

1943, Oct. 9

B354	SP180	50c + 1fr "O"	.50	.50
B355	SP180	60c + 1.90fr "R"	.30	.25
B356	SP180	1fr + 3fr "V"	.30	.25
B357	SP180	1.75fr + 5.25fr "A"	.30	.25
B358	SP180	3.25fr + 16.75fr "L"	.40	.40
B359	SP185	5fr + 30fr dp brn	.85	.85
		Nos. B354-B359 (6)	2.65	2.50
		Set, never hinged	4.50	

Surtax aided restoration of Orval Abbey.

St. Leonard Church, Leau SP186

St. Martin Church, Courtrai — SP190   Basilica of St. Martin, Angre — SP191

Notre Dame, Hal — SP193

St. Martin SP194

35c+5c, St. Martin Church, Dion-le-Val. 50c+15c, St. Martin Church, Alost. 60c+20c, St. Martin Church, Liege. 3.25fr+11.75fr, St. Martin Church, Loppem. No. B369, St. Martin, beggar & Meuse landscape.

1943-44

B360	SP186	10c + 5c dp brn	.25	.25
B361	SP186	35c + 5c dk bl grn	.25	.25
B362	SP186	50c + 15c ol blk	.30	.30
B363	SP186	60c + 20c brt red vio	.30	.40
B364	SP190	1fr + 1fr rose brn	.40	.40
B365	SP191	1.75fr + 4.25fr dp ultra	.90	.60
B366	SP186	3.25fr + 11.75fr red lil	1.25	1.25
B367	SP193	5fr + 25fr dk bl	1.90	1.90
B368	SP194	10fr + 30fr gray grn ('44)	1.50	1.50
B369	SP194	10fr + 30fr blk brn ('44)	1.50	1.50
		Nos. B360-B369 (10)	8.55	8.35
		Set, never hinged	18.00	

Surtax for winter relief.

> Catalogue values for unused stamps in this section, from this point to the end of the section, are for Never Hinged items.

"Daedalus and Icarus" SP196   Sir Anthony Van Dyck, Self-portrait SP200

Paintings by Van Dyck: 50c+2.50fr. "The Good Samaritan." 60c+3.40fr, "Christ Healing the Paralytic." 1fr+5fr, "Madonna & Child." 5fr+30fr, "St. Sebastian."

1944, Apr. 16   **Photo.**   **Perf. 11½**
Crosses in Carmine

B370	SP196	35c + 1.65fr dk sl grn	.45	.30
B371	SP196	50c + 2.50fr grnsh blk	.45	.30
B372	SP196	60c + 3.40fr blk brn	.45	.30
B373	SP196	1fr + 5fr dk car	.70	.45
B374	SP200	1.75fr + 8.25fr int bl	.75	.60
B375	SP196	5fr + 30fr cop brn	1.10	.70
		Nos. B370-B375 (6)	3.90	2.65

The surtax was for the Belgian Red Cross.

Jan van Eyck — SP202   Godfrey of Bouillon — SP203

Designs: 50c+25c, Jacob van Maerlant. 60c+40c, Jean Joses de Dinant. 1fr+50c, Jacob van Artevelde. 1.75fr+4.25fr, Charles Joseph de Ligne. 2.25fr+8.25fr, Andre Gretry. 3.25fr+11.25fr, Jan Moretus-Plantin. 5fr+35fr, Jan van Ruysbroeck.

1944, May 31

B376	SP202	10c + 15c dk pur	.75	.25
B377	SP203	35c + 15c green	.50	.25
B378	SP203	50c + 25c chnt brn	.50	.25
B379	SP203	60c + 40c ol blk	.50	.25
B380	SP203	1fr + 50c rose brn	.50	.25
B381	SP203	1.75fr + 4.25fr ultra	.50	.25
B382	SP203	2.25fr + 8.25fr grnsh blk	1.10	.55
B383	SP203	3.25fr + 11.25fr dk brn	.50	.25
B384	SP203	5fr + 35fr sl bl	1.60	.70
		Nos. B376-B384 (9)	6.45	3.00

The surtax was for prisoners of war.

Sons of Aymon Astride Bayard SP211

Brabo Slaying the Giant Antigoon SP212   Till Eulenspiegel Singing to Nele SP214

50c+10c, St. Hubert converted by stag with crucifix. 1fr+15fr, St. George slaying the dragon. 1.75fr+5.25fr, Genevieve of Brabant with son & roe-deer. 3.25fr+11.75fr, Tchantches wrestling with the Saracen. 5fr+25fr, St. Gertrude rescuing the knight with the cards.

1944, June 25

B385	SP211	10c + 5c choc	.25	.25
B386	SP212	35c + 5c dk bl grn	.25	.25
B387	SP214	50c + 10c dl vio	.25	.25
B388	SP214	60c + 10c blk brn	.25	.25
B389	SP214	1fr + 15c rose brn	.25	.25
B390	SP214	1.75fr + 5.25fr ultra	.25	.30
B391	SP211	3.25fr + 11.75fr grnsh blk	.35	.50
B392	SP211	5fr + 25fr dk bl	.45	.70
		Nos. B385-B392 (8)	2.30	2.75

The surtax was for the control of tuberculosis.

Nos. B385-B389 were overprinted "Breendonk+10fr." in 1946 by the Union Royale Philatelique for an exhibition at Brussels. They had no postal validity. Value same as unused set without overprint.

Union of the Flemish and Walloon Peoples in their Sorrow — SP219

Union in Reconstruction — SP220

Perf. 11½

1945, May 1   **Unwmk.**   **Photo.**

B395	SP219	1fr + 30fr carmine	1.60	.90
B396	SP220	1¾fr + 30fr brt ultra	1.60	.90

1945, July 21
Size: 34½x23½mm

B397	SP219	1fr + 9fr scarlet	.40	.25
B398	SP220	1fr + 9fr car rose	.40	.25
		Nos. B395-B398 (4)	4.00	2.30

Surtax for the postal employees' relief fund.

Prisoner of War SP221

Reunion SP222   Awaiting Execution SP223

Symbolical Figures "Recovery of Freedom" SP225

Design: 70c+30c, 3.50fr+3.50fr, Member of Resistance Movement.

1945, Sept. 10

B399	SP221	10c + 15c orange	.25	.25
B400	SP222	20c + 20c dp pur	.25	.25
B401	SP223	60c + 25c sepia	.25	.25
B402	SP221	70c + 30c dp yel grn	.25	.25
B403	SP221	75c + 50c org brn	.25	.25
B404	SP222	1fr + 75c brt bl	.25	.25
B405	SP223	1.50fr + 1fr brt red	.25	.25
B406	SP221	3.50fr + 3.50fr brt bl	1.60	1.10
B407	SP225	5fr + 40fr brown	2.25	1.25
		Nos. B399-B407 (9)	5.60	4.10

The surtax was for the benefit of prisoners of war, displaced persons, families of executed victims and members of the Resistance Movement.

Arms of West Flanders — SP226

Arms of Provinces: 20c+20c, Luxembourg. 60c+25c, East Flanders. 70c+30c, Namur. 75c+50c, Limburg. 1fr+75c, Hainaut. 1.50fr+1fr, Antwerp. 3.50fr+1.50fr, Liege. 5fr+45fr, Brabant.

1945, Dec. 1

B408	SP226	10c + 15c sl blk & sl gray	.25	.25
B409	SP226	20c + 20c rose car & rose	.25	.25
B410	SP226	60c + 25c dk brn & pale brn	.25	.25
B411	SP226	70c + 30c dk grn & lt grn	.25	.25
B412	SP226	75c + 50c org brn & pale org brn	.25	.25
B413	SP226	1fr + 75c pur & lt pur	.25	.25
B414	SP226	1.50fr + 1fr car & rose	.25	.25
B415	SP226	3.50fr + 1.50fr dp bl & gray bl	.60	.50
B416	SP226	5fr + 45fr mag & cer	3.75	2.00
		Nos. B408-B416 (9)	6.10	4.25

The surtax was for tuberculosis prevention.

322   BELGIUM

Father Joseph Damien — SP227   Father Damien Comforting Leper — SP229

Leper Colony, Molokai Island, Hawaii SP228

Perf. 11½

1946, July 15   Unwmk.   Photo.
B417 SP227   65c + 75c dk blue   1.90   .65
B418 SP228   1.35fr + 2fr brown   1.90   .65
B419 SP229   1.75fr + 18fr rose
          brn   1.90   1.10

The surtax was for the erection of a museum in Louvain.

Symbols of Wisdom and Patriotism SP230   "In Memoriam" SP232

François Bovesse SP231

1946, July 15
B420 SP230   65c + 75c violet   1.90   .65
B421 SP231   1.35fr + 2fr dk org
          brn   1.90   .80
B422 SP232   1.75fr + 18fr car
          rose   1.90   1.10

The surtax was for the erection of a "House of the Fine Arts" at Namur.

Emile Vandervelde SP233   Sower SP235

Vandervelde, Laborer and Family — SP234

1946, July 15
B423 SP233   65c + 75c dk sl
          grn   1.90   .65
B424 SP234   1.35fr + 2fr dk vio
          bl   1.90   .80

B425 SP235   1.75fr + 18fr dp
          car   1.90   1.10
    Nos. B417-B425 (9)   17.10   7.50

The surtax was for the Emile Vanderveide Institute, to promote social, economic and cultural activities.
For surcharges see Nos. CB4-CB12.

Pepin of Herstal — SP236

1fr+50c, Charlemagne. 1.50fr+1fr, Godfrey of Bouillon. 3.50fr+1.50fr, Robert of Jerusalem. Nos. B430-B431, Baldwin of Constantinople.

1946, Sept. 15   Engr.   Perf. 11½x11
B426 SP236   75c + 25c grn   .60   .35
B427 SP236   1fr + 50c vio   .90   .50
B428 SP236   1.50fr + 1fr plum   1.25   .65
B429 SP236   3.50fr + 1.50fr brt
          bl   1.50   .75
B430 SP236   5fr + 45fr red
          vio   12.00   7.00
B431 SP236   5fr + 45fr red
          org   15.00   7.75
    Nos. B426-B431 (6)   31.25   17.00

The surtax on Nos. B426-B429 was for the benefit of former prisoners of war, displaced persons, the families of executed patriots, and former members of the Resistance Movement.
The surtax on Nos. B430-B431 was divided among several welfare, national celebration and educational organizations.
Issue dates: Nos. B426-B429, Apr. 15; No. B430, Sept. 15; No. B431, Nov. 15.
See Nos. B437-B441, B465-B466, B472-B476.

Malines — SP241

Coats of Arms: 90c+60c, Dinant. 1.35fr+1.15fr, Ostend. 3.15fr+1.85fr, Verviers. 4.50fr+45.50fr, Louvain.

1946, Dec. 2   Perf. 11½
B432 SP241   65c + 35c rose
          car   .55   .50
B433 SP241   90c + 60c lem   .65   .50
B434 SP241   1.35fr + 1.15fr dp
          grn   .65   .50
B435 SP241   3.15fr + 1.85fr bl   1.50   1.25
B436 SP241   4.50fr + 45.50fr
          dk vio brn   16.00   14.00
    Nos. B432-B436 (5)   19.35   16.75

The surtax was for anti-tuberculosis work.
See Nos. B442-B446.

Type of 1946

Designs: 65c+35c, John II, Duke of Brabant. 90c+60c, Count Philip of Alsace. 1.35fr+1.15fr, William the Good. 3.15fr+1.85fr, Bishop Notger of Liege. 20fr+20fr, Philip the Noble.

1947, Sept. 25   Engr.   Perf. 11½x11
B437 SP236   65c + 35c Prus
          grn   1.10   .50
B438 SP236   90c + 60c yel
          grn   1.60   .75
B439 SP236   1.35fr + 1.15fr car   3.00   1.10
B440 SP236   3.15fr + 1.85fr ul-
          tra   3.75   1.60
B441 SP236   20fr + 20fr red
          vio   52.50   42.50
    Nos. B437-B441 (5)   61.95   46.45

The surtax was for victims of World War II.

Arms Type of 1946 Dated "1947"

Coats of Arms: 65c+35c, Nivelles. 90c+60c, St. Trond. 1.35fr+1.15fr, Charleroi. 3.15fr+1.85fr, St. Nicolas. 20fr+20fr, Bouillon.

1947, Dec. 15   Perf. 11½
B442 SP241   65c + 35c org   .80   .65
B443 SP241   90c + 60c dp cl   .70   .65
B444 SP241   1.35fr + 1.15fr dk
          brn   1.00   .70
B445 SP241   3.15fr + 1.85fr dp
          bl   2.60   1.75
B446 SP241   20fr + 20fr dk
          grn   24.00   15.00
    Nos. B442-B446 (5)   29.10   18.75

The surtax was for anti-tuberculosis work.

St. Benedict and King Totila — SP247

Achel Abbey SP248

3.15fr+2.85fr, St. Benedict, legislator & builder. 10fr+10fr, Death of St. Benedict.

1948, Apr. 5   Photo.
B447 SP247   65c + 65c red
          brn   1.25   .55
B448 SP248   1.35fr + 1.35fr
          grnsh blk   1.75   .55
B449 SP247   3.15fr + 2.85fr dp
          ultra   2.50   1.90
B450 SP247   10fr + 10fr brt
          red vio   12.50   10.00
    Nos. B447-B450 (4)   18.00   13.00

The surtax was to aid the Abbey of the Trappist Fathers at Achel.

St. Begga and Chevremont Castle — SP249

Chevremont Basilica and Convent SP250

3.15fr+2.85fr, Madonna of Chevremont & Chapel. 10fr+10fr, Madonna of Mt. Carmel.

1948, Apr. 5   Unwmk.
B451 SP249   65c + 65c bl
          grn   1.00   .55
B452 SP250   1.35fr + 1.35fr dk
          car rose   1.60   .55
B453 SP249   3.15fr + 2.85fr dp
          bl   2.75   1.90
B454 SP249   10fr + 10fr dp
          brn   12.00   10.00
    Nos. B451-B454 (4)   17.35   13.00

The surtax was to aid the Basilica of the Carmelite Fathers of Chèvremont.

Anseele Monument Showing French Inscription — SP251

90c+60c, View of Ghent. 1.35fr+1.15fr, Van Artevelde monument, Ghent. 3.15fr+1.85fr, Anseele Monument, Flemish inscription.

1948, June 21   Perf. 14x13½
B455 SP251   65c + 35c
          rose red   2.75   1.10
B456 SP251   90c + 60c
          gray   3.50   1.90
B457 SP251   1.35fr + 1.15fr
          hn brn   2.25   1.50
B458 SP251   3.15fr + 1.85fr
          brt bl   8.50   5.00
   a.   Souv. sheet, #B455-B458   200.00   85.00
    Nos. B455-B458 (4)   17.00   9.50

Issued to honor Edouard Anseele, statesman, founder of the Belgian Socialist Party. No. B458a sold for 50fr.
For surcharges see Nos. 395-398.

Statue "The Unloader" SP252   Underground Fighter SP253

1948, Sept. 4   Perf. 11½x11
B460 SP252   10fr + 10fr gray
          grn   52.50   24.50
B461 SP253   10fr + 10fr red
          brn   22.50   12.50

The surtax was used toward erection of monuments at Antwerp and Liege.

Portrait Type of 1946 and

Double Barred Cross — SP254

Designs: 4fr+3.25fr, Isabella of Austria. 20fr+20fr, Archduke Albert of Austria.

1948, Dec. 15   Photo.   Perf. 13½x14
B462 SP254   20c + 5c dk sl grn   .50   .25
B463 SP254   1.20fr + 30c mag   1.25   .70
B464 SP254   1.75fr + 25c red   1.75   .60

Engr.   Perf. 11½x11
B465 SP236   4fr + 3.25fr ultra   9.50   6.50
B466 SP236   20fr + 20fr Prus
          grn   42.50   30.00
    Nos. B462-B466 (5)   55.50   38.05

The surtax was divided among several charities.

Souvenir Sheets

Rogier van der Weyden Paintings — SP255

Paintings by van der Weyden (No. B466A): 90c, Virgin and Child. 1.75fr, Christ on the Cross. 4fr, Mary Magdalene.
Paintings by Jordaens (No. B466B): 90c, Woman Reading. 1.75fr, The Flutist. 4fr, Old Woman Reading Letter.

1949, Apr. 1   Photo.   Perf. 11½
B466A SP255   Sheet of 3   200.00   175.00
   c.   90c deep brown   55.00   50.00
   d.   1.75fr deep rose lilac   55.00   50.00
   e.   4fr dark violet blue   55.00   50.00
B466B SP255   Sheet of 3   200.00   175.00
   f.   90c dark violet   55.00   50.00
   g.   1.75fr red   55.00   50.00
   h.   4fr blue   55.00   50.00

The surtax went to various cultural and philanthropic organizations. Sheets sold for 50fr each.
Gum on Nos. B466A-B466B is irregularly applied.

Guido
Gezelle — SP256

1949, Nov. 15   Photo.   Perf. 14x13½
B467 SP256 1.75fr + 75c dk Prus
                grn   2.50 1.75

50th anniversary of the death of Guido
Gezelle, poet. The surtax was for the Guido
Gezelle Museum, Bruges.

Portrait Type of 1946 and

Arnica — SP257

Designs: 65c+10c, Sand grass. 90c+10c,
Wood myrtle. 1.20fr+30c, Field poppy.
1.75fr+25c, Philip the Good. 3fr+1.50fr,
Charles V. 4fr+2fr, Maria-Christina. 6fr+3fr,
Charles of Lorraine. 8fr+4fr, Maria-Theresa.

1949, Dec. 20   Typo.   Perf. 13½x14
B468 SP257 20c + 5c multi   .55 .55
B469 SP257 65c + 10c multi 1.40 1.25
B470 SP257 90c + 10c multi 2.25 1.60
B471 SP257 1.20fr + 30c multi 2.75 1.90

Engr.   Perf. 11½x11
B472 SP236 1.75fr + 25c red
                org   1.50   .90
B473 SP236 3fr + 1.50fr dp
                claret   11.00 7.50
B474 SP236 4fr + 2fr ultra 11.00 8.75
B475 SP236 6fr + 3fr choc   20.00 12.00
B476 SP236 8fr + 4fr dl grn 21.00 12.50
    Nos. B468-B476 (9)   71.45 46.95

The surtax was apportioned among several
welfare organizations.

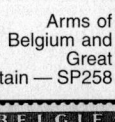

Arms of
Belgium and
Great
Britain — SP258

British
Memorial — SP260

Design: 2.50fr+50c, British tanks at Hertain.

Perf. 13½x14, 11½
1950, Mar. 15   Engr.
B477 SP258 80c + 20c grn   1.50 1.00
B478 SP258 2.50fr + 50c red 5.00 3.25
B479 SP260 4fr + 2fr dp bl 9.25 6.25
    Nos. B477-B479 (3)   15.75 11.00

6th anniv. of the liberation of Belgian territory by the British army.

Hurdling   Relay Race
SP261   SP262

Designs: 90c+10c, Javelin throwing. 4fr+2fr,
Pole vault. 8fr+4fr, Foot race.

Perf. 14x13½, 13½x14
1950, July 1   Engr.   Unwmk.
B480 SP261 20c + 5c brt
                grn   .45   .25
B481 SP261 90c + 10c vio
                brn   3.75 1.50
B482 SP262 1.75fr + 25c car 7.25 1.75
    a.   Souvenir sheet of 1 80.00 50.00
B483 SP261 4fr + 2fr lt bl 35.00 17.00
B484 SP261 8fr + 4fr dp
                grn   37.50 24.00
    Nos. B480-B484 (5)   83.95 44.50

Issued to publicize the European Athletic
Games, Brussels, August 1950.

The margins of No. B482a were trimmed in
April, 1951, and an overprint ("25 Francs pour
le Fonds Sportif-25e Foire Internationale Bruxelles") was added in red in French and in black
in Flemish by a private committee. These pairs
of altered sheets were sold at the Brussels
Fair. Value, set of 2 altered sheets, $25.

Gentian — SP263

Sijsele
Sanatorium
SP264

Tombeek
Sanatorium
SP265

Designs: 65c+10c, Cotton Grass. 90c+10c,
Foxglove. 1.20fr+30c, Limonia. 4fr+2fr, Jauche
Sanatorium.

1950, Dec. 20   Typo.   Perf. 14x13½
B485 SP263 20c + 5c multi   .80   .40
B486 SP263 65c + 10c multi 1.50   .85
B487 SP263 90c + 10c multi 1.60 1.10
B488 SP263 1.20fr + 30c multi 2.75 2.25

Perf. 11½
Engr.
Cross in Red
B489 SP264 1.75fr + 25c car 2.50 1.40
B490 SP264 4fr + 2fr blue 18.00 8.25
B491 SP265 8fr + 4fr bl grn 25.00 17.50
    Nos. B485-B491 (7)   52.15 31.75

The surtax was for tuberculosis prevention
and other charitable purposes.

Chemist   Allegory of Peace
SP266   SP268

Colonial
Instructor
and Class
SP267

1951, Mar. 27   Unwmk.
B492 SP266 80c + 20c grn   1.40 1.00
B493 SP267 2.50fr + 50c vio
                brn   10.00 5.50
B494 SP268 4fr + 2fr dp bl 12.00 6.75
    Nos. B492-B494 (3)   23.40 13.25

Surtax for the reconstruction fund of the
UNESCO.

Monument to
Political
Prisoners — SP269

Fort of
Breendonk
SP270

8fr+4fr, Monument: profile of figure on
pedestal.

1951, Aug. 20   Photo.   Perf. 11½
B495 SP269 1.75fr + 25c blk
                brn   3.00 1.90
B496 SP270 4fr + 2fr bl &
                sl gray   32.50 17.50
B497 SP269 8fr + 4fr dk bl
                grn   32.50 20.00
    Nos. B495-B497 (3)   68.00 39.40

The surtax was for the erection of a national
monument.

Queen
Elisabeth — SP271

1951, Sept. 22
B498 SP271 90c + 10c
                grnsh
                gray   4.00   .90
B499 SP271 1.75fr + 25c
                plum   9.00 2.00
B500 SP271 3fr + 1fr grn   32.50 15.00
B501 SP271 4fr + 2fr gray
                bl   35.00 16.00
B502 SP271 8fr + 4fr se-
                pia   45.00 20.00
    Nos. B498-B502 (5)   125.50 53.90

The surtax was for the Queen Elisabeth
Medical Foundation.

Cross, Sun Rays and
Dragon — SP272

Beersel
Castle
SP273

Horst
Castle — SP274

Castles: 4fr+2fr, Lavaux St. Anne. 8fr+4fr,
Veves.

1951, Dec. 17   Engr.   Unwmk.
B503 SP272 20c + 5c red   .35   .25
B504 SP272 65c + 10c dp
                ultra   .85   .60
B505 SP272 90c + 10c sep   .90   .80
B506 SP272 1.20fr + 30c rose
                vio   1.40   .90

B507 SP273 1.75fr + 75c red
                brn   4.00 1.50
B508 SP274 3fr + 1fr yel
                grn   14.00 8.25
B509 SP273 4fr + 2fr blue 17.00 9.25
B510 SP274 8fr + 4fr gray 26.50 14.50
    Nos. B503-B510 (8)   65.00 36.05

The surtax was for anti-tuberculosis work.
See Nos. B523-B526, B547-B550.

Main Altar   Basilica of the
SP275   Sacred Heart
                   Koekelberg
                   SP276

Procession Bearing Relics of St.
Albert of Louvain — SP277

1952, Mar. 1   Photo.   Perf. 11½
B511 SP275 1.75fr + 25c blk
                brn   1.50 1.25
B512 SP276 4fr + 2fr indigo 16.00 8.25

Engr.
B513 SP277 8fr + 4fr vio brn 25.00 11.50
    a.   Souv. sheet, #B511-
          B513   425.00 175.00
    Nos. B511-B513 (3)   42.50 21.00

25th anniv. of the Cardinalate of J. E. Van
Roey, Primate of Belgium. The surtax was for
the Basilica. No. B513a sold for 30fr.

Beaulieu Castle,
Malines — SP278

1952, May 14   Engr.
Laid Paper
B514 SP278 40fr + 10fr lt
                grnsh bl   140.00 100.00

Issued on the occasion of the 13th Universal
Postal Union Congress, Brussels, 1952.

August Vermeylen
SP279

Portraits: 80c+40c, Karel Van de Woestijne.
90c+45c, Charles de Coster. 1.75fr+75c, M.
Maeterlinck. 4fr+2fr, Emile Verhaeren. 8fr+4fr,
Hendrik Conscience.

Perf. 11½
1952, Oct. 24   Unwmk.   Photo.
B515 SP279 65c + 30c pur   5.75 2.25
B516 SP279 80c + 40c dk
                grn   6.00 2.75
B517 SP279 90c + 45c se-
                pia   6.25 3.00
B518 SP279 1.75fr + 75c cer 14.50 5.00
B519 SP279 4fr + 2fr bl
                vio   37.50 17.50

B520 SP279   8fr + 4fr dk
      brn   45.00   22.50
Nos. B515-B520 (6)   115.00   53.00

1952, Nov. 15

4fr, Emile Verhaeren. 8fr, Hendrik Conscience.

B521 SP279   4fr (+ 9fr) blue   160.00   80.00
B522 SP279   8fr (+ 9fr) dk
      car rose   160.00   80.00

On Nos. B521-B522, the denomination is repeated at either side of the stamp. The surtax is expressed on se-tenant labels bearing quotations of Verhaeren (in French) and Conscience (in Flemish). Value is for stamp with label.

A 9-line black overprint was privately applied to these labels: "Conference Internationale de la Musique Bruxelles UNESCO International Music Conference Brussels 1953*" Value, $125.

Type of 1951 Dated "1952," and

Arms of
Malmédy — SP281

Castle
Ruins,
Burgreuland
SP282

Designs: 4fr+2fr, Vesdre Dam, Eupen. 8fr+4fr, St. Vitus, patron saint of Saint-Vith.

1952, Dec. 15   **Engr.**
B523 SP272   20c + 5c red
      brn   .50   .50
B524 SP272   80c + 20c grn   .95   .70
B525 SP272   1.20fr + 30c lil
      rose   2.00   1.10
B526 SP272   1.50fr + 50c ol
      brn   2.00   1.10
B527 SP281   2fr + 75c car   3.50   3.50
B528 SP282   3fr + 1.50fr
      choc   22.50   13.50
B529 SP281   4fr + 2fr blue   21.00   12.00
B530 SP281   8fr + 4fr vio
      brn   22.50   16.00
Nos. B523-B530 (8)   74.95   48.40

The surtax on Nos. B523-B530 was for anti-tuberculosis and other charitable works.

Walthère
Dewé — SP283

1953, Feb. 16   **Photo.**
B531 SP283 2fr + 1fr brn car   3.25   1.75

The surtax was for the construction of a memorial to Walthère Dewé, Underground leader in World War II.

Princess Josephine-
Charlotte — SP284

1953, Mar. 14   **Cross in Red**
B532 SP284   80c + 20c ol
      grn   3.50   1.50
B533 SP284   1.20fr + 30c brn   3.25   1.25

B534 SP284   2fr + 50c rose
      lake   2.75   1.25
   a.   Booklet pane of 8   80.00   65.00
B535 SP284   2.50fr + 50c crim   17.50   10.00
B536 SP284   4fr + 1fr brt
      blue   19.00   8.75
B537 SP284   5fr + 2fr sl grn   19.00   8.75
Nos. B532-B537 (6)   65.00   31.50

The surtax was for the Belgian Red Cross. The selvage of No. B534a is inscribed in French. Value for selvage inscribed in Dutch, $220.

Boats at
Dock
SP285

Bridge and Citadel,
Namur — SP286

Designs: 1.20fr+30c, Bridge at Bouillon. 2fr+50c, Antwerp waterfront. 4fr+2fr, Wharf at Ghent. 8fr+4fr, Meuse River at Freyr.

1953, June 22   **Unwmk.**   **Perf. 11½**
B538 SP285   80c + 20c grn   2.25   1.00
B539 SP285   1.20fr + 30c
      redsh brn   6.00   2.75
B540 SP285   2fr + 50c sep   6.75   2.75
B541 SP286   2.50fr + 50c dp
      mag   16.00   8.00
B542 SP286   4fr + 2fr vio bl   26.50   13.00
B543 SP286   8fr + 4fr gray
      blk   32.50   15.00
Nos. B538-B543 (6)   90.00   42.50

The surtax was used to promote tourism in the Ardenne-Meuse region and for various cultural works.

Allegory — SP287

1953, Oct. 26   **Engr.**
B544 SP287   80c + 20c grn   3.50   2.50
B545 SP287   2.50fr + 1fr rose
      car   32.50   24.00
B546 SP287   4fr + 1.50fr
      blue   37.50   30.00
Nos. B544-B546 (3)   73.50   56.50

The surtax was for the European Bureau of Childhood and Youth.

Type of 1951 Dated "1953," and

Ernest
Malvoz — SP288

Robert Koch
SP289

Portraits: 3fr+1.50fr, Carlo Forlanini. 4fr+2fr, Leon Charles Albert Calmette.

1953, Dec. 15
B547 SP272   20c + 5c blue   .60   .55
B548 SP272   80c + 20c rose
      vio   1.60   .70
B549 SP272   1.20fr + 30c choc   2.50   1.00
B550 SP272   1.50fr + 50c dk
      gray   3.00   1.25
B551 SP288   2fr + 75c dk
      grn   4.00   1.75
B552 SP288   3fr + 1.50fr dk
      red   17.50   9.25
B553 SP288   4fr + 2fr ultra   20.00   11.00
B554 SP289   8fr + 4fr choc   25.00   13.50
Nos. B547-B554 (8)   74.20   39.00

The surtax was for anti-tuberculosis and other charitable works.

King Albert I
Statue — SP290

Albert I
Monument,
Namur
SP291

9fr+4.50fr, Cliffs of Marche-les-Dames.

1954, Feb. 17   **Photo.**
B555 SP290   2fr + 50c chnt brn   10.00   3.75
B556 SP291   4fr + 2fr blue   32.50   14.50
B557 SP290   9fr + 4.50fr ol blk   27.50   15.00
Nos. B555-B557 (3)   70.00   33.25

20th anniv. of the death of King Albert I. The surtax aided in the erection of the monument pictured on No. B556.

Political Prisoners'
Monument
SP292

Camp and
Fort,
Breendonk
SP293

Design: 9fr+4.50fr, Political prisoners' monument (profile).

1954, Apr. 1   **Unwmk.**   **Perf. 11½**
B558 SP292   2fr + 1fr red   22.50   11.00
B559 SP293   4fr + 2fr dk brn   50.00   22.50
B560 SP292   9fr + 4.50fr ol
      grn   52.50   26.50
Nos. B558-B560 (3)   125.00   60.00

The surtax was used toward the creation of a monument to political prisoners.

Gatehouse
and Gateway
SP294

Nuns in Courtyard
SP295

Our Lady of
the Vine
SP296

2fr+1fr, Swans in stream. 7fr+3.50fr Nuns at well. 8fr+4fr, Statue above door.

1954, May 15
B561 SP294   80c + 20c dk bl
      grn   1.00   .75
B562 SP294   2fr + 1fr crim   12.00   1.60
B563 SP295   4fr + 2fr violet   17.00   10.00
B564 SP295   7fr + 3.50fr lil
      rose   40.00   21.00
B565 SP296   8fr + 4fr brown   40.00   21.00
B566 SP296   9fr + 4.50fr
      gray bl   65.00   32.50
Nos. B561-B566 (6)   175.00   86.85

The surtax was for the Friends of the Beguinage of Bruges.

Child's
Head — SP297

"The Blind
Man and the
Paralytic," by
Antoine
Carte
SP298

1954, Dec. 1   **Engr.**
B567 SP297   20c + 5c dk grn   .50   .50
B568 SP297   80c + 20c dk
      gray   1.00   .90
B569 SP297   1.20fr + 30c org
      brn   2.00   1.00
B570 SP297   1.50fr + 50c pur   3.50   2.00
B571 SP298   2fr + 75c rose
      car   8.00   3.75
B572 SP298   4fr + 1fr brt
      blue   20.00   12.50
Nos. B567-B572 (6)   35.00   20.65

The surtax was for anti-tuberculosis work.

Ernest
Solvay
SP299

Jean-Jacques
Dony — SP300

Portraits: 1.20fr+30c, Egide Walschaerts. 2fr+50c, Leo H. Baekeland. 3fr+1fr, Jean-Etienne Lenoir. 4fr+2fr, Emile Fourcault and Emile Gobbe.

Perf. 11½

1955, Oct. 22   Unwmk.   Photo.

B573	SP299	20c + 5c brn & dk brn	.40	.35
B574	SP300	80c + 20c vio	1.00	.50
B575	SP299	1.20fr + 30c ind	6.25	3.25
B576	SP300	2fr + 50c dp car	5.50	3.00
B577	SP300	3fr + 1fr dk grn	14.50	8.50
B578	SP299	4fr + 2fr brown	14.50	8.50
	Nos. B573-B578 (6)		42.15	24.10

Issued in honor of Belgian scientists. The surtax was for the benefit of various cultural organizations.

"The Joys of Spring" by E. Canneel SP301

Einar Holböll SP302

Portraits: 4fr+2fr, John D. Rockefeller. 8fr+4fr, Sir Robert W. Philip.

1955, Dec. 5   Unwmk.   Perf. 11½

B579	SP301	20c + 5c red lil	.70	.30
B580	SP301	80c + 20c grn	1.00	.65
B581	SP301	1.20fr + 30c redsh brn	2.50	.90
B582	SP301	1.50fr + 50c vio bl	3.00	1.10
B583	SP302	2fr + 50c car	9.50	4.75
B584	SP302	4fr + 2fr ultra	26.00	12.00
B585	SP302	8fr + 4fr ol gray	27.50	15.00
	Nos. B579-B585 (7)		70.20	34.70

The surtax was for anti-tuberculosis work.

Palace of Charles of Lorraine — SP303

Queen Elisabeth and Sonata by Mozart — SP304

Design: 2fr+1fr, Mozart at age 7.

1956, Mar. 19   Engr.

B586	SP303	80c + 20c steel bl	1.00	1.00
B587	SP303	2fr + 1fr rose lake	4.25	3.00
B588	SP304	4fr + 2fr dull pur	8.00	4.25
	Nos. B586-B588 (3)		13.25	8.25

200th anniversary of the birth of Wolfgang Amadeus Mozart, composer. The surtax was for the benefit of the Pro-Mozart Committee in Belgium.

Queen Elisabeth — SP305

1956, Aug. 16   Photo.

B589	SP305	80c + 20c slate grn	1.00	1.00
B590	SP305	2fr + 1fr deep plum	3.50	1.90
B591	SP305	4fr + 2fr brown	5.00	2.75
	Nos. B589-B591 (3)		9.50	5.65

Issued in honor of the 80th birthday of Queen Elisabeth. The surtax went to the Queen Elisabeth Foundation. See No. 659.

Ship with Cross — SP306

Infant on Scales SP307

Rehabilitation SP308

Design: 4fr+2fr, X-Ray examination.

1956, Dec. 17   Engr.

B592	SP306	20c + 5c redsh brn	.35	.30
B593	SP306	80c + 20c grn	.75	.60
B594	SP306	1.20fr + 30c dl lil	.90	.60
B595	SP306	1.5fr + 50c lt sl bl	1.10	.90
B596	SP307	2fr + 50c ol grn	3.50	2.10
B597	SP307	4fr + 2fr dl pur	14.50	8.75
B598	SP308	8fr + 4fr dp car	16.00	10.50
	Nos. B592-B598 (7)		37.10	23.75

The surtax was for anti-tuberculosis work.

Charles Plisnier and Albrecht Rodenbach SP309

80c+20c, Emiel Vliebergh & Maurice Wilmotte. 1.20fr+30c, Paul Pastur & Julius Hoste. 2fr+50c, Lodewijk de Raet & Jules Destree. 3fr+1fr, Constant Meunier & Constant Permeke. 4fr+2fr, Lieven Gevaert & Edouard Empain.

Perf. 11½

1957, June 8   Unwmk.   Photo.

B599	SP309	20c + 5c brt vio	.40	.35
B600	SP309	80c + 20c lt red brn	.55	.35
B601	SP309	1.20f + 30c blk brn	.70	.60
B602	SP309	2fr + 50c claret	1.90	1.25
B603	SP309	3fr + 1fr dk ol grn	2.75	1.90
B604	SP309	4fr + 2fr vio bl	3.25	2.50
	Nos. B599-B604 (6)		9.55	6.95

The surtax was for the benefit of various cultural organizations.

Dogs and Antarctic Camp SP310

1957, Oct. 18   Engr.   Perf. 11½

B605	SP310	5fr + 2.50fr gray, org & vio brn	3.25	2.25
a.		Sheet of 4, #B605b	175.00	140.00
b.		Blue, slate & red brown	35.00	29.00

Surtax for Belgian Antarctic Expedition, 1957-58.

Gen. Patton's Grave and Flag SP311

Gen. George S. Patton, Jr. — SP312

Designs: 2.50fr+50c, Memorial, Bastogne. 3fr+1fr, Gen. Patton decorating Brig. Gen. Anthony C. McAuliffe. 6fr+3fr, Tanks of 1918 and 1944.

1957, Oct. 28   Photo.

Size: 36x25mm, 25x36mm

B606	SP311	1fr + 50c dk gray	2.00	1.00
B607	SP311	2.50fr + 50c ol grn	3.00	1.60
B608	SP311	3fr + 1fr red brn	3.75	2.10
B609	SP312	5fr + 2.50fr grysh bl	8.75	5.50

Size: 53x35mm

B610	SP311	6fr + 3fr pale brn car	12.00	8.00
	Nos. B606-B610 (5)		29.50	18.20

The surtax was for the General Patton Memorial Committee and Patriotic Societies.

Adolphe Max — SP313

1957, Nov. 10   Engr.

B611	SP313	2.50fr + 1fr ultra	1.25	.75

18th anniversary of the death of Adolphe Max, mayor of Brussels. The surtax was for the national "Adolphe Max" fund.

"Chinels," Fosses SP314

"Op Signoorken," Malines SP315

Infanta Isabella Shooting Crossbow SP316

Legends: 1.50fr+50c, St. Remacle and the wolf. 2fr+1fr, Longman and the pea soup. 5fr+2fr, The Virgin with Inkwell, vert. 6fr+2.50fr, "Gilles" (clowns), Binche.

1957, Dec. 14   Engr. & Photo.

B612	SP314	30c + 20c	.25	.30
B613	SP314	1fr + 50c	.40	.30
B614	SP314	1.50fr + 50c	.80	.50
B615	SP315	2fr + 1fr	1.10	1.00
B616	SP316	2.50fr + 1fr	1.90	1.40
B617	SP316	5fr + 2fr	3.50	2.75
B618	SP316	6fr + 2.50fr	4.50	3.25
	Nos. B612-B618 (7)		12.45	9.50

The surtax was for anti-tuberculosis work. See Nos. B631-B637.

Benelux Gate SP317

Designs: 1fr+50c, Civil Engineering Pavilion. 1.50fr+50c, Belgian Congo & Ruanda-Urundi Pavilion. 2.50fr+1fr, Belgium 1900. 3fr+1.50fr, Atomium. 5fr+3fr, Telexpo Pavilion.

Perf. 11½

1958, Apr. 15   Unwmk.   Engr.

Size: 35½x24½mm

B619	SP317	30c + 20c multi	.25	.25
B620	SP317	1fr + 50c multi	.25	.25
B621	SP317	1.50fr + 50c multi	.25	.25
B622	SP317	2.50fr + 1fr multi	.45	.45
B623	SP317	3fr + 1.50fr multi	.90	.50

Size: 49x33mm

B624	SP317	5fr + 3fr multi	1.50	1.00
	Nos. B619-B624 (6)		3.60	2.70

World's Fair, Brussels, Apr. 17-Oct. 19.

Marguerite van Eyck by Jan van Eyck — SP318

Christ Carrying Cross, by Hieronymus Bosch SP319

Paintings: 1.50fr+50c, St. Donatien, Jan Gossart. 2.50fr+1fr, Self-portrait, Lambert Lombard. 3fr+1.50fr, The Rower, James Ensor. 5fr+3fr, Henriette, Henri Evenepoel.

1958, Oct. 30   Photo.   Perf. 11½
Various Frames in Ocher and Brown

B625	SP318	30c + 20c dk ol grn	.45	.30
B626	SP319	1fr + 50c mar	.75	.70
B627	SP318	1.50fr + 50c vio bl	1.10	.75
B628	SP318	2.50fr + 1fr dk brn	2.25	1.60
B629	SP319	3fr + 1.50fr dl red	3.25	2.00
B630	SP318	5fr + 3fr brt bl	5.25	5.00
	Nos. B625-B630 (6)		13.05	10.35

The surtax was for the benefit of various cultural organizations.

Type of 1957

Legends: 40c+10c, Elizabeth, Countess of Hoogstraten. 1fr+50c, Jean de Nivelles. 1.50fr+50c, St. Evermare play, Russon. 2fr+1fr, The Penitents of Furnes. 2.50fr+1fr, Manger and "Pax." 5fr+2fr, Sambre-Meuse procession. 6fr+2.50fr, Our Lady of Peace and "Pax," vert.

Engraved and Photogravure

1958, Dec. 6   Unwmk.   Perf. 11½

B631	SP314	40c + 10c ultra & brt grn	.30	.25
B632	SP315	1fr + 50c gray brn & grn	.40	.30
B633	SP315	1.50fr + 50c cl & brt grn	.60	.35
B634	SP314	2fr + 1fr brn & red	.70	.50
B635	SP316	2.50fr + 1fr vio brn & bl grn	2.50	1.90
B636	SP316	5fr + 2fr cl & bl	3.75	3.00
B637	SP316	6fr + 2.50fr bl & rose red	4.75	4.50
	Nos. B631-B637 (7)		13.00	10.80

The surtax was for anti-tuberculosis work.

"Europe of
the Heart"
SP320

1959, Feb. 25   Photo.   Unwmk.

B638	SP320	1fr + 50c red lil	.55	.30
B639	SP320	2.50fr + 1fr dk grn	.95	.90
B640	SP320	5fr + 2.50fr dp brn	1.25	1.10
		Nos. B638-B640 (3)	2.75	2.30

The surtax was for aid for displaced persons.

Allegory of Blood
Transfusion
SP321

Henri Dunant and Battlefield at
Solferino — SP322

Design: 2.50fr+1fr, 3fr+1.50fr, Red Cross, broken sword and drop of blood, horiz.

1959, June 10   Photo.   Perf. 11½

B641	SP321	40c + 10c	.60	.30
B642	SP321	1fr + 50c	1.10	.45
B643	SP321	1.50fr + 50c	3.00	1.60
B644	SP321	2.50fr + 1fr	3.50	1.90
B645	SP321	3fr + 1.50fr	6.00	3.50
B646	SP322	5fr + 3fr	11.50	5.50
		Nos. B641-B646 (6)	25.70	13.25

Cent. of the Intl. Red Cross idea. Surtax for the Red Cross and patriotic organizations.

Philip the
Good — SP323

Arms of
Philip the
Good
SP324

Designs: 1fr+50c, Charles the Bold. 1.50fr+50c, Emperor Maximilian of Austria. 2.50fr+1fr, Philip the Fair. 3fr+1.50fr, Charles V. Portraits from miniatures by Simon Bening (c. 1483-1561).

1959, July 4   Engr.

B647	SP323	40c + 10c multi	.50	.35
B648	SP323	1fr + 50c multi	.80	.50
B649	SP323	1.50fr + 50c multi	1.25	.80
B650	SP323	2.50fr + 1fr multi	1.90	

B651	SP323	3fr + 1.50fr multi	4.00	3.00
B652	SP324	5fr + 3fr multi	5.50	4.00
		Nos. B647-B652 (6)	14.30	10.55

The surtax was for the Royal Library, Brussels.
Portraits show Grand Masters of the Order of the Golden Fleece.

Whale, Antwerp
SP325

Carnival, Stavelot
SP326

Designs: 1fr+50c, Dragon, Mons. 2fr+50c, Prince Carnival, Eupen. 3fr+1fr, Jester and cats, Ypres. 6fr+2fr, Holy Family, horiz. 7fr+3fr, Madonna, Liége, horiz.

Engraved and Photogravure

1959, Dec. 5   Perf. 11½

B653	SP325	40c + 10c cit, Prus bl & red	.45	.40
B654	SP325	1fr + 50c ol & grn	.75	.60
B655	SP325	2fr + 50c lt brn, org & cl	.50	.40
B656	SP326	2.50fr + 1fr gray, pur & ultra	.80	.60
B657	SP326	3fr + 1fr gray, mar & yel	1.75	1.25
B658	SP326	6fr + 2fr ol, brt bl & hn brn	4.00	2.50
B659	SP326	7fr + 3fr chlky bl & org yel	5.25	4.25
		Nos. B653-B659 (7)	13.50	10.00

The surtax was for anti-tuberculosis work.

Child
Refugee — SP327

Designs: 3fr+1.50fr, Man. 6fr+3fr, Woman.

1960, Apr. 7   Engr.

B660	SP327	40c + 10c rose claret	.25	.25
B661	SP327	3fr + 1.50fr gray brn	.65	.50
B662	SP327	6fr + 3fr dk bl	1.60	1.10
a.		Souvenir sheet of 3	85.00	75.00
		Nos. B660-B662 (3)	2.50	1.85

World Refugee Year, 7/1/59-6/30/60.
No. B662a contains Nos. B660-B662 with colors changed: 40c+10c, dull purple; 3fr+1.50fr, red brown; 6fr+3fr, henna brown.

Parachutists
and Plane
SP328

Designs: 2fr+50c, 2.50fr+1fr, Parachutists coming in for landing, vert 3fr+1fr, 6fr+2fr, Parachutist walking with parachute.

Photogravure and Engraved
1960, June 13   Perf. 11½
Multicolored

B663	SP328	40c + 10c	.25	.25
B664	SP328	1fr + 50c	1.50	.70
B665	SP328	2fr + 50c	3.25	2.10
B666	SP328	2.50fr + 1fr	6.00	3.25
B667	SP328	3fr + 1fr	6.00	3.25
B668	SP328	6fr + 2fr	7.00	4.50
		Nos. B663-B668 (6)	24.00	14.05

The surtax was for various patriotic and cultural organizations.

Mother and
Child,
Planes and
Rainbow
SP329

Designs: 40c+10c, Brussels Airport, planes and rainbow. 6fr+3fr, Rainbow connecting Congo and Belgium, and planes, vert.

Perf. 11½
1960, Aug. 3   Unwmk.   Photo.
Size: 35x24mm

B669	SP329	40c + 10c grnsh blue	.25	.25
B670	SP329	3fr + 1.50fr brt red	2.50	2.25

Size: 35x52mm

B671	SP329	6fr + 3fr violet	4.75	3.50
		Nos. B669-B671 (3)	7.50	6.00

The surtax was for refugees from Congo.

Infant, Milk Bottle
and Mug — SP330

UNICEF: 1fr+50c, Nurse and children of 3 races. 2fr+50c, Refugee woman carrying gift clothes. 2.50fr+1fr, Negro nurse weighing infant. 3fr+1fr, Children of various races dancing. 6fr+2fr, Refugee boys.

Photogravure and Engraved
1960, Oct. 8   Perf. 11½

B672	SP330	40c + 10c gldn brn, yel & bl grn	.25	.25
B673	SP330	1fr + 50c ol gray, mar & slate	1.40	.75
B674	SP330	2fr + 50c vio, pale brn & brt grn	1.90	1.40
B675	SP330	2.50fr + 1fr dk red, sep & lt bl	2.00	1.40
B676	SP330	3fr + 1fr bl grn, red org & dl vio	2.50	1.60
B677	SP330	6fr + 2fr ultra, emer & brn	4.00	3.25
		Nos. B672-B677 (6)	12.05	8.65

Tapestry
SP331

Belgian handicrafts: 1fr+50c, Cut crystal vases, vert. 2fr+50c, Lace, vert. 2.50fr+1fr, Metal plate & jug. 3fr+1fr, Diamonds. 6fr+2fr, Ceramics.

1960, Dec. 5   Perf. 11½
Multicolored

B678	SP331	40c + 10c	.25	.25
B679	SP331	1fr + 50c	1.00	1.00
B680	SP331	2fr + 50c	2.00	1.50
B681	SP331	2.50fr + 1fr	3.00	2.25
B682	SP331	3fr + 1fr	3.50	2.25
B683	SP331	6fr + 2fr	5.00	4.00
		Nos. B678-B683 (6)	14.75	11.25

The surtax was for anti-tuberculosis work.

Jacob Kats
and Abbe
Nicolas
Pietkin
SP332

Portraits: 1fr+50c, Albert Mockel and J. F. Willems. 2fr+50c, Jan van Rijswijck and Xavier M. Neujean. 2.50fr+1fr, Joseph Demarteau

and A. Van de Perre. 3fr+1fr, Canon Jan-Baptist David and Albert du Bois. 6fr+2fr, Henri Vieuxtemps and Willem de Mol.

1961, Apr. 22   Unwmk.   Perf. 11½
Multicolored
Portraits in Gray Brown

B684	SP332	40c + 10c	.50	.30
B685	SP332	1fr + 50c	2.25	1.25
B686	SP332	2fr + 50c	3.75	3.00
B687	SP332	2.50fr + 1fr	3.75	3.00
B688	SP332	3fr + 1fr	4.25	3.00
B689	SP332	6fr + 2fr	6.00	4.50
		Nos. B684-B689 (6)	20.50	15.05

The surtax was for the benefit of various cultural organizations.

White Rhinoceros
SP333

Animals: 1fr+50c, Przewalski horses. 2fr+50c, Okapi. 2.50fr+1fr, Giraffe, horiz. 3fr+1fr, Lesser panda, horiz. 6fr+2fr, European elk, horiz.

Perf. 11½
1961, June 5   Unwmk.   Photo.
Multicolored

B690	SP333	40c + 10c	.25	.25
B691	SP333	1fr + 50c	1.10	1.00
B692	SP333	2fr + 50c	1.60	1.40
B693	SP333	2.50fr + 1fr	2.00	1.50
B694	SP333	3fr + 1fr	2.25	1.50
B695	SP333	6fr + 2fr	2.75	2.10
		Nos. B690-B695 (6)	9.95	7.75

The surtax was for various philanthropic organizations.

Antonius Cardinal
Perrenot de
Granvelle — SP334

Designs: 3fr+1.50fr, Arms of Cardinal de Granvelle. 6fr+3fr, Tower and crosier, symbolic of collaboration between Malines and the Archbishopric.

1961, July 29   Engr.

B696	SP334	40c + 10c mag, car & brn	.25	.25
B697	SP334	3fr + 1.50fr multi	.70	.60
B698	SP334	6fr + 3fr mag pur & bis	1.40	1.10
		Nos. B696-B698 (3)	2.35	1.95

400th anniv. of Malines as an Archbishopric.

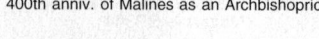

Mother and Child
by Pierre
Paulus — SP335

Plaintings: 1fr+50c, Mother Love, Francois-Joseph Navez. 2fr+50c, Motherhood, Constant Permeke. 2.50fr+1fr, Madonna and Child, Rogier van der Weyden. 3fr+1fr, Madonna with Apple, Hans Memling. 6fr+2fr, Madonna of the Forget-me-not, Peter Paul Rubens.

1961, Dec. 2   Photo.   Perf. 11½
Gold Frame

B699	SP335	40c + 10c dp brn	.25	.25
B700	SP335	1fr + 50c brt bl	.60	.55
B701	SP335	2fr + 50c rose red	1.00	.90
B702	SP335	2.50fr + 1fr mag	1.10	.90
B703	SP335	3fr + 1fr vio bl	1.00	.90

B704 SP335 6fr + 2fr dk sl
grn   1.75 1.50
Nos. B699-B704 (6)   5.70 5.00

The surtax was for anti-tuberculosis work.

Castle of the
Counts of
Male — SP336

Designs: 90c+10c, Royal library, horiz.
1fr+50c, Church of Our Lady, Tongres.
2fr+50c, Collegiate Church, Soignies, horiz.
2.50fr+1fr, Church of Our Lady, Malines.
3fr+1fr, St. Denis Abbey, Broqueroi. 6fr+2fr,
Cloth Hall, Ypres, horiz.

1962, Mar. 12   **Engr.**   **Perf. 11½**
B705 SP336 40c + 10c brt grn   .25   .25
B706 SP336 90c + 10c lil rose   .25   .25
B707 SP336 1fr + 50c dl vio   .40   .45
B708 SP336 2fr + 50c violet   .70   .60
B709 SP336 2.50fr + 1fr red brn   1.10   .85
B710 SP336 3fr + 1fr bl grn   1.25   .85
B711 SP336 6fr + 2fr car rose   1.90 1.40
   Nos. B705-B711 (7)   5.85 4.65

The surtax was for various cultural and philanthropic organizations.

Andean Cock of
the Rock — SP337

Birds: 1fr+50c, Red lory. 2fr+50c, Guinea
touraco. 2.50fr+1fr, Keel-billed toucan. 3fr+1fr,
Great bird of paradise. 6fr+2fr, Congolese
peacock.

Engraved and Photogravure
1962, June 23   **Unwmk.**   **Perf. 11½**
B712 SP337 40c + 10c multi   .25   .25
B713 SP337 1fr + 50c multi   .45   .50
B714 SP337 2fr + 50c multi   .75   .70
B715 SP337 2.50fr + 1fr multi   1.00   .90
B716 SP337 3fr + 1fr multi   1.40 1.25
B717 SP337 6fr + 2fr multi   2.00 1.75
   Nos. B712-B717 (6)   5.85 5.10

The surtax was for various philanthropic
organizations.

Handicapped
Child — SP338

Handicapped Children: 40c+10c, Reading
Braille. 2fr+50c, Deaf-mute girl with earphones
and electronic equipment, horiz. 2.50fr+1fr,
Child with ball (cerebral palsy). 3fr+1fr, Girl
with crutches (polio). 6fr+2fr, Sitting boys playing ball, horiz.

1962, Sept. 22   **Photo.**
B718 SP338 40c + 10c choc   .25   .25
B719 SP338 1fr + 50c rose
red   .45   .45
B720 SP338 2fr + 50c brt lil   1.00   .90
B721 SP338 2.50fr + 1fr dl grn   1.00   .90
B722 SP338 3fr + 1fr dk blue   1.00   .90
B723 SP338 6fr + 2fr dk brn   1.50 1.25
   Nos. B718-B723 (6)   5.20 4.65

The surtax was for various institutions for
handicapped children.

Queen Louise-
Marie
SP339

Belgian Queens: No. B725, like No. B724
with "ML" initials. 1fr+50c, Marie-Henriette.
2fr+1fr, Elisabeth. 3fr+1.50fr, Astrid.
8fr+2.50fr, Fabiola.

1962, Dec. 8   **Photo. & Engr.**
       Gray, Black & Gold
B724 SP339 40c + 10c ("L")   .25   .25
B725 SP339 40c + 10c ("ML")   .25   .25
B726 SP339 1fr + 50c   .60   .50
B727 SP339 2fr + 1fr   1.25 1.10
B728 SP339 3fr + 1.50fr   1.60 1.40
B729 SP339 8fr + 2.50fr   1.90 1.60
   Nos. B724-B729 (6)   5.85 5.10

The surtax was for anti-tuberculosis work.

British War
Memorial
(Porte de
Menin),
Ypres
SP340

1962, Dec. 26   **Engr.**   **Perf. 11½**
B730 SP340 1fr + 50c multi   .50   .50
Millennium of the city of Ypres. Issued in
sheets of eight.

Peace Bell Ringing
over
Globe — SP341

Engraved and Photogravure
1963, Feb. 18   **Unwmk.**   **Perf. 11½**
B731 SP341 3fr +1.50fr multi   1.60 1.60
   a.   Sheet of 4   7.75 7.75
B732 SP341 6fr +3fr multi   .80   .80

The surtax was for the installation of the
Peace Bell (Bourdon de la Paix) at Koekelberg
Basilica and for the benefit of various cultural
organizations.
No. B731 was issued in sheets of 4, No.
B732 in sheets of 30.

The Sower by
Brueghel — SP342

Designs: 3fr+1fr, The Harvest, by Brueghel,
horiz. 6fr+2fr, "Bread," by Anton Carte, horiz.

1963, Mar. 21   **Perf. 11½**
B733 SP342 2fr +1fr multi   .25   .25
B734 SP342 3fr + 1fr multi   .40   .30
B735 SP342 6fr +2fr multi   .55   .50
   Nos. B733-B735 (3)   1.20 1.05

FAO "Freedom from Hunger" campaign.

2fr+1fr, Bicyclists at check point, horiz.
3fr+1.50fr, Team racing, horiz. 6fr+3fr, Pace
setters.

      Perf. 11½
1963, July 13   **Unwmk.**   **Engr.**
B736 SP343 1fr + 50c multi   .25   .25
B737 SP343 2fr + 1fr bl, car, blk
& ol gray   .25   .25
B738 SP343 3fr + 1.50fr multi   .35   .35
B739 SP343 6fr + 3fr multi   .55   .55
   Nos. B736-B739 (4)   1.40 1.40

80th anniversary of the founding of the Belgian Bicycle League. The surtax was for athletes at the 1964 Olympic Games.

Princess Paola with
Princess
Astrid — SP344

Prince Albert and Family — SP345

Designs: 40c+10c, Prince Philippe. 2fr+50c,
Princess Astrid. 2.50fr+1fr, Princess Paola.
6fr+2fr, Prince Albert.

1963, Sept. 28   **Photo.**
B740 SP344 40c + 10c   .25   .25
B741 SP344 1fr + 50c   .35   .30
B742 SP344 2fr + 50c   .45   .40
B743 SP344 2.50fr + 1fr   .45   .40
B744 SP345 3fr + 1fr brn &
multi   .65   .65
B745 SP345 3fr + 1fr yel
grn & mul-
ti   2.00 2.00
   a.   Booklet pane of 8   19.00 19.00
B746 SP344 6fr + 2fr   1.60 1.60
   Nos. B740-B746 (7)   5.75 5.60

Cent. of the Intl. Red Cross. No. B745
issued in booklet panes of 8, which are in two
forms: French and Flemish inscriptions in top
and bottom margins transposed. Value the
same.

Daughter of
Balthazar Gerbier,
Painted by
Rubens — SP346

Jesus, St. John and Cherubs by
Rubens — SP347

Portraits (Rubens' sons): 1fr+40c, Nicolas, 2
yrs. old. 2fr+50c, Franz. 2.50fr+1fr, Nicolas, 6
yrs. old. 3fr+1fr, Albert.

Photogravure and Engraved
1963, Dec. 7   **Unwmk.**   **Perf. 11½**
B747 SP346 50c + 10c   .25   .25
B748 SP346 1fr + 40c   .25   .25
B749 SP346 2fr + 50c   .30   .30
B750 SP346 2.50fr + 1fr   .65   .65

B751 SP346 3fr + 1fr   .55   .55
B752 SP347 6fr + 2fr   .90   .90
   Nos. B747-B752 (6)   2.90 2.90

The surtax was for anti-tuberculosis work.
See No. B771.

John Quincy Adams and Lord
Gambier Signing Treaty of Ghent, by
Amédée Forestier — SP348

1964, May 16   **Photo.**   **Perf. 11½**
B753 SP348 6fr + 3fr dk blue   .75   .75

Signing of the Treaty of Ghent between the
US and Great Britain, Dec. 24, 1814.

Philip van
Marnix — SP349

Portraits: 3fr+1.50fr, Ida de Bure Calvin.
6fr+3fr, Jacob Jordaens.

1964, May 30   **Engr.**
B754 SP349 1fr + 50c blue gray   .25   .25
B755 SP349 3fr + 1.50fr rose
pink   .25   .25
B756 SP349 6fr + 3fr redsh brn   .70   .70
   Nos. B754-B756 (3)   1.20 1.20

Issued to honor Protestantism in Belgium.
The surtax was for the erection of a Protestant
church.

Foot Soldier,
1918 — SP350

Designs: 2fr+1fr, Flag bearer, Guides Regiment, 1914. 3fr+1.50fr, Trumpeter of the Grenadiers and drummers, 1914.

1964, Aug. 1   **Photo.**   **Perf. 11½**
B757 SP350 1fr + 50c multi   .25   .25
B758 SP350 2fr + 1fr multi   .25   .25
B759 SP350 3fr + 1.50fr multi   .35   .35
   Nos. B757-B759 (3)   .85   .85

50th anniversary of the German aggression
against Belgium in 1914. The surtax aided
patriotic undertakings.

Battle of
Bastogne — SP351

6fr+3fr, Liberation of the estuary of the
Escaut.

1964, Aug. 1   **Unwmk.**
B760 SP351 3fr + 1fr multi   .25   .25
B761 SP351 6fr + 3fr multi   .70   .70

Belgium's Resistance and liberation of
World War II. The surtax was to help found an
International Student Center at Antwerp and
to aid cultural undertakings.

Souvenir Sheets

Rogier van der Weyden
Paintings — SP352

Descent From the Cross — SP353

1964, Sept. 19   **Photo.**   *Perf. 11½*
B762	SP352	Sheet of 3	4.25 4.25
a.		1fr Philip the Good	1.10 1.10
b.		2fr Portrait of a Lady	1.10 1.10
c.		3fr Man with Arrow	1.10 1.10

Engr.
B763	SP353	8fr red brown	4.25 4.25

Rogier van der Weyden (Roger de La Pasture, 1400-64). The surtax went to various cultural organizations. No. B762 sold for 14fr, No. B763 for 16fr.

Ancient View of the Pand — SP354

3fr+1fr, Present view of the Pand from Lys River.

1964, Oct. 10   **Photo.**
B764	SP354	2fr + 1fr blk, grnsh bl & ultra	.40 .40
B765	SP354	3fr + 1fr lil rose, bl & dk brn	.40 .40

The surtax was for the restoration of the Pand Dominican Abbey in Ghent.

Type of 1963 and

Child of Charles I, Painted by Van Dyck — SP355

Designs: 1fr+40c, William of Orange with his bride, by Van Dyck. 2fr+1fr, Portrait of a small boy with dogs by Erasmus Quellin and Jan Fyt. 3fr+1fr, Alexander Farnese by Antonio Moro. 4fr+2fr, William II, Prince of Orange by Van Dyck. 6fr+3fr, Artist's children by Cornelis De Vos.

1964, Dec. 5   **Engr.**   *Perf. 11½*
B766	SP355	50c + 10c rose clar	.25 .25
B767	SP355	1fr + 40c car rose	.25 .25
B768	SP355	2fr + 1fr vio brn	.25 .25
B769	SP355	3fr + 1fr gray	.30 .30
B770	SP355	4fr + 2fr vio bl	.50 .50
B771	SP347	6fr + 3fr brt pur	.70 .70
	Nos. B766-B771 (6)		2.25 2.25

The surtax was for anti-tuberculosis work.

Liberator, Shaking Prisoner's Hand, Concentration Camp — SP356

Designs: 1fr+50c, Prisoner's hand reaching for the sun. 3fr+1.50fr, Searchlights and tank breaking down barbed wire, horiz. 8fr+5fr, Rose growing amid the ruins, horiz.

Engraved and Photogravure
1965, May 8   **Unwmk.**   *Perf. 11½*
B772	SP356	50c + 50c tan, blk & buff	.25 .25
B773	SP356	1fr + 50c multi	.25 .25
B774	SP356	3fr + 1.50fr dl lil & blk	.35 .35
B775	SP356	8fr + 5fr multi	.70 .70
	Nos. B772-B775 (4)		1.55 1.55

20th anniv. of the liberation of the concentration camps for political prisoners and prisoners of war.

Stoclet House, Brussels SP357

Stoclet House: 6fr+3fr, Hall with marble foundation, vert. 8fr+4fr, View of house from garden.

1965, June 21
B776	SP357	3fr + 1fr slate & tan	.30 .30
B777	SP357	6fr + 3fr sepia	.50 .50
B778	SP357	8fr + 4fr vio brn & tan	.65 .65
	Nos. B776-B778 (3)		1.45 1.45

Austrian architect Josef Hoffmann (1870-1956), builder of the art nouveau residence of Adolphe Stoclet, engineer and financier.

Jackson's Chameleon SP358

Animals from Antwerp Zoo: 2fr+1fr, Common iguanas. 3fr+1.50fr, African monitor. 6fr+3fr, Komodo monitor. 8fr+4fr, Nile softshell turtle.

1965, Oct. 16   **Photo.**   *Perf. 11½*
B779	SP358	1fr + 50c multi	.25 .25
B780	SP358	2fr + 1fr multi	.25 .25
B781	SP358	3fr + 1.50fr multi	.35 .35
B782	SP358	6fr + 3fr multi	.50 .50
	Nos. B779-B782 (4)		1.35 1.35

Miniature Sheet
B783	SP358	8fr + 4fr multi	1.75 1.75

The surtax was for various cultural and philanthropic organizations. No. B783 contains one stamp, size: 52x35mm.

Boatmen's and Archers' Guild Halls SP359

Buildings on Grand-Place, Brussels: 1fr+40c, Brewers' Hall. 2fr+1fr, "King of Spain." 3fr+1.50fr, "Dukes of Brabant." 10fr+4.50fr, Tower of City Hall and St. Michael.

1965, Dec. 4   **Engr.**   *Perf. 11½*
Size: 35x24mm
B784	SP359	50c + 10c ultra	.25 .25
B785	SP359	1fr + 40c bl grn	.25 .25
B786	SP359	2fr + 1fr rose cl	.25 .25
B787	SP359	3fr + 1.50fr violet	.35 .35

Size: 24x44mm
B788	SP359	10fr + 4.50fr sep & gray	.80 .80
	Nos. B784-B788 (5)		1.90 1.90

The surtax was for anti-tuberculosis work.

Souvenir Sheets

Queen Elisabeth — SP360

Design: No. B790, Types of 1931 and 1956.

1966, Apr. 16   **Photo.**   *Perf. 11½*
B789	SP360	Sheet of 2 + label	1.50 1.50
a.		SP74 3fr dk brn & gray grn	.60 .60
b.		SP87 3fr dk brn, yel grn & gold	.60 .60
B790	SP360	Sheet of 2 + label	1.50 1.50
a.		SP42 3fr dk brn & dl bl	.60 .60
b.		SP304 3fr dk brn & gray	.60 .60

The surtax went to various cultural organizations.
Each sheet sold for 20fr.

Luminescent Paper
was used in printing Nos. B789-B790, B801-B806, B808-B809, B811-B823, B825-B831, B833-B835, B837-B840, B842-B846, B848-B850, B852-B854, B856-B863, and from B865 onward unless otherwise noted. In many cases the low value of the set is not on luminescent paper. This will not be noted.

Diver — SP361

Design: 10fr+4fr, Swimmer at start.

1966, May 9   **Engr.**
B791	SP361	60c + 40c Prus grn, ol & org brn	.25 .25
B792	SP361	10fr + 4fr ol grn, org brn & mag	.80 .80

Issued to publicize the importance of swimming instruction.

Minorites' Convent, Liège — SP362

Designs: 1fr+50c, Val-Dieu Abbey, Aubel. 2fr+1fr, View and seal of Huy. 10fr+4.50fr, Statue of Ambiorix by Jules Bertin, and tower, Tongeren.

1966, Aug. 27   **Engr.**   *Perf. 11½*
B793	SP362	60c + 40c multi	.25 .25
B794	SP362	1fr + 50c multi	.25 .25
B795	SP362	2fr + 1fr multi	.25 .25
B796	SP362	10fr + 4.50fr multi	.80 .80
	Nos. B793-B796 (4)		1.55 1.55

The surtax was for various patriotic and cultural organizations.

Surveyor and Dog Team SP363

3fr+1.50fr, Adrien de Gerlache, "Belgica." 6fr+3fr, Surveyor, weather balloon, ship. 10fr+5fr, Penguins, "Magga Dan" (ship used for 1964, 1965 & 1966 expeditions).

1966, Oct. 8   **Engr.**   *Perf. 11½*
B797	SP363	1fr + 50c bl grn	.25 .25
B798	SP363	3fr + 1.50fr pale vio	.25 .25
B799	SP363	6fr + 3fr dk car	.50 .50
	Nos. B797-B799 (3)		1.00 1.00

Souvenir Sheet
Engraved and Photogravure
B800	SP363	10fr + 5fr dk gray, sky bl & dk red	1.00 1.00

Belgian Antarctic expeditions. No. B800 contains one 52x35mm stamp.

Boy with Ball and Dog — SP364

Designs: 2fr+1fr, Girl skipping rope. 3fr+1.50fr, Girl and boy blowing soap bubbles. 6fr+3fr, Girl and boy rolling hoops, horiz. 8fr+3.50fr, Four children at play and cat, horiz.

1966, Dec. 3   *Perf. 11½*
B801	SP364	1fr + 1fr pink & blk	.25 .25
B802	SP364	2fr + 1fr lt bluish grn & blk	.25 .25
B803	SP364	3fr + 1.50fr lt vio & blk	.25 .25
B804	SP364	6fr + 3fr pale sal & dk brn	.50 .50
B805	SP364	8fr + 3.50fr lt yel grn & dk brn	.65 .65
	Nos. B801-B805 (5)		1.90 1.90

The surtax was for anti-tuberculosis work.

Souvenir Sheet

Refugees — SP365

1fr, Boy receiving clothes. 2fr, Tibetan children. 3fr, African mother and children.

1967, Mar. 11   **Photo.**   *Perf. 11½*
B806	SP365	Sheet of 3	1.25 1.25
a.		1fr black & yellow	.30 .30
b.		2fr black & blue	.30 .30
c.		3fr black & orange	.40 .40

Issued to help refugees around the world. Sheet has black border with Belgian P.T.T. and UN Refugee emblems. Sold for 20fr.

Robert Schuman
SP366

Colonial
Brotherhood
Emblem
SP368

Kongolo
Memorial,
Gentinnes
SP367

1967, June 24   Engr.   Perf. 11½
B807 SP366 2fr + 1fr gray blue   .25 .25

Engraved and Photogravure
B808 SP367 5fr + 2fr brn & ol   .40 .40
B809 SP368 10fr + 5fr multi   .85 .85
  Nos. B807-B809 (3)   1.50 1.50

Robert Schuman (1886-1963), French statesman, one of the founders of European Steel and Coal Community, 1st pres. of European Parliament (2fr+1fr); Kongolo Memorial, erected in memory of missionary and civilian victims in the Congo (5fr+2fr); a memorial for African Troops, Brussels (10fr+5fr).

Preaching Fool
from "Praise of
Folly" by Erasmus
SP369

Erasmus, by
Quentin Massys
SP370

Designs: 2fr+1fr, Exhorting Fool from Praise of Folly. 5fr+2fr, Thomas More's Family, by Hans Holbein, horiz. 6fr+3fr, Pierre Gilles (Aegidius), by Quentin Massys.

Photogravure and Engraved (SP369); Photogravure (SP370)
1967, Sept. 2   Unwmk.   Perf. 11
B810 SP369 1fr + 50c tan, blk, bl
  & car   .25 .25
B811 SP369 2fr + 1fr tan, blk &
  car   .25 .25
B812 SP370 3fr + 1.50fr multi   .25 .25
B813 SP369 5fr + 2fr tan, blk &
  car   .45 .45
B814 SP370 6fr + 3fr multi   .55 .55
  Nos. B810-B814 (5)   1.75 1.75

Issued to commemorate Erasmus (1466(?)-1536), Dutch scholar and his era.

Souvenir Sheet

Pro-Post Association
Emblem — SP371

Engraved and Photogravure
1967, Oct. 21   Perf. 11½
B815 SP371 10fr + 5fr multi   1.00 1.00

Issued to publicize the POSTPHILA Philatelic Exhibition, Brussels, Oct. 21-29.

Detail from Brueghel's "Children's
Games" — SP372

Designs: Various Children's Games. Singles of Nos. B816-B821 arranged in 2 rows of 3 show complete painting by Pieter Brueghel.

1967, Dec. 9   Photo.   Perf. 11½
B816 SP372 1fr + 50c multi   .25 .25
B817 SP372 2fr + 50c multi   .25 .25
B818 SP372 3fr + 1fr multi   .30 .30
B819 SP372 6fr + 3fr multi   .50 .50
B820 SP372 10fr + 4fr multi   .85 .85
B821 SP372 13fr + 6fr multi   1.10 1.10
  Nos. B816-B821 (6)   3.25 3.25

Queen Fabiola
Holding Refugee
Child from
Congo — SP373

6fr+3fr, Queen Elisabeth & Dr. Depage.

1968, Apr. 27   Photo.   Perf. 11½
Cross in Red
B822 SP373 6fr + 3fr sepia & gray .65 .65
B823 SP373 10fr + 5fr sepia & gray .95 .95

The surtax was for the Red Cross.

Woman
Gymnast
and
Calendar
Stone
SP374

Yachting and "The
Swimmer" by
Andrien — SP375

Designs: 2fr+1fr, Weight lifter and Mayan motif. 3fr+1.50fr, Hurdler, colossus of Tula and animal head from Kukulkan. 6fr+2fr, Bicyclists and Chichen Itza Temple.

Engraved and Photogravure
1968, May 27   Perf. 11½
B824 SP374 1fr + 50c multi   .25 .25
B825 SP374 2fr + 1fr multi   .25 .25
B826 SP374 3fr + 1.50fr multi   .25 .25
B827 SP374 6fr + 2fr multi   .55 .55
Photo.
B828 SP375 13fr + 5fr multi   1.10 1.10
  Nos. B824-B828 (5)   2.40 2.40

Issued to publicize the 19th Olympic Games, Mexico City, Oct. 12-27.

"Explosion"
SP376

Designs (Paintings by Pol Mara): 12fr+5fr, "Fire." 13fr+5fr, "Tornado."

1968, June 22   Photo.
B829 SP376 10fr + 5fr multi   .80 .80
B830 SP376 12fr + 5fr multi   .95 .95
B831 SP376 13fr + 5fr multi   1.25 1.25
  Nos. B829-B831 (3)   3.00 3.00

The surtax was for disaster victims.

Undulate
Triggerfish
SP377

Tropical Fish: 3fr+1.50fr, Angelfish. 6fr+3fr, Turkeyfish (Pterois volitans). 10fr+5fr, Orange butterflyfish.

1968, Oct. 19   Engr. & Photo.
B832 SP377 1fr + 50c multi   .25 .25
B833 SP377 3fr + 1.50fr multi   .25 .25
B834 SP377 6fr + 3fr multi   .55 .55
B835 SP377 10fr + 5fr multi   .80 .80
  Nos. B832-B835 (4)   1.85 1.85

King Albert
and Queen
Elisabeth
Entering
Brussels
SP378

Tomb of the Unknown Soldier and
Eternal Flame, Brussels — SP379

Designs: 1fr+50c, King Albert, Queen Elisabeth and Crown Prince Leopold on balcony, Bruges, vert. 6fr+3fr, King and Queen entering Liège.

1968, Nov. 9   Photo.   Perf. 11½
B836 SP378 1fr + 50c multi   .25 .25
B837 SP378 3fr + 1.50fr multi   .25 .25
B838 SP378 6fr + 3fr multi   .50 .50

Engraved and Photogravure
B839 SP379 10fr + 5fr multi   .80 .80
  Nos. B836-B839 (4)   1.80 1.80

50th anniv. of the victory in World War I.

Souvenir Sheet

The Painter and the Amateur, by Peter
Brueghel — SP380

1969, May 10   Engr.   Perf. 11½
B840 SP380 10fr + 5fr sepia   1.10 1.10

Issued to publicize the POSTPHILA 1969 Philatelic Exhibition, Brussels, May 10-18.

Huts, by Ivanka D.
Pancheva,
Bulgaria — SP381

Children's Drawings and UNICEF Emblem: 3fr+1.50fr, "My Art" (Santa Claus), by Claes Patric, Belgium. 6fr+3fr, "In the Sun" (young boy), by Helena Rejchlova, Czechoslovakia. 10fr+5fr, "Out for a Walk" by Phillis Sporn, US, horiz.

1969, May 31   Photo.   Perf. 11½
B841 SP381 1fr + 50c multi   .25 .25
B842 SP381 3fr + 1.50fr multi   .25 .25
B843 SP381 6fr + 3fr multi   .55 .55
B844 SP381 10fr + 5fr multi   .85 .85
  Nos. B841-B844 (4)   1.90 1.90

The surtax was for philanthropic purposes.

Msgr. Victor
Scheppers
SP382

1969, July 5   Engr.
B845 SP382 6fr + 3fr rose claret   .70 .70

Msgr. Victor Scheppers (1802-77), prison reformer and founder of the Brothers of Mechlin (Scheppers).

Moon Landing Type of 1969
Souvenir Sheet

Design: 20fr+10fr, Armstrong, Collins and Aldrin and moon with Tranquillity Base, vert.

1969, Sept. 20   Photo.   Perf. 11½
B846 A245 20fr + 10fr indigo   3.00 3.00

See note after No. 726.

Heads from Alexander the Great Tapestry, 15th Century — SP383

Designs from Tapestries: 3fr+1.50fr, Fiddler from "The Feast," c. 1700. 10fr+4fr, Head of beggar from "The Healing of the Paralytic," 16th century.

1969, Sept. 20

B847	SP383	1fr + 50c multi	.25	.25
B848	SP383	3fr + 1.50fr multi	.40	.40
B849	SP383	10fr + 4fr multi	1.00	1.00
	Nos. B847-B849 (3)		1.65	1.65

The surtax was for philanthropic purposes.

Bearded Antwerp Bantam SP384

1969, Nov. 8   Engr. & Photo.

B850	SP384	10fr + 5fr multi	1.00	1.00

Angel Playing Lute — SP385

Designs from Stained Glass Windows: 1.50fr+50c, Angel with trumpet, St. Waudru's, Mons. 7fr+3fr, Angel with viol, St. Jacques', Liege. 9fr+4fr, King with bagpipes, Royal Art Museum, Brussels.

1969, Dec. 13   Photo.

Size: 24x35mm

B851	SP385	1.50fr + 50c multi	.25	.25
B852	SP385	3.50fr + 1.50fr multi	.30	.30
B853	SP385	7fr + 3fr multi	.65	.65

Size: 35x52mm

B854	SP386	9fr + 4fr multi	1.00	1.00
	Nos. B851-B854 (4)		2.20	2.20

The surtax was for philanthropic purposes.

Farm and Windmill, Open-air Museum, Bokrijk SP386

Belgian Museums: 3.50fr+1.50fr, Stage Coach Inn, Courcelles. 7fr+3fr, "The Thresher of Trevires," Gallo-Roman sculpture, Gaumais Museum, Virton. 9fr+4fr, "The Sovereigns," by Henry Moore, Middelheim Museum, Antwerp.

Engraved and Photogravure

1970, May 30   Perf. 11½

B855	SP386	1.50fr + 50c multi	.25	.25
B856	SP386	3.50fr + 1.50fr multi	.30	.30
B857	SP386	7fr + 3fr multi	.60	.60
B858	SP386	9fr + 4fr multi	.75	.75
	Nos. B855-B858 (4)		1.90	1.90

The surtax went to various culture organizations.

"Resistance" SP387

Design: 7fr+3fr, "Liberation of Camps." The designs were originally used as book covers.

1970, July 4   Photo.   Perf. 11½

B859	SP387	3.50fr + 1.50fr blk, gray grn & dp car	.35	.35
B860	SP387	7fr + 3fr blk, lil & dp car	.60	.60

Honoring the Resistance Movement and 25th anniv. of the liberation of concentration camps.

Fishing Rod and Reel SP388

Design: 9fr+4fr, Hockey stick and puck, vert.

1970, Sept. 19   Engr. & Photo.

B861	SP388	3.50fr + 1.50fr multi	.30	.30
B862	SP388	9fr + 4fr multi	.70	.70

Souvenir Sheet

Belgium Nos. 31, 36, 39 — SP389

1970, Oct. 10   Perf. 11½

B863	SP389	Sheet of 3	4.75	4.75
a.		1.50fr + 50c black & dull lilac	1.40	1.40
b.		3.50fr + 1.50fr black & lilac	1.40	1.40
c.		9fr + 4fr black & red brown	1.40	1.40

BELGICA 72 International Philatelic Exhibition, Brussels, June 24-July 9.

Camille Huysmans (1871-1968) SP390

3.50fr+1.50fr, Joseph Cardinal Cardijn (1882-1967). 7fr+3fr, Maria Baers (1883-1959). 9fr+4fr, Paul Pastur (1866-1938).

1970, Nov. 14   Perf. 11½

Portraits in Sepia

B864	SP390	1.50fr + 50c car rose	.25	.25
B865	SP390	3.50fr + 1.50fr lilac	.30	.30
B866	SP390	7fr + 3fr green	.55	.55
B867	SP390	9fr + 4fr blue	.75	.75
	Nos. B864-B867 (4)		1.85	1.85

"Anxious City" (Detail) by Paul Delvaux — SP391

7fr+3fr, "The Memory," by Rene Magritte.

1970, Dec. 12   Photo.

B868	SP391	3.50fr + 1.50fr multi	.30	.30
B869	SP391	7fr + 3fr multi	.65	.65

Notre Dame du Vivier, Marche-les-Dames — SP392

7fr+3fr, Turnhout Beguinage and Beguine.

1971, Mar. 13   Perf. 11½

B870	SP392	3.50fr + 1.50fr multi	.30	.30
B871	SP392	7fr + 3fr multi	.65	.65

The surtax was for philanthropic purposes.

Red Cross — SP393

1971, May 22   Photo.   Perf. 11½

B872	SP393	10fr + 5fr crim & blk	.80	.80

Belgian Red Cross.

Discobolus and Munich Cathedral — SP394

1971, June 19   Engr. & Photo.

B873	SP394	7fr + 3fr bl & blk	.65	.65

Publicity for the 20th Summer Olympic Games, Munich 1972.

Festival of Flanders — SP395

Design: 7fr+3fr, Wallonia Festival.

1971, Sept. 11   Photo.   Perf. 11½

B874	SP395	3.50fr + 1.50fr multi	.30	.30
B875	SP395	7fr + 3fr multi	.65	.65

Attre Palace — SP396

Steen Palace, Elewijt — SP397

Design: 10fr+5fr, Royal Palace, Brussels.

1971, Oct. 23   Engr.

B876	SP396	3.50fr + 1.50fr sl grn	.30	.30
B877	SP397	7fr + 3fr red brn	.65	.65
B878	SP396	10fr + 5fr vio bl	.90	.90
	Nos. B876-B878 (3)		1.85	1.85

Surtax was for BELGICA 72, International Philatelic Exposition.

Ox Fly, tabanus bromius SP398

Insects: 1.50fr+50c, Luna moth, vert. 7fr+3fr, Wasp, polistes gallicus. 9fr+4fr, Tiger beetle, vert.

1971, Dec. 11   Photo.   Perf. 11½

B879	SP398	1.50fr + 50c multi	.25	.25
B880	SP398	3.50fr + 1.50fr multi	.30	.30
B881	SP398	7fr + 3fr multi	.65	.65
B882	SP398	9fr + 4fr multi	.75	.75
	Nos. B879-B882 (4)		1.95	1.95

Surtax was for philanthropic purposes.

Leopold I on #1 — SP399

2fr+1fr, Leopold I on #5. 2.50fr+1fr, Leopold II on #45. 3.50fr+1.50fr, Leopold II on #48. 6fr+3fr, Albert I on #135. 7fr+3fr, Albert I on #214. 10fr+5fr, Albert I on #231. 15fr+7.50fr, Leopold III on #290. 20fr+10fr, King Baudouin on #718.

Engraved and Photogravure

1972, June 24   Perf. 11½

B883	SP399	1.50fr + 50c	.25	.25
B884	SP399	2fr + 1fr	.25	.25
B885	SP399	2.50 + 1fr	.30	.30
B886	SP399	3.50fr + 1.50fr	.35	.35
B887	SP399	6fr + 3fr	.50	.50
B888	SP399	7fr + 3fr	.70	.70
B889	SP399	10fr + 5fr	.90	.90
B890	SP399	15fr + 7fr	1.25	1.25
B891	SP399	20fr + 10fr	2.00	2.00
	Nos. B883-B891 (9)		6.50	6.50

Belgica 72, Intl. Philatelic Exhibition, Brussels, June 24-July 9. Nos. B883-B891 issued in sheets of 10 and of 20 (2 tete beche sheets with gutter between). Sold in complete sets.

Epilepsy Emblem — SP400

1972, Sept. 9   Photo.   Perf. 11½

B892	SP400	10fr + 5fr multi	.80	.80

The surtax was for the William Lennox Center for epilepsy research and treatment.

Gray Lag Goose — SP401

Designs: 4.50fr+2fr, Lapwing. 8fr+4fr, Stork. 9fr+4.50fr, Kestrel, horiz.

1972, Dec. 16	Photo.	Perf. 11½	
B893 SP401	2fr + 1fr multi	.25	.25
B894 SP401	4.50fr + 2fr multi	.45	.45
B895 SP401	8fr + 4fr multi	.75	.75
B896 SP401	9fr + 4.50fr multi	.80	.80
Nos. B893-B896 (4)		2.25	2.25

Bijloke Abbey, Ghent — SP402

4.50fr+2fr, St. Ursmer Collegiate Church, Lobbes. 8fr+4fr, Park Abbey, Heverle. 9fr+4.50fr, Abbey, Floreffe.

1973, Mar. 24	Engr.	Perf. 11½	
B897 SP402	2fr + 1fr sl grn	.25	.25
B898 SP402	4.50fr + 2fr brown	.40	.40
B899 SP402	8fr + 4fr rose lil	.75	.75
B900 SP402	9fr + 4.50fr brt bl	.90	.90
Nos. B897-B900 (4)		2.30	2.30

Basketball SP403

1973, Apr. 7	Photo. & Engr.	
B901 SP403	10fr + 5fr multi	.80 .80

First World Basketball Championships of the Handicapped, Bruges, Apr. 16-21.

Dirk Martens' Printing Press — SP404

Lady Talbot, by Petrus Christus — SP405

Hadrian and Marcus Aurelius Coins SP406

Council of Malines, by Coussaert — SP407

Designs: 3.50fr+1.50fr, Head of Amon and Tutankhamen's cartouche. 10fr+5fr, Three-master of Ostend Merchant Company.

Photogravure and Engraved; Photogravure (#B906)

1973, June 23	Perf. 11½	
B902 SP404	2fr + 1fr multi	.25 .25
B903 SP404	3.50fr + 1.50fr multi	.30 .30
B904 SP405	4.50fr + 2fr multi	.35 .35
B905 SP406	8fr + 4fr multi	.65 .65
B906 SP407	9fr + 4.50fr multi	.85 .85
B907 SP407	10fr + 5fr multi	1.50 1.50
Nos. B902-B907 (6)		3.90 3.90

500th anniv. of 1st book printed in Belgium (No. B902); 50th anniv. of Queen Elisabeth Egyptological Foundation (No. B903); 500th anniv. of death of painter Petrus Christus (No. B904); Discovery of Roman treasure at Luttre-Liberchies (No. B905); 500th anniv. of Great Council of Malines (No. B906); 250th anniv. of the Ostend Merchant Company (No. B907). No. B902 is not luminescent.

Queen of Hearts — SP408

Old Playing Cards: No. B909, King of Clubs. No. B910, Jack of Diamonds. No. B911, King of Spades.

1973, Dec. 8	Photo.	Perf. 11½	
B908 SP408	5fr + 2.50fr multi	.50	.50
B909 SP408	5fr + 2.50fr multi	.50	.50
B910 SP408	5fr + 2.50fr multi	.50	.50
B911 SP408	5fr + 2.50fr multi	.50	.50
a. Strip of 4, #B908-B911		2.00	2.00

Surtax was for philanthropic purposes.

Symbol of Blood Donations SP409

Design: 10fr+5fr, Traffic lights, Red Cross (symbolic of road accidents).

1974, Feb. 23	Photo.	Perf. 11½	
B912 SP409	4fr + 2fr multi	.35	.35
B913 SP409	10fr + 5fr multi	.90	.90

The Red Cross as blood collector and aid to accident victims.

Armand Jamar, Self-portrait SP410

Designs: 5fr+2.50fr, Anton Bergmann and view of Lierre. 7fr+3.50fr, Henri Vieuxtemps and view of Verviers. 10fr+5fr, James Ensor, self-portrait, and masks.

1974, Apr. 6	Photo.	Perf. 11½	
Size: 24x35mm			
B914 SP410	4fr + 2fr multi	.35	.35
B915 SP410	5fr + 2.50fr multi	.40	.40
B916 SP410	7fr + 3.50fr multi	.55	.55
Size: 35x52mm			
B917 SP410	10fr + 5fr multi	.85	.85
Nos. B914-B917 (4)		2.15	2.15

Van Gogh, Self-portrait and House at Cuesmes — SP411

1974, Sept. 21	Photo.	Perf. 11½	
B918 SP411	10fr + 5fr multi	.90	.90

Opening of Vincent van Gogh House at Cuesmes, where he worked as teacher.

Gentian — SP412

Spotted Cat's Ear — SP414

Badger SP413

Design: 7fr+3.50fr, Beetle.

1974, Dec. 8	Photo.	Perf. 11½	
B919 SP412	4fr + 2fr multi	.35	.35
B920 SP413	5fr + 2.50fr multi	.50	.50
B921 SP413	7fr + 3.50fr multi	.60	.60
B922 SP414	10fr + 5fr multi	.95	.95
Nos. B919-B922 (4)		2.40	2.40

Pesaro Palace, Venice SP415

St. Bavon Abbey, Ghent SP416

Virgin and Child, by Michelangelo SP417

1975, Apr. 12	Engr.	Perf. 11½	
B923 SP415	6.50fr + 2.50fr brn	.55	.55
B924 SP416	10fr + 4.50 vio brn	.85	.85
B925 SP417	15fr + 6.50fr brt bl	1.25	1.25
Nos. B923-B925 (3)		2.65	2.65

Surtax was for various cultural organizations.

Frans Hemerijckx and Leprosarium, Kasai — SP418

1975, Sept. 13	Photo.	Perf. 11½	
B926 SP418	20fr + 10fr multi	1.75	1.75

Dr. Frans Hemerijckx (1902-1969), tropical medicine and leprosy expert.

Emile Moyson — SP419

Beheading of St. Dympna — SP420a

Hand Reading Braille SP420

No. B928, Dr. Ferdinand Augustin Snellaert.

1975, Nov. 22	Engr.	Perf. 11½	
B927 SP419	4.50fr + 2fr dp mag	.35	.35
B928 SP419	6.50fr + 3fr green	.60	.60
Engraved and Photogravure			
B929 SP420	10fr + 5fr multi	.90	.90
Photo.			
B930 SP420a	13fr + 6fr multi	1.10	1.10
Nos. B927-B930 (4)		2.95	2.95

Emile Moyson (1838-1868), freedom fighter for the rights of Flemings and Walloons; Dr. Snellaert (1809-1872), physician and Flemish patriot; Louis Braille (1809-1852), sesquicentennial of invention of Braille system of writing for the blind; St. Dympna, patron saint of Geel, famous for treatment of mentally ill.

The Cheese Vendor — SP421

Designs (THEMABELGA Emblem and): No. B932, Potato vendor. No. B933, Basket carrier. No. B934, Shrimp fisherman with horse, horiz. No. B935, Knife grinder, horiz. No. B936, Milk vendor with dog cart, horiz.

1975, Dec. 13	Engr. & Photo.	
B931 SP421	4.50fr + 1.50fr multi	.35 .35
B932 SP421	6.50fr + 3fr multi	.55 .55
B933 SP421	6.50fr + 3fr multi	.55 .55
B934 SP421	10fr + 5fr multi	.80 .80
B935 SP421	10fr + 5fr multi	.80 .80
B936 SP421	30fr + 15fr multi	2.40 2.40
Nos. B931-B936 (6)		5.45 5.45

THEMABELGA Intl. Topical Philatelic Exhib., Brussels, Dec. 13-21. Issued in sheets of 10 (5x2).

Blackface Fund Collector — SP422

1976, Feb. 14   Photo.   Perf. 11½
B937 SP422 10fr + 5fr multi   .90 .90

"Conservatoire Africain" philanthropic soc., cent., and to publicize the Princess Paola creches.

Swimming and Olympic Emblem SP423

Montreal Olympic Games Emblem and: 5fr+2fr, Running, vert. 6.50fr+2.50fr, Equestrian.

1976, Apr. 10   Photo.   Perf. 11½
B938 SP423 4.50fr + 1.50fr multi   .35 .35
B939 SP423 5fr + 2fr multi   .40 .40
B940 SP423 6.50fr + 2.50fr multi   .55 .55
    Nos. B938-B940 (3)   1.30 1.30

21st Olympic Games, Montreal, Canada, July 17-Aug. 1.

Queen Elisabeth Playing Violin SP424

and Perf. 11½
1976, May 1   Engr.   Photo.
B941 SP424 14fr + 6fr blk & cl   1.10 1.10

Queen Elisabeth International Music Competition, 25th anniversary.

Souvenir Sheet

Jan Olieslagers, Bleriot Monoplane, Aero Club Emblem — SP425

Engraved and Photogravure
1976, June 12   Perf. 11½
B942 SP425 25fr + 10fr multi   2.25 2.25

Royal Belgian Aero Club, 75th anniversary, and Jan Olieslagers (1883-1942), aviation pioneer.

Adoration of the Shepherds (detail), by Rubens — SP426

Rubens Paintings (Details): 4.50fr, Descent from the Cross. No. B945, The Virgin with the Parrot. No. B946, Adoration of the Kings. No. B947, Last Communion of St. Francis. 30fr+15fr, Virgin and Child.

1976, Sept. 4   Photo.   Perf. 11½
    Size: 35x52mm
B943 SP426 4.50fr + 1.50fr multi   .45 .45
    Size: 24x35mm
B944 SP426 6.50fr + 3fr multi   .55 .55
B945 SP426 6.50fr + 3fr multi   .55 .55
B946 SP426 10fr + 5fr multi   .90 .90
B947 SP426 10fr + 5fr multi   .90 .90
    Size: 35x52mm
B948 SP426 30fr + 15fr multi   2.40 2.40
    Nos. B943-B948 (6)   5.75 5.75

Peter Paul Rubens (1577-1640), Flemish painter, 400th birth anniversary.

Dwarf, by Velazquez SP427

1976, Nov. 6   Photo.   Perf. 11½
B949 SP427 14fr + 6fr multi   1.25 1.25

Surtax was for the National Association for the Mentally Handicapped.

Dr. Albert Hustin SP428

Red Cross and Rheumatism Year Emblem SP429

1977, Feb. 19   Photo.   Perf. 11½
B950 SP428 6.50fr + 2.50 multi   .60 .60
B951 SP429 14fr + 7fr multi   1.10 1.10

Belgian Red Cross.

Bordet Atheneum, Empress Maria Theresa SP430

Conductor and Orchestra, by E. Tytgat SP431

Lucien Van Obbergh, Stage SP432

Humanistic Society Emblem SP433

Camille Lemonnier SP434

Design: No. B953, Marie-Therese College, Herve, and coat of arms.

1977, Mar. 21   Photo.   Perf. 11½
B952 SP430 4.50fr + 1fr multi   .35 .35
B953 SP430 4.50fr + 1fr multi   .35 .35
B954 SP431 5fr + 2fr multi   .40 .40
B955 SP432 6.50fr + 2fr multi   .55 .55
B956 SP433 6.50fr + 2fr blk & red   .55 .55
    Engr.
B957 SP434 10fr + 5fr slate bl   .80 .80
    Nos. B952-B957 (6)   3.00 3.00

Bicentenaries of the Jules Bordet Atheneum, Brussels, and the Marie-Therese College, Herve (Nos. B952-B953); 50th anniv. of the Brussels Philharmonic Soc., and Artists' Union (Nos. B954-B955); 25th anniv. of the Flemish Humanistic Organization (No. B956); 75th anniv. of the French-speaking Belgian writers' organization (No. B957).

Young Soccer Players — SP435

1977, Apr. 18   Photo.
B958 SP435 10fr + 5fr multi   .90 .90

30th Intl. Junior Soccer Tournament.

Albert-Edouard Janssen, Financier — SP436

Famous Men: No. B960, Joseph Wauters (1875-1929), editor of Le Peuple, and newspaper. No. B961, Jean Capart (1877-1947), Egyptologist, and hieroglyph. No. B962, August de Boeck (1865-1937), composer, and score.

1977, Dec. 3   Engr.   Perf. 11½
B959 SP436 5fr + 2.50fr brown   .40 .40
B960 SP436 5fr + 2.50fr red   .40 .40
B961 SP436 10fr + 5fr magenta   .80 .80
B962 SP436 10fr + 5fr blue gray   .80 .80
    Nos. B959-B962 (4)   2.40 2.40

Abandoned Child SP437

Checking Blood Pressure SP438

De Mick Sanatorium, Brasschaat — SP439

1978, Feb. 18   Photo.   Perf. 11½
B963 SP437 4.50fr + 1.50fr multi   .35 .35
B964 SP438 6fr + 3fr multi   .50 .50
B965 SP439 10fr + 5fr multi   .80 .80
    Nos. B963-B965 (3)   1.65 1.65

Help for abandoned children (No. B963); fight against hypertension (No. B964); fight against tuberculosis (No. B965).

Actors and Theater SP440

Karel van de Woestijne SP441

Designs: No. B967, Harquebusier, Harquebusier Palace and coat of arms. 10fr+5fr, John of Austria and his signature.

Engraved and Photogravure
1978, June 17   Perf. 11½
B966 SP440 6fr + 3fr multi   .50 .50
B967 SP440 6fr + 3fr multi   .50 .50
    Engr.
B968 SP441 8fr + 4fr black   .65 .65
B969 SP441 10fr + 5fr black   .80 .80
    Nos. B966-B969 (4)   2.45 2.45

Cent. of Royal Flemish Theater, Brussels (No. B966); 400th anniv. of Harquebusiers' Guild of Vise, Liege (No. 967); Karel van de Woestijne (1878-1929), poet (No. B968); 400th anniv. of signing of Perpetual Edict by John of Austria (No. 969).

Lake Placid '80 and Belgian Olympic Emblems — SP442

Moscow '80 Emblem and: 8fr+3.50fr, Kremlin Towers, Belgian Olympic Committee emblem. 7fr+3fr, Runners from Greek vase, Lake Placid '80 emblem, Olympic rings. 14fr+6fr, Olympic flame, Lake Placid '80, Belgian emblems, Olympic rings.

1978, Nov. 4   Photo.   Perf. 11½
B970 SP442 6fr + 2.50fr multi   .50 .50
B971 SP442 8fr + 3.50fr multi   .65 .65
    Souvenir Sheet
B972 Sheet of 2   1.90 1.90
  a.   SP442 7fr + 3fr multi   .65 .65
  b.   SP442 14fr + 6fr multi   1.25 1.25

Surtax was for 1980 Olympic Games.

Great Synagogue,
Brussels — SP443

Dancers
SP444

Father Pire,
African
Village
SP445

1978, Dec. 2   Engr.   Perf. 11½
B973 SP443 6fr + 2fr gray grn &
sepia   .50 .50
Photo.
B974 SP444 8fr + 3fr multi   .65 .65
B975 SP445 14fr + 7fr multi   1.25 1.25
    Nos. B973-B975 (3)   2.40 2.40

Centenary of Great Synagogue of Brussels;
Flemish Catholic Youth Action Organization,
50th anniversary; Nobel Peace Prize awarded
to Father Dominique Pire for his "Heart Open
to the World" movement, 20th anniversary.

Young People
Giving First
Aid — SP446

Skull with Bottle,
Cigarette,
Syringe — SP447

1979, Feb. 10   Photo.   Perf. 11½
B976 SP446 8fr + 3fr multi   .70 .70
B977 SP447 16fr + 8fr multi   1.40 1.40

Belgian Red Cross.

Beatrice
Soetkens
with Statue
of Virgin
Mary
SP448

Details from Tapestries, 1516-1518, Showing Legend of Our Lady of Sand: 8fr+3fr, Francois de Tassis accepting letter from Emperor
Frederick III (beginning of postal service).
14fr+7fr, Arrival of statue, Francois de Tassis
and Philip the Fair. No. B981, Statue carried in
procession by future Emperor Charles V and
his brother Ferdinand. No. B982, Ship carrying Beatrice Soetkens with statue to Brussels,
horiz.

1979, May 5   Photo.   Perf. 11½
B978 SP448 6fr + 2fr multi   .50 .50
B979 SP448 8fr + 3fr multi   .65 .65
B980 SP448 14fr + 7fr multi   1.25 1.25
B981 SP448 20fr + 10fr multi   1.90 1.90
    Nos. B978-B981 (4)   4.30 4.30
Souvenir Sheet
B982 SP448 20fr + 10fr multi   2.00 2.00

The surtax was for festivities in connection
with the millennium of Brussels.

Notre Dame Abbey,
Brussels — SP449

Designs: 8fr+3fr, Beauvoorde Castle.
14fr+7fr, 1st issue of "Courrier de L'Escaut"
and Barthelemy Dumortier, founder. 20fr+10fr,
Shrine of St. Hermes, Renaix.

Engraved and Photogravure
1979, Sept. 15   Perf. 11½
B983 SP449 6fr + 2fr multi   .50 .50
B984 SP449 8fr + 3fr multi   .65 .65
B985 SP449 14fr + 7fr multi   1.25 1.25
B986 SP449 20fr + 10fr multi   1.90 1.90
    Nos. B983-B986 (4)   4.30 4.30

50th anniv. of restoration of Notre Dame de
la Cambre Abbey; historic Beauvoorde Castle,
15th cent. sesquicentennial of the regional
newspaper "Le Courrier de L'Escaut"; 850th
anniv. of the consecration of the Collegiate
Church of St. Hermes, Renaix.

Grand-Hornu Coal Mine — SP450

1979, Oct. 22   Engr.   Perf. 11½
B987 SP450 10fr + 5fr blk   .90 .90

Henry Heyman
SP451

Veterans
Organization
Medal
SP452

Boy and IYC Emblem — SP453

1979, Dec. 8   Photo.   Perf. 11½
B988 SP451 8fr + 3fr multi   .65 .65
B989 SP452 10fr + 5fr multi   .80 .80
B990 SP453 16fr + 8fr multi   1.25 1.25
    Nos. B988-B990 (3)   2.70 2.70

Henri Heyman (1879-1958), Minister of
State; Disabled Veterans' Organization, 50th
anniv.; Intl. Year of the Child.

Ivo Van Damme,
Olympic
Rings — SP454

1980, May 3   Photo.   Perf. 11½
B991 SP454 20fr + 10fr multi   1.75 1.75

Ivo Van Damme (1954-1976), silver medal-
ist, 800-meter race, Montreal Olympics, 1976.
Surtax was for Van Damme Memorial
Foundation.

Queen Louis-Marie, King Leopold
I — SP455

150th Anniversary of Independence
(Queens and Kings): 9fr+3fr, Marie Henriette.
Leopold II. 14fr+6fr, Elisabeth, Albert I.
17fr+8fr, Astrid, Leopold III. 25fr+10fr, Fabiola,
Baudouin.

Photogravure and Engraved
1980, May 31   Perf. 11½
B992 SP455 6.50 + 1.50fr multi   .55 .55
B993 SP455 9 + 3fr multi   .75 .75
B994 SP455 14 + 6fr multi   1.25 1.25
B995 SP455 17 + 8fr multi   1.40 1.40
B996 SP455 25 + 10fr multi   2.10 2.10
    Nos. B992-B996 (5)   6.05 6.05

Miner, by
Constantine
Meunier
SP456

Seal of Bishop Notger, First Prince-
Bishop — SP457

9fr+3fr, Brewer, 16th century, from St. Lam-
bert's reliquary, vert. 25fr+10fr, Virgin and
Child, 13th century, St. John's Collegiate
Church, Liege.

1980, Sept. 13   Photo.   Perf. 11½
B997 SP456 9 + 3fr multi   .75 .75
B998 SP456 17 + 6fr multi   1.40 1.40
B999 SP456 25 + 10fr multi   2.10 2.10
    Nos. B997-B999 (3)   4.25 4.25
Souvenir Sheet
B1000 SP457 20 + 10fr multi   2.00 2.00

Millennium of the Principality of Liege.

Visual and
Oral
Handicaps
SP458

Intl. Year of the Disabled: 10fr+5fr, Cerebral
handicap, vert.

1981, Feb. 9   Photo.   Perf. 11½
B1001 SP458 10 + 5fr multi   1.00 1.00
B1002 SP458 25 + 10fr multi   2.25 2.25

Dove with
Red Cross
Carrying
Globe
SP459

Design: 10fr+5fr, Atomic model, vert.

1981, Apr. 6   Photo.   Perf. 11½
B1003 SP459 10 + 5fr multi   .90 .90
B1004 SP459 25 + 10fr multi   2.10 2.10

Red Cross and: 15th Intl. Radiology Congress, Brussels, June 24-July 1 (No. B1003);
intl. disaster relief (No. B1004).

Ovide
Decroly
SP460

1981, June 1   Photo.   Perf. 11½
B1005 SP460 35 + 15fr multi   3.00 3.00

Ovide Decroly (1871-1932), developer of
educational psychology.

Mounted Police
Officer — SP461

Anniversaries: 9fr+4fr, Gendarmerie (State
Police Force), 150th. 20fr+7fr, Carabineers
Regiment, 150th. 40fr+20fr, Guides Regiment.

1981, Dec. 7   Photo.   Perf. 11½
B1006 SP461 9 + 4fr multi   .85 .85
B1007 SP461 20 + 7fr multi   1.75 1.75
B1008 SP461 40 + 20fr multi   3.50 3.50
    Nos. B1006-B1008 (3)   6.10 6.10

Billiards — SP462

1982, Mar. 29   Photo.   Perf. 11½
B1009 SP462 6 + 2fr shown   .80 .80
B1010 SP462 9 + 4fr Cycling   1.10 1.10
B1011 SP462 10 + 5fr Soccer   1.25 1.25
B1012 SP462 50 + 14fr
              Yachting   4.00 4.00
    Nos. B1009-B1012 (4)   7.15 7.15
Souvenir Sheet
B1013   Sheet of 4   7.50 7.50
  a.   SP462 25fr like #B1009   1.75 1.75
  b.   SP462 25fr like #B1010   1.75 1.75
  c.   SP462 25fr like #B1011   1.75 1.75
  d.   SP462 25fr like #B1012   1.75 1.75

No. B1013 shows designs in changed colors.

Christmas
SP463

1982, Nov. 6
B1014 SP463 10 + 1fr multi   .80 .80

Surtax was for tuberculosis research.

Belgica '82 Intl. Stamp Exhibition, Brussels, Dec. 11-19 SP464

Messengers (Prints). Nos. B1016-B1018 vert.

Photogravure and Engraved
1982, Dec. 11   **Perf. 11½**
B1015	SP464	7 + 2fr multi	.55 .55
B1016	SP464	7.50 + 2.50fr multi	.60 .60
B1017	SP464	10 + 3fr multi	.80 .80
B1018	SP464	17 + 7fr multi	1.40 1.40
B1019	SP464	20 + 9fr multi	1.60 1.60
B1020	SP464	25 + 10fr multi	2.00 2.00
		Nos. B1015-B1020 (6)	6.95 6.95

Souvenir Sheet
B1021	SP464	50 + 25fr multi	6.00 6.00

No. B1021 contains one 48x37mm stamp.

50th Anniv. of Catholic Charities — SP465

1983, Jan. 22   **Photo.**   **Perf. 11½**
B1022	SP465	10 + 2fr multi	.80 .80

Mountain Climbing — SP466

1983, Mar. 7   **Photo.**
B1023	SP466	12 + 3fr shown	1.00 1.00
B1024	SP466	20 + 5fr Hiking	1.75 1.75

Surtax was for Red Cross.

Madonna by Jef Wauters — SP467

1983, Nov. 21   **Photo.**   **Perf. 11½**
B1025	SP467	11 + 1fr multi	.80 .80

Rifles Uniform — SP468

No. B1027, Lancers uniform. No. B1028, Grenadiers uniform.

1983, Dec. 5   **Photo.**   **Perf. 11½**
B1026	SP468	8 + 2fr shown	.75 .75
B1027	SP468	11 + 2fr multi	1.25 1.25
B1028	SP468	50 + 12fr multi	4.00 4.00
		Nos. B1026-B1028 (3)	6.00 6.00

Type of 1984 Summer Olympics
No. B1029, Judo, horiz. No. B1030, Wind surfing.

1984, Mar. 3   **Photo.**   **Perf. 11½**
B1029	A495	8 + 2fr multi	.65 .65
B1030	A495	12 + 3fr multi	1.00 1.00

50th Anniv. of Natl. Lottery SP469

1984, Mar. 31   **Photo.**   **Perf. 11½**
B1031	SP469	12 + 3fr multi	1.00 1.00

Brussels Modern Art Museum Opening SP470

Paintings: 8fr+2fr, Les Masques Singuliers, by James Ensor. 12fr+3fr, Empire des Lumieres, by Rene Magritte. 22fr+5fr, The End, by Jan Cox. 50fr+13fr, Rhythm No. 6, by Jo Delahaut.

1984, Sept. 1   **Photo.**
B1032	SP470	8 + 2fr multi	.75 .75
B1033	SP470	12 + 3fr multi	1.25 1.25
B1034	SP470	22 + 5fr multi	1.75 1.75
B1035	SP470	50 + 13fr multi	4.00 4.00
		Nos. B1032-B1035 (4)	7.75 7.75

Child with Parents — SP471

No. B1037, Siblings. No. B1038, Merry-go-round.

1984, Nov. 3   **Photo.**
B1036	SP471	10 + 2fr shown	.80 .80
B1037	SP471	12 + 3fr multi	1.00 1.00
B1038	SP471	15 + 3fr multi	1.25 1.25
		Nos. B1036-B1038 (3)	3.05 3.05

Surtax was for children's programs.

Christmas 1984 SP472

No. B1039, Three Kings.

1984, Dec. 1   **Photo.**
B1039	SP472	12 + 1fr multi	1.00 1.00

Belgian Red Cross Blood Transfusion Service, 50th Anniv. — SP473

1985, Mar. 4   **Photo.**   **Perf. 11½**
B1040	SP473	9 + 2fr Tree	.80 .80
B1041	SP473	23 + 5fr Hearts	1.90 1.90

Surtax was for the Belgian Red Cross.

Solidarity SP474

Castles: No. B1042, Trazegnies. No. B1043, Laarne. No. B1044, Turnhout. No. B1045, Colonster.

1985, Nov. 4   **Photo. & Engr.**
B1042	SP474	9 + 2fr multi	.80 .80
B1043	SP474	12 + 3fr multi	1.00 1.00
B1044	SP474	23 + 5fr multi	1.90 1.90
B1045	SP474	50 + 12fr multi	4.00 4.00
		Nos. B1042-B1045 (4)	7.70 7.70

Christmas 1985, New Year 1986 — SP475

Painting: Miniature from the Book of Hours, by Jean duc de Berry.

1985, Nov. 25   **Photo.**
B1046	SP475	12 + 1fr multi	.90 .90

King Baudouin Foundation SP476

1986, Mar. 24   **Photo.**
B1047	SP476	12 + 3fr Emblem	1.25 1.25

Surtax for the foundation.

Madonna SP477

Adoration of the Mystic Lamb, St. Bavon Cathedral Altarpiece, Ghent — SP478

Paintings by Hubert van Eyck (c. 1370-1426): No. B1049, Christ in Majesty. No. B1050, St. John the Baptist.

1986, Apr. 5   **Photo.**   **Perf. 11½**
B1048	SP477	9 + 2fr shown	.75 .75
B1049	SP477	13 + 3fr multi	1.10 1.10
B1050	SP477	24 + 6fr multi	2.00 2.00
		Nos. B1048-B1050 (3)	3.85 3.85

Souvenir Sheet
B1051	SP478	50 + 12fr multi	8.00 8.00

Surtax for cultural organizations.

Antique Automobiles SP479

No. B1052, Lenoir, 1863. No. B1053, Pipe de Tourisme, 1911. No. B1054, Minerva 22 HP, 1930. No. B1055, FN 8 Cylinder, 1931.

1986, Nov. 3   **Photo.**
B1052	SP479	9 + 2fr multi	.75 .75
B1053	SP479	13 + 3fr multi	1.10 1.10
B1054	SP479	24 + 6fr multi	2.00 2.00
B1055	SP479	26 + 6fr multi	2.10 2.10
		Nos. B1052-B1055 (4)	5.95 5.95

Christmas 1986, New Year 1987 SP480

No. B1056, Village in winter.

1986, Nov. 24   **Photo.**
B1056	SP480	13 + 1fr multi	1.00 1.00

Natl. Red Cross — SP482

Nobel Prize winners for physiology (1938) and medicine (1974): No. B1058, Corneille Heymans (1892-1968). No. B1059, A. Claude (1899-1983).

Photogravure and Engraved
1987, Feb. 16   **Perf. 11½**
B1058	SP482	13 + 3fr dk brn & red	1.25 1.25
B1059	SP482	24 + 6fr dk brn & red	2.25 2.25

European Conservation Year — SP483

No. B1060, Bee orchid. No. B1061, Horse-shoe bat. No. B1062, Peregrine falcon.

1987, Mar. 16   **Photo.**
B1060	SP483	9 + 2fr multi	.90 .90
B1061	SP483	24 + 6fr multi	2.00 2.00
B1062	SP483	26 + 6fr multi	2.50 2.50
		Nos. B1060-B1062 (3)	5.40 5.40

Castles — SP484

No. B1063, Rixensart. No. B1064, Westerlo. No. B1065, Fallais. No. B1066, Gaasbeek.

1987, Oct. 17   **Photo. & Engr.**
B1063	SP484	9 + 2fr multi	.80 .80
B1064	SP484	13 + 3fr multi	1.10 1.10
B1065	SP484	26 + 5fr multi	2.10 2.10
B1066	SP484	50 + 12fr multi	4.00 4.00
		Nos. B1063-B1066 (4)	8.00 8.00

Christmas
1987 — SP485

Painting: Holy Family, by Rev. Father Lens.

1987, Nov. 14   Photo.
B1067 SP485 13 + 1fr multi   1.10 1.10

White and Yellow
Cross of Belgium,
50th
Anniv. — SP486

1987, Dec. 5
B1068 SP486   9 + 2fr multi   1.00 1.00

Promote
Philately — SP487

Various flowers from Sixty Roses for a
Queen, by P. J. Redoute (1759-1840).

1988, Apr. 25   Photo.   Perf. 11½
B1069 SP487 13 + 3fr shown   1.25 1.25
B1070 SP487 24 + 6fr multi, diff.   2.10 2.10

Souvenir Sheet
B1071 SP487 50 + 12fr multi,
          diff.   8.00 8.00
See Nos. B1081-B1083, B1089-B1091,
1346.

1988 Summer Olympics,
Seoul — SP488

No. B1072, Table tennis. No. B1073,
Cycling. No. B1074, Marathon runners.

1988, June 6   Photo.   Perf. 11½
B1072 SP488 9fr + 2fr multi   1.10 1.10
B1073 SP488 13fr + 3fr multi   1.25 1.25

Souvenir Sheet
B1074 SP488 50fr + 12fr multi   9.00 9.00

Solidarity — SP489

No. B1075, Jacques Brel. No. B1076, Jef
Denyn. No. B1077, Fr. Ferdinand Verbiest.

1988, Oct. 24   Photo.   Perf. 12x11½
B1075 SP489 9fr + 2fr multi   1.25 1.25
B1076 SP489 13fr + 3fr multi   1.40 1.40
B1077 SP489 26fr + 6fr multi   2.10 2.10
     Nos. B1075-B1077 (3)   4.75 4.75

Belgian Red
Cross
SP490

Paintings: No. B1078, Crucifixion of Christ,
by Rogier van der Weyden (c. 1399-1464). No.
B1079, Virgin and Child, by David (c. 1460-
1523). B1089, The Good Samaritan, by Denis
van Alsloot.

1989, Feb. 20   Photo.   Perf. 11½
B1078 SP490 9fr + 2fr multi   1.00 1.00
B1079 SP490 13fr + 3fr multi   1.40 1.40
B1080 SP490 24fr + 6fr multi   2.10 2.10
     Nos. B1078-B1080 (3)   4.50 4.50

**Stamp Collecting Promotion Type of
1988**

Various flowers from Sixty Roses for a
Queen, by P.J. Redoute (1759-1840) and
inscriptions: No. B1081, "Centfeuille unique
melee de rouge." No. B1082, "Bengale a
grandes feuilles." No. B1083, Aeme vibere
(tea roses).

1989, Apr. 17
B1081 SP487 13fr + 5fr multi   1.40 1.40
B1082 SP487 24fr + 6fr multi   2.10 2.10

Souvenir Sheet
B1083 SP487 50fr + 17fr multi   8.00 8.00

Solidarity
SP491

Royal Greenhouses of Laeken: No. B1084,
Exterior. No. B1085, Interior, vert. No. B1086,
Dome exterior, vert. No. B1087, Dome interior,
vert.

1989, Oct. 23
B1084 SP491 9fr + 3fr multi   1.00 1.00
B1085 SP491 13fr + 4fr multi   1.40 1.40
B1086 SP491 24fr + 5fr multi   1.90 1.90
B1087 SP491 26fr + 6fr multi   2.10 2.10
     Nos. B1084-B1087 (4)   6.40 6.40

Queen Elisabeth Chapelle Musicale,
50th Anniv. — SP492

1989, Nov. 6
B1088 SP492 24fr + 6fr G clef   2.00 2.00

**Stamp Collecting Promotion Type of
1988**

Various flowers from Sixty Roses for a
Queen, by P.J. Redoute (1759-1840): No.
B1089, Bengale desprez. No. B1090, Bengale
philippe. No. B1091, Maria leonida.

1990, Feb. 5
B1089 SP487 14fr + 7fr multi   1.50 1.50
B1090 SP487 25fr + 12fr multi   2.50 2.50

Souvenir Sheet
B1091 SP487 50fr + 20fr multi   8.00 8.00

Youth and Music — SP493

14fr+3fr, Beethoven & Lamoraal, Count of
Egmont (1522-1568). 25fr+6fr, Joseph Cantre
(1890-1957), drawing & sculpture.

1990, Oct. 6
B1092 SP493 10fr + 2fr multi   1.90 1.90
B1093 SP493 14fr + 3fr multi   2.40 2.40
B1094 SP493 25fr + 6fr multi   3.25 3.25
     Nos. B1092-B1094 (3)   7.55 7.55

King Baudouin & Queen Fabiola, 30th
Wedding Anniv. — SP494

1990, Dec. 10
B1095 SP494 50fr +15fr multi   8.00 8.00

Belgian Red
Cross
SP495

Details from paintings: No. B1096, The
Temptation of St. Anthony by Hieronymus
Bosch. No. B1097, The Annunciation by Dirk
Bouts.

1991, Feb. 25,   Photo.   Perf. 11½
B1096 SP495 14fr +3fr multi   2.25 2.25
B1097 SP495 25fr +6fr multi   3.25 3.25

Belgian Film Personalities — SP496

10fr+2fr, Charles Dekeukeleire (1905-71),
producer. 14fr+3fr, Jacques Ledoux (1921-
88), film conservationist. 25fr+6fr, Jacques
Feyder (1899-1948), director.

1991, Oct. 28   Photo.   Perf. 11½
B1098 SP496 10fr +2fr multi   1.00 1.00
B1099 SP496 14fr +3fr multi   1.50 1.50
B1100 SP496 25fr +6fr multi   2.75 2.75
     Nos. B1098-B1100 (3)   5.25 5.25

1992 Winter and
Summer Olympics,
Albertville and
Barcelona
SP497

No. B1101, Speed skating. No. B1102,
Baseball. No. B1103, Women's tennis, horiz.
No. B1104, Skeet shooting.

1992, Jan. 20   Photo.   Perf. 11½
B1101 SP497 10fr +2fr multi   1.10 1.10
B1102 SP497 10fr +2fr multi   1.10 1.10
B1103 SP497 14fr +3fr multi   1.60 1.60
B1104 SP497 25fr +6fr multi   3.00 3.00
     Nos. B1101-B1104 (4)   6.80 6.80

Folk
Legends
SP498

11fr + 2fr, Proud Margaret. 15fr + 3fr, Gus-
tine Maca & the Witches. 28fr + 6fr, Reynard
the Fox.

1992, June 22   Photo.   Perf. 11½
B1105 SP498 11fr +2fr multi   1.25 1.25
B1106 SP498 15fr +3fr multi   1.75 1.75
B1107 SP498 28fr +6fr multi   3.00 3.00
     Nos. B1105-B1107 (3)   6.00 6.00

Belgian Red
Cross
SP499

Paintings: 15fr + 3fr, Man with the Pointed
Hat, by Adriaen Brouwer (1605-1638). 28fr +
7fr, Nereid and Triton, by Peter Paul Rubens,
horiz.

1993, Feb. 15   Photo.   Perf. 11½
B1108 SP499 15fr +3fr multi   1.90 1.90
B1109 SP499 28fr +7fr multi   4.00 4.00

Fight
Against
Cancer
SP500

1993, Sept. 20   Photo.   Perf. 11½
B1110 SP500 15fr +3fr multi   1.50 1.50

Intl. Olympic
Committee,
Cent. — SP501

No. B1112, Soccer players. No. B1113, Figure skater.

1994, Feb. 14   Photo.   Perf. 11½
B1111 SP501 16fr +3fr multi   1.75 1.75
B1112 SP501 16fr +3fr multi   1.75 1.75
B1113 SP501 16fr +3fr multi   1.75 1.75
     Nos. B1111-B1113 (3)   5.25 5.25

1994 World Cup Soccer Championships,
Los Angeles (No. B1112). 1994 Winter Olympics, Lillehammer, Norway (No. B1113).

Porcelain — SP502

Designs: No. B1114, Tournai plate, Museum
of Mariemont-Morlanweiz. No. B1115,
Etterbeek cup, saucer, Municipal Museum,
Louvain. 50fr+11fr, Delft earthenware jars,
Pharmacy Museum of Maaseik.

1994, June 27   Photo.   Perf. 11½
B1114 SP502 16fr +3fr multi   1.50 1.50

B1115 SP502 16fr +3fr multi 1.50 1.50
Souvenir Sheet
B1116 SP502 50fr +11fr multi 7.50 7.50
No. B1116 contains one 49x38mm stamp.

Solidarity
SP503

Design: 16fr+3fr, Hearing-impaired person.

1994, Nov. 14   Photo.   Perf. 11½
B1117 SP503 16fr +3fr multi 1.25 1.25

Museums — SP504

No. B1118, Natl. Flax Museum, Kortrijk. No. B1119, Natl. Water & Fountain Museum, Genval. 34fr+6fr, Intl. Carnival and Mask Museum, Binche.

1995, Jan. 30   Photo.   Perf. 11½
B1118 SP504 16fr +3fr multi 1.25 1.25
B1119 SP504 16fr +3fr multi 1.25 1.25
Souvenir Sheet
B1120 SP504 34fr +6fr multi 3.00 3.00
Surtax for promotion of philately.

"Souvenir Sheets"
Beginning in 1995 items looking like souvenir sheets have appeared in the market. The 1995 one has the design used for No. B1120. The 1996 one has the design similar to the one used for No. B1128. The 1997 one has the design used for No. B1131. In 2000, the design of No. 1811 was used. These have no postal value.

Royal Belgian Soccer Assoc., Cent. SP505

1995, Aug. 21   Photo.   Perf. 11½
B1121 SP505 16fr +4fr multi 1.40 1.40

Belgian Red Cross SP506

No. B1122, Princess Astrid, chairwoman of Belgian Red Cross. No. B1123, Wilhelm C. Röntgen (1845-1923), discoverer of the X-ray. No. B1124, Louis Pasteur (1822-95), scientist.

1995, Sept. 11
B1122 SP506 16fr +3fr multi 1.25 1.25
B1123 SP506 16fr +3fr multi 1.25 1.25
B1124 SP506 16fr +3fr multi 1.25 1.25
Nos. B1122-B1124 (3) 3.75 3.75

Solidarity — SP507

1995, Nov. 6   Photo.
B1125 SP507 16fr +4fr multi 1.25 1.25
Surtax for fight against AIDS.

Museums — SP508

No. B1126, Museum of Walloon Life, Liège. No. B1127, Natl. Gin Museum, Hasselt. 34fr+6fr, Butchers' Guild Hall Museum, Antwerp.

1996, Feb. 19   Photo.   Perf. 11½
B1126 SP508 16fr +4fr multi 1.25 1.25
B1127 SP508 16fr +4fr multi 1.25 1.25
Souvenir Sheet
B1128 SP508 34fr +6fr multi 3.00 3.00

Modern Olympic Games, Cent. SP509

No. B1129, Table tennis. No. B1130, Swimming. No. B1131, High jump.

1996, July 1   Photo.   Perf. 11½
B1129 SP509 16fr +4fr multi 1.25 1.25
B1130 SP509 16fr +4fr multi 1.25 1.25
Souvenir Sheet
B1131 SP509 34fr +6fr multi 2.75 2.75
No. B1131 contains one 49x38mm stamp.

UNICEF, 50th Anniv. SP510

1996, Nov. 18   Photo.   Perf. 11½
B1132 SP510 16fr +4fr multi 1.40 1.40

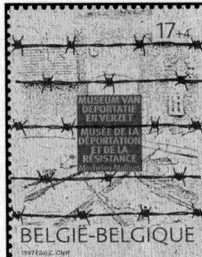

Museums SP511

No. B1133, Deportation and Resistance Museum, Mechlin. No. B1134, Iron Museum, Saint Hubert. 41fr+9fr, Horta Museum, Saint Gilles.

1997, Jan. 20   Photo.   Perf. 11½
B1133 SP511 17fr +4fr multi 1.40 1.40
B1134 SP511 17fr +4fr multi 1.40 1.40
Souvenir Sheet
B1135 SP511 41fr +9fr multi 4.50 4.50
Surtax for "Pro-Post" association.

Judo — SP512

No. B1136, Men's (10a). No. B1137, Women's (10b).

1997, May 5   Photo.   Perf. 11½
B1136 SP512 17fr +4fr multi 1.25 1.25
B1137 SP512 17fr +4fr multi 1.25 1.25
Surtax for Belgian Olympic Committee.

Solidarity — SP513

1997, Oct. 25
B1138 SP513 17fr +4fr multi 1.25 1.25
Surtax for Multiple Sclerosis research.

King Leopold III — SP514

32fr+15fr, King Baudouin I. 50fr+25fr, King Albert II.

1998, Feb. 16   Engr.   Perf. 11½
B1139 SP514 17fr +8fr dk grn 1.50 1.50
B1140 SP514 32fr +15fr dk brn 2.75 2.75
Souvenir Sheet
B1141 SP514 50fr +25fr dk vio brn 5.50 5.50
See Nos. B1146-B1148, 1748, B1154-B1156, 1842, B1158-B1160.

Sports SP515

1998, June 8   Photo.   Perf. 11½
B1142 SP515 17fr +4fr Pelota 1.25 1.25
B1143 SP515 17fr +4fr Handball 1.25 1.25
Souvenir Sheet
B1144 SP515 30fr +7fr Soccer 2.50 2.50
1998 World Cup Soccer Championships, France (No. B1144).

Assist the Blind — SP516

Photo. & Embossed
1998, Nov. 9   Perf. 11½
B1145 SP516 17fr +4fr multi 1.40 1.40
Face value is indicated in Braille.

Royalty Type of 1998
Designs: 17fr+8fr, King Albert I. 32fr+15fr, King Leopold II. 50fr+25fr, King Leopold I.

1999, Jan. 25   Engr.   Perf. 11½
B1146 SP514 17fr +8fr dp grn 1.50 1.50
B1147 SP514 32fr +15fr black 2.75 2.75
Souvenir Sheet
B1148 SP514 50fr +25fr dp brn 4.50 4.50

Motorcycles — SP517

No. B1149, Speed race. No. B1150, Trial, vert. No. B1151, Motocross, vert.

1999, May 17   Photo.   Perf. 11½
B1149 SP517 17fr +4fr multi 1.40 1.40
B1150 SP517 17fr +4fr multi 1.40 1.40
Souvenir Sheet
B1151 SP517 30fr +7fr multi 2.50 2.50

Solidarity SP518

No. 1152, First aid. No. 1153, Dental care, vert.

1999, Nov. 8   Photo.   Perf. 11½
B1152 SP518 17fr +4fr multi 1.40 1.40
B1153 SP518 17fr +4fr multi 1.40 1.40

Royalty Type of 1998
Queens: 17fr + 8fr, Astrid (1905-35). 32fr +15fr, Fabiola (b. 1928). 50fr +25fr, Paola (b. 1937).

Photo. & Engr.
2000, Jan. 24   Perf. 11½
B1154 SP514 17fr +8fr green 1.50 1.50
B1155 SP514 32fr +15fr black 2.75 2.75
Souvenir Sheet
B1156 SP514 50fr +25fr claret 4.00 4.00

Red Cross/Red Crescent SP519

2000, Mar. 27   Photo.   Perf. 11½
B1157 SP519 17fr +4fr multi 1.10 1.10

Royalty Type of 1998
Queens: 17fr+8fr, Elisabeth (1876-1965). 32fr+15fr, Marie-Henriette (1836-1902). 50fr+25fr, Louise-Marie (1812-50).

Photo. & Engr.
2001, Feb. 12   Perf. 11½
B1158 SP514 17fr +8fr green 1.50 1.50

B1159 SP514 32fr +15fr black   2.75 2.75
Souvenir Sheet
B1160 SP514 50fr +25fr brown   4.00 4.00

Sports
SP520

World championship meets: No. B1161, Cycle track racing, Antwerp. No. B1162, Artistic gymnastics, Ghent.

2001, June 14   Photo.   Perf. 11½
B1161 SP520 17fr +4fr multi   1.40 1.40
B1162 SP520 17fr +4fr multi   1.40 1.40

Red Cross
Volunteers
SP521

2001, Sept. 10
B1163 SP521 17fr +4fr multi   1.40 1.40

Winning Drawing in Belgica 2001 Children's Stamp Design Contest SP522

2002, Feb. 11   Photo.   Perf. 11½
B1164 SP522 42c +10c multi   1.25 1.25

Red Cross
Emergency
Aid
SP523

2002, June 5   Photo.   Perf. 11½
B1165 SP523 84c +12c multi   2.50 2.50

Red Cross — SP524

No. B1166: a, Helicopter and rescue worker (6a). b, Rescue worker on shoulders of another (6b). c, Nurse attending to accident victim (6c).

2003, Mar. 31   Photo.   Perf. 11½
B1166   Vert. strip of 3 + 2 labels   4.00 4.00
a.-c. SP524 41c +9c any single   1.25 1.25

Argenteuil, by Edouard Manet — SP525

2003, Sept. 15   Photo.   Perf. 11½
B1167 SP525 49c +11c multi   1.50 1.50
Margins on sheets, inscribed "Prior," served as etiquettes.

The Temptation of Saint Anthony, by Salvador Dali
SP526

2004, Apr. 19   Photo.   Perf. 11½
B1168 SP526 49c +11c multi   1.50 1.50
Margins on sheets, inscribed "Prior," served as etiquettes.

Red Cross
Workers
SP527

2004, July 12   Photo.   Perf. 11½
B1169 SP527 50c +11c multi   1.50 1.50
Margins on sheets, inscribed "Prior," served as etiquettes.

The Violinist, by Kees van Dongen — SP528

2005, Jan. 17   Photo.   Perf. 11½
B1170 SP528 50c +12c multi   1.60 1.60
Margins on sheets, inscribed "Prior," served as etiquettes.

Dec. 26, 2004 Tsunami Victim Relief SP529

2005, Feb. 28
B1171 SP529 50c +12c multi   1.75 1.75
Margins on sheets, inscribed "Prior," served as etiquettes. Surtax for Red Cross health care infrastructure relief efforts.

Red Cross
SP530

2006, May 15   Photo.   Perf. 11½
B1172 SP530 52c +12c multi   1.75 1.75
Margins on sheets, inscribed "Prior," served as etiquettes.

The Kleptomaniac, by Théodore Gericault, and Ghent Museum of Fine Arts — SP531

2006, Oct. 23   Photo.   Perf. 11½
B1173 SP531 52c +12c multi   1.75 1.75
Printed in sheets of 5. Margins on sheets, inscibed "Prior," served as etiquettes. Surtax for promotion of philately.

Souvenir Sheet

Seated Nude, by Amedeo Modigliani — SP532

2007, Jan. 8   Photo.   Perf. 11½
B1174 SP532 60c +30c multi   2.40 2.40
Surtax for promotion of philately.

Red Cross
Mobile
Library for
Hospitals
SP533

2007, Feb. 26
B1175 SP533 52c +25c multi   2.10 2.10
Printed in sheets of 10. Margins on sheets, inscribed "Prior," served as etiquettes.

Red Cross
Blood
Donation
SP534

2008, Jan. 21   Photo.   Perf. 11½
B1176 SP534 1 +25c multi   2.25 2.25
No. B1176 sold for 77c on day of issue.

Souvenir Sheet

La Luz que se Apaga, by José Maria Sicilia — SP535

2008, Jan. 21
B1177 SP535 2 +40c multi   4.25 4.25
No. B1177 sold for €1.44 on day of issue.

Red Cross Drinking Water Projects — SP536

2009, Feb. 23   Litho.   Perf. 11½
B1178 SP536 1 +25c multi   2.25 2.25
On day of issue, No. B1178 sold for 84c.

Souvenir Sheet

Belgium No. 139a — SP537

2009, Nov. 3   Litho.   Perf. 11½
B1179 SP537 (90c) + 40c multi   4.00 4.00
Surtax for promotion of philately.

Miniature Sheet

Grand Place, Brussels — SP538

No. B1180: a, Statue of St. Michael, spire of City Hall. b, Star, Swan and Golden Tree Guildhouses. c, House of the Dukes of Brabant (one building), horiz. d, King of Spain, Wheelbarrow, Bag and Claw Guildhouses, horiz. e, Breadhouse (Maison du Roi).

	Photo. & Engr.		
2011, Sept. 19		**Perf. 11½**	
B1180	SP538	Sheet of 5	17.50 17.50
a.-e.		1 + (61c) Any single	3.50 3.50

On day of issue, Nos. B1180a-B1180e each had a franking value of 61c.

Miniature Sheet

Grand-Place, Bruges — SP539

No. B1181: a, Statue of Jan Breydel and Pieter de Coninck. b, Belfry. c Provincial House, horiz. d, Boechoute, Craenenburg, Die Maene Houses, Pathé Cinema, horiz..e, Spainge, Diephuis and Le Panier d'Or Houses.

2012, Oct. 29			
B1181	SP539	Sheet of 5	17.50 17.50
a.-e.		SP539 1 + (65c) Any single	3.50 3.50

On day of issue, Nos. B1181a-B1181e each had a franking value of 65c.

Statue of Marie-Christine de Lalaing — SP540

Belfry — SP541

Cloth Hall — SP542

Grange Aux Dimes — SP543

"The Oath" Statue — SP544

	Photo. & Engr.		
2013, Oct. 28		**Perf. 11½**	
B1182		Sheet of 5	19.00 19.00
a.	SP540	1+(67c) multi	3.75 3.75
b.	SP541	1+(67c) multi	3.75 3.75
c.	SP542	1+(67c) multi	3.75 3.75
d.	SP543	1+(67c) multi	3.75 3.75
e.	SP544	1+(67c) multi	3.75 3.75

Capture of Tournai by King Henry VIII of England, 500th anniv. Nos. B1182a-B1182e each had a franking value of 67c on day of issue.

Miniature Sheet

Grand-Place, Antwerp — SP545

No. B1183: a, Hand from Brabo Fountain (28x40mm). b, Notre-Dame Cathedral (28x40mm). c, Town Hall (56x40mm). d, Guild houses, "1" at LR (28x40mm). e, Guild houses, "1" at UL (28x40mm).

	Engr. With Photo. Sheet Margin		
2014, Sept. 8		**Perf. 11½**	
B1183	SP545	Sheet of 5	19.00 19.00
a.-e.		1+(70c) Any single	3.75 3.75

Nos. B1183a-B1183e each had a franking value of 70c on day of issue. Surtax for the promotion of philately. Photogravure imperforate examples of No. B1183 were given away as gifts to standing-order customers.

Miniature Sheet

Grand-Place, Mons — SP546

No. B1184: a, Hôtel de Blanc Lévrier (woman in LL corner, 28x40mm). b, City Hall (building with tower, 28x40mm). c, St. George's Chapel (building with railing along steps, 28x40mm). d, Hôtel de la Couronne Impériale (building with solid doors, 55x40mm). e, Royal Theater (building with doors with windows, 55x40mm).

	Photo. & Engr.		
2015, June 1		**Perf. 11½**	
B1184	SP546	Sheet of 5	16.50 16.50
a.-e.		1+(72c) Any single	3.25 3.25

Nos. B1184a-B1184e each had a franking value of 72c on day of issue. Surtax for promotion of philately. A horse hair is affixed to the sheet margin with adhesive tape.

Miniature Sheet

Ghent — SP547

No. B1185: a, Belfry of Ghent. b, St. Nicholas's Church. c, St. Bavo's Cathedral. d, Old City Hall. e, New City Hall.

	Photo. & Engr.		
2016, Mar. 14		**Perf. 11½**	
B1185	SP547	Sheet of 5 + label	17.50 17.50
a.-e.		1+(74c) Any single	3.50 3.50

Nos. B1185a-B1185e each had a franking value of 74c on day of issue. Surtax was for promotion of philately.

Miniature Sheet

Eupen — SP548

No. B1186: a, Franco-German War Memorial, Werthplatz (28x41mm). b, Franciscan Sisters Convent, Marktplatz (28x41mm). c, Merchant's house, Werthplatz (56x41mm). d, St. Nicholas Church, Marktplatz (28x41mm). e, City Hall, Rathausplatz (56x41mm).

	Photo. & Engr.		
2017, June 12		**Perf. 11½**	
B1186	SP548	Sheet of 5 + label	17.50 17.50
a.-e.		1+(74c) Any single	3.50 3.50

Nos. B1186a-B11856e each had a franking value of 74c on day of issue. Surtax was for promotion of philately.

AIR POST STAMPS

Fokker FVII/3m over Ostend AP1

Designs: 1.50fr, Plane over St. Hubert. 2fr, over Namur. 5fr, over Brussels.

		Perf. 11½		
1930, Apr. 30		**Unwmk.**	**Photo.**	
C1	AP1	50c blue	.45	.45
C2	AP1	1.50fr black brn	2.50	2.50
C3	AP1	2fr deep green	2.00	.90
C4	AP1	5fr brown lake	2.00	1.10
		Nos. C1-C4 (4)	6.95	4.95
		Set, never hinged	22.50	

Nos. C1-C4 exist imperf.

1930, Dec. 5				
C5	AP1	5fr dark violet	30.00	30.00
		Never hinged	65.00	

Issued for use on a mail carrying flight from Brussels to Leopoldville, Belgian Congo, starting Dec. 7.
Exists imperf.

Nos. C2 and C4 Surcharged in Carmine or Blue

1935, May 23				
C6	AP1	1fr on 1.50fr (C)	.55	.40
C7	AP1	4fr on 5fr (Bl)	8.75	8.00
		Set, never hinged	42.50	

Catalogue values for unused stamps in this section, from this point to the end of the section, are for Never Hinged items.

DC-4 Skymaster, Sabena Airline AP5

1946, Apr. 20		**Engr.**	**Perf. 11½**	
C8	AP5	6fr blue	.75	.25
C9	AP5	8.50fr violet brn	1.00	.45
C10	AP5	50fr yellow grn	5.00	.90
a.		Perf. 12x11½ ('54)	325.00	1.40
C11	AP5	100fr gray	8.25	2.00
a.		Perf. 12x11½ ('54)	100.00	1.40
		Nos. C8-C11 (4)	15.00	3.60

Evolution of Postal Transportation — AP6

1949, July 1				
C12	AP6	50fr dark brown	52.50	20.00

Centenary of Belgian postage stamps.

Glider — AP7

Design: 7fr, "Tipsy" plane.

1951, June 18		**Photo.**	**Perf. 13½**	
C12A		Strip of 2 + label	82.50	65.00
b.	AP7	6fr dark blue	32.50	20.00
c.	AP7	7fr carmine rose	32.50	20.00

For the 50th anniv. of the Aero Club of Belgium. The strip sold for 50fr.

1951, July 25			**Perf. 13½**	
C13	AP7	6fr sepia	5.75	.25
C14	AP7	7fr Prus green	5.75	.95

UN Types of Regular Issue, 1958

Designs: 5fr, ICAO. 6fr, World Meteorological Organization. 7.50fr, Protection of Refugees. 8fr, General Agreement on Tariffs and Trade. 9fr, UNICEF. 10fr, Atomic Energy Agency.

			Perf. 11½	
1958, Apr. 17		**Unwmk.**	**Engr.**	
C15	A137	5fr dull blue	.25	.30
C16	A136	6fr yellow grn	.30	.45
C17	A137	7.50fr lilac	.35	.30
C18	A136	8fr sepia	.40	.30
C19	A137	9fr carmine	.45	.50
C20	A136	10fr redsh brown	.75	.60
		Nos. C15-C20 (6)	2.50	2.45

World's Fair, Brussels, Apr. 17-Oct. 19. See note after No. 476.

AIR POST SEMI-POSTAL STAMPS

Catalogue values for unused stamps in this section are for Never Hinged items.

American Soldier in Combat — SPAP1

Perf. 11x11½

1946, June 15   Unwmk.   Engr.
CB1 SPAP1 17.50fr + 62.50fr dl
                brn   2.00 .90
CB2 SPAP1 17.50fr + 62.50fr dl
                gray grn   2.00 .90

Surtax for an American memorial at Bastogne.

An overprint, "Hommage a Roosevelt," was privately applied to Nos. CB1-CB2 in 1947 by the Association Belgo-Americaine. Value, $5.

In 1950 another private overprint was applied, in red, to Nos. CB1-CB2. It consists of "16-12-1944, 25-1-1945, Dedication July 16, 1950" and outlines of the American eagle emblem and the Bastogne Memorial. Value, $12. Similar overprints were applied to Nos. 265 and 361.

Flight Allegory SPAP2

1946, Sept. 7   Perf. 11½
CB3 SPAP2 2fr + 8fr brt vio   .60 1.00

The surtax was for the benefit of aviation.

Nos. B417-B425 Surcharged in Various Arrangements in Red or Dark Blue

Type I   Type II

Type I — Top line "POSTE AERIENNE"
Type II — Top line "LUCHTPOST"

1947, May 18   Photo.   Perf. 11½
Type I
CB4 SP227 1fr + 2fr (R)   .75 .50
CB5 SP228 1.50fr + 2.50fr   .75 .50
CB6 SP229 2fr + 45fr   .75 .50
CB7 SP230 1fr + 2fr (R)   .75 .50
CB8 SP231 1.50fr + 2.50fr   .75 .50
CB9 SP232 2fr + 45fr   .75 .50
CB10 SP233 1fr + 2fr (R)   .75 .50
CB11 SP234 1.50fr + 2.50fr (R) .75 .50
CB12 SP235 2fr + 45fr   .75 .50
Type II
CB4A SP227 1fr + 2fr (R)   .75 .50
CB5A SP228 1.50fr + 2.50fr   .75 .50
CB6A SP229 2fr + 45fr   .75 .50
CB7A SP230 1fr + 2fr (R)   .75 .50
CB8A SP231 1.50fr + 2.50fr   .75 .50
CB9A SP232 2fr + 45fr   .75 .50
CB10A SP233 1fr + 2fr (R)   .75 .50
CB11A SP234 1.50fr + 2.50fr (R) .75 .50
CB12A SP235 2fr + 45fr   .75 .50
    Nos. CB4-CB12A (18)   13.50 9.00

Issued for CIPEX, NYC. In 1948 Nos. CB4-CB12 and CB4A-CB12A were punched with the letters "IMABA," and the inscription "Imaba du 21 au 29 aout 1948" was applied to the backs. Value $20.

Helicopter Leaving Airport SPAP3

1950, Aug. 7
CB13 SPAP3 7fr + 3fr blue   9.00 5.25
Surtax for the Natl. Aeronautical Committee.

SPECIAL DELIVERY STAMPS

From 1874 to 1903 certain hexagonal telegraph stamps were used as special delivery stamps.

Town Hall, Brussels — SD1

2.35fr, Street in Ghent. 3.50fr, Bishop's Palace, Liege. 5.25fr, Notre Dame Cathedral, Antwerp.

1929   Unwmk.   Photo.   Perf. 11½
E1 SD1 1.75fr dark blue   .80 .30
E2 SD1 2.35fr carmine   1.75 .45
E3 SD1 3.50fr dark violet 11.00 10.00
E4 SD1 5.25fr olive green 10.50 10.00

Eupen — SD2

1931
E5 SD2 2.45fr dark green   17.00 2.50
    Nos. E1-E5 (5)   41.05 23.25
    Set, never hinged   110.00

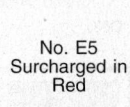

No. E5 Surcharged in Red

1932
E6 SD2 2.50fr on 2.45fr dk grn 18.00 2.00
    Never hinged   60.00

REGISTRATION STAMPS

Catalogue values in this section are for Never Hinged items.

Osprey — R1

2011, Jan. 3   Litho.   Perf. 11½x11¾
F1 R1 (€4.70)multi   12.50 6.25

Short-eared Owl — R2

2012, Feb. 13   Perf. 11½
F2 R2 (€4.35) multi   11.50 5.75

Arctic Tern — R3

2013, Jan. 21   Perf. 11½x11¾
F3 R3 (€5.03) multi   14.00 7.00

Lapwing — R4

2013, Sept. 13   Litho.   Perf. 11½
F4 R4 (€1.20) multi   3.25 1.60

Northern Shoveler — R5

2015, June 1   Litho.   Perf. 11½
F5 R5 (€5.13) multi   11.50 5.75

Water Rail — R6

2017, Jan. 30   Litho.   Perf. 11½
F6 R6 (€5.29) multi   11.50 5.75

POSTAGE DUE STAMPS

D1

1870   Unwmk.   Typo.   Perf. 15
J1 D1 10c green   3.75 2.00
J2 D1 20c ultra, thin paper 30.00 3.75
    Set, never hinged   140.00

In 1909 many bisects of Nos. J1-J2 were created. The 10c bisect used as 5c on piece sells for $3.50.

No. J2 was also printed in aniline ink on thin paper. Value about the same.

D2

1895-09   Perf. 14
J3 D2 5c yellow grn   .25 .25
J4 D2 10c orange brn   17.50 1.75
J5 D2 10c carmine ('00)   .25 .25

J6 D2 20c olive green   .25   .25
J7 D2 30c pale blue ('09) .30   .25
J8 D2 50c yellow brn   17.50 5.00
J9 D2 50c gray ('00)   .75   .45
J10 D2 1fr carmine   20.00 11.50
J11 D2 1fr ocher ('00)   6.50 5.00
    Nos. J3-J11 (9)   63.30 24.70
    Set, never hinged   175.00

1916   Redrawn
J12 D2 5c blue grn   25.00 7.00
J13 D2 10c carmine   42.50 11.00
J14 D2 20c dp gray grn   42.50 15.00
J15 D2 30c brt blue   6.00 5.00
J16 D2 50c gray   125.00 60.00
    Nos. J12-J16 (5)   241.00 98.00
    Set, never hinged   790.00

In the redrawn stamps the lions have a heavy, colored outline. There is a thick vertical line at the outer edge of the design on each side.

D3

1919   Perf. 14
J17 D3 5c green   .40   .50
J18 D3 10c carmine   .95   .35
J19 D3 20c gray green   7.25 1.25
J20 D3 30c bright blue   1.40   .40
J21 D3 50c gray   2.75   .50
    Nos. J17-J21 (5)   12.75 3.00
    Set, never hinged   40.00

The 5c, 10c, 20c and 50c values also exist perf 14x15.

D4

1922-32
J22 D4 5c dk gray   .25   .25
J23 D4 10c green   .25   .25
J24 D4 20c deep brown   .25   .25
J25 D4 30c ver ('24)   .65   .25
  a.   30c rose red   1.00   .45
J26 D4 40c red brn ('25)   .25   .25
J27 D4 50c ultra   1.90   .25
J28 D4 70c red brn ('29)   .30   .25
J29 D4 1fr violet ('25)   .45   .25
J30 D4 1fr rose lilac ('32) .55 .25
J31 D4 1.20fr ol grn ('29) .65   .45
J32 D4 1.50fr ol grn ('32) .65   .45
J33 D4 2fr violet ('29)   .75   .25
J34 D4 3.50fr dp blue ('29) 1.00 .25
    Nos. J22-J34 (13)   7.90 3.65
    Set, never hinged   15.00

1934-46   Perf. 14x13½
J35 D4 35c green ('35)   .40   .45
J36 D4 50c slate   .25   .25
J37 D4 60c carmine ('38) .40   .30
J38 D4 80c slate ('38)   .30   .25
J39 D4 1.40fr gray ('35) .65   .45
J39A D4 3fr org brn ('46) 1.50 .60
J39B D4 7fr brt red vio ('46) 2.25 3.25
    Nos. J35-J39B (7)   5.75 5.55
    Set, never hinged   12.00

See Nos. J54-J61.

Catalogue values for unused stamps in this section, from this point to the end of the section, are for Never Hinged items.

D5

1945   Typo.   Perf. 12½
Inscribed "TE BETALEN" at Top
J40 D5 10c gray olive   .25   .25
J41 D5 20c ultramarine   .25   .25
J42 D5 30c carmine   .25   .25
J43 D5 40c black violet   .25   .25
J44 D5 50c dl bl grn   .25   .25
J45 D5 1fr sepia   .25   .25
J46 D5 2fr red orange   .25   .25

Inscribed "A PAYER" at Top
J47 D5 10c gray olive   .25   .25
J48 D5 20c ultramarine   .25   .25
J49 D5 30c carmine   .25   .25
J50 D5 40c black vio   .25   .25

J51 D5 50c dl bl grn .25 .25
J52 D5 1fr sepia .25 .25
J53 D5 2fr red orange .25 .25
Nos. J40-J53 (14) 3.50 3.50

Type of 1922-32
1949-53 Typo. Perf. 14x13½
J54 D4 65c emerald 7.00 3.75
J55 D4 1.60fr lilac rose ('53) 14.00 6.50
J56 D4 1.80fr red 15.00 6.50
J57 D4 2.40fr gray lilac ('53) 9.00 4.00
J58 D4 4fr deep blue ('53) 11.00 .50
J59 D4 5fr red brown 3.50 .25
J60 D4 8fr lilac rose 10.00 3.75
J61 D4 10fr dark violet 7.25 3.75
Nos. J54-J61 (8) 76.75 29.15

 D6

Numerals 6½mm or More High
1966-70 Photo.
J62 D6 1fr brt pink .25 .25
J63 D6 2fr blue green .25 .25
J64 D6 3fr blue .25 .25
J65 D6 5fr purple .30 .25
J66 D6 6fr bister brn .45 .25
J67 D6 7fr red org ('70) .50 .30
J68 D6 20fr slate grn 1.75 1.00
Nos. J62-J68 (7) 3.75 2.55

Printed on various papers.

Numerals 4½-5½mm High
1985-87 Photo. Perf. 14x13½
J69 D6 1fr lilac rose .25 .25
J70 D6 2fr dull blue grn .25 .25
J71 D6 3fr greenish blue .25 .25
J72 D6 4fr green .25 .25
J73 D6 5fr lt violet .30 .25
J73A D6 6fr brown .35 .25
J74 D6 7fr brt orange .40 .30
J75 D6 8fr pale gray .45 .30
J76 D6 9fr rose lake .50 .35
J77 D6 10fr lt red brown .55 .40
J78 D6 20fr lt olive grn 1.25 1.10
Nos. J69-J78 (11) 4.80 3.95

Printed on various papers.
Issue dates: 3fr, 4fr, 8fr-10fr, Mar. 25, 1985.
6fr, 9/5/86. 20fr, 9/8/86. 2fr, 11/12/86. 6fr,
9/5/86. 1fr, 5fr, 7fr, 1987.

MILITARY STAMPS

Catalogue values for unused stamps in this section are for Never Hinged items.

King Baudouin — M1

Unwmk.
1967, July 17 Photo. Perf. 11
M1 M1 1.50fr greenish gray .25 .25

King Baudouin — M2

1971-75 Engr. Perf. 11½
M2 M2 1.75fr green .50 .45
M3 M2 2.25fr gray green ('72) .35 .30
M4 M2 2.50fr gray green ('74) .25 .25
M5 M2 3.25fr vio brown ('75) .30 .25
Nos. M2-M5 (4) 1.40 1.25

Nos. M1-M3 are luminescent, Nos. M4-M5 are not.

MILITARY PARCEL POST STAMP

Type of Parcel Post Stamp of 1938 Srchd. in Blue

1939 Unwmk. Perf. 13½
MQ1 PP19 3fr on 5.50fr copper red .30 .25
Never hinged .60

OFFICIAL STAMPS

For franking the official correspondence of the Administration of the Belgian National Railways.

Most examples of Nos. O1-O25 in the marketplace are counterfeits. Values are for genuine examples.

Regular Issue of 1921-27 Overprinted in Black

1929-30 Unwmk. Perf. 14
O1 A58 5c gray .25 .25
O2 A58 10c blue green .30 .40
O3 A58 35c blue green .40 .30
O4 A58 60c olive green .45 .30
O5 A58 1.50fr brt blue 8.00 6.25
O6 A58 1.75fr ultra ('30) 1.75 2.00
Nos. O1-O6 (6) 11.15 9.50

Same Overprint, in Red or Black, on Regular Issues of 1929-30
1929-31
O7 A63 5c slate (R) .25 .35
O8 A63 10c olive grn (R) .50 .40
O9 A63 25c rose red (Bk) 1.50 .85
O10 A63 35c dp green (R) 1.75 .50
O11 A63 40c red vio (Bk) 1.25 .45
O12 A63 50c dp blue (R) ('31) .80 .35
O13 A63 60c rose (Bk) 10.00 6.00
O14 A63 70c orange brn (Bk) 4.25 1.25
O15 A63 75c black vio (R) ('31) 4.00 .85
Nos. O7-O15 (9) 24.30 11.00

Overprinted on Regular Issue of 1932
1932
O16 A73 10c olive grn (R) .50 .60
O17 A74 35c dp green 9.00 .75
O18 A71a 75c bister brn (R) 1.50 .30
Nos. O16-O18 (3) 11.00 1.65

Overprinted on No. 262 in Red
1935 Perf. 13½x14
O19 A80 70c olive black 2.75 .25

Regular Stamps of 1935-36 Overprinted in Red
1936-38 Perf. 13½, 13½x14, 14
O20 A82 10c olive bister .25 .35
O21 A82 35c green .25 .40
O22 A82 50c dark blue .45 .35
O23 A83 70c brown 1.50 .65

Overprinted in Black or Red on Regular Issue of 1938
Perf. 13½x14
O24 A82 40c red violet (Bk) .30 .35
O25 A85 75c olive gray (R) .65 .30
Nos. O20-O25 (6) 3.40 2.40

Regular Issues of 1935-41 Overprinted in Red or Dark Blue

1941-44 Perf. 14, 14x13½, 13½x14
O26 A82 10c olive bister .25 .25
a. Inverted overprint 65.00 65.00
O27 A82 40c red violet .55 .75
O28 A82 50c dark blue .25 .25
a. Inverted overprint 77.50 77.50
O29 A83a 1fr rose car (Bl) .45 .35
O30 A85 1fr rose pink (Bl) .25 .25

O31 A83a 2.25fr grnsh blk ('44) .30 .50
O32 A84 2.25fr gray violet .45 .70
Nos. O26-O32 (7) 2.50 3.05

Nos. O21, O23 and O25 Surcharged with New Values in Black or Red
1942
O33 A82 10c on 35c green .25 .35
O34 A83 50c on 70c brown .25 .25
O35 A85 50c on 75c ol gray (R) .25 .25
Nos. O33-O35 (3) .75 .85

Counterfeits exist of Nos. O26-O35.

Catalogue values for unused stamps in this section, from this point to the end of the section, are for Never Hinged items.

O1

1946-48 Unwmk. Perf. 14
O36 O1 10c olive bister .25 .25
O37 O1 20c brt violet 3.00 .90
O38 O1 50c dk blue .25 .25
O39 O1 65c red lilac ('48) 4.00 1.10
O40 O1 75c lilac rose .25 .25
O41 O1 90c brown violet 5.00 .35
Nos. O36-O41 (6) 12.75 3.10

Types A99, A101 and A102 with "B" Emblem Added to Design
1948 Perf. 11½
O42 A99 1.35fr red brown 4.25 .75
O43 A99 1.75fr dk gray green 6.00 .45
O44 A101 3fr brt red violet 27.50 8.00
O45 A102 3.15fr deep blue 11.00 7.00
O46 A102 4fr brt ultra 22.50 13.00
Nos. O42-O46 (5) 71.25 29.20

O2

1953-66 Typo. Perf. 13½x14
O47 O2 10c orange .65 .25
O48 O2 20c red lilac 3.50 .70
O49 O2 30c gray green ('58) 1.40 .55
O50 O2 40c olive gray .50 .25
O51 O2 50c light blue .75 .25
O51A O2 60c lilac rose ('66) 1.10 .55
O52 O2 65c red lilac 30.00 22.50
O53 O2 80c emerald 4.50 1.10
O54 O2 90c deep blue 6.75 1.10
O55 O2 1fr rose .45 .25
Nos. O47-O55 (10) 49.60 27.50

See Nos. O66, O68.

King Baudouin — O3

1954-70 Photo. Perf. 11½
O56 O3 1.50fr gray .30 .25
O57 O3 2fr rose red 40.00 .25
O58 O3 2fr blue grn ('59) .30 .25
O59 O3 2.50fr red brown ('58) 32.50 .75
O60 O3 3fr red lilac ('58) 1.50 .25
O61 O3 3.50fr yel green ('70) .75 .25
O62 O3 4fr brt blue 1.00 .25
O63 O3 6fr car rose ('58) 1.50 .60
Nos. O56-O63 (8) 77.85 2.85

Printed on various papers.

Type of 1953-66 Redrawn
1970-75 Typo. Perf. 13½x14
O66 O2 1.50fr grnsh gray ('75) .25 .25
O68 O2 2.50fr brown .25 .25

King Baudouin — O4

1971-73 Engr. Perf. 11½
O71 O4 3.50fr org brn ('73) .35 .25
O72 O4 4.50fr brown ('73) .35 .25
O73 O4 7fr red .40 .50
O74 O4 15fr violet .75 .30
Nos. O71-O74 (4) 1.85 1.30

Nos. O71-O74 were printed on various papers.

1974-80
O75 O4 3fr yellow grn 1.50 1.00
O76 O4 4fr blue 1.50 .50
O77 O4 4.50fr grnsh bl ('75) .30 .25
O78 O4 5fr lilac .30 .25
O79 O4 6fr carmine ('78) .35 .25
O80 O4 6.50fr black ('76) .40 .35
O81 O4 8fr bluish blk ('78) .50 .25
O82 O4 9fr lt red brn ('80) .55 .25
O83 O4 10fr rose carmine .60 .25
O84 O4 25fr lilac ('76) 1.50 .50
O85 O4 30fr org brn ('78) 1.75 .50
Nos. O75-O85 (11) 9.25 4.35

Heraldic Lion — O5

1977-82 Typo. Perf. 13½x14
O87 O5 50c brown ('82) .25 .25
O92 O5 1fr lilac ('82) .25 .25
O94 O5 2fr orange ('82) .25 .25
O95 O5 4fr red brown .25 .25
O96 O5 5fr green ('80) .25 .25
Nos. O87-O96 (5) 1.25 1.25

Nos. O87-O96 were printed on various papers.

NEWSPAPER STAMPS

Most examples of Nos. P1-P40 in the marketplace are counterfeits. Values are for genuine examples.

Parcel Post Stamps of 1923-27 Overprinted

Perf. 14½x14, 14x14½
1928 Unwmk.
P1 PP12 10c vermilion .25 .40
P2 PP12 20c turq blue .25 .40
P3 PP12 40c olive grn .25 .40
P4 PP12 60c orange .70 .90
P5 PP12 70c dk brown .45 .40
P6 PP12 80c violet .60 .70
P7 PP12 90c slate 2.25 2.00
P8 PP13 1fr brt blue .90 .60
a. 1fr ultramarine 12.00 5.00
P10 PP13 2fr olive grn 1.50 .60
P11 PP13 3fr orange red 1.60 .90
P12 PP13 4fr rose 2.25 1.10
P13 PP13 5fr violet 2.25 1.00
P14 PP13 6fr bister brn 4.50 1.75
P15 PP13 7fr orange 5.00 2.25
P16 PP13 8fr dk brown 6.00 2.75
P17 PP13 9fr red violet 10.00 3.00
P18 PP13 10fr blue green 9.00 2.75
P19 PP13 20fr magenta 15.00 7.00
Nos. P1-P8,P10-P19 (18) 62.75 28.90

Parcel Post Stamps
of 1923-28
Overprinted

JOURNAUX DAGBLADEN

1929-31

P20	PP12	10c vermilion	.25	.25
P21	PP12	20c turq blue	.25	.25
P22	PP12	40c olive green	.30	.25
a.		Inverted overprint		
P23	PP12	60c orange	.55	.35
P24	PP12	70c dk brown	.55	.25
P25	PP12	80c violet	.60	.25
P26	PP12	90c gray	2.00	1.00
P27	PP13	1fr ultra	.60	.25
a.		1fr bright blue	4.00	2.50
P28	PP13	1.10fr org brn ('31)	6.25	1.40
P29	PP13	1.50fr gray vio ('31)	6.25	1.90
P30	PP13	2fr olive green	2.00	.25
P31	PP13	2.10fr sl gray ('31)	17.00	12.00
P32	PP13	3fr orange red	2.25	.45
P33	PP13	4fr rose	2.25	.70
P34	PP13	5fr violet	3.00	.55
P35	PP13	6fr bister brn	3.75	1.00
P36	PP13	7fr orange	3.75	1.00
P37	PP13	8fr dk brown	3.75	1.00
P38	PP13	9fr red violet	5.25	1.50
P39	PP13	10fr blue green	3.75	1.10
P40	PP13	20fr magenta	13.00	4.50
		Nos. P20-P40 (21)	77.35	30.20

PARCEL POST AND RAILWAY STAMPS

Values for used Railway Stamps (Chemins de Fer) stamps are for copies with railway cancellations. Railway Stamps with postal cancellations sell for twice as much.

Coat of Arms — PP1

1879-82   Unwmk.   Typo.   Perf. 14

Q1	PP1	10c violet brown	110.00	5.75
Q2	PP1	20c blue	275.00	17.50
Q3	PP1	25c green ('81)	375.00	10.00
Q4	PP1	50c carmine	1,750.	10.00
Q5	PP1	80c yellow	2,000.	57.50
Q6	PP1	1fr gray ('82)	275.00	16.00

Used examples of Nos. Q1-Q6 with pinholes, a normal state, sell for approximately 40-60 percent of the values given.

Most of the stamps of 1882-1902 (Nos. Q7 to Q28) are without watermark. Twice in each sheet of 100 stamps they have one of three watermarks: (1) A winged wheel and "Chemins de Fer de l'Etat Belge," (2) Coat of Arms of Belgium and "Royaume de Belgique," (3) Larger Coat of Arms, without inscription.

PP2

1882-94   Perf. 15½x14¼

Q7	PP2	10c brown ('86)	20.00	1.50
Q8	PP2	15c gray ('94)	8.75	7.25
Q9	PP2	20c blue ('86)	65.00	7.00
Q10	PP2	25c yel grn ('91)	72.50	4.25
Q11	PP2	50c carmine	72.50	2.50
Q12	PP2	80c brnsh buff	72.50	.90
Q13	PP2	80c lemon	75.00	1.60
Q14	PP2	1fr lavender	350.00	3.00
Q15	PP2	2fr yel buff ('94)	210.00	67.50

Counterfeits exist.

PP3

Name of engraver below frame

1895-97
Numerals in Black, except 1fr, 2fr

Q16	PP3	10c red brown ('96)	11.00	.60
Q17	PP3	15c gray	11.00	7.00
Q18	PP3	20c blue	17.50	1.00
Q19	PP3	25c green	17.50	1.25
Q20	PP3	50c carmine	25.00	.80
Q21	PP3	60c violet ('96)	50.00	1.00
Q22	PP3	80c ol yel ('96)	50.00	1.40
Q23	PP3	1fr lilac brown	175.00	3.00
Q24	PP3	2fr yel buff ('97)	200.00	15.00

Counterfeits exist.

1901-02   Numerals in Black

Q25	PP3	30c orange	21.00	2.00
Q26	PP3	40c green	26.00	1.75
Q27	PP3	70c blue	50.00	1.40
a.		Numerals omitted	750.00	
b.		Numerals printed on reverse	750.00	
Q28	PP3	90c red	65.00	2.00
		Nos. Q25-Q28 (4)	162.00	7.15

Winged Wheel PP4

Without engraver's name

1902-14   Perf. 15

Q29	PP3	10c yel brn & slate	.25	.25
Q30	PP3	15c slate & vio	.25	.25
Q31	PP3	20c ultra & yel brn	.25	.25
Q32	PP3	25c yel grn & red	.25	.25
Q33	PP3	30c orange & bl grn	.25	.25
Q34	PP3	35c bister & bl grn ('12)	.35	.25
Q35	PP3	40c blue grn & vio	.25	.25
Q36	PP3	50c pale rose & vio	.25	.25
Q37	PP3	55c lilac brn & ultra ('14)	.35	.25
Q38	PP3	60c violet & red	.25	.25
Q39	PP3	70c blue & red	.25	.25
Q40	PP3	80c lemon & vio brn	.25	.25
Q41	PP3	90c red & yel grn	.25	.25
Q42	PP4	1fr vio brn & org	.25	.25
Q43	PP4	1.10fr rose & blk ('06)	.25	.25
Q44	PP4	2fr ocher & bl grn	.25	.25
Q45	PP4	3fr black & ultra	.35	.25
Q46	PP4	4fr yel grn & red ('13)	1.25	.70
Q47	PP4	5fr org & bl grn ('13)	.55	.55
Q48	PP4	10fr ol yel & brn vio ('13)	.90	.55
		Nos. Q29-Q48 (20)	7.25	6.05

Regular Issues of 1912-13 Handstamped in Violet

1915   Perf. 14

Q49	A42	5c green	190.00	160.00
Q50	A43	10c red	1,400.	1,400.
Q51	A45	10c red	230.00	200.00
a.		With engraver's name	775.00	775.00
Q52	A43	20c olive grn	1,600.	1,600.
Q53	A45	20c olive grn	260.00	225.00
a.		With engraver's name	775.00	775.00
Q54	A45	25c ultra	260.00	225.00
a.		With engraver's name	775.00	775.00
Q55	A43	35c bister brn	350.00	300.00
Q55A	A40	40c green	2,500.	2,500.
Q56	A45	40c green	325.00	275.00
Q57	A43	50c gray	325.00	275.00
Q58	A43	1fr orange	325.00	275.00
Q59	A43	2fr violet	1,900.	1,650.
Q60	A44	5fr plum	4,000.	3,500.

Excellent forgeries of this overprint exist.

PP5

1916   Litho.   Perf. 13½

Q61	PP5	10c pale blue	1.10	.25
Q62	PP5	15c olive grn	1.40	.50
Q63	PP5	20c red	2.25	.50
Q64	PP5	25c lt brown	2.25	.50
Q65	PP5	30c lilac	1.40	.50
Q66	PP5	35c gray	1.40	.45
Q67	PP5	40c orange yel	3.00	1.50
Q68	PP5	50c bister	2.25	.45
Q69	PP5	55c brown	3.00	2.25
Q70	PP5	60c gray vio	2.25	.45
Q71	PP5	70c green	2.25	.45
Q72	PP5	80c red brown	2.25	.45
Q73	PP5	90c blue	2.25	.45
Q74	PP5	1fr gray	2.25	.45
Q75	PP6	1.10fr ultra (Franken)	27.50	21.00
Q76	PP6	2fr red	25.00	.45
Q77	PP6	3fr violet	25.00	.45
Q78	PP6	4fr emerald	45.00	1.50
Q79	PP6	5fr brown	45.00	3.00
Q80	PP6	10fr orange	45.00	1.50
		Nos. Q61-Q80 (20)	241.80	37.05

Type of 1916 Inscribed "FRANK" instead of "FRANKEN"

1920

Q81	PP6	1.10fr ultra	2.00	.45

PP7

PP8

1920   Perf. 14

Q82	PP7	10c blue grn	1.75	.75
Q83	PP7	15c olive grn	1.75	1.10
Q84	PP7	20c red	1.75	.75
Q85	PP7	25c gray brn	2.50	.75
Q86	PP7	30c red vio	27.00	22.50
Q87	PP7	40c pale org	11.00	.75
Q88	PP7	50c bister	9.00	.75
Q89	PP7	55c pale brown	5.50	4.50
Q90	PP7	60c dk violet	10.00	.75
Q91	PP7	70c green	18.00	1.10
Q92	PP7	80c red brown	40.00	1.50
Q93	PP7	90c dull blue	10.00	.75
Q94	PP8	1fr gray	85.00	1.50
Q95	PP8	1.10fr ultra	26.00	2.00
Q96	PP8	1.20fr dk green	11.00	.75
Q97	PP8	1.40fr black brn	11.00	.75
Q98	PP8	2fr vermilion	110.00	1.25
Q99	PP8	3fr red vio	125.00	.85
Q100	PP8	4fr yel grn	125.00	.75
Q101	PP8	5fr bister brn	125.00	.75
Q102	PP8	10fr brown org	125.00	.75
		Nos. Q82-Q102 (21)	881.25	45.30

PP9

PP10

Types PP7 and PP9 differ in the position of the wheel and the tablet above it.

Types PP8 and PP10 differ in the bars below "FR".

There are many other variations in the designs.

1920-21   Typo.

Q103	PP9	10c carmine	.30	.25
Q104	PP9	15c yel grn	.30	.25
Q105	PP9	20c blue grn	.70	.25
Q106	PP9	25c ultra	.65	.25
Q107	PP9	30c chocolate	.85	.25
Q108	PP9	35c orange brn	.90	.30
Q109	PP9	40c orange	1.10	.25
Q110	PP9	50c rose	1.10	.25
Q111	PP9	55c yel ('21)	4.50	3.25
Q112	PP9	60c dull rose	1.10	.25
Q113	PP9	70c emerald	3.00	.40
Q114	PP9	80c violet	2.25	.25
Q115	PP9	90c lemon	37.50	21.00
Q116	PP9	90c claret	4.50	.40
Q117	PP10	1fr buff	4.50	.35
Q118	PP10	1fr red brown	4.00	.30
Q119	PP10	1.10fr ultra	1.60	.45
Q120	PP10	1.20fr orange	6.25	.30
Q121	PP10	1.40fr yellow	10.00	1.75
Q122	PP10	1.60fr turq blue	18.00	.70
Q123	PP10	1.60fr emerald	40.00	.70
Q124	PP10	2fr pale rose	26.00	.30
Q125	PP10	3fr dp rose	24.00	.30
Q126	PP10	4fr emerald	24.00	.30
Q127	PP10	5fr lt violet	17.50	.30
Q128	PP10	10fr lemon	110.00	9.00
Q129	PP10	10fr dk brown	22.50	.30
Q130	PP10	15fr dp rose ('21)	22.50	.30
Q131	PP10	20fr dk blue ('21)	325.00	3.00
		Nos. Q103-Q131 (29)	714.60	45.95

PP11

1922   Engr.   Perf. 11½

Q132	PP11	2fr black	4.00	.25
Q133	PP11	3fr brown	37.50	.25
Q134	PP11	4fr green	9.00	.25
Q135	PP11	5r claret	9.00	.25
Q136	PP11	10fr yel brown	10.00	.25
Q137	PP11	15fr rose red	10.00	.25
Q138	PP11	20fr blue	67.50	.25
		Nos. Q132-Q138 (7)	147.00	1.75

PP12

PP13

Perf. 14x13½, 13½x14

1923-40   Typo.

Q139	PP12	5c red brn	.25	.25
Q140	PP12	10c vermilion	.25	.25
Q141	PP12	15c ultra	.25	.30
Q142	PP12	20c turq blue	.25	.25
Q143	PP12	30c brn vio ('27)	.25	.25
Q144	PP12	40c olive grn	.25	.25
Q145	PP12	50c mag ('27)	.25	.25
Q146	PP12	60c orange	.25	.25
Q147	PP12	70c dk brn ('24)	.25	.25
Q148	PP12	80c violet	.25	.25
Q149	PP12	90c sl ('27)	1.25	.25
Q150	PP13	1fr ultra	.35	.25
Q151	PP13	1fr brt blue ('28)	.55	.25
Q152	PP13	1.10fr orange	3.00	.30
Q153	PP13	1.50fr turq blue	3.25	.30
Q154	PP13	1.70fr dp brn ('31)	.75	.60
Q155	PP13	1.80fr claret	4.25	.60
Q156	PP13	2fr ol grn ('24)	.35	.25
Q157	PP13	2.10fr gray grn	7.50	.85
Q158	PP13	2.40fr dp violet	4.00	.85
Q159	PP13	2.70fr gray ('24)	35.00	1.40
Q160	PP13	3fr org red	.45	.25

Q161	PP13	3.30fr brn ('24)	55.00	1.40
Q162	PP13	4fr rose ('24)	.55	.25
Q163	PP13	5fr vio ('24)	.90	.25
Q163A	PP13	5fr brn vio ('40)	.45	.30
Q164	PP13	6fr bis brn ('27)	.50	.25
Q165	PP13	7fr org ('27)	.90	.25
Q166	PP13	8fr dp brn ('27)	.75	.25
Q167	PP13	9fr red vio ('27)	2.50	.25
Q168	PP13	10fr blue grn ('27)	1.10	.25
Q168A	PP13	10fr blk ('40)	5.75	5.00
Q169	PP13	20fr mag ('27)	1.90	.25
Q170	PP13	30fr turq grn ('31)	6.00	.40
Q171	PP13	40fr gray ('31)	55.00	.75
Q172	PP13	50fr bis ('27)	9.00	.30
		Nos. Q139-Q172 (36)	203.50	18.85

See Nos. Q239-Q262. For overprints see Nos. Q216-Q238. Stamps overprinted "Bagages Reisgoed" are revenues.

No. Q158 Srchd.

1924 — **Green Surcharge**

Q173	PP13	2.30fr on 2.40fr vio	5.00	.85
		Never hinged	30.00	
a.		Inverted surcharge	57.50	

Type of Regular Issue of 1926-27 Overprinted

1928 — **Perf. 14**

Q174	A61	4fr buff	7.50	1.10
Q175	A61	5fr bister	7.50	1.25
		Set, never hinged	55.00	

Central P.O., Brussels PP15

1929-30 — **Engr.** — **Perf. 11½**

Q176	PP15	3fr black brn	2.00	.25
Q177	PP15	4fr gray	2.00	.25
Q178	PP15	5fr carmine	2.00	.25
Q179	PP15	6fr vio brn ('30)	29.00	32.50
		Nos. Q176-Q179 (4)	35.00	33.25
		Set, never hinged	115.00	

No. Q179 Surcharged in Blue

1933

Q180	PP15	4(fr) on 6fr vio brn	25.00	.25
		Never hinged	105.00	

Modern Locomotive PP16

1934 — **Photo.** — **Perf. 13½x14**

Q181	PP16	3fr dk green	40.00	9.00
Q182	PP16	4fr red violet	9.50	.25
Q183	PP16	5fr dp rose	37.50	.25
		Nos. Q181-Q183 (3)	87.00	9.50
		Set, never hinged	275.00	

Modern Railroad Train — PP17

Old Railroad Train — PP18

1935 — **Engr.** — **Perf. 14x13½, 13½x14**

Q184	PP17	10c rose car	.45	.25
Q185	PP17	20c violet	.50	.25
Q186	PP17	30c black brn	.65	.45
Q187	PP17	40c dk blue	.80	.25
Q188	PP17	50c orange red	.80	.25
Q189	PP17	60c green	.90	.25
Q190	PP17	70c ultra	1.00	.25
Q191	PP17	80c olive blk	.90	.25
Q192	PP17	90c rose lake	1.25	.65
Q193	PP18	1fr brown vio	1.25	.25
Q194	PP18	2fr gray blk	2.75	.25
Q195	PP18	3fr red org	3.50	.25
Q196	PP18	4fr violet brn	4.25	.25
Q197	PP18	5fr plum	4.50	.25
Q198	PP18	6fr dp green	5.00	.25
Q199	PP18	7fr dp violet	24.00	.25
Q200	PP18	8fr olive blk	24.00	.25
Q201	PP18	9fr dk blue	24.00	.25
Q202	PP18	10fr car lake	24.00	.25
Q203	PP18	20fr green	125.00	.25
Q204	PP18	30fr violet	125.00	2.75
Q205	PP18	40fr black brn	125.00	3.50
Q206	PP18	50fr rose car	140.00	2.75
Q207	PP18	100fr ultra	350.00	62.50
		Nos. Q184-Q207 (24)	989.50	77.10
		Set, never hinged	3,375.	

Centenary of Belgian State Railway.

Winged Wheel PP19

Surcharged in Red or Blue

1938 — **Photo.** — **Perf. 13½**

Q208	PP19	5fr on 3.50fr dk grn	22.50	1.50
Q209	PP19	5fr on 4.50fr rose vio (Bl)	.25	.25
Q210	PP19	6fr on 5.50fr cop red (Bl)	.50	.25
a.		Half used as 3fr on piece	8.00	
		Nos. Q208-Q210 (3)	23.25	2.00
		Set, never hinged	75.00	

Nos. Q208-Q210 exist without surcharge. Value, set, $750.
See Nos. MQ1, Q297-Q299.

Symbolizing Unity Achieved Through Railroads PP20

1939 — **Engr.** — **Perf. 13½x14**

Q211	PP20	20c redsh brn	5.00	5.25
Q212	PP20	50c vio bl	5.00	5.25
Q213	PP20	2fr rose red	5.00	5.25
Q214	PP20	9fr slate grn	5.00	5.25
Q215	PP20	10fr dk vio	5.00	5.25
		Nos. Q211-Q215 (5)	25.00	26.25
		Set, never hinged	30.00	

Railroad Exposition and Cong. held at Brussels.

Parcel Post Stamps of 1925-27 Overprinted in Blue or Carmine

Perf. 14½x14, 14x14½

1940 — **Unwmk.**

Q216	PP12	10c vermilion	.25	.25
Q217	PP12	20c turq bl (C)	.25	.25
Q218	PP12	30c brn vio (C)	.25	.25
Q219	PP12	40c ol grn (C)	.25	.25
Q220	PP12	50c magenta	.25	.25
Q221	PP12	60c orange	.60	*.55*
Q222	PP12	70c dk brn	.25	.25
Q223	PP12	80c vio (C)	.25	.25
Q224	PP12	90c slate (C)	.25	.25
Q225	PP13	1fr ultra (C)	.25	.25
Q226	PP13	2fr ol grn (C)	.25	.25
a.		Ovpt. inverted	140.00	75.00
Q227	PP13	3fr org red	.25	.25
Q228	PP13	4fr rose	.25	.25
Q229	PP13	5fr vio (C)	.25	.25
Q230	PP13	6fr bis brn	.35	.25
Q231	PP13	7fr orange	.35	.25
Q232	PP13	8fr dp brn	.35	.25
Q233	PP13	9fr red vio	.35	.25
Q234	PP13	10fr bl grn (C)	.35	.25
Q235	PP13	20fr magenta	.60	.25
Q236	PP13	30fr turq grn (C)	1.10	.75
Q237	PP13	40fr gray (C)	2.25	*2.10*
Q238	PP13	50fr bister	1.60	1.10
		Nos. Q216-Q238 (23)	11.15	9.25
		Set, never hinged	18.00	

Types of 1923-40

1941

Q239	PP12	10c dl olive	.25	.25
Q240	PP12	20c lt vio	.25	.25
Q241	PP12	30c fawn	.25	.25
Q242	PP12	40c dull blue	.25	.25
Q243	PP12	50c lt grn	.25	.25
Q244	PP12	60c gray	.25	.25
Q245	PP12	70c chalky grn	.25	.25
Q246	PP12	80c orange	.25	.25
Q247	PP12	90c rose lilac	.25	.25
Q248	PP13	1fr lt yel grn	.25	.25
Q249	PP13	2fr vio brn	.40	.25
Q250	PP13	3fr slate	.45	.25
Q251	PP13	4fr dl olive	.50	.25
Q252	PP13	5fr rose lilac	.50	.25
Q253	PP13	5fr black	.85	.30
Q254	PP13	6fr org ver	.75	.30
Q255	PP13	7fr lilac	.75	.25
Q256	PP13	8fr chalky grn	.75	.25
Q257	PP13	9fr blue	.90	.25
Q258	PP13	10fr rose lilac	.90	.25
Q259	PP13	20fr milky blue	2.75	.40
Q260	PP13	30fr orange	5.00	.80
Q261	PP13	40fr rose	6.25	.80
Q262	PP13	50fr brt red vio	10.00	.70
		Nos. Q239-Q262 (24)	33.25	7.80
		Set, never hinged	90.00	

Adjusting Tie Plates — PP21

Engineer at Throttle — PP22

Freight Station Interior — PP23

Signal and Electric Train — PP24

1942 — **Engr.** — **Perf. 14x13½**

Q263	PP21	9.20fr red org	.60	*.85*
Q264	PP22	12.30fr dp grn	.60	*.90*
Q265	PP23	14.30fr dk car	.80	*1.25*

Perf. 11½

Q266	PP24	100fr ultra	20.00	17.00
		Nos. Q263-Q266 (4)	22.00	20.00
		Set, never hinged	25.00	

Catalogue values for unused stamps in this section, from this point to the end of the section, are for Never Hinged items.

PP25 PP26

PP27

1945-46 — **Photo.** — **Unwmk.**

Q267	PP25	10c ol blk ('46)	.35	.30
Q268	PP25	20c dp vio	.35	.30
Q269	PP25	30c chnt brn ('46)	.35	.30
Q270	PP25	40c dp bl ('46)	.35	.30
Q271	PP25	50c peacock grn	.35	.30
Q272	PP25	60c blk ('46)	.35	.30
Q273	PP25	70c emer ('46)	.45	.30
Q274	PP25	80c orange	.75	.30
Q275	PP25	90c brn vio ('46)	.35	.30
Q276	PP26	1fr bl grn ('46)	.35	.30
Q277	PP26	2fr blk brn	.35	.30
Q278	PP26	3fr grnsh blk ('46)	2.00	.30
Q279	PP26	4fr dark blue	.45	.30
Q280	PP26	5fr sepia	.50	.30
Q281	PP26	6fr dk ol grn ('46)	2.25	.30
Q282	PP26	7fr dk vio ('46)	.75	.30
Q283	PP26	8fr red org	.75	.30
Q284	PP26	9fr dp bl ('46)	.90	.30
Q285	PP27	10fr dk red ('46)	3.25	.30
Q286	PP27	10fr sepia ('46)	1.90	.30
Q287	PP27	20fr dk yel grn ('46)	1.00	.30
Q288	PP27	30fr blk ('46)	1.00	.30
Q289	PP27	40fr rose pink	1.00	.30
Q290	PP27	50fr brt bl ('46)	16.00	.70
		Nos. Q267-Q290 (24)	36.10	7.60

Mercury — PP28

1945-46 — **Perf. 13½x13**

Q291	PP28	3fr emer ('46)	.25	.25
Q292	PP28	5fr ultra	.25	.25
Q293	PP28	6fr red	.25	.25

Inscribed "Belgique-Belgie"

Q294	PP28	3fr emer ('46)	.25	.25
Q295	PP28	5fr ultra	.25	.25
Q296	PP28	6fr red	.25	.25
		Nos. Q291-Q296 (6)	1.50	1.50

Winged Wheel Type of 1938

Carmine Surcharge

1946 — **Perf. 13½x14**

Q297	PP19	8fr on 5.50fr brn	.65	.25
Q298	PP19	10fr on 5.50fr dk bl	.75	.25
Q299	PP19	12fr on 5.50fr vio	1.10	.25
		Nos. Q297-Q299 (3)	2.50	.75

Railway Crossing PP29

1947 — **Engr.** — **Perf. 12½**

Q300	PP29	100fr dark green	7.00	.25

Crossbowman with Train — PP30

1947		Photo.	Perf. 11½		
Q301	PP30	8fr dark olive brn		1.00	.25
Q302	PP30	10fr gray & blue		1.10	.25
Q303	PP30	12fr dark violet		1.60	.45
		Nos. Q301-Q303 (3)		3.70	.95

Nos.
Q301-3
Srchd.

1948					
Q304	PP30	9fr on 8fr		1.25	.25
Q305	PP30	11fr on 10fr		1.25	.25
Q306	PP30	13.50fr on 12fr		2.00	.25
		Nos. Q304-Q306 (3)		4.50	.75

Delivery of
Parcel
PP31

1948					
Q307	PP31	9fr chocolate		6.50	.25
Q308	PP31	11fr brown car		7.00	.25
Q309	PP31	13.50fr gray		10.50	.25
		Nos. Q307-Q309 (3)		24.00	.75

Locomotive
of 1835
PP32

Various Locomotives.

Lathe Work in Frame Differs

1949		Engr.	Perf. 12½		
Q310	PP32	½fr dark brown		.65	.25
Q311	PP32	1fr carmine rose		.80	.25
Q312	PP32	2fr deep ultra		1.10	.25
Q313	PP32	3fr dp magenta		2.25	.25
Q314	PP32	4fr blue green		3.00	.25
Q315	PP32	5fr orange red		3.00	.25
Q316	PP32	6fr brown vio		3.25	.30
Q317	PP32	7fr yellow grn		4.50	.25
Q318	PP32	8fr grnsh blue		5.50	.25
Q319	PP32	9fr yellow brn		6.50	.30
Q320	PP32	10fr citron		8.00	.25
Q321	PP32	20fr orange		12.00	.25
Q322	PP32	30fr blue		20.00	.25
Q323	PP32	40fr lilac rose		35.00	.30
Q324	PP32	50fr violet		60.00	.35
Q325	PP32	100fr red		100.00	.25

Engraved; Center Typographed

Q326	PP32	10fr car rose & blk		12.00	1.75
		Nos. Q310-Q326 (17)		277.55	6.00

See No. Q337.

1949			Engr.		

Design: Electric locomotive.

Q327	PP32	60fr black brown		25.00	.25

Opening of Charleroi-Brussels electric railway line, Oct. 15, 1949.

Mailing
Parcel Post
PP33

Sorting
PP34

Loading
PP35

1950-52		Perf. 12x12½, 12½		
Q328	PP33	11fr red orange	6.00	.25
Q329	PP33	12fr red vio ('51)	20.00	1.50
Q330	PP34	13fr dk blue grn	6.00	.25
Q331	PP34	15fr ultra ('51)	15.00	.30
Q332	PP35	16fr gray	6.00	.25
Q333	PP35	17fr brown ('52)	8.00	.25
Q334	PP35	18fr brt car ('51)	16.00	.45
Q335	PP35	20fr brn org ('52)	8.00	.25
		Nos. Q328-Q335 (8)	85.00	3.50

For surcharges see Nos. Q338-Q340.

Mercury and Winged Wheel — PP36

1951				
Q336	PP36	25fr dark blue	15.00	11.50

25th anniv. of the founding of the Natl. Soc. of Belgian Railroads.

Type of 1949

Design: Electric locomotive.

1952		Unwmk.	Perf. 11½	
Q337	PP32	300fr red violet	150.00	.50

Nos. Q331, Q328 and Q334 Surcharged with New Value and "X" in Red, Blue or Green

1953			Perf. 12x12½	
Q338	PP34	13fr on 15fr (R)	60.00	3.00
Q339	PP33	17fr on 11fr (Bl)	35.00	2.25
Q340	PP35	20fr on 18fr (G)	30.00	2.50
		Nos. Q338-Q340 (3)	125.00	7.75

Electric
Train, 1952
PP37

1953				Engr.
Q341	PP37	200fr dk yel grn & vio brn	250.00	4.00
Q342	PP37	200fr dk red brn	225.00	1.00

No. Q341 was issued to commemorate the opening of the railway link connecting Brussels North and South Stations, Oct. 4, 1952.

New North Station,
Brussels — PP38

Chapelle
Station,
Brussels
PP39

Designs: No. Q348, 15fr, Congress Station. 10fr, 20fr, 30fr, 40fr, 50fr, South Station. 100fr, 200fr, 300fr, Central Station.

1953-57		Unwmk.	Perf. 11½	
Q343	PP38	1fr bister		.30	.25
Q344	PP38	2fr slate		.45	.25
Q345	PP38	3fr blue grn		.60	.25
Q346	PP38	4fr orange		.90	.25
Q347	PP38	5fr red brn		2.75	.25
Q348	PP38	5fr dk red brn		10.00	.25

Q349	PP38	6fr rose vio	1.10	.25
Q350	PP38	7fr brt green	1.10	.25
Q351	PP38	8fr rose red	1.40	.25
Q352	PP38	9fr brt grnsh bl	2.00	.25
Q353	PP38	10fr lt grn	2.25	.25
Q354	PP38	15fr dl red	13.00	.25
Q355	PP38	20fr blue	4.00	.25
Q356	PP38	30fr purple	6.25	.25
Q357	PP38	40fr brt purple	8.00	.25
Q358	PP38	50fr lilac rose	10.00	.25
Q359	PP39	60fr brt purple	20.00	.25
Q360	PP39	80fr brown vio	35.00	.25
Q361	PP39	100fr emerald	18.00	.25
Q361A	PP39	200fr brt vio bl	95.00	1.60
Q361B	PP39	300fr lilac rose	175.00	2.25
		Nos. Q343-Q361B (21)	407.10	8.60

Issued: #Q347, 20fr, 30fr, 1953; 80fr, 1955; 200fr, 1956; 300fr, 1957; others, 1954.
See Nos. Q407, Q431-Q432.

Electric
Train — PP40

1954				
Q362	PP40	13fr chocolate	22.50	.25
Q363	PP40	18fr dark blue	22.50	.25
Q364	PP40	21fr lilac rose	22.50	.50
		Nos. Q362-Q364 (3)	67.50	1.00

Nos. Q362-Q364 Surcharged with New Value and "X" in Blue, Red or Green

1956				
Q365	PP40	14fr on 13fr (B)	8.00	.25
Q366	PP40	19fr on 18fr (R)	8.25	.25
Q367	PP40	22fr on 21fr (G)	8.75	.45
		Nos. Q365-Q367 (3)	25.00	.95

Mercury and
Winged
Wheel — PP41

1957		Engr.	Perf. 11½	
Q368	PP41	14fr brt green	7.75	.25
Q369	PP41	19fr olive gray	8.00	.25
Q370	PP41	22fr carmine rose	8.75	.30
		Nos. Q368-Q370 (3)	24.50	.80

Nos. Q369-Q370 Surcharged with New Value and "X" in Pink or Green

1959				
Q371	PP41	20fr on 19fr (P)	22.50	.35
Q372	PP41	20fr on 22fr (G)	27.50	.55

Old North
Station,
Brussels
PP42

1959		Engr.	Perf. 11½	
Q373	PP42	20fr olive green	12.50	.25

See Nos. Q381, Q383. For surcharges see Nos. Q378, Q382, Q384.

Diesel and
Electric
Locomotives
and
Association
Emblem
PP43

1960		Unwmk.	Perf. 11½	
Q374	PP43	20fr red	45.00	30.00
Q375	PP43	50fr dark blue	45.00	30.00
Q376	PP43	60fr red lilac	45.00	30.00
Q377	PP43	70fr emerald	45.00	30.00
		Nos. Q374-Q377 (4)	180.00	120.00

Intl. Assoc. of Railway Congresses, 75th anniv.

No. Q373 Surcharged with New Value and "X" in Red

1961				
Q378	PP42	24fr on 20fr ol grn	60.00	.25

South Station,
Brussels — PP44

1962		Unwmk.	Perf. 11½	
Q379	PP44	24fr dull red	6.25	.25

No. Q379 Surcharged with New Value and "X" in Light Green

1963				
Q380	PP44	26fr on 24fr dl red	6.50	.25

Type of 1959

Design: 26fr, Central Station, Antwerp.

1963		Engr.	Perf. 11½	
Q381	PP42	26fr blue	6.25	1.75

No. Q381 Surcharged in Red

1964, Apr. 20				
Q382	PP42	28fr on 26fr blue	6.25	.25

Type of 1959

Design: 28fr, St. Peter's Station, Ghent.

1965		Engr.	Perf. 11½	
Q383	PP42	28fr red lilac	6.25	1.40

Nos. Q383
Surcharged
in Green

1966				
Q384	PP42	35fr on 28fr red lil	6.25	.25

Arlon
Railroad
Station
PP45

		Perf. 11½		
1967, Aug.		Unwmk.	Engr.	
Q385	PP45	25fr bister	10.00	.25
Q386	PP45	30fr blue green	5.00	.25
Q387	PP45	35fr deep blue	7.00	.35
		Nos. Q385-Q387 (3)	22.00	.85

No. Q385 exists on luminescent paper. Value, $500.
See #Q408. For surcharges see #Q410-Q412.

Electric
Train
PP46

Designs: 2fr, 3fr, 4fr, 5fr, 6fr, 7fr, 8fr, 9fr, like 1fr. 10fr, 20fr, 30fr, 40fr, Train going right. 50fr, 60fr, 70fr, 80fr, 90fr, Train going left. 100fr, 200fr, 300fr, Diesel train.

1968-73　　Engr.　　Perf. 11½

Q388	PP46	1fr olive bis	.25	.25
Q389	PP46	2fr slate	.25	.25
Q390	PP46	3fr blue green	.55	.55
Q391	PP46	4fr orange	.55	.25
Q392	PP46	5fr brown	.65	.25
Q393	PP46	6fr plum	.55	.25
Q394	PP46	7fr brt green	.65	.25
Q395	PP46	8fr carmine	.85	.25
Q396	PP46	9fr blue	1.40	.25
Q397	PP46	10fr green	2.75	.25
Q398	PP46	20fr dk blue	1.60	.25
Q399	PP46	30fr dk purple	4.00	.25
Q400	PP46	40fr brt lilac	5.50	.25
Q401	PP46	50fr brt pink	6.75	.25
Q402	PP46	60fr brt violet	8.25	.30
Q402A	PP46	70fr dp bister		
		('73)	10.00	.30
Q403	PP46	80fr dk brown	6.75	.25
Q403A	PP46	90fr yel grn		
		('73)	5.50	.30
Q404	PP46	100fr emerald	11.00	.25
Q405	PP46	200fr violet blue	13.00	.50
Q406	PP46	300fr lilac rose	22.50	1.25
	Nos. Q388-Q406 (21)		103.30	6.65

Printed on various papers.
See No. Q409.

Types of 1953-68

10fr, Congress Station, Brussels. 40fr, Arlon Station. 500fr, Electric train going left.

1968, June　　Engr.　　Perf. 11½

Q407	PP38	10fr gray	1.50	.25
Q408	PP45	40fr vermilion	22.50	.25
Q409	PP46	500fr yellow	32.50	1.90
	Nos. Q407-Q409 (3)		56.50	2.40

Nos. Q385, Q387 and Q408 Surcharged with New Value and "X"

1970, Dec.

Q410	PP45	37fr on 25fr bister	45.00	6.00
Q411	PP45	48fr on 35fr dp bl	13.00	5.00
Q412	PP45	53fr on 40fr ver	15.00	6.00
	Nos. Q410-Q412 (3)		73.00	17.00

No. Q410 was also issued on non-luminescent paper. Value $175.

Ostend Station
PP47

1971, Mar.　　Engr.　　Perf. 11½

Q413	PP47	32fr bis & blk	2.50	2.25
Q414	PP47	37fr gray & blk	5.00	4.00
Q415	PP47	42fr bl & blk	4.00	3.00
Q416	PP47	44fr brt rose & blk	4.50	3.00
Q417	PP47	46fr vio & blk	4.50	3.00
Q418	PP47	50fr brick red & blk	5.25	3.25
Q419	PP47	52fr sep & blk	7.00	4.75
Q420	PP47	54fr yel grn & blk	5.75	3.25
Q421	PP47	61fr grnsh bl & blk	5.75	4.00
	Nos. Q413-Q421 (9)		44.25	30.50

Nos. Q413-Q416, Q419-Q421 Surcharged with New Value and "X"

1971, Dec. 15

Denomination in Black

Q422	PP47	34fr on 32fr bister	2.00	.65
Q423	PP47	40fr on 37fr gray	2.50	.75
Q424	PP47	47fr on 44fr brt		
		rose	2.75	.85
Q425	PP47	53fr on 42fr blue	3.25	.90
Q426	PP47	56fr on 52fr sepia	3.25	1.10
Q427	PP47	59fr on 54fr yel		
		grn	3.25	1.10
Q428	PP47	66fr on 61fr grnsh		
		blue	4.00	1.25
	Nos. Q422-Q428 (7)		21.00	6.60

Track, Underpinning of Railroad Car and Emblems — PP48

1972, Mar.　　　　　Photo.

Q429	PP48	100fr emer, red &	
		blk	10.00 1.90

Centenary of International Railroad Union.

Congress Emblem PP49

1974, Apr.　　Photo.　　Perf. 11½

Q430	PP49	100fr yel, blk & red	8.00 2.25

4th International Symposium on Railroad Cybernetics, Washington, DC, Apr. 1974.

Type of 1953-1957

1975, June 1　　Engr.　　Perf. 11½

Q431	PP38	20fr emerald	1.75	.40
Q432	PP38	50fr blue	3.75	.60

Railroad Tracks PP50

1976, June 10　　Photo.　　Perf. 11½

Q433	PP50	20fr ultra & multi	3.00	.70
Q434	PP50	50fr brt grn &		
		multi	1.75	1.00
Q435	PP50	100fr dp org &		
		multi	4.00	1.50
Q436	PP50	150fr brt lil & multi	6.25	2.25
	Nos. Q433-Q436 (4)		15.00	5.45

Railroad Station — PP51

1977　　　Photo.　　Perf. 11½

Q437	PP51	1000fr multi	55.00 22.50

Also issued on luminescent paper.
See note following No. Q465.

Freight Car — PP52

Designs: 1fr-9fr, Freight car. 10fr-40fr, Hopper car. 50fr-90fr, Maintenance car. 100fr-500fr, Liquid fuel car.

1980, Dec. 16　　Engr.　　Perf. 11½

Q438	PP52	1fr bis brn &		
		blk	.30	.30
Q439	PP52	2fr claret & blk	.30	.30
Q440	PP52	3fr brt bl & blk	.30	.30
Q441	PP52	4fr grnsh blk &		
		blk	.30	.30
Q442	PP52	5fr sepia & blk	.30	.30
Q443	PP52	6fr dp org &		
		blk	.40	.40
Q444	PP52	7fr purple & blk	.50	.50
Q445	PP52	8fr black	.50	.50
Q446	PP52	9fr green & blk	.50	.50
Q447	PP52	10fr yel bis &		
		blk	.50	.50
Q448	PP52	20fr grnsh bl &		
		blk	1.25	.50
Q449	PP52	30fr bister & blk	2.25	.50
Q450	PP52	40fr lt lil & blk	2.50	.50
Q451	PP52	50fr dk brn &		
		blk	2.75	.70
Q452	PP52	60fr olive & blk	3.25	.70
Q453	PP52	70fr vio bl & blk	5.00	5.00
Q454	PP52	80fr vio brn &		
		blk	5.25	1.00
Q455	PP52	90fr lil rose &		
		blk	7.00	7.00
Q456	PP52	100fr crim rose &		
		blk	6.25	1.50
Q457	PP52	200fr brn & blk	12.50	1.75
Q458	PP52	300fr ol gray &		
		blk	18.00	2.50
Q459	PP52	500fr dl pur & blk	32.50	5.25
	Nos. Q438-Q459 (22)		102.40	30.80

Train in Station — PP53

1982　　　Engr.　　Perf. 11½

Q460	PP53	10fr red & blk	1.75	.25
Q461	PP53	20fr green & blk	1.25	.50
Q462	PP53	50fr sepia & blk	4.25	.75
Q463	PP53	100fr blue & blk	7.25	2.75
	Nos. Q460-Q463 (4)		14.50	4.25

Electric Locomotives PP54

1985, May 3　　Photo.　　Perf. 11½

Q464	PP54	250fr BB-150	15.00	12.00
Q465	PP54	500fr BB-120	35.00	17.50

Seven limited edition souvenir sheets exist. These include souvenir sheets of 4 of #Q437, Q464-Q465 with French or Flemish inscriptions, value $2,500, and a bilingual sheet with one each of #Q437, Q464-Q465, value $150.

Stylized Castle, Gabled Station and Electric Rail Car — PP55

1987, Oct. 12　　Engr.　　Perf. 11½

Q466	PP55	10fr dk red & blk	1.00	.75
Q467	PP55	20fr dk grn & blk	1.50	1.50
Q468	PP55	50fr dk brn & blk	4.50	2.50
Q469	PP55	100fr dk lil & blk	8.00	4.00
Q470	PP55	150fr dark olive		
		bister & blk	12.50	6.25
	Nos. Q466-Q470 (5)		27.50	15.00

Beginning in 1996, items looking like Parcel Post and Railway stamps have appeared in the market. Though sold by the Philatelic Bureau of the Belgian Post Office, these stamps are part of an ongoing series of Charity items that lack postal validity.

Kilopost — PP56

Maximum package weights: Nos. Q471, Q480, 0.5kg. Nos. Q472, Q481, 1kg. Nos. Q473, Q482, 2kg. Nos. Q474, Q483, 3kg. No. Q475, Q484, 4kg. No. Q476, Q485, 5kg. Nos. Q477, Q486, 10kg. Nos. Q478, Q487, 20kg. No. Q479, Q488, 30kg.

2003-04　　Litho.　　Perf. 11½

Color of Box

Q471	PP56	(€2.48) org	18.00	2.00
Q472	PP56	(€3.10) red	18.00	2.00
Q473	PP56	(€3.72) blue	18.00	3.00
Q474	PP56	(€5.21) yel	24.00	4.00
Q475	PP56	(€5.95) pur	30.00	4.00
Q476	PP56	(€6.69) grn	29.00	6.00
Q477	PP56	(€7.44) mar	30.00	9.00
Q478	PP56	(€8.68) brn	42.00	16.00
Q479	PP56	(€11.16) aqua	55.00	35.00

Self-Adhesive Booklet Stamps
Serpentine Die Cut 8 Horiz.

Q480	PP56	(€2.48) org	12.00	2.00
a.		Booklet pane of 5	60.00	
Q481	PP56	(€3.10) red	13.00	2.50
a.		Booklet pane of 5	65.00	
Q482	PP56	(€3.72) blue	15.00	3.00
a.		Booklet pane of 5	75.00	
Q483	PP56	(€5.21) yel	20.00	1.50
a.		Booklet pane of 5	125.00	
Q484	PP56	(€5.95) pur	24.00	2.00
a.		Booklet pane of 5	150.00	
Q485	PP56	(€6.69) grn	26.00	3.00
a.		Booklet pane of 5	175.00	
Q486	PP56	(€7.44) mar	30.00	6.00
a.		Booklet pane of 5	190.00	
Q487	PP56	(€8.68) brn	35.00	10.00
a.		Booklet pane of 5	225.00	
Q488	PP56	(€11.16) aqua	45.00	20.00
a.		Booklet pane of 5	275.00	
	Nos. Q471-Q488 (18)		480.00	130.00

Issued: Nos. Q471-Q482, 11/17. Nos. Q486-Q487, 2004. Nos. Q483-Q485, Q488, 2004.

Kilopost — PP57

Booklet Stamps
Die Cut Perf. 9¾ on 3 Sides

2005-07　　Photo.　　Self-Adhesive

Color of Box

Q489	PP57	(€3.10) red	9.00	.50
a.		Booklet pane of 5	45.00	
Q490	PP57	(€13) blue	32.50	2.00
a.		Booklet pane of 5	165.00	
Q491	PP57	(€2.60) green		
		('07)	7.00	.40
a.		Booklet pane of 5	35.00	

Kilopost — PP58

Die Cut Perf. 10 on 3 Sides

2007, Aug. 1　　　　　Litho.

Booklet Stamps

Self-Adhesive

Q492	PP58	(€3) "Prior" at		
		left	10.00	5.00
Q493	PP58	(€3) "Prior" at		
		right	10.00	5.00
a.		Booklet pane of 5, 3 #Q492, 2 #Q493	50.00	

ISSUED UNDER GERMAN OCCUPATION

German Stamps of 1906-11 Surcharged

Nos. N1-N6

Nos. N7-N9

Wmk. Lozenges (125)

1914-15　　　　　Perf. 14, 14½

N1	A16	3c on 3pf brn	.45	.25
N2	A16	5c on 5pf grn	.40	.25
N3	A16	10c on 10pf car	.50	.25
N4	A16	25c on 20pf ul-		
		tra	.50	.25
N5	A16	50c on 40pf lake		
		& blk	2.50	1.25
N6	A16	75c on 60pf		
		mag	.90	1.25
N7	A16	1fr on 80pf lake		
		& blk, *rose*	2.50	1.75
N8	A17	1fr25c on 1m car	20.00	12.50

N9	A21	2fr50c on 2m gray		
		bl	18.00	15.00
		Nos. N1-N9 (9)	45.75	32.75
		Set, never hinged	160.00	

German Stamps of 1906-18 Surcharged

Nos. N10-N21   No. N22

Nos. N23-N25

1916-18

N10	A22	2c on 2pf drab	.25	.25
N11	A16	3c on 3pf brn	.35	.25
N12	A16	5c on 5pf grn	.35	.25
N13	A22	8c on 7½pf org	.65	.35
N14	A16	10c on 10pf car	.25	.25
N15	A22	15c on 15pf yel		
		brn	.65	.25
N16	A22	15c on 15pf dk		
		vio	.65	.45
N17	A16	20c on 25pf org		
		& blk, *yel*	.35	.35
N18	A16	25c on 20pf ul-		
		tra	.35	.25
a.		25c on 20pf blue	.40	.25
N19	A16	40c on 30pf org		
		& blk, *buff*	.40	.30
N20	A16	50c on 40pf lake		
		& blk	.35	.30
N21	A16	75c on 60pf		
		mag	1.00	*12.50*
N22	A16	1fr on 80pf lake		
		& blk, *rose*	2.00	*2.50*
N23	A17	1fr25c on 1m car	2.00	2.00
N24	A21	2fr50c on 2m gray		
		bl	27.50	25.00
a.		2fr50c on 1m car (error)		*3,500.*
N25	A20	6fr25c on 5m sl &		
		car	40.00	37.50
		Nos. N10-N25 (16)	77.10	82.75
		Set, never hinged	145.00	

A similar series of stamps without "Belgien" was used in parts of Belgium and France while occupied by German forces. See France Nos. N15-N26.

BELIZE

bə-'lēz

LOCATION — Central America bordering on Caribbean Sea to east, Mexico to north, Guatemala to west
GOVT. — Independent state
AREA — 8,867 sq. mi.
POP. — 219,296 (1996 est.)
CAPITAL — Belmopan

Belize was known as British Honduras until 1973. The former British colony achieved independence in September 1981.

100 Cents = 1 Dollar

Catalogue values for all unused stamps in this country are for Never Hinged items.

British Honduras Regular Issue 1968-72 Ovptd. in Black on Silver Panel

Wmk. 314 (½c, 5c, $5), Unwmkd.

1973, June 1		**Litho.**	**Perf. 13x12½**	
312	A37	½c multi (#235)	.25	.25
313	A37	1c multi (#214)	.25	.25
314	A37	2c multi (#215)	.25	.25
315	A37	3c multi (#216)	.25	.25
316	A37	4c multi (#217)	.25	.25
317	A37	5c multi (#238)	.25	.25
318	A37	10c multi (#219)	.25	.25
319	A37	15c multi (#220)	.25	.25
320	A37	25c multi (#221)	.45	.45
321	A37	50c multi (#222)	.85	.85
322	A37	$1 multi (#223)	1.00	1.40
323	A37	$2 multi (#224)	1.75	2.75
324	A37	$5 multi (#240)	2.00	5.50
		Nos. 312-324 (13)	8.05	12.95

No. 315 with silver panel omitted exists canceled. Nos. 313 and 319 exist with silver panel double.

Common Design Types pictured following the introduction.

Princess Anne's Wedding Issue
Common Design Type

1973, Nov. 14		**Wmk. 314**	**Perf. 14**	
325	CD325	26c blue grn & multi	.25	.25
326	CD325	50c ocher & multi	.25	.25

Crana
A50

1c, Jewlfish. 2c, White-lipped peccary. 3c, Grouper. 4c, Collared anteater. 5c, Bonefish. 10c, Paca. 15c, Dolphinfish. 25c, Kinkajou. 50c, Muttonfish. $1, Tayra. $2, Great barracudas. $5, Mountain lion.

1974, Jan. 1		**Litho.**	**Perf. 13½**	
327	A50	½c shown	.25	.70
328	A50	1c multicolored	.25	.40
329	A50	2c multicolored	.25	.40
330	A50	3c multicolored	.25	.30
331	A50	4c multicolored	.25	.40
332	A50	5c multicolored	.25	.30
333	A50	10c multicolored	.25	.30
334	A50	15c multicolored	.30	.30
335	A50	25c multicolored	.50	.50
336	A50	50c multicolored	.85	.90
337	A50	$1 multicolored	1.00	1.75
338	A50	$2 multicolored	1.75	3.00
339	A50	$5 multicolored	2.00	5.50
		Nos. 327-339 (13)	8.15	14.75

Stag, Mayan Pottery
A51

Designs: Mayan pottery decorations.

1974, May 1			**Perf. 14½**	
340	A51	3c shown	.25	.25
341	A51	6c Fire snake	.25	.25
342	A51	16c Mouse	.25	.25
343	A51	26c Eagle	.45	.45
344	A51	50c Parrot	.80	.80
		Nos. 340-344 (5)	2.00	1.80

Parides Arcas
A52

Butterflies of Belize: 1c, Thecla regalis. 2c, Colobura dirce. 3c, Catonephele numilia. 4c, Battus belus. 5c, Callicore patelina. 10c, Callicore astala. 15c, Nessaea aglaura. 16c, Prepona pseudojoiceyi. 25c, Papilio thoas. 26c, Hamadryas arethusa. 50c, Thecla bathildis. $1, Caligo uranus. $2, Heliconius sapho. $5, Eurytides philolaus. $10, Philaethria dido.

Wmk. 314 Sideways

1974-77			**Perf. 14**	
345	A52	½c shown	1.15	5.75
346	A52	1c multicolored	1.15	2.00
347	A52	2c multicolored	.60	.80
348	A52	3c multicolored	1.45	.80
349	A52	4c multicolored	3.50	.35
350	A52	5c multicolored	3.75	.35
351	A52	10c multicolored	1.75	.80

		Perf. 14x15; 14 (26, 35c)		
352	A52	15c multicolored	1.40	.80
a.		Watermark upright ('75)	.90	2.00
353	A52	16c multicolored	5.75	10.00
354	A52	25c multicolored	7.50	.45
a.		Watermark upright ('77)	5.00	1.75
355	A52	26c multicolored	2.25	5.00
356	A52	50c multicolored	3.75	.75
a.		Watermark upright ('77)	5.00	1.75
357	A52	$1 multicolored	7.50	8.00
358	A52	$2 multicolored	4.50	1.45
359	A52	$5 multicolored	6.50	7.00
a.		Watermark upright ('75)	5.00	8.00
360	A52	$10 multicolored	11.50	4.50
		Nos. 345-360 (16)	64.00	48.80

Issue dates: No. 355A, July 25, 1977; No. 360, Jan. 2, 1975; others Sept. 2, 1974.
For surcharges & overprint see Nos. 380, 386, 395.

1975-78			**Wmk. 373**	
345a	A52	½c multicolored	2.00	10.00
347a	A52	2c multi ('77)	.50	.75
348a	A52	3c multi ('77)	1.25	.75
349a	A52	4c multi ('77)	3.00	.35
350a	A52	5c multi ('77)	3.25	.35
351a	A52	10c multicolored	3.50	.35
352b	A52	15c multi ('77)	.75	.70
354b	A52	25c multi ('78)	6.50	.50
355A	A52	35c Parides arcas ('77)	13.50	6.25
		Nos. 345a-355A (9)	34.25	20.00

For overprints and surcharges see Nos. 395-396, 424, 426-427.

Churchill and Coronation Coach of Queen Elizabeth II — A53

$1, Churchill & Williamsburg, VA Liberty Bell.

		Wmk. 373		
1974, Nov. 30		**Litho.**	**Perf. 14**	
363	A53	50c multicolored	.25	.25
364	A53	$1 multicolored	.35	.35

Sir Winston Churchill (1874-1965).

Mayan Urn — A54

Designs: Various Mayan vessels.

1975, June 2		**Wmk. 314**	**Perf. 14**	
365	A54	3c lt green & multi	.25	.25
366	A54	6c lt blue & multi	.25	.25
367	A54	16c dull yel & multi	.30	.25
368	A54	26c lilac & multi	.45	.25
369	A54	50c lt brown & multi	.50	1.75
		Nos. 365-369 (5)	1.75	2.75

Musicians
A55

Christmas: 26c, Nativity (Thatched hut and children). 50c, Drummers, vert. $1, Map of Belize, star, fleeing family, vert.

		Perf. 14x14½, 14½x14		
1975, Nov. 17		**Litho.**	**Wmk. 314**	
370	A55	6c multicolored	.25	.25
371	A55	26c multicolored	.30	.25
372	A55	50c multicolored	.45	.55
373	A55	$1 multicolored	.75	1.60
		Nos. 370-373 (4)	1.75	2.65

William Wrigley, Jr., Sapodilla Tree — A56

Bicentennial Emblem and: 35c, Charles Lindbergh and "Spirit of St. Louis." $1, John Lloyd Stephens and Mayan temple.

1976, Mar. 29		**Wmk. 373**	**Perf. 14½**	
374	A56	10c multicolored	.25	.25
375	A56	35c multicolored	.25	.40
376	A56	$1 multicolored	.55	1.50
		Nos. 374-376 (3)	1.05	2.15

American Bicentennial.

Bicycling
A57

		Wmk. 373		
1976, July 17		**Litho.**	**Perf. 14½**	
377	A57	35c shown	.50	.25
378	A57	45c Running	.25	.25
379	A57	$1 Shooting	.50	1.40
		Nos. 377-379 (3)	1.25	1.90

21st Olympic Games, Montreal, Canada, July 17-Aug. 1.

No. 355 Surcharged

		Wmk. 314		
1976, Aug. 30		**Litho.**	**Perf. 14**	
380	A52	20c on 26c multi	2.50	2.75

Map of West Indies, Bats, Wicket and Ball — A57a

Prudential Cup — A57b

		Unwmk.		
1976, Oct. 18		**Litho.**	**Perf. 14**	
381	A57a	35c lt blue & multi	.50	.60
382	A57b	$1 lilac rose & blk	1.25	1.75

World Cricket Cup, won by West Indies Team, 1975.

Royal Visit, 1975
A58

Designs: 35c, Rose window and Queen's head. $2, Queen surrounded by bishops.

1977, Feb. 7			**Perf. 13½x14**	
383	A58	10c multicolored	.25	.25
384	A58	35c multicolored	.25	.25
385	A58	$2 multicolored	.50	.90
		Nos. 383-385 (3)	1.00	1.40

25th anniv. of the reign of Elizabeth II.

No. 352 Surcharged

1977		**Wmk. 314**	**Perf. 14x15**	
386	A52	5c on 15c multi	3.00	3.00

Stamps from the first overprinting process have the "5c" close to the right edge of the block (varies). Stamps from the second, and more common, overprinting process have about 7mm from the right edge to the "5c."

Red-capped Manakin — A59

Birds of Belize: 10c, Hooded oriole. 25c, Blue-crowned motmot. 35c, Slaty-breasted tinamou. 45c, Ocellated turkey. $1, White hawk.

		Wmk. 373		
1977, Sept. 3		**Litho.**	**Perf. 14½**	
387	A59	8c shown	.90	.60
388	A59	10c multicolored	1.10	.35
389	A59	25c multicolored	1.50	.65
390	A59	35c multicolored	1.90	.85
391	A59	45c multicolored	2.10	1.50
392	A59	$1 multicolored	3.75	6.00
a.		Souvenir sheet of 6, #387-392	12.00	14.00
		Nos. 387-392 (6)	11.25	9.95

See Nos. 398-403, 416-421, 500-501. For overprints and surcharges see No. 502.

Medical
Laboratory
A60

Design: $1, Mobile medical unit and children
receiving treatment.

1977, Dec. 2   **Perf. 13½**
393 A60 35c multicolored   .25 .25
394 A60 $1 multicolored   .70 .70
 a.   Souvenir sheet of 2, #393-394   1.50 1.60

Pan American Health Org., 75th anniv.

**Nos. 351 and 355A Overprinted in
Gold: "BELIZE DEFENCE FORCE /
1ST JANUARY 1978"**
Wmk. 314, 373
1978, Feb. 15   Litho.   Perf. 14
395 A52 10c multicolored   1.00 1.00
396 A52 35c multicolored   2.50 2.50

**Elizabeth II Coronation Anniversary
Issue**
Common Design Types
Souvenir Sheet
1978, Apr. 21   Unwmk.   Perf. 15
397   Sheet of 6   1.40 1.75
 a.   CD326 75c White lion of Mortimer .25 .30
 b.   CD327 75c Elizabeth II   .25 .30
 c.   CD328 75c Jaguar (Maya god)   .25 .30

No. 397 contains 2 se-tenant strips of Nos.
397a-397c, separated by horizontal gutter with
commemorative and descriptive inscriptions
and showing central part of coronation procession with coach.

Bird Type of 1977
10c, White-crowned parrot. 25c, Crimson-
collared tanager. 35c, Citreoline trogon. 45c,
Sungrebe. 50c, Muscovy duck. $1, King
vulture.

Wmk. 373
1978, July 31   Litho.   Perf. 14½
398 A59 10c multicolored   .75 .40
399 A59 25c multicolored   1.10 .50
400 A59 35c multicolored   1.50 .75
401 A59 45c multicolored   1.75 1.75
402 A59 50c multicolored   1.90 2.00
403 A59 $1 multicolored   2.75 6.00
 a.   Souvenir sheet of 6, #398-403 11.50 12.00
      Nos. 398-403 (6)   9.75 11.40

Russelia
Sarmentosa
A61

Wild Flowers and Ferns: 15c, Lygodium
polymorphum. 35c, Heliconia aurantiaca. 45c,
Adiantum tetraphyllum. 50c, Angelonia ciliaris.
$1, Thelypteris obliterata.

1978, Oct. 16   Litho.   Perf. 14x13½
404 A61 10c multicolored   .25 .25
405 A61 15c multicolored   .35 .35
406 A61 35c multicolored   .35 .35
407 A61 45c multicolored   .35 .35
408 A61 50c multicolored   .50 .50
409 A61 $1 multicolored   .80 .95
      Nos. 404-409 (6)   2.60 2.75

Christmas.

Internal Airmail Service, 1937 — A62

Mail Service: 10c, MV Heron, 1949. 35c,
Dugout canoe on river, 1920. 45c, Stann

Creek railroad, 1910. 50c, Mounted courier,
1882. $2, RMS Eagle, 1856, and "paid"
cancel.

Perf. 13½x14
1979, Jan. 15   Wmk. 373
410 A62 5c multicolored   .45 .45
411 A62 10c multicolored   .45 .25
412 A62 35c multicolored   .45 .30
413 A62 45c multicolored   .80 .80
414 A62 50c multicolored   .80 .80
415 A62 $2 multicolored   1.50 2.50
      Nos. 410-415 (6)   4.45 5.10

Centenary of membership in UPU.

Bird Type of 1977
10c, Boat-billed heron. 25c, Gray-necked
wood rail. 35c, Lineated woodpecker. 45c,
Blue gray tanager. 50c, Laughing falcon. $1,
Long-tailed hermit.

1979, Apr. 16   Unwmk.   Perf. 14½
416 A59 10c multicolored   .75 .35
417 A59 25c multicolored   1.10 .35
418 A59 35c multicolored   1.25 .60
419 A59 45c multicolored   1.35 .75
420 A59 50c multicolored   1.40 1.25
421 A59 $1 multicolored   2.10 4.00
 a.   Souvenir sheet of 6, #416-421 8.50 9.00
      Nos. 416-421 (6)   7.95 7.30

**Nos. 477, 354b, 595, 355A, 599, 651
Surcharged**

No. 422

No. 424

No. 428

1979-83   Litho.   Perf. 14
422 A67 10c on 15c multi   7.50 5.00
423 A67 10c on 35c multi   17.50
424 A52 10c on 25c multi   3.00 2.25
424A A67 10c on 35c multi   70.00 70.00
 b.   Round obliterator   300.00
425 A76 10c on 35c multi   60.00
426 A52 15c on 35c multi   100.00
427 A52 15c on 35c multi   4.00 2.25
428 A76 $1.25 on $2 multi   30.00 16.00
429 A81 $1.25 on $2 multi   200.00 12.00

No. 422 has a square the width of the "10c"
obliterating the old value. No. 423 has a rectangle that is wider than the "10c."
No. 424A has a square obliterator.
No. 426 has "15c" at top of stamp, No. 427
has "15c" at right of rectangle. Type differs.
No. 429 has rectangular obliterator with new
value at top of stamp.
Many errors exist from printer's waste.
Nos. 422 and 427, possibly others, exist fiscally used prior to the stated issue dates.
Issued: No. 426, 3/79; No. 427, 6/79; No.
424, 3/31/80; No. 422, 8/22/81; No. 423,
1/28/83; No. 425, 4/15/83; Nos. 428-429,
6/9/83.

Used Stamps
Postally used stamps are valued
the same as unused. Canceled-to-
order stamps are of minimal value.
Most used stamps from No. 430-679
exist CTO. Most of these appeared
on the market after the contract was
canceled and were not authorized.
The cancellations are printed and the
paper differs from the issued
stamps.

Imperforate Stamps
Many stamps from No. 430-692
exist imperforate in small quantities.
Values up to three times those of
perforated stamps.

Queen Elizabeth II, 25th Anniv. of
Coronation — A63

Designs: 25c, No. 439, Paslow Bldg.,
#397c. 50c, Parliament, London, #397a. 75c,
Coronation coach, vert. $2, Prince of Wales,
vert. $3, Queen and
Prince Philip, vert. $4, Queen Elizabeth II, por-
trait, vert. No. 437, St. Edward's Crown, vert.
No. 438a, $5, Princess Anne on horseback,
Montreal Olympics, vert. No. 438b, $10,
Queen, Montreal Olympics, vert.

Unwmk.
1979, May 31   Litho.   Perf. 14
430 A63 25c multicolored   2.00
431 A63 50c multicolored   2.50
432 A63 75c multicolored   3.25
433 A63 $1 multicolored   4.25
434 A63 $2 multicolored   4.25
435 A63 $3 multicolored   4.25
436 A63 $4 multicolored   4.25
437 A63 $5 multicolored   4.50
      Nos. 430-437 (8)   29.25

Souvenir Sheets
438 A63   Sheet of 2, #a.-b.   19.00
439 A63 $15 multicolored   19.00

Powered Flight, 75th Anniv. — A64

4c, Safety, 1909. 25c, Boeing 707. 50c,
Concorde. 75c, Handley Page W8b, 1922. $1,
AVRO F, 1912. $1.50, Cody, 1910. $2, Tri-
plane Roe II, 1909. $3, Santos-Dumont, 1906.
$4, Wright Brothers Flyer, 1903.
$10, Belize Airways Jet.

1979, July 30
440 A64   4c multicolored   .70
441 A64   25c multicolored   2.10
442 A64   50c multicolored   6.00
443 A64   75c multicolored   2.75
444 A64 $1 multicolored   2.75
445 A64 $1.50 multicolored   3.75
446 A64 $2 multicolored   3.75
447 A64 $3 multicolored   3.25
448 A64 $4 multicolored   4.25
      Nos. 440-448 (9)   29.30

Souvenir Sheets
Perf. 14½
449   Sheet of 2   14.50
 a.   A64 $5 Dunne D.5, 1910   7.25
 b.   A64 $5 Great Britain #581   7.25
450 A64 $10 multi   14.50

Sir Rowland Hill, death cent., "75th anniv."
of ICAO.

1980 Summer
Olympics,
Moscow — A65

1979, Oct. 10   Perf. 14
451 A65 25c Handball   .50
452 A65 50c Weight lifting   .80
453 A65 75c Track   1.10
454 A65 $1 Soccer   1.50
455 A65 $2 Sailing   2.10
456 A65 $3 Swimming   2.50
457 A65 $4 Boxing   3.00
458 A65 $5 Cycling   13.50
      Nos. 451-458 (8)   25.00

Souvenir Sheets
Perf. 14½
459   Sheet of 2   17.00
 a.   A65 $5 Track, diff.   6.00
 b.   A65 $10 Boxing, diff.   10.00
460 A65 $15 Cycling, diff.   17.00

1980 Winter
Olympics,
Lake
Placid — A66

25c, Torch. 50c, Slalom skiing. 75c, Figure
skating. $1, Downhill skiing. $2, Speed skating. $3, Cross country skiing. $4, Biathlon. $5,
Olympic medals.

1979, Dec. 4   Perf. 14
461 A66 25c multi   .25
462 A66 50c multi   .60
463 A66 75c multi   .85
464 A66 $1 multi   1.05
465 A66 $2 multi   2.10
466 A66 $3 multi   3.25
467 A66 $4 multi   4.00
468 A66 $5 multi   4.75
      Nos. 461-468 (8)   16.85

Souvenir Sheets
Perf. 14½
469   Sheet of 2   13.50
 a.   A66 $5 Torch bearers   4.00
 b.   A66 $10 Medals, diff.   7.50
470 A66 $15 Torch, diff.   13.50

See Nos. 503-512.

Cypraea
Zebra
A67

2c, Macrocallista maculata. 3c, Arca zebra,
vert. 4c, Chama macerophylla, vert. 5c,
Latirus cariniferus. 10c, Conus spurius, vert.
15c, Murex cabritii, vert. 20c, Atrina rigida.
25c, Chlamys imbricata, vert. 35c, Conus
granulatus. 45c, Tellina radiata, vert. 50c,
Leucozonia nassa. 85c, Tripterotyphis triangu-
laris. $1, Strombus gigas, vert. $2, Strombus
gallus, vert. $5, Fasciolaria tulipa. $10, Arene
cruentata.

1980, Jan. 7   Litho.   Perf. 14
Inscribed "1980"
471 A67 1c shown   1.00
472 A67 2c multicolored   1.25
473 A67 3c multicolored   1.40
474 A67 4c multicolored   1.40
475 A67 5c multicolored   1.40
476 A67 10c multicolored   2.10
477 A67 15c multicolored   2.75
478 A67 20c multicolored   2.75
479 A67 25c multicolored   2.75
480 A67 35c multicolored   3.50
481 A67 45c multicolored   4.00
482 A67 50c multicolored   4.00
483 A67 85c multicolored   6.25

484	A67	$1 multicolored	6.75
485	A67	$2 multicolored	9.75
486	A67	$5 multicolored	13.50
487	A67	$10 multicolored	15.50
	Nos. 471-487 (17)		80.05

1981　　　　　　**Inscribed "1981"**

476a	A67	10c	12.50
482a	A67	50c	12.50
483a	A67	85c	12.50
484a	A67	$1	17.50
	Nos. 476a-484a (4)		55.00

Souvenir Sheets

| 488 | A67 | Sheet of 2, 85c, $5 | 32.50 | 12.00 |
| 489 | A67 | Sheet of 2, $2, $10 | 45.00 | 22.50 |

Stamps in Nos. 488-489 have different color border and are of a slightly different size than the sheet stamps.

For overprints and surcharges see Nos. 422-423, 424A, 572-589, 592-593.

Intl. Year of the Child — A68

Various children. No. 498a, Three children. No. 498b, Madonna and Child by Durer. No. 499, Children before Christmas tree.

1980, Mar. 15　　Litho.　　Perf. 14

490	A68	25c multicolored	.75
491	A68	50c multicolored	1.20
492	A68	75c multicolored	1.75
493	A68	$1 multicolored	1.75
494	A68	$1.50 multicolored	2.50
495	A68	$2 multicolored	3.00
496	A68	$3 multicolored	3.75
497	A68	$4 multicolored	4.25
	Nos. 490-497 (8)		18.95

Souvenir Sheets
Perf. 13½

498	A68	$5 Sheet of 2, #a.-	12.50
	b.		
499	A68	$10 multicolored	12.50

No. 498 contains two 35x54mm stamps. No. 499 contains one 73x110mm stamp.

Bird Type of 1977
Souvenir Sheets

1980, June 16　Unwmk.　Perf. 13½

500		Sheet of 6	55.00	55.00
a.	A59	10c Jabiru	7.00	7.00
b.	A59	25c Barred antshrike	7.50	7.50
c.	A59	35c Royal flycatcher	8.25	8.25
d.	A59	45c White-necked puffbird	8.25	8.25
e.	A59	50c Ornate hawk-eagle	8.50	8.50
f.	A59	$1 Golden-masked tanager	8.75	8.75
g.		Sheet of 12	150.00	150.00
501		Sheet of 2	42.50	42.50
a.	A59	$2 Jabiru	17.00	17.00
b.	A59	$3 Golden-masked tanager	23.00	23.00

No. 500g contains 2 each Nos. 500a-500f with gutter between; inscribed "Protection of Environment" and "Wildlife Protection."

No. 500 Surcharged

1980, Oct. 3　　Litho.　　Perf. 13½

502		Sheet of 6	80.00	80.00
a.	A59	10c multicolored	9.75	9.75
b.	A59	25c multicolored	11.00	11.00
c.	A59	35c multicolored	11.00	11.00
d.	A59	40c on 45c multi	12.00	12.00
e.	A59	40c on 50c multi	12.00	12.00
f.	A59	40c on $1 multi	12.00	12.00

ESPAMER '80 Stamp Exhibition, Madrid, Spain, Oct. 3-12.

1980 Winter Olympics, Lake Placid — A69

Events and winning country: 25c, Men's speed skating, US. 50c, Ice hockey, US. 75c, No. 512, Men's figure skating, Great Britain. $1, Alpine skiing, Austria. $1.50, Women's giant slalom, Germany. $2, Women's speed skating, Netherlands. $3, Cross country skiing, Sweden. $5, Men's giant slalom, Sweden. Nos. 511a ($5), 511b ($10), Speed skating, US.

1980, Aug. 20　　Litho.　　Perf. 14

503	A69	25c multicolored	.65
504	A69	50c multicolored	1.10
505	A69	75c multicolored	1.20
506	A69	$1 multicolored	1.60
507	A69	$1.50 multicolored	2.25
508	A69	$2 multicolored	2.60
509	A69	$3 multicolored	3.25
510	A69	$5 multicolored	5.25
	Nos. 503-510 (8)		17.90

Souvenir Sheets
Perf. 14½

| 511 | A69 | Sheet of 2, #a.-b. | 13.50 |
| 512 | A69 | $10 multicolored | 13.50 |

Nos. 503-510 were each issued in sheets of 20 + 10 labels. The 2nd and 5th vertical rows consist of labels.

Intl. Year of the Child — A70

Nos. 513-521: Scenes from Sleeping Beauty. $8, Detail from Paumgartner Family Altarpiece by Albrecht Durer.

1980, Nov. 24　　　　　　Perf. 14

513	A70	35c multicolored	3.00
514	A70	40c multicolored	3.25
515	A70	50c multicolored	3.75
516	A70	75c multicolored	4.00
517	A70	$1 multicolored	4.00
518	A70	$1.50 multicolored	5.00
519	A70	$3 multicolored	6.00
520	A70	$4 multicolored	6.00
	Nos. 513-520 (8)		35.00

Souvenir Sheets
Perf. 14½

521		Sheet of 2	21.00
a.	A70	$5 Marriage	7.00
b.	A70	$5 Couple on horseback	7.00
522	A70	$8 multicolored	17.00

Nos. 513-520 issued with se-tenant label.

Queen Mother Elizabeth, 80th Birthday — A71

1980, Dec. 12

| 523 | A71 | $1 multicolored | 3.25 |

Souvenir Sheet
Perf. 14½

| 524 | A71 | $5 multicolored | 18.50 |

No. 524 contains one 46x31mm stamp. No. 523 issued in sheet of 6.

MERRY CHRISTMAS 1980
11016

Christmas — A72

25c, Annunciation. 50c, Bethlehem. 75c, Holy Family. $1, Nativity. $1.50, Flight into Egypt. $2, Shepherds. $3, With angel. $4, Adoration.

$5, Nativity. $10, Madonna & Child.

1980, Dec. 30　　Litho.　　Perf. 14

525	A72	25c multicolored	.85
526	A72	50c multicolored	1.60
527	A72	75c multicolored	2.00
528	A72	$1 multicolored	2.10
529	A72	$1.50 multicolored	2.25
530	A72	$2 multicolored	2.60
531	A72	$3 multicolored	3.00
532	A72	$4 multicolored	3.00
	Nos. 525-532 (8)		17.40

Souvenir Sheets
Perf. 14½

| 533 | A72 | $5 multicolored | 8.00 |
| 534 | A72 | $10 multicolored | 17.00 |

Nos. 525-532 each issued in sheets of 20 + 10 labels. The 2nd and 5th vertical rows consist of labels.

Nos. 529, 532, 534 Surcharged

1981, May 22

| 535 | A72 | $1 on $1.50 multi | 19.00 |
| 536 | A72 | $2 on $4 multi | 20.00 |

Souvenir Sheet
Perf. 14½

| 537 | A72 | $2 on $10 multi | 37.50 |

Location of overprint and surcharge varies.

Intl. Rotary Club — A73

Designs: 25c, Paul P. Harris, founder. 50c, No. 546, Rotary, project emblem. $1, No. 545b, 75th anniv. emblem. $1.50 Diploma, horiz. $2, No. 545a, Project Hippocrates. $3, 75th anniv. project emblems, horiz. No. 544, Hands reach out, horiz.

1981, May 26　　　　　　Perf. 14

538	A73	25c multicolored	3.00
539	A73	50c multicolored	3.75
540	A73	$1 multicolored	4.50
541	A73	$1.50 multicolored	5.25
542	A73	$2 multicolored	6.00

543	A73	$3 multicolored	8.00
544	A73	$5 multicolored	9.50
	Nos. 538-544 (7)		40.00

Souvenir Sheets
Perf. 14½

545		Sheet of 2	45.00
a.	A73	$5 multicolored	15.00
b.	A73	$10 multicolored	30.00
546	A73	$10 multicolored	30.00

Originally scheduled to be issued Mar. 30, the set was postponed and issued without a 75c stamp. Supposedly some of the 75c were sold to the public. Value $2,500.

For overprints and surcharges see Nos. 563-571, 590-591.

Royal Wedding of Prince Charles and Lady Diana — A74

1981, July 16　　　　Perf. 13½x14
Size: 22.5x38mm

548	A74	50c Coat of Arms	.50
549	A74	$1 Prince Charles	.90
550	A74	$1.50 Couple	1.25

Size: 25x43mm
With Thin Gold Border

551	A74	50c like No. 548	.50
552	A74	$1 like No. 549	.90
553	A74	$1.50 like No. 550	1.25
	Nos. 548-553 (6)		5.30

Miniature Sheet
Perf. 14½

554		Sheet of 3, #554a-554c	2.75
a.	A74	$3 like No. 550	.90
b.	A74	$3 like No. 548	.90
c.	A74	$3 like No. 549	.90

Nos. 551-553 issued in sheets of 6 + 3 labels. No. 554 contains three 35x50mm stamps.

For overprints see Nos. 659-665.

1984 Olympics A75

85c, Track. $1, Cycling. $1.50, Boxing. $2, Emblems. $3, Baron Coubertin. $5, Torch, emblems.

1981, Sept. 14　　　　　Perf. 14

555	A75	85c multicolored	3.25
556	A75	$1 multicolored	11.00
557	A75	$1.50 multicolored	4.00
558	A75	$2 multicolored	5.25
559	A75	$3 multicolored	6.50
560	A75	$5 multicolored	7.50
	Nos. 555-560 (6)		37.50

Souvenir Sheets
Perf. 13½

561		Sheet of 2	40.00
a.	A75	$5 like No. 559	10.00
b.	A75	$10 like No. 560	30.00

Perf. 14½

| 562 | A75 | $15 like No. 558 | 40.00 |

No. 561 contains two 35x54mm stamps. No. 562 contains one 46x68mm stamp. Nos. 561-562 exist with gold background.

Nos. 538-546
Overprinted in
Black or Gold

1981, Sept. 21   *Perf. 14*
563	A73	25c multicolored (G)	3.00
564	A73	50c multicolored	4.00
565	A73	$1 multicolored	5.00
566	A73	$1.50 multicolored	6.25
567	A73	$2 multicolored (G)	7.00
568	A73	$3 multicolored	8.25
569	A73	$5 multicolored	10.00
		Nos. 563-569 (7)	43.50

Souvenir Sheets
Perf. 14½
570	A73	Sheet of 2, #a.-b. (G)	35.00
571	A73	$10 multicolored	30.00

Size of overprint varies.

Nos. 471-
483, 485-
489 Ovptd.

1981, Sept. 21
572	A67	1c multicolored	1.90
573	A67	2c multicolored	1.90
574	A67	3c multicolored	1.90
575	A67	4c multicolored	1.90
576	A67	5c multicolored	2.25
577	A67	10c multicolored	3.00
a.		Inscribed "1980"	225.00
578	A67	15c multicolored	4.25
579	A67	20c multicolored	4.25
580	A67	25c multicolored	4.75
581	A67	35c multicolored	4.75
582	A67	45c multicolored	5.50
583	A67	50c multicolored	5.50
584	A67	85c multicolored	8.50
585	A67	$2 multicolored	15.00
586	A67	$5 multicolored	18.50
587	A67	$10 multicolored	22.00
		Nos. 572-587 (16)	105.85

Souvenir Sheets
588	A67	Sheet of 2, #488	45.00
589	A67	Sheet of 2, #489	52.50

Size and style of overprint varies, italic on
horiz. stamps, upright on vert. stamps and
upright capitals on souvenir sheets.
The 10c is dated 1981. Less than 16 sheets
dated 1980 were also overprinted.

Nos. 541, 545 Surcharged

1981, Nov. 13   *Perf. 14*
590	A73	$1 on $1.50 multi	24.00

Souvenir Sheet
Perf. 14½
591		Sheet of 2	37.50
a.	A73	$1 on $5 multicolored	18.50
b.	A73	$1 on $10 multicolored	18.50

Espamer '81.

Nos. 488,
489
Surcharged
in Red

1981, Nov. 14   *Perf. 14½*
Souvenir Sheets
592		Sheet of 2	72.50
a.	A67	$1 on 85c	27.50
b.	A67	$1 on $5	27.50
593		Sheet of 2	72.50
a.	A67	$1 on $2	27.50
b.	A67	$1 on $10	27.50

Independence — A76

10c, Flag. 35c, Map, vert. 50c, Black orchid,
vert. 85c, Tapir. $1, Mahogany tree, vert. $2,
Keel-billed toucan.

1981-82   *Perf. 14*
594	A76	10c multicolored	3.75
595	A76	35c multicolored	9.00
596	A76	50c multicolored	12.50
597	A76	85c multicolored	4.25
598	A76	$1 multicolored	3.50
599	A76	$2 multicolored	19.00
		Nos. 594-599 (6)	52.00

Souvenir Sheet
Perf. 14½
600	A76	$5 like 10c	40.00

Issued: 50c-$2, 12/18; 10c, 35c, $5, 2/10/82.
For surcharges see Nos. 425, 428, 616.

1982 World Cup Soccer
Championships, Spain — A77

10c, Uruguay '30, '50. 25c, Italy '34, '38.
50c, Germany '54, '74. $1, Brazil '58, '62, '70.
$1.50, Argentina '78. $2, England '66.
No. 607, Emblem. No. 608, Player.

1981, Dec. 28   *Perf. 14*
601	A77	10c multicolored	2.75
602	A77	25c multicolored	4.00
603	A77	50c multicolored	5.00
604	A77	$1 multicolored	6.25
605	A77	$1.50 multicolored	8.00
606	A77	$2 multicolored	8.75
		Nos. 601-606 (6)	34.75

Souvenir Sheets
Perf. 14½
607	A77	$2 multicolored	16.50
608	A77	$3 multicolored	21.00

No. 608 contains one 46x78mm stamp.
For surcharge see No. 617.

Sailing Ships — A78

10c, Man of war, 19th cent. 25c, Madagascar, 1837. 35c, Whitby, 1838. 50c, China,
1838. 85c, Swiftsure, 1850. $2, Windsor Cas-
tle, 1857.
$5, 19th cent. ships.

1982, Mar. 15   *Perf. 14*
609	A78	10c multicolored	3.50
610	A78	25c multicolored	5.00
611	A78	35c multicolored	6.00
612	A78	50c multicolored	7.00
613	A78	85c multicolored	8.50
614	A78	$2 multicolored	12.00
		Nos. 609-614 (6)	42.00

Souvenir Sheet
Perf. 14½
615	A78	$5 multicolored	45.00

Nos. 599 and 606 Surcharged

1982, Apr. 28
616	A76	$1 on $2 multi	25.00
617	A77	$1 on $2 multi	25.00

Essen '82 Philatelic Exhibition.

Princess of Wales,
21st
Birthday — A79

Various portraits.

1982, May 20   *Perf. 13½x14*
618	A79	50c multicolored	1.75
619	A79	$1 multicolored	2.25
620	A79	$1.50 multicolored	2.25
		Nos. 618-620 (3)	6.25

Size: 25x42mm
Perf. 13½
621	A79	50c like No. 618	1.75
622	A79	$1 like No. 619	2.25
623	A79	$1.50 like No. 620	2.25
		Nos. 621-623 (3)	6.25

Souvenir Sheet
Stamp Size: 31x47mm
Perf. 14½
624	A79	$3 Sheet of 3, #a.-c. like #618-620	10.00

Nos. 618-620 also exist with gold borders,
size: 30x45mm. Value, set $16.

Overprinted in
Silver

1982, Oct. 21   *Perf. 13½x14*
628	A79	50c multicolored	.55
629	A79	$1 multicolored	.70
630	A79	$1.50 multicolored	.95

Size: 25x42mm
Perf. 13½
631	A79	50c multicolored	.55
632	A79	$1 multicolored	.70
633	A79	$1.50 multicolored	.95
		Nos. 628-633 (6)	4.40

Souvenir Sheet
Perf. 14½
634	A79	$3 Sheet of 3, #a.-c.	12.50

Size of overprint varies. The overprint exists
on the gold bordered stamps. Value, set $25.
No. 634 exists with a gold overprint. Value
$11.

Boy Scouts — A80

10c, Building camp fire. 25c, Bird watching.
35c, Playing guitar. 50c, Hiking. 85c, Flag,
scouts. $2, Salute.
No. 644, Scout holding flag, vert. No. 645,
Lord Baden Powell, vert.

1982, Aug. 31   *Perf. 14*
638	A80	10c multicolored	1.90
639	A80	25c multicolored	5.50
640	A80	35c multicolored	3.00
641	A80	50c multicolored	3.50
642	A80	85c multicolored	5.00
643	A80	$2 multicolored	5.50
		Nos. 638-643 (6)	24.40

Souvenir Sheets
Perf. 14½
644	A80	$2 multicolored	24.00
645	A80	$3 multicolored	24.00

Scouting, 75th anniv. and Lord Baden Powell, 125th birth anniv.
For overprints see Nos. 653-658.

Marine Life — A81

10c, Gorgonia ventalina. 35c, Carpilius
corallinus. 50c, Plexaura flexuosa. 85c, Con-
dylactis gigantea. $1, Stenopus hispidus. $2,
Abudefduf saxatilis.
$5, Scyllarides aequinoctialis.

1982, Sept. 20   *Perf. 14*
646	A81	10c multicolored	3.50
647	A81	35c multicolored	5.50
648	A81	50c multicolored	6.00
649	A81	85c multicolored	6.25
650	A81	$1 multicolored	8.50
651	A81	$2 multicolored	10.50
		Nos. 646-651 (6)	40.25

Souvenir Sheet
Perf. 14½
652	A81	$5 multicolored	55.00

For surcharge see No. 429.

Nos. 638-643 Overprinted in Gold

1982, Oct. 1   *Perf. 14*
653	A80	10c Building camp fire	3.50
654	A80	25c Bird watching	8.50
655	A80	35c Playing guitar	4.50
656	A80	50c Hiking	5.00
657	A80	85c Flag, scouts	12.50
658	A80	$2 Salute	13.50
		Nos. 653-658 (6)	47.50

Overprint is different on Nos. 654-655.
Sheets include labels with native Christmas
themes.

**Nos. 548-554 Overprinted in Gold
Similar to Nos. 628-634**

1982, Oct. 25   *Perf. 13½x14*
659	A74	50c Coat of Arms	3.50
660	A74	$1 Prince Charles	6.50
661	A74	$1.50 Couple	9.25
		Nos. 659-661 (3)	19.25

Size: 25x43mm
Perf. 13½

662	A74	50c like No. 659	.65
663	A74	$1 like No. 660	.90
664	A74	$1.50 like No. 661	1.40
		Nos. 662-664 (3)	2.95

Miniature Sheet
Perf. 14½

665		Sheet of 3, #665a-665c	9.50
a.		A74 $3 like No. 661	3.00
b.		A74 $3 like No. 659	3.00
c.		A74 $3 like No. 660	3.00

Nos. 662-664 issued in sheets of 6 plus 3 labels. No. 665 contains three 35x50mm stamps. Size and style of overprint varies.

Visit by Pope John Paul II A82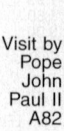

50c, Belize Cathedral. $2.50, Pope John Paul II.

1983, Mar. 7   *Perf. 13½*

666	A82	50c multicolored	4.50

Souvenir Sheet
Perf. 14½

667	A82	$2.50 multicolored	32.50

No. 667 contains one 30x47mm stamp. No. 666 issued in sheet of 6.

Commonwealth Day — A83

35c, Map, vert. 50c, Maya Stella. 85c, Supreme Court Building. $2, University Center.

1983, Mar. 14   *Perf. 13½*

668	A83	35c multicolored	.60
669	A83	50c multicolored	.65
670	A83	85c multicolored	.85
671	A83	$2 multicolored	1.50
		Nos. 668-671 (4)	3.60

Issued in miniature sheets of 4. Other formats are suspect.

First Manned Flight, Bicent. — A84

10c, Flying boat, 1670. 25c, Flying machine, 1709. 50c, Airship Guyton de Morveau. 85c, Dirigible. $1, Clement Bayard. $1.50, Great Britain R-34.

No. 678, Nassau Balloon. No. 679, Montgolfier Brothers balloon, vert.

1983, May 16   *Perf. 14*

672	A84	10c multicolored	3.50
673	A84	25c multicolored	4.50
674	A84	50c multicolored	4.75
675	A84	85c multicolored	5.75
676	A84	$1 multicolored	6.50
677	A84	$1.50 multicolored	7.25
		Nos. 672-677 (6)	32.25

Souvenir Sheets
Perf. 14½

678	A84	$3 multicolored	20.00
679	A84	$3 multicolored	20.00

"Errors"
Many "errors," including imperforates, exist of Nos. 680-898. These unauthorized varieties were printed without the knowledge of the Belize postal service. There may be large quantities of them.

Mayan Monuments — A85

1983, Nov. 14   *Litho.*   *Perf. 13½x14*

680	A85	10c Altun Ha	.25	.25
681	A85	15c Xunantunich	.25	.25
682	A85	75c Cerros	.55	.55
683	A85	$2 Lamanai	1.25	1.75
		Nos. 680-683 (4)	2.30	2.80

Souvenir Sheet

684	A85	$3 Xunantunich, diff.	2.40	2.40

World Communications Year — A86

10c, Belmopan Earth Station. 15c, Telstar 2. 75c, UPU monument. $2, Mail boat.

1983, Nov. 28   *Perf. 14*

685	A86	10c multicolored	.45	.25
686	A86	15c multicolored	.65	.25
687	A86	75c multicolored	.90	1.10
688	A86	$2 multicolored	2.00	4.50
		Nos. 685-688 (4)	4.00	6.10

Jaguar, World Wildlife Fund Emblem A87

1983, Dec. 9

689	A87	5c Sitting	.55	.80
690	A87	10c Standing	.65	.50
691	A87	85c Swimming	2.50	3.00
692	A87	$1 Walking	2.60	3.25
		Nos. 689-692 (4)	6.30	7.55

Souvenir Sheet

693	A87	$1 Sitting in tree	3.50	3.50

No. 693 contains one stamp 45x28mm.

Christmas — A88

Scenes from mass celebrated by Pope John Paul II during visit, Mar.

1983, Dec. 22

694	A88	10c multicolored	.50	.25
695	A88	15c multicolored	.50	.25
696	A88	75c multicolored	1.00	1.00
697	A88	$2 multicolored	1.50	2.00
		Nos. 694-697 (4)	3.50	3.50

Souvenir Sheet

698	A88	$3 multicolored	3.75	3.75

Foureye Butterflyfish — A89

2c, Cushion star. 3c, Flower coral. 4c, Fairy basslets. 5c, Spanish hogfish. 6c, Star-eyed hermit crab. 10c, Sea fans, fire sponge. 15c, Blueheads. 25c, Blue-striped grunt. 50c, Coral crab. 60c, Tube sponge. 75c, Brain coral. $1, Yellow-tail snapper. $2, Common lettuce slug. $5, Yellow damselfish. $10, Rock beauty.

1984, Feb. 27   *Perf. 15*

699	A89	1c shown	.60	1.50
700	A89	2c multicolored	.70	1.50
701	A89	3c multicolored	.70	1.50
702	A89	4c multicolored	.85	1.50
703	A89	5c multicolored	.95	1.50
704	A89	6c multicolored	.95	1.75
705	A89	10c multicolored	.95	.35
706	A89	15c multicolored	1.35	.60
707	A89	25c multicolored	1.35	.80
708	A89	50c multicolored	1.35	1.75
709	A89	60c multicolored	1.35	2.00
710	A89	75c multicolored	1.35	1.50
711	A89	$1 multicolored	1.35	1.25
712	A89	$2 multicolored	1.35	.60
713	A89	$5 multicolored	1.75	.75
714	A89	$10 multicolored	2.00	1.15
		Nos. 699-714 (16)	18.90	20.00

Nos. 699-714 exist imperforate, issued at a later date by a liquidator. Value $10 each.

Other denominations, not issued contemporaneously, exist perforated 13½. A 2c stamp perforated 13½ may have been issued in 1988. The editors would like to examine any in period use.

Nos. 709 and 711 exist overprinted "HURRICANE HATTIE". Value $20.

For overprints and surcharge see Nos. 715-716, 762A-762C, 922.

The 50c, 60c, 75c, $1 exist inscribed "1986" in selvage.

1988, July   *Perf. 13½*

705a	A89	10c	.75	.75
706a	A89	15c	1.00	1.00
707a	A89	25c	1.40	1.40
708a	A89	50c	2.10	2.10
709a	A89	60c	2.10	2.10
711a	A89	$1	2.75	2.75
		Nos. 705a-711a (6)	10.10	10.10

Nos. 705, 708 Overprinted: "VISIT OF THE LORD / ARCHBISHOP OF CANTERBURY / 8th-11th MARCH 1984"

1984, Mar. 8

715	A89	10c multicolored	1.40	.70
716	A89	50c multicolored	2.40	2.75

1984 Summer Olympics — A90

1984, Apr. 30   *Perf. 13½x14*

717	A90	25c Shooting	.35	.25
718	A90	75c Boxing	.60	.75
719	A90	$1 Running	.70	1.00
720	A90	$2 Bicycling	3.00	2.75
		Nos. 717-720 (4)	4.65	4.75

Souvenir Sheet

721	A90	$3 Discus	3.00	3.00

1984 Summer Olympics — A91

1984, Apr. 30   *Litho.*   *Perf. 14½*
Booklet Stamps

722	A91	5c Running	.50	.90
a.		Booklet pane of 4	2.25	
723	A91	20c Javelin	.60	.90
a.		Booklet pane of 4	2.75	
724	A91	25c Shot put	.60	.90
a.		Booklet pane of 4	2.75	
725	A91	$2 Torch	.80	1.25
a.		Booklet pane of 4	4.00	
		Complete booklet, #722a-725a	12.00	
		Nos. 722-725 (4)	2.50	3.95

Ausipex '84 — A92

15c, Br. Honduras #3. 30c, Bath-Bristol mail coach, 1784. 65c, Penny Black, Rowland Hill.

75c, Railroad Pier, Commerce Bight. $2, Royal Exhibition Buildings.
$3, Australia #132, Br. Hond. #3.

1984, Sept. 26   *Litho.*   *Perf. 15*

726	A92	15c multicolored	.30	.25
727	A92	30c multicolored	.45	.30
728	A92	65c multicolored	.80	.80
729	A92	75c multicolored	.90	.95

Perf. 14

730	A92	$2 multicolored	1.25	2.00
		Nos. 726-730 (5)	3.70	4.30

Souvenir Sheet

731	A92	$3 multicolored	1.50	1.50

House of Tudor, 500th Anniv. — A93

1984, Oct. 15   *Perf. 14*

732	A93	50c Queen Victoria	.35	.35
733	A93	50c Prince Albert	.35	.35
a.		Sheet of 4, 2 each, #732-733	1.50	
734	A93	75c King George VI	.40	.55
735	A93	75c Queen Elizabeth	.40	.55
a.		Sheet of 4, 2 each, #734-735	1.75	
736	A93	$1 Prince Charles	.65	.75
737	A93	$1 Princess Diana	.65	.75
a.		Sheet of 4, 2 each, #736-737	2.75	
		Nos. 732-737 (6)	2.80	3.30

Souvenir Sheet

738		Sheet of 2	2.00	2.00
a.		A93 $1.50 Prince Philip	1.00	1.00
b.		A93 $1.50 Queen Elizabeth II	1.00	1.00

Parrots — A94

a, White-fronted Parrot. b, White-capped, horiz. c, Red-lored. d, Mealy, horiz. $3, Scarlet macaw.

1984, Nov. 1   *Perf. 11*

739	A94	Block of 4	11.00	11.00
a.-d.		$1 any single	2.50	2.50

Miniature Sheet
Perf. 14

740	A94	$3 multicolored	5.50	5.50

No. 740 contains one 48x32mm stamp.

Mayan Artifacts — A95

25c, Incense holder, 1450. 75c, Cylindrical vase, 675. $1, Tripod vase, 500. $2, Kinich Ahau (sun god).

1984, Nov. 30   *Perf. 15*

741	A95	25c multicolored	.40	.40
742	A95	75c multicolored	.80	.80
743	A95	$1 multicolored	.85	.85
744	A95	$2 multicolored	1.25	1.25
		Nos. 741-744 (4)	3.30	3.30

Girl Guides 75th Anniv., Intl. Youth Year A96

25c, Gov.-Gen. Gordon. 50c, Camping. 90c, Map reading. $1.25, Students in laboratory. $2, Lady Baden-Powell.

1985, Mar. 15   Litho.   Perf. 15

745	A96	25c multicolored	.40	.40
746	A96	50c multicolored	.60	.60
747	A96	90c multicolored	.80	.80
748	A96	$1.25 multicolored	.95	.95
749	A96	$2 multicolored	1.20	1.20
		Nos. 745-749 (5)	3.95	3.95

Each stamp shows the scouting and IYY emblems.
For overprints see Nos. 777-781.

Audubon Birth Bicentenary — A97

Illustrations by Audubon: 10c, White-tailed kite. 15c, Cuvier's kinglet. 25c, Painted bunting. 75c, Belted kingfisher. $1, Northern cardinal. $3, Long-billed curlew.
$5, Portrait of Audubon, 1826, by John Syme.
10c, 25c, 75c, $1, $5 vert.

Perf. 14, 15 ($1)

1985, May 30   Litho.

750	A97	10c multicolored	1.00	1.00
751	A97	15c multicolored	1.00	1.00
752	A97	25c multicolored	1.20	1.20
753	A97	75c multicolored	1.20	1.40
754	A97	$1 multicolored	1.20	1.40
755	A97	$3 multicolored	2.00	2.25
		Nos. 750-755 (6)	7.60	8.25

Souvenir Sheet
Perf. 13½x14

756	A97	$5 multicolored	5.75	5.75

No. 756 contains one 38x51mm stamp. See No. 909A.

Queen Mother, 85th Birthday — A98

Designs: 10c, The Queen Consort and Princess Elizabeth, 1928. 15c, Queen Mother, Elizabeth. 75c, Queen Mother waving a greeting. No. 760, Royal family photograph, christening of Prince Henry. $2, Holding the infant Prince Henry. No. 762, Queen Mother, diff.

1985, June 20

757	A98	10c shown	.25	.25
758	A98	15c multicolored	.25	.25
759	A98	75c multicolored	.70	.70
760	A98	$5 multicolored	2.75	2.75
		Nos. 757-760 (4)	3.95	3.95

Souvenir Sheets

761	A98	$2 multicolored	2.25	2.25
762	A98	$5 multicolored	4.00	4.00

Nos. 761-762 contain one 38x51mm stamp.
For overprints see Nos. 771-776.

Nos. 705-706, 708 Ovptd.

1985, June 24   Perf. 15

762A	A89	10c multicolored	2.00	1.00
762B	A89	15c multicolored	2.00	1.00
762C	A89	50c multicolored	3.25	4.50
		Nos. 762A-762C (3)	7.25	6.50

Miniature Sheet

Commonwealth Stamp Omnibus, 50th Anniv. — A99

British Honduras Nos. 111-112, 127, 129, 143, 194, 307 and Belize Nos. 326, 385 and 397b on: a, George V and Queen Mary in an open carriage. b, George VI and Queen Consort Elizabeth crowned. c, Civilians celebrating the end of WWII. d, George VI and Queen Consort at mass service. e, Elizabeth II wearing robes of state and the imperial crown. f, Winston Churchill, WWII fighter planes. g, Bridal photograph of Elizabeth II and Prince Philip. h, Bridal photograph of Princess Anne and Capt. Mark Phillips. i, Elizabeth II. j, Imperial crown.
$5, Elizabeth II coronation photograph.

1985, July 25   Perf. 14½x14

763	A99	Sheet of 10	6.75	6.75
a.-j.		50c any single	.55	.55

Souvenir Sheet
Perf. 14

764	A99	$5 multicolored	5.00	5.00

No. 764 contains one 38x51mm stamp.
For overprints see Nos. 796-797.

British Post Office, 350th Anniv. A100

10c, Postboy, letters. 15c, Packet, privateer. 25c, Duke of Marlborough. 75c, Diana. $1, Falmouth P.O. packet. $3, S. S. Conway.

1985, Aug. 1   Perf. 15

765	A100	10c multicolored	.45	.45
766	A100	15c multicolored	.55	.55
767	A100	25c multicolored	.70	.70
768	A100	75c multicolored	1.20	1.20
769	A100	$1 multicolored	1.20	1.20
770	A100	$3 multicolored	2.25	2.25
		Nos. 765-770 (6)	6.35	6.35

Nos. 757-762 Overprinted

1985, Sept. 5   Litho.   Perf. 15

771	A98	10c multicolored	.50	.40
772	A98	15c multicolored	.60	.45
773	A98	75c multicolored	1.25	1.00
774	A98	$5 multicolored	3.25	3.75
		Nos. 771-774 (4)	5.60	5.60

Souvenir Sheets

775	A98	$2 multicolored	1.50	1.50
776	A98	$5 multicolored	4.25	4.25

Nos. 745-749 Ovptd.

1985, Sept. 25   Perf. 15

777	A96	25c multicolored	.75	.35
778	A96	50c multicolored	1.25	.75
779	A96	90c multicolored	1.75	1.90
780	A96	$1.25 multicolored	2.25	2.50
781	A96	$2 multicolored	3.00	3.50
		Nos. 777-781 (5)	9.00	9.00

Royal Visit — A101

25c, Royal and natl. flags. 75c, Elizabeth II. $4, Britannia.
$5, Elizabeth II, diff.

1985, Oct. 9   Perf. 15x14½

782	A101	25c multicolored	1.10	1.10
783	A101	75c multicolored	1.40	1.40

Size: 81x38mm

784	A101	$4 multicolored	5.00	5.00
a.		Strip of 3, #782-784	7.75	7.75
			7.50	7.50

Souvenir Sheet
Perf. 13½x14

785	A101	$5 multicolored	5.25	5.25

No. 785 contains one 38x51mm stamp.

Disneyland, 30th Anniv. A102

Characters from "It's a Small World" — 1c, Royal Canadian Mounted Police. 2c, American Indian. 3c, Inca of the Andes. 4c, Africa. 5c, Far East. 6c, Belize. 50c, Balkans. $1.50, Saudi Arabia. $3, Japan.
$4, Montage.

1985, Nov. 1   Perf. 11

786	A102	1c multicolored	.25	.25
787	A102	2c multicolored	.25	.25
788	A102	3c multicolored	.25	.25
789	A102	4c multicolored	.25	.25
790	A102	5c multicolored	.25	.25
791	A102	6c multicolored	.25	.25
792	A102	50c multicolored	2.00	2.00
793	A102	$1.50 multicolored	3.25	3.25
794	A102	$3 multicolored	4.25	4.25
		Nos. 786-794 (9)	11.00	11.00

Souvenir Sheet
Perf. 14

795	A102	$4 multicolored	8.00	8.00

Christmas.

Nos. 763-764 Overprinted

1985, Dec. 20   Perf. 14½x14

796		Sheet of 10	8.75	8.75
a.-j.		A99 50c, any single	.85	.85

Souvenir Sheet

797	A99	$5 multicolored	5.75	5.75

Women in Folk Costumes — A103

1986, Jan. 15   Perf. 15

798	A103	5c India	.90	.35
799	A103	10c Maya	1.00	.35
800	A103	15c Garifuna	1.20	.45
801	A103	25c Creole	1.50	.45
802	A103	50c China	2.10	1.50
803	A103	75c Lebanon	2.40	2.40
804	A103	$1 Europe	2.40	3.00
805	A103	$2 South America	3.25	4.50
		Nos. 798-805 (8)	14.75	13.00

Souvenir Sheet
Perf. 14

806	A103	$5 Maya, So. America	9.25	9.25

No. 806 contains one 38x51mm stamp.

Miniature Sheet

A104

Easter — A105

Papal arms, crucifix and: a, Pius X. b, Benedict XV. c, Pius XI. d, Pius XII. e, John XXIII. f, Paul VI. g, John Paul I. h, John Paul II. No. 573, John Paul II saying mass in Belize.

1986, Apr. 15   Litho.   Perf. 11

807	A104	Sheet of 8 + label	11.50	11.50
a.-h.		50c, any single	1.25	1.25

Souvenir Sheet
Perf. 14

808	A105	$4 multi	13.00	13.00

No. 807 contains center label picturing the Vatican, and papal crest.

Queen Elizabeth II, 60th Birthday — A106

A107

1986, Apr. 21 — Perf. 14

809		Strip of 3	1.25	1.25
a.	A106	25c Age 2	.25	.25
b.	A106	50c Coronation	.40	.40
c.	A106	75c Riding horse	.60	.60
810	A106	$3 Wearing crown jewels	2.40	2.40

Souvenir Sheet

811	A107	$4 Portrait	3.75	3.75

Halley's Comet — A109

1986, Apr. 30

812		Strip of 3	1.90	3.00
a.	A108	10c Planet-A probe	.40	.80
b.	A108	15c Sighting, 1910	.50	.95
c.	A108	50c Giotto probe	1.00	1.25
813		Strip of 3	4.60	5.25
a.	A108	75c Weather bureau	1.00	1.10
b.	A108	$1 US space telescope, shuttle	1.10	1.40
c.	A108	$2 Edmond Halley	2.50	2.75

Souvenir Sheet

814	A109	$4 Computer graphics	8.50	8.50

Miniature Sheet

A110

US Presidents — A111

1986, May — Perf. 11

815	A110	Sheet of 6 + 3 labels	4.50	4.50
a.		10c George Washington	.25	.25
b.		20c John Adams	.25	.25
c.		30c Thomas Jefferson	.30	.30
d.		50c James Madison	.45	.45
e.		$1.50 James Monroe	1.20	1.20
f.		$2 John Quincy Adams	1.60	1.60

Souvenir Sheet
Perf. 14

816	A111	$4 Washington	5.25	5.25

No. 815 contains 3 center labels picturing the great seal of the US.
Issue dates: No. 815, May 5; No. 816, May 7.

A112

Statue of Liberty, Cent. — A113

Designs: 25c, Bartholdi, statue. 50c, Statue, US centennial celebration, Philadelphia, 1876. 75c, Statue close-up, flags, 1886 unveiling. $3, Flags, statue close-up. $4, Statue, New York City skyline.

1986, May 15 — Perf. 14

817		Strip of 3	3.75	3.75
a.	A112	25c multicolored	.35	.35
b.	A112	75c multicolored	.80	.80
c.	A112	$3 multicolored	2.60	2.60
818	A112	50c multicolored	.50	.50

Souvenir Sheet

819	A113	$4 multicolored	5.00	5.00

A114

AMERIPEX '86, Chicago, May 22-June 1 — A115

1986, May 22

820		Strip of 3	2.50	2.50
a.	A114	10c British Honduras No. 3	.60	.60
b.	A114	15c Stamp of 1981	.75	.75
c.	A114	50c US No. C3a	1.20	1.20
821		Strip of 3	3.75	4.25
a.	A114	75c USS Constitution	1.15	1.25
b.	A114	$1 Liberty Bell	1.25	1.40
c.	A114	$2 White House	1.35	1.60

Souvenir Sheet

822	A115	$4 Capitol Building	5.00	5.00

For overprints see Nos. 835-837.

1986 World Cup Soccer Championships, Mexico — A116

Designs: 25c, England vs. Brazil. 50c, Mexican player, Mayan statues. 75c, Belize players. $3, Aztec calendar stone, Mexico. $4, Flags composing soccer balls.

1986, June 16 — Litho. — Perf. 11

823	A116	25c multicolored	1.75	1.75
824	A116	50c multicolored	2.00	2.00
825	A116	75c multicolored	2.25	2.25
826	A116	$3 multicolored	2.50	2.50
		Nos. 823-826 (4)	8.50	8.50

Souvenir Sheet
Perf. 14

827	A116	$4 multicolored	7.50	7.50

Nos. 823-826 printed in sheets of 8 plus label picturing Azteca Stadium, 2 each value per sheet.

Nos. 823-827 Overprinted

1986, Aug. 15

828	A116	25c multicolored	1.75	1.75
829	A116	50c multicolored	2.00	2.00
830	A116	75c multicolored	2.50	2.50
831	A116	$3 multicolored	3.50	3.50
		Nos. 828-831 (4)	9.75	9.75

Souvenir Sheet

832	A116	$4 multicolored	9.75	9.75

A117

Wedding of Prince Andrew and Sarah Ferguson A118

1986, July 23 — Perf. 14x14½

833		Strip of 3	3.50	3.50
a.	A117	25c Sarah	.75	.50
b.	A117	75c Andrew	1.00	1.00
c.	A117	$3 Couple	1.75	2.00

Souvenir Sheet
Perf. 14½

834		Sheet of 2	4.75	4.75
a.	A118	$1 Sarah, diff.	1.25	1.25
b.	A118	$3 Andrew, diff.	3.50	3.50

Size of No. 833c: 92x41mm.

Nos. 820-822 Overprinted

1986, Aug. 28 — Litho. — Perf. 14

835		Strip of 3	2.50	2.50
a.	A114	10c multicolored	.65	.65
b.	A114	15c multicolored	.85	.85
c.	A114	50c multicolored	1.00	1.00
836		Strip of 3	5.00	5.00
a.	A114	75c multicolored	1.25	1.25
b.	A114	$1 multicolored	1.75	1.75
c.	A114	$2 multicolored	2.00	2.00

Souvenir Sheet

837	A115	$4 multicolored	6.75	6.75

A119

Intl. Peace Year — A120

Children.

1986, Oct. 3 — Litho. — Perf. 14

838	A119	25c Infant	.80	.80
839	A119	50c Caucasians	1.00	1.00
840	A119	75c Oriental	1.20	1.20
841	A119	$3 Indian, caucasian	2.25	2.25
		Nos. 838-841 (4)	5.25	5.25

Souvenir Sheet

842	A120	$4 shown	6.25	6.25

Nos. 838-841 printed se-tenant in sheets of 8 (2 each) plus center label.

Fungi — A121

Toucans — A122

5c, Amanita lilloi. 10c, Keel-billed toucan. 20c, Boletellus cubensis. 25c, Collared aracari. 75c, Psilocybe caerulescens. $1, Emerald toucanet. $1.25, Crimson-rumped toucan. $2, Russula puiggarii.

1986, Oct. 30 — Perf. 14

843	A121	5c multicolored	1.50	1.50
844	A122	10c multicolored	1.50	1.50
845	A121	20c multicolored	1.75	1.75
846	A122	25c multicolored	1.75	1.75
847	A121	75c multicolored	2.25	2.25
848	A122	$1 multicolored	2.25	2.25
849	A122	$1.25 multicolored	2.50	2.50
850	A121	$2 multicolored	2.50	2.50
		Nos. 843-850 (8)	16.00	16.00

Stamps of the same design printed in sheets of 8 plus center label picturing Audubon Society emblem. Value $18 each.

Christmas
A123

Disney characters.

1986, Nov. 14			**Perf. 11**	
851		Sheet of 9	12.00	12.00
a.	A123	2c Jose Carioca	.25	.25
b.	A123	3c Carioca, Panchito, Donald		
c.	A123	4c Daisy	.25	.25
d.	A123	5c Mickey, Minnie	.25	.25
e.	A123	6c Carioca playing music	.25	.25
f.	A123	50c Panchito, Donald	1.50	1.50
g.	A123	65c Donald, Carioca	1.75	1.75
h.	A123	$1.35 Donald	2.75	2.75
i.	A123	$2 Goofy	4.00	4.00

Souvenir Sheet
Perf. 14

852	A123	$4 Donald	11.00	11.00

Marriage of Queen
Elizabeth II and
the Duke of
Edinburgh, 40th
Anniv. — A124

A125

1987, Oct. 7		**Litho.**	**Perf. 15**	
853	A124	25c Elizabeth, 1947	.30	.30
854	A124	75c Couple, c. 1980	.55	.55
855	A124	$1 Elizabeth, 1986	.60	.60
856	A124	$4 Wearing robes of Order of the Garter	1.20	1.20
		Nos. 853-856 (4)	2.65	2.65

Souvenir Sheet
Perf. 14

857	A125	$6 shown	6.50	6.50

A126

America's Cup 1986-87 — A127

Yachts that competed in the 1987 finals.

1987, Oct. 21			**Perf. 15**	
858	A126	25c America II	.50	.50
859	A126	75c Stars and Stripes	.60	.60
860	A126	$1 Australia II	.80	.80
861	A126	$4 White Crusader	1.60	1.60
		Nos. 858-861 (4)	3.50	3.50

Souvenir Sheet
Perf. 14

862	A127	$6 Australia II sails	7.00	7.00

Woodcarvings by
Sir George Gabb
(b. 1928) — A128

A129

25c, Mother and Child. 75c, Standing Form. $1, Love-Doves. $4, Depiction of Music. $6, African Heritage.

1987, Nov. 4			**Perf. 15**	
863	A128	25c multicolored	.25	.25
864	A128	75c multicolored	.55	.55
865	A128	$1 multicolored	.60	.60
866	A128	$4 multicolored	1.60	1.60
		Nos. 863-866 (4)	3.00	3.00

Souvenir Sheet
Perf. 14

867	A129	$6 multicolored	5.75	5.75

A130

Indigenous Primates — A131

25c, Black spider monkey. 75c, Male black howler. $1, Spider monkeys. $4, Howler monkeys. $6, Black spider, diff.

1987, Nov. 11			**Perf. 15**	
868	A130	25c multicolored	.40	.40
869	A130	75c multicolored	.70	.70
870	A130	$1 multicolored	.75	.75
871	A130	$4 multicolored	1.90	1.90
		Nos. 868-871 (4)	3.75	3.75

Souvenir Sheet
Perf. 14

872	A131	$6 multicolored	7.25	7.25

Natl. Girl Guides Movement, 50th
Anniv. — A132

Lady Olave Baden-Powell,
Founder — A133

25c, Flag-bearers. 75c, Camping. $1, On parade, camp. $4, Olave Baden-Powell. $6, Lady Olave, diff.

1987, Nov. 25			**Perf. 15**	
873	A132	25c multicolored	.65	.65
874	A132	75c multicolored	1.00	1.00
875	A132	$1 multicolored	1.35	1.35
876	A132	$4 multicolored	4.00	4.00
		Nos. 873-876 (4)	7.00	7.00

Souvenir Sheet
Perf. 14

877	A133	$6 multicolored	6.00	6.00

Intl. Year
of Shelter
for the
Homeless
A134

1987, Dec. 3			**Perf. 15**	
878	A134	25c Tent dwellings	.75	.75
879	A134	75c Urban slum	1.25	1.25
880	A134	$1 Tents, diff.	1.50	1.50
881	A134	$4 Construction	2.75	2.75
		Nos. 878-881 (4)	6.25	6.25

Orchids
A135

Illustrations from Reichenbachia, published by Henry F. Sander in 1886: 1c, Laelia euspatha. 2c, Cattleya citrina. 3c, Masdevallia bachousiana. 4c, Cypripedium tautzianum. 5c, Trichopilia suavis alba. 6c, Odontoglossum hebraicum. 7c, Cattleya trianaei schroederiana. 10c, Saccolabium giganteum. 30c, Cattleya warscewiczii. 50c, Chysis bractescens. 70c, Cattleya rochellensis. $1, Laelia elegans schilleriana. $1.50, Laelia anceps percivaliana. #895, $3, Laelia gouldiana. #896, $3, Odontoglossum roezlii. $5, Cattleya dowiana aurea.

1987, Dec. 16		**Litho.**	**Perf. 14**	
882-895	A135	Set of 14	18.50	18.50

Miniature Sheets

896-897	A135	Set of 2	16.00	16.00

Nos. 882-887 and 889-894 printed in blocks of six. Sheets of 14 contain 2 blocks of Nos. 882-887 plus 2 No. 888 and center label or 2 blocks of Nos. 889-894 plus center strip containing 2 No. 895 and center label. Center labels picture various illustrations from Reichenbachia.

Nos. 896-897 contain one 44x51mm stamp.

Miniature Sheet

Easter — A136

Stations of the Cross (in sequential order): a, Jesus condemned to death. b, Carries the cross. c, Falls the first time. d, Meets his mother, Mary. e, Cyrenean takes up the cross. f, Veronica wipes Jesus's face. g, Falls the second time. h, Consoles the women of Jerusalem. i, Falls the third time. j, Stripped of his robes. k, Nailed to the cross. l, Dies. m, Taken down from the cross. n, Laid in the sepulcher.

1988, Mar. 21			**Perf. 14**	
898	A136	Sheet of 14 + label	8.00	8.00
a.-n.		40c, any single	.50	.50

A $6 souvenir sheet was prepared but not issued.

1988 Summer
Olympics,
Seoul — A137

10c, Basketball. 25c, Volleyball. 60c, Table tennis. 75c, Diving. $1, Judo. $2, Field hockey. $3, Women's gymnastics.

1988, Aug. 15		**Litho.**	**Perf. 14**	
899	A137	10c multi	3.00	1.00
900	A137	25c multi	1.25	.40
901	A137	60c multi	1.25	.75
902	A137	75c multi	1.25	.95
903	A137	$1 multi	1.40	1.25
904	A137	$2 multi	7.00	5.00
		Nos. 899-904 (6)	15.15	9.35

Souvenir Sheet

905	A137	$3 multi	8.00	8.00

Intl. Red
Cross,
125th
Anniv.
A138

60c, Travelling nurse, 1912. 75c, Hospital ship, ambulance boat, 1937. $1, Ambulance, 1956. $2, Ambulance plane, 1940.

1988, Nov. 18		**Litho.**	**Perf. 14**	
906	A138	60c multicolored	3.50	1.40
907	A138	75c multicolored	3.75	1.60
908	A138	$1 multicolored	4.50	2.25
909	A138	$2 multicolored	6.00	6.50
		Nos. 906-909 (4)	17.75	11.75

Audubon Type of 1985

1988
909A A97 60c Painted bunting ... 2,000. 750.00

Indigenous Small Animals — A139

10c, Gibnut (agouti). 25c, Four-eyed opossum, vert. 50c, Ant bear. 75c, Antelope. $2, Peccary.

1989 Litho. Wmk. 384 Perf. 14
910 A139 10c multi ... 4.00 4.00

Unwmk.
911 A139 25c multi ... 4.00 4.00
  a. Wmk. 384 ... 5.50 5.50
912 A139 50c multi ... 4.75 3.75
913 A139 60c like 10c ... 4.75 4.00
914 A139 75c multi ... 4.75 4.00
915 A139 $2 multi ... 7.75 7.75
    Nos. 910-915 (6) ... 30.00 27.50

Issued: 10c, 7/23; No. 911a, 12/6; others, 2/24.

Moon Landing, 20th Anniv.
Common Design Type

Apollo 9: 25c, Command service and lunar modules docked in space. 50c, Command service module. 75c, Mission emblem. $1, First manned lunar module in space. $5, Apollo 11 command service module.

Perf. 14x13½
Size of Nos. 680-681: 29x29mm
916 CD342 25c multicolored ... 2.10 .60
917 CD342 50c multicolored ... 2.50 1.00
918 CD342 75c multicolored ... 2.75 1.50
919 CD342 $1 multicolored ... 3.00 2.50
    Nos. 916-919 (4) ... 10.35 5.60

Souvenir Sheet
920 CD342 $5 multi ... 12.50 12.50

No. 920 Overprinted

1989, Nov. 17 Perf. 14x13½
921 CD342 $5 multicolored ... 13.50 13.50
World Stamp Expo '89.

No. 704 Surcharged

1989, Nov. 15 Perf. 15
922 A89 5c on 6c multi ... 45.00

Christmas
A140

Old churches: 10c, Wesley. 25c, Baptist. 60c, St. John's Cathedral. 75c, St. Andrew's Presbyterian. $1, Holy Redeemer Cathedral.

Wmk. 384
1989, Dec. 13 Litho. Perf. 14
927 A140 10c multicolored ... .40 .25
928 A140 25c multicolored ... .50 .40
929 A140 60c multicolored ... 1.00 .90
930 A140 75c multicolored ... 1.30 1.25
931 A140 $1 multicolored ... 1.60 2.00
    Nos. 927-931 (5) ... 4.80 4.80

A141

Birds and Butterflies: 5c, Piranga leucoptera, Catonephele numilia female. 10c, Ramphastos sulfuratus, Nessaea aglaura. 15c, Fregata magnificens, Eurytides philolaus. 25c, Jabiru mycteria, Heliconius sapho. 30c, Ardea herodias, Colobura dirce. 50c, Icterus galbula, Hamadryas arethusia. 60c, Ara macao, Thecla regalis. 75c, Cyanerpes cyaneus, Callicore patelina. $1, Pulsatrix perspicillata, Caligo uranus. $2, Cyanocorax yncas, Philaethria dido. $5, Cathartes aura, Battus belus. $10, Pandion haliaetus, Papilio thoas.

Wmk. 373
1990, Mar. 1 Litho. Perf. 14
932 A141 5c multicolored ... .85 1.50
933 A141 10c multicolored ... 1.15 1.00
  a. Inscribed "1993" ... 2.00 2.00
934 A141 15c multicolored ... 1.15 .50
935 A141 25c multicolored ... 1.15 .50
936 A141 30c multicolored ... 1.15 .60
937 A141 50c multicolored ... 1.50 .75
938 A141 60c multicolored ... 1.75 .90
939 A141 75c multicolored ... 1.75 .95
940 A141 $1 multicolored ... 3.25 2.00
941 A141 $2 multicolored ... 4.00 4.25
942 A141 $5 multicolored ... 6.50 7.75
943 A141 $10 multicolored ... 12.00 14.50
    Nos. 932-943 (12) ... 36.20 35.20

For overprints and surcharge see Nos. 944, 1021, 1030.

No. 940 Overprinted

1990, Mar. 1
944 A141 $1 multicolored ... 6.50 6.50

Turtles
A142

10c, Green. 25c, Hawksbill. 60c, Loggerhead. 75c, Loggerhead, diff. $1, Bocatora. $2, Hicatee.

Wmk. 373
1990, Aug. 8 Litho. Perf. 14
945 A142 10c multicolored ... 1.20 .70
946 A142 25c multicolored ... 1.90 .70
947 A142 60c multicolored ... 2.75 2.75
948 A142 75c multicolored ... 3.00 3.00
949 A142 $1 multicolored ... 3.75 3.75
950 A142 $2 multicolored ... 5.00 6.00
    Nos. 945-950 (6) ... 17.60 16.90

Battle of Britain, 50th Anniv. A143

Aircraft: 10c, Fairey Battle. 25c, Bristol Beaufort. 60c, Bristol Blenheim. 75c, Armstrong-Whitworth Whitley. $1, Vickers-Armstrong Wellington. $2, Handley-Page Hampden.

1990, Sept. 15 Wmk. 384 Perf. 13½
951 A143 10c multicolored ... 2.25 .90
952 A143 25c multicolored ... 3.00 1.00
953 A143 60c multicolored ... 4.00 2.00
954 A143 75c multicolored ... 4.00 2.00
955 A143 $1 multicolored ... 4.00 2.00
956 A143 $2 multicolored ... 5.00 4.00
    Nos. 951-956 (6) ... 22.25 11.90

Orchids — A144

25c, Cattleya bowringiana. 50c, Rhyncholaelia digbyana. 60c, Sobralia macrantha. 75c, Chysis bractescens. $1, Vanilla planifolia. $2, Epidendrum polyanthum.

1990, Nov. 1 Wmk. 384 Perf. 14
957 A144 25c multicolored ... 1.40 .30
958 A144 50c multicolored ... 2.00 .70
959 A144 60c multicolored ... 2.50 1.60
960 A144 75c multicolored ... 2.50 1.60
961 A144 $1 multicolored ... 3.00 3.00
962 A144 $2 multicolored ... 4.00 4.00
    Nos. 957-962 (6) ... 15.40 11.20

Christmas.

Indigenous Fauna — A145

1991, Apr. 10
963 A145 25c Iguana ... 1.50 .50
964 A145 50c Crocodile ... 2.25 1.25
965 A145 60c Manatee ... 2.75 2.75
966 A145 75c Boa constrictor ... 3.25 3.25
967 A145 $1 Tapir ... 3.75 3.75
968 A145 $2 Jaguar ... 5.00 5.00
    Nos. 963-968 (6) ... 18.50 16.50

Elizabeth & Philip, Birthdays
Common Design Types
1991, June 17 Perf. 14½
969 CD345 $1 multicolored ... 1.50 1.50
970 CD346 $1 multicolored ... 1.50 1.50
  a. Pair, #969-970 + label ... 3.75 3.75

Hurricanes — A146

60c, Weather radar. 75c, Weather observation station. $1, Scene after hurricane. $2, Hurricane Gilbert.

1991, July 31 Wmk. 373 Perf. 14
971 A146 60c multicolored ... 2.40 2.00
972 A146 75c multicolored ... 2.50 2.25
973 A146 $1 multicolored ... 2.75 2.25
974 A146 $2 multicolored ... 4.00 4.75
    Nos. 971-974 (4) ... 11.65 11.75

Independence, 10th Anniv. — A147

Famous Men: 25c, Thomas V. Ramos (1887-1955). 60c, Sir Isaiah Morter (1860-1924). 75c, Antonio Soberanis (1897-1975). $1, Santiago Ricalde (1920-1975).

1991, Sept. 4 Wmk. 384
975 A147 25c multicolored ... .90 .40
976 A147 60c multicolored ... 1.90 2.00
977 A147 75c multicolored ... 1.90 2.00
978 A147 $1 multicolored ... 2.25 2.50
    Nos. 975-978 (4) ... 6.95 6.90

Folktales A148

Christmas: 25c, Anansi. 50c, Jack-O-Lantern. 60c, Tata Duende, vert. 75c, Xtabai. $1, Warrie Massa, vert. $2, Old Heg.

Wmk. 373
1991, Nov. 6 Litho. Perf. 14
979 A148 25c multicolored ... 2.00 .45
980 A148 50c multicolored ... 2.50 .55
981 A148 60c multicolored ... 2.90 1.25
982 A148 75c multicolored ... 2.90 1.25
983 A148 $1 multicolored ... 3.25 2.25
984 A148 $2 multicolored ... 4.50 7.00
    Nos. 979-984 (6) ... 18.05 12.75

See Nos. 999-1002.

Orchids — A149

Easter: 25c, Gongora quinquenervis. 50c, Oncidium sphacelatum. 60c, Encyclia bractescens. 75c, Epidendrum ciliare. $1, Psygmorchis pusilla. $2, Galeandra batemanii.

1992, Apr. 1
985 A149 25c multicolored ... 1.75 .30
986 A149 50c multicolored ... 2.40 1.10
987 A149 60c multicolored ... 2.75 2.50
988 A149 75c multicolored ... 2.75 2.50
989 A149 $1 multicolored ... 3.00 3.00
990 A149 $2 multicolored ... 4.75 7.50
    Nos. 985-990 (6) ... 17.40 16.90

Famous Belizeans A150

Designs: 25c, Gwendolyn Lizarraga, MBE (1901-75). 60c, Rafael Fonseca, CMG, OBE (1921-78). 75c, Vivian Seay, MBE (1881-1971). $1, Samuel A. Haynes (1898-1971).

1992, Aug. 26 Perf. 13x12½
991 A150 25c multicolored ... .90 .35
992 A150 60c multicolored ... 1.75 1.75
993 A150 75c multicolored ... 2.10 2.10
994 A150 $1 multicolored ... 2.25 2.25
    Nos. 991-994 (4) ... 7.00 6.45

See Nos. 1013-1016.

Discovery of America, 500th
Anniv. — A151

Mayan ruins, modern buildings: 25c, Xunan-
tunich, National Assembly. 60c, Altun Ha,
Supreme Court Building. 75c, Santa Rita,
Tower Hill Sugar Factory. $5, Lamanai, The
Citrus Company.

Perf. 13½x14
1992, Oct. 1   Litho.   Wmk. 384

995	A151	25c multicolored	1.40	.35
996	A151	60c multicolored	2.10	1.40
997	A151	75c multicolored	2.25	1.75
998	A151	$5 multicolored	11.00	13.00
		Nos. 995-998 (4)	16.75	16.50

Folklore Type of 1991

Christmas.

Perf. 13x12½
1992, Nov. 16   Litho.   Wmk. 373

999	A148	25c Hashishi Pampi	.45	.30
1000	A148	60c Cadejo	.95	.95
1001	A148	$1 La Sucia, vert.	1.25	1.25
1002	A148	$5 Sisimito	6.25	6.50
		Nos. 999-1002 (4)	8.90	9.00

Royal Air Force, 75th Anniv.
Common Design Type

Designs: 25c, Aerospatiale Puma. 50c, British Aerospace Harrier. 60c, DeHavilland Mosquito. 75c, Avro Lancaster. $1, Consolidated
Liberator. $3, Short Stirling.

Wmk. 373
1993, Apr. 1   Litho.   Perf. 14

1003	CD350	25c multicolored	1.90	.90
1004	CD350	50c multicolored	2.25	1.15
1005	CD350	60c multicolored	2.40	1.60
1006	CD350	75c multicolored	2.40	1.60
1007	CD350	$1 multicolored	2.60	2.00
1008	CD350	$3 multicolored	5.00	9.25
		Nos. 1003-1008 (6)	16.55	16.50

1993 World
Orchid
Conference,
Glasgow — A152

25c, Lycaste aromatica. 60c, Sobralia
decora. $1, Maxillaria alba. $2, Brassavola
nodosa.

Perf. 14½x14
1993, Apr. 24   Litho.   Wmk. 384

1009	A152	25c multicolored	.70	.45
1010	A152	60c multicolored	1.30	1.30
1011	A152	$1 multicolored	1.75	1.75
1012	A152	$2 multicolored	3.00	3.25
		Nos. 1009-1012 (4)	6.75	6.75

Famous Belizeans Type of 1992

Designs: 25c, Herbert Watkin Beaumont
(1880-1978). 60c, Dr. Selvyn Walford Young
(1899-1977). 75c, Cleopatra White (1898-
1987). $1, Dr. Karl Heusner (1872-1960).

Wmk. 384
1993, Aug. 11   Litho.   Perf. 14

1013	A150	25c multicolored	.55	.35
1014	A150	60c multicolored	1.05	1.00
1015	A150	75c multicolored	1.25	1.25
1016	A150	$1 multicolored	1.50	1.50
		Nos. 1013-1016 (4)	4.35	4.10

Christmas
A153

25c, Boom and chime band. 60c, John
Canoe dance. 75c, Cortez dance. $2, Maya
Musical Group.

Wmk. 373
1993, Nov. 3   Litho.   Perf. 14

1017	A153	25c multicolored	1.25	.50
1018	A153	60c multicolored	2.25	1.25
1019	A153	75c multicolored	2.25	1.25
1020	A153	$2 multicolored	5.25	8.00
		Nos. 1017-1020 (4)	11.00	11.00

No. 940
Overprinted

Wmk. 373
1994, Feb. 18   Litho.   Perf. 14

1021	A141	$1 multicolored	4.75	4.25

Royal
Visit — A154

Designs: 25c, Belize, United Kingdom
Flags. 60c, Queen Elizabeth II wearing hat.
75c, Queen. $1, Queen, Prince Philip.

Perf. 14½x14
1994, Feb. 24   Litho.   Wmk. 373

1022	A154	25c multicolored	2.25	.70
1023	A154	60c multicolored	2.90	1.60
1024	A154	75c multicolored	3.25	2.00
1025	A154	$1 multicolored	3.50	3.25
		Nos. 1022-1025 (4)	11.90	7.55

Bats
A155

25c, Insect feeder. 60c, Fruit feeder. 75c,
Fish feeder. $2, Common vampire.

Wmk. 384
1994, May 30   Litho.   Perf. 14

1026	A155	25c multicolored	.75	.35
1027	A155	60c multicolored	1.40	1.20
1028	A155	75c multicolored	1.60	1.30
1029	A155	$2 multicolored	3.75	4.50
		Nos. 1026-1029 (4)	7.50	7.35

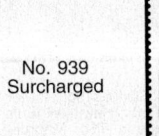

No. 939
Surcharged

Wmk. 373
1994, Aug. 18   Litho.   Perf. 14

1030	A141	10c on 75c multi	3.00	3.00

Christmas
A156

Orchids: 25c, Cycnoches chlorochilon. 60c,
Brassavolas cucullata. 75c, Sobralia
mucronata. $1, Nidema Boothii.

1994, Nov. 7   Wmk. 384

1031	A156	25c multicolored	.90	.40
1032	A156	60c multicolored	1.50	1.40
1033	A156	75c multicolored	1.75	1.75
1034	A156	$1 multicolored	2.25	2.75
		Nos. 1031-1034 (4)	6.40	6.30

For overprints see Nos. 1051-1054.

Insects
A157

5c, Ground beetle. 10c, Harlequin beetle.
15c, Giant water bug. 25c, Peanut-head bug.
30c, Coconut weevil. 50c, Mantis. 60c, Taran-
tula wasp. 75c, Rhinoceros beetle. $1, Metallic
wood borer. $2, Dobson fly. $5, Click beetle.
$10, Long-horned beetle.

Wmk. 373
1995, Jan. 11   Litho.   Perf. 14
Without date imprint

1035	A157	5c multicolored	.60	1.00
1036	A157	10c multicolored	.75	1.00
1037	A157	15c multicolored	.80	1.00
1038	A157	25c multicolored	.95	.30
1039	A157	30c multicolored	.95	.35
1040	A157	50c multicolored	1.10	.40
1041	A157	60c multicolored	1.60	.65
1042	A157	75c multicolored	1.75	.75
1043	A157	$1 multicolored	2.25	1.10
1044	A157	$2 multicolored	4.75	5.00
1045	A157	$5 multicolored	9.00	9.50
1046	A157	$10 multicolored	13.50	15.00
		Nos. 1035-1046 (12)	38.00	36.05

For overprints see Nos. 1063-1066.

1996, Oct. 14   Inscribed "1996"

1035a	A157	5c	.60	1.00
1036a	A157	10c	.75	1.00
1037a	A157	15c	.80	1.00
1038a	A157	25c	.95	.30
1039a	A157	30c	.95	.35
1040a	A157	50c	1.10	.40
1041a	A157	60c	1.60	.65
1042a	A157	75c	1.75	.75
1043a	A157	$1	2.25	1.10
1044a	A157	$2	4.75	5.00
1045a	A157	$5	8.75	9.00
1046a	A157	$10	13.00	15.00
		Nos. 1035a-1046a (12)	37.25	35.55

End of World War II, 50th Anniv.
Common Design Type

Designs: 25c, War Memorial Cenotaph. 60c,
Remembrance Sunday. 75c, British Honduras
Forestry Unit. $1, Wellington Bomber.

Wmk. 373
1995, May 8   Litho.   Perf. 13½

1047	CD351	25c multicolored	.55	.40
1048	CD351	60c multicolored	1.50	1.50
1049	CD351	75c multicolored	1.75	1.75
1050	CD351	$1 multicolored	2.25	2.25
		Nos. 1047-1050 (4)	6.05	5.90

Nos. 1031-1034
Ovptd. in Blue

1995, Sept. 1   Wmk. 384   Perf. 14

1051	A156	25c on No. 1031	1.25	.35
1052	A156	60c on No. 1032	1.75	1.10
1053	A156	75c on No. 1033	2.10	2.10
1054	A156	$1 on No. 1034	2.40	2.75
		Nos. 1051-1054 (4)	7.50	6.30

UN, 50th Anniv.
Common Design Type

Designs: 25c, M113 Light reconnaissance
vehicle. 60c, Sultan, armored command vehicle. 75c, Leyland/DAF 8x4 "Drops" vehicle. $2,
Warrior infantry combat vehicle.

Wmk. 384
1995, Oct. 24   Litho.   Perf. 14

1055	CD353	25c multicolored	.40	.30
1056	CD353	60c multicolored	.95	.90

1057	CD353	75c multicolored	1.10	1.10
1058	CD353	$2 multicolored	2.25	2.40
		Nos. 1055-1058 (4)	4.70	4.70

Christmas
A158

Doves: 25c, Blue ground. 60c, White-
fronted. 75c, Ruddy ground. $1, White-
winged.

1995, Nov. 6   Wmk. 373

1059	A158	25c multicolored	.60	.30
1060	A158	60c multicolored	1.20	1.20
1061	A158	75c multicolored	1.45	1.45
1062	A158	$1 multicolored	2.00	2.25
		Nos. 1059-1062 (4)	5.25	5.20

Nos. 1037, 1039-1040, 1044 Ovptd.

Wmk. 373
1996, May 17   Litho.   Perf. 14

1063	A157	15c on #1037	.30	.25
1064	A157	30c on #1039	.65	.50
1065	A157	50c on #1040	.90	.80
1066	A157	$2 on #1044	2.75	3.00
		Nos. 1063-1066 (4)	4.60	4.55

CAPEX
'96
A159

Trains: 25c, Unloading banana train onto
freighter, Commerce Bight Pier. 60c, Engine
No. 1, Stann Creek Station. 75c, Mahogany
log train, Hunslet 0-6-0 Side Tank Engine No.
4. $3, LMS Jubilee Class 4-6-0 Locomotive
No. 5602 "British Honduras."

Perf. 13½x13
1996, June 6   Litho.   Wmk. 373

1067	A159	25c multicolored	1.40	.50
1068	A159	60c multicolored	2.00	1.25
1069	A159	75c multicolored	2.00	1.40
1070	A159	$3 multicolored	3.50	5.75
		Nos. 1067-1070 (4)	8.90	8.90

Christmas — A160

Orchids: 25c, Epidendrum stamfordianum.
60c, Oncidium carthagenense. 75c, Oer-
stedella verrucosa. $1, Coryanthes speciosa.

Wmk. 373
1996, Nov. 6   Litho.   Perf. 14

1071	A160	25c multicolored	.80	.30
1072	A160	60c multicolored	1.25	.95
1073	A160	75c multicolored	1.40	1.25
1074	A160	$1 multicolored	1.90	2.00
		Nos. 1071-1074 (4)	5.35	4.50

Hong Kong '97
A161

Cattle: 25c, Red poll. 60c, Brahman. 75c, Longhorn. $1, Charbray.

Wmk. 373

1997, Feb. 12		**Litho.**		**Perf. 14**
1075	A161	25c multicolored	.75	.30
1076	A161	60c multicolored	1.15	1.20
1077	A161	75c multicolored	1.50	1.60
1078	A161	$1 multicolored	1.75	2.00
		Nos. 1075-1078 (4)	5.15	5.10

Snakes — A162

25c, Coral snake. 60c, Green vine snake. 75c, Yellow-jawed tommygoff. $1, Speckled racer.

Wmk. 373

1997, May 28		**Litho.**		**Perf. 14**
1079	A162	25c multicolored	.70	.30
1080	A162	60c multicolored	1.10	1.10
1081	A162	75c multicolored	1.25	1.25
1082	A162	$1 multicolored	1.50	1.90
		Nos. 1079-1082 (4)	4.55	4.55

Howler Monkeys — A163

World Wildlife Fund: 10c, Adult male. 25c, Female feeding. 60c, Female with infant. 75c, Juvenile feeding.

Wmk. 373

1997, Aug. 13		**Litho.**		**Perf. 14**
1083	A163	10c multicolored	.40	.25
1084	A163	25c multicolored	.60	.30
1085	A163	60c multicolored	1.00	1.00
1086	A163	75c multicolored	1.20	1.50
		Nos. 1083-1086 (4)	3.20	3.05

Christmas A164

Orchids: 25c, Maxillaria elatior. 60c, Dimerandra emarginata. 75c, Macradenia brassavolae. $1, Ornithocephalus gladiatus.

Wmk. 373

1997, Nov. 21		**Litho.**		**Perf. 14**
1087	A164	25c multicolored	.80	.30
1088	A164	60c multicolored	1.30	.80
1089	A164	75c multicolored	1.40	1.30
1090	A164	$1 multicolored	1.90	2.10
		Nos. 1087-1090 (4)	5.40	4.50

Diana, Princess of Wales (1961-97)
Common Design Type

Designs: a, Up close portrait, smiling. b, Wearing evening dress. c, Up close portrait, serious. d, Holding bouquet of flowers.

Perf. 14½x14

1998, Mar. 31		**Litho.**		**Wmk. 373**
1091	CD355	$1 Sheet of 4, #a.-d.	5.00	5.00

University of West Indies, 50th Anniv. A165

Wmk. 373

1998, July 22		**Litho.**		**Perf. 13**
1092	A165	$1 multicolored	1.45	1.45

Organization of American States, 50th Anniv. A166

Designs: 25c, Children working computers, connecting high schools to the internet. $1, Map of Central America, Inter American Drug Abuse Control Commission.

1998, July 22				
1093	A166	25c multicolored	.25	.25
1094	A166	$1 multicolored	1.90	1.90

Battle of St. George's Cay, Bicent. A167

Views of Old Belize from St. George, vert: No. 1095, Woman, child beside small boat. No. 1096, Soldiers at dock, cannon. No. 1097, Cannon balls, cannon, boats in water. 25c, Bayman gun flats. 60c, Bayman sloops. 75c, Schooners. $1, HMS Merlin. $2, Spanish flagship.

1998, Aug. 5				***Perf. 13½***
1095	A167	10c multicolored	.65	.90
1096	A167	10c multicolored	.65	.90
1097	A167	10c multicolored	.65	.90
a.		Strip of 3, #1095-1097	2.00	3.00
1098	A167	25c multicolored	.95	.30
1099	A167	60c multicolored	1.35	1.10
1100	A167	75c multicolored	1.50	1.20
1101	A167	$1 multicolored	1.75	1.75
1102	A167	$2 multicolored	2.75	3.25
		Nos. 1095-1102 (8)	10.25	10.30

A168

Christmas — Flowers: 25c, Brassia maculata. 60c, Encyclia radiata. 75c, Stanhopea ecornuta. $1, Isochilus carnosiflorus.

1998, Nov. 4				***Perf. 14***
1103	A168	25c multicolored	.55	.30
1104	A168	60c multicolored	.80	.65
1105	A168	75c multicolored	.80	.85
1106	A168	$1 multicolored	1.00	1.25
		Nos. 1103-1106 (4)	3.15	3.05

A169

Easter — Orchids: 10c, Eucharis grandiflora. 25c, Hippeastrum puniceum. 60c, Zephyranthes citrina. $1, Hymenocallis littoralis.

1999, Mar. 17				***Perf. 13***
1107	A169	10c multicolored	.40	.25
1108	A169	25c multicolored	.55	.30
1109	A169	60c multicolored	.95	.95
1110	A169	$1 multicolored	1.15	1.50
		Nos. 1107-1110 (4)	3.05	3.00

UPU, 125th Anniv. A170

1999, Oct. 18				***Perf. 13¼***
1111	A170	25c Bicycle	.65	.40
1112	A170	60c Truck	.80	.65
1113	A170	75c Mailship "Dee"	1.00	.85
1114	A170	$1 Airplane	1.30	1.50
		Nos. 1111-1114 (4)	3.75	3.40

Christmas — A171

Designs: 25c, Holy Family with Jesus and St. John, by school of Peter Paul Rubens. 60c, The Holy Family with St. John, by unknown artist. 75c, Madonna with Child, St. John and Angel, by unknown artist. $1, Madonna with Child and St. John by Andrea da Salerno.

1999, Dec. 6				***Perf. 14***
1115	A171	25c multicolored	.40	.20
1116	A171	60c multicolored	.75	.60
1117	A171	75c multicolored	.85	.80
1118	A171	$1 multicolored	1.25	1.40
		Nos. 1115-1118 (4)	3.25	3.00

Fauna A172

5c, Iguana. 10c, Gibnut. 15c, Howler monkey. 25c, Ant bear. 30c, Hawksbill turtle. 50c, Antelope. 60c, Jaguar. 75c, Manatee. $1, Crocodile. $2, Tapir. $5, Collared peccary. $10, Boa constrictor.

Wmk. 373

2000, Feb. 15		**Litho.**		***Perf. 14***
		Without date imprint		
1119	A172	5c multicolored	.25	.60
1120	A172	10c multicolored	.25	.60
1121	A172	15c multicolored	.35	.60
1122	A172	25c multicolored	.50	.25
1123	A172	30c multicolored	.50	.25
1124	A172	50c multicolored	.80	.30
1125	A172	60c multicolored	.95	.35
1126	A172	75c multicolored	1.10	.50
1127	A172	$1 multicolored	1.50	.80
1128	A172	$2 multicolored	2.75	3.00
1129	A172	$5 multicolored	6.00	6.75
1130	A172	$10 multicolored	12.00	13.00
		Nos. 1119-1130 (12)	26.95	27.00

For surcharges see Nos. 1181-1183.

2003, Sept.			**Inscribed "2003"**	
1120a	A172	10c	.30	.65
1121a	A172	15c	.40	.65
1122a	A172	25c	.55	.25
1123a	A172	30c	.55	.25
1124a	A172	50c	.85	.35
1125a	A172	60c	1.00	.45
1126a	A172	75c	1.20	.65
1127a	A172	$1	1.50	.80
1128a	A172	$2	3.00	3.00
1129a	A172	$5	7.50	7.75
1130a	A172	$10	13.00	15.00
		Nos. 1120a-1130a (11)	29.85	29.80

Fruits A173

Wmk. 373

2000, Apr. 19		**Litho.**		***Perf. 14***
1131	A173	25c Mango	.50	.25
1132	A173	60c Cashew	.90	.75
1133	A173	75c Papaya	1.20	1.00
1134	A173	$1 Banana	1.40	2.00
		Nos. 1131-1134 (4)	4.00	4.00

People's United Party, 50th Anniv. A174

10c, Birth of party politics, 9/29/50. 25c, People gain voting rights, 4/28/54. 60c, Self-government, 1/1/64. 75c, Building the new capital Belmopan, 1967-70. $1, Independence, 9/21/81.

Perf. 13¼x13¾

2000, Sept. 18	**Litho.**	**Wmk. 373**	
1135-1139	A174	Set of 5	4.75 4.75

Christmas A175

Orchids: 25c, Bletia purpurea. 60c, Cyrtopodium punctata. 75c, Cycnoches egertonianum. $1, Catasetum integerrimum.

Perf. 14½x14¼

2000	**Litho.**	**Wmk. 373**	
1140-1143	A175	Set of 4	6.25 6.25

Independence, 20th Anniv. — A176

Designs: 25c, Education. 60c, Shrimp farming. 75c, Privassion Cascade, vert. $2, Map, vert.

Wmk. 373

2001, Oct. 3	**Litho.**	***Perf. 14***	
1144-1147	A176	Set of 4	6.75 6.75

Christmas — A177

Orchids: 25c, Sobralia fragrans. 60c, Encyclia cordigera. 75c, Maxillaria fulgens. $1, Epidendrum nocturnum.

Wmk. 373

2001, Dec. 28	**Litho.**	***Perf. 14***	
1148-1151	A177	Set of 4	5.25 5.25

Reign Of Queen Elizabeth II, 50th Anniv. Issue
Common Design Type

Designs: Nos. 1152, 1156a, 25c, Princess Elizabeth, 1943. Nos. 1153, 1156b, 60c, In 1952. Nos. 1154, 1156c, 75c, With Prince Charles and Princess Anne. Nos. 1155, 1156d, $1, In 1995. No. 1156e, $5, 1955 portrait by Annigoni (38x50mm).

Perf. 14¼x14½, 13¾ (#1156e)
2002, Feb. 6   Litho.   Wmk. 373
With Gold Frames

1152	CD360 25c multicolored	.50	.25
1153	CD360 60c multicolored	.80	.60
1154	CD360 75c multicolored	.95	.85
1155	CD360 $1 multicolored	1.15	1.30
	Nos. 1152-1155 (4)	3.40	3.00

Souvenir Sheet
Without Gold Frames

1156	CD360	Sheet of 5, #a-e	9.25	9.25

Christmas — A178

Orchids: 25c, Dichaea neglecta. 50c, Epidendrum hawkesii. 60c, Encyclia belizensis. 75c, Eriopsis biloba. $1, Harbenaria monorrhiza. $2, Mormodes buccinator.

Wmk. 373
2002, Dec. 12   Litho.   Perf. 14
1157-1162 A178   Set of 6   10.00 10.00

Belize Defense Force, 25th Anniv. A179

Wmk. 373
2003, Jan. 29   Litho.   Perf. 14
1163 A179 25c multi   .55 .55

Powered Flight, Cent. — A180

Designs: 25c, Avro Shackleton Mk 3. 60c, Lockheed L-749 Constellation. 75c, SEPECAT Jaguar GR 1. $3, British Aerospace Harrier GR 3.
$5, Spirit of St. Louis lands in Belize, Dec. 30, 1927.

Wmk. 373
2003, Sept. 17   Litho.   Perf. 14
Stamps + Label
1164-1167 A180   Set of 4   7.75 7.75
Souvenir Sheet
1168 A180 $5 multi   7.50 7.50
For surcharge see No. 1185.

Christmas A181

Scarlet macaw: 25c, Close-up of head. 60c, Pair on tree. 75c, Three eating clay. $5, Pair in flight.

2003, Nov. 5   Perf. 13¾
1169-1172 A181   Set of 4   12.25 12.25
For surcharge see No. 1184.

Whale Shark A182

Various depictions of whale shark: 25c, 60c, 75c, $5.

Wmk. 373
2004, Aug. 16   Litho.   Perf. 13½
1173-1176 A182   Set of 4   12.00 12.00

Worldwide Fund for Nature (WWF) — A183

Various depictions of Central American wooly opossum with denominations in: 25c, Green, vert. 60c, Blue, vert. 75c, Orange. $5, Red violet.

Perf. 14¼x14, 14x14¼
2004, Nov. 8   Litho.   Wmk. 373
1177-1180 A183   Set of 4   11.00 11.00

Nos. 1124-1126 Surcharged

Wmk. 373
2004-2005   Litho.   Perf. 14
1181 A172 10c on 50c #1124   1.75 1.75
1182 A172 10c on 60c #1125 ('05)   — —
1183 A172 15c on 75c #1126   1.75 1.75
Issued: Nos. 1181, 1183, 10/4/04. No. 1182, 1/31/05.
Nos. 1181 and 1182 exist dated "2003."

No. 1170 Surcharged

Wmk. 373
2005, July 15   Litho.   Perf. 13¾
1184 A181 10c on 60c #1170   11.00 11.00

No. 1165 Surcharged

Wmk. 373
2005, July   Litho.   Perf. 14
1185 A180 10c on 60c #1165   3.00 3.00

Pope John Paul II (1920-2005) A184

Wmk. 373
2005, Aug. 18   Litho.   Perf. 14
1186 A184 $1 multi   2.00 2.00

Ecological and Heritage Sites A185

Designs: 5c, Guanacaste National Park. 10c, Government House of Culture. 15c, Lubaantun Archaeological Reserve. 25c, Altun Ha Archaeological Reserve. 30c, Nohoch Che'n Archaeological Reserve. 50c, Goff's Caye. 60c, Nlue Hole Natural Monument. 75c, Lamanai Archaeological Reserve. $1, Half Moon Caye and Lighthouse. $2, Placencia Peninsula. $5, Museum of Belize. $10, Cerros Archaeological Reserve.

2005, Aug. 31   Wmk. 373   Perf. 14
1187 A185 5c multi   .25 .25
1188 A185 10c multi   .25 .25
1189 A185 15c multi   .25 .25
1190 A185 25c multi   .30 .30
a.   Wmk. 406   .50 .50
1191 A185 30c multi   .35 .35
1192 A185 50c multi   .60 .60
1193 A185 60c multi   .70 .70
1194 A185 75c multi   .85 .85
1195 A185 $1 multi   1.10 1.10
1196 A185 $2 multi   2.50 2.50
1197 A185 $5 multi   5.50 5.50
1198 A185 $10 multi   11.00 11.00
Nos. 1187-1198 (12)   23.65 23.65
Issued: No. 1190a, Feb. 2009.

Europa Stamps, 50th Anniv. A186

Stamps commemorating 125th anniv. of the UPU: 25c, #1111. 75c, #1112. $3, #1113. $5, #1114.

Perf. 13x13¼
2006, Mar. 22   Litho.   Unwmk.
1199-1202 A186   Set of 4   16.00 16.00
1202a   Souvenir sheet, #1199-1202   15.75 15.75

Independence, 25th Anniv. — A187

Designs: 25c, Prime Minister George Price. 30c, National symbols, horiz. 60c, Map of Belize. $1, 1981 Independence logo. $5, Constitution, horiz.

Perf. 13¼x12½, 12½x13¼
2006, July 3   Litho.   Wmk. 373
1203-1207 A187   Set of 5   9.00 9.00

Breast Cancer Research — A188

2006, Oct. 26   Litho.   Perf. 13½x13¼
1208 A188 $1 multi   2.50 2.50

Art by Belizean Artists — A189

Designs: 25c, Sleeping Giant, sculpture, by George Gabb. 30c, Market Scene, by Louis Belisle, horiz. 60c, The Original Turtle Shell Band, by Pen Cayetano, horiz. 75c, Have Some Coconut Water, by Benjamin Nicholas. $2, Untitled sculpture by Reuben Miguel. $3, Mural at Corozal Town Hall, by Manuel Villamor.

Wmk. 373
2007, May 9   Litho.   Perf. 14
1209-1214 A189   Set of 6   7.00 7.00

Abolition of the Slave Trade Act, Bicent. — A190

Perf. 12½x13
2007, Sept. 26   Litho.   Wmk. 373
1215 A190 $2 multi   2.00 2.00

University of the West Indies, 60th Anniv. A191

Wmk. 373
2008, Nov. 14   Litho.   Perf. 13
1216 A191 $1 multi   1.50 1.50

Endangered Birds — A192

Designs: 25c, Yellow-headed parrot. 60c, Harpy eagle. $1, Slate-colored seedeater. $2, Green honeycreeper. $5, Great curassow.

Wmk. 406
2009, July 8   Litho.   Perf. 12½
1217-1221 A192   Set of 5   10.00 10.00

Christmas — A193

Orchids: 25c, Encyclia polybulbon. 60c, Oncidium ensatum. $2, Encyclia livida. $5, Epidendrum difforme.

Wmk. 406

2010, Dec. 8	**Litho.**		**Perf. 12½**
1222-1225	A193	Set of 4	8.00 8.00

Reign of Queen Elizabeth II, 60th Anniv. — A194

Various photographs of Queen Elizabeth II: 25c, 60c, 75c, $1, $2, $5.
$10, Queen Elizabeth II, diff.

Perf. 13¼

2012, Feb. 6	**Litho.**		**Unwmk.**
1226-1231	A194	Set of 6	10.00 10.00
1231a		Sheet of 6, #1226-1231, + 3 labels	10.00 10.00
		Souvenir Sheet	
1232	A194	$10 multi	10.00 10.00

No. 1188 Surcharged in Black and Silver

Method, Perf. and Watermark As Before

2012, Aug.
1233	A185	25c on 10c #1188	15.00 —

A195

Coronation of Queen Elizabeth II, 60th Anniv. — A196

Various photographs of Queen Elizabeth II: 25c, 60c, 75c, $5.

Perf. 13½x13¼

2013, Apr. 19	**Litho.**		**Wmk. 406**
1234-1237	A195	Set of 4	6.50 6.50
		Souvenir Sheet	
		Perf. 14¾x14¼	
1238	A196	$10 multi	10.00 10.00

Pallottine Sisters in Belize, Cent. A197

Designs: 25c, Landing of Sisters at Cayo. 60c, Novitiate Nazareth Chapel, Toledo. $10, Centenary emblem.

Wmk. 406

2013, Oct. 9	**Litho.**		**Perf. 13**
1239-1241	A197	Set of 3	11.00 11.00

Salvation Army in Belize, Cent. — A198

Designs: 25c, Girl putting money in donation bucket. $2, Belize Salvation Army headquarters, horiz.

Wmk. 406

2015, Apr. 8	**Litho.**		**Perf. 14**
1242-1243	A198	Set of 2	2.25 2.25

SEMI-POSTAL STAMPS

World Cup Soccer Championship — SP1

Designs: 20c+10c, 30c+15c, Scotland vs. New Zealand (diff.). 40c+20c, Kuwait vs. France. 60c+30c, Italy vs. Brazil. No. B5,

---

France vs. Northern Ireland. $1.50+75c, Austria vs. Chile. No. B7, Italy vs. Germany, vert. $2+$1, England vs. France, vert.

1982, Dec. 10	**Litho.**		**Perf. 14**
B1	SP1	20c +10c multi	3.00 1.50
B2	SP1	30c +15c multi	3.00 1.50
B3	SP1	40c +20c multi	3.25 1.90
B4	SP1	60c +30c multi	3.75 1.90
B5	SP1	$1 +50c multi	4.50 2.25
B6	SP1	$1.50 +75c multi	5.25 3.00
		Nos. B1-B6 (6)	22.75 11.65
		Souvenir Sheets	
		Perf. 14½	
B7	SP1	$1 +50c multi	13.50 7.25
B8	SP1	$2 +$1 multi	13.50 7.25

Nos. B7-B8 each contain one 50x70mm stamp.

POSTAGE DUE STAMPS

Numeral — D2

Each denomination has different border.

1976, July 1	**Litho.**		**Wmk. 373**
J6	D2	1c green & red	.25 1.50
J7	D2	2c violet & rose lil	.25 1.50
J8	D2	5c ocher & brt grn	.25 1.90
J9	D2	15c brown org & yel grn	.30 2.40
J10	D2	25c slate grn & org	.45 2.75
		Nos. J6-J10 (5)	1.50 10.05

CAYES OF BELIZE

Catalogue values for all unused stamps in this country are for Never Hinged items.

Spiny Lobster A1

2c, Blue crab. 5c, Red-footed booby. 10c, Brown pelican. 15c, White-tailed deer. 25c, Lighthouse, English Caye. 75c, Spanish galleon, Santa Yaga, c. 1750. $3, Map of Ambergris Caye, vert. $5, Jetty, windsurfers.

Perf. 14½x14, 14x14½

1984, May 30	**Litho.**		**Unwmk.**
1	A1	1c shown	.25 .25
2	A1	2c multicolored	.25 .25
3	A1	5c multicolored	.25 .25
4	A1	10c multicolored	.25 .25
5	A1	15c multicolored	.25 .25
6	A1	25c multicolored	.25 .25
7	A1	75c multicolored	.85 .85
8	A1	$3 multicolored	4.50 4.50
a.		Souvenir booklet	20.00
9	A1	$5 multicolored	8.00 8.00
		Nos. 1-9 (9)	14.85 14.85

No. 8a contains four panes. One has one $3 stamp, one has a block of four 25c stamps, two have blocks of four 75c stamps but different text. The stamps are larger than Nos. 6-8, have slightly different colors and are perf. 14½.
The $1 stamp was not issued. Eighteen sheets of 40 were sold for postage by accident.

Lloyd's List Issue
Common Design Type

25c, Queen Elizabeth 2. 75c, Lutine Bell. $1, Loss of the Fishburn. $2, Trafalgar Sword.

1984, June 6			**Perf. 14½x14**
10	CD335	25c multi	.25 .25
11	CD335	75c multi	.50 .50
12	CD335	$1 multi	.65 .65
13	CD335	$2 multi	1.25 1.25
		Nos. 10-13 (4)	2.65 2.65

1984 Summer Olympics, Los Angeles — A2

1984, Oct. 5			**Perf. 15**
14	A2	10c Yachting	.25 .25
15	A2	15c Windsurfing	.25 .25
16	A2	75c Swimming	.70 .70
17	A2	$2 Kayaking	1.60 1.60
		Nos. 14-17 (4)	2.80 2.80

No. 17 inscribed Canoeing.

First Cayes Stamps, 90th Anniv. A3

10c, 1895 cover. 15c, Sydney Cuthbert. 75c, Cuthbert's steam yacht. $2, British Honduras #133.

1984, Nov. 5			
18	A3	10c multicolored	.25 .25
19	A3	15c multicolored	.25 .25
20	A3	75c multicolored	.50 .50
21	A3	$2 multicolored	1.75 1.75
		Nos. 18-21 (4)	2.75 2.75

Audubon Birth Bicentenary — A4

Illustrations by Audubon: 25c, Blue-winged teal. 75c, Semipalmated sandpiper. $1, Yellow-crowned night heron, vert. $3, Common gallinule.

1985, May 20			**Perf. 14**
22	A4	25c multicolored	.25 .25
23	A4	75c multicolored	.70 .70
24	A4	$1 multicolored	.85 .85
25	A4	$3 multicolored	2.50 2.50
		Nos. 22-25 (4)	4.30 4.30

Shipwrecks — A5

a, Oxford, c. 1675. b, Santa Yaga, 1780. c, No. 27, Comet, 1822. d, Yeldham, 1800.

1985, June 5			**Perf. 15**
26	A5	$1 Strip of 4 + label	4.25 4.25
		Souvenir Sheet	
		Perf. 13½x14	
27	A5	$5 multicolored	4.75 4.75

No. 27 contains one 38x51mm stamp. No. 26 has continuous design.

BENIN

bə-'nin

French Colony

LOCATION — West Coast of Africa
GOVT. — French Possession
AREA — 8,627 sq. mi.
POP. — 493,000 (approx.)
CAPITAL — Benin

In 1895 the French possessions known as Benin were incorporated into the colony of Dahomey and postage stamps of Dahomey superseded those of Benin. Dahomey took the name Benin when it became a republic in 1975.

100 Centimes = 1 Franc

Catalogue values for unused stamps in this country are for Never Hinged items, beginning with Scott 342 in the regular postage section, Scott C240 in the airpost section, Scott J44 in the postage due section, and Scott Q8 in the parcel post section.

Watermark

Wmk. 385

Handstamped on Stamps of French Colonies

1892		**Unwmk.**	**Perf. 14x13½**	
		Black Overprint		
1	A9	1c blk, *bluish*	200.00	170.00
2	A9	2c brn, *buff*	180.00	150.00
3	A9	4c claret, *lav*	120.00	80.00
4	A9	5c grn, *grnsh*	40.00	32.50
5	A9	10c blk, *lavender*	100.00	80.00
6	A9	15c blue	40.00	32.50
7	A9	20c red, *grn*	250.00	220.00
8	A9	25c blk, *rose*	125.00	80.00
9	A9	30c brn, *yelsh*	225.00	200.00
10	A9	35c blk, *orange*	225.00	200.00
11	A9	40c red, *straw*	200.00	180.00
12	A9	75c car, *rose*	500.00	350.00
13	A9	1fr brnz grn, *straw*	475.00	400.00
		Red Overprint		
14	A9	15c blue	120.00	100.00
		Blue Overprint		
15	A9	5c grn, *grnsh*	2,600.	1,200.
15A	A9	15c blue	2,600.	1,200.

For inverted overprints and double overprints and pairs, one without overprint, see the *Scott Classic Specialized Catalogue.*
The overprints of Nos. 1-15A are of four types, three without accent on "E." They exist diagonal.
Counterfeits exist of Nos. 1-19.

Additional Surcharge in Red or Black

1892				
16	A9	01c on 5c grn, *grnsh*	360.00	275.00
a.		Double surcharge	1,000.	1,000.
17	A9	40c on 15c blue	225.00	120.00
a.		Double surcharge		3,800.
18	A9	75c on 15c blue	1,000.	600.00
19	A9	75c on 15c bl (Bk)	3,500.	2,800.

Counterfeits exist.

Navigation and Commerce — A3

1893		**Typo.**	**Perf. 14x13½**	
		Name of Colony in Blue or Carmine		
20	A3	1c blk, *bluish*	5.25	3.25
21	A3	2c brn, *buff*	6.75	4.75
22	A3	4c claret, *lav*	6.75	4.75
23	A3	5c grn, *grnsh*	8.00	5.50
24	A3	10c blk, *lavender*	10.00	6.50
a.		Name of country omitted		6,500.
25	A3	15c blue, quadrille paper	40.00	27.50
26	A3	20c red, *grn*	20.00	16.00
27	A3	25c blk, *rose*	52.50	32.50
28	A3	30c brn, *bis*	27.50	21.00
29	A3	40c red, *straw*	8.00	5.50
30	A3	50c car, *rose*	8.00	7.25
31	A3	75c vio, *org*	12.50	12.50
32	A3	1fr brnz grn, *straw*	72.50	72.50
		Nos. 20-32 (13)	277.75	219.50

Perf. 13½x14 stamps are counterfeits.

Navigation and Commerce — A4

1894			**Perf. 14x13½**	
33	A4	1c blk, *bluish*	2.50	3.25
34	A4	2c brn, *buff*	4.00	3.25
35	A4	4c claret, *lav*	4.00	3.25
36	A4	5c grn, *grnsh*	6.50	4.00
37	A4	10c blk, *lavender*	7.25	5.50
38	A4	15c bl, quadrille paper	16.00	4.75
39	A4	20c red, *grn*	12.00	9.50
40	A4	25c blk, *rose*	16.00	7.25
41	A4	30c brn, *bis*	12.00	10.50
42	A4	40c red, *straw*	24.00	16.00
43	A4	50c car, *rose*	32.50	16.00
44	A4	75c vio, *org*	32.50	14.50
45	A4	1fr brnz grn, *straw*	8.00	6.50
		Nos. 33-45 (13)	177.25	104.25

Perf. 13½x14 stamps are counterfeits.

PEOPLE'S REPUBLIC OF BENIN

LOCATION — West Coast of Africa
GOVT. — Republic.
AREA — 43,483 sq. mi.
POP. — 6,305,567 (1999 est.)
CAPITAL — Porto Novo (Cotonou is the seat of government)

The Republic of Dahomey proclaimed itself the People's Republic of Benin on Nov. 30, 1975. See Dahomey for stamps issued before then. The country became the Republic of Benin in 1990.

Catalogue values for unused stamps in this section are for Never Hinged items.

Allamanda Cathartica — A83

Flowers: 35fr, Ixora coccinea. 45fr, Hibiscus, 60fr, Phaemeria magnifica.

			Unwmk.	
1975, Dec. 8		**Photo.**	**Perf. 13**	
342	A83	10fr lilac & multi	.45	.35
343	A83	35fr gray & multi	1.10	.50
344	A83	45fr multi	1.25	.70
345	A83	60fr blue & multi	1.90	1.10
		Nos. 342-345 (4)	4.70	2.65

For surcharges see Nos. 612, 618, 690B, 719, 723, 788, 1364, 1413, 1416, 1418, 1463, Q18A.

Flag Bearers, Arms of Benin — A84

Design: 60fr, Pres. Kerekou, map with "PRPB," flag and arms of Benin. 100fr, Flag and arms of Benin.

1976, Apr. 30		**Litho.**	**Perf. 12**	
346	A84	50fr ocher & multi	.70	.35
347	A84	60fr ocher & multi	1.10	.35
348	A84	100fr multi	1.75	.70
		Nos. 346-348 (3)	3.55	1.40

Proclamation of the People's Republic of Benin. Nov. 30, 1975.
For surcharge, see No. Q16A.

A.G. Bell, Satellite and 1876 Telephone — A85

1976, July 9		**Litho.**	**Perf. 13**	
349	A85	200fr lilac, red & brn	2.75	1.60

Centenary of first telephone call by Alexander Graham Bell, Mar. 10, 1876.
For overprints, see Nos. Q16, Q16A and Q16B.

Dahomey Nos. 277-278 Surcharged

1976, July 19		**Photo.**	**Perf. 12½x13**	
350	A57	50fr on 1fr multi	.70	.35
351	A57	60fr on 2fr multi	.80	.45

For overprint & surcharge see Nos. 654A, 711.

African Jamboree, Nigeria 1976 — A86

1976, Aug. 16		**Litho.**	**Perf. 12½x13**	
352	A86	50fr Scouts Cooking	.70	.45
353	A86	70fr Three scouts	1.00	.55

Blood Bank, Cotonou — A87

Designs: 50fr, Accident and first aid station. 60fr, Blood donation.

1976, Sept. 24		**Litho.**	**Perf. 13**	
354	A87	5fr multicolored	.25	.25
355	A87	50fr multicolored	.55	.35
356	A87	60fr multicolored	1.00	.55
		Nos. 354-356 (3)	1.80	1.15

National Blood Donors Day.
For overprint, see No. Q12.

A88

1976, Oct. 4		**Litho.**	**Perf. 13x12½**	
357	A88	20fr Manioc	.45	.25
358	A88	50fr Corn	.80	.35
359	A88	60fr Cacao	1.10	.45
360	A88	150fr Cotton	2.50	1.10
		Nos. 357-360 (4)	4.85	2.15

Natl. agricultural production campaign.
For opverprint and surcharge see Nos. 565, Q10C.

Classroom A89

1976, Oct. 25				
361	A89	50fr multicolored	1.10	.55

Third anniversary of KPARO newspaper, used in local language studies.

Roan Antelope — A90

Penhari National Park: 30fr, Buffalo. 50fr, Hippopotamus, horiz. 70fr, Lion.

1976, Nov. 8   **Photo.**
362 A90 10fr multicolored   .35   .25
363 A90 30fr multicolored   .70   .65
364 A90 50fr multicolored   1.60   1.00
365 A90 70fr multicolored   1.75   1.20
   Nos. 362-365 (4)   4.40   3.10

Flags, Map of
Benin (Bricks),
Broken
Chains — A91

150fr, Corn, raised hands with weapons.

1976, Nov. 30   **Litho.**   **Perf. 12½**
366 A91 40fr multicolored   .55   .25
367 A91 150fr multicolored   1.75   .90

First anniversary of proclamation of the People's Republic of Benin.
   For surcharge, see No. Q14.

Table Tennis, Map of Africa (Games'
Emblem) — A92

Design: 50fr, Stadium, Cotonou.

1976, Dec. 26   **Litho.**   **Perf. 13**
368 A92 10fr multi   .55   .25
369 A92 50fr multi   .80   .25

West African University Games, Cotonou,
Dec. 26-31.
   For overprint, see No. Q25.

Europafrica Issue

Planes over Africa
and Europe — A93

1977, May 13   **Litho.**   **Perf. 13**
370 A93 200fr multi   2.75   2.50

   For surcharge see No. 590.

Snake
A94

1977, June 13 **Litho.** **Perf. 13x13½**
371 A94 2fr shown   .50   .25
372 A94 3fr Tortoise   .60   .25
373 A94 5fr Zebus   .75   .25
374 A94 10fr Cats   1.25   .25
   Nos. 371-374 (4)   3.10   1.00

   For surcharge, see No. 446A.

Patients at
Clinic
A95

1977, Aug. 2   **Litho.**   **Perf. 12½**
375 A95 100fr multi   1.75   .80

World Rheumatism Year.
   For overprint, see No. Q21.

Karate, Map of
Africa — A96

Designs: 100fr, Javelin, map of Africa, Benin
Flag, horiz. 150fr, Hurdles.

1977, Aug. 30   **Litho.**   **Perf. 12½**
376 A96 90fr multi   1.25   .70
377 A96 100fr multi   1.25   .90
378 A96 150fr multi   2.00   1.20
   a. Souvenir sheet of 3, #376-378   7.00   7.00
   Nos. 376-378 (3)   4.50   2.80

2nd West African Games, Lagos, Nigeria.
   For surcharges, see Nos. 925, Q20, Q33.

Chairman
Mao — A97

1977, Sept. 9   **Litho.**   **Perf. 13x12½**
379 A97 100fr multicolored   3.50   2.00
   Mao Tse-tung (1893-1976), Chinese communist leader.

Lister and
Vaporizer — A98

Designs: 150fr, Scalpels and flames, symbols of antisepsis, and Red Cross.

1977, Sept. 20   **Engr.**   **Perf. 13**
380 A98 150fr multi   2.00   1.00
381 A98 210fr multi   2.50   1.60
   Joseph Lister (1827-1912), surgeon,
founder of antiseptic surgery.
   For surcharges, see Nos. 560, 566, 919.

Guelege Mask, Ethnographic Museum,
Porto Novo — A99

Designs: 50fr, Jar, symbol of unity, emblem
of King Ghezo, Historical Museum, Abomey,
vert. 210fr, Abomey Museum.

1977, Oct. 17   **Perf. 13**
382 A99 50fr red & multi   .75   .50
383 A99 60fr blk, bl & bister   1.25   .60
384 A99 210fr multi   3.00   1.40
   Nos. 382-384 (3)   5.00   2.50

   For surcharge see Nos. 562, 920.

Atacora
Falls — A100

Tourist Publicity: 60fr, Pile houses, Ganvie,
horiz. 150fr, Round huts, Savalou.

1977, Oct. 24   **Litho.**   **Perf. 12½**
385 A100 50fr multi   .60   .35
386 A100 60fr multi   .90   .55
387 A100 150fr multi   2.00   1.20
   a. Souvenir sheet of 3, #385-387   5.50   5.50
   Nos. 385-387 (3)   3.50   2.10

Mother and
Child, Owl of
Wisdom — A101

150fr, Chopping down magical tree, horiz.

Perf. 12½x13, 13x12½
1977, Dec. 3   **Photo.**
388 A101 60fr multi   1.25   .50
389 A101 150fr multi   2.25   1.00
   Campaign against witchcraft.
   For surcharge see No. 576.

Battle Scene — A102

1978, Jan. 16   **Litho.**   **Perf. 12½**
390 A102 50fr multi   1.20   .45
   Victory of people of Benin over imperialist
forces.

Map, People and
Houses of
Benin — A103

1978, Feb. 1
391 A103 50fr multi   .80   .45
   General population and dwelling census.

Alexander Fleming, Microscope and
Penicillin — A104

1978, Mar. 12   **Litho.**   **Perf. 13**
392 A104 300fr multi   4.50   2.10
   Alexnader Fleming (1881-1955), 50th anniversary of discovery of penicillin.

Abdoulaye
Issa,
Weapons
and
Fighters
A105

1978, Apr. 1   **Perf. 12½x13**
393 A105 100fr red, blk & gold   1.25   .60
   First anniversary of death of Abdoulaye Issa
and National Day of Benin's Youth.

El Hadj Omar and Horseback
Rider — A106

Design: 90fr, L'Almamy Samory Toure
(1830-1900) and horseback riders.

1978, Apr. 10   **Perf. 13x12½**
394 A106 90fr red & multi   1.25   .50
395 A106 100fr multi   1.25   .60
   African heroes of resistance against
colonialism.

ITU Emblem,
Satellite,
Landscape — A107

1978, May 17   **Litho.**   **Perf. 13**
396 A107 100fr multi   1.50   .80
   10th World Telecommunications Day.

Soccer Player, Stadium, Argentina '78
Emblem — A108

Designs (Argentina '78 Emblem and): 300fr,
Soccer players and ball, vert. 500fr, Soccer
player, globe with ball on map.

1978, June 1   Litho.   Perf. 12½
397	A108	200fr multi	2.10	1.10
398	A108	300fr multi	2.75	1.60
399	A108	500fr multi	5.00	2.75
a.		Souvenir sheet of 3, perf. 12	13.50	12.50
		Nos. 397-399 (3)	9.85	5.45

11th World Cup Soccer Championship, Argentina, June 1-25. No. 399a contains 3 stamps similar to Nos. 397-399 in changed colors.

For surcharges and overprints see Nos. 591, 593, 595, 1477.

Nos. 397-399a Overprinted in Red Brown

a

b

c

1978, June 25   Litho.   Perf. 12½
400	A108 (a)	200fr multi	1.75	1.20
401	A108 (b)	300fr multi	2.60	2.00
402	A108 (c)	500fr multi	5.00	3.25
a.		Souvenir sheet of 3	13.50	12.50
		Nos. 400-402 (3)	9.35	6.45

Argentina's victory in 1978 Soccer Championship.

For surcharges and overprints, see Nos. 596, 591A, 1478.

Games' Flag over Africa, Basketball Players — A109

Designs: 60fr, Map of Africa, volleyball players. 80fr, Map of Benin, bicyclists.

1978, July 13   Perf. 13x12½
403	A109	50fr lt bl & multi	.55	.25
404	A109	60fr ultra & multi	.80	.45
405	A109	80fr multi	1.00	.55
a.		Souvenir sheet of 3	3.50	3.50
		Nos. 403-405 (3)	2.35	1.25

3rd African Games, Algiers, July 13-28. No. 405a contains 3 stamps in changed colors similar to Nos. 403-405.

Martin Luther King, Jr. — A110

1978, July 30   Perf. 12½
| 406 | A110 | 300fr multi | 3.50 | 1.75 |

Martin Luther King, Jr. (1929-1968), American civil rights leader.
For surcharge see No. 592.

Kanna Taxi, Oueme A111

60fr Leatherworker & goods. 70fr, Drummer & tom-toms. 100fr, Metalworker & calabashes.

1978, Aug. 26
407	A111	50fr multi	1.20	.30
408	A111	60fr multi	1.00	.30
409	A111	70fr multi	1.20	.50
410	A111	100fr multi	1.50	.65
		Nos. 407-410 (4)	4.90	1.75

Getting to know Benin through its provinces.

Map of Italy and Exhibition Poster — A112

1978, Aug. 26   Litho.   Perf. 13
| 411 | A112 | 200fr multi | 2.50 | 1.25 |

Riccione 1978 Philatelic Exhibition.
For overprint see No. 537.

Poultry Breeding — A113

1978 Oct. 5   Photo.   Perf. 12½x13
412	A113	10fr Turkeys	.35	.25
413	A113	20fr Ducks	.80	.30
414	A113	50fr Chicken	2.25	.70
415	A113	60fr Guinea fowl	2.50	.90
		Nos. 412-415 (4)	5.90	2.15

Royal Messenger, UPU Emblem — A114

UPU Emblem and: 60fr, Boatsman, ship & car. 90fr, Special messenger & plane.

1978, Oct. 16   Perf. 13x12½, 12½x13
416	A114	50fr multi	1.00	.35
417	A114	60fr multi, vert.	1.00	.45
418	A114	90fr multi, vert.	1.25	.60
		Nos. 416-418 (3)	3.25	1.40

Centenary of change of "General Postal Union" to "Universal Postal Union."
For surcharge see No. 1009.

Raoul Follereau A115

1978, Dec. 17   Litho.   Perf. 12½
| 419 | A115 | 200fr multi | 2.25 | 1.00 |

Raoul Follereau (1903-1977), apostle to the lepers and educator of the blind.

IYC Emblem A116

Intl. Year of the Child: 20fr, Globe as balloon carrying childern. 50fr, Children of various races surrounding globe.

1979, Feb. 20   Litho.   Perf. 12x13
420	A116	10fr multi	.25	.25
421	A116	20fr multi	.30	.25
422	A116	50fr multi	.50	.35
		Nos. 420-422 (3)	1.05	.85

Hydrangea — A117

Flowers: 25fr, Assangokan. 30fr, Geranium. 40fr, Water lilies, horiz.

Perf. 13x12½, 12½x13

1979, Feb. 28   Litho.
423	A117	20fr multi	.25	.25
424	A117	25fr multi	.55	.25
425	A117	30fr multi	.90	.35
426	A117	40fr mutli	1.00	.35
		Nos. 423-426 (4)	2.70	1.20

Emblem: Map of Africa and Members' Flags A118

60fr, Map of Benin & flags. 80fr, OCAM flag & map of Africa showing member states.

1979, Mar. 20   Litho.   Perf. 12x13
427	A118	50fr multi	.55	.35
428	A118	60fr multi	.90	.45
429	A118	80fr multi	1.10	.60
		Nos. 427-429 (3)	2.55	1.40

OCAM Summit Conf., Cotonou, Mar. 20-28.
For overprints see Nos. 434-436.

Tower, Waves, Satellite, ITU Emblem A119

1979, May 17   Litho.   Perf. 12½
| 430 | A119 | 50fr multi | .85 | .50 |

World Telecommunications Day.

Bank Building and Sculpture A120

1979, May 26   Litho.
| 431 | A120 | 50fr multi | 1.75 | .50 |

Opening of Headquarters of West African Savings Bank in Dakar.

Guelede Mask, Abomey Tapestry, Malaconotus Bird — A121

Design: 50fr, Jet, canoe, satellite, UPU and exhibition emblems.

1979, June 8   Litho.   Perf. 13
| 432 | A121 | 15fr multi | 2.00 | .80 |

Engr.
| 433 | A121 | 50fr multi | 1.60 | 1.10 |

Philexafrique II, Libreville, Gabon, June 8-17. Nos. 432, 433 each printed in sheets of 10 with 5 labels showing exhibition emblem.
For surcharges, see Nos. 1061A-1061C.

Nos. 427-429 Overprinted: "26 au 28 juin 1979" and Dots

1979, June 26
434	A118	50fr multi	.70	.35
435	A118	60fr multi	.90	.55
436	A118	80fr multi	1.10	.55
		Nos. 434-436 (3)	2.70	1.45

2nd OCAM Summit Conf., June 26-28.

Olympic Flame, and Emblems A122

Pre-Olympic Year: 50fr, High jump.

1979, July 1   Litho.
437 A122 10fr multi   .25   .25
438 A122 50fr multi   1.00   .45

Antelope A123

Animals: 10fr, Giraffes, map of Benin, vert 20fr, Chimpanzee. 50fr, Elephants, map of Benin, vert.

1979, Oct. 1   Litho.   Perf. 13
439 A123 5fr multi   .50   .25
440 A123 10fr multi   .65   .45
441 A123 20fr multi   .95   .55
442 A123 50fr multi   2.25   .65
       Nos. 439-442 (4)   4.35 1.90

Map of Africa, Emblem and Jet — A124

1979, Dec. 12   Litho.   Perf. 12½
443 A124 50fr multi   .55   .25
444 A124 60fr multi   .55   .25

ASECNA (Air Safety Board), 20th anniv.

Mail Services A125

50fr, Post Office and headquarters, vert.

1979, Dec. 19   Litho.   Perf. 13
445 A125 50fr multi   .55   .25
446 A125 60fr multi   .55   .25

Office of Posts and Telecommunications, 20th anniversary.

No. 371 Surcharged
Methods and Perfs As Before
1979
446A A94 50fr on 2fr #371   160.00 40.00

Lenin and Globe — A126

Design: 150fr, Lenin and his published books.

1980, Apr. 22   Litho.   Perf. 12½
447 A126 50fr shown   .70   .25
448 A126 150fr multicolored   1.75   .80

Lenin, 110th birth anniversary.

For surcharge, see No. Q8.

Monument to King Behanzin — A126a

Litho. & Embossed
1980, May 31   Perf. 12½
448A A126a 1000fr gold &
              multi   12.50   8.50

For overprint see No. Q10A.

Cotonou Club Emlem — A127

200fr, Rotary emblem on globe, horiz.

1980, Feb. 23   Litho.   Perf. 12½
449 A127 90fr shown   .90   .45
450 A127 200fr multicolored   1.80   .95

Rotary International, 75th anniversary. For surcharge see No. 915.

Galileo, Astrolabe — A128

100fr, Copernicus, solar system.

1980, Apr. 2
451 A128 70fr shown   .80   .45
452 A128 100fr multicolored   1.20   .55

Discovery of Pluto, 50th anniversary.

Abu Simbel, UNESCO Emblem — A129

1980, Apr. 15   Perf. 13
453 A129 50fr Column, vert.   .65   .25
454 A129 60fr Ramses II, vert.   .75   .45
455 A129 150fr shown   1.75   .90
       Nos. 453-455 (3)   3.15 1.60

UNESCO campaign to save Nubian monuments, 20th anniversary.

Monument, Martyrs' Square, Cotonou A130

Designs: Various monuments in Martyrs' Square. Cotonou. 60fr, 70fr, 100fr, horiz.

1980, May 2   Perf. 12½x13, 13x12½
456 A130 50fr multi   .50   .25
457 A130 60fr multi   .65   .25
458 A130 70fr multi   .75   .35
459 A130 100fr multi   1.25   .50
       Nos. 456-459 (4)   3.15 1.35

For overprint, see No. Q9. For surcharge see No. 539.

Musical Instruments — A131

5fr, Assan, vert. 10fr, Tinbo. 15fr, Tam-tam sato, vert. 20fr, Kora. 30fr, Gangan. 50fr, Sinhoun.

1980, May 20   Perf. 12½
460 A131 5fr multicolored   .35   .25
461 A131 10fr multicolored   .35   .25
462 A131 15fr multicolored   .50   .25
463 A131 20fr multicolored   .50   .25
464 A131 30fr multicolored   1.10   .60
465 A131 50fr multicolored   1.75   .90
       Nos. 460-465 (6)   4.55 2.50

First Non-stop Flight, Paris-New York — A132

100fr, Dieudonnée Costes, Maurice Bellonte.

1980, June 2   Litho.   Perf. 12½
466 A132 90fr shown   1.25   .60
467 A132 100fr multicolored   1.25   .60

For surcharges see Nos. 564, 926.

Lunokhod I on the Moon — A133

1980, June 15   Engr.   Perf. 13
468 A133 90fr multi   1.00   .60

Lunokhod I Soviet unmanned moon mission, 10th anniv. See No. C290.

Olympic Flame and Mischa, Moscow '80 Emblem — A134

60fr, Equestrian, vert. 70fr, Judo. 200fr, Flag, sports, globe, vert. 300fr, Weight lifting, vert.

1980, July 16   Litho.   Perf. 12½
469 A134 50fr shown   .55   .25
470 A134 60fr multicolored   .55   .35
471 A134 70fr multicolored   .80   .45
472 A134 200fr multicolored   1.80   .90
473 A134 300fr multicolored   2.90 1.50
       Nos. 469-473 (5)   6.60 3.45

22nd Summer Olympic Games, Moscow, July 19-Aug. 3.
For overprint, see No. Q10. For surcharges see Nos. 559, 561.

Telephone and Rising Sun A135

World Telecommunications Day: 50fr, Farmer on telephone, vert.

1980, May 17   Litho.   Perf. 12½
474 A135 50fr multi   .60   .30
475 A135 60fr multi   .60   .30

Cotonou West African Community Village A136

Designs: View of Cotonou.

1980, July 26   Perf. 13x13½
476 A136 50fr multi   .70   .30
477 A136 60fr multi   .70   .35
478 A136 70fr multi   1.10   .45
       Nos. 476-478 (3)   2.50 1.45

For surcharge see No. 540.

Agbadja Dancers — A137

Designs: Dancers and musicians.

1980, Aug. 1   Perf. 12½
479 A137 30fr multi   .55   .25
480 A137 50fr multi   .90   .45
481 A137 60fr multi   .90   .55
       Nos. 479-481 (3)   2.35 1.25

Fisherman — A138

Designs: 5fr, Throwing net. 15fr, Canoe and shore fishing. 20fr, Basket traps. 50fr, Hauling net. 60fr, River fishing. All horiz.

1980, Sept. 1
482	A138	5fr multi	.35 .25
483	A138	10fr multi	.50 .25
484	A138	15fr multi	.55 .25
485	A138	20fr multi	.75 .25
486	A138	50fr multi	1.25 .45
487	A138	60fr multi	1.50 .45

Nos. 482-487 (6)   4.90 1.90

For surcharge see No. 535.

Philippines under Magnifier — A139

World Tourism Conference, Manila, Sept. 27: 60fr, Emblem on flag, hand pointing to Manila on globe, horiz.

Perf. 13x13½, 13x½x13
1980, Sept. 27
488	A139	50fr multi	.55 .25
489	A139	60fr multi	.90 .35

For surcharge see No. 557.

A140

40fr, Othreis materna. 50fr, Othreis fullonia. 200fr, Oryctes sp.

1980, Oct. 1   **Perf. 12½**
490	A140	40fr multicolored	1.25 .40
491	A140	50fr multicolored	1.60 .60
492	A140	200fr multicolored	5.00 1.50

Nos. 490-492 (3)   7.85 2.50

A141

1980, Oct. 24   **Photo.**   **Perf. 13½**
493	A141	75fr multi	.80 .30

African Postal Union, 5th Anniv.

A142

1980, Nov. 4   **Perf. 12½x13**
494	A142	30fr shown	.30 .25
495	A142	50fr Freed prisoner	.70 .25
496	A142	60fr Man holding torch	.75 .30

Nos. 494-496 (3)   1.75 .80

Declaration of human rights, 30th anniv. For surcharge, see No. Q15.

A143

Self-portrait, by Vincent van Gogh, 1888.

1980, Dec. 1   **Litho.**   **Perf. 13**
497	A143	100fr shown	3.50 .80
498	A143	300fr Facteur Roulin	8.50 2.25

Vincent van Gogh (1853-1890), artist. For surcharge see No. 579.

Offenbach and Scene from Orpheus in the Underworld — A144

1980, Dec. 15   **Engr.**
499	A144	50fr shown	1.40 .80
500	A144	60fr Paris Life	2.00 1.00

Jacques Offenbach (1819-1880), composer. For surcharge, see No. Q13.

Kepler and Satellites — A145

50fr, Kepler, diagram, vert.

1980, Dec. 20
501	A145	50fr multicolored	.80 .35
502	A145	60fr shown	1.00 .50

Johannes Kepler (1571-1630), astronomer.

Intl. Year of the Disabled — A146

1981, Apr. 10   **Litho.**   **Perf. 12½**
503	A146	115fr multi	1.30 .60

For surcharge see No. 582.

20th Anniv. of Manned Space Flight — A147

1981, May 30   **Perf. 13**
504	A147	500fr multi	5.00 3.00

For surcharges see Nos. 580, 790.

13th World Telecommunications Day — A148

1981, May 30   **Litho.**   **Perf. 12½**
505	A148	115fr multi	1.25 .50

For surcharge see No. 583.

Amaryllis A149

20fr, Eichhornia crassipes, vert. 80fr, Parkia biglobosa, vert.

1981, June 20   **Perf. 12½**
506	A149	10fr shown	.30 .25
507	A149	20fr multicolored	.60 .35
508	A149	80fr multicolored	2.10 .50

Nos. 506-508 (3)   3.00 1.10

For surcharge see No. 542.

Benin Sheraton Hotel A150

1981, July
509	A150	100fr multi	1.25 .50

For surcharge see No. 541.

Guinea Pig — A151

1981, July 31   **Perf. 13x13½**
510	A151	5fr shown	.55 .35
511	A151	60fr Cat	1.40 .60
512	A151	80fr Dogs	2.00 1.10

Nos. 510-512 (3)   3.95 2.05

For surcharges see Nos. 536, 543, 563.

World UPU Day — A152

1981, Oct. 9   **Engr.**   **Perf. 13**
513	A152	100fr red brn & blk	1.00 .50

25th Intl. Letter Writing Week, Oct. 6-12 — A153

1981, Oct. 15
514	A153	100fr dk bl & pur	1.00 .50

For surcharge see No. 558.

West African Economic Community A154

1981, Nov. 20   **Litho.**   **Perf. 12½**
515	A154	60fr multi	.80 .30

West African Rice Development Assoc. 10th Anniv. — A155

1981, Dec. 10   **Perf. 13x13½**
516	A155	60fr multi	.80 .30

TB Bacillus Centenary A156

1982, Mar. 1   **Litho.**   **Perf. 13**
517	A156	115fr multi	1.90 .75

For surcharge see No. 584.

West African Economic Community, 5th Summit Conference A157

1982, May 27   **Perf. 12½**
518	A157	60fr multi	.70 .30

1982 World Cup — A158

1982, June 1   **Perf. 13**
519	A158	90fr Players	1.00 .45
520	A158	300fr Flags on leg	3.25 1.25

For overprints and surcharges see Nos. 523-524, 594, 789.

France No. B349 Magnified, Map of
France — A159

1982, June 11
521 A159 90fr multi   1.10   .50
For surcharge see No. 916.

PHILEXFRANCE '82 Stamp Exhibition,
Paris, June 11-21.

George Washington — A160

200fr, Washington, flag, map.

1982, Mar. 10   Litho.   Perf. 14
522 A160 200fr multicolored   2.50 1.00
For surcharge see No. 577.

Nos. 519-520 Overprinted

1982, Aug. 16   Perf. 12½
523 A158 90fr multi   1.25   .55
524 A158 300fr multi   4.00 1.50

Italy's victory in 1982 World Cup.
For surcharge see No. 811.

Bluethroat
A161

5fr, Daoelo gigas, vert. 15fr, Swallow, vert.
20fr, Kingfisher, weaver bird, vert. 30fr, Great
sedge warbler. 60fr, Common warbler. 80fr,
Owl, vert. 100fr, Cockatoo, vert.

1982, Sept. 1   Perf. 14x14½, 14½x14
525 A161 5fr multicolored   1.10   .45
526 A161 10fr shown   1.60   .45
527 A161 15fr multicolored   1.60   .45
528 A161 20fr multicolored   2.50   .60
529 A161 30fr multicolored   3.75   .80
530 A161 60fr multicolored   5.25 1.10
531 A161 80fr multicolored   9.50 2.50
532 A161 100fr multicolored   12.00 3.25
  Nos. 525-532 (8)   37.30 9.60

ITU Plenipotentiaries Conference,
Nairobi, Sept. — A162

1982, Sept. 26   Perf. 13
533 A162 200fr Map   2.00 1.00
For surcharge see No. 585.

13th World UPU Day — A163

1982, Oct. 9   Engr.   Perf. 13
534 A163 100fr Monument   1.10   .45

**Nos. 482, 510, 411 Overprinted in
Red or Blue**

No. 535

No. 536 —
"UAPT
1982" 3mm
tall

No.
537

Perf. 13, 12½, 13x13½

1982, Nov.   Litho.
535 A138 60fr on 5fr multi   10.00 5.00
536 A151 60fr on 5fr multi   4.00 3.00
  a.   "UAPT 1982" 2mm tall   25.00
537 A112 200fr multi (BI)   2.40 1.00
  Nos. 535-537 (3)   16.40 9.00

Visit of
French
Pres.
Francois
Mitterand
A164

1983, Jan. 15   Litho.   Perf. 12½x13
538 A164 90fr multi   1.60   .75
For surcharge see No. 917.

**Nos. 458, 476, 508-509, 512
Surcharged**

No.
539

No. 540

No. 541

No. 542

No. 543

Perf. 13x12½, 13x13½, 12½

1983   Litho.
539 A130 60fr on 70fr multi   2.10   .70
540 A136 60fr on 50fr multi   2.10   .70
541 A150 60fr on 100fr multi   2.10   .95
542 A149 75fr on 80fr multi   2.10 1.40
543 A151 75fr on 80fr multi   2.10 1.40
  Nos. 539-543 (5)   10.50 5.15

Seme Oil
Rig — A165

1983, Apr. 28   Litho.   Perf. 13x12½
544 A165 125fr multi   2.00   .70

World Communications Year — A166

1983, May 17   Litho.   Perf. 13
545 A166 185fr multi   2.00   .75
For surcharge see No. 898.

Riccione '83, Stamp Show — A167

1983, Aug. 27   Litho.   Perf. 13
546 A167 500fr multi   5.00 2.00
For surcharge see No. 922.

Benin Red
Cross, 20th
Anniv.
A168

1983, Sept. 5   Photo.   Perf. 13
547 A168 105fr multi   1.40   .60
For surcharge see No. 581.

Handicrafts
A169

Designs: 75fr, Handcarved lion chairs and
table. 90fr, Natural tree table and stools. 200fr,
Monkeys holding jar.

1983, Sept. 18   Litho.   Perf. 13
548 A169 75fr multi   .95   .35
549 A169 90fr multi   1.25   .45
550 A169 200fr multi   2.00   .85
  Nos. 548-550 (3)   4.20 1.65
For surcharge see No. 578.

14th UPU Day — A170

1983, Oct. 9   Engr.   Perf. 13
551 A170 125fr multi   1.40   .70
For surcharge see No. 575.

Religious
Movements
A171

1983, Oct. 31   Litho.   Perf. 14x15
552 A171 75fr Zangbeto   1.10   .55
553 A171 75fr Egoun   1.10   .55

Plaited Hair
Styles — A172

1983, Nov. 14
554 A172 30fr Rockcoco   .30   .25
555 A172 75fr Serpent   .80   .50
556 A172 90fr Songas   1.40   .60
  Nos. 554-556 (3)   2.50 1.35

Stamps of 1976-81 Surcharged

No. 557

No.
558

15ᶠ

No. 559

15ᵖ

No. 560

25ᶠ

No. 561

25ᶠ

No. 562

75ᶠ

No. 563

75ᶠ

No. 564

75ᶠ

No. 565

75ᶠ

No. 566

1983, Nov.
557	A139	5fr on 50fr #488	6.50	1.25
558	A153	10fr on 100fr #514	6.50	1.25
559	A134	15fr on 200fr #472	6.50	1.25
560	A98	15fr on 210fr #381	6.50	1.25
561	A134	25fr on 70fr #471	6.50	1.25

562	A99	25fr on 210fr #384	6.50	1.25
563	A151	75fr on 5fr #510	6.50	1.25
564	A132	75fr on 100fr #467	6.50	1.25
565	A88	75fr on 150fr #360	6.50	1.25
566	A98	75fr on 150fr #380	6.50	1.25
		Nos. 557-566 (10)	65.00	12.50

Alfred Nobel (1833-96)
A173

1983, Dec. 19   Litho.   Perf. 15x14
567	A173	300fr multi	3.00	1.40

For surcharge see No. 923.

Council of Unity — A174

1984, May 29   Litho.   Perf. 12
568	A174	75fr multi	.80	.30
569	A174	90fr multi	1.10	.35

For surcharge see No. 918.

1984 UPU Congress A175

1984, June 18   Litho.   Perf. 13
570	A175	90fr multi	1.00	.50

Abomey Calavi Earth Station A176

1984, June 29   Litho.   Perf. 12½x13
571	A176	75fr Satellite dish	.80	.45

Traditional Costumes A177

1984, July 2   Litho.   Perf. 13½x13
572	A177	5fr Koumboro	.30	.25
573	A177	10fr Taka	.40	.25
574	A177	20fr Toko	.50	.30
		Nos. 572-574 (3)	1.20	.80

Nos. 389, 498, 503-505, 517, 522, 533, 547, 550 and 551 Surcharged

No. 575

No. 576

No. 577

No. 578

No. 579

No. 580

No. 581

No. 582

No. 583

No. 584

No. 585

1984, Sept.
575	A170	5fr on 125fr #551	7.25	1.40
576	A101	5fr on 150fr #389	7.25	1.40
577	A160	10fr on 200fr #522	7.25	1.40
578	A169	10fr on 200fr #550	7.25	1.40
579	A143	15fr on 300fr #498	7.25	1.40
580	A147	40fr on 500fr #504	7.25	1.40
581	A168	75fr on 105fr #547	7.25	1.40
582	A146	75fr on 115fr #503	7.25	1.40
583	A148	75fr on 115fr #505	7.25	1.40
584	A156	75fr on 115fr #517	7.25	1.40
585	A162	75fr on 200fr #533	7.25	1.40
		Nos. 575-585 (11)	79.75	15.40

World Food Day — A178

100fr, Malnourished child.

1984, Oct. 16   Litho.   Perf. 12½
586	A178	100fr multicolored	1.00	.50

Dinosaurs A179

75fr, Anatosaurus. 90fr, Brontosaurus.

1984, Dec. 14   Litho.   Perf. 13½
587	A179	75fr multicolored	6.00	1.00
588	A179	90fr multicolored	6.00	1.00

Cultural & Technical Cooperation Agency, 15th Anniv. — A180

300fr, Emblem, globe, hands, book.

1985, Mar 20   Litho.   Perf. 13
589	A180	300fr multicolored	3.00	1.25

Stamps of 1977-82 Surcharged

No. 590

No. 591

No. 591A

No. 592

No. 593

No. 594

No. 595

No. 596

1985, Mar.

590	A93	75fr on 200fr #370	13.00	2.50
591	A108	75fr on 200fr #397	13.00	2.50
591A	A108(a)	75fr on 200fr #400	50.00	3.00
592	A110	75fr on 300fr #406	13.00	2.50
593	A108	75fr on 300fr #398	13.00	2.50
594	A158	90fr on 300fr #520	13.00	2.50
595	A108	90fr on 500fr #399	13.00	2.50
596	A108	90fr on 500fr #402	13.00	2.50

Nos. 590-591,592-596 (7)   91.00   17.50

End of World War II, 40th Anniv. — A180a

1985, May   Litho.   Perf. 12
596A   A180a   100fr multicolored   70.00   17.50

Traditional Dances A181

75fr, Teke, Borgou Tribe. 100fr, Tipen'ti, L'Atacora Tribe.

1985, June 1   Litho.   Perf. 15x14½
597	A181	75fr multicolored	1.10	.50
598	A181	100fr multicolored	1.40	.65

Intl. Youth Year — A182

1985, July 16   Perf. 13½
599   A182   150fr multi   1.50   .75

1986 World Cup Soccer Championships, Mexico — A183

1985, July 22   Perf. 13x12½
600   A183   200fr multi   2.00   1.00

Beginning with Scott 601, Benin again surcharged stamps of Dahomey with a variety of surcharges. While the listings that follow contain hundreds of surcharged stamps, the Scott editors still need to examine many more other stamps, in order to list all of those that are currently known to exist.

The size and location of the surcharge varies from stamp to stamp. The type face used in the surcharge may also vary from issue to issue.

a

b

c

d

e

f

g

h

i

j

Dahomey No. 336 Surcharged with Black Bars and New Value
1985, Aug.   Perf. 12½
601   A78(a)   15fr on 40fr multi   6.00   1.10

ASECNA (Air Safety Board), 25th Anniv. — A184

1985, Sept. 16   Perf. 13
602   A184   150fr multi   2.00   .75

UN 40th Anniv. A185

1985, Oct. 24   Perf. 12½
603   A185   250fr multi   2.50   1.25

Benin UN membership, 25th anniv.

ITALIA'85, Rome A186

1985, Oct. 25   Perf. 13½
604   A186   200fr multi   2.00   1.25

PHILEXAFRICA '85, Lome — A187

No. 605, Labor emblem & #569. No. 606, Magnified stamp, #C252 & Gabon #366.

1985, Nov. 16   Perf. 13
605 A187 250fr multi   5.00 3.00
606 A187 250fr multi   4.00 2.75
a. Pair, Nos. 605-606 + label   11.00 11.00

For surcharges, see Nos. 653B-653C.

Audubon Birth Bicent. — A188

1985, Oct. 17   Litho.   Perf. 14x15
607 A188 150fr Skua gull   3.50 1.50
608 A188 300fr Oyster catcher   8.50 2.50

Mushrooms and Toadstools A189

35fr, Boletus edible. 40fr, Amanite phalloide. 100fr, Brown chanterelle.

1985, Oct. 17
609 A189 35fr multicolored   1.50 .60
610 A189 40fr multicolored   2.00 1.00
611 A189 100fr multicolored   5.00 2.00
Nos. 609-611 (3)   8.50 3.60

Dahomey #282, 292, Benin #343 Surcharged

1986, Mar.   Photo.
612 A83(b) 75fr on 35fr #343   5.00 1.10
613 A57(c) 90fr on 70fr #282   5.00 1.10
614 A60(b) 90fr on 140fr #292   5.00 1.10
Nos. 612-614 (3)   15.00 3.30

African Parliamentary Union, 10th Anniv. — A190

1986, May 8   Litho.   Perf. 13x12½
615 A190 100fr multi   1.00 .50

9th Conference, Cotonou, May 8-10.

Halley's Comet — A191

1986, May 30   Perf. 12½x12
616 A191 205fr multi   3.25 1.50
For surcharge see No. 809.

Dahomey No. 283, Benin No. 344 Surcharged

Engraved, Photogravure
1986, June   Perf. 13
617 A58(b) 100fr on 40fr #283   4.00 1.25
618 A83(b) 150fr on 45fr #344   4.00 1.25

1986 World Cup Soccer Championships, Mexico — A192

1986, June 29   Litho.
619 A192 500fr multi   5.00 2.50
For surcharge see No. 792.

Fight against Desert Encroachment — A193

1986, July 16   Perf. 13½
620 A193 150fr multi   1.75 .95

King Behanzin — A194

Amazon — A194a

1986-88   Engr.   Perf. 13
621 A194 40fr black   .30 .25
622 A194a 100fr brt blue   .80 .50
623 A194 125fr maroon   1.10 .75
624 A194a 150fr violet   1.60 .80
625 A194 190fr dark ultra   1.75 1.10
627 A194 220fr dark grn   2.00 1.25
Nos. 621-627 (6)   7.55 4.65

Issued: 100fr, 150fr, 8/1; others, 10/1/88. See No. 636. For surcharge see No. 787.

Flowers — A195

100fr, Haemanthus. 205fr, Hemerocalle, horiz.

Perf. 13x12½, 12½x13
1986, Sept. 1   Litho.
631 A195 100fr multi   1.10 .70
632 A195 205fr multi   3.00 1.10
For surcharge see No. 1061F.

Butterflies A196

No. 633, Day peacock, little tortoiseshell, morio. No. 634, Aurora, machaon and fair lady.

1986, Sept. 15
633 A196 150fr shown   4.00 2.00
634 A196 150fr multi   4.00 2.00

Dahomey Nos. 290, 307 Overprinted Perfs. & Printing Methods as Before
1985, Oct. 15
634A A67(b) 50fr on #307   55.00 25.00
634B A60(d) 150fr on 100fr #290   55.00 25.00

Statue of Liberty, Cent. — A197

1986, Oct. 28   Litho.   Perf. 12½
635 A197 250fr multi   3.00 1.25

King Behanzin — A198

1986, Oct. 30   Perf. 13½
636 A198 440fr multi   5.50 2.50

Behanzin, leader of resistance movement against French occupation (1886-1894). For surcharge see No. 921.

Brazilian Cultural Week, Cotonou — A200

1987, Jan. 17   Perf. 12½
638 A200 150fr multi   2.00 .75

Rotary Intl. District 910 Conference, Cotonou, Apr. 23-25 — A201

300fr, Center for the Blind, Cotonou.

1987, Apr. 23   Litho.   Perf. 13½
639 A201 300fr multi   4.00 1.50

Automobile Cent. — A202

Modern car and: 150fr, Steam tricycle, by De Dion-Bouton and Trepardoux, 1887. 300fr, Gas-driven Victoria, by Daimler, 1886.

1987, July 1   Perf. 12½
640 A202 150fr multi   1.75 .75
641 A202 300fr multi   3.75 1.50
For surcharge see No. 679B.

Snake Temple
Baptism — A203

1987, July 20   *Perf. 13½*
642　A203　100fr multi   1.75 .75

Shellfish
A204

1987, July 24   *Perf. 12½*
643　A204　100fr Crayfish   1.50 .80
644　A204　150fr Crab   2.25 1.00

G. Hansen, R.
Follereau
A205

1987, Sept. 4   *Perf. 13*
645　A205　200fr Cure Leprosy   2.75 1.25

Beginning of
Benin Revolution,
15th Anniv. —
A205a

1987, Oct. 28 Litho.   *Perf. 12x12½*
645A　A205a　100fr multi   115.00 3.00

October
Revolution, 70th
Anniv. — A205b

1987, Nov. 7 Litho.   *Perf. 12x12½*
645B　A205b　150fr multi   115.00 3.00

Locust
Control
A206

1987, Dec. 7 Litho.   *Perf. 12½x13*
646　A206　100fr multi   1.50 .75

Christmas
1987
A207

1987, Dec. 21   *Perf. 13*
647　A207　150fr multi   1.60 1.00

**Dahomey No. 268 overprinted and
No. 284 Surcharged**

1987   **Engr.**   *Perf. 13*
647A　A58(b)　15fr on 100fr
　　　　#284   50.00 25.00
647B　A53(b)　40fr on #268   65.00 25.00
See Nos. C362, C369.

Intl. Red Cross and Red Crescent
Organizations, 125th Anniv. — A208

1988, May 25 Litho.   *Perf. 13½*
648　A208　200fr multi   2.00 1.00

A209

1988, July 11   *Perf. 12½*
649　A209　200fr multi   2.50 1.25
Martin Luther King, Jr. (1929-68), American
civil rights leader.

A210

1988, May 25 Litho.   *Perf. 13½*
650　A210　125fr multi   1.50 .65
Organization of African Unity, 25th anniv.

WHO, 40th Anniv. — A211

1988, Sept. 1 Litho.   *Perf. 13x12½*
651　A211　175fr multi   1.60 .90
Alma Ata Declaration, 10th anniv.; Health
Care for All on Earth by the Year 2000.
For surcharge see No. 786.

Ganvie Lake Village — A212

190fr, Boatman, part of boat, village.

1988, Sept. 4   *Perf. 13½*
652　A212　125fr shown   1.25 .65
653　A212　190fr multicolored   2.00 1.00

Benin Nos. 605, 606 Surcharged

1988   **Method and Perf. as Before**
653B　A187　190fr on 250fr
　　　　#605   35.00 17.50
653C　A187　190F on 250fr
　　　　#606   35.00 17.50

A213

1988, Aug. 14   *Perf. 12½*
654　A213　125fr multi   1.75 1.75
1st Benin Scout Jamboree, Aug. 12-19.

**Benin No. 351, Dahomey Nos. 296,
328 Surcharged**

1988
Printing Method & Perfs as Before
654A　A57(d)　10fr on 60fr on
　　　　　　　2fr #351   50.00 25.00
654B　A62(d)　10fr on 65fr
　　　　　　　#296   50.00 25.00
654E　A74(d)　150fr on 200fr
　　　　　　　#328   50.00 25.00

A214

Ritual Offering to Hebiesso, God of Thunder
and Lightning.

1988, Dec. 30   **Litho.**   *Perf. 13*
655　A214　125fr multicolored   1.40 .60

**Dahomey Nos. 161, 247, 302, 309,
333, 339, 341 Surcharged**
1988   **Photo.**   *Perf. 12½x13*
655A　A19(d)　5fr on 3fr #161   50.00 25.00
655B　A68(d)　20fr on 100fr
　　　　　　　#309   50.00 25.00
655C　A82(d)　30fr on 150fr
　　　　　　　#341   50.00 25.00
655D　A76(d)　25fr on 100fr
　　　　　　　#333   50.00 25.00
655E　A45(b)　50fr on 45fr #247   60.00 35.00
655F　A81(d)　55fr on 200fr
　　　　　　　#339   80.00 40.00
655G　A65(b)　65fr on 85fr #302   80.00 40.00

These are part of a set of 10. Another set of
19 surcharges also is known to exist. The editors need to see the rest of these stamps
before listings can be created.

No. 380
Overprinted

1989   **Engr.**   *Perf. 13*
655H　A98　150fr multi   240.00 —

Rural Development Council, 30th
Anniv. — A214a

1989, May 29 Litho.   *Perf. 15x14*
655K　A214a　75fr multicolored   95.00

World Wildlife Fund — A216

Roseate terns, *Sterna dougalli*: 10fr, Three
terns. 15fr, Feeding on fish. 50fr, Perched.
125fr, In flight.

1989, Jan. 30   **Litho.**   *Perf. 13*
657　A216　10fr multi   1.75 .50
658　A216　15fr multi   2.00 .50
659　A216　50fr multi   3.75 1.75
660　A216　125fr multi   6.50 3.25
Nos. 657-660 (4)   14.00 6.00

Eiffel Tower
Cent. — A217

1989, Apr. 24   Litho.   Perf. 13x12½
661 A217 190fr multi   2.75 1.25

PHILEXFRANCE '89, French
Revolution Bicent. — A218

Design: Bastille, emblems, Declaration of
Human Rights and Citizenship, France No.
B252-B253.

1989, July 7   Perf. 13
662 A218 190fr multicolored   2.75 1.50

Electric
Corp. of
Benin, 20th
Anniv.
A219

1989, Oct.   Litho.   Perf. 12½x13
663 A219 125fr multicolored   1.50   .70

Fish
A220

1989, Sept. 22   Perf. 13½
664 A220 125fr Lote   1.75   .70
665 A220 190fr Pike, salmon   2.75 1.10

Death of King
Glele,
Cent. — A221

1989, Dec. 16   Litho.   Perf. 13½
666 A221 190fr multicolored   2.00 1.00

Christmas
A222

1989, Dec. 25   Perf. 13
667 A222 200fr Holy family   2.00 1.00

Benin Posts & Telecommunications,
Cent. — A223

1990, Jan. 1   Perf. 13½
668 A223 125fr multicolored   1.40   .70

Fruits and
Flora
A224

60fr, Oranges. 190fr, Kaufmann Tulips, vert.
250fr, Cashews, vert.

1990, Jan. 23   Litho.   Perf. 11½
669 A224 60fr multi   .65   .45
670 A224 190fr multi   2.50 1.25
671 A224 250fr multi   2.75 1.40
     Nos. 669-671 (3)   5.90 3.10
        Dated 1989.
No. 669 exists with "Populaire" obliterated
by black marker.

Moon
Landing,
20th Anniv.
A225

1990, Jan. 23
672 A225 190fr multicolored   2.00   .90
        Dated 1989.

World Cup Soccer Championships,
Italy — A226

190fr, Character trademark, vert.

1990, June 8   Litho.   Perf. 12½
673 A226 125fr shown   1.25   .60
674 A226 190fr multi   2.00   .90
        For overprint see No. 676.

Post, Telephone
& Telegraph
Administration in
Benin,
Cent. — A227

1990, July 1   Perf. 13
675 A227 150fr multicolored   1.75   .70

No. 673
Overprinted

1990   Litho.   Perf. 12½
676 A226 125fr multicolored   1.40   .70

Charles de Gaulle (1890-
1970) — A228

1990, Nov. 22   Litho.   Perf. 13
677 A228 190fr multicolored   2.25 1.50
        See No. 689.

Galileo
Probe and
Jupiter
A229

1990, Dec. 1
678 A229 100fr multicolored   1.10   .65
        For overprint see No. 681.

Christmas
A230

1990, Dec. 25   Litho.   Perf. 12½x13
679 A230 200fr multicolored   2.25 1.25

Benin No. 641 Surcharged

1990
Perf. & Printing Method as Before
679B A202(e) 190fr on 300fr
        #641   65.00 24.00

A230a

1990   Litho.   Perf. 11½x12
679C A230a 125fr multi   125.00 —
National Conference of Active Forces.

A231

1991, Sept. 3   Litho.   Perf. 13½
680 A231 125fr multicolored   1.50   .70
Independence, 31st anniv.

No. 678
Ovptd. in
Red

1991   Perf. 13
681 A229 100fr multicolored   1.10   .75

French Open Tennis Championships,
Cent. — A232

1991   Perf. 13½
682 A232 125fr multicolored   1.60 1.00

African Tourism Year — A233

1991
683　A233　190fr multicolored　　　2.25　1.50

Christmas
A234

1991, Dec. 2　　Litho.　　Perf. 13½
684　A234　125fr multicolored　　　1.40　.70

Dancer of
Guelede — A235

1991, Dec. 2
685　A235　190fr multicolored　　　2.25　1.00

Wolfgang
Amadeus Mozart,
Death
Bicent. — A236

1991, Dec. 2
686　A236　1000fr multicolored　　12.00　7.75
For surcharge see No. 793.

Discovery
of America,
500th
Anniv.
A237

1000fr, Columbus coming ashore, horiz.

1992, Apr. 24　　Litho.　　Perf. 13
687　A237　500fr blk, blue &
　　　　　brn　　　　　　　　　　5.25　3.50
688　A237　1000fr multicolored　　10.50　7.00
　a.　Souvenir sheet, #687-688　17.50　16.00

De Gaulle Type of 1990
1992　　Litho.　　Perf. 13
689　A228　300fr like #677　　　　3.25　2.00

Intl. Conference
on Nutrition,
Rome — A238

1992, Dec. 5　　Litho.　　Perf. 13
690　A238　190fr multicolored　　　2.00　1.40
For surcharge see 928.

**Dahomey Nos. 160, 266, 303, 311,
327, 334, 338, C161 Surcharged or
Overprinted (No. 690A), Benin No.
342 Overprinted (No. 690B)**
1992
Perfs. & Printing Methods as Before

690A	A66(e)	5fr on	#303	67.50	32.50
690B	A83(e)	10fr on	#342	55.00	32.50
690E	A80(f)	35fr on	#338	50.00	25.00
690F	A19(e)	125fr on 2fr	#160	55.00	32.50
690G	AP54(f)	125fr on 65fr	#C161	80.00	40.00
690H	A77(f)	125fr on 65fr	#334 (G)	80.00	40.00
690I	CD137(e)	125fr on 100fr	#311	125.00	72.50
690J	A52(f)	190fr on 45fr	#266	60.00	35.00
690K	A74(f)	125fr on 100fr	#327	125.00	65.00

Visit of Pope John
Paul II, Feb. 3-
5 — A239

1993, Feb. 3　　Litho.　　Perf. 13x12½
691　A239　190fr multicolored　　　2.25　1.25

Ouidah 92, First
Festival of
Voodoo
Culture — A240

1993, Feb. 8　　　　Perf. 13½
692　A240　125fr multicolored　　　1.40　.80

Well of
Possotome,
Eurystome
A241

1993, May 25　　Litho.　　Perf. 12½
693　A241　125fr multicolored　　　3.25　1.25

OAU,
30th
Anniv.
A242

1993, June 7　　Litho.　　Perf. 13½
694　A242　125fr multicolored　　　1.25　.75

John F. Kennedy — A243

No. 696, Martin Luther King, vert.

1993, June 24　　　　Perf. 13
695　A243　190fr shown　　　　　2.25　1.25
696　A243　190fr multi　　　　　2.25　1.25

Assassinations of Kennedy, 30th anniv. (No.
695), and King, 25th anniv. (No. 696).

**Dahomey Nos. 161, 173, 175, 277,
312, 335 Overprinted or Surcharged**
1993
Perfs. & Printing Methods as Before

697	A21(e)	5fr on #175	60.00	32.50
698	A69(f)	5fr on #312	80.00	40.00
700	A19(f)	10fr on 3fr #161	50.00	24.00
701	A77(f)	10fr on 100fr #335	45.00	24.00
703	A57(f)	20fr on 1fr #277	40.00	25.00
704	A21(f)	25fr on 1fr #173	140.00	70.00

**Benin Nos. 343, 345, 350, Dahomey
Nos. 169, 226-227, 249, 256, 273,
276, 295, 283, 286, 319, 328, 333
Surcharged or Overprinted (Nos.
711, 713)**

No. 727

1994-95

707	A38(f)	5fr on 1fr #226	60.00	32.50
708	A47(e)	10fr on 90fr #256	40.00	25.00
709	A71(f)	25fr on #319	40.00	25.00
710	A59(e)	40fr on #286	60.00	35.00
711	A57(e)	50fr on 1fr #350	50.00	25.00
712	A58(e)	80fr on 40fr #283	40.00	20.00
713	A76(g)	100fr on #333	50.00	25.00
715	A38(f)	135fr on 3fr #227	75.00	—
718	A62(e)	135fr on 30fr #295	75.00	—
719	A83(g)	135fr on 35fr #343	75.00	35.00
720	A56(h)	135fr on 40fr #276	35.00	—
722	A20(e)	135fr on 60fr #169	50.00	25.00
723	A83(g)	135fr on 60fr #345	75.00	40.00
724	A55(e)	135fr on 70fr #273	65.00	35.00
725	A45(e)	200fr on 30fr #249	60.00	30.00
727	A74(f)	200fr on Dahomey #328	250.00	125.00

UNESCO
Conference on
The Slave
Route — A244

1994　　Litho.　　Perf. 13x13½
728　A244　135fr multicolored　　55.00　17.50
729　A244　200fr multicolored　　85.00　25.00
730　A244　300fr multicolored　　55.00　17.50

Natitingou Scout
Encampment
A245

1994　　　　Perf. 12¾x12½
731　A245　135fr multi　　　　　65.00　1.25

Intl. Year of
the Family
A246

1994　　Litho.　　Perf. 12½
732　A246　200fr multicolored　　65.00　1.25

1994 World Cup
Soccer
Championships,
US — A247

1994　　Litho.　　Perf. 13x13½
733　A247　300fr multicolored　　160.00　6.25

1996 Summer Olympics,
Atlanta — A248

45fr, Water polo. 50fr, Javelin. 75fr, Weight
lifting. 100fr, Tennis. 135fr, Baseball. 200fr,
Synchronized swimming.
300fr, Diving.

Perf. 12½x13, 13x12½
1995, Apr. 30　　　　　　Litho.
734　A248　45fr multicolored　　　　.30　.30
735　A248　50fr multicolored　　　　.35　.35
736　A248　75fr multicolored　　　　.55　.55
737　A248　100fr multicolored　　　.75　.75
738　A248　135fr multicolored　　　.95　.95
739　A248　200fr multicolored　　1.40　1.40
　Nos. 734-739 (6)　　　　　　4.30　4.30

Souvenir Sheet
740　A248　300fr multicolored　　3.00　3.00

Nos. 735-740 are vert. No. 740 contains one
32x40mm stamp.
For surcharges, see Nos. 1241, 1257.

Dogs
A249

40fr, German shepherd. 50fr, Beagle. 75fr,
Great dane. 100fr, Boxer. 135fr, Pointer. 200fr,
Fox terrier.
300fr, Schnauzer.

1995, Aug. 23 Litho. Perf. 12½

741	A249	40fr multi	.30	.30
742	A249	50fr multi	.40	.40
743	A249	75fr multi	.55	.55
744	A249	100fr multi	.75	.75
745	A249	135fr multi	.95	.95
746	A249	200fr multi	1.40	1.40

Nos. 741-746 (6) 4.35 4.35

Souvenir Sheet

747	A249	300fr multi	3.75	3.75

For surcharges, see Nos. 1222, 1258.

Ships
A250

Designs: 40fr, Steam driven paddle boat, 1788. 50fr, Paddle steamer Charlotte, 1802. 75fr, Transatlantic steamship, Citta de Catania. 100fr, Hovercraft Mountbatten SR-N4. 135fr, QE II. 200fr, Japanese experimental atomic energy ship, Mutsu-NEF.
300fr, Paddle-steamer Savannah, 1819.

1995, May 20

748	A250	40fr multicolored	.30	.30
749	A250	50fr multicolored	.40	.40
750	A250	75fr multicolored	.55	.55
751	A250	100fr multicolored	.75	.75
752	A250	135fr multicolored	.95	.95
753	A250	200fr multicolored	1.40	1.40

Nos. 748-753 (6) 4.35 4.35

Souvenir Sheet

754	A250	300fr multicolored	3.00	3.00

No. 754 contains one 40x32mm stamp.
For surcharges, see Nos. 1223, 1259.

Primates
A251

50fr, Pan troglodytes. 75fr, Mandrillus sphinx. 100fr, Colobus. 135fr, Macaca sylvanus. 200fr, Comopithecus hamadryas.
300fr, Papio cynocephalus.

1995, June 30

755	A251	50fr multicolored	.30	.30
756	A251	75fr multicolored	.35	.35
757	A251	100fr multicolored	.60	.60
758	A251	135fr multicolored	.80	.80
759	A251	200fr multicolored	1.10	1.10

Nos. 755-759 (5) 3.15 3.15

Souvenir Sheet

760	A251	300fr multicolored	3.50	3.50

No. 760 contains one 32x40mm stamp.
For surcharges, see Nos. 1242, 1260.

Domestic
Cats
A252

1995, July 30 Litho. Perf. 12½x13

761	A252	40fr Shorthair tabby	.30	.30
762	A252	50fr Ruddy red	.40	.40
763	A252	75fr White longhair	.60	.60
764	A252	100fr Seal color point	.80	.80
765	A252	135fr Tabby point	1.00	1.00
766	A252	200fr Black shorthair	1.50	1.50

Nos. 761-766 (6) 4.60 4.60

Souvenir Sheet

767	A252	300fr Cat in basket	3.75	3.75

No. 767 contains one 40x32mm stamp.
For surcharges, see Nos. 1224, 1261.

Flowers — A253

Designs: 40fr, Dracunculus vulgaris. 50fr, Narcissus watieri. 75fr, Amaryllis belladonna. 100fr, Nymphaea capensis. 135fr, Chrysanthemum carinatum. 200fr, Iris tingitana.

1995, Oct. 15 Litho. Perf. 12½

768	A253	40fr multicolored	.25	.25
769	A253	50fr multicolored	.35	.35
770	A253	75fr multicolored	.50	.50
771	A253	100fr multicolored	.65	.65
772	A253	135fr multicolored	.75	.75
773	A253	200fr multicolored	1.10	1.10

Nos. 768-773 (6) 3.60 3.60

For surcharges, see Nos. 1225, 1262.

Wild
Animals
A254

50fr, Panthera leo. 75fr, Syncerus caffer. 100fr, Pan troglodytes. 135fr, Aepyceros melampus. 200fr, Geosciurus inaurus.
300fr, Loxodonta, vert.

Perf. 13x12½, 12½x13

1995, Sept. 20

774	A254	50fr multicolored	.35	.35
775	A254	75fr multicolored	.45	.45
776	A254	100fr multicolored	.65	.65
777	A254	135fr multicolored	.95	.95
778	A254	200fr multicolored	1.25	1.25

Nos. 774-778 (5) 3.65 3.65

Souvenir Sheet

779	A254	300fr multicolored	3.50	3.50

Nos. 774-777 are vert. No. 779 contains one 32x40mm stamp.
For surcharge, see No. 1263.

Birds Feeding
Their
Chicks — A255

Designs: 40fr, Coccothraustes coccothraustes. 50fr, Streptopelia chinensis. 75fr, Falco peregrinus. 100fr, Dendroica fusca. 135fr, Larus ridibundus. 200fr, Pelecanus onocrotalus.

1995, Aug. 28 Perf. 12½x13

780	A255	40fr multicolored	.25	.25
781	A255	50fr multicolored	.35	.35
782	A255	75fr multicolored	.50	.50
783	A255	100fr multicolored	.70	.70
784	A255	135fr multicolored	.75	.75
785	A255	200fr multicolored	1.20	1.20

Nos. 780-785 (6) 3.75 3.75

For surcharges, see Nos. 1226, 1243.

Benin Nos. 344, 504, 519, 619, 627, 651, 686 and Dahomey No. 291 Surcharged

1994-95

Printing Method and Perfs as Before

786	A211	25fr on 175fr		
		#651	50.00	25.00
787	A194	50fr on 175fr		
		#627	27.50	—
788	A83(h)	150fr on 45fr #344	40.00	
789	A158	150fr on 90fr #519	60.00	30.00
790	A147	150fr on 500fr		
		#504	60.00	15.00

791	A60(f)	200fr on 135fr		
		#291	60.00	30.00
792	A192	200fr on 500fr		
		#619	75.00	35.00
793	A236	250fr on 1000fr		
		#686	60.00	30.00

Natl.
Arms — A256

Denomination 3½mm Wide

1995, Dec. 26 Litho. Perf. 12½

793A	A256	135fr yellow & multi	1.00	1.00
b.		Denomination 3mm wide	6.00	2.50
793B	A256	150fr yel grn & multi	1.10	1.10
794	A256	200fr multicolored	1.25	1.10
a.		Denomination 3mm wide	6.00	2.50

See Nos. 948-951. For surcharge see No. 1021A.
Nos. 793Ab and 794a issued 8/24/95.

Orchids — A257

Designs: 40fr, Angraecum sesquipedale. 50fr, Polystachya virginea. 75fr, Disa uniflora. 100fr, Ansellia africana. 135fr, Angraecum eichlerianum. 200fr, Jumellea confusa.

1995, Nov. 10 Litho. Perf. 12½

795	A257	40fr multicolored	.25	.25
796	A257	50fr multicolored	.35	.35
797	A257	75fr multicolored	.50	.50
798	A257	100fr multicolored	.70	.70
799	A257	135fr multicolored	.75	.75
800	A257	200fr multicolored	1.20	1.20

Nos. 795-800 (6) 3.75 3.75

For surcharges, see Nos. 1227, 1244.

Butterflies
A258

Designs: 40fr, Graphium policenes. 50fr, Vanessa atalanta. 75fr, Polymmatus icarus. 100fr, Danaus chrysipus. 135fr, Cynthia cardui. 200fr, Argus celbulina.
1000fr, Charaxes jasius.

1996, Mar. 10

801	A258	40fr multicolored	.40	.40
802	A258	50fr multicolored	.40	.40
803	A258	75fr multicolored	.80	.80
804	A258	100fr multicolored	.90	.90
805	A258	135fr multicolored	1.25	1.25
806	A258	200fr multicolored	2.00	2.00

Nos. 801-806 (6) 5.75 5.75

Souvenir Sheet

807	A258	1000fr multicolored	7.00	7.00

For surcharge, see No. 1228.

CHINA '96, Beijing — A259

Designs: a, 40fr, Dancer in traditional Chinese costume. b, 50fr, Exhibition emblem. c, 75fr, Water lily. d, 100fr, Temple of Heaven.

1996, Apr. 8

808	A259	Block of 4, #a.-d.	4.50	4.50

Benin Nos. 523, 616 and Dahomey No. 306 Surcharged or Overprinted (No. 810)

1996?

Perfs. & Printing Methods as Before

809	A191	5fr on 205fr		
		#616	60.00	35.00
810	A67(g)	35fr on #306	60.00	35.00
811	A158	150fr on 90fr		
		#523	140.00	65.00

15th Lions Intl. District
Convention — A260

1996 Litho. Perf. 12½

811A	A260	100fr multicolored	.40	.40
811B	A260	135fr green & multi	1.25	1.25
812	A260	150fr yellow & multi	1.25	1.25
813	A260	200fr red & multi	1.60	1.60

Nos. 811A-813 (4) 4.50 4.50

For surcharge see No. 1021B.
Issued: No. 811A, 12/27; others, 5/2.

La
Francophonie
Conference
A261

1995, Dec. 2 Litho. Perf. 12½

814	A261	150fr pink & multi	1.00	.80
815	A261	200fr blue & multi	1.50	1.00

Cats — A262

1995, Nov. 2 Litho. Perf. 13

816	A262	40fr Lynx lynx	.35	.35
817	A262	50fr Felis concolor	.45	.45
818	A262	75fr Acinonyx jubatus	.55	.55
819	A262	100fr Panthera pardus	.75	.75
820	A262	135fr Panthera tigris	1.00	1.00
821	A262	200fr Panthera leo	1.50	1.50

Nos. 816-821 (6) 4.60 4.60

For surcharges, see Nos. 1229, 1245, 1264.

1998 World Cup
Soccer
Championships,
France — A263

Various soccer players.

1996, Feb. 10 Litho. Perf. 13

822	A263	40fr multicolored	.35	.35
823	A263	50fr multicolored	.45	.45
824	A263	75fr multicolored	.60	.60
825	A263	100fr multicolored	.90	.90

826	A263	135fr multicolored	1.00	1.00
827	A263	200fr multicolored	1.60	1.60
		Nos. 822-827 (6)	4.90	4.90

Souvenir Sheet
Perf. 12½

828	A263	1000fr multicolored	5.00	5.00

No. 828 contains one 32x40mm stamp.
For surcharges, see Nos. 1246, 1265.

1996 Summer Olympic Games, Atlanta — A264

1996, Jan. 28　　Litho.　　Perf. 13

829	A264	40fr Diving	.30	.30
830	A264	50fr Tennis	.30	.30
831	A264	75fr Running	.70	.70
832	A264	100fr Gymnastics	.80	.80
833	A264	135fr Weight lifting	1.10	1.10
834	A264	200fr Shooting	1.40	1.40
		Nos. 829-834 (6)	4.60	4.60

Souvenir Sheet

835	A264	1000fr Water polo	5.50	5.50

No. 835 contains one 32x40mm stamp.
For surcharges, see Nos. 1230, 1247, 1266.

Christmas Paintings — A265

Entire paintings or details: 40fr, Holy Family Under the Oak Tree, by Raphael. 50fr, The Holy Family, by Raphael. 75fr, St. John the Baptist as a Child, by Murillo. 100fr, The Virgin of Balances, by Leonardo da Vinci. 135fr, The Virgin and the Infant, by Gerard David. 200fr, Adoration of the Magi, by Juan Bautista Mayno.
1000fr, Rest on the Flight into Egypt, by Murillo.

1996, May 5　　Litho.　　Perf. 13

836	A265	40fr multicolored	.30	.30
837	A265	50fr multicolored	.30	.30
838	A265	75fr multicolored	.75	.75
839	A265	100fr multicolored	.95	.95
840	A265	135fr multicolored	1.10	1.10
841	A265	200fr multicolored	1.75	1.75
		Nos. 836-841 (6)	5.15	5.15

Souvenir Sheet

842	A265	1000fr multicolored	5.00	5.00

No. 842 contains one 40x32mm stamp.
For surcharges, see Nos. 1231, 1248, 1267.

Wild Cats — A266

Designs: 40fr, Leptailurus serval. 50fr, Profelis temmincki. 75fr, Leopardus pardalis. 100fr, Lynx rufus. 135fr, Prionailurus bengalensis. 200fr, Felis euptilura.
1000fr, Neofelis nebulosa.

1996, June 10　　Litho.　　Perf. 12x12½

843	A266	40fr multicolored	.25	.25
844	A266	50fr multicolored	.25	.25
845	A266	75fr multicolored	.45	.45
846	A266	100fr multicolored	.55	.55

847	A266	135fr multicolored	.80	.80
848	A266	200fr multicolored	1.25	1.25
		Nos. 843-848 (6)	3.55	3.55

Souvenir Sheet
Perf. 12½

849	A266	1000fr multicolored	5.00	5.00

No. 849 contains one 32x40mm stamp.
For surcharges, see Nos. 1232, 1268.

Sailing Ships A267

40fr, Thermopylae. 50fr, 5-masted bark. 75fr, Nightingale. 100fr, Opium clipper. 135fr, The Torrens. 200fr, English clipper. 1000fr, Opium clipper, diff.

1996, May 27　　　　Perf. 13x12½

850	A267	40fr multi	.25	.25
851	A267	50fr multi	.30	.30
852	A267	75fr multi	.55	.55
853	A267	100fr multi	.65	.65
854	A267	135fr multi	1.00	1.00
855	A267	200fr multi	1.40	1.40
		Nos. 850-855 (6)	4.15	4.15

Souvenir Sheet
Perf. 13

856	A267	1000fr multi	5.00	5.00

No. 856 contains one 32x40mm stamp.
For surcharges, see Nos. 1209, 1249, 1269.

Olymphilex '96 — A268

1996, July 2　　　　Perf. 13

857	A268	40fr Running	.30	.30
858	A268	50fr Kayaking	.30	.30
859	A268	75fr Gymnastics	.65	.65
860	A268	100fr Soccer	.75	.75
861	A268	135fr Tennis	1.00	1.00
862	A268	200fr Baseball	1.50	1.50
		Nos. 857-862 (6)	4.50	4.50

Souvenir Sheet

863	A268	1000fr Basketball	5.00	5.00

No. 863 contains one 32x40mm stamp.
For surcharges, see Nos. 1233, 1250, 1270.

Modern Olympic Games, Cent. — A269

a, 40fr, Gold medal, woman hurdler. b, 50fr, Runner, Olympic flame. c, 75fr, Pierre de Coubertin, map of US. d, 100fr, Map of US, "1996."

1996, June 20

864	A269	Block of 4, #a.-d.	4.00	4.00

No. 864 is a continuous design.

For surcharge, see No. 1236.

Horses A270

Various horses.

1996, Aug. 10　　Litho.　　Perf. 13

865	A270	40fr multi, vert.	.30	.30
866	A270	50fr multi, vert.	.30	.30
867	A270	75fr multi, vert.	.60	.60
868	A270	100fr multi, vert.	.70	.70
869	A270	135fr multi, vert.	1.00	1.00
870	A270	200fr multicolored	1.50	1.50
		Nos. 865-870 (6)	4.40	4.40

For surcharges, see Nos. 1251, 1271.

Flowering Cacti — A271

40fr, Parodia subterranea. 50fr, Astrophytum senile. 75fr, Echinocereus melanocentrus. 100fr, Turbinicarpus kinkerianus. 135fr, Astrophytum capricorne. 200fr, Nelloydia grandiflora.

1996, July 25

871	A271	40fr multicolored	.30	.30
872	A271	50fr multicolored	.30	.30
873	A271	75fr multicolored	.70	.70
874	A271	100fr multicolored	.80	.80
875	A271	135fr multicolored	1.00	1.00
876	A271	200fr multicolored	1.50	1.50
		Nos. 871-876 (6)	4.60	4.60

For surcharges, see Nos. 1210, 1234, 1272.

Mushrooms A272

Designs: 40fr, Stropharia cubensis. 50fr, Psilocybe zapotecorum. 75fr, Psilocybe mexicana. 100fr, Conocybe siligineoides. 135fr, Psilocybe caerulescens mazatecorum. 200fr, Psilocybe caerulescens nigripes.
1000fr, Psilocybe aztecorum, horiz.

1996, Sept. 30

877	A272	40fr multicolored	.30	.30
878	A272	50fr multicolored	.30	.30
879	A272	75fr multicolored	.70	.70
880	A272	100fr multicolored	.80	.80
881	A272	135fr multicolored	1.00	1.00
882	A272	200fr multicolored	1.50	1.50
		Nos. 877-882 (6)	4.60	4.60

Souvenir Sheet
Perf. 12½

883	A272	1000fr multicolored	5.00	5.00

No. 883 contains one 40x32mm stamp.
For surcharge on No. 877, see No. 1235.

Prehistoric Animals — A273

40fr, Longisquama, vert. 50fr, Dimophodon, vert. 75fr, Dunkleosteus. 100fr, Eryops. 135fr, Peloneustes. 200fr, Deinonychus.

1996, Aug. 30　　　　Perf. 12½

884	A273	40fr multicolored	.30	.30
885	A273	50fr multicolored	.30	.30
886	A273	75fr multicolored	.60	.60
887	A273	100fr multicolored	.70	.70
888	A273	135fr multicolored	1.00	1.00
889	A273	200fr multicolored	1.60	1.60
		Nos. 884-889 (6)	4.50	4.50

For surcharges on No. 886, see Nos. 1236 and 1252.

Birds — A274

Designs: 40fr, Campephilus principalis. 50fr, Picathartes oreas. 75fr, Strigops habroptilus. 100fr, Amazona vittata. 135fr, Nipponia nippon. 200fr, Gymnogyps californianus.
1000fr, Paradisea rudolphi.

1996, Sept. 10

890	A274	40fr multicolored	.25	.25
891	A274	50fr multicolored	.25	.25
892	A274	75fr multicolored	.50	.50
893	A274	100fr multicolored	.60	.60
894	A274	135fr multicolored	.85	.85
895	A274	200fr multicolored	1.40	1.40
		Nos. 890-895 (6)	3.85	3.85

Souvenir Sheet

896	A274	1000fr multicolored	4.50	4.50

No. 896 contains one 32x40mm stamp.
For surcharges, see Nos. 1253, 1315.

Dahomey No. 235 Overprinted, Benin No. 545 Surcharged

199?
Perfs. & Printing Methods as Before

897	A40(e)	30fr on #235	37.50	20.00
898	A166	75fr on 185fr #545	60.00	30.00

Dahomey Nos. 208, 239-241, 257-258, 261, 269, 274, 283, 320, 326, 334-336, 337 Surcharged or Overprinted (No. 899)

1996?
Perfs. & Printing Methods as Before

899	A77(f)	100fr on #335	60.00	30.00
900	A79(e)	125fr on 150fr #337	35.00	20.00
901	A77(h)	135fr on 65fr #334	120.00	60.00
902	A42(e)	150fr on 30fr #239	32.50	20.00
903	A43(h)	150fr on 30fr #241	35.00	
904	A48(h)	150fr on 30fr #257	32.50	
905	A50(h)	150fr on 30fr #261	32.50	
906	CD132(h)	150fr on 40fr #269	28.00	
907	A58(h)	150fr on 40fr #283	32.50	
908	A71(e)	150fr on 40fr #320	72.50	
909	A74(e)	150fr on 40fr #326	240.00	
910	A78(e)	150fr on 40fr #336	32.50	
911	A32(e)	150fr on 50fr #208	72.50	
912	A42(e)	150fr on 70fr #240	32.50	
913	A48(h)	150fr on 70fr #258	28.00	
914	A55(h)	150fr on 70fr #274		

Benin Nos. 381, 384, 449, 521, 538, 546, 567, 569, 636, Surcharged

1996?
Perfs. & Printing Methods as Before

915	A127	10fr on 90fr #449	50.00	
916	A159	10fr on 90fr #521	50.00	25.00
917	A164	10fr on 90fr #538	50.00	25.00
918	A174	10fr on 90fr #569	40.00	25.00
919	A98	40fr on 210fr #381	65.00	—
920	A99	40fr on 210fr #384	70.00	—

921 A198 75fr on 440fr #636 60.00 30.00
922 A167 100fr on 500fr #546 60.00 30.00
923 A173 125fr on 500fr #567 45.00 25.00

Obliterator on No. 922 has either one or two bars. Pairs of No. 922 exist with each stamp having a different obliterator.

Nos. 376, 466, 690 Surcharged

No. 926

1995	**Method and Perf. as Before**		
925	A96	10fr on 90fr #376	45.00 25.00
926	A132	10fr on 90fr #466	45.00 —
928	A238	Lsciina on 190fr #690	25.00 15.00

Ungulates — A275

Designs: 40fr, Aepyceros melampus. 50fr, Kobus ellipsiprymnus. 75fr, Caffer caffer. 100fr, Connochaetes taurinus. 135fr, Okapia johnstoni. 200fr, Tragelaphus strepsiceros.

1996, Oct. 15	**Litho.**	**Perf. 12½x12**	
930	A275	40fr multicolored	.30 .30
931	A275	50fr multicolored	.30 .30
932	A275	75fr multicolored	.60 .60
933	A275	100fr multicolored	.75 .75
934	A275	135fr multicolored	.90 .90
935	A275	200fr multicolored	1.40 1.40
		Nos. 930-935 (6)	4.25 4.25

For surcharges, see Nos. 1237, 1254.

Marine Mammals — A276

Designs: 40fr, Delphinapterus leucas. 50fr, Tursiops truncatus. 75fr, Belaenoptera musculus. 100fr, Eubalaena australis. 135fr, Gramphidelphis griseus. 200fr, Orcinus orca.

1996, Nov. 5		**Perf. 13**	
936	A276	40fr multicolored	.30 .30
937	A276	50fr multicolored	.30 .30
938	A276	75fr multicolored	.60 .60
939	A276	100fr multicolored	.70 .70
940	A276	135fr multicolored	1.00 1.00
941	A276	200fr multicolored	1.60 1.60
		Nos. 936-941 (6)	4.50 4.50

For surcharges, see Nos. 1238, 1255, 1273.

Fish A277

50fr, Pomacanthidae, vert. 75fr, Acanthuridae. 100fr, Carangidae. 135fr, Chaetodontidae. 200fr, Chaetodontidae, diff. 1000fr, Scaridae.

1996, Dec. 4		**Litho.**	**Perf. 12½**
942	A277	50fr multicolored	.35 .35
943	A277	75fr multicolored	.50 .50
944	A277	100fr multicolored	.70 .70
945	A277	135fr multicolored	.85 .85
946	A277	200fr multicolored	1.40 1.40
		Nos. 942-946 (5)	3.80 3.80

Souvenir Sheet

947 A277 1000fr multicolored 5.00 5.00

No. 947 contains one 40x32mm stamp. For surcharges, see Nos. 1256, 1274.

Coat of Arms Type of 1995

1996-97			**Perf. 12½**
948	A256	100fr multicolored	.50 .50
949	A256	135fr lt yellow & multi	.70 .35
950	A256	150fr lt bl grn & multi	1.10 .70
951	A256	200fr lt orange & multi	1.20 .70
		Nos. 948-951 (4)	3.50 2.25

Nos. 949-951 have "Republique du Benin" at bottom.
Issued: 100fr, 12/27/96; 135fr, 150fr, 200fr, 5/15/97.
For surcharge see No. 1021A.

Military Uniforms — A278

Regiments of European infantry: 135fr, Grenadier, Glassenapp. 150fr, Officer, Von Groben. 200fr, Musketeer, Comte Dohna. 270fr, Bombardier. 300fr, Gendarme. 400fr, Dragoon, Mollendorf. 1000fr, Soldiers, flag, horses, vert.

1997, Feb. 20			
952	A278	135fr multicolored	.60 .40
953	A278	150fr multicolored	.90 .40
954	A278	200fr multicolored	1.00 .80
955	A278	270fr multicolored	1.20 .90
956	A278	300fr multicolored	1.50 1.25
957	A278	400fr multicolored	1.75 1.75
		Nos. 952-957 (6)	6.95 5.50

Souvenir Sheet
Perf. 13

958 A278 1000fr multicolored 5.00 4.50

No. 958 contains one 32x40mm stamp. For surcharge on No. 955, see No. 1275.

Trains A279

135fr, Steam turbine, Reid Maclead, 1920. 150fr, Experimental high speed, 1935. 200fr, Renard Argent, 1935. 270fr, Class No. 21-C-6, 1941. 300fr, Diesel, 1960. 400fr, Diesel, 1960, diff. 1000fr, Coronation Scot, 1937.

1997, Mar. 26		**Litho.**	**Perf. 13**
959	A279	135fr multicolored	.60 .40
960	A279	150fr multicolored	.90 .50
961	A279	200fr multicolored	1.00 .70
962	A279	270fr multicolored	1.20 1.00
963	A279	300fr multicolored	1.50 1.00
964	A279	400fr multicolored	1.75 1.40
		Nos. 959-964 (6)	6.95 5.00

Souvenir Sheet

965 A279 1000fr multicolored 5.00 4.50

No. 965 contains one 40x32mm stamp. For surcharge on No. 962, see No. 1276.

1998 World Cup Soccer Championship, France — A280

Various soccer plays.

1997, Apr. 9			**Perf. 12½x13**
966	A280	135fr multicolored	.60 .40
967	A280	150fr multicolored	.70 .40
968	A280	200fr multicolored	1.00 .80
969	A280	270fr multicolored	1.20 .90

970	A280	300fr multi, horiz.	1.50 1.25
971	A280	400fr multi, horiz.	2.00 1.90
		Nos. 966-971 (6)	7.00 5.65

Souvenir Sheet

972 A280 1000fr multicolored 5.00 4.50

No. 972 contains one 40x32mm stamp. For surcharge on No. 969, see No. 1277.

Orchids — A281

Phalaenopsis: 135fr, Penetrate. 150fr, Golden sands. 200fr, Sun spots. 270fr, Fuscata. 300fr, Christi floyd. 400fr, Cayanne. 1000fr, Janet kuhn.

1997, June 9		**Litho.**	**Perf. 12½x13**
973	A281	135fr multicolored	.75 .45
974	A281	150fr multicolored	.90 .60
975	A281	200fr multicolored	1.10 .75
976	A281	270fr multicolored	1.25 .90
977	A281	300fr multicolored	1.50 1.20
978	A281	400fr multicolored	2.25 1.50
		Nos. 973-978 (6)	7.75 5.40

Souvenir Sheet
Perf. 12½

979 A281 1000fr multicolored 5.00 4.50

No. 979 contains one 32x40mm stamp. For surcharge on No. 976, see No. 1278.

Dogs — A282

Designs: 135fr, Irish setter. 150fr, Saluki. 200fr, Doberman pinscher. 270fr, Siberian husky. 300fr, Basenji. 400fr, Boxer. 1000fr, Rhodesian ridgeback.

1997, May 30			**Perf. 13**
980	A282	135fr multicolored	.70 .40
981	A282	150fr multicolored	.80 .60
982	A282	200fr multicolored	1.10 .70
983	A282	270fr multicolored	1.25 .90
984	A282	300fr multicolored	1.50 1.10
985	A282	400fr multicolored	2.10 1.25
		Nos. 980-985 (6)	7.45 4.95

Souvenir Sheet
Perf. 12½

986 A282 1000fr multicolored 5.00 4.50

No. 986 contains one 32x40mm stamp. For surcharge on No. 983, see No. 1279.

Antique Automobiles — A283

135fr, 1905 Buick. 150fr, 1903 Ford. 200fr, 1913 Stanley. 270fr, 1911 Stoddar-Dayton. 300fr, 1934 Cadillac. 400fr, 1931 Cadillac. 1000fr, 1928 Ford.

1997, July 5		**Litho.**	**Perf. 13x12½**
987	A283	135fr multi	.70 .50
988	A283	150fr multi	.80 .60
989	A283	200fr multi	1.00 .80
990	A283	270fr multi	1.20 .90
991	A283	300fr multi	1.40 1.20
992	A283	400fr multi	2.00 1.50
		Nos. 987-992 (6)	7.10 5.50

Souvenir Sheet
Perf. 13

993 A283 1000fr multi 5.00 4.50

No. 993 contains one 40x32mm stamp. For surcharge on No. 990, see No. 1280.

Songbirds — A284

Designs: 135fr, Pyrrhula pyrrhula. 150fr, Carduelis spinus. 200fr, Turdus torquatus. 270fr, Parus cristatus. 300fr, Nucifraga caryocatactes. 400fr, Luscinia megarhynchos. 1000fr, Motacilla flava.

1997, July 30			**Perf. 13x12½**
994	A284	135fr multicolored	.70 .40
995	A284	150fr multicolored	.80 .50
996	A284	200fr multicolored	1.00 .70
997	A284	270fr multicolored	1.20 .90
998	A284	300fr multicolored	1.40 1.00
999	A284	400fr multicolored	2.00 1.50
		Nos. 994-999 (6)	7.10 5.00

Souvenir Sheet
Perf. 12½

1000 A284 1000fr multicolored 5.00 4.50

No. 1000 contains one 32x40mm stamp. For surcharge on No. 997, see No. 1281.

Flowering Cactus — A285

Designs: 135fr, Faucaria lupina. 150fr, Conophytum bilobun. 200fr, Lithops aucampiae. 270fr, Lithops helmutii. 300fr, Stapelia grandiflora. 400fr, Lithops fulviceps. 1000fr, Pleiospilos willowmorensis.

1997, Aug. 30		**Litho.**	**Perf. 13x12½**
1001	A285	135fr multicolored	.70 .40
1002	A285	150fr multicolored	.80 .60
1003	A285	200fr multicolored	1.00 .80
1004	A285	270fr multicolored	1.20 1.00
1005	A285	300fr multicolored	1.40 1.10
1006	A285	400fr multicolored	2.00 1.75
		Nos. 1001-1006 (6)	7.10 5.65

Souvenir Sheet
Perf. 12½

1007 A285 1000fr multicolored 5.00 4.50

No. 1007 contains one 32x40mm stamp. For surcharge on No. 1004, see No. 1282.

Benin No. 418 Surcharged

1995
Perfs. & Printing Methods as Before
1009 A114 10fr on 90fr #418 50.00 25.00

Dahomey No. 307 Surcharged

1995 **Method and Perf. As Before**
1011 A67 135fr on 50fr Dahomey #307 — —

Benin Nos. 813, 948 Surcharged
Printing Methods and Perfs as before

1997-99 (?)

1021A	A256	135fr on 100fr		
		#948	45.00	25.00
1021B	A260	135fr on 200fr		
		#813	45.00	25.00

Early Locomotives — A286

Designs: 135fr, Puffing Billy, 1813. 150fr, La Fusée, 1829. 200fr, Royal George, 1827. 270fr, Nouveauté, 1829. 300fr, Locomotion, 1825, vert. 400fr, Sans Pareil, 1829, vert. 1000fr, Trevithick locomotive.

1997, Dec. 3　Litho.　Perf. 13

1022	A286	135fr multicolored	.70	.40
1023	A286	150fr multicolored	.80	.50
1024	A286	200fr multicolored	1.00	.70
1025	A286	270fr multicolored	1.20	.90
1026	A286	300fr multicolored	1.40	1.00
1027	A286	400fr multicolored	2.00	1.25
		Nos. 1022-1027 (6)	7.10	4.75

Souvenir Sheet

1028	A286	1000fr multicolored	5.00	4.50

No. 1028 contains one 40x32mm stamp.
For surcharge on No. 1025, see No. 1283.

Mushrooms A287

Designs: 135fr, Amanita caesarea. 150fr, Cortinarius collinitus. 200fr, Amanita bisporigera. 270fr, Amanita rubescens. 300fr, Russula virescens. 400fr, Amanita inaurata. 1000fr, Amanita muscaria.

1997, Nov. 5　Litho.　Perf. 13

1029	A287	135fr multicolored	.70	.40
1030	A287	150fr multicolored	.80	.50
1031	A287	200fr multicolored	1.00	.70
1032	A287	270fr multicolored	1.20	.90
1033	A287	300fr multicolored	1.40	1.00
1034	A287	400fr multicolored	2.00	1.25
		Nos. 1029-1034 (6)	7.10	4.75

Souvenir Sheet

1035	A287	1000fr multicolored	5.00	4.50

No. 1035 contains one 32x40mm stamp.
For surcharge on No. 1032, see No. 1284.

Assoc. of African Petroleum Producers, 10th Anniv. — A288

1997, Oct. 20　Litho.　Perf. 13

1036	A288	135fr green & multi	.70	.40
1037	A288	200fr orange & multi	1.00	.60
1038	A288	300fr multi & multi	1.50	.90
1039	A288	500fr yellow & multi	2.00	1.20
		Nos. 1036-1039 (4)	5.20	3.10

For surcharge, see No. 1061E.

Old Sailing Vessels — A289

Designs: 135fr, Egyptian. 150fr, Greek. 200fr, Assyrian-Phoenician. 270fr, Roman. 300fr, Norman. 400fr, Mediterranean. 1000fr, English.

1997, Sept. 10　Litho.　Perf. 12½

1040	A289	135fr multicolored	.70	.40
1041	A289	150fr multicolored	.90	.50
1042	A289	200fr multicolored	1.10	.70
1043	A289	270fr multicolored	1.25	.90
1044	A289	300fr multicolored	1.50	1.00
1045	A289	400fr multicolored	2.00	1.25
		Nos. 1040-1045 (6)	7.45	4.75

Souvenir Sheet

1046	A289	1000fr multicolored	5.00	4.50

No. 1046 contains one 32x40mm stamp.
For surcharge on No. 1043, see No. 1285.

Fish A290

Designs: 135fr, Epinephelus fasciatus. 150fr, Apogon victoriae. 200fr, Scarus gibbus. 270fr, Pygoplites diacanthus. 300fr, Cirrhilabrus punctatus. 400fr, Cirrhitichthys oxycephalus. 1000fr, Bodianus bilunulatus.

1997, Sept. 15　Litho.　Perf. 12½

1047	A290	135fr multicolored	.70	.40
1048	A290	150fr multicolored	.80	.50
1049	A290	200fr multicolored	1.00	.70
1050	A290	270fr multicolored	1.20	.90
1051	A290	300fr multicolored	1.40	1.00
1052	A290	400fr multicolored	2.00	1.25
		Nos. 1047-1052 (6)	7.10	4.75

Souvenir Sheet
Perf. 13

1053	A290	1000fr multicolored	5.00	4.50

No. 1053 contains one 40x32mm stamp.
For surcharge, see Nos. 1286, 1408.

Arabian Horse — A291

Various horses. Denominations and background colors: d, 135fr, pale green. e, 150fr, orange brown. f, 200fr, yellow. g, 270fr, orange brown. h, 300fr, tan. i, 400fr, pale green.

1997, May 25　　　　Perf. 12½

1053A	A291	Pair, #d.-e.	1.50	1.00
1053B	A291	Pair, #f.-g.	2.25	1.60
1053C	A291	Pair, #h.-i.	3.50	2.25
		Nos. 1053A-1053C (3)	7.25	4.85

Souvenir Sheet

1054	A291	1000fr multicolored	5.00	4.50

Dahomey No. 266 Surcharged
Methods and Perfs As Before

1997

1054B	A52(h)	35fr on 45fr		
		#266	75.00	40.00

Mushrooms A292

135fr, Tephrocybe carbonaria. 150fr, Suillus luteus. 200fr, Pleurotus ostreatus. 270fr, Hohenbuehelia geogenia. 300fr, Tylopilus felleus. 400fr, Lepiota leucothites. 1000fr, Gymnopilus junonius.

1998, Apr. 28　Litho.　Perf. 12½

1055	A292	135fr multicolored	.70	.40
1056	A292	150fr multicolored	.80	.50
1057	A292	200fr multicolored	1.00	.70
1058	A292	270fr multicolored	1.20	.90
1059	A292	300fr multicolored	1.40	1.00
1060	A292	400fr multicolored	2.00	1.25
		Nos. 1055-1060 (6)	7.10	4.75

Souvenir Sheet

1061	A292	1000fr multicolored	4.50	4.50

For surcharge on No. 1058, see No. 1287.

Nos. 432, 433, 632, 1037 Surcharged or Overprinted

No. 1061F

1998　　Method and Perf. as Before

1061A	A121(h)	15fr on #432	87.50	47.50
1061B	A121(h)	35fr on 50fr		
		#433	47.50	24.00
1061C	A121(h)	50fr on #433	47.50	24.00
1061E	A288	135fr on 200fr		
		#1037	47.50	24.00
1061F	A195(h)	150fr on 205fr		
		#632	47.50	24.00

Fire Fighting Apparatus — A293

135fr, Philadelphia Double Deck, 1885. 150fr, Veteran, 1850. 200fr, Merry Weather, 1894. 270fr, Horse-drawn wagon, 19th cent. 300fr, 1948 Jeep. 400fr, Chevrolet 6400. 1000fr, 1952 American-La France-Foamite Corp.

1998, Apr. 30　Litho.　Perf. 12¾

1062	A293	135fr multicolored	.70	.40
1063	A293	150fr multicolored	.80	.50
1064	A293	200fr multicolored	1.00	.70
1065	A293	270fr multicolored	1.20	.80
1066	A293	300fr multicolored	1.40	1.00
1067	A293	400fr multicolored	2.00	1.25
		Nos. 1062-1067 (6)	7.10	4.65

Souvenir Sheet

1068	A293	1000fr multicolored	4.50	4.50

No. 1068 contains one 40x32mm stamp.
For surcharge on No. 1065, see No. 1288.

Minerals — A294

No. 1069a, 135fr, Uranifere. No. 1069b, 150fr, Quartz. No. 1070a, 200fr, Aragonite. No. 1070b, 270fr, Malachite. No. 1071a, 300fr, Turquoise. No. 1071b, 400fr, Corundum. 1000fr, Marble.

1998, June 5　Litho.　Perf. 12½

1069	A294	Pair, #a.-b.	1.50	.90
1070	A294	Pair, #a.-b.	2.25	1.25
1071	A294	Pair, #a.-b.	3.25	2.25
		Nos. 1069-1071 (3)	7.00	4.75

Souvenir Sheet

1072	A294	1000fr multicolored	4.50	4.50

Locomotives — A295

Designs: 135fr, Red 0-6-0. 150fr, 0-4-4. 200fr, Brown 0-6-0. 270fr, Purple 0-6-0. 300fr, Blue 0-6-0. 400fr, "Helvetia" 0-6-0. 1000fr, "Shelby Steel" 0-6-0.

1998, June 30　Litho.　Perf. 12¾

1073	A295	135fr multicolored	.70	.40
1074	A295	150fr multicolored	.80	.50
1075	A295	200fr multicolored	1.00	.70
1076	A295	270fr multicolored	1.20	.90
1077	A295	300fr multicolored	1.40	1.00
1078	A295	400fr multicolored	2.00	1.25
		Nos. 1073-1078 (6)	7.10	4.75

Souvenir Sheet
Perf. 13

1079	A295	1000fr multicolored	4.50	4.50

No. 1079 contains one 40x32mm stamp.
For surcharge on No. 1076, see No. 1289.

Diana, Princess of Wales (1961-97) — A296

Portraits: a, 135fr. b, 150fr. c, 200fr. d, 270fr. e, 300fr. f, 400fr. g, 500fr. h, 600fr. i, 700fr.

1998, July 10　Litho.　Perf. 12½

1083	A296	Sheet of 9, #a.-i.	15.00	15.00

Dahomey No. 302 Surcharged
1997?
Perfs. & Printing Method as Before

1084	A65(h)	35fr on 85fr #302	75.00	40.00

Dinosaurs — A297

No. 1085: a, 135fr, Sordes. b, 150fr, Scaphognatus. c, 200fr, Dsungaripterus. d, 270fr, Brontosaurus. e, 300fr, Diplodocus. f, 400fr, Coelurus, Baryonyx. g, 500fr, Kronosaurus, Ichthyosaurus. h, 600fr, Ceratosaurus. i, 700f, Yangchuansaurus.

1998, July 25	Litho.	Perf. 12¾
1085 A297 Sheet of 9, #a-i		15.00 15.00

Python Regius A298

Various views of python: a, 135fr. b, 150fr. c, 200fr. d, 2000fr.

1999, Apr. 27	Litho.	Perf. 13
1086 A298 Strip of 4, #a.-d.		10.00 10.00

World Wildlife Fund.

Dogs — A299

135fr, Beagle. 150fr, Dalmatian. 200fr, Dachshund. 270fr, Cairn terrier. 300fr, Shih Tzu. 400fr, Pug.
1000fr, Springer spaniel, horiz.

1998, July 31	Litho.	Perf. 12¾
1087 A299	135fr multi	.60 .40
1088 A299	150fr multi	.65 .50
1089 A299	200fr multi	.80 .70
1090 A299	270fr multi	1.00 .90
1091 A299	300fr multi	1.20 1.00
1092 A299	400fr multi	1.60 1.25
	Nos. 1087-1092 (6)	5.85 4.75

Souvenir Sheet
Perf. 13

1093 A299 1000fr multi	4.50 4.00

No. 1093 contains one 40x32mm stamp.
For surcharge on No. 1090, see No. 1290.

Cats A300

135fr, Abyssinian. 150fr, Striped shorthair. 200fr, Siamese. 270fr, Red striped cat. 300fr, Gray cat with black stripes. 400fr, Manx.
1000fr, Cat with orange, black and white fur.

Perf. 12¼x12½, 12½x12¼

1998, Aug. 10		Litho.
1094 A300	135fr multi, vert.	.55 .40
1095 A300	150fr multi, vert.	.75 .50
1096 A300	200fr multi, vert.	1.10 .70
1097 A300	270fr multi	1.25 .90
1098 A300	300fr multi	1.40 1.00
1099 A300	400fr multi	1.75 1.25
	Nos. 1094-1099 (6)	6.80 4.75

Souvenir Sheet
Perf. 13

1100 A300 1000fr multicolored	4.50 4.00

No. 1100 contains one 40x32mm stamp.
For surcharge on No. 1097, see No. 1291.

Antique Automobiles — A301

Designs: 135fr, 1910 Bugatti 13. 150fr, 1903 Clément. 200fr, 1914 Stutz Bearcat. 270fr, 1907 Darracq. 300fr, 1913 Napier. 400fr, 1911 Pierce-Arrow.
1000fr, 1904 Piccolo, vert.

1998, Oct. 12		Litho.	Perf. 12¾
1101 A301	135fr multi		.60 .40
1102 A301	150fr multi		.65 .50
1103 A301	200fr multi		.85 .70
1104 A301	270fr multi		1.00 .90
1105 A301	300fr multi		1.20 1.00
1106 A301	400fr multi		1.60 1.25
	Nos. 1101-1106 (6)		5.90 4.75

Souvenir Sheet
Perf. 12¾x12½

1107 A301 1000fr multi	4.50 4.00

No. 1107 contains one 32x40mm stamp.
For surcharge on No. 1104, see No. 1292.

Butterflies — A301a

Designs: 135fr, Parnassius apollo. 150fr, Anthocharis cardamines. 200fr, Nymphalis antiopa. 250fr, Parage aegeria. 300fr, Palaeochrysophanus hippothoe. 400fr, Carterocephalus palaemon.
1000fr, Aglais urticae.

1998, Dec. 10	Litho.	Perf. 12¾
1107A-1107F A301a Set of 6		7.00 4.50

Souvenir Sheet
Perf. 13

1107G A301a 1000fr multi	4.00 4.00

No. 1107G contains one 40x32mm stamp.

African Wildlife — A302

Designs: 50fr, Ceratotherium simun. 100fr, Hipotragus niger. No. 1110, Phacochoerus aethiopicus. No. 1111, Hyaena brunnea. No. 1112, Colobus guereza. No. 1113, Hippopotamus amphibius. No. 1114, Cyncerus caffer caffer. No. 1115, Equus zebra. No. 1116, Acinonyx jubatus. No. 1117, Panthera leo leo. 400fr, Lycaon pictus. 500fr, Perodicticus potto.

Perf. 12¼x12½

1999, Mar. 10			Litho.
1108 A302	50fr	gray	.25 .25
1109 A302	100fr	brt violet	.45 .30
1110 A302	135fr	gray green	.60 .40
1111 A302	135fr	black	.60 .40
1112 A302	150fr	gray blue	.70 .50
1113 A302	150fr	emerald	.70 .50
1114 A302	200fr	dull brown	.90 .70
1115 A302	200fr	blue	.90 .70
1116 A302	300fr	henna brown	1.40 1.00
1117 A302	300fr	brown	1.40 1.00
1118 A302	400fr	red brown	1.90 1.50
1119 A302	500fr	deep bister	2.10 1.75
	Nos. 1108-1119 (12)		11.90 9.00

Birds — A303

Designs: 135fr, Chloebia gouldiae. 150fr, Sicalis flaveola. 200fr, Quelea quelea. 270fr, Euplectes afer. 300fr, Paroaria coronata. 400fr, Emberiza flaviventris.
1000fr, Mandingoa nitidula.

1999, Jan. 30	Litho.	Perf. 12¾
1120-1125 A303 Set of 6		6.00 5.00

Souvenir Sheet
Perf. 12½

1126 A303 1000fr multi	4.00 4.00

No. 1126 contains one 32x40mm stamp.
For No. 1123 surcharge, see No. 1293.

Orchids A304

Designs: 50fr, Brassocattleya cliftonii. 100fr, Wilsonara. 150fr, Cypripedium paeony. 300fr, Cymbidium babylon. 400fr, Cattleya. 500fr, Miltonia minx.

1999, Apr. 25		Litho.	Perf. 12¾
1127 A304	50fr multi		.25 .25
1128 A304	100fr multi		.45 .45
1129 A304	150fr multi		.70 .70
1130 A304	300fr multi		1.40 .90
1131 A304	400fr multi		1.90 1.10
1132 A304	500fr multi		2.10 1.75
	Nos. 1127-1132 (6)		6.80 5.15

Souvenir Sheet
Perf. 13

1133 A304 1000fr Miltonia (isis)	4.50 4.00

No. 1133 contains one 28x36mm stamp.
For surcharge, see No. 1239.

Chess Players A305

Designs: 135fr, Mikhail Tal. 150fr, Emanuel Lasker. 200fr, José Raul Capablanca. 270fr, Alexander Alekhine. 300fr, Max Euwe. 400fr, Mikhail Botvinnik.
1000fr, Wilhelm Steinitz.

1999, Mar. 28	Litho.	Perf. 12¾
1134-1139 A305 Set of 6		5.50 5.00

Souvenir Sheet
Perf. 13

1140 A305 1000fr multi	4.50 4.00

No. 1140 contains one 32x40mm stamp.
For surcharge on No. 1137, see No. 1294.

Ancient Sailing Ships A306

Designs: 135fr, Ceylonese canot. 150fr, Tanka-tim. 200fr, Sampan. 270fr, Polynesian canot. 300fr, Japanese junk. 400fr, Daccapulwar.
1000fr, Chinese junk.

1999, Feb. 15	Litho.	Perf. 12¾
1141-1146 A306 Set of 6		5.50 5.00

Souvenir Sheet
Perf. 12½

1147 A306 1000fr multi	3.75 3.75

No. 1147 contains one 40x32mm stamp.
For surcharge on No. 1144, see No. 1295.

Fish — A307

Designs: 135fr, Notopterus chitala. 150fr, Puntius filamentosus. 200fr, Epaizeorhynchos bicolor. 270fr, Rasbora maculata. 300fr, Pristolepis fasciatus. 400fr, Betta splendens.
1000fr, Trichogaster trichopterus.

1999, May 10	Litho.	Perf. 12½x12¼
1148 A307	135fr multi	.55 .40
1149 A307	150fr multi	.65 .50
1150 A307	200fr multi	.80 .70
1151 A307	270fr multi	.95 .90
1152 A307	300fr multi	1.10 1.00
1153 A307	400fr multi	1.60 1.50
	Nos. 1148-1153 (6)	5.65 5.00

Souvenir Sheet
Perf. 13x13¼

1154 A307 1000fr multi	4.00 4.00

No. 1154 contains one 40x32mm stamp.
For surcharge, see No. 1347.

Grand Prix de l'Amitie of France Afrique — A308

1999	Litho.	Perf. 13½x13
1154A A308	135fr multi	— —
1155 A308	150fr multi	— —
1156 A308	200fr multi	— —
1157 A308	300fr multi	— —
1157A A308	500fr multi	— —
1158 A308	1000fr multi	400.00 —
	Nos. 1154A-1158 (6)	400.00 —

No. 1157A exists as a souvenir sheet of 1. Value, unused $200.

Early Steam Vehicles A309

Designs: 135fr, 1786 tricycle made by A. Murdock. 150fr, 1800 locomotive made by Richard Trevithick. 200fr, 1803 locomotive made by Trevithick. 270fr, 1811 locomotive made by John Blenkinsop. 300fr, 1829 locomotive, Stourbridge Lion. 400fr, 1830 locomotive, Tom Thumb.
1000fr, 1760 locomotive made by Isaac Newton, horiz.

1999, June 18	Litho.	Perf. 12¾
1159-1164 A309 Set of 6		6.00 5.00

Souvenir Sheet
Perf. 13

1165 A309 1000fr multi	4.00 4.00

No. 1165 contains one 40x32 mm stamp.

Council of
the
Entente,
40th Anniv.
A310

1999-2001 Litho. Perf. 13x13¼
1166 A310 135fr multi, dated
"1999" — —
a. Perf. 13½x13¼, dated "2000" — —
b. Perf. 13½x13¼, dated "2001" — —
c. Perf. 13, dated "2001" — —
d. Perf. 13x13¼, dated "2000" — —
e. Perf. 13x13¼, dated "2001" — —
1167 A310 150fr multi, dated
"1999" — —
a. Perf. 13½x13¼, dated "2001" — —
b. Perf. 13x13¼, dated "2001" — —
c. Perf. 13x13¼, dated "2000" — —
d. Perf. 13½x13¼, dated "2000" — —
1168 A310 200fr multi, dated
"1999" — —
a. Perf. 13½x13¼, dated "2000" — —
b. Perf. 13½x13¼, dated "2001" — —
c. Perf. 13x13¼, dated "2001" — —
d. Perf. 13½x13¼, dated "2000" — —

The editors suspect other stamps in this set
have been issued and would like to examine
them.
For surcharges, see Nos. 1316-1322.

Snakes
A311

Designs: 135fr, Elaphe longissima. 150fr,
Pituophis melanoleucus. 200fr, Natrix natrix.
270fr, Oxybelis fulgidus. 300fr, Epicrates sub-
flavus. 400fr, Crotalus atrox.
1000fr, Vipera berus.

1999, July 18 Litho. Perf. 12¾
1170-1175 A311 Set of 6 6.00 5.00
Souvenir Sheet
Perf. 13
1176 A311 1000fr multi 4.50 4.00
No. 1176 contains one 40x32mm stamp.

China 1999 World Philatelic
Exhibition — A312

No. 1177: a, 50fr, Rocket testing, 14th cent.
b, 100fr, Jiuquan space launch center. c,
135fr, DFH-3 communications satellite. d,
150fr, Launch of a foreign satellite. e, 200fr,
Long March rocket CZ-2C. f, 300fr, Ship Yuan
Wang. g, 400fr, Satellite dish. h, 500fr,
Cacheted stamped covers.

1999, Aug. 22 Perf. 12½
1177 A312 Sheet of 8, #a-h 10.00 10.00

SOS Children's Villages, 50th
Anniv. — A313

Denominations and panel colors: 135fr,
Light green. 200fr, Pink. 300fr, Light blue.
500fr, Yellow.

1999, Oct. 15 Litho. Perf. 12¾
1178-1181 A313 Set of 4 5.25 5.25
For surcharges, see Nos. 1208, 1240, 1296.

Souvenir Sheet

Manchester United, 1999 English
Soccer Champions — A314

No. 1182: a, 135fr, Players celebrating on
platform. b, 200fr, Players in action. c, 300fr,
Players celebrating. d, 400fr, Stadium. e,
500fr, Trophies. f, 1000fr, Player with trophy.

1999, Oct. 15 Perf. 13¼
1182 A314 Sheet of 6, #a-f 11.00 10.00

The sets formerly listed as Nos.
1183-1189 (New Year 2000 - Year of
the Dragon) and 1211-1217 (Dogs)
were apparently prepared but not
issued. These and two other sets,
depicting insects (5 stamps and a
souvenir sheet) and songbirds (12
stamps) were not sold in Benin, and
they were not valid for postage.

Wild
Cats
A316

Designs: 135fr, Acinonyx jubatus. 150fr,
Panthera onca. 200fr, Panthera pardus. 270fr,
Panthera uncia. 300fr, Felis concolor. 400fr,
Panthera tigris.
1000fr, Panthera leo.

Perf. 12½x12¼
1999, Sept. 28 Litho.
1190-1195 A316 Set of 6 6.50 5.00
Souvenir Sheet
1196 A316 1000fr multi 4.50 4.00
For surcharge, see No. 1350.

Cacti — A317

Designs: 135fr, Mammillaria lenta. 150fr,
Oehmea nelsonii. 200fr, Neobesseya rosiflora.
270fr, Opuntia gosseliniana. 300fr, Parodia
nivosa. 400fr, Rebutia senilis.
1000fr, Opuntia retrorsa, vert.

1999, Oct. 10 Litho. Perf. 12¼
1197-1202 A317 Set of 6 6.50 5.00
Souvenir Sheet
Perf. 12½
1203 A317 1000fr multi 4.50 4.00
No. 1203 contains one 32x40mm rectangular stamp.

Birds — A318

No. 1204: a, 135fr, Estrilda locustella. b,
150fr, Estrilda melanotis.
No. 1205: a, 200fr, Pytelia melba. b, 270fr,
Uraeginthus bengalensis.
No. 1206: a, 300fr, Pyromelana orix. b,
400fr, Ploceus cucullatus.
1000fr, Steganura paradisea.

1999, Dec. 7 Litho. Perf. 12¼
Pairs, #a-b
1204-1206 A318 Set of 3 5.50 5.00
Souvenir Sheet
1207 A318 1000fr multi 3.75 3.75

No. 1180 Surcharged
Method and Perf. as Before
2000 ?
1208 A313 135fr on 300fr #1180

Nos. 850, 873 Surcharged

Methods and Perfs. as Before
2000 ?
1209 A267 135fr on 40fr #850 150.00 75.00
1210 A271 150fr on 75fr #873 75.00 40.00

Lions
A319

Designs: 135fr, Lion lying on side. 150fr,
Lion walking. 200fr, Lions hunting zebras.

2001 Litho. Perf. 12
1211 A319 135fr multi 1.40 1.40
1212 A319 150fr multi 1.50 1.50
Size: 65x22mm
1213 A319 200fr multi 2.10 2.10

Three 750fr stamps and a 1500fr souvenir
sheet depicting lions and their prey were not
authorized by Benin postal officials.

Fire
Vehicles —
A319a

Designs: 135fr, 1890 hose wagon. 150fr,
1900 fire truck. 200fr, 1903 fire truck. No.
1214C, 750fr, 1913 ladder truck. No. 1214D,
750fr, 1923 ladder truck.

2001 Litho. Perf. 12
1214 A319a 135fr multi 15.00 —
1214A A319a 150fr multi 15.00 —
1214B A319a 200fr multi 15.00 —
1214C A319a 750fr multi 15.00 —
1214D A319a 750fr multi 15.00 —
Nos. 1214-1214D (5) 75.00

Benin postal authorities declared a 750fr
stamp depicting a 1940 ladder truck and a

1500fr souvenir sheet depicting an 1877
pumper as "not authorized."

A319b

A319c

Primates —
A319d

Designs: 150fr, Head of gorilla. 200fr,
Gorilla.

2001 Litho. Perf. 12
1215 A319b 135fr shown 15.00 —
1215A A319b 150fr multi 15.00 —
1215B A319b 200fr multi 15.00 —
1215C A319c 750fr shown 15.00 —
1215D A319d 750fr shown 15.00 —
Nos. 1215-1215D (5) 75.00

Benin postal authorities declared another
750fr stamp depicting a primate and a 1500fr
souvenir sheet depicting a gorilla as "not
authorized."

Abdus Salam,
1979 Nobel
Physics
Laureate — A320

Abdus
Salam and
Building
A321

2001 Litho. Perf. 13¼x13
1218 A320 135fr multi 5.00 —
1219 A321 150fr multi 5.00 —
1220 A321 200fr multi 5.00 —

Edward Bouchet Abdus Salam Institute Intl.
Conference on Physics and High Technology
for the Development of Africa, Cotonou. The
editors suspect there may be additional
stamps in this set and would like to examine
any examples. Numbers may change.
Nos. 1218-1220 exist dated 2002.
For surcharge on No. 1219, see No. 1323.

**Various Stamps of 1995-99
Surcharged Like No. 1209**

No. 1222

No. 1296

Methods and Perfs As Before

2000

1222	A249 135fr on 40fr #741	160.00	80.00
1223	A250 135fr on 40fr #748	160.00	80.00
1224	A252 135fr on 40fr #761	160.00	80.00
1225	A253 135fr on 40fr #768	160.00	80.00
1226	A255 135fr on 40fr #780	160.00	80.00
1227	A257 135fr on 40fr #795	160.00	80.00
1228	A258 135fr on 40fr #801	160.00	80.00
1229	A262 135fr on 40fr #816	160.00	80.00
1230	A264 135fr on 40fr #829	160.00	80.00
1231	A265 135fr on 40fr #836	160.00	80.00
1232	A266 135fr on 40fr #843	160.00	80.00
1233	A268 135fr on 40fr #857	160.00	80.00
1234	A271 135fr on 40fr #871	160.00	80.00
1235	A272 135fr on 40fr #877	160.00	80.00
1236	A273 135fr on 40fr #884	160.00	80.00
1237	A275 135fr on 40fr #930	160.00	80.00
1238	A276 135fr on 40fr #936	160.00	80.00
1239	A304 135fr on 400fr #1131	160.00	80.00
1240	A313 135fr on 500fr #1181	400.00	200.00
1241	A248 150fr on 75fr #736	80.00	40.00
1242	A251 150fr on 75fr #756	80.00	40.00
1243	A255 150fr on 75fr #782	80.00	40.00
1244	A257 150fr on 75fr #797	80.00	40.00
1245	A262 150fr on 75fr #818	80.00	40.00
1246	A263 150fr on 75fr #824	80.00	40.00
1247	A264 150fr on 75fr #831	80.00	40.00
1248	A265 150fr on 75fr #838	80.00	40.00
1249	A267 150fr on 75fr #852	80.00	40.00
1250	A268 150fr on 75fr #859	80.00	40.00
1251	A270 150fr on 75fr #867	80.00	40.00
1252	A273 150fr on 75fr #886	80.00	40.00
1253	A274 150fr on 75fr #892	80.00	40.00
1254	A275 150fr on 75fr #932	80.00	40.00
1255	A276 150fr on 75fr #938	80.00	40.00
1256	A277 150fr on 75fr #943	80.00	40.00
1257	A248 150fr on 100fr #737	80.00	40.00
1258	A249 150fr on 100fr #744	80.00	40.00
1259	A250 150fr on 100fr #751	80.00	40.00
1260	A251 150fr on 100fr #757	80.00	40.00
1261	A252 150fr on 100fr #764	80.00	40.00
1262	A253 150fr on 100fr #771	80.00	40.00
1263	A254 150fr on 100fr #776	80.00	40.00
1264	A262 150fr on 100fr #819	80.00	40.00
1265	A263 150fr on 100fr #825	80.00	40.00

1266	A264 150fr on 100fr #832	80.00	40.00
1267	A265 150fr on 100fr #839	80.00	40.00
1268	A266 150fr on 100fr #846	80.00	40.00
1269	A267 150fr on 100fr #853	80.00	40.00
1270	A268 150fr on 100fr #860	80.00	40.00
1271	A270 150fr on 100fr #868	80.00	40.00
1272	A271 150fr on 100fr #874	80.00	40.00
1273	A276 150fr on 100fr #939	80.00	40.00
1274	A277 150fr on 100fr #944	80.00	40.00
1275	A278 150fr on 270fr #955	80.00	40.00
1276	A279 150fr on 270fr #962	80.00	40.00
1277	A280 150fr on 270fr #969	80.00	40.00
1278	A281 150fr on 270fr #976	80.00	40.00
1279	A282 150fr on 270fr #983	80.00	40.00
1280	A283 150fr on 270fr #990	80.00	40.00
1281	A284 150fr on 270fr #997	80.00	40.00
1282	A285 150fr on 270fr #1004	80.00	40.00
1283	A286 150fr on 270fr #1025	80.00	40.00
1284	A287 150fr on 270fr #1032	80.00	40.00
1285	A289 150fr on 270fr #1043	80.00	40.00
1286	A290 150fr on 270fr #1050	80.00	40.00
1287	A292 150fr on 270fr #1058	80.00	40.00
1288	A293 150fr on 270fr #1065	80.00	40.00
1289	A295 150fr on 270fr #1076	80.00	40.00
1290	A299 150fr on 270fr #1090	80.00	40.00
1291	A300 150fr on 270fr #1097	80.00	40.00
1292	A301 150fr on 270fr #1104	80.00	40.00
1293	A303 150fr on 270fr #1123	80.00	40.00
1294	A305 150fr on 270fr #1137	80.00	40.00
1295	A306 150fr on 270fr #1144	80.00	40.00
1296	A313 150fr on 500fr #1181	80.00	40.00

Items inscribed "Republique du Benin" that were not authorized by Benin postal officials but which have appeared on the philatelic market include:

Sheet of 15 stamps with various denominations depicting dogs.

Sheet of 9 stamps with various denominations depicting American movie stars, Isabella Rosselini.

Sheets of 6 stamps of various denominations depicting Pope John Paul II, bats, deer, dolphins, frogs, geckos, hares, hummingbirds, kangaroos, lemurs, owls (2 different), pandas, penguins, pigeons, porcupines, rodents, sea gulls, snakes, squirrels, thrushes, toads, turtles.

Souvenir sheets with one 1000fr stamp depicting Isabella Rosselini (2 different), bats, deer, dolphins, frogs, geckos, hares, hummingbirds, kangaroos, lemurs, pigeons, porcupines, rodents, sea gulls, snakes, squirrels, thrushes, toads, turtles.

Sheet of 9 stamps with various denominations depicting Polar bears, Dogs, Wild cats.

Sheet of 8 stamps with various denominations depicting Spiderman, Vin Diesel.

Sheet of 6 stamps with various denominations depicting Lighthouses (2 different), Tigers (2 different), Turtles, Military aircraft.

Sheet of 12 stamps with various denominations depicting Marilyn Monroe (2 different), French firefighters, Carlos Cartagena, Sean Gallimore, Land of the Rising Fun.

Sheets of 10 stamps with various denominations depicting Wolves, Bears, Birds, Elvis Presley.

Sheet of 9 stamps with 100fr denominations depicting Pope John Paul II with Princess Diana.

Sheets of 9 stamps with various denominations depicting Lighthouses (4 different), Windmills (3 different), Looney Tunes characters (3 different), English soccer players and teams (3 different), Paintings of nudes (2 different), Harry Potter (2 different), The Lord of the Rings: The Two Towers (2 different), Terminator 3, Britney Spears, Elvis Presley, Marilyn Monroe, Red Cross, Endangered Animals, Nature Conservancy, Orchids, Gorillas, Cheetahs, Elephants, Lions, Tigers, Horses, Dinosaurs (with Scout emblem), Dinosaurs (without emblems), Trains, Al Buell, Billy DeVorss, Boris Lopez, Edward D'Ancona, Luis Royo Nude Miyazawa, Pearl Frush, Sexy Models, Top Models.

Sheet of 8 stamps with various denominations depicting Horses, Robbie Williams.

Sheet of 6 stamps with 500fr denominations depicting Marilyn Monroe (2 different), Lighthouses, Motorcycles, Trains, Ferrari racing cars, Actresses, Partially nude models.

Sheet of 6 stamps with 300fr denominations depicting Shunga.

Sheets of 6 stamps with 200fr denominations depicting Scenes from Lighthouses, French tales, Wild cats (with scout emblem), Trains.

Sheets of 6 stamps with 100fr denominations depicting Dinosaurs (2 different), Dinosaurs (with Rotary emblem) (2 different), Fire Engines (2 different), Arctic Animals, Lions, Wolves, Prehistoric Elephants, Domestic Cats (with Scout and Rotary emblem), Domestic Cats (without emblems), Dogs, Owls (with Scout emblem), Owls (without emblems), Sparrowhawks, Falcons, Trains, Elvis Presley, Marilyn Monroe, The Beatles.

Sheets of 6 stamps with various denominations depicting Paintings in the Prado (11 differerent), Impressionist Paintings (5 different), Classic Movies (3 different), Marilyn Monroe (3 different), Elvis Presley (perf. and imperf.) (3 different), 75th Academy Awards (2 different), Turtles (2 different), Parrots (with Scout emblem) (2 different), Owl paintings of Pollyanna Pickering (2 different), Trains (2 different), Motorcycles (2 different), Ferrari racing cars, Classic automobiles, Scenes from Japanese tale "Spirited Away," Dogs, Butterflies on Orchids, Dinosaurs, Audubon paintings of animals, Nature Conservancy, James Bond films, Vincent van Gogh, paintings of Nudes, Military aircraft, Pope John Paul II, Elvis Presley, Japanese women, Jazz musicians, Anton Corbijo, Baron Jerry von Lind, Dorian Cleavenger, Drew Posada, Helmut Newton, Matt Hughes, Edvard Runci, Top Models.

Sheet of 4 stamps with 1000fr denominations depicting Winnie the Pooh.

Sheet of 4 stamps with various denominations depicting Madonna, AC/DC, Backstreet Boys, The Beatles, Bee Gees, The Doors, Freddy Mercury, Kiss, Led Zeppelin, Metallica, Mick Jagger, Queen, Bob Hope.

Sheet of 3 stamps with 1000fr denominations depicting Scenes from children's stories.

Sheets of 3 stamps with various denominations depicting Nature Conservancy (2 different), Fighter Airplanes, Trains, Automobiles, Pope John Paul II with Mother Teresa and Princess Diana (perf. and imperf.).

Sheets of 2 stamps with 1000fr denominations depicting Nature Conservancy, Pope John Paul II.

Sheets of 2 stamps with 500fr denominations depicting Dinosaurs, Pandas, Chess, Trains, Elvis Presley.

Souvenir sheets of 1 stamp with 3000fr denomination depicting Gullivera Part I, Gullivera Part II.

Souvenir sheets of 1 stamp with 1000fr denomination depicting Disney Characters, Elvis Presley and various scenes from children's stories (15 different), Marilyn Monroe (11 different), Birds (10 different), Elvis Presley (6 different), Windmills (4 different), Aircraft

(4 different), Pope John Paul II with Princess Diana (4 different), Lighthouses (3 different); Ricky Carralero (3 different), Pope John Paul II (2 different), Automobiles (2 different), Trains (2 different), Endangered Animals (2 different), Dinosaurs (with Scout emblem) (2 different), Dinosaurs (without emblems) (2 different), Baron Jerry von Lind (2 different), Dorian Cleavenger (2 different), Drew Posada (2 different), Dogs, Penguins, Water Birds, Sea Creatures, Audubon painting of a fox, Nature Conservancy, Madonna, Nadja Auermann, Vincent van Gogh, Painting of a Nude, Japanese Women, Manchester United soccer team, Firefighters, Matt Hughes, Carlos Cartagena, Pope John Paul II with Mother Teresa.

Souvenir sheets of 1 stamp with 500fr denomination depicting James Bond films (3 different), The Beatles (2 different), Owls, Al Buell, Freeman Elliot, Peter Driben, Land of the Rising Fun, Pope John Paul II.

Gate of No Return Slave Route Monument, Ouidah — A322

2003, June 23   Litho.   Perf. 12¾

1297	A322	135fr multi	—	—
1298	A322	150fr multi	—	—
1299	A322	200fr multi	—	—
1300	A322	300fr multi	—	—
1301	A322	1000fr multi	—	—

Souvenir Sheet

1301A	A322	1000fr Gate, vert.	—	—

Two additional stamps were released in this set. The editors would like to examine any examples.

Da Silva Museum of Afro-Brazilian Arts and Culture, Porto-Novo — A323

2003, Nov. 10   Litho.   Perf. 13x13¼

Panel Color

1302	A323	25fr blue	—	—
1303	A323	175fr red violet	—	—
1304	A323	250fr green	—	—
1305	A323	300fr olive green	—	—
1306	A323	500fr blue	—	—
1307	A323	1000fr black	—	—

For surcharges, see Nos. 1355, 1406.

Cercopithecus
Erythrogaster
Erythrogaster
A324

2003, Dec. 19   Litho.   Perf. 13¼x13

Panel Color

1308	A324	50fr gray blue	—	—
1309	A324	175fr blue	—	—
1310	A324	250fr bister	—	—
1311	A324	300fr green	—	—
1312	A324	400fr brown	—	—
1313	A324	500fr orange	—	—
1314	A324	600fr dk blue gray	—	—
a.		Souvenir sheet of 2, #1313-1314	—	—

For surcharges, see Nos. 1334, 1356-1361, 1411, 1448.

Nos. 890 and 1167b Surcharged

No. 1316

1000fr surcharges: Type 1, Top serif on "1." Type 2, Top and bottom serif on "1." Type 3, No serifs on "1."

Methods and Perfs. As Before
2003-04 ?

1315	A274	135fr on 40fr #890	75.00	40.00
1316	A310	135fr on 150fr #1167b	60.00	30.00
1317	A310	300fr on 150fr #1167b	12.00	8.00
1318	A310	500fr on 150fr #1167b	12.00	8.00
1319	A310	500fr on 150fr #1167b, large "5"	—	—
1320	A310	1000fr on 150fr #1167b, type 1	—	—
1321	A310	1000fr on 150fr #1167b, type 2	—	—
1322	A310	1000fr on 150fr #1167b, type 3	—	—

No. 1319 has a large "5" with a top line that curves. No. 1318 has a smaller "5" with a top line that is straight but has an upward-pointing serif.

No. 1219 Surcharged

135 F

Methods and Perfs As Before
2003 ?

1323	A321	135fr on 150fr multi	15.00	8.00

Fight Against Child Trafficking A325

Denomination color: 175fr, Yellow. 250fr, Dark blue. 300fr, White. 400fr, Light blue.

2004, Aug. 31   Litho.   Perf. 13x13¼

1324-1327	A325	Set of 4	15.00	—

For surcharges, see Nos. 1365, 1446.

Rotary International, Cent — A326

Denomination color: 50fr, Purple. 175fr, Red. 250fr, Black. 300fr, Brown. 400fr, Green. 500fr, Orange. Inscription on 175fr, 250fr, 300fr reads "ACD / Cotonou du 13 au 16 Avril 2005."

2005, Feb. 1   Perf. 13¼x13

1328-1333	A326	Set of 6	16.00	—
1333a		Souvenir sheet of 1	16.00	

Benin postal officials have declared as "not authorized" the following items:

Sheet of 9 stamps with various denominations depicting Harry Potter and the Prisoner of Azkaban, The Lord of the Rings: The Return of the King, Prince William, Princess Diana, Asian lighthouses.

Sheet of 8 stamps with various denominations depicting Marilyn Monroe.

Strip of 8 stamps with various denominations depicting Cats.

Sheet of 6 stamps with various denominations depicting Shells.

Souvenir sheets of one stamp with 1000fr denomination depicting Asian lighthouses (2), Cats.

Benin Nos. 1151, 1193, 1305, 1308, 1310-1311 Surcharged

No. 1357   175F

Methods and Perfs As Before
2005-08 ?

1334	A324	175fr on 50fr #1308	4.50	3.00
1347	A307	175fr on 270fr #1151	45.00	30.00
1350	A316	175fr on 270fr #1193	45.00	30.00
1355	A323	175fr on 300fr #1305	4.50	4.50
1356	A324	175fr on 300fr #1311	4.50	4.50
1357	A324	175fr on 250fr #1310	4.00	2.50
1358	A324	200fr on 250fr #1310, thin numerals and "F"	—	—
1359	A324	200fr on 250fr #1310, thick numerals, "F" with short arms	—	—
1360	A324	200fr on 250fr #1310, thick numerals and "F"	—	—
1361	A324	200fr on 250fr #1310, thick numerals and thin "F"	—	—

Dahomey Nos. 317, 338, C169 and Benin Nos. 342, 1325 Srchd. or Ovptd.

No. 1364

Methods and Perfs As Before
2008 ?

1362	A80(f)	175fr on 35fr Dahomey #338	35.00	25.00
1363	A71(f)	175fr on 5fr Dahomey #317	35.00	25.00
1364	A83(f)	175fr on 10fr #342	30.00	20.00
1365	A325	175fr on 250fr #1325	4.00	2.50

1366	AP59(f)	250fr on Dahomey #C169	20.00	10.00

Benin postal officials have declared as "illegal" various items commemorating the 50th anniversary of Europa stamps.

Dahomey Nos. 179, 195, 287, 319 and 331 Overprinted Type "g"
Methods and Perfs As Before
2005-09 (?)

1367	A23(g)	25fr multi (#179)	110.00	60.00
1368	A27(g)	25fr multi (#195)	30.00	15.00
1369	A60(g)	25fr multi (#287)	50.00	25.00
1370	A71(g)	25fr multi (#319)	110.00	60.00
1371	A76(g)	25fr multi (#331)	20.00	10.00
Nos. 1367-1371 (5)			320.00	170.00

Various Dahomey and Benin Stamps Surcharged With Various Surcharge Types and

25F

k

Methods and Perfs As Before
2005-09 (?)

1372	A21(k)	25fr on 1fr Dah. #173	25.00	12.00
1373	A57(k)	25fr on 1fr Dah. #277	40.00	20.00
a.		With obliterator over "Dahomey" omitted	—	
1374	A15(k)	25fr on 3fr Dah. #143	70.00	35.00
1375	A19(k)	25fr on 3fr Dah. #161	20.00	10.00
1376	A38(k)	25fr on 3fr Dah. #227	150.00	75.00
1377	A24(k)	25fr on 4fr Dah. #182	30.00	15.00
1378	A69(k)	25fr on 5fr Dah. #312	175.00	85.00
1379	A71(k)	25fr on 5fr Dah. #317	150.00	75.00
1380	A63(k)	25fr on 10fr Dah. #297	150.00	75.00
1381	A71(k)	25fr on 10fr Dah. #318	125.00	70.00
1382	A21(k)	25fr on 15fr Dah. #176	40.00	20.00
1383	A69(k)	25fr on 15fr Dah. #313	200.00	100.00
1384	A21(k)	25fr on 20fr Dah. #177	30.00	15.00
1385	A33(k)	25fr on 30fr Dah. #210	20.00	10.00
1386	A41(k)	25fr on 30fr Dah. #237	50.00	25.00
1387	A46(k)	25fr on 30fr Dah. #250	40.00	20.00
1388	A52(k)	25fr on 30fr Dah. #265	50.00	25.00
1389	A62(k)	25fr on 30fr Dah. #295	40.00	20.00
1390	A38(k)	50fr on 30fr Dah. #231	60.00	30.00
1391	A42(k)	50fr on 30fr Dah. #239	40.00	20.00
1392	A43(k)	50fr on 30fr Dah. #241	30.00	15.00
1393	A63(k)	50fr on 35fr Dah. #298	75.00	35.00

1394	A69(k)	50fr on 35fr Dah. #314	75.00	35.00
1395	A74(k)	50fr on 35fr Dah. #325	75.00	35.00
1396	CD132(k)	50fr on 40fr Dah. #269	75.00	35.00
1397	A63(k)	50fr on 40fr Dah. #299	100.00	50.00
1398	A72(k)	50fr on 40fr Dah. #321	50.00	25.00
1399	A74(k)	50fr on 40fr Dah. #326	100.00	50.00
1400	A78(k)	50fr on 40fr Dah. #336	20.00	10.00
1401	A57(f)	175fr on 1fr Dah. #277	15.00	10.00
1402	A38(f)	175fr on 3fr Dah. #227	45.00	30.00
1403	A66(f)	175fr on 5fr Dah. #303	15.00	7.50
1406	A323	175fr on 250fr Ben. #1304	4.50	4.50
1408	A290	175fr on 270fr Ben. #1050	200.00	—
1411	A324	175fr on 400fr #1312	4.00	2.50
1413	A63(k)	200fr on 35fr Ben. #343	90.00	45.00
1414	A76(k)	200fr on 40fr Dah. #332	30.00	15.00
1415	A45(k)	200fr on 45fr Dah. #247	75.00	35.00
1416	A83(k)	200fr on 45fr Ben. #344	150.00	75.00
1417	A19(k)	200fr on 50fr #168	120.00	60.00
1418	A83(k)	200fr on 60fr Ben. #345	90.00	45.00
1419	A77(k)	200fr on 65fr Dah. #334	30.00	15.00
1420	A45(k)	200fr on 70fr Dah. #248	75.00	35.00
1421	A45(k)	200fr on 100fr Dah. #249	50.00	25.00
1422	A60(k)	200fr on 100fr Dah. #290	25.00	12.50
1423	A77(k)	200fr on 100fr Dah. #335	25.00	12.50
1429	A58(k)	300fr on 40fr Dah. #283	40.00	20.00
1430	A59(k)	300fr on 40fr Dah. #286	50.00	25.00
1431	A60(k)	300fr on 40fr Dah. #289	20.00	10.00
1432	A71(k)	300fr on 40fr Dah. #320	75.00	35.00
1433	A52(k)	300fr on 45fr Dah. #266	40.00	20.00
1434	A67(k)	300fr on 50fr Dah. #307	40.00	20.00
1435	A72(k)	300fr on 50fr Dah. #322	85.00	45.00
1436	A82(k)	300fr on 50fr Dah. #340	40.00	20.00
1437	A65(k)	300fr on 85fr Dah. #302	40.00	20.00
1438	A47(k)	300fr on 90fr Dah. #256	90.00	45.00
1439	A68(k)	300fr on 100fr Dah. #309	45.00	20.00
1440	CD137(k)	300fr on 100fr Dah. #311	35.00	20.00
1441	A72(k)	300fr on 100fr Dah. #323	90.00	45.00
1442	A74(k)	300fr on 100fr Dah. #327	90.00	45.00
1443	A76(k)	300fr on 100fr Dah. #333	40.00	20.00

1444 A74(f) 300fr on 200fr
Dah.
#328 50.00 30.00
1445 A81(f) 300fr on 200fr
Dah.
#339 35.00 25.00
1446 A325 500fr on 300fr
Ben.
#1326 7.50 4.50
1448 A324 1000fr on
300fr
Ben.
#1311 11.50 11.50

Léopold Sédar Senghor (1906-2001),
First President of Senegal — A327

Denomination color: 175fr, Red. 300fr, Blue
green.

2006 Litho. Perf. 13x13¼
1451-1452 A327 Set of 2 4.00 4.00

Benin Coat of
Arms — A328

2008, Jan. 1 Litho. Perf. 13¼x13½
Denomination Color
1453 A328 25fr blue green .25 .25
1454 A328 50fr org brown .40 .40
1455 A328 75fr brown .60 .60
1456 A328 100fr red .80 .80

Size: 36x27mm
Perf. 13x13¼
1457 A328 200fr purple 1.60 1.60
1458 A328 250fr green 1.90 1.90
1459 A328 500fr blue gray 4.00 4.00
1460 A328 5000fr red brown 40.00 40.00
Nos. 1453-1460 (8) 49.55 49.55
For surcharges see Nos. 1461, 1473-1476.

No. 1458
Surcharged

2008 ? Litho. Perf. 13x13¼
1461 A328 200fr on 250fr
#1458 65.00 40.00

Miniature Sheet

2008 Summer Olympics,
Beijing — A329

No. 1462: a, Running. b, Taekwondo. c,
Swimming. d, Taekwondo, swimming and
running.

2008, Oct. 1 Litho. Perf. 12¾x13½
1462 A329 200fr Sheet of 4,
#a-d 10.00 10.00

Dahomey Nos. 181, 251, 276, 292,
329, 341 and Benin No. 342 Srchd.

No. 1463

Methods and Perfs As Before
2009
1463 A83(k) 25fr on 10fr
Ben.
#342 125.00 65.00
1464 A56(k) 50fr on 40fr
Dah.
#276 25.00 10.00
1465 A46(k) 300fr on 70fr
Dah.
#251 70.00 35.00
1466 A23(k) 300fr on 100fr
Dah.
#181 25.00 10.00
1467 A60(k) 400fr on 140fr
Dah.
#292 25.00 15.00
1468 A75(k) 1000fr on 35fr
Dah.
#329 75.00 35.00
1469 A82(k) 1000fr on 150fr
Dah.
#341 25.00 16.50
Nos. 1463-1469 (7) 370.00 186.50

Dahomey Nos. 291 and 306
Surcharged
Methods and Perfs As Before
2009
1470 A60(k) 400fr on 135fr
Dahomey
#291 60.00 30.00
1471 A67(k) 1000fr on 35fr Dahomey
#306 45.00 25.00

Dahomey No. C35 Surcharged With
"Poste Aerienne" Obliterated
Method and Perf. As Before
2009 ?
1472 AP15(f) 500fr on 200fr
Dah.
#C35 75.00 45.00

No. 1457
Surcharged

2009 Method and Perf. As Before
1473 A328 250fr on 200fr
#1457 6.00 6.00
1474 A328 300fr on 200fr
#1457 6.00 6.00
1475 A328 500fr on 200fr
#1457 6.00 6.00
1476 A328 600fr on 200fr
#1457 6.00 6.00
Nos. 1473-1476 (4) 24.00 24.00

Benin Nos. 399a, 402a With
"POPULAIRE" Obliterated
Methods and Perfs As Before
2009
1477 A108 On sheet of 3,
#a-c (#399a) 27.50 27.50
1478 A108 On sheet of 3,
#a-c (#402a) 32.50 32.50

Independence, 50th Anniv. — A330

50th anniversary emblem and: 250fr,
Dancer. 300fr, Tractor, flags of Benin since
1960. 500fr, Godomey highway interchange.

2010, Aug. 1 Litho. Perf. 12¾x13
1479-1481 A330 Set of 3 10.50 10.50

Bernardin
Cardinal Gantin
(1922-2008)
A331

Country name and outline of denomination
in: 250fr, Green. 300fr, Red. 600fr, Black.

2011 Perf. 13¼x13
1482-1484 A331 Set of 3 10.00 10.00

Visit of
Pope
Benedict
XVI to
Benin
A332

Color of top panel: 250fr, Blue. 300fr, Red
violet. 400fr, Purple. 500fr, Red. 1000fr, Bister.

2011, Sept. 22 Perf. 13¼x13¼
1485-1489 A332 Set of 5 24.00 24.00

National Day of
Traditional
Religions — A333

Color of panel at left: 250fr, Blue. 300fr,
Light green. 1000fr, Light orange.

2013 Litho. Perf. 13¼x13
1490-1492 A333 Set of 3 14.00 14.00

Dr. Boni Yayi,
2012-13
President of the
African
Union — A334

Denomination color: 300fr, Dark blue green.
1000fr, Green.

2013 Litho. Perf. 13¼x13
1493-1494 A334 Set of 2 14.00 14.00

Pres. Sourou-
Migan Apithy
(1913-89) — A335

Denominations: 600fr, 1000fr

2013 Litho. Perf. 13¼x13
1495-1496 A335 Set of 2 14.00 14.00

Two additional stamps were issued in this
set. The editors would like to examine any
examples.

Behanzin
High
School,
Porto-Novo,
Cent.
A336

Denomination color: 250fr, Blue. 600fr,
Magenta. 1000fr, Red.

2013 Litho. Perf. 13x13¼
1497-1499 A336 Set of 3 17.00 17.00

An additional stamp was issued in this set.
The editors would like to examine any
example.

AIR POST STAMPS

PEOPLE'S REPUBLIC

Catalogue values for unused
stamps in this section are for
Never Hinged items.

Nativity, by Aert van Leyden — AP84

Christmas: 85fr, Adoration of the Kings, by
Rubens, vert. 140fr, Adoration of the Shepherds, by Charles Lebrun. 300fr, The Virgin
with the Blue Diadem, by Raphael, vert.

1975, Dec. 19 Litho. Perf. 13
C240 AP84 40fr gold & multi .90 .45
C241 AP84 85fr gold & multi 1.25 .80
C242 AP84 140fr gold & multi 2.50 1.10
C243 AP84 300fr gold & multi 5.40 2.75
Nos. C240-C243 (4) 10.05 5.10

For surcharges see Nos. C357C, C362,
C367, C407, C407A, C424, C432, C583,
C589.

Slalom, Innsbruck Olympic
Emblem — AP85

Innsbruck Olympic Games Emblem and:
150fr, Bobsledding, vert. 300fr, Figure skating,
pairs.

1976, June 28 Litho. Perf. 12½
C244 AP85 60fr multi 1.50 .65
C245 AP85 150fr multi 2.50 1.60
C246 AP85 300fr multi 5.25 3.25
Nos. C244-C246 (3) 9.25 5.50

12th Winter Olympic Games, Innsbruck,
Austria, Feb. 4-15.
For overprint on No. C246, see No. Q22.

Dahomey Nos. C263-C265
Overprinted or Surcharged

No. C247

1976, July 4   Engr.   Perf. 13
C247 AP86 135fr multi   1.90 1.25
C248 AP86 210fr on 300fr multi   2.75 1.60
C249 AP86 380fr on 500fr multi   5.75 2.75
  Nos. C247-C249 (3)   10.40 5.60

The overprint includes a bar covering "DU DAHOMEY" in shades of brown; "POPULAIRE DU BENIN" is blue on Nos. C247-C248, red on No. C249. The surcharge and bars over old value are blue on No. C248, red, brown on No. C249.

Long Jump AP86

Designs (Olympic Rings and): 150fr, Basketball, vert. 200fr, Hurdles.

1976, July 16   Photo.   Perf. 13
C250 AP86 60fr multi   1.00 .55
C251 AP86 150fr multi   2.25 1.25
C252 AP86 200fr multi   3.00 1.75
  a.   Souv. sheet of 3, #C250-C252 8.75 8.75
  Nos. C250-C252 (3)   6.25 3.55

21st Olympic Games, Montreal, Canada, July 17-Aug 1.

Konrad Adenauer and Cologne Cathedral — AP87

Design: 90fr, Konrad Adenauer, vert.

1976, Aug. 27   Engr.   Perf. 13
C253 AP87 90fr multi   1.60 .90
C254 AP87 250fr multi   4.75 1.90

Konrad Adenauer (1876-1967), German Chancellor, birth centenary.
For surcharges, see Nos. C289B, Q17, Q17A, Q26, Q27.

Children's Heads and Flying Fish (Dahomey Type A32) — AP88

210fr, Lion cub's head, Benin design A3, vert.

1976, Sept. 13
C255 AP88 60fr Prus bl & vio bl 1.25 .60
C256 AP88 210fr multi   3.50 1.60

JUVAROUEN 76, Intl. Youth Phil. Exhib., Rouen, France, Apr. 25-May 2.
For surcharges see Nos. C300, C494, C542, C543.

Apollo 14 Emblem and Blast-off — AP89

270fr, Landing craft and man on moon.

1976, Oct. 18   Engr.   Perf. 13
C257 AP89 130fr multi   1.75 .75
C258 AP89 270fr multi   3.50 1.50

Apollo 14 Moon Mission, 5th anniversary.
For surcharges see Nos. C312, C454.

Annunciation, by Master of Jativa — AP90

Christmas: 60fr, Nativity, by Gerard David. 270fr, Adoration of the Kings, Dutch School. 300fr, Flight into Egypt, by Gentile Fabriano, horiz.

1976, Dec. 20   Litho.   Perf. 12½
C259 AP90 50fr gold & multi   .95 .50
C260 AP90 60fr gold & multi   1.00 .65
C261 AP90 270fr gold & multi   4.00 2.10
C262 AP90 300fr gold & multi   4.50 2.50
  Nos. C259-C262 (4)   10.45 5.75

For surcharges see Nos. C310, C321, C484.

Gamblers and Lottery Emblem — AP91

1977, Mar. 13   Litho.   Perf. 13
C263 AP91 50fr multi   .90 .50

National lottery, 10th anniversary.

Sassenage Castle, Grenoble — AP92

1977, May 16   Perf. 12½
C264 AP92 200fr multi   2.75 1.25

10th anniv. of Intl. French Language Council.
For surcharge see No. C334.

Concorde, Supersonic Plane — AP93

Designs: 150fr, Zeppelin. 300fr, Charles A. Lindbergh and Spirit of St. Louis. 500fr, Charles Nungesser and François Coli, French aviators lost over Atlantic, 1927.

1977, July 25   Engr.   Perf. 13
C265 AP93 80fr ultra & red   1.00 .50
C266 AP93 150fr multi   2.10 1.00
C267 AP93 300fr multi   3.25 2.10
C268 AP93 500fr multi   6.50 4.00
  Nos. C265-C268 (4)   12.85 7.60

Aviation history.
For overprint and surcharges see Nos. C274, C316, C336, C496.

Soccer Player — AP94

200fr, Soccer players and Games' emblem.

1977, July 28   Litho.   Perf. 12½x12
C269 AP94 60fr multi   .95 .55
C270 AP94 200fr multi   2.75 1.90

World Soccer Cup elimination games.
For surcharges see Nos. C289A, C308.

Miss Haverfield, by Gainsborough — AP95

Designs: 150fr, Self-portrait, by Rubens. 200fr, Anguish, man's head by Da Vinci.

1977, Oct. 3   Engr.   Perf. 13
C271 AP95 100fr sl grn & mar   2.50 .80
C272 AP95 150fr red brn & dk
            brn   4.00 1.90
C273 AP95 200fr brn & red   5.50 2.50
  Nos. C271-C273 (3)   12.00 5.20

For surcharges see Nos. C309, C317.

No. C265 Overprinted

1977, Nov. 22   Engr.   Perf. 13
C274 AP93 80fr ultra & red   2.00 .90

Concorde, 1st commercial flight, Paris to NY.

Viking on Mars — AP96

150fr, Isaac Newton, apple globe, stars. 200fr, Vladimir M. Komarov, spacecraft and earth. 500fr, Dog Laika, rocket and space.

1977, Nov. 28   Engr.   Perf. 13
C275 AP96 100fr multi   1.00 .65
C276 AP96 150fr multi   1.90 1.00
C277 AP96 200fr multi   3.00 1.25
C278 AP96 500fr multi   7.00 3.50
  Nos. C275-C278 (4)   12.90 6.40

Operation Viking on Mars; Isaac Newton (1642-1727); 10th death anniv. of Russian cosmonaut Vladimir M. Komarov; 20th anniv. of 1st living creature in space.
For surcharges see Nos. C301, C314, C497, Q18.

Monument, Red Star Place, Cotonou AP97

Lithographed; Gold Embossed
1977 Nov. 30   Perf. 12½
C279 AP97 500fr multi   6.50 3.00

Suzanne Fourment, by Rubens AP98

380fr, Nicholas Rubens, by Rubens.

1977, Dec. 12   Engr.   Perf. 13
C280 AP98 200fr multi   3.50 1.50
C281 AP98 380fr claret & ocher   6.00 2.50

For surcharges see Nos. C311, C313, C483.

Parthenon and UNESCO Emblem — AP99

Designs: 70fr, Acropolis and frieze showing Pan-Athenaic procession, vert. 250fr, Parthenon and frieze showing horsemen, vert.

1978, Sept. 22   Litho.   Perf. 12½x12
C282 AP99 70fr multi   .75 .25
C283 AP99 250fr multi   2.75 1.60
C284 AP99 500fr multi   5.50 2.50
  Nos. C282-C284 (3)   9.00 4.35

Save the Parthenon in Athens campaign.
For surcharge see No. C338.

Philexafrique II — Essen Issue
Common Design Types
Designs: No. C285, Buffalo and Dahomey #C33. No. C286, Wild ducks and Baden #1.

1978, Nov. 1   Litho.   Perf. 12½
C285 CD138 100fr multi   4.50 1.75
C286 CD139 100fr multi   4.50 1.75
  a.   Pair, #C285-C286   9.00 8.50

For surcharges, see Nos, C535-C536.

Wilbur and Orville Wright and Flyer — AP100

1978, Dec. 28   Engr.   Perf. 13
C287 AP100 500fr multi   6.50 3.00

75th anniversary of 1st powered flight.
For surcharge see No. C339.

Cook's Ships, Hawaii, World
Map — AP101

Design: 50fr, Battle at Kowrowa.

1979, June 1   Engr.   Perf. 13
C288 AP101 20fr multi   .90   .30
C289 AP101 50fr multi   1.10   .50

Capt. James Cook (1728-1779), explorer.

No. C253, C269 Surcharged
1979
Perfs. & Printing Method as Before
C289A AP94 50fr on 60fr
       #C269   80.00 40.00
C289B AP87 50fr on 90fr
       #C253   80.00 40.00

Lunokhod I —
A101a

1980, June 15   Engr.   Perf. 13
Size: 27x48mm
C290 A101a210fr multi   3.00   1.40

For surcharges see Nos. C305, C450.

Soccer
Players — AP102

1981, Mar. 31   Litho.   Perf. 13
C291 AP102 200fr Ball, globe   2.00   .80
C292 AP102 500fr shown   5.00   2.00

ESPANA '82 World Soccer Cup eliminations.
For surcharges see Nos. C335, C455,
Q10B.

Prince Charles and Lady Diana,
London Bridge — AP103

1981, July 29   Litho.   Perf. 12½
C293 AP103 500fr multi   5.00   2.25

Royal wedding.
For surcharges see Nos. C323, C500.

Three Musicians, by Pablo Picasso
(1881-1973) — AP104

Perf. 12½x13, 13x12½
1981, Nov. 2   Litho.
C294 AP104 300fr Dance, vert.   3.25   1.25
C295 AP104 500fr shown   6.00   2.00

For surcharges see Nos. C320, C340.

1300th Anniv. of
Bulgaria
AP105

1981, Dec. 2   Litho.   Perf. 13
C296 AP105 100fr multi   1.00   .45

Visit of Pope John Paul II — AP106

1982, Feb. 17   Litho.   Perf. 13
C297 AP106 80fr multi   2.25   1.00

20th Anniv. of
John Glenn's
Flight — AP107

1982, Feb. 21   Litho.   Perf. 13
C298 AP107 500fr multi   6.00   2.50

For surcharge see No. C315.

Scouting
Year
AP108

1982, June 1   Perf. 12½
C299 AP108 105fr multi   1.25   .70

For surcharge see No. C324.

Nos. C256, C275 Surcharged

No. C300

No. C301

1982, Nov.   Engr.   Perf. 13
C300 AP88 50fr on 210fr multi   3.00   3.00
C301 AP96 50fr on 100fr multi   3.00   3.00

(Claude) Monet in His Studio Boat, by
(Edouard) Manet — AP109

1982, Dec. 6   Litho.   Perf. 13x12½
C302 AP109 300fr multi   7.00   2.50

For surcharge see No. C326.

Christmas
1982
AP110

Virgin and Child Paintings: 200fr, Matthias
Grunewald. 300fr, Correggio.

1982, Dec. 20   Perf. 12½x13
C303 AP110 200fr gold & multi   2.50   1.25
C304 AP110 300fr gold & multi   3.50   1.60

For surcharges see Nos. C325, C337.

No. C290
Surcharged

1983   Engr.   Perf. 13
C305 A133 75fr on 210fr multi   2.25   1.25

Bangkok
'83 Stamp
Exhibition
AP111

1983, Aug. 4   Photo.   Perf. 13
C306 AP111 300fr multi   3.25   1.50

For surcharge see No. C322.

Christmas
1983
AP112

200fr, Loretto Madonna, by Raphael.

1983, Dec. 26   Litho.   Perf. 12½x13
C307 AP112 200fr multicolored   3.00   1.20

For surcharge see No. C319.

Types of 1976-82 Surcharged

No. C308

No. C309

No. C310

No. C311

No. C312

No. C313

No. C314

No. C315

No. C316

No. C317

1983, Nov.

C308	AP94	10fr on 200fr C270	6.50	1.10
C309	AP95	15fr on 200fr C273	6.50	1.10
C310	AP90	15fr on 270fr C261	6.50	1.10
C311	AP98	20fr on 200fr C280	6.50	1.10
C312	AP89	25fr on 270fr C258	6.50	1.10
C313	AP98	25fr on 380fr C281	6.50	1.10
C314	AP96	30fr on 200fr C277	6.50	1.10
C315	AP107	40fr on 500fr C298	6.50	1.10
C316	AP93	75fr on 150fr C266	6.50	1.10
C317	AP95	75fr on 150fr C272	6.50	1.10
		Nos. C308-C317 (10)	65.00	11.00

Summer Olympics — AP113

300fr, Sam the Eagle, mascot.

1984, July 16 Litho. Perf. 13x13½
C318 AP113 300fr multicolored 3.25 1.50

Nos. C262, C293-C294, C299, C302, C304, C306-C307 Surcharged

No. C319

No. C320

No. C321

No. C322

1984, Sept.

C319	AP112	15fr on 200fr #C307	7.25	2.00
C320	AP104	15fr on 300fr #C294	7.25	2.00
C321	AP90	25fr on 200fr #C262	7.25	2.00
C322	AP111	25fr on 300fr #C306	7.25	2.00
C323	AP103	40fr on 500fr #C293	7.25	2.00
C324	AP108	75fr on 105fr #C299	7.25	2.00
C325	AP110	90fr on 200fr #C304	7.25	2.00
C326	AP109	90fr on 300fr #C302	7.25	2.00
		Nos. C319-C326 (8)	58.00	16.00

No. C323

No. C324

No. C325

No. C326

Christmas 1984 AP114

500fr, Virgin and Child, by Murillo.

1984, Dec. 17 Litho. Perf. 12½x13
C327 AP114 500fr multicolored 6.00 2.50
For surcharge see No. C486.

Ships — AP115

90fr, Sidon merchant ship. 125fr, Wavertree, vert.

1984, Dec. 28 Litho. Perf. 13
C328 AP115 90fr multicolored 1.40 .65
C329 AP115 125fr multicolored 2.25 .90

Benin-S.O.M. Postal Convention AP116

No. C330, Benin arms. No. C331, Sovereign Order of Malta.

Wmk. 385
1985, Apr. 15 Litho. Perf. 13½
C330 AP116 75fr multicolored .90 .30
C331 AP116 75fr multicolored .90 .30
a. Pair, #C330-C331 2.40 2.40

PHILEXAFRICA III, Lome — AP117

No. C332, Oil platform. No. C333, Soccer players.

1985, June 24 Perf. 13
C332 200fr multicolored 2.50 1.50
C333 200fr multicolored 2.50 1.50
a. AP117 Pair, #C332-C333 + label 6.00 4.50
For surcharges see Nos. C485-C485A.

Stamps of 1977-82 Surcharged

No. C334

No. C335

No. C336

No. C337

No. C338

No. C339

No. C340

1985, Mar.

C334	AP92	75fr on 200fr		
		#C264	10.00	2.50
C335	AP102	75fr on 200fr		
		#C291	10.00	2.50
C336	AP93	75fr on 300fr		
		#C267	10.00	2.50
C337	AP110	75fr on 300fr		
		#C304	10.00	2.50
C338	AP99	90fr on 500fr		
		#C284	10.00	2.50
C339	AP100	90fr on 500fr		
		#C287	10.00	2.50
C340	AP104	90fr on 500fr		
		#C295	10.00	2.50
	Nos. C334-C340 (7)		70.00	17.50

**Dahomey Stamps of 1971-75
Surcharged**

No. C341

No. C342

No. C343

No. C343A

No. C344

No. C345

No. C346

No. C347

No. C348

No. C349

No. C350

1985, Aug.

C341	AP87(i)	25fr on 40fr		
		#C266	6.00	1.10
C342	AP49(a)	40fr #C142	6.00	1.10
C343	AP56(i)	75fr on 85fr		
		#C164	6.00	1.10
C343A	AP56(b)(i)	75fr on 85fr		
		Daho-		
		mey		
		#C171	75.00	2.50
C344	AP60(a)	75fr on		
		100fr		
		#C173	6.00	1.10
C345	AP64(i)	75fr on		
		125fr		
		#C186	6.00	1.10
C346	AP56(i)	90fr on 20fr		
		#C163	6.00	1.10
C347	A61(i)	90fr on		
		150fr		
		#C153	6.00	1.10
C348	AP49(a)	90fr on		
		200fr		
		#C143	6.00	1.10
C349	AP78(j)	90fr on		
		200fr		
		#C237	6.00	1.10
C350	AP78(j)	150fr on #C236	6.00	1.10
	Nos. C341-C350 (11)		135.00	13.50

Christmas — AP118

1985, Dec. 20   Litho.   Perf. 13x12½
C351 AP118 500fr multi   5.50 3.00
For surcharge see No. C449.

**Dahomey Nos. C34-C37, C84, C131
Surcharged or Overprinted**

No. C352

No. C353

No. C354

No. C355

No. C356

No. C357

1986	Photo.		Perfs. as before	
C352	AP33(b)	75fr on 70fr		
		#C84	5.50	1.00
C353	AP14(b)	75fr on 100fr		
		#C34	5.50	1.00
C354	AP15(b)	75fr on 200fr		
		#C35	5.50	1.00
C355	AP15(b)	90fr on 250fr		
		#C36	5.50	1.00
C356	AP45(b)	100fr #C131	5.00	1.00
C357	AP14(b)	150fr on 500fr		
		#C37	5.00	1.00
	Nos. C352-C357 (6)		32.00	6.00

Issued: 75fr, 90fr, Mar; 100fr, 150fr, June.

Dahomey Nos. C82, C139, C141, C146, Benin No. C243 Surcharged

1986

Perfs. & Printing Methods as Before

C357A	AP33(d)	15fr on 45fr #C82	50.00	25.00
C357B	AP48(d)	25fr on 200fr #C141 (S)	50.00	25.00
C357C	AP84(d)	30fr on 300fr Benin #C243	40.00	25.00
C357D	AP48(d)	100fr on #C139	50.00	25.00
C357E	CD135(d)	100fr on #C146	60.00	25.00

Christmas — AP119

1986, Dec. 24   Litho.   Perf. 13x12½

C358	AP119	300fr multi	3.50	1.50

Air Africa, 25th Anniv. AP120

1986, Dec. 30   Perf. 12½

C359	AP120	100fr multi	1.10	.55

Intl. Agricultural Development Fund (FIDA), 10th Anniv. — AP121

1987, Dec. 14   Litho.   Perf. 13½

C360	AP121	500fr multi	5.00	2.50

Christmas — AP122

500fr, Adoration of the Magi, storyteller.

1988, Dec. 23   Litho.   Perf. 13x12½

C361	AP122	500fr multi	5.00	2.40

No. C241 Surcharged

1989, Apr. 24   Litho.   Perf. 13

C362	AP84(b)	15fr on 85fr multi	30.00	15.00

Dahomey Nos. C37, C53, C152, C156, C165, C175, C182, C234, Benin No. C242 Surcharged or Overprinted

1987

Perfs. & Printing Methods as Before

C363	AP77	20fr on 250fr #C234	50.00	20.00
C364	AP48(b)	25fr on 150fr #C175 (S&B)	50.00	20.00
C365	AP63(b)	40fr on 15fr #C182	42.50	20.00
C366	AP48(b)	40fr on 100fr #C152	40.00	20.00
C367	AP84(b)	50fr on 140fr #C242	50.00	25.00
C368	AP14(b)	50fr on 500fr #C37	50.00	25.00
C369	AP22(b)	80fr on #C53	50.00	25.00
C370	AP56(b)	80fr on 100fr #C165	50.00	25.00
C373	AP52(b)	100fr on #C156	50.00	20.00

Dahomey Nos. C140, C144, C158, C166, C177, C185, C188 C191, C195, C207, C233, C260, C262 Surcharged

No. C376

No. C382

1988

Perfs. & Printing Methods as Before

C374	AP50(d)	10fr on 50fr #C144	50.00	25.00
C375	AP64(d)	10fr on 65fr #C185	50.00	25.00
C376	AP72(d)	15fr on 150fr #C207	50.00	25.00
C377	AP67(d)	25fr on 200fr #C191	50.00	25.00
C378	AP61(d)	40fr on 35fr #C195	50.00	25.00
C380	AP53(d)	70fr on 250fr #C158	50.00	25.00
C381	AP48(d)	100fr on #C140	30.00	15.00
C382	AP65(d)	100fr on #C188	40.00	20.00
C383	AP84(d)	100fr on #C260	45.00	20.00
C384	AP61(f)	125fr on #C177	40.00	20.00
C385	AP86(d)	125fr on 75fr #C262	45.00	20.00
C386	AP57(d)	150fr on 100fr #C166	50.00	20.00
C387	AP77(d)	190fr on 100fr #C233	45.00	20.00

Dahomey Nos. C179, C181, C196, C203, C208 Surcharged in Black or Violet

1988-89

Perfs. & Printing Methods as Before

C388	AP61(d)	25fr on 100fr #C196	60.00	30.00
C390	AP62	40fr on 100fr #C181	60.00	30.00
C391	AP73(d)	40fr on 150fr #C208	45.00	25.00

C391A	AP70(j)	125fr on 150fr #C203 (V)	45.00	25.00
C392	AP61(d)	125fr on 250fr #C179	45.00	25.00
C393	AP87(d)	190fr on 250fr Dah. #C267	75.00	40.00

Issued: No. C391A, 1989.

Dahomey Nos. C108, C147-C148, C162, C167, C178, C187, C194 Surcharged or Overprinted

No. C394A

1992

Perfs. & Printing Methods as Before

C394	AP51(f)	70fr on #C148	60.00	30.00
C394A	AP51(e)	70fr on #C148	60.00	30.00
C395	AP55(e)	100fr on #C162	45.00	25.00
C396	AP68(g)	100fr on #C194	120.00	60.00
C397	AP51(e)	125fr on 40fr #C147	20.00	12.50
C398	A52(f)	125fr on 70fr #C108	60.00	30.00
C400	AP64a(e)	125fr on 100fr #C187	45.00	25.00
C401	AP61(f)	190fr on 140fr #C178	45.00	25.00
C402	AP58(f)	190fr on 150fr #C167	60.00	30.00

Dahomey Nos. C145, C149-C150, C163, C182, C189, C198, C257, C264 Surcharged, Benin No. C241 Surcharged

No. C407A

1993

Perfs. & Printing Methods as Before

C403	AP51(e)	5fr on 100fr #C149	45.00	25.00
C404	AP50(f)	10fr on 100fr #C145	45.00	25.00
C404A	AP56(f)	20fr on #C163	30.00	15.00
C405	AP51(f)	20fr on 200fr #C150	50.00	35.00
C406	AP83(f)	20fr on 500fr #C257	50.00	35.00
C407	AP84(e)	25fr on 85fr #C241	45.00	25.00
C407A	AP84(f)	25fr on 85fr #C241		25.00
C409	AP63(f)	30fr on 15fr #C182	32.50	15.00
C410	AP61(f)	30fr on 200fr #C198	21.00	12.50

C411	AP66(b)	35fr on #C189	45.00	25.00
C412	AP86(g)	300fr on #C264	50.00	25.00

Dahomey Nos. C14, C31, C33, C34, C54, C101, C110, C128, C144, C151, C152, C153, C155, C179, C191, C197, C198, C203, C222, C234, C236, C250, C253, C254-C256, C261, Benin C240, C242 Surcharged or Overprinted

No. C420

1994-95?

Perfs. & Printing Methods as Before

C413	AP61(g)	10fr on 100fr #C253	85.00	40.00
C414	AP52(e)	15fr on 40fr #C155	45.00	25.00
C415	AP83(f)	25fr on 200fr #C256	50.00	25.00
C416	AP83(f)	35fr on #C255	45.00	25.00
C417	AP49(g)	50fr on #C101	62.50	35.00
C418	AP48(g)	75fr on 40fr #C151	40.00	20.00
C419	AP4(g)	100fr on #C14	40.00	20.00
C420	AP22(h)	100fr on #C54	50.00	25.00
C421	AP50(e)	125fr on 50fr #C144	40.00	20.00
C422	AP75(e)	135fr on 65fr #C222	40.00	20.00
C424	AP84(g)	135fr on 40fr #C240	50.00	—
C425	AP21(f)	135fr on 45fr #C110	62.50	—
C426	AP14(e)	135fr on 50fr #C33	62.50	—
C429	AP43(e)	135fr on 70fr #C128	90.00	—
C430	AP81(f)	135fr on 250fr #C250	50.00	—
C431	AP61(g)	135fr on 250fr #C254	50.00	25.00
C432	AP84(f)	150fr on 140fr #C242	25.00	15.00
C433	A61(b)	150fr on #C153	75.00	
C434	AP61(f)	150fr on #C197	50.00	25.00
C435	AP13(e)	200fr on 100fr #C31	125.00	65.00
C436	AP14(e)	200fr on 100fr #C34	50.00	25.00
C437	AP48(e)	200fr on 100fr #C152	45.00	20.00
C439	AP61(e)	200fr on 100fr #C253	45.00	25.00
C440	AP78(f)	200fr on 150fr #C236	80.00	40.00
C441	AP67(f)	200fr on #C191	60.00	35.00
C442	AP61(g)	200fr on #C198	45.00	20.00
C444	AP61(e)	200fr on 250fr #C179	45.00	—
C445	AP61(e)	200fr on 250fr #C234	75.00	
C446	AP61(e)	200fr on 250fr #C254	50.00	
C447	AP85(f)	300fr on #C261	65.00	35.00

Benin No. C351 Surcharged

1994-95

Printing Method and Perfs as Before

C449	AP118	200fr on 500fr #C351	60.00	30.00

Benin No. C290 Surcharged,
Dahomey Nos. C206, C257
Surcharged

1996?
Perfs. & Printing Methods as Before
C450 A133   40fr on 210fr
         #C290   60.00 30.00
C451 AP83(f) 200fr on 500fr
         #C257   65.00 35.00
C452 AP72(f) 1000fr on 150fr
         #C206   50.00 25.00

Dahomey No. C265 Surcharged,
Benin Nos. C258, C292 Surcharged

1996?
Perfs. & Printing Methods as Before
C453 AP86(g) 25fr on 500fr
         #C265   42.50 25.00
C454 AP89   35fr on 270fr
         #C258   62.50   —
C455 AP102 100fr on 500fr
         #C292   62.50 30.00

Dahomey Nos. C61, C74, C85, C88,
C94, C106, C109, C111, C113, C115,
C120, C124-C125, C130, C135-C136,
C138, C142-C143, C150, C157, C204-
C205, C207-C208, C260, C263
Surcharged

No. C458

No. C461

No. C464

No. C465

No. C467

No. C469

No. C471

No. C474

No. C475

No. C476

No. C478

No. C479

No. C480

No. C482

1996?
Perfs. & Printing Methods as Before
C456	AP48(e)	70fr on 100fr		
		#C138	75.00	40.00
C457	AP34(h)	150fr on #C88	35.00	—
C458	AP21(e)	150fr on		
		#C115	45.00	—
C459	AP72(e)	150fr on		
		#C207	35.00	—
C460	AP73(h)	150fr on		
		#C208	35.00	—
C461	AP34(e)	150fr on 30fr		
		#C85	40.00	—
C462	AP31(h)	150fr on 30fr		
		#C74	35.00	—
C463	AP21(e)	150fr on 30fr		
		#C109	35.00	—
C464	AP40(e)	150fr on 40fr on 30fr		
		#C120	35.00	—
C465	AP47(e)	150fr on 40fr		
		#C136	35.00	—
C466	AP49(e)	150fr on 40fr		
		#C142	35.00	—
C467	CD128(h)	150fr on 50fr		
		#C94	40.00	—
C468	AP38(h)	150fr on 50fr		
		#C106	27.50	—
C469	AP71(e)	150fr on 50fr		
		#C204	35.00	—
C470	AP54(h)	150fr on 70fr		
		#C124	35.00	—
C471	CD124(h)	150fr on 100fr		
		#C61	35.00	—
C472	AP21(e)	150fr on 100fr		
		#C113	35.00	—
C473	AP53(h)	150fr on 100fr		
		#C157	29.00	—
C474	AP84(h)	150fr on 100fr		
		#C260	12.50	—
C475	AP21(h)	150fr on 110fr		
		#C111	35.00	—
C476	AP44(h)	150fr on 110fr		
		#C130	40.00	—
C477	AP54(h)	150fr on 120fr		
		#C125	35.00	—
C478	AP86(g)	150fr on 135fr		
		#C263	62.50	—
C479	AP46(h)	150fr on 200fr		
		#C135	35.00	—
C480	AP49(e)	150fr on 200fr		
		#C143	35.00	—
C481	AP51(h)	150fr on 200fr		
		#C150	35.00	—
C482	AP71(e)	150fr on 200fr		
		#C205	29.00	—

Benin Nos. C261, C281, C327, C332-
C333 Surcharged, Dahomey Nos.
C201, C127, C175 Surcharged

No. C483

No. C488

1996-97?
Perfs. & Printing Methods as Before
C483	AP98	30fr on 380fr		
		#C281	42.50	20.00
C484	AP90	35fr on 270fr		
		#C261	60.00	35.00
C485	AP117	125fr on 200fr		
		#C332	35.00	15.00
C485A	AP117	125fr on 200fr		
		#C333	35.00	15.00
C486	AP114	200fr on 500fr		
		#C327	60.00	30.00
C488	AP43(h)	150fr on 40fr		
		#C127	22.50	—
C489	AP70(f)	150fr on 50fr		
		#C201	35.00	15.00
C490	AP48(e)	200fr on 150fr		
		#C175	62.50	35.00

No. C256, C268, C278 Surcharged

No. C494

No. C497

Method and Perf. as Before
1995-96 ?
C494	AP88	40fr on 210fr		
		#C256 ('96)	50.00	25.00
C496	AP93	150fr on 500fr		
		#C268	30.00	15.00
C497	AP96	150fr on 500fr		
		#C278	22.50	12.00

Benin No. C293 Surcharged,
Dahomey Nos. C147, C250
Surcharged Type e or f

No. C503

1995-97?
Perf. & Printing Methods as Before
C500	AP103	150fr on 500fr		
		#C293	22.50	—
C503	AP51(e)	135fr on 40fr		
		#C147	70.00	35.00
C509	AP81(f)	150fr on 250fr		
		#C250	80.00	40.00

Dahomey Nos. #C86, C126, C70 Surcharged

No. C513

1995-99?
Perfs. & Printing Methods as Before

C513	AP34(h)	35fr on 45fr #C86	80.00	40.00
C515	AP42(h)	35fr on 100fr on 200fr #C126	80.00	40.00
C516	AP29(h)	35fr on 100fr #C70	50.00	25.00

Dahomey Nos. C72, C93, C105, C112, C139, C168, C223, Benin Nos. C285-C286 Surcharged or Overprinted

No. C523

No. C537

Method and Perf. as Before 1997 ?

C517	AP30(h)	35fr on 55fr Dahomey #C72	80.00	40.00
C522	AP35(h)	35fr on 100fr Dahomey #C93	50.00	25.00
C523	A51(h)	35fr on 100fr Dahomey #C105	50.00	25.00
C526	AP48(h)	35fr on 100fr #C139	80.00	40.00
C530	AP75(h)	35fr on 125fr Dahomey #C223	80.00	40.00
C532	AP21(h)	35fr on 200fr Dahomey #C112	80.00	40.00
C535	CD138(h)	100fr on #C285	50.00	25.00
C536	CD139(h)	100fr on #C286	50.00	25.00
C537	AP58	300fr on 200fr Dahomey #C168	30.00	20.00

Dahomey Nos. C15, C172, C206, C224, C256, C257 Surcharged or Overprinted

No. C538

No. C539

No. C540

No. C541

No. C542

No. C543

Method and Perf. as Before 1997 ?

C538	AP56(f)	175fr on 150fr Dahomey #C172	50.00	35.00
C539	AP72(f)	175fr on 150fr Dahomey #C206	50.00	35.00
C540	AP75(f)	300fr on 200fr Dahomey #C224	55.00	30.00
C541	AP4(f)	500fr on Dahomey #C15	40.00	25.00
C542	AP63(f)	500fr on 200fr Dahomey #C256	30.00	20.00
C543	AP63(f)	500fr on Dahomey #C257	40.00	25.00

Dahomey Nos. C36, C48, C141, C150, C191, C237, C256, C261, C264, C265 Overprinted Types "f" or "g"
Methods and Perfs As Before 2005-09 (?)

C544	AP21(g)	200fr multi (#C48)	50.00	25.00
C545	AP48(g)	200fr multi (#C141)	35.00	15.00
C546	AP51(g)	200fr multi (#C150)	40.00	20.00
C547	AP67(g)	200fr multi (#C191)	40.00	20.00
C548	AP78(g)	200fr multi (#C237)	100.00	50.00
C549	AP83(g)	200fr multi (#C256)	125.00	65.00
C550	AP15(f)	250fr multi (#C36)	80.00	40.00
C554	AP35(f)	300fr multi (#C261)	55.00	30.00
C555	AP86(f)	300fr multi (#C264)	30.00	20.00
C557	AP86(f)	500fr multi (#C265)	35.00	20.00

Various Stamps of Dahomey and Benin Surcharged Type "f" or "k"
Methods and Perfs As Before 2005-09 (?)

C558	AP63(k)	25fr on 15fr Dah. #C182	125.00	70.00
C559	AP56(k)	25fr on 20fr Dah. #C163	40.00	20.00
C560	AP63(k)	25fr on 20fr Dah. #C183	110.00	60.00
C561	AP30(k)	50fr on 30fr Dah. #C71	25.00	12.00
C562	AP31(k)	50fr on 30fr Dah. #C74	25.00	12.00
C563	AP35(k)	50fr on 30fr Dah. #C89	30.00	15.00
C564	AP66(k)	50fr on 35fr Dah. #C189	40.00	20.00
C565	AP61(k)	50fr on 35fr Dah. #C195	25.00	12.00
C566	AP43(k)	50fr on 40fr Dah. #C127	25.00	12.00
C567	AP47(k)	50fr on 40fr Dah. #C136	150.00	75.00
C568	AP49(k)	50fr on 40fr Dah. #C142	40.00	20.00
C569	AP52(k)	50fr on 40fr Dah. #C155	40.00	20.00
C570	AP62(k)	50fr on 40fr Dah. #C180	60.00	30.00
C571	AP63(k)	50fr on 40fr Dah. #C184	75.00	40.00
C572	AP24(f)	175fr on 70fr Dah. #C58	40.00	20.00
C574	AP32(f)	175fr on 70fr Dah. #C79	35.00	20.00
C576	AP86(f)	175fr on 135fr Dah. #C263	17.50	10.00
C578	AP48(f)	175fr on 150fr Dah. #C175	30.00	20.00
C579	AP72(f)	175fr on 150fr Dah. #C207	40.00	25.00
C580	AP83(k)	200fr on 35fr Dah. #C255	100.00	50.00
C581	AP51(k)	200fr on 40fr Dah. #C147	35.00	17.50
C582	AP87(k)	200fr on 40fr Dah. #C266	40.00	20.00
C583	AP84(k)	200fr on 40fr Ben. #C240	40.00	20.00
C584	AP33(k)	200fr on 45fr Dah. #C82	60.00	30.00
C585	AP50(k)	200fr on 50fr Dah. #C144	35.00	17.50
C586	AP75(k)	200fr on 65fr Dah. #C222	125.00	70.00
C587	AP28(k)	200fr on 70fr Dah. #C68	40.00	20.00
C588	AP86(k)	200fr on 75fr Dah. #C262	35.00	17.50
C589	AP84(k)	200fr on 85fr Ben. #C241	100.00	50.00
C590	AP14(k)	200fr on 100fr Dah. #C34	110.00	60.00
C591	AP68(k)	200fr on 100fr Dah. #C194	50.00	25.00
C592	AP48(k)	300fr on 40fr Dah. #C151	60.00	30.00
C593	AP66(k)	300fr on 40fr Dah. #C190	35.00	17.50
C594	AP32(k)	300fr on 45fr Dah. #C78	75.00	40.00
C595	AP21(k)	300fr on 45fr Dah. #C110	35.00	17.50
C596	A49(k)	300fr on 50fr Dah. #C101	20.00	10.00
C597	AP70(k)	300fr on 50fr Dah. #C201	35.00	17.50
C598	AP71(k)	300fr on 50fr Dah. #C204	100.00	50.00
C599	AP36(k)	300fr on 60fr Dah. #C98	70.00	35.00
C600	AP54(k)	300fr on 65fr Dah. #C161	35.00	17.50
C601	AP64(k)	300fr on 65fr Dah. #C185	50.00	25.00
C602	AP24(k)	300fr on 70fr Dah. #C58	40.00	20.00
C603	AP31(k)	300fr on 70fr Dah. #C76	40.00	20.00
C604	AP51(k)	300fr on 70fr Dah. #C148	35.00	17.50
C605	AP36(k)	300fr on 75fr Dah. #C99	70.00	35.00
C606	AP22(k)	300fr on 80fr Dah. #C53	85.00	42.50
C607	AP56(b)(k)	300fr on 85fr Dah. #C171	40.00	20.00
C608	AP44(k)	300fr on 90fr Dah. #C129	40.00	20.00
C609	AP4(k)	300fr on 100fr Dah. #C14	25.00	12.50
C610	AP6(k)	300fr on 100fr Dah. #C20	25.00	12.50
C611	AP10(k)	300fr on 100fr Dah. #C28	40.00	20.00
C612	AP22(k)	300fr on 100fr Dah. #C54	60.00	30.00
C613	AP30(k)	300fr on 100fr Dah. #C73	35.00	17.50
C614	AP32(k)	300fr on 100fr Dah. #C80	80.00	40.00
C615	AP35(k)	300fr on 100fr Dah. #C91	35.00	17.50
C616	AP45(k)	300fr on 100fr Dah. #C131	35.00	17.50
C617	AP48(k)	300fr on 100fr Dah. #C139	35.00	17.50
C618	AP48(k)	300fr on 100fr Dah. #C140	35.00	17.50
C619	CD135(k)	300fr on 100fr Dah. #C146	60.00	30.00
C620	AP55(k)	300fr on 100fr Dah. #C162	40.00	20.00
C621	AP57(k)	300fr on 100fr Dah. #C166	40.00	20.00
C622	AP60(k)	300fr on 100fr Dah. #C173	40.00	20.00
C623	AP62(k)	300fr on 100fr Dah. #C181	40.00	20.00
C624	AP65(k)	300fr on 100fr Dah. #C188	40.00	20.00
C625	AP69(k)	300fr on 100fr Dah. #C200	35.00	17.50

C626	AP77(k)	300fr on 100fr Dah. #C233	40.00	20.00
C628	AP61(k)	400fr on 35fr Dah. #C176	40.00	20.00
C629	AP35(k)	400fr on 100fr Dah. #C93	40.00	20.00
C630	AP50(k)	400fr on 100fr Dah. #C145	35.00	17.50
C631	AP51(k)	400fr on 100fr Dah. #C149	40.00	20.00
C632	AP70(k)	400fr on 125fr Dah. #C202	40.00	20.00
C634	AP70(k)	1000fr on 150fr Dah. #C203	30.00	15.00
C635	AP73(k)	1000fr on 150fr Dah. #C208	70.00	35.00
C636	AP78(k)	1000fr on 150fr Dah. #C236	90.00	45.00

There are three surcharge types on No. C560. Values are for the least expensive type.

Dahomey Nos. C92, C116, C138, C152, C153, C157, C158, C167, C186, C192, C197, C207, C250 and C253 Surcharged
Methods and Perfs As Before
2009

C637	AP39(k)	400fr on 100fr #C116	30.00	15.00
C638	AP48(k)	400fr on 100fr #C138	40.00	20.00
C639	AP48(k)	400fr on 100fr #C152	30.00	15.00
C640	AP53(k)	400fr on 100fr #C157	25.00	15.00
C641	AP61(k)	400fr on 100fr #C253	40.00	20.00
C642	AP64(k)	400fr on 125fr #C186	50.00	25.00
C643	AP58(k)	400fr on 150fr #C167	25.00	15.00
C644	AP68(k)	1000fr on 35fr #C192	60.00	30.00
C645	A61(k)	1000fr on 150fr #C153	40.00	20.00
C646	AP61(k)	1000fr on 150fr #C197	40.00	20.00
C647	AP72(k)	1000fr on 150fr #C207	90.00	45.00
C648	AP35(k)	1000fr on 200fr #C92	25.00	15.00
C649	AP53(k)	1000fr on 250fr #C158	25.00	15.00
C650	AP81(k)	1000fr on 250fr #C250	40.00	20.00
		Nos. C637-C650 (14)	560.00	290.00

Dahomey No. C164 Surcharged
2009   **Method and Perf. As Before**

| C651A | AP56(k) | 300fr on 85fr
Dah.
#C164 | 40.00 | 20.00 |

Dahomey No. C177 Surcharged
2009   **Method and Perf. As Before**

| C652 | AP61(k) | 400fr on 125fr
Dahomey
#C177 | 40.00 | 20.00 |

Dahomey No. C223 Surcharged
2009   **Method and Perf. As Before**

| C653 | AP75(k) | 400fr on 125fr
#C223 | 50.00 | 25.00 |

POSTAGE DUE STAMPS

French Colony

Handstamped in Black on Postage Due Stamps of French Colonies

---

1894		**Unwmk.**		**Imperf.**
J1	D1	5c black	175.00	70.00
J2	D1	10c black	175.00	70.00
J3	D1	20c black	175.00	70.00
J4	D1	30c black	175.00	70.00
		Nos. J1-J4 (4)	700.00	280.00

Nos. J1-J4 exist with overprint in various positions.

> Catalogue values for unused stamps in this section are for Never Hinged items.

People's Republic

Pineapples D6

Mail Delivery D7

Designs: 20fr, Cashew, vert. 40fr, Oranges. 50fr, Akee. 80fr, Mail delivery by boat.

1978, Sept. 5			**Photo.**	**Perf. 13**
J44	D6	10fr multicolored	.30	.25
J45	D6	20fr multicolored	.55	.45
J46	D6	40fr multicolored	1.00	.65
J47	D6	50fr multicolored	1.40	.90

Engr.

J48	D7	60fr multi	1.10	.65
J49	D7	80fr multi	1.40	.90
		Nos. J44-J49 (6)	5.75	3.80

PARCEL POST STAMPS

> Catalogue values for unused stamps in this section are for Never Hinged items.

Nos. 448-448A, 459, 473, C292 Overprinted or Surcharged "Colis Postaux"

No. Q8

No. Q9

No. Q10

No. Q10A

No. Q10B

Perfs. and Printing Methods as Before

1982, Nov.

Q8	A126	100fr on 150fr	20.00	12.50
Q9	A130	100fr multi	70.00	35.00
Q10	A134	300fr multi	20.00	12.50
Q10A	A126a	1000fr multi	25.00	12.50
Q10B	AP102	5000fr on 500fr	70.00	35.00
		Nos. Q8-Q10B (5)	205.00	107.50

No. 358 Overprinted "COLIS / POSTAUX" Vertically Reading Down
Method and Perf as Before

1984 ?

| Q10C | A88 | 50fr multi | 170.00 | 85.00 |

Dahomey No. C205 Surcharged

| 1989 | | | **Photo.** | **Perf. 12½x13** |
| Q11 | AP71 | 500fr on 200fr multi | 25.00 | 12.50 |

Dahomey No. C224, Benin Nos. 344, 349, 354, 367, 495, 499, C254, C278 Overprinted or Surcharged

No. Q14

Methods and Perfs as Before

1989-90

Q12	A87	5fr multi (#354)	70.00	35.00
Q13	A144	15fr on 50fr multi (#499)	35.00	17.50
Q14	A91	60fr on 150fr multi (#367)	50.00	25.00
Q15	A142	75fr on 50fr multi (#495)	35.00	17.50

Q16	A85	200fr multi (#349)	50.00	25.00
Q16A	A85	200fr multi (#349)	50.00	25.00
Q16B	A85	200fr multi (#349)	—	—
Q17	AP87	250fr multi (#C254)	50.00	25.00
Q17A	AP87	250fr multi (#C254)	50.00	25.00
Q17B	AP75	300fr on 200fr multi (Da- homey #C224)	50.00	25.00
Q18	AP96	500fr multi (#C278)	70.00	35.00
Q18A	A83	500fr on 45fr multi (#344)	90.00	45.00

Nos. Q14, Q15 have "Republique de Benin" overprint.

Nos. Q16 and Q17 have overprint in sans-serif type. Nos. Q16A and Q17A have overprint in serifed type.

Nos. Q16A, Q16B, Q17, Q17A have obliterator over "POPULAIRE." No. Q16B has overprint in sans-serif type.

Nos. 375, 378, C246 Surcharged or Overprinted "Colis Postaux"
Methods and Perfs as Before

1998

Q20	A96	60fr on 150fr multi (#378)	50.00	25.00
Q21	A95	100fr multi (#375)	50.00	25.00
Q22	AP85	300fr multi (#C246)	90.00	45.00

Dahomey No. C157, Benin Nos. 368, C254 Overprinted "COLIS / POSTAUX"

1998 ? Method and Perf as Before

Q25	A92	10fr on #368	350.00	225.00
Q25A	AP53	10fr on 10fr (Daho- mey #C157)	175.00	100.00
Q26	AP87	5000fr on 250fr (#C254)	50.00	25.00
Q27	AP87	5000fr on 250fr (#C254)	50.00	25.00

No. Q25A has the overprinted word "Populaire" obliterated. No. Q26 has "Colis Postaux" in sans-serif type. Nos. Q27 has "Colis Postaux" in serifed type.

No. 378 Surcharged With "Colis Postaux" in Serifed Type
Method and Perf. As Before

2009 (?)

| Q33 | A96 | 60fr on 150fr #378 | 50.00 | 25.00 |

No. Q20 has "Colis Postaux" in sans-serif type.

BERMUDA

ˌbər-'myü-də

LOCATION — A group of about 150 small islands of which only 20 are inhabited, lying in the Atlantic Ocean about 580 miles southeast of Cape Hatteras.
GOVT. — British Crown Colony
AREA — 20.5 sq. mi.
POP. — 62,471 (1999 est.)
CAPITAL — Hamilton

Bermuda achieved internal self-government in 1968.

4 Farthings = 1 Penny
12 Pence = 1 Shilling
20 Shillings = 1 Pound
100 Cents = 1 Dollar (1970)

> Catalogue values for unused stamps in this country are for Never Hinged items, beginning with Scott 131.

POSTMASTER STAMPS

PM1

1848-56   **Unwmk.**   *Imperf.*
X1	PM1	1p blk, *bluish* (1848)		180,000.
a.		Dated 1849		200,000.
X2	PM1	1p red, *bluish* (1856)		200,000.
a.		Dated 1854		400,000.
X3	PM1	1p red (1853)		200,000.

PM2

Same inscribed "ST GEORGES"
1860
X4	PM2	(1p) red, *yellowish*	100,000.

Same inscribed "HAMILTON"
1861
X5	PM2	(1p) red, *bluish*	140,000.	130,000.
X6	PM2	(1p) red		38,500.

Nos. X1-X3 were produced and used by Postmaster William B. Perot of Hamilton. No. X4 is attributed to Postmaster James H. Thies of St. George's.

Only a few of each stamp exist. Values reflect actual sales figures for stamps in the condition in which they are found.

GENERAL ISSUES

Values for unused stamps are for examples with original gum as defined in the catalogue introduction. Very fine examples of Nos. 1-1a, 2-15b will have perforations touching the design (or frameline where applicable) on at least one side due to the narrow spacing of the stamps on the plates. Stamps with perfs clear of the design on all four sides are scarce and will command higher prices.

Queen Victoria
A1   A2

A3   A4

A5

1865-74   **Typo.**   **Wmk. 1**   *Perf. 14*
1	A1	1p rose red	110.00	1.75
b.		Imperf.	85,000.	27,000.
2	A2	2p blue ('66)	525.00	40.00
3	A3	3p buff ('73)	600.00	80.00
4	A4	6p brown lilac	2,300.	90.00
5	A4	6p lilac ('74)	30.00	17.00
6	A5	1sh green	450.00	70.00
		Nos. 1-6 (6)	4,015.	298.75

See Nos. 7-9, 19-21, 23, 25. For surcharges see Nos. 10-15.
No. 1b is a proof.

1882-1903   *Perf. 14x12½*
7	A3	3p buff	210.00	75.00
8	A4	6p violet ('03)	17.00	27.50
9	A5	1sh green ('94)	200.00	150.00
a.		Vert. strip of 3, perf. all around & imperf. btwn.	13,750.	
		Nos. 7-9 (3)	247.00	252.50

Handstamped Diagonally

1874   *Perf. 14*
10	A5	3p on 1sh green	1,700.	950.

Handstamped Diagonally

11	A1	3p on 1p rose	19,000.	20,000.
12	A5	3p on 1sh green	2,850.	975.
a.		"P" with top like "R"	2,300.	1,100.

No. 11 is stated to be an essay, but a few examples are known used. Nos. 10-12 are found with double or partly double surcharges.

Surcharged in Black   One Penny.

1875
13	A2	1p on 2p blue	875.00	475.00
a.		Without period	27,500.	13,250.
14	A3	1p on 3p buff	550.00	425.00
15	A5	1p on 1sh green	675.00	310.00
a.		Inverted surcharge	—	50,000.
b.		Without period	40,000.	20,000.

A6   A7

1880   **Wmk. 1**
16	A6	½p brown	8.75	5.25
17	A7	4p orange	21.00	2.50

See Nos. 18, 24.

A8

1883-1904   **Wmk. 2**
18	A6	½p dp gray grn ('93)	5.00	1.00
a.		½p green ('92)	9.00	4.50
19	A1	1p aniline car ('89)	21.00	.30
a.		1p dull rose	200.00	5.25
b.		1p rose red	100.00	4.00
c.		1p carmine rose ('86)	75.00	1.00
20	A2	2p blue ('86)	75.00	8.25
21	A2	2p brn pur ('98)	6.00	2.75
a.		2p aniline pur ('93)	17.50	6.00
22	A8	2½p ultra ('84)	24.00	.50
a.		2½p deep ultra	37.50	3.75
23	A3	3p gray ('86)	27.50	11.00
24	A7	4p brown org ('04)	37.50	62.50
25	A5	1sh ol bis ('93)	19.00	24.00
a.		1sh yellow brown	25.00	24.00
		Nos. 18-25 (8)	215.00	110.30

ONE FARTHING   A9

1901   **Black Surcharge**
26	A9	1f on 1sh gray	6.00	1.25

Dry Dock — A10

1902-03
28	A10	½p gray grn & blk ('03)	15.00	4.50
29	A10	1p car rose & brown	10.00	.35
30	A10	3p ol grn & violet	6.50	3.50
		Nos. 28-30 (3)	31.50	8.35

1906-10   **Wmk. 3**
31	A10	¼p pur & brn ('08)	2.10	1.90
32	A10	½p gray grn & blk	24.00	1.25
33	A10	½p green ('09)	25.00	4.50
34	A10	1p car rose & brn	45.00	.25
35	A10	1p carmine ('08)	26.00	.50
36	A10	2p orange & gray	9.25	13.50
37	A10	2½p blue & brown	35.00	9.50
38	A10	2½p ultra ('10)	28.00	9.50
39	A10	4p vio brn & blue ('09)	3.75	20.00
		Nos. 31-39 (9)	198.10	60.90

Caravel   King George V
A11   A12

1910-24   **Engr.**   *Perf. 14*
40	A11	¼p brown ('12)	2.10	3.00
a.		¼p pale brown	2.50	1.75
41	A11	½p yel green	3.75	.30
a.		½p dark green ('18)	15.00	1.50
42	A11	1p red (I)	20.00	.35
a.		1p carmine (I) ('19)	67.50	10.00
43	A11	2p gray ('13)	6.50	21.00
44	A11	2½p ultra (I) ('12)	4.25	.75
45	A11	3p vio, *yel* ('13)	3.50	7.50
46	A11	4p red, *yel* ('19)	14.00	16.00
47	A11	6p claret ('24)	12.50	9.00
48	A11	1sh blk, *grn* ('12)	6.50	5.00
a.		1sh black, *olive* ('25)	6.50	23.00

Typographed
Chalky Paper
49	A12	2sh ultra & dl vio, *bl* ('20)	22.50	62.50
50	A12	2sh6p red & blk, *bl*	37.50	100.00
51	A12	4sh car & blk ('20)	75.00	200.00

52	A12	5sh red & grn, *yellow*	75.00	150.00
53	A12	10sh red & grn, *green*	225.00	425.00
54	A12	£1 blk & vio, *red*	400.00	700.00
		Nos. 40-54 (15)	908.10	1,700.

Types I of 1p and 2½p are illustrated above Nos. 81-97.
The 1p was printed from two plates, the 2nd of which, No. 42a, exists only in carmine on opaque paper with a bluish tinge. Compare No. MR1 (as No. 42) and MR2 (as No. 42a). Revenue cancellations are found on Nos. 52-54.
See Nos. 81-97.

Seal of the Colony and King George V
A13

1920-21   **Wmk. 3**   **Ordinary Paper**
55	A13	¼p brown	4.00	28.00
56	A13	½p green	9.50	19.00
57	A13	2p gray	18.00	55.00

Chalky Paper
58	A13	3p vio & dl vio, *yel*	15.00	55.00
59	A13	4p red & blk, *yel*	15.00	42.50
60	A13	1sh blk, *gray grn*	25.00	65.00

Ordinary Paper
Wmk. 4
67	A13	1p rose red	4.50	.35
68	A13	2½p ultra	19.00	20.00

Chalky Paper
69	A13	6p red vio & dl vio	32.50	95.00
		Nos. 55-60,67-69 (9)	142.50	379.85

Issued: 6p, 1/19/21; others, 11/11/20.

King George V
A14

1921, May 12   **Engr.**
71	A14	¼p brown	4.25	4.50
72	A14	½p green	3.50	9.00
73	A14	1p carmine	12.00	.45

Wmk. 3
74	A14	2p gray	12.00	55.00
75	A14	2½p ultra	15.00	7.00
76	A14	3p vio, *orange*	7.00	20.00
77	A14	4p scarlet, *org*	20.00	42.50
78	A14	6p claret	19.00	65.00
79	A14	1sh blk, *green*	29.00	65.00
		Nos. 71-79 (9)	121.75	268.45

Tercentenary of "Local Representative Institutions" (Nos. 55-79).

Types of 1910-20 Issue

Type I

Types of 1p

Type II

Type III

Type I, figure "1" has pointed serifs, scroll at top left very weak.

Type II, thick "1" with square serifs, scroll weak.
Type III, thinner "1" with long square serifs, scroll complete with strong line.

Types of 2½p

Type I

Type II

Type I, small "d," short, thick figures of value.
Type II, larger "d," taller, thinner figures of value.

			1922-34		Wmk. 4	
81	A11	¼p brown ('28)			1.90	3.75
82	A11	½p green			1.90	.25
83	A11	1p car, III ('28)			17.00	.35
a.		1p carmine, II ('26)			55.00	8.50
b.		1p carmine, I			21.00	.75
84	A11	1½p red brn ('34)			11.00	.45
85	A11	2p gray ('23)			1.90	1.90
86	A11	2½p ap grn ('23)			3.75	1.90
87	A11	2½p ultra, II ('32)			2.10	.90
a.		2½p ultra, I ('26)			5.50	.60
88	A11	3p ultra ('24)			20.00	32.50
89	A11	3p vio, yel ('26)			5.00	1.25
90	A11	4p red, yel ('24)			2.50	1.25
91	A11	6p claret ('24)			1.50	1.00
92	A11	1sh blk, emer ('27)			9.00	11.00
93	A11	1sh brn blk, yel grn ('34)			42.50	62.50

Chalky Paper

94	A12	2sh ultra & vio, bl ('27)			55.00	87.50
a.		2sh bl & dp vio, dp bl ('31)			67.50	100.00
95	A12	2sh 6p red & blk, bl ('27)			75.00	125.00
a.		2sh6p pale org ver & blk, gray bl ('30)			3,500.	3,250.
b.		2sh6p dp ver & blk, deep blue ('31)			100.00	150.00
96	A12	10sh red & grn, emer ('24)			160.00	300.00
a.		10sh dp red & pale grn, dp emer ('31)			175.00	350.00
97	A12	12sh 6p ocher & gray blk ('32)			300.00	425.00
		Nos. 81-97 (17)			710.05	1,057.

Revenue cancellations are found on Nos. 94-97.
For the 12sh6p with "Revenue" on both sides, see No. AR1.

Common Design Types pictured following the introduction.

Silver Jubilee Issue
Common Design Type

			1935, May 6		Perf. 11x12	
100	CD301	1p car & dk bl			.55	2.50
101	CD301	1½p blk & ultra			.85	3.50
102	CD301	2½p ultra & brn			1.40	2.50
103	CD301	1sh brn vio & ind			14.00	50.00
		Nos. 100-103 (4)			16.80	58.50
		Set, never hinged			32.50	

Hamilton Harbor — A15

South Shore — A16

Yacht "Lucie" — A17

Grape Bay — A18

Typical Cottage — A19

Scene at Par-la-Ville — A20

			1936-40		Perf. 12	
105	A15	½p blue green			.25	.25
106	A16	1p car & black			.50	.35
107	A16	1½p choc & black			1.15	.60
108	A17	2p lt bl & blk			5.75	2.00
109	A17	2p brn blk & turq bl ('38)			52.50	16.00
109A	A17	2p red & ultra ('40)			1.15	1.25
110	A18	2½p dk bl & lt bl			1.15	.30
111	A19	3p car & black			3.00	2.75
112	A20	6p vio & rose lake			.90	.25
113	A18	1sh deep green			3.75	23.00
114	A15	1sh6p brown			.55	.25
		Nos. 105-114 (11)			70.65	47.00
		Set, never hinged			95.00	

No. 108, blue border and black center.
No. 109, black border, blue center.

Coronation Issue
Common Design Type

			1937, May 14		Perf. 13½x14	
115	CD302	1p carmine			.25	1.50
116	CD302	1½p brown			.35	1.75
117	CD302	2½p bright ultra			.65	1.75
		Nos. 115-117 (3)			1.25	5.00
		Set, never hinged			1.75	

Hamilton Harbor — A21

Grape Bay — A22

St. David's Lighthouse A23

King George VI A25

Bermudian Water Scene and Yellow-billed Tropic Bird — A24

			1938-51		Wmk. 4	Perf. 12
118	A21	1p red & blk			.60	.25
a.		1p rose red & black			16.00	1.40
119	A21	1½p vio brn & blue			4.75	1.40
a.		1½p dl vio brn & bl ('43)			4.00	.25
120	A22	2½p blue & lt bl			8.50	1.00
120A	A22	2½p ol brn & lt bl ('41)			2.50	1.25
b.		2½p dk ol blk & pale blue ('43)			2.50	1.40
121	A23	3p car & blk			16.00	2.25
121A	A23	3p dp ultra & blk ('42)			1.40	.25
c.		3p brt ultra & blk ('41)			1.40	.25
		Complete booklet, 6 each #118, 119, 109A, 120Ab, 121Ac			160.00	
		Complete booklet, 6 #121Ac and 18 #112, in blocks of 6, and 12 air mail labels			180.00	
121D	A24	7½p yel grn, bl & blk ('41)			5.00	2.00

122	A22	1sh green			1.60	.55

Typo.
Perf. 13

123	A25	2sh ultra & red vio, bl ('50)			13.50	12.00
a.		2sh ultra & vio, bl, perf. 14			9.25	3.50
b.		2sh ultra & dl vio, bl (mottled paper), perf. 14 ('42)			9.25	3.50
124	A25	2sh 6p red & blk, bl			14.50	8.75
a.		Perf. 14			26.00	8.75
125	A25	5sh red & grn, yel			17.00	15.00
a.		Perf. 14			60.00	20.00
126	A25	10sh red & grn, grn ('51)			40.00	32.50
a.		10sh brn lake & grn, grn, perf. 14			140.00	100.00
b.		10sh red & grn, grn, perf. 14 ('39)			225.00	200.00
127	A25	12sh 6p org & gray blk			87.50	72.50
a.		12sh 6p org & gray, perf. 14			110.00	60.00
b.		12sh 6p yel & gray, perf. 14 ('47)			725.00	600.00
c.		12sh 6p brn org & gray, perf. 14			275.00	100.00

Wmk. 3

128	A25	£1 blk & vio, red ('51)			52.50	62.50
a.		£1 blk & pur, red, perf. 14			300.00	140.00
b.		£1 blk & dk vio, salmon, perf. 14 ('42)			87.50	67.50
		Nos. 118-128 (14)			265.35	212.20
		Set, never hinged			450.00	

No. 127b is the so-called "lemon yellow" shade.
Revenue cancellations are found on Nos. 123-128. Stamps with removed revenue cancellations and forged postmarks are abundant.

No. 118a
Surcharged in Black

			1940, Dec. 20		Wmk. 4	Perf. 12
129	A21	½p on 1p rose red & blk			.30	3.00
		Never hinged			1.00	

Catalogue values for unused stamps in this section, from this point to the end of the section, are for Never Hinged items.

Peace Issue
Common Design Type
Perf. 13½x14

			1946, Nov. 6	Engr.	Wmk. 4	
131	CD303	1½p brown			.25	.25
132	CD303	3p deep blue			.30	.30

Silver Wedding Issue
Common Design Types

			1948, Dec. 1	Photo.	Perf. 14x14½	
133	CD304	1½p red brown			.25	.25

Engr.; Name Typo.
Perf. 11½x11

134	CD305	£1 rose carmine			47.50	55.00

Postmaster Stamp of 1848 — A26

1949, Apr. 11   Engr.   Perf. 13x13½

135	A26	2½p dk brown & dp bl	.25	.25
136	A26	3p dp blue & black	.25	.25
137	A26	6p green & rose vio	.45	.45
		Nos. 135-137 (3)	.95	.95

No. 137 shows a different floral arrangement. Bermuda's first postage stamp, cent.

UPU Issue
Common Design Types
Engr.; Name Typo.

1949, Oct. 10   Perf. 13½, 11x11½

138	CD306	2½p slate	.50	2.00
139	CD307	3p indigo	1.25	1.25
140	CD308	6p rose violet	1.00	.90
141	CD309	1sh blue green	2.00	2.00
		Nos. 138-141 (4)	4.75	6.15

Coronation Issue
Common Design Type

1953, June 4   Engr.   Perf. 13½x13

142	CD312	1½p dk blue & blk	.85	.50

A27

Easter Lilies — A28

Designs: 1p, 4p, Perot stamp. 2p, Racing dinghy. 2½p, Sir George Somers and "Sea Venture." 3p, 1sh3p, Map. 4½p, 9p, "Sea Venture," boat, hog coin and Perot stamp. 6p, 8p, Yellow-billed tropic bird. 1sh, Hog coins. 2sh, Arms of St. George. 2sh6p, Warwick Fort. 5sh, Hog coin. 10sh, Earliest hog coin. £1, Arms of Bermuda.

1953-58   Perf. 13½x13, 13x13½

143	A27	½p olive green	.50	3.00
144	A27	1p rose red & blk	1.25	.55
145	A28	1½p dull green	.30	.25
146	A27	2p red & ultra	.55	.55
147	A27	2½p carmine rose	2.10	.60
148	A27	3p vio (Sandy's)	.35	.25
149	A27	3p vio (Sandys) ('57)	1.10	.25
150	A27	4p dp ultra & blk	.30	1.40
151	A27	4½p green	.55	1.25
152	A27	6p dk bluish grn & blk	5.00	.75
153	A27	8p red & blk ('55)	2.50	.45
154	A27	9p violet ('58)	7.25	3.00
155	A27	1sh orange	.55	.25
156	A27	1sh3p blue (Sandy's)	3.75	.45
157	A27	1sh3p blue (Sandys) ('57)	7.25	.60
158	A27	2sh yellow brown	4.00	1.10
159	A28	2sh6p scarlet	4.75	.70
160	A27	5sh dp car rose	19.50	1.10
161	A27	10sh deep ultra	13.50	9.00

Engr. and Typo.

162	A27	£1 dp ol grn & multi	35.00	24.00
		Nos. 143-162 (20)	110.05	49.50

For overprints, see Nos. 164-167.

Type of 1953 Inscribed "ROYAL VISIT 1953"
Design: 6p, Yellow-billed tropic bird.

1953, Nov. 26   Engr.

163	A27	6p dk bluish grn & blk	.50	.25

Visit of Queen Elizabeth II and the Duke of Edinburgh, 1953.

Nos. 148 and 156 Overprinted in Violet Blue or Red

1953, Dec. 8   Perf. 13½x13

164	A27	3p violet	.25	.25
165	A27	1sh3p blue (R)	.25	.25

Three Power Conference, Tucker's Town, December 1953.

Nos. 153 and 156 Overprinted in Black or Red

1956, June 22

166	A27	8p red & black	.35	.60
167	A27	1sh3p blue (R)	.35	.60

Newport-Bermuda Yacht Race, 50th anniv.

Perot Post Office, Hamilton A29

Perf. 13½x13

1959, Jan. 1   Engr.   Wmk. 4

168	A29	6p lilac & black	1.35	.25

Restoration and reopening of the post office operated at Hamilton by W. B. Perot in the mid-nineteenth century.

Arms of James I and Elizabeth II — A30

Engr. and Litho.

1959, July 29   Wmk. 314   Perf. 13
Coats of Arms in Blue, Yellow & Red

169	A30	1½p dark blue	.35	.35
170	A30	3p gray	.40	.40
171	A30	4p rose violet	.50	.50
172	A30	8p violet gray	.50	.50
173	A30	9p olive green	.50	.50
174	A30	1sh3p orange brown	.50	.50
		Nos. 169-174 (6)	2.75	2.75

350th anniv. of the shipwreck of the "Sea Venture" which resulted in the first permanent settlement of Bermuda.

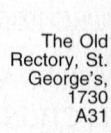

The Old Rectory, St. George's, 1730 A31

Designs: 2p, Church of St. Peter. 3p, Government House. 4p, Cathedral, Hamilton. 5p, No. 185A, H.M. Dockyard. 6p, Perot's Post Office, 1848. 8p, General Post Office, 1869. 9p, Library and Historical Society. 1sh, Christ Church, Warwick, 1719. 1sh3p, City Hall, Hamilton. 10p, No. 185, Bermuda Cottage, 1705. 2sh, Town of St. George. 2sh6p, Bermuda House, 1710. 2sh6p, Bermuda House, 18th century. 5sh, Colonial Secretariat, 1833. 10sh, Old Post Office, Somerset, 1890. £1, House of Assembly, 1815.

Wmk. 314 Upright

1962-65   Photo.   Perf. 12½

175	A31	1p org, lil & blk	.25	.75
176	A31	2p sl, lt vio, grn & yel	.25	.25
a.		Light vio omitted	1,000.	1,000.
b.		Green omitted	7,500.	
d.		Imperf., pair	2,250.	
177	A31	3p lt bl & yel brn	.25	.25
178	A31	4p car rose & red brn	.25	.40
179	A31	5p dk bl & pink	1.50	3.00
180	A31	6p emer, lt & dk bl	.25	.30
181	A31	8p grn, dp org & ultra	.30	.40
182	A31	9p org brn & grnsh bl	.25	.50
182A	A31	10p brt vio & bis ('65)	8.75	2.00
183	A31	1sh multi	.25	.25
184	A31	1sh3p sl, lem & rose car	.90	.25
185	A31	1sh6p brt vio & bis	2.50	2.50
186	A31	2sh brn & org	2.75	1.40
187	A31	2sh3p brn & brt yel grn	2.10	7.00
188	A31	2sh6p grn, yel & sep	.65	.50
189	A31	5sh choc & brt grn	1.10	1.50
190	A31	10sh dl grn, buff & rose car	4.50	7.00
191	A31	£1 cit, bis, blk & org	14.00	14.00
		Nos. 175-191 (18)	40.80	42.25

See No. 252a. For surcharges see Nos. 238-254.

No. 177a, yellow-brown omitted, is no longer listed. All reported examples show traces of the yellow-brown.

1966-69   Wmk. 314 Sideways
Unnamed Colors as in 1962-65 Issue

176c	A31	2p ('69)	6.50	8.00
181a	A31	8p ('67)	.65	1.60
182b	A31	10p	1.90	.90
183a	A31	1sh ('67)	2.25	1.40
185A	A31	1sh6p indigo & rose	4.50	2.75
186a	A31	2sh ('67)	4.50	5.00

For surcharges see Nos. 239, 245-246, 248-249.

Freedom from Hunger Issue
Common Design Type

1963, June 4   Perf. 14x14½

192	CD314	1sh3p sepia	1.00	.50

Red Cross Centenary Issue
Common Design Type
Wmk. 314

1963, Sept. 2   Litho.   Perf. 13

193	CD315	3p black & red	.50	.30
194	CD315	1sh3p ultra & red	2.50	2.50

Finn Boat — A32

Wmk. 314

1964, Sept. 28   Photo.   Perf. 13½

195	A32	3p blue, vio & red	.40	.40

18th Olympic Games, Tokyo, Oct. 10-25.

ITU Issue
Common Design Type
Perf. 11x11½

1965, May 17   Litho.   Wmk. 314

196	CD317	3p blue & emerald	.65	.50
197	CD317	2sh yel & vio blue	1.50	1.75

Scout Badge and Royal Cipher A33

1965, July 24   Photo.   Perf. 12½

198	A33	2sh multicolored	.55	.55

50th anniversary of Scouting in Bermuda.

Intl. Cooperation Year Issue
Common Design Type

1965, Oct. 25   Litho.   Perf. 14½

199	CD318	4p blue grn & cl	.45	.25
200	CD318	2sh6p lt violet & grn	1.60	1.00

Churchill Memorial Issue
Common Design Type

1966, Jan. 24   Photo.   Perf. 14
Design in Black, Gold and Carmine Rose

201	CD319	3p bright blue	.55	.55
202	CD319	6p green	.85	.85
203	CD319	10p brown	1.10	1.10
204	CD319	1sh3p violet	1.50	2.25
		Nos. 201-204 (4)	4.00	4.75

World Cup Soccer Issue
Common Design Type

1966, July 1   Perf. 14

205	CD321	10p multicolored	.50	.50
206	CD321	2sh6p multicolored	1.25	1.25

UNESCO Anniversary Issue
Common Design Type

1966, Dec. 1   Litho.   Perf. 14

207	CD323	4p "Education"	.45	.40
208	CD323	1sh3p "Science"	1.25	1.25
209	CD323	2sh "Culture"	2.10	2.25
		Nos. 207-209 (3)	3.80	3.90

Post Office, Hamilton A34

Wmk. 314

1967, June 23   Photo.   Perf. 14½

210	A34	3p vio blue & multi	.25	.25
211	A34	1sh orange & multi	.25	.25
212	A34	1sh6p green & multi	.30	.25
213	A34	2sh6p red & multi	.30	.75
		Nos. 210-213 (4)	1.10	1.50

Opening of the new GPO, Hamilton.

Cable Ship Mercury A35

Designs: 1sh, Map of Bermuda and Virgin Islands, telephone and microphone. 1sh6p, Radio tower, television set, telephone and cable. 2sh6p, Cable at sea bottom and ship.

1967, Sept. 14   Photo.   Wmk. 314

214	A35	3p multicolored	.25	.25
215	A35	1sh multicolored	.30	.30
216	A35	1sh6p multicolored	.30	.30
217	A35	2sh6p multicolored	.50	.75
		Nos. 214-217 (4)	1.35	1.60

Completion of the Bermuda-Tortola, Virgin Islands, telephone link.

Human Rights Flame, Globe and Doves A36

1968, Feb. 1   Litho.   Perf. 14x14½

218	A36	3p indigo, lt grn & bl	.30	.25
219	A36	1sh brown, lt bl & bl	.30	.25
220	A36	1sh6p black, pink & blue	.30	.30
221	A36	2sh6p green, yellow & bl	.30	.30
		Nos. 218-221 (4)	1.20	1.05

International Human Rights Year.

Mace
A37

Nos. 224-225, House of Assembly, Bermuda, Parliament, London & royal cipher.

1968, July 1   Photo.   Perf. 14½

222	A37	3p rose red & multi	.30	.25
223	A37	1sh ultra & multi	.30	.25
224	A37	1sh6p yellow & multi	.30	.25
225	A37	2sh6p multicolored	.30	.50
		Nos. 222-225 (4)	1.20	1.25

New constitution.

Olympic
Sports and
Rings
A38

1968, Sept. 24   Wmk. 314   Perf. 12½

226	A38	3p lilac & multi	.25	.25
a.		Rose brown omitted ("3d BERMUDA")	4,750.	5,000.
227	A38	1sh multi	.35	.35
228	A38	1sh6p multi	.60	.60
229	A38	2sh6p multi	.90	1.25
		Nos. 226-229 (4)	2.10	2.45

19th Olympic Games, Mexico City, 10/12-27.

Girl
Guides
A39

Designs: 1sh, Like 3p. 1sh6p, 2sh6p, Girl Guides and arms of Bermuda.

1969, Feb. 17   Litho.   Perf. 14

230	A39	3p lilac & multi	.25	.25
231	A39	1sh green & multi	.35	.25
232	A39	1sh6p gray & multi	.40	.40
233	A39	2sh6p red & multi	.60	1.40
		Nos. 230-233 (4)	1.60	2.30

Bermuda Girl Guides, 50th anniv.

Gold and
Emerald
Cross — A40

Design: 4p, 2sh, Different background.

1969, Sept. 29   Photo.   Perf. 14½x14

Cross in Yellow, Brown and Emerald

234	A40	4p violet	.30	.25
235	A40	1sh3p green	.45	.25
236	A40	2sh black	.55	.90
237	A40	2sh6p carmine rose	.60	1.75
		Nos. 234-237 (4)	1.90	3.15

Treasures salvaged off the coast of Bermuda. The cross shown is from the Tucker treasure from the 16th century Spanish galleon San Pedro.

Buildings Issue and Type of 1962-69 Surcharged with New Value and Bar in Black or Brown

1970, Feb. 6   Wmk. 314   Perf. 12½

238	A31	1c on 1p multi	.25	1.75
239	A31	2c on 2p multi	.25	.25
a.		Watermark upright	3.00	6.50
b.		Light violet omitted	1,000.	
c.		Pair, one without surch.	7,500.	
240	A31	3c on 3p multi	.25	.25
241	A31	4c on 4p multi (Br)	.25	.25
242	A31	5c on 8p multi	.25	2.25
243	A31	6c on 6p multi	.25	1.75
244	A31	9c on 9p multi (Br)	.40	2.75
245	A31	10c on 10p multi	.40	.25
246	A31	12c on 1sh multi	.40	1.25
247	A31	15c on 1sh3p multi	2.00	1.75
248	A31	18c on 1sh6p multi	1.00	.70
249	A31	24c on 2sh multi	1.10	4.25
250	A31	30c on 2sh6p multi	1.25	3.00
251	A31	36c on 2sh3p multi	2.25	8.00
252	A31	60c on 5sh multi	2.90	4.00
a.		Surcharge omitted	1,500.	
253	A31	$1.20 on 10sh multi	5.25	13.00
254	A31	$2.40 on £1 multi	8.00	17.00
		Nos. 238-254 (17)	26.45	62.45

Watermark upright on 1c, 3c to 9c and 36c; sideways on others. Watermark is sideways on No. 252a, upright on No. 189.

Spathiphyllum — A41

Flowers: 2c, Bottlebrush. 3c, Oleander, vert. 4c, Bermudiana. 5c, Poinsettia. 6c, Hibiscus. 9c, Cereus. 10c, Bougainvillea, vert. 12c, Jacaranda. 15c, Passion flower. 18c, Coralita. 24c, Morning glory. 30c, Tecoma. 36c, Angel's trumpet. 60c, Plumbago. $1.20, Bird of paradise. $2.40, Chalice cup.

Wmk. 314, Sideways on Horiz. Stamps

1970, July 6   Perf. 14

255	A41	1c lt grn & multi	.35	.50
256	A41	2c pale bl & multi	.60	.50
257	A41	3c yellow & multi	.35	.50
258	A41	4c buff & multi	.35	.50
259	A41	5c pink & multi	.85	.50
a.		Imperf. pair	1,500.	
260	A41	6c org & multi	.85	.60
261	A41	9c lt grn & multi	.60	.50
262	A41	10c pale sal & multi	.60	.50
263	A41	12c pale yel & multi	2.10	1.75
264	A41	15c buff & multi	2.50	1.50
265	A41	18c pale sal & multi	6.50	2.50
266	A41	24c pink & multi	4.25	4.25
267	A41	30c plum & multi	2.90	1.60
268	A41	36c dk gray & multi	3.50	2.40
269	A41	60c gray & multi	4.75	4.00
270	A41	$1.20 blue & multi	7.75	7.25
271	A41	$2.40 multicolored	15.00	15.00
		Nos. 255-271 (17)	53.80	44.35

See Nos. 322-328. For overprints see Nos. 288-291.

1974-76   Wmk. 314 Upright

259b	A41	5c multicolored	3.25	3.75
260a	A41	6c multicolored	7.25	8.25
263a	A41	12c multicolored	6.00	7.00
267a	A41	30c multicolored ('76)	9.75	11.00
		Nos. 259b-267a (4)	26.25	30.00

Issued: 30c, June 11; others, June 13.

1975-76   Wmk. 373

256a	A41	2c multicolored	1.75	1.25
260b	A41	6c multicolored	8.00	7.00

Issued: 2c, Dec. 8; 6c, June 11, 1976.

State House, St. George's, 1622-1815 — A42

Designs: 15c, The Sessions House, Hamilton, 1893. 18c, First Assembly House, St. Peter's Church, St. George's. 24c, Temporary Assembly House, Hamilton, 1815-26.

1970, Oct. 12   Litho.   Perf. 14

272	A42	4c multicolored	.25	.25
273	A42	15c multicolored	.25	.25
274	A42	18c multicolored	.30	.30
275	A42	24c multicolored	.50	.90
a.		Souvenir sheet of 4, #272-275	2.25	2.25
		Nos. 272-275 (4)	1.30	1.70

350th anniv. of Bermuda's Parliament.

Street in
St.
George's
A43

"Keep Bermuda Beautiful": 15c, Horseshoe Bay. 18c, Gibb's Hill Lighthouse. 24c, View of Hamilton Harbor.

1971, Feb. 8   Wmk. 314   Perf. 14

276	A43	4c multicolored	.25	.25
277	A43	15c multicolored	.70	.75
278	A43	18c multicolored	1.90	2.10
279	A43	24c multicolored	1.50	1.75
		Nos. 276-279 (4)	4.35	4.80

Building of "Deliverance" — A44

Designs: 15c, "Deliverance" and "Patience" arriving in Jamestown, Va., 1610, vert. 18c, Wreck of "Sea Venture," vert. 24c, "Deliverance" and "Patience" under sail, 1610.

1971, May 10   Litho.   Wmk. 314

280	A44	4c multicolored	.80	.30
281	A44	15c brown & multi	2.25	2.40
282	A44	18c purple & multi	2.25	2.40
283	A44	24c blue & multi	2.50	2.75
		Nos. 280-283 (4)	7.80	7.85

Voyage of Sir George Somers to Jamestown, Va., from Bermuda, 1610.

Ocean
View Golf
Course
A45

Golf Courses: 15c, Port Royal. 18c, Castle Harbour. 24c, Belmont.

1971, Nov. 1   Perf. 13

284	A45	4c multicolored	1.00	.25
285	A45	15c multicolored	1.90	.90
286	A45	18c multicolored	2.00	1.40
287	A45	24c multicolored	2.50	2.75
		Nos. 284-287 (4)	7.40	5.30

Golfing in Bermuda.

Nos. 258, 264-266 Overprinted: "HEATH-NIXON / DECEMBER 1971"

1971, Dec. 20   Photo.   Perf. 14

288	A41	4c buff & multi	.25	.25
289	A41	15c buff & multi	.25	.25
290	A41	18c pale sal & multi	.30	.50
291	A41	24c pink & multi	.40	.75
		Nos. 288-291 (4)	1.20	1.75

Meeting of President Richard M. Nixon and Prime Minister Edward Heath of Great Britain, at Hamilton, Dec. 20-21, 1971.

Bonefish
A46

1972, Aug. 7   Litho.   Perf. 13½x14

292	A46	4c shown	.50	.25
293	A46	15c Wahoo	.50	.50
294	A46	18c Yellowfin tuna	.60	.75
295	A46	24c Greater amberjack	.65	1.00
		Nos. 292-295 (4)	2.25	2.50

World fishing records.

Silver Wedding Issue, 1972
Common Design Type

Design: Queen Elizabeth II, Prince Philip, Admiralty oar and mace.

1972, Nov. 20   Photo.   Perf. 14x14½

296	CD324	4c violet & multi	.25	.25
297	CD324	15c car rose & multi	.25	.40

Palmettos — A47

1973, Sept. 3   Wmk. 314   Perf. 14

298	A47	4c shown	.40	.25
299	A47	15c Olivewood	1.10	1.10
a.		Brown (Queen's head, "15c") omitted	2,250.	
300	A47	18c Bermuda cedar	1.25	1.25
301	A47	24c Mahogany	1.25	1.50
		Nos. 298-301 (4)	4.00	4.10

Bermuda National Trust, and "Plant a Tree" campaign.

Princess Anne's Wedding Issue
Common Design Type

1973, Nov. 21   Litho.

302	CD325	15c lilac & multi	.25	.25
303	CD325	18c slate & multi	.25	.25

National Tennis Stadium, Pembroke, 1973 — A48

15c, Bermuda's 1st tennis court, Pembroke, 1873. 18c, Britain's 1st tennis court, Leamington Spa, 1872. 24c, 1t US tennis club, Staten Island, 1874.

1973, Dec. 17   Wmk. 314

304	A48	4c black & multi	.35	.25
305	A48	15c black & multi	.70	.70
306	A48	18c black & multi	.85	1.25
307	A48	24c black & multi	1.00	1.50
		Nos. 304-307 (4)	2.90	3.70

Centenary of tennis in Bermuda.

Rotary
Emblem,
Weather
Vane, City
Hall,
Hamilton
A49

Rotary Emblem and: 17c, St. Peter's Church, St. George's. 20c, Somerset Drawbridge, Somerset. 25c, Map of Bermuda on globe, 1626.

1974, June 24   Perf. 14

308	A49	5c emerald & multi	.25	.25
309	A49	17c blue & multi	.60	.45
310	A49	20c yel org & multi	.65	1.25
311	A49	25c lt violet & multi	.80	1.75
		Nos. 308-311 (4)	2.30	3.70

50th anniv. of Rotary Intl. in Bermuda.

Jack of Clubs and a Good Bridge Hand — A50

Bermuda Bowl and: 17c, Queen of diamonds. 20c, King of hearts. 25c, Ace of spades.

1975, Jan. 27   Litho.   Wmk. 314
312 A50 5c blue & multi   .35   .25
313 A50 17c dull yel & multi   .65   .65
314 A50 20c ver & multi   .75   1.50
315 A50 25c lilac & multi   .75   2.25
    Nos. 312-315 (4)   2.50   4.65

World Bridge Championship, Bermuda, Jan. 1975.

Queen Elizabeth II and Prince Philip — A51

Perf. 14x14½
1975, Feb. 17   Photo.   Wmk. 373
316 A51 17c multicolored   .85   .85
317 A51 20c dk blue & multi   .95   1.25

Royal Visit, Feb. 16-18, 1975.

British Cavalier Flying Boat, 1937 A52

17c, U.S. Navy airship "Los Angeles," 1925, flying from Lakehurst, NJ to Hamilton, Bermuda. 20c, Constellation over Kindley Field, 1946. 25c, Boeing 747 on tarmac, 1970.

1975, Apr. 28   Litho.   Perf. 14
318 A52 5c lt green & multi   .45   .25
319 A52 17c lt ultra & multi   1.75   1.40
320 A52 20c multicolored   1.90   2.25
321 A52 25c rose lil & multi   2.25   2.50
    a. Souvenir sheet of 4, #318-321   14.00 14.00
    Nos. 318-321 (4)   6.35   6.40

Airmail service to Bermuda, 50th anniv.

Flower Type of 1970
1975, June 2   Photo.   Wmk. 314
322 A41 17c Passion flower   3.00   4.00
323 A41 20c Coralita   3.00   4.00
324 A41 25c Morning glory   3.00   4.00
325 A41 40c Angel's trumpet   3.00   4.00
326 A41 $1 Plumbago   3.50   4.50
327 A41 $2 Bird-of-paradise flower   6.00   7.50
328 A41 $3 Chalice cup   12.00 15.00
    Nos. 322-328 (7)   33.50 43.00

Royal Magazine Break-in A54

17c, Sympathizers rowing towards magazine. 20c, Loading gun powder barrels onto ships. 25c, Gun powder barrels on beach.

Perf. 13x13½
1975, Oct. 27   Litho.   Wmk. 373
329 A54 5c multicolored   .25   .25
330 A54 17c multicolored   .50   .55
331 A54 20c multicolored   .60   1.40

332 A54 25c multicolored   .65   1.50
    a. Souv. sheet, #329-332, perf 14   4.50   7.00
    Nos. 329-332 (4)   2.00   3.70

Gunpowder Plot, 1775, American War of Independence.

Bermuda Biological Station A55

Designs: 5c, Launching of bathysphere from "Ready," vert. 20c, Sailing ship Challenger, 1873. 25c, Descent of Beebe's bathysphere, 1934, and marine life, vert.

1976, Mar. 29   Litho.   Perf. 14
333 A55 5c multicolored   .40   .25
334 A55 17c multicolored   .80   .80
335 A55 20c multicolored   .95   1.50
336 A55 25c multicolored   1.10   2.25
    Nos. 333-336 (4)   3.25   4.80

Bermuda Biological Station, 50th anniv.

Christian Radich, Norway A56

Tall Ships: 12c, Juan Sebastian de Elcano, Spain. 17c, Eagle, US. 20c, Sir Winston Churchill, Great Britain. 40c, Kruzenshtern, USSR. $1, Cutty Sark (silver trophy).

1976, June 15   Litho.   Perf. 13
337 A56 5c lt green & multi   1.10   .25
338 A56 12c violet & multi   1.20   2.00
339 A56 17c ultra & multi   1.20   1.50
340 A56 20c blue & multi   1.20   1.50
341 A56 40c yellow & multi   1.50   2.25
342 A56 $1 sl grn & multi   1.90   5.25
    Nos. 337-342 (6)   8.10 12.75

Trans-Atlantic Cutty Sark International Tall Ships Race, Plymouth, England-New York City (Operation Sail '76).

Silver Cup Trophy and Crossed Club Flags A57

Designs: 17c, St. George's Cricket Club and emblem. 20c, Somerset Cricket Club and emblem. 25c, Cricket match.

1976, Aug. 16   Wmk. 373   Perf. 14½
343 A57 5c multicolored   .45   .25
344 A57 17c multicolored   .85   .85
345 A57 20c multicolored   1.10   1.75
346 A57 25c multicolored   1.75   2.75
    Nos. 343-346 (4)   4.15   5.60

St. George's and Somerset Cricket Club matches, 75th anniversary.

Queen's Visit to Bermuda, 1975 — A58

Designs: 20c, St. Edward's Crown. $1, Queen seated in Chair of Estate.

1977, Feb. 7   Litho.   Perf. 14x13½
347 A58 5c silver & multi   .30   .30
348 A58 20c silver & multi   .30   .30
349 A58 $1 silver & multi   .60   1.10
    Nos. 347-349 (3)   1.20   1.70

Reign of Queen Elizabeth II, 25th anniv.

Stockdale House, St. George's A59

UPU Emblem and: 15c, Perot Post Office and Perot Stamp. 17c, St. George's Post Office, c. 1860. 20c, Old GPO, Hamilton, c. 1935. 40c, New GPO, Hamilton, 1967.

1977, June 20   Litho.   Perf. 13x13½
350 A59 5c multicolored   .25   .25
351 A59 15c multicolored   .40   .45
352 A59 17c multicolored   .40   .45
353 A59 20c multicolored   .45   .50
354 A59 40c multicolored   .75   .85
    Nos. 350-354 (5)   2.25   2.50

Bermuda's UPU membership, cent.

Sailing Ship, 17th Century, Approaching Castle Island — A60

Designs: 15c, King's pilot leaving 18th century naval ship at Murray's Anchorage. 17c, Pilot gigs racing to meet steamship, early 19th century. 20c, Harvest Queen, late 19th century. 40c, Pilot cutter and Queen Elizabeth II off St. David's Lighthouse.

Perf. 13½x14
1977, Sept. 26   Wmk. 373
355 A60 5c multicolored   .60   .25
356 A60 15c multicolored   .90   .90
357 A60 17c multicolored   1.00   .90
358 A60 20c multicolored   1.10   2.00
359 A60 40c multicolored   2.00   3.25
    Nos. 355-359 (5)   5.60   7.30

Piloting in Bermuda waters.

Elizabeth II A61

Designs: 8c, Great Seal of Elizabeth I. 50c, Great Seal of Elizabeth II.

1978, Aug. 28   Litho.   Perf. 14x13½
360 A61 8c gold & multi   .25   .25
361 A61 50c gold & multi   .35   .35
362 A61 $1 gold & multi   .70   .80
    Nos. 360-362 (3)   1.30   1.40

25th anniv. of coronation of Elizabeth II.

White-tailed Tropicbird — A62

4c, White-eyed vireo. 5c, Eastern bluebird. 7c, Whistling tree frog. 8c, Cardinal. 10c, Spiny lobster. 12c, Land crab. 15c, Skink. 20c, Four-eyed butterflyfish. 25c, Red hind. 30c, Monarch butterfly. 40c, Rock beauty. 50c, Banded butterflyfish. $1, Blue angelfish. $2, Humpback whale. $3, Green turtle. $5, Bermuda Petrel.

Perf. 14; 14x14½ (4c, 5c, $2, $3, $5)
1978-79   Photo.   Wmk. 373
363 A62 3c shown   2.25   2.50
364 A62 4c multicolored   2.60   3.00
365 A62 5c multicolored   1.15   1.60
366 A62 7c multicolored   .45   1.25

367 A62 8c multicolored   1.25   .45
368 A62 10c multicolored   .25   .25
369 A62 12c multicolored   .30   .60
370 A62 15c multicolored   .30   .30
371 A62 20c multicolored   .35   .35
372 A62 25c multicolored   .45   .45
    a. Greenish blue (background) omitted 4,750.
373 A62 30c multicolored   1.90   2.00
374 A62 40c multicolored   .60   1.50
375 A62 50c multicolored   .75   1.25
376 A62 $1 multicolored   2.10   2.10
377 A62 $2 multicolored   3.00   3.00
378 A62 $3 multicolored   4.50   4.50
379 A62 $5 multicolored   7.75   7.75
    Nos. 363-379 (17)   29.95 32.85

Issued: 3c, 4c, 5c, 8c, $5, 1978; others, 1979.
For surcharge see No. 509.

Map of Bermuda, by George Somers, 1609 — A63

Old Maps of Bermuda: 15c, by John Seller, 1685. 20c, by Herman Moll, 1729, vert. 25c, by Desbruslins, 1740. 50c, by John Speed, 1626.

1979, May 14   Litho.   Perf. 13½
380 A63 8c multicolored   .25   .25
381 A63 15c multicolored   .30   .25
382 A63 20c multicolored   .35   .30
383 A63 25c multicolored   .40   .40
384 A63 50c multicolored   .55   .85
    Nos. 380-384 (5)   1.85   2.00

Bermuda Police Centenary — A64

20c, Traffic direction, horiz. 25c, Water patrol, horiz. 50c, Motorbike and patrol car.

1979, Nov. 26   Wmk. 373   Perf. 14
385 A64 8c multicolored   .45   .25
386 A64 20c multicolored   .75   .75
387 A64 25c multicolored   .90   .90
388 A64 50c multicolored   1.15   1.15
    Nos. 385-388 (4)   3.25   3.05

Bermuda No. X1, Penny Black — A65

Bermuda #X1 and: 20c, Hill. 25c, "Paid 1" marking on cover. 50c, "Paid 1" marking.

1980, Feb. 25   Litho.   Perf. 13½x14
389 A65 8c multicolored   .25   .25
390 A65 20c multicolored   .40   .40
391 A65 25c multicolored   .40   .40
392 A65 50c multicolored   .45   .90
    Nos. 389-392 (4)   1.50   1.95

Sir Rowland Hill (1795-1879), originator of penny postage.

Tristar-500, London 1980 Emblem — A66

50c, "Orduna," 1926. $1, "Delta," 1856. $2, "Lord Sidmouth," 1818.

1980, May 6		**Litho.**		**Perf. 13x14**	
393	A66	25c	shown	.40	.25
394	A66	50c	multicolored	.65	.50
395	A66	$1	multicolored	1.25	1.25
396	A66	$2	multicolored	1.90	2.25
		Nos. 393-396 (4)		4.20	4.25

London 1980 Intl. Stamp Exhib., May 6-14.

Gina Swainson, Miss World, 1979-80, Arms of Bermuda — A67

20c, After crowning ceremony. 50c, Welcome home party. $1, In carriage.

1980, May 8				**Perf. 14**	
397	A67	8c	shown	.30	.30
398	A67	20c	multicolored	.40	.40
399	A67	50c	multicolored	.70	.70
400	A67	$1	multicolored	1.50	1.50
		Nos. 397-400 (4)		2.90	2.90

Queen Mother Elizabeth Birthday Issue
Common Design Type

1980, Aug. 4		**Wmk. 373**		**Perf. 14**	
401	CD330	25c multicolored		.45	.75

Camden, Prime Minister's House A68

8c, View from satellite. 25c, Princess Hotel, Hamilton. 50c, Government House.

1980, Sept. 24		**Litho.**		**Perf. 14**	
402	A68	8c	multicolored	.25	.25
403	A68	20c	shown	.30	.30
404	A68	30c	multicolored	.30	.50
405	A68	50c	multicolored	.60	1.50
		Nos. 402-405 (4)		1.45	2.55

Commonwealth Finance Ministers Meeting, Bermuda, Sept.

18th Century Kitchen A69

25c, Gathering Easter lilies. 30c, Fisherman. 40c, Stone cutting, 19th cent. 50c, Onion shipping, 19th cent. $1, Ships, 17th cent.

1981, May 21		**Wmk. 373**		**Perf. 14**	
406	A69	8c	shown	.25	.25
407	A69	25c	multicolored	.40	.40
408	A69	30c	multicolored	.55	.55
409	A69	40c	multicolored	.75	.75
410	A69	50c	multicolored	.90	.90
411	A69	$1	multicolored	1.75	1.75
		Nos. 406-411 (6)		4.60	4.60

Royal Wedding Issue
Common Design Type

1981, July 22		**Wmk. 373**		**Perf. 14**	
412	CD331	30c	Bouquet	.30	.30
413	CD331	50c	Charles	.60	.60
414	CD331	$1	Couple	1.10	1.10
		Nos. 412-414 (3)		2.00	2.00

Girl Helping Blind Man Cross Street — A70

25c, Kayaking, Paget Island. 30c, Mountain climbing, St. David's Island. $1, Duke of Edinburgh.

1981, Sept. 28		**Litho.**		**Perf. 14**	
415	A70	10c	shown	.25	.25
416	A70	25c	multicolored	.30	.30
417	A70	30c	multicolored	.35	.35
418	A70	$1	multicolored	.75	1.10
		Nos. 415-418 (4)		1.65	2.00

Duke of Edinburgh's Awards, 25th anniv.

Conus Species A71

25c, Bursa finlayi. 30c, Sconsia striata. $1, Murex pterynotus lightbourni.

1982, May 13		**Wmk. 373**		**Perf. 14**	
419	A71	10c	shown	.65	.25
420	A71	25c	multicolored	1.25	1.25
421	A71	30c	multicolored	1.60	1.60
422	A71	$1	multicolored	4.25	4.25
		Nos. 419-422 (4)		7.75	7.35

Bermuda Regiment A72

10c, Color guard. 25c, Queen's birthday parade. 30c, Governor inspecting honor guard. 40c, Beating the retreat. 50c, Ceremonial gunners. $1, Royal visit, 1975.

1982, June 17		**Litho.**		**Wmk. 373**	
423	A72	10c	multicolored	.75	.25
424	A72	25c	multicolored	1.10	.90
425	A72	30c	multicolored	1.50	1.50
426	A72	40c	multicolored	1.60	1.60
427	A72	50c	multicolored	1.60	1.60
428	A72	$1	multicolored	2.75	2.75
		Nos. 423-428 (6)		9.30	8.60

Southampton Fort — A73

10c, Charles Fort, vert. 25c, Pembroke Fort, vert. $1, Smiths and Pagets Forts.

1982, Nov. 18		**Litho.**		**Wmk. 373**	
429	A73	10c	multicolored	.30	.30
430	A73	25c	multicolored	.80	.80
431	A73	30c	shown	.90	.90
432	A73	$1	multicolored	1.90	1.90
		Nos. 429-432 (4)		3.90	3.90

Arms of Sir Edwin Sandys (1561-1629) A74

Coats of Arms: 25c, Bermuda Company. 50c, William Herbert, 3rd Earl of Pembroke (1584-1630). $1, Sir George Somers (1554-1610).

1983, Apr. 14		**Litho.**		**Perf. 13½**	
433	A74	10c	multicolored	.45	.25
434	A74	25c	multicolored	1.40	1.25
435	A74	50c	multicolored	2.50	3.00
436	A74	$1	multicolored	3.50	5.00
		Nos. 433-436 (4)		7.85	9.50

See Nos. 457-460, 474-477.

Fitted Dinghies — A75

Old and modern boats.

1983, July 21		**Wmk. 373**		**Perf. 14**	
437	A75	12c	multicolored	.55	.25
438	A75	30c	multicolored	.75	.75
439	A75	40c	multicolored	.85	.85
440	A75	$1	multicolored	2.00	2.75
		Nos. 437-440 (4)		4.15	4.60

Manned Flight Bicentenary — A76

Designs: 12c, Curtiss Jenny, 1919 (first flight over Bermuda). 30c, Stinson Pilot Radio, 1930 (first completed US-Bermuda flight). 40c, Cavalier, 1937 (first scheduled passenger flight). $1, USS Los Angeles airship moored to USS Patoka, 1925.

1983, Oct. 13		**Litho.**		**Perf. 14**	
441	A76	12c	multicolored	.80	.30
442	A76	30c	multicolored	1.50	1.50
443	A76	40c	multicolored	1.75	1.75
444	A76	$1	multicolored	3.00	4.25
		Nos. 441-444 (4)		7.05	7.80

Newspaper and Postal Services, 200th Anniv. — A77

12c, Joseph Stockdale. 30c, First Newspaper. 40c, Stockdale's Postal Service, horiz. $1, "Lady Hammond," horiz.

1984, Jan. 26		**Litho.**		**Perf. 14**	
445	A77	12c	multicolored	.45	.25
446	A77	30c	multicolored	.75	.75
447	A77	40c	multicolored	.95	.95
448	A77	$1	multicolored	3.00	3.25
		Nos. 445-448 (4)		5.15	5.20

375th Anniv. of Bermuda Settlement — A78

Designs: 12c, Thomas Gates, George Somers. 30c, Jamestown, Virginia, US. 40c, Sea Venture shipwreck. $1, Fleet leaving Plymouth, England.

1984, May 3		**Litho.**		**Wmk. 373**	
449	A78	12c	multicolored	.25	.25
450	A78	30c	multicolored	.70	.70
451	A78	40c	multicolored	1.25	1.25

452	A78	$1	multicolored	2.75	5.00
a.		Souv. sheet of 2, #450, 452		5.75	8.50
		Nos. 449-452 (4)		4.95	7.20

1984 Summer Olympics A79

1984, July 19		**Litho.**		**Perf. 14**	
453	A79	12c	Swimming, vert.	.50	.25
454	A79	30c	Track & field	.95	.95
455	A79	40c	Equestrian, vert.	1.60	1.60
456	A79	$1	Sailing	3.25	5.00
		Nos. 453-456 (4)		6.30	7.80

Arms Type of 1983

1984, Sept. 27		**Litho.**		**Perf. 13½**	
457	A74	12c	Southampton	.75	.25
458	A74	30c	Smith	1.50	1.25
459	A74	40c	Devonshire	1.90	1.90
460	A74	$1	St. George	4.25	4.25
		Nos. 457-460 (4)		8.40	7.65

Architecture, Buttery — A80

1985, Jan. 24		**Litho.**		**Perf. 13½x13**	
461	A80	12c	shown	.40	.25
462	A80	30c	Rooftops	1.10	1.00
463	A80	40c	Chimneys	1.25	1.25
464	A80	$1.50	Archway	4.25	4.25
		Nos. 461-464 (4)		7.00	6.75

Audubon Birth Bicentenary — A81

12c, Osprey, vert. 30c, Yellow-crowned night heron, vert. 40c, Great egret. $1.50, Bluebird, vert.

1985, Mar. 21		**Wmk. 373**		**Perf. 14**	
465	A81	12c	multicolored	2.75	.85
466	A81	30c	multicolored	2.75	1.25
467	A81	40c	multicolored	3.25	1.60
468	A81	$1.50	multicolored	5.25	5.25
		Nos. 465-468 (4)		14.00	8.95

Queen Mother 85th Birthday Issue
Common Design Type

Designs: 12c, Queen Consort, 1937. 30c, With grandchildren, 80th birthday. 40c, At Clarence House, 83rd birthday. $1.50, Holding Prince Henry. No. 473, In coach with Prince Charles.

		Perf. 14½x14			
1985, June 7		**Wmk. 384**			
469	CD336	12c	gray, bl & blk	.35	.35
470	CD336	30c	multicolored	.70	.70
471	CD336	40c	multicolored	1.10	1.10
472	CD336	$1.50	multicolored	3.25	3.25
		Nos. 469-472 (4)		5.40	5.40

Souvenir Sheet

473	CD336	$1	multicolored	4.00	4.00

Arms Type of 1983

Coats of Arms: 12c, James Hamilton, 2nd Marquess of Hamilton (1589-1625). 30c, William Paget, 4th Lord Paget (1572-1629). 40c, Robert Rich, 2nd Earl of Warwick (1587-1658). $1.50, Hamilton, 1957.

1985, Sept. 19		**Litho.**		**Perf. 13½**	
474	A74	12c	multicolored	.90	.25
475	A74	30c	multicolored	1.75	1.10
476	A74	40c	multicolored	2.10	2.10
477	A74	$1.50	multicolored	4.50	4.50
		Nos. 474-477 (4)		9.25	7.95

Halley's Comet A82

15c, Bermuda Archipelago. 40c, Nuremberg Chronicles, 1493. 50c, Peter Apian woodcut, 1532. $1.50, Painting by Samuel Scott (c.1702-72).

1985, Nov. 21   Wmk. 384   Perf. 14½

478	A82	15c multicolored	1.10	.35
479	A82	40c multicolored	2.10	2.10
480	A82	50c multicolored	2.50	2.50
481	A82	$1.50 multicolored	4.25	6.00
		Nos. 478-481 (4)	9.95	10.95

Shipwrecks — A83

3c, Constellation, 1943. 5c, Early Riser, 1876. 7c, Madiana, 1903. 10c, Curlew, 1856. 12c, Warwick, 1619. 15c, HMS Vixen, 1890. 20c, San Pedro, 1594. 25c, Alert, 1877. 40c, North Carolina, 1880. 50c, Mark Antonie, 1777. 60c, Mary Celestia, 1864. $1, L'Herminie, 1839. $1.50, Caesar, 1818. $2, Lord Amherst, 1778. $3, Minerva, 1849. $5, Caraquet, 1923. $8, HMS Pallas, 1783.

1986   Wmk. 384   Perf. 14
Without date imprint

482	A83	3c multicolored	.80	1.75
483	A83	5c multicolored	.30	.30
484	A83	7c multicolored	.65	2.75
485	A83	10c multicolored	.30	.30
486	A83	12c multicolored	.65	.60
487	A83	15c multicolored	.45	.60
488	A83	20c multicolored	1.10	.75
489	A83	25c multicolored	.75	3.00
490	A83	40c multicolored	.80	1.25
491	A83	50c multicolored	1.60	3.25
492	A83	60c multicolored	1.75	1.75
493	A83	$1 multicolored	2.50	4.25
494	A83	$1.50 multicolored	6.00	7.00
495	A83	$2 multicolored	5.75	7.50
496	A83	$3 multicolored	9.25	9.25
497	A83	$5 multicolored	15.00	15.00
498	A83	$8 multicolored	24.00	24.00
		Nos. 482-498 (17)	71.65	83.45

See Nos. 545-546. For surcharges see Nos. 598-600.

Inscribed "1989" or "1990"
1989-90

482a	A83	3c 1990	1.75	3.00
488a	A83	20c 1990	3.00	4.50
493a	A83	$1 1989	1.50	1.50
495a	A83	$2 1989	2.50	4.50
496a	A83	$3 1989	4.50	8.25
		Nos. 482a-496a (5)	13.25	21.75

Issued: Nos. 493a-496a, 7/89; Nos. 482a, 483a, 1/8/90.

Inscribed "1992"
1992   Litho.   Wmk. 373   Perf. 14

485a	A83	10c	2.60	2.60
487a	A83	15c	3.25	3.25
488b	A83	20c	3.25	3.25
489a	A83	25c	3.25	3.25
492a	A83	60c	5.50	5.50
497a	A83	$5	22.00	22.00
498a	A83	$8	32.50	32.50
		Nos. 485a-498a (7)	72.35	72.35

Queen Elizabeth II 60th Birthday
Common Design Type

15c, Age 3. 40c, With the Earl of Rosebury, Oaks May Meeting, Epsom, 1954. 50c, With Prince Philip, state visit,1979. 60c, At the British embassy in Paris, state visit, 1972. $1.50, Visiting Crown Agents' offices, 1983.

1986, Apr. 21   Wmk. 384   Perf. 14½

499	CD337	15c scar, blk & sil	.25	.25
500	CD337	40c ultra & multi	.65	.65
501	CD337	50c green & multi	.80	.80
502	CD337	60c violet & multi	.95	.95
503	CD337	$1.50 rose vio & multi	2.00	2.50
		Nos. 499-503 (5)	4.65	5.15

AMERIPEX '86 — A84

$1.50, Statue of Liberty, S.S. Queen of Bermuda.

1986, May 22   Perf. 14

504	A84	15c No. 452a	1.50	.40
505	A84	40c No. 307	2.25	.85
506	A84	50c No. 441	2.25	1.25
507	A84	$1 No. 339	3.75	3.25
		Nos. 504-507 (4)	9.75	5.75

Souvenir Sheet

508	A84	1.50 multi	11.00 11.00

Statue of Liberty, cent.

No. 378 Surcharged
Perf. 14x14½

1986, Dec. 4   Photo.   Wmk. 373

509	A62	90c on $3 multi	7.75 7.75

Exists with double surcharge. Value $110.

Transport Railway, c. 1931-1947 — A85

15c, Front Street, c. 1940. 40c, Springfield Trestle. 50c, No. 101, Bailey's Bay Sta. $1.50, No. 31, ship Prince David.

Wmk. 373

1987, Jan. 22   Litho.   Perf. 14

510	A85	15c multicolored	2.00	.40
511	A85	40c multicolored	2.50	1.40
512	A85	50c multicolored	2.50	1.90
513	A85	$1.50 multicolored	4.00	5.50
		Nos. 510-513 (4)	11.00	9.20

Paintings by Winslow Homer (1836-1910) A86

15c, Bermuda Settlers, 1901. 30c, Bermuda, 1900. 40c, Bermuda Landscape, 1901. 50c, Inland Water, 1901. $1.50, Salt Kettle, 1899.

1987, Apr. 30   Perf. 14½

514	A86	15c multicolored	.80	.40
515	A86	30c multicolored	1.15	.65
516	A86	40c multicolored	1.35	.90
517	A86	50c multicolored	1.60	1.00
518	A86	$1.50 multicolored	3.00	3.00
		Nos. 514-518 (5)	7.90	5.95

Booklet Stamps

519	A86	40c like 15c	1.75	1.75
520	A86	40c like 30c	1.75	1.75
521	A86	40c like No. 516	1.75	1.75
522	A86	40c like 50c	1.75	1.75
523	A86	40c like $1.50	1.75	1.75
a.		Bklt. pane, 2 each #519-523	17.50	
		Complete booklet, #523a	17.50	

Nos. 519-523 printed in strips of 5 within pane. "ER" at lower left.

Intl. Flights Inauguration — A87

15c, Sikorsky S-42B, 1937. 40c, Shorts S-23 Cavalier. 50c, S-42B Bermuda Clipper. $1.50, Cavalier, Bermuda Clipper.

1987, June 18   Perf. 14

524	A87	15c multicolored	2.40	.25
525	A87	40c multicolored	3.50	.95
526	A87	50c multicolored	3.75	1.10
527	A87	$1.50 multicolored	6.75	6.75
		Nos. 524-527 (4)	16.40	9.05

Bermuda Telephone Company, Cent. — A88

15c, Telephone poles on wagon. 40c, Operators. 50c, Telephones. $1.50, Satellite, fiber optics, world.

1987, Oct. 1   Litho.   Wmk. 384

528	A88	15c multicolored	1.00	.25
529	A88	40c multicolored	2.00	1.00
530	A88	50c multicolored	2.25	1.10
531	A88	$1.50 multicolored	3.75	3.75
		Nos. 528-531 (4)	9.00	6.10

Horse-drawn Commercial Vehicles — A89

15c, Mail wagon, c. 1869. 40c, Open cart, c. 1823. 50c, Closed cart, c. 1823. $1.50, Two-wheel wagon, c. 1930.

1988, Mar. 3   Litho.   Perf. 14

532	A89	15c multicolored	.40	.75
533	A89	40c multicolored	.90	.90
534	A89	50c multicolored	1.10	1.10
535	A89	$1.50 multicolored	3.50	3.50
		Nos. 532-535 (4)	5.90	5.75

Old Garden Roses A90

15c, Old blush. 30c, Anna Olivier. 40c, Rosa chinensis semperflorens, vert. 50c, Archduke Charles. $1.50, Rosa chinensis viridiflora, vert.

1988, Apr. 21   Wmk. 373

536	A90	15c multicolored	1.25	.40
537	A90	30c multicolored	1.75	.70
538	A90	40c multicolored	1.90	1.25
539	A90	50c multicolored	2.00	1.75
540	A90	$1.50 multicolored	4.00	4.00
		Nos. 536-540 (5)	10.90	8.10

See Nos. 561-575.

Lloyds of London, 300th Anniv.
Common Design Type

18c, Loss of the H.M.S. Lutine, 1799. 50c, Cable ship Sentinel. 60c, The Bermuda, Hamilton, 1931. $2, Valerian, lost during a hurricane, 1926.

1988, Oct. 13   Litho.   Wmk. 384

541	CD341	18c multi	1.00	.30
542	CD341	50c multi, horiz.	1.75	.80
543	CD341	60c multi, horiz.	2.00	1.00
544	CD341	$2 multi	3.25	4.50
		Nos. 541-544 (4)	8.00	6.60

Shipwreck Type of 1986

1988   Litho.   Wmk. 384   Perf. 14

545	A83	18c like 7c	5.50	4.00
546	A83	70c like $1.50	6.25	7.00

Issue dates: 18c, Sept. 22; 70c, Oct. 27.

Military Uniforms — A91

18c, Devonshire Parish Militia, 1812. 50c, 71st Regiment Highlander, 1831-34. $1, Cameron Highlander, 1942. $2, Troop of Horse, 1774.

1988, Nov. 10   Wmk. 373   Perf. 14½

547	A91	18c multicolored	1.60	.40
548	A91	50c multicolored	2.25	1.50
549	A91	60c multicolored	2.50	1.60
550	A91	$2 multicolored	5.25	7.50
		Nos. 547-550 (4)	11.60	11.00

Ferry Service A92

18c, Corona. 50c, Rowboat ferry. 60c, St. George's Ferry. $2, Laconia.

1989   Litho.   Wmk. 384   Perf. 14

551	A92	18c multicolored	.60	.40
552	A92	50c multicolored	1.10	1.10
553	A92	60c multicolored	1.25	1.25
554	A92	$2 multicolored	4.00	4.25
		Nos. 551-554 (4)	6.95	7.00

Photography, Sesquicent. A93

18c, Morgan's Island. 30c, Front Street, Hamilton (seascape). 50c, Front Street (seascape). 60c, Crow Lane, Hamilton Harbor. 70c, Hamilton Harbor (shipbuilding). $1, Dockyard.

Perf. 14x14½

1989, May 11   Litho.   Wmk. 373

555	A93	18c multicolored	1.10	.40
556	A93	30c multicolored	1.10	.60
557	A93	50c multicolored	1.60	1.60
558	A93	60c multicolored	1.75	1.75
559	A93	70c multicolored	2.10	2.50
560	A93	$1 multicolored	2.25	3.00
		Nos. 555-560 (6)	9.90	9.85

Old Garden Roses Type of 1988

18c, Agrippina. 30c, Smith's Parish. 50c, Champney's pink cluster. 60c, Rosette delizy. $1.50, Rosa bracteata.

1989, July 13   Perf. 14

561	A90	18c multicolored	1.25	.40
562	A90	30c multicolored	1.25	.65
563	A90	50c multicolored	1.75	1.60
564	A90	60c multicolored	2.00	1.75
565	A90	$1.50 multicolored	3.25	5.75
		Nos. 561-565 (5)	9.50	10.15

Nos. 561-562 vert.

Old Garden Roses Type of 1988 with Royal Cipher Instead of Queen's Silhouette

1989, July 13   Booklet Stamps

566	A90	50c like No. 562	2.50	3.00
567	A90	50c like No. 540	2.50	3.00
568	A90	50c like No. 561	2.50	3.00
569	A90	50c like No. 538	2.50	3.00
570	A90	50c like No. 563	2.50	3.00
571	A90	50c like No. 536	2.50	3.00
572	A90	50c like No. 564	2.50	3.00
573	A90	50c like No. 537	2.50	3.00
574	A90	50c like No. 565	2.50	3.00
575	A90	50c like No. 539	2.50	3.00
a.		Bklt. pane of 10, #566-575	25.00	
		Complete booklet, #575a	27.50	

Bermuda Library, 150th Anniv. A94

18c, Hamilton Main Library. 50c, St. George's, The Old Rectory. 60c, Springfield, Sommerset Library. $2, Cabinet Building.

1989, Sept. 14   **Perf. 13½x14**
576	A94	18c multicolored	.40	.40
577	A94	50c multicolored	1.10	1.10
578	A94	60c multicolored	1.25	1.25
579	A94	$2 multicolored	4.00	5.50
		Nos. 576-579 (4)	6.75	8.25

Commonwealth Postal Conference — A95

1989, Nov. 3   Wmk. 384   Perf. 14
580	A95	18c No. 1	1.25	.40
581	A95	50c No. 2	2.25	1.00
582	A95	60c Type A4	2.50	1.60
583	A95	$2 No. 6	4.00	5.50
		Nos. 580-583 (4)	10.00	8.50

For overprints see Nos. 594-597.

Fairylands, Bermuda, c. 1890, by Ross Sterling Turner A96

Paintings: 50c, *Shinebone Alley, c. 1953,* by Ogden M. Pleissner. 60c, *Salt Kettle, 1916,* by Prosper Senat. $2, *St. George's, 1934,* by Jack Bush.

1990, Apr. 19
590	A96	18c multicolored	.80	.40
591	A96	50c multicolored	1.50	1.50
592	A96	60c multicolored	1.50	1.50
593	A96	$2 multicolored	4.00	5.50
		Nos. 590-593 (4)	7.80	8.90

Nos. 580-583 Overprinted

1990, May 3
594	A95	18c multicolored	1.50	.40
595	A95	50c multicolored	2.00	1.75
596	A95	60c multicolored	2.25	2.10
597	A95	$2 multicolored	4.00	5.50
		Nos. 594-597 (4)	9.75	9.75

Stamp World London '90.

Nos. 486, 491, 494 Surcharged

1990, Aug. 13
598	A83	30c on 12c No. 486	2.50	2.50
599	A83	55c on 50c No. 491	3.25	3.25
600	A83	80c on $1.50 No. 494	4.00	5.75
		Nos. 598-600 (3)	9.75	11.50

Nova Scotia-Bermuda Cable, Cent. — A97

20c, Office. 55c, Cableship SS Westmeath. 70c, Radio station, 1928. $2, Cableship Sir Eric Sharp.

1990, Oct. 18   Litho.   Unwmk.
601	A97	20c multicolored	.80	.40
602	A97	55c multicolored	2.25	1.60
603	A97	70c multicolored	2.25	2.25
604	A97	$2 multicolored	5.75	7.00
		Nos. 601-604 (4)	11.05	11.25

Nos. 601-602 with Added Inscription "BUSH-MAJOR / 16 MARCH 1991"

1991, Mar.   Unwmk.   Perf. 14
605	A97	20c like #601	2.25	2.00
606	A97	55c like #602	4.25	4.25

Carriages A98

Designs: 20c, Two-seat pony cart, c. 1805. 30c, Varnished rockaway, c. 1830. 55c, Vis-a-Vis Victoria, c. 1895. 70c, Semi-formal phaeton, c. 1900. 80c, Pony runabout, c. 1905. $1, Ladies' phaeton, c. 1910.

Perf. 14x14½
1991, Mar. 21   Litho.   Wmk. 373
607	A98	20c green & multi	.80	.40
608	A98	30c bl gray & multi	.90	.85
609	A98	55c dk car & multi	1.75	1.40
610	A98	70c blue & multi	2.50	2.75
611	A98	80c yel org & multi	2.75	3.50
612	A98	$1 dk gray & multi	3.00	4.25
		Nos. 607-612 (6)	11.70	13.15

Paintings A99

Designs: 20c, Bermuda by Prosper Senat, vert. 55c, Bermuda Cottage by Frank Allison. 70c, Old Maid's Lane by Jack Bush, vert. $2, St. George's by Ogden M. Pleissner.

Perf. 14x13½
1991, May 16   Litho.   Wmk. 373
613	A99	20c multicolored	1.10	.40
614	A99	55c multicolored	2.25	1.90
615	A99	70c multicolored	2.75	3.25
616	A99	$2 multicolored	6.25	8.00
		Nos. 613-616 (4)	12.35	13.55

Elizabeth & Philip, Birthdays
Common Design Types

1991, June 20   Wmk. 384   Perf. 14½
617	CD346	55c multicolored	1.75	2.00
618	CD345	70c multicolored	1.75	2.00
a.		Pair, #617-618 + label	3.50	4.00

Bermuda in World War II A100

Designs: 20c, Floating drydock. 55c, Kindley Air Field. 70c, Trans-atlantic air route, Boeing 314. $2, Censored trans-atlantic mail.

1991, Sept. 19   Wmk. 373   Perf. 14
619	A100	20c multicolored	2.00	.45
620	A100	55c multicolored	3.25	2.40
621	A100	70c multicolored	4.00	4.25
622	A100	$2 multicolored	6.75	8.00
		Nos. 619-622 (4)	16.00	15.10

Queen Elizabeth II's Accession to the Throne, 40th Anniv.
Common Design Type

1992, Feb. 6
623	CD349	20c multicolored	.75	.40
624	CD349	30c multicolored	.90	.75
625	CD349	55c multicolored	1.50	1.40
626	CD349	70c multicolored	2.00	2.25
627	CD349	$1 multicolored	2.25	2.75
		Nos. 623-627 (5)	7.40	7.55

Age of Exploration — A101

Artifacts: 25c, Rings, medallion. 35c, Ink wells. 60c, Gold pieces. 75c, Bishop button, crucifix. 85c, Pearl earrings and buttons. $1, 8-real coin, jug and measuring cups.

1992, July 23   Perf. 13½
628	A101	25c multicolored	1.50	.55
629	A101	35c multicolored	1.60	1.00
630	A101	60c multicolored	2.50	2.75
631	A101	75c multicolored	3.00	3.25
632	A101	85c multicolored	3.25	3.75
633	A101	$1 multicolored	3.50	4.00
		Nos. 628-633 (6)	15.35	15.30

Stained Glass Windows — A102

Designs: 25c, Ship wreck. 60c, Birds in tree. 75c, St. Francis feeding bird. $2, Seashells.

1992, Sept. 24   Perf. 14
634	A102	25c multicolored	1.75	.55
635	A102	60c multicolored	3.25	2.75
636	A102	75c multicolored	4.00	4.00
637	A102	$2 multicolored	8.50	10.00
		Nos. 634-637 (4)	17.50	17.30

7th World Congress of Kennel Clubs A103

25c, German shepherd. 35c, Irish setter. 60c, Whippet, vert. 75c, Border terrier, vert. 85c, Pomeranian, vert. $1, Schipperke, vert.

Perf. 13½x14, 14x13½
1992, Nov. 12   Litho.   Wmk. 373
638	A103	25c multicolored	1.60	.55
639	A103	35c multicolored	2.25	1.10
640	A103	60c multicolored	3.00	2.75
641	A103	75c multicolored	3.00	3.25
642	A103	85c multicolored	3.50	4.00
643	A103	$1 multicolored	3.75	4.50
		Nos. 638-643 (6)	17.10	16.15

A104

Tourist Posters — A105

25c, Cyclist, carriage, ship. 60c, Golf course. 75c, Coastline. $2, Dancers.

1993, Feb. 25   Wmk. 373   Perf. 14
644	A104	25c multi	2.25	1.00
645	A105	60c multi	3.00	3.00
646	A105	75c multi	2.75	2.75
647	A104	$2 multi	4.75	6.50
		Nos. 644-647 (4)	12.75	13.25

Royal Air Force, 75th Anniv.
Common Design Type

Designs: 25c, Consolidated Catalina. 60c, Supermarine Spitfire. 75c, Bristol Beaufighter. $2, Handley Page Halifax.

1993, Apr. 1
648	CD350	25c multicolored	.90	.45
649	CD350	60c multicolored	2.00	2.00
650	CD350	75c multicolored	2.50	2.50
651	CD350	$2 multicolored	4.25	5.50
		Nos. 648-651 (4)	9.65	10.45

Duchesse de Brabant Rose, Bee — A106

1993, Apr. 1   Wmk. 384
Booklet Stamps
652	A106	10c green & multi	.75	1.60
653	A106	25c violet & multi	.75	.75
a.		Booklet pane of 5	3.75	
654	A106	50c sepia & multi	2.50	4.50
a.		Booklet pane, 2 #652, 3 #654	9.00	
		Complete booklet, #653a, 654a	13.00	
655	A106	60c vermilion & multi	1.75	1.90
a.		Booklet pane of 5	8.75	
		Complete booklet, #653a, 655a	18.00	
		Nos. 652-655 (4)	5.75	8.75

Hamilton, Bicent. — A107

Designs: 25c, Modern skyline. 60c, Front Street, ships at left. 75c, Front Street, horse carts. $2, Hamilton Harbor, 1823.

Wmk. 373
1993, Sept. 16   Litho.   Perf. 14½
656	A107	25c multicolored	1.75	.55
657	A107	60c multicolored	3.25	3.25
658	A107	75c multicolored	3.25	3.25
659	A107	$2 multicolored	8.25	8.25
		Nos. 656-659 (4)	16.50	15.30

Furness Lines — A108

25c, Furness Liv-Aboard Bermuda cruises, vert. 60c, SS Queen of Bermuda entering port. 75c, SS Queen of Bermuda, SS Ocean Monarch. $2, Starlit night aboard ship, vert.

Perf. 15x14, 14x15
1994, Jan. 20   Litho.   Wmk. 373

660	A108	25c multicolored	.85	.45
661	A108	60c multicolored	2.10	2.10
662	A108	75c multicolored	2.25	2.25
663	A108	$2 multicolored	4.75	6.00
		Nos. 660-663 (4)	9.95	10.80

Royal Visit — A109

25c, Queen Elizabeth II. 60c, Queen Elizabeth II, Duke of Edinburgh. 75c, Royal yacht Britannia.

Wmk. 373
1994, Mar. 9   Litho.   Perf. 13½

664	A109	25c multicolored	1.25	.50
665	A109	60c multicolored	3.00	2.75
666	A109	75c multicolored	6.00	5.00
		Nos. 664-666 (3)	10.25	8.25

Flowering Fruits A110

5c, Peach. 7c, Fig. 10c, Calabash, vert. 15c, Natal plum. 18c, Locust & wild honey. 20c, Pomegranate. 25c, Mulberry, vert. 35c, Grape, vert. 55c, Orange, vert. 60c, Surinam cherry. 75c, Loquat. 90c, Sugar apple. $1, Prickly pear, vert. $2, Paw paw. $3, Bay grape. $5, Banana, vert. $8, Lemon.

1994-95   Litho.   Wmk. 373   Perf. 14

668	A110	5c multi	.40	.40
669	A110	7c multi	.45	.45
670	A110	10c multi	.45	.45
671	A110	15c multi	.70	.40
672	A110	18c multi	4.00	3.00
b.		Inscribed "1996"	1.25	1.25
673	A110	20c multi	.70	.45
674	A110	25c multi	1.00	.60
675	A110	35c multi	1.25	.80
676	A110	55c multi	1.60	1.10
677	A110	60c multi	2.25	1.40
678	A110	75c multi	2.25	2.50
679	A110	90c multi	2.75	2.75
680	A110	$1 multi	3.25	3.25
681	A110	$2 multi	5.00	5.00
682	A110	$3 multi	7.25	7.25
683	A110	$5 multi	9.75	9.75
684	A110	$8 multi	16.00	16.00
		Nos. 668-684 (17)	59.05	55.55

Issued: 5c, 7c, 15c, 20c, $8, 7/14/94; 10c, 25c, 35c, 55c, $1, $5, 10/6/94; 18c, 60c, 75c, 90c, $2, $3, 3/23/95. No. 672a, 9/1/96.

1998, Sept. 1   Wmk. 384

668a	A110	5c	.80	1.25
671a	A110	15c	1.40	.50
672a	A110	18c	1.40	.50
673a	A110	20c	1.40	.60
674a	A110	25c	4.00	.60
678a	A110	75c	4.00	2.00
679a	A110	90c	5.00	2.50
680a	A110	$1	6.00	3.75
		Nos. 668a-680a (8)	24.00	11.70

No. 672a exists dated "1998."
Issued: Nos. 668a, 671a, 673a-674a, 678a-680a, 9/1/98.

Hospital Care, Cent. — A111

1994, Sept. 15   Perf. 15x14

685	A111	25c Child birth	1.10	.45
686	A111	60c Dialysis	2.25	2.25
687	A111	75c Emergency	3.25	3.25
688	A111	$2 Therapy	6.00	6.75
		Nos. 685-688 (4)	12.60	12.70

Christmas — A112

25c, Gombey dancers. 60c, Carollers. 75c, Marching band. $2, Natl. dance group.

1994, Nov. 10   Perf. 14x15

689	A112	25c multi	.80	.45
690	A112	60c multi	1.50	1.50
691	A112	75c multi	3.00	2.50
692	A112	$2 multi	5.25	6.75
		Nos. 689-692 (4)	10.55	11.20

Decimalization, 25th Anniv. — A113

Stamps, 1970 coins: 25c, #255, one cent. 60c, #259, five cents. 75c, #262, ten cents. $2, #324, twenty-five cents.

Wmk. 373
1995, Feb. 6   Litho.   Perf. 14

693	A113	25c multicolored	.90	.40
694	A113	60c multicolored	1.50	1.50
695	A113	75c multicolored	2.00	2.00
696	A113	$2 multicolored	5.50	6.25
		Nos. 693-696 (4)	9.90	10.15

Outdoor Celebrations — A114

25c, Kite flying. 60c, Majorettes. 75c, Portuguese dancers. $2, Floral float.

Perf. 14x15
1995, May 30   Litho.   Wmk. 373

697	A114	25c multi	.75	.45
698	A114	60c multi	2.00	2.00
699	A114	75c multi	2.25	2.25
700	A114	$2 multi	5.00	5.75
		Nos. 697-700 (4)	10.00	10.45

Parliament, 375th Anniv. — A115

Designs: 25c, $1, Bermuda coat of arms.

Perf. 14x13½
1995, Nov. 3   Litho.   Wmk. 373

701	A115	25c blue & multi	1.10	.40
702	A115	$1 green & multi	2.40	3.00
		See No. 731.		

Military Bases A116

Force insignia and: 20c, Ordnance Island Submarine Base. 25c, Royal Naval Dockyard. 60c, Fort Bell and Kindley Field. 75c, Darrell's Island. 90c, US Navy Operating Base. $1, Canadian Forces Station, Daniel's Head.

1995, Dec. 4   Perf. 14

703	A116	20c multicolored	.75	.75
704	A116	25c multicolored	.90	.45
705	A116	60c multicolored	1.90	1.90
706	A116	75c multicolored	2.25	2.25
707	A116	90c multicolored	2.25	3.00
708	A116	$1 multicolored	2.25	3.00
		Nos. 703-708 (6)	10.30	11.35

Modern Olympic Games, Cent. — A117

Wmk. 384
1996, May 21   Litho.   Perf. 14

709	A117	25c Track & field	1.10	.60
710	A117	30c Cycling	4.00	1.60
711	A117	65c Sailing	2.75	2.75
712	A117	80c Equestrian	2.75	2.75
		Nos. 709-712 (4)	10.60	7.70

CAPEX '96 A118

Methods of transportation: 25c, Sommerset Express, c. 1900. 60c, Bermuda Railway, 1930's. 75c, First bus, 1946. $2, Early sightseeing bus, c.1947.

Perf. 13½x14
1996, June 7   Litho.   Wmk. 373

713	A118	25c multicolored	1.50	.60
714	A118	60c multicolored	3.00	2.00
715	A118	75c multicolored	3.00	2.40
716	A118	$2 multicolored	5.50	7.00
		Nos. 713-716 (4)	13.00	12.00

Panoramas of Hamilton and St. George's, by E. J. Holland, 1933 A119

Hamilton, looking across water from Bostock Hill: No. 717, Palm trees, Furness Line ship coming through Two Rock Passage. No. 718, House, buildings on other side. No. 719, Sailboats on water, Princess Hotel. No. 720, Island, Bermudiana Hotel, Cathedral. No. 721, Coral roads on hillside, city of Hamilton.
St. George's, looking across water from St. David's: No. 722, Island, harbor. No. 723, Sailboat, buildings along shore. No. 724, Sailboat, St. George's Hotel, buildings. No. 725, Hillside, ship. No. 726, Homes on hill top, passage out of harbor.

Perf. 14x14½
1996, May 21   Wmk. 373
Booklet Stamps

717	A119	60c multicolored	2.75	2.75
718	A119	60c multicolored	2.75	2.75
719	A119	60c multicolored	2.75	2.75
720	A119	60c multicolored	2.75	2.75
721	A119	60c multicolored	2.75	2.75
a.		Strip of 5, #717-721	14.00	14.00
722	A119	60c multicolored	2.75	2.75
723	A119	60c multicolored	2.75	2.75
724	A119	60c multicolored	2.75	2.75
725	A119	60c multicolored	2.75	2.75

726	A119	60c multicolored	2.75	2.75
a.		Strip of 5, #722-726	14.00	14.00
b.		Booklet pane, #721a, 726a	28.00	
		Complete booklet, #726b	30.00	

Lighthouses A120

Designs: 30c, Hog Fish Beacon. 65c, Gibbs Hill Lighthouse. 80c, St. David's Lighthouse. $2, North Rock Beacon.

Perf. 14x13½
1996, Aug. 15   Litho.   Wmk. 373

727	A120	30c multicolored	2.10	.85
728	A120	65c multicolored	2.75	2.25
729	A120	80c multicolored	3.25	2.75
730	A120	$2 multicolored	5.25	7.00
		Nos. 727-730 (4)	13.35	12.85

See Nos. 737-740.

Bermuda Coat of Arms Type of 1995
Inscribed "Commonwealth Finance Ministers Meeting"
Perf. 14x13½
1996, Sept. 24   Litho.   Wmk. 373

731	A115	$1 red & multi	3.50	3.50

Queen Elizabeth II — A121

1996, Nov. 7

732	A121	$22 blue & org brn	47.50	55.00

Architectural Heritage — A122

30c, Waterville. 65c, Bridge House. 80c, Fannie Fox's Cottage. $2.50, Palmetto House.

Wmk. 384
1996, Nov. 28   Litho.   Perf. 14

733	A122	30c multicolored	1.10	.55
734	A122	65c multicolored	1.60	1.60
735	A122	80c multicolored	2.00	2.00
736	A122	$2.50 multicolored	4.50	6.50
		Nos. 733-736 (4)	9.20	10.65

Lighthouse Type of 1996 Redrawn
Wmk. 373
1997, Feb. 12   Litho.   Perf. 14

737	A120	30c Like #727	2.50	1.10
738	A120	65c Like #728	3.75	2.75
739	A120	80c Like #729	4.25	3.25
740	A120	$2.50 Like #730	8.00	11.00
		Nos. 737-740 (4)	18.50	18.10

Nos. 737-740 each have Hong Kong '97 emblem. No. 738 inscribed "Gibbs Hill Lighthouse c. 1900." No. 739 inscribed "St. David's Lighthouse c. 1900."

Birds A123

Designs: 30c, White-tailed tropicbird. 60c, White-tailed tropicbird, adult, chick, vert. 80c, Cahow, adult, chick, vert. $2.50, Cahow.

Wmk. 384

1997, Apr. 17   **Litho.**   *Perf. 14*

741	A123	30c multicolored	1.10	.75
742	A123	60c multicolored	2.25	1.90
743	A123	80c multicolored	3.00	2.75
744	A123	$2.50 multicolored	6.75	7.50
		Nos. 741-744 (4)	13.10	12.90

See Nos. 798-801.

Queen Elizabeth II and Prince Philip, 50th Wedding Anniv. A124

Perf. 14x14½

1997, Oct. 9   **Litho.**   **Wmk. 373**

745	A124	30c Queen, crowd	.75	.75
746	A124	$2 Queen, Prince	5.00	5.00
a.		Souvenir sheet of 2, #745-746	6.50	6.50

Education in Bermuda A125

Designs: 30c, Man, children using blocks. 40c, Teacher, students with map. 60c, Boys holding sports trophy. 65c, Students in front of Berkeley Institute. 80c, Students working in lab. 90c, Students in graduation gowns.

Wmk. 384

1997, Dec. 18   **Litho.**   *Perf. 14*

747	A125	30c multicolored	.80	.60
748	A125	40c multicolored	.90	.90
749	A125	60c multicolored	1.25	1.25
750	A125	65c multicolored	1.25	1.25
751	A125	80c multicolored	1.90	1.90
752	A125	90c multicolored	2.10	2.10
		Nos. 747-752 (6)	8.20	8.00

Diana, Princess of Wales (1961-97)
Common Design Type

Various portraits: a. 30c. b, 40c. c, 65c. d, 80c.

Perf. 14x14½

1998, Mar. 31   **Litho.**   **Wmk. 373**

753	CD355	Sheet of 4, #a.-d.	5.00	5.00

No. 753 sold for $2.15 + 25c, with surtax from international sales being donated to the Princess Diana Memorial Fund and surtax from national sales being donated to designated local charity.

Paintings of the Islands A126

Designs: 30c, Fox's Cottage, St. David's. 40c, East Side, Somerset. 65c, Long Bay Road, Somerset. $2, Flatts Village.

1998, June 4   *Perf. 13½x14*

754	A126	30c multicolored	1.50	.70
755	A126	40c multicolored	1.90	1.25
756	A126	65c multicolored	2.75	2.50
757	A126	$2 multicolored	6.50	8.50
		Nos. 754-757 (4)	12.65	12.95

Hospitality for Tourists in Bermuda — A127

Designs: 25c, Carriage ride. 30c, Golfer at registration desk. 65c, Maid leaving flowers on hotel bed. 75c, Chefs preparing food. 80c, Waiter serving couple. 90c, Singer, bartender, guests.

Wmk. 384

1998, Sept. 24   **Litho.**   *Perf. 14½*

758	A127	25c multicolored	1.40	.60
759	A127	30c multicolored	2.10	1.10
760	A127	65c multicolored	2.10	1.75
761	A127	75c multicolored	2.10	2.10
762	A127	80c multicolored	2.25	2.25
763	A127	90c multicolored	2.50	3.00
		Nos. 758-763 (6)	12.45	10.80

Bermuda's Botanical Gardens, Cent. — A128

30c, Agave attenuata. 65c, Bermuda palmetto tree. $1, Banyan tree. $2, Cedar tree.

Wmk. 373

1998, Oct. 15   **Litho.**   *Perf. 14*

764	A128	30c multi	1.75	.70
765	A128	65c multi	2.25	1.25
766	A128	$1 multi	3.50	3.50
767	A128	$2 multi	5.50	7.50
		Nos. 764-767 (4)	13.00	12.95

Christmas A129

Children's paintings: 25c, Lizard in Santa hat stringing Christmas lights, vert. 40c, Stairway, wreath on door.

Wmk. 373

1998, Nov. 26   **Litho.**   *Perf. 14*

768	A129	25c multicolored	1.75	1.40
769	A129	40c multicolored	2.25	2.25

Beaches — A130

30c, Shelly Bay. 60c, Catherine's Bay. 65c, Jobson's Cove. $2, Warwick Long Bay.

Wmk. 373

1999, Apr. 29   **Litho.**   *Perf. 13½*

770	A130	30c multi	1.10	.50
771	A130	60c multi	1.25	1.25
772	A130	65c multi	1.60	1.40
773	A130	$2 multi	4.75	6.00
		Nos. 770-773 (4)	8.70	9.15

Common Design Type and

First Manned Moon Landing, 30th Anniv. A131

30c, Ground station. 60c, Lift-off, vert. 75c, Aerial view of ground station. $2, Moon walk, vert.
65c, Looking at earth from moon.

Wmk. 373

1999, July 20   **Litho.**   *Perf. 13*

774	A131	30c multicolored	1.25	.50
775	A131	60c multicolored	1.90	1.25
776	A131	75c multicolored	2.10	1.75
777	A131	$2 multicolored	4.75	6.25
		Nos. 774-777 (4)	10.00	9.75

Souvenir Sheet
Wmk. 384
Perf. 14

778	CD357	65c multicolored	9.00	9.00

No. 778 contains one 40mm circular stamp.

Mapmaking — A132

30c, Somerset Is., theodolite. 65c, 1901 street map. 80c, Aerial photo, modern street map. $1, Satellite, island.

Wmk. 373

1999, Aug. 19   **Litho.**   *Perf. 14*

779	A132	30c multicolored	1.60	.60
780	A132	65c multicolored	2.75	2.75
781	A132	80c multicolored	3.00	3.00
782	A132	$1 multicolored	3.50	4.00
		Nos. 779-782 (4)	10.85	10.35

Mail Boxes and Stamps — A133

30c, Victoria era, #6. 75c, George V era, #49. 95c, George VI era, #121. $1, Elizabeth II era, #142.

Wmk. 373

1999, Oct. 5   **Litho.**   *Perf. 14¼*

783	A133	30c multicolored	1.75	.80
784	A133	75c multicolored	2.75	2.75
785	A133	95c multicolored	3.00	3.00
786	A133	$1 multicolored	3.00	3.00
		Nos. 783-786 (4)	10.50	9.55

Pioneers of Progress — A134

No. 787: a, Dr. E. F. Gordon, labor leader. b, Sir Henry Tucker, banker. c, Gladys Morrell, suffragist.

Perf. 13½x13¼

2000, May 1   **Litho.**   **Wmk. 373**

787	A134	30c Horiz. strip of 3, #a-c	3.75	3.75

See Nos. 933-937, 963-964.

Sailing Ships — A135

Designs: 30c, Amerigo Vespucci. 60c, Europa. 80c Juan Sebastian de Elcano.

2000, May 23   *Perf. 14*

788	A135	30c multi	1.60	.90
789	A135	60c multi	2.25	2.25
790	A135	80c multi	2.75	3.25
		Nos. 788-790 (3)	6.60	6.40

Royal Family Birthdays — A136

35c, Prince William, 18th. 40c, Prince Andrew, 40th. 50c, Princess Anne, 50th. 70c, Princess Margaret, 70th. $1, Queen Mother, 100th.

2000, Aug. 7

791	A136	35c multi	1.75	.95
792	A136	40c multi	1.90	1.10
793	A136	50c multi	2.10	1.75
794	A136	70c multi	2.25	2.75
795	A136	$1 multi	3.00	3.50
a.		Souvenir sheet, #791-795	12.00	12.00
		Nos. 791-795 (5)	11.00	10.05

Christmas A137

Children's art: 30c, Santa Claus and Bermuda onion, by Meghan Jones. 45c, Christmas tree, by Carlita Lodge.

Wmk. 384

2000, Sept. 26   **Litho.**   *Perf. 13¾*

796-797	A137	Set of 2	3.25	3.25

Bird Type of 1997 Redrawn with WWF Emblem

Designs: No. 798, 15c, White-tailed tropic bird. No. 799, 15c, Cahow. No. 800, 20c, Cahow, vert. No. 801, 20c, White-tailed tropic bird, vert.

Wmk. 373

2001, Feb. 1   **Litho.**   *Perf. 14*

798-801	A123	Set of 4	4.50	4.50
801a		Miniature sheet, 4 each #798-801	19.00	19.00

Hong Kong 2001 Stamp Exhibition (No. 801a).

Historical Tourist Attractions, St. George's A138

Designs: 35c, King's Castle. 50c, Bridge House. 55c, Whitehall. 70c, Fort Cunningham. 85c, St. Peter's Church. 95c, Water Street.

2001, May 1   *Perf. 13¾*

802-807	A138	Set of 6	14.50	14.50

Boer War, Cent. — A139

Designs: 35c, Crowded boat, plow. 50c, Men, boot last. 70c, Man with children, rings and pin. 95c, Men and women, stamped cover.

2001, June 28   *Perf. 14*

808-811	A139	Set of 4	7.75	7.75

Aquarium, Museum and Zoo, 75th Anniv. — A140

Designs: 35c, Child, sea urchins, starfish, vert. 50c, Child, museum display. 55c, Child, tortoise. 70c, Aquarium. 80c, Diver in aquarium tank, vert. 95c, Turtle, vert.

Perf. 14¾x14¼, 14¼x14¾

2001, Aug. 9		Litho.		Wmk. 373
812-817	A140	Set of 6	12.00	12.00

Paintings by Charles Lloyd Tucker — A141

Various paintings: 35c, 70c, 85c, $1.

Perf. 14¼x14¾

2001, Oct. 9				
818-821	A141	Set of 4	11.50	11.50

Reign Of Queen Elizabeth II, 50th Anniv. Issue
Common Design Type

Designs: Nos. 822, 826a, 10c, Princess Elizabeth with dog, 1952. Nos. 823, 826b, 35c, In 1965. Nos. 824, 826c, 70c, Waving. Nos. 825, 826d, 85c, In 1991. No. 826e, $1, 1955 portrait by Annigoni (38x50mm).

Perf. 14¼x14½, 13¾ (#826e)

2002, Feb. 6		Litho.		Wmk. 373
With Gold Frames				
822	CD360	10c multicolored	.50	.50
823	CD360	35c multicolored	1.25	1.25
824	CD360	70c multicolored	2.75	2.75
825	CD360	85c multicolored	3.50	3.50
		Nos. 822-825 (4)	8.00	8.00

Souvenir Sheet
Without Gold Frames

826	CD360	Sheet of 5, #a-e	10.00	10.00

Caves A142

Designs: 35c, Fantasy Cave. 70c, Crystal Cave. 80c, Prospero's Cave. $1, Cathedral Cave.

Wmk. 373

2002, May 1		Litho.		*Perf. 14*
827-830	A142	Set of 4	11.50	11.50

Cricket Cup Match, Cent. — A143

Details from "One Hundred Up," by Robert D. Bassett: No. 831, 35c, Umpire and fielder. No. 832, 35c, Batsman and wicketkeeper. $1, Entire painting, horiz.

Wmk. 373

2002, July 4		Litho.		*Perf. 14*
831-832	A143	Set of 2	5.00	5.00
Souvenir Sheet				
833	A143	$1 multi	6.00	6.00

See Nos. 869-870.

Queen Mother Elizabeth (1900-2002)
Common Design Type

Designs: Nos. 834, 836a, 30c, Without hat (sepia photograph). Nos. 835, 836b, $1.25, Wearing blue hat.

Perf. 13¾x14¼

2002, Aug. 5		Litho.		Wmk. 373
With Purple Frames				
834	CD361	30c multicolored	1.25	1.25
835	CD361	$1.25 multicolored	4.00	4.00

Souvenir Sheet
Without Purple Frames

Perf. 14½x14¼

836	CD361	Sheet of 2, #a-b	7.00	7.00

Shells — A144

Designs: 5c, Slit worm-shell. 10c, Netted olive. 20c, Angular triton. 25c, Frog shell. 30c, Colorful Atlantic moon. 35c, Noble wentletrap. 40c, Atlantic trumpet triton. 45c, Zigzag scallop. 50c, Bermuda cone. 75c, Very distorted distorsio. 80c, Purple sea snail. 90c, Flame helmet. $1, Scotch bonnet. $2, Gold mouth triton. $3, Bermuda's slit shell. $4, Reticulated cowrie-helmet. $5, Dennison's morum. $8, Sunrise tellin.

2002-03		Litho. Wmk. 373		*Perf. 14*
837	A144	5c multi	.25	.25
838	A144	10c multi	.30	.30
839	A144	20c multi	.55	.55
840	A144	25c multi	.65	.65
841	A144	30c multi	.75	.75
842	A144	35c multi	.90	.90
a.		Inscribed "2008"	.90	.90
843	A144	40c multi	1.10	1.10
844	A144	45c multi	1.25	1.25
845	A144	50c multi	1.50	1.50
846	A144	75c multi	2.00	2.00
847	A144	80c multi	2.25	2.75
848	A144	90c multi	2.50	2.50
849	A144	$1 multi	2.50	3.00
850	A144	$2 multi	5.25	6.50
851	A144	$3 multi	8.00	8.00
852	A144	$4 multi	9.00	10.00
853	A144	$5 multi	10.00	11.00
854	A144	$8 multi	17.00	18.00
		Nos. 837-854 (18)	65.75	71.00

Issued: Nos. 5c, 10c, 35c, 45c, 50c, $8, 9/10/02. 20c, 40c, 80c, 90c, $3, $4, 1/23/03. 25c, 30c, 75c, $1, $2, $5, 3/20/03.

World Peace Day — A145

Dove facing: 35c, Right. 70c, Left.

Wmk. 373

2002, Nov. 7		Litho.		*Perf. 14¼*
855-856	A145	Set of 2	5.25	5.25

Bermuda Biological Station for Research, Cent. A146

Designs: 35c, Biological Station and ship, vert. 70c, Fish. 85c, Researcher probing reef. $1, Shrimp, vert.

Wmk. 373

2003, Feb. 4		Litho.		*Perf. 14*
857-860	A146	Set of 4	9.00	9.00

Items Made in Bermuda — A147

Designs: 35c, Dolls. 70c, Model of ship. 80c, Wooden sculpture. $1, Silver tankard and goblets.

Perf. 14½x14¼

2003, May 15		Litho.		Wmk. 373
861-864	A147	Set of 4	7.50	7.50

See Nos. 880-883, 898-901, 925-928.

Head of Queen Elizabeth II
Common Design Type
Wmk. 373

2003, June 2		Litho.		*Perf. 13¾*
865	CD362	$25 multi	50.00	50.00

Coronation of Queen Elizabeth II, 50th Anniv.
Common Design Type

Designs: Nos. 866, 35c, 868a, $1.25, Queen in carriage. Nos. 867, 70c, 868b, $2, Queen with crown at coronation.

Perf. 14¼x14½

2003, June 2		Litho.		Wmk. 373
Vignettes Framed, Red Background				
866-867	CD363	multicolored	3.25	3.25

Souvenir Sheet
Vignettes Without Frame, Purple Panel

868	CD363	Sheet of 2, #a-b	11.00	11.00

Cricket Cup Type of 2002 with "30th Anniversary CARICOM" Added at Left

Designs: No. 869, 35c, Umpire and fielder. No. 870, 35c, Batsman and wicketkeeper.

Wmk. 373

2003, July 4		Litho.		*Perf. 14*
869-870	A143	Set of 2	4.00	4.00

Poinsettias A148

Bract color: 30c, Red. 45c, White. 80c, Mottled.

Perf. 14½x14¼

2003, Oct. 9		Litho.		Wmk. 373
871-873	A148	Set of 3	5.75	5.75

Royal Naval Dockyard — A149

Various views: 25c, 35c, 70c, 85c, 95c, $1.

Wmk. 373

2004, Feb. 19		Litho.		*Perf. 13¾*
874-879	A149	Set of 6	14.00	14.00

Items Made in Bermuda Type of 2003

Designs: 35c, Chair. 70c, Pitcher and plate. 80c, Decorative glassware. $1.25, Quilt.

Wmk. 373

2004, May 15		Litho.		*Perf. 13¾*
880-883	A147	Set of 4	6.25	6.25

Worldwide Fund for Nature (WWF) — A150

Various depictions of school of bluefin tuna: 10c, 35c, 85c, $1.10.

Wmk. 373

2004, Aug. 19		Litho.		*Perf. 14*
884-887	A150	Set of 4	7.25	7.25
887a	A150	Sheetlet, 4 each #884-887		30.00

Nos. 884-887 were issued issued both in sheets of 50 (with gutter between panes of 25) and in miniature sheets of 16, with 4 se-tenant strips.

Bermuda Orchid Society, 50th Anniv. — A151

Various orchids: 35c, 45c, 85c, $1.10.

Wmk. 373

2004, Nov. 18		Litho.		*Perf. 13¾*
888-891	A151	Set of 4	9.50	9.50

Discovery of Bermuda, 500th Anniv. — A152

Map of Bermuda and: 25c, Compass. 35c, Sextant. 70c, Chronometer. $1.10, Telescope. $1.25, Divider. $5, Aerial photograph of Bermuda.

Perf. 14x14¾

2005, Jan. 13		Litho.		Wmk. 373
892-896	A152	Set of 5	12.50	12.50
Souvenir Sheet				
897	A152	$5 multi	14.00	14.00

Items Made in Bermuda Type of 2003

Designs: 35c, Carnival reveler dolls. 70c, Fish and coral sculpture. 85c, Lion and lamb stained glass. $1, Earrings and necklace.

Wmk. 373

2005, May 19		Litho.		*Perf. 13¾*
898-901	A147	Set of 4	8.50	8.50

Battle of Trafalgar, Bicent. — A153

Designs: 10c, HMS Victory. 35c, HMS Pickle under construction in Bermuda. 70c, HMS Pickle picking up survivors from the Achille. 85c, HMS Pickle racing back to England.

Wmk. 373, Unwmkd (10c)

2005, June 23		Litho.		*Perf. 13¼*
902-905	A153	Set of 4	7.25	7.25

No. 902 has particles of wood from the HMS Victory embedded in the areas covered by a thermographic process that produces a shiny, raised effect.

Birds and Habitats A154

Various birds and: 10c, Sandy beach, 25c, Fresh water pond. 35c, Rocky shore. 70c, Upland forest (blue bird). 85c, Upland forest (owl). $1, Mangroves.

2005, Aug. 18   *Perf. 13¾*
906-911 A154 Set of 6   11.50 11.50

Christmas A155

Light displays: 30c, Christmas tree. 45c, Dolphin. 80c, Snowman.

Wmk. 373
2005, Oct. 27 Litho. *Perf. 13¾*
912-914 A155 Set of 3   3.75 3.75

Bermuda Electric Light Company, Cent. A156

Designs: 35c, Worker in cherry picker working on overhead electric wires. 70c, Worker in cherry picker. 85c, Worker on elevated walkway near equipment. $1, Building.

2006, Jan. 13 Litho. *Perf. 13¼x13*
915-918 A156 Set of 4   6.25 6.25

Queen Elizabeth II, 80th Birthday A157

Designs: 35c, As child, with dog. 70c, Wearing tiara and small earrings. 85c, Wearing tiara and large earrings. No. 922, $1.25, Wearing blue hat.
No. 923: a, $1.25, Like 70c. b, $2, Like 85c.

Wmk. 373
2006, Apr. 21 Litho. *Perf. 14*
With White Frames
919-922 A157 Set of 4   7.00 7.00
Souvenir Sheet
Without White Frames
923 A157 Sheet of 2, #a-b   7.25 7.25

Map of Bermuda A158

2006, May 27   *Perf. 13¾x13¼*
924 A158 $1.10 multi   2.50 2.50
 a.   Souvenir sheet of 1   3.00 3.00
Washington 2006 World Philatelic Exhibition.

Items Made in Bermuda Type of 2003

Designs: 35c, Jar of honey. 70c, Stonecutters, by Sharon Wilson. 85c, I've Caught Some Whoppers, sculpture by Desmond Fountain. $1.25, Bottle of perfume.

2006, June 22   *Perf. 13x13¼*
925-928 A147 Set of 4   9.00 9.00

Christmas A159

Various wreaths: 30c, 35c, 45c, 80c.

Wmk. 373
2006, Oct. 12 Litho. *Perf. 13¾*
929-932 A159 Set of 4   6.00 6.00

Pioneers of Progress Type of 2000

Teachers: No. 933, 35c, Millie Neversen (1883-1975). No. 934, 35c, Edith (1880-1978) and Matilda Crawford (1879-1948). No. 935, 35c, May Francis (1899-1985). No. 936, 35c, Francis L. Patton (1843-1932). No. 937, 35c, Adele Tucker (1868-1971).

      Perf. 13¾x13½
2007, Feb. 15 Litho.   **Wmk. 373**
933-937 A134 Set of 5   4.00 4.00

Spirit of Bermuda A160

Various views of sloop: 10c, 35c, 70c, 85c, $1.10, $1.25.

      Perf. 13¼x13½
2007, May 17 Litho.   **Wmk. 373**
938-943 A160 Set of 6   10.00 10.00

Voyage of Deliverance From Bermuda to Jamestown, Va. — A161

Ship and coastline with panel colors of: 35c, Olive green. $1.10, Blue.

      Perf. 12½x12¾
2007, June 21 Litho.   **Wmk. 373**
944-945 A161 Set of 2   5.00 5.00
Jamestown, Va., 400th anniv.

Scouting, Cent. A162

Designs: 35c, 1930 photograph of Bishop's Own Cubs, hand with compass. 70c, 1930 photograph of Lord Robert Baden-Powell inspecting Cubs, hands lashing rope. 85c, 1930 photograph of Scout parade, hands of trumpeter. $1.10, Dance of Kaa, hands tying knot.
No. 950, vert.: a, $1.25, Emblem of Bermuda Scouts. b, $2, Baden-Powell inspecting Cubs.

2007, Aug. 23   *Perf. 13¾*
946-949 A162 Set of 4   7.00 7.00
Souvenir Sheet
950 A162 Sheet of 2, #a-b   8.00 8.00

Poster Art for Troubador Acts A163

Designs: 35c, Celeste & Harris. 70c, Calypsos Hubert Smith, Sydney Bean, Erskine Zuill, Four Deuces. 85c, Calypso Varieties from Bermuda. $1.10, The Talbot Brothers.

Wmk. 373
2008, Mar. 19 Litho. *Perf. 13¾*
951-954 A163 Set of 4   7.00 7.00

Bermuda No. X1, 160th Anniv. — A164

Panel color: 35c, Brown. 70c, Gray blue. 85p, Gold. $1.25, Silver

Wmk. 373
2008, Apr. 23 Litho. *Perf. 13¾*
955-958 A164 Set of 4   8.00 8.00

Local Scenes A165

Designs: (35c), Deep Bay, West Pembroke. (70c), Spanish Point Park. (85c), Flatts Inlet. (95c), Tucker's Town Bay.

Die Cut Perf. 12x12½
2008, May 1   **Unwmk.**
Booklet Stamps
Self-Adhesive
959 A165 (35c) multi   .70 .70
 a.   Booklet pane of 10   7.00
960 A165 (70c) multi   1.40 2.00
 a.   Booklet pane of 10   14.00
961 A165 (85c) multi   1.75 2.25
 a.   Booklet pane of 10   17.50
962 A165 (95c) multi   1.90 2.75
 a.   Booklet pane of 10   19.00
   Nos. 959-962 (4)   5.75 7.70
No. 959 is inscribed "Postage Paid Local;" No. 960, "Postage Paid Zone 1;" No. 961, "Postage Page Zone 2;" No. 962, "Postage Paid Zone 3."

Pioneers of Progress Type of 2000

Designs: No. 963, 35c, Dr. Pauulu Roosevelt Brown Kamarakafego (1932-2007), political activist. No. 964, 35c, Dame Lois Browne-Evans (1927-2007), attorney general.

Perf. 13¾x13½
2008, June 11   **Wmk. 373**
963-964 A134 Set of 2   2.00 2.00

2008 Summer Olympics, Beijing A166

Designs: 10c, Running. 35c, Swimming. 70c, Equestrian. 85c, Yachting.

Perf. 12½x13
2008, July 23   **Wmk. 373**
965-968 A166 Set of 4   5.25 5.25

Lighted Christmas Decorations — A167

Various decorations: 30c, 35c, 45c, 80c.

Wmk. 406
2008, Oct. 1 Litho. *Perf. 13½*
969-972 A167 Set of 4   4.75 4.75

Settlement of Bermuda, 400th Anniv. — A168

Old and modern: 35c, City photographs. 70c, Harbor scenes. 85c, Harbor scenes, diff. $1.25, Maps.

Perf. 12½x12¾
2009, Jan. 22 Litho.   **Wmk. 406**
973-976 A168 Set of 4   8.75 8.75

First Man on the Moon, 40th Anniv. A169

Designs: 35c, Aerial view of tracking station, Cooper's Island. 70c, Antenna at tracking station, Cooper's Island. 85c, Apollo 11 Lunar Module. 95c, Space Shuttle (STS 126). $1.25, International Space Station. $1.10, Lunar Module on Moon, vert.

Wmk. 406
2009, Apr. 16 Litho. *Perf. 13¼*
977-981 A169 Set of 5   10.50 10.50
Souvenir Sheet
Perf. 13x13¼
982 A169 $1.10 multi   3.00 3.00
No. 982 contains one 40x60mm stamp.

Marathon Derby, Cent. A170

Designs: 35c, Athlete with trophy and cup. 70c, Athlete with trophy, window at left. 85c, Motorcyclist following runner. $1.10, Woman racing with men.

2009, May 21   *Perf. 14*
983-986 A170 Set of 4   7.00 7.00

Atlantic Challenge 2009 Tall Ship Races — A171

Ships: 35c, Concordia. 70c, Picton Castle. 85c, Jolie Brise, horiz. 95c, Tecla. $1.10, Europa. $1.25, Etoile, horiz.

Perf. 13¾x13¼, 13¼x13¾
2009, June 11   Litho.   Wmk. 373
987-992 A171   Set of 6   12.50 12.50

Bermuda Theater Boycott, 50th Anniv. — A172

Designs: 35c, People. 70c, Stylized people, vert. 85c, Sculpture, vert. $1.25, Photograph of protestors.

2009, July 2   Wmk. 406   Perf. 12½
993-996 A172   Set of 4   8.00 8.00

Christmas — A173

Christmas tree ornaments: 30c, Basket. 35c, Angel. 70c, Basket, diff. 85c, Angel, diff.

Perf. 14x13¾
2009, Sept. 24   Litho.   Wmk. 406
997-1000 A173   Set of 4   6.00 6.00

Girl Guides, Cent. — A174

Girl Guides: 35c, At ceremony. 70c, Camping. 85c, Marching. $1.10, With parade float. $1.25, Bermuda's first black Girl Guides unit.

Perf. 14x14¾
2010, Feb. 18   Litho.   Wmk. 406
1001-1004 A174   Set of 4   7.00 7.00
Souvenir Sheet
1005 A174 $1.25 multi   3.50 3.50

African Diaspora Heritage Trail — A175

Designs: 35c, Cobbs Hill Methodist Church. 70c, Bermudian Heritage Museum. 85c, St. Peter's Church. $1.10, Barr's Bay Park.

Perf. 13x12½
2010, May 20   Litho.   Wmk. 406
1006-1009 A175   Set of 4   7.75 7.75

Worldwide Fund for Nature (WWF) — A176

Lined seahorse: 35c, Head. 70c, Pair of seahorses. 85c, Pair of seahorses in seaweed. $1.25, Adults and juveniles.

Wmk. 406
2010, June 17   Litho.   Perf. 14
1010-1013 A176   Set of 4   8.00 8.00
1013a   Sheet of 16, 4 each #1010- 32.00 32.00
1013

Dockyard Apprentices A177

Designs: 35c, Hull of boat under construction, plumb bob. 70c, Dockyard gates, gears. 85c, Worker and equipment, wooden rudder pattern. $1.10, Apprentices, tools.

Wmk. 406
2010, Sept. 23   Litho.   Perf. 14
1014-1017 A177   Set of 4   8.00 8.00

Service of Queen Elizabeth II and Prince Philip — A178

Designs: 10c, Queen Elizabeth II. 35c, Queen and Prince Philip. 70c, Queen and Prince Philip, diff. 85c, Queen and Prince Philip, diff. $1.10, Queen and Prince Philip, diff. $1.25, Prince Philip. $2.50, Queen and Prince Philip, diff.

Perf. 13¼
2011, Mar. 3   Litho.   Unwmk.
1018-1023 A178   Set of 6   9.00 9.00
1023a   Sheet of 6, #1018-1023, + 9.00 9.00
3 labels
Souvenir Sheet
1024 A178 $2.50 multi   5.25 5.25

Boat Piloting — A179

Designs: 35c, People dragging boat ashore, nautical chart. 70c, Boats. 85c, Boat, sailor. $1.10, Boat in water, sailors and children on shore.

Perf. 14x14¼
2011, May 19   Wmk. 406
1025-1028 A179   Set of 4   7.00 7.00

Casemate Barracks — A180

Designs: 35c, Casemate Barracks, Great Eastern Storehouse and Commissioner's House, 1857, painting by Gaspard Le

---

Marchant Tupper. 70c, Casemate Barracks and Victualling Yard, 1857, painting by Tupper. 85c, Casemate Barracks and Bermuda Dockyard, 1856, painting by unknown artist. $1.25, 1899 photograph of Casemate Barracks and Lower Ordnance Yard.

Perf. 14¼x14¾
2011, July 21   Wmk. 406
1029-1032 A180   Set of 4   7.00 7.00

Miniature Sheet

Wedding of Prince William and Catherine Middleton — A181

No. 1033 — Couple: a, 35c, Holding hands. b, 70c, Waving in coach, horiz. c, 85c, In automobile, horiz. d, $1.25, Kissing.

2011, Sept. 1   Perf. 14x14¼
1033 A181   Sheet of 4, #a-d   7.00 7.00

Reign of Queen Elizabeth II, 60th Anniv. — A182

Various photographs of Queen Elizabeth II: 10c, 35c, 70c, 85c, $1.10, $1.25. $2.50, Queen Elizabeth II wearing crown.

2012, Feb. 9   Unwmk.   Perf. 13¼
1034-1039 A182   Set of 6   10.50 10.50
1039a   Souvenir sheet of 6,   10.50 10.50
#1034-1039, + 3 labels
Souvenir Sheet
1040 A182 $2.50 multi   8.00 8.00

Bermuda Postal Service, 200th Anniv. — A183

Designs: 25c, Postmaster William B. Perot, Bermuda #X1. 35c, Ferry, 1800s, Bermuda #1. 70c, Mail carriage, 1920s, Bermuda #56. 95c, Flying boat, 1930s, Bermuda #109A. $1.10, Mail van, 1960s, Bermuda #225. $1.25, Envelope, binary digits.

2012, Apr. 19   Wmk. 406   Perf. 13
1041-1046 A183   Set of 6   11.00 11.00

Paintings — A184

Designs: 35c, South Shore, Bermuda, by Thomas Anschutz. 70c, St. George's, by Ogden Pleissner. 80c, Front Street, 1922, by André Biéler. $1.10, Street Scene, Bermuda (Elliott Street), by Dorothy Austen Stevens. $1.25, La Maison du Gouverneur, by Albert Gleizes, vert. $1.65, The Welcoming Smile, by Frank Small, vert.

Perf. 13¼x13¾, 13¾x13¼
2012, July 12
1047-1052 A184   Set of 6   13.50 13.50

Masterworks Foundation, 25th anniv.

St. Peter's Church, 400th Anniv. — A185

Designs: 35c, Clock tower. 95c, Chandelier and ceiling. $1.10, Bronze plaque for graveyard for blacks and slaves. $1.25, Church exterior.

2012, Oct. 18   Perf. 13¾x13¼
1053-1056 A185   Set of 4   8.75 8.75

Items Commemorating British Coronations — A186

Coronation of Queen Elizabeth II, 60th Anniv. — A187

Various items commemorating the coronation of: 10c, Queen Victoria. 35c, King Edward VII. 70c, King George V. 85c, King George VI. $1.10, Queen Elizabeth II.

2013, Feb. 21   Perf. 14
1057-1061 A186   Set of 5   7.00 7.00
Souvenir Sheet
Perf. 14¾x14¼
1062 A187 $2.50 multi   5.75 5.75

Beaches — A188

Designs: 35c, Jobson's Cove Beach, Warwick. $1.25, Southlands Beach, Warwick. $1.50, Astwood Park Beach. $1.65, Warwick Long Bay Beach.

2013, May 16   Perf. 13¾
1063-1066 A188   Set of 4   10.00 10.00

Gombey Dancers — A189

Various Gombey dancers with frame color of: 35c, Blue. $1.25, Green. $1.50, Red. $1.65, Black.

2013, July 18   *Perf. 14*
1067-1070 A189   Set of 4   11.50 11.50

Mystery Roses — A190

Rose varieties: 35c, Pacific. 70c, Maitland White. 85c, Soncy. $1.10, Spice.

Wmk. 406
2013, Nov. 21   Litho.   *Perf. 12½*
1071-1074 A190   Set of 4   7.50 7.50

Eastern Bluebird A191

Eastern bluebird: 35c, Male perched on spruce branch. 85c, Female in nest. $1.10, Male at entrance to birdbox. $1.25, Male and female at birdbox.

Wmk. 406
2014, May 15   Litho.   *Perf. 12½*
1075-1078 A191   Set of 4   8.00 8.00

Flowers A192

Designs: 5c, Allamanda cathartica. 10c, Plumeria rubra. 25c, Bougainvillea sp. 35c, Erythrina variegata. $10, Thunbergia grandiflora.

Perf. 13x12¾
2014, July 15   Litho.   Wmk. 406
1079-1083 A192   Set of 5   23.00 23.00
   See Nos. 1098-1103, 1115-1120.

A193

A194

A195

A196

A197

A198

A199

A200

A201

Roses — A202

Wmk. 406
2014, Dec. 11   Litho.   *Perf. 13¾*
1084   Horiz. strip of 5   8.00 8.00
a. A193 (70c) multi   1.60 1.60
b. A194 (70c) multi   1.60 1.60
c. A195 (70c) multi   1.60 1.60
d. A196 (70c) multi   1.60 1.60
e. A197 (70c) multi   1.60 1.60

1085   Horiz. strip of 5   8.00 8.00
a. A198 (70c) multi   1.60 1.60
b. A199 (70c) multi   1.60 1.60
c. A200 (70c) multi   1.60 1.60
d. A201 (70c) multi   1.60 1.60
e. A202 (70c) multi   1.60 1.60
f. Booklet pane of 10, #1084a-1084e, 1085a-1085e   16.00 —
   Complete booklet, #1085f   16.00

Botanical Paintings by Charlotte Anna Lefroy — A203

No. 1086: a, Clematis sp. b, Magnolia grandiflora. c, Cleome speciosa. d, Hibiscus rosa-sinensis. e, Plumeria rubra.
No. 1087: a, Clitoria ternatea. b, Dendrobium moschatum. c, Passiflora edulis. d, Pereskia aculeata and Pereskia bleo. e, Capsicum baccatum.

Wmk. 406
2015, Jan. 15   Litho.   *Perf. 14*
1086   Horiz. strip of 5   9.50 9.50
a.-e. A203 (85c) Any single   1.90 1.90
1087   Horiz. strip of 5   9.50 9.50
a.-e. A203 (85c) Any single   1.90 1.90
f. Booklet pane of 10, #1086a-1086e, 1087a-1087e   19.00 —
   Complete booklet, #1087f   19.00

Nos. 1086a-1086e, 1087a-1087e are each inscribed "Zone 2."

Bermuda Regiment, 50th Anniv. A204

Designs: 35c, Soldier with ear protection crouching. 70c, Soldiers in boat. 80c, Drummers in parade. $1, Queen Elizabeth II inspecting soldiers. $1.25, Soldiers with regimental flags.

Wmk. 406
2015, Apr. 16   Litho.   *Perf. 14*
1088-1092 A204   Set of 5   10.00 10.00

Fish A205

Designs: 35c, Bicolor coney. 70c, Blue angelfish. 80c, Gray snapper. 85c, Queen parrotfish. 95c, Yellowhead wrasse.

Wmk. 406
2015, May 21   Litho.   *Perf. 14*
1093-1097 A205   Set of 5   8.25 8.25

Flowers Type of 2014
Designs: 50c, Bauhinia variegata. $1, Nerium oleander. $1.15, Macfadyena unguis-cati. $1.20, Hibiscus rosa-sinensis. $1.35, Delonix regia. $1.55, Solanum wendlandii.

Perf. 13x12¾
2015, July 16   Litho.   Wmk. 406
1098-1103 A192   Set of 6   15.00 15.00

Bermuda Postage Stamps, 150th Anniv. A206

Designs: 50c, Bermuda #1, hand with quill pen. $1.15, Bermuda #2, hand with fountain pen. $1.20, Bermuda #3, hands at typewriter keys. $1.35, Bermuda #4, hands at computer keyboard. $1.65, Bermuda #6, hands with smartphone.

Wmk. 406
2015, Sept. 17   Litho.   *Perf. 14*
1104-1108 A206   Set of 5   13.00 13.00

Bermuda in World War I — A207

Poppy and: 50c, Bermuda Volunteer Rifle Corps awaiting deployment at Hamilton docks, medals. $1, Bermuda members of Royal Garrison Artillery, map of battle engagements. $1.15, Letter to W. F. Anderson of the Lincolnshire Regiment with "Killed in Action" notation. $1.20, Postcard to Bermuda, photograph of Cyril Chesterfield Easton of Bermuda Militia Artillery. $1.35, Recruitment poster for Bermuda Militia Artillery, Royal Garrison Artillery cap badge. $1.55, Cecil Montgomery-Moore and his plane, Royal Flying Corps badge.

Wmk. 406
2016, May 19   Litho.   *Perf. 13½*
1109-1114 A207   Set of 6   15.00 15.00

Flowers Type of 2014
Designs: 20c, Datura aurea. 60c, Petrea volubilis. 75c, Cassia javanica. 90c, Lagerstroemia indica. $1.95, Antigonon leptopus. $3, Ipomoea pes-caprae.

Perf. 13¼x13½
2016, Aug. 8   Litho.   Wmk. 406
1115-1120 A192   Set of 6   16.50 16.50

Lifecycle of the Monarch Butterfly — A208

Designs: 50c, Caterpillar. $1, Caterpillar and chrysalis. $1.15, Adult with folded wings. $1.35, Adult with open wings.

Wmk. 406
2016, Oct. 20   Litho.   *Perf. 13¾*
1121-1124 A208   Set of 4   8.75 8.75
1124a   Souvenir sheet of 4, #1121-1124   8.75 8.75

Queen Elizabeth II — A209

Queen Elizabeth II wearing: 50c, Pale blue hat with pink ribbon. $1.15, Pale orange hat. $1.35, Light blue and white hat.

Wmk. 406
2017, June 29   Litho.   *Perf. 13¾*
1125-1127 A209   Set of 3   6.00 6.00

Tall Ships A210

Designs: 50c, STV Spirit of Bermuda. $1.15, Pride of Baltimore II. $1.35, Alexander von Humboldt II. $1.55, Oosterschelde.

Perf. 13¼x13½
2017, Aug. 31   Litho.   Wmk. 406
1128-1131 A210   Set of 4   9.25 9.25

Bermuda National
Gallery, 25th
Anniv. — A211

Designs: 50c, Old Bermuda House, by William Howe Foote. $1.15, Cerise, by Janet Fish. $1.35, Painting by Sir Joshua Reynolds. $1.55, Bamum wooden mask, Cameroun.

Wmk. 406

2017, Sept. 21	Litho.	Perf. 13¾		
1132-1135	A211	Set of 4	9.25	9.25

POSTAL-FISCAL STAMP

"Revenue
Revenue" — PF1

1936   Typo.   Wmk. 4   Perf. 14
Chalky Paper

AR1	PF1	12sh6p org & grayish blk	1,250.	1,750.
		Revenue cancel		75.00

#AR1 was authorized for postal use from Feb. 1 through May, 1937 and during Nov. and Dec. 1937. Used values are for examples with dated postal cancels indicating usage during the authorized periods. Beware of bogus and improperly dated favor cancels.

WAR TAX STAMPS

No. 42 Overprinted

1918   Wmk. 3   Perf. 14

MR1	A11	1p rose red	1.25	2.00

No. 42a Overprinted

1920

MR2	A11	1p carmine	4.00	3.50

BHUTAN
bü-'tän

LOCATION — Eastern Himalayas
GOVT. — Kingdom
AREA — 18,000 sq. mi.
POP. — 1,951,965(?) (1999 est.)
CAPITAL — Thimphu

100 Chetrum = 1 Ngultrum or Rupee

Watermark

Wmk. 388 — Multiple "SPM"

Catalogue values for all unused
stamps in this country are for
Never Hinged items.

Postal
Runner — A1

Designs: 3ch, 70ch, Archer. 5ch, 1.30nu,
Yak. 15ch, Map of Bhutan, portrait of Druk
Gyalpo (Dragon King) Ugyen Wangchuk
(1867-1902) and Paro Dzong (fortress-monas-
tery). 33ch, Postal runner. All horiz. except
2ch and 33ch.

Perf. 14x14½, 14½x14

			1962, Oct. 10	Litho.	Unwmk.
1	A1	2ch red & gray		.30	.30
2	A1	3ch red & ultra		.35	.35
3	A1	5ch green & brown		1.90	1.90
4	A1	15ch red, blk & org yel		.30	.30
5	A1	33ch blue grn & lil		.35	.35
6	A1	70ch dp ultra & lt blue		1.00	1.00
7	A1	1.30nu blue & black		2.40	2.40
		Nos. 1-7 (7)		6.60	6.60

Nos. 1-7 were made available to the trade in
April, 1962, and became valid for postage with
the inauguration of the postal service and
opening of the first post office on Oct. 10,
1962.
Imperforates of this issue are from printer's
archive.
For overprint & surcharges see Nos. 42, 72-
73.

Refugee
Year
Emblem
and Arms
of Bhutan
A2

			1962, Oct. 10		Perf. 14½x14
8	A2	1nu dk blue & dk car rose		1.60	1.60
9	A2	2nu yel grn & red lilac		5.50	5.50

World Refugee Year. For surcharges see
Nos. 68-69.

Malaria Eradication
A set of three (33ch, 70ch, and
1.30nu) was prepared in 1962 but not
issued. All three exist perforated, and
the 33ch also exists imperforate. Value,
perforated set $375.

Equipment of
Ancient
Warrior — A3

Perf. 14x14½

			1963, May 12		Unwmk.
10	A3	33ch multicolored		.45	.45
11	A3	70ch multicolored		.90	.90
12	A3	1.30nu multicolored		2.25	2.25
		Nos. 10-12 (3)		3.60	3.60

Bhutan's membership in Colombo Plan.
For overprints and surcharges, see B1-3.

Boy Filling Grain Box
and Wheat
Emblem — A4

			1963, July 15		Perf. 13½x14
13	A4	20ch lt blue, yel & red brn		1.00	1.00
14	A4	1.50nu rose lil, bl & red brn		2.10	2.10

FAO "Freedom from Hunger" campaign.
For surcharge see No. 117M.

Masked Dancer — A5

Various Bhutanese Dancers (Five Designs;
2ch, 5ch, 20ch, 1nu, 1.30nu vert.)

			1964, Apr. 16	Perf. 14½x14, 14x14½
15	A5	2ch multicolored	.30	.30
16	A5	3ch multicolored	.30	.30
17	A5	5ch multicolored	.30	.30
18	A5	20ch multicolored	.30	.30
19	A5	33ch multicolored	.30	.30
20	A5	70ch multicolored	.30	.30
21	A5	1nu multicolored	1.10	1.10
22	A5	1.30nu multicolored	1.25	1.25
23	A5	2nu multicolored	1.90	1.90
		Nos. 15-23 (9)	6.05	6.05

For surcharges & overprints see nos. 70-71,
74-75, 129A, 129G, C1-C3, C11-C13.

Stone
Throwing
A6

Sport: 5ch, 33ch, Boxing. 1nu, 3nu, Archery.
2nu, Soccer.

			1964, Oct. 10	Litho.	Perf. 14½
24	A6	2ch emerald & multi		.30	.30
25	A6	5ch orange & multi		.30	.30
26	A6	15ch brt citron & multi		.30	.30
27	A6	33ch rose lil & multi		.30	.30
28	A6	1nu multicolored		1.00	1.00
29	A6	2nu rose lilac & multi		1.60	1.60
a.		*Souv. sheet, #28-29*		13.00	13.00
30	A6	3nu lt blue & multi		2.25	2.25
		Nos. 24-30 (7)		6.05	6.05

18th Olympic Games, Tokyo, Oct. 10-25.
See No. B4.
Nos. 24-30 exist imperf. Value $17.50. No.
29a exists imperf. Value, $13.

Flags of the World at Half-mast — A7

1964, Nov. 22 Unwmk. Perf. 14½
Flags in Original Colors

31	A7	33ch steel gray	.45	.45
32	A7	1nu silver	1.10	1.10
33	A7	3nu gold	3.00	3.00
a.		*Souv. sheet, perf. 13½ or imperf.*	7.50	7.50
		Nos. 31-33 (3)	4.55	4.55

Issued in memory of those who died in the
service of their country. Nos. 31-33 exist
imperf. Value $20.
No. 33a contains 2 stamps similar to Nos.
32-33.
Overprints on No. 31 were not officially
issued. For overprints see Nos. 44, 46.

Flowers — A8

			1965, Jan. 6	Litho.	Perf. 13
34	A8	2ch Primrose		.25	.25
35	A8	5ch Gentian		.25	.25
36	A8	15ch Primrose		.25	.25
37	A8	33ch Gentian		.25	.25
38	A8	50ch Rhododendron		.90	.90
39	A8	75ch Peony		.90	.90
40	A8	1nu Rhododendron		.90	.90
41	A8	2nu Peony		2.25	2.25
		Nos. 34-41 (8)		5.95	5.95

Overprints on No. 37 were not officially
issued. For overprints see Nos. 43, 45, C4-C5,
C14-C15.

**Nos. 5, 40, 32, 41 and 33
Overprinted "WINSTON CHURCHILL
1874-1965"**

1965, Feb. 27

42	A8	33ch bl grn & lilac	.75	.75
43	A8	1nu pink, grn & dk gray	1.25	1.25
44	A7	1nu silver & multi	1.25	1.25
45	A8	2nu sepia, yel & grn	1.75	1.75
46	A7	3nu gold & multi	2.25	2.25
		Nos. 42-46 (5)	7.25	7.25

Issued in memory of Sir Winston Churchill
(1874-1965), British statesman. The overprint
is in three lines on Nos. 42-43 and 45; in two
lines on Nos. 43 and 46.
Nos. 44, 46 exist imperf. Value, both, $4.50.

Skyscraper, Pagoda and World's Fair
Emblem — A9

Designs: 10ch, 2nu, Pieta by Michelangelo
and statue of Khmer Buddha. 20ch, Skyline of
NYC and Bhutanese village. 33ch, George
Washington Bridge, NY, and foot bridge,
Bhutan.

			1965, Apr. 21	Litho.	Perf. 14½
47	A9	1ch blue & multi		.25	.25
48	A9	10ch green & multi		.25	.25
49	A9	20ch rose lilac & multi		.25	.25
50	A9	33ch bister & multi		.25	.25
51	A9	1.50nu bister & multi		2.00	2.00
52	A9	2nu multicolored		3.00	3.00
a.		*Souv. sheet, perf. 13½ or imperf.*		8.00	8.00
		Nos. 47-52 (6)		6.00	6.00

Nos. 47-52 exist imperf.; value $5.00.
No. 52a contains two stamps similar to Nos.
51-52.
For overprints see Nos. 87-87B.

Telstar, Short-wave Radio and ITU
Emblem — A10

Designs (ITU Emblem and): 2nu, Telstar
and Morse key. 3nu, Syncom and ear phones.

			1966, Mar. 2	Litho.	Perf. 14½
53	A10	35ch multicolored		.25	.25
54	A10	2nu multicolored		.80	.80
55	A10	3nu multicolored		1.40	1.40
		Nos. 53-55 (3)		2.45	2.45

Cent. (in 1965) of the ITU. Souvenir sheets
exist containing two stamps similar to Nos. 54-
55, perf. 13½ and imperf. Value, 2 sheets,
$7.50.

Leopard — A11

Animals: 1ch, 4nu, Asiatic black bear. 2ch,
3nu, Leopard. 4ch, 2nu, Pigmy hog. 8ch, 75ch,
Tiger. 10ch, 1.50nu, Dhole (Asiatic hunting
dog). 1nu, 5nu, Takin (goat).

			1966, Mar. 24	Litho.	Perf. 13
56	A11	1ch yellow & blk		.25	.25
57	A11	2ch pale grn & blk		.25	.25
58	A11	4ch lt citron & blk		.25	.25
59	A11	8ch lt blue & blk		.25	.25
60	A11	10ch lt lilac & blk		.35	.35
61	A11	75ch lt yel grn & blk		.50	.50
62	A11	1nu lt green & blk		.85	.85
63	A11	1.50nu lt bl grn & blk		1.10	1.10
64	A11	2nu dull org & blk		1.40	1.40
65	A11	3nu bluish lil & blk		2.00	2.00
66	A11	4nu lt green & blk		2.50	2.50
67	A11	5nu pink & black		3.50	3.50
		Nos. 56-67 (12)		13.20	13.20

Exists imperf. Value $25.00.
For surcharges see Nos. 115C, 115E, 115I,
117N, 117P, 129B, 129J. For overprints see
Nos. C6-C10, C16-C20.

Nos. 6-9,
20-23
Surcharged

			1965	Perf. 14½x14, 14x14½
68	A2	5ch on 1nu	52.50	50.00
69	A2	5ch on 2nu	52.50	50.00
70	A5	10ch on 70ch	100.00	14.00
71	A5	10ch on 2nu	16.00	14.00
72	A1	15ch on 70ch	14.00	11.00
73	A1	15ch on 1.30nu	14.00	11.00
74	A5	20ch on 1nu	18.00	16.00
75	A5	20ch on 1.30nu	18.00	16.00
		Nos. 68-75 (8)	285.00	182.00

The surcharges on Nos. 68-69 contain two
bars at left and right obliterating the denomination on both sides of the design. Four bars on
Nos. 72-73.

Simtokha
Dzong
A12

Tashichho Dzong — A13

Daga Dzong
A14

Designs: 5ch, Rinpung Dzong. 50ch, Tongsa Dzong. 1nu, Lhuntsi Dzong.

Perf. 14½x14 (A12), 13½ (A13, A14)

1966-70   **Photo.**

76	A12	5ch orange brn ('67)	4.00	2.40
77	A13	10ch dk grn & rose vio ('68)	4.00	2.40
78	A12	15ch brown	4.00	3.25
79	A12	20ch green	4.00	3.25
80	A13	25ch blue grn ('68)	2.00	1.75
81	A14	75ch dk bl & ol gray ('70)	3.25	1.25
82	A14	1nu dk vio & vio bl ('70)	3.25	1.25
		Nos. 76-82 (7)	24.50	15.55

Sizes: 5ch, 15ch, 20ch, 37x20½mm. 10ch, 53½x28½mm. 50ch, 35½x25½mm.

King Jigme
Wangchuk
— A14a

Coins: 1.30nu, 3nu, 5nu, reverse.

Litho. & Embossed on Gold Foil

1966, July 8   **Die Cut**   **Imperf.**

83	A14a	10ch green	.80	.80
83A	A14a	25ch green	.95	.95
83B	A14a	50ch green	1.40	1.40
83C	A14a	1nu red	2.25	2.25
83D	A14a	1.30nu red	3.00	3.00
83E	A14a	2nu red	3.75	3.75
83F	A14a	3nu red	5.50	5.50
83G	A14a	4nu red	7.00	7.00
83H	A14a	5nu red	8.50	8.50
		Nos. 83-83H (9)	33.15	33.15

Two dies were used for the embossed coin and show different initials to the lower left of the king's chin, resulting in two types of each of the following: On No. 83: GK or RH; on No. 83A: NR or JM; on No. 83B: JM or AT; on No. 83C: GK or RH, and on No. 83E: NR or JM.

Stamps denominated 15ch, 33ch, and 9nu were prepared but not issued. See Nos. 98-98B.

Abominable Snowman — A14b

1966, Oct. 10   **Photo.**   **Perf. 13½**

84	A14b	1ch multicolored	.35	.35
84A	A14b	2ch multi, diff.	.35	.35
84B	A14b	3ch multi, diff.	.35	.35
84C	A14b	4ch multi, diff.	.35	.35
84D	A14b	5ch multi, diff.	.35	.35
84E	A14b	15ch like #84	.35	.35
84F	A14b	30ch like #84A	.35	.35
84G	A14b	40ch like #84B	.35	.35
84H	A14b	50ch like #84C	.35	.35
84I	A14b	1.25nu like #84D	.50	.50
84J	A14b	2.50nu like #84	1.10	1.10
84K	A14b	3nu like #84A	1.20	1.20
84L	A14b	5nu like #84B	2.00	2.00
84M	A14b	6nu like #84C	2.00	2.00
84N	A14b	7nu like #84D	2.00	2.00
		Nos. 84-84N (15)	11.95	11.95

Nos. 84-84N exist imperf. Value, set $25.

For overprints see Nos. 93-93G. For surcharges see Nos. 115D, 115K, 115O, 115P, 117I, 117S.

Flowers
A14c

Designs: 3ch, 50ch, Lilium sherriffiae. 5ch, 1nu, Meconopsis dhwoju. 7ch, 2.50nu, Rhododendron chaetomallum. 10ch, 4nu, Pleione hookeriana. 5nu, Rhododendron giganteum.

1967, Feb. 9   **Litho.**   **Perf. 13**

85	A14c	3ch multicolored	.35	.35
85A	A14c	5ch multicolored	.35	.35
85B	A14c	7ch multicolored	.35	.35
85C	A14c	10ch multicolored	.35	.35

Gray Background

85D	A14c	50ch multicolored	.40	.40
85E	A14c	1nu multicolored	.75	.75
85F	A14c	2.50nu multicolored	1.50	1.50
85G	A14c	4nu multicolored	2.25	2.25
85H	A14c	5nu multicolored	3.00	3.00
		Nos. 85-85H (9)	9.30	9.30

Exists imperf.
For surcharges see Nos. 115F, 115L.

Boy Scouts — A14d

5ch, Planting tree. 10ch, Cooking. 15ch, Mountain climbing.

1967, Mar. 28   **Photo.**   **Perf. 13½**

86	A14d	5ch multi	.35	.35
86A	A14d	10ch multi	.35	.35
86B	A14d	15ch multi	.35	.35

Emblem, Border in Gold

86C	A14d	50ch like #86	.55	.55
86D	A14d	1.25nu like #86A	1.15	1.15
86E	A14d	4nu like #86B	3.25	3.25
f.		Souv. sheet of 2, #86D, 86E	8.00	8.00
		Nos. 86-86E (6)	6.00	6.00

Exist imperf. Value: set $6.50; souvenir sheet $8.

See Nos. 89-89E for overprints. For surcharges see Nos. 115G, 117J, 129K.

Nos. 50-52, 52a Overprinted

Perfs. as Before

1967, May 25   **Litho.**

87	A9	33ch on #50	1.25	1.25
87A	A9	1.50nu on #51	1.40	1.40
87B	A9	2nu on #52	1.75	1.75
c.		Souv. sheet of 2, on #52a	7.50	7.50
		Nos. 87-87B (3)	4.40	4.40

Nos. 87-87B exist imperf. Value: set $8; souvenir sheet $8.

Airplanes — A14f

1967, June 26   **Litho.**   **Perf. 13½**

88	A14f	45ch Lancaster	.50	.50
88A	A14f	2nu Spitfire	1.00	1.00
88B	A14f	4nu Hurricane	2.50	2.50
c.		Souv. sheet of 2, #88A, 88B	5.25	5.25
		Nos. 88-88B (3)	4.00	4.00

Churchill and Battle of Britain. Exist imperf. Value: set $6; souvenir sheet $6.
For surcharges see Nos. 117Q, 117T.

Nos. 86-86E, 86Ef Overprinted "WORLD JAMBOREE / IDAHO, U.S.A. / AUG. 1-9,/67"

5ch, Planting tree. 10ch, Cookout. 15ch, Mountain climbing.

1967, Aug. 8   **Photo.**   **Perf. 13½**

89	A14d	5ch multi	.35	.35
89A	A14d	10ch multi	.45	.45
89B	A14d	15ch multi	.50	.50
89C	A14d	50ch like #89	.75	.75
89D	A14d	1.25nu like #89A	1.10	1.10
89E	A14d	4nu like #89B	3.25	3.25
f.		Souv. sheet of 2, #89D, 89E	7.00	7.00
		Nos. 89-89E (6)	6.40	6.40

No. 89Ef sold for 6.25nu. Exist imperf. Value: set $16; souvenir sheet $8.

Girl Scouts — A14g

5ch, Painting. 10ch, Making music. 15ch, Picking fruit.

1967, Sept. 28   **Photo.**   **Perf. 13½**

90	A14g	5ch multi	.25	.25
90A	A14g	10ch multi	.25	.25
90B	A14g	15ch multi	.30	.30

Emblem, Border in Gold

90C	A14g	1.50nu like #90	.85	.85
90D	A14g	2.50nu like #90A	1.75	1.75
90E	A14g	5nu like #90B	4.00	4.00
f.		Souv. sheet of 2, #90D, 90E	7.40	7.40
		Nos. 90-90E (6)	7.40	7.40

Exist imperf. Value: set $8.50; souvenir sheet $10.
For surcharge see No. 266.

Astronaut, Space Capsule — A14h

Astronaut walking in space and: 5ch, 30ch, 4nu, Orbiter, Lunar modules docked. 7ch, 50ch, 5nu, Lunar module. 10ch, 1.25nu, 9nu, Other astronauts.

1967, Oct. 30   **Litho.**   **Imperf.**

91	A14h	3ch multi	.30	.30
91A	A14h	5ch multi	.30	.30
91B	A14h	7ch multi	.30	.30
91C	A14h	10ch multi	.40	.40
m.		Souv. sheet of 4, #91-91C	8.00	8.00
91D	A14h	15ch multi	.50	.50
91E	A14h	30ch multi	1.10	1.10
91F	A14h	50ch multi	1.90	1.90
91G	A14h	1.25nu multi	4.50	4.50
n.		Souv. sheet of 4, #91D-91G	12.00	12.00

91H	A14h	2.50nu multi	2.75	2.75
91I	A14h	4nu multi	4.50	4.50
91J	A14h	5nu multi	5.50	5.50
91K	A14h	9nu multi	9.75	9.75
o.		Souv. sheet of 4, #91H-91K	20.00	20.00
		Nos. 91-91K (12)	31.80	31.80

Nos. 91H-91K are airmail. Nos. 91H-91K exist missing "Air Mail" inscription. Simulated 3-dimensions using a plastic overlay.
For other space issues see designs A15a, A15e.
Officially issued with trial perforations. Set of three perforated souvenir sheets, value $350.

Pheasants — A14i

Designs: 1ch, 2nu, Tragopan satyra. 2ch, 4nu, Lophophorus sclateri. 4ch, 5nu, Lophophorus impejanus. 8ch, 7nu, Lophura leucomelanos. 15ch, 9nu, Crossoptilon crossoptilon.

1968, Jan. 20   **Photo.**   **Perf. 13½**

92	A14i	1ch multicolored	.25	.25
92A	A14i	2ch multicolored	.25	.25
92B	A14i	4ch multicolored	.25	.25
92C	A14i	8ch multicolored	.25	.25
92D	A14i	15ch multicolored	.25	.25

Border in Gold

92E	A14i	2nu multicolored	.75	.75
92F	A14i	4nu multicolored	1.00	1.00
92G	A14i	5nu multicolored	1.25	1.25
92H	A14i	7nu multicolored	1.75	1.75
92I	A14i	9nu multicolored	2.10	2.10
		Nos. 92-92I (10)	8.10	8.10

Unauthorized imperfs exist. Value, $16.
For surcharges see Nos. 115H, 117R, 117V, 129D, 129L.

Nos. 84G, 84I, 84K, 84M Ovptd. in Black on Silver

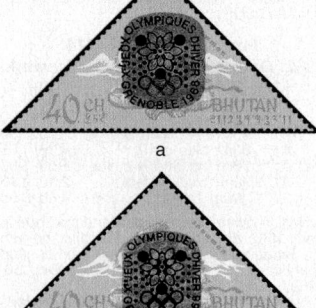

a

b

Perfs. as Before

1968, Feb. 16   **Photo.**

Overprint Type "a"

93	A14b	40ch on #84G	1.50	1.50
93A	A14b	1.25nu on #84I	1.75	1.75
93B	A14b	3nu on #84K	2.25	2.25
93C	A14b	6nu on #84M	3.00	3.00

Overprint Type "b"

93D	A14b	40ch on #84G	1.50	1.50
93E	A14b	1.25nu on #84I	1.75	1.75
93F	A14b	3nu on #84K	2.25	2.25
93G	A14b	6nu on #84M	3.00	3.00
		Nos. 93-93G (8)	17.00	17.00

Nos. 93-93C and 93D-93G exist imperf. Value, either set $40.

Snow Lion — A14j

Mythological Creatures: 2ch, Elephant. 3ch, Garuda. 4ch, Monastery Tiger. 5ch, Wind Horse. 15ch, Snow Lion.

1968, Mar. 14   Photo.   Perf. 12½

94	A14j	2ch multicolored	.35	.35
94A	A14j	3ch multicolored	.35	.35
94B	A14j	4ch multicolored	.35	.35
94C	A14j	5ch multicolored	.35	.35
94D	A14j	15ch multicolored	.35	.35
94E	A14j	20ch like #94	.35	.35
94F	A14j	30ch like #94A	.35	.35
94G	A14j	50ch like #94B	.35	.35
94H	A14j	1.25nu like #94C	.45	.45
94I	A14j	1.50nu like #94	.45	.45
94J	A14j	2nu like #94D	.80	.80
94K	A14j	2.50nu like #94A	.80	.80
94L	A14j	4nu like #94B	1.50	1.50
94M	A14j	5nu like #94C	2.00	2.00
94N	A14j	10nu like #94D	3.75	3.75
		Nos. 94-94N (15)	12.55	12.55

Nos. 94I, 94K-94N are airmail. All exist imperf. Value, set $25.
For surcharges see Nos. 115, 115M, 115Q, 117-117E, 129C, C35-C36.

Butterflies — A14k

Designs: 15ch, Catagramma sorana. 50ch, Delias hyparete. 1.25nu, Anteos maerula. 2nu, Ornithoptera priamus urvilleanus. 3nu, Euploea mulciber. 4nu, Morpho rhetenor. 5nu, Papilio androgeous. 6nu, Troides magellanus.

1968, May 20   Litho.   Imperf.

95	A14k	15ch multi	.85	.85
95A	A14k	50ch multi	1.20	1.20
95B	A14k	1.25nu multi	2.40	2.40
95C	A14k	2nu multi	3.50	3.50
h.		Souv. sheet of 4, #95-95C	15.00	15.00
95D	A14k	3nu multi	4.00	4.00
95E	A14k	4nu multi	4.50	4.50
95F	A14k	5nu multi	5.50	5.00
95G	A14k	6nu multi	5.75	5.75
i.		Souv. sheet of 4, #95D-95G	22.50	22.50
		Nos. 95-95G (8)	27.70	27.20

Souv. sheets issued Oct. 23. Nos. 95D-95G, 95Gi are airmail. Simulated 3-dimensions using a plastic overlay.

Paintings — A14m

1968   Litho. & Embossed   Imperf.

96	A14m	2ch Van Gogh	.25	.25
96A	A14m	4ch Millet	.25	.25
96B	A14m	5ch Monet	.25	.25
96C	A14m	2nu Corot	.25	.25
p.		Souv. sheet of 4, #96-96C	1.60	1.60
96D	A14m	45ch like #96	.25	.25
96E	A14m	80ch like #96A	.35	.35
96F	A14m	1.05nu like #96B	.45	.45
96G	A14m	1.40nu like #96C	.60	.60
q.		Souv. sheet of 4, #96D-96G	2.40	2.40
96H	A14m	1.50nu like #96	.65	.65
96I	A14m	2nu like #96	.85	.85
96J	A14m	2.50nu like #96A	1.10	1.10
96K	A14m	3nu like #96A	1.25	1.25
96L	A14m	4nu like #96B	1.50	1.50

96M	A14m	5nu like #96C	1.60	1.60
r.		Souv. sheet of 4, #96I, 96K-96M	4.00	4.00
96N	A14m	6nu like #96B	2.25	2.25
96O	A14m	8nu like #96C	3.25	3.25
s.		Souv. sheet of 4, #96H, 96J, 96N-96O	8.00	8.00
		Nos. 96-96O (16)	15.10	15.10

Issued: nos. 96-96G, 96I, 96K-96M, 7/8; Nos. 96Cp, 96Gq, 96Mr, 8/5; others, 8/28.
Nos. 96H, 96J, 96N-96O are airmail.
See Nos. 114-114O, 144-144G.

Summer Olympics, Mexico, 1968 — A14n

1968, Oct. 1   Photo.   Perf. 13½

97	A14n	5ch Discus	.25	.25
97A	A14n	45ch Basketball	.25	.25
97B	A14n	60ch Javelin	.25	.25
97C	A14n	80ch Shooting	.25	.25
97D	A14n	1.05nu like #97	.25	.25
97E	A14n	2nu like #97B	.25	.25
97F	A14n	3nu like #97C	.45	.45
97G	A14n	5nu Soccer	.75	.75
h.		Souv. sheet of 2, #97D, 97G	2.50	2.50
		Nos. 97-97G (8)	2.70	2.70

Exist imperf. Values: set $75 unused, $5 used; souvenir sheet $2.75.
For surcharges see Nos. 129E, B5-B7.

Coin Type of 1966 Overprinted

Embossed on Gold Foil
1968, Nov. 12   Die Cut   Imperf.

98	A14a	15ch green	2.00	2.00
98A	A14a	33ch green	3.00	3.00
98B	A14a	9nu on 75ch green	7.50	7.50
		Nos. 98-98B (3)	12.50	12.50

Human Rights Year.
Nos. 98-98B exist without overprinting. Value, $100.

Birds — A14p

2ch, 20ch, 1.50nu, Crimson-winged laughing thrush. 3ch, 30ch, 2.50nu, Ward's trogon. 4ch, 50ch, 4nu, Grey peacock-pheasant. 5ch, 1.25nu, 5nu, Rufous necked hornbill. 15ch, 2nu, 10nu, Myzornis.

1968, Dec. 7   Photo.   Perf. 12½

99	A14p	2ch multi	.25	.25
99A	A14p	3ch multi, vert.	.25	.25
99B	A14p	4ch multi, vert.	.25	.25
99C	A14p	5ch multi, vert.	.25	.25
99D	A14p	15ch multi	.30	.30
99E	A14p	20ch multi	.35	.35
99F	A14p	30ch multi, vert.	.40	.40
99G	A14p	50ch multi	.40	.40
99H	A14p	1.25nu multi	.60	.60
99I	A14p	1.50nu multi	.75	.75
99J	A14p	2nu multi	1.00	1.00
99K	A14p	2.50nu multi	1.00	1.00
99L	A14p	4nu multi	1.25	1.25
99M	A14p	5nu multi	1.75	1.75
99N	A14p	10nu multi	3.25	3.25
		Nos. 99-99N (15)	12.05	12.05

1.50nu, 2.50nu, 4nu, 5nu, 10nu are airmail. Exist imperf. Value $17.50.
For surcharges see Nos. 115A-115B, 115I, 115M, 115R, 117F-117G, 117K, 117O, 129H.

Fish — A14q

1969, Feb. 27   Litho.   Imperf.

100	A14q	15ch multicolored	1.60	1.60
100A	A14q	20ch multi, diff.	2.10	2.10
100B	A14q	30ch multi, diff.	3.25	3.25
100C	A14q	5nu multi, diff.	4.25	4.25
100D	A14q	6nu multi, diff.	5.25	5.25
100E	A14q	7nu multi, diff.	6.25	6.25
f.		Souv. sheet, #100B-100E	18.00	18.00
		Nos. 100-100E (6)	22.70	22.70

Nos. 100C-100E are airmail. Simulated 3-dimensions using a plastic overlay.

Insects — A14r

1969, Apr. 10   Litho.   Imperf.

101	A14r	10ch multi	.90	.90
101A	A14r	75ch multi, diff.	1.50	1.50
101B	A14r	1.25nu multi, diff.	2.00	2.00
101C	A14r	2nu multi, diff.	2.75	2.75
h.		Souv. sheet, #101-101C	22.50	22.50
101D	A14r	3nu multi, diff.	3.50	3.50
101E	A14r	4nu multi, diff.	3.75	3.75
101F	A14r	5nu multi, diff.	4.00	4.00
101G	A14r	6nu multi, diff.	4.50	4.50
i.		Souv. sheet, #101D-101G	18.50	18.50
		Nos. 101-101G (8)	22.90	22.90

Nos. 101D-101G, 101i are airmail. Simulated 3-dimensions using a plastic overlay.

Admission to UPU — A14s

1969, May 2   Photo.   Perf. 13

102	A14s	5ch multi	.25	.25
102A	A14s	10ch multi	.25	.25
102B	A14s	15ch multi	.25	.25
102C	A14s	45ch multi	.25	.25
102D	A14s	60ch multi	.25	.25
102E	A14s	1.05nu multi	.30	.30
102F	A14s	1.40nu multi	.40	.40
102G	A14s	4nu multi	.90	.90
		Nos. 102-102G (8)	2.85	2.85

Exist imperf. Value $5.50.
For surcharges see Nos. 117H, 117L, 117U, 129.

History of Steel Making — A14t

Designs: 2ch, Pre-biblical. 5ch, Damascus sword. 15ch, 3nu, Saugus Mill. 45ch, Beehive coke ovens. 75ch, 4nu, Bessemer converter. 1.50nu, 5nu, Rolling mill. 1.75nu, Steel mill. 2nu, 6nu, Future applications.

Litho. on Steel Foil
1969, June 2   Imperf.
Without Gum

103	A14t	2ch multicolored	.60	.60
103A	A14t	5ch multicolored	.60	.60
103B	A14t	15ch multicolored	.60	.60
m.		Souv. sheet #103A-103B	2.50	2.50
103C	A14t	45ch multicolored	.60	.60
n.		Souv. sheet, #103, 103C	2.50	2.50
103D	A14t	75ch multicolored	.60	.60
103E	A14t	1.50nu multicolored	1.25	1.25
103F	A14t	1.75nu multicolored	1.75	1.75
o.		Souv. sheet #103E-103F	3.00	3.00
103G	A14t	2nu multicolored	2.50	2.50
p.		Souv. sheet, #103D, 103G	3.00	3.00
103H	A14t	3nu multicolored	3.00	3.00
103I	A14t	4nu multicolored	3.50	3.50
103J	A14t	5nu multicolored	4.00	4.00
q.		Souv. sheet #103I-103J	8.00	8.00
103K	A14t	6nu multicolored	5.50	5.50
r.		Souv. sheet, #103H,103K	10.00	10.00
		Nos. 103-103K (12)	24.50	24.50

Nos. 103H-103K, 103q, 103r are airmail. Souv. sheets issued June 30. Stamps from souvenir sheets have inscriptions in either the left or right margin.

Birds — A14u

15ch, Owl. 50ch, Red birds. 1.25nu, Hawk. 2nu, Penguin. 3nu, Macaws. 4nu, Bird of paradise. 5nu, Duck. 6nu, Pheasant.

1969, Aug. 5   Litho.   Imperf.

104	A14u	15ch multi	5.50	5.50
104A	A14u	50ch multi	5.50	5.50
104B	A14u	1.25nu multi	5.50	5.50
104C	A14u	2nu multi	5.50	5.50
h.		Souv. sheet, #104-104C	37.50	37.50
104D	A14u	3nu multi	5.00	5.00
104E	A14u	4nu multi	3.75	3.75
104F	A14u	5nu multi	4.00	4.00
104G	A14u	6nu multi	4.75	4.75
i.		Souv. sheet, #104D-104G	37.50	37.50
		Nos. 104-104G (8)	39.50	39.50

Nos. 104D-104G, 104Gi are airmail. Simulated 3-dimensions using a plastic overlay. Souv. sheets issued Aug. 28.

Buddhist Prayer Banners — A14v

Litho. on Cloth
1969, Sep. 30   Imperf.
Self-adhesive
Sizes: 15ch, 75ch, 2nu, 57x57mm, 5nu, 6nu, 70x37mm

105	A14v	15ch multicolored	13.00	13.00
105A	A14v	75ch multi, diff.	14.00	14.00
105B	A14v	2nu multi, diff.	15.00	15.00
105C	A14v	5nu multi, diff.	16.00	16.00
105D	A14v	6nu multi, diff.	17.50	17.50
		Nos. 105-105D (5)	75.50	75.50

Souvenir Sheet

105E		Sheet of 3	80.00	80.00

No. 105E shows denominations of 75ch, 5nu, 6nu with design elements of Nos. 105A, 105C, 105D with gray frame. Exists perf. 13½. Value, $70.

Mahatma Gandhi — A15

1969, Oct. 2   Litho.   Perf. 13x13½

106	A15	20ch light blue & brn	.85	.85
107	A15	2nu lemon & brn olive	4.50	4.50

Mohandas K. Gandhi (1869-1948), leader in India's struggle for independence.

Apollo 11 Moon Landing — A15a

Designs: 3ch, Separation from third stage. 5ch, Entering lunar orbit. 15ch, Lunar module separating from orbiter. 20ch, 3nu, Astronaut standing on lunar module's foot pad. 25ch, Astronaut, lunar module on moon. 45ch, Astronaut, flag. 50ch, 4nu, Setting up experiments. 1.75nu, Lunar module docking with orbiter. 5nu, Lift-off from Cape Canaveral. 6nu, Recovery at sea.

1969   Litho.   Imperf.

108	A15a	3ch multi	.75	.75
108A	A15a	5ch multi	.75	.75
108B	A15a	15ch multi	.75	.75
108C	A15a	20ch multi	1.00	1.00
m.		Souv. sheet, #108-108C	13.50	13.50
108D	A15a	25ch multi	1.00	1.00
108E	A15a	45ch multi	1.25	1.25
108F	A15a	50ch multi	1.40	1.40
108G	A15a	1.75nu multi	2.50	2.50
n.		Souv. sheet, #108D-108G	18.00	18.00
108H	A15a	3nu multi	3.50	3.50
108I	A15a	4nu multi	4.50	4.50
108J	A15a	5nu multi	5.00	5.00
108K	A15a	6nu multi	5.75	5.75
o.		Souv. sheet, #108H-108K	35.00	35.00
		Nos. 108-108K (12)	28.15	28.15

Nos. 108H-108K, 108Ko are airmail. Simulated 3-dimensions using a plastic overlay. "Aldrin" misspelled on No. 108Ko.
Issue dates: Nos. 108-108G, Nov. 3; Nos. 108H-108K, Nov. 20; Souv. sheets, Dec. 20.

Paintings
A15b

5ch, Clouet. 10ch, van Eyck. 15ch, David. 2.75nu, Rubens. 3nu, Homer. 4nu, Gentileschi. 5nu, Raphael. 6nu, Ghirlandaio.

1970, Jan. 19   Litho.   Imperf.

109	A15b	5ch multi	1.50	1.50
109A	A15b	10ch multi	1.50	1.50
109B	A15b	15ch multi	1.50	1.50
109C	A15b	2.75nu multi	2.50	2.50
h.		Souv. sheet, #109-109C	13.50	13.50
109D	A15b	3nu multi	2.00	2.00
109E	A15b	4nu multi	2.75	2.75
109F	A15b	5nu multi	3.50	3.50
109G	A15b	6nu multi	4.50	4.50
i.		Souv. sheet, #109D-109G	13.50	13.50
		Nos. 109-109G (8)	19.75	19.75

Nos. 109D-109G, 109Gi are airmail. Simulated 3-dimensions using a plastic overlay. Souv. sheets issued Feb. 25.

Various Forms of Mail Transport, UPU Headquarters, Bern — A15c

1970, Feb. 27   Photo.   Perf. 13½

110	A15c	3ch ol grn & gold	.50	.50
111	A15c	10ch red brn & gold	.65	.65
112	A15c	20ch Prus bl & gold	.75	.75
113	A15c	2.50nu dp mag & gold	2.00	2.00
		Nos. 110-113 (4)	3.90	3.90

New Headquarters of Universal Postal Union, Bern, Switzerland.
Exist imperf. Value $10.

For surcharge see No. 129I.

Painting Type of 1968

Paintings of flowers.

Litho. & Embossed

1970, May 6   Imperf.

114	A14m	2ch Van Gogh	.35	.35
114A	A14m	3ch Redon	.35	.35
114B	A14m	5ch Kuroda	.35	.35
114C	A14m	10ch Renoir	.40	.40
p.		Souv. sheet, #114-114C	2.00	2.00
114D	A14m	15ch Renoir, diff.	.40	.40
114E	A14m	75ch Monet	.40	.40
114F	A14m	80ch like #114	.80	.80
114G	A14m	90ch like #114A	.80	.80
114H	A14m	1nu La Tour	.80	.80
114I	A14m	1.10nu like #114B	.80	.80
114J	A14m	1.40nu Oudot	.80	.80
q.		Souv. sheet, #114D, 114E, 114H, 114J	3.50	3.50
114K	A14m	1.40nu like #114D	.80	.80
r.		Souv. sheet, #114F, 114G, 114I, 114K	5.75	5.75
114L	A14m	1.20nu like #114D	1.20	1.20
114M	A14m	1.70nu like #114E	1.50	1.50
114N	A14m	3nu like #114H	1.60	1.60
114O	A14m	3.50nu like #114J	2.25	2.25
s.		Souv. sheet, #114L-114O	8.00	8.00
		Nos. 114-114O (16)	13.60	13.60

Nos. 114F-114G, 114I, 114K-114O are airmail.

Stamps of 1966-69 Surcharged

1970, June 19

115	A14j	20ch on 2nu, #94J	4.75	4.75
115A	A14p	20ch on 2nu, #99J	4.75	4.75
115B	A14p	20ch on 2.50nu, #99K	4.75	4.75
115C	A11	20ch on 3nu, #65	4.75	4.75
115D	A14b	20ch on 3nu, #84K	4.75	4.75
115E	A11	20ch on 4nu, #66	4.75	4.75
115F	A14c	20ch on 4nu, #85G	4.75	4.75
115G	A14d	20ch on 4nu, #86E	20.00	20.00
115H	A14i	20ch on 4nu, #92F	4.75	4.75
115I	A14p	20ch on 4nu, #99L	4.75	4.75
115J	A11	20ch on 5nu, #67	4.75	4.75
115K	A14b	20ch on 5nu, #84L	4.75	4.75
115L	A14c	20ch on 5nu, #85H	4.75	4.75
115M	A14j	20ch on 5nu, #94M	4.75	4.75
115N	A14p	20ch on 5nu, #99M	4.75	4.75
115O	A14b	20ch on 6nu, #84M	4.75	4.75
115P	A14b	20ch on 7nu, #84N	4.75	4.75
115Q	A14j	20ch on 10nu, #94N	5.00	5.00
115R	A14p	20ch on 10nu, #99N	5.00	5.00
		Nos. 115-115R (19)	106.00	106.00

Nos. 115B, 115I, 115M-115N, 115Q-115R are airmail.

Animals — A15d

5ch, African elephant. 10ch, Leopard. 20ch, Ibex. 25ch, Tiger. 30ch, Abominable snowman. 40ch, Water buffalo. 65ch, Rhinoceros. 75ch, Giant pandas. 85ch, Snow leopard. 2nu, Young deer. 3nu, Wild boar, vert. 4nu, Collared bear, vert. 5nu, Takin.

1970, Oct. 15   Litho.   Imperf.

116	A15d	5ch multi	1.00	1.00
116A	A15d	10ch multi	1.00	1.00
116B	A15d	20ch multi	1.40	1.40
116C	A15d	25ch multi	1.40	1.40
116D	A15d	30ch multi	2.00	2.00
116E	A15d	40ch multi	2.00	2.00
116F	A15d	65ch multi	2.50	2.50
116G	A15d	75ch multi	2.75	2.75
116H	A15d	85ch multi	3.00	3.00
116I	A15d	2nu multi	3.00	3.00
116J	A15d	3nu multi	3.50	3.50

116K	A15d	4nu multi	4.00	4.00
116L	A15d	5nu multi	5.00	5.00
		Nos. 116-116L (13)	32.55	32.55

Nos. 116I-116L are airmail. Simulated 3-dimensions using a plastic overlay.

Stamps of 1963-69 Surcharged

1970, Nov. 2

117	A14j	5ch on 30ch, #94F	1.75	1.75
117A	A14j	5ch on 50ch, #94G	1.75	1.75
117B	A14j	5ch on 1.25nu, #94H	1.75	1.75
117C	A14j	5ch on 1.50nu, #94I	1.75	1.75
117D	A14j	5ch on 2nu, #94J	1.75	1.75
117E	A14j	5ch on 2.50nu, #94K	1.75	1.75
117F	A14p	20ch on 30ch, #99F	4.75	4.75
117G	A14p	20ch on 50ch, #99G	4.75	4.75
117H	A14s	20ch on 1.05nu, #102E	4.75	4.75
117I	A14b	20ch on 1.25nu, #84I	4.75	4.75
117J	A14d	20ch on 1.25nu, #86D	4.75	4.75
117K	A14p	20ch on 1.25nu, #99H	4.75	4.75
117L	A14s	20ch on 1.40nu, #102F	4.75	4.75
117M	A4	20ch on 1.50nu, #14	4.75	4.75
117N	A11	20ch on 1.50nu, #63	4.75	4.75
117O	A14p	20ch on 1.50nu, #99I	4.75	4.75
117P	A11	20ch on 2nu, #64	4.75	4.75
117Q	A14f	20ch on 2nu, #88A	4.75	4.75
117R	A14i	20ch on 2nu, #92E	4.75	4.75
117S	A14b	20ch on 2.50nu, #84J	4.75	4.75
117T	A14f	20ch on 4nu, #88B	4.75	4.75
117U	A14s	20ch on 4nu, #102G	4.75	4.75
117V	A14i	20ch on 7nu, #92H	4.75	4.75
		Nos. 117-117V (23)	91.25	91.25

Nos. 117C, 117E, 117O are airmail.
No. 117C exists with overprint intended for No. 117 (5CH centered to the right of the obliterating bars, rather than adjacent to the lower bar).

Conquest of Space — A15e

Designs: 2ch, Jules Verne's "From the Earth to the Moon." 5ch, V-2 rocket. 15ch, Vostok. 25ch, Mariner 2. 30ch, Gemini 7. 50ch, Lift-off. 75ch, Edward White during space walk. 1.50nu, Apollo 13. 2nu, View of Earth from moon. 3nu, Another galaxy. 6nu, Moon, Earth, Sun, Mars, Jupiter. 7nu, Future space station.

1970   Litho.   Imperf.

118	A15e	2ch multi	1.00	1.00
118A	A15e	5ch multi	1.00	1.00
118B	A15e	15ch multi	1.00	1.00
118C	A15e	25ch multi	1.25	1.25
m.		Souv. sheet, #118-118C	10.00	10.00
118D	A15e	30ch multi	1.50	1.50
118E	A15e	50ch multi	2.00	2.00
118F	A15e	75ch multi	2.50	2.50
118G	A15e	1.50nu multi	2.75	2.75
n.		Souv. sheet, #118D-118G	15.00	15.00
118H	A15e	2nu multi	3.25	3.25
118I	A15e	3nu multi	4.00	4.00
118J	A15e	6nu multi	6.00	6.00
118K	A15e	7nu multi	7.00	7.00
o.		Souv. sheet, #118H-118K	30.00	30.00
		Nos. 118-118K (13)	33.25	33.25

Issued: Nos. 118-118G, 11/9; Nos. 118H-118K, 11/30. Souv. sheets, Dec. 18. Nos. 118H-118K are airmail. Simulated 3-dimensions using a plastic overlay.
See Nos. 127-127C. For surcharge see No. 129F.

Wangdiphodrang Dzong and Bridge A15f

1971, Feb. 22   Photo.   Perf. 13½

119	A15f	2ch gray	1.50	1.50
120	A15f	3ch deep red lilac	1.60	1.60
121	A15f	4ch violet	2.00	2.00
122	A15f	5ch dark green	.65	.65
123	A15f	10ch orange brown	.80	.80
124	A15f	15ch deep blue	1.40	1.40
125	A15f	20ch deep plum	1.40	1.40
		Nos. 119-125 (7)	8.95	8.95

Funeral Mask of King Tutankhamen A15g

History of Sculpture: 75ch, Winged Bull. 1.25nu, Head of Zeus. 2nu, She-wolf Suckling Romulus and Remus, horiz. 3nu, Head of Cicero. 4nu, Head of David, by Michaelangelo. 5nu, Age of Bronze, by Rodin. 6nu, Head of Woman, by Modigliani.

1971, Feb. 27   Litho.   Imperf.
Self-adhesive

126	A15g	10ch multi	.70	.70
126A	A15g	75ch multi	.85	.85
126B	A15g	1.25nu multi	1.75	1.75
126C	A15g	2nu multi	2.75	2.75
h.		Souv. sheet, #126-126C	6.50	6.50
126D	A15g	3nu multi	4.75	4.75
126E	A15g	4nu multi	5.75	5.75
126F	A15g	5nu multi	7.75	7.75
126G	A15g	6nu multi	5.75	5.75
i.		Souv. sheet, #126D-126G	16.00	16.00
		Nos. 126-126G (8)	30.05	30.05

Stamps are plastic heat molded into three dimensions. Nos. 126D-126G are airmail.

Conquest of Space Type of 1970

Designs: 10ch, 2.50nu, Lunokhod 1. 1.70nu, 4nu, Apollo 15.

1971, Mar. 20   Litho.   Imperf.

127	A15e	10ch multi	1.40	1.40
127A	A15e	1.70nu multi	2.10	2.10
127B	A15e	2.50nu multi	3.50	3.50
127C	A15e	4nu multi	4.25	4.25
d.		Souv. sheet of 4, #127-127C	22.50	22.50
		Nos. 127-127C (4)	11.25	11.25

Nos. 127B-127C are airmail. Simulated 3-dimensions using a plastic overlay.
No. 127 exists with erroneous surcharge of 90ch that was intended for use on No. 129A to create No. 129F.

Antique Automobiles — A15h

2ch, Mercedes Benz, Germany. 5ch, Ford, US. 10ch, Alfa Romeo, Italy. 15ch, Cord, US. 20ch, Hispano Suiza, Spain. 30ch, Invicta, Britain. 60ch, Renault, France. 75ch, Talbot, Britain. 85ch, Mercer, US. 1nu, Sunbeam, Britain. 1.20nu, Austrian Daimler. 1.55nu, Bugatti, Italy. 1.80nu, Simplex, US. 2nu, Amilcar, France. 2.50nu, Bentley, Britain. 4nu, Morris Garage, Britain. 6nu, Duesenberg, US. 7nu,

Aston Martin, Britain. 9nu, Packard, US. 10nu, Rolls Royce, Britain.

1971   Litho.   *Imperf.*
128-128S A15h   Set of 20   30.00 30.00

Issued: Nos. 128-128F, 5/20; Nos. 128G-128N, 6/10; Nos. 128O-128S, 7/5. Nos. 128O-128S are airmail. Simulated 3-dimensions using a plastic overlay.
"Romeo" misspelled.

Stamps of 1964-71 Surcharged

No. 129F, sans-serif type, 8mm surcharge bars

No. 129F, sans-serif type, 18mm surcharge bars

No. 129F, bold serif type, 18mm surcharge bars

1971, July 1
129	A14s	55ch on 60ch, #102D	2.50	2.50
129A	A5	55ch on 1.30nu, #22	2.50	2.50
129B	A11	55ch on 3nu, #65	2.50	2.50
129C	A14j	55ch on 4nu, #94L	2.50	2.50
129D	A14i	55ch on 5nu, #92G	2.50	2.50
129E	A14n	90ch on 1.05nu, #97D	3.00	3.00
129F	A15e	90ch on 1.70nu, #127A	50.00	50.00
129G	A5	90ch on 2nu, #23	2.50	2.50
129H	A14p	90ch on 2nu, #99J	4.00	4.00
129I	A15c	90ch on 2.50nu, #113	3.00	3.00
129J	A11	90ch on 4nu, #66	3.00	3.00
129K	A14d	90ch on 4nu, #86E	4.00	4.00
129L	A14i	90ch on 9nu, #92I	4.00	4.00
		Nos. 129-129L (13)	86.00	86.00

No. 129C is airmail. No. 129F exists in three varieties: with 90ch surcharge in sans-serif type with bars 8mm or 18mm long, and with surcharge in bold serif type with bars 18mm long. Bold surcharge exists erroneously applied to No. 127.
All values except No. 129F exist with inverted surcharges. Value: each $35, unused or used.

UN Emblem and Bhutan Flag — A16

Designs (Bhutan Flag and): 10ch, UN Headquarters, NY. 20ch, Security Council Chamber and mural by Per Krohg. 3nu, General Assembly Hall.

1971, Sept. 21   Photo.   *Perf. 13½*
130	A16	5ch gold, bl & multi	.25	.25
131	A16	10ch gold & multi	.25	.25
132	A16	20ch gold & multi	.25	.25
133	A16	3nu gold & multi	.50	.50
		Nos. 130-133,C21-C23 (7)	3.05	3.05

Bhutan's admission to the UN. Exist imperf. Values, unused or used: set, $6.

For overprints see Nos. 140-143. For surcharge see No. 252.

Boy Scout Crossing Stream in Rope Sling — A17

Emblem & Boy Scouts: 20ch, 2nu, mountaineering. 50ch, 6nu, reading map. 75ch, as 10ch.

1971, Nov. 30   Litho.   *Perf. 13½*
134	A17	10ch gold & multi	.25	.25
135	A17	20ch gold & multi	.25	.25
136	A17	50ch gold & multi	.25	.25
137	A17	75ch silver & multi	.50	.50
138	A17	2nu silver & multi	.65	.65
139	A17	6nu silver & multi	2.00	2.00
a.		Souv. sheet of 2, #138-139 + 2 labels	4.50	4.50
		Nos. 134-139 (6)	3.90	3.90

60th anniv. of the Boy Scouts. Exist imperf. Value $7.50. No. 139a imperf., value, $30.
For overprint and surcharge see Nos. 253, 383.

Nos. 130-133 Overprinted in Gold

1971, Dec. 23
140	A16	5ch gold & multi	.30	.30
141	A16	10ch gold & multi	.30	.30
142	A16	20ch gold & multi	.30	.30
143	A16	3nu gold & multi	.60	.60
		Nos. 140-143,C24-C26 (7)	4.35	4.35

World Refugee Year. Exist imperf. Values: set, unused $10, used $9.

The Bathing Girl by Renoir A17a

Designs: 20ch, A Bar at the Follies, by Manet, horiz. 90ch, Mona Lisa, by da Vinci. 1.70nu, Cart of Father Juniet, by Rousseau, horiz. 2.50nu, The Gleaners, by Millet, horiz. 4.60nu, White Horse, by Gaugin. 5.40nu, The Dancing Lesson, by Degas. 6nu, After the Rain, by Guillaumin, horiz.

1972   Litho. & Embossed   *Imperf.*
144	A17a	15ch multi	.50	.50
144A	A17a	20ch multi	.75	.75
144B	A17a	90ch multi	.85	.85
144C	A17a	1.70nu multi	1.50	1.50
144D	A17a	2.50nu multi	1.50	1.50
h.		Souv. sheet of 4, #144-144B, 144D	7.00	7.00
144E	A17a	4.60nu multi	2.25	2.25
144F	A17a	5.40nu multi	2.75	2.75

144G	A17a	6nu multi	2.75	2.75
i.		Souv. sheet of 4, #144C, 144E-144G	8.00	8.00
		Nos. 144-144G (8)	12.85	12.85

Issued: Nos. 144-144B, 144D, 1/29; others, 2/28.
Nos. 144C, 144E-144G are airmail.

Famous Men A17b

10ch, John F. Kennedy. 15ch, Gandhi. 55ch, Churchill. 2nu, De Gaulle. 6nu, Pope John XXIII. 8nu, Eisenhower.

1972, Apr. 17   Litho.   *Imperf.*
Self-adhesive
145	A17b	10ch multi	.60	.60
145A	A17b	15ch multi	.75	.75
145B	A17b	55ch multi	1.10	1.10
145C	A17b	2nu multi	1.25	1.25
145D	A17b	6nu multi	2.00	2.00
145E	A17b	8nu multi	2.75	2.75
f.		Souv. sheet, #145B-145E	7.50	7.50
		Nos. 145-145E (6)	8.45	8.45

Nos. 145C-145E are airmail. Stamps are plastic heat molded into three dimensions.

Book Year Emblem A17c

1972, May 15   Photo.   *Perf. 13½x13*
146	A17c	2ch multicolored	.25	.25
146A	A17c	3ch multicolored	.25	.25
146B	A17c	5ch multicolored	.25	.25
146C	A17c	20ch multicolored	.25	.25
		Nos. 146-146C (4)	1.00	1.00

International Book Year.

1972 Summer Olympics, Munich — A17d

1972, June 6   Photo.   *Perf. 13½*
147	A17d	10ch Handball	.25	.25
147A	A17d	15ch Archery	.25	.25
147B	A17d	20ch Boxing	.25	.25
147C	A17d	30ch Discus	.25	.25
147D	A17d	35ch Javelin	.25	.25
147E	A17d	45ch Shooting	.25	.25
147F	A17d	1.35nu like #147A	.80	.80
147G	A17d	7nu like #147	1.25	1.25
h.		Souv. sheet of 3, #147D, 147F-147G	3.00	3.00
		Nos. 147-147G (8)	3.55	3.55

Nos. 147D, 147F-147G are airmail and have a gold border.
Exist imperf. Value: set $6; souvenir sheet $6.
For overprint see No. 384.

Apollo 11 Type of 1969

Apollo 16: 15ch, Lift-off, vert. 20ch, Achieving lunar orbit. 90ch, Astronauts Young, Mattingly, Duke, vert. 1.70nu, Lunar module. 2.50nu, Walking on moon. 4.60nu, Gathering rock samples. 5.40nu, Apollo 16 on launch pad, vert. 6nu, Looking at earth, vert.

1972, Sept. 1   Litho.   *Imperf.*
148	A15a	15ch multi	1.25	1.25
148A	A15a	20ch multi	1.25	1.25
148B	A15a	90ch multi	1.25	1.25
148C	A15a	1.70nu multi	1.75	1.75

148D	A15a	2.50nu multi	2.25	2.25
h.		Souv. sheet of 4, #148-148B, 148D	17.50	17.50
148E	A15a	4.60nu multi	3.00	3.00
148F	A15a	5.40nu multi	3.50	3.50
148G	A15a	6nu multi	4.75	4.75
i.		Souv. sheet of 4, #148C, 148E-148G	27.50	27.50
		Nos. 148-148G (8)	19.00	19.00

Nos. 148C, 148E-148G are airmail. Simulated 3-dimensions using a plastic overlay.

Dogs A17f

2ch, Pointer. 3ch, Irish Setter. 5ch, Lhasa Apso, vert. 10ch, Dochi. No. 149D, 15ch, Damci. No. 149E, 15ch, Collie. 20ch, Basset hound. 25ch, Damci, diff. 30ch, Fox terrier. 55ch, Lhasa Apso, diff. 99ch, Boxer. 2.50nu, St. Bernard. 4nu, Cocker Spaniel. 8nu, Damci, diff.
18nu, Poodle.

1972-73   Photo.   *Perf. 13½*
149	A17f	2ch multi	.25	.25
149A	A17f	3ch multi	.25	.25
149B	A17f	5ch multi	.25	.25
149C	A17f	10ch multi	.25	.25
149D	A17f	15ch multi	.25	.25
149E	A17f	15ch multi	.25	.25
149F	A17f	20ch multi	.25	.25
149G	A17f	25ch multi	.35	.35
149H	A17f	30ch multi	.25	.25
149I	A17f	55ch multi	.35	.35
149J	A17f	99ch multi	.25	.25
149K	A17f	2.50nu multi	.50	.50
149L	A17f	4nu multi	1.50	1.50
o.		Souv. sheet of 3, #149J-149L, perf. 14	6.00	6.00
149M	A17f	8nu multi	2.50	2.50
p.		Souv. sheet of 2, #149I, 149M, perf. 14	5.50	5.50
		Nos. 149-149M (14)	7.45	7.45

Souvenir Sheet
Perf. 14
149N	A17f	18nu multi	8.00	8.00

Issued: Nos. 149B-149D, 149G, 149I, 149M, 149Mp, 10/5; Nos. 149-149A, 149E-149F, 149H, 149J-149L, 149Lo, 1/1/73; No. 149N, 1/15/73. No. 149N is airmail. All exist imperf. Values: set (14), $11; No. 149Lo, $9; 149Mp, $7.50; 149N, $8.
For surcharges & overprints see Nos. 268-269, 385.

Roses — A17g

15ch, Wendy Cussons. 25ch, Iceberg. 30ch, Marchioness of Urquio. 3nu, Pink parfait. 6nu, Roslyn. 7nu, Blue moon.

Scented Paper

1973, Jan. 30   Photo.   *Perf. 13½*
150	A17g	15ch multi	.25	.25
150A	A17g	25ch multi	.25	.25
150B	A17g	30ch multi	.25	.25
150C	A17g	3nu multi	.80	.80
150D	A17g	6nu multi	1.00	1.00
150E	A17g	7nu multi	1.60	1.60
f.		Souv. sheet, #150D-150E	3.50	3.50
		Nos. 150-150E (6)	4.15	4.15

Nos. 150D-150E are airmail. Exist imperf. Value: set $10; souvenir sheet $8.

Apollo 11 Type of 1969

Apollo 17: 10ch, Taking photographs on moon. 15ch, Setting up experiments. 55ch, Earth. 2nu, Driving lunar rover. 7nu, Satellite. 9nu, Astronauts Cernan, Evans, Schmitt.

1973, Feb. 28　　Litho.　　Imperf.
Size: 50x49mm

151	A15a	10ch multicolored	1.50	1.50
151A	A15a	15ch multicolored	1.50	1.50
151B	A15a	55ch multicolored	2.00	2.00
151C	A15a	2nu multicolored	3.00	3.00
f.		Souv. sheet of 4, #151-151C	12.00	12.00
151D	A15a	7nu multicolored	6.00	6.00
151E	A15a	9nu multicolored	8.00	8.00
g.		Souv. sheet of 2, #151D-151E	50.00	50.00
		Nos. 151-151E (6)	22.00	22.00

Simulated 3-dimensions using a plastic overlay. Nos. 151D-151E are airmail. No. 151g is circular, 160mm in diameter.

Phonograph Records

A17h

Recordings: 10ch, Bhutanese History. 25ch, Royal Bhutan Anthem. 1.25nu, Bhutanese History (English). 3nu, Bhutanese History (Bhutanese), Folk Song No. 1. 7nu, Folk Song No. 1. 8nu, Folk Song No. 2. 9nu, History in English, Folk Songs Nos. 1 & 2.

Diameter: Nos. 152-152B, 152D-152E, 69mm, Nos. 152C, 152F, 100mm

1973, Apr. 15　　Self-adhesive

152	A17h	10ch yel on red	15.00	15.00
152A	A17h	25ch gold on grn	20.00	20.00
152B	A17h	1.25nu sil on bl	30.00	30.00
152C	A17h	3nu sil on pur	85.00	85.00
152D	A17h	7nu sil on blk	50.00	50.00
152E	A17h	8nu red on white	75.00	75.00
152F	A17h	9nu blk on yel	125.00	125.00
		Nos. 152-152F (7)	400.00	400.00

Nos. 152C, 152F are airmail. Nos. 152-152F exist in trial colors.

A 6nu stamp, silver on green, exists but was not issued. Value, unused $900.

King Jigme Dorji Wangchuk (d. 1972)
A17i

Embossed on Gold Foil

1973, May 2　　Die Cut　　Imperf.

153	A17i	10ch orange	2.00	2.00
153A	A17i	25ch red	2.00	2.00
153B	A17i	3nu green	3.00	3.00
153C	A17i	6nu blue	5.00	5.00
153D	A17i	8nu purple	6.00	6.00
e.		Souv. sheet of 2, #153C-153D	20.00	20.00
		Nos. 153-153D (5)	18.00	18.00

Nos. 153C-153D are airmail.

Mushrooms — A17j

Different mushrooms.

1973, Sept. 25　　Litho.　　Imperf.

154	A17j	15ch multicolored	.60	.60
154A	A17j	25ch multicolored	.85	.85
154B	A17j	30ch multicolored	1.00	1.00
154C	A17j	3nu multicolored	2.00	2.00
f.		Souv. sheet, #154-154C	15.00	15.00
154D	A17j	6nu multicolored	7.50	7.50
154E	A17j	7nu multicolored	11.00	11.00
g.		Souv. sheet, #154D-154E	50.00	50.00
		Nos. 154-154E (6)	22.95	22.95

Simulated 3-dimensions using a plastic overlay. Nos. 154D-154E are airmail.

Bhutanese Mail Service — A17k

Designs: 5ch, 6nu, Letter carrier at mail box. 10ch, 5nu, Postmaster, letter carrier. 15ch, Sacking mail. 25ch, Mailtruck. 1.25nu, Sorting mail. 3nu, Hand-delivered mail.

1973, Nov. 14　　Photo.　　Perf. 13½

155	A17k	5ch multi	.25	.25
155A	A17k	10ch multi	.25	.25
155B	A17k	15ch multi	.25	.25
155C	A17k	25ch multi	.25	.25
155D	A17k	1.25nu multi	.25	.25
155E	A17k	3nu multi	.75	.75
155F	A17k	5nu multi	1.25	1.25
155G	A17k	6nu multi	1.50	1.50
h.		Souv. sheet, #155F-155G	5.50	5.50
		Nos. 155-155G (8)	4.75	4.75

Indipex '73. Nos. 155F-155G are airmail. All exist imperf. Values: set $7; souvenir sheet $6.50.
For surcharges and overprint see Nos. 267, 382, C37-C38.

King Jigme Singye Wangchuk and Royal Crest — A18

Designs (King and): 25ch, 90ch, Flag of Bhutan. 1.25nu, Wheel with 8 good luck signs. 2nu, 4nu, Punakha Dzong, former winter capital. 3nu, 5nu, Crown. 5ch, same as 10ch.

1974, June 2　　Litho.　　Perf. 13½

157	A18	10ch maroon & multi	.25	.25
158	A18	25ch gold & multi	.25	.25
159	A18	1.25nu multi	.25	.25
160	A18	2nu gold & multi	.40	.40
161	A18	3nu multi	.50	.50
		Nos. 157-161 (5)	1.65	1.65

Souvenir Sheets
Perf. 13½, Imperf.

162		Sheet of 2	3.00	3.00
a.	A18 5ch maroon & multi		.50	
b.	A18 5nu red orange & multi		2.50	
163		Sheet of 2	3.00	3.00
a.	A18 90ch gold & multi		.90	
b.	A18 4nu gold & multi		2.10	

Coronation of King Jigme Singye Wangchuk, June 2, 1974.

Mailman on Horseback　　Old and New Locomotives
A19　　　　　　　　A20

Designs (UPU Emblem, Carrier Pigeon and): 3ch, Sailing and steam ships. 4ch, Old biplane and jet. 25ch, Mail runner and jeep.

1974, Oct. 9　　Litho.　　Perf. 14½

164	A19	1ch grn & multi	.60	.60
165	A20	2ch lilac & multi	.60	.60
166	A20	3ch ocher & multi	.60	.60
167	A20	4ch yel grn & multi	.60	.60
168	A20	25ch salmon & multi	.60	.60
		Nos. 164-168, C27-C29 (8)	5.50	5.50

Centenary of Universal Postal Union. Issued in sheets of 50 and sheets of 5 plus label with multicolored margin. Exist imperf. Values, unused or used: set $6.

Family and WPY Emblem — A21

1974, Dec. 17　　Perf. 13½

169	A21	25ch bl & multi	.25	.25
170	A21	50ch org & multi	.25	.25
171	A21	90ch ver & multi	.30	.30
172	A21	2.50nu brn & multi	.65	.65
a.		Souvenir sheet, 10nu	2.75	2.75
		Nos. 169-172 (4)	1.45	1.45

For surcharge see No. 254.

Sephisa Chandra — A22

Indigenous butterflies: 2ch, Lethe kansa. 3ch, Neope bhadra. 4ch, Euthalia duda. 5ch, Vindula erota. 10ch, Bhutanitis Lidderdale. 3nu, Limenitis zayla. 5nu, Delis thysbe. 10nu, Dabasa gyas.

1975, Sept. 15　　Litho.　　Perf. 14½

173	A22	1ch multicolored	.30	.30
174	A22	2ch multicolored	.30	.30
175	A22	3ch multicolored	.30	.30
176	A22	4ch multicolored	.30	.30
177	A22	5ch multicolored	.30	.30
178	A22	10ch multicolored	.30	.30
179	A22	3nu multicolored	.75	.75
180	A22	5nu multicolored	1.60	1.60
		Nos. 173-180 (8)	4.15	4.15

Souvenir Sheet
Perf. 13

181	A22	10nu multicolored	3.00	3.00

For surcharges see Nos. 255-256.

Apollo and Apollo-Soyuz Emblem — A23

Design: No. 183, Soyuz and emblem.

1975, Dec. 1　　Litho.　　Perf. 14x13½

182	A23	10nu multicolored	3.00	3.00
183	A23	10nu multicolored	3.00	3.00
a.		Souvenir sheet of 2, 15nu	6.00	6.00

Apollo Soyuz link-up in space, July 17. Nos. 182-183 printed se-tenant in sheets of 10. Sheets exist imperf. Values: single stamp, $6 each; se-tenant pair $15. No. 183a contains two 15nu stamps similar to Nos 182-183.
For surcharges see Nos. 257-258.

Jewelry — A24

Designs: 2ch, Coffee pot, bell and sugar cup. 3ch, Container and drinking horn. 4ch, Pendants and box cover. 5ch, Painter. 15ch, Silversmith. 20ch, Wood carver with tools. 1.50nu, Mat maker. 5nu, 10nu, Printer.

1975, Dec. 17　　Perf. 14½

184	A24	1ch multicolored	.30	.30
185	A24	2ch multicolored	.30	.30
186	A24	3ch multicolored	.30	.30
187	A24	4ch multicolored	.30	.30
188	A24	5ch multicolored	.30	.30
189	A24	15ch multicolored	.30	.30
190	A24	20ch multicolored	.30	.30
191	A24	1.50nu multicolored	.35	.35
192	A24	2.25 multicolored	2.25	2.25
		Nos. 184-192 (9)	4.70	4.70

Souvenir Sheet
Perf. 13

193	A24	multicolored	4.25	4.25

Handicrafts and craftsmen.
For surcharges see No. 259, 381.

King Jigme Singye Wangchuk
A25

Designs: 25ch, 90ch, 1nu, 2nu, 4nu, like 15ch. 1.30nu, 3nu, 5nu, Coat of arms. Sizes (Diameter): 15ch, 1nu, 1.30nu, 38mm. 25ch, 2nu, 3nu, 49mm. 90ch, 4nu, 5nu, 63mm.

Lithographed, Embossed on Gold Foil

1975, Nov. 11　　Imperf.

194	A25	15ch emerald	.65	.65
195	A25	25ch emerald	.90	.90
196	A25	90ch emerald	1.40	1.40
197	A25	1nu bright carmine	1.50	1.50
198	A25	1.30nu bright carmine	1.90	1.90
199	A25	2nu bright carmine	2.10	2.10
200	A25	3nu bright carmine	2.75	2.75
201	A25	4nu bright carmine	4.75	4.75
202	A25	5nu bright carmine	6.00	6.00
		Nos. 194-202 (9)	21.95	21.95

King Jigme Singye Wangchuk's 20th birthday.
Two dies were used to print Nos. 196, 197, 199, and 201. These stamps exist with either the initials "AT" or "GK" to the left of the king's chin.

Rhododendron Cinnabarinum
A28

Rhododendron: 2ch, Campanulatum. 3ch, Fortunei. 4ch, Red arboreum. 5ch, Pink arboreum. 1nu, Falconeri. 3nu, Hodgsonii. 5nu, Keysii. 10nu, Cinnabarinum.

1976, Feb. 15　　Litho.　　Perf. 15

203	A28	1ch rose & multi	.25	.25
204	A28	2ch lt grn & multi	.25	.25
205	A28	3ch gray & multi	.25	.25

206	A28	4ch lil & multi	.25	.25
207	A28	5ch ol gray & multi	.25	.25
208	A28	1nu brn org & multi	.30	.30
209	A28	3nu ultra & multi	.90	.90
210	A28	5nu gray & multi	1.40	1.40
		Nos. 203-210 (8)	3.85	3.85

Souvenir Sheet
Perf. 13½

211	A28	10nu multicolored	3.75	3.75

For surcharge see No. 260.

Slalom and Olympic Games Emblem — A29

Olympic Games Emblem and: 2ch, 4-men bobsled. 3ch, Ice hockey. 4ch, Cross-country skiing. 5ch, Figure skating, women's. 2nu, Downhill skiing. 4nu, Speed skating. 6nu, Ski jump. 10nu, Figure skating, pairs.

1976, Mar. 29   Litho.   Perf. 13½

212	A29	1ch multicolored	.25	.25
213	A29	2ch multicolored	.25	.25
214	A29	3ch multicolored	.25	.25
215	A29	4ch multicolored	.25	.25
216	A29	5ch multicolored	.25	.25
217	A29	2nu multicolored	.40	.40
218	A29	4nu multicolored	.90	.90
219	A29	10nu multicolored	2.50	2.50
		Nos. 212-219 (8)	5.05	5.05

Souvenir Sheet

220	A29	6nu multicolored	2.75	2.75

12th Winter Olympic Games, Innsbruck, Austria, Feb. 4-15.
For surcharges see Nos. 261-262.
Exist imperf. Values, unused or used: set 7.50; souvenir sheet $7.50.

Ceremonial Masks — A29a

Various masks. Nos. 220E-220K are horiz. stamps.

1976, Apr. 23   Litho.   Imperf.

220A	A29a	5ch multi	.40	.40
220B	A29a	10ch multi	.40	.40
220C	A29a	15ch multi	.40	.40
220D	A29a	20ch multi	.40	.40
220E	A29a	25ch multi	.40	.40
220F	A29a	30ch multi	.40	.40
220G	A29a	35ch multi	.40	.40
220H	A29a	1nu multi	2.40	2.40
220I	A29a	2nu multi	2.75	2.75
220J	A29a	2.50nu multi	2.75	2.75
220K	A29a	3nu multi	3.25	3.25
		Nos. 220A-220K (11)	13.95	13.95

Souvenir Sheets

220L	A29a	5nu like #220C	5.50	5.00
220M	A29a	10nu like #220F	12.50	12.50

Simulated 3-dimensions using a plastic overlay. Nos. 220H-220M are airmail.
Sizes of stamps: No. 220L, 59x70mm, No. 220M, 69x57mm.

Orchid
A30

Designs: Various flowers.

1976, May 29   Litho.   Perf. 14½

221	A30	1ch multicolored	.25	.25
222	A30	2ch multicolored	.25	.25
223	A30	3ch multicolored	.25	.25
224	A30	4ch multicolored	.25	.25

225	A30	5ch multicolored	.25	.25
226	A30	2nu multicolored	.70	.70
227	A30	4nu multicolored	1.25	1.25
228	A30	6nu multicolored	2.00	2.00
		Nos. 221-228 (8)	5.20	5.20

Souvenir Sheet
Perf. 13½

229	A30	10nu multicolored	4.00	4.00

For surcharges see Nos. 263-264.

Double Carp Design A31

Designs: Various symbolic designs and Colombo Plan emblem.

1976, July 1   Litho.   Perf. 14½

230	A31	3ch red & multi	.25	.25
231	A31	4ch ver & multi	.25	.25
232	A31	5ch multicolored	.25	.25
233	A31	25ch bl & multi	.25	.25
234	A31	1.25nu multicolored	.35	.35
235	A31	2nu yel & multi	.60	.60
236	A31	2.50nu vio & multi	.75	.75
237	A31	3nu multicolored	.90	.90
		Nos. 230-237 (8)	3.60	3.60

Colombo Plan, 25th anniversary.
For surcharge see No. 265.

Bandaranaike Conference Hall — A32

1976, Aug. 16   Litho.   Perf. 13½

238	A32	1.25nu multicolored	.80	.80
239	A32	2.50nu multicolored	1.90	1.90

5th Summit Conference of Non-aligned Countries, Colombo, Sri Lanka, Aug. 9-19.

Elizabeth II — A33

Liberty Bell — A34

Spirit of St. Louis — A35

Bhutanese Archer, Olympic Rings — A36

Designs: No. 242, Alexander Graham Bell. No. 245, LZ 3 Zeppelin docking, 1907. No. 246, Alfred B. Nobel.

1978, Nov. 15   Litho.   Perf. 14½

240	A33	20nu multicolored	4.00	4.00
241	A34	20nu multicolored	5.25	5.25
242	A33	20nu multicolored	5.25	5.25
243	A35	20nu multicolored	5.25	5.25
244	A36	20nu multicolored	5.25	5.25
245	A35	20nu multicolored	6.75	6.75
246	A33	20nu multicolored	5.75	5.75
		Nos. 240-246 (7)	37.50	37.50

25th anniv. of coronation of Elizabeth II; American Bicentennial; cent. of 1st telephone call by Alexander Graham Bell; Charles A. Lindbergh crossing the Atlantic, 50th anniv.; Olympic Games; 75th anniv. of the Zeppelin; 75th anniv. of Nobel Prize. Seven souvenir sheets exist, each 25nu, commemorating same events with different designs. Size: 103x80mm. Value $50.

Issues of 1967-1976 Surcharged

Perforations and Printing as Before 1978

252	A16	25ch on 3nu (#133)		
253	A17	25ch on 6nu (#139)		
254	A21	25ch on 2.50nu (#172)		
255	A22	25ch on 3nu (#179)		
256	A22	25ch on 5nu (#180)		
257	A23	25ch on 10nu (#182)		
258	A23	25ch on 10nu (#183)		
259	A24	25ch on 10nu (#192)		
260	A28	25ch on 5nu (#210)		
261	A29	25ch on 4nu (#218)		
262	A29	25ch on 10nu (#219)		
263	A30	25ch on 4nu (#227)		
264	A30	25ch on 6nu (#228)		
265	A31	25ch on 2.50nu (#236)		
266	A14g	25ch on 5nu (#90E)		
267	A17k	25ch on 3nu (#155E)		
268	A17f	25ch on 4nu (#149L)		
269	A17f	25ch on 8nu (#149M)		
		Nos. 252-269, C31-C38 (26)	120.00	120.00

Mother and Child, IYC Emblem — A37

IYC Emblem and: 5nu, Mother and two children. 10nu, Boys with blackboards and stylus.

1979, June   Litho.   Perf. 14x13½

289	A37	2nu multicolored	.65	.65
290	A37	5nu multicolored	1.75	1.75
291	A37	10nu multicolored	3.00	3.00
a.		Souv. sheet of 3, #289-291 + label, perf. 15x13½	7.00	7.00
		Nos. 289-291 (3)	5.40	5.40

International Year of the Child. Exist imperf. Values: set $8; souvenir sheet $11.
For overprints see Nos. 761-763.

Conference Emblem and Dove — A38

10nu, Emblem and Bhutanese symbols.

1979, Sept. 3   Litho.   Perf. 14x13½

292	A38	25ch multicolored	.25	.25
293	A38	10nu multicolored	3.25	3.25

6th Non-Aligned Summit Conference, Havana, August 1979.

Silver Rattle, Dorji A39

Antiques: 10ch, Silver handbell, Dilbu, vert. 15ch, Cylindrical jar, Jadum, vert. 25ch, Ornamental teapot, Jamjee. 1nu, Leather container, Kem, vert. 1.25nu, Brass teapot, Jamjee. 1.70nu, Vessel with elephant-head legs, Sangphor, vert. 2nu, Teapot with ornamental spout, Jamjee, vert. 3nu, Metal pot on claw-shaped feet, Yangtho, vert. 4nu, Dish inlaid with precious stones, Battha. 5nu, Metal circular flask, Chhap, vert.

1979, Dec. 17   Photo.   Perf. 14

294	A39	5ch multicolored	.25	.25
295	A39	10ch multicolored	.25	.25
296	A39	15ch multicolored	.25	.25
297	A39	25ch multicolored	.25	.25
298	A39	1nu multicolored	.45	.45
299	A39	1.25nu multicolored	.50	.50
300	A39	1.70nu multicolored	.70	.70
301	A39	2nu multicolored	.90	.90
302	A39	3nu multicolored	1.25	1.25
303	A39	4nu multicolored	1.60	1.60
304	A39	5nu multicolored	2.25	2.25
		Nos. 294-304 (11)	8.65	8.65

For surcharges, see Nos. 1409, 1409A-1409B.

Hill, Rinpiang Dzong — A40

Hill Statue, Stamps of Bhutan and: 2nu, Dzong. 5nu, Ounsti Dzong. 10nu, Lingzi

Dzong, Gt. Britain Type 81. 20nu, Rope bridge, Penny Black.

1980, Mar 15		Litho.		*Perf. 14x13½*
305	A40	1nu multicolored	.40	.40
306	A40	2nu multicolored	.75	.75
307	A40	5nu multicolored	2.00	2.00
308	A40	10nu multicolored	3.75	3.75
		Nos. 305-308 (4)	6.90	6.90

Souvenir Sheet

309	A40	20nu multicolored	11.00	11.00

Sir Rowland Hill (1795-1879), originator of penny postage.

Exist imperf. Values, unused or used: set $7; souvenir sheet $9.

Kichu Lhakhang Monastery, Phari — A41

Guru Padma Sambhava's Birthday — Monasteries: 1nu, Dungtse, Phari, vert. 2.25nu, Kurjey. 3nu, Tangu, Thimphu. 4nu, Cheri, Thimphu. 5nu, Chorten, Kora. 7nu, Tak-Tsang, Phari, vert.

1981, July 11		Litho.		*Perf. 14*
310	A41	1nu multi	.25	.25
311	A41	2nu shown	.40	.40
312	A41	2.25nu multi	.60	.60
313	A41	3nu multi	.70	.70
314	A41	4nu multi	.95	.95
315	A41	5nu multi	1.40	1.40
316	A41	7nu multi	1.75	1.75
		Nos. 310-316 (7)	6.05	6.05

Prince Charles and Lady Diana — A42

1nu, St. Paul's Cathedral.
No 321, Wedding procession.

1981, Sept. 10		Litho.		*Perf. 14½*
317	A42	1nu multi	.80	.80
318	A42	5nu like #317	2.00	2.00
319	A42	20nu shown	3.00	3.00
320	A42	25nu like #319	3.25	3.25
		Nos. 317-320 (4)	9.05	9.05

Souvenir Sheet

321	A42	20nu multi	3.00	3.00

Royal wedding. Nos. 318-319 issued in sheets of 5 plus label.
For surcharges see Nos. 471-475.
Exist imperf. Values, unused or used: set $16; souvenir sheet $9.

Orange-bellied Chloropsis — A43

3nu, Monal pheasant. 5nu, Ward's trogon. 10nu, Mrs. Gould's sunbird. 25nu, Maroon oriole.

1982, Apr. 19		Litho.		*Perf. 14*
322	A43	2nu shown	.70	.70
323	A43	3nu multi	1.75	1.75
324	A43	5nu multi	2.50	2.50
325	A43	10nu multi	2.75	2.75
		Nos. 322-325 (4)	7.70	7.70

Souvenir Sheet

326	A43	25nu multi	7.50	7.50

1982 World Cup — A44

Designs: Various soccer players.

1982, June 25		Litho.		*Perf. 14½x14*
327	A44	1nu multicolored	.25	.25
328	A44	2nu multicolored	.60	.60
329	A44	3nu multicolored	.90	.90
330	A44	20nu multicolored	5.25	5.25
		Nos. 327-330 (4)	7.00	7.00

Souvenir Sheets

331	A44	25nu multicolored	6.00	6.00
331A	A44	25nu multicolored	6.00	6.00

Nos. 331-331A have margins continuing design and listing finalists (No. 331, Algeria-Honduras; No. 331A, Hungary-Yugoslavia). Nos. 327-331A exist imperf.
For surcharges see Nos. 481-485.

21st Birthday of Princess Diana — A45

1nu, St. James' Palace. 10nu, Diana, Charles. 15nu, Windsor Castle. 25nu, Wedding.
20nu, Diana.

1982, Aug.				
332	A45	1nu multi	.50	.50
332A	A45	10nu multi	4.50	4.50
332B	A45	15nu multi	8.00	8.00
333	A45	25nu multi	12.00	12.00
		Nos. 332-333 (4)	25.00	25.00

Souvenir Sheet

334	A45	20nu multi	16.00	7.50

10nu-15nu issued only in sheets of 5 + label.
For overprints and surcharges see Nos. 361-363, 455-459, 476-480.
Exist imperf. Values unused or used: set $25; souvenir sheet $20.

Rama and Cubs with Mowgli — A47

Scenes from Disney's The Jungle Book. No. 349, Baloo and Mowgli in forest. No. 350, Baloo and Mowgli floating.

1982, Sept. 1				*Perf. 11*
340	A47	1ch multicolored	.25	.25
341	A47	2ch multicolored	.25	.25
342	A47	3ch multicolored	.25	.25
343	A47	4ch multicolored	.25	.25
344	A47	5ch multicolored	.25	.25
345	A47	10ch multicolored	.25	.25
346	A47	30ch multicolored	.25	.25
347	A47	2nu multicolored	.40	.40
348	A47	2nu multicolored	6.00	6.00
		Nos. 340-348 (9)	8.15	8.15

Souvenir Sheets
Perf. 13½

349	A47	20nu multicolored	6.50	6.50
350	A47	20nu multicolored	6.50	6.50

George Washington Surveying — A48

1nu, FDR, Harvard. 2nu, Washington at Valley Forge. 3nu, FDR, family. 4nu, Washington, Battle of Monmouth. 5nu, FDR, White House. 15nu, Washington, Mt. Vernon. 20nu, FDR, Churchill, Stalin.
No. 359, Washington, vert. No. 360, FDR, vert.

1982, Nov. 15		Litho.		*Perf. 15*
351	A48	50ch shown	.25	.25
352	A48	1nu multi	.30	.30
353	A48	2nu multi	.35	.35
354	A48	3nu multi	.50	.50
355	A48	4nu multi	.70	.70
356	A48	5nu multi	1.00	1.00
357	A48	15nu multi	2.50	2.50
358	A48	20nu multi	3.25	3.25
		Nos. 351-358 (8)	8.85	8.85

Souvenir Sheets

359	A48	25nu multi	4.50	4.50
360	A48	25nu multi	4.50	4.50

Washington and Franklin D. Roosevelt.
Exist imperf. Values unused or used: set $12; souvenir sheet each $6.

Nos. 332-334 Overprinted: "ROYAL BABY / 21.6.82"

1982, Nov. 19				*Perf. 14½x14*
361	A45	1nu multicolored	.25	.25
361A	A45	10nu multicolored	2.50	2.50
361B	A45	15nu multicolored	3.50	3.50
362	A45	25nu multicolored	5.75	5.75
		Nos. 361-362 (4)	12.00	12.00

Souvenir Sheet

363	A45	20nu multi	7.50	7.50

Birth of Prince William of Wales, June 21.
Exist imperf. Values unused or used: set $17; souvenir sheet $12.

500th Birth Anniv. of Raphael A51

Portraits: 1nu, Angelo Doni. 4nu, Maddalena Doni. 5nu, Baldassare Castiglione. 20nu, La Donna Velata.
No. 379, Expulsion of Heliodorus. No. 380, Mass of Bolsena.

1983, Mar. 23				*Perf. 13½*
375	A51	1nu multi	.30	.30
376	A51	4nu multi	1.10	1.10
377	A51	5nu multi	1.50	1.50
378	A51	20nu multi	6.00	6.00
		Nos. 375-378 (4)	8.90	8.90

Souvenir Sheets

379	A51	25nu multi	8.00	8.00
380	A51	25nu multi	8.00	8.00

Exist imperf. Values unused or used: set $9; souvenir sheets each $6.25.

Nos. 184, 155F, 139, 147G, 149M Srchd. or Ovptd. "Druk Air"

1983, Feb. 11				
381	A24	30ch on 1ch multi	2.00	2.00
382	A17k	5nu multicolored	2.75	2.75
383	A17	6nu multicolored	3.00	3.00
384	A17d	7nu multicolored	4.25	4.25
385	A17f	8nu multicolored	4.50	4.50
		Nos. 381-385 (5)	16.50	16.50

Druk Air Service inauguration. Overprint of 8nu all caps. Nos. 382, 384 air mail.

Manned Flight Bicentenary — A52

1983, Aug. 15		Litho.		*Perf. 15*
386	A52	50ch Dornier Wal	.25	.25
387	A52	3nu Savoia-Marchetti S-66	.95	.95
388	A52	10nu Hawker Osprey	2.50	2.50
389	A52	20nu Ville de Paris	5.00	5.00
		Nos. 386-389 (4)	8.70	8.70

Souvenir Sheet

390	A52	25nu Balloon Captif	7.50	7.50

Exist imperf. Values unused or used: set $25; souvenir sheet $7.

Buddhist Symbols — A53

25ch, Sacred vase. 50ch, Five Sensory Symbols. 2nu, Seven Treasures. 3nu, Five Sensory Organs. 8nu, Five Fleshes. 9nu, Sacrificial cake.

1983, Aug. 11		Litho.		*Perf. 13½*
391	A53	25ch multicolored	.25	.25
392	A53	50ch multicolored	.25	.25
393	A53	2nu multicolored	.40	.40
394	A53	3nu multicolored	.85	.85
395	A53	8nu multicolored	1.90	1.90
396	A53	9nu multicolored	2.50	2.50
a.		Souv. sheet of 6, #391-396	7.50	7.50
		Nos. 391-396 (6)	6.15	6.15

Size of Nos. 393, 396: 45x40mm.

World Communications Year (1983) — A54

Various Disney characters and history of communications.
No. 406, Donald Duck on phone, horiz. No. 407, Mickey Mouse on TV.

1984, Apr. 10   Litho.   Perf. 14½x14

397	A54	4ch multicolored	.25	.25
398	A54	5ch multicolored	.25	.25
399	A54	10ch multicolored	.25	.25
400	A54	20ch multicolored	.25	.25
401	A54	25ch multicolored	.25	.25
402	A54	50ch multicolored	.25	.25
403	A54	1nu multicolored	.50	.50
404	A54	5nu multicolored	1.50	1.50
405	A54	20nu multicolored	4.25	4.25
		Nos. 397-405 (9)	7.75	7.75

Souvenir Sheets
Perf. 14x14½

406	A54	20nu multicolored	5.50	5.50
407	A54	20nu multicolored	5.50	5.50

Nos. 397-407 exist imperf.

1984 Winter
Olympics — A55

50ch, Skiing. 1nu, Cross-country skiing.
3nu, Speed skating. 20nu, Bobsledding.
25nu, Hockey.

1984, June 16   Perf. 14

408	A55	50ch multicolored	.30	.30
409	A55	1nu multicolored	.40	.40
410	A55	3nu multicolored	.75	.75
411	A55	20nu multicolored	4.00	4.00
		Nos. 408-411 (4)	5.45	5.45

Souvenir Sheet

412	A55	25nu multicolored	6.25	6.25

Exist imperf. Values unused or used: set $7;
souvenir sheet $7.

Golden Langur
(WWF) — A56

1nu, Group in tree, horiz. 2nu, Family, horiz.
4nu, Group walking.
No. 417, Snow leopard. No. 418, Yak. No.
419, Blue sheep, horiz.

1984, June 10   Litho.   Perf. 14½

413	A56	50ch shown	.70	.70
414	A56	1nu multicolored	.70	.70
415	A56	2nu multicolored	1.75	1.75
416	A56	4nu multicolored	3.25	3.25
		Nos. 413-416 (4)	6.40	6.40

Souvenir Sheets

417	A56	20nu multicolored	8.00	8.00
418	A56	25nu multicolored	8.00	8.00
419	A56	25nu multicolored	8.00	8.00

Locomotives
A57

50ch, Sans Pareil, 1829. 1nu, Planet, 1830.
3nu, Experiment, 1832. 4nu, Black Hawk,
1835. 5.50nu, Jenny Lind, 1847. 8nu, Sem-
mering-Bavaria, 1851. 10nu, Great Northern
#1, 1870. 25nu, German Natl. Tinder, 1880.
No. 428, Darjeeling Himalayan Railway,
1984. No. 429, Sondermann Freight, 1896.
No. 430, Crampton's locomotive, 1846. No.
431, Erzsebet, 1870.

1984, July 16

420	A57	50ch multi	.25	.25
421	A57	1nu multi	.30	.30
422	A57	3nu multi	.65	.65
423	A57	4nu multi	1.00	1.00
424	A57	5.50nu multi	1.25	1.25
425	A57	8nu multi	1.75	1.75
426	A57	10nu multi	2.10	2.10
427	A57	25nu multi	2.70	2.70
		Nos. 420-427 (8)	12.80	12.80

Souvenir Sheets

428	A57	20nu multi	5.00	5.00
429	A57	20nu multi	5.00	5.00
430	A57	20nu multi	5.00	5.00
431	A57	20nu multi	5.00	5.00

Nos. 424-427 horiz.

Classic
Cars
A58

50ch, Riley Sprite, 1936. 1nu, Lanchester,
1919. 3nu, Itala, 1907. 4nu, Morris Oxford
Bullnose, 1913. 5.50nu, Lagonda LG6, 1939.
6nu, Wolseley, 1903. 8nu, Buick Super, 1952.
20nu, Maybach Zeppelin, 1933.
No. 440, Simplex, 1912. No. 441, Renault,
1901.

1984, Aug. 29   Litho.   Perf. 14

432	A58	50ch multi	.25	.25
433	A58	1nu multi	.30	.30
434	A58	3nu multi	.70	.70
435	A58	4nu multi	1.00	1.00
436	A58	5.50nu multi	1.25	1.25
437	A58	6nu multi	1.40	1.40
438	A58	8nu multi	1.60	1.60
439	A58	20nu multi	3.75	3.75
		Nos. 432-439 (8)	10.25	10.25

Souvenir Sheets

440	A58	25nu multi	5.00	5.00
441	A58	25nu multi	5.00	5.00

Summer Olympic
Games — A59

15ch, Women's archery. 25ch, Men's archery. 2nu, Table tennis. 2.25nu, Basketball.
5.50nu, Boxing. 6nu, Running. 8nu, Tennis.
25nu, Archery.

1984, Oct. 27   Litho.

442	A59	15ch multi	.25	.25
443	A59	25ch multi	.25	.25
444	A59	2nu multi	.65	.65
445	A59	2.25nu multi	.95	.95
446	A59	5.50nu multi	1.25	1.25
447	A59	6nu multi	1.50	1.50
448	A59	8nu multi	2.25	2.25
		Nos. 442-448 (7)	7.10	7.10

Souvenir Sheet

449	A59	25nu multi	6.75	6.75

For overprints see Nos. 537-544.
Exist imperf. Values unused or used: set $8;
souvenir sheet $7.

Nos. 335-339 Surcharged with New Values and Bars in Black or Silver

1985   Litho.   Perf. 14

450	A46	10nu on 3nu multi	2.50	2.25
451	A46	10nu on 5nu multi	2.50	2.25
452	A46	10nu on 15nu multi	2.50	2.25
453	A46	10nu on 20nu multi	2.50	2.25
		Nos. 450-453 (4)	10.00	9.00

Souvenir Sheet

454	A46	20nu on 25nu multi	6.00	6.00

Nos. 450-454 exist imperf. Value, set Nos.
450-453: $100.

Nos. 332, 332A, 332B, 333-334 Surcharged with New Values and Bars

1985, Feb. 28

455	A45	5nu on 1nu multi	1.45	1.30
456	A45	5nu on 10nu multi	1.45	1.30
457	A45	5nu on 15nu multi	1.45	1.30
458	A45	40nu on 25nu multi	11.00	11.00
		Nos. 455-458 (4)	15.35	14.90

Souvenir Sheet

459	A45	25nu on 20nu multi	11.00	11.00

Nos. 455-459 exist imperf.

50th Anniv.
of Donald
Duck — A60

4ch, Magician Mickey. 5ch, Slide, Donald.
Slide. 10ch, Donald's Golf Game. 20ch, Mr.
Duck Steps Out. 25ch, Lion Around. 50ch,
Alpine Climbers. 1nu, Flying Jalopy. 5nu,
Frank Duck. 20nu, Good Scouts.
No. 469, Three Caballeros. No. 470, Sea
Scouts.

1984, Dec. 10   Litho.   Perf. 13½x14

460	A60	4ch multicolored	.25	.25
461	A60	5ch multicolored	.25	.25
462	A60	10ch multicolored	.25	.25
463	A60	20ch multicolored	.25	.25
464	A60	25ch multicolored	.25	.25
465	A60	50ch multicolored	.25	.25
466	A60	1nu multicolored	.25	.25
467	A60	5nu multicolored	1.00	1.00
468	A60	20nu multicolored	4.50	4.50
		Nos. 460-468 (9)	7.25	7.25

Souvenir Sheets

469	A60	20nu multicolored	6.00	6.00
470	A60	20nu multicolored	6.00	6.00

Exist imperf. Values unused or used: set
$12; souvenir sheets each $7.

Nos. 317-321 Surcharged with New Values and Bars

1985, Feb. 28   Litho.   Perf. 14½

471	A42	10nu on 1nu multi	4.50	4.00
472	A42	10nu on 5nu multi	4.50	4.00
473	A42	10nu on 20nu multi	4.50	4.00
474	A42	10nu on 25nu multi	4.50	4.00
		Nos. 471-474 (4)	18.00	16.00

Souvenir Sheet

475	A42	30nu on 20nu multi	11.00	11.00

Nos. 471-475 exist imperf.

Nos. 361, 361A, 361B, 362-363 Surcharged with New Values and Bars

1985, Feb. 28   Perf. 14½x14

476	A45	5nu on 1nu multi	1.45	1.30
477	A45	5nu on 10nu multi	1.45	1.30
478	A45	5nu on 15nu multi	1.45	1.30
479	A45	40nu on 25nu multi	11.00	11.00
		Nos. 476-479 (4)	15.35	14.90

Souvenir Sheet

480	A45	25nu on 20nu multi	11.00	9.00

Nos. 476-480 exist imperf.

Nos. 327-331A Surcharged with New Values and Bars in Black or Silver

1985, June

481	A44	5nu on 1nu multi	2.25	2.00
482	A44	5nu on 2nu multi	2.25	2.00
483	A44	5nu on 3nu multi	2.25	2.00
484	A44	5nu on 20nu multi	2.25	2.00
		Nos. 481-484 (4)	9.00	8.00

Souvenir Sheets

485	A44	20nu on 25nu multi	4.50	4.25
485A	A44	20nu on 25nu multi	4.50	4.25

Nos. 481-485A exist imperf.

Mask Dance of
the Judgement
of Death — A61

5ch, Shinje Choegyel. 35ch, Raksh Lango.
50ch, Druelgo. 2.50nu, Pago. 3nu, Telgo. 4nu,
Due Nakcung. 5nu, Lha Karpo. 5.50nu,
Nyalbum. 6nu, Khimda Pelkyi.

1985, Apr. 27   Perf. 13½

486	A61	5ch multi	.35	.35
487	A61	35ch multi	.35	.35
488	A61	50ch multi	.35	.35
489	A61	2.50nu multi	.50	.50

490	A61	3nu multi	.70	.70
491	A61	4nu multi	.90	.90
492	A61	5nu multi	1.00	1.00
a.	Souv. sheet, #486-487, 491-492		4.50	4.50
493	A61	5.50nu multi	1.25	1.25
494	A61	6nu multi	1.40	1.40
		Nos. 486-494 (9)	6.80	6.80

For overprints see Nos. 764-772.

Monasteries
A62

10ch, Domkhar. 25ch, Shemgang. 50ch,
Chapcha. 1nu, Tashigang. 2nu, Pungthang
Chhug. 5nu, Dechhenphoda.

1984, Dec. 1   Litho.   Perf. 12

495	A62	10ch chalky blue	.30	.30
496	A62	25ch lake brown	.30	.30
497	A62	50ch brt violet	.30	.30
498	A62	1nu brown	.30	.30
499	A62	2nu red	.45	.45
500	A62	5nu olive green	1.00	1.00
		Nos. 495-500 (6)	2.65	2.65

For surcharges, see Nos. 1344-1347B.

Veteran's
War
Memorial
Building,
San
Francisco
A63

50ch, Flags of Bhutan, UN, vert. 15nu,
Headquarters, NY, vert.
25nu, UN Human Rights Declaration.

1985, Oct. 24   Litho.   Perf. 14

502	A63	50ch multicolored	.25	.25
503	A63	15nu multicolored	2.75	2.75
504	A63	20nu shown	3.75	3.75
		Nos. 502-504 (3)	6.75	6.75

Souvenir Sheet

505	A63	25nu multicolored	6.50	6.50

UN, 40th anniv.

Audubon Birth Bicentenary — A64

Illustrations of North American bird species
by Audubon: 50ch, Anas breweri. 1nu,
Lagopus lagopus. 2nu, Charadrius montanus.
3nu, Gavia stellata. 4nu, Canachites canadensis. 5nu, Mergus cucullatus. 15nu, Olor buccinator. 20nu, Bucephala clangula.
No. 514, Accipiter striatus. No. 515, Parus
bicolor.

1985

506	A64	50ch multicolored	.25	.25
507	A64	1nu multicolored	.35	.35
508	A64	2nu multicolored	.55	.55
509	A64	3nu multicolored	.60	.60
510	A64	4nu multicolored	.90	.90
511	A64	5nu multicolored	1.00	1.00
512	A64	15nu multicolored	2.50	2.50
513	A64	20nu multicolored	4.00	4.00
		Nos. 506-513 (8)	10.15	10.15

Souvenir Sheets

514	A64	20nu multicolored	5.00	5.00
515	A64	25nu multicolored	5.00	5.00

Issued: Nos. 507, 510-512, 514, 11/15; Nos.
506, 508-509, 513, 515, 12/6.
Exist imperf. Values unused or used: set
$20; souvenir sheets, each $7.50.

A Tramp Abroad, by Mark Twain (1835-1910) A65

Walt Disney animated characters. 25nu, Goofy, Mickey Mouse.

1985, Nov. 15
516	A65	50ch multicolored	.30	.25
517	A65	2nu multicolored	.50	.50
518	A65	5nu multicolored	1.10	1.10
519	A65	9nu multicolored	2.00	2.00
520	A65	20nu multicolored	4.25	4.25
		Nos. 516-520 (5)	8.15	8.10

Souvenir Sheet
521	A65	25nu multicolored	6.50	6.50

Intl. Youth Year.
For overprints see Nos. 554, 556-557.
Nos. 516-521 exist imperf.

Rapunzel, by Jacob and Wilhelm Grimm A66

Walt Disney animated characters.

1985, Nov. 15
522	A66	1nu multicolored	.25	.25
523	A66	4nu multicolored	.75	.75
524	A66	7nu multicolored	1.40	1.40
525	A66	8nu multicolored	1.75	1.75
526	A66	15nu multicolored	3.00	3.00
		Nos. 522-526 (5)	7.15	7.15

Souvenir Sheet
527	A66	25nu multicolored	6.50	6.50

No. 525 printed in sheets of 8.
For overprints see Nos. 553, 555, 558.
Nos. 522-527 exist imperf.

First South Asian Regional Cooperation Summit, Dec. 7-8, Dacca, Bangladesh A67

1985, Dec. 8 Perf. 14
528	A67	50ch multicolored	.25	.25
529	A67	5nu multicolored	1.00	1.00

Seven Precious Attributes of the Universal King — A68

1986, Feb. 12 Litho. Perf. 13x12½
530	A68	30ch Wheel	.25	.25
531	A68	50ch Gem	.25	.25
532	A68	1.25nu Queen	.25	.25
533	A68	2nu Minister	.45	.45
534	A68	4nu Elephant	.80	.80

535	A68	6nu Horse	1.25	1.25
536	A68	8nu General	1.60	1.60
		Nos. 530-536 (7)	4.85	4.85

Nos. 442-443, 445-449 Ovptd. with Medal, Winners' Names and Countries. No. 449 Ovptd. for Men's and Women's Events

15ch, Hyang Soon Seo, So. Korea. 25ch, Darrell Pace, US. 2.25nu, Gold Medal, US. 5.50nu, Mark Breland, US. 6nu, Daley Thompson, Britain. 8nu, Stefan Edberg, Sweden. No. 543, Hyang Soon Seo. No. 544, Darrel Pace.

1986, May 5 Litho. Perf. 14
537	A59	15ch multi	.25	.25
538	A59	25ch multi	.25	.25
539	A59	2.25nu multi	.45	.45
540	A59	5.50nu multi	1.10	1.10
541	A59	6nu multi	1.25	1.25
542	A59	8nu multi	1.60	1.60
		Nos. 537-542 (6)	4.90	4.90

Souvenir Sheets
543	A59	25nu multi	5.00	5.00
544	A59	25nu multi	5.00	5.00

Nos. 537-544 exist imperf.

Kilkhor Mandalas, Deities — A69

Religious art: 10ch, 1nu, Phurpa, ritual dagger. 25ch, 3nu, Amitayus in wrath. 50ch, 5nu, Overpowering Deities. 75ch, 7nu, Great Wrathful One, Guru Rinpoche.

1986, June 17 Perf. 13½
545	A69	10ch multicolored	.50	.50
546	A69	25ch multicolored	.50	.50
547	A69	50ch multicolored	.50	.50
548	A69	75ch multicolored	.50	.50
549	A69	1nu multicolored	.50	.50
550	A69	3nu multicolored	.65	.65
551	A69	5nu multicolored	1.10	1.10
552	A69	7nu multicolored	1.60	1.60
		Nos. 545-552 (8)	5.85	5.85

Nos. 525, 519, 526, 520, 521 and 527 Ovptd. with AMERIPEX '86 Emblem

1986, June 16 Litho. Perf. 14
553	A65	8nu multi	1.40	1.40
554	A65	9nu multi	2.25	2.25
555	A66	15nu multi	3.50	3.50
556	A65	20nu multi	4.50	4.50
		Nos. 553-556 (4)	11.65	11.65

Souvenir Sheets
557	A65	25nu #521	6.00	6.00
558	A66	25nu #527	6.00	6.00

Nos. 553-558 exist imperf. Value, set Nos. 553-556: $100.

Nos. 335-339 Overprinted

1986, July 23 Litho. Perf. 14
559	A46	3nu multi	1.90	1.90
560	A46	5nu multi	3.75	3.75
561	A46	15nu multi	10.00	10.00
562	A46	20nu multi	14.00	14.00
		Nos. 559-562 (4)	29.65	29.65

Souvenir Sheet
563	A46	25nu multi	15.00	15.00

Nos. 559-563 exist imperf. Value, set Nos. 559-562: $100.

A70

A71

Halley's Comet — A72

Designs: 50ch, Babylonian tablet fragments, 2349 B.C. sighting. 1nu, 17th cent. print, A.D. 66 sighting. 2nu, French silhouette art, 1835 sighting. 3nu, Bayeux Tapestry, 1066 sighting. 4nu, Woodblock, 684 sighting. 5nu, Illustration from Bybel Printen, 1650. 15nu, 1456 Sighting, Cancer constellation. 20nu, Delft plate, 1910 sighting. No. 572, Comet over Himalayas. No. 573, Comet over domed temple Dug-gye Jong.

1986, Nov. 4 Litho. Perf. 15
564	A70	50ch multicolored	.30	.30
565	A70	1nu multicolored	.30	.30
566	A71	2nu multicolored	.45	.45
567	A70	3nu multicolored	.60	.60
568	A70	4nu multicolored	.90	.90
569	A71	5nu multicolored	1.10	1.10
570	A70	15nu multicolored	3.00	3.00
571	A70	20nu multicolored	4.50	4.50
		Nos. 564-571 (8)	11.15	11.15

Souvenir Sheets
572	A72	25nu multicolored	5.00	5.00
573	A72	25nu multicolored	5.00	5.00

Exist imperf. Values unused or used: set $20; souvenir sheets, each $11.

A73

Statue of Liberty, Cent. — A74

Statue and ships: 50ch, Mircea, Romania. 1nu, Shalom, Israel. 2nu, Leonardo da Vinci, Italy. 3nu, Libertad, Argentina. 4nu, France, France. 5nu, SS United States, US. 15nu, Queen Elizabeth II, England. 20nu, Europa, West Germany. No. 582, Statue. No. 583, Statue, World Trade Center.

1986, Nov.
574	A73	50ch multicolored	.25	.25
575	A73	1nu multicolored	.25	.25
576	A73	2nu multicolored	.45	.45
577	A73	3nu multicolored	.65	.65
578	A73	4nu multicolored	.80	.80
579	A73	5nu multicolored	1.10	1.10
580	A73	15nu multicolored	3.00	3.00
581	A73	20nu multicolored	4.50	4.50
		Nos. 574-581 (8)	11.00	11.00

Souvenir Sheets
582	A74	25nu multicolored	5.00	5.00
583	A74	25nu multi, diff.	5.00	5.00

Exist imperf. Values unused or used: set $11; souvenir sheets each $6.

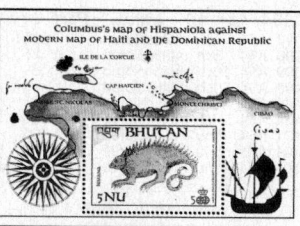

Discovery of America, 500th Anniv. — A75

20ch, Santa Maria. 25ch, Queen Isabella. 50ch, Ship, flying fish. 1nu, Columbus's coat of arms. 2nu, Christopher Columbus. 3nu, Landing in the New World.
No. 590, Pineapple. No. 591, Indian hammock. No. 592, Tobacco plant. No. 593, Flamingo. No. 594, Navigator, astrolabe, 15th cent. No. 595, Lizard. No. 596, Iguana.

1987, May 25 Litho. Perf. 14
584	A75	20ch multicolored	.90	.90
585	A75	25ch multicolored	.90	.90
586	A75	50ch multicolored	.90	.90
587	A75	1nu multicolored	1.75	1.75
588	A75	2nu multicolored	3.00	3.00
589	A75	3nu multicolored	4.50	4.50
a.		Miniature sheet of 6, #584-589	16.00	16.00
		Nos. 584-589 (6)	11.95	11.95

Souvenir Sheets
590	A75	20ch multicolored	2.50	2.50
591	A75	25ch multicolored	2.50	2.50
592	A75	50ch multicolored	2.50	2.50
593	A75	1nu multicolored	2.50	2.50
594	A75	2nu multicolored	2.50	2.50
595	A75	3nu multicolored	2.50	2.50
596	A75	5nu multicolored	2.50	2.50

All stamps are vertical except those contained in Nos. 591, 595 and 596. Stamps from No. 589a have white background.
Exist imperf. Values unused or used: $18; souvenir sheets each $4. Value No. 589a imperf, $40.

CAPEX '87 — A76

Locomotives: 50ch, Canadian Natl. U1-f. 1nu, Via Rail L.R.C. 2nu, Canadian Natl. GM GF-30t. 3nu, Canadian Natl. 4-8-4. 8nu, Canadian Pacific 4-6-2. 10nu, Via Express passenger train. 15nu, Canadian Nat. Turbotrain. 20nu, Canadian Pacific Diesel-Electric Express.
No. 605, Royal Hudson 4-6-4. No. 606, Canadian Natl. 4-8-4, diff.

1987, June 15
597	A76	50ch multicolored	.25	.25
598	A76	1nu multicolored	.25	.25
599	A76	2nu multicolored	.45	.45
600	A76	3nu multicolored	.75	.75
601	A76	8nu multicolored	1.75	1.75
602	A76	10nu multicolored	1.90	1.90
603	A76	15nu multicolored	2.50	2.50
604	A76	20nu multicolored	3.25	3.25
		Nos. 597-604 (8)	11.10	11.10

Souvenir Sheet
605	A76	50ch multicolored	5.50	5.50
606	A76	25nu multicolored	5.50	5.50

Two Faces, Sculpture by Marc Chagall (1887-1984) A77

Paintings: 1nu, At the Barber's. 2nu, Old Jew with Torah. 3nu, Red Maternity. 4nu, Eve of Yom Kippur. 5nu, The Old Musician. 6nu, The Rabbi of Vitebsk. 7nu, Couple at Dusk. 9nu, The Artistes. 10nu, Moses Breaking the Tablets of the Law. 12nu, Bouquet with Flying Lovers. 20nu, In the Sky of the Opera.
No. 619, Romeo and Juliet. No. 620, Magician of Paris. No. 621, Maternity. No. 622, The Carnival for Aleko: Scene II. No. 623,

Visit to the Grandparents. No. 624, The Smolensk Newspaper. No. 625, The Concert. No. 626, Composition with Goat. No. 627, Still Life. No. 628. The Red Gateway. No. 629, Cow with Parasol. No. 630, Russian Village.

1987, Dec. 17   Litho.   Perf. 14

| 607-618 | A77 | Set of 12 | 20.00 | 20.00 |

Size: 110x95mm

Imperf

| 619-630 | A77 | 25nu Set of 12 | 65.00 | 65.00 |

1988 Winter Olympics, Calgary — A78

Emblem and Disney animated characters as competitors in Olympic events: 50ch, Slalom. 1nu, Downhill skiing. 2nu, Ice hockey. 4nu, Biathlon. 7nu, Speed skating. 8nu, Minnie Mouse(yellow outfit) figure skating. 9nu, Minnie Mouse (red outfit) figure skating. 20nu, Bobsled.

No. 639, Ski jumping. No. 640, Ice dancing.

1988, Feb. 15   Litho.   Perf. 14

631	A78	50ch multi	.30	.30
632	A78	1nu multi	.30	.30
633	A78	2nu multi	.50	.50
634	A78	4nu multi	1.00	1.00
635	A78	7nu multi	1.75	1.75
636	A78	8nu multi	2.00	2.00
637	A78	9nu multi	2.40	2.40
638	A78	20nu multi	5.00	5.00
	Nos. 631-638 (8)		13.25	13.25

Souvenir Sheets

| 639 | A78 | 25nu multi | 6.25 | 6.25 |
| 640 | A78 | 25nu multi | 6.25 | 6.25 |

Nos. 631-640 exist imperf.

Transportation Innovations — A79

50ch, Pullman Pioneer, 1865. 1nu, Stephenson's Rocket, 1829. 2nu, Pierre L'Allement's Velocipede, 1866. 3nu, Benz Velocipede, 1886. 4nu, Volkswagen Beetle, c. 1960. 5nu, Natchez Vs. Robert E. Lee, 1870. 6nu, American La France, 1910. 7nu, USS Constitution, 1787, vert. 8nu, Bell Rocket Belt, 1961, vert. 10nu, Trevithick Locomotive, 1804. No. 651, Concorde jet. No. 652, Mallard, 1938, vert. No. 653, Shinkansen. No. 654, TGV, 1981.

1988, Mar. 31

641	A79	50ch multicolored	.25	.25
642	A79	1nu multicolored	.25	.25
643	A79	2nu multicolored	.35	.35
644	A79	3nu multicolored	.50	.50
645	A79	4nu multicolored	.60	.60
646	A79	5nu multicolored	.70	.70
647	A79	6nu multicolored	.90	.90
648	A79	7nu multicolored	1.00	1.00
649	A79	9nu multicolored	1.45	1.45
650	A79	10nu multicolored	1.50	1.50
	Nos. 641-650 (10)		7.50	7.50

Souvenir Sheets

651	A79	25nu multicolored	6.00	6.00
652	A79	25nu multicolored	6.00	6.00
653	A79	25nu multicolored	6.00	6.00
654	A79	25nu multicolored	6.00	6.00

1988 Summer Olympics, Seoul A80

50ch, Women's gymnastics. 1nu, Tae kwon do. 2nu, Shot put. 4nu, Women's volleyball. 7nu, Basketball. 8nu, Soccer. 9nu, Women's high jump. 20nu, Running.

No. 663, Archery, vert. No. 664, Fencing. Nos. 7nu-20nu are vertical stamps.

1989, Feb. 15   Litho.

655	A80	50ch multicolored	.25	.25
656	A80	1nu multicolored	.25	.25
657	A80	2nu multicolored	.35	.35
658	A80	4nu multicolored	.75	.75
659	A80	7nu multicolored	1.25	1.25
660	A80	8nu multicolored	1.50	1.50
661	A80	9nu multicolored	1.75	1.75
662	A80	20nu multicolored	3.75	3.75
	Nos. 655-662 (8)		9.85	9.85

Souvenir Sheets

| 663 | A80 | 25nu multicolored | 5.00 | 5.00 |
| 664 | A80 | 25nu multicolored | 5.00 | 5.00 |

Exist imperf. Values unused or used: set $10; souvenir sheets each $5.

Paintings by Titian — A81

Designs: 50ch, *Gentleman with a Book.* 1nu, *Venus and Cupid, with a Lute Player.* 2nu, *Diana and Actaeon.* 3nu, *Cardinal Ippolito dei Medici.* 4nu, *Sleeping Venus.* 5nu, *Venus Risen from the Waves.* 6nu, *Worship of Venus.* 7nu, *Fete Champetre.* 10nu, *Perseus and Andromeda.* 15nu, *Danae.* 20nu, *Venus at the Mirror.* 25nu, *Venus and the Organ Player.* No. 677, *The Pardo Venus,* horiz. No. 678, *Venus and Cupid, with an Organist.* No. 679, *Miracle of the Irascible Son.* No. 680, *Diana and Callisto.* No. 681, *Saint John the Almsgiver.* No. 682, *Danae with the Shower of Gold,* horiz. No. 683, *Bacchus and Ariadne.* No. 684, *Venus Blindfolding Cupid.* No. 685, *Portrait of Laura Dianti.* No. 686, *Venus of Urbino.* No. 687, *Portrait of Johann Friedrich.* No. 688, *Mater Dolorosa with Raised Hands.*

Perf. 13½x14, 14x13½

1989, Feb. 15   Litho.

665	A81	50ch multicolored	.25	.25
666	A81	1nu multicolored	.30	.30
667	A81	2nu multicolored	.50	.50
668	A81	3nu multicolored	.70	.70
669	A81	4nu multicolored	.85	.85
670	A81	5nu multicolored	1.25	1.25
671	A81	6nu multicolored	1.40	1.40
672	A81	7nu multicolored	1.60	1.60
673	A81	10nu multicolored	2.10	2.10
674	A81	15nu multicolored	3.25	3.25
675	A81	20nu multicolored	4.00	4.00
676	A81	25nu multicolored	5.00	5.00
	Nos. 665-676 (12)		21.20	21.20

Souvenir Sheets

| 677-688 | A81 | 25nu Set of 12 | 60.00 | 60.00 |

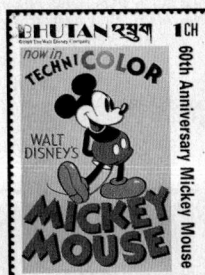

Mickey Mouse, 60th Anniv. (in 1988) — A82

Movie posters: 1ch, Mickey Mouse, 1930s. 2ch, *Barnyard Olympics,* 1932. 3ch, *Society Dog Show,* 1939. 4ch, *Fantasia,* 1980s re-release. 5ch, *The Mad Dog,* 1932. 10ch, *A Gentleman's Gentleman,* 1941. 50ch, *Symphony hour,* 1942. 10nu, *The Moose Hunt,* 1931. 15nu, *Wild Waves,* 1929. 20nu, *Mickey in Arabia,* 1932. 25nu, *Tugboat Mickey,* 1940. 30nu, *Building a Building,* 1933.

No. 701, *The Mad Doctor,* 1933. No. 702, *The Meller Drammer,* 1933. No. 703, *Ye Olden Days,* 1933. No. 704, *Mickey's Good Deed,* 1932. No. 705, *Mickey's Pal Pluto,* 1933. No. 706, *Trader Mickey,* 1932. No. 707, *Touchdown Mickey,* 1932. No. 708, *Steamboat Willie,* 1928. No. 709, *The Whoopee Party,* 1932. No. 710, *Mickey's Nightmare,* 1932. No. 711, *The Klondike Kid,* 1932. No. 712, *The Wayward Canary,* 1932.

1989, June 20   Litho.   Perf. 13½x14

| 689-700 | A82 | Set of 12 | 22.50 | 22.50 |

Souvenir Sheets

| 701-712 | A82 | 25nu Set of 12 | 65.00 | 65.00 |

Mushrooms — A83

Designs: 50ch, Tricholoma pardalotum. 1nu, Suillus placidus. 2nu, Boletus regius. 3nu, Gomphidius glutinosus. 4nu, Boletus calopus. 5nu, Suillus grevillei. 6nu, Boletus appendiculatus. 7nu, Lactarius torminosus. 10nu, Macrolepiota rhacodes. 15nu, Amanita rubescens. 20nu, Amanita phalloides. No. 724, Amanita citrina.

No. 725, Russula aurata. No. 726, Gyroporus castaneus. No. 727, Cantharellus cibarius. No. 728, Boletus rhodoxanthus. No. 729, Paxillus involutus. No. 730, Gyroporus cyanescens. No. 731, Lepista nuda. No. 732, Dentinum repandum. No. 733, Lepista saeva. No. 734, Hydnum imbricatum. No. 735, Xerocomus subtomentosus. No. 736, Russula olivacea.

1989, Aug. 22   Litho.   Perf. 14

713	A83	50ch multicolored	.25	.25
714	A83	1nu multicolored	.25	.25
715	A83	2nu multicolored	.40	.40
716	A83	3nu multicolored	.65	.65
717	A83	4nu multicolored	.80	.80
718	A83	5nu multicolored	1.00	1.00
719	A83	6nu multicolored	1.10	1.10
720	A83	7nu multicolored	1.40	1.40
721	A83	10nu multicolored	2.00	2.00
722	A83	15nu multicolored	3.00	3.00
723	A83	20nu multicolored	4.00	4.00
724	A83	25nu multicolored	5.00	5.00
	Nos. 713-724 (12)		19.85	19.85

Souvenir Sheets

725	A83	25nu multicolored	5.50	5.50
726	A83	25nu multicolored	5.50	5.50
727	A83	25nu multicolored	5.50	5.50
728	A83	25nu multicolored	5.50	5.50
729	A83	25nu multicolored	5.50	5.50
730	A83	25nu multicolored	5.50	5.50
731	A83	25nu multicolored	5.50	5.50
732	A83	25nu multicolored	5.50	5.50
733	A83	25nu multicolored	5.50	5.50
734	A83	25nu multicolored	5.50	5.50
735	A83	25nu multicolored	5.50	5.50
736	A83	25nu multicolored	5.50	5.50
	Nos. 725-736 (12)		66.00	66.00

Intl. Maritime Organization, 30th Anniv. — A84

Ships: 50ch, Spanish galleon *La Reale,* 1680. 1 nu, Submersible *Turtle,* 1776. 2nu, *Charlote Dundas,* 1802. 3nu, *Great Eastern,* c. 1858. 4nu, HMS *Warrior,* 1862. 5nu, Mississippi steamer, 1884. 6nu, *Preussen,* 1902. 7nu, USS *Arizona,* 1915. 10nu, *Bluenose,* 1921. 15nu, Steam trawler, 1925. 20nu, American liberty ship, 1943. No. 748, S.S. *United States,* 1952.

Each 25nu: No. 749, Moran tug, c. 1950. No. 750, Sinking of the *Titanic,* 1912. No. 751, U-boat, c. 1942. No. 752, Japanese warship *Yamato,* 1944. No. 753, HMS *Dreadnought.* No. 754, S.S. *Normandie,* c. 1933, and a Chinese junk. No. 755, HMS *Victory,* 1805. No. 756, USS *Monitor,* 1862. No. 757, *Cutty Sark,* 1869. No. 758, USS *Constitution.* No. 759, HMS *Resolution.* No. 760, Chinese junk.

1989, Aug. 24   Litho.   Perf. 14

737	A84	50ch multicolored	.25	.25
738	A84	1nu multicolored	.40	.40
739	A84	2nu multicolored	.75	.75
740	A84	3nu multicolored	1.00	1.00
741	A84	4nu multicolored	1.25	1.25
742	A84	5nu multicolored	1.40	1.40
743	A84	6nu multicolored	1.90	1.90
744	A84	7nu multicolored	2.00	2.00
745	A84	10nu multicolored	2.50	2.50
746	A84	15nu multicolored	3.50	3.50
747	A84	20nu multicolored	4.25	4.25
748	A84	25nu multicolored	5.75	5.75
	Nos. 737-748 (12)		24.95	24.95

Souvenir Sheets

| 749-760 | A84 | Set of 12 | 66.00 | 66.00 |

Nos. 289-291 Overprinted: WORLD / AIDS DAY

1988, Dec. 1   Litho.   Perf. 14x13½

761	A37	2nu multicolored	.60	.60
762	A37	5nu multicolored	1.40	1.40
763	A37	10nu multicolored	3.50	3.50
	Nos. 761-763 (3)		5.50	5.50

Nos. 486-494 Ovptd. in Silver: AISA-PACIFIC EXPOSITION / FUKUOKA '89

1989, Mar. 17   Perf. 13½

764	A61	5ch multicolored	.25	.25
765	A61	35ch multicolored	.25	.25
766	A61	50ch multicolored	.25	.25
767	A61	2.50nu multicolored	.45	.45
768	A61	3nu multicolored	.55	.55
769	A61	4nu multicolored	.70	.70
770	A61	5nu multicolored	.95	.95
771	A61	5.50nu multicolored	1.00	1.00
772	A61	10nu multicolored	1.10	1.10
	Nos. 764-772 (9)		5.50	5.50

Nos. 764-772 exist overprinted in Japanese. Value, set $125.

Chhukha Hydroelectric Project — A85

1988, Oct. 21   Litho.   Perf. 13½

| 773 | A85 | 50ch multicolored | .50 | .50 |

No. 773 exists imperf. Value, $40.

Jawaharlal Nehru (1889-1964), Indian Prime Minister A85a

1989, Nov. 14   Photo.   Perf. 14

| 773A | A85a | 100ch olive brown | .40 | .40 |

Denomination is shown as 1.00ch in error.

Birds A86

Designs: 50ch, Larger goldenbacked woodpecker. 1nu, Black-naped monarch. 2nu, White-crested laughing thrush. 3nu, Bloodpheasant. 4nu, Blossom-headed parakeet. 5nu, Rosy minivet. 6nu, Chestnut-headed tit babbler. 7nu, Blue pitta. 10nu, Black-naped oriole. 15nu, Green magpie. 20nu, Indian three-toed kingfisher. No. 785, Ibisbill.

Each 25nu: No. 786, Great pied hornbill. No. 787, Himalayan redbreasted falconet. No. 788, Lammergeier. No. 789, Large racket-tailed drongo. No. 790, Fire-tailed sunbird. No. 791, Indian crested swift. No. 792, White-eared pheasant. No. 793, Satyr tragopan. No. 794, Wallcreeper. No. 795, Fairy bluebird. No. 796, Little spiderhunter. No. 797, Spotted forktail. Nos. 774-779 vert.

1989, Nov. 22   Litho.   Perf. 14

774	A86	50ch multicolored	.25	.25
775	A86	1nu multicolored	.40	.40
776	A86	2nu multicolored	.75	.75
777	A86	3nu multicolored	1.00	1.00
778	A86	4nu multicolored	1.25	1.25
779	A86	5nu multicolored	1.40	1.40
780	A86	6nu multicolored	1.90	1.90
781	A86	7nu multicolored	2.00	2.00
782	A86	10nu multicolored	2.50	2.50
783	A86	15nu multicolored	3.50	3.50
784	A86	20nu multicolored	4.25	4.25
785	A86	25nu multicolored	5.75	5.75
	Nos. 774-785 (12)		24.95	24.95

Souvenir Sheets

| 786-797 | A86 | Set of 12 | 60.00 | 60.00 |

Steam Locomotives — A87

Designs: 50ch, *Best Friend of Charleston*, 1830, US 1nu, Class U, 1949, France. 2nu, *Consolidation*, 1866, US. 3nu, *Luggage Engine*, 1843, Great Britain. 4nu, Class 60-3 *Shay*, 1913, US. 5nu, *John Bull* 1831, US. 6nu, *Hercules*, 1837, US. 7nu, Eight-wheel tank engine, 1874, Great Britain. 10nu, *The Illinois*, 1852, US. 15nu, German State 4-6-4, 1935. 20nu, American Standard, 1865. No. 809, Class Ps-4, 1926, US.

Each 25nu: No. 810, *Puffing Billy*, 1814, Great Britain. No. 811, Stephenson's *Rocket*, 1829, Great Britain. No. 812, *Cumberland*, 1845, US, vert. No. 813, *John Stevens*, 1849, US, vert. No. 814, No. 22 Baldwin Locomotive Works, 1873, US. No. 815, *Ariel*, 1877, US. No. 816, 1899 *No. 1301* Webb Compound Engine, Great Britain. No. 817, 1893 *No. 999* Empire State Express. No. 818, 1923 Class K-36, US. No. 819, 1935 Class A4, Great Britain. No. 820, 1935 Class A, US. No. 821, 1943 Class P-1, US.

1990, Jan. 30

798	A87	50ch	multi	.25	.25
799	A87	1nu	multi	.25	.25
800	A87	2nu	multi	.40	.40
801	A87	3nu	multi	.65	.65
802	A87	4nu	multi	.80	.80
803	A87	5nu	multi	1.00	1.00
804	A87	6nu	multi	1.10	1.10
805	A87	7nu	multi	1.40	1.40
806	A87	10nu	multi	2.00	2.00
807	A87	15nu	multi	3.00	3.00
808	A87	20nu	multi	4.00	4.00
809	A87	25nu	multi	5.00	5.00
		Nos. 798-809 (12)		19.85	19.85

Souvenir Sheets

810-821	A87	Set of 12	60.00	60.00

Butterflies A88

Designs: 50ch, Charaxes harmodius. 1nu, Prioneris thestylis. 2nu, Sephisa chandra. 3nu, Penthema usarda. 4nu, Troides aecus. 5nu, Polyura eudamippus. 6nu, Polyura dolon. 7nu, Neope bhadra. 10nu, Delias descombesis. 15nu, Childreni childrena. 20nu, Kallima inachus. No. 833, Elymnias malelas.

No. 834, Red lacewing. No. 835, Bhutan glory. No. 836, Great eggfly. No. 837, Kaiser-I-Hind. No. 838, Chestnut tiger. No. 839, Common map. No. 840, Swallowtail. No. 841, Jungle glory. No. 842, Checkered swallowtail. No. 843, Common birdwing. No. 844, Blue banded peacock. No. 845, Camberwell beauty.

1990, Jan. 30   Litho.   Perf. 14

822	A88	50ch	multicolored	.25	.25
823	A88	1nu	multicolored	.25	.25
824	A88	2nu	multicolored	.45	.45
825	A88	3nu	multicolored	.75	.75
826	A88	4nu	multicolored	.90	.90
827	A88	5nu	multicolored	1.10	1.10
828	A88	6nu	multicolored	1.25	1.25
829	A88	7nu	multicolored	1.50	1.50
830	A88	10nu	multicolored	2.25	2.25
831	A88	15nu	multicolored	3.50	3.50
832	A88	20nu	multicolored	4.75	4.75
833	A88	25nu	multicolored	5.75	5.75
		Nos. 822-833 (12)		22.70	22.70

Souvenir Sheets

834	A88	25nu	multicolored	5.00	5.00
835	A88	25nu	multicolored	5.00	5.00
836	A88	25nu	multicolored	5.00	5.00
837	A88	25nu	multicolored	5.00	5.00
838	A88	25nu	multicolored	5.00	5.00
839	A88	25nu	multicolored	5.00	5.00
840	A88	25nu	multicolored	5.00	5.00
841	A88	25nu	multicolored	5.00	5.00
842	A88	25nu	multicolored	5.00	5.00
843	A88	25nu	multicolored	5.00	5.00
844	A88	25nu	multicolored	5.00	5.00
845	A88	25nu	multicolored	5.00	5.00
		Nos. 834-845 (12)		60.00	60.00

Nos. 822-824, 826-827, 830-831, 834-835, 844-845 are vert.

Paintings by Hiroshige A89

10ch, Plum Estate, Kameido. 20ch, Yatsumi Bridge. 50ch, Ayase River and Kanegafuchi. 75ch, View of Shiba Coast. 1nu, Grandpa's Teahouse, Meguro. 2nu, Kameido Tenjin Shrine. 6nu, Yoroi Ferry, Koami-cho. 7nu, Sakasai Ferry. 10nu, Fukagawa Lumberyards. 15nu, Suido Bridge & Surugadai. 20nu, Meguro Drum Bridge, Sunset Hill. #857, Atagoshita & Yabu Lane.

Each 25nu: No. 858, Towboats Along the Yotsugi-dori Canal. No. 859, Minowa, Kanasugi, Mikawashima. No. 860, Horikiri Iris Garden. No. 861, Fukagawa Susaki & Jumantsubo. No. 862, Suijin Shrine & Massaki on the Sumida River. No. 863, New Year's Eve Foxfires at the Changing Tree, Oji. No. 864, Nihonbashi, Clearing After Snow. No. 865, View to the North from Asukayama. No. 866, Komakata Hall & Azuma Bridge. No. 867, The City Flourishing, Tanabata Festival. No. 868, Suruga-cho. No. 869, Sudden Shower over Shin-Ohashi Bridge & Atake.

1990, May 21   Litho.   Perf. 13½

846	A89	10ch	multicolored	.25	.25
847	A89	20ch	multicolored	.25	.25
848	A89	50ch	multicolored	.25	.25
849	A89	75ch	multicolored	.25	.25
850	A89	1nu	multicolored	.25	.25
851	A89	2nu	multicolored	.40	.40
852	A89	6nu	multicolored	1.40	1.40
853	A89	7nu	multicolored	1.50	1.50
854	A89	10nu	multicolored	2.25	2.25
855	A89	15nu	multicolored	3.50	3.50
856	A89	20nu	multicolored	4.50	4.50
857	A89	25nu	multicolored	5.25	5.25
		Nos. 846-857 (12)		20.05	20.05

Souvenir Sheets

858-869	A89	Set of 12	62.50	62.50

Hirohito (1901-1989) and enthronement of Akihito as emperor of Japan.

Orchids — A90

Designs: 10ch, Renanthera monachica. 50ch, Vanda coerulea. 1nu, Phalaenopsis violacea. 2nu, Dendrobium nobile. 5nu, Vandopsis lissochiloides. 6nu, Paphiopedilum rothschildianum. 7nu, Phalaenopsis schilleriana. 9nu, Paphiopedilum insigne. 10nu, Paphiopedilum bellatulum. 20nu, Doritis pulcherrima. 25nu, Cymbidium giganteum. 35nu, Phalaenopsis mariae.

No. 882, Vanda coerulescens. No. 883, Vandopsis parishi. No. 884, Dendrobium aphyllum. No. 885, Phalaenopsis amabilis. No. 886, Paphiopedilum haynaldianum. No. 887, Dendrobium loddigesii. No. 888, Vanda alpina. No. 889, Phalaenopsis equestris. No. 890, Vanda cristata. No. 891, Phalaenopsis cornu cervi. No. 892, Paphiopedilum niveum. No. 893, Dendrobium margaritaceum.

1990, Apr. 6   Litho.   Perf. 14

870	A90	10ch	multicolored	.25	.25
871	A90	50ch	multicolored	.25	.25
872	A90	1nu	multicolored	.25	.25
873	A90	2nu	multicolored	.45	.45
874	A90	5nu	multicolored	1.00	1.00
875	A90	6nu	multicolored	1.25	1.25
876	A90	7nu	multicolored	1.40	1.40
877	A90	9nu	multicolored	1.75	1.75
878	A90	10nu	multicolored	1.90	1.90
879	A90	20nu	multicolored	3.50	3.50
880	A90	25nu	multicolored	4.25	4.25
881	A90	35nu	multicolored	5.75	5.75
		Nos. 870-881 (12)		22.00	22.00

Souvenir Sheets

882	A90	30nu	multicolored	6.00	6.00
883	A90	30nu	multicolored	6.00	6.00
884	A90	30nu	multicolored	6.00	6.00
885	A90	30nu	multicolored	6.00	6.00
886	A90	30nu	multicolored	6.00	6.00
887	A90	30nu	multicolored	6.00	6.00
888	A90	30nu	multicolored	6.00	6.00
889	A90	30nu	multicolored	6.00	6.00
890	A90	30nu	multicolored	6.00	6.00
891	A90	30nu	multicolored	6.00	6.00
892	A90	30nu	multicolored	6.00	6.00
893	A90	30nu	multicolored	6.00	6.00
		Nos. 882-893 (12)		72.00	72.00

EXPO '90 Intl. Garden and Greenery Exposition, Osaka, Apr. 1-Dec. 31.

G.P.O., Thimphu — A90a

1990, May 29   Photo.   Perf. 14

893A	A90a	1nu	multicolored	.75	.75

Penny Black, 150th Anniv. A90b

Penny Black and: 50ch, Bhutan #1. 1nu, Oldenburg #1. 2nu, Bergedorf #3. 4nu, German Democratic Republic #48. 5nu, Brunswick #1. 6nu, Basel #3L1. 8nu, Geneva #2L1. 10nu, Zurich #1L1. No. 902, France #3. 20nu, Vatican City #1. 25nu, Israel #1. No. 905, Japan #1.

Each 15nu: Penny Black and: No. 906a, Mecklenburg-Schwerin #1. b, Mecklenburg-Strelitz #1. No. 907a, Germany #5, #9. b, Prussia #2. No. 908a, Hamburg #1. b, North German Confederation #1, #7. No. 909a, Baden #1. b, Wurttemberg #1. No. 910a, Heligoland #1. b, Hanover #1. No. 911a, Thurn & Taxis #3. b, Thurn & Taxis #42. No. 912a, Schleswig-Holstein #1. b, Lubeck #5.

Each 30nu: No. 913, Saxony #1. No. 914, Berlin #9N1. No. 915, No other stamp. No. 916, US #1. No. 917, Bavaria #1.

1990, Oct. 9   Perf. 14

894	A90b	50ch	multicolored	.25	.25
895	A90b	1nu	multicolored	.25	.25
896	A90b	2nu	multicolored	.30	.30
897	A90b	4nu	multicolored	.65	.65
898	A90b	5nu	multicolored	.80	.80
899	A90b	6nu	multicolored	1.00	1.00
900	A90b	8nu	multicolored	1.25	1.25
901	A90b	10nu	multicolored	1.50	1.50
902	A90b	15nu	multicolored	2.50	2.50
903	A90b	20nu	multicolored	3.00	3.00
904	A90b	25nu	multicolored	3.75	3.75
905	A90b	30nu	multicolored	4.75	4.75
		Nos. 894-905 (12)		20.00	20.00

Souvenir Sheets
Sheets of 2 (#906-912) or 1

906-912	A90b	Set of 7	40.00	40.00
913-917	A90b	Set of 5	25.00	25.00

Stamp World London '90.

Panda Bear A91

Tiger A92

Endangered wildlife of Asia: 50ch, Panda sitting up. 1nu, Panda sitting on branch. 2nu, Panda and cub. 4nu, Panda on back eating. 6nu, Adult panda getting food with cub. 7nu, Cub laying on adult panda. 10nu, Elephant. 15nu, Adult panda by fallen tree. 20nu, Barking deer. No. 929, 25nu, Snow leopard.

No. 930, Rhinoceros. No. 931, Clouded leopard. No. 932, Asiatic wild dog. No. 933, Himalayan shou. No. 934, Golden cat. No. 935, Himalayan musk deer. No. 936, Head of panda. No. 937, Asiatic black bear. No. 938, Gaur. No. 939, Pygmy hog. No. 940, Wolf. No. 941, Sloth bear.

1990   Perf. 14

918	A91	50ch	multi	.30	.25
919	A91	1nu	multi	.40	.40
920	A91	2nu	multi	.60	.60
921	A91	3nu	shown	1.00	1.00
922	A91	4nu	multi	1.25	1.25
923	A92	5nu	shown	1.40	1.40
924	A91	6nu	multi	1.60	1.60
925	A91	7nu	multi	1.90	1.90
926	A92	10nu	multi	2.50	2.50
927	A92	15nu	multi	3.50	3.50
928	A92	20nu	multi	4.75	4.75
929	A92	25nu	multi	5.75	5.75
		Nos. 918-929 (12)		24.95	24.90

Souvenir Sheets

930	A92	25nu	multi	5.50	5.50
931	A92	25nu	multi	5.50	5.50
932	A92	25nu	multi	5.50	5.50
933	A92	25nu	multi	5.50	5.50
934	A92	25nu	multi	5.50	5.50
935	A92	25nu	multi	5.50	5.50
936	A91	25nu	multi	5.50	5.50
937	A92	25nu	multi	5.50	5.50
938	A92	25nu	multi	5.50	5.50
939	A92	25nu	multi	5.50	5.50
940	A92	25nu	multi	5.50	5.50
941	A92	25nu	multi	5.50	5.50
		Nos. 930-941 (12)		66.00	66.00

Nos. 919-920 and 927 vert.

Buddhist Musical Instruments — A93

1990, Sept. 29   Litho.   Perf. 13½x13

942	A93	10ch	Dungchen	.25	.25
943	A93	20ch	Dungkar	.25	.25
944	A93	30ch	Roim	.25	.25
945	A93	50ch	Tinchag	.25	.25
946	A93	1nu	Dradu & drilbu	.25	.25
947	A93	2nu	Gya-ling	.40	.40
948	A93	2.50nu	Nga	.50	.50
a.		Souv. sheet, #943, 945, 947-948		20.00	20.00
949	A93	3.50nu	Kang-dung	.75	.75
a.		Souv. sheet, #942, 944, 946, 949		50.00	50.00
		Nos. 942-949 (8)		2.90	2.90

Year of the Girl Child — A94

1990, Dec. 8

950	A94	50ch	shown	.25	.25
951	A94	20nu	Young girl	4.00	4.00

Wonders of the World — A95

Walt Disney characters viewing: 1ch, Temple of Artemis, Ephesus. 2ch, Statue of Zeus, Olympia. 3ch, Egyptian pyramids. 4ch, Lighthouse, Alexandria. 5ch, Mausoleum at Halicarnassus. 10ch, Colossus of Rhodes. 50ch, Hanging gardens of Babylon. 5nu, Mauna Loa volcano, Hawaii. 6nu, Carlsbad Caverns, New Mexico. 10nu, Rainbow Bridge, Utah. 15nu, Grand Canyon of the Colorado, Arizona. 20nu, Old Faithful geyser, Wyoming. 25nu, Giant sequoias, California. 30nu, Crater Lake and

Wizard Island, Oregon. 5nu, 6nu, 10nu, 15nu, 20nu, 25nu, 30nu are horiz.

Each 25nu, Walt Disney characters viewing: No. 966, Great Wall of China, horiz. No. 967, Mosque of St. Sophia, Istanbul, Turkey. No. 968, The Leaning Tower of Pisa, Italy. No. 969, Colosseum, Rome. No. 970, Stonehenge, England. No. 971, Catacombs of Alexandria, Egypt. No. 972, Porcelain Tower, Nanking, China, horiz. No. 973, The Panama Canal, horiz. No. 974, Golden Gate Bridge, San Francisco, horiz. No. 975, Sears Tower, Chicago, horiz. No. 976, Gateway Arch, St. Louis. No. 977, Alcan Highway, Alaska and Canada, horiz. No. 978, Hoover Dam, Nevada. No. 979, Empire State Building, New York.

1991, Feb. 2   Litho.   Perf. 14

952	A95	1ch multicolored	.25	.25
953	A95	2ch multicolored	.25	.25
954	A95	3ch multicolored	.25	.25
955	A95	4ch multicolored	.25	.25
956	A95	5ch multicolored	.25	.25
957	A95	10ch multicolored	.25	.25
958	A95	50ch multicolored	.25	.25
959	A95	5nu multicolored	1.40	1.40
960	A95	6nu multicolored	1.75	1.75
961	A95	10nu multicolored	2.25	2.25
962	A95	15nu multicolored	3.00	3.00
963	A95	20nu multicolored	4.25	4.25
964	A95	25nu multicolored	4.50	4.50
965	A95	30nu multicolored	6.00	6.00

Nos. 952-965 (14) 24.90 24.90

Souvenir Sheets
Perf. 14x13½, 13½x14

966-979 A95 Set of 14   63.00 63.00

Peter Paul Rubens (1577-1640), Painter A96

Entire paintings or different details from: 10ch, 5nu, 6nu, 10nu, No. 992, Atalanta and Meleager. 50ch, Fall of Phaethon. 1nu, No. 993, Feast of Venus Verticordia. 2nu, Achilles Slaying Hector. 3nu, No. 994, Arachne Punished by Minerva. 4nu, No. 995, Jupiter Receives Psyche on Olympus. 7nu, Venus in Vulcan's Furnace. 20nu, No. 996, Briseis Returned to Achilles. 30nu, No. 997, Mars and Rhea Sylvia. No. 998, Venus Shivering. No. 999, Ganymede and the Eagle. No. 1000, Origin of the Milky Way. No. 1001, Adonis and Venus. No. 1002, Hero and Leander. No. 1003, Fall of the Titans.

Nos. 992-1003, each 25nu.
Nos. 994, 996-997, 1000-1003 are horiz.

1991, Feb. 2   Litho.   Perf. 13½

980	A96	10ch multicolored	.40	.40
981	A96	50ch multicolored	.40	.40
982	A96	1nu multicolored	.50	.50
983	A96	2nu multicolored	.60	.60
984	A96	3nu multicolored	.90	.90
985	A96	4nu multicolored	1.15	1.15
986	A96	5nu multicolored	1.40	1.40
987	A96	6nu multicolored	1.50	1.50
988	A96	7nu multicolored	1.60	1.60
989	A96	10nu multicolored	2.50	2.50
990	A96	20nu multicolored	3.75	3.75
991	A96	30nu multicolored	5.50	5.50

Nos. 980-991 (12) 20.20 20.20

Souvenir Sheets

992-1003 A96 Set of 12   75.00 75.00

Vincent Van Gogh (1853-1890), Painter — A97

Paintings: 10ch, Cottages, Reminiscence of the North. 50ch, Head of a Peasant Woman with Dark Cap. 1nu, Portrait of a Woman in

Blue. 2nu, The Midwife. 8nu, Vase with Hollyhocks. 10nu, Portrait of a Man with a Skull Cap. 12nu, Agostina Segatori Sitting in the Cafe du Tambourin. 15nu, Vase with Daisies and Anemones. 18nu, Fritillaries in a Copper Vase. 20nu, Woman Sitting in the Grass. 25nu, On the Outskirts of Paris, horiz. 30nu, Chrysanthemums and Wild Flowers in a Vase.

Each 30nu: No. 1016, Le Moulin de la Galette. No. 1017, Bowl with Sunflowers, Roses and Other Flowers, horiz. No. 1018, Poppies and Butterflies. No. 1019, Trees in the Garden of Saint-Paul Hospital. No. 1020, Le Moulin de Blute Fin. No. 1021, Le Moulin de la Galette, diff. No. 1022, Vase with Peonies. No. 1023, Vase with Zinnias. No. 1024, Fishing in the Spring, Pont de Clichy, horiz. No. 1025, Village Street in Auvers, horiz. No. 1026, Vase with Zinnias and Other Flowers, horiz. No. 1027, Vase with Red Poppies.

1991, July 22   Litho.   Perf. 13½

1004	A97	10ch multicolored	.30	.30
1005	A97	50ch multicolored	.30	.30
1006	A97	1nu multicolored	.30	.30
1007	A97	2nu multicolored	.40	.40
1008	A97	8nu multicolored	1.60	1.60
1009	A97	10nu multicolored	2.00	2.00
1010	A97	12nu multicolored	2.50	2.50
1011	A97	15nu multicolored	3.00	3.00
1012	A97	18nu multicolored	4.00	4.00
1013	A97	20nu multicolored	4.25	4.25
1014	A97	25nu multicolored	5.00	5.00
1015	A97	30nu multicolored	6.25	6.25

Nos. 1004-1015 (12) 29.90 29.90

Size: 76x102mm, 102x76mm
Imperf

1016-1027 A97 Set of 12   84.00 84.00

History of World Cup Soccer — A98

Winning team pictures, plays or possible future site: 50ch, Uruguay, 1930. 1nu, Italy, 1934. 2nu, Italy, 1938. 3nu, Uruguay, 1950. 5nu, West Germany, 1954. 10nu, Brazil, 1958. 20nu, Brazil, 1962. 25nu, England, 1966. 29nu, Brazil, 1970. 30nu, West Germany, 1974. 31nu, Argentina, 1978. 32nu, Italy, 1982. 33nu, Argentina, 1986. 34nu, West Germany, 1990. 35nu, Los Angeles Coliseum, 1994.

Players, each 30nu: No. 1043, Claudio Caniggia, Argentina, vert. No. 1044, Salvatore Schillaci, Italy, vert. No. 1045, Roberto Baggio, Italy, vert. No. 1046, Peter Shilton, England, vert. No. 1047, Lothar Matthaus, West Germany, vert. No. 1048, Paul Gascoigne, England, vert.

1991, Aug. 1   Litho.   Perf. 13½

1028	A98	50ch multi	.25	.25
1029	A98	1nu multi	.25	.25
1030	A98	2nu multi	.35	.35
1031	A98	3nu multi	.60	.60
1032	A98	5nu multi	.90	.90
1033	A98	10nu multi	1.90	1.90
1034	A98	20nu multi	3.75	3.75
1035	A98	25nu multi	4.50	4.50
1036	A98	29nu multi	5.50	5.50
1037	A98	30nu multi	5.50	5.50
1038	A98	31nu multi	5.75	5.75
1039	A98	32nu multi	6.00	6.00
1040	A98	33nu multi	6.25	6.25
1041	A98	34nu multi	6.25	6.25
1042	A98	35nu multi	6.50	6.50

Nos. 1028-1042 (15) 54.25 54.25

Souvenir Sheets

1043-1048 A98 Set of 6   40.00 40.00

Nos. 1028-1042 and 1043-1048 exist imperf. These were unauthorized but inadvertently sent to Bhutan and distributed. Values, set: $225 and $400, respectively.

Phila Nippon '91 — A99

1991, Nov. 16   Perf. 13

1049 A99 15nu multicolored   3.50 3.50

Education in Bhutan A100

1992, Mar. 5   Photo.   Perf. 13½

1050 A100 1nu multicolored   1.00 1.00

A101

1992 Summer Olympics, Barcelona — A102

1992, July 24   Litho.   Perf. 12

1051 A101 25nu Pair, #a.-b.   4.50 4.50

Souvenir Sheet

1052 A102 25nu Archer   3.50 3.50

German Reunification — A103

1992, Oct. 3   Litho.   Perf. 12

1053 A103 25nu multicolored   1.50 1.50

Souvenir Sheet

1054 A103 25nu multicolored   1.50 1.50

Stamp from No. 1054 does not have white inscription or border.

Bhutan Postal Service, 30th Anniv. A104

Designs: 1nu, Mail truck, plane. 3nu, Letter carrier approaching village. 5nu, Letter carrier emptying mail box.

1992, Oct. 9

1055	A104	1nu multicolored	.30	.30
1056	A104	3nu multicolored	.40	.40
1057	A104	5nu multicolored	.75	.75

Nos. 1055-1057 (3) 1.45 1.45

Environmental Protection — A105

Designs: a, 7nu, Red panda. b, 20nu, Takin. c, 15nu, Black-necked crane, blue poppy. d, 10nu, One-horned rhinoceros.

1993, July 1   Litho.   Perf. 14

1058 A105 Sheet of 4, #a.-d.   9.00 9.00

No. 1058 was delayed from its originally scheduled release in 1992, although some examples were made available to the trade at that time.

Ship — A106

1992, Sept. 18   Perf. 12

| 1059 | A106 | 15nu shown | 2.50 | 2.50 |
| 1060 | A106 | 20nu Portrait | 3.25 | 3.25 |

Souvenir Sheet

1061 A106 25nu like #1060   5.00 5.00

Discovery of America, 500th anniv. Stamp from No. 1061 does not have silver inscription or white border.

A107

Reign of King Jigme Singye Wangchuk, 20th Anniv.: a, 1nu, Man tilling field, factory. b, 5nu, Airplane. c, 10nu, House, well. d, 15nu, King.
20nu, People, flag, King, horiz.

1992, Nov. 11   Litho.   Perf. 12

1062 A107 Block of 4, #a.-d.   6.00 6.00

Souvenir Sheet

1063 A107 20nu multicolored   6.00 6.00

Intl. Volunteer Day — A108

a, 1.50nu, White inscription. b, 9nu, Green inscription. c, 15nu, Red inscription.

1992, Dec. 5   Litho.   Perf. 14
1067 A108 Block of 4, #a.-c. +
             label   5.00   5.00

Medicinal
Plants — A109

1.50nu, Meconopsis grandis prain. 7nu, Meconopsis sp. 10nu, Meconopsis wallichii. 12nu, Meconopsis horridula. 20nu, Meconopsis discigera.
25nu, Meconopsis horridula, diff.

1993, Jan. 1   Litho.   Perf. 12
1068 A109 1.50nu multicolored .40   .40
1069 A109 7nu multicolored   1.10 1.10
1070 A109 10nu multicolored   1.40 1.40
1071 A109 12nu multicolored   1.90 1.90
1072 A109 20nu multicolored   3.25 3.25
      Nos. 1068-1072 (5)   8.05 8.05

Souvenir Sheet
1073 A109 25nu multicolored   6.00 6.00

Miniature Sheet

Lunar New Year — A110

1993, Feb. 22   Litho.   Perf. 14
1074 A110 25nu multicolored   7.75 7.75
Exists with overprint "ROCKPEX '93 KAOH-SIUNG" in sheet margin.

No. 1074 Surcharged "TAIPEI '93" in Silver and Black

1993, Aug. 14   Litho.   Perf. 14
1075 A110 30nu on 25nu   7.75 7.75

Paintings
A111

Designs: No. 1076, 1ch, No. 1081, 15ch, No. 1086, 1nu, The Love Letter, by Jean-Honoré Fragonard. No. 1077, 2ch, No. 1082, 25ch, No. 1087, 1.25nu, The Writer, by Vittore Carpaccio. No. 1078, 3ch, No. 1083, 50ch, No. 1088, 2nu, Mademoiselle Lavergne, by Jean-Etienne Liotard. No. 1079, 5ch, No. 1084, 60ch, No. 1089, 3nu, Portrait of Erasmus, by Hans Holbein, the Younger. No. 1080, 10ch, No. 1085, 80ch, No. 1090, 6nu, Woman Writing a Letter, by Gerard Terborch.
Color of frames and text outlines: Nos. 1076-1080, bronze, Nos. 1081-1085, silver, Nos. 1086-1090, gold.

1993, May 2   Photo.   Perf. 13½
1076-1090 A111 Set of 15   8.00   —
1090a Souvenir sheet, #1088-
       1089, with bronze frames
       and text outlines, perf.   6.50   —
Nos. 1076-1090, 1090a were prepared and distributed in 1974 but were not made valid until 1993. Nos. 1076-1090 exist imperf. Value, set $15. No. 1090a exists imperf. Value, $6.50. Nos. 1088-1090 are air mail.

Door
Gods — A112

1.50nu, Namtheo-Say. 5nu, Pha-Ke-Po. 10nu, Chen-Mi-Jang. 15nu, Yul-Khor-Sung.

1993, Dec. 17   Litho.   Perf. 12
1091 A112 1.50nu multi   .35   .35
1092 A112 5nu multi   .95   .95
1093 A112 10nu multi   1.90 1.90
1094 A112 15nu multi   2.75 2.75
      Nos. 1091-1094 (4)   5.95 5.95

Flowers — A113

Designs: a, Rhododendron mucronatum. b, Anemone rupicola. c, Polemonium coeruleum. d, Rosa marophylla. e, Paraquilegia microphylla. f, Aquilegia nivalis. g, Geranium wallichianum. h, Rhododendron campanulatum. i, Viola suavis. j, Cyananthus lobatus.
13nu, Red flower, horiz.

1994, Jan. 1   Perf. 13
1095   Strip of 10   10.00 10.00
  a. A113 1nu multicolored   .30   .25
  b. A113 1.5nu multicolored .30   .25
  c. A113 2nu multicolored   .35   .25
  d. A113 2.5nu multicolored .35   .25
  e. A113 4nu multicolored   .40   .30
  f. A113 5nu multicolored   .75   .40
  g. A113 6nu multicolored 1.00   .50
  h. A113 7nu multicolored 1.25   .60
  i. A113 9nu multicolored 1.50   .70
  j. A113 10nu multicolored 2.00 1.00

Souvenir Sheet
1096 A113 13nu multicolored 3.50 3.50

New Year
1994 (Year of the Dog) — A114

1994, Feb. 11   Litho.   Perf. 14
1097 A114 11.50nu multi   1.75 1.75

Souvenir Sheet
1098 A114 20nu like #1097   3.50 3.50
      Hong Kong '94.

Stamp Cards — A115

Designs: 16nu, Tagtshang Monastery. 20nu, Map of Bhutan.

Rouletted 26 on 2 or 3 Sides
1994, Aug. 15   Litho.
Self-Adhesive
Cards of 6 + 6 labels
1099 A115 16nu #a.-f.   12.00 12.00
1100 A115 20nu #a.-f.   13.00 13.00

Individual stamps measure 70x9mm and have a card backing. Se-tenant labels inscribed "AIR MAIL."

Souvenir Sheet

First Manned Moon Landing, 25th Anniv. — A116

a, 30nu, Astronaut on moon. b, 36nu, Space shuttle, earth, moon.

1994, Nov. 11   Litho.   Perf. 14x14½
1101 A116 Sheet of 2, #a.-b. 12.00 12.00

Nos. 1101a, 1101b have holographic images. Soaking in water may affect the holograms.

Souvenir Sheet

Victory Over Tibet-Mongol Army, 350th Anniv. — A117

Battle scene: a, Mounted officer. b, Hand to hand combat, soldiers in yellow or blue armor. c, Soldier on gray horse. d, Soldiers in red, drummer, horn player.

1994, Dec. 17   Litho.   Perf. 12½
Granite Paper
1102 A117 15nu Sheet of 4,
            #a.-d.   6.00 6.00

Souvenir Sheet

Bridges — A118

a, 15nu, Tower Bridge, London, cent. b, 16nu, Wangdue Bridge, Bhutan, 250th anniv.

1994, Nov. 11   Perf. 12
1103 A118 Sheet of 2, #a.-b. 4.50 4.50

1994 World Cup Soccer
Championships, US — A119

1994, July 17   Litho.   Perf. 12
1104 A119 15nu multicolored 2.00 2.00

Souvenir Sheet

World Tourism Year — A120

Scenes of Bhutan: a, 1.50nu, Paro Valley. b, 5nu, Chorten Kora. c, 10nu, Thimphu Tshechu. d, 15nu, Wangdue Tshechu.

1995, Apr. 2   Litho.   Perf. 12
1105 A120 Sheet of 4, #a.-d. 5.00 5.00

Miniature Sheet

New Year 1995 (Year of the Boar) — A121

Symbols of Chinese Lunar New Year: a, 10ch, Rat. b, 20ch, Ox. c, 30ch, Tiger. d, 40ch, Rabbit. e, 1nu, Dragon. f, 2nu, Snake. g, 3nu, Horse. h, 4nu, Sheep. i, 5nu, Monkey. j, 7nu, Rooster. k, 8nu, Dog. l, 9nu, Boar.
10nu, Wood Hog.

1995, Mar. 2
1106 A121 Sheet of 12,
            #a.-l.   6.00 6.00

Souvenir Sheet
1107 A121 10nu multicolored 2.00 2.00
No. 1107 is a continuous design.

A122

Flowers: 9nu, Pleione praecox. 10nu, Primula calderina. 16nu, Primula whitei. 18nu, Notholirion macrophyllum.

1995, May 2   Litho.   Perf. 12
1108-1111 A122 Set of 4   5.50 5.50

A123

UN, 50th Anniv.: a, Human resources development. b, Health & population. c, Water & sanitation. d, Transport & communications. e, Forestry & environment. f, Peace & security. g, UN in Bhutan.

1995, June 26			Perf. 14	
1112		Strip of 7	8.00	8.00
a.	A123	1.5nu multicolored	.25	.25
b.	A123	9nu multicolored	.35	.35
c.	A123	10nu multicolored	.50	.50
d.	A123	5nu multicolored	.60	.60
e.	A123	16nu multicolored	.75	.75
f.	A123	18nu multicolored	1.00	1.00
g.	A123	11.5nu multicolored	1.25	1.25

Miniature Sheet of 6

Singapore '95 — A124

Birds — No. 1113: a, 1nu, Himalayan pied kingfisher. b, 2nu, Blyth's tragopan. c, 3nu, Long-tailed minivet. d, 10nu, Red junglefowl. e, 15nu, Black-capped sibia. f, 20nu, Red-billed chough.
No. 1114, Black-neck crane.

1995, June 2		Litho.	Perf. 12	
1113	A124	#a.-f. + 3 labels	3.50	3.50
		Souvenir Sheet		
1114	A124	20nu multicolored	2.50	2.50

Traditional Crafts — A125

1nu, Drying parchment. 2nu, Making tapestry. 3nu, Restoring archaeological finds. 10nu, Weaving textiles. 15nu, Sewing garments. No. 1120, 20nu, Carving wooden vessels.
No. 1121, Mosaic.

1995, Aug. 15		Litho.	Perf. 14	
1115-1120	A125	Set of 6	5.50	5.50
		Souvenir Sheet		
1121	A125	20nu multicolored	3.25	3.25

New Year 1996 (Year of the Rat) — A126

Designs: a, Monkey. b, Rat, fire. c, Dragon.

1996, Jan. 1		Litho.	Perf. 14	
1122	A126	10nu Sheet of 3, #a.-c.	4.00	4.00

Butterflies A127

a, 2nu, Blue pansy. b, 3nu, Blue peacock. c, 5nu, Great Mormon. d, 10nu, Fritillary. e, 15nu, Blue duke. f, 25nu, Brown Gorgon.
No. 1124, 30nu, Xanthomelas. No. 1124A, 30 nu, Fivebar swordtail.

1996, May 2		Litho.	Perf. 14	
1123	A127	Sheet of 6, #a.-f.	6.00	6.00
		Souvenir Sheets		
1124-1124A	A127	Set of 2	6.50	6.50

1996 Summer Olympic Games, Atlanta A128

5nu, Silver 300n coin, soccer. 7nu, Silver 300n coin, basketball. 10nu, Gold 5s coin, judo. 15nu, Archery.

1996, June 15		Litho.	Perf. 14	
1125-1127	A128	Set of 3	3.00	3.00
		Souvenir Sheet		
1128	A128	15nu multicolored	3.50	3.50

Olymphilex '96.

Folktales — A129

Designs: a, 1nu, The White Bird. b, 2nu, Sing Sing Lhamo and the Moon. c, 3nu, The Hoopoe. d, 5nu, The Cloud Fairies. e, 10nu, The Three Wishes. f, 20nu, The Abominable Snowman.

1996, Apr. 15			Perf. 12	
1129	A129	Sheet of 6, #a.-f.	3.00	3.00
		Souvenir Sheet		
1130	A129	25nu like #1129d	3.00	3.00

Locomotives — A130

No. 1131, each 20nu: a, 0-6-4 Tank engine (Chile). b, First Pacific locomotive in Europe (France). c, 4-6-0 Passenger engine (Norway). d, Atlantic type express (Germany). e, 4-Cylinder 4-6-0 express (Belgium). f, Standard type "4" diesel-electric (England).
No. 1132, each 20nu: a, Standard 0-6-0 Goods engine (India). b, Main-line 1,900 horsepower diesel-electric (Finland). c, 0-8-0 Shunting tank engine (Russia). d, Alco "PA-1" diesel-electric (US). e, "C11" Class 2-6-4 branch passenger tank engine (Japan). f, "Settebello" deluxe high-speed electric train (Italy).
No. 1133, 70nu, Class "KD" 0-6-0 Goods locomotive, 1900 (Sweden). No. 1134, 70nu, Shinkansen "New Railway" series 200 (Japan).

1996, Nov. 25		Litho.	Perf. 14	
		Sheets of 6, #a-f		
1131-1132	A130	Set of 2	20.00	20.00
		Souvenir Sheets		
1133-1134	A130	Set of 2	15.00	15.00

Penny Black — A131

Litho. & Embossed

1996, Dec. 17			Perf. 13½	
1135	A131	140nu black & gold	10.00	10.00

A132

Winter Olympic Medalists: 10nu, Vegard Ulvang, cross-country skiing, 1992. 15nu, Kristi Yamaguchi, figure skating, 1992. 25nu, Markus Wasmeier, giant slalom, 1994. 30nu, Georg Hackl, luge, 1992.
No. 1140: a, Andreas Ostler, 2-man bobsled, 1952. b, Wolfgang Hoppe, 4-man bobsled, 1984. c, Stein Eriksen, giant slalom, 1952. d, Alberto Tomba, giant slalom, 1988.
Each 70nu: No. 1141, Henri Oreiller, downhill, 1948. No. 1142, Eduard Scherrer, 4-man bobsled, 1924.

1997, Jan. 1			Perf. 14	
1136-1139	A132	Set of 4	7.50	7.50
1140	A132	15nu Strip of 4, #a.-d.	5.50	5.50
		Souvenir Sheets		
1141-1142	A132	Set of 2	14.50	14.50

No. 1140 was issued in sheets of 8 stamps.

Insects and Arachnids — A133

a, 1ch, Apis laboriosa smith. b, 2ch, Neptunides polychromus. c, 3ch, Conocephalus maculctus. d, 4ch, Blattidae. e, 5ch, Dytiscus marginalis. f, 10ch, Dynastes hercules. g, 15ch, Hippodamia. h, 20ch, Sarcophaga haemorrhoidalis. i, 25ch, Lucanus cervus. j, 30ch, Caterpillar. k, 35ch, Lycia hirtaria. l, 40ch, Clytarlus pennatus. m, 45ch, Ephemera denica. n, 50ch, Gryllus campestris. o, 60ch, Deilephila elpenor. p, 65ch, Gerris. q, 70ch, Agrion splendens. r, 80ch, Tachyta nana. s, 90ch, Eurydema pulchra. t, 1nu, Hadrurus hirsutus. u, 1.50nu, Vespa germanica. v, 2nu, Pyrops. w, 2.50nu, Mantis religiosa. x, 3nu, Araneus diadematus. y, 3.50nu, Atrophaneura.
15nu, Melolontha.

1997, Jan. 15			Perf. 13	
1143	A133	Sheet of 25, #a.-y.	6.50	6.50
		Souvenir Sheet		
1144	A133	15nu multicolored	4.00	4.00

Hong Kong '97 — A134

Wildlife: a, Thalarctos maritimus. b, Phascolarctos cinereus. c, Selenarctos thibetanus. d, Ailurus fulgens.
20nu, Ailuropoda melanoleuca.

1997, Feb. 1		Litho.	Perf. 14	
1145	A134	10nu Sheet of 4, #a.-d.	5.50	5.50
		Souvenir Sheet		
1146	A134	20nu multicolored	3.50	3.50

Signs of the Chinese Zodiac — A135

No. 1147: a, 1ch, Mouse. b, 2ch, Ox. c, 3ch, Tiger. d, 4ch, Rabbit. e, 5nu, Dragon. f, 6nu, Snake. g, 7nu, Horse. h, 8nu, Sheep. i, 90ch, Monkey. j, 10nu, Rooster. k, 11nu, Dog. l, 12nu, Pig.
20nu, Ox, diff.

1997, Feb. 8		Litho.	Perf. 14	
1147	A135	Sheet of 12, #a.-l. + label	9.50	9.50
		Souvenir Sheet		
1148	A135	20nu multicolored	5.50	5.50

Fauna A136

Cuon alpinus: No. 1149: a, Adult, hind legs off ground. b, Adult walking right. c, Mother nursing young. d, Two seated.
Endangered species: No. 1150: a, Lynx. b, Red panda. c, Takin. d, Musk deer. e, Snow leopard. f, Golden langur. g, Tiger. h, Muntjac. i, Marmot.
No. 1151, 70nu, Pseudois nayaur. No. 1152, 70nu, Ursus thibetanus.

1997, Apr. 24				
1149	A136	10nu Block or strip of 4, #a.-d.	5.50	5.50
1150	A136	10nu Sheet of 9, #a.-i.	8.00	8.00
		Souvenir Sheets		
1151-1152	A136	Set of 2	14.50	14.50

World Wildlife Fund (No. 1149). No. 1149 issued in sheets of 12 stamps.

UNESCO,
50th Anniv.
A137

No. 1153: a, Mount Hungshan, China. b, Mausoleum of first Qin Emperor, China. c, Imperial Bronze Dragon, China. d, Tikal Natl. Park, Guatemala. e, Evora, Portugal. f, Shirakami-Sanchi, Japan. g, Paris, France. h, Valley Below the Falls, Plitvice Lakes Natl. Park, Croatia.

Sites in Germany: No. 1154: a, Cathedral, Bamberg. b, Bamberg. c, St. Michael's Church, Hildesheim. d, Potsdam Palace. e, Potsdam Church. f, Lubeck. g, Quedlinberg. h, Benedictine Church, Lorsch.

No. 1155, 60nu, Goslar, Germany, horiz. No. 1156, 60nu, Cathedral, Comenzada, Portugal, horiz.

1997, May 15   Sheets of 8 + Label
1153 A137 10nu #a.-h.   9.00 9.00
1154 A137 15nu #a.-h.   11.00 11.00
Souvenir Sheets
1155-1156 A137 Set of 2   13.50 13.50

Chernobyl
Disaster,
10th Anniv.
A138

1997, May 2   Litho.   Perf. 13½x14
1157 A138 35nu UNESCO   4.75 4.75

Dogs — A139

Designs: 10nu, Dalmatian. 15nu, Siberian husky. 20nu, Saluki. 25nu, Shar pei.
No. 1162: a, Dandie Dinmont terrier. b, Chinese crested. c, Norwich terrier. d, Basset hound. e, Cardigan welsh corgi. f, French bulldog.
60nu, Hovawart.

1997, July 15   Perf. 14
1158-1161 A139 Set of 4   5.00 5.00
1162 A139 20nu Sheet of 6, #a.-f.   9.00 9.00
Souvenir Sheet
1163 A139 60nu multicolored   4.50 4.50

Cats — A140

Designs: 10nu, Turkish angora. 15nu, Oriental shorthair. 20nu, British shorthair. 25nu, Burmese.
No. 1168: a, Japanese bobtail. b, Ceylon. c, Exotic. d, Rex. e, Ragdoll. f, Russian blue.

60nu, Tonkinese.

1997, July 15
1164-1167 A140 Set of 4   5.00 5.00
1168 A140 15nu Sheet of 6, #a.-f.   9.00 9.00
Souvenir Sheet
1169 A140 60nu multicolored   4.50 4.50

1998 World
Cup Soccer,
France
A141

English players: 5nu, Pearce. 10nu, Gascoigne. 15nu, Beckham. 20nu, McManaman. 25nu, Adams. 30nu, Ince.
World Cup captains, horiz.: No. 1176: a, Maradona, Argentina, 1986. b, Alberto, Brazil, 1970. c, Dunga, Brazil, 1994. d, Moore, England, 1966. e, Walter, Germany, 1954. f, Matthaus, Germany, 1990. g, Beckenbauer, Germany, 1974. h, Passarella, Argentina, 1978.
Winning teams, horiz.: No. 1177: a, Italy, 1938. b, W. Germany, 1954. c, Uruguay, 1958. d, England, 1966. e, Argentina, 1978. f, Brazil, 1962. g, Italy, 1934. h, Brazil, 1970. i, Uruguay, 1930.
No. 1178, 35nu, Philippe Albert, Belgium. No. 1179, 35nu, Salvatore (Toto) Schillaci, Italy, horiz.

Perf. 13½x14, 14x13½
1997, Oct. 9   Litho.
1170-1175 A141 Set of 6   8.00 8.00
Sheets of 8 or 9
1176 A141 10nu #a.-h. + label   6.25 6.25
1177 A141 10nu #a.-i.   7.00 7.00
Souvenir Sheets
1178-1179 A141 Set of 2   8.75 8.75

Friendship
Between India
and Bhutan
A142

3nu, Jawaharlal Nehru, King Jigme Dorji Wangchuk. 10nu, Rajiv Gandhi, King Jigme Singye Wangchuk.
20nu, Indian Pres. R. V. Venkataraman, King Jigme Singye Wangchuk.

1998   Litho.   Perf. 13x13½
1180 A142 3nu multicolored   .40   .40
1181 A142 10nu multicolored   .90   .90
Souvenir Sheet
1182 A142 20nu multicolored   2.00 2.00
No. 1182 contains one 76x35mm stamp.

A143

Indepex '97: No. 1183: a, 3nu, Buddha seated with legs crossed. b, 15nu, Buddha seated with legs down. c, 7nu, Gandhi with hands folded. d, 10nu, Gandhi.
No. 1184, 15nu, Buddha. No. 1185, 15nu, Gandhi holding staff.

1998   Perf. 13½x13
1183 A143 Sheet of 4, #a.-d.   2.50 2.50
Souvenir Sheets
1184-1185 A143 Set of 2   3.50 3.50
India's independence, 50th anniv.

A144

New Year 1998 (Year of the Tiger): 3nu, Stylized tiger walking right.
Tigers: No. 1187: a, 5nu, Lying down. b, 15nu, Adult walking forward. c, 17nu, Cub walking over rocks.
20nu, Adult up close.

1998, Feb. 28   Litho.   Perf. 14
1186 A144 3nu multicolored   .25   .25
1187 A144 Sheet of 4, #a.-c., #1186   3.50 3.50
Souvenir Sheet
1188 A144 20nu multicolored   2.40 2.40

WHO,
50th
Anniv.
A145

1998, Apr. 7   Litho.   Perf. 13½
1189 A145 3nu multicolored   .25   .25
1190 A145 10nu multicolored   .70   .70
Souvenir Sheet
Perf. 14
1191 A145 15nu Mother, child   1.10 1.10
Safe Motherhood. No. 1191 contains one 35x35mm stamp.

Mother Teresa
(1910-97)
A146

No. 1191A, Mother Teresa, Princess Diana. No. 1192: a, Portrait (shown). b, Holding child. c, Holding starving infant. d, Seated among nuns. e, Looking down at sick. f, With hands folded in prayer. g, With Pope John Paul II. h, Portrait, diff.
No. 1193: a, like No. 1191A. b, like No. 1192g.

1998, May 25   Litho.   Perf. 13½
1191A A146 10nu multi   4.50 4.50
1192 A146 10nu Sheet of 9, #a.-h., 1191A   9.00 9.00
Souvenir Sheet of 2
1193 A146 25nu #a.-b.   3.00 3.00
No. 1192 exists imperf. Value, $40.
No. 1193 contains two 38x43mm stamps.

Birds — A147

No. 1194: a, 10ch, Red-billed chough. b, 30ch, Great hornbill. c, 50ch, Singing lark. d, 70ch, Chestnut-flanked white-eye. e, 90ch, Magpie-robin. f, 1nu, Mrs. Gould's sunbird. g, 2nu, Tailorbird. h, 3nu, Duck. i, 5nu, Spotted cuckoo. j, 7nu, Gold crest. k, 9nu, Common mynah. l, 10nu, Green cochoa.
15nu, Turtle dove.

1998, July 28   Litho.   Perf. 13
1194 A147 Sheet of 12, #a.-l.   5.00 5.00
Souvenir Sheet
1195 A147 15nu multicolored   2.00 2.00
No. 1195 contains one 40x30mm stamp.

New Year
1999 (Year
of the
Rabbit)
A148

4nu, White rabbit. 15nu, Brown rabbit. 20nu, Rabbit facing forward.

1999, Jan. 1   Litho.   Perf. 13
1196 A148 4nu multi   .35   .35
1197 A148 16nu multi   1.25 1.25
Souvenir Sheet
Perf. 13½
1198 A148 20nu multi   2.25 2.25
No. 1198 contains one 35x35mm stamp.

King Jigme Singye Wangchuk, 25th
Anniv. of Coronation — A149

Various portraits, background color — No. 1199: a, Blue. b, Yellow. c, Orange. d, Green. No. 1200, Bright pink background.

1999, June 2   Litho.   Perf. 12¼
1199 A149 25nu Sheet of 4, #a.-d.   7.00 7.00
Souvenir Sheet
1200 A149 25nu multicolored   1.90 1.90

Trains
A150

Designs: 5nu, Early German steam. 10nu, EID 711 electric. 20nu, Steam engine. 30nu, Trans Europe Express, Germany.
No. 1205: a, Bullet train, Japan, 1964. b, 2-D-2 Class 26, South Africa, 1953. c, Super Chief, US, 1946. d, Magleus Magnet, Japan, 1991. e, The Flying Scotsman, UK, 1922. f, Kodama Train, Japan, 1958. g, Blue Train, South Africa, 1969. h, Inter-City, Germany, 1960. i, High Speed ET 403, Germany, 1973. j, US Standard 4-4-0, 1855. k, Bayer Garratt, South Africa, 1954. l, Settebello train, Italy, 1953.
No. 1206, each 15nu: a, Diesel-electric, France. b, 6-4-4-6 Pennsylvania RR, US. c, 2-8-2 Steam, Germany. d, Amtrak, US. e, GS&W 2-2-2, Britain. f, Class P steam, Denmark. g, French electric. h, First Japanese locomotive. i, 2-8-2 Germany.
No. 1207, each 15nu: a, Pacific Class 01, Germany. b, Neptune Express, Germany. c, 4-4-0 Steam, Britain. d, Shovelnose streamliner, US. e, German electric. f, Early steam, Germany. g, Union Pacific, US. h, Borsig steam, Germany, 1881. i, Borsig 4-6-4, Germany.
No. 1208, 80nu, Union Pacific electric locomotive E2 streamliner, US. No. 1209, 80nu, Great Northern diesel electric streamliner, US.

1999, July 21   Perf. 14
1201-1204 A150 Set of 4   4.50 4.50
Sheet of 12
1205 A150 10nu Sheet of 12, #a.-l.   6.00 6.00
Sheets of 9
1206-1207 A150 Set of 2   13.50 13.50
Souvenir Sheets
1208-1209 A150 Set of 2   8.00 8.00

Paintings by
Hokusai
(1760-1849)
A151

Details or entire paintings — No. 1210, each 15nu: a, Suspension Bridge Between Hida and Etchu. b, Drawings of Women (partially nude). c, Exotic Beauty. d, The Poet Nakamaro in China. e, Drawings of Women (clothed). f, Chinese Poet in Snow.

No. 1211, each 15nu: a, Festive Dancers (with umbrella). b, Drawings of Women (holding book). c, Festive Dancers (man wearing checked pattern). d, Festive Dancers (person wearing black outfit). e, Drawings of Women (holding baby). f, Festive Dancers (woman with scarf tied under chin).

No. 1212, horiz., each 15nu: a, Mount Fuji Seen Above Mist on the Tama River. b, Mount Fuji Seen from Shichirigahama. c, Sea Life (turtle). d, Sea Life (fish). e, Mount Fuji Reflected in a Lake. f, Mount Fuji Seen Through the Piers of Mannenbashi.

Each 80nu: No. 1213, The Lotus Pedestal. No. 1214, Kushunoki Masashige. No. 1215, Peasants Leading Oxen.

1999, July 27   Perf. 13½x14, 14x13½
Sheets of 6
1210-1212 A151 Set of 3   18.00 18.00
Souvenir Sheet
1213-1215 A151 Set of 3   18.00 18.00

Souvenir Sheet

IBRA '99,
Nuremberg
A152

a, 35nu, City view. b, 40nu, Show emblem.

1999, Apr. 27   Litho.   Perf. 13¾
1216 A152 Sheet of 2, #a.-b.   4.50 4.50

Prehistoric Animals — A153

No. 1217, each 10nu: a, Pterodactylus, Brachiosaurus. b, Pteranodon. c, Anurognathus, Tyrannosaurus. d, Brachiosaurus. e, Corythosaurus. f, Iguanodon. g, Lesothosaurus. h, Allosaurus. i, Velociraptor. j, Triceratops. k, Stegosaurus. l, Compsognathus.

No. 1218, each 10nu: a, Tyrannosaurus, black inscriptions b, Dimorphodon. c, Diplodocus. d, Pteranodon. e, Tyrannosaurus, white inscriptions. f, Edmontosaurus. g, Apatosaurus. h, Deinonychus. i, Hypsilophodon. j, Oviraptor. k, Stegosaurus, diff. l, Triceratops, diff.

No. 1219: a, Moeritherium. b, Platybelodon. c, Wooly mammoth. d, African elephant. e, Deinonychus, diff. f, Dimorphodon, diff. g, Archaeopteryx. h, Ring-necked pheasant.

Each 80nu: No. 1220, Triceratops, vert. No. 1221, Pteranodon. No. 1222, Hoatzin, vert. No. 1223, Ichthyosaur, vert.

1999, Aug. 10   Litho.   Perf. 14
Sheets of 12
1217-1218 A153 Set of 2   6.00 6.00

Sheet of 8
1219 A153 20nu a.-h.   9.00 9.00
Souvenir Sheets
1220-1223 A153 Set of 4   22.00 22.00

No. 1221 is incorrectly inscribed "Triceratops" instead of "Pteranodon," and No. 1223 is "Present Day Dolphin" instead of "Ichthysoaur."

Fauna — A154

Designs: a, Musk deer. b, Takin. c, Blue sheep. d, Yak. e, Goral.

1999, Aug. 21   Litho.   Perf. 12¾
1224 A154 20nu Sheet of 5, #a.-
        e. + label   8.00 8.00

Birds
A155

No. 1225, each 15nu: a, Chestnut-bellied chlorophonia. b, Yellow-faced Amazon parrot. c, White ibis. d, Caique. e, Green jay. f, Tufted coquette. g, Common troupial. h, Purple gallinule. i, Copper-rumped hummingbird.

No. 1226, each 15nu: a, Common egret. b, Rufous-browed peppershrike. c, Glittering-throated emerald. d, Great kiskadee. e, Cuban green woodpecker. f, Scarlet ibis. g, Belted kingfisher. h, Barred antshrike. i, Caribbean parakeet.

No. 1227, vert., each 15nu: a, Rufous-tailed jacamar. b, Scarlet macaw. c, Channel-billed toucan. d, Tricolored heron. e, St. Vincent parrot. f, Blue-crowned motmot. g, Horned screamer. h, Black-billed plover. i, Common meadowlark.

Each 80nu: No. 1228, Toco toucan. No. 1229, Red-billed scythebill, vert. No. 1230, Military macaws, vert.

1999, Oct. 17   Litho.   Perf. 14
Sheets of 9, #a.-i.
1225-1227 A155 Set of 3   27.00 27.00
Souvenir Sheets
1228-1230 A155 Set of 3   16.00 16.00

Butterflies
A156

Designs: 5nu, Sara orange tip. 10nu, Pipepine swallowtail. 15nu, Longwings. 20nu, Viceroy. 25nu, Silver-spotted skipper, vert. 30nu, Great spangled fritillary, vert. 35nu, Little copper.

No. 1238, each 20nu: a, Frosted skipper. b, Fiery skipper. c, Banded hairstreak. d, Clouded sulphur. e, Milberts tortoise shell. f, Eastern tailed blue.

No. 1239, each 20nu: a, Zebra swallowtail. b, Colorado hairstreak. c, Pink-edged sulphur. d, Fairy yellow. e, Red-spotted purple. f, Aphrodite.

Each 80nu: No. 1240, Checkered white. No. 1241, Gray hairstreak, vert. No. 1242, Gulf fritillary, vert. No. 1243, Monarch, vert.

1999, Oct. 4   Litho.   Perf. 14
1231-1237 A156 Set of 7   9.50 9.50
Sheets of 6
1238-1239 A156 Set of 2   16.00 16.00
Souvenir Sheets
1240-1243 A156 Set of 4   22.00 22.00

First Manned Moon Landing, 30th
Anniv. — A157

No. 1244, each 20nu: a, Neil A. Armstrong (with name patch). b, Michael Collins. c, Edwin E. Aldrin, Jr. d, Command and service modules. e, Lunar module. f, Aldrin on Moon.

No. 1245, each 20nu: a, X-15 rocket. b, Gemini 8. c, Apollo 11 Saturn V rocket. d, Command and service modules (docked with lunar module). e, Lunar module (docked with command and service modules). f, Aldrin on lunar module ladder.

No. 1246, each 20nu: a, Yuri Gagarin. b, Alan B. Shepard, Jr. c, John H. Glenn, Jr. d, Valentina Tereshkova. e, Edward H. White II. f, Armstrong (no name patch).

Each 80nu: No. 1247, Armstrong, diff. No. 1248, Apollo 11 splashdown. No. 1249, Gemini 8 docked with Agena rocket, horiz.

1999, Nov. 1   Litho.   Perf. 14
Sheets of 6
1244-1246 A157 Set of 3   25.00 25.00
Souvenir Sheets
1247-1249 A157 Set of 3   16.00 16.00

No. 1249 contains one 57x42mm stamp.

Cats,
Horses,
Dogs
A158

Cats: No. 1250, 5nu, Tortoiseshell. No. 1251, 5nu, Woman and cat. 10nu, Chinchilla Golden Longhair.

No. 1253: a, Russian Blue. b, Birman. c, Devon Rex. d, Pewter Longhair. e, Bombay. f, Sorrel Somali. g, Red Tabby Manx. h, Blue Smoke Longhair. i, Oriental Tabby Shorthair.

70nu, Norwegian Shorthair.

1999, Nov. 15   Litho.   Perf. 14
1250-1252 A158 Set of 3   3.50 3.50
Sheet of 9
1253 A158 12nu #a.-i.   7.00 7.00
Souvenir Sheet
1254 A158 70nu multicolored   5.00 5.00

1999, Nov. 15

Horses: 15nu, Lipizzaner. 20nu, Andalusian. No. 1257: a, Przewalski. b, Shetland. c, Dutch Gelderlander. d, Shire. e, Arabian. f, Boulonnais. g, Falabella. h, Orlov Trotter. i, Suffolk Punch.

70nu, Connemara.

1255-1256 A158 Set of 2   3.50 3.50
Sheet of 9
1257 A158 12nu #a.-i.   8.00 8.00
Souvenir Sheet
1258 A158 70nu multicolored   5.00 5.00

1999, Nov. 15

Dogs: 25nu, Weimaraner. 30nu, German Shepherd.
No. 1261: a, Australian Silky Terrier. b, Samoyed. c, Basset Bleu de Gascogne. d, Bernese Mountain Dog. e, Pug. f, Bergamasco. g, Basenji. h, Wetterhoun. i, Drever.

70nu, Labrador Retriever.

1259-1260 A158 Set of 2   6.00 6.00
Sheet of 9
1261 A158 12nu #a.-i.   8.00 8.00
Souvenir Sheet
1262 A158 70nu multicolored   5.00 5.00

Birds,
Mushrooms,
Anilmals
A159

No. 1263, each 20nu: a, Crested lark. b, Ferruginous duck. c, Blood pheasant. d, Laughing thrush. e, Golden eagle. f, Siberian rubythroat.

No. 1264, each 20nu: a, Red-crested pochard. b, Satyr tragopan. c, Lammergeier vulture. d, Kalij pheasant. e, Great Indian hornbill. f, Stork.

No. 1265, each 20nu: a, Rufous-necked hornbill. b, Drongo. c, Himalayan monal pheasant. d, Black-necked crane. e, Little green bee-eater. f, Ibis.

Each 100nu: No. 1266, Siberian rubythroat. No. 1267, Black-naped monarch. No. 1268, Mountain peacock pheasant.

1999, Dec. 17   Perf. 13¾
Sheets of 6. #a.-f.
1263-1265 A159 Set of 3   27.00 27.00
Souvenir Sheets
1266-1268 A159 Set of 3   20.00 20.00

1999, Dec. 17

No. 1269, each 20nu: a, Boletus frostii. b, Morchella estculenta. c, Hypomyces lactifuorum. d, Polyporus auricularius. e, Cantarellus lateritius. f, Volvariella pusilla.

No. 1270, each 20nu: a, Microglossum rufum. b, Lactarius hygrophoroides. c, Lactarius speciousus complex. d, Calostoma cinnabarina. e, Clitocybe clavipes. f, Microstoma floccosa.

No. 1271, each 20nu: a, Mutinus elegans. b, Pholiota squarrosoides. c, Coprinus quadrifudus. d, Clavulinopsis fusiformis. e, Spathularia velutipes. f, Ganoderma lucidum.

Each 100nu: No. 1272, Pholiota aurivella. No. 1273, Ramaria grandis. No. 1274, Oudemansiella lucidum.

Sheets of 6, #a.-f.
1269-1271 A159 Set of 3   27.00 27.00
Souvenir Sheets
1272-1274 A159 Set of 3   20.00 20.00

1999, Nov. 24   Litho.   Perf. 13¾

No. 1275, each 20nu: a, Otter. b, Tibetan wolf. c, Himalayan black bear. d, Snow leopard. e, Flying s quirrel. f, Red fox.

No. 1276, each 20nu: a, Bharal. b, Lynx. c, Rat snake. d, Elephant. e, Langur. f, Musk deer.

No. 1277, each 20nu: a, Ibex. b, Takin. c, Agama lizard. d, Marmot. e, Red panda. f, Leopard cat.

Each 100nu: No. 1278, Rhinoceros. No. 1279, Cobra. No. 1280, Tiger.

Sheets of 6, #a-f
1275-1277 A159 Set of 3   27.00 27.00
Souvenir Sheets
1278-1280 A159 Set of 3   20.00 20.00

Millennium
A160

Frame background color: 10nu, Dark blue green. 20nu, Bright violet.

1999, Dec. 15
1281-1282 A160 Set of 2   2.00 2.00

New Year 2000 (Year of the Dragon) A161

Various dragons. Denominations: 3nu, 5nu, 8nu, 12nu.
15nu, Dragon, vert.

2000
1283-1286 A161 Set of 4   2.50 2.50
Souvenir Sheet
Perf. 12¾
1287 A161 15nu multi   1.50 1.50
No. 1287 contains one 30x40mm stamp.

Space — A162

No. 1288, horiz., each 25nu: a, Victor Patsayev. b, Vladislav Volkov. c, Georgi Dobrovolski. d, Virgil Grissom. e, Roger Chaffee. f, Edward White.
No. 1289, horiz., each 25nu: a, NASA shuttle Challenger. b, X-15. c, Buran. d, Hermes. e, X-33 Venturi Star. f, Hope.
No. 1290, horiz., each 25nu: a, Luna 3. b, Ranger 9. c, Lunar Orbiter. d, Lunar Prospector. e, Apollo 11. f, Selene.
Each 80nu: No. 1291, Challenger. No. 1292, Buran. No. 1293, Astronaut on moon.

2000, May 15   Litho.   Perf. 14
Sheets of 6, #a-f
1288-1290 A162 Set of 3   30.00 30.00
Souvenir Sheets
1291-1293 A162 Set of 3   15.00 15.00
World Stamp Expo 2000, Anaheim.

First Zeppelin Flight, Cent. — A163

No. 1294, horiz., each 25nu: a, LZ-1 and hills. b, LZ-9. c, LZ-6 in hangar. d, LZ-10. e, LZ-7. f, LZ-11.
No. 1295, horiz., each 25nu: a, LZ-1 and sky. b, LZ-2 and treetops. c, LZ-3 and ground. d, LZ-127. e, LZ-129. f, LZ-130.
No. 1296, horiz., each 25nu: a, LZ-1 and treetops. b, LZ-2 and mountains. c, LZ-3 and sky. d, LZ-4. e, LZ-5. f, LZ-6.
Each 80nu: No. 1297, Ferdinand von Zeppelin, without hat. No. 1298, Zeppelin with white hat. No. 1299, Zeppelin with black hat.

2000, May 15   Sheets of 6, #a-f
1294-1296 A163 Set of 3   30.00 30.00
Souvenir Sheets
1297-1299 A163 Set of 3   16.00 16.00

Souvenir Sheet

2000 Summer Olympics, Sydney — A164

No. 1300, each 20nu: a, Jesse Owens. b, Kayaking. c, Fulton County Stadium, Atlanta. d, Ancient greek broad jump.

2000, July 24
1300 A164 Sheet of 4, #a-d   5.00 5.00

British Railway System, 175th Anniv. — A165

No. 1301, each 50nu: a, George Stephenson's Rocket. b, London and Birmingham Railway, 1828. c, Northumbrian engine, 1825. 100nu, Stockton and Darlington Railway opening, 1825.

2000, July 31   Litho.   Perf. 14
1301 A165 Sheet of 3, #a-c   10.00 10.00
Souvenir Sheet
1302 A165 100nu multi   6.50 6.50

Airplanes — A166

No. 1303, 25nu: a, Laird Commercial. b, Ryan Brougham. c, Cessna AW. d, Travel Air 4000. e, Fairchild F-71. f, Command Aire.
No. 1304, 25nu: a, WACO YMF. b, Piper J4 Cub Coupe. c, Ryan ST-A. d, Spartan Executive. e, Luscombe 8. f, Stinson SR5 Reliant.
No. 1305, 25nu: a, Cessna 195. b, WACO SRE. c, Erco Ercoupe. d, Boeing Stearman. e, Beech Staggerwing. f, Republic Seabee.
No. 1306, 100nu, WACO CSO. No. 1307, 100nu, Curtiss-Wright 19W. No. 1308, 100nu, Grumman G-44 Widgeon.

2000, Aug. 7   Perf. 13¾
Sheets of 6, #a-f
1303-1305 A166 Set of 3   26.00 26.00
Souvenir Sheets
1306-1308 A166 Set of 3   18.00 18.00

Berlin Film Festival, 50th Anniv. — A167

No. 1309, each 25nu: a, A Kind of Loving. b, Bushido Zankoku Monogatari. c, Hobson's Choice. d, El Lazarillo de Tormes. e, In the Name of the Father. f, Les Cousins.
100nu, Die Ratten.

2000, Aug. 15   Perf. 14
1309 A167 Sheet of 6, #a-f   9.00 9.00
Souvenir Sheet
1310 A167 100nu multi   6.50 6.50

Souvenir Sheet

Albert Einstein (1879-1955) — A168

2000, Sept. 1   Perf. 12x12¼
1311 A168 100nu multi   7.50 7.50

Flowers — A169

No. 1312, 25nu: a, Crinum amoenum. b, Beaumontia grandiflora. c, Trachelospermum lucidum. d, Curcuma aromatica. e, Barleria cristata. f, Holmskioldia sanguinea.
No. 1313, 25nu: a, Meconopsis villosa. b, Salvia hians. c, Caltha palustris. d, Anemone polyanthes. e, Cypripedium cordigerum. f, Cryptochilus luteus.
No. 1314, 25nu: a, Androsace globifera. b, Tanacetum atkinsonii. c, Aster stracheyi. d, Arenaria glanduligera. e, Sibbaldia purpurea. f, Saxifraga parnassifolia.
No. 1315, 100nu, Dendrobium densiflorum, vert. No. 1316, 100nu, Rhododendron arboreum, vert. No. 1317, Gypsophila cerastioides.

Perf. 14¼x14½, 14½x14¼
2000, Sept. 5
Sheets of 6, #a-f
1312-1314 A169 Set of 3   26.00 26.00
Souvenir Sheets
1315-1317 A169 Set of 3   18.00 18.00

St. Thomas Aquinas (1225-1274) A170

2000, Sept. 18   Perf. 14x14¾
1318 A170 25nu multi   1.50 1.50
No. 1318 printed in sheets of 4.

A171

Millennium — A172

Medical pioneers — No. 1319, 25nu: a, Albert Calmette. b, Camillo Golgi and Santiago Ramón y Cajal. c, Alexander Fleming. d, Jonas Salk. e, Christiaan Barnard. f, Luc Montagnier.
Olympic movement — No. 1320, 25nu: a, Baron Pierre de Coubertin. b, 1896 Athens Games. c, Jesse Owens. d, 1972 Munich Games. e, 2000 Sydney Games. f, 2004 Athens Games.
100nu, Paro Taktsang.

2000, Sept. 18   Perf. 14
Sheets of 6, #a-f
1319-1320 A171 Set of 2   18.00 18.00
Souvenir Sheet
1321 A172 100nu multi   6.00 6.00
Souvenir Sheets

Explorers — A173

No. 1322, Christopher Columbus. No. 1323, Capt. James Cook.

2000, Sept. 18
1322-1323 A173 100nu Set of
2   12.00 12.00

Expo 2000, Hanover — A174

No. 1324 — Dzongs: a, 3nu, Trashigang. b, 4nu, Lhuentse. c, 6nu, Gasa. d, 7nu, Punakha. e, 10nu, Trashichhoe. f, 20nu, Paro.

No. 1325 — Flora and Fauna, 10nu: a, Snow leopard, b, Raven. c, Golden langur. d, Rhododendron. e, Black-necked crane. f, Blue poppy.

Perf. 13x13¼ (#1324), 12¾
2000, June 1   Litho.
Sheets of 6, #a-f
1324-1325 A174 Set of 2   4.75 4.75
Souvenir Sheet
1326 A174 15nu Temple   1.75 1.75
Size of stamps in Nos. 1325-1326: 40x31mm.

Paintings from the Prado — A175

No. 1327, 25nu: a, Portrait of an Old man, by Joos van Cleve. b, Mary I, by Anthonis Mor. c, Portrait of a Man, by Jan van Scorel. d, The Court Jester Pejerón, by Mor. e, Elizabeth of France, by Frans Pourbus, the Younger. f, King James I, by Paul van Somer.

No. 1328, 25nu: a, Isabella of Portugal, by Titian. b, Lucrecia di Baccia del Fede, the Painter's Wife, by Andrea del Sarto. c, Self-portrait, by Titian. d, Philip II, by Sofonisba Anguisciola. e, Portrait of a Doctor, by Lucia Anguisciola. f, Anna of Austria, by Sofonisba Anguisciola.

No. 1329, 25nu: a, Duchess. b, Child. c, Duke. d, Isidoro Maiquez, by Goya. e, Doña Juana Galarza de Goicoechea, by Goya. f, Ferdinand VII in an Encampment, by Goya. a-c from #1332.

No. 1330, 100nu, Charles V on Horseback at the Battle of Mühlberg. No. 1331, 100nu, The Relief of Genoa, by Antonio de Pereda y Salgado. No. 1332, 100nu, The Duke and Duchess of Osuna With Their Children, by Goya, horiz.

2000, Oct. 6   *Perf. 12x12¼, 12¼x12*
Sheets of 6, #a-f
1327-1329 A175 Set of 3   32.00 32.00
Souvenir Sheets
1330-1332 A175 Set of 3   21.00 21.00
España 2000 Intl. Philatelic Exhibition.

Indepex 2000 Philatelic Exhibition, India — A176

No. 1333: a, 5nu, Butterfly. b, 8nu, Red jungle fowl. c, 10nu, Zinnia elegans. d, 12nu, Tiger. 15nu, Spotted deer.

2000   Litho.   *Perf. 13¾*
1333 A176   Sheet of 4, #a-d   2.00 2.00
Souvenir Sheet
Perf. 13¼x13½
1334 A176 15nu multi   1.90 1.90

New Year 2001
(Year of the
Snake) — A177

Various snakes and flowers with panel colors of: 3nu, Light blue. No. 1337a, 10nu, Dark blue. No. 1337b, 15nu, Green. 20nu, Red.

2001   *Perf. 12¾*
1335-1336 A177   Set of 2   1.50 1.50
Souvenir Sheet
1337 A177   Sheet, #a-b, 1335-
             1336   3.00 3.00

Souvenir Sheet

Hong Kong 2001 Stamp
Exhibition — A178

No. 1338: a, Uncia uncia. b, Aceros nipalensis. c, Grus nigricollis. d, Panthera tigris.

2001
1338 A178 15nu Sheet of 4, #a-d 4.75 4.75

Intl. Volunteers Year A179

Various children's drawings: 3nu, 4nu, 10nu, 15nu.

2001
1339-1342 A179   Set of 4   2.75 2.75
  a. Souvenir sheet, #1339-1342   3.00 3.00

Souvenir Sheet

Choelong Trulsum — A180

No. 1343: a, 10nu, Chenrezig. b, 15nu, Guru Rimpoche. c, 20nu, Sakyamuni.

2001, Sept. 23   Litho.   *Perf. 13¼*
1343 A180   Sheet of 3, #a-c   3.25 3.25

Nos. 495-498
Surcharged

2001, Oct. 9   Litho.   *Perf. 11¾*
1344 A62 4nu on 10ch #495   .50   .50
1345 A62 10nu on 25ch #496   1.00 1.00
1346 A62 15nu on 50ch #497   1.60 1.60
1347 A62 20nu on 1nu #498   2.25 2.25
1347A A62 4nu on 10ch #495   *3.00* —
1347B A62 10nu on 25ch #496   *6.00* —
  Nos. 1344-1347B (6)   14.35 5.35

Obliterator on Nos. 1347A-1347B has deeper curve than that on Nos. 1344-1345. Two surcharge settings exist on Nos. 1344 and 1345.

Souvenir Sheet

Snow Leopards — A181

No. 1348: a, Face, vert. b, Two leopards. c, Three kittens. d, Leopard walking, vert.

2001, Dec. 17   Litho.   *Perf. 13½*
1348 A181 10nu Sheet of 8, 2
          each #a-d   3.50 3.50

Souvenir Sheet

Mountains — A182

No. 1349: a, Teri Gang. b, Tsenda Gang. c, Jomolhari. d, Gangheytag. e, Jitchudrake. f, Tse-rim Gang.

2002, Feb. 5   *Perf. 12¾*
1349 A182 20nu Sheet of 6, #a-f 8.00 8.00

Souvenir Sheet

Orchids — A183

No. 1350: a, Rhomboda lanceolata. b, Odontochilus lanceolatus. c, Zeuxine glandulosa. d, Goodyera schlechtendaliana. e, Anoectochilus lanceolatus. f, Goodyera hipsida.

2002, Apr. 3   *Perf. 13x13¼*
1350 A183 10nu Sheet of 6 #a-f 4.50 4.50

Souvenir Sheet

Rhododendrons — A184

No. 1351: a, Rhododendron arboreum. b, Rhododendron niveum. c, Rhododendron dalhousiae. d, Rhododendron glaucophyllum. e, Rhododendron barbatum. f, Rhododendron grande.

2002, May 1   *Perf. 13¾*
1351 A184 15nu Sheet of 6, #a-f,
          + label   7.50 7.50

New Year 2002 (Year of the
Horse) — A185

No. 1352: a, Tan horse. b, White horse. 25nu, Yellow horse, horiz.

2002, Jan. 1   *Perf. 12¾*
1352 A185 20nu Horiz. pair, #a-b 2.40 2.40
Souvenir Sheet
1353 A185 25nu multi   1.90 1.90

Medicinal
Plants — A186

Designs: No. 1354, 10nu, Bombax ceiba. No. 1355, 10nu, Brugmansia suaveolens. No. 1356, 10nu, Podophyllum hexandrum. No. 1357, 10nu, Phytolacca acinosa.

2002, June 2   Litho.   *Perf. 12¾*
1354-1357 A186   Set of 4   3.25 3.25
  a. Souvenir sheet, #1354-1357   3.50 3.50

United We Stand — A187

2002, Sept. 16   **Perf. 14**
1358 A187 25nu multi   5.50 5.50
Printed in sheets of 4.

Souvenir Sheet

2002 Winter Olympics, Salt Lake City — A188

No. 1359: a, Ski jumper. b, Cross-country skier.

2002, Sept. 16
1359 A188 50nu Sheet of 2, #a-b 5.50 5.50

Reign of Queen Elizabeth II, 50th Anniv. — A189

No. 1360: a, Wearing blue hat. b, Wearing green and white hat. c, Wearing red violet hat. d, Wearing white hat with blue trim.
90nu, Wearing tiara.

2002, Sept. 16   **Perf. 14¼**
1360 A189 40nu Sheet of 4, #a-d 7.25 7.25
Souvenir Sheet
1361 A189 90nu multi   6.75 6.75

Intl. Year of Ecotourism — A190

No. 1362: a, Lotus. b, Northern jungle queen butterfly. c, Bengal tiger.
90nu, Peacock.

2002, Oct. 14   **Perf. 14**
1362 A190 50nu Sheet of 3, #a-c 7.00 7.00
Souvenir Sheet
1363 A190 90nu multi   5.50 5.50

20th World Scout Jamboree, Thailand — A191

No. 1364, horiz.: a, Scout. b, Four scouts. c, Boy saluting, 1908.
90nu, Daniel Beard.

2002, Oct. 14
1364 A191 50nu Sheet of 3, #a-c 7.00 7.00
Souvenir Sheet
1365 A191 90nu multi   5.50 5.50

First Solo Transatlantic Flight, 75th Anniv. — A192

No. 1366: a, Charles Lindbergh and The Spirit of St. Louis. b, Lindbergh.
90nu, Lindbergh, diff.

2002, Oct. 14
1366 A192 75nu Sheet of 2, #a-b 7.00 7.00
Souvenir Sheet
1367 A192 90nu multi   5.00 5.00

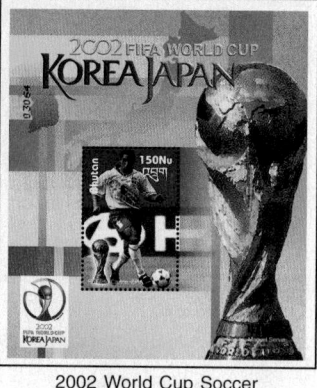

2002 World Cup Soccer Championships, Japan and Korea — A193

No. 1368: a, Zinedine Zidane. b, Michael Owen. c, Miyagi Stadium, Japan. d, Cuauhtemoc Blanco. e, Gabriel Batistuta. f, Incheon Stadium, Korea.
150nu, Roberto Carlos.

2002
1368 A193   25nu Sheet of 6, #a-
     f   7.00 7.00
Souvenir Sheet
1369 A193 150nu multi   7.00 7.00

A194

Flora, Fauna and Mushrooms — A195

No. 1370, 25nu — Flowers: a, Primula cawdoriana. b, Meconopsis aculeata. c, Primula wigramiana. d, Primula stuartii. e, Saxifraga andersonii. f, Rheum nobile.
No. 1371, 25nu — Orchids: a, Coelogyne rhodeana. b, Coelogyne virescens. c, Phalaenopsis schilleriana. d, Angraecum eburneum. e, Dendrobium aureum. f, Dendrobium Caesar x Jag.
No. 1372, 25nu — Mushrooms: a, Entire russula. b, March wax cap. c, Fawn tricholoma. d, Sulfur tuft. e, Poplar tricholoma. f, Annatto-colored cortinarius.
No. 1373, 25nu — Butterflies: a, Dead leaf. b, Troides aeacus. c, Atrophaneura latreillei. Teinopalpus imperialis. e, Zeuxidia aurelius. f, Euploea dufresne.
No. 1374, 25nu — Birds: a, Yellow-legged gull. b, Sand martin. c, Asian openbill. d, White stork. e, Eurasian oystercatcher. f, Indian pitta.
No. 1375, 25nu — Animals: a, Gaur. b, Hog badger. c, Indian cobra. d, Leopard gecko. e, Gavial. f, Hispid hare.
No. 1376, 90nu, Paris polyphylla. No. 1377, 90nu, Dendrobium chrysotoxum. No. 1378, 90nu, Red tentacle fungus. No. 1379, 90nu, Portia philota. No. 1380, 90nu, Mandarin duck. No. 1381, 90nu, Estuarine crocodile.

2002, Dec. 16   **Litho.**   **Perf. 14**
Sheets of 6, #a-f
1370-1373 A194 Set of 4   25.00 25.00
1374-1375 A195 Set of 2   12.50 12.50
Souvenir Sheets
1376-1379 A194 Set of 4   15.00 15.00
1380-1381 A195 Set of 2   7.50 7.50

Pres. John F. Kennedy (1917-63) — A196

No. 1382: a, As Choate graduate, 1935. b, With John, Jr. c, As congressman, 1946. d, At White House, 1961. e, With wife at tennis court. f, Wife and children at funeral, 1963.
90nu, Portrait.

2003, Feb. 3
1382 A196 25nu Sheet of 6,
     #a-f   11.00 11.00
Souvenir Sheet
1383 A196 90nu multi   5.00 5.00

Princess Diana (1961-97) — A197

No. 1384: a, Wearing red dress. b, Wearing blue violet dress. c, Wearing black sweater and blue blouse. d, Wearing tiara and yellow gown.
90nu, Wearing red hat.

2003, Feb. 3
1384 A197 40nu Sheet of 4,
     #a-d   12.00 12.00
Souvenir Sheet
1385 A197 90nu multi   5.00 5.00

Elvis Presley (1935-77) — A198

No. 1386 — Various photos of Presley with guitar in color of: a, Greenish gray. b, Sepia. c, Bluish gray. d, Lilac.
No. 1387 — Presley without guitar in color of: a, Violet brown. b, Bluish gray. c, Sepia. d, Greenish gray. e, Brown. f, Lilac.

2003, Feb. 3
1386 A198 25nu Sheet of 4, #a-d 6.00 6.00
1387 A198 25nu Sheet of 6, #a-f 9.00 9.00

No. 548
Surcharged

2003, Feb. 25   Litho.   Perf. 13½
1388 A69 8nu on 75ch multi   .60 .60

Souvenir Sheet

New Year 2003 (Year of the Sheep) — A199

No. 1389: a, 15nu, Lambs. b, 20nu, Sheep, vert.

2003, Mar. 3   Perf. 12½
1389 A199 Sheet of 2, #a-b   3.00 3.00

Japanese Art — A200

No. 1390, 25nu, vert.: a, Beauty Reading Letter, by Kunisada Utagawa. b, Two Beauties, by Shunsho Katsukawa. c, Beauty Arranging Her Hair, by Doshin Kaigetsudo. d, Dancing, by Kiitsu Suzuki. e, Two Beauties, by Kikumaro Kitagawa. f, Kambun Beauty, by unknown Edo Period artist.
No. 1391, 25nu, vert.: a, Detail of Egret and Willow, by Suzuki. b, Cranes, by Jakuchu Ito. c, Detail of Cranes, by Kiitsu Suzuki. d, Mandarin Ducks Amid Snow-covered Reeds, by Ito. e, Rooster, Hen and Hydrangeas, by Ito. f, Hawk Perched on a Snow-covered Branch, by Zeshin Shibata.
No. 1392, 25nu, vert. — The Thirty-six Poets, by Hoitsu Sakai: a, Poet in black with arms folded. b, Poet in green with object in hand. c, Poet touching head. d, Poets with white, light blue, red and black kimonos. e, Poets with dark blue, black, gray and tan kimonos. f, Poets with white, green, light blue and black kimonos.
No. 1393, 90nu, Detail of Heads of Nine Beauties in a Roundel With Plum Blossom, by Eishi Hosoda. No. 1394, 90nu, Chrysanthemums by a Stream, With Rocks, by Ito. No. 1395, 90nu, Hawk Carrying Off a Monkey, by Shibata.

Perf. 14x14¾, 14¼ (#1392)
2003, Mar. 10
Sheets of 6, #a-f
1390-1392 A200 Set of 3 27.00 27.00
Size: 90x90mm
Imperf
1393-1395 A200 Set of 3 13.50 13.50
Nos. 1390-1391 each contain six 26x77mm stamps; No. 1392 contains six 38x50mm stamps.

Souvenir Sheet

Move for Health Walk — A201

2003, May 19   Litho.   Perf. 13¾
1396 A201 50nu multi   2.75 2.75

Souvenir Sheet

Education for Every Girl and Boy — A202

No. 1397: a, 5nu, Girl and parrot. b, 5nu, Girl reading book. c, 10nu, Boy and girl. d, 20nu, Girl with soccer ball.

2003, Nov. 11   Litho.   Perf. 12¾
1397 A202 Sheet of 4, #a-d 2.50 2.50

Souvenir Sheet

Worldwide Fund for Nature (WWF) — A203

No. 1398: a, 2nu, Lophura leucomelanus. b, 5nu, Tragopan blythii. c, 8nu, Tragopan satyra. d, 15nu, Lophophorus impejanus.

2003, Dec. 17
1398 A203 Sheet of 4, #a-d 3.00 3.00

Souvenir Sheet

New Year 2004 (Year of the Monkey) — A204

No. 1399 — Golden langurs: a, Langur with elbow on knee. b, Langur on branch, "Golden Langur" at left. c, Langur with legs spread apart. d, Three langurs.

2004, Jan. 30
1399 A204 10nu Sheet of 4, #a-d 4.00 3.25
2004 Hong Kong Stamp Expo.

FIFA (Fédération Internationale de Football Association), Cent. — A205

No. 1400 — World Cup Champions: a, Brazil, 2002. b, France, 1998.

2004   Litho.   Perf. 11¾x12
1400 A205 10nu Vert. pair, #a-b 1.50 1.50

Expo 2005, Aichi, Japan — A206

No. 1401 — Masked dancers: a, 10nu, Jugging-cham. b, 10nu, Durdhak-cham. c, 20nu, Nga-cham. d, 20nu, Shazam-cham. 30nu, Buddha.

2005, Mar. 25   Litho.   Perf. 13¼
1401 A206 Sheet of 4, #a-d 4.00 4.00
Souvenir Sheet
Perf. 12
1402 A206 30nu multi   2.00 2.00
No. 1401 contains four 35x70mm stamps.

Souvenir Sheet

Rotary International, Cent. — A207

2005, Aug. 24   Perf. 12¾
1403 A207 85nu multi   7.50 7.50

Miniature Sheet

Pope John Paul II (1920-2005) — A208

No. 1404: a, Pink sky showing below LL corner of vignette, purple mountain sloping upward at right. b, Purple mountain at right slightly above top of Pope's shoulder. c, Purple mountain at right below top of Pope's shoulder. d, Pink frame.

2005, Aug. 24
1404 A208 15nu Sheet of 9, #a-c, 6 #d   13.00 13.00

Locomotives — A209

No. 1405, horiz.: a, P36 N0097. b, VIA F 40 6428. c, InterRegio train. d, Amtrak 464. 85nu, P36 N0032.

2005, Aug. 24
1405 A209 30nu Sheet of 4,
              #a-d   10.00 10.00
       Souvenir Sheet
1406 A209 85nu multi   7.50 7.50

World Cup Soccer Championships, 75th Anniv. — A210

No. 1407: a, Guido Buchwald. b, Mario Basler. c, Torsten Frings. 85nu, Fredi Bobic.

2005, Aug. 24   **Perf. 12¼x12**
1407 A210 40nu Sheet of 3,
              #a-c   10.00 10.00
       Souvenir Sheet
1408 A210 85nu multi   7.50 7.50

No. 298
Surcharged

Nu 5

2005   **Perf. 14**
1409   A39 5nu on 1nu #298   1.00   .40
1409A A39 5nu on 1.25nu
              #299   —   35.00
1409B A39 5nu on 1.70nu
              #300   —   35.00
No. 1409 exists with inverted surcharge. Value $35.

Souvenir Sheet

New Year 2005 (Year of the Rooster) — A211

No. 1410: a, 15nu, Jungle rooster and hen. b, 20nu, Domestic rooster and hen.

2005   **Perf. 11¾x12**
1410 A211 Sheet of 2, #a-b   2.75 2.75

Japanese Assistance, 20th Anniv. — A212

No. 1411, horiz.: a, Traditional plowing. b, Traditional transplanting. c, Traditional threshing. d, Modern plowing. e, Modern transplanting. f, Modern threshing. 30nu, King Jigme Singye Wangchuk at plow.

2005   **Perf. 11¾x12**
1411 A212 5nu Sheet of 6, #a-f 2.50 2.50
       Souvenir Sheet
       Perf. 12x11¾
1412 A212 30nu multi   2.50 2.50

Miniature Sheet

My Dream For Peace One Day — A213

No. 1413 — Children's drawings: a, Doves, flags, people, world map. b, Candle, flags. c, Children and jigsaw puzzle. d, Hands, globe, dove. e, Hands, doves, olive branch. f, Globe holding umbrella.

2005, Sept. 21   **Perf. 13¼**
1413 A213 10nu Sheet of 6, #a-f 5.50 5.50

Miniature Sheet

King Jigme Singye Wangchuk, 50th Birthday — A214

No. 1414: a, Standing, with other men. b, At microphone. c, With fruit bowl. d, Shaking hands with man. e, Standing on platform (39x87mm).

2005, Nov. 11 Litho.   Perf. 13¼
1414 A214 20nu Sheet of 5, #a-e 9.00 9.00

Miniature Sheet

Bridges — A215

No. 1415: a, 10nu, Wachy Bridge. b, 10nu, Chain bridge. c, 10nu, Wooden cantilever bridge. d, 20nu, Mo Chu Bridge. e, 20nu,

Langjo Bridge. f, 20nu, Punatshang Chu Bridge.

2005   **Perf. 11¾x12**
1415 A215 Sheet of 6, #a-f   8.00 8.00

New Year 2006 (Year of the Dog) — A216

Designs: Nos. 1416, 1420a, 5nu, St. Bernard. Nos. 1417, 1420b, 10nu, Lhasa Apso. Nos. 1418, 1420c, 15nu, Maltese. Nos. 1419, 1420d, 20nu, Papillon. No. 1420e, 25nu, Husky, vert. (33x68mm).

2006, Feb. 28 Litho.   Perf. 13¼
Denominations in White or Purple (#1416)
1416-1419 A216 Set of 4   2.50 2.50
       Miniature Sheet
       Denominations in Yellow
1420 A216 Sheet of 5, #a-e   3.75 3.75

Europa Stamps, 50th Anniv. — A217

Designs: 150nu, Jakar Dzong. 250nu, Archery.

2006   **Perf. 12¾x13½**
1421-1422 A217 Set of 2   20.00 20.00
1422a   Souvenir sheet, #1421-
              1422   20.00 20.00
Nos. 1421-1422, 1422a exist imperf. Values, unused or used: set $25; souvenir sheet $25.

Miniature Sheet

National Symbols — A218

No. 1423: a, 10nu, Raven. b, 10nu, Takins. c, 20nu, Cypress trees. d, 20nu, Blue poppy.

2006   **Perf. 13¼**
1423 A218 Sheet of 4, #a-d   2.75 2.75

A219

New Year 2007 (Year of the Pig) — A220

2007   Litho.   Perf. 12x11¾
1424 A219 20nu multi   1.00 1.00
       Souvenir Sheet
       Perf. 13¼
1425 A220 25nu multi   1.25 1.25

Miniature Sheet

Monasteries — A221

No. 1426: a, 8nu, Taktsang Monastery. b, 10nu, Kichu Monastery. c, 15nu, Kurjey Monastery. d, 20nu, Jambay Monastery.

2007   **Perf. 13¼**
1426 A221 Sheet of 4, #a-d   —   —

A222

New Year 2008 (Year of the Rat) — A223

No. 1428: a, Rat facing right. b, Rat facing left.

2008
1427 A222 20nu multi   1.00 1.00
       Souvenir Sheet
       Perf. 13½x13¼
1428 A223 20nu Sheet of 2, #a-b 1.75 1.75

Kings — A224

Kings — A225

In Harmony With Nature — A226

No. 1429 — King: a, 5nu, Ugyen Wangchuck. b, 10nu, Jigme Wangchuck. c, 15nu, Jigme Dorji Wangchuck. d, 20nu, Jigme Singye Wangchuck. e, 25nu, Jigme Khesar Namgyel Wangchuck.

2008	Litho.	Perf. 14¼x14½
1429 A224	Sheet of 5, #a-e, + label	4.25 4.25

Souvenir Sheets
Imperf
Self-Adhesive

| 1430 A225 | 225nu multi | 15.00 15.00 |
| 1431 A226 | 225nu multi | 15.00 15.00 |

Nos. 1430-1431 are sealed envelopes containing compact discs. Values are for sealed envelopes containing the discs.

Miniature Sheet

2008 Summer Olympics, Beijing — A227

No. 1432: a, 10nu, Archer aiming arrow. b, 15nu, Archer holding bow. c, 25nu, Dragon, denomination in maroon. d, 25nu, Dragon, denomination in white.

2008		Perf. 13
1432 A227	Sheet of 4, #a-d	4.25 4.25

Bhutan at the Smithsonian Folklore Festival — A228

No. 1433: a, Two people wearing Bhutanese masks. b, Archer. c, Farmer plowing. d, Dancers. e, Carver holding knife.
No. 1434, 50nu, Drawing of building. No. 1435, 50nu, Fireworks over building, horiz.

2008		Perf. 13¼
1433 A228	20nu Sheet of 5, #a-e	6.00 6.00

Souvenir Sheets
Perf. 14

| 1434-1435 A228 | Set of 2 | 6.00 6.00 |

No. 1433 contains five 50x50mm diamond-shaped stamps.

Miniature Sheet

Visit to Bhutan of Indian Prime Minister Manmohan Singh — A229

No. 1436: a, Bhutan Prime Minister Jigme Thinley and Indian Prime Minister Singh shaking hands in front of plaque. b, Thinley and Singh, flags of India and Bhutan. c, Thinley. d, Singh, wearing turban.

2008	Litho.	Perf. 13¼
1436 A229	25nu Sheet of 4, #a-d	4.75 4.75

Souvenir Sheets

Coronation of King Jigme Khesar Namgyel Wangchuck — A230

Voting for Happiness — A231

2009, Feb. 21	Litho.	Imperf.

Self-Adhesive

| 1437 A230 | 225nu multi | 15.00 15.00 |
| 1438 A231 | 225nu multi | 15.00 15.00 |

Nos. 1437-1438 are sealed envelopes containing compact discs. Values are for sealed envelopes containing the discs.

New Year 2009 (Year of the Ox) — A232

Ox with background in: 20nu, Brown. 30nu, Brown black.

2009, Feb. 25	Litho.	Perf. 13
1439 A232	20nu multi	.80 .80

Souvenir Sheet
Perf. 13½

| 1440 A232 | 30nu multi | 1.25 1.25 |

No. 1440 contains one 40x30mm stamp.

Punakha Dzong Bridge A233

Designs: 20nu, Entire bridge.
No. 1442: a, Bridge at right. b, Bridge at left.

2009, Mar. 20		Perf. 12½x12¾
1441 A233	20nu multi	.80 .80

Souvenir Sheet
Perf. 13½x13¼

| 1442 A233 | 25nu Sheet of 2, #a-b | 2.00 2.00 |

Souvenir Sheet

July 22, 2009, Total Solar Eclipse — A234

No. 1443 — Solar eclipse, buildings and: a, One man. b, Three men.

2009, June 22		Perf. 12½
1443 A234	25nu Sheet of 2, #a-b	2.10 2.10

Miniature Sheet

A235

World Food Program in Bhutan, 35th Anniv. — A236

No. 1444: a, 10nu, Child leading oxen carrying rice bags. b, 10nu, Man near oxen carrying ricebags. c, 10nu, Stacked rice bags and vegetable oil boxes. d, 10nu, Farmer with hoe. e, 10nu, Farmers planting crops. f, 10nu, Men removing rocks near house. g, 20nu, Children eating. h, 20nu, Children on food line. i, 20nu, Children studying.
25nu, People holding cups.

2009, June 27		Perf. 13¼
1444 A235	Sheet of 9, #a-i	5.00 5.00

Souvenir Sheet
Perf. 13

| 1445 A236 | 25nu multi | 1.10 1.10 |

Miniature Sheet

Textiles — A237

No. 1446: a, Kushuthara. b, Mentse Mathra. c, Lungserma. d, Yathra.

Perf. 12¾x12½

2009, Sept. 28	Litho.	Wmk. 388
1446 A237	20nu Sheet of 4, #a-d	3.50 3.50

Worldwide Fund for Nature (WWF) — A238

No. 1447 — Red panda: a, 20nu, Adult and juvenile. b, 20nu, Adult. c, 25nu, Adult and juvenile, diff. d, 25nu, Adult, diff.

2009, Oct. 9	Unwmk.	Perf. 13½
1447 A238	Block of 4, #a-d	4.00 4.00

Souvenir Sheets

New Year 2010 (Year of the Tiger) — A239

No. 1448: a, Tiger at night. b, Tiger in daylight.
50nu, Tiger, vert.

Perf. 12½x12¾

2010, Feb. 14   **Wmk. 388**
1448 A239 30nu Sheet of 2, #a-b 2.60 2.60
Perf. 13¼x13½
1449 A239 50nu multi   2.25 2.25
Worldwide Fund for Nature (WWF).

World Health Day — A240

No. 1450: a, Memorial Chorten (temple). b, Thimphu buildings, cars on street. c, Aerial view of Thimphu. d, Golfer. e, Cars on highway. f, Building, clock tower and plaza, Thimphu.
25nu, Jigme Dorji Wangchuk National Referral Hospital, Thimphu.

Perf. 12½x12¾
2010, Apr. 7   **Litho.**   **Wmk. 388**
1450 A240 10nu Sheet of 6, #a-f 2.75 2.75
Souvenir Sheet
Perf. 14
1451 A240 25nu multi   1.25 1.25
No. 1451 contains one 50x39mm stamp.

16th South Asian Association for Regional Cooperation Summit, Thimphu — A241

No. 1452 — Flag of participating nation: a, Afghanistan. b, Bangladesh. c, Bhutan. d, India. e, Maldive Islands. f, Nepal. g, Pakistan. h, Sri Lanka.
25nu, Leaf, flags of the participating nations.

2010, Apr. 23   **Unwmk.**   *Perf. 13¼*
1452 A241 10nu Sheet of 8, #a-h 3.75 3.75
Souvenir Sheet
1453 A241 25nu multi   1.25 1.25
No. 1452 contains eight 40x30mm stamps.

A242

A243

A244

A245

King Jigme Khesar Namgyel Wangchuck — A246

No. 1454 — King: a, With bow and arrow. b, Throwing dart. c, Playing soccer with children. d, Playing basketball. e, Holding water polo ball. f, Bicycling.
No. 1455 — King: a, Bending with arms out, in front of children. b, Sitting in doorway with children. c, Standing and waving in middle of group of children. d, Standing in front of children. e, Standing, with hands on wall. f, With girl and baby.
No. 1456 — King: a, with Buddhist monk. b, Writing in book. c, Sitting in doorway with children, diff. d, With hands together touching chin. e, Sitting with children. f, Sitting on wall in front of crowd.
No. 1457 — King with background color of: a, Gold. b, Silver. c, Bronze.

Perf. 13½x13¼
2010, Nov. 1   **Unwmk.**
1454 A242 10nu Sheet of 6,
          #a-f   2.75 2.75
1455 A243 10nu Sheet of 6,
          #a-f   2.75 2.75
1456 A244 20nu Sheet of 6,
          #a-f   5.50 5.50
Perf.
1457 A245 30nu Sheet of 3,
          #a-c   4.25 4.25
Nos. 1454-1457 (4)   15.25 15.25
Souvenir Sheet
Perf. 13¼x13½
1458 A246 20nu multi   .95 .95

Miniature Sheets

Wangchuck Dynasty Kings — A247

Queens of Bhutan — A248

No. 1459: a, Desi Jigme Namgyel (1825-81) (30x46mm). b, King Ugyen Wangchuck (1826-1926) (30x46mm). c, King Jigme Wangchuck (1905-52) (30x46mm). d, King Jigme Khesar Namgyel Wangchuck (30x76mm). e, King Jigme Dorji Wangchuck (1928-72) (45x30mm). f, King Jigme Singye Wangchuck (45x30mm). No. 1460: a, Queen Ashi Tsendu Lhamo Wangchuck (1886-1922). b, Queen Ashi Phuntsho Choden Wangchuck (1911-2003). c, Queen Ashi Pema Dechen Wangchuck (1918-91). d, Royal Grandmother Ashi Kezang Choeden Wangchuck. e, Queen Mother Ashi Dorji Wangmo Wangchuck. f, Queen Mother Ashi Tshering Pem Wangchuck. g, Queen Mother Ashi Tshering Yangdon Wangchuck. h, Queen Mother Ashi Sangay Choden Wangchuck.

2010, Dec. 17   **Unwmk.**   *Perf. 14*
1459 A247 15nu Sheet of 6, #a-f   4.00 4.00
Perf. 12¾x12½
Wmk. 388
1460 A248 15nu Sheet of 8, #a-h 5.25 5.25

Souvenir Sheet

New Year 2011 (Year of the Rabbit) — A249

2011, Feb. 3   **Wmk. 388**   *Perf. 12¼*
1461 A249 25nu multi   1.10 1.10

Miniature Sheet

Diplomatic Relations Between Bhutan and Japan, 25th Anniv. — A250

No. 1462 — Flags of Bhutan and Japan and: a, Cherry blossoms, Mt. Fuji, flower. b, Bridge in Bhutan. c, Agricultural equipment. d, Farmer inspecting fruit.

Wmk. 388
2011, May 28   **Litho.**   *Perf. 13½*
1462 A250 20nu Sheet of 4, #a-d 3.75 3.75

A251

1958 Visit to Bhutan of Indian Prime Minister Jawaharlal Nehru — A252

No. 1463: a, King Jigme Dorji Wangchuck greeting Nehru. b, Nehru reviewing troops. c, Nehru, King Jigme Dorji Wangchuck and family. d, Meeting.
25nu, Nehru riding ox.

Wmk. 388
2011, Aug. 15   **Litho.**   *Perf. 13½*
1463 A251 10nu Sheet of 4, #a-d 1.75 1.75
Souvenir Sheet
Perf. 13½x14
1464 A252 25nu multi   1.10 1.10

A253

A253a

A253b

A254

Wedding of King Jigme Khesar
Namgyel Wangchuk and Jetsun Pema
— A254a

No. 1465: a, Couple, white and bister decorative background. b, Bride, white and bister
decorative background. c, Couple, foliage in
background. d, Bride, dark brown netting in
background.

2011, Oct. 9   Litho.   Perf. 13¼
1465   A253   25nu Sheet of 4,
                #a-d   —   —
Souvenir Sheets
1465E   A253a   50nu multi   —   —
1465F   A253b   50nu multi   —   —
Litho. & Embossed
Perf. 13
1466   A254   50nu multi   —   —
Perf. 13¼
1466A   A254a   100nu multi   —   —

Souvenir Sheet

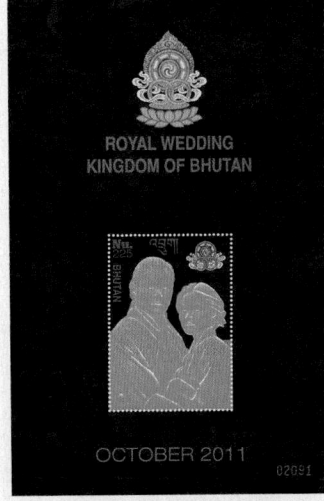

Wedding of King Jigme Khesar
Namgyel Wangchuk and Jetsun
Pema — A255

Litho. & Embossed With Foil
Application
2011, Oct. 9   Perf. 13¼
1467   A255   225nu multi   9.25   9.25

King Jigme Singye Wangchuk —
A255a

No. 1467A — King Jigme Singye Wangchuk
and: b, Subjects, text starting with "So long
as . . ." c, Subjects, text starting with "As a
king . . ." d, Subjects, text starting with "One of
the most . . ." e, King Jigme Khesar Namgyel
Wangchuk, text starting with "It is my wish . . ."
100nu, King Jigme Singye Wangchuk and
copy of first Bhutanese constitution.

2011, Nov.   Litho.   Perf. 13½x13¼
1467A   A255a   25nu Sheet of 4,
                 #b-e   4.00   4.00
Souvenir Sheet
Perf. 14¼
1467F   A255a   100nu multi   4.00   4.00
No. 1467F contains one 45x35mm stamp.

Miniature Sheet

South Asian Association for Regional
Cooperation, 25th Anniv. — A255b

No. 1467G — Flags of: h, Bhutan. i, Sri
Lanka. j, Afghanistan. k, Pakistan. l, Ban-
gladesh. m, Nepal. n, India. o, Maldive
Islands.

2011   Litho.   Wmk. 388   Perf. 14
1467G   A255b   15nu Sheet of 8,
                  #h-o, + cen-
                  tral label   —   —

Education
in Bhutan,
Cent.
(Sherig
Century) —
A255c

Designs: 10nu, Children and candle.
No. 1467Q: r, School building, candle and
ring of text. s, School building, children and
candle.
50nu, Like 10nu.

Wmk. 388
2012, May   Litho.   Perf. 12½
1467P   A255c   10nu multi   —   —
1467Q   A255c   30nu Sheet of 2,
                  #r-s   —   —
Souvenir Sheet
Perf. 13½
1467T   A255c   50nu multi   —   —

Bhutan Post, 50th Anniv. — A256

No. 1468: a, Bhutan #4. b, Bhutan #83H. c,
Bhutan #84B. d, Bhutan #105B. e, Bhutan
#152B. f, Bhutan #153B.
50nu, Postal messenger running.

Perf. 13¼x13
2012, Oct. 10   Litho.   Unwmk.
1468   A256   20nu Sheet of 6, #a-f   4.50   4.50
Souvenir Sheet
Perf. 13½
1469   A256   50nu multi   1.90   1.90
No. 1469 contains one 40x40mm stamp.

Souvenir Sheets

A257

A258

A259

A260

A261

Wedding of King Jigme Khesar
Namgyel Wangchuk and Jetsun Pema,
1st Anniv. — A262

No. 1470 — Royal couple with: a, Trees with green foliage in background. b, Cherry blossoms in background.

2012, Oct. 13   Litho.   Perf. 13
1470 A257 50nu Sheet of 2, #a-b, + central label   3.75 3.75

Perf.
1471 A258 100nu multi   3.75 3.75

Perf. 13¼
1472 A259 200nu multi   7.50 7.50
1473 A260 200nu multi   7.50 7.50
1474 A261 200nu multi   7.50 7.50

Perf. 14x14½
1475 A262 200nu multi   7.50 7.50
Nos. 1470-1475 (6)   37.50 37.50

New Year 2012 (Year of the Dragon) A263

2013, Jan. 1   Litho.   Perf. 12½x12¾
1476 A263 20nu shown   .75 .75

Souvenir Sheet
Perf. 12
1477 A263 50nu Dragon, diff.   1.90 1.90
No. 1477 contains one 45x35mm stamp.

New Year 2013 (Year of the Snake) A264

2013, Feb. 11   Litho.   Perf. 13x13¼
1478 A264 20nu shown   .75 .75

Souvenir Sheet
1479 A264 50nu Snake, diff.   1.90 1.90

Eight Manifestations of Guru Padmasambhava — A265

No. 1480: a, Guru Tshokey Dorji. b, Guru Pema Gyalpo. c, Guru Shakya Sengye. d, Guru Loden Chogsey. e, Guru Pema Jungney. f, Guru Nima Yoezer. g, Guru Sengye Dradok. h, Guru Dorji Drolo.
40nu, Guru Padmasambhava.

2013, June 18   Litho.   Perf. 13¼x13
1480 A265 20nu Sheet of 8, #a-h 5.50 5.50

Souvenir Sheet
Perf. 13¼x13½
1481 A265 40nu multi   1.40 1.40
No. 1481 contains one 42x56mm stamp.

Lama Drukpa Kunley (1455-1529), Buddhist Poet and Teacher — A266

No. 1482 — Drawings on building of: a, Ejaculating penis. b, Penis with white ribbon. c, Penis with eyes and ribbon. d, Penis pointing downward with red and black ribbon.

Perf. 13½x13
2013, Dec. 9   Litho.   Unwmk.
1482 A266 20nu Sheet of 4, #a-d 2.60 2.60

Souvenir Sheet
Perf. 13¼x13¾
1483 A266 40nu multi   1.40 1.40
No. 1482 contains four 30x40mm stamps.

New Year 2014 (Year of the Horse) A268

Designs: 10nu, 50nu, Horse.
No. 1487: a, Rat. b, Ox. c, Tiger. d, Rabbit. e, Dragon. f, Snake. g, Horse, diff. h, Sheep. i, Monkey. j, Bird. k, Dog. l, Pig.

2014, Mar. 2   Litho.   Perf. 13x13¼
1486 A268 10nu multi   .35 .35
1487 A268 20nu Sheet of 12, #a-l   7.75 7.75

Souvenir Sheet
1488 A268 50nu multi   1.60 1.60

Chhoetens (Stupas) — A269

No. 1489: a, National Memorial Stupa, Thimphu. b, Khamsum Yuelley Namgyel Stupa, Punakha. c, Kyichu Lhakhang Stupa, Paro. d, Heyjo Stupa, Thimphu. e, Khuruthang Stupa, Punakha. f, Nemizampa Stupa, Paro. g, Druk Wangyel Stupa, Dochula. h, Dechenphodrang Stupa, Thimphu.
No.1490: a, Chorten Kora Stupa, Trashiyangtse. b, Chendebji Stupa, Trongsa.

2014, Apr. 15   Litho.   Perf. 13x13¼
1489 A269 20nu Sheet of 8, #a-h 5.50 5.50

Souvenir Sheet
1490 A269 25nu Sheet of 2, #a-b 1.75 1.75

A270

Flora and Fauna — A271

No. 1491: a, Rheum nobile. b, Himalayan blue sheep.
No. 1492: a, Melastoma. b, Golden langur. c, Primula. d, Himalayan black bear. e, Red panda. f, Michelia. g, Muntjac. h, Geranium.
50nu, White-bellied heron.

2014, May 10   Litho.   Perf. 13¼x13
1491 A270 10nu Vert. pair, #a-b
1492 A271 20nu Sheet of 8, #a-h 5.50 5.50

Souvenir Sheet
1493 A271 50nu multi   1.75 1.75

A272

A273

Flowers — A274

Designs: 10nu, Primula sikkimensis.
No. 1495: a, Clematis fongulensis. b, Iris goniocarpa. c, Oxygraphis glacialis. d, Rosa macrophylla.
No. 1496: a, Primula griffithii. b, Beaumontia grandiflora. c, Roscoea alpina. d, Lloydia flavonutans. e, Barleria strigosa. f, Primula spathulifolia. g, Curcuma aromatica. h, Rhododendron bhutanense. i, Saxifraga hirculus.

Perf. 13¼x13, 13x13¼ (#1495)
2014, June 15   Litho.
1494 A272 10nu multi   .35 .35
1495 A273 10nu Sheet of 4, #a-d 1.40 1.40
1496 A274 20nu Sheet of 9, #a-i 6.00 6.00

Twelve Deeds of Lord Buddha — A275

Shakyamuni Buddha — A276

No. 1497: a, Descent from Tushita Pure Land. b, Entry into his mother's womb. c, Birth in the garden of Lumbini. d, Mastery of arts and skills. e, Marriage and fathering of a child. f, Renunciation of Samsara. g, Practice of austerities for six years. h, Resolve to meditate under the Bodhi tree. i, Conquest of Mara. j, Enlightenment. k, Turning the Wheel of Dharma. l, Mahaparinirvana.

2014, July 31   Litho.   Perf. 13¼x13
1497 A275 20nu Sheet of 12, #a-l   8.00 8.00

Souvenir Sheet
1498 A276 50nu multi   1.75 1.75

Miniature Sheets

Cultural Ties Between Bhutan and the University of Texas at El Paso, Cent. — A277

No. 1499: a, Rapa dancer, denomination at UR. b, Durdag dance. c, Rapa dancers, denomination at LL. d, University centennial emblem. e, Minding Minds sculpture. f, Opera Bhutan, Thimphu. g, UTEP Pedestrian bridge and campus building. h, Lhakang Building, UTEP. i, Ceremonial flags.
No. 1500: a, Like #1499a. b, Like #1499i. c, Like #1499g. d, Like #1499b.

2014, Aug. 25   Litho.   Perf. 13x13¼
1499 A277 20nu Sheet of 9, #a-i 6.00 6.00
1500 A277 25nu Sheet of 4, #a-d 3.50 3.50

Diplomatic Relations Between Bhutan and Thailand, 25th Anniv. — A278

No. 1501: a, Meconopsis grandis. b, Khon (Thai mask dance). c, Paro Taktsang, Bhutan. d, Cassia fistula. e, Shawa shachi (mask dance). f, Grand Palace, Bangkok.
80nu, Temple of the Emerald Buddha, Thailand and Punakha Dzong, Bhutan.

2014, Nov. 14   Litho.   Perf. 13x13¼
1501 A278 20nu Sheet of 6, #a-f 4.00 4.00

Souvenir Sheet
1502 A278 80nu multi   2.60 2.60

Strong Men — A279

No. 1503: a, Three men dragging logs. b, Two men carrying logs. c, Man carrying sack on shoulder. d, Wrestlers. e, Man cutting log. f, Man lifting tires.
80nu, Man carrying sack on shoulder, vert.

2014, Nov. 17 Litho. Perf. 13x13¼
1503 A279 20nu Sheet of 6, #a-f 4.00 4.00
Souvenir Sheet
Perf. 13¼x13
1504 A279 80nu multi 2.60 2.60

Jewelry — A280

No. 1505: a, Brooch necklace. b, Bracelet. c, Necklace. d, Two round brooches. e, Two brooches (connected diamonds). f, Earrings.
80nu, Betel nut container.

2014, Nov. 17 Litho. Perf. 13x13¼
1505 A280 20nu Sheet of 6, #a-f 4.00 4.00
Souvenir Sheet
1506 A280 80nu multi 2.60 2.60

Butterflies — A281

No. 1507: a, Orinoma damaris. b, Neurosigma siva. c, Euthalia durga. d, Junonia orithiya.
80nu, Bhutanitis ludlowi.

2014, Nov. 17 Litho. Perf. 13x13¼
1507 A281 25nu Sheet of 4, #a-d 3.25 3.25
Souvenir Sheet
1508 A281 80nu multi 2.60 2.60

New Year 2015 (Year of the Sheep) — A282

No. 1509: a, Rat. b, Ox. c, Tiger. d, Rabbit. e, Dragon. f, Snake. g, Horse. h, Sheep. i, Monkey. j, Rooster. k, Dog. l, Pig.
30nu, Sheep, horiz.

2015, Feb. 19 Litho. Perf. 13¼x13
1509 A282 10nu Sheet of 12, #a-l 4.00 4.00
Souvenir Sheet
Perf. 13x13¼
1510 A282 30nu multi 1.00 1.00

Drubthop Thangtong Gyalpo (c. 1385-c.1464), Yogi and Bridge Builder — A283

No. 1511: a, Drubthop Thangtong Gyalpo. b, Dungtsi Lhakhang. c, Man on chain bridge. d, Gateway Tschorten. e, Iron Chain Bridge. f, Buddha Sakyamuni. g, Iron chain. h, Aerial view of Iron Chain Bridge.
40nu, Head of Drubthop Thangtong Gyalpo statue.

2015, Apr. 29 Litho. Perf. 13¼x13
1511 A283 20nu Sheet of 8, #a-h 5.00 5.00
Souvenir Sheet
1512 A283 40nu multi 1.25 1.25

A284

Atsaras — A285

Designs: 5nu, Two atsaras in purple costumes. 10nu, Two atsaras in orange costumes. 15nu, Atsara. 30nu, Two atsaras in red and orange costumes.
No. 1517: a, Two atsaras, dancer with dragon mask. b, Two atsaras, one crouching, c, Atsara with arm extended, holding phallus near head, dancers in background. d, Two atsaras, one holding phallus. e, Atsara with arms raised, two dancers in background. f, Atsara on back of other atsara.
40nu, Seated atsara holding phallus.

2015, Sept. 10 Litho. Perf. 13¼x13
1513-1516 A284 Set of 4 1.90 1.90
1517 A285 20nu Sheet of 6, #a-f 3.75 3.75
Souvenir Sheet
1518 A285 40nu multi 1.25 1.25

Bhutanese Foods — A286

No. 1519: a, Ngya Tshoem. b, Sikam Paa. c, Kewa Datshi. d, Bjasha Maru. e, Haapi Hoentoe. f, Nakey Nosha Paa. g, Nosha Phim. h, Mengay. i, Khuley.
No. 1520: a, Puta. b, Ema Datshi and rice.

2015, Oct. 9 Litho. Perf. 13x13¼
1519 A286 15nu Sheet of 9, #a-i 4.25 4.25
Souvenir Sheet
1520 A286 30nu Sheet of 2, #a-b 1.90 1.90

King Jigme Khesar Namgyel Wangchuk — A287

No. 1521: a, Archers (38mm diameter). b, King Jigme Khesar Namgyel Wangchuk greeting crowd (38mm diameter). c, People seated (38mm diameter). d, Crowd (38mm diameter). e, King Jigme Khesar Namgyel, his father, King Jigme Singye Wangchuk, Queen Jetsun (40x30mm). f, King Jigme Khesar Namgyel Wangchuk and women (40x30mm).
No. 1522, King Jigme Khesar Namgyel Wangchuk and man.

Perf. 13x13¼ (#1521e, 1521f, 1522), Perf.
2015, Oct. 9 Litho.
1521 A287 50nu Sheet of 6, #a-f 9.25 9.25
Souvenir Sheet
1522 A287 50nu multi 1.60 1.60

United Nations, 70th Anniv. — A288

No. 1523: a, United Nations Peacekeeper receiving medal. b, Woman writing in book. c, HeForShe campaign. d, Two Bhutanese men.
50nu, People and candles.

2015, Oct. 24 Litho. Perf. 13x13¼
1523 A288 30nu Sheet of 4, #a-d 3.75 3.75
Souvenir Sheet
1524 A288 50nu multi 1.60 1.60

Dzongs — A289

No. 1525: a, Rimpung Dzong. b, Semtokha Dzong. c, Punakha Dzong. d, Trongsa Dzong. e, Trashigang Dzong. f, Jakar Dzong.
60nu, Tashichho Dzong.

2015, Nov. 2 Litho. Perf. 13¼x13
1525 A289 30nu Sheet of 6, #a-f 5.50 5.50
Souvenir Sheet
1526 A289 60nu multi 1.90 1.90

Monasteries — A290

No. 1527: a, Kurje Lhakhang. b, Jambay Lhakhang. c, Kyichu Lhakhang. d, Changangkha Lhakhang. e, Gangtey Goenpa. f, Tango Monastery.
60nu, Taktshang (Tiger's Nest), vert.

2015, Nov. 3 Litho. Perf. 13x13¼
1527 A290 30nu Sheet of 6, #a-f 5.50 5.50
Souvenir Sheet
1528 A290 60nu multi 1.90 1.90
No. 1528 contains one 40x60mm stamp.

A291

A292

A293

A294

A295

A296

King Jigme Singye Wangchuk, 60th Birthday — A297

Various photographs of King Jigme Singye Wangchuk taken during his reign, as shown.

2015, Nov. 7   Litho.   Perf. 13
1529 A291 15nu Sheet of 4,
       #a-d   1.90 1.90
1530 A292 15nu Sheet of 4,
       #a-d   1.90 1.90
1531 A293 15nu Sheet of 4,
       #a-d   1.90 1.90
1532 A294 15nu Sheet of 4,
       #a-d   1.90 1.90
1533 A295 15nu Sheet of 4,
       #a-d   1.90 1.90
   Nos. 1529-1533 (5)   9.50 9.50

Souvenir Sheets
Perf. 13¼x13
1534 A296 100nu multi   3.00 3.00

Litho. & Embossed
Perf. 13x13¼
1535 A297 500nu multi   15.00 15.00

Bird Conservation — A298

No., 1536: a, Four black-necked cranes (40x30mm). b, Two black-necked cranes on ground (40x30mm). c, Emblem of Royal Society for Protection of Nature (40x30mm). d, Two black-necked cranes in flight (40x30mm). e, White-bellied heron (40x60mm). f, One black-necked crane in flight (40x30mm). g, Dancers in black-necked crane costumes, Black-necked Crane Festival, Gangtey Goepta (40x30mm). h, Two black-necked cranes and people of Phobji Gewog.
No. 1537: a, Three black-necked cranes in flight (40x30mm). b, White-bellied heron (40x30mm).

2015, Nov. 11   Litho.   Perf. 13x13¼
1536 A298 15nu Sheet of 8, #a-h 3.75 3.75
Souvenir Sheet
1537 A298 50nu Sheet of 2, #a-b 3.00 3.00

Worldwide Fund for Nature (WWF) — A299

No. 1538: a, Asiatic water buffalo (40x30mm). b, Red panda (40x60mm). c, Snow leopards (40x30mm). d, Golden mahseers (40x30mm). e, Asian elephant (40x30mm). f, White-bellied heron (40x30mm). g, Golden langurs (40x30mm). h, Royal Bengal tiger (40x30mm).
   50nu, Himalayan blue sheep.

2015, Nov. 11   Litho.   Perf. 13x13¼
1538 A299 30nu Sheet of 8, #a-h 7.25 7.25
Souvenir Sheet
1539 A299 50nu multi   1.50 1.50

Royal Visits to Merak and Sakteng — A300

No. 1540: a, King Jigme Khesar Namgyel Wangchuk and crowd of children. b, King Jigme and Queen Jetsun near stove. c, Queen Jetsun. d, Queen Jetsun and crowd of children. e, King Jigme and Queen Jetsun walking. f, King Jigme and Queen Jetsun looking at items on table.
   150nu, King Jigme and Queen Jetsun seated.

2015, Nov. 11   Litho.   Perf. 13x13¼
1540 A300 50nu Sheet of 6, #a-
       f   9.00 9.00
Souvenir Sheet
1541 A300 150nu multi   4.50 4.50

Traditional Sports — A301

No. 1542: a, Khuru. b, Soksom. c, Bjigdum. d, Dego.
   80nu, Archery.

2015, Dec. 17   Litho.   Perf. 13¾x14
1542 A301 30nu Sheet of 4, #a-d 3.75 3.75
Souvenir Sheet
1543 A301 80nu multi   2.40 2.40

New Year 2016 (Year of the Monkey) — A302

No. 1544: a, Monkey. b, Dragon. c, Rat.
   50nu, Four harmonious friends (bird, rabbit, monkey, elephant), vert.

2016, Feb. 9   Litho.   Perf. 13
1544 A302 30nu Sheet of 3, #a-c 2.75 2.75
Souvenir Sheet
1545 A302 50nu multi   1.50 1.50

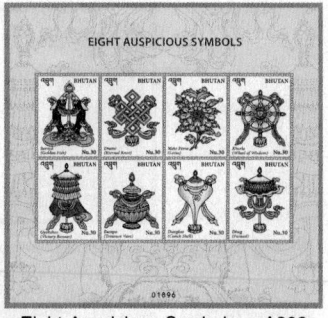

Eight Auspicious Symbols — A303

No. 1546: a, Golden fish. b, Eternal knot. c, Lotus. d, Wheel of wisdom. e, Victory banner. f, Treasure vase. g, Conch shell. h, Parasol.
   60nu, Tashi Tagye.

2016, Apr. 16   Litho.   Perf. 13
1546 A303 30nu Sheet of 8, #a-h 7.25 7.25
Souvenir Sheet
Perf. 13¼
1547 A303 60nu multi   1.90 1.90
No. 1547 contains one 42x70mm stamp.

Birth of Prince Jigme Namgyel Wangchuk — A304

No. 1548 — Inscriptions: a, His Majesty the Fourth Druk Gyalpo. b, His Majesty the King. c, HRH the Gyalsey (King Jigme holding son). d, HRH the Gyalsey (Grandmother, Queen Jetsun and Prince Jigme). e, HRH the Gyalsey (King Jigme, Queen Jestun and Prince Jigme).
   200nu, HRH the Gyalsey (Prince Jigme).

Litho. With Foil Application
2016, May 21   Perf. 13¾x13½
1548 A304 50nu Sheet of 5, #a-
       e   7.50 7.50
Souvenir Sheet
1549 A304 200nu multi   6.00 6.00

Four Mythical Animals — A305

No. 1550: a, Tiger. b, Snow lion. c, Garuda. d, Dragon.
   80nu, Dragon, diff.

2016, July 18   Litho.   Perf. 14¼
1550 A305 30nu Sheet of 4, #a-d 3.75 3.75
Souvenir Sheet
1551 A305 80nu multi   2.40 2.40

Miniature Sheet

Diplomatic Relations Between Bhutan and Japan, 30th Anniv. — A306

No. 1552: a, King Jigme Khesar Namgyel Wangchuk, Queen Jetsun Pema, and Empress Michiko of Japan. b, 30th anniv. emblem. c, King and Queen, Japanese Prime Minister Shinzo Abe, soldiers with flags. d, King and Queen with children. e, King and Queen praying with other worshipers. f, Tea ceremony.

2016, Sept. 5   Litho.   Perf. 14¼
1552 A306 30nu Sheet of 6, #a-f 5.50 5.50

Buddhist Statues and Sites — A307

No. 1553: a, Buddha Dordenma. b, Guru Nangsi Zilnoen. c, Tashichhodzong. d, Lhuntse Dzong.
No. 1554, horiz.: a, Buddha Dordenma, diff. b, Guru Nangsi Zilnoen, diff.

2016, Sept. 6   Litho.   Perf. 14¼
1553 A307 30nu Sheet of 4, #a-d 3.75 3.75
Souvenir Sheet
Perf. 14x14¼
1554 A307 50nu Sheet of 2, #a-b 3.00 3.00

Miniature Sheet

Tourism — A308

No. 1555: a, Layap woman with yak. b, Punakha Dzong. c, Burning Lake. d, Children of Sakteng. e, Tiger's Nest. f, Takins. g, Bamboo baskets.

2016, Oct. 18   Litho.   Perf. 14x14¼
1555 A308 30nu Sheet of 7, #a-g 6.25 6.25

National Flora and Fauna — A309

No. 1556: a, Raven (national bird). b, Blue poppies (national flower). c, Ludlow's Bhutan swallowtail (national butterfly). d, Takin and cypress tree (national animal and tree).
No. 1557, 60nu, Raven, diff. No. 1558, 60nu, Blue poppies, diff. No. 1559, 60nu, Ludlow's Bhutan swallowtail, diff. No. 1560, 60nu, Takin and cypress tree, diff.

2016, Oct. 18   Litho.   Perf. 14¼x14
1556 A309 30nu Sheet of 4, #a-d 3.75 3.75
Souvenir Sheets
1557-1560 A309 Set of 4 7.25 7.25

Druk Wangyel Festival — A310

No. 1561: a, Raven-headed deity. b, Jetsun Milarepa. c, Tshering Chednga. d, Combat of the Heroes, mountains in background. e, Gadpo and Ganmo. f, Combat of the Heroes, no mountains. g, Azhe Lhamo. h, Farewell of the Heroes.
40nu, Vision of Bodhisattvas.

2016, Dec. 17   Litho.   Perf. 14¼
1561 A310 20nu Sheet of 8, #a-h 4.75 4.75
Souvenir Sheet
Perf. 14¼x14
1562 A310 40nu multi 1.25 1.25
No. 1562 contains one 70x46mm stamp.

Prayer Flags — A311

No. 1563: a, Flags above stone monument. b, Flags attached to pole above pile of stones. c, Poles and flags. c, Tree and flags.
40nu, Flags and buildings.

2016, Dec. 17   Litho.   Perf. 14¼
1563 A311 30nu Sheet of 4, #a-d 3.50 3.50
Souvenir Sheet
1564 A311 40nu multi 1.25 1.25
No. 1564 contains one 40x56mm stamp.

Six Elements of Longevity — A312

No. 1565: a, Old man. b, Tree. c, Cliff. d, Water. e, Bird. f, Deer.
50nu, Old man, vert.

2016, Dec. 17   Litho.   Perf. 14x14¼
1565 A312 25nu Sheet of 6, #a-f 4.50 4.50
Souvenir Sheet
1566 A312 50nu multi 1.50 1.50
No. 1566 contains one 46x70mm stamp.

Tashigomangs — A313

No. 1567 — Various tashigomangs: a, 9nu. b, 13nu. c, 21nu. d, 37nu.
50nu, Tashigomang, diff.

2016, Dec. 17   Litho.   Perf. 14¼
1567 A313 Sheet of 4, #a-d 2.40 2.40
Souvenir Sheet
1568 A313 50nu multi 1.50 1.50

New Year 2017 (Year of the Rooster) — A314

No. 1569: a, Rooster. b, Dog. c, Pig. d, Rat. e, Ox. f, Tiger. g, Rabbit. h, Dragon. i, Snake. j, Horse. k, Sheep. l, Monkey.
60nu, Rooster and flames.

Litho. & Embossed   Perf. 14¼
2017, Jan. 1
1569 A314 30nu Sheet of 12, #a-l 10.50 10.50
Souvenir Sheet
1570 A314 60nu multi 1.75 1.75
No. 1570 contains one 70x46mm stamp.

Pilgrimage Sites — A315

No. 1571: a, Kyichu Lhakhang. b, Jampa Lhakhang. c, Kurjey Lhakhang. d, Aja Nye. e, The Burning Lake. f, Singye Dzong. g, Tachog Lhakhang. h, Chhorten Kora. i, Dungtse Lhakhang.
100nu, Taktshang.

2017, Mar. 19   Litho.   Perf. 14x14¼
1571 A315 20nu Sheet of 9, #a-i 5.75 5.75
Souvenir Sheet
1572 A315 100nu multi 3.25 3.25

Prayer Wheel — A316

No. 1573: a, 5nu, Buddhist holding prayer wheel. b, 15nu, Prayer wheels in niches. c, 25nu, Prayer wheels on black base. d, 35nu, Temples.
50nu, Buddhists praying.

2017, June 19   Litho.   Perf. 14¼x14
1573 A316 Sheet of 4, #a-d 2.50 2.50
Souvenir Sheet
Perf. 14x14¼
1574 A316 50nu multi 1.60 1.60
No. 1574 contains one 48x70mm stamp.

Fruits and Nuts — A317

No. 1575: a, Mandarin oranges. b, Bananas. c, Passion fruit. d, Apples. e, Peaches. f, Pears. g, Pineapples. h, Plums.
30nu, Walnuts, vert.

2017, June 19   Litho.   Perf. 14x14¼
1575 A317 15nu Sheet of 8, #a-h 3.75 3.75
Souvenir Sheet
1576 A317 30nu multi .95 .95

Utensils and Household Items — A318

No. 1577: a, Wine container and lid. b, Teapot. c, Flour strainer. d, Cane baskets. e, Rice thresher. f, Cereal grinder.
50nu, Tea strainer and brass pot.

2017, June 19   Litho.   Perf. 14x14¼
1577 A318 30nu Sheet of 6, #a-f 5.75 5.75
Souvenir Sheet
Perf. 14¼x14
1578 A318 50nu multi 1.60 1.60
No. 1578 contains one 70x46mm stamp.

Musical Instruments — A319

No. 1579: a, Pod shaker. b, Hammered dulcimer. c, Mouth harp. d, Flute. e, Fiddle. f, Horn.
50nu, Lute, vert.

2017, Sept. 1   Litho.   Perf. 14x14¼
1579 A319 20nu Sheet of 6, #a-f 3.75 3.75
Souvenir Sheet
Perf. 14¼x14
1580 A319 50nu multi 1.60 1.60
No. 1579b has "Dulcimer" spelled incorrectly on stamp.

Diplomatic Relations Between Bhutan and South Korea, 30th Anniv. — A320

No. 1581: a, Blue flower. b, Puppeteer with puppet. c, Dzong. d, White and red flower. e, Costumed performers and audience. f, Temple and walkway.
60nu, Dzong, temple, flags of Bhutan and South Korea.

2017, Sept. 22   Litho.   Perf. 14x14¼
1581 A320 30nu Sheet of 6, #a-f 5.75 5.75
Souvenir Sheet
Perf. 14¼
1582 A320 60nu multi 1.90 1.90
No. 1582 contains one 56x40mm stamp.

SEMI-POSTAL STAMPS

Nos. 10-12
Surcharged

Perf. 14x14½

1964, Mar.   **Litho.**   **Unwmk.**

B1	A3	33ch + 50ch multi	4.00	4.00
B2	A3	70ch + 50ch multi	4.00	4.00
B3	A3	1.30nu + 50ch multi	4.00	4.00
		Nos. B1-B3 (3)	12.00	12.00

9th Winter Olympic Games, Innsbruck, Jan. 29-Feb. 9, 1964.

Olympic Games Type of Regular Issue, 1964

Souvenir Sheet

1964, Oct. 10   **Perf. 13½, Imperf.**

B4	A6	Sheet of 2	20.00	20.00
a.		1nu + 50ch Archery	6.50	6.50
b.		2nu + 50ch Soccer	13.50	13.50

18th Olympic Games, Tokyo, Oct. 10-25.

Nos. 97, 97C, 97E Surcharged

1968, Dec. 7   **Photo.**   **Perf. 13½**

B5	A14n	5ch +5ch	.30	.30
B6	A14n	80ch +25ch	.50	.50
B7	A14n	2nu +50ch	1.25	1.25
		Nos. B5-B7 (3)	2.05	2.05

AIR POST STAMPS

Nos. 19-21, 38-39, 63-67 Ovptd.

a

Perfs. as Before

1967, Jan. 10   **Litho.**

Overprint "a"

C1	A5	33ch on #19	.30	.30
C2	A5	70ch on #20	.55	.40
C3	A5	1nu on #21	.65	.55
C4	A8	50ch on #38	.40	.30
C5	A8	75ch on #39	.55	.40
C6	A11	1.50nu on #63	1.00	.90
C7	A11	2nu on #64	1.25	1.25
C8	A11	3nu on #65	1.90	1.75
C9	A11	4nu on #66	2.75	2.50
C10	A11	5nu on #67	3.00	2.75

b

Overprint "b"

C11	A5	33ch on #19	.30	.30
C12	A5	70ch on #20	.50	.40
C13	A5	1nu on #21	.65	.55
C14	A8	50ch on #38	.40	.30
C15	A8	75ch on #39	.50	.40
C16	A11	1.50nu on #63	1.00	.90
C17	A11	2nu on #64	1.50	1.25
C18	A11	3nu on #65	1.90	1.75
C19	A11	4nu on #66	2.75	2.50
C20	A11	5nu on #67	3.50	3.40
		Nos. C1-C20 (20)	25.35	22.85

UN Type of Regular Issue

Bhutan Flag and: 2.50nu, UN Headquarters, NYC. 5nu, Security Council Chamber and mural by Per Krohg. 6nu, General Assembly Hall.

1971, Sept. 21   **Photo.**   **Perf. 13½**

C21	A16	2.50nu silver & multi	.40	.40
C22	A16	5nu silver & multi	.60	.60
C23	A16	6nu silver & multi	.80	.80
		Nos. C21-C23 (3)	1.80	1.80

Bhutan's admission to the United Nations. Exist imperf.

Nos. C21-C23 Overprinted in Gold: "UNHCR / UNRWA / 1971" like Nos. 145-145C

1971, Dec. 23   **Perf. 13½**

C24	A16	2.50nu silver & multi	.45	.45
C25	A16	5nu silver & multi	1.00	1.00
C26	A16	6nu silver & multi	1.40	1.40
		Nos. C24-C26 (3)	2.85	2.85

World Refugee Year. Exist imperf.

UPU Types of 1974

UPU Emblem, Carrier Pigeon and: 1nu, Mail runner and jeep. 1.40nu, 10nu, Old and new locomotives. 2nu, Old biplane and jet.

1974, Oct. 9   **Litho.**   **Perf. 14½**

C27	A19	1nu salmon & multi	.35	.35
C28	A20	1.40nu lilac & multi	.90	.90
C29	A20	2nu multicolored	1.25	1.25
		Nos. C27-C29 (3)	2.50	2.50

Souvenir Sheet

Perf. 13

C30	A20	10nu lilac & multi	5.75	5.75

Cent. of the UPU. Nos. C27-C29 were issued in sheets of 50 and sheets of 5 plus label with multicolored margin. Exist imperf.

Issues of 1968-1974 Surcharged 25ch and Bars

1978   **Perf. & Printing as Before**

C31	A16	25ch on 5nu, #C22	3.00	3.00
C32	A16	25ch on 6nu, #C23	3.00	3.00
C33	A20	25ch on 1.40nu, #C28	4.00	4.00
C34	A20	25ch on 2nu, #C29	4.00	4.00
C35	A14j	25ch on 4nu, #94L	4.00	4.00
C36	A14j	25ch on 10nu, #94N	4.00	4.00
C37	A17k	25ch on 5nu, #155F	4.00	4.00
C38	A17k	25ch on 6nu, #155G	4.00	4.00
		Nos. C31-C38 (8)	30.00	30.00

POSTAL-FISCAL STAMPS

Nos. AR1-AR4 are revenue stamps, authorized for use as postage stamps. After the issue of regular postage stamps in 1962, their use diminished when expansion of the modern postal system made the monastery fortresses' postal runner system obsolete. They were demonitized for postal use in the mid- to late 1980s, but remained on sale in post offices for fiscal use.

2 Shiki = 1 Thala = ½ Rupee (India)

Dorje (thunderbolt) — PF1

Perf. 12½

1955, Sept. 28   **Unwmk.**

AR1	PF1	(1sh) blue	1.40	—
AR2	PF1	(2sh) rose red	4.25	—
AR3	PF1	(4sh) green	7.00	—
AR4	PF1	(8sh) orange	19.00	—
		Nos. AR1-AR4 (4)	31.65	

Prior to April 1, 1957, the shiki denominations of Nos. AR1-AR4 equalled 1 anna, 2a, 4a, and 8a, respectively. Beginning April 2, 1957, the denominations equalled ¼ rupee, ½r, 1r, and 5r, respectively.

No. AR1 exists with 10 new paisa and 25np surcharges. There is no official government notice of its issuance.

BIAFRA

bē-af-rə

LOCATION — West Africa on the Gulf of Guinea, between Nigeria and Cameroun.
GOVT. — Republic
AREA — 29,848 sq. mi.
POP. — 13,500,000 (1967 est.)
CAPITAL — Enugu

After independence in 1960, Nigeria was torn by ethnic tensions between the Muslim north and the Christian and Animist south. During 1966, two coups, the first staged by Christian Igbo military officers from the oil-rich southeast (Biafra), with a subsequent counter-coup by Muslim officers, resulted in ethnic riots in which more than 30,000 Igbos were killed. Efforts at reconciliation between the regions failed, and on May 30, 1967, Biafra declared its independence. Hostilities between the central government and Biafra began in July, and after a bitter civil war, Biafra surrendered in Jan. 1970, and the region was reunited with Nigeria. Some 1,000,000 Biafrans died during the hostilities, either in battle or from starvation.

12 Pence = 1 Shilling
20 Shillings = 1 Biafran Pound

> Catalogue values for all unused stamps in this country are for Never Hinged items.

Values for used stamps are for favor-canceled examples bearing an UMUAHIA postmark with a four-digit year date, rather than the two-digit date used on normal postal cancels. This device is 31mm in diameter, and the city name is 3mm high, both elements larger than postal cancels. Postally used examples sell for much higher prices.

Map of Biafra — A1

Arms, Flag, Date — A2

Mother and Child — A3

Perf. 12½

1968, Feb. 5   **Litho.**   **Unwmk.**

1	A1	2p multi	.30	.80
2	A2	4p multi	.30	.80
3	A3	1s multi	.30	2.25
		Nos. 1-3 (3)	.90	3.85

Nigeria Nos. 184-187, 189-197 Overprinted

No. 4

No. 12

Arms in red on Nos. 11-14, 16

1968, Apr. 1

4	A49	½p multi (#184)	2.00	6.75
5	A49	1p multi (#185)	3.25	10.00
6	A49	1½p multi (#186)	12.00	20.00
7	A49	2p multi (#187)	37.50	60.00
8	A49	4p multi (#189)	19.00	60.00
9	A49	6p multi (#190)	9.50	18.00
10	A49	9p multi (#191)	3.75	4.50
11	A49	1sh multi (#192)	65.00	135.00
12	A49	1sh3p multi (#193)	35.00	60.00
13	A49	2sh6p multi (#194)	4.25	19.00
14	A49	5sh multi (#195)	3.50	18.50
15	A49	10sh multi (#196)	11.00	47.50
16	A49	£1 multi (#197)	12.00	47.50
		Nos. 4-16 (13)	217.75	506.75

Nos. 4-16 were overprinted locally by the Government Printer, Enugu. Overprint errors and varieties exist.

1st Anniv. Indep. — A4

Designs: 4p, Biafran flag, workers, missiles. 1sh, Igbo victim of 1966 Nigerian pogrom. 2sh6p, nurse and refugees. 5sh, Biafran arms, £1 banknote. 10sh, Biafran orphan.

1968, May 30   **Perf. 12½**

17	A4	4p multi	.25	.25
18	A4	1sh multi	.35	.30
19	A4	2sh6p multi	.80	3.50
20	A4	5sh multi	.90	4.50
21	A4	10sh multi	1.40	5.00
		Nos. 17-21 (5)	3.70	13.55

> During 1968 several sets were sold by the Biafran philatelic agents but were not released to post offices within the country and did not perform postal duty: Nigeria Nos. 184 and 185 overprinted "Biafra France Friendship" and surcharged 5sh and £1, respectively. Value, $27.50. Biafra Nos. 17-21 overprinted "Help Biafran Children" and surcharged with additional values. Value, $4. Butterflies and plants, 4 values. Value, $11.; later overprinted with Olympic rings and "Mexico Olympics 1968." Value, $14.

2nd Anniv. Indep. — A5

1969, May 30   **Perf. 13¼x13½**

22	A5	2p multi	1.75	5.00
23	A5	4p multi	1.75	5.00
24	A5	1sh multi	3.00	8.00
25	A5	2sh6p multi	3.50	16.00
		Nos. 22-25 (4)	10.00	34.00

Souvenir Sheet

26	A5	10sh Biafran children	42.50

No. 26 exists imperf. Value, $65.
No. 26 was numbered on the back. Examples without number are presentation proofs.

Pope Paul VI's Visit to Africa — A6

1969, Aug. 1

27	A6	4p multi, org background	1.25	3.50
28	A6	6p multi, blue background	1.40	9.00
29	A6	9p multi, green background	1.60	10.00
30	A6	3sh multi, rose car background	4.00	19.00
a.		Brown background	75.00	
		Nos. 27-30 (4)	8.25	41.50

Souvenir Sheet

31	A6	10sh multi, mag background	55.00	
a.		Plum background	55.00	

In Dec. 1969 and Jan. 1970, as Biafra was collapsing, three sets were issued by Biafra's philatelic agents but were not available within Biafra: Nos. 27-30 overprinted "Christmas 1969 Peace on Earth and Goodwill to All Men." Value, $9. This overprint also was applied to Nos. 31 and 31a, with denomination surcharged to £1; value, each $45. Nos. 22-26 overprinted "Save Biafra 9th Jan. 1970" with added surtax. Values: set $42.50, souvenir sheet $47.50. No. 26 imperf. with this overprint also exists. Nos. 28 and 29 overprinted with UN emblem, "Human Rights" and added surtax. Value, $10.

BOLIVIA

bə-'li-vē-ə

LOCATION — Central South America, separated from the Pacific Ocean by Chile and Peru.
GOVT. — Republic
AREA — 424,165 sq. mi.
POP. — 7,949,933 (1998 est.)
CAPITAL — Sucre (La Paz is the actual seat of government).

100 Centavos = 1 Boliviano
100 Centavos = 1 Peso Boliviano (1963)
100 Centavos = 1 Boliviano (1987)

Catalogue values for unused stamps in this country are for Never Hinged items, beginning with Scott 308 in the regular postage section, Scott C112 in the airpost section, Scott RA5 in the postal tax section, and Scott RAC1 in airpost postal tax section.

On Feb. 21, 1863, the Bolivian Government decreed contracts for carrying the mails should be let to the highest bidder, the service to commence on the day the bid was accepted, and stamps used for the payment of postage. The winner of the contract would be responsible for expenses and would keep the profits. On Mar. 18, the contract was awarded to Sr. Justiniano Garcia and was in effect until Apr. 29, 1863, when it was rescinded. Stamps in the form illustrated above were prepared in denominations of ½, 1, 2 and 4 reales. All values exist in black and in blue. The blue are

twice as scarce as the black. Value, black, $75 each.

It is said that used examples exist on covers, but the authenticity of these covers remains to be established.

Condor — A1

A2

A3

72 varieties of each of the 5c, 78 varieties of the 10c, 30 varieties of each of the 50c and 100c.

The plate of the 5c stamps was entirely reengraved 4 times and retouched at least 6 times. Various states of the plate have distinguishing characteristics, each of which is typical of most, though not all the stamps in a sheet. These characteristics (usually termed types) are found in the shading lines at the right side of the globe. a, vertical and diagonal lines. b, diagonal lines only. c, diagonal and horizontal with traces of vertical lines. d, diagonal and horizontal lines. e, horizontal lines only. f, no lines except the curved ones forming the outlines of the globe.

1867-68   Unwmk.   Engr.   Imperf.

1	A1	5c yel grn, thin paper (a, b)	11.00	25.00
a.		5c blue green (a)	11.00	30.00
b.		5c deep green (a)	11.00	30.00
c.		5c ol grn, thick paper (a)	450.00	450.00
d.		5c yel grn, thick paper (a)	300.00	300.00
e.		5c yel grn, thick paper (b)	300.00	300.00
f.		5c blue green (b)	11.00	30.00
2	A1	5c green (d)	10.00	25.00
a.		5c green (c)	15.00	30.00
b.		5c green (e)	15.00	30.00
c.		5c green (f)	15.00	30.00
3	A1	5c vio ('68)	375.00	375.00
a.		5c rose lilac ('68)	375.00	375.00
		Revenue cancel		150.00
4	A3	10c brown	400.00	350.00
		Revenue cancel		175.00
5	A2	50c orange	35.00	
		Revenue cancel		15.00
6	A2	50c blue ('68)	500.00	
a.		50c dark blue ('68)	500.00	
		Revenue cancel		250.00
7	A3	100c blue	80.00	
		Revenue cancel		45.00
8	A3	100c green ('68)	250.00	
a.		100c pale blue grn ('68)	250.00	
		Revenue cancel		175.00

Used values are for postally canceled stamps. Pen cancellations usually indicate that the stamps have been used fiscally and such stamps sell for about one-fifth as much as those with postal cancellations.

The 500c is an essay.

Reprints of Nos. 3,4, 6 and 8 are common. Value, $10 each. Reprints of Nos. 2 and 5 are scarcer. Value, $25 each.

Coat of Arms
A4   A5

1868-69   Perf. 12

Nine Stars

10	A4	5c green	27.50	18.00
11	A4	10c vermilion	45.00	25.00
12	A4	50c blue	70.00	45.00
13	A4	100c orange	80.00	55.00
14	A4	500c black	1,000.	1,000.

Eleven Stars

15	A5	5c green	18.00	12.00
16	A5	10c vermilion	25.00	20.00
a.		Half used as 5c on cover		600.00
17	A5	50c blue	50.00	40.00
18	A5	100c dp orange	60.00	50.00
19	A5	500c black	3,500.	3,500.

See Nos. 26-27, 31-34.

Arms and "The Law" — A6

1878   Various Frames   Perf. 12

20	A6	5c ultra	15.00	7.00
21	A6	10c orange	12.00	6.00
a.		Half used as 5c on cover		250.00
22	A6	20c green	45.00	10.00
a.		Half used as 10c on cover		200.00
23	A6	50c dull carmine	120.00	30.00
		Nos. 20-23 (4)	192.00	53.00

(11 Stars) — A7

Numerals Upright

1887   Rouletted

24	A7	1c rose	4.00	3.00
25	A7	2c violet	6.00	6.00
26	A5	5c blue	14.50	8.00
27	A5	10c orange	14.50	8.00
		Nos. 24-27 (4)	37.00	22.00

See No. 37.

(9 Stars) — A8

1890   Perf. 12

28	A8	1c rose	3.00	2.00
29	A8	2c violet	8.00	4.00
30	A4	5c blue	6.00	2.00
31	A4	10c orange	12.00	3.00
32	A4	20c dk green	25.00	6.00
33	A4	50c red	12.00	8.00
34	A4	100c yellow	25.00	30.00
		Nos. 28-34 (7)	91.00	55.00

See Nos. 35-36, 38-39.

1893   Litho.   Perf. 11

35	A8	1c rose	6.00	5.00
a.		Imperf. pair	100.00	
b.		Horiz. pair, imperf. vert.	100.00	
c.		Horiz. pair, imperf. btwn.	100.00	
36	A8	2c violet	6.00	5.00
a.		Block of 4 imperf. vert. and horiz. through center	200.00	
b.		Horiz. pair, imperf. btwn.	100.00	
c.		Vert. pair, imperf betwn.	100.00	
37	A7	5c blue	8.00	4.00
a.		Vert. pair, imperf. horiz.	100.00	
b.		Horiz. pair, imperf. btwn.	100.00	
38	A8	10c orange	25.00	8.00
a.		Horiz. pair, imperf. btwn.	100.00	
39	A8	20c dark green	100.00	45.00
a.		Imperf. pair, vert. or horiz.	200.00	
b.		Pair, imperf. btwn., vert. or horiz.	175.00	
		Nos. 35-39 (5)	145.00	67.00

Coat of Arms — A9

1894   Unwmk.   Engr.   Perf. 14, 14½
Thin Paper

40	A9	1c bister	1.50	1.25
41	A9	2c red orange	3.00	2.25
42	A9	5c green	1.50	1.25
43	A9	10c yellow brn	1.50	1.25
44	A9	20c dark blue	8.00	8.00
45	A9	50c claret	20.00	20.00
46	A9	100c brown rose	40.00	40.00
		Nos. 40-46 (7)	75.50	74.00

Stamps of type A9 on thick paper were surreptitiously printed in Paris on the order of an official and without government authorization. Some of these stamps were substituted for part of a shipment of stamps on thin paper, which had been printed in London on government order.

When the thick paper stamps reached Bolivia they were at first repudiated but afterwards were allowed to do postal duty. A large

quantity of the thick paper stamps were fraudulently canceled in Paris with a cancellation of heavy bars forming an oval. Value of unused set: $5.

To be legitimate, stamps of the thick paper stamps must have genuine cancellations of Bolivia. Value, on cover, each $150.

The 10c blue on thick paper is not known to have been issued.

Some examples of Nos. 40-46 show part of a papermakers' watermark "1011."

For overprints see Nos. 55-59.

President Tomas Frias — A10   President Jose M. Linares — A11

Pedro Domingo Murillo A12   Bernardo Monteagudo A13

Gen. Jose Ballivian — A14   Gen. Antonio Jose de Sucre — A15

Simon Bolivar — A16   Coat of Arms — A17

1897   Litho.   Perf. 12

47	A10	1c pale yellow grn	2.00	2.00
a.		Vert. pair, imperf. horiz.	100.00	
b.		Vert. pair, imperf. btwn.	100.00	
48	A11	2c red	3.00	2.00
49	A12	5c dk green	2.00	2.00
a.		Horiz. pair, imperf. btwn.	100.00	
50	A13	10c brown vio	2.00	2.00
a.		Vert. pair, imperf. btwn.	100.00	
51	A14	20c lake & blk	10.00	5.00
a.		Imperf., pair	100.00	
52	A15	50c orange	10.00	10.00
53	A16	1b Prus blue	20.00	20.00
54	A17	2b red, yel, grn & blk	60.00	90.00
		Nos. 47-54 (8)	109.00	133.00

Excellent forgeries of No. 54, perf and imperf, exist, some postally used.

Reprint of No. 53 has dot in numeral. Same value.

Nos. 40-44
Handstamped in Violet or Blue

1899   Perf. 14½

55	A9	1c yellow bis	30.00	30.00
56	A9	2c red orange	40.00	50.00
57	A9	5c green	17.00	17.00

58	A9	10c yellow brn	30.00	30.00
59	A9	20c dark blue	50.00	75.00
		Nos. 55-59 (5)	167.00	202.00

The handstamp is found inverted, double, etc. Values twice the listed amounts. Forgeries of this handstamp are plentiful. "E.F." stands for Estado Federal.

The 50c and 100c (Nos. 45-46) were overprinted at a later date in Brazil. Value, $500.

Antonio José de Sucre — A18

Perf. 11½, 12

1899		Engr.		Thin Paper
62	A18	1c gray blue	5.00	2.00
63	A18	2c brnsh red	5.00	2.00
64	A18	5c dk green	5.00	2.00
65	A18	10c yellow org	4.00	2.00
66	A18	20c rose pink	5.00	2.00
67	A18	50c bister brn	10.00	5.00
68	A18	1b gray violet	8.00	4.00
		Nos. 62-68 (7)	42.00	19.00

1901				
69	A18	5c dark red	3.00	2.00

Col. Adolfo Ballivian A19

Eliodoro Camacho A20

President Narciso Campero A21

Jose Ballivian A22

Gen. Andres Santa Cruz — A23

Coat of Arms — A24

1901-04			Engr.	
70	A19	1c claret	.85	.30
71	A20	2c green	1.00	.50
73	A21	5c scarlet	1.00	.30
74	A22	10c blue	3.00	.50
75	A23	20c violet & blk	2.00	1.00
76	A24	2b brown	7.00	5.00

			Litho.	
77	A19	1c claret ('04)	3.00	1.00
		Nos. 70-77 (7)	17.85	8.60

In No. 70 the panel above "CENTAVO" is shaded with continuous lines. In No. 77 the shading is of dots.

Nos. 73-74 exist imperf. Value, pairs, each $50.

See Nos. 103-105, 107, 110.

For surcharges see Nos. 95-96, 193.

Coat of Arms of Dept. of La Paz — A25

Murillo — A26

Jose Miguel Lanza — A27

Ismael Montes — A28

1909		Litho.		Perf. 11
78	A25	5c blue & blk	15.00	11.00
79	A26	10c green & blk	15.00	11.00
80	A27	20c orange & blk	15.00	11.00
81	A28	2b red & black	15.00	11.00
		Nos. 78-81 (4)	60.00	44.00

Centenary of Revolution of July, 1809.

Nos. 78-81 exist imperf. and tête bêche. Values: imperf. pairs, each $80; tête bêche pairs, each $95. Nos. 79-81 exist with center inverted. Value, each $95.

Miguel Betanzos A29

Col. Ignacio Warnes A30

Murillo A31

Monteagudo A32

Esteban Arce — A33

Antonio Jose de Sucre — A34

Simon Bolivar — A35

Manuel Belgrano — A36

1909		Dated 1809-1825		Perf. 11½
82	A29	1c lt brown & blk	1.00	.40
83	A30	2c green & blk	1.50	.60
84	A31	5c red & blk	1.50	.50
85	A32	10c dull bl & blk	2.00	.50
86	A33	20c violet & blk	1.75	.70
87	A34	50c olive bister & blk	2.00	.80
88	A35	1b gray brn & blk	2.50	1.50
89	A36	2b chocolate & blk	2.50	2.00
		Nos. 82-89 (8)	14.75	7.00

War of Independence, 1809-1825.

Nos. 82-89 exist imperf. Value, set of pairs $400.

For surcharge see No. 97.

Warnes A37

Betanzos A38

Arce — A39

Dated 1910-1825

1910			Perf. 13x13½	
92	A37	5c green & black	.50	.30
a.		Imperf., pair	15.00	
93	A38	10c claret & indigo	.60	.50
a.		Imperf., pair	50.00	
94	A39	20c dull blue & indigo	1.00	.80
a.		Imperf., pair	20.00	
		Nos. 92-94 (3)	2.10	1.60

War of Independence.

Nos. 92-94 may be found with parts of a papermaker's watermark: "A I & Co/EXTRA STRONG/9303."

Both perf. and imperf. exist with inverted centers.

Nos. 71 and 75 Surcharged in Black

1911			Perf. 11½, 12	
95	A20	5c on 2c green	.75	.30
a.		Inverted surcharge	10.00	10.00
b.		Double surcharge	12.00	10.00
c.		Period after "1911"	4.50	1.50
d.		Blue surcharge	100.00	80.00
e.		Double dsurch., one invtd.	20.00	20.00
96	A23	5c on 20c vio & blk	30.00	30.00
a.		Inverted surcharge	60.00	60.00
b.		Double surch., one invtd.	80.00	
c.		Period after "1911"	40.00	40.00

No. 83 Handstamp Surcharged in Green

97	A30	20c on 2c grn & blk		2,500.

This provisional was issued by local authorities at Villa Bella, a town on the Brazilian border. The 20c surcharge was applied after the stamp had been affixed to the cover. Excellent forgeries of No. 96-97 exist.

"Justice" A40

A41

1912
Black or Dark Blue Overprint On Revenue Stamps

98	A40	2c green (Bk)	.75	.30
a.		Inverted overprint	15.00	
99	A41	10c ver (Bl)	6.00	1.00
a.		Inverted overprint	20.00	

A42   A43

Red or Black Overprint
Engr.

100	A42	5c orange (R)	.75	.65
a.		Inverted overprint	20.00	
b.		Pair, one without overprint	50.00	
c.		Black overprint	35.00	

Red or Black Surcharge

101	A43	10c on 1c bl (R)	1.00	.60
a.		Inverted surcharge	25.00	
b.		Double surcharge	25.00	
c.		Dbl. surcharge, one invtd.	40.00	
d.		Black surcharge	200.00	150.00
e.		As "d," inverted	250.00	
f.		As "d," double surcharge	225.00	
g.		Pair, one without black surch.	800.00	

Fakes of No. 101d are plentiful.

Revenue Stamp Surcharged

Type 1 —Serifed "1"s in date

Type 2 — Sans-serif "1"s in date

1917			Litho.	
102		10c on 1c blue, Type 1	5,000.	1,750.
a.		10c on 1c, Type 2		2,000.

Design similar to type A43.

1,000 examples of Nos. 102 and 102a were reportedly produced, with 90 percent of the issue being type 1 and the balance type 2. No. 102a also exists with overprint in black. Value, used, $2,500.

Excellent forgeries exist.

Types of 1901 and

Frias — A45

Sucre — A46

Bolivar — A47

1913		Engr.		Perf. 12
103	A19	1c car rose	.75	.30
104	A20	2c vermilion	.75	.30
105	A21	5c green	1.00	.25
106	A45	8c yellow	1.50	1.00
107	A22	10c gray	1.50	.25
108	A46	50c dull violet	3.00	1.50
109	A47	1b slate blue	6.00	2.00
110	A24	2b black	10.00	5.00
		Nos. 103-110 (8)	24.50	10.60

No. 107, litho., was not regularly issued.

Nine values commemorating the Guaqui-La Paz railroad were printed in 1915 but never issued. Value, set $25. The original set is engraved. Crude, typographed forgeries exist.

Monolith of Tiahuanacu A48 — Mt. Potosí A49

Lake Titicaca — A50 — Mt. Illimani — A51

Legislature Building — A53

FIVE CENTAVOS.
Type I — Numerals have background of vertical lines. Clouds formed of dots.
Type II — Numerals on white background. Clouds near the mountain formed of wavy lines.

1916-17		Litho.	Perf. 11½	
111	A48	½c brown	.40	.30
a.		Horiz. pair, imperf. vert.	50.00	40.00
112	A49	1c gray green	.50	.30
a.		Imperf., pair	40.00	30.00
113	A50	2c car & blk	.50	.30
a.		Imperf., pair	40.00	30.00
b.		Vert. pair, imperf. horiz.	40.00	30.00
c.		Center inverted	150.00	100.00
d.		Imperf., center inverted	250.00	150.00
114	A51	5c dk blue (I)	1.25	.30
a.		Imperf., pair	40.00	30.00
b.		Vert. pair, imperf. horiz.	40.00	30.00
c.		Horiz. pair, imperf. vert.	40.00	30.00
115	A51	5c dk blue (II)	1.00	.50
a.		Imperf., pair	40.00	30.00
116	A53	10c org & bl	1.00	.50
a.		Imperf., pair	60.00	40.00
b.		No period after "Legislativo"	1.00	.30
c.		Center inverted	200.00	125.00
d.		Vertical pair, imperf. between	60.00	50.00
		Nos. 111-116 (6)	4.65	2.00

For surcharges see Nos. 194-196.

Coat of Arms
A54   A55

Printed by the American Bank Note Co.

1919-20		Engr.	Perf. 12	
118	A54	1c carmine	.40	.30
119	A54	2c dk violet	8.00	4.00
120	A54	5c dk green	.75	.30
121	A54	10c vermilion	.75	.30
122	A54	20c dk blue	2.25	.40
123	A54	22c lt blue	1.40	.90
124	A54	24c purple	.90	.60
125	A54	50c orange	7.00	.70
126	A55	1b red brown	9.00	2.50
127	A55	2b black brn	13.50	6.75
		Nos. 118-127 (10)	43.95	16.75

Printed by Perkins, Bacon & Co., Ltd.

1923-27		Re-engraved	Perf. 13½	
128	A54	1c carmine ('27)	.40	.30
129	A54	2c dk violet	.40	.30
130	A54	5c dp green	1.00	.30
131	A54	10c vermilion	25.00	18.00
132	A54	20c slate blue	2.50	.50
135	A54	50c orange	5.50	1.50
136	A55	1b red brown	1.50	1.00
137	A55	2b black brown	2.00	.60
		Nos. 128-137 (8)	38.30	22.50

There are many differences in the designs of the two issues but they are too minute to be illustrated or described.
Nos. 128-137 exist imperf. Value, $50 each pair.
See Nos. 144-146, 173-177. For surcharges see Nos. 138-143, 160, 162, 181-186, 236-237.

Stamps of 1919-20
Surcharged in Blue, Black or Red

1924			Perf. 12	
138	A54	5c on 1c car (Bl)	.40	.30
a.		Inverted surcharge	10.00	6.00
b.		Double surcharge	10.00	6.00
139	A54	10c on 10c ver (Bk)	1.00	.70
a.		Inverted surcharge	12.00	6.00
140	A54	15c on 22c lt bl (Bk)	1.00	.75
a.		Inverted surcharge	12.00	6.00
b.		Double surcharge, one inverted	16.00	6.00

No. 140 surcharged in red or blue probably are trial impressions. They appear jointly, and with black in blocks.

Same Surcharge on No. 131
Perf. 13½

142	A54	15c on 10c ver (Bk)	1.00	.30
a.		Inverted surcharge	12.00	6.00

No. 121 Surcharged

Perf. 12

143	A54	15c on 10c ver (Bk)	1.00	.50
a.		Inverted surcharge	12.00	6.00
b.		Double surcharge	12.00	6.00
		Nos. 138-143 (5)	4.40	2.55

Type of 1919-20 Issue
Printed by Waterlow & Sons
Second Re-engraving

1925		Unwmk.	Perf. 12½	
144	A54	5c deep green	1.00	.50
145	A54	15c ultra	1.00	.50
146	A54	20c dark blue	1.00	.50
		Nos. 144-146 (3)	3.00	1.50

These stamps may be identified by the perforation.

Miner — A56

Condor Looking Toward the Sea A57

Designs: 2c, Sower. 5c, Torch of Eternal Freedom. 10c, National flower (kantuta). 15c, Pres. Bautista Saavedra. 50c, Liberty head. 1b, Archer on horse. 2b, Mercury. 5b, Gen. A. J. de Sucre.

1925		Engr.	Perf. 14	
150	A56	1c dark green	1.50	
151	A56	2c rose	1.50	
152	A56	5c red, grn	1.50	.50
153	A56	10c car, yel	2.50	1.00
154	A56	15c red brown	.80	.50
155	A57	25c ultra	2.50	1.00
156	A56	50c dp violet	3.00	1.00
157	A56	1b red	5.00	2.50
158	A57	2b orange	6.00	3.00
159	A56	5b black brn	6.00	3.00
		Nos. 150-159 (10)	30.30	

Cent. of the Republic. The 1c and 2c were not released for general use.
Nos. 150-159 exist imperf. Value, $60 each pair.
For surcharges see Nos. C59-C62.

Stamps of 1919-27
Surcharged in Blue, Black or Red

1927				
160	A54	5c on 1c car (Bl)	4.50	3.25
a.		Inverted surcharge	15.00	15.00
b.		Black surcharge	40.00	40.00
		Perf. 12		
162	A54	10c on 24c pur (Bk)	4.50	3.25
a.		Inverted surcharge	50.00	50.00
b.		Red surcharge	70.00	70.00

Coat of Arms — A66

Printed by Waterlow & Sons

1927		Litho.	Perf. 13½	
165	A66	2c yellow	.50	.35
166	A66	3c pink	.90	.90
167	A66	4c red brown	.75	.75
168	A66	20c lt ol grn	1.00	.35
169	A66	25c deep blue	1.00	.50
170	A66	30c violet	1.50	1.50
171	A66	40c orange	2.00	2.00
172	A66	50c dp brown	2.00	1.00
173	A55	1b red	2.50	2.00
174	A55	2b plum	4.00	3.50
175	A55	3b olive grn	4.50	4.50
176	A55	4b claret	7.50	6.00
177	A55	5b bister brn	8.00	6.50
		Nos. 165-177 (13)	36.15	29.85

For overprints and surcharges see Nos. 178-180, 208, 211-212.

Type of 1927 Issue
Overprinted

1927				
178	A66	5c dark green	.50	.30
179	A66	10c slate	.75	.30
180	A66	15c carmine	.75	.35
		Nos. 178-180 (3)	2.00	.95

Exist with inverted overprint. Value $30 each.

Stamps of 1919-27
Surcharged

1928		Perf. 12, 12½, 13½		
		Red Surcharge		
181	A54	15c on 20c #122	15.00	15.00
a.		Inverted surcharge	22.50	22.50
182	A54	15c on 20c #132	15.00	15.00
a.		Inverted surcharge	25.00	25.00
b.		Black surcharge	45.00	
183	A54	15c on 20c #146	250.00	160.00
		Black Surcharge		
184	A54	15c on 24c #124	2.25	1.25
a.		Inverted surcharge	8.00	8.00
b.		Blue surcharge	75.00	
185	A54	15c on 50c #125	90.00	400.00
a.		Inverted surcharge	120.00	
186	A54	15c on 50c #135	1.75	1.25
a.		Inverted surcharge	10.00	10.00
		Nos. 181-186 (6)	374.00	592.50

Condor — A67 — Hernando Siles — A68

Map of Bolivia — A69

Printed by Perkins, Bacon & Co., Ltd.

1928		Engr.	Perf. 13½	
189	A67	5c green	1.50	.25
190	A68	10c slate	.50	.25
191	A69	15c carmine lake	3.00	.25
		Nos. 189-191 (3)	5.00	.75

Nos. 104, 111, 113, Surcharged in Various Colors

1930			Perf. 12, 11½	
193	A20	1c on 2c (Bl)	2.00	2.00
a.		"0.10" for "0.01"	35.00	35.00
194	A50	3c on 2c (Br)	2.00	2.00
195	A48	25c on ½c (Bk)	2.00	2.00
196	A50	25c on 2c (V)	2.00	2.00
		Nos. 193-196 (4)	8.00	8.00

The lines of the surcharges were spaced to fit the various shapes of the stamps. The surcharges exist inverted, double, etc.
Trial printings were made of the surcharges on Nos. 193 and 194 in black and on No. 196 in brown.

Mt. Potosi — A70 — Mt. Illimani — A71

Eduardo Abaroa — A72 — Map of Bolivia — A73

Sucre — A74 — Bolivar — A75

1931		Engr.	Perf. 14	
197	A70	2c green	2.00	1.00
198	A71	5c light blue	2.00	.30
199	A72	10c red orange	2.00	.30
200	A73	15c violet	4.50	.40
201	A73	35c carmine	3.00	1.25
202	A73	45c orange	3.00	1.25
203	A74	50c gray	1.50	1.00
204	A75	1b brown	2.50	1.40
		Nos. 197-204 (8)	20.50	6.90

No. 198 exists imperf.
See Nos. 207, 241. For surcharges see Nos. 209-210.

Symbols of 1930 Revolution — A76

1931　　Litho.　　Perf. 11

205	A76	15c scarlet	6.00	1.00
a.		Pair, imperf. between	25.00	
206	A76	50c brt violet	1.50	1.25
a.		Pair, imperf. between	30.00	

Revolution of June 25, 1930.
For surcharges see Nos. 239-240.

Map Type of 1931
Without Imprint

1932　　　　　　　　Litho.

207	A73	15c violet	4.00	.35

Stamps of 1927-31
Surcharged

1933　　　　Perf. 13½, 14

208	A66	5c on 1b red	1.00	.50
a.		Without period after "Cts"	3.00	3.00
209	A73	15c on 35c car	.50	.50
a.		Inverted surcharge	30.00	20.00
210	A73	15c on 45c orange	.60	.60
a.		Inverted surcharge	30.00	20.00
211	A66	15c on 50c dp brn	2.00	.50
212	A66	25c on 40c orange	1.00	.50
		Nos. 208-212 (5)	5.10	2.60

The hyphens in "13-7-33" occur in three positions: type 1, both hyphens in middle (shown); type 2, both hyphens on base line of numbers; type 3, left hyphen in middle, right hyphen on base line. Values are the same for all types.

Coat of Arms — A77

1933　　Engr.　　Perf. 12

213	A77	2c blue green	.50	.30
214	A77	5c blue	.50	.30
215	A77	10c red	1.00	.75
216	A77	15c deep violet	.50	.30
217	A77	25c dark blue	1.50	.75
		Nos. 213-217 (5)	4.00	2.40

For surcharges see Nos. 233-235, 238.

Mariano
Baptista — A78

1935

218	A78	15c dull violet	.75	.50

Map of
Bolivia — A79

1935

219	A79	2c dark blue	.50	.30
220	A79	3c yellow	.50	.30
221	A79	5c vermilion	.50	.30
222	A79	5c blue grn	.50	.30
223	A79	10c black brn	.50	.30
224	A79	15c deep rose	.50	.30
225	A79	15c ultra	.50	.30
226	A79	20c yellow grn	1.00	.60
227	A79	25c lt blue	1.50	.30
228	A79	30c deep rose	1.00	.60
229	A79	40c orange	2.25	1.00
230	A79	50c gray violet	2.25	1.00
231	A79	1b yellow	1.25	.60
232	A79	2b olive brown	3.00	1.50
		Nos. 219-232 (14)	15.75	7.70

Regular Stamps of
1925-33 Surcharged
in Black

1937　　　　Perf. 11, 12, 13½

233	A77	5c on 2c bl grn	.30	.30
234	A77	15c on 25c dk bl	.50	.50
235	A77	30c on 25c dk bl	.80	.80
236	A55	45c on 1b red brn	1.00	1.00
237	A55	1b on 2b plum	1.00	1.00
a.		"1" missing	15.00	15.00
238	A77	2b on 25c dk bl	1.00	1.00

"Comunicaciones" on one line

239	A76	3b on 50c brt vio	2.00	2.00
a.		"3" of value missing	20.00	
240	A76	5b on 50c brt vio	3.00	3.00
		Nos. 233-240 (8)	9.60	9.60

Exist inverted, double, etc.

President
Siles — A80

1937　　Unwmk.　　Perf. 14

241	A80	1c yellow brown	.50	.50

Native
School — A81

Oil Wells — A82

Modern
Factories
A83

Torch of
Knowledge
A84

Map of the Sucre-
Camiri
R. R. — A85

Allegory of Free
Education — A86

Allegorical
Figure of
Learning — A87

Symbols of
Industry — A88

Modern
Agriculture — A89

1938　　Litho.　　Perf. 10½, 11

242	A81	2c dull red	.80	.60
243	A82	10c pink	.90	.50
244	A83	15c yellow grn	1.40	.40
245	A84	30c yellow	1.75	.60
246	A85	45c rose red	3.00	1.25
247	A86	60c dk violet	2.50	1.25
248	A87	75c dull blue	2.00	1.75
249	A88	1b lt brown	4.50	1.00
250	A89	2b bister	4.00	1.50
		Nos. 242-250 (9)	20.85	8.85

For surcharge see No. 314.

Llamas — A90　　　Vicuna — A91

Coat of
Arms — A92

Cocoi
Herons — A93

Chinchilla — A94

Toco
Toucan — A95

Condor — A96

Jaguar — A97

1939, Jan. 21　　Perf. 10½, 11½x10½

251	A90	2c green	1.50	.75
252	A90	4c fawn	1.50	.75
253	A90	5c red violet	1.50	.75
254	A91	10c black	1.50	.75
255	A91	15c emerald	3.00	1.25
256	A91	20c dk slate grn	3.00	1.25
257	A92	25c lemon	1.50	.75
258	A92	30c dark blue	1.50	.75
259	A93	40c vermilion	2.50	1.00
260	A93	45c gray	2.50	1.00
261	A94	60c rose red	2.50	1.00
262	A94	75c slate blue	2.50	1.00
263	A95	90c orange	5.00	1.25
264	A95	1b blue	5.00	1.25
265	A96	2b rose lake	7.00	1.25
266	A96	3b dark violet	10.00	1.75
267	A97	4b brown org	10.00	1.75
268	A97	5b gray brown	11.50	2.00
		Nos. 251-268 (18)	73.50	20.25

All but 20c exist imperf. Value, each pair $40.
Imperf. counterfeits with altered designs exist of some values.
For surcharges see Nos. 315-317.

Flags of 21 American
Republics — A98

1940, Apr.　　Litho.　　Perf. 10½

269	A98	9b multicolored	4.50	2.25

Pan American Union, 50th anniversary.

Statue of
Murillo — A99

Urns of Murillo and
Sagarnaga — A100

Dream of
Murillo — A101

Murillo — A102

1941, Apr. 15

270	A99	10c dull vio brn	.25	.25
271	A100	15c lt green	.50	.30
a.		Imperf., pair	25.00	
b.		Double impression	8.00	8.00
272	A101	45c carmine rose	.50	.25
a.		Double impression	10.00	10.00
273	A102	1.05b dk ultra	.80	.40
		Nos. 270-273 (4)	2.05	1.20

130th anniv. of the execution of Pedro Domingo Murillo (1759-1810), patriot.
For surcharge see No. 333.

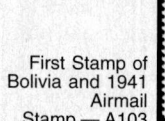

First Stamp of
Bolivia and 1941
Airmail
Stamp — A103

1942, Oct.　　Litho.　　Perf. 13½

274	A103	5c pink	1.00	1.00
275	A103	10c orange	1.00	1.00
276	A103	20c yellow grn	1.50	1.00
277	A103	40c carmine rose	1.50	1.00
278	A103	90c yellow	3.00	2.25
279	A103	1b violet	5.00	3.75
280	A103	10b olive bister	20.00	16.00
		Nos. 274-280 (7)	33.00	26.00

1st School Phil. Exposition held in La Paz, Oct., 1941.

Gen. Ballivian
Leading Cavalry
Charge, Battle of
Ingavi — A104

1943　　Photo.　　Perf. 12½

281	A104	2c lt blue grn	.30	.25
282	A104	3c orange	.30	.25
283	A104	25c deep plum	.60	.35
284	A104	45c ultra	.60	.35
285	A104	3b scarlet	1.40	.70
286	A104	4b brt rose lilac	1.50	.80
287	A104	5b black brown	1.50	.90
		Nos. 281-287 (7)	6.20	3.60

Souvenir Sheets
Perf. 13, Imperf.

288	A104	Sheet of 4	6.00	6.00
289	A104	Sheet of 3	15.00	15.00

Centenary of the Battle of Ingavi, 1841. No. 288 contains 4 stamps similar to Nos. 281-284, No. 289 three stamps similar to Nos. 285-287.

Potosi
A107

Quechisla
A108

Miner — A109

Dam
A110

Mine
Interior
A111

Chaquiri
Dam
A112

Entrance
to
Pulacayo
Mine
A113

1943   Engr.   Perf. 12½

290	A107	15c red brown	.50	.30
291	A108	45c vio blue	.60	.30
292	A109	1.25b brt rose vio	1.00	.50
293	A110	1.50b emerald	.80	.50
294	A111	2b brown blk	1.00	.70
295	A112	2.10b lt blue	1.00	.70
296	A113	3b red orange	4.00	1.10
		Nos. 290-296 (7)	8.90	4.10

General
José
Ballivián
and
Cathedral
at
Trinidad
A114

1943, Nov. 18

297	A114	5c dk green & brn	.50	.30
298	A114	10c dull pur & brn	.50	.30
299	A114	30c rose red & brn	.50	.30
300	A114	45c brt ultra & brn	.75	.50
301	A114	2.10b dp org & brn	1.50	1.00
		Nos. 297-301,C91-C95 (10)	6.40	4.30

Department of Beni centenary.

"Honor, Work,
Law" — A115

"United for the
Country" — A116

1944   Litho.   Perf. 13½

302	A115	20c orange	.30	.30
303	A115	90c ultra	.30	.30
304	A116	1b brt red vio	.30	.30
305	A116	2.40b dull brown	.30	.30

1945

306	A115	20c green	.30	.30
307	A115	90c dp rose	.50	.30
		Nos. 302-307,C96-C99 (10)	3.35	2.80

Nos. 302-307 were issued to commemorate the Revolution of Dec. 20, 1943.

> Catalogue values for unused stamps in this section, from this point to the end of the section, are for Never Hinged items.

Leopold Benedetto Vincenti, Joseph Ignacio de Sanjines and Bars of Anthem — A117

1946, Aug. 21   Litho.   Perf. 10½

308	A117	5c rose vio & blk	.25	.25
309	A117	10c ultra & blk	.25	.25
310	A117	15c blue grn & blk	.25	.25
311	A117	30c vermilion & brn	.55	.25
a.		Souv. sheet of 1, imperf.	2.50	2.50
312	A117	90c dk blue & brn	.50	.30
313	A117	2b black & brn	1.20	1.00
a.		Souv. sheet of 1, imperf.	4.50	4.50
		Nos. 308-313 (6)	3.00	2.30

Adoption of Bolivia's natl. anthem, cent. Nos. 311a and 313a sold for 4b over face.

Nos. 248 and 262
Surcharged in
Carmine, Black or
Orange

1947, Mar. 12   Perf. 10½, 11

314	A87	1.40b on 75c (C)	.35	.25
315	A94	1.40b on 75c (Bk)	.35	.25
316	A94	1.40b on 75c (C)	.35	.25
317	A94	1.40b on 75c (O)	.35	.25
		Nos. 314-317,C112 (5)	1.75	1.25

People Attacking
Presidential
Palace — A118

1947, Sept.   Litho.   Perf. 13½

318	A118	20c blue grn	.25	.25
319	A118	50c lilac rose	.30	.25
320	A118	1.40b grnsh bl	.30	.25
321	A118	3.70b dull org	1.00	.30
322	A118	4b violet	1.00	.30
323	A118	10b olive	3.00	1.00
		Nos. 318-323,C113-C117 (11)	7.15	3.60

1st anniv. of the Revolution of July 21, 1946. Nos. 318-323 exist imperf. Value, each pair $40.

Arms of Bolivia
and Argentina
A119

1947, Oct. 23

324	A119	1.40b deep orange	.40	.25

Meeting of Presidents Enrique Hertzog of Bolivia and Juan D. Peron of Argentina at Yacuiba on Oct. 23, 1947. Exist imperf. See No. C118.

Statue of Christ
above La
Paz — A120

2b, Child kneeling before cross of Golgotha. 3b, St. John Bosco. No. 328, Virgin of Copacabana. No. 329, Pope Pius XII blessing University of La Paz.

1948, Sept. 26   Unwmk.   Perf. 11½

325	A120	1.40b blue & yel	.60	.25
326	A120	2b yel grn & sal	.90	.25
327	A120	3b green & gray	1.75	.25
328	A120	5b violet & sal	2.25	.25
329	A120	5b red brn & lt grn	3.00	.60
		Nos. 325-329,C119-C123 (10)	14.30	3.50

3rd Inter-American Cong. of Catholic Education.

Map and Emblem of
Bolivia Auto
Club — A125

1948, Oct. 20

330	A125	5b indigo & salmon	2.50	.60

Intl. Automobile Races of South America, Sept.-Oct. 1948. See No. C124.

Pres. Gregorio
Pacheco, Map and
Post Horn — A126

1950, Jan. 2   Litho.   Perf. 11½

331	A126	1.40b violet blue	.30	.25
332	A126	4.20b red	.50	.25
		Nos. 331-332,C125-C127 (5)	1.90	1.25

75th anniv. of the UPU.

No. 273 Surcharged
in Black

1950   Perf. 10½

333	A102	2b on 1.05b dk ultra	.45	.25

Crucifix and View
of Potosi — A127

Perf. 11½
1950, Sept. 14   Litho.   Unwmk.

334	A127	20c violet	.25	.25
335	A127	30c dp orange	.25	.25
336	A127	50c lilac rose	.25	.25
337	A127	1b carmine	.25	.25
338	A127	2b blue	.35	.25
339	A127	6b chocolate	.35	.25
		Nos. 334-339 (6)	1.70	1.50

400th anniv. of the appearance of a crucifix at Potosi. Exist imperf.

Symbols of United
Nations — A128

1950, Oct. 24

340	A128	60c ultra	1.40	.25
341	A128	2b green	2.25	.35
		Nos. 340-341,C138-C139 (4)	6.65	1.20

5th anniv. of the UN, Oct. 24, 1945.

Gate of the
Sun and
Llama
A129

Church of San
Francisco — A130

40c, Avenue Camacho. 50c, Consistorial Palace. 1b, Legislative Palace. 1.40b, Communications Bldg. 2b, Arms. 3b, La Gasca ordering Mendoza to found La Paz. 5b, Capt. Alonso de Mendoza founding La Paz. 10b, Arms; portrait of Mendoza.

1951, Mar.   Engr.   Perf. 12½
Center in Black

342	A129	20c green	.25	.25
343	A130	30c dp orange	.25	.25
344	A129	40c bister brn	.25	.25
345	A129	50c dk red	.25	.25
346	A129	1b dp purple	.25	.25
347	A129	1.40b dk vio blue	.30	.25
348	A129	2b dp purple	.40	.25
349	A129	3b red lilac	.40	.40
a.		Sheet, Nos. 345, 346, 348, 349	3.00	3.00
b.		As "a," imperf.	3.00	3.00
350	A129	5b dk red	.50	.30
a.		Sheet, Nos. 344, 347, 350	3.50	3.50
b.		As "a," imperf.	3.50	3.50
351	A129	10b sepia	1.00	.40
a.		Sheet, Nos. 342, 343, 351	3.00	3.00
b.		As "a," imperf.	3.00	3.00
		Nos. 342-351,C140-C149 (20)	9.90	8.65

400th anniv. of the founding of La Paz. For surcharges see Nos. 393-402.

Boxing
A131

Perf. 12½
1951, July 1   Unwmk.   Engr.

352	A131	20c shown	.35	.25
353	A131	50c Tennis	.50	.25
354	A131	1b Diving	.50	.25
355	A131	1.40b Soccer	.55	.25
356	A131	2b Skiing	.75	.40
357	A131	3b Handball	2.50	1.75
a.		Sheet, #352-353, 356-357	7.00	7.00
b.		As "a," imperf.	7.00	7.00
358	A131	4b Cycling	3.50	2.50
a.		Sheet, #354-355, 358	7.00	7.00
b.		As "a," imperf.	7.00	7.00
		Nos. 352-358,C150-C156 (14)	24.70	12.20

The stamps were intended to commemorate the 5th athletic championship matches held at La Paz, October 1948.

An imperforate souvenir sheet denominated 54b, depicting Nos. 354, 654 and 659 with simulated perforations, was issued March 24, 1982, to celebrate the España '82 World Cup soccer championship games. Value $50.

A souvenir sheet denominated 2b, containing No. 356 perf 14¼, was issued June 15, 1988, to mark the 1988 Calgary Winter Olympic Games. Value $25.

Eagle and Flag of Bolivia A132

1951, Nov. 5   Litho.   Perf. 11½
Flag in Red, Yellow and Green.

359	A132	2b aqua	.25	.25
360	A132	3.50b ultra	.25	.25
361	A132	5b purple	.25	.25
362	A132	7.50b gray	.50	.25
363	A132	15b dp car	.65	.30
364	A132	30b sepia	1.40	.65
		Nos. 359-364 (6)	3.30	1.95

Cent. of the adoption of Bolivia's natl. flag.

Eduardo Abaroa — A133

1952, Mar.   Perf. 11

365	A133	80c dk carmine	.25	.25
366	A133	1b red orange	.25	.25
367	A133	2b emerald	.25	.25
368	A133	5b ultra	.50	.25
369	A133	10b lilac rose	1.50	.30
370	A133	20b dk brown	2.50	.50
		Nos. 365-370,C157-C162 (12)	11.70	4.90

73rd anniv. of the death of Eduardo Abaroa.

Queen Isabella I — A134

1952, July 16   Unwmk.   Perf. 13½

371	A134	2b vio bl	.45	.25
372	A134	6.30b carmine	.45	.25
		Nos. 371-372,C163-C164 (4)	3.15	1.10

Birth of Isabella I of Spain, 500th anniv.

Columbus Lighthouse — A135

1952, July 16   Litho.

373	A135	2b vio bl, bl	.25	.25
374	A135	5b car, sal	.80	.50
375	A135	9b emer, grn	1.10	1.00
		Nos. 373-375,C165-C168 (7)	3.50	2.75

An imperforate souvenir sheet denominated 1,000,000b, depicting No. 374 with simulated perforations, was issued May 12, 1986, to

---

mark the 500th anniversary of the discovery of America. Value $30.

Miner — A136

1953, Apr. 9

376	A136	2.50b vermilion	.30	.25
377	A136	8b violet	.30	.25

Nationalization of the mines.

Gualberto Villarroel, Victor Paz Estenssoro and Hernan Siles Zuazo A137

1953, Apr. 9   Perf. 11½

378	A137	50c rose lil	.25	.25
379	A137	1b brt rose	.25	.25
380	A137	2b vio bl	.30	.25
381	A137	3b lt grn	.30	.25
382	A137	4b yel org	.50	.30
383	A137	5b dl vio	.50	.30
		Nos. 378-383,C169-C175 (13)	5.65	4.30

Revolution of Apr. 9, 1952, 1st anniv.

Map of Bolivia and Cow's Head — A138

25b, 85b, Map and ear of wheat.

1954, Aug. 2   Perf. 12x11½

384	A138	5b car rose	.25	.25
385	A138	17b aqua	.25	.25
386	A138	25b chalky blue	.25	.25
387	A138	85b blk brn	.30	.25
		Nos. 384-387,C176-C181 (10)	5.85	2.55

Nos. 384-385 for the agrarian reform laws of 1953-54. Nos. 386-387 for the 1st National Congress of Agronomy. Exist imperf.

Oil Refinery A139

1955, Oct. 9   Unwmk.   Perf. 12x11½

388	A139	10b ultra & lt ultra	.35	.25
389	A139	35b rose car & rose	.35	.25
390	A139	40b dk & lt yel grn	.35	.25
391	A139	50b red vio & lil rose	.50	.25
392	A139	80b brn & bis brn	.75	.25
		Nos. 388-392,C182-C186 (10)	12.15	4.25

Nos. 388-392 exist imperf. Value, set of pairs $250.

Nos. 342-351, Surcharged with New Values and Bars in Ultramarine

1957, Feb. 14   Engr.   Perf. 12½
Center in Black

393	A129	50b on 3b red lilac	.25	.25
394	A129	100b on 2b dp pur	.25	.25
395	A129	200b on 1b dp pur	.25	.25
396	A129	300b on 1.40b dk vio bl	.30	.25
397	A129	350b on 20c green	.50	.25
398	A129	400b on 40c bis brn	.60	.25
399	A130	600b on 30c dp org	.50	.30
400	A129	800b on 50c dk red	.75	.30
401	A129	1000b on 10b sepia	.75	.30
402	A129	2000b on 5b dk red	1.25	.50
		Nos. 393-402 (10)	5.40	2.90

See Nos. C187-C196.

CEPAL Building, Santiago de Chile, and Meeting Hall in La Paz — A140

1957, May 15   Litho.   Perf. 13

403	A140	150b gray & ultra	.25	.25
404	A140	350b bis brn & gray	.30	.25
405	A140	550b chlky bl & brn	.40	.25
406	A140	750b dp rose & grn	.45	.30
407	A140	900b grn & brn blk	1.50	.60
		Nos. 403-407,C197-C201 (10)	10.80	5.20

7th session of the C. E. P. A. L. (Comision Economica para la America Latina de las Naciones Unidas), La Paz. Nos. 403-407 exist imperf. Value, set of pairs $250.

For surcharges see Nos. 482-484.

Presidents Siles Zuazo and Aramburu A141

1957, Dec. 15   Unwmk.   Perf. 11½

408	A141	50b dp red org & org	.25	.25
409	A141	350b dp blue & blue	.55	.25
410	A141	1000b dp brn & brn rose	1.25	.30
		Nos. 408-410,C202-C204 (6)	5.55	1.80

Opening of the Santa Cruz-Yacuiba Railroad and the meeting of the Presidents of Bolivia and Argentina. Nos. 408-410, C202-C204 exist imperf. Value, set of pairs $160.

For surcharge see No. 699.

Flags of Bolivia and Mexico and Presidents Hernan Siles Zuazo and Adolfo Lopez Mateos A142

1960, Jan. 30   Litho.   Perf. 11½

411	A142	350b olive	.30	.25
412	A142	600b red brown	.40	.25
413	A142	1500b black brown	1.00	.35
		Nos. 411-413,C205-C207 (6)	6.20	3.10

Issued for an expected visit of Mexico's President Adolfo Lopez Mateos. On sale Jan. 30-Feb. 1, 1960.

Indians and Mt. Illimani A143

1960, Mar. 26   Unwmk.

414	A143	500b olive bister	.75	.40
415	A143	1000b blue	1.50	.60
416	A143	2000b brown	3.75	1.00
417	A143	4000b green	6.00	4.50
		Nos. 414-417,C208-C211 (8)	36.75	18.75

Refugee Children — A144

1960, Apr. 7   Perf. 11½

418	A144	50b brown	.25	.25
419	A144	350b claret	.25	.25
420	A144	400b steel blue	.40	.25
421	A144	1000b gray brown	.80	.50
422	A144	3000b slate green	2.00	1.25
		Nos. 418-422,C212-C216 (10)	8.30	5.20

World Refugee Year, 7/1/59-6/30/60.
For surcharges see Nos. 454-458, 529.

Jaime Laredo A145

1960, Aug. 15   Litho.   Perf. 11½

423	A145	100b olive	.50	.25
424	A145	350b deep rose	.70	.25
425	A145	500b Prus green	1.00	.30
426	A145	1000b brown	1.25	.70
427	A145	1500b violet blue	2.25	1.25
428	A145	5000b gray	5.50	2.25
		Nos. 423-428,C217-C222 (12)	29.45	11.05

Issued to honor violinist Jaime Laredo.
For surcharge see No. 485.

Rotary Emblem and Nurse with Children — A146

1960, Nov. 19   Perf. 11½

429	A146	350b multi	.30	.25
430	A146	500b multi	.45	.30
431	A146	600b multi	.75	.30
432	A146	1000b multi	1.00	.50
		Nos. 429-432,C223-C226 (8)	9.90	4.30

Issued for the Children's Hospital, sponsored by the Rotary Club of La Paz.
For surcharges see Nos. 486-487.

 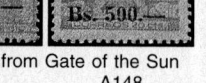

Designs from Gate of the Sun A147   A148

Designs: Various prehistoric gods and ornaments from Tiahuanacu excavations.

Surcharged in Black or Dark Red Gold Background
1960, Dec. 16   Perf. 13x12, 12x13
Sizes: 21x23mm, 23x21mm

433	A147	50b on ½c red	.80	.45
434	A147	100b on 1c red	.50	.25
435	A147	200b on 2c blk	1.60	.25
436	A147	300b on 5c grn (DR)	.35	.25
437	A147	350b on 10c grn	1.25	1.10
438	A148	400b on 15c ind	.50	.25
439	A148	500b on 20c red	.50	.25
440	A148	500b on 50c red	.60	.25
441	A148	600b on 22½c grn	.80	.40
442	A148	600b on 60c vio	.90	.50
443	A148	700b on 25c vio	1.25	.30
444	A148	700b on 1b grn	1.75	1.00
445	A148	800b on 30c red	1.00	.30
446	A148	900b on 40c grn	.75	.40
447	A148	1000b on 2b bl	1.00	.50
448	A148	1800b on 3b gray	10.00	6.00

Perf. 11
Size: 49½x23mm

449	A148	4000b on 4b gray	75.00	60.00

Perf. 11x13½
Size: 49x53mm

450	A147	5000b on 5b gray	18.00	12.50
		Nos. 433-450 (18)	116.55	84.95

Nos. 433-450 were not regularly issued without surcharge. Value, set $60.

The decree for Nos. 433-450 stipulated that 7 were for air mail (500b on 50c, 600b on 60c, 700b on 1b, 1000b, 1800b, 4000b and 5000b), but the overprinting failed to include "Aereo."

The 800b surcharge also exists on the 1c red and gold. This was not listed in the decree. Value $20.

An imperforate 1,000,000b souvenir sheet, depicting the 5c and 3b values of the unissued set was issued May 12, 1986, to commemorate Halley's Comet. Value $75.
For surcharges see Nos. 528, 614.

Miguel de Cervantes — A149

1961, Nov.   Photo.   Perf. 13x12½
451 A149 600b ocher & dl vio   .60   .25
Cervantes' appointment as Chief Magistrate of La Paz. See No. C230.

Nuflo de Chaves — A150

1961, Nov.   Unwmk.
452 A150 1500b dk bl, *buff*   1.25   .50
Founding of Santa Cruz de la Sierra, 400th anniv. See Nos. 468, C246. For surcharge see No. 533.

People below Eucharist Symbol — A151

1962, Mar. 19   Litho.   Perf. 10½
453 A151 1000b gray grn, red & yel   1.25   .75
4th Natl. Eucharistic Congress, Santa Cruz, 1961. See No. C231.

Nos. 418-422 Surcharged Horizontally with New Value and Bars or Greek Key Border Segment

No. 454   No. 455

No. 456   Nos. 457-458

1962, June   Perf. 11½
454 A144 600b on 50b brown   .40   .25
455 A144 900b on 350b claret   .50   .25
456 A144 1000b on 400b steel blue   .60   .25
457 A144 2000b on 1000b gray brn   1.00   .50

458 A144 3500b on 3000b slate grn   1.25   1.00
Nos. 454-458,C232-C236 (10)   10.55   5.45
Old value obliterated with two short bars on No. 454; four short bars on Nos. 455-456 and Greek key border on Nos. 457-458. The Greek key obliteration comes in two positions: two full "keys" on top, and one full and two half keys on top.

Flowers — A152

1962, June 28   Litho.   Perf. 10½
459 A152 200b Hibiscus   .75   .30
460 A152 400b Bicolored vanda   1.25   .30
461 A152 600b Lily   2.00   .40
462 A152 1000b Orchid   2.50   .40
Nos. 459-462,C237-C240 (8)   19.75   6.70

Bolivia's Armed Forces — A153

1962, Sept. 5   Perf. 11½
463 A153 400b Infantry   .25   .25
464 A153 500b Cavalry   .45   .25
465 A153 600b Artillery   .40   .30
466 A153 2000b Engineers   1.00   .40
Nos. 463-466,C241-C244 (8)   6.10   3.50

Anti-Malaria Emblem — A154

1962, Oct. 4
467 A154 600b dk & lt vio & yel   .50   .30
WHO drive to eradicate malaria. See No. C245.

Portrait Type of 1961
Design: 600b, Alonso de Mendoza.

1962   Photo.   Perf. 13x12½
468 A150 600b rose vio, *bluish*   .50   .30

Soccer and Flags A155

Design: 1b, Goalkeeper catching ball, vert.

1963, Mar. 21   Litho.   Perf. 11½
Flags in National Colors
469 A155 60c orange   .65   .35
470 A155 1b gray   1.00   .45
21st South American Soccer Championships. See Nos. C247-C248.
An imperforate 20b souvenir sheet, depicting Nos. 469 and C247 with simulated perforations, was issued April 28, 1980, to commemorate the Argentina 1978 and España 1982 World Cup championship soccer games. Value $45.
Two imperforate souvenir sheets commemorating España '82 were issued Aug. 11, 1981. One depicts Nos. 469 and 654 with simulated perforations and is denominated 14.80b (value $75). The other depicts No. 470 with simulated perforations (value$45).

Globe and Wheat Emblem A156

1963, Aug. 1   Unwmk.   Perf. 11½
471 A156 60c dk bl, bl & yel   .45   .25
"Freedom from Hunger" campaign of the FAO. See No. C249.

Oil Derrick and Chart — A157

Designs: 60c, Map of Bolivia. 1b, Students.

1963, Dec. 21   Litho.   Perf. 11½
472 A157 10c green & dk brn   .25   .25
473 A157 60c ocher & dk brn   .25   .25
474 A157 1b dk blue, grn & yel   .35   .25
Nos. 472-474,C251-C253 (6)   3.15   2.30
Revolution of Apr. 9, 1952, 10th anniv.

Flags of Bolivia and Peru A158

1966, Aug. 10   Wmk. 90   Perf. 13½
Flags in National Colors
475 A158 10c black & tan   .25   .25
476 A158 60c black & lt grn   .25   .25
477 A158 1b black & gray   .40   .25
478 A158 2b black & rose   .70   .25
Nos. 475-478,C254-C257 (8)   4.20   3.50
Marshal Andrés Santa Cruz (1792-1865), president of Bolivia and of Peru-Bolivian Confederation.

Children — A159

Perf. 13½
1966, Dec. 16   Unwmk.   Litho.
479 A159 30c ocher & sepia   .40   .25
Issued to help poor children. See No. C258.

Map and Flag of Bolivia and Generals Ovando and Barrientos A160

1966, Dec. 16   Litho.   Perf. 13½
Flag in Red, Yellow and Green
480 A160 60c violet brn & tan   .45   .25
481 A160 1b dull grn & tan   .45   .25
Issued to honor Generals Rene Barrientos Ortuno and Alfredo Ovando C., co-Presidents, 1965-66. See Nos. C259-C260.

Various Issues 1957-60 and Type A161 Surcharged

No. 403 Surcharged

1966, Dec. 21
482 A140 20c on 150b gray & ultra   .25   .25

Nos. 405-406 Surcharged

483 A140 30c on 550b chlky bl & brn   .35   .25
484 A140 2.80b on 750b dp rose & grn   1.00   .60

No. 424 Surcharged

485 A145 60c on 350b dp rose   .65   .25

Nos. 429-430 Surcharged

486 A146 1.60b on 350b multi   1.00   .60
487 A146 2.40b on 500b multi   1.25   .90

Revenue Stamps of 1946 Surcharged

488 A161 20c on 5b red   .25   .25

Revenue Stamps of 1946 Surcharged

489 A161 60c on 2b grn   .35   .25

Revenue Stamps of 1946 Surcharged

490 A161 1b on 10b brn   .60   .25

Revenue Stamps of 1946 Surcharged

491 A161 1.60b on 50c vio .60 .25
Nos. 482-491,C261-C272 (22) 20.35 11.90

For surcharge see No. C272.

Sower — A162

1967, Sept. 20 Litho. Perf. 13½x13
492 A162 70c multicolored .40 .25

50th anniv. of Lions Intl. See Nos. C273-C273a.

"Macheteros" A163

Designs (Folklore characters): 60c, Chunchos. 1b, Wiphala. 2b, Diablada.

1968, June 24 Perf. 13½x13
493 A163 30c gray & multi .25 .25
494 A163 60c sky bl & multi .35 .30
495 A163 1b gray & multi .50 .25
496 A163 2b gray ol & multi .80 .25
a. Souvenir sheet of 4, #493-496, imperf 15.00 15.00
Nos. 493-496,C274-C277 (8) 5.10 2.25

Issued to publicize the 9th Congress of the Postal Union of the Americas and Spain.

Arms of Tarija — A164

1968, Oct. 29 Litho. Perf. 13½x13
497 A164 20c pale sal & multi .25 .25
498 A164 30c gray & multi .25 .25
499 A164 40c dl yel & multi .25 .25
500 A164 60c lt yel grn & multi .35 .25
Nos. 497-500,C278-C281 (8) 4.25 2.65

Battle of Tablada sesquicentennial.

Pres. Gualberto Villaroel — A165

1968, Nov. 6 Unwmk.
501 A165 20c sepia & org .80 .25
502 A165 30c sepia & dl bl grn .80 .25
503 A165 40c sepia & dl rose .80 .25
504 A165 50c sepia & yel grn .80 .25
505 A165 1b sepia & ol bister .80 .25
Nos. 501-505 (5) 4.00 1.25

4th centenary of the founding of Cochabamba. See Nos. C282-C286.

ITU Emblem A166

1968, Dec. 3 Litho. Perf. 13x13½
506 A166 10c gray, blk & yel .25 .25
507 A166 60c org, blk & ol .50 .50

Cent. (in 1965) of the ITU. See Nos. C287-C288.

Polychrome Painted Clay Cup, Inca Period — A167

1968, Nov. 14 Perf. 13½x13
508 A167 20c dk bl grn & multi .35 .25
509 A167 60c vio bl & multi .70 .40

20th anniv. (in 1966) of UNESCO. See Nos. C289-C290.

John F. Kennedy A168

1968, Nov. 22 Perf. 13x13½
510 A168 10c yel grn & blk .25 .25
511 A168 4b vio & blk 2.00 1.90
a. Souvenir sheet of 1, type of #511 2.50 2.50

See Nos. C291-C292.

Tennis Player — A169

1968, Dec. 10 Perf. 13x13½
512 A169 10c gray, blk & lt brn .35 .35
513 A169 20c yel, blk & lt brn .35 .35
514 A169 30c ultra, blk & lt brn .35 .35
a. Souvenir sheet #512-514, imperf 2.50 2.50
Nos. 512-514 (3) 1.05 1.05

32nd South American Tennis Championships, La Paz, 1965. See Nos. C293-C294.

Issue of 1863 — A170

1968, Dec. 23 Litho. Perf. 13x13½
515 A170 10c yel grn, brn & blk 1.00 .25
516 A170 30c lt bl, brn & blk 1.00 .40
517 A170 2b gray, brn & blk 1.00 .40
a. Souvenir sheet #515-517, imperf 6.00 6.00
Nos. 515-517,C295-C297 (6) 8.45 4.20

Cent. of Bolivian postage stamps. See Nos. C295-C297.

Rifle Shooting A171

Sports: 50c, Equestrian. 60c, Canoeing.

1969, Oct. 29 Litho. Perf. 13x13½
518 A171 40c red brn, org & blk .50 .50
519 A171 50c emer, red & blk .50 .50
520 A171 60c bl, emer & blk .50 .50
a. Souvenir sheet #518-520, imperf 6.00 6.00
Nos. 518-520,C299-C301 (6) 5.65 5.00

19th Olympic Games, Mexico City, 10/12-27/68.

Temenis Laothoe Violetta A172

Butterflies: 10c, Papilio crassus. 20c, Catagramma cynosura. 30c, Eunica eurota flora. 80c, Ituna phenarete.

1970, Apr. 24 Litho. Perf. 13x13½
521 A172 5c pale lil & multi 2.00 1.00
522 A172 10c pink & multi 4.00 2.00
523 A172 20c gray & multi 4.00 2.00
524 A172 30c yel & multi 4.00 2.00
525 A172 80c multicolored 4.00 2.00
a. Souvenir sheet #521-523, imperf 30.00 30.00
Nos. 521-525,C302-C306 (10) 58.00 28.50

A souvenir sheet exists containing 3 imperf. stamps similar to Nos. 521-523. Black marginal inscription. Size: 129½x80mm. Value $45.

Boy Scout — A173

Design: 10c, Girl Scout planting rose bush.

1970, June 17 Perf. 13½x13
526 A173 5c multicolored .25 .25
527 A173 10c multicolored .25 .25
Nos. 526-527,C307-C308 (4) 1.25 1.25

Honoring the Bolivian Scout movement.
A 1,000,000b imperforate souvenir sheet, depicting No. 526 with simulated perforations, was issued May 12, 1986, to mark the explosion of the U.S. Space Shuttle Challenger. Value $30.

No. 437 Surcharged Red

1970, Dec. 6 Litho. Perf. 13x12
528 A147 30c on 350b on 10c .50 .35

EXFILCA 70, 2nd Interamerican Philatelic Exhib., Caracas, Venezuela, Nov. 27-Dec. 6.

Nos. 455 and 452 Surcharged in Black or Red

1970, Dec. Photo. Perf. 11½
529 A144 60c on 900b on 350b .35 .25
533 A150 1.20b on 1500b (R) .60 .25

Amaryllis Yungacensis A174

Bolivian Flowers: 30c, Amaryllis escobaruriae, horiz. 40c, Amaryllis evansae, horiz. 2b, Gymnocalycium chiquitanum.

Perf. 13x13½, 13½x13
1971, Aug. 9 Litho. Unwmk.
534 A174 30c gray & multi .35 .25
535 A174 40c multi .35 .25
536 A174 50c multi .50 .25
537 A174 2b multi 1.25 .60
a. Souvenir sheet of 4, #534, 535, C310, C312, imperf 15.00 15.00
b. Souvenir sheet of 4, #536, 537, C311, C313, imperf 15.00 15.00
Nos. 534-537,C310-C313 (8) 8.75 5.80

Sica Sica Church, EXFILIMA Emblem — A175

1971, Nov. 6 Perf. 14x13½
538 A175 20c red & multi .45 .25

EXFILIMA '71, 3rd Inter-American Philatelic Exhibition, Lima, Peru, Nov. 6-14.

A176

Design: Pres. Hugo Banzer Suarez.

1972, Jan. 24 Litho. Perf. 13½
539 A176 1.20b blk & multi 2.00 .25

Bolivia's development, 8/19/71-1/24/72.

A177

Folk Dances: 20c, Chiriwano de Achocalla. 40c, Rueda Chapaca. 60c, Kena-kena. 1b, Waca Thokori.

1972, Mar. 23 Litho. Perf. 13½x13
540 A177 20c red & multi .25 .25
541 A177 40c rose lil & multi .45 .35
542 A177 60c cream & multi .60 .25
543 A177 1b citron & multi .80 .35
a. Souvenir sheet of 4, #540, 541, C315, imperf 35.00 35.00
b. Souvenir sheet of 4, #542, 543, C314 imperf 35.00 35.00
Nos. 540-543,C314-C315 (6) 3.85 1.70

Madonna and
Child by B.
Bitti — A178

Bolivian paintings: 10c, Nativity, by Melchor Perez de Holguin. 50c, Coronation of the Virgin, by G. M. Berrio. 70c, Harquebusier, anonymous. 80c, St. Peter of Alcantara, by Holguin.

1972   **Litho.**   **Perf. 14x13½**
544	A178	10c gray & multi	.35	.25
545	A178	50c sal & multi	.50	.25
546	A178	70c lt grn & multi	.60	.25
547	A178	80c buff & multi	.70	.25
548	A178	1b multi	1.00	.25
a.		Souvenir sheet of 2, #548, C318, imperf	45.00	45.00
b.		Souvenir sheet of 4, #C317, C318 imperf	45.00	45.00

Nos. 544-548,C316-C319 (9)   6.40   2.35

Issue dates: 1b, Aug. 17; others, Dec. 4.
An imperforate 20b souvenir sheet. depicting No. 548 with simulated perforations, was issued March 16, 1979, to mark the International Year of the Child. Value $45.
An imperf 1b souvenir sheet, depicting No. 548 with simulated perforations, was issued Aug. 1, 1982, to celebrate Christmas. Value $65.
A 2b souvenir sheet containing No. 548, perf 13¼ was issued Dec. 16, 1987, for Christmas. Value $30.

Tarija Cathedral,
EXFILBRA
Emblem — A179

1972, Aug. 26
549	A179	30c multi	.45	.25

4th Inter-American Philatelic Exhibition, EXFILBRA, Rio de Janeiro, Brazil, 8/26-9/2.

Echinocactus
Notocactus
A180

Designs: Various cacti.

1973, Aug. 6   **Litho.**   **Perf. 13½**
550	A180	20c crim & multi	.55	.30
551	A180	40c multi	.55	.30
552	A180	50c multi	.55	.30
553	A180	70c multi	.60	.40
a.		Souvenir sheet of 2, #553, C321, imperf	40.00	40.00
b.		Souvenir sheet of 4, #551, C323 imperf	40.00	40.00

Nos. 550-553,C321-C323 (7)   5.75   2.40

Power
Station,
Santa
Isabel
A181

Designs: 20c, Tin industry. 90c, Bismuth industry. 1b, Natural gas plant.

1973, Nov. 26   **Litho.**   **Perf. 13½**
554	A181	10c gray & multi	1.25	.25
555	A181	20c tan & multi	1.25	.25
556	A181	90c lt grn & multi	1.50	.25
557	A181	1b yel & multi	1.50	.25

Nos. 554-557,C324-C325 (6)   11.75   1.50
Bolivia's development.

Cattleya
Nobilior — A182

Orchids: 50c, Zygopetalum bolivianum. 1b, Huntleya melagris.

1974, May 15   **Perf. 13½**
558	A182	20c gray & multi	1.50	.25
559	A182	50c lt bl & multi	1.50	.25
560	A182	1b cit & multi	1.50	.25
a.		Souvenir sheet of 2, #558, C328, imperf	50.00	20.00
b.		Souvenir sheet of 4, #559, 560 imperf	50.00	20.00

Nos. 558-560,C327-C330 (7)   27.00   3.60

For surcharge see No. 704.
Four imperforate souvenir sheets were issued May 31, 1974, to publicize 1975-77 Bolivian philatelic expositions. They depict: 14.90b, Nos. 18, 544 and C330; 15.50b, Nos. 18, 545 and C329; 16b, Nos. 18 and C320; 16.70b, Nos. 18, 547 and C327. Value, each $5. These sheets were later (Sept. 21) overprinted for various 1974 special events. Vale, set of 4: unused $275; used $150.

UPU and Philatelic Exposition
Emblems — A183

1974, Oct. 9
561	A183	3.50b grn, blk & bl	1.25	.50

Centenary of Universal Postal Union: PRENFIL-UPU Philatelic Exhibition, Buenos Aires, Oct. 1-12; EXPO-UPU Philatelic Exhibition, Montevideo, Oct. 20-27.

Gen. Sucre, by
I. Wallpher
A184

1974, Dec. 9   **Litho.**   **Perf. 13¾**
562	A184	5b multicolored	1.50	.75

Sesquicentennial of the Battle of Ayacucho.
An imperforate 5b souvenir sheet, depicting No. 562 with simulated perforations, was issued Dec. 31, 1982, to honor Peter Paul Reubens. Value $50.
An imperforate 1,000,000b souvenir sheet, containing No. 562 perf 13¼, was issued Sept. 25, 1986, to mark the Seoul Summer Olympic Games. Value $40.

Lions
Emblem
and
Steles
A185

1975, Mar. 17   **Litho.**   **Perf. 13½**
563	A185	30c red & multi	.60	.40

Lions Intl. in Bolivia, 25th anniv.

España
75
Emblem
A186

1975, Mar.
564	A186	4.50b yel, red & blk	1.00	.45

Espana 75 International Philatelic Exhibition, Madrid, Apr. 4-13.

Emblem
A187

1975   **Litho.**   **Perf. 13½**
565	A187	2.50b lil, blk & sil	1.00	.35

First meeting of Postal Ministers, Quito, Ecuador, March 1974, and for the Cartagena Agreement.
Four 20b imperforate souvenir sheets were issued in March 1975 to publicize 1975-77 Bolivian stamp exhibitions. Each depicts No. 14, with Nos. 562, 563, 564 or 565. Value, each $5. These sheets were also overprint to commemorate special events of 1974. Value, set $175.
Two of the unoverprinted 1974 sheets, those depicting Nos. 563 and 564, were overprinted in April 1981 to commemorate the 150th anniv. of the death of Símon Bolívar. Value, each $5. These sheets were also overprinted to mark the 50th anniv. of the first Bolivia-Brazil flight. Value, each $5.

Pando Coat of
Arms — A188

Designs: Departmental coats of arms.

1975, July 16   **Litho.**   **Perf. 13½**
566	A188	20c shown	.45	.25
567	A188	2b Chuquisaca	1.00	.50
568	A188	3b Cochabamba	1.25	.75

Nos. 566-568,C336-C341 (9)   10.80   5.60
Sesquicentennial of Republic of Bolivia.

Simón
Bolívar — A189

Presidents and Statesmen of Bolivia: 30c, Victor Paz Estenssoro. 60c, Tomas Frias. 1b, Ismael Montes. 2.50b, Aniceto Arce. 7b, Bautista Saavedra. 10b, Jose Manuel Pando. 15b, Jose Maria Linares. 50b, Simon Bolivar.

1975   **Litho.**   **Perf. 13½**
Size: 24x32mm
569	A189	30c multi	.25	.25
569A	A189	60c multi	.25	.25
570	A189	1b multi	.25	.25
571	A189	2.50b multi	.75	.25
572	A189	7b multi	1.75	1.00
573	A189	10b multi	3.00	1.50
574	A189	15b multi	4.00	1.75

Size: 28x39mm
575	A189	50b multi	15.00	10.00

Nos. 569-575,C346-C353 (16)   54.90   34.80
Sesquicentennial of Republic of Bolivia.
An imperforate 20b souvenir sheet, depicting No. 575 with simulated perforations, was issued Oct. 13, 1980, to celebrate the 1980

Lake Placid Winter Olympic Games. Value $20.
An imperforate 10b souvenir sheet, depicting No. 573 with simulated perforations, was issued March 24, 1982, to commemorate the España '82 World Cup soccer championship games. Value $35.

"EXFIVIA
75"
A190

1975, Dec. 1   **Litho.**   **Perf. 13½**
576	A190	3b multicolored	1.20	.80
a.		Souvenir sheet	2.50	2.50

EXFIVIA 75, 1st Bolivian Philatelic Exposition. No. 576a contains one stamp similar to #576 with simulated perforations. Sold for 5b.
No. 576a was overprinted in 1981 for EXFIVA 77 and EXFILMAR 79. Value $5.
An imperforate 20b souvenir sheet, depicting No. 576 with simulated perforations, was issued June 1, 1978, commemorating the 75th anniv. of the Nobel Prize (in 1976). Value $85.

A191

Chiang Kai-shek, flags of Bolivia and China.

1976, Apr. 4   **Litho.**   **Perf. 13½**
577	A191	2.50b multi, red circle	4.50	1.50
578	A191	2.50b multi, bl circle	4.50	1.50

Pres. Chiang Kai-shek of China (1887-1975).
Erroneous red of sun's circle on Chinese flag of No. 577 was corrected on No. 578 with a dark blue overlay.

Navy
Day — A192

1976, Apr.   **Litho.**   **Perf. 13½**
579	A192	50c Naval insignia	.60	.50

Geological Map, Pickax and
Lamp — A193

1976, May
580	A193	4b multicolored	1.25	.50

Bolivian Geological Institute.

Lufthansa Jet, Bolivian and German Colors A194

1976, May
581 A194 3b multicolored   1.25   .60

Lufthansa, 50th anniversary.

An imperforate 20b souvenir sheet, depicting No. 581 with simulated perforations, was issued June 1, 1978, to celebrate the Argentina 78 World Cup. Value $35.

Two imperforate 20b souvenir sheets, depicting No. 581 with simulated perforations, were issued Oct. 13, 1980, to celebrate the 50th anniversary of Zeppelin flights to South America.

Boy Scout and Scout Emblem — A195

1976, May   Litho.   Perf. 13½
582 A195 1b multicolored   .75   .65

Bolivian Boy Scouts, 60th anniversary.

An imperforate 125,000b souvenir sheet, depicting Nos. 582 and 683 with simulated perforations, was issued June 24, 1985, to mark the 75th anniv. of the Boy Scouts. Value $10. This sheet was overprinted, surcharged 1,500,000b and reissued Apr. 18, 1986, to honor the 1987/88 World Jamboree in Australia. Value $20.

Battle Scene, US Bicentennial Emblem — A196

1976, May 25
583 A196 4.50b bis & multi   2.00   1.00
   a.   Souenir sheet of 1   25.00   25.00

American Bicentennial.

No. 583a contains one stamp similar to No. 583 with simulated perforations. Size: 130x80mm.

Three imperforate souvenir sheets, each denominated 20b, depicting No. 583 with simulated perforations and various historic U.S. motifs, were issued Dec. 20, 1976, to commemorate the U.S. Bicentennial. Value, each $6.

Family, Map of Bolivia — A197

1976   Perf. 13½
584 A197 2.50b multicolored   .85   .50

National Census 1976.

Vicente Bernedo — A198

1976, Oct.
585 A198 1.50b multicolored   .50   .40

Brother Vicente Bernedo de Potosi (1544-1619), missionary to the Indians.

Four imperforate souvenir sheets, each denominated 20b, depicting No. 585 with simulated perforations, were issued Dec. 20, 1976, celebrating various themes. These comprise: 75th anniv. Nobel prize, value $50; 1976 Montreal Summer Olympics, value $25; U.S. Bicentennial / Space, value $35; 100th anniv. telephone, 25th anniv. United Nations, 110th anniv. ITU, value $35.

Policeman with Dog, Rainbow over La Paz — A199

1976, Oct.
586 A199 2.50b multicolored   .80   .80

Bolivian Police, 150 years of service.

Emblem, Bolivar and Sucre A200

1976, Nov. 18   Litho.   Perf. 13½
587 A200 1.50b multicolored   1.00   .50

Intl. Congress of Bolivarian Societies.

Pedro Poveda, View of La Paz — A201

1976, Dec.
588 A201 1.50b multicolored   .50   .25

Pedro Poveda (1874-1936), educator.

A202

1976, Dec. 17   Perf. 10½
594 A202   20c brown   .35   .25
595 A202   1b ultra   .65   .25
596 A202 1.50b green   1.10   .60
   Nos. 594-596 (3)   2.10   1.10

Boy and Girl — A203

1977, Feb. 4   Litho.   Perf. 13½
599 A203 50c multicolored   .40   .25

Christmas 1976, and for 50th anniversary of the Inter-American Children's Institute.

Staff of Aesculapius A204

1977, Mar. 18   Litho.   Perf. 13½x13
600 A204 3b multicolored   1.00   .30

National Seminar on Chagas' disease, Cochabamba, Feb. 21-26.

Supreme Court, Sucre — A205

Designs: 4b, Manuel Maria Urcullu, first President of Supreme Court. 4.50b, Pantaleon Dalence, President 1883-1889.

1977, May 3
601 A205 2.50b multi   .45   .25
602 A205   4b multi   .65   .25
603 A205 4.50b multi   .90   .30
   Nos. 601-603 (3)   2.00   .80

Sesquicentennial of Bolivian Supreme Court.

Newspaper Mastheads — A206

Designs: 2.50b, Alfredo Alexander and Hoy, horiz. 3b, Jose Carrasco and El Diario, horiz. 4b, Demetrio Canelas and Los Tiempos. 5.50b, Frontpage of Presencia.

1977, June   Litho.   Perf. 13½
604 A206 1.50b multi   .40   .30
605 A206 2.50b multi   .60   .30
606 A206   3b multi   .60   .30
607 A206   4b multi   .75   .40
608 A206 5.50b multi   1.00   .30
   Nos. 604-608 (5)   3.35   1.60

Bolivian newspapers and their founders.

Map of Bolivia, Tower and Flag — A207

1977, June
609 A207 3b multi   .75   .30

90th anniversary of Oruro Club.

Games' Poster — A208

1977, Oct. 20   Litho.   Perf. 13½
610 A208 5b blue & multi   1.00   .40

8th Bolivian Games, La Paz, Oct. 1977.

Four imperforate souvenir sheets, each denominated 20b, depicting No. 610 with simulated perforations were issued June 1, 1978. Each sheet celebrated an upcoming philatelic

exhibition: Honduras '78; Capex '78; Praga '78; and Philaserdica '79. Value, each $15.

Tin Miner and Emblem — A209

1977, Oct. 31   Litho.   Perf. 13
611 A209 3b multicolored   1.00   .30

Bolivian Mining Corp., 25th anniv.

Miners, Globe, Tin Symbol — A210

1977, Nov. 3
612 A210 6b silver & multi   1.50   .60

Intl. Tin Symposium, La Paz, Nov. 14-21.

Two souvenir sheets, denominated 1,000,000b, containing No. 612 perf 13¼, were issued Sept. 25, 1986, to commemorate the Uncia-Antofagasto railway. Value, each $30.

Map of Bolivia, Radio Masts — A211

1977, Nov. 11
613 A211 2.50b blue & multi   .75   .50

Radio Bolivia, ASBORA, 50th anniversary.

No. 450 Surcharged in Black

1977, Nov. 25   Litho.   Perf. 11x13½
614 A147 5b on 5000b on 5b   3.00   2.00

EXFIVIA '77 Philatelic Exhibition, Cochabamba.

Eye, Compass, Book of Law — A212

1978, May 3   Litho.   Perf. 13½x13
615 A212 5b multi   1.10   .30

Audit Department, 50th anniversary.

Mt. Illimani
A213

Pre-
Columbian
Monolith
A214

Design: 1.50b, Mt. Cerro de Potosi.

Perf. 11x10½, 10½x11

1978, June 1			Litho.	
616	A213	50c bl & Prus bl	.30	.25
617	A214	1b brn & lemon	.30	.25
618	A213	1.50b red & bl gray	.50	.35
		Nos. 616-618 (3)	1.10	.85

Andean Countries,
Staff of
Aesculapius — A215

1978, June 1   Perf. 10½x11
626 A215 2b org & blk   .60   .30

Health Ministers of Andean Countries, 5th meeting.

Map of Americas with
Bolivia — A216

1978, June 1
627 A216 2.50b dp ultra & red   .80   .30

World Rheumatism Year.
For surcharges see Nos. 697, 972.

Central Bank
Building — A217

1978, July 26   Litho.   Perf. 13½
628 A217 7b multi   1.75   .40

50th anniversary of Bank of Bolivia.

Jesus and
Children — A218

1979, Feb. 20   Litho.   Perf. 13½
629 A218 8b multicolored   1.50   .50

International Year of the Child.
An imperforate 20b souvenir sheet, depicting No. 629 with simulated perforations, was issued March 16, 1979, for the International Year of the Child. Value $50.
An imperforate 20b souvenir sheet, depicting Nos. 599 and 629 with simulated perforations, was issued April 28, 1980, marking the Year of the Child. Value $25.

Antofagasta
Cancel — A219

Eduardo
Abaroa,
Chain — A220

Designs: 1b, La Chimba cancel. 1.50b, Mejillones cancel. 5.50b, View of Antofagasta. 6.50b, Woman in chains, symbolizing captive province, vert. 8b, Map of Antofagasta Province, 1876, vert. 10b, Arms of province, vert.

1979, Mar. 23   Perf. 10½
630	A219	50e buff & blk	.40	.25
631	A219	1b pink & blk	.60	.40
632	A219	1.50b pale grn & blk	.70	.40

Perf. 13½
633	A220	5.50b multi	1.00	.40
634	A220	6.50b multi	1.20	.40
635	A220	7b multi	1.20	.40
636	A220	8b multi	1.40	.50
637	A220	10b multi	1.75	.50
		Nos. 630-637 (8)	8.25	3.25

Loss of Antofagasta coastal area to Chile, cent.
For surcharge see No. 696.
An imperforate 1000b souvenir sheet, depicting No. 637 with simulated perforations, was issued March 26, 1984, to mark the 1984 World Postal Congress in Hamburg. Value $25.

Emblem and Map
of Bolivia — A221

1979, Mar. 26   Perf. 13½x13
638 A221 3b multicolored   1.20   .70

Radio Club of Bolivia.

Gymnast — A222

6.50b, Runner and Games emblem, horiz.

1979, Mar. 27   Perf. 13x13½, 13½x13
639	A222	6.50b multi	1.25	.25
640	A222	10b multi	2.00	.50
a.		Souvenir sheet of one	5.50	5.50

Southern Cross Sports Games, Bolivia, Nov. 3-12, 1978.
No. 640a contains No. 640 with simulated perforations. Sold for 20b. Size: 80x130mm.
For surcharge see No. 965.
No. 640a was overprinted in two versions in 1981, the first overprint commemorating the 10th anniv. of the Santa Cruz Philatelic Center, the second celebrating the 10th anniv. of the Bolivian Philatelic Federation. Value, each $5.
Two imperforate 20b souvenir sheets, one depicting No. 639, the other No. 640, both with simulated perforations, were issued March 16, 1979, to mark the 1980 Olympic Games. Values, each $30.
Two imperforate souvenir sheets, each denominated 20b, one depicting No. 639, the other No. 640, both with simulated perforations, were issued Oct. 13, 1980, to commemorate the 1980 Moscow Olympic Games. Values, each $75.

Bulgaria
No. 1 — A223

1979, Mar. 30   Perf. 10½
641 A223 2.50b multi   .60   .40

PHILASERDICA '79 International Philatelic Exhibition, Sofia, Bulgaria, May 18-27.
For surcharge see No. 694.

EXFILMAR
Emblem — A224

1979, Apr. 2
642 A224 2b multi   2.00   .65

Bolivian Maritime Philatelic Exhibition, La Paz, Nov. 18-28.
For surcharge see No. 698.

OAS Emblem,
Map of
Bolivia — A226

1979, Oct. 22   Litho.   Perf. 14x13½
644 A226 6b multi   1.20   .40

Organization of American States, 9th Congress, La Paz, Oct.-Nov.

Franz
Tamayo — A227

Bolivian and
Japanese Flags,
Hospital — A228

UN Emblem and
Meeting — A229

Radio Tower and
Waves — A230

1979, Dec.
645	A227	2.80b blk & gray	.60	.50
646	A228	5b multi	1.00	.25
648	A229	5b multi	1.00	.25
649	A230	6b multi	1.25	.50
		Nos. 645-649 (4)	3.85	1.50

Franz Tamayo, lawyer, birth centenary; Japanese-Bolivian health care cooperation; CEPAL, 18th Congress, La Paz, Sept. 18-26; Bolivian National Radio, 50th anniversary.
For surcharge see No. 695.
An imperforate 500,000b souvenir sheet, depicting No. 645 with simulated perforations, was issued Dec. 1985 to mark the 850th anniv. of Malmonides, Jewish philosopher (1135-1204). Value $10.

Puerto
Suarez
Iron Ore
Deposits
A231

1979   Litho.   Perf. 13½x14
650 A231 9.50b multi   3.50   .80

Bolivia No. 19, EXFILMAR Emblem,
Bolivian Flag — A232

1980   Litho.   Perf. 13½
651 A232 4b multi   1.25   .40

EXFILMAR, Bolivian Maritime Philatelic Exhibition, La Paz, Nov. 18-28, 1979.
An imperforate 4b souvenir sheet, depicting No. 651 with simulated perforations, was issued Dec. 31, 1982, to commemorate space exploration. Value $75.

Juana Azurduy
on Horseback
A233

1980   Litho.   Perf. 14x13½
652 A233 4b multi   .80   .40

Juana Azurduy de Padilla, independence fighter, birth bicentenary.
A souvenir sheet containing No. 652 perforated 13¼ was issued Oct. 19, 1990, to commemorate the 700th anniv. of the Swiss Confederation.

La Salle
and
World
Map
A234

1980   Perf. 13½x14
653 A234 9b multi   1.75   .70

St. Jean Baptiste de la Salle (1651-1719), educator.
For surcharge see No. 966.

"Victory" in Chariot, Madrid, Exhibition Emblem, Flags of Bolivia and Spain
A235

1980, Oct. Litho. Perf. 13½x14
654 A235 14b multi   2.50 .75

ESPAMER '80 Stamp Exhibition, Madrid.

Map of South America, Flags of Argentina, Bolivia and Peru — A236

1980, Oct. Perf. 14x13½
655 A236 2b multi   1.10 .30

Ministers of Public Works and Transport of Argentina, Bolivia and Peru meeting.

Santa Cruz-Trinidad Railroad, Inauguration of Third Section — A237

1980, Oct.
656 A237 3b multi   .75 .30

An imperforate 1500b souvenir sheet, depicting No. 656 and the 50c value of the unissued 1915 set, both with simulated perforations, was issued June 20, 1984, to mark the World Postal Congress in Hamburg. Value $30.

Flag on Provincial Map — A238

1b, Soldier, flag, map. 3b, Flag, map. 40b, Soldier, civilians, horiz.

Perf. 14x13½, 13½x14
1981, May 11   Litho.
657 A238 1b multi   25.00 30.00
658 A238 3b multi   25.00 30.00
659 A238 40b shown   10.00   4.00
660 A238 50b multi   10.00   4.00
    Nos. 657-660 (4)   70.00 68.00

July 17 Revolution memorial.
An imperforate 40b souvenir sheet, depicting No. 659 with simulated perforations, was issued March 24, 1982, to honor Princess Diana. Value $30.

Parrots — A239

4b, Ara macao. 7b, Ara chloroptera. 8b, Ara ararauna. 9b, Ara rubrogenys. 10b, Ara auricollis. 12b, Anodorhynchus hyacinthinus. 15b, Ara militaris. 20b, Ara severa.

1981, May 11   Perf. 14x13½
661 A239 4b multi   .75   .25
662 A239 7b multi   1.40   .25
663 A239 8b multi   1.75   .50
664 A239 9b multi   1.75   .60
665 A239 10b multi   2.00   .60
666 A239 12b multi   2.50 1.00
667 A239 15b multi   3.25 1.20
668 A239 20b multi   4.00 1.50
    Nos. 661-668 (8)   17.40 5.90

Christmas 1981 — A240

1b, Virgin and Child, vert. 2b, Child, star.

1981, Dec. 7   Litho.   Perf. 10½
669 A240 1b red   .25   .25
670 A240 2b blue, pale blue .40 .25

American Airforces Commanders' 22nd Conference, Buenos Aires — A241

1982, Apr. 12   Litho.   Perf. 13½
671 A241 14b multi   2.25 1.25

75th Anniv. of Cobija — A242

1982, July 8   Litho.   Perf. 13½
672 A242 28b multi   .60   .40

Simon Bolivar Birth Bicentenary (1983) A243

1982, July 12
673 A243 18b multi   .40   .30

1983 World Telecommunications Year — A244

1982, July 15
674 A244 26b Receiving station .60 .40

An imperforate 1b souvenir sheet, depicting No. 674 with simulated perforations, was issued March 20, 1987, to honor Wernher von Braun. Value $60.

1982 World Cup — A245

100b, Final Act, by Picasso.

1982, July 21   Perf. 11
675 A245 4b shown   .30   .30
676 A245 100b multicolored 2.50 1.50

For surcharge see No. 701.
Two imperforate souvenir sheets, each denominated 104b, were issued Aug. 1, 1982, to celebrate España '82. The first depicts No. 676 with a stamp similar to No. 675, both with simulated perforations. Value $35. The second depicts No. 677 with simulated perforations. Value $65.
Two imperforate souvenir sheets were issued Dec. 31, 1982, to commemorate the victory of the Italian team in the España '82 World Cup games. One depicts Nos. 675 and 676 with simulated perfs and is denominated 104b. The second depicts Nos. 676 and 677 and is denominated 116b. Values, each $30.

Girl Playing Piano — A246

16b, Boy playing soccer, vert.

1982, July 25   Perf. 13½
677 A246 16b multicolored 1.50 .75
678 A246 20b shown   2.00 .75

An imperforate 200b souvenir sheet, depicting Nos. 678 and 629 with simulated perforations, was issued Sept. 16, 1983, for the International Year of the Child. Value $75.
An imperforate 27,500b souvenir sheet, depicting No. 678 with simulated perfs, was issued April 4, 1985, to mark the International Year of the Child. Value $50.

Bolivian-Chinese Agricultural Cooperation, 1972-1982 — A247

1982, Aug. 12
679 A247 30b multi   1.25 .75

First Bolivian-Japanese Gastroenterology Conference, La Paz, Jan. — A248

1982, Aug. 26
680 A248 22b multi   1.50 .80

Stamps — A249

1982, Aug. 31   Litho.   Perf. 14x13½
681 A249 19b multicolored 1.75 .60

10th Anniv. of Bolivian Philatelic Federation.

A250

1982, Sept. 1
682 A250 20b tan & dk brown .50 .30

Pres. Hernando Siles, birth centenary.

Scouting Year — A251

1982, Sept. 3   Perf. 11
683 A251 5b Baden-Powell .40 .30

For surcharge see No. 703.

Cochabamba Philatelic Center, 25th Anniv. — A252

1982, Sept. 14
684 A252 3b multicolored .40 .30

For surcharge see No. 700.

Cochabamba Superior Court of Justice Sesquicentennial — A253

1982 **Litho.** **Perf. 13½**
685 A253 10b multicolored   .50   .30

For surcharge see No. 970.

Enthronement of Virgin of Copacabana, 400th Anniv. — A254

1982, Nov. 15 **Litho.** **Perf. 13½**
686 A254 13b multicolored   .50   .30

For surcharge see No. 971.

Navy Day — A255

14b, Port Busch Naval Base.

1982, Nov. 17
687 A255 14b multicolored   .40   .30

An imperforate 1,000,000b souvenir sheet, depicting No. 687 with simulated perforations, was issued Jan. 5, 1987, to mark the 500th anniv. of Columbus' discovery of America. Value $20.

Christmas — A256

1982, Nov. 19 **Perf. 11**
688 A256 10b green & gray   .90   .25

For surcharge see No. 702.

An imperforate 1,000,000b souvenir sheet, depicting No. 688 with simulated perforations, was issued Dec.24, 1986, for Christmas. Value $27.50.

A257

1983, Feb. 13 **Litho.** **Perf. 13½**
689 A257 50b multicolored   1.25   .60

10th Youth Soccer Championship, Jan. 22-Feb. 13.

A 2b souvenir sheet containing Nos. 689 and 726, both perf 13¼, was issued Dec. 15, 1988, to mark the Italia 1990 World Cup. Value $25.

EXFIVIA '83 Philatelic Exhibition A258

1983, Nov. 5 **Litho.** **Perf. 13½**
690 A258 150b brown carmine   1.50   .75

An imperforate 1000b souvenir sheet, depicting Nos. 690 and 356 with simulated perforations, was issued March 26, 1984, to mark the 1984 Sarajevo Winter Olympic Games. Value $27.50.

An imperforate 500,000b souvenir sheet, depicting No. 690 with simulated perforartions, was issued Dec. 3, 1985, to celebrate Halley's Comet. Value $30.

Visit of Brazilian Pres. Joao Figueiredo, Feb. — A259

1984, Feb. 7 **Litho.** **Perf. 13½x14**
691 A259 150b multicolored   .75   .25

Simon Bolivar Entering La Paz, by Carmen Baptista A260

Paintings of Bolivar: 50b, Riding Horse, by Mulato Gil de Quesada, vert.

Perf. 14x13½, 13½x14
1984, Mar. 30
692 A260 50b multi   .30   .25
693 A260 200b multi   1.00   .40

An imperforate 1500b souvenir sheet, depicting No. 692 with simulated perforations, was issued June 20, 1984, to mark the 1984 Los Angeles Summer Olympic Games. Value $20.

A 2b souvenir sheet containing No. 692, perf. 13¼, was issued Dec. 16, 1987, to mark the 1988 Seoul Summer Olympc Games. Value $25.

Types of 1957-79 Surcharged

1984, Mar.
694 A223 40b on 2.50b #641   .30   .25
695 A227 40b on 2.80b #645   .30   .25
696 A219 60b on 1.50b #632   .30   .25
697 A216 60b on 2.50b #627   .30   .25
698 A224 100b on 2b #642   .50   .30
699 A141 200b on 350b #409   1.00   .40
   Nos. 694-699 (6)   2.70 1.70

See No. 972 for surcharge similar to No. 697.

Nos. 675, 683-684, 688, C328 Surcharged

1984, June 27 **Litho.** **Perf. 11**
700 A252 500b on 3b #684   1.25   .50
701 A245 1000b on 4b #675   2.50 1.25
702 A256 2000b on 10b #688   5.00 2.00
703 A251 5000b on 5b #683   12.00 5.00

Perf. 13½
704 A182 10,000b on 3.80b #C328   16.00 10.00
   Nos. 700-704 (5)   36.75 18.75

An imperforate 500,000b souvenir sheet, depicting No. 704 with simulated perforations, was issued Dec. 31, 1985, picturing Raphael's *The Three Graces.* Value $20.

Road Safety Education — A261

Cartoons: 80b, Jaywalker. 120b, Motorcycle policeman, ambulance.

1984, Sept. 7 **Litho.** **Perf. 11**
705 A261 80b multicolored   2.00   .25
706 A261 120b multicolored   2.00   .25

Jose Eustaquio Mendez, 200th Birth Anniv. — A262

Paintings: 300b, Birthplace, by Jorge Campos. 500b, Mendez Leading the Battle of La Tablada, by M. Villegas, horiz.

Perf. 14x13½, 13½x14
1984, Sept. 19
707 A262 300b multi   .30   .25
708 A262 500b multi   .30   .25

1983 World Cup Soccer Championships, Mexico — A263

Sponsoring shoe-manufacturers' trademarks and: 100b, 200b, Outline map of Bolivia, natl. colors. 600b, World map, soccer ball.

1984, Oct. 26 **Perf. 11**
709 A263 100b multi   .50   .25
710 A263 200b multi   .50   .25
711 A263 600b multi, horiz.   .50   .25
   Nos. 709-711 (3)   1.50   .75

An imperforate 125,000b souvenir sheet, depicting No. 711 with simulated perforations, was issued June 24, 1985, to mark the 1984 Los Angeles Summer Olympic Games. Value $20.

Chasqui, Postal Runner — A264

1985
712 A264 11000b vio bl   1.00   .30

For surcharge see No. 962.

Intl. Year of Professional Education — A265

2000b, Natl. Manual Crafts emblem.

1985, Apr. 25
713 A265 2000b red, blue   .30   .25

For surcharges see Nos. 721-722, 959.

Intl. Anti-Polio Campaign — A266

1985, May 22
714 A266 20000b lt bl & vio   .50   .25

Endangered Wildlife — A267

23000b, Altiplano boliviano. 25000b, Sarcorhamphus gryphus. 30000b, Blastocaros dichotomus.

1985, May 22
715 A267 23000b multi   1.50   .60
716 A267 25000b multi   .60   .40
717 A267 30000b multi   .70   .50
   Nos. 715-717 (3)   2.80 1.50

Nos. 716-717 vert.
For surcharge see No. 963.

Dona Vicenta Juaristi Eguino (b. 1785), Independence Heroine — A268

1985, Oct. **Litho.** **Perf. 13½**
718 A268 300000b multi   1.40   .60

UN, 40th Anniv. — A269

1985, Oct. 24 **Perf. 11**
719 A269 1000000b bl & gold   4.50   .50

For surcharge see No. 964.
A 3b souvenir sheet containing No. 719, perforated 12½x11½, was issued Nov. 30, 1991, to promote world peace. Value $10.

A270

1985, Nov.
720 A270 200000b multi   .85   .50

Soccer Team named "The Strongest," 75th anniv.

No. 713 Surcharged
1986 **Litho.** **Perf. 11**
721 A265 200000b on 2000b   .75   .25
722 A265 5000000b on 2000b   8.00 5.00

A271

300000, Emblems, vert. 550000, Pique trademark, vert. 1000000, Azteca Stadium. 2500000, World cup, vert.

1986
723	A271	300000 multi	.50	.30
724	A271	550000 multi	1.00	.50
725	A271	1000000 multi	1.50	.80
726	A271	2500000 multi	5.00	2.00
		Nos. 723-726 (4)	8.00	3.60

1986 World Cup Soccer Championships. For surcharges see Nos. 961, 1257-1258.
A 1,000,000b souvenir sheet containing No. 723 perforated 13¼ was issued Sept. 25, 1986, to mark the World Cup finals in Mexico City. Value $30.
A 2b souvenir sheet containing Nos. 723 and 739, perf 13¼ was issued Jan. 25, 1989, to mark the Italia 1990 World Cup championships. Value $25.

Intl. Youth Year
A272   A273

1986
727	A272	150000b brt car rose	.40	.30
728	A272	500000b bl grn	1.25	.50
729	A273	3000000b multi	7.50	2.50
		Nos. 727-729 (3)	9.15	3.30

Inscribed 1985.
For surcharge see No. 958.

Alfonso Sobieta Viaduct, Carretera Quillacollo, Confital
A274

1986   **Perf. 13½**
730	A274	400000 int bl & gray	.65	.30

Inter-American Development Bank, 25th anniv.

Admission of Bolivia to the UPU, Cent. — A275

1986, Apr. 3   **Perf. 11**
731	A275	800000 multi	1.60	1.00

A 2b souvenir sheet containing No. 731 perforated 13¼ was issued Dec. 7, 1989, to honor the 500th anniv. of the Imperial Reichspost. Value $50.

Postal Workers Soc., 50th Anniv. — A276

1986, Sept. 5
732	A276	2000000 brn & pale brn	5.50	1.50

For surcharge see No. 967.

Founding of Trinidad, 300th Anniv.
A277

No. 733, Bull and Rider, by Vaca.

1986, May 25   **Perf. 13½x14**
733	A277	1400000 multi	2.50	1.50

For surcharge see No. 960.

Bolivian Philatelic Federation, 15th Anniv. — A278

1986, Nov. 28
734	A278	600000b No. 19	1.00	.50

Death of a Priest, by Jose Antonio Zampa — A279

1986, Nov. 21   **Perf. 13¾x13½**
735	A279	400000b multi	1.20	.50

Intl. Peace Year — A280

1986, Sept. 16   **Perf. 11**
736	A280	200000 yel grn & pale grn	.60	.30

Natl. Oil Corp. (YPBF), 50th Anniv. — A281

1986, Dec. 22   **Litho.**   **Perf. 11**
737	A281	1000000b multi	2.25	1.10

For surcharge see No. 1259.

Photograph of a Devil-mask Dancer, by Jimenez Cordero.

Perf. 13¾x13½

1987, Feb. 13   **Litho.**
738	A282	20c multi	1.10	.30

February 10th Society, cent. (in 1985).

A283

Perf. 13¾x13½

1987, Mar. 20   **Litho.**
739	A283	30c Crossed flags	1.10	.50

State Visit of Richard von Weizsacker, Pres. of Germany, Mar. 20.
A 2b souvenir sheet containing No. 739 perforated 13¼ was issued Dec. 16, 1987, to commemorate the 750th anniv. of the founding of Berlin. Value $35.
A 2b souvenir sheet containing No. 739 perforated 13¼ was issued March 18, 1990, to promote world peace. Value $15.

State Visit of King Juan Carlos of Spain, May 20
A284

1987, May 20   **Perf. 13½x13¾**
740	A284	60c Natl. arms	1.50	.60

A 2b souvenir sheet containing No. 740 perforated 13¼ was issued Dec. 15, 1988, to mark the Summer Olympic Games in Seoul (1988) and Barcelona (1992). Value $25.

EXFIVIA '87 — A285

Mount Potosi, 18th cent. engraving.

1987, Oct.   **Litho.**   **Perf. 13½**
741	A285	50c multi	2.50	.60

See No. 750.

Wildlife Conservation
A286

1987, Oct.
742	A286	20c Condor	.80	.30
743	A286	20c Tapir	.80	.30
744	A286	30c Vicuna	1.25	.40
745	A286	30c Armadillo	1.25	.40
746	A286	40c Spectacled bears	1.50	.50
747	A286	60c Toucans	2.50	.70
		Nos. 742-747 (6)	8.10	2.60

Wildlife in danger of extinction.
A 2b souvenir sheet containing No. 742 perforated 13½ was issued Dec. 7, 1989, to mark the 20th anniv. of the Apollo XI moon landing. Value $20.
A 3b souvenir sheet containing No. 742 perforated 13x13¾ was issued Nov. 30, 1991, to honor Otto Lilienthal and Lilienthal '91. Value $12.
A 3b souvenir sheet containing No. 742 perforated 13½ was issued July 6, 1992, to mark various aviation anninersaries. Value $15.

ESPAMER '87, La Coruna — A287

No. 748, Nina, stern of Santa Maria. No. 749, Bow of Santa Maria, Pinta.

1987, Oct.   **Litho.**   **Perf. 14x13½**
748		20c multicolored	.60	.30
749		20c multicolored	.60	.30
a.	A287	Pair, #748-749	3.00	3.00

No. 749a has a continuous design.
A 2b souvenir sheet containing No. 749a, perforated 13¼ around and imperforate between, was issued Aug. 15, 1988, to celebrate the 500th anniv. of the discovery of America and the 1992 Barcelona Summer Olympic Games. Value $20.

EXFIVIA Type of 1987

Photograph of Mt. Potosi by Jimenez Cordero.

1987, Aug. 5   **Litho.**   **Perf. 13½**
750	A285	40c multi	1.00	.50

Musical Instruments — A288

50c, Zampona and quena (wind instruments). 1b, Charango, vert.

1987, Dec. 3   **Perf. 13½x14, 14x13½**
751	A288	50c multicolored	1.20	.50
752	A288	1b multicolored	2.50	1.10

A289

State Visit of Pope John Paul II
A290

Pontiff, religious architecture and art: No. 753, Cathedral of Kings, Beni. No. 754, Carabuco Church. No. 755, Tihuanacu Church. No. 756, St. Francis's Church, Sucre. No. 757, St. Joseph's of Chiquitos Church. 40c, Cobija Chapel, vert. No. 759, Jayu Kcota Church. No. 760, Cochabamba Cathedral, vert. 60c, St. Francis's Basilica, La Paz, vert. No. 762, Christ of Machaca Church. No. 763, St. Lawrence's Church, Potosi, vert. No. 764, *The Holy Family*, by Rubens, vert. No. 765, *The Virgin of Copacabana*, statue, vert. No. 766, Vallegrande Church. No. 767, Tarija Cathedral, vert. No. 768, Concepcion Church.

1988   **Litho.**   **Perf. 13½x14, 14x13½**
753	A289	20c multi	.50	.30
754	A289	20c multi	.50	.30
755	A289	20c multi	.50	.30
756	A289	30c multi	.80	.30
757	A289	30c multi	.80	.30
758	A289	40c multi	1.00	.40
759	A289	50c multi	1.50	.40
760	A289	50c multi	1.50	.40
761	A289	60c multi	1.75	.50
762	A289	70c multi	1.90	.50
763	A289	70c multi	1.90	.50
764	A289	80c multi	2.25	.50

765	A289	80c multi	2.25	.80
766	A289	80c multi	2.25	.80
767	A289	1.30b multi	3.25	1.50
768	A289	1.30b multi	3.25	1.50
769	A290	1.50b shown	3.75	1.50

Nos. 753-769 (17)   29.65 11.10

Issue dates: 1.50b, May 9; others, Mar. 3.

A 2b souvenir sheet containing No. 764 perforated 13¼ was issued July 16, 1989, to honor Peter Paul Reubens. Value $50.

A 2b souvenir sheet containing No. 764 perforated 13¼ was issued June 2, 1990, to mark the 350th anniv. of the death of artist Peter Paul Reubens (1577-1640). Value $35.

An imperforate souvenir sheet depicting Nos. 769 and 901F with simulated perforations was issued Oct. 20, 1994. Value $5.

An imperforate souvenir sheet depicting Nos. 769 and 934 with simulated perforations was issued Nov. 9, 1994, to celebrate Christmas. Value $25.

Visit of Pres. Jose Sarney of Brazil A291

1988, Aug. 2   **Litho.**   **Perf. 13½x14**
770 A291 50c multi   1.10   .50

St. John Bosco (1815-1888) A292

1988, Aug. 16   **Perf. 13½**
771 A292 30c multi   .80   .30

Bolivian Railways, Cent. — A293

Design: 1b, Steam locomotive from the La Paz-Beni line, made by Marca Shy Ohio, Natl. Railway Museum, Sucre.

1988, Aug. 29
772 A293 1b multi   3.00 1.00

Nataniel Aguirre (b. 1888), Author — A294

1988, Sept. 14   **Litho.**   **Perf. 13½**
773 A294 1b blk & beige   2.00 1.00

Department of Pando, 50th Anniv. — A295

Designs: 40c, *Columna Porvenir,* memorial to the Battle of Bahio. 60c, Siringuero rubber production (worker sapping latex from *Hevea brasiliensis*).

1988, Sept. 26   **Perf. 13½**
774 A295 40c multi   .90   .50
775 A295 60c multi   1.50   .70

1988 Summer Olympics, Seoul — A296

1988, Sept. 27
776 A296 1.50b multi   3.50 1.75

A 2b souvenir sheet containing No. 776 perforated 13¼ was issued Jan. 25, 1989, to honor the German gold medal winners in the equestrian competition at the 1988 Seoul Summer Olympic Games. Value $20.

An imperforate souvenir sheet depicting Nos. 776 and 85, with simulated perforations, was issued July 4, 1995, to mark the 1996 Atlanta Summer Olympic Games. Value $8.

A297

Designs: 70c, Archbishop Bernardino de Cardenas (1579-1668). 80c, Mother Rosa Gattorno (1831-1900), founder of the Sisters of Santa Ana.

1988
777 A297 70c multi   1.60   .75
778 A297 80c multi   1.75   .80

Issue dates: 70c, Oct. 20, 80c, Oct. 14.

Ministry of Transportation & Communications A298

1988, Oct. 24   **Litho.**   **Perf. 14x13½**
779 A298 2b dp car, blk & pale ol grn   4.00 2.00

Army Communications, 50th Anniv. (in 1987) — A299

1988, Nov. 29   **Litho.**   **Perf. 13½**
780 A299 70c multi   1.75   .75

Bolivian Automobile Club, 50th Anniv. A300

1988, Dec. 29   **Litho.**   **Perf. 13½**
781 A300 1.50b multi   2.75 1.25

An imperforate souvenir sheet depicting No. 781 with simulated perforations was issued July 12, 1995, to mark the first anniv. of the death of Ayrton Senna, Brazilian Formula-1 race driver. Value $8.

Flowering Plants and Emblems A301

50c, Orchid, BULGARIA '89 emblem. 60c, Kantuta blossoms, ITALIA '90 emblem. 70c, *Heliconia humilis,* Albertville '86 emblem. 1b, Hoffmanseggia, Barcelona '92 Games emblem. 2b, Puya raymondi, Seoul '88 Games and five-ring emblems.

1989, Feb. 17   **Litho.**   **Perf. 13½**
782	A301	50c multi, vert.	1.60	.50
783	A301	60c multi	2.00	.55
784	A301	70c multi, vert.	3.00	1.25
785	A301	1b multi, vert.	4.00	1.50
786	A301	2b multi, vert.	7.00	3.00

Nos. 782-786 (5)   17.60 6.80

A 2b souvenir sheet containing No. 783 perforated 13¼ was issued May 18, 1990, to mark the Italia 1990 World Cup games. Value $20.

A 2b souvenir sheet, containing two No. 783, perforated 13¼ aound and imperforate between, was issued Aug. 2, 1990, marking Italia 1990 and picturing the final Germany-Argentina match. Value $20.

Two 2b souvenir sheets, one containing No. 784 perforated 13¼x13½, the other containing two No. 784, perforated 13¼x13½ around and imperforate between, were issued Dec. 27, 1990, to mark the 1992 Albertville Winter Olympic Games. Value, each $10.

A 3b souvenir sheet containing No. 785 perforated 13¾x13, was issued July 6, 1992, to mark Barcelona 1992, Atlanta 1996 and Berlin 2000 Olympic Games. Value $10.

Radio FIDES, 50th Anniv. A302

1989, Feb. 2
787 A302 80c multi   1.50   .75

Gold Quarto of 1852 A303

1989, Feb. 9   **Perf. 13½x14**
788 A303 1b multi   2.00 1.00

A 3b souvenir sheet containing No. 788 perforated 11¾x12½, was issued April 30, 1993, to mark the 40th anniv. of silver coinage in the German Federal Republic. Value $10. A second sheet, also denominated 3b, depicting No. 788 in tan, rather than blue, and with different marginal design, was issued July 26. Value $12.

French Revolution, Bicent. — A304

1989, June 23   **Litho.**   **Perf. 14x13½**
789 A304 70c red, blk & blue   1.75   .70

Uyuni Township, Cent. — A305

1989, July 9   **Litho.**   **Perf. 14x13½**
790 A305 30c bl, blk & gray   1.00   .35

Noel Kempff Mercado Natl. Park, Santa Cruz — A306

1.50b, Federico Ahlfeld Falls, Pauserna River. 3b, *Ozotoceros bezcarticus* (deer).

1989, Sept. 24   **Litho.**   **Perf. 13½x14**
791 A306 1.50b multicolored   3.50 1.50
792 A306 3b multicolored   7.00 3.00

UPAEP — A306a

50c, Metalworking. 1b, Temple of Kalasasaya.

1989, Oct. 12   **Litho.**   **Perf. 13½**
792A A306a 50c multicolored   2.00   .60
792B A306a 1b multicolored   4.00 1.00

See Nos. 808-809.

A 2b souvenir sheet containing Nos. 792A and 792B, perforated 13¼ around and imperforate between, was issued June 2, 1990, to celebrate the 500th anniv. of the discovery of America, UPAEP and Expo '92 Sevila. Value $25.

State Visit by Dr. Carlos Andres Perez, Pres. of Venezuela — A306b

1989, Oct. 14
792C A306b 2b multi   3.50 1.50

See Nos. 825-826, 832.

City of Potosi — A306c

1989, Nov. 10   **Litho.**   **Perf. 13½**
792D A306c 60c Cobija Arch   .85   .60
792E A306c 80c Mint   1.25   .90
f. Pair, #792D-792E   3.50 2.50

Christmas — A307

Paintings: 40c, *Andean Stillwaters*, by Arturo Borda. 60c, *The Virgin of the Roses*, anonymous. 80c, *The Conquistador*, by Jorge de la Reza. 1b, *Native Harmony*, by Juan Rimsa. 1.50b, *Woman with Jug*, by Cecilio Guzman de Rojas. 2b, *Bloom of Tenderness*, by Gil Imana. Nos. 794-798 vert.

1989, Dec. 18 *Perf. 13½x14, 14x13½*

793	A307	40c multicolored	1.00	.30
794	A307	60c multicolored	1.60	.40
795	A307	80c multicolored	2.25	.60
796	A307	1b multicolored	2.50	.70
797	A307	1.50b multicolored	3.75	1.25
798	A307	2b multicolored	4.75	1.50
		Nos. 793-798 (6)	15.85	4.75

A 3b souvenir sheet containing No. 797, perforated 12½x11¾, was issued Jan. 27, 19930 to commemorate the 200th anniv. of the Louvre. Value $20.

Fight Against Drug Abuse — A308

1990, Jan. 23 *Litho.* *Perf. 13½*
799 A308 80c multicolored 1.50 .75

Penny Black, 150th Anniv. — A309

Great Britain #1, Sir Rowland Hill, Bolivia #1

1990, May 13 *Perf. 14x13½*
800 A309 4b multicolored 6.00 3.00

World Cup Soccer Championships, Italy — A310

1990, June 16 *Perf. 13½*
801 A310 2b Stadium, Milan 2.75 1.40
802 A310 6b Game 10.00 4.50

A 3b souvenir sheet containing No. 801 perforated 13x13¾ and 817 perforated 11½x12½ was issued July 6, 1992, to honor World Cup soccer. Value $10.

Organization of American States, Cent. — A311

1990, Apr. 14
803 A311 80c dark bl & brt bl 1.50 .50

A312

1990, Apr. 16
804 A312 1.20b multi 2.00 1.00

Telecommunications — A313

1990 *Litho.* *Perf. 14x13½*
805 A313 70c multi 1.25 .90

A 3b souvenir sheet containing No. 805 perforated 12½x11¾ was issued on April 27, 1992, on the theme of the creation of the Milky Way. Value $15.

A 3b souvenir sheet containing No. 805 perforated 12½x11¾ was issued on Feb. 17, 1993, to mark the 450th anniv. of the death of astronomer Nikolaus Kopernikus (1473-1543). Value $12.

National Chamber of Commerce, Cent. — A314

1990, June
806 A314 50c gold, blk & bl 1.00 .60

Cochabamba Social Club, Cent. — A315

1990, Sept. 14 *Litho.* *Perf. 13½*
807 A315 40c multicolored .65 .40

UPAEP Type of 1989

80c, Huts. 1b, Mountains, lake, vert.

Perf. 13½x14, 14x13½

1990, Oct. 12 *Litho.*
808 A306a 80c multicolored 4.50 .80
809 A306a 1b multicolored 6.00 1.00

A317

1990, Oct. 19 *Perf. 14x13½*
810 A317 1.20b multicolored 1.75 1.00

Magistrate's District of Larecaja, 400th Anniv.

A318

1990, Oct. 12 *Perf. 14x13½*
811 A318 2b multicolored 2.75 1.50

Discovery of America, 500th anniv. (in 1992).

German Reunification A319

1990, Nov. 19 *Litho.* *Perf. 14x13½*
812 A319 2b multicolored 3.50 1.50

An imperforate 5b souvenir sheet depicting No. 812 with simulated perforations was issued Nov. 20, 1990, to celebrate German reunification and the Philatelia '90 philatelic exhibition in Berlin. Exists with either black or red control number. Value, each $15.

A 3b souvenir sheet containing No. 812, perforated 12½x11½ was issued April 27, 1992, to commemorate the 200th anniv. of the port of Brandenburg. Value $12.

Visit of Carlos Salinas de Gortari, Pres. of Mexico A320

Design: 80c, Visit of Rodrigo Borja Cevallos, Pres. of Ecuador.

1990, Dec. 13 *Litho.* *Perf. 13½*
813 A320 60c multicolored 2.00 .80
814 A320 80c multicolored 2.25 .80

4th Congress of the Andean Presidents — A321

1990, Nov. 29 *Perf. 13½x14*
815 A321 1.50b multicolored 2.50 1.00

Exfivia '90 — A322

1990, Dec. 9 *Perf. 13½*
816 A322 40c dk blue .70 .30

Christmas — A323

1990, Nov. 20 *Perf. 11*
817 A323 50c multicolored .80 .30

Express Mail Service A324

1990, Dec. 14 *Perf. 13½x14*
818 A324 1b multicolored 1.50 .50

A 3b souvenir sheet containing No. 818, perforated 11¾x12½ was issued Dec. 31, 1993, honoring Dr. Hermann Oberth. Value $15.

Bolivian Radio Club, 50th Anniv. — A325

1991, Mar. 1 *Litho.* *Perf. 14x13½*
819 A325 2.40b multicolored 3.25 1.50

End of Chaco War, 56th Anniv. — A326

Map of Heroes of Chaco Highway.

1991, June 14 *Litho.* *Perf. 14x13½*
820 A326 60c multicolored 1.00 .50

National Museums — A327

No. 821, Archaeology. No. 822, Art. No. 823, Ethnology, Folklore.

1991, June 13 *Perf. 13½*
821 A327 50c multi .75 .35
822 A327 50c multi .75 .35
823 A327 1b multi 1.50 .60
 a. Strip of 3, #821-823 3.00 3.00

Espamer '91.

A328

Our Lady of Peace, Metropolitan Cathedral.

1991, July 15   Litho.   Perf. 14x13½
824 A328 1.20b multicolored   2.25   .75

Presidential State Visit Type of 1989

Jaime Paz Zamora, Pres. of Bolivia and: No. 825, Dr. Carlos Saul Menem, Pres. of Argentina. No. 826, Dr. Luis Alberto Lacalle, Pres. of Uruguay.

1991   Perf. 13½x14
825 A306b 1b multicolored   1.50   .50
826 A306b 1b multicolored   1.50   .50

Issue dates: No. 825, Aug. 5; No. 826, Aug. 12.

World Wildlife Fund — A329

Tremarctos ornatus: No. 827, Adult, two cubs. No. 828, Adult's head. No. 829, Adult on tree limb. No. 830, Adult, cubs on tree limb.

1991, May 31   Perf. 13½
827 A329 30c multicolored   2.25   .50
828 A329 30c multicolored   2.25   .50
829 A329 30c multicolored   2.25   .50
830 A329 30c multicolored   2.25   .50
    Nos. 827-830 (4)   9.00 2.00

A330

1991, Aug. 21 Litho.   Perf. 14x13½
831 A330 70c multicolored   1.25   .50

Bolivian Philatelic Federation, 20th anniv.

Presidential State Visit Type of 1989

Design: 50c, Jaime Paz Zamora, Pres. of Bolivia and Alberto Fujimori, Pres. of Peru.

1991, Aug. 29   Perf. 13½x14
832 A306b 50c multicolored   .90   .40

National Census — A331

1991, Nov. 19 Litho.   Perf. 14x13½
833 A331 50c multicolored   .80   .40

America Issue — A332

UPAEP emblem and: 60c, First Discovery of Chuquiago, 1535, by Arturo Reque M. 1.20c, Founding of the City of La Paz, 1548, by J. Rimsa, vert.

1991, Oct. 12   Perf. 13½x14, 14x13½
834 A332 60c multicolored   2.50   .60
835 A332 1.20b multicolored   5.00 1.10

First National Grand Prix Auto and Motorcycle Race — A332a

1991, Sept. 5   Litho.   Perf. 14x13½
835A A332a 50c multicolored   .85   .40

ECOBOL, Postal Security System — A333

1991, Sept. 9   Perf. 13½x14
836 A333 1.40b multicolored   2.00   .75

Simon Bolivar — A334

1992, Feb. 15 Litho.   Perf. 13½
837 A334 1.20b buff, brn & org brn   2.00   .75

Exfilbo '92.

Scouting in Bolivia, 75th Anniv. (in 1990) and 1992 Andes Jamboree A335

1992, Jan. 13   Perf. 13½x14
838 A335 1.20b multicolored   2.00 1.00

Dated 1991.
An imperforate souvenir sheet, depicting Nos. 838, 936 and type of 683 valued 2b, was issued Nov. 7, 1994. Value $5.

Christmas A336

Paintings: 2b, Landscape, by Daniel Pena y Sarmiento. 5b, Woman with Fruit, by Cecilio Guzman de Rojas. 15b, Native Mother, by Crespo Gastelu.

1991, Dec.19   Litho.   Perf. 13½
839 A336 2b multicolored   3.25 1.50
840 A336 5b multicolored   7.00 3.00
841 A336 15b multicolored   20.00 9.00
    Nos. 839-841 (3)   30.25 13.50

Pacific Ocean Access Pact Between Bolivia and Peru A337

Designs: 1.20b, Pres. Zamora raising flag, vert. 1.50b, Pres. Jaime Paz Zamora of Bolivia and Pres. Alberto Fujimori, Peru. 1.80b, Shoreline of access zone near Ilo, Peru.

1992, Mar. 23 Perf. 14x13½, 13½x14
842 A337 1.20b multicolored   1.50 1.00
843 A337 1.50b multicolored   2.00 1.00
844 A337 1.80b multicolored   2.50 1.25
    Nos. 842-844 (3)   6.00 3.25

Expo '92, Seville A338

1992, Apr. 15   Perf. 13½x14
845 A338 30c multicolored   .50   .30
846 A338 50c Columbus' ships   .85   .40

Miraflores Rotary Club, District 4690, Mt. Illimani A339

1992, Apr. 30 Litho.   Perf. 13½
847 A339 90c multicolored   1.40   .70

Prof. Elizardo Perez, Founder of Ayllu of Warisata School, Birth Cent. — A340

1992, June 6   Litho.   Perf. 13½
848 A340 60c multicolored   .90   .50

Government Palace, Sucre — A341

1992, July 10 Litho.   Perf. 13½x14
849 A341 50c multicolored   1.50   .50

A342

1992, Sept. 11   Perf. 14x13½
850 A342 50c multicolored   .75   .50

Los Tiempos Newpaper, 25th anniv.

1992 Summer Olympics, Barcelona — A343

Mario Martinez Guzman, tennis player.

1992, Aug. 9   Perf. 13½
851 A343 1.50b multicolored   2.00 1.00

A 3b souvenir sheet containing No. 851, perforated 14x13, was issued Jan. 27, 1993, to mark the Barcelona 1992 and Atlanta 1996 Olympic Games. Value $30.

First Intl. Whitewater Canoe Regatta, Bermejo River A343a

1992, Sept. 17 Litho.   Perf. 13½
851A A343a 1.20b multicolored 2.00 1.00

1994 World Cup Soccer Championships, US — A344

1992, Oct. 2   Litho.   Perf. 13½
852 A344 1.20b multicolored   3.50 1.50

A 3b souvenir sheet containing No. 852, perf 13x13¾, was issued Dec. 31, 1993, to mark the 1994 World Cup. Value $10.

Oruro Technical University, Cent. — A345

1992, Oct. 15   Perf. 13½x14
853 A345 50c multicolored   .85   .50

Interamerican Institute for Agricultural Cooperation, 50th Anniv. — A346

1.20b, Chenopodium quinoa.

1992, Oct. 7   Perf. 13½
854 A346 1.20b multi   2.00 1.00

Discovery of America, 500th Anniv. A347

Paintings: 60c, Columbus departing from Palos, vert. 2b, Columbus with Caribbean natives.

1992, Oct. 1   Perf. 14x13½, 13½x14
855 A347 60c multicolored   1.25   .50
856 A347 2b multicolored   4.50 1.50

Battle of Ingavi, 150th Anniv. (in 1991) A348

1992, Nov. 18   Litho.   Perf. 13½x14
857 A348 1.20b sepia & black   2.75   .80

12th Bolivian Games, Cochabamba and Santa Cruz — A349

1992, Nov. 13
858 A349 2b multicolored   3.00 1.25

Fauna, Events A350

Event emblem and fauna: 20c, Beni Dept., sesquicentennial, caiman. 50c, Polska '93, paca. 1b, Bangkok '93, chinchilla. 2b, 1994 Winter Olympics, Lillehammer, Norway, anteater. 3b, Brandenburg Gate, jaguar. 4b, Brasiliana '93, hummingbird, vert. 5b, 1994 World Cup Soccer Championships, US, piranhas.

1992, Nov. 18   Litho.   Perf. 13½
859 A350 20c multicolored   .50   .25
860 A350 50c multicolored   1.00   .40
861 A350 1b multicolored   1.50   .75
862 A350 2b multicolored   3.00 1.25
863 A350 3b multicolored   5.00 2.00
864 A350 4b multicolored   6.00 2.50
865 A350 5b multicolored   8.00 3.50
    Nos. 859-865 (7)   25.00 10.65

A 3b souvenir sheet containing No. 862 perforated 13x13¾ was issued Dec. 31, 1993, to mark the 1994 Lillehammer Winter Olympic Games. Value $30.

A 4b souvenir sheet depicting Nos. 864 and C224 with simulated perforations was issued July 3, 1995, to recognize Rotary International and to promote nature conservation. Value $10.

Christmas — A350a

Designs: 1.20b, Man in canoe, star. 2.50b, Star over churches. 6b, Flowers, church, infant on hay.

1992, Dec. 1   Litho.   Perf. 13½
865A A350a 1.20b multi   1.60   .50
865B A350a 2.50b multi   3.25 1.25
865C A350a 6b multi   8.75 3.25
     Nos. 865A-865C (3)   13.60 5.00

A351

Nicolaus Copernicus (1473-1543), Polish Astronomer: 50c, Santa Ana Intl. astrometrical observatory, Tarija, horiz.

Perf. 13x13½, 13½x13
1993, Feb. 18   Litho.
866 A351 50c multicolored   .70   .30
867 A351 2b black   2.50   .80

An imperforate 3.50b souvenir sheet depicting Nos. 867 and 923 with simulated perforations was issued Oct. 21, 1994. Value $10.

A352

1993, Apr. 14   Litho.   Perf. 13½
868 A352 60c multicolored   1.10   .40

Beatification of Mother Nazaria.

12th Bolivar Games A353

1993, Apr. 24   Perf. 13½x14
869 A353 2.30b multicolored   2.75 1.10

Bolivia #C240, Brazil #3 A354

1993, May 31
870 A354 2.30b multicolored   3.00 1.10

First Brazilian Stamp, 150th anniv.

A355

Eternal Father, by Gaspar de la Cueva.

1993, June 9   Litho.   Perf. 13½
871 A355 1.80b multicolored   2.75 1.00

Virgin of Urkupina A356

1993, July 31   Litho.   Perf. 14x13½
872 A356 50c multi   1.20   .35

City of Quillacollo, 400th anniv.

Pedro Domingo Murillo Industrial School A357

1993, Aug. 4   Perf. 13½
873 A357 60c multicolored   .85   .35

Butterflies A358

No. 874, Archaeoprepona demophon. No. 875, Morpho sp. No. 876, Papilio sp. No. 877, Historis odius. No. 878, Euptoieta hegesia. No. 879, Morpho deidamia. No. 880, Papilio thoas. No. 881, Danaus plexippus. No. 882, Caligo sp. No. 883, Anaea marthesia. No. 884, Rothschildia sp. No. 885, Heliconius sp. No. 886, Marpesia corinna. No. 887, Prepona chromus. No. 888, Heliconius sp., diff. No. 889, Siproeta epaphus.

1993, June 4   Perf. 13½x14
874 A358 60c multicolored   1.25   .40
875 A358 60c multicolored   1.25   .40
876 A358 80c multicolored   1.60   .75
877 A358 80c multicolored   1.60   .75
878 A358 80c multicolored   1.60   .75
879 A358 1.80b multicolored   3.50 1.00
880 A358 1.80b multicolored   3.50 1.00
881 A358 1.80b multicolored   3.50 1.00
882 A358 2.30b multicolored   4.75 1.25
883 A358 2.30b multicolored   4.75 1.25
884 A358 2.30b multicolored   4.75 1.25
885 A358 2.70b multicolored   6.00 1.50
886 A358 2.70b multicolored   6.00 1.50
887 A358 2.70b multicolored   6.00 1.50
888 A358 3.50b multicolored   7.50 1.75
889 A358 3.50b multicolored   7.50 1.75
  a. Sheet of 16, #874-889   85.00 85.00
     Nos. 874-889 (16)   65.05 17.80

Pan-American Health Organization, 90th Anniv. — A359

1993, Oct. 13   Litho.   Perf. 13½
890 A359 80c multicolored   1.00   .50

An imperforate souvenir sheet depicting Nos. 890 and 789 with simulated perforations was issued July 8, 1995, to honor Louis Pasteur. Value $10.

Archaeological Finds — A360

Location of cave paintings: No. 891, Oruro. No. 892, Santa Cruz, vert. No. 893, Beni, vert. No. 894, Chuquisaca, vert. No. 895, Chuquisaca. No. 896, Potosi. No. 897, La Paz, vert. No. 898, Tarija, vert. No. 899, Cochabamba.

1993, Sept. 28
891 A360 80c multicolored   2.25   .40
892 A360 80c multicolored   2.25   .40
893 A360 80c multicolored   2.25   .40
894 A360 80c multicolored   2.25   .40
895 A360 80c multicolored   2.25   .40
896 A360 80c multicolored   2.25   .40
897 A360 80c multicolored   2.25   .40
898 A360 80c multicolored   2.25   .40
899 A360 80c multicolored   2.25   .40
     Nos. 891-899 (9)   20.25 3.60

America Issue — A361

80c, Saimiri sciureus. 2.30b, Felis pardalis.

1993, Oct. 9   Litho.   Perf. 13½
900 A361 80c multi   1.50   .50
901 A361 2.30b multi   4.50 1.50

Famous People — A361a

Designs: 50c, Yolanda Bedregal, poet. 70c, Simon Martinic, President of Cochabamba Philatelic Center. 90c, Eugenio von Boeck, politician, President of Bolivian Philatelic Federation. 1b, Marina Nunez del Prado, sculptor.

1993, Nov. 17   Litho.   Perf. 11
901A A361a 50c sepia   .50   .30
901B A361a 70c sepia   .80   .30
901C A361a 90c sepia   1.25   .50
901D A361a 1b sepia   1.25   .50
     Nos. 901A-901D (4)   3.80 1.60

Christmas — A361b

Paintings: 2.30b, Adoration of the Shepherds, by Leonardo Flores. 3.50b, Virgin with Child and Saints, by unknown artist. 6b, Virgin of the Milk, by Melchor Perez de Holguin.

1993, Dec. 8   Perf. 14x13½
901E A361b 2.30b multicolored   5.00 1.10
901F A361b 3.50b multicolored   7.50 1.50
901G A361b 6b multicolored   12.00 3.00
     Nos. 901E-901G (3)   24.50 5.60

Town of Riberalta, Cent. — A362

1994, Feb. 3   Litho.   Perf. 13½
902 A362 2b multicolored   2.50   .80

World Population Day — A363

1994, Feb. 17   Litho.   Perf. 13½
903 A363 2.30b multicolored   3.50 1.25

A364

1994, Feb. 21   **Perf. 13½**
904 A364   2b buff & multi   2.25   .80
905 A364 2.30b multi   2.75 1.25
   Inauguration of Pres. Gonzalo Sanchez de Lozada.

A365

   1994 World Cup Soccer Championships, US: 80c, Mascot. 1.80b, Bolivia, Uruguay. 2.30b, Bolivia, Venezuela. No. 909, Part of Bolivian team, goalies in black. No. 910, Part of Bolivian team, diff. 2.70b, Bolivia, Ecuador. 3.50b, Bolivia, Brazil.

1994, Mar. 22
906 A365   80c multicolored   1.00   .40
907 A365 1.80b multicolored   2.00 1.00
908 A365 2.30b multicolored   3.00 1.25
909 A365 2.50b multicolored   3.00 1.25
910 A365 2.50b multicolored   3.00 1.25
   a.   Pair, #909-910   8.00 8.00
911 A365 2.70b multicolored   3.25 1.25
912 A365 3.50b multicolored   4.25 1.75
    Nos. 906-912 (7)   19.50 8.15

   An imperforate souvenir sheet depicting Nos. 907-908 and 911-912 with simulated perforations was issued May 9, 1994. Value $10. On Sept. 18, this sheet was re-released with the overprint "Brasil Campeon." Value $10.

SOS Children's Village, Bolivia — A366

1994, Apr. 12   **Litho.**   **Perf. 13½**
913 A366 2.70b multicolored   3.00 1.25

Catholic Archdiocese La Paz, 50th Anniv. — A367

   Churches, priests: 1.80b, Church of San Pedro, Msgr. Jorge Manrique Hurtado. 2b, Archbishop Abel I. Antezana y Rojas, Church of the Sacred Heart of Mary, vert. 3.50b, Msgr. Luis Sainz Hinojosa, Church of Santo Domingo, vert.

1994, July 12   **Litho.**   **Perf. 13½**
914 A367 1.80b multicolored   2.75   .80
915 A367   2b multicolored   3.25 1.00
916 A367 3.50b multicolored   6.00 1.75
    Nos. 914-916 (3)   12.00 3.55

A368

   Design: 2b, Pres. Victor Paz Estenssoro.

1994, Oct. 2   **Litho.**   **Perf. 13½**
917 A368 2b multicolored   2.25 1.00

A369

1994, Oct. 9
918 A369 1.80b No. 46   1.90   .90

Battle of Ft. Boqueron A370

   Col. Manuel Marzana Oroza, battle scene.

1994, Oct. 6
919 A370 80c multicolored   1.25   .40

San Borja, 300th Anniv. A371

1994, Oct. 14
920 A371 1.60b Erythrina fusca   1.75   .60

America Issue — A372

   Old, new methods of postal transport: 1b, Streetcar, van. 5b, Airplane, ox cart.

1994, Oct. 12
921 A372 1b multicolored   1.25   .40
922 A372 5b multicolored   5.25 2.25

1994 Solar Eclipse — A373

1994 Oct. 21
923 A373 3.50b multicolored   3.75 1.25

Environmental Protection — A374

   Trees: 60c, Buddleja coriacea. 1.80b, Bertholletia exelsa. 2b, Schinus molle, horiz. 2.70b, Polylepis racemosa. 3, Tabebuia chrysantha. 3.50b, Erythrina falcata, horiz.

1994, Sept. 21
924 A374   60c multicolored   .75   .25
925 A374 1.80b multicolored   1.60   .75
926 A374   2b multicolored   1.90   .80
927 A374 2.70b multicolored   2.50 1.25
928 A374   3b multicolored   3.25 1.50
929 A374 3.50b multicolored   3.50 1.75
    Nos. 924-929 (6)   13.50 6.30

   An imperforate souvenir sheet depicting Nos. 925 and 928 with simulated perforations was issued Nov. 3, 1994. Value $12.

Gen. Antonio Jose de Sucre (1795-1830) A375

1995, Jan. 25   **Litho.**   **Perf. 13½**
930 A375 1.80b shown   2.25   .90
931 A375 3.50b red, yel, grn background   4.00 1.25

Christmas A377

   2b, Tarija girl. 5b, High plateau child. 20b, Eastern girl.

1994, Nov. 25   **Litho.**   **Perf. 13½**
933 A377   2b multi   3.25   .80
934 A377   5b multi   8.00 2.25
935 A377 20b multi   30.00 9.00
    Nos. 933-935 (3)   41.25 12.05

A378

1994, Nov. 28   **Litho.**   **Perf. 13½**
936 A378 1.80b multicolored   2.00 1.00
   Pan-American Scout Jamboree, Cochabamba

Cathedral of St. Anne — A379

1995, Apr. 21   **Litho.**   **Perf. 13½**
937 A379 1.90b black & multi   2.25 1.00
938 A379 2.90b blue & multi   3.25 1.25
   Yacuma-Beni Province, cent.

Franciscans at Copacabana Natl. Sanctuary, Cent. — A380

1995, May 2
939 A380 60c gray & multi   1.00   .30
940 A380 80c bister & multi   1.50   .35

A381

1995   **Litho.**   **Perf. 13½**
941 A381 2b multicolored   2.00 1.00
   Peace Between Bolivia and Paraguay. Dated 1994.

A382

1995, July 25
942 A382 2.40b multicolored   2.75 1.10
   Andes Development Corporation (CAF), 25th anniv.

50th Anniv. of Publication of "Nationalism and the Colonial Age," by Carlos Montenegro (1904-53) A383

1995, Aug. 8
943 A383 1.20b pink & black   2.75   .60

FAO, 50th Anniv. — A384

1995, Sept. 26
944 A384 1b multicolored   2.00   .60

UN, 50th Anniv. — A385

1995, Oct. 24 *Perf. 14½*
945 A385 2.90b multicolored 2.25 1.25

America Issue A386

1995, Nov. 21 *Perf. 14*
946 A386 5b Condor 5.00 2.00
947 A386 5b Llamas 5.00 2.00
a. Pair, #946-947 10.00 10.00

ICAO, 50th Anniv. — A387

1995, Dec. 4 *Perf. 13½x13*
948 A387 50c multicolored 1.25 .40

Temple of Samaipata — A388

Archaeological finds and: a, 1.90b, Top of ruins. b, 1b, Top of ruins, diff. c, 2.40b, Lower excavation. d, 2b, Floor, tiers.

1995, Dec. 4 *Perf. 13x13½*
949 A388 Block of 4, #a.-d. 10.00 10.00
No. 949 is a continuous design.

Taquiña Brewery, Cent. — A389

1995, Dec. 8 *Perf. 14*
950 A389 1b multicolored 2.50 .60

Christmas A390

Paintings: 1.20b, The Annunciation, by Cima da Conegliano. 3b, The Nativity, by Hans Baldung. 3.50b, Adoration of the Magi, by Rogier van der Weyden.

1995, Dec. 15 *Perf. 14x13½*
951 A390 1.20b multicolored 1.25 .50
952 A390 3b multicolored 3.00 1.10
953 A390 3.50b multicolored 3.75 1.40
Nos. 951-953 (3) 8.00 3.00

Natl. Anthem, 150th Anniv. — A391

Designs: 1b, J.I. de Sanjines, lyricist. 2b, B. Vincenti, composer.

1995, Dec. 18 *Litho.* *Perf. 13½*
954 1b multicolored 1.40 .70
955 2b multicolored 2.50 1.40
a. A391 Pair, #954-955 5.00 5.00

Decree to Abolish Abuse of Indian Labor, 50th Anniv. — A392

Designs: 1.90b, Modern representations of industry, Gov. Gualberto Villarroel. 2.90, Addressing labor policies, silhouettes of people rejoicing.

1996, Jan. 26 *Perf. 14*
956 1.90b multicolored 1.75 1.00
957 2.90b multicolored 2.50 1.50
a. A392 Pair, #956-957 5.00 5.00

Nos. 639, 653, 685-686, 712-713, 715, 719, 726, 729, 732-733, C332, C348 Srchd.

Perfs. and Printing Methods as Before

1996
958 A273 50c on 3,000,000b #729 .50 .25
959 A265 60c on 2000b #713 .85 .25
960 A277 60c on 1,400,000b #733 .85 .25
961 A271 1b on 2,500,000b #726 .85 .50
962 A264 1.50b on 11,000b #712 1.50 .60
963 A267 2.50b on 23,000b #715 2.25 1.00
964 A269 3b on 1,000,000b #719 2.75 1.25
965 A222 3.50b on 6.50b #639 3.25 1.40
966 A234 3.50b on 9b #653 3.25 1.40

---

967 A276 3.50b on 2,000,000b #732 3.25 1.40
968 AP67 3.80b on 3.80b #C332 3.25 1.40
969 A189 20b on 3.80b #C348 18.00 8.00
970 A253 20b on 10b #685 18.00 8.00
971 A254 20b on 13b #686 18.00 8.00
Nos. 958-971 (14) 76.55 33.70
Size and location of surcharge varies.

No. 627 Surcharged

1996 *Litho.* *Perf. 10½*
972 A216 60c on 2.50b multi .90 .25
See No. 697 for similar surcharge.

10th Summit of the Chiefs of State and Government (Rio Group), Cochabamba A393

Designs: 2.50b, Stylized person. 3.50b, Stylized globe surrounded by lines.

1996, Sept. 4 *Perf. 14*
973 A393 2.50b multicolored 2.25 .90
974 A393 3.50b multicolored 3.25 1.25

Anniversaries A394

50c, Natl. Bank of Bolivia, 125th anniv. 1b, Jose Joaquin de Lemoine (1776-1851), first postal administrator, vert.

1996, Dec. 8 *Litho.* *Perf. 13½*
975 A394 50c multicolored .50 .25
976 A394 1b multicolored 1.00 .40

Summit of the Americas to Sustain Development A395

1996, Dec. 8 *Perf. 14x13½*
977 A395 2.50b org brn & multi 2.25 1.00
978 A395 5b black & multi 4.50 2.00

CARE in Bolivia, 20th Anniv. — A396

1996, Dec. 19 *Perf. 13½*
979 A396 60c Family, horiz. .50 .25
980 A396 70c shown .60 .30

Natl. Symphony Orchestra, 50th Anniv. — A397

1.50b, Flute, saxophone. 2b, String instruments.

1996, Dec. 24
981 1.50b multicolored 1.50 .75
982 2b multicolored 1.90 1.10
a. A397 Pair, #981-982 4.00 4.00
No. 982a is a continuous design.

Tourism in Oruro A398

Designs: 50c, Miners' Monument, vert. 60c, Folklore costume, vert. 1b, Virgin of Socavon, vert. 1.50b, Sajama mountains. 2.50b, Chipaya child, building, vert. 3b, Raul Shaw, "Moreno."

1997, Feb. 3 *Litho.* *Perf. 14½*
983 A398 50c multicolored .50 .50
984 A398 60c multicolored .75 .75
985 A398 1b multicolored 1.25 1.25
986 A398 1.50b multicolored 1.25 1.25
987 A398 2.50b multicolored 2.00 2.00
988 A398 3b multicolored 3.00 3.00
Nos. 983-988 (6) 8.75 8.75
Dated 1996.

Tourism in Chuquisaca — A399

Designs: 60c, La Glorieta. 1b, Governor's Palace, vert. No. 991, Dinosaur tracks. No. 992, House of Liberty. 2b, Tarabaqueno, vert. 3b, Statue of Juana Azurduy of Padilla, vert.

1997, Jan. 30 *Perf. 13½x14, 14x13½*
989 A399 60c multicolored .45 .45
990 A399 1b multicolored .70 .70
991 A399 1.50b multicolored 1.50 1.50
992 A399 1.50b multicolored 1.50 1.50
993 A399 2b multicolored 2.00 2.00
994 A399 3b multicolored 3.00 3.00
Nos. 989-994 (6) 9.15 9.15
Dated 1996.

Tourism in Tarija — A400

Designs: 50c, House of Culture, Dorada, vert. 60c, Church of Entre Rios, vert. 80c, San Luis Falls. 1b, Monument to the Chaco War. 3b, Temple, Statue of the Virgin Mary, Chaguaya. 20b, Eustaquio Mendez house, monument.

1997, Jan. 24 *Perf. 14x13½, 13½x14*
995 A400 50c multicolored .50 .30
996 A400 60c multicolored .65 .35
997 A400 80c multicolored .85 .55
998 A400 1b multicolored 1.10 .60

999 A400 3b multicolored 3.25 1.90
1000 A400 20b multicolored 20.00 11.00
Nos. 995-1000 (6) 26.35 14.75
Dated 1996.

Visit of French Pres. Jacques Chirac A401

Design: Bolivian Pres. Gonzalo Sanchez de Lozada, Chirac.

1997, Mar. 15 **Perf. 14**
1001 A401 4b multicolored 4.00 4.00

Salesian Order in Bolivia, Cent. — A402

Designs: 1.50b, St. John Bosco (1815-88), church. 2b, Statue of St. John Bosco talking with boy, church.

1997, Apr. 29 Litho. Perf. 13½
1002 A402 1.50b multicolored 1.50 1.50
1003 A402 2b multicolored 2.00 2.00

UNICEF, 50th Anniv. A403

Children's drawings: 50c, Houses, children on playground. 90c, Child running, cactus, rock, lake. 1b, Boys, girls arm in arm across globe. 2.50b, Girl on swing, others in background.

1997
1004 A403 50c multicolored .50 .45
1005 A403 90c multicolored .95 .75
1006 A403 1b multicolored 1.20 .75
1007 A403 2.50b multicolored 2.75 2.10
Nos. 1004-1007 (4) 5.40 4.05

Department of La Paz — A404

Tourism: 50c, Mt. Chulumani, Las Yungas, vert. 80c, Inca monolith, vert. 1.50b, City, Mt. Illimani, vert. 2b, Gate of the Sun, Tiwanacu. 2.50b, Traditional dancers, vert. 10b, Virgin of Copacabana, reed boat.

1997, May 28 Litho. Perf. 13½
1008 A404 50c multicolored .50 .45
1009 A404 80c multicolored .75 .70
1010 A404 1.50b multicolored 1.40 1.25
1011 A404 2b multicolored 1.75 1.60
1012 A404 2.50b multicolored 2.25 2.00
1013 A404 10b multicolored 9.25 8.50
Nos. 1008-1013 (6) 15.90 14.50

1997 America Cup Soccer Championships, Bolivia — A405

1998 World Cup Soccer Championships, France — A406

1997, June 13
1014 A405 3b multicolored 3.00 3.00
1015 A406 5b multicolored 5.00 5.00

National Congress A407

1997, July 8 Litho. Perf. 13½
1016 A407 1b multicolored .80 .40

America Issue — A408

Women in traditional costumes: 5b, From valley region. 15b, From eastern Bolivia.

1997, July 14 Litho. Perf. 13½
1017 A408 5b multicolored 5.00 5.00
1018 A408 15b multicolored 14.00 14.00

Mercosur (Common Market of Latin America) A409

1997, Sept. 26
1019 A409 3b multicolored 2.75 2.00
See Argentina No. 1975, Brazil No. 2646, Paraguay No. 2565, Uruguay No. 1681.

Christmas A410

Paintings: 2b, Virgen del Cerro, by unknown artist. 5b, Virgen de la Leche, by unknown artist. 10b, The Holy Family, by Melchor Pérez de Holguin.

1997, Dec. 19 Litho. Perf. 13½
1020 A410 2b multicolored 2.50 1.40
1021 A410 5b multicolored 5.50 3.50
1022 A410 10b multicolored 10.00 5.00
Nos. 1020-1022 (3) 18.00 9.90

Diana, Princess of Wales (1961-97) A411

1997, Dec. 29
1023 A411 2b Portrait, vert. 2.00 1.40
1024 A411 3b In mine field 2.75 2.10

Visit of Prime Minister of Spain A412

Hugo Banzer Suarez, Pres. of Bolivia and José Maria Aznar.

1998, Mar. 16
1025 A412 6b multicolored 6.00 3.50

Bolivian Society of Engineers, 75th Anniv. A413

1998, Apr. 28
1026 A413 3.50b multicolored 3.00 1.50

Rotary Intl. in Bolivia, 70th Anniv. — A414

1998, Apr. 30 Litho. Perf. 13½
1027 A414 5b multicolored 4.00 2.25

A415

America Issue: 4b, Letter Carriers, 1942, horiz.

1998, July 9
1028 A415 3b multicolored 2.50 1.25
1029 A415 4b multicolored 3.50 1.50

Famous Men — A416

1.50b, Werner Guttentag Tichauer, bibliographer. 2b, Dr. Martin Cardenas Hermosa, botanist. 3.50b, Adrian Patiño Carpio, composer.

1998, July 10
1030 A416 1.50b brown 1.00 .50
1031 A416 2b green, vert 1.50 .75
1032 A416 3.50b black, vert 2.40 .90
Booklet, 4 each #1030-1032 50.00
Nos. 1030-1032 (3) 4.90 2.15

Regions in Bolivia A417

Beni: 50c, Victoria regia. 1b, Calliandra. 1.50b, White Tajibo tree, vert. 3.50b, Amazon mask. 5b, Nutria. 7b, King vulture.

1998, Oct. 11 Litho. Perf. 13½
1033 A417 50c black & multi .30 .25
1034 A417 1b black & multi .75 .40
1035 A417 1.50b black & multi 1.25 .70
1036 A417 3.50b black & multi 3.00 1.50
1037 A417 5b black & multi 4.25 2.00
1038 A417 7b black & multi 5.75 4.00
Nos. 1033-1038 (6) 15.30 8.85

Pando: 50c, Acre River. 1b, Sloth climbing bamboo tree, vert. 1.50b, Bahia Arroyo, vert. 4b, Boa. 5b, Family of capybaras. 7b, Houses, palm trees, vert.

1039 A417 50c green & multi .50 .30
1040 A417 1b green & multi .75 .40
1041 A417 1.50b green & multi 1.25 .70
1042 A417 4b green & multi 3.25 1.75
1043 A417 5b green & multi 4.50 2.00
1044 A417 7b green & multi 6.50 4.00
Nos. 1039-1044 (6) 16.75 9.15
Nos. 1033-1044 (12) 32.05 18.00

Women of Bolivia — A418

First Lady Yolanda Prada de Banzer and: 1.50b, Women working in fields, making pottery, weaving. 2b, Women working on computer, standing at blackboard.

1998, Oct. 11
1045 A418 1.50b multicolored 1.10 .60
1046 A418 2b multicolored 1.75 1.00
a. Pair, #1045-1046 3.00 3.00
America Issue.

City of La Paz, 450th Anniv. A419

2b, Plaza de Laja Church.

1998, Oct. 14
1047 A419 2b multicolored 2.00 1.00

A420

1998, Nov. 6 Litho. Perf. 13½x13¾
1048 A420 3.50b blue & yellow 2.75 .75
Organization of American States, 50th anniv.

A421

1998, Nov. 12   *Perf. 13¼x13½*
1049 A421 2b multicolored   1.50   .50

Bolivian Philatelic Federation, 25th anniv., Espamer '98, Buenos Aires.

Christmas — A422

2b, Child's drawing of church. 6b, Pope John Paul II. 7b, John Paul II, Mother Teresa.

Perf. 13¼x13½, 13½x13¼
1998, Nov. 26
1050 A422 2b multi, horiz.   1.60   .50
1051 A422 6b multi   3.75   1.75
1052 A422 7b multi   4.50   2.00
    Nos. 1050-1052 (3)   9.85   4.25

UPU, 125th Anniv. A423

1999, Jan. 26   **Litho.**   *Perf. 13½*
1053 A423 3.50b multicolored   3.00   .70

AFC Soccer Club, 75th Anniv. — A424

1999, Apr. 22   **Litho.**   *Perf. 13½*
1054 A424 5b multicolored   4.50   2.25

Geneva Convention and Bolivian Red Cross, 50th Anniv. A425

1999, May 18
1055 A425 5b multicolored   4.25   1.25

Bernardo Guarachi, First Bolivian to Reach Summit of Mt. Everest A426

1999, May 25
1056 A426 6b multicolored   6.00   3.00

Special Olympics of Bolivia, 30th Anniv. — A427

Designs: 2b, Medalists on podium. 2.50b, Winners of swimming event, running event.

1999
1057 A427   2b multicolored   1.50   .50
1058 A427   2.50b multicolored   1.75   .60

Japanese Immigration to Bolivia, Cent. — A428

Designs: 3b, Golden Pavilion, Kyoto. 6b, Sun setting across water, vert.

1999, June 3
1059 A428 3b multicolored   2.25   .70
1060 A428 6b multicolored   4.50   1.75

Bolivian Cinema, 100th Anniv. A429

No. 1061, Hacia la Gloria, 1932-33. No. 1062, Jonas y la Ballena Rosada, 1995. No. 1063, Wara Wara, 1929. No. 1064, Vuelve Sebastiana, 1953. No. 1065, La Campana del Chaco, 1933. No. 1066, La Vertiente, 1958. No. 1067, Yawar Mallku, 1969. No. 1068, Mi Socio, 1982.

1999   **Litho.**   *Perf. 13½*
1061 A429 50c multi   .35   .25
1062 A429 50c multi   .35   .25
1063 A429 1b multi   .65   .45
1064 A429 1b multi   .65   .45
1065 A429 3b multi   2.25   .75
1066 A429 3b multi   2.25   .75
1067 A429 6b multi   4.00   2.00
1068 A429 6b multi   4.00   2.00
   a.   Sheet of 8, #1061-1068   13.00   13.00
    Nos. 1061-1068 (8)   14.50   6.90

SOS Children's Village, 50th Anniv. — A430

1999, July 8
1069 A430 3.50b multicolored   2.50   1.40

Intl. Day Against Illegal Drugs A431

Perf. 13¼x13½
1999, June 26   **Litho.**
1070 A431 3.50b multicolored   2.50   1.40

Completion of Bolivian-Brazilian Gas Pipeline — A432

Designs: 3b, Presidents of Bolivia and Brazil, map of pipeline. 6b, Presidents, gas flame.

1999, July 1   **Litho.**   *Perf. 13½*
1071 A432 3b multicolored   2.50   1.25
1072 A432 6b multicolored   4.50   2.75

La Paz Lions Club, 50th Anniv. — A433

1999   *Perf. 13½x13¼*
1073 A433 3.50b multicolored   2.50   1.40

Cochabamba Tourism — A434

50c, Mt. Tunari. 1b, Cochabamba Valley. 2b, Container from Omerque culture, idol from Pachamama culture. 3b, Totora. 5b, Composer Teofilo Vargas Candia. 6b, Statue of Jesus Christ.

1999   *Perf. 13½x13¾, 13¾x13½*
1074 A434 50c multi   .45   .25
1075 A434 1b multi   .85   .40
1076 A434 2b multi, vert.   1.40   .60
1077 A434 3b multi   1.90   .85
1078 A434 5b multi, vert.   3.00   1.25
1079 A434 6b multi, vert.   3.50   1.50
    Nos. 1074-1079 (6)   11.10   4.85

Potosí Tourism A435

50c, Tarapaya Lake. 1b, Obverse and reverse of 1827 Bolivian coin. 2b, Mt. Chorolque. 3b, Lake, llama, birds. 5b, "Mestizo Woman with a Cigarette Case," by Teofilo Loaiza. 6b, Alfredo Dominguez Romero, musician.

Perf. 13¾x13½, 13½x13¾
1999   **Litho.**
1080 A435 50c multi, vert.   .45   .25
1081 A435 1b multi   .85   .40
1082 A435 2b multi   1.40   .60
1083 A435 3b multi   1.90   .85
1084 A435 5b multi, vert.   3.00   1.25
1085 A435 6b multi, vert.   3.50   1.50
    Nos. 1080-1085 (6)   11.10   4.85

America Issue, A New Millennium Without Arms — A436

1999   *Perf. 13½x13¼*
1086 A436 3.50b shown   2.50   1.50
1087 A436 3.50b Globe, flower   2.50   1.50

Christmas A437

2b, Children, Christmas tree. 6b, The Birth of Jesus, by Gaspar Miguel de Berrios. 7b, Our Families of the World, by Omar Medina.

1999   *Perf. 13¼x13½, 13½x13¼*
1088 A437 2b multi   1.30   .50
1089 A437 6b multi, vert.   3.50   1.40
1090 A437 7b multi, vert.   4.50   1.60
    Nos. 1088-1090 (3)   9.30   3.50

Discovery of Brazil, 500th Anniv. A438

2000   **Litho.**   *Perf. 13½x13¾*
1091 A438 5b multi   4.00   1.50

2000 Doble Copacabana Bicycle Race — A439

Various views of racers.

2000
1092 A439 1b multi   .90   .50
1093 A439 3b multi   2.00   1.10
1094 A439 5b multi   4.00   1.60
1095 A439 7b multi   6.00   2.25
    Nos. 1092-1095 (4)   12.90   5.45

Sgt. Maximiliano Paredes Military School, Cent. — A440

2000   **Litho.**   *Perf. 13½x13¾*
1096 A440 2.50b multi   2.00   1.00

Federal Republic of Germany, 50th Anniv. (in 1999) A441

2000
1097 A441 6b multi   4.50   1.25

Paintings of Cecilio Guzmán de Rojas (1900-51) — A442

Designs: 1b, Self-portrait, vert. 2.50b, Triunfo de la Naturaleza. 5b, Andina, vert. 6b, Riña de Estudiantes.

2000   *Perf. 13¾x13½, 13½x13¾*
1098-1101 A442 Set of 4   10.00   4.00

Artifacts from Natl. Archaeological Museum — A443

Artifacts from: No. 1102, 50c, Pando. No. 1103, 50c, Potosí. 70c, Beni. 90c, Tarija. No. 1106, 1b, Chuquisaca. No. 1107, 1b, Oruro. 3b, Cochabamba. 5b, Santa Cruz. 20b, La Paz.

2000   *Perf. 11¼x11*
1102-1110 A443 Set of 9   24.00   12.00

America Issue, Fight Against AIDS — A444

Designs: No. 1111, 3.50b, Symbols for male and female in whirlwind. No. 1112, 3.50b, Man, woman, clouds, brick wall.

2000			Perf. 13¼x13½	
1111-1112	A444	Set of 2	6.00	2.50

Victor Agustin Ugarte, Soccer Player — A445

2000, Apr. 24		Litho.	Perf. 13½x13¼	
1113	A445	3b multi	2.50	1.00

Santa Cruz Tourism A446

Designs: 50c, Fountains, Parque el Arenal. 1b, Ox cart. 2b, Writers Raúl Otero Reiche, Gabriel René Moreno, Hernando Sanabria Fernández. 3b, Virgin of Cotoca, vert. 5b, Anthropomorphic vessel, vert. 6b, Speothos venaticus.

		Perf. 13½x13¾, 13¾x13½		
2000, Apr. 28				
1114-1119	A446	Set of 6	14.00	6.25

Javier del Granado (1913-96), Writer — A447

2000, May 26		Litho.	Perf. 13¼x13½	
1120	A447	3b multi	3.00	.90

Millennium — A448

2000		Litho.	Perf. 13½x13¼	
1121	A448	5b multi	3.50	1.00

Sovereign Military Order of Malta, 900th Anniv. — A449

2000			Perf. 13¾x13½	
1122	A449	6b multi	4.25	1.25

Christmas — A450

Angels from Calamarca Church: 3b, Gabriel. 5b, Angel of Virtue. 10b, Angel with spike of grain.

2000				
1123-1125	A450	Set of 3	12.50	4.25

Holy Year 2000 — A451

Holy Year emblem and: 4b, Basilica de San Francisco, La Paz. 6b, Wheat stalks, barbed wire.

2000		Litho.	Perf. 13½x13¼	
1126-1127	A451	Set of 2	8.00	3.00

Promotion of Philately A452

National Symbols A453

Designs: 50c, Man carrying first day covers up stairs. 1b, Child, six stamps. 1.50b, Stamp collector. 2b, Child, three stamps. 2.50b, Envelope in bin. 10b, Patuju bandera, current national flower. 20b, La kantuta, previous national flower. 30b, Coat of arms, 1825. 50b, Coat of arms, 1826. 100b, Coat of arms, 1851.

2001		Litho.	Perf. 10½	
1128	A452	50c green	.30	.25
1129	A452	1b green	.70	.30
1130	A452	1.50b green	1.10	.50
1131	A452	2b green	1.40	.70
1132	A452	2.50b green	2.00	.80
a.		Horiz. strip, #1128-1132, + label	6.75	6.75

		Perf. 13¾x13½		
1133	A453	10b multi	8.00	4.00
1134	A453	20b multi	15.00	8.00
1135	A453	30b multi	22.50	12.00
1136	A453	50b multi	37.50	25.00
1137	A453	100b multi	75.00	40.00
		Nos. 1128-1137 (10)	163.50	91.55

Issued: 50c, 1b, 1.50b, 2b, 2.50b, 6/12; 10b, 6/29; 20b, 6/8; 30b, 5/16; 50b, 3/16; 100b, 4/16.

Bolivia - European Union Cooperation, 25th Anniv. — A454

2001, May 8		Litho.	Perf. 13½x13¾	
1138	A454	6b multi	4.25	1.25

Law and Political Science Faculty of San Andres University, 171st Anniv. — A455

2001, May 18			Perf. 13¾x13½	
1139	A455	6b multi	4.25	1.25

Muela del Diablo A457

2001, July 6		Litho.	Perf. 13½x13¾	
1141	A457	1.50b multi	1.25	.40

2001 Census — A458

2001, Aug. 1			Perf. 11	
1142		Horiz. strip of 5	8.00	8.00
a.	A458	1b purple & multi	1.00	.30
b.	A458	1.50b red & multi	1.10	.40
c.	A458	1.50b green & multi	1.10	.40
d.	A458	2.50b blue & multi	2.00	.65
e.	A458	3b violet & multi	2.40	.70

Butterflies and Insects A459

Butterflies: No. 1143, 1b, Heliconinae. 1.50b, Philaethria dido. No. 1145, 2.50b, Diathria clymene. No. 1146, 5b, Arctiidae. No. 1147, 6b, Morpho godarti. No. 1148, 6b, Caligo idomineus.
Insects: No. 1149, 1b, Orthopteridae. No. 1150, 2.50b, Mantidae. No. 1151, 3b, Tropidacris latreillei. 4b, Dynastidae. No. 1153, 5b, Acrocinus longimanus. No. 1154, 5b, Lucanidae.

		Perf. 13¼x13½		
2001, Aug. 30				Litho.
1143-1148	A459	Set of 6	16.50	6.75
1149-1154	A459	Set of 6	16.50	6.75

21st Inter-American Scout Conference A460

2001, Sept. 13			Perf. 13¾x13½	
1155	A460	3.50b multi	3.00	2.25

America Issue, UNESCO World Heritage Sites — A461

Designs: 1.50b, Door from Church of St. Francis, Potosi. 5b, Tiwanakwu monoliths, horiz.

		Perf. 13¾x13½, 13½x13¾		
2001, Sept. 26				
1156-1157	A461	Set of 2	6.00	4.00

Breast Cancer Prevention A462

2001, Oct. 18		Litho.	Perf. 13¼x13½	
1158	A462	1.50b multi	1.25	1.00

Christmas — A463

Sculptures by Gaspar de la Cueva: 3b, St. Mary Magdalene. 5b, St. Apolonia. 10b, St. Teresa of Avila.

2001, Nov. 15			Perf. 13½x13¼	
1159-1161	A463	Set of 3	15.00	9.25

Joaquin Gantier, Historian, and Casa de la Libertad — A464

2001, Nov. 20				
1162	A464	4b multi	3.75	2.00

Bolivian-Belgian Cooperation — A465

2001, Nov. 21			Perf. 13¼x13½	
1163	A465	6b multi	5.00	2.50

Meeting of Bolivian and Peruvian Presidents A466

Arms of Bolivia and Peru and: 50c, Dam, aerial view of Lake Titicaca. 3b, Bridge, Route from La Paz, Bolivia to Ilo, Peru.

2002, Jan. 26			Perf. 13¾x13½	
1164-1165	A466	Set of 2	3.00	1.75

Mauro Nuñez, Composer, Cent. of Birth — A467

No. 1166: a, 1b, Musical score and stringed instruments. b, 6b, Musical score and Nuñez.

2002, Jan. 29
1166 A467   Horiz. pair, #a-b   6.00 4.50

Naming of Oruro Carnival as UNESCO Masterpiece of Oral and Intangible Heritage of Humanity A468

Dances: 50c, Diablada. 1.50b, Morenada. 2.50b, Caporales. 5b, Tobas. No. 1171, 7b, Suri Sikuri, vert. No. 1172, 7b, Pujllay, vert.

Perf. 13¼x13½, 13½x13¼
2002, Feb. 8
1167-1172 A468   Set of 6   17.50 14.00

Butterfly and insect Type of 2001
Miniature Sheet

No. 1173: a, Urania leilus. b, Tropidacris latreillei. c, Papilio cresphontes. d, Acrocinus longimanus. e, Preponia buckleyana. f, Half of Thysannia agripyna, denomination at left. g, Half of Thysannia agripyna, denomination at right. h, Lucanidae. i, Nymphalidae. j, Dynastidae. k, Nymphalidae-heliconinae. l, Orthopteridae.

Perf. 13¼x13½
2002, Feb. 15
1173 A459 3b Sheet of 12,   30.00 30.00
     #a-l

3rd Intl. Theater Festival, La Paz — A469

2002, Mar. 21   *Perf. 13¾x13½*
1174 A469 3b multi   2.50 1.25

Intl. Year of Mountains and Intl. Year of Ecotourism A470

Designs: 80c, Viscachas Mountain, Potosi Department. 1b, Tree, Cochabamba Department, vert. 1.50, Mount Huayna Potosi, La Paz Department. No. 1178, 2.50b, Mt. Sajama, Oruro Department, vert. No. 1179, 2.50b, Mt. Payachatas, Oruro Department.

Perf. 13¼x13½, 13½x13¼
2002, Apr. 2
1175-1179 A470   Set of 5   7.75 3.00

Dr. Gunnar Mendoza, Historian A471

2002, May 25   *Perf. 13¼x13½*
1180 A471 4b multi   3.25 2.00

Gen. Germán Busch Military Aviation College, 50th Anniv. A472

Designs: 4b, Airplane over mountains. 5b, Two airplanes, vert. 6b, Three helicopters.

Perf. 13¼x13½, 13½x13¼
2002, June 14
1181-1183 A472   Set of 3   12.00 8.00

Museo de la Recoleta, Sucre, 400th Anniv. — A473

2002, July 12   *Perf. 13¾x13½*
1184 A473 4b multi   3.25 2.00

Birds — A474

Designs: 50c, Neochen jubata. 4b, Falco deiroleucus. 6b, Dryocopus schulzi.

2002, July 12   *Perf. 13½x13¼*
1185-1187 A474   Set of 3   9.00 5.50

Cefilco Philatelic Co., Cochabamba (50c), Bolivian Philatelic Federation, 30th anniv. (4b), Phila Korea 2002 World Stamp Exhibition, Seoul (6b).

Art by Maria Luisa Pacheco A475

Designs: 70c, Untitled work, vert. 80c, Cordillera, 1967, vert. 5b, Cerros, 1967.

Perf. 13½x13¼, 13¼x13½
2002, July 29
1188-1190 A475   Set of 3   5.25 3.25

Sculptures by Marina Nuñez del Prado — A476

Designs: 70c, Madona India. 80c, Madre India. 5b, Venus Negra.

2002, July 29 Litho.   *Perf. 13½x13¼*
1191-1193 A476   Set of 3   5.25 3.25

Armando Alba Zambrana (1901-74), Historian A477

Perf. 13¼x13½
2002, Aug. 30   **Litho.**
1194 A477 3b multi   2.75 1.75

Pan-American Health Organization, Cent. — A478

2002, Apr. 24   *Perf. 13½x13¾*
1195 A478 3b multi   2.75 1.75

America Issue, Education A479

Students: 1b, In classroom. 2.50b, At computer.

2002, Oct. 11   *Perf. 13¼x13½*
1196-1197 A479   Set of 2   3.50 2.25

Alcide d'Orbigny (1802-57), Naturalist A480

Designs: 1b, D'orbigny and man and woman in native costumes, vert. 4b, D'Orbigny and boat. 6b, Portrait, vert.

Perf. 13¾x13½, 13½x13¾
2002, Sept. 26
1198-1200 A480   Set of 3   9.00 5.50

Christmas — A481

Designs: 3b, Madonna and Child. 5b, Andean nativity. 6b, Adoration of the Magi.

Perf. 13½x13¼
2002, Nov. 14   **Litho.**
1201-1203 A481   Set of 3   8.00 8.00

Apolinar Camacho (1917-2002), Composer A482

2003, Jan. 10   *Perf. 13¾x13½*
1204 A482 2.50b multi   1.50 1.25

Battle of Bahia, Cent. (in 2002) — A483

No. 1205: a, 50c, One statue. b, 1b, Three statues.

2003, May 5 Litho.   *Perf. 13½x13¼*
1205 A483   Pair, #a-b   1.00 1.00

Permanent Assembly for Human Rights in Bolivia, 25th Anniv. — A484

2003, June 5
1206 A484 6b blue   3.25 1.50

Central Bank of Bolivia, 75th Anniv. — A485

2003, July 18   *Perf. 13¾x13½*
1207 A485 4b multi   2.50 1.10

Constitutional Tribunal, 5th Anniv. A486

2003, July 25   *Perf. 13¼x13½*
1208 A486 1.50b multi   1.10 .50

Indigenous Flora and Fauna A487

No. 1209: a, 6b, Quinoa. b, 7b, Llamas.

2003, Sept. 23
1209 A487   Pair, #a-b   7.50 5.00

Republic of Panama, Cent. A488

2003, Nov. 3 Litho.   *Perf. 13½x13¾*
1210 A488 7b multi   3.50 1.50

13th Iberoamerican Heads of State Summit, Santa Cruz de la Sierra — A489

No. 1211: a, Flags, Western hemisphere. b, Flags, Eastern hemisphere.

2003, Nov. 7
1211 A489 6b Horiz. pair, #a-b   6.00 3.00

Porfirio Díaz Machicao (1909-81), Rosendo Villalobos (1859-1932), and Msgr. Juan Quiros (1914-92) — A490

Virgin of Guadalupe A491

2003   *Perf. 13½x13¾, 13¾x13½*
1212 A490 6b multi   3.50   1.50
1213 A491 6b multi   3.50   1.50
   a.   Pair, #1212-1213   7.50   5.00
Bolivian Language Academy, 75th anniv. (No. 1212), La Plata Archdiocese, 450th anniv. (No. 1213).
Issued: No. 1212, 11/12; No. 1213, 11/25.

Christmas A492

Paintings depicting the Adoration of the Shepherds by: 1.50b, Leonardo Flores, vert. 6b, Bernardo Bitti, vert. 7b, Melchor Pérez de Holguín.

Perf. 13¾x13½, 13½x13¾
2003, Dec. 16
1214-1216 A492   Set of 3   8.00 4.00

Pontificate of Pope John Paul II, 25th Anniv. A493

Designs: 1b, Pope waving, vert. 1.50b, Painting, vert. 5b, Pope blessing Indians. 6b, Pope waving, diff., vert. 7b, Photograph, vert. 20b, Arms of Bolivia and Vatican City, Pope John Paul II, aerial view of Vartican City, #1013, 1161.

2003   *Perf. 13¾x13½, 13½x13¾*
1217-1221 A493   Set of 5   12.50 11.50
   Imperf
   Size: 150x110mm
1222 A493 20b multi   12.50 11.50

Arco Iris Foundation, 10th Anniv. — A494

2004, Apr. 4   Litho.   *Perf. 13¾x13½*
1223 A494 1.80b multi   1.25   .50

Academy of Military History, 25th Anniv. — A495

2004, Oct. 19   Litho.   *Perf. 13¾x13½*
1224 A495 1b multi   .60   .30

2004 Summer Olympics, Athens — A496

Designs: 1.50b, Shooting, gymnastics, judo. 7b, Track, swimming.

2004, Nov. 8
1225-1226 A496   Set of 2   4.00 1.50

Christmas A497

Designs: 1.50b, Nativity. 3b, Shepherd praying. 6b, Candle.

2004, Dec. 16
1227-1229 A497   Set of 3   5.50 2.00

La Paz Journalist's Association, 75th Anniv. — A498

2004, Dec. 23
1230 A498 1.50b multi   .85   .50

America Issue - Environmental Protection A499

Designs: 5b, Palm tree. 6b, Parrots.

2004, Dec. 30
1231-1232 A499   Set of 2   6.00 2.75

Rotary International, Cent. — A500

No. 1233 — Emblem of Rotary International and: a, Emblem of PolioPlus, map of Bolivia. b, Paul Harris, flag of Bolivia.

2005, Mar. 4   Litho.   *Perf. 13¼x13½*
1233 A500 3b Horiz. pair, #a-b   3.50 1.25

Projects of Bolivia and the European Union A501

Designs: 5b, PRAS PANDO, Pando water and drainage project. 6b, PRAEDAC, Chapare alternate development program, vert.

Perf. 13¼x13½, 13½x13¼
2005, Mar. 16
1234-1235 A501   Set of 2   6.00 2.00

Textiles — A502

Designs: 50c, Aguayo Calamarca. 1b, Aqsu Bolivar. 1.50b, Incuña Camacho. No. 1239, 6b, Llixlla Challa. No. 1240, 6b, Unku Santo Lago Titicaca, horiz.

Perf. 13½x13¼, 13¼x13½
2005, Apr. 1
1236-1240 A502   Set of 5   7.75 3.25

Marshal Otto Felipe Braun — A503

2005, May 20   *Perf. 13¾x13½*
1241 A503 6b multi   3.25 1.25

Birds — A504

Designs: 1b, Harpia harpyja. 1.50b, Penelope dabbenei. 7b, Aulacorhynchus coeruleicinctus.

2005, June 28   *Perf. 13½x13¼*
1242-1244 A504   Set of 3   5.00 1.50
Interexpo '05, Dominican Republic (1b), Bolivian Philatelic Federation, 35th anniv. (1.50b), Washington 2006 Intl. Philatelic Exhibition (7b).

Pope John Paul II (1920-2005) — A505

Pope Benedict XVI — A506

2005, Aug. 1   Litho.   *Perf. 13½x13¾*
1245 A505 5b multi   2.50 1.25
   Perf. 13¾x13½
1246 A506 5b multi   2.50 1.25

Pacific War, 125th Anniv. A507

Perf. 13½x13¾
2005, Aug. 17   Litho.
1247 A507 5b multi   3.00 1.25

Publication of *Don Quixote,* by Miguel de Cervantes, 400th Anniv. — A508

2005, Aug. 26
1248 A508 4b multi   2.50 1.00

America Issue — Fight Against Poverty A509

Paintings by Gilka Wara Libermann: 6b, Mother and child. 7b, Sailboat and fish skeleton.

2005, Aug. 26
1249-1250 A509   Set of 2   7.50 3.50

Gen. Ildefonso Murguia and Presidential Escort Regiment A510

2005, Sept. 3 Litho. Perf. 13¾x13½
1251 A510 2b multi   1.25   .50
Presidential Escort Regiment, 184th anniv.

Tourism A511

2005, Sept. 27   Perf. 13½x13¾
1252 A511 6b multi   3.25 1.50

Environmental Protection League — A512

2005, Oct. 5
1253 A512 6b multi   3.25 1.50

Miniature Sheet

Stamp Day — A513

No. 1254: a, 2b, Unissued Bolivian stamps of 1863. b, 2b, Imperf. Bolivia #C7. c, 2b, Brazil #1, stamp similar to Great Britain #1. d, 4b, Bolivia #2-3. e, 4b, Bolivia #C25. f, 4b, Bolivia #740.

2005, Oct. 9   Perf. 13¼x13½
1254 A513   Sheet of 6, #a-f   10.00 10.00

Christmas A514

Designs: 1.50b on 60c, Magi on camels, Star of Bethlehem. 3b on 80c, Holy Family.

2005, Oct. 9 Litho.   Perf. 13¾x13½
1255-1256 A514   Set of 2   2.50 1.10
Dark gray and dark blue portions of the designs of Nos. 1255-1256 were overprinted on unissued stamps.

Nos. 724, 725, 737 Surcharged

Methods and Perfs As Before
2006, Feb. 12
1257 A271   1b on 1,000,000b
                      #725   .55   .50
1258 A271   2b on 550,000b
                      #724   1.10 1.00
1259 A281 2.50b on 1,000,000b
                      #737   1.40 1.25
    Nos. 1257-1259 (3)   3.05 2.75
Size and location of surcharge varies.

National Faculty of Engineering, Cent. — A515

2006, July 4 Litho.   Perf. 13½x13¾
1260 A515 6b multi   2.25 1.50

Pres. Evo Morales Ayma — A516

President: 1.50b, Waving. 5b, With flag. 6b, Wearing traditional Indian costume.

2006, Aug. 15   Perf. 13¾x13½
1261-1263 A516   Set of 3   4.25 3.50

Bolivian Red Cross — A517

2006, Aug. 16
1264 A517 5b multi   1.75 1.00

Bolivia Post Corporation, 15th Anniv. — A518

Incan post runner and envelopes in: 1b, Green. 1.50b, Blue.

Perf. 13½x13¼
2006, Aug. 21   Litho.
1265-1266 A518   Set of 2   1.00   .65

Miniature Sheet

Stamp Day — A519

No. 1267: a, 1.50b, Boy Scouts viewing exhibits at Exfivia 75. b, 1.50b, Stamp collector with open album. c, 1.50b, Bolivia #189, Honduras #C1052i. d, 6b, People viewing exhibits at Exfilmar 80. e, 6b, Bolivia #1247, Iceland #990a. f, 6b, Bolivia #C240, Dominican Republic #1308a.

2006, Aug. 24   Perf. 13½x13¾
1267 A519   Sheet of 6, #a-f   7.50 7.50

History of the National Flag — A520

Designs: 1.50b, Legislative Palace and flag of 1851. 5b, Exterior of Casa de la Libertad and flag of 1826. 6b, Interior of Casa de la Libertad, flag of 1825.

2006, Sept. 21   Perf. 13¾x13½
1268-1270 A520   Set of 3   4.50 3.50

Franciscan Order in Tarija, 400th Anniv. — A521

Designs: No. 1271, 2b, Franciscan monk and donkey. No. 1272, 2b, Exterior of San Francisco Church. No. 1273, 6b, Interior of San Francisco Basilica, vert. No. 1274, 6b, Painting of Virgin Mary and angels, vert.

Perf. 13½x13¾, 13¾x13½
2006, Oct. 2
1271-1274 A521   Set of 4   5.50 4.00
Nos. 1271 and 1273 are dated "2005."

First Flight of Alberto Santos-Dumont, Cent. — A522

2006, Oct. 23   Perf. 13½x13¾
1275 A522 1.50b multi   .70   .50

Oruro, 400th Anniv. A523

2006, Oct. 23
1276 A523 4b multi   1.50 1.00

Puerto Bahia, Cent. A524

Designs: 1b, Avenida 9 de Febrero. 1.50b, German Busch Plaza. 2.50b, Chestnut tree, vert. 3b, Potosi Plaza. 4b, Bahía Pando River. 6b, Bolivia-Brazil Friendship Bridge. 7b, Avenida del Puerto, vert.

Perf. 13½x13¾, 13¾x13½
2006, Nov. 24   Litho.
1277-1283 A524   Set of 7   8.00 6.25

America Issue, Energy Conservation A525

Designs: 3b, Fluorescent light bulb on flower stalk, doctor, patient and people. 4b, Light bulb containing money.

2006, Dec. 4 Litho.   Perf. 13¾x13½
1284-1285 A525   Set of 2   4.50 2.00

Manco Kapac Province, 50th Anniv. A526

Designs: 5b, Ruins of astronomical observatory. 6b, Copacabana Church. 7b, Boat on Lake Titicaca.

2006, Dec. 4   Perf. 13½x13¾
1286-1288 A526   Set of 3   6.50 4.00
No. 1288 is dated "2003."

Deserts and Desertification — A527

Designs: 1.50b, Mine degradation in Potosi Department. 2b, Gullies, Tarija Department. 3b, Terraces, La Paz. 4b, Deforested area, Caranavi.

2006, Dec. 4
1289-1292 A527   Set of 4   4.00 3.00

Endangered Animals
A528

Designs: 1b, Vicuna. 1.50b, Caiman, horiz. 5b, Caiman, diff., horiz. 7b, Vicuna, horiz.

Perf. 13¾x13½, 13½x13¾
2006, Dec. 4
1293-1296 A528 Set of 4 5.00 4.00

Christmas
A529

Designs: 4b, Virgin of Rosario. 5b, Adoration of the Magi. 6b, Adoration of the Shepherds.

2006, Dec. 4 **Perf. 13¾x13½**
1297-1299 A529 Set of 3 5.50 3.50

Birds — A530

Designs: 2.50b, Toucan, Pando Department. 3.50b, Horned curassow, Santa Cruz Department. 6b, Blue bird, Pando Department. 7b, Harpy eagle, Santa Cruz Department.

2006, Dec. 11
1300-1303 A530 Set of 4 6.50 5.00

Dogs — A531

Designs: 1b, Miniature schnauzer. 3b, Husky. 4b, Boxer. 6b, Mixed-breed.

2006, Dec. 21
1304-1307 A531 Set of 4 5.00 3.50

36th Lions International Forum for Latin America and the Caribbean, Cochabamba — A532

2007, Jan. 7 Litho. Perf. 13½x13¾
1308 A532 6b multi 2.25 1.40

Treaty of Rome, 50th Anniv. — A533

No. 1309: a, 3.50b, Map of Europe. b, 7b, European Union flag.

2007, Mar. 27
1309 A533 Horiz. pair, #a-b 3.50 2.50

Cochabamba Philatelic Center (CEFILCO), 50th Anniv — A534

Designs: 50c, Brochures on philately for young people. 1b, Arnold Glaeser, first President of CEFILCO, Bolivia #C270. 2.50b, Bolivia #901B, 1999 CEFILCO stamp catalogue. 3b, Philatelists Franz Steimbach and Oscar Roca.
No. 1314: a, 3.50b, Cochabamba Cathedral and monument. b, 6b, Sculpture of Christ, Cochabamba Cathedral.

2007, Apr. 18
1310-1313 A534 Set of 4 2.50 1.50
1314 A534 Horiz. pair, #a-b 3.25 2.50

Charangos
A535

Designs: 4b, Charangos, Bolivian arms. 6b, Charango, mountain, horiz.

Perf. 13¾x13½, 13½x13¾
2007, Apr. 27
1315-1316 A535 Set of 2 3.25 2.75

Bolivian Red Cross, 90th Anniv. A536

2007, May 24 Perf. 13½x13¾
1317 A536 2.50b multi 1.00 .50

Francis Harrington, Founder of American Institute, La Paz — A537

2007, May 30 Litho.
1318 A537 7.50b multi 2.50 1.75

American Institute, cent.

Natl. Chamber of Industry, 75th Anniv. — A538

No. 1319: a, 9b, Gears, map of Bolivia. b, 12b, Gears.

2007, June 28
1319 A538 Horiz. pair, #a-b 9.00 5.00

Santa Cruz Zoo — A539

Cats: 6b, Jaguar. 9b, Puma.

2007 Perf. 13¾x13½
1320-1321 A539 Set of 2 6.00 4.00

Scouting, Cent. A540

Designs: 7.50b, Lord Robert Baden-Powell blowing kudu horn. 8.50b, Scouting emblem, vert.

2007 Perf. 13½x13¾, 13¾x13½
1322-1323 A540 Set of 2 6.75 5.00

57th Conference of the Chiefs of American Air Forces, Santa Cruz de la Sierra — A541

2007 Perf. 13½x13¾
1324 A541 10.50b multi 5.00 4.00

Birds — A542

Designs: 4b, Opisthocomus hoazin, La Paz Department. No. 1326, 5.50b,Tunqui, La Paz Department, horiz. No. 1327, 5.50b, Ara ararauna, Santa Cruz Department, horiz. 7.50b, Porphyrula martinica, Santa Cruz Department, horiz.

2007 Perf. 13¾x13½, 13½x13¾
1325-1328 A542 Set of 4 9.00 6.25
Issued: Nos. 1325-1326, 7/28; Nos. 1327-1328, 7/20.

Birds Type of 2007

Designs: 3.50b, Cyclarhis guyanensis, Tarija Department, horiz. 4b, Egretta alba, Cochabamba Department. 5.50b, Ramphastos toco, Beni Department, horiz. No. 1332, 6.50b, Bubo virginianus, Cochabamba Department. No. 1333, 6.50b, Trogon melanurus, Pando Department. No. 1334, 6.50b, Falco sparverius, Potosí Department, horiz. No. 1335, 6.50b, Hymantopus mexicanus, Oruro Department. No. 1336, 7.50b, Opisthocomus hoazin, Beni Department, horiz. No. 1337, 7.50b, Platalea ajaja, Oruro Department, horiz. No. 1338, 8.50b, Sarcoramphus papa, Tarija Department, horiz. No. 1339, 8.50b, Momotus momota, Chuquisaca Department, horiz. No. 1340, 9b, Tinamotis pentlandii, Potosí Department, horiz. No. 1341, 9b, Chlorostilbon aureoventris, Chuquisaca Department. 10.50b, Ardea cocoi, Pando Department.

Perf. 13½x13¾, 13¾x13½
2008 Litho.
1329-1342 A542 Set of 14 35.00 35.00
Issued: Nos. 1329, 1338, 8/20; Nos. 1330, 1332, 8/21; Nos. 1333, 1342, 8/22; Nos. 1331, 1336, 8/23; Nos. 1334, 1340, 8/24; Nos. 1339, 1341, 8/27; Nos. 1335, 1337, 8/28.

Death of Ernesto "Che" Guevara in Bolivia, 40th Anniv. A543

Designs: 30b, Autograph of Guevara. 50b, Various images of Guevara, vert.

Perf. 13½x13¾, 13¾x13½
2007, Oct. 8
1343-1344 A543 Set of 2 30.00 30.00

Bolivian Air Force, 50th Anniv. A544

Anniversary emblem and: 7.50b, Planes on ground. 9b, Plane in flight.

2007, Oct. 12 Perf. 13½x13¾
1345-1346 A544 Set of 2 6.50 6.00

Intl. Civil Aviation Day A545

Airplane and: 6.50b, Globe. 8.50b, World map.

2007, Dec. 10
1347-1348 A545 Set of 2 7.00 6.50

America Issue, Education For All — A546

No. 1349: a, 3b, Three schoolgirls in classroom. b, 5b, Text, map of Bolivia. c, 6b, Teacher and student. d, 9b, School building, girl and flowers.

Perf. 13¼x13½

2007, Dec. 12　　　　　　**Litho.**
1349 A546　Block of 4, #a-d　　8.50 6.00

Tourism
A547

Designs: 2b, Maragua Syncline, Chuquisaca Department. 2.50b, Festuca grass pasturelands, Oruro Department. 3.50b, Lagoon, Pando Department. 5b, Lake on Beni River, Beni Department. No. 1354, Manuripi River, Beni Department. No. 1355, Valley, Tarija Department. No. 1356, Zongo Valley, La Paz Department. No. 1357, Trees along Orthon River, Pando Department. No. 1358, Tornado in Sajama Valley, Oruro Department, vert. No. 1359, Sucre Bridge over Pilcomayo River, Chuquisaca Department. No. 1360, Cactus, Isla del Pescador, Potosí Department, vert. 10b, Chapare River, Cochabamba Department. No. 1362, Trichocereus camarguensis, Tarija Department. No. 1363, Uyuni Salt Flats, Potosí Department. 20b, Lake Caimán, Santa Cruz Department. 30b, Zongo, La Paz Department, vert. 50b, Plaza Sucre, Cochabamba Department. 100b, Arcoiris Waterfall, Santa Cruz Department, vert.

Perf. 13½x13¾, 13¾x13½

2007　　　　　　　　　　　**Litho.**
1350 A547	2b multi	.75	.55
1351 A547	2.50b multi	.85	.65
1352 A547	3.50b multi	1.50	.95
1353 A547	5b multi	2.25	1.40
1354 A547	5.50b multi	2.40	1.50
1355 A547	5.50b multi	2.40	1.50
1356 A547	5.50b multi	2.40	1.50
1357 A547	7.50b multi	3.25	2.00
1358 A547	7.50b multi	3.25	2.00
1359 A547	9b multi	4.00	2.40
1360 A547	9b multi	4.00	2.40
1361 A547	10b multi	4.25	2.60
1362 A547	10b multi	4.25	2.75
1363 A547	10.50b multi	4.25	2.75
1364 A547	20b multi	8.50	5.25
1365 A547	30b multi	12.50	8.00
1366 A547	50b multi	22.50	16.00
1367 A547	100b multi	42.50	40.00
Nos. 1350-1367 (18)		125.80	94.20

Issued: Nos. 1352-1355, 1357, 1362, 12/13; Nos. 1350, 1351, 1356, 1358-1361, 1363-1367, 12/14. Six additional stamps were issued in this set. The editors would like to examine any examples.

Christmas — A548

No. 1368: a, 3.50b, Holy Family. b, 4b, Adoration of the Shepherds. c, 6.50b, Epiphany.

Perf. 13¾x13½

2007, Dec. 19　　　　　　**Litho.**
1368 A548　Horiz. strip of 3, #a-c　　5.00 5.00

World Post Day — A549

2008, Jan. 15
1369 A549 1b multi　　　.45 .30
Dated 2007.

Bolivian Episcopal Commission of Pastoral Social Charities, 50th Anniv. — A550

Designs: 10b, Jesus, icons, people, map of Bolivia and South America. 15b, Church and indigenous people, vert.

Perf. 13½x13¾, 13¾x13½

2008, Jan. 24
1370-1371 A550　Set of 2　　9.50 7.50

Jesuit Church, Santa Cruz A551

Various views of church: 5b, 9b.

2008, Feb. 15　　**Perf. 13½x13¾**
1372-1373 A551　Set of 2　　5.50 3.75
Dated 2007.

Cochabamba Rotary Club, 80th Anniv. (in 2007) — A552

2008, Mar. 7　　**Perf. 13¾x13½**
1374 A552 20b multi　　8.50 5.25
Dated 2007.

Superior Court of Oruro, 150th Anniv. (in 2005) — A553

2008, Apr. 5
1375 A553 20b multi　　8.50 7.00
Dated 2007.

The Strongest Soccer Team, Cent. — A554

No. 1376: a, 1.50b, Team emblem. b, 2.50b, Team crest. c, 5.50b, Trophy. d, 6.50b, 1908 team.

2008, Apr. 11　　**Perf. 13½x13¾**
1376 A554　Block of 4, #a-d　　7.00 6.00

Pope Benedict XVI — A555

Pope Benedict XVI wearing: 12b, White vestments. 15b, Colored vestments.

2008, May 29　Litho.　Perf. 13¾x13½
1377-1378 A555　Set of 2　　11.00 9.00
Dated 2007.

Mountain, Soccer Stadium and Ball A556

2008, June 13　　**Perf. 13½x13¾**
1379 A556 3b multi　　1.25 1.00

Protest against FIFA proposal to ban international soccer matches at altitudes above 2500 meters.

Sucre Rebellion of May 25, 1809 A557

Designs: 1.50b, Clock tower. 5.50b, Liberty Belltower. 7.50b, Clock tower, building with anniversary banner. 9b, San Francisco Xavier University.

2008, June 18
1380-1383 A557　Set of 4　　10.00 8.00

Superintendent of Banks and Financial Institutions, 80th Anniv. — A558

Designs: 3b, Emblem. 7b, Building, vert.

Perf. 13½x13¾, 13¾x13½

2008, July 10
1384-1385 A558　Set of 2　　4.25 3.50

Acquisition of MA-60 Airplanes by Bolivian Air Force — A559

Airplane: 1.50b, In flight. 9b, On ground.

2008, Aug. 14　　**Perf. 13½x13¾**
1386-1387 A559　Set of 2　　4.50 4.00

Intl. Year of the Potato A560

Potato varieties and their blossoms: 1.50b, Luk'i Negra. 5.50b, Sani Imilla. 7.50b, Saq'ampaya. 10.50b, Waych'a.

2008, Oct. 10
1388-1391 A560　Set of 4　　12.00 10.00

Map of Bolivia and Envelopes — A561

2009, May 1　Litho.　Perf. 13½x13¾
1392 A561 1.50b multi　　.75 .60

No. 1392 paid an additional postage fee for mail that was to be handled by private postal services in Bolivia.

Nationalization of Entel, 1st Anniv. — A562

Designs: 2b, Emblem. 3b, Emblem and people, horiz.

Perf. 13¾x13½, 13½x13¾

2009, May 5
1393-1394 A562　Set of 2　　2.75 2.25

Rainbow Foundation, 15th Anniv. — A563

2009, May 11　　**Perf. 13½x13¾**
1395 A563 5b multi　　2.75 2.25

Marshal Sucre National University, Cent. — A564

2009, June 6
1396 A564 3b multi　　1.75 1.00

Solidarity With Cuba A565

2009, June 10
1397 A565 7.50b multi　　4.00 3.25

Inter-American Development Bank, 50th Anniv. — A566

2009, June 22   **Perf. 13¾x13½**
1398 A566 5b multi   2.75 2.25

La Paz Revolution, Bicent. — A567

2009, July 14
1399 A567 2b multi   1.10 .90

Ayllu and Normal School, Warisata, 75th Anniv. A568

2009, Aug. 2   **Perf. 13½x13¾**
1400 A568 2.50b multi   1.40 1.10

National Institute of Health Laboratories, Cent. — A569

2009, Aug. 4   **Perf. 13¾x13½**
1401 A569 1.50b multi   .90 .70

Venezuela National High School, Cent. — A570

Designs: 1b, Medals. 3b, School building.

2009, Aug. 10   **Perf. 13½x13¾**
1402-1403 A570   Set of 2   2.25 1.75

Enrique Lindemann B Educational Unit — A571

2009, Aug. 19   **Litho.**
1404 A571 3.50b multi   2.00 1.50

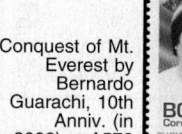

Conquest of Mt. Everest by Bernardo Guarachi, 10th Anniv. (in 2008) — A572

Guarachi, first Bolivian to reach summit of Mt. Everest wearing: 50c, Ski cap. 7b, Red parka, horiz.

Perf. 13¾x13½, 13½x13¾
2009, Aug. 28
1405-1406 A572   Set of 2   4.00 3.50

San Ramon Home for the Elderly, Cent. A573

2009, Oct. 26   **Perf. 13½x13¾**
1407 A573 2b multi   1.10 .90

16th Bolivarian Games, Sucre — A574

Designs: 1.50b, Emblem. 9b, Emblem, diff.

2009, Nov. 14   **Perf. 13¾x13½**
1408-1409 A574   Set of 2   4.50 4.00

America Issue — A575

Children playing with traditional toys: 1b, Top. 7b, Kite.

2009, Nov. 20
1410-1411 A575   Set of 2   3.25 3.00

Japan Intl. Cooperation Agency in Bolivia, 30th Anniv. — A576

Various agency workers with Bolivians: 1b, 1.50b, 3b, 9b.

2009, Dec. 4   **Perf. 13½x13¾**
1412-1415 A576   Set of 4   6.00 5.50
Dated 2008.

Bolivian Philatelic Federation, 38th Anniv. — A577

2009, Dec. 10
1416 A577 3.50b multi   1.50 1.50

Christmas A578

Designs: 7b, Flight into Egypt. 9b, Jesus in manger.

Perf. 13¾x13½
2009, Dec. 21   **Litho.**
1417-1418 A578   Set of 2   6.50 4.75

Re-election of Pres. Evo Morales Ayma — A579

Pres. Morales: 12.50b, Holding poles. 9b, Waving.

2010, Jan. 20 Litho. Perf. 13¾x13½
1419-1420 A579   Set of 2   4.50 3.50

Airplane and Letter to France A580

2010, Mar. 15   **Perf. 13½x13¾**
1421 A580 9b multi   3.50 3.25
First airmail flight from the Pyrenees to the Andes, 80th anniv.

Global Warming — A581

Mt. Chacaltaya with: 2.50b, Little snow cover. 10b, More snow cover.

2010, Apr. 20
1422-1423 A581   Set of 2   5.00 4.50

Túpac Katari (c. 1750-81), and Wife, Bartolina Sisa (c. 1750-82), Leaders of Rebellion of Indigenous People — A582

2010, Apr. 25   **Perf. 13¾x13½**
1424 A582 1.50b brown   .65 .60

Bolivian Traditions A583

Designs: 1.50b, Items associated with All Saint's Day. 10.50b, Ekeko, god of abundance.

2010, May 10   **Perf. 13½x13¾**
1425-1426 A583   Set of 2   5.00 5.00

Masks — A584

Designs: 1b, Pepino. 2b, Moreno. 9b, Chuncho. 10b, Kusillo.

2010, May 10   **Perf. 13¾x13½**
1427-1430 A584   Set of 4   9.00 9.00

Flowers — A585

No. 1431: a, Flowers. b, Flowers and butterfly.

2010, May 27   **Perf. 13½x13¾**
1431 A585 1.50b Horiz. pair, #a-
b   1.50 1.00

Rose, Barbed Wire, Rainer and José Luis Ibsen A586

2010, Aug. 31
1432 A586 3b multi   1.40 1.00
Rainer Ibsen (1949-72), and his father, José Luis (1925-73), were kidnapped and murdered political prisoners of the Banzer regime.

Bolivian Army, 200th Anniv. A587

Flags and: 3.50b, Bulldozer and tank. 9b, Military leaders and battle scene.

2010, Aug. 31
1433-1434 A587 Set of 2   5.00 4.25

2010 Youth Olympics, Singapore — A588

Emblem and: 2b, Soccer player, cyclist. 9b, Swimmer, runner.

2010, Sept. 8   Litho.   Perf. 13½x13¾
1435-1436 A588 Set of 2   4.50 3.75

Declaration of Independence of Cochabamba, Bicent. — A589

2010, Sept. 10   Perf. 13¾x13½
1437 A589 9b multi   3.50 3.00

Rebellion Against Spanish Rule of Santa Cruz, Bicent. A590

2010, Sept. 20   Perf. 13½x13¾
1438 A590 5b multi   2.25 1.75

America Issue, National Symbols — A591

No. 1439 — Government Palace, La Paz and: a, 2.50b, Andean condor, Bolivian national bird. b, 5b, Patuju, Bolivian national flower.

2010, Oct. 20
1439 A591   Horiz. pair, #a-b   3.25 2.50

Military Engineering School, 60th Anniv. — A592

2010, Oct. 26
1440 A592 7b multi   2.75 2.75

Endangered Species A593

Designs: 1b, Puya raimondii. 2b, Leopardus jacobita, horiz. 2.50b, Atelopus tricolor, horiz. 3.50b, Anairetes alpinus, horiz.

Perf. 13¾x13½, 13½x13¾
2010, Nov. 1   Set of 4   4.50 3.75
1441-1444 A593

Rebellion Against Spanish Rule of Potosí, Bicent. A594

2010, Nov. 10   Perf. 13½x13¾
1445 A594 3.50b multi   1.40 1.10

Zampona, Woodcut by Fausto Aoiz Vilaseca (1908-94) A595

2010, Dec. 13   Perf. 13¾x13½
1446 A595 2b multi   1.10 1.00

Christmas A596

Items in Santa Clara Museum of Religious Art, Sucre: 3b, Archangel Michael, wooden sculpture. 9b, Adoration of the Shepherds, painting, horiz.

Perf. 13¾x13½, 13½x13¾
2010, Dec. 17
1447-1448 A596 Set of 2   5.50 5.00

Jaime Escalante (1930-2010), Bolivian-born American High School Mathematics Teacher — A597

2011, Jan. 20   Perf. 13½x13¾
1449 A597 2b multi   1.10 1.00

Fruits A598

Designs: 1.50b, Oranges (naranja). 5.50b, Mangos. 7.50b, Papayas. 9b, Avocados (palta). 10.50b, Bananas (platano).

2011
1450-1454 A598   Set of 5   12.00 12.00

Nos. 1450-1454 paid an additional postage fee for mail that was to be handled by private postal services in Bolivia.

Grains — A599

Designs: 1b, Chenopodium quinoa. 2b, Amaranthus. 2.50b, Chenopodium pallidicaule. 5b, Lupinus mutabilis.

2011, July 5   Perf. 13¾x13½
1455-1458 A599   Set of 4   5.50 4.00

Boliviana de Aviación, 4th Anniv. A600

2011, July 22   Perf. 13½x13¾
1459 A600 3b multi   1.75 1.25

Bolivian Cooperation With Cuba — A601

Designs: 2b, Doctor administering eye examination on patient. 2.50b, People in map of bolivia, dove, vert. 3b, Teacher and adult student.

Perf. 13½x13¾, 13¾x13½
2011, Sept. 2
1460-1462 A601 Set of 3   4.00 2.75

Intl. Registry of Bolivian Ships, 10th Anniv. A602

Designs: 1.50b, Barge. 9b, Bolivian Navy boat.

2011, Sept. 2   Perf. 13½x13¾
1463-1464 A602   Set of 2   5.50 4.00

Blood Donation Campaign — A603

2011, Sept. 15
1465 A603 3b multi   1.75 1.25

Postal Union of the Americas, Spain and Portugal (UPAEP), Cent. — A604

2011, Oct. 6   Perf. 13¾x13½
1466 A604 9b multi   5.00 3.25

Endangered Fish — A605

Designs: 1b, Orestias agassii. 1.50b, Cichla pleiozona. 3b, Colossoma macropomum. 9b, Orestias luteus.

2011, Oct. 21   Perf. 13½x13¾
1467-1470 A605   Set of 4   7.50 6.50

National Institute of Statistics, 75th Anniv. A606

2011, Oct. 25
1471 A606 9b multi   5.00 3.25

Mailboxes A607

Designs: 1.50b, Rectangular mailbox. 9b, Mailbox with rounded top.

2011, Dec. 6
1472-1473 A607   Set of 2   5.50 4.00

Christmas A608

Children's drawings: 1b, Child, star, Christmas tree, gifts, by Sarah Laura Zailes Azeñas. 9b, Children and Christmas tree, by Adriana Nahir Peñaloza Cusi, horiz.

Perf. 13¾x13½, 13½x13¾
2011, Dec. 7
1474-1475 A608   Set of 2   5.50 3.75

Human
Rights
A609

2011, Dec. 9   **Perf. 13½x13¾**
1476 A609 9b multi   5.00 3.25

Intl. Year of
Forests — A610

Emblem and: 2.50b, Bertholletia excelsa.
3b, Swietenia macrophylla.

2011, Dec. 11   **Perf. 13¾x13½**
1477-1478 A610 Set of 2   3.00 2.00

Traditional Cuisine — A611

Designs: 1b, Saice. 1.50b, Majao. 2.50b,
Silpancho. 9b, Plato Paceño.

2011, Dec. 16   **Perf. 13½x13¾**
1479-1482 A611 Set of 4   8.00 5.25

Coca Production — A612

Designs: 50c, Coca plantation and products
using coca. 9b, Coca leaves and berries, vert.

Perf. 13½x13¾, 13¾x13½
2011, Dec. 19
1483-1484 A612 Set of 2   5.00 3.75

Yacimientos Petroliferos Fiscales
Bolivianos Corporation, 75th
Anniv. — A613

Designs: 50c, Line of workers. 9b, Dionisio
Foianini, nationalizer of Bolivian oil fields, oil
derrick, workers with Bolivian flag, vert.

2011, Dec. 21
1485-1486 A613 Set of 2   5.00 3.50

Coin Commemorating New Bolivian
Constitution — A614

2012, Jan. 20   **Perf. 13¾x13½**
1487 A614 3b multi   1.75 1.25

Bolivia's
Seacoast
Claim — A615

2012, Mar. 12
1488 A615 5b multi   2.75 2.50

Year Against Violence Towards
Children and Adolescents — A616

2012, Apr. 12   **Perf. 13½x13¾**
1489 A616 3.50b multi   1.90 1.50

Workers
A617

Designs: 50c, Sugar cane cutter (zafra). 1b,
Seamstresses (fabril). 3b, Miner (minero). 5b,
Petroleum worker (petrolero), vert.

Perf. 13½x13¾, 13¾x13½
2012, May 1
1490-1493 A617 Set of 4   5.00 4.00

42nd General
Assembly of
Organization of
American
States,
Cochabamba
A618

2012, May 7   **Perf. 13¾x13½**
1494 A618 10b multi   5.50 3.00

World Internet
Day — A619

Designs: 1b, Map of Western Hemisphere,
"@." 1.50b, Stylized globe, pointing finger
icon. 3b, "@" and emblems of internet
websites.

2012, May 17   **Litho.**
1495-1497 A619 Set of 3   3.50 2.50

Heroic
Resistance of
Cochabamba
Women,
Bicent. — A620

2012, May 22   **Perf. 13¾x13½**
1498 A620 1.50b multi   1.00 .75

Domesticated Animals — A621

Designs: 50c, Chickens (gallina). 1b, Burro.
3b, Sheep (oveja). 5b, Rabbit (conejo).

2012, May 28   **Perf. 13½x13¾**
1499-1502 A621 Set of 4   6.00 4.00

Dinosaurs and Their Tracks — A622

Designs: 50c,   Theropod.   1.50b,
Ankylosaurus.   3b,   Sauropod.   5b,
Stegosaurus.

2012, June 8   **Litho.**
1503-1506 A622 Set of 4   7.00 3.75

Emblem
of the
Attorney
General
A623

2012, June 25
1507 A623 3.50b multi   2.25 1.50

Minerals
A624

Designs: 1b, Andorite. 1.50b, Bismuthinite.
2b, Amethyst. 5b, Cassiterite.

2012, July 11
1508-1511 A624 Set of 4   6.25 3.75

Folk
Dances — A625

Designs: 50c, Ch'utas. 1b, Llamerada.
1.50b, Kullawada. 2b, Caporales. 10b,
Morenada.

2012, July 24   **Perf. 13¾x13½**
1512-1516 A625 Set of 5   10.00 6.00
        See Nos. 1569-1572.

Television
Show "La
Bicicleta
de los
Huanca,"
25th
Anniv.
A626

2012, Aug. 17   **Perf. 13½x13¾**
1517 A626 4b multi   2.50 1.75

Bolivian
Dishes
A627

Designs: 50c, Locro de Gallina. 1b,
Mondongo. 1.50b, K'ala Phurka. 5b,
Charquekan.

2012, Sept. 18
1518-1521 A627 Set of 4   5.25 3.25

Orchids
A628

Designs: 50c, Vasqueziella boliviana. 1.50b,
Masdevallia yungasensis. 3b, Cattleya rex. 5b,
Restrepia vasquezii.

2012, Sept. 19
1522-1525 A628 Set of 4   6.50 4.00

Congressional Library, Cent. — A629

2012, Sept. 21
1526 A629 3.50b multi   2.25 1.50

Decolonization Day — A630

Designs: 1b, Mother Earth and alignment of planets (end of Mayan calendar cycle). 1.50b, 1492 discovery of America by Christopher Columbus, vert. 2.50b, Amazonian collective marriage ceremony, vert.

Perf. 13½x13¾, 13¾x13½
2012, Oct. 6
1527-1529 A630   Set of 3   3.50 2.00

America Issue — A631

Myths and legends: 1b, La Palliri. 5b, El amor maldito transformalo en culebra (Cursed love transformed into a snake).

2012, Oct. 12   *Perf. 13¾x13½*
1530-1531 A631   Set of 2   4.00 2.50

Intl. Year of Sustainable Energy For All — A632

Emblem and: 1b, Christ of Peace statue, Cochabamba, wind generators, power lines. 3.50b, Mountain, solar panels.

2012, Oct. 25   Litho.
1532-1533 A632   Set of 2   3.00 2.00

Leaders of 1781 Siege of La Paz A633

Designs: 50c, Tupac Katari (c. 1750-81), and torture of prisoner. 1.50b, Micaela Bastidas (1745-81), Bartolina Sisa (c. 1750-82), wife of Katari, vert. 3b, Katari and Sisa.

Perf. 13½x13¾, 13¾x13½
2012, Oct.
1534-1536 A633   Set of 3   3.50 2.00

Mentisan Ointment, 75th Anniv. A634

2012, Nov. 6   *Perf. 13½x13¾*
1537 A634 30b multi   20.00 12.50

Christmas A635

Children's art: 1.50b, Bolivians and Holy Family, by Wara Bascopé Céspedes. 2.50b, Christmas tree, by Stefany Gissell Robles.

2012, Nov. 12   *Perf. 13¾x13½*
1538-1539 A635   Set of 2   2.75 1.75

Avelino Siñani - Elizardo Pérez Education Law, 2nd Anniv. A636

2012, Dec. 14   *Perf. 11¼x11*
1540 A636 2.50b multi   1.60 1.00

Quinoa Cultivation A637

Quinoa seeds and: 1b, Chenopodium quinoa plants. 3.50b, Quinoa harvesters, horiz. 4b, Quinoa plants in field, horiz.

Perf. 13¾x13½, 13½x13¾
2012, Dec. 18
1541-1543 A637   Set of 3   5.50 3.25

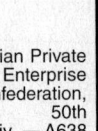

Bolivian Private Enterprise Confederation, 50th Anniv. — A638

2012, Dec. 19   Litho.   *Perf. 11x11½*
1544 A638 4b multi   2.60 1.25

Intl. Day Against Corruption A639

Emblem and: 2b, Man, flag of Bolivia. 3b, Pres. Evo Morales, man, horiz.

Perf. 11x11½, 11½x11
2013, Feb. 27   Litho.
1545-1546 A639   Set of 2   3.00 1.50

World Health Day — A640

2013, Apr. 9   Litho.   *Perf. 13¾x13½*
1547 A640 20b multi   12.00 5.75

Bolivian Institute of High Altitude Biology, 50th Anniv. — A641

2013, Apr. 13   Litho.   *Perf. 13¾x13½*
1548 A641 9b multi   6.00 2.60

Higher University of San Andrés Law and Political Science Faculty, 182nd Anniv. A642

2013, Apr. 29   Litho.   *Perf. 13½x13¾*
1549 A642 30b multi   20.00 8.75

Oruro Carnaval, Cent. — A643

Designs: 1b, Tobas Fraternity Central Zone costumes. 1.50b, Hijos del Sol Fraternity Inca costumes. 10.50b, Morenada Folklore Team Northern Zone costumes. 12b, Diablada Oruro costumes.

2013, May 17   Litho.   *Perf. 13¾x13½*
1550-1553 A643   Set of 4   15.00 7.25

Special Anti-Drug Trafficking Police Force, 25th Anniv. A644

2013, May 20   Litho.   *Perf. 13½x13¾*
1554 A644 100b multi   29.00 29.00

Public University of El Alto, 13th Anniv. — A645

2013, May 29   Litho.   *Perf. 13¾x13½*
1555 A645 4b multi   1.25 1.25

World Environment Day — A646

2013, July 9   Litho.   *Perf. 13¾x13½*
1556 A646 15b multi   4.50 4.50

Endangered Animals — A647

Designs: 50c, Hippocamelus antisensis. 1b, Lonchorhina aurita. 9b, Nymphargus pluvialis, horiz. 10.50b, Vultur gryphus, horiz.

Perf. 13¾x13½, 13½x13¾
2013, July 9   Litho.
1557-1560 A647   Set of 4   6.25 6.25

Endangered Flora — A648

Designs: 1.50b, Cedrela angustifolia. 2.50b, Parajubaea sunkha. 3b, Trichocereus atacamensis. 10.50b, Azorella compacta.

2013, July 9   Litho.   *Perf. 13½x13¾*
1561-1564 A648   Set of 4   5.25 5.25

San Ignacio College, La Paz, 50th Anniv. A649

2013, July 25   Litho.   *Perf. 13½x13¾*
1565 A649 4b multi   1.25 1.25

Torotoro Conservation Association, 25th Anniv. — A650

2013, Sept. 6 Litho. *Perf. 13¾x13½*
1566 A650 1.50b multi .45 .45

Bolivian Migrants A651

Perf. 13½x13¾
2013, Sept. 19 Litho.
1567 A651 50b multi 14.50 14.50

Doctor Examining Child, Arco Iris Hospital — A652

Perf. 13½x13¾
2013, Sept. 28 Litho.
1568 A652 7.50b multi 2.25 2.25

Folk Dances Type of 2012
Designs: 50c, Pujllay. 1.50b, Tinku. 2b, Waka Wakas. 7.50b, Diablada.

2013, Oct. 8 Litho. *Perf. 13¾x13½*
1569-1572 A625 Set of 4 3.50 3.50

Water and Life — A653

2013, Oct. 14 Litho. *Perf. 11¼x11*
Granite Paper
1573 A653 10.50b multi 3.00 3.00

Giovanni Boccaccio (1313-75), Writer — A654

2013, Oct. 25 Litho. *Perf. 13¾x13½*
1574 A654 9b multi 2.60 2.60

Christmas — A655

Designs: 50c, Child holding Christmas gift, line of wagons carrying gifts. 9b, Child holding toy truck, gift distribution volunteers.

2013, Dec. 3 Litho. *Perf. 13½x13¾*
1575-1576 A655 Set of 2 2.75 2.75

Campaign Against Discrimination — A656

America issue: 50c, Three men. 15b, Red apple and six green apples.

2013, Dec. 6 Litho. *Perf. 13½x13¾*
1577-1578 A656 Set of 2 4.50 4.50

Giuseppe Verdi (1813-1901), Composer A657

Perf. 13¾x13½
2013, Dec. 13 Litho.
1579 A657 20b multi 5.75 5.75

Simón Bolívar (1783-1830), First President of Bolivia — A658

Bolívar and flag of Bolivia: 1.50b, 9b. No. 1581 is vert.

Perf. 13½x13¾, 13¾x13½
2013, Dec. 17 Litho.
1580-1581 A658 Set of 2 3.00 3.00

Tupac Katari Satellite A659

Designs: 1.50b, Pres. Evo Morales. 9b, Emblem of Bolivian Space Agency, vert.

Perf. 13½x13¾, 13¾x13½
2013, Dec. 18 Litho.
1582-1583 A659 Set of 2 3.00 3.00

La Paz Soccer Association, Cent. — A660

2014, Jan. 8 Litho. *Perf. 13¾x13½*
1584 A660 1.50b multi .45 .45
Dated 2013.

2014 Dakar Rally A661

Designs: 10b, Dakar Rally emblem, motorcyclist. 20b, Dakar Rally emblem, Salar de Uyuni, vert.

Perf. 13½x13¾, 13¾x13½
2014, Jan. 12 Litho.
1585-1586 A661 Set of 2 8.75 8.75
Dated 2013.

La Paz-El Alto Cable Car — A663

2014, May 30 Litho. *Perf. 13¾x13½*
1588 A663 1b multi .30 .30

Bolivian Presidency of Group of 77 and China — A664

Perf. 13½x13¾
2014, June 12 Litho.
1589 A664 2b multi .60 .60

2014 World Cup Soccer Championships, Brazil — A665

Perf. 13¾x13½
2014, June 12 Litho.
1590 A665 5b multi 1.50 1.50

Pope Francis — A666

2014, July 3 Litho. *Perf. 13¾x13½*
1591 A666 5b multi 1.50 1.50

Father Joseph Kentenich (1885-1968), Founder of Schoenstatt Movement and Refuge of Sinners Madonna, by Luigi Crosio — A667

2014, July 6 Litho. *Perf. 13½x13¾*
1592 A667 5b multi 1.50 1.50
Schoenstatt Movement, cent.

Diplomatic Relations Between Bolivia and Japan, Cent. — A668

2014, July 10 Litho. *Perf. 13½x13¾*
1593 A668 10b multi 3.00 3.00

America Issue A669

Designs: 1b, Bolivian Pres. Evo Morales, Venezuelan Pres. Hugo Chávez (1954-2013). 25b, Chávez holding map, vert.

Perf. 13½x13¾, 13¾x13½
2014, July 28 Litho.
1594-1595 A669 Set of 2 7.50 7.50

Gunnar Mendoza Loza (1914-94), Historian A670

2014, Sept. 3 Litho. *Perf. 13¾x13½*
1596 A670 4b multi 1.25 1.25

Mauricio Otazo, Conductor of National Symphony Orchestra A671

2014, Oct. 24 Litho. *Perf. 13¾x13½*
1597 A671 15b multi 4.50 4.50

St. Francis of Assisi University, La Paz — A672

2014, Oct. 30 Litho. *Perf. 13½x13¾*
1598 A672 2b multi .60 .60

Mountains — A673

No. 1599: a, Mt. Condoriri, mountain climber at left. b, Mt. Condoriri, mountain climber at right.
9b, Mt. Illampu and mountain climber. 23b, Mt. Huayna Potosí and mountain climber.

Perf. 13½x13¾
2014, Dec. 16 Litho.
1599 A673 2b Horiz. pair, #a-b 1.25 1.25
1600 A673 9b multi 2.60 2.60
1601 A673 23b multi 6.75 6.75
Nos. 1599-1601 (3) 10.60 10.60

Christmas A674

Perf. 13¾x13½
2014, Dec. 17 Litho.
1602 A674 15b multi 4.50 4.50

Galaxy and Telescope — A675

2014, Dec. 19 Litho. *Perf. 11x11¼*
1603 A675 100b multi 29.00 29.00
Galileo Galilei (1564-1642), astronomer.

2015 Dakar Rally — A676

2014, Dec. 31 Litho. *Perf. 11¼x11*
1604 A676 7.50b multi 2.25 2.25

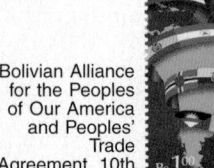

Bolivian Alliance for the Peoples of Our America and Peoples' Trade Agreement, 10th Anniv. — A677

Designs, 1b, Flags wrapped around map of South America. 12b, Flags to right of map of South America.

2015, Feb. 4 Litho. *Perf. 13¾x13½*
1605-1606 A677 Set of 2 3.75 3.75

Carnival Dancers — A679

Designs: 1b, Cueca Chapaca. 2b, Llamerada. 2.50b, Tinku.

2015, Apr. 29 Litho. *Perf. 13¾x13½*
1608-1610 A679 Set of 3 1.60 1.60

National Telecommunications Company (ENTEL), 50th Anniv. — A680

2015, Apr. 30 Litho. *Perf. 13¾x13½*
1611 A680 4b multi 1.25 1.25

Endangered Animals — A681

Designs: 5.50b, Fulica cornuta. 9b, Dynastes satanas. 15b, Chaetophractus nationi. 50b, Harpia harpyja.

2015, May 16 Litho. *Perf. 13¾x13½*
1612-1615 A681 Set of 4 23.00 23.00

Diplomatic Relations Between Bolivia and South Korea, 50th Anniv. — A682

No. 1616: a, Mergus squamatus. b, Phibalura flavirostris.

Perf. 13½x13¾
2015, June 25 Litho.
1616 A682 2b Horiz. pair, #a-b 1.25 1.25
See South Korea No. 2443.

Visit to Bolivia of Pope Francis — A683

2015, July 2 Litho. *Perf. 13¾x13½*
1617 A683 20b multi 5.75 5.75

San José de la Recoleta Convent, 90th Anniv. — A684

2015, Aug. 1 Litho. *Perf. 13¾x13½*
1618 A684 3b multi .90 .90

International Telecommunication Union, 150th Anniv. — A685

Perf. 13½x13¾
2015, Aug. 18 Litho.
1619 A685 10b multi 3.00 3.00

La Paz Department Tourism — A686

No. 1620: a, 1b, Thatch house. b, 4b, Indigenous musicians.

Perf. 13½x13¾
2015, Sept. 24 Litho.
1620 A686 Horiz. pair, #a-b 1.50 1.50

Bolivia Post Corporation, 25th Anniv. — A687

2015, Oct. 15 Litho. *Perf. 13¾x13½*
1621 A687 2b multi .60 .60

Pres. Andrés de Santa Cruz y Calahumana (1792-1865) A690

Perf. 13¾x13½
2015, Nov. 27 Litho.
1624 A690 2b multi .60 .60

San Andrés University, 185th Anniv. — A691

Perf. 13½x13¾
2015, Nov. 27 Litho.
1625 A691 3b multi .90 .90

Fe y Alegría Foundation in Bolivia, 50th Anniv. — A692

Perf. 13½x13¾
2016, Aug. 16 Litho.
1626 A692 100b multi 29.00 29.00

Bolivian Cuisine A694

Designs: 3b, Guiso de cumanda. 4b, Majao. 5b, Chairo, vert. 7.50b, Sillp'ancho. 10b, Map of Bolivia's four gastronomic regions, vert.

Perf. 13½x13¾, 13¾x13½
2016, Oct. 15 Litho.
1631-1635 A694 Set of 5 8.75 8.75

Friends of the City Organization, La Paz, Cent. — A695

2016, Oct. 17 Litho. *Perf. 13½x13¾*
1636 A695 50b multi 14.50 14.50

Silala Springs — A698

Designs: 14b, Spring. 18b, Animals near spring, horiz.

Perf. 13¾x13½, 13½x13¾
2016, Dec. 29 Litho.
1640-1641 A698 Set of 2 9.50 9.50

International Court of Justice's 2015 Decision on Bolivia's Claim for Sea Access — A699

2017, Feb. 8 Litho. *Perf. 13½x13¾*
1642 A699 1b multi .30 .30
Dated 2016.

AIR POST STAMPS

Aviation School
AP1   AP2

1924, Dec.   Unwmk.   Engr.   Perf. 14
C1	AP1	10c ver & blk	1.00	.50
a.		Inverted center	2,500.	
C2	AP1	15c carmine & blk	2.00	2.00
C3	AP1	25c dk bl & blk	1.50	1.00
C4	AP1	50c orange & blk	10.00	5.00
C5	AP2	1b red brn & blk	3.00	3.00
C6	AP2	2b blk brn & blk	20.00	10.00
C7	AP2	5b dk vio & blk	25.00	20.00
		Nos. C1-C7 (7)	62.50	41.50

Natl. Aviation School establishment.
These stamps were available for ordinary postage. Nos. C1, C3, C5 and C6 exist imperforate. Value, $400. each pair.
Proofs of the 2b with inverted center exist imperforate and privately perforated. Value, $2,750.
For overprints and surcharges see Nos. C11-C23, C56-C58.

Emblem of Lloyd Aéreo Boliviano
AP3

1928   Litho.   Perf. 11
C8	AP3	15c green	2.50	1.50
a.		Imperf., pair	70.00	60.00
C9	AP3	20c dark blue	4.00	3.25
C10	AP3	35c red brown	3.25	2.50
		Nos. C8-C10 (3)	9.75	7.25

No. C8 exists imperf. between. Value, $60 pair.
For surcharges see Nos. C24-C26, C53-C55.

Graf Zeppelin Issues
Nos. C1-C5 Surcharged or Overprinted in Various Colors

Nos. C11, C19   Nos. C12-C18, C20-C23

1930, May 6   Perf. 14
C11	AP1	5c on 10c ver & blk (G)	20.00	20.00
C12	AP1	10c ver & blk (Bl)	20.00	20.00
C13	AP1	10c ver & blk (Brn)	2,500.	2,500.
C14	AP1	15c car & blk (V)	20.00	20.00
C15	AP1	25c dk bl & blk (R)	20.00	20.00
C16	AP1	50c org & blk (Brn)	20.00	20.00
C17	AP1	50c org & blk (R)	1,000.	1,000.
C18	AP2	1b red brn & blk (gold)	350.00	350.00

Experts consider the 50c with gold or silver overprint and 5c with black to be trial color proofs.
Nos. C11-C18 exist with the surcharges inverted, double, or double with one inverted, but the regularity of these varieties is questioned.
See notes following No. C23.

Surcharged or Overprinted in Bronze Inks of Various Colors
C19	AP1	5c on 10c ver & blk (G)	120.00	150.00
a.		Inverted surcharge	200.00	
C20	AP1	10c ver & blk (Bl)	100.00	150.00
a.		Inverted surcharge		150.00
C21	AP1	15c car & blk (V)	100.00	150.00
a.		Inverted surcharge		150.00
C22	AP1	25c dk bl & blk (cop)	100.00	150.00
a.		Inverted surcharge		150.00
C23	AP2	1b red brn & blk (gold)	700.00	900.00
a.		Inverted surcharge		
		Nos. C19-C23 (5)	1,120.	1,500.

Flight of the airship Graf Zeppelin from Europe to Brazil and return via Lakehurst, NJ. Nos. C19 to C23 were intended for use on postal matter forwarded by the Graf Zeppelin.

No. C18 was overprinted with light gold or gilt bronze ink. No. C23 was overprinted with deep gold bronze ink. Nos. C13 and C17 were overprinted with trial colors but were sold with the regular printings. The 5c on 10c is known surcharged in black and in blue.

No. C8-C10 Surcharged

1930, May 6   Perf. 11
C24	AP3	1.50b on 15c	80.00	80.00
a.		Inverted surcharge	300.00	300.00
b.		Comma instead of period after "1"	100.00	100.00
C25	AP3	3b on 20c	80.00	80.00
a.		Inverted surcharge	350.00	350.00
b.		Comma instead of period after "3"	125.00	125.00
C26	AP3	6b on 35c	80.00	80.00
a.		Inverted surcharge	375.00	375.00
b.		Comma instead of period after "6"	125.00	125.00
		Nos. C24-C26 (3)	240.00	240.00

Airplane and Bullock Cart — AP6

Airplane and River Boat — AP7

1930, July 24   Litho.   Perf. 14
C27	AP6	5c dp violet	1.50	1.10
C28	AP7	15c red	1.50	1.10
C29	AP7	20c yellow	1.10	.90
C30	AP6	35c yellow grn	1.00	.75
C31	AP7	50c deep blue	2.50	1.50
C32	AP6	1b lt brown	3.50	1.75
C33	AP7	2b deep rose	4.50	2.50
C34	AP6	3b slate	8.00	6.00
		Nos. C27-C34 (8)	23.60	15.60

Nos. C27 to C34 exist imperforate. Value, $60 each pair.
For surcharge see No. C52.

Air Service Emblem AP8

1932, Sept. 16   Perf. 11
C35	AP8	5c ultra	3.25	2.40
C36	AP8	10c gray	2.00	1.50
C37	AP8	15c dark rose	2.00	1.50
C38	AP8	25c orange	2.00	1.50
C39	AP8	30c green	1.25	.80
C40	AP8	50c violet	3.25	2.50
C41	AP8	1b dk brown	3.25	2.50
		Nos. C35-C41 (7)	17.00	12.70

Map of Bolivia — AP9

1935, Feb. 1   Engr.   Perf. 12
C42	AP9	5c brown red	.30	.30
C43	AP9	10c dk green	.30	.30
C44	AP9	20c dk violet	.30	.30
C45	AP9	30c ultra	.30	.30
C46	AP9	50c orange	.50	.50
C47	AP9	1b bister brn	.50	.50
C48	AP9	1½b yellow	1.25	.75
C49	AP9	2b carmine	1.25	1.00
C50	AP9	5b green	1.50	1.25
C51	AP9	10b dk brown	5.00	1.75
		Nos. C42-C51 (10)	11.20	6.95

Nos. C1, C4, C10, C30 Srchd. in Red (#C52-C56) or Green (#C57-C58) — c

1937, Oct. 6   Perf. 11, 14
C52	AP6	5c on 35c yel grn	.50	.40
a.		"Carreo"	30.00	30.00
b.		Inverted surcharge	20.00	
C53	AP3	20c on 35c red brn	.75	.60
a.		Inverted surcharge	20.00	20.00
C54	AP3	50c on 35c red brn	1.50	1.00
a.		Inverted surcharge	50.00	50.00
C55	AP3	1b on 35c red brn	2.00	1.50
a.		Inverted surcharge	25.00	20.00
C56	AP1	2b on 50c org & blk	2.50	2.00
a.		Inverted surcharge	20.00	15.00
C57	AP1	12b on 10c ver & blk	15.00	15.00
a.		Inverted surcharge	75.00	50.00
C58	AP1	15b on 10c ver & blk	15.00	10.00
a.		Inverted surcharge	75.00	30.00

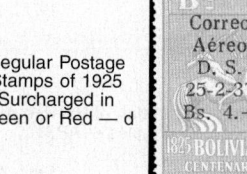

Regular Postage Stamps of 1925 Surcharged in Green or Red — d

Perf. 14
C59	A56 (d)	3b on 50c dp vio (G)	5.00	5.00
C60	A56 (d)	4b on 1b red (G)	5.00	5.00
C61	A57 (c)	5b on 2b org (G)	6.00	6.00
a.		Double surcharge	175.00	
C62	A56 (d)	10b on 5b blk brn	8.50	7.00
a.		Double surcharge	50.00	
		Nos. C52-C62 (11)	61.75	48.50

No. C59-C62 exist with inverted surcharge, No. C62a with black and black and red surcharges.

Courtyard of Potosi Mint — AP10

Miner — AP11

Emancipated Woman AP12

Pincers, Torch and Good Will Principles AP15

Airplane over Field AP13

Airplanes and Liberty Monument AP14

Airplane over River AP16

Emblem of New Government AP17

Transport Planes over Map of Bolivia AP18

1938, May   Litho.   Perf. 10½
C63	AP10	20c deep rose	.60	.30
C64	AP11	30c gray	.60	.30
C65	AP12	40c yellow	.70	.40
C66	AP13	50c yellow grn	.60	.30
C67	AP14	60c dull blue	.75	.40
C68	AP15	1b dull red	.75	.40
C69	AP16	2b bister	1.50	.50
C70	AP17	3b lt brown	2.25	1.00
C71	AP18	5b dk violet	3.00	1.00
		Nos. C63-C71 (9)	10.75	4.60

40c, 1b, 2b exist imperf.

Chalice — AP19

Virgin of Copacabana AP20

Jesus Christ — AP21

Church of San Francisco, La Paz AP22

St. Anthony of Padua — AP23

1939, July 19   Litho.   Perf. 13½, 10½
C72	AP19	5c dull violet	.75	.50
a.		Pair, imperf. between	80.00	
C73	AP20	30c lt bl grn	1.00	.50
C74	AP21	45c violet bl	1.00	.50
a.		Vertical pair, imperf. between	90.00	

C75	AP22	60c carmine	1.50	.75
C76	AP23	75c vermilion	1.50	1.25
C77	AP23	90c deep blue	1.50	.60
C78	AP22	2b dull brown	2.50	.50
C79	AP21	4b deep plum	3.00	1.00
C80	AP20	5b lt blue	7.00	.80
C81	AP19	10b yellow	12.00	1.25
		Nos. C72-C81 (10)	31.75	7.65

2nd National Eucharistic Congress.
For surcharge see No. C112.

Plane over Lake
Titicaca — AP24

Mt. Illimani and
Condor — AP25

1941, Aug. 21   *Perf. 13½*

C82	AP24	10b dull green	15.00	2.00
C83	AP24	20b light ultra	7.00	2.50
C84	AP25	50b rose lilac	15.00	5.00
C85	AP25	100b olive bister	25.00	8.00
		Nos. C82-C85 (4)	62.00	17.50

Counterfeits exist.
A souvenir sheet containing Nos. C84 and 356, perforated 13¼ and 14¼ respectively, was issued Dec. 16, 1987, to mark the 1988 Calgary Winter Olympic Games. Value $20.

Liberty and Clasped
Hands — AP26

1942, Nov. 12

C86	AP26	40c rose lake	.50	.50
C87	AP26	50c ultra	.50	.50
C88	AP26	1b orange brn	1.50	.75
C89	AP26	5b magenta	2.00	.60
a.		Double impression	90.00	
C90	AP26	10b dull brn vio	6.50	3.50
		Nos. C86-C90 (5)	11.00	5.85

Conference of Chancellors, Jan. 15, 1942.

Ballivián Type of Regular Issue

General José Ballivián; old and modern transportation.

1943, Nov. 18   Engr.   *Perf. 12½*

C91	A114	10c rose vio & brn	.30	.25
C92	A114	20c emerald & brn	.30	.25
C93	A114	30c rose car & brn	.30	.25
C94	A114	3b blue & brn	.75	.40
C95	A114	5b black & brn	1.00	.75
		Nos. C91-C95 (5)	2.65	1.90

Condor and Sun
Rising — AP28

Plane — AP29

1944, Sept. 19   Litho.   *Perf. 13½*

C96	AP28	40c red violet	.25	.25
C97	AP28	1b blue violet	.30	.25
C98	AP29	1.50b yellow green	.30	.25
C99	AP29	2.50b dk gray blue	.50	.25
		Nos. C96-C99 (4)	1.35	1.00

Revolution of Dec. 20, 1943.

Map of Natl.
Airways — AP30

1945, May 31   *Perf. 11*

C100	AP30	10c red	.30	.25
a.		Imperf., pair	25.00	
C101	AP30	50c yellow	.30	.25
a.		Imperf., pair	30.00	
C102	AP30	90c lt green	.40	.30
a.		Imperf., pair	30.00	
C103		5b lt ultra	1.00	.50
C104	AP30	20b deep brown	2.00	1.00
		Nos. C100-C104 (5)	4.00	2.30

10th anniversary of first flight, La Paz to Tacna, Peru, by Panagra Airways.
For surcharges see Nos. C128-C129.

Map of Bolivian Air
Lines — AP31

1945, Sept. 15   *Perf. 13½*
Centers in Red and Blue

C105	AP31	20c violet	.25	.25
C106	AP31	30c orange brn	.25	.25
C107	AP31	50c brt blue grn	.25	.25
C108	AP31	90c brt violet	.25	.25
C109	AP31	2b blue	.40	.25
C110	AP31	3b magenta	.50	.25
C111	AP31	4b olive bister	.90	.50
		Nos. C105-C111 (7)	2.80	2.00

Founding of Lloyd Aéreo Boliviano, 20th anniv.

> Catalogue values for unused stamps in this section, from this point to the end of the section, are for Never Hinged items.

No. C76
Surcharged in
Blue

1947, Mar. 23

C112	AP23	1.40b on 75c ver	.35	.25

Mt.
Illimani — AP32

1947, Sept. 15   Litho.   *Perf. 11½*

C113	AP32	1b rose car	.25	.25
C114	AP32	1.40b emerald	.25	.25
a.		Imperf, pair	20.00	
C115	AP32	2.50b blue	.25	.25
a.		Imperf, pair	20.00	
C116	AP32	3b dp orange	.30	.25
C117	AP32	4b rose lilac	.90	.50
		Nos. C113-C117 (5)	1.30	1.25

1st anniv. of the Revolution of July 21, 1946.
For surcharge see No. C137.

Bolivia/Argentina Arms Type

1947, Oct. 23   *Perf. 13½*

C118	A119	2.90b ultra	.45	.35
a.		Imperf., pair	30.00	
b.		Perf. 10½	7.50	6.00

Statue of Christ Type

Designs: 2.50b, Statue of Christ above La Paz. 3.70b, Child kneeling before cross. No. C121, St. John Bosco. No. C122, Virgin of Copacabana. 13.60b, Pope Plus XII blessing University of La Paz.

1948, Sept. 26   *Perf. 11½*

C119	A120	2.50b ver & yellow	.80	.35
C120	A120	3.70b rose & cream	1.00	.50
C121	A120	4b rose lil & gray	1.25	.35
C122	A120	4b lt ultra & sal	1.50	.35
C123	A120	13.60b ultra & lt grn	1.25	.35
		Nos. C119-C123 (5)	5.80	1.90

Bolivia Auto Club Type

1948, Oct.

C124	A125	10b emerald & salmon	4.00	.35

Pacheco Type of Regular Issue

1950, Jan. 2   Unwmk.

C125	A126	1.40b orange brown	.35	.25
C126	A126	2.50b orange	.40	.25
C127	A126	3.30b rose violet	.35	.25
		Nos. C125-C127 (3)	1.10	.75

75th anniv. of the UPU.
No. C126 exists imperf. Value, pair $25.

Nos. C100 and
C104 Surcharged in
Black

1950, May 31   *Perf. 11*

C128	AP30	4b on 10c red	.25	.25
a.		Inverted surcharge	35.00	35.00
C129	AP30	10b on 20b dp brn	.50	.40
a.		Inverted surcharge	35.00	35.00

Panagra air services in Bolivia, 15th anniv.

L. A. B.
Plane — AP35

1950, Sept. 15   Litho.   *Perf. 13½*

C130	AP35	20c red orange	.25	.25
C131	AP35	30c purple	.25	.25
C132	AP35	50c green	.25	.25
C133	AP35	1b orange	.25	.25
C134	AP35	3b ultra	.25	.25
C135	AP35	15b carmine	.60	.50
C136	AP35	50b chocolate	1.50	1.00
		Nos. C130-C136 (7)	3.35	2.75

25th anniv. of the founding of Lloyd Aero Boliviano. 30c, 50c, 15b exist imperforate.
No. C132 exists without imprint at bottom of stamp.

No. C116
Surcharged in
Black

1950, Sept. 24   *Perf. 11½*

C137	AP32	1.40b on 3b dp org	.30	.25

1st anniv. of the ending of the Civil War of Aug. 24-Sept. 24, 1949.
Exists with inverted and double surcharge.

UN Type of Regular Issue

1950, Oct. 24   Unwmk.

C138	A128	3.60b crimson rose	1.00	.25
C139	A128	4.70b black brown	2.00	.35

La Paz Type of Regular Issue

20c, Gate of the Sun and llama. 30c, Church of Old San Francisco. 40c, Avenue Camacho. 50c, Consistorial Palace. 1b, Legislative Palace. 2b, Communications Bldg. 3b, Arms. 4b, La Gasca ordering Mendoza to found La Paz. 5b, Capt. Alonso de Mendoza founding La Paz. 10b, Arms; portrait of Mendoza.

1951, Mar. 1   Engr.   *Perf. 12½*
Center in Black

C140	A129	20c carmine	.25	.25
C141	A130	30c dk vio bl	.25	.25
C142	A129	40c dark blue	.25	.25
C143	A129	50c blue green	.30	.30
C144	A129	1b red	.50	.30
C145	A129	2b red orange	.70	.60

C146	A129	3b deep blue	.70	.60
C147	A129	4b vermilion	.80	.75
a.		Souvenir sheet of 4	3.00	3.00
b.		As "a," imperf.	3.00	3.00
C148	A129	5b dark green	.80	.75
a.		Souvenir sheet of 3	3.00	3.00
b.		As "a," imperf.	3.00	3.00
C149	A129	10b red brown	1.50	1.75
a.		Souvenir sheet of 3	3.00	3.00
b.		As "a," imperf.	3.00	3.00
		Nos. C140-C149 (10)	6.05	5.80

Nos. C147a-C147b contain #C143-C145, C147; Nos. C148a-C148b contain #C142, C146, C148; Nos. C149a-C149b contain #C140, C141, C149.
For surcharges see Nos. C187-C196.

Athletic Type of Regular Issue

20c, Horsemanship. 30c, Basketball. 50c, Fencing. 1b, Hurdling. 2.50b, Javelin throwing. 3b, Relay race. 5b, La Paz stadium.

1951, Aug. 23   Unwmk.
Center in Black

C150	A131	20c purple	.60	.25
C151	A131	30c rose vio	1.00	.25
C152	A131	50c dp red org	1.10	.25
C153	A131	1b chocolate	1.10	.25
C154	A131	2.50b orange	2.25	.55
C155	A131	3b black brn	4.00	2.00
a.		Souv. sheet, #C153-C155	10.00	10.00
b.		As "a," imperf.	10.00	10.00
C156	A131	5b red	6.00	3.00
a.		Souv. sheet of 4, #C150-C152, C156	17.50	17.50
b.		As "a," imperf.	17.50	17.50
		Nos. C150-C156 (7)	16.05	6.55

Eduardo Abaroa Type

1952, Mar. 24   Litho.   *Perf. 11*

C157	A133	70c rose red	.25	.25
C158	A133	2b orange yel	.45	.25
C159	A133	3b yellow green	.25	.25
C160	A133	5b blue	1.00	.50
C161	A133	50b rose lilac	1.50	.60
C162	A133	100b gray black	3.00	1.25
a.		Perf. 14	60.00	30.00
		Nos. C157-C162 (6)	6.45	3.10

Queen Isabella I Type

1952, July 16   *Perf. 13½*

C163	A134	50b emerald	.75	.25
C164	A134	100b brown	1.50	.35

Nos. C163-C164 exist imperforate. Value, $40 each pair.
An imperforate 500,000b souvenir sheet depicting No. C164 with simulated perforations was issued Dec. 31, 1985, to mark the 500th anniv. of the discovery of America. Value $20.

Columbus Lighthouse Type

1952, July 16

C165	A135	2b rose lil, *sal*	.25	.25
C166	A135	3.70b blue grn, *bl*	.25	.25
C167	A135	4.40b orange, *salmon*	.25	.25
C168	A135	20b dk brn, *cream*	.60	.25
		Nos. C165-C168 (4)	1.35	1.00

No. C168 exists imperforate. Value, $60 pair.

Revolution Type and

Soldiers — AP43

Perf. 13½ (AP43), 11½ (A137)

1953, Apr. 9   Litho.

C169	A137	3.70b chocolate	.75	.75
C170	AP43	6b red violet	.30	.25
C171	A137	9b brown rose	.30	.25
C172	A137	10b aqua	.30	.25
C173	A137	16b vermilion	.30	.30
C174	AP43	22.50b dk brown	1.00	.60
C175	A137	40b gray	.60	.30
		Nos. C169-C175 (7)	3.55	2.70

Nos. C169-C170 and C174 exist imperf. Value, $40 each pair.

Map and Peasant Type and

Pres. Victor Paz
Estenssoro
Embracing
Indian — AP45

1954, Aug. 2   **Perf. 12x11½**

C176	AP45	20b orange brn	.30	.25
C177	A138	27b brt pink	.25	.25
C178	A138	30b red org	.30	.25
C179	A138	45b violet brn	.50	.25
C180	AP45	100b blue grn	1.00	.25
C181	A138	300b yellow grn	2.00	.30
		Nos. C176-C181 (6)	4.35	1.55

AP45 for 3rd Inter-American Indian Cong. A138 agrarian reform laws of 1953-54.

Nos. C176-C180 exist imperf. Value, $25 each pair.

For surcharge see No. C261.

Oil Derricks — AP47

1955, Oct. 9   **Perf. 10½**

C182	AP47	55b dk & lt grnsh bl	.35	.25
C183	AP47	70b dk gray & gray	.60	.25
C184	AP47	90b dk & lt grn	.90	.25

Perf. 13

C185	AP47	500b red lilac	3.00	.75
C186	AP47	1000b blk brn & fawn	5.00	1.50
		Nos. C182-C186 (5)	9.85	3.00

For surcharge see No. C262.

Nos. C140-C149 Surcharged in Black or Carmine

1957   **Engr.**
Center in Black   **Perf. 12½**

C187	A129	100b on 3b (C)	.25	.25
C188	A129	200b on 2b	.25	.25
C189	A129	500b on 4b	.30	.25
C190	A129	600b on 1b	.30	.25
C191	A129	700b on 20c	.50	.25
C192	A129	800b on 40c (C)	.60	.25
C193	A130	900b on 30c (C)	.75	.25
C194	A129	1800b on 50c (C)	1.20	.50
C195	A129	3000b on 5b (C)	1.75	1.00
C196	A129	5000b on 10b (C)	3.00	2.00
		Nos. C187-C196 (10)	8.90	5.30

See Nos. 393-402.

Map of South America and Bolivian National Arms — AP48

Unwmk.
1957, May 25   **Litho.**   **Perf. 12**

C197	AP48	700b lilac & vio	.55	.35
C198	AP48	1200b pale brn	.85	.60
C199	AP48	1350b rose car	1.00	.60
C200	AP48	2700b blue grn	2.00	.75
C201	AP48	4000b violet bl	3.50	1.25
		Nos. C197-C201 (5)	7.90	3.55

Nos. C197-C201 exist imperf. Value, $50 each pair.

For surcharges see Nos. C263-C265.

Type of Regular Issue, 1957

1957, Dec. 19   **Perf. 11½**

C202	A141	600b dp mag & pink	.50	.30
C203	A141	700b vio blue & blue	1.00	.30
C204	A141	900b dk grn & pale grn	2.00	.40
		Nos. C202-C204 (3)	3.50	1.00

Type of Regular Issue, 1960

1960, Jan. 30

C205	A142	400b rose claret	1.00	1.00
C206	A142	800b slate blue	1.25	.75
C207	A142	2000b slate	2.25	1.00
		Nos. C205-C207 (3)	4.50	2.25

Gate of the Sun, Tiahuanacu AP49

1960, Mar. 26   **Litho.**   **Perf. 11½**

C208	AP49	3000b gray	3.25	2.00
C209	AP49	5000b orange	4.50	2.00
C210	AP49	10,000b rose cl	7.00	3.25
C211	AP49	15,000b blue violet	10.00	5.00
		Nos. C208-C211 (4)	24.75	12.25

Uprooted Oak Emblem — AP50

1960, Apr. 7   **Perf. 11½**

C212	AP50	600b ultra	.50	.25
C213	AP50	700b lt red brn	.50	.30
C214	AP50	900b dk bl grn	.60	.30
C215	AP50	1800b violet	1.25	.60
C216	AP50	2000b gray	1.75	1.25
		Nos. C212-C216 (5)	4.60	2.70

WRY, July 1, 1959-June 30, 1960.

No. C215 exists with "1961" overprint in dark carmine, but was not regularly issued in this form.

Jaime Laredo Type

Laredo facing left, Bolivia in color.

Perf. 11½

1960, Aug. 15   **Unwmk.**   **Litho.**

C217	A145	600b rose vio	1.25	.45
C218	A145	700b ol gray	1.25	.50
C219	A145	800b vio brn	1.75	.50
C220	A145	900b dk bl	3.00	.60
C221	A145	1800b green	4.00	2.00
C222	A145	4000b dk gray	7.00	2.00
		Nos. C217-C222 (6)	18.25	6.05

Issued to honor the violinist Jaime Laredo. For surcharges see Nos. C266-C267.

Children's Hospital Type of 1960

1960, Nov. 21   **Perf. 11½**

C223	A146	600b multi	.75	.35
C224	A146	1000b multi	.75	.35
C225	A146	1800b multi	1.40	.75
C226	A146	5000b multi	4.50	1.50
		Nos. C223-C226 (4)	7.40	2.95

For surcharges see No. C268-C269.

Pres. Paz Estenssoro and Pres. Getulio Vargas of Brazil AP52

1960, Dec. 14   **Litho.**   **Perf. 11½**

C227	AP52	1200b on 10b org & blk	1.00	.75

Exists with surcharge inverted. Value, $75.

No. C227 without surcharge was not regularly issued, although a decree authorizing its circulation was published. Value, $1.

Postally used counterfeits of surcharge exist.

Pres. Paz Estenssoro and Pres. Frondizi of Argentina AP53

4000b, Flags of Bolivia and Argentina.

1961, May 23   **Perf. 10½**

C228	AP53	4000b brn, red, yel, grn & bl	1.25	1.00
C229	AP53	6000b dk grn & blk	2.00	1.25

Visit of the President of Argentina, Dr. Arturo Frondizi, to Bolivia.

For surcharge see No. C309.

Miguel de Cervantes — AP54

1961, Oct.   **Photo.**   **Perf. 13**

C230	AP54	1400b pale grn & dk ol grn	1.00	.45

Cervantes' appointment as Chief Magistrate of La Paz. See No. 451.

Virgin of Cotoca and Symbol of Eucharist — AP55

1962, Mar. 19   **Litho.**   **Perf. 10½**

C231	AP55	1400b brn, pink & yel	.80	.35

4th Natl. Eucharistic Cong., Santa Cruz, 1961.

Nos. C212-C216 Surcharged

1962, June   **Unwmk.**   **Perf. 11½**

C232	AP50	1200b on 600b	1.10	.50
C233	AP50	1300b on 700b	1.10	.50
C234	AP50	1400b on 900b	1.10	.50
C235	AP50	2800b on 1,800b	1.75	.70
C236	AP50	3000b on 2,000b	1.75	1.00
		Nos. C232-C236 (5)	6.80	3.20

The overprinted segment of Greek key border on Nos. C232-C236 comes in two positions: two full "keys" on top, and one full and two half keys on top.

Flower Type of 1962

Flowers: 100b, 1800b, Cantua buxifolia. 800b, 10,000b, Cantua bicolor.

1962, June 28   **Litho.**   **Perf. 10½**
Flowers in Natural Colors

C237	A152	100b dk bl	.75	.25
C238	A152	800b green	1.25	.30
C239	A152	1800b violet	2.75	.75
a.		Souvenir sheet of 3	12.00	12.00
C240	A152	10,000b dk bl	8.50	4.00
		Nos. C237-C240 (4)	13.25	5.30

No. C239a contains 3 imperf. stamps similar to Nos. C237-C239, but with the 1,800b background color changed to dark violet blue.

For surcharges see Nos. C270-C271.

Planes and Parachutes AP56

1200b, 5000b, Plane and oxcart. 2000b, Aerial photography (plane over South America).

1962, Sept. 5   **Litho.**   **Perf. 11½**
Emblem in Red, Yellow & Green

C241	AP56	600b blk & bl	.50	.25
C242	AP56	1200b multi	.60	.30
C243	AP56	2000b multi	.90	.50
C244	AP56	5000b multi	2.00	1.25
		Nos. C241-C244 (4)	4.00	2.30

Armed Forces of Bolivia.

An imperforate 200b souvenir sheet depicting No. C241 with simulated perforations was issued Sept. 16, 1983, to celebrate 200 years of manned flight. Value $50.

Malaria Type of 1962

Design: Inscription around mosquito, laurel around globe.

1962, Oct. 4

C245	A154	2000b ind, grn & yel	2.00	.50

Type of Regular Issue, 1961

Design: Pedro de la Gasca (1485-1567).

1962 Unwmk. Photo.   **Perf. 13x12½**

C246	A150	1200b brn, *yel*	.60	.30

Condor, Soccer Ball and Flags — AP57

1.80b, Map of Bolivia, soccer ball, goal and flags.

1963, Mar. 21   **Litho.**   **Perf. 11½**

C247	AP57	1.40b multi	1.50	1.00
C248	AP57	1.80b multi	1.50	1.00

21st South American Soccer Championships.

An imperforate 20b souvenir sheet depicting No. C248 with simulated perforations was issued March 16, 1979 to celebrate the 1979 World Cup soccer championship games. Value $40.

Two imperforate 20b souvenir sheets, one containing No. C247 and the other containing No. C248, both with simulated perforations, were issued Oct. 13, 1980, to mark various World Cup competitions. Value, each $45.

Freedom from Hunger Type

Design: Wheat, globe and wheat emblem.

1963, Aug. 1   **Unwmk.**   **Perf. 11½**

C249	A156	1.20b dk grn, bl & yel	1.00	.75

Alliance for Progress Emblem — AP58

1963, Nov. 15   **Perf. 11½**

C250	AP58	1.20b dl yel, ultra & grn	1.25	.75

2nd anniv. of the Alliance for Progress, which aims to stimulate economic growth and raise living standards in Latin America.

Type of Regular Issue, 1963

1.20b, Ballot box and voters. 1.40b, Map and farmer breaking chain. 2.80b, Miners.

1963, Dec. 21   **Perf. 11½**

C251	A157	1.20b gray, dk brn & rose	.60	.25
C252	A157	1.40b bister & grn	.70	.40
C253	A157	2.80b slate & buff	1.00	.90
		Nos. C251-C253 (3)	2.30	1.55

Andrés Santa
Cruz — AP59

Perf. 13½
1966, Aug. 10   Wmk. 90   Litho.
C254 AP59 20c dp bl   .30 .25
C255 AP59 60c dp grn   .30 .30
C256 AP59 1.20b red brn   .75 .60
C257 AP59 2.80b black   1.25 1.00
  Nos. C254-C257 (4)   2.60 2.15
Cent. (in 1965) of the death of Marshal Andrés Santa Cruz (1792-1865), pres. of Bolivia and of Peru-Bolivia Confederation.

Children Type of 1966
Design: 1.40b, Mother and children.

1966, Dec. 16   Unwmk.   Perf. 13½
C258 A159 1.40b gray bl & blk   2.25 .50

Co-Presidents Type of Regular Issue
1966, Dec. 16   Litho.   Perf. 12½
Flag in Red, Yellow and Green
C259 A160 2.80b gray & tan   1.50 .80
C260 A160 10b sep & tan   3.00 1.00
  a. Souvenir sheet of 4   9.00 9.00
No. C260a contains 4 imperf. stamps similar to Nos. 480-481 and C259-C260. Dark green marginal inscription. Size: 135x82mm.

Various Issues 1954-62 Surcharged with New Values and Bars

On No. C177

1966, Dec. 21
C261 A138 10c on 27b   .30 .30
  a. Agraria/Agraria   20.00 10.00

On No. C182

C262 AP47 10c on 55b   .30 .30

On No. C199

C263 AP48 60c on 1350b   .75 .30

On No. C200

C264 AP48 2.80b on 2700b   3.00 2.25

On No. C201

C265 AP48 4b on 4000b   2.00 1.50

On No. C219

C266 A145 1.20b on 800b   1.50 .30

On No. C222

C267 A145 1.40b on 4,000b   1.10 .75

Nos. C224-C225

C268 A146 1.40b on 1,000b   .75 .75
C269 A146 1.40b on 1,800b   .75 .75

Nos. C238-C239

C270 A152 1.20b on 800b   1.50 .30
C271 A152 1.20b on 1,800b   1.50 .30

Revenue Stamp
of 1946
Surcharged

C272 A161 1.20b on 1b dk bl   .60 .25
  Nos. C261-C272 (12)   14.05 8.05

Lions Emblem
and Pre-
historic
Sculptures
AP60

1967, Sept. 20   Litho.   Perf. 13x13½
C273 AP60 2b red & multi   1.20 .75
  a. Souvenir sheet of 2   5.50 5.50
50th anniv. of Lions Intl. No. C273a contains 2 imperf. stamps similar to Nos. 492 and C273.

Folklore Type of Regular Issue
Folklore characters: 1.20p, Pujllay. 1.40p, Ujusiris. 2p, Morenada. 3p, Auki-aukis.

1968, June 24   Perf. 13½x13
C274 A163 1.20b lt yel grn &
              multi   .45 .25
C275 A163 1.40b gray & multi   .50 .25
C276 A163 2b dk ol bis &
              multi   1.00 .35

C277 A163 3b sky bl & mul-
              ti   1.25 .35
  a. Souvenir sheet of 4, #C274-
      C277 imperf   15.00 15.00
  Nos. C274-C277 (4)   3.20 1.20

Moto
Mendez — AP61

1968, Oct. 29   Litho.   Perf. 13½x13
C278 AP61 1b multi   .40 .25
C279 AP61 1.20b multi   .50 .25
C280 AP61 2b multi   1.00 .45
C281 AP61 4b multi   1.25 .70
  Nos. C278-C281 (4)   3.15 1.65
Battle of Tablada sesquicentennial.

Pres.
Gualberto
Villarroel
AP62

1968, Nov. 6   Perf. 13x13½
C282 AP62 1.40b org & blk   .90 .30
C283 AP62 3b lt bl & blk   1.50 .40
C284 AP62 4b rose & blk   2.00 .50
C285 AP62 5b gray grn &
              blk   2.25 .75
C286 AP62 10b pale pur &
              blk   4.00 1.40
  Nos. C282-C286 (5)   10.65 3.35
4th centenary of Cochabamba.

ITU Type of Regular Issue
1968, Dec. 3   Litho.   Perf. 13x13½
C287 A166 1.20b gray, blk & yel .75 .40
C288 A166 1.40b bl, blk & gray ol .75 .25

UNESCO
Emblem — AP63

1968, Nov. 14   Perf. 13½x13
C289 AP63 1.20b pale vio & blk   .70 .50
C290 AP63 2.80b yel grn & blk   1.25 .75
20th anniv. (in 1966) of UNESCO.

Kennedy Type of Regular Issue
1968, Nov. 22   Unwmk.
C291 A168 1b grn & blk   .35 .25
C292 A168 10b scar & blk   4.00 3.75
  a.   7.50 7.50
No. C292a contains one imperf. stamp similar to No. C291. Dark violet marginal inscription. Size: 131x81½mm.

Tennis Type of Regular Issue
1968, Dec. 10   Perf. 13x13½
C293 A169 1.40b org, blk & lt
              brn   1.25 .45
C294 A169 2.80b sky bl, blk &
              lt brn   2.00 .75
  a. Souvenir sheet of 1 #C293,
      imperf   15.00 15.00
A 1,000,000b souvenir sheet containing Nos. C294 and 353, perforated 13¼ and 14¼ respectively, was issued Sept. 25, 1986, with a tennis theme. Value $30.

Stamp Centenary Type
Design: 1.40b, 2.80b, 3b, Bolivia No. 1.

1968, Dec. 23   Litho.   Perf. 13x13½
C295 A170 1.40b org, grn &
              blk   1.25 .65
C296 A170 2.80b pale rose,
              grn & blk   2.10 1.25

C297 A170 3b lt vio, grn &
              blk   2.10 1.25
  a. Souvenir sheet of 3, #C295-
      C297, imperf   6.00 6.00
  Nos. C295-C297 (3)   5.45 3.15

An imperforate 20b souvenir sheet depicting No. C297 with simulated perforations was issued March 16, 1979, to mark the 100th anniv. of the death of Sir Rowland Hill (1795-1879), inventor of the postage stamp. Value $50.

Two additional imperforate 20b souvenir sheets, one depicting Nos. C297 and C358, with Bolivia Nos. 14 and 19 and Great Britain No. 1, the other depicting Nos. C297, C11, C12, C17, a trial color surcharge on No. C4, and Great Britain No. 1, were issued April 28, 1980, to mark the 100th anniv. of the death of Sir Rowland Hill. Value, both sheets $60.

Franklin D.
Roosevelt — AP64

1969, Oct. 29   Litho.   Perf. 13½x13
C298 AP64 5b brn, blk & buff   2.00 1.50

Olympic Type of Regular Issue
Sports: 1.20b, Woman runner, vert. 2.80b, Discus thrower, vert. 5b, Hurdler.

Perf. 13½x13, 13x13½
1969, Oct. 29   Litho.
C299 A171 1.20b yel grn, bis
              & blk   .75 .50
C300 A171 2.80b red, org &
              blk   1.40 1.00
C301 A171 5b bl, lt bl, red
              & blk   2.00 2.00
  a. Souvenir sheet of 3, #C299-
      C301 imperf   12.50 12.50
  Nos. C299-C301 (3)   4.15 3.50

Two imperforate 20b souvenir sheets depicting Nos. C300 and C301 with simulated perforations were issued April 28, 1980, to commemorate the 1980 Moscow Olympics. Value, both sheets $75.

An imperforate 200b souvenir sheet depicting Nos. C300 and 639 with simulated perforations was issued Sept. 16, 1983, to mark the 1983 Los Angeles Summer Olympic Games. Value $25.

An imperforate 27,500b souvenir sheet depicting No. C299 with simulated perforations was issued April 4, 1985, to mark the 1984 Los Angeles Summer Olympic Games. Value $25.

A 2b souvenir sheet containing Nos. C299 and 712, perforated 13¼, was issued April 13, 1987, to mark the 1988 Seoul Summer Olympic Games. Value $20.

An additional 2b souvenir sheet containing No. C300, perforated 13¼, was issued Aug. 15, 1988, to mark the Seoul Olympics. Value $30.

Butterfly Type of Regular Issue
1b, Metamorpha dido wernichei. 1.80b, Heliconius felix. 2.80b, Morpho casica. 3b, Papilio yuracares. 4b, Heliconius melitus.

1970, Apr. 24   Litho.   Perf. 13x13½
C302 A172 1b sal & multi   4.00 2.00
C303 A172 1.80b lt bl & multi 6.00 3.00
C304 A172 2.80b multi   9.00 4.50
C305 A172 3b multi   9.00 4.50
C306 A172 4b multi   12.00 5.50
  a. Souvenir sheet of 3, #C302-
      C304   25.00 25.00
  Nos. C302-C306 (5)   40.00 19.50

A souvenir sheet exists containing 3 imperf. stamps similar to Nos. C302-C304. Black marginal inscription. Size: 129½x80mm.

Scout Type of Regular Issue
Designs: 50c, Boy Scout building brick wall. 1.20b, Bolivian Boy Scout emblem.

1970, June 17   Litho.   Perf. 13½x13
C307 A173 50c yel & multi   .25 .25
C308 A173 1.20b multi   .50 .50

No. C228
Surcharged

1970, Dec. Litho. Perf. 10½
C309 AP53 1.20b on 4000b multi .45 .25

Flower Type of Regular Issue

Bolivian Flowers: 1.20b, Amaryllis pseudopardina, horiz. 1.40b, Rebutia kruegeri. 2.80b, Lobivia pentlandii, horiz. 4b, Rebutia tunariensis.

Perf. 13x13½, 13½x13
1971, Aug. 9 Litho. Unwmk.
C310	A174	1.20b multi	.80	.60
C311	A174	1.40b multi	1.00	.75
C312	A174	2.80b multi	2.00	1.10
C313	A174	4b multi	2.50	2.00
		Nos. C310-C313 (4)	6.30	4.45

Folk Dance Type of Regular Issue
1972, Mar. 23 Litho. Perf. 13½x13
C314	A177	1.20b Kusillo	.75	.25
a.		Souvenir sheet of 3, #542-543, C314 imperf	40.00	40.00
C315	A177	1.40b Taquirari	1.00	.25
a.		Souvenir sheet of 3, #540-541, C315 imperf	40.00	40.00

Painting Type of Regular Issue

Bolivian Paintings: 1.40b, Portrait of Chola Paceña, by Cecilio Guzman de Rojas. 1.50b, Adoration of the Kings, by G. Gamarra. 1.60b, Adoration of Pachamama (mountain), by A. Borda. 2b, The Kiss of the Idol, by Guzman de Rojas.

1972 Litho. Perf. 13½
C316	A178	1.40b multi	.75	.25
C317	A178	1.50b multi	.75	.25
C318	A178	1.60b multi	.75	.25
a.		Souvenir sheet of 2, #548, C318 imperf	50.00	50.00
C319	A178	2b multi	1.00	.35
a.		Souvenir sheet of 2, #C317, C319, imperf	50.00	50.00
		Nos. C316-C319 (4)	3.25	1.10

Issued: 1.40b, Dec. 4; others Aug. 17.

An imperforate 20b souvenir sheet depicting No. C318 with simulated perforations was issued March 16, 1979, to mark the 1980 Olympic Games. Value \$25.

An imperforate 1.50b souvenir sheet depicting No. C317 with simulated perforations was issued Aug. 1, 1982, for Christmas 1982. Value \$60.

An imperforate 200b souvenir sheet depicting Nos. C318 and 616 with simulated perforations was issued Sept. 16, 1983, to celebrate the 1984 Sarajevo Winter Olympic Games. Value \$30.

An imperforate 7500b souvenir sheet depicting No. C319 with simulated perforations was issued Nov. 12, 1984, to honor Peter Paul Reubens (pictures *Diana and Calisto*). Value \$50.

An imperforate 1b souvenir sheet depicting No. C319 with simulated perforations was issued March 20, 1987, to honor Peter Paul Reubens (pictures *Juno and Argus*). Value \$25.

Bolivian Coat of Arms AP65

1972, Dec. 4 Perf. 13½x13¾
C320 AP65 4b lt bl & multi 2.75 .75

An imperforate 20b souvenir sheet depicting Nos. C320 and 651 with simulated perforations was issued Oct. 13, 1980, to celebrate the 1980 Lake Placid Winter Olympics. Value \$75.

An imperforate 4b souvenir sheet depicting No. C320 with simulated perforations was issued Aug. 11, 1981, to celebrate the wedding of Prince Charles and Lady Diana. Value \$25.

An imperforate 4b souvenir sheet depicting No. C320 with simulated perforations was issued March 24, 1982, to honor Princess Diana. Value \$25.

An imperforate 7500b souvenir sheet depicting Nos. C320 and 703 with simulated perforations was issued Nov. 12, 1984, to mark the

---

1984 Sarajevo Winter Olympic Games. Value \$50.

An imperforate 500,000b souvenir sheet depicting No. C320 with simulated perforations was issued Dec. 3, 1985, to mark the World Chess Congress. Value \$65.

A 1,000,000b souvenir sheet containing Nos. C320 and 616 perforated 13¼ was issued Sept. 25, 1986, to mark the 1988 Calgary Winter Olympic Games. Value \$30.

A 2b souvenir sheet containing No. C320 perforated 13¼ was issued April 13, 1987, to mark the 1988 Calgary Winter Olympic Games. Value \$27.50.

A 2b souvenir sheet containing No. C320 perforated 13¼ was issued Dec. 16, 1987, to honor U.S. and Soviet space flights. Value \$25.

A 2b souvenir sheet containing No. C320 perforated 13¼ was issued July 16, 1989, to commemorate the 200th anniv. of the French Revolution. Value \$20.

A 2b souvenir sheet containing No. C320 perforated 13¼ was issued May 18, 1990, to mark the 700th anniv. of the Swiss Confederation. Value \$40.

Cactus Type of Regular Issue

Designs: Various cacti.

1973, Aug. 6 Litho. Perf. 13½
C321	A180	1.20b tan & multi	.75	.25
C322	A180	1.90b org & multi	1.00	.35
C323	A180	2b multi	1.75	.50
		Nos. C321-C323 (3)	3.50	1.10

Development Type of Regular Issue

1.40b, Highway 1Y4. 2b, Rail car on bridge.

1973, Nov. 26 Litho. Perf. 13½
C324	A181	1.40b salmon & multi	2.50	.25
C325	A181	2b multi	3.75	.25

A 2b souvenir sheet containing No. C325 perforated 13¼ was issued June 15, 1988, to mark the 1931 Bentley/Zug auto/train race in England. Value \$35.

Santos-Dumont and 14-Bis Plane — AP66

1973, July 20
C326 AP66 1.40b yel & blk 1.00 .40

Alberto Santos-Dumont (1873-1932), Brazilian aviation pioneer.

Orchid Type of 1974

Orchids: 2.50b, Cattleya luteola, horiz. 3.80b, Stanhopaea. 4b, Catasetum, horiz. 5b, Maxillaria.

1974 Litho. Perf. 13½
C327	A182	2.50b multi	3.50	.40
C328	A182	3.80b rose & multi	5.00	.65
C329	A182	4b multi	5.00	.80
C330	A182	5b sal & multi	9.00	1.00
		Nos. C327-C330 (4)	22.50	2.85

Air Force Emblem, Plane over Map of Bolivia AP67

Designs: 3.80b, Plane over Andes. 4.50b, Triple decker and jet. 8b, Rafael Pabon and double decker. 15b, Jet and "50."

1974 Litho. Perf. 13x13½
C331	AP67	3b multi	1.00	.60
C332	AP67	3.80b multi	1.50	1.00
C333	AP67	4.50b multi	1.50	1.00
C334	AP67	8b multi	2.50	2.00
C335	AP67	15b multi	5.00	2.75
		Nos. C331-C335 (5)	11.50	7.35

Bolivian Air Force, 50th anniv. Nos. C331-C335 exist imperf. Value, \$40 each pair.
For surcharge see No. 968.

Coat of Arms Type of 1975

Designs: Departmental coats of arms.

1975, July 16 Litho. Perf. 13½
C336	A188	20c Beni	.50	.25
C337	A188	30c Tarija	.50	.25
C338	A188	50c Potosi	.70	.30
C339	A188	1b Oruro	1.40	.80
C340	A188	2.50b Santa Cruz	2.50	1.25
C341	A188	3b La Paz	2.50	1.25
		Nos. C336-C341 (6)	8.10	4.10

LAB Emblem — AP68

Bolivia on Map of Americas AP69

Map of Bolivia, Plane and Kyllmann AP70

1975 Litho. Perf. 13½
C342	AP68	1b gold, bl & blk	.60	.50
C343	AP69	1.50b multi	.90	.50
C344	AP70	2b multi	1.25	.60
		Nos. C342-C344 (3)	2.75	1.60

Lloyd Aereo Boliviano, 50th anniversary, founded by Guillermo Kyllmann.

Bolivar, Presidents Perez and Banzer, and Flags — AP71

1975, Aug. 4 Litho. Perf. 13½
C345 AP71 3b gold & multi 1.00 .75

Visit of Pres. Carlos A. Perez of Venezuela.

Eight imperforate souvenir sheets, each denominated 5.50b, depicting No. 19 with various contemporaneous Bolivian stamps with simulated perforations were issued on Nov. 7, 1975, celebrating various anniversaries and philatelic events. These comprise: No. 345, Innsbruck 1976, value \$25; No. C345, Interphil '76, value \$6; No. C350, Concorde/Zeppelin, value \$50; No. C350, Wien '75, value \$6; No. C3251, U.S. Bicentennial, value \$30; No. C351, Hafnia '76, value \$6; No. C352, Montreal Olympics/Argentina '78, value \$35; No. C352, Exfilmo '75, value \$6. Four of these sheets were overprinted in April 1981 for WIPA 81 (value \$5), Espamer 81 (value \$5), Philatokyo 81 (value \$5) and Philexfrance 1982 (value \$12.50).

An imperforate 25b souvenir sheet depicting No. C345 with simulated perforations was issued June 1, 1978, to commemorate the 25th anniv. of the coronation of Queen Elizabeth II. Value \$25.

Bolivar Type of 1975

Presidents and Statesmen of Bolivia: 50c, Rene Barrientos O. 2b, Francisco B. O'Connor. 3.80b, Gualberto Villarroel. 4.20b, German Busch. 4.50b, Hugo Banzer Suarez. 20b, José Ballivian. 30b, Andres de Santa Cruz. 40b, Antonio Jose de Sucre.

1975 Litho. Perf. 13½
Size: 24x33mm
C346	A189	50c multi	.25	.25
C347	A189	2b multi	1.40	.50
C348	A189	3.80b multi	1.50	.80
C349	A189	4.20b multi	2.00	1.00

Size: 28x39mm
C350	A189	4.50b multi	1.50	1.00

Size: 24x33mm
C351	A189	20b multi	6.00	4.00
C352	A189	30b multi	7.00	5.00
C353	A189	40b multi	10.00	7.00
		Nos. C346-C353 (8)	29.65	19.55

For surcharge see No. 969.

An imperforate 20b souvenir sheet depicting No. C353 with simulated perforations was issued March 16, 1979, to commemorate the 75th anniv. of powered flight. Value \$40.

An imperforate 54b souvenir sheet depicting Nos. C346 and C358 with simulated perforations was issued April 28, 1980, to celebrate the 1980 Lake Placid Winter Olympics. Value \$25.

UPU Emblem AP72

1975, Dec. 7 Litho. Perf. 13½
C358	AP72	25b blue & multi	4.00	3.50
a.		Souvenir sheet of 1, imperf	20.00	20.00

Cent. of UPU (in 1974).

No. C358a contains a single No. C358, imperforate with simulated perforations. Size: 130x80mm.

An imperforate 25b souvenir sheet depicting No. C358 with simulated perforations was issued Jan. 1, 1978, to recognize Charles Lindbergh and Zeppelin flights. Value \$100.

POSTAGE DUE STAMPS

D1

1931 Unwmk. Engr. Perf. 14, 14½
J1	D1	5c ultra	1.75	*3.50*
J2	D1	10c red	2.50	*3.50*
J3	D1	15c yellow	2.50	*5.00*
J4	D1	30c deep green	2.50	*6.00*
J5	D1	40c deep violet	6.00	*8.00*
J6	D1	50c black brown	12.00	*15.00*
		Nos. J1-J6 (6)	27.25	41.00

Symbol of Youth — D2

Torch of Knowledge D3

Symbol of the Revolution of May 17, 1936 — D4

1938 Litho. Perf. 11
J7	D2	5c deep rose	1.75	1.50
a.		Pair, imperf. between	10.00	
J8	D3	10c green	2.00	1.50
J9	D4	30c gray blue	2.00	1.60
		Nos. J7-J9 (3)	5.75	4.60

POSTAL TAX STAMPS

Worker — PT1

Imprint: "LITO. UNIDAS LA PAZ."

Perf. 13½x10½, 10½, 13½

		1939	Litho.	Unwmk.	
RA1	PT1	5c dull violet		1.00	.50
a.		Double impression		15.00	15.00

Redrawn

Imprint: "TALL. OFFSET LA PAZ."

		1940		*Perf. 12x11, 11*	
RA2	PT1	5c violet		.75	.30
a.		Horizontal pair, imperf. between		3.00	2.00
b.		Imperf. horiz., pair		10.00	
c.		Double impression		15.00	10.00

Tax of Nos. RA1-RA2 was for the Workers' Home Building Fund.

Communications Symbols — PT2

		1944-45	Litho.	*Perf. 10½*	
RA3	PT2	10c salmon		.75	.30
RA4	PT2	10c blue ('45)		.75	.30

A 30c orange inscribed "Centenario de la Creacion del Departamento del Beni" was issued in 1946 and required to be affixed to all air and surface mail to and from the Department of Beni in addition to regular postage. Values: unused $1; used 50¢.Five higher denominations in the same scenic design were used for local revenue purposes.

Catalogue values for unused stamps in this section, from this point to the end of the section, are for Never Hinged items.

Type of 1944 Redrawn

		1947-48	Unwmk.	*Perf. 10½*	
RA5	PT2	10c carmine		2.50	.25
RA6	PT2	10c org yel ('48)		2.50	.25
RA7	PT2	10c yel brn ('48)		2.50	.25
RA8	PT2	10c emerald ('48)		2.50	.25
		Nos. RA5-RA8 (4)		10.00	1.00

Post horn and envelope reduced in size.

Condor, Envelope and Post Horn — PT3

		1951-52			
RA9	PT3	20c deep orange		.70	.30
a.		Imperf., pair		25.00	
RA10	PT3	20c green ('52)		.70	.30
a.		Imperf., pair		25.00	
RA11	PT3	20c blue ('52)		.70	.30
a.		Imperf., pair		25.00	
		Nos. RA9-RA11 (3)		2.10	.90

For surcharges see Nos. RA17-RA18.

Communication Symbols — PT4

		1952-54	*Perf. 13½, 10½, 10½x12*		
RA12	PT4	50c green		.70	.25
RA13	PT4	50c carmine		1.00	.25
RA14	PT4	3b green		.70	.30
RA15	PT4	3b olive bister		.85	.30
RA16	PT4	5b violet ('54)		2.50	1.00
		Nos. RA12-RA16 (5)		5.75	2.10

For surcharges see Nos. RA21-RA22.

No. RA10 and Type of 1951-52 Surcharged with New Value in Black

		1953		*Perf. 10½*	
RA17	PT3	50c on 20c green		.60	.25
RA18	PT3	50c on 20c red vio		.60	.25

Postman Blowing Horn — PT5

		1954-55	Unwmk.	*Perf. 10½*	
RA19	PT5	1b brown		1.25	.25
RA20	PT5	1b car rose ('55)		1.25	.25

Nos. RA19-RA20 exist imperf. Value, $25 each pair.

Nos. RA15 and RA14 Surcharged in Black

		1955		*Perf. 10½, 10½x12*	
RA21	PT4	5b on 3b olive bister		1.00	.25
RA22	PT4	5b on 3b green		2.00	.30

Tax of Nos. RA3-RA22 was for the Communications Employees Fund.

No. RA21 is known with surcharge in thin type of different font and with comma added after "55." Value, $10.

Plane over Airport — PT6

Planes — PT7

		1955	Unwmk.	*Perf. 10½, 12, 13½*	
RA23	PT6	5b dp ultra		1.00	.30
a.		Vertical pair imperf. between		30.00	
				Perf. 11½	
RA24	PT7	10b light green		1.00	.30

PT8

PT9

		1955	Litho.	*Perf. 10½*	
RA25	PT8	5b red		15.00	10.00
a.		Imperf., pair		40.00	
				Perf. 12	
RA26	PT9	20b dark brown		1.10	.30

Tax of Nos. RA23-RA26 was for the building of new airports.

General Alfredo Ovando and Three Men — PT10

		1970, Sept. 26	Litho.	*Perf. 13x13½*	
RA27	PT10	20c black & red		.70	.30

See No. RAC1.

Pres. German Busch PT11

		1971, May 13	Litho.	*Perf. 13x13½*	
RA28	PT11	20c lilac & black		.70	.30

AIR POST POSTAL TAX STAMPS

Catalogue values for unused stamps in this section are for Never Hinged items.

Type of Postal Tax Issue

Design: 30c, General Ovando and oil well.

		1970, Sept. 26	Litho.	*Perf. 13x13½*	
RAC1	PT10	30c blk & grn		.80	.30

Pres. Gualberto Villarroel, Refinery PTAP1

		1971, May 25	Litho.	*Perf. 13x13½*	
RAC2	PTAP1	30c lt bl & blk		1.00	.30

Inscribed: "XXV ANIVERSARIO DE SU GOBIERNO"

		1975	Litho.	*Perf. 13x13½*	
RAC3	PTAP1	30c lt bl & blk		10.00	2.75

BOSNIA & HERZEGOVINA

ˈbäz-nē-ə and ˌhert-sə-gō-ˈvē-nə

LOCATION — Between Dalmatia and Serbia
GOVT. — Provinces of Turkey under Austro-Hungarian occupation, 1879-1908; provinces of Austria-Hungary 1908-1918
AREA — 19,768 sq. mi.
POP. — 2,000,000 (approx. 1918)
CAPITAL — Sarajevo

Following World War I Bosnia and Herzegovina united with the kingdoms of Montenegro and Serbia, and Croatia, Dalmatia and Slovenia, to form the

---

Kingdom of Yugoslavia (See Yugoslavia.)

100 Novcica (Neukreuzer) = 1 Florin (Gulden)
100 Heller = 1 Krone (1900)

Watermark

Wmk. 91 — BRIEF-MARKEN or (from 1890) ZEITUNGS-MARKEN in Double-lined Capitals, Across the Sheet

Coat of Arms — A1

Type I — The heraldic eaglets on the right side of the escutcheon are entirely blank. The eye of the lion is indicated by a very small dot, which sometimes fails to print.
Type II — There is a colored line across the lowest eaglet. A similar line sometimes appears on the middle eaglet. The eye of the lion is formed by a large dot which touches the outline of the head above it.
Type III — The eaglets and eye of the lion are similar to type I. Each tail feather of the large eagle has two lines of shading and the lowest feather does not touch the curved line below it. In types I and II there are several shading lines in these feathers, and the lowest feather touches the curved line.

Varieties of the Numerals

2 NOVCICA:
A — The "2" has curved tail. All are type I.
B — The "2" has straight tail. All are type II.

15 NOVCICA:
C — The serif of the "1" is short and forms a wide angle with the vertical stroke.
D — The serif of the "1" forms an acute angle with the vertical stroke.
The numerals of the 5n were retouched several times and show minor differences, especially in the flag.

Other Varieties

½ NOVCICA:
There is a black dot between the curved ends of the ornaments near the lower spandrels.
G — This dot touches the curve at its right. Stamps of this (1st) printing are litho.
H — This dot stands clear of the curved lines. Stamps of this (2nd) printing are typo.

10 NOVCICA:
Ten stamps in each sheet of type II show a small cross in the upper section of the right side of the escutcheon.

		Perf. 9 to 13½ and Compound			
		1879-94	Litho.	**Wmk. 91**	
			Type I		
1	A1	½n blk (type II)			
		('94)		26.00	*37.50*
2	A1	1n gray		15.00	2.25
c.		1n gray lilac			3.00
4	A1	2n yellow		22.50	1.50
5	A1	3n green		26.00	3.00
6	A1	5n rose red		37.50	.40
7	A1	10n blue		150.00	1.50
8	A1	15n brown (D)		150.00	9.75
a.		15n brown (C)		360.00	50.00
9	A1	20n gray green ('93)		500.00	13.50
10	A1	25n violet		130.00	11.00
		Nos. 1-10 (9)		1,057.	80.40

No. 2c was never issued. It is usually canceled by blue pencil marks and "mint" examples generally have been cleaned.

		Perf. 10½ to 13 and Compound			
		1894-98			**Typo.**
			Type II		
1a	A1	½n black		16.50	*22.50*
2a	A1	1n gray		5.25	1.50
4a	A1	2n yellow		3.25	.75
5a	A1	3n green		5.25	1.50
6a	A1	5n rose red		125.00	1.50
7a	A1	10n blue		7.50	1.10
b.		Pair, imperf btw, perf 10½ all around			12,500.

8b	A1	15n brown	6.75	4.50
9a	A1	20n gray green	7.50	6.00
10a	A1	25n violet	9.00	13.50
		Nos. 1a-10a (9)	186.00	52.10

Type III

6b	A1	5n rose red ('98)	3.75	.75

All the preceding stamps exist in various shades.

Nos. 1a to 10a were reprinted in 1911 in lighter colors, on very white paper and perf. 12½. Value, set $32.50.

A2   A3

Perf. 10½, 12½ and Compound

1900				Typo.
11	A2	1h gray black	.25	.25
12	A2	2h gray	.25	.25
13	A2	3h yellow	.25	.25
14	A2	5h green	.25	.25
15	A2	6h brown	.40	.25
16	A2	10h red	.25	.25
17	A2	20h rose	130.00	12.00
18	A2	25h blue	1.10	1.10
19	A2	30h bister brown	130.00	13.00
20	A2	40h orange	190.00	15.00
21	A2	50h red lilac	.75	.75
22	A3	1k dark rose	1.00	.60
23	A3	2k ultra	1.50	1.90
24	A3	5k dull blue grn	3.25	6.00
		Nos. 11-24 (14)	459.25	51.85

All values of this issue except the 3h exist on ribbed paper.

Nos. 17, 19 and 20 were reprinted in 1911. The reprints are in lighter colors and on whiter paper than the originals. Reprints of Nos. 17 and 19 are perf. 10½ and those of No. 20 are perf. 12½. Value each $5. Reprints also exist imperf.

Numerals in Black

1901-04			Perf. 12½	
25	A2	20h pink ('02)	.90	.60
26	A2	30h bister brn ('03)	.90	.60
27	A2	35h blue	1.40	.90
a.		35h ultramarine	175.00	9.00
28	A2	40h orange ('03)	1.10	.90
29	A2	45h grnsh blue ('04)	1.10	.90
		Nos. 25-29 (5)	5.40	3.90

Nos. 11-16, 18, 21-29 exist imperf. Most of Nos. 11-29 exist perf. 6½; compound with 12½; part perf.; in pairs imperf. between. These were supplied only to some high-ranking officials and never sold at any P.O.

For surcharges, see Yugoslavia Nos. 1LJ14-1LJ22.

View of Deboj A4

The Carsija at Sarajevo — A5

Designs: 2h, View of Mostar. 3h, Pliva Gate, Jajce. 5h, Narenta Pass and Prenj River. 6h, Rama Valley. 10h, Vrbas Valley. 20h, Old Bridge, Mostar. 25h, Bey's Mosque, Sarajevo. 30h, Donkey post. 35h, Jezero and tourists' pavilion. 40h, Mail wagon. 45h, Bazaar at Sarajevo. 50h, Postal car. 2k, St. Luke's Campanile, Jajce. 5k, Emperor Franz Josef.

Perf. 6½, 9½, 10½ and 12½, also Compounds

1906			Engr.	Unwmk.
30	A4	1h black	.25	.25
31	A4	2h violet	.25	.25
32	A4	3h olive	.25	.25
33	A4	5h dark green	.35	.35
34	A4	6h brown	.25	.35
a.		Perf. 13½	.75	1.50
35	A4	10h carmine	.45	.35
36	A4	20h dark brown	.75	.75
a.		Perf. 13½	2.10	4.00
37	A4	25h deep blue	1.50	2.25
38	A4	30h green	1.50	1.10
39	A4	35h myrtle green	1.50	1.10
40	A4	40h orange red	1.50	1.10
41	A4	45h brown red	1.50	2.60
42	A4	50h dull violet	2.25	2.60
43	A5	1k maroon	6.00	3.75
44	A5	2k gray green	7.50	13.00
45	A5	5k dull blue	4.50	9.00
		Nos. 30-45 (16)	30.30	39.05

Nos. 30-45 exist imperf. Value, set $91.35 unused, $107 canceled. Many perforation varieties exist. See the *Scott Classic Specialized Catalogue of Stamps and Covers 1840-1940* for detailed listings.

For overprints and surcharges see Nos. 126, B1-B4, Yugoslavia Nos. 1L38, 1LB5-1LB7.

Birthday Jubilee Issue

Designs of 1906 Issue, with "1830-1910" in Label at Bottom

1910			Perf. 12½	
46	A4	1h black	.40	.40
47	A4	2h violet	.40	.40
48	A4	3h olive	.40	.40
49	A4	5h dark green	.40	.40
50	A4	6h orange brn	.40	.40
51	A4	10h carmine	.75	.25
52	A4	20h dark brown	1.50	2.25
53	A4	25h deep blue	2.25	3.75
54	A4	30h green	2.25	3.75
55	A4	35h myrtle grn	2.25	3.75
56	A4	40h orange red	2.25	3.75
57	A4	45h brown red	3.00	7.50
58	A4	50h dull violet	3.75	7.50
59	A5	1k maroon	4.50	7.50
60	A5	2k gray green	15.00	52.50
61	A5	5k dull blue	1.50	9.00
		Nos. 46-61 (16)	41.00	103.50

80th birthday of Emperor Franz Josef. For overprints, see Yugoslavia Nos. 1L1-1L16.

Scenic Type of 1906

Views: 12h, Jaice. 60h, Konjica. 72h, Vishegrad.

1912				
62	A4	12h ultra	5.25	6.75
63	A4	60h dull blue	3.00	4.50
64	A4	72h carmine	11.00	22.50
		Nos. 62-64 (3)	19.25	33.75

Value, imperf set, $110.

See Austria for similar designs inscribed "FELDPOST" instead of "MILITARPOST."

Emperor Franz Josef
A23   A24

A25

A26

1912-14			Various Frames	
65	A23	1h olive green	.40	.25
66	A23	2h brt blue	.40	.25
67	A23	3h claret	.40	.25
68	A23	5h green	.40	.25
69	A23	6h dark gray	.40	.25
70	A23	10h rose car	.40	.25
71	A23	12h dp olive grn	.55	.40
72	A23	20h orange brn	2.75	.25
73	A23	25h ultra	1.50	.25
74	A23	30h orange red	1.50	.25
75	A24	35h myrtle grn	1.50	.25
76	A24	40h dk violet	4.50	.25
77	A24	45h olive brn	2.25	.40
78	A24	50h slate blue	2.25	.25
79	A24	60h brown vio	1.50	.25
80	A24	72h dark blue	3.25	5.25
81	A25	1k brn vio, *straw*	8.25	.75
82	A25	2k dk gray, *bl*	7.50	.75
83	A26	3k carmine, *grn*	8.25	11.00
84	A25	5k dk vio, *gray*	15.00	30.00
85	A25	10k dk ultra, *gray*	90.00	125.00
		Nos. 65-85 (21)	152.95	176.80

Value, imperf set, $325.

For overprints and surcharges see Nos. 127, B5-B8, Austria M1-M21.

A27

A28

1916-17			Perf. 12½	
86	A27	3h dark gray	.25	.40
87	A27	5h olive green	.30	.60
88	A27	6h violet	.60	.75
89	A27	10h olive brown	2.25	3.00
a.		10h bister	2.25	3.75
90	A27	12h blue gray	.75	1.10
91	A27	15h car rose	.25	.25
92	A27	20h brown	.75	1.10
93	A27	25h blue	.75	1.10
94	A27	30h dark green	.75	1.10
95	A27	40h vermilion	.75	1.10
96	A27	50h green	.75	1.10
97	A27	60h lake	.75	1.10
98	A27	80h orange brn	3.75	1.50
a.		Perf. 11½	3.75	7.50
99	A27	90h dark violet	3.00	1.90
a.		Perf. 11½	1,050.	
101	A28	2k claret, *straw*	1.90	3.00
102	A28	3k green, *bl*	2.25	3.75
103	A28	4k carmine, *grn*	7.50	13.50
104	A28	10k dp vio, *gray*	19.00	37.50
		Nos. 86-104 (18)	46.30	73.85

Value, imperf set: hinged $260; never hinged $525.

For overprints see Nos. B11-B12.

Emperor Karl I
A29   A30

1917			Perf. 12½	
105	A29	3h olive gray	.25	.30
a.		Perf. 11½	110.00	240.00
b.		Perf. 12½x11½	22.50	52.50
106	A29	5h olive green	.25	.30
107	A29	6h violet	.40	.90
108	A29	10h orange brn	.25	.25
a.		Perf. 11½x12½	190.00	260.00
b.		Perf. 11½	260.00	560.00
109	A29	12h blue	.40	.90
110	A29	15h brt rose	.25	.25
111	A29	20h red brown	.25	.25
112	A29	25h ultra	.75	.75
113	A29	30h gray green	.40	.40
114	A29	40h olive bis	.40	.40
115	A29	50h dp green	.75	.75
116	A29	60h car rose	.55	.75
a.		Perf. 11½	26.00	60.00
117	A29	80h steel blue	.40	.65
118	A29	90h dull violet	1.10	1.90
119	A30	2k carmine, *straw*	1.50	.75
120	A30	3k green, *bl*	21.00	24.00
121	A30	4k carmine, *grn*	7.50	15.00
122	A30	10k dp violet, *gray*	3.75	13.50
		Nos. 105-122 (18)	40.15	62.00

Value, imperf set, $190.

Nos. 47 and 66 Overprinted in Red

1918				
126	A4	2h violet	.50	*1.50*
b.		Inverted overprint	37.50	
d.		Double overprint	19.00	
f.		Double overprint, one inverted	30.00	
127	A23	2h bright blue	.50	*1.50*
a.		Pair, one without overprint	15.00	
b.		Inverted overprint	15.00	
c.		Double overprint	11.00	
d.		Double overprint, one inverted	22.50	

Emperor Karl I — A31

1918		Typo.	Perf. 12½, Imperf.	
128	A31	2h orange	11.00	
129	A31	3h dark green	11.00	
130	A31	5h lt green	11.00	
131	A31	6h blue green	11.00	
132	A31	10h brown	11.00	
133	A31	20h brick red	11.00	
134	A31	25h ultra	11.00	
135	A31	45h dk slate	11.00	
136	A31	50h lt bluish grn	11.00	
137	A31	60h blue violet	11.00	
138	A31	70h ocher	11.00	
139	A31	80h rose	11.00	
140	A31	90h violet brn	11.00	

		Engr.		
141	A30	1k ol grn, *grnsh*	*1,900.*	
		Nos. 128-140 (13)	143.00	

Nos. 128-141 were prepared for use in Bosnia and Herzegovina, but were not issued there. They were sold after the Armistice at the Vienna post office for a few days.

Nos. 128-141 exist imperf. Value, set $190.

SEMI-POSTAL STAMPS

Nos. 33 and 35 Surcharged in Red

1914, Nov. 1		Unwmk.	Perf. 12½	
B1	A4	7h on 5h dk grn	.40	.75
B2	A4	12h on 10h car	.40	.75

Three varieties of the surcharge include "4" with open top, narrow "4" and wide "4." See the *Scott Classic Specialized Catalogue of Stamps and Covers* for detailed listings.

Nos. B1-B2 exist with double and inverted surcharges. Values, double surcharge, each: unused $22.50, never hinged $37.50. Values, inverted surcharge, each: unused $26, never hinged $45.

Nos. 33, 35 Surcharged in Red or Blue

1915, July 10			Perf. 12½	
B3	A4	7h on 5h (R)	12.00	19.00
a.		Perf. 9¼	240.00	275.00
B4	A4	12h on 10h (Bl)	.40	.55

Nos. B3-B4 exist with double and inverted surcharges. Value about $30 each.

Nos. 68, 70 Surcharged in Red or Blue

1915, Dec. 1

B5	A23	7h on 5h (R)	.75	2.10
a.		"1915" at top and bottom	37.50	67.50
B6	A23	12h on 10h (Bl)	1.50	5.25
a.		Surcharged "7 Heller."	37.50	75.00

Nos. B5-B6 are found in four types differing in length of surcharge lines. See the *Scott Classic Specialized Catalogue of Stamps and Covers* for detailed listings.

Nos. B5-B6 exist with double and inverted surcharges. Values, each: unused $22.50, never hinged $37.50.

Nos. B5a and B6a exist double and inverted. Value: each, $750.

Nos. 68, 70
Surcharged in Red
or Blue

1916. Feb. 1

B7	A23	7h on 5h (R)	.75	.75
B8	A23	12h on 10h (Bl)	.75	.75

The overprint on Nos. B7-B8 is found in two types, differing in length of surcharge lines. See the *Scott Classic Specialized Catalogue of Stamps and Covers* for detailed listings.

Nos. B7-B8 exist with double and inverted surcharges. Values: double surcharge, each $19 unused $37.50 never hinged; inverted surcharge, each $15 unused, $30 never hinged.

Wounded	Blind
Soldier — SP1	Soldier — SP2

1916, July 10   **Engr.**

B9	SP1	5h (+ 2h) green	.85	1.90
B10	SP2	10h (+ 2h) magenta	1.50	2.60

Nos. B9-B10 exist imperf. Value, set $110. For overprints, see Yugoslavia Nos. 1LB3-1LB4.

Nos. 89, 89a, 91
Overprinted

1917, May 9

B11	A27	10h bister (#89a)	.25	.25
B12	A27	15h carmine rose	.25	.50

Nos. B11-B12 exist imperf. Value set $150.

Nos. B11-B12 exist with double and inverted overprint. Values: double surcharge, each $15 unused; $30 never hinged; inverted surcharge, each $22.50 unused, $45 never hinged.

Design
for
Memorial
Church at
Sarajevo
SP3

Archduke Francis
Ferdinand — SP4

Duchess
Sophia
and
Archduke
Francis
Ferdinand
SP5

1917, June 20   Typo.   Perf. 12½

B13	SP3	10h violet black	.35	.40
B14	SP4	15h claret	.35	.40
B15	SP5	40h deep blue	.25	.40
		Nos. B13-B15 (3)	.95	1.20

Assassination of Archduke Ferdinand and Archduchess Sophia. Sold at a premium of 2h each, which helped build a memorial church at Sarajevo.

Exist perf 11½. See Scott Classic Specialized catalogue for detailed listings.

Exist imperf. Value set, $35.

Blind
Soldier — SP6

Design: 15h, Wounded soldier.

1918, Mar. 1   Engr.   Perf. 12½

B16	SP6	10h (+ 10h) grnsh bl	.65	1.50
B17	SP6	15h (+ 10h) red brn	.65	1.50

Nos. B16-B17 exist imperf. Value, set $67.50. For overprints, see Yugoslavia Nos. 1LB1-1LB2.

Emperor
Karl I — SP8

Design: 15h, Empress Zita.

1918, July 20   Typo.   Perf. 12½x13

B18	SP8	10h gray green	.50	1.25
B19	SP8	15h brown red	.50	1.25
B20	SP8	40h violet	.50	1.25
		Nos. B18-B20 (3)	1.50	3.75

Sold at a premium of 10h each which went to the "Karl's Fund."
Nos. B18-B20 exist imperf. Value, set: $75.

POSTAGE DUE STAMPS

D1

1904   Unwmk.   Perf. 12½

J1	D1	1h black, red & yel	.75	.30
J2	D1	2h black, red & yel	.75	.30
J3	D1	3h black, red & yel	.75	.30
J4	D1	4h black, red & yel	.75	.30
J5	D1	5h black, red & yel	3.75	.30
J6	D1	6h black, red & yel	.75	.30
J7	D1	7h black, red & yel	5.25	3.75
J8	D1	8h black, red & yel	5.25	2.25
J9	D1	10h black, red & yel	.75	.30
J10	D1	15h black, red & yel	.75	.30
J11	D1	20h black, red & yel	6.00	.30
J12	D1	50h black, red & yel	3.00	.40

J13	D1	200h black, red & grn	26.00	3.00
		Nos. J1-J13 (13)	54.50	12.10
		Set, never hinged	105.00	

Nos. J1-J13 exists with a wide variety of perforations. See the *Scott Classic Specialized Catalogue of Stamps and Covers* for detailed listings.

Nos. J1-J13 also exist perf. 10½, 9¼, 6¼, and in various compound combinations.

Value, imperf set: hinged $125; never hinged $300.

For overprints and surcharges see Western Ukraine Nos. 61-72, Yugoslavia Nos. 1LJ23-1LJ26.

D2

1916-18   Perf. 12½

J14	D2	2h red ('18)	.40	1.50
J15	D2	4h red ('18)	.25	1.50
J16	D2	5h red	.40	1.50
J17	D2	6h red ('18)	.25	1.50
J18	D2	10h red	.40	1.50
J19	D2	15h red	3.00	9.00
J20	D2	20h red	.40	1.50
J21	D2	25h red	1.10	3.75
J22	D2	30h red	.90	3.75
J23	D2	40h red	8.25	21.00
J24	D2	50h red	26.00	62.50
J25	D2	1k dark blue	3.75	11.00
J26	D2	3k dark blue	15.00	40.00
		Nos. J14-J26 (13)	60.10	160.00
		Set, never hinged	185.00	

Nos. J25-J26 have colored numerals on a white tablet.

Value, imperf. set: unused $135, never hinged $300.

For surcharges see Italy Nos. NJ1-NJ7, Yugoslavia 1LJ1-1LJ13.

NEWSPAPER STAMPS

Bosnian Girl — N1

1913   Unwmk.   Imperf.

P1	N1	2h ultra	.75	.75
P2	N1	6h violet	2.25	3.50
P3	N1	10h rose	2.60	3.50
P4	N1	20h green	3.00	3.75
		Nos. P1-P4 (4)	8.60	11.50

Used values are for postally used examples. Favor-canceled stamps are valued the same as unused.

After Bosnia and Herzegovina became part of Yugoslavia, stamps of type N1 perf., and imperf. copies surcharged with new values, were used as regular postage stamps. See Yugoslavia Nos. 1L17-1L22, 1L43-1L45.

SPECIAL DELIVERY STAMPS

"Lightning" — SH1

1916   Unwmk.   Engr.   Perf. 12½

QE1	SH1	2h vermilion	.25	.75
a.		Perf. 11½x12½	375.00	
QE2	SH1	5h deep green	.40	1.10
a.		Perf. 11½	15.00	37.50

Nos. QE1-QE2 exist imperf. Values, set: unused $130, never hinged $260.

For surcharges see Italy Nos. NE1-NE2, Yugoslavia Nos. 1LE1-1LE2.

BOSNIA & HERZEGOVINA (BOSNIAK GOVERNMENT)

'băz-nē-ak

LOCATION — Bordering on Croatia, Seribia & Montenegro.
GOVT. — Republic
CAPITAL — Sarajevo

Formerly part of Yugoslavia. Proclamation of independence in 1992 was followed by protracted civil war that was ended by the Dayton Peace Agreement of Nov. 21, 1995.

While Dinars were the official currency until 6/22/98, a currency pegged to the German mark was in use for some time prior to that. Stamps are denominated in pfennigs and marks in 11/97.

100 Paras = 1 Dinar
100 Pfennig = 1 Mark (6/22/98)

Catalogue values for all unused stamps in this country are for Never Hinged items.

Muslim Government in Sarajevo

Natl.
Arms — A50

Denominations: 100d, 500d, 1000d, 5000d, 10,000d, 20,000d, 50,000d.

1993, Oct. 27   Litho.   Imperf.
Booklet Stamps

200-206	A50	Set of 7	16.00	16.00

Nos. 200-206 each were available in bklts. of 50 (10 strips of 5).

1984 Winter
Olympic
Games,
Sarajevo, 10th
Anniv. — A51

No. 207, Games emblem. No. 208a, 100,000d, Four man bobsled. No. 208b, 200,000d, Hockey.

1994, Feb. 8

207	A51	50,000d org & blk	2.50	2.50

Souvenir Sheet

208	A51	Sheet of 2, #a.-b.	11.50	11.50

No. 208 contains 45x27mm stamps.

Souvenir Sheet

Bairam Festival — A52

Various illustrations from Koran: a, 400d. b, 600d.

1995, May 12   Perf. 14

209	A52	Sheet of 2, #a.-b.	16.00	16.00

Main Post Office, Sarajevo
A53

Designs: 10d, Facade. 20d, 30d, Demolished interior. 35d, 50d, Pre-civil war exterior. 100d, 200d, Post-war exterior.

1995, June 12
210-216 A53 Set of 7   8.00 8.00
216a   Pane of 7   9.00 9.00
No. 216a sold unattached in booklet covers.

Bosnian History
A54

Designs: 35d, Historical map, 10th-15th cent. 100d, Tomb, vert. 200d, Arms, Kotromanic Dynasty, vert. 300d, Charter by Ban Kulin, 1189.

1995, Aug. 12   *Perf. 11½*
217-220 A54 Set of 4   9.00 9.00

Peace & Freedom, Europa
A55

1995, Sept. 25
221 A55 200d multicolored   *3.50 3.50*

World Post Day — A56

1995, Sept. 25
222 A56 100d multicolored   1.60 1.60

A57

Flowers: No. 223: a, 100d, Simphyandra hofmannii. b, 200d, Lilium bosniacum.

1995, Oct. 12
223 A57 Pair, #a.-b.   4.75 4.75

Fish
A58

No. 224: a, 100d, Aulopyge hugeli. b, 200d, Paraphoxinus alepidotus.

1995, Oct. 12
224 A58 Pair, #a.-b.   4.75 4.75

Children's Week
A59

1995, Oct. 12
225 A59 100d multicolored   1.60 1.60

Electric Tram System, Sarajevo, Cent.
A60

1995, Oct. 12
226 A60 200d multicolored   3.00 3.00

Bridges
A61

Designs: 20d, Kozija, Sarajevo. 30d, Arslanagica, Trebinje. 35d, Latinska, Sarajevo. 50d, Old Bridge, Mostar. 100d, Visegrad.

1995, Dec. 12
227-231 A61 Set of 5   3.75 3.75

Christmas
A62

Designs: 100d, Visiting friends. 200d, Madonna and Child, vert.

1995, Dec. 24
232-233 A62 Set of 2   4.00 4.00

Queen Jelena's Tomb — A63

1995, Dec. 31
234 A63 30d multicolored   .50   .50

A64

Design: Husein Gradascevic (1802-33).

1995, Dec. 31
235 A64 35d multicolored   .50   .50

Mirza Safvet Basagic (1870-1934) — A65

1995, Dec. 31
236 A65 100d multicolored   1.10 1.10

Religious Diversity
A66

1995, Dec. 31
237 A66 35d multicolored   .60   .60

Destruction of Olympic Stadium, Sarajevo — A67

35d, Stadium, various skaters. 100d, Stadium ablaze, vert.

1995, Dec. 31
238-239 A67 Set of 2   2.25 2.25

Famous Women — A68

Europa: 80d, Bahrija Hadzic (1904-93), opera singer. 120d, Nasiha Hadzic (1932-95), writer.

1996, Apr. 15   *Perf. 15*
240-241 A68 Set of 2   3.50 3.50

UNICEF, 50th Anniv. — A69

Designs: a, 50d, Child stepping on land mine. b, 150d, Child's handprint.

1996, Apr. 15   *Perf. 11½*
242 A69 Pair, #a.-b.   3.25 3.25

Bobovac Castle — A70

1996, May 5   *Perf. 11½*
243 A70 35d multicolored   .55   .55

Bairam Festival — A71

1996, May 5   *Perf. 14*
244 A71 80d multicolored   1.50 1.50
No. 244 was issued in sheets of 2. Value $3.50.

Sarajevo Town Hall, Cent.
A72

1996, May 5   *Perf. 11½*
245 A72 80d multicolored   1.10 1.10

Bosnian Journalists Assoc., Cent.
A73

1996, May 5
246 A73 100d multicolored   1.60 1.60

Essen '96, Intl. Philatelic Expo
A74

1996, May 25   *Perf. 11½*
247 A74 200d multicolored   2.75 2.75

1996 Summer Olympic Games, Atlanta — A75

No. 248: a, 120d, Baron de Coubertin. b, 80d, Olympic Torch. c, 30d, Runners. d, 35d, Atlanta Games emblem.

1996, May 25
248 A75 Block of 4, #a.-d.   4.00 4.00
Background of No. 248 differs with location on sheet.

Alexander Graham Bell's Telephone, 120th Anniv.
A76

1996, July 10   *Perf. 11½*
249 A76 80d multicolored   1.00 1.00

Extension of Privleges to Dubrovnik by Ban Stepan II, 1333
A77

1996, July 10
250 A77 100d multicolored 1.50 1.50

Use of Mail Vans in Bosnia, Cent. A78

1996, July 10
251 A78 120d multicolored 1.50 1.50

Flowers — A79

No. 252: a, 30d, Campanula hercegovina. b, 35d, Iris bosniaca.

1996, July 10
252 A79 Pair, #a.-b. 1.00 1.00
Printed checkerwise on the sheet.

Dogs A80

No. 253: a, 35d, Barak. b, 80d, Tornjak.

1996, July 10
253 A80 Pair, #a.-b. 2.00 2.00
Printed checkerwise on the sheet.

SOS Children's Village, Sarajevo — A81

1996, Sept. 1
254 A81 100d multicolored 1.50 1.50

A83   A84

Traditional costumes — No. 255: a, 50d, Moslem, Bjelasnice. b, 80d, Croatian. c, 100d, Moslem, Sarajevo.
Uniforms — No. 256: a, 35d, Bogomil soldier. b, 80d, Austro-Hungarian rifleman. c,

100d, Turkish light cavalry. d, 120d, Medieval Bosnian king.

1996, Sept. 20
255 A83 Strip of 3, #a.-c. + label 3.00 3.00
256 A84 Strip of 4, #a.-d. 5.00 5.00

Winter Festival, Sarajevo A85

1996, Nov. 25
257 A85 100d multicolored 1.50 1.50

Bosnia Day — A86

1996, Nov. 25
258 A86 120d Map, natl. arms 1.75 1.75

Christmas A87

1996, Dec. 21
259 A87 100d multicolored 1.50 1.50

Visit by Pope John Paul II — A88

1996, Dec. 21   **Perf. 14**
260 A88 500d multicolored 8.00 8.00

Archaeological Finds — A89

Designs: 35d, Paleolithic rock carving, Badanj. 50d, Neolithic ceramic head, Butmir. 80d, Bronze age bird wagon, Glasinac.
Walls of Daorson, Illyria — No. 264: a, 100d, Walls, rock face at L. b, 120d, Low wall outside city wall.

1997, Mar. 31   **Perf. 15**
261-263 A89 Set of 3 2.25 2.25
    Souvenir Sheet
264 A89 Sheet of 2, #a.-b. 3.25 3.25

Children's Week — A90

1997, Apr. 15   **Perf. 11½**
265 A90 100d multicolored 1.50 1.50

Bairam Festival — A91

200d, Ferhad Pasha Mosque.

1997, Apr. 15   **Perf. 11½**
266 A91 200d multi 3.00 3.00

A92

1997, Apr. 25   **Perf. 14**
267 A92 100d multicolored 1.50 1.50
Mujaga Komadina (1839-1925), mayor of Mostar.

A93

Europa (Myths & Legends): 100d, Trojan warriors, map. 120d, Man on prayer mat, castle from The Miraculous Spring of Ajvatovica.

1997, May 3   **Perf. 11½**
268-269 A93 Set of 2 3.50 3.50

Greenpeace, 25th Anniv. — A94

Rainbow Warrior, inscribed: a, 35d, Grace. b, 80d, Dorreboom. c, 100d, Beltra. d, 120d, Morgan.

1997, May 25
270 A94 Block or strip of 4, #a.-d. 6.50 6.50

Third Intl. Film Festival, Sarajevo A95

1997, June 15
271 A95 110d multicolored 1.75 1.75

Mediterranean Games, Bari — A96

Designs: 40d, Games emblem. 130d, Boxing, basketball, kick boxing.

1997, June 15
272-273 A96 Set of 2 2.50 2.50

Discovery of Electrons, Cent. A97

1997, June 25
274 A97 40d multicolored .85 .85

Vasco da Gama's Voyage Around Africa, 500th Anniv. — A98

1997, June 25
275 A98 110d multicolored 1.75 1.75

Stamp Day — A99

1997, June 25
276 A99 130d multicolored 2.00 2.00

Railroads in Bosnia & Herzegovina, 125th Anniv. — A100

1997, June 25
277 A100 150d multicolored 2.25 2.25

Fauna — A101

No. 278: a, 40d, Dinaromys bogdanovi. b, 80d, Triturus alpestris.
No. 279: a, 40d, Oxytropis prenja. b, 110d, Dianthus freynii.

1997, Aug. 25
278 A101 Pair, #a.-b. 2.50 2.50
279 A101 Pair, #a.-b. 2.75 2.75

World Peace
Day — A102

a, 50d, Sweden, Switzerland, Australia &
other flags. b, 60d, Flags, globe showing
Europe, Africa. c, 70d, Flags, globe showing
North & South America. d, 110d, US, UK,
Canadian & other flags.

1997, Aug. 25
280 A102 Strip of 4, #a.-d. 4.50 4.50

Great Sarajevo
Fire, 300th
Anniv. — A103

1997, Sept. 15
281 A103 110d multicolored 2.00 2.00

Architecture — A104

Designs: 40d, House with attic. 50d, Tiled
stove, door. 130d, Three-storied house.

1997, Sept. 15
282-284 A104 Set of 3 3.00 3.00

Italian Pioneer Corps Aid in
Reconstruction of Sarajevo — A105

1997, Nov. 1 *Perf. 14*
285 A105 1.40m multicolored 2.00 2.00

Famous
Men
A106

1.30m, Augustin Tin Ujevic (1891-1955),
writer. 2m, Zaim Imamovic (1920-94), singer,
vert.

1997, Nov. 1 *Perf. 11½*
286-287 A106 Set of 2 4.50 4.50

Diana, Princess of Wales (1961-
97) — A107

1997, Nov. 3 *Perf. 14*
288 A107 2.50m multicolored 3.50 3.50

Gnijezdo,
by Fikret
Libovac
A108

Sarajevo
Library, by
Nusret
Pasic
A109

1997, Nov. 6 *Perf. 11½*
289 A108 35pf multicolored .50 .50
290 A109 80pf multicolored 1.25 1.25

Samac-Sarajevo Railway, 50th
Anniv. — A110

1997, Nov. 17 *Perf. 14*
291 A110 35pf multicolored .60 .60

Religious
Holidays — A111

50pf, Nativity Scene, Orthodox Christmas.
No. 293, 1.10m, Wreath on door, Christmas.
No. 294, 1.10m, Pupils before teacher,
Hagada.

1997, Dec. 22 *Perf. 11½*
292-294 A111 Set of 3 4.00 4.00

A112

Designs: a, 35pf, Sports. b, 1m, Games
emblem.

1998, Jan. 15 *Perf. 14*
295 A112 Sheet of 2, #a.-b. 2.00 2.00
1998 Winter Olympic Games, Nagano.

Bairam
Festival — A113

1998, Jan. 28
296 A113 1m Mosque fountain 1.50 1.50

Ahmed Muradbegovic (1898-1972),
Writer — A114

1998, Mar. 20
297 A114 1.50m multicolored 2.25 2.25

Fortified Towns — A115

No. 298: a, 35pf, Zvornik. b, 70pf, Bihac. c,
1m, Pocitelj. d, 1.20m, Gradacac.

1998, Mar. 20
298 A115 Booklet pane of 4,
#a.-d. 5.00 5.00
Complete booklet, #298 5.50 5.50

A116

1998, May 5 *Perf. 11½*
299 A116 1.10m multicolored 3.00 3.00
Intl. Theater Festival, Sarajevo, Europa.

A117

Former Presidents of Univ. of Arts and Science: 40pf, Branislav Durdev (1908-93). 70pf,
Alojz Benac (1914-92). 1.30m, Edhem Camo
(1909-96).

1998, May 5
300-302 A117 Set of 3 3.50 3.50

A118

Ciconia Ciconia — No. 303: a, 70pf, Three
in water. b, 90pf, Two in flight. c, 1.10m, Two in
nest. d, 1.30m, Adult, chicks.

1998, May 5
303 A118 Strip of 4, #a.-d. 6.00 6.00

A119

1998, May 22
304 A119 2m Sheet with 2 labels 3.00 3.00

World Congress of Intl. League of Human-
ists, Sarajevo.

1998 World Cup Soccer
Championships, France — A120

50pf, Soccer balls. 1m, Map, soccer ball.
1.50m, Asim Ferhatovic Hase (1934-87), soccer player.

1998, May 22 *Perf. 14½*
305-307 A120 Set of 3 4.50 4.50

Sarajevo Tunnel,
5th Anniv. — A121

1998, July 20 *Perf. 11½*
308 A121 1.10m multicolored 1.60 1.60

Mushrooms
A122

50pf, Morchella esculenta. 80pf, Canthurel-
lus cibarius. 1.10m, Boletus edulis. 1.35m,
Amanita caesarea.

1998, July 30
309-312 A122 Set of 4 5.50 5.50

Paris
Subway
A123

1998, Aug. 30
313 A123 2m violet blue & green   2.75   2.75

Henri
Dunant — A124

1998, Sept. 14   *Perf. 14*
314 A124 50pf multicolored   .85   .85
Intl. Red Cross fight against tuberculosis.

Cities — A125

1998, Sept. 24
315 A125   5pf Travnik   .30   .30
316 A125 38pf Sarajevo   .45   .45

Chess — A126

Bosnian players — No. 317: a, 20pf,
Woman at chess board. b, 40pf, Silver medal
team, 31st Chess Olympiad. c, 60pf, Women's
team, 32nd Chess Olympiad. d, 80pf, Men,
Women's teams, 11th European Chess
Championships.

1998, Sept. 24
317 A126   Sheet of 4, #a.-d.   3.00   3.00

World Post
Day — A127

1998, Oct. 9   *Perf. 11½*
318 A127 1m multicolored   1.50   1.50

Musical Instruments
A128

1998, Oct. 23
319 A128 80pf multicolored   1.25   1.25

Intl. Day of
Disabled
Persons
A129

1998, Dec. 3
320 A129 1m multicolored   1.50   1.50

Mt.
Bjelasnica
A130

1998, Dec. 3
321 A130 1m multicolored   1.50   1.50

Universal Declaration of Human
Rights, 50th Anniv. — A131

1998, Dec. 10   *Perf. 14½*
322 A131 1.35m multicolored   2.00   2.00

New Year
A132

Christmas — A133

Designs: 1m, Child's drawing. 1.50m, Fr.
Andeo Zvizdovic (1420?-98).

1998, Dec. 18   *Perf. 11½*
323 A132   1m multicolored   1.50   1.50
324 A133   1.50m multicolored   2.25   2.25

School Anniversaries — A134

Designs: No. 325, 40pf, First Sarajevo High
School, 120th anniv. No. 326, 40pf, Sarajevo
University, 50th anniv., vert.

1999, Apr. 22   *Litho.*   *Perf. 11¾*
325-326 A134   Set of 2   1.20   1.20

Flora and
Fauna
A135

80pf, Pigeons. 1.10m, Knautia sarajevensis.

1999, Apr. 22   *Litho.*   *Perf. 11¾*
327-328 A135   Set of 2   3.50   3.50

First Manned Moon
Landing, 30th
Anniv. — A136

1999, May 20   *Litho.*   *Perf. 11¾*
329 A136 2m multicolored   2.75   2.75

Una River
— A137

1999, May 20
330 A137 2m multicolored   *3.50 3.50*
Europa

Gorazde
A137a

1999, June 9   *Litho.*   *Perf. 14x14¼*
330A A137a 40pf multi   .60   .60

World
Environmental
Protection
Day — A138

80pf, Buna River Wellspring.

1999, June 15   *Litho.*   *Perf. 11¾*
331 A138 80pf multi   1.25   1.25

Philex
France
99 — A139

1999, June 15
332 A139 2m multicolored   2.75   2.75

Special
Olympics
A140

1999, June 15
333 A140 50pf multicolored   .70   .70

Bosnia & Herzegovina Postage
Stamps, 120th Anniv. — A141

1999, July 1
334 A141 1m multicolored   1.75   1.75

UPU, 125th
Anniv. — A142

1999, July 1   *Litho.*   *Perf. 11¾*
335 A142 1.50m multi   2.25   2.25

Minerals
A143

Designs: 40pf, Tuzlite. 60pf, Siderite. 1.20m,
Hijelofan. 1.80m, Quartz, vert.

1999, July 27   *Litho.*   *Perf. 11¾*
336-339 A143   Set of 4   6.00   6.00

Dzuzovi
Mehmed
Pasha
Sokolovic
Koran
Manuscript
A144

1999, Sept. 23
340 A144 1.50m multicolored   2.00   2.00

Kursumli Medresa
Library, Founded
1537 — A145

1999, Sept. 23
341 A145 1m multicolored   1.40   1.40

Radiology in Bosnia & Herzegovina,
Cent. — A146

1999, Oct. 5
342 A146 90pf multicolored   1.40   1.40

Handija Kasevljakovic (1888-1959),
Historian — A147

1999, Oct. 5
343 A147 1.30m multicolored   1.75   1.75

25th European Chess Club Cup
Finals — A148

1999, Oct. 29   Litho.   Perf. 14
344 A148 1.10m multicolored   1.75 1.75

Hvalov Zbornik,
Book in Glagolitic
Text — A149

1999, Sept. 23   Litho.   Perf. 11¾
345 A149 1.10m multicolored   1.60 1.60

Sarajevo
Summit
A150

1999, July 29   Litho.   Perf. 14
346 A150 2m multi   3.00 3.00

Expo
2000,
Hanover
A151

1999, Nov. 9   Litho.   Perf. 11¾
347 A151 1m multi   1.40 1.40

Painting by
Afan
Ramic
A152

1999, Nov. 25
348 A152 1.20m multi   1.60 1.60

Birth of Six
Billionth
Person
A153

1999, Nov. 25   Perf. 14
349 A153 2.50m multi   4.00 4.00

Souvenir Sheet

Bjelasnica Weather Observatory,
105th Anniv. — A154

1999, Dec. 15
350 A154 1.10m multi   1.60 1.60

Sarajevo   Sarajevo Intl.
Philharmonic   Music Festival
A155   A156

1999, Dec. 20
351 A155 40pf multi   .60 .60
352 A156 1.10m multi   1.40 1.40

Mehmed Spaho
(1883-1939),
Politician — A157

2000, Mar. 15   Perf. 11¾
353 A157 1m multi   1.60 1.60

Bairam
Festival — A158

2000, Mar. 15
354 A158 1.10m multi   1.75 1.75

Amateur Radio in
Bosnia and
Herzegovina, 50th
Anniv. — A159

2000, Mar. 15
355 A159 1.50m multi   2.50 2.50

Oriental Institute,
Sarajevo, 50th
Anniv. — A160

2000, Mar. 15
356 A160 2m multi   3.00 3.00

Souvenir Sheet

2000 Summer Olympics,
Sydney — A161

Emblem of Sydney Olympics and map of: a,
1.30m, Bosnia & Herzegovina. b, 1.70m,
Australia.

2000, Apr. 10   Litho.   Perf. 14¾
357 A161 Sheet of 2, #a-b   5.00 5.00

Europa, 2000
Common Design Type
2000, May 9   Perf. 11¾
358 CD17 2m multi   4.75 4.75

Birds
A162

1m, Gyps fulvus. 1.50m, Platalea
leucorodia.

2000, May 9   Litho.   Perf. 11¾
359-360 A162 Set of 2   4.00 4.00

Lake
Boracko
A163

River Una
Emeralds — A164

2000, May 9
361 A163 40pf multi   .65 .65
362 A164 1m multi   1.60 1.60
World Environmental Protection Day.

Souvenir Sheet

Greenpeace — A165

a, 50pf, Fish. b, 60pf, Lobster. c, 90pf,
Anemones. d, 1.50m, Diver on shipwreck.

2000, May 9   Perf. 11¾x11½
363 A165 Sheet of 4, #a-d   6.00 6.00

First
Zeppelin
Flight,
Cent.
A166

2000, June 10   Perf. 11¾
364 A166 1.50m multi   2.25 2.25

Cities — A167

2000, June 9   Litho.   Perf. 14
365 A167 50pf Zenica   .90   .90
366 A167 1m Mostar   1.20 1.20
367 A167 1.10m Bihac   1.40 1.40
368 A167 1.50m Tuzla, vert. 2.00 2.00
    Nos. 365-368 (4)   5.50 5.50

Vranduk
A168

Kraljeva
Sutjeska
A169

2000, Sept. 20   Perf. 11¾x11½
369 A168 1.30m multi   1.75 1.75
370 A169 1.50m multi   2.50 2.50

The
Adventures
of Tom
Sawyer, by
Mark
Twain
A170

2000, Sept. 20
371 A170 1.50m multi   2.50 2.50

Souvenir Sheet

Millennium — A171

2000, Sept. 20   *Perf. 11¾*
372 A171 2m multi   3.00 3.00

No. 372 contains one 29x57mm 80pf "stamp," and one 57x57mm 1.20m "stamp," but both lack the country name, which appears only in the sheet margin.

Intl. Children's Week — A172

2000, Oct. 5   *Perf. 11½x11¾*
373 A172 1.60m multi   2.50 2.50

Paintings A173

Paintings by: 60pf, J. Mujezinovic. 80pf, I. Seremet.

2000, Oct. 5   *Perf. 11¾x11½*
374-375 A173 Set of 2   2.25 2.25

UN High Commissioner for Refugees, 50th Anniv. — A174

2000, Dec. 14   *Perf. 11¾x11½*
376 A174 1m multi   1.50 1.50

Cities — A175

2001, Mar. 22   *Perf. 14*
377 A175 10pf Tesanj, vert.   .25 .25
378 A175 20pf Bugojno   .30 .30
379 A175 30pf Konjic   .40 .40
380 A175 35pf Zivinice   .80 .80
381 A175 2m Cazin   3.00 3.00
    Nos. 377-381 (5)   4.75 4.75

Animals — A176

No. 382, vert.: a, 90pf, Alcedo atthis. b, 1.10m, Bombycilla garrulus. No. 383: a, 1.10m, Equus caballus facing right. b, 1.90m, Equus caballus facing left.

2001, Mar. 22   **Litho.**   *Perf. 11¾*
382 A176 Horiz. pair, #a-b   2.50 2.50
    Perf. 11¾x11½
383 A176 Horiz. pair, #a-b   3.00 3.00

Walt Disney (1901-66) — A177

Perf. 11½x11¾
2001, Mar. 22   **Litho.**
384 A177 1.10m multi   1.25 1.25

Shell Fossils — A178

Denominations in: a, 1.30m, Blue. b, 1.80m, Black.

2001, Mar. 22   *Perf. 11¾x11½*
385 A178 Horiz. pair, #a-b   3.50 3.50

Souvenir Sheet

Comic Strips — A179

Inscriptions: a, Ti si moje janje. b, Ti si moj medo. c, Ti si moja maca. d, Ti si moj cvijet. e, Ti si moje pile.

2001, Mar. 22   **Litho.**   *Perf. 11¾*
    Granite Paper
386 A179 30pf Sheet of 5, #a-e   2.50 2.50
    See No. 419.

Souvenir Sheet

Europa — A180

2001, Apr. 10   *Perf. 11½x11¾*
387 A180 2m multi   3.50 3.50

Souvenir Sheet

Bosnia Institute, Sarajevo — A181

2001, May 25   **Litho.**   *Perf. 14*
388 A181 1.10m multi   1.90 1.90

Souvenir Sheet

Emir Balic, Mostar Bridge Diver — A182

2001, May 30   *Perf. 11½x11¾*
389 A182 2m multi   3.50 3.50

14th Mediterranean Games, Tunis — A183

2001, May 30   **Litho.**   *Perf. 14x14¼*
390 A183 1.30m multi   2.00 2.00

Ferrari Race Cars — A184

No. 391: a, 40pf, 15954 625 F1. b, 60pf, 1970 312 B. c, 1.30m, 1978 312 T3. d, 1.70m, 1983 126 C3.

2001, June 20   **Litho.**   *Perf. 14x14¼*
391 A184   Block of 4, #a-d   6.00 6.00

Zeljeznic, Soccer Champions — A185

2001, July 18
392 A185 1m multi   1.50 1.50

Nobel Prizes, Cent. A186

2001, July 18
393 A186 1.50m multi   2.25 2.25

Charlie Chaplin (1889-1977) A187

2001, July 18   *Perf. 14x13¾*
394 A187 1.60m multi   2.50 2.50

Art by Edin Numankadic — A188

Perf. 12½x12¾
2001, Sept. 10   **Litho.**
395 A188 80pf multi   1.25 1.25

Portions of the design were applied by a thermographic process producing a shiny, raised effect.

David, by Michelangelo, 500th Anniv. — A189

2001, Sept. 10
396 A189 2m multi   3.00 3.00

Portions of the design were applied by a thermographic process producing a shiny, raised effect.

Breastfeeding Week — A190

2001, Oct. 1   **Litho.**   *Perf. 14*
397 A190 1.10m multi   1.75 1.75

World Post
Day — A191

2001, Oct. 9
398 A191 1.30m multi   3.00 3.00

Horse-drawn Mail
Delivery
Railcar — A192

2001, Oct. 30 Litho. Perf. 14¼x14
399 A192 1.10m multi   1.75 1.75

Alija Bejtic (1920-81),
Historian — A193

2001, Nov. 10 Litho. Perf. 14
400 A193 80pf multi   1.25 1.25

Albert
Einstein
A194

2001, Dec. 14
401 A194 1.50m multi   2.50 2.50

Musical
Group
"Indexi"
A195

2002, Apr. 5 Litho. Perf. 14
402 A195 38pf multi   .65 .65

Mustafa Ejubovic
(Sejh Jujo, 1651-
1707),
Writer — A196

2002, Apr. 15 Litho. Perf. 13¾x14
403 A196 1m multi   1.50 1.50

Juraj
Neidhardt
(1901-79),
Architect
A197

2002, Apr. 15   Perf. 14x13¾
404 A197 1m multi   1.50 1.50

Dr. Sevala Zildzic-
Iblizovic (1903-
78) — A198

2002, Apr. 15   Perf. 13¾x14
405 A198 1.30m multi   2.25 2.25

Sarajevo's
Candidacy to Host
2010 Winter
Olympics — A199

2002, Apr. 15 Litho. Perf. 13¾x14
406 A199 1.50m multi   2.50 2.50

Intl. Earth
Day — A200

2002, Apr. 15 Litho. Perf. 13¾
407 A200 2m multi   2.75 2.75

Bosnia & Herzegovina Scouting
Organization, 80th Anniv. — A201

2002, Apr. 20 Litho. Perf. 14x13¾
408 A201 1m multi   1.75 1.75

Europa — A202

2002, Apr. 20   Perf. 13¾x14
409 A202 2.50m multi   4.00 4.00

Independence, 10th Anniv. — A203

2002, Apr. 20   Perf. 14x13¾
410 A203 2.50m multi   3.75 3.75

Souvenir Sheet

Sarajevo Fire Fighters — A204

2002, Apr. 20   Perf. 13¾x14
411 A204 2.20m multi   3.50 3.50

Flowers — A205

Designs: 1m, Gentiana dinarica. 1.50m,
Aquilegia dinarica.

2002, Apr. 20 Litho. Perf. 13¾x14
412-413 A205   Set of 2   4.00 4.00

Butterflies — A206

Designs: 1.50m, Parnassus apollo. 2.50m,
Iphiclides podalirius.

2002, Apr. 20 Litho. Perf. 13¾x14
414-415 A206   Set of 2   6.00 6.00

Traditional
Food
A207

2002, June 28 Litho. Perf. 14
416 A207 1.10m multi   1.75 1.75

30th Una
River
Regatta
A208

2002, June 28
417 A208 1.30m multi   2.25 2.25

Souvenir Sheet

Ships — A209

No. 418: a, 1.20m, Galley. b, 1.80m,
Galleon.

2002, June 28
418 A209   Sheet of 2, #a-b   5.00 5.00

Comic Strips Type of 2001
Inscriptions: a, Ako mi se ne javis! b, Ako
me ne volis! c, Ako ti dosadujem! d, Ako me ne
odgovoris! e, Ako me foliras.

2002, June 28
419 A179 40pf Sheet of 5, #a-e   3.50 3.50

Napredak, Croatian
Cultural
Organization,
Cent. — A210

Perf. 13¾x13½
2002, Sept. 14   Litho.
420 A210 1m multi   1.60 1.60

Mountaineering, Cent. — A211

2002, Sept. 14   Perf. 13½x13¾
421 A211 1m multi   1.40 1.40

Sarajevo
Synagogue,
Cent.
A212

2002, Sept. 14
422 A212 2m multi   3.50 3.50

Miniature Sheet

Handicrafts — A213

No. 423: a, 80pf, Ironsmithing. b, 1.10m,
Basketry. c, 1.20m, Filigree. d, 1.30m,
Embroidery.

2002, Oct. 10
423 A213   Sheet of 4, #a-d   7.00 7.00

Bosnia & Herzegovina Flag — A214

2002, Nov. 20
424   A214   1m multi   1.60   1.60

Introduction of Euro Currency in Europe A215

2002, Nov. 20
425   A215   2m multi   3.25   3.25

Campaign Against Drug Abuse — A216

2002, Dec. 10   **Perf. 14**
426   A216   10pf multi   .50   .50

Mother and Child Institute — A217

2002, Dec. 10
427   A217   38pf multi   .95   .95

Mak Dizdar (1917-71), Writer — A218

2002, Dec. 10
428   A218   1m multi   1.75   1.75

Coins — A219

Coins from reign of: 20pf, King Tvrtko (1376-91). 30pf, King Stjepan Tomas (1443-61). 50pf, King Stjepan Tomasevic (1461-63).

2002, Dec. 10
429-431   A219   Set of 3   1.50   1.50

Paintings by Mersad Berber (b. 1940) — A220

Designs: 40pf, Horse's head (34x34mm). 1.10m, Portrait of a woman. 1.50m, Angel statue, two women, horiz.

2002, Dec. 10   **Perf. 13¾ (40pf), 14**
432-434   A220   Set of 3   5.00   5.00

Archbishop Josip Stadler (1843-1918) — A221

2003, Jan. 24   Litho.   Perf. 14
435   A221   50pf multi   .90   .90
No. 435 was sold by the post offices of the Moslem Administration as well as the Croat Administration.

Preporod, Bosnian Cultural Association, Cent. — A222

2003, Feb. 20   Litho.   Perf. 13x13¼
436   A222   1m multi   1.60   1.60
Portions of the design were applied by a thermographic process producing a shiny, raised effect.

2006 European Foresters' Competition in Nordic Skiing, Sarajevo — A223

2003, Feb. 20   **Perf. 13¼x13½**
437   A223   1m multi   1.60   1.60

Mother and Child, by Omer Mujadzic (1903-91) A224

2003, Mar. 31   **Perf. 13¼**
438   A224   70pf multi   1.20   1.20

Svetozar Zimonjic (1928-99), Electrical Engineer — A225

2003, Mar. 31   **Perf. 13½x13¼**
439   A225   90pf multi   1.50   1.50

Bosnian Sitting Volleyball Team, 2002 World Champions — A226

2003, Mar. 31   **Perf. 13½x13**
440   A226   1m multi   1.60   1.60

Flowers — A227

No. 441: a, Leontopodium alpinum (38mm diameter). b, Gentiana symphyandra.

2003, Mar. 31   **Perf. 12¾**
441   A227   90pf Pair, #a-b   3.00   3.00

Europa — A228

2003, May 9   **Perf. 13½x13¼**
442   A228   2.50m multi   4.00   4.00
a.   Booklet pane of 4   16.00
       Complete booklet, #442a   20.00

Visit of Pope John Paul II — A229

Perf. 13¼x13½
2003, June 22   **Litho.**
443   A229   1.50m multi   2.50   2.50

Discovery of Structure of DNA, 50th Anniv. — A230

2003, June 30   **Perf. 13**
444   A230   50pf multi   .90   .90

San Monstruma, Comic Strip by Enki Bilal — A231

Designs: a, Man on roof of building (30x24mm). b, Hotel and street (30x24mm). c, Man and woman (40x26mm). d, Woman and two men (40x26mm).

Perf. 13¼ (#a, b), 13 (#c, d)
2003, June 30
445   A231   50pf Sheet of 4, #a-d   3.50   3.50

Skakavac Waterfall — A232

2003, Sept. 30   Litho.   Perf. 13½
446   A232   1.50m multi   2.50   2.50
Printed in sheets of 8 + 2 labels.

Decorations in Cekrekci Musilhudin Mosque — A233

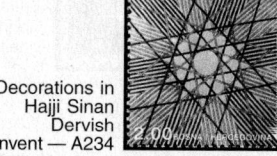

Decorations in Hajji Sinan Dervish Convent — A234

2003, Sept. 30   **Perf. 13¼**
447   A233   1m multi   1.50   1.50
                                Perf. 13¼
448   A234   2m multi   3.50   3.50

Children's Week A235

2003, Oct. 3   **Perf. 13¼x13½**
449   A235   50pf multi   .90   .90
Self-Adhesive
Serpentine Die Cut 12½
450   A235   50pf multi   24.00 24.00

Souvenir Sheet

Pres. Alija Izetbegovic (1925-2003) — A236

2003, Nov. 27   *Perf. 13½x13¼*
451 A236 2m multi   3.50 3.50

Souvenir Sheet

Sarajevo Post Office, by Josip Vancas, 90th Anniv. — A237

2003, Nov. 27   *Perf. 13*
452 A237 3m multi   4.75 4.75

Animals — A238

Designs: 30pf, Rupicapra rupicapra balcanica. 50pf, Ursus arctos bosniensis.

2003, Dec. 9   *Perf. 13¼*
453-454 A238 Set of 2   2.00 2.00

Christmas A239

2003, Dec. 18   Litho.   *Perf. 13¼*
455 A239 20pf multi   .45 .45

Pleminitas II, by Dzevad Hozo — A240

2003, Dec. 18   *Perf. 13½x13¼*
456 A240 10pf multi   .25 .25

Painting by Ibrahim Ljubovic — A241

2003, Dec. 20   *Perf. 12½*
457 A241 1.50m multi   2.50 2.50

Powered Flight, Cent. A242

2003, Dec. 20   *Perf. 13¼x13½*   Litho.
458 A242 1m multi   1.75 1.75

Bayram Festival — A243

2004, Jan. 19   Litho.   *Perf. 13¼*
459 A243 50pf multi   .90 .90

Ban Kulin, 800th Anniv. of Death — A244

2004, Jan. 26   *Perf. 12½*
460 A244 50pf multi   .90 .90

Love A245

2004, Feb. 2   *Perf. 13*
461 A245 2m multi   3.50 3.50

Values are for stamps with surrounding selvage.

Sarajevo Winter Olympics, 20th Anniv. — A246

2004, Feb. 7   *Perf. 13¼*
462 A241 1.50m multi + 2 flanking labels   2.10 2.10

Cities — A247

Designs: 20pf, Jajce, vert. 50pf, Jablanica. 2m, Stolac. 4m, Gradacac, vert. 5m, Fojnica.

2004   *Perf. 13½x13¼, 13¼x13½*
463 A247 20pf multi   .40 .40
464 A247 50pf multi   1.00 1.00
465 A247 2m multi   3.75 3.75
466 A247 4m multi   7.75 7.75
467 A247 5m multi   10.00 10.00
   Nos. 463-467 (5)   22.90 22.90
Issued: 20pf, 50pf, 4/5; 2m, 3/15; 4m, 5m, 2/23.

FIFA (Fédération Internationale de Football Association), Cent. — A248

2004, Mar. 31   *Perf. 13*
468 A248 2m multi   3.50 3.50

Flora — A249

No. 469 — Orchids: a, 1.50m, Cattleya intermedia. b, 2m, Brassavola David Sander.
No. 470 — Succulents: a, 1.50m, Aloe barbadensis. b, 2.50, Carnegiea gigantea.

2004, Mar. 31   *Perf. 13½x13¼*
Vert. Pairs, #a-b
469-470 A249 Set of 2   10.00 10.00

Zodiac Signs — A250

Nos. 471 and 472: a, Aries. b, Taurus. c, Gemini. d, Cancer. e, Leo. f, Virgo. g, Libra. h, Scorpio. i, Sagittarius. j, Capricorn. k, Aquarius. l, Pisces.

2004, Apr. 15   *Perf. 13¼*
471 A250 50pf Sheet of 12, #a-l   9.50 9.50

Booklet Stamps
Self-Adhesive
Serpentine Die Cut 12½

472   Booklet of 12   10.00 10.00
  a.-l. A250 50pf Any single   .75 .75

Europa — A251

No. 473: a, 1m, Clock on skis. b, 1.50m, Clocks at beach.

2004, Apr. 26   *Perf. 13½x13¼*
473 A251 Pair, #a-b   4.00 4.00
  c. Booklet pane, 3 each #473a-473b   12.00 12.00
   Complete booklet, #473c   13.00 13.00

European Youth Peace Summit — A252

2004, Apr. 26   Litho.
474 A252 1.50m multi   2.50 2.50

Greetings — A253

2004, May 15   *Perf. 13*
475   Horiz. pair, #a-b, with alternating labels   3.00 3.00
  a. A253 50pf Clown and balloons   .75 .75
  b. A253 1.50m Bride and groom   2.25 2.25

Souvenir Sheet

Bees — A254

No. 476: a, On flower. b, In flight.

2004, May 15   *Perf. 13x13¼*
476 A254 2m Sheet of 2, #a-b   6.00 6.00

Reconstruction of Old Bridge, Mostar — A255

Old Bridge: 50pf, Close-up. 1m, From distance, horiz.

Perf. 13½x13¼, 13¼x13½
2004, June 23
477-478 A255 Set of 2   2.50 2.50
478a   Souvenir sheet, #477-478,
            perf. 13   2.50 2.50

No. 478a is rouletted in five sections with
stamps which have printer's inscription at bottom, in the central section.

2004 Summer Olympics,
Athens — A256

2004, July 5   *Perf. 13*
479 A256 2m multi   3.50 3.50

10th Sarajevo Film
Festival — A257

2004, July 26   *Perf. 13½x13¼*
480 A257 1.50m multi   2.10 2.10

Cities Type of 2004 and

A258

Designs: 10pf, Brcko. 20pf, Livno, vert. 30pf,
Visoko. 1m, Sanski Most, vert.

2004, Dec. 31   *Litho.*   *Perf. 13*
481 A258 10pf multi   .25   .25
482 A247 20pf multi   .35   .35
483 A258 30pf multi   .40   .40
484 A258 1m multi   1.40 1.40
        Nos. 481-484 (4)   2.40 2.40

The New Year, by
Adin
Hebib — A259

2004, Dec. 31
485 A259 1m multi   1.25 1.25

European Cultural Convention, 50th
Anniv. — A260

2004, Dec. 31
486 A260 1.50m multi   2.50 2.50

Windows,
by Safet
Zec
A261

2004, Dec. 31
487 A261 2m multi   2.75 2.75

Nikola Sop (1904-
82), Poet — A262

2004, Dec. 31
488 A262 3m multi   4.00 4.00

Family
Houses
A263

House of: No. 489, 1m, Svrzo family (blue
denomination). No. 490, 1m, Despic family
(red denomination).

2004, Dec. 31
489-490 A263 Set of 2   2.75 2.75

Chamber
Theater
55,
Sarajevo,
50th
Anniv.
A264

2005, Mar. 7   *Litho.*   *Perf. 13*
491 A264 40pf multi   .65   .65

Jablanica Hydroelectric Plant, 50th
Anniv. — A265

2005, Mar. 7
492 A265 60pf multi   1.10 1.10

Electric Lighting
and Trams in
Sarajevo, 110th
Anniv. — A266

2005, Mar. 7
493 A266 2m multi   3.50 3.50

Izet Kiko Sarajlic (1930-2002),
Poet — A267

2005, Mar. 10
494 A267 1m multi   1.25 1.25

Hasan Kikic (1905-42), Writer — A268

2005, Mar. 10
495 A268 1.50m multi   2.50 2.50

Europa
A269

Designs: No. 496, 2m, Baklava (denomination in black). No. 497, 2m, Stuffed onions
(denomination in white).

2005, Apr. 20
496-497 A269 Set of 2   6.50 6.50
    a.   Souvenir sheet, #496-497 6.50 6.50

Roses — A270

Designs: 80pf, Rosa damascena. 1.20m,
Rosa alba.

2005, Apr. 20   *Litho.*   *Perf. 13*
498-499 A270 Set of 2   3.50 3.50

Fauna
A271

Designs: 2m, Tetrao urogalius. 3m, Castor
fiber.

2005, Apr. 20   *Litho.*   *Perf. 13*
500-501 A271 Set of 2   8.50 8.50

Nos. 500-501 each printed in sheets of 8 + 2
labels.

Mediterranean
Games, Almería,
Spain — A272

2005, May 20   *Litho.*   *Perf. 13*
502 A272 1m multi   1.75 1.75

Sarajevo
Music
Academy,
50th
Anniv.
A273

2005, May 31
503 A273 1m multi   1.75 1.75

Friendship
Between
Sarajevo
and Doha,
Qatar
A274

2005, June 30
504 A274 2m multi   2.75 2.75
        See Qatar No. 1000.

Srebrenica
Massacre, 10th
Anniv. — A275

2005, July 1   *Litho.*   *Perf. 13*
505 A275 1m multi   1.75 1.75

Mail
Services
A276

Running mailman with letter and: 10pf, Mail
van, EMS emblem. 20pf, Printing press. 30pf,
Text. 50pf, Bosnia & Herzegovina #327.

2005, Sept. 1
506 A276 10pf multi   .25   .25
507 A276 20pf multi   .40   .40
508 A276 30pf multi   .50   .50
509 A276 50pf multi   .80   .80
        Nos. 506-509 (4)   1.95 1.95

Fruit — A277

Designs: 1m, Pyrus communis. 1.50m,
Orange carica. 2m, Ficus carica. 2.50m,
Prunus domestica. 5m, Prunus avium.

2005, Sept. 1
510 A277 1m multi   1.75 1.75
511 A277 1.50m multi   2.60 2.60
512 A277 2m multi   3.50 3.50
513 A277 2.50m multi   4.50 4.50
514 A277 5m multi   8.50 8.50
        Nos. 510-514 (5)   20.85 20.85

Aladza Mosque,
Foca — A278

2005, Sept. 15   Litho.   Perf. 13
515 A278 1m multi   1.75 1.75

Zitomislici
Moanastery,
Mostar — A279

2005, Sept. 15
516 A279 1m multi   1.75 1.75

St. Mark the Evangelist Monastery,
Plehan — A280

2005, Sept. 15
517 A280 1m multi   1.75 1.75

The Bay, by Hakija
Kulenovic (1905-
87) — A281

2005, Sept. 15
518 A281 2m multi   3.50 3.50

Souvenir Sheet

Cartoon Characters — A282

No. 502: a, Girl and dogs. b, Windsurfing
hedgehog.

2005, Sept. 15
519 A282 50pf Sheet of 2, #a-b   1.75 1.75

Trade Unions in
Bosnia &
Herzegovina,
Cent. — A283

2005, Sept. 15   Litho.   Perf. 13
520 A283 1m multi   1.75 1.75

Bogomil
Culture
A284

Designs: No. 521, 50pf, Ban Kulin (1180-
1203). No. 522, 50pf, King Tvrtko I Kotromanic
(1353-91). 1m, Stone carving of Bogomil burning at stake. 2m, Bull of Pope Eugene IV.

2005, Oct. 10   Perf. 13¾x13¼
521-524 A284 Set of 4   6.50 6.50

2004 Exhibition at
Bosniac Institute,
Istanbul — A285

Designs: 70pf, Exhibit hall. 4m, Entryway
and exhibits.

2005, Nov. 15   Perf. 13
525-526 A285 Set of 2   7.50 7.50
Nos. 525-526 each printed in sheets of 8 + 2
labels.

Dayton Peace
Accords, 10th
Anniv. — A286

2005, Nov. 21   Perf. 13¾x13¼
527 A286 1.50m multi   2.50 2.50
Printed in sheets of 8 + label.

End of World
War II, 60th
Anniv. — A287

2005, Nov. 25
528 A287 1m multi   1.75 1.75

Europa
Stamps,
50th
Anniv. (in
2006)
A288

No. 529: a, Flags and Western Hemisphere.
b, Flags and Eastern Hemisphere. c, Map of
Europe and 1-euro coin. d, Stars and chess
organization emblems.

2005, Nov. 30   Perf. 13
529   Horiz. strip of 4   18.00 18.00
a.-d. A288 3m Any single   4.00 4.00
e.   Souvenir sheet, #529a-529d   18.00 18.00
No. 529e exists imperf. Value $30.

World
Vision — A289

2005, Dec. 3   Perf. 13¾x13¼
530 A289 50pf multi   1.60 1.60

Souvenir Sheet

2006 Winter Olympics, Turin — A290

No. 531: a, 1m, Skiing. b, 2m, Speed
skating.

2006, Feb. 1   Litho.   Perf. 13
531 A290 Sheet of 2, #a-b   5.00 5.00

Tourism
A291

Designs: No. 532, 1m, Treskavica, Trnovo.
No. 533, 1m, Raft in water, Gorazde, vert.

Perf. 13¼x13¾, 13¾x13¼
2006, Mar. 10
532-533 A291 Set of 2   3.50 3.50

Souvenir Sheet

Automobiles — A292

No. 534: a, 50pf, 1935 Mercedes-Benz 500k
Cabriolet B. b, 50pf, 1939 Dodge D11 Graber

Cabriolet. c, 1m, 1929, Mercedes-Benz SS
Schwarzer. d, 2m, 1939 Bugatti T57 Ventoux.

2006, Apr. 5   Perf. 13
534 A292 Sheet of 4, #a-d   7.00 7.00

Europa
A293

Designs: No. 535, 2m, Upper arc of circle,
denomination at left. No. 536, 2m, Lower arc
of circle, denomination at right.

2006, Apr. 5   Perf. 13
535-536 A293 Set of 2   7.00 7.00
536a   Souvenir sheet, #535-536   7.00 7.00

Fauna and
Fungi — A294

Designs: 1.50m, Formica rufa. 3m,
Sarcosphaera crassa.

2006, Apr. 20   Perf. 13¾x13¼
537-538 A294 Set of 2   7.50 7.50

Prisoners of War Association, 10th
Anniv. — A295

2006, May 9   Perf. 13¼x13¾
539 A295 1m multi   1.75 1.75

Bosnia & Herzegovina Art Gallery,
60th Anniv. — A296

2006, May 20   Perf. 13
540 A296 1m multi   1.75 1.75

Isak Samokovlija (1889-1955), Writer,
and Samuel, the Porter — A297

2006, May 20
541 A297 1m multi   1.75 1.75

Academicians — A298

Designs: No. 542, 1m, Muhamed Kadic (1906-83). No. 543, 1m, Mustafa Kamaric (1906-73).

2006, May 20	Litho.	Perf. 13
542-543 A298	Set of 2	3.50 3.50

Sarajevo Soccer Team, 60th Anniv. A299

2006, June 10	Litho.	Perf. 13½
544 A299	1m multi	1.75 1.75
a.	Booklet pane of 2	4.50 4.50

A circle of perforations is in the middle of the stamp.

2006 World Cup Soccer Championships, Germany — A300

2006, June 10		
545 A300	3m multi	5.00 5.00
a.	Booklet pane of 2	10.00 10.00
	Complete booklet, #544a, 545a	15.00

A circle of perforations is in the middle of the stamp.

49th European Junior Table Tennis Championships A301

2006, July 5		Perf. 13
546 A301	1m multi	1.75 1.75

Breza Basilica Archaeological Site — A302

2006, Sept. 10		Perf. 13¼x13¾
547 A302	1m multi	1.75 1.75

Semiz Ali Pasha's Mosque, Praca — A303

2006, Sept. 10		Perf. 13¾x13¼
548 A303	1m multi	1.75 1.75

Souvenir Sheet

Cartoon Characters From "Ptice Kao Mi" — A304

No. 549: a, Red bird. b, Yellow bird.

2006, Sept. 10		Litho.
549 A304	50pf Sheet of 2, #a-b	1.75 1.75

Vegetables — A305

Designs: 10pf, Potatoes (Solanum tuberosum). 20pf, Cauliflower (Brassica oleracea var. botrytis). 30pf, Savoy cabbage (Brassica oleracea var. sabauda). 40pf, Cabbage (Brassica oleracea var. capitata). 50pf, Garlic (Allium sativum). 1m, Carrots (Dauctus carota).

2006, Mar.	Litho.	Perf. 13½x13¾
550 A305	10pf multi	.25 .25
551 A305	20pf multi	.35 .35
552 A305	30pf multi	.50 .50
553 A305	40pf multi	.85 .85
554 A305	50pf multi	.95 .95
555 A305	1m multi	1.75 1.75
	Nos. 550-555 (6)	4.65 4.65

Wild Animals A306

Designs: 1.50m, Lepus europaeus. 2m, Capreolus capreolus. 2.50m, Anas sp., horiz. 4m, Vulpes vulpes. 5m, Canis lupus, horiz.

Perf. 13¾x13¼, 13¼x13¾

2006, June 30		
556 A306	1.50m multi	2.50 2.50
557 A306	2m multi	3.25 3.25
558 A306	2.50m multi	4.00 4.00
559 A306	4m multi	6.50 6.50
560 A306	5m multi	8.00 8.00
	Nos. 556-560 (5)	24.25 24.25

Each stamp printed in sheets of 8 + label.

Children's Week — A307

2006, Oct. 6		Die Cut
Self-Adhesive		
561 A307	50pf multi	.90 .90

Elci Ibrahim-Pasha Madrassa, Travnik, 300th Anniv. — A308

2006, Oct. 25		Perf. 13¼x13¾
562 A308	1m multi	1.75 1.75

Tuzla University, 30th Anniv. — A309

2006, Oct. 25		Perf. 13¾x13¼
563 A309	1m multi	1.75 1.75

Nobel Laureates A310

Designs: 1m, Vladimir Prelog (1906-98), 1975 Chemistry laureate. 2.50m, Ivo Andric (1892-1975), 1961 Literature laureate.

2006, Oct. 25		
564-565 A310	Set of 2	5.50 5.50

Museum Exhibits — A311

2006, Nov. 24		Perf. 13
566 A311	1m multi	1.75 1.75

Trains A312

Designs: 50pf, Steam locomotive. 1m, Electric train.

2006, Nov. 24		Litho.
567-568 A312	Set of 2	2.50 2.50

Sarajevo National Opera, 60th Anniv. — A313

2007, Feb. 15		Perf. 13¾x13¼
569 A313	50pf multi	.90 .90

Prokos Lake A314

2007, Feb. 15		Perf. 13¼x13¾
570 A314	2.50m multi	4.00 4.00

Europa A315

Scouts and: No. 571, 2m, Backpacks. No. 572, 2m. Tent and campfire.

2007, Feb. 15		Perf. 13
571-572 A315	Set of 2	7.00 7.00
572a	Souvenir sheet, #571-572 + 2 labels	7.00 7.00
572b	Booklet pane, 2 each #571-572 + label	15.00 —
	Complete booklet, #572b	15.00

Scouting, cent. Nos. 571-572 each were printed in sheets of 8 + label.

Domesticated Animals — A316

Designs: 10pf, Ovis aries. 20pf, Capra hircus. 30pf, Bos taurus. 40pf, Equus asinus. 70pf, Equus caballus. 1m, Felis silvestris.

2007, Jan. 31	Litho.	Perf. 13
573 A316	10pf multi	.25 .25
574 A316	20pf multi	.30 .30
575 A316	30pf multi	.50 .50
576 A316	40pf multi	.75 .75

	Perf. 13¼x13¾	
	Size: 40x33mm	
577 A316	70pf multi	1.25 1.25
578 A316	1m multi	1.60 1.60
	Nos. 573-578 (6)	4.65 4.65

Nos. 573-578 each printed in sheets of 8 + label.

Knautia Travnicensis A317

Sciurus Vulgaris A318

2007, Mar. 15		Perf. 13
579 A317	80pf multi	1.25 1.25
580 A318	1.20m multi	2.25 2.25

Nos. 579-580 each printed in sheets of 8 + label.

Kozarac
A319

2007, Mar. 15   *Perf. 13¾x13¼*
581 A319 1m multi   1.75 1.75

Dr. Abdulah Nakas Hospital, 140th Anniv. A320

2007, Apr. 10   *Perf. 13¼x13¾*
582 A320 1.50m sil & maroon   2.50 2.50

Madrassa, Cazin, 140th Anniv. — A321

2007, Apr. 10   *Perf. 13*
583 A321 2m multi   3.50 3.50

Fountain, Tuzla — A322

Fountain, Mostar A323

Fountain, Sanski Most — A324

Fountain, Sarajevo A325

Fountain Near Bey's Mosque A326

Perf. 13¾x13¼, 13¼x13¾
2007, Apr. 10
584 A322 1.50m multi   2.25 2.25
585 A323 2m multi   3.00 3.00
586 A324 2.50m multi   4.00 4.00
587 A325 4m multi   6.25 6.25
588 A326 5m multi   7.50 7.50
    Nos. 584-588 (5)   23.00 23.00
Nos. 584-588 each printed in sheets of 8 + label.

Gajret Newspaper, Cent. — A327

2007, Apr. 16   *Perf. 13*
589 A327 1m multi   1.75 1.75

Gazi Husrev-Begova Library — A328

2007, Apr. 16
590 A328 1.50m multi   2.50 2.50

Islamic Sciences Faculty, Sarajevo, 30th Anniv. A329

2007, Apr. 16
591 A329 2m multi   3.50 3.50

Pocitelj Art Colony A330

2007, May 4   Litho.   *Perf. 13¼x13¾*
592 A330 1m multi   1.75 1.75

Painting by Ismet Rizvic A331

2007, May 4   Litho.   *Perf. 13*
593 A331 1.50m multi   2.50 2.50

Bear Figurine, 3500 B.C. A332

2007, June 1   *Perf. 13¼x13¾*
594 A332 1m multi   1.75 1.75

Karel Parik (1857-1942), Architect — A333

2007, June 6   *Perf. 13*
595 A333 2.50m multi   4.00 4.00

Karate — A334

2007, July 2   Litho.   *Perf. 13*
596 A334 1m multi   1.50 1.50

Zulfikar Zuko Dzumhur (1920-89), Cartoonist A335

2007, July 2
597 A335 1m multi   1.75 1.75

Sarajevo University Medical Faculty, 61st Anniv. A336

2007, July 2
598 A336 1m multi   1.75 1.75

Sepp Blatter, Fédération Internationale de Football Association (FIFA) President — A337

Juan Antonio Samaranch, Former Pres. of Intl. Olympic Committee — A338

Perf. 13¼x13¾
2007, Sept. 20   **Litho.**
599 A337 2m multi   3.50 3.50
600 A338 2m multi   3.50 3.50
Honorary Ambassadors of Sport and Culture of Peace.

Fortress, Samobor A339

Perf. 13¾x13¼
2007, Sept. 28   **Litho.**
601 A339 1m multi   1.75 1.75

Ecology A340

Children's art by: No. 602, 50pf, Amira Halilovic. No. 603, 50pf, Maida Hasanic.

2007, Sept. 28   *Perf. 13*
602-603 A340 Set of 2   1.75 1.75
603a   Souvenir sheet, #602-603 1.75 1.75

Meat Pie A341

2007, Oct. 1   *Perf. 13½*
604 A341 2m multi   3.50 3.50
Values are for stamps with surrounding selvage.

Stegosaurus — A342

2007, Nov. 15   *Perf. 13¼x13¾*
605 A342 2m multi   3.50 3.50

Space Flight of Dog, Laika, on Sputnik 2, 50th Anniv. — A343

2007, Nov. 15   *Perf. 13¾x13¼*
606 A343 3m multi   5.00 5.00

Bosnian University Sports Association, 60th Anniv. — A344

2007, Dec. 3   *Perf. 13*
607 A344 50pf multi   .90   .90
Printed in sheets of 4.

Bosnian Handball Team, 60th Anniv. — A345

2007, Dec. 31
608 A345 50pf multi   .90   .90

Merhamet Charitable Organization, 95th Anniv. — A346

2008, Feb. 15
609 A346 70pf multi   1.20 1.20

Europa A347

Designs: 2m, Letter, candle, quill pen. 3m, Person writing on postcard.

2008, Mar. 8 Litho. *Perf. 13½x13¾*
610-611 A347 Set of 2   8.50 8.50
611a Souvenir sheet, #610-611   8.50 8.50

University of Sarajevo College of Pharmacy — A348

2008, Feb. 15 Litho. *Perf. 13*
612 A348 2m multi   3.50 3.50

Local Cuisine A349

Designs: 1m, Shishkebabs. 2m, Apple stuffed with whipped cream.

2008, Feb. 15   *Perf. 13¼x13¾*
613-614 A349 Set of 2   5.00 5.00
Nos. 613-614 each were printed in sheets of 8 + label.

Blood Transfusion Institute, Sarajevo, 50th Anniv. A350

2008, Mar. 8   *Perf. 13*
615 A350 1.50m multi   2.50 2.50

Intl. Women's Day — A351

2008, Mar. 8
616 A351 2m multi   3.50 3.50
Printed in sheets of 8 + label.

Bosanska Krupa — A352

Velika Kladusa A353

2008, Mar. 8
617 A352 70pf multi   1.25 1.25
618 A353 1m multi   1.75 1.75
Nos. 617-618 each were printed in sheets of 8 + label.

Sarajevo Shooting Club, 60th Anniv. A354

2008, Apr. 10
619 A354 1.50m multi   2.50 2.50

Universal Esperanto Association, Cent. — A355

2008, Apr. 10
620 A355 1.50m multi   2.50 2.50

2008 Summer Olympics, Beijing A356

Designs: 1m, Judo. 1.50m, Track and field.

2008, May 5   *Perf. 13¾x13¼*
621-622 A356 Set of 2   3.50 3.50
Nos. 621-622 each were printed in sheets of 8 + label.

Motorcycles A357

Designs: No. 623, 1.50m, Jawa Trail 90. No. 624, 1.50m, Ural-3.

2008, May 5   *Perf. 13*
623-624 A357 Set of 2   4.50 4.50

Vjetrenica Cave A358

2008, June 10   Litho.
625 A358 1m multi   1.75 1.75

Stabilization and Association Agreement with European Union — A359

2008, June 16
626 A359 70pf multi   1.20 1.20

Krivaja House, Zavidovici A360

2008, July 1   *Perf. 13¾x13¼*
627 A360 2.50m multi   4.00 4.00

Pond Flora and Fauna A361

Designs: 1.50m, Nymphaea alba. 2m, Rana esculenta.

2008, July 1   *Perf. 13*
628-629 A361 Set of 2   6.00 6.00
Nos. 628-629 each were printed in sheets of 9 + label.

Musalla, Kamengrad A362

Ostrovica A363

2008, July 11
630 A362 1m multi   1.75 1.75
631 A363 1.50m multi   2.50 2.50

Turritella Turris Fossil Shell A364

2008, Sept. 1   *Perf. 13¼x13¾*
632 A364 1.50m multi   2.50 2.50
Printed in sheets of 8 + label.

Friendship Between Bosnia and Herzegovina and Kuwait — A365

2008, Sept. 9   *Perf. 13*
633 A365 3m multi   5.00 5.00

Sarajevo Ski Club, 80th Anniv. A366

2008, Nov. 1   *Perf. 13¼x13¾*
634 A366 2m multi   3.50 3.50
Printed in sheets of 8 + label.

Fauna — A367

Designs: 5pf, Lynx lynx. 70pf, Accipiter gentilis. 5m, Strigiformes.

2008, Dec. 15   *Perf. 13¾x13¼*
635-637 A367 Set of 3   7.50 7.50

Douglas
Fir
A368

Birch
A369

Cypress
A370

2008, Dec. 15   *Perf. 13¼x13¾*
638 A368 70c multi   .90 .90
639 A369 70c multi   .90 .90
640 A370 70c multi   .90 .90
     Nos. 638-640 (3)   2.70 2.70

Europa
A371

Designs: 2m, Planets. 3m, Space telescope.

2009, Sept. 10   Litho.   *Perf. 13*
641-642 A371   Set of 2   8.50 8.50
642a   Souvenir sheet of 2,
     #641-642, + 2 labels   8.50 8.50
     Intl. Year of Astronomy.

Intl. Day of
Missing
Persons
A372

2009, Aug. 30   Litho.   *Perf. 13*
643 A372 20pf multi   .40 .40

Hirundo
Rustica
A373

2009, Sept. 10   *Perf. 13¼x13*
644 A373 70pf multi   1.20 1.20
   Printed in sheets of 8 + label.

Historical Archives of Sarajevo
Museum — A374

2009, Sept. 10   *Perf. 13*
645 A374 70pf multi   1.10 1.10

Academic Culture Center of Sarajevo
University, 60th Anniv. — A375

2009, Sept. 10   *Perf. 13¼x13*
646 A375 1m multi   1.50 1.50

Council of Europe,
60th
Anniv. — A376

2009, Sept. 10   *Perf. 13x13¼*
647 A376 1m multi   1.50 1.50

Sarajevo
Museum, 60th
Anniv.
A377

2009, Sept. 10   *Perf. 13*
648 A377 1m multi   1.50 1.50

Bosnian
Coffee — A378

2009, Sept. 10   Litho.
649 A378 1m multi   1.50 1.50
   Printed in sheets of 8 + label.

Charles Darwin (1809-82),
Naturalist — A379

2009, Sept. 10   *Perf. 13¼x13*
650 A379 2m multi   3.50 3.50

World Track and Field Championships,
Berlin — A380

Designs: 1.50m, Runners. 2m, Stylized
runners.

2009, Sept. 10
651-652 A380   Set of 2   5.50 5.50
652a   Souvenir sheet, #651-652   5.50 5.50

Children's
Week
A381

2009, Oct. 1   *Perf. 13*
653 A381 70pf multi   1.20 1.20

Pansies
A382

2009, Oct. 9   *Perf. 13¼x13*
654 A382 1m multi   1.50 1.50
   Printed in sheets of 8 + label.

Sarajevo
Canton
Tribunal,
130th
Anniv.
A383

2009, Oct. 9   *Perf. 13*
655 A383 1m multi   1.75 1.75

Postal Cooperation Between Bosnia &
Herzegovina and Turkey — A384

2009, Oct. 9
656 A384 2m multi   2.90 2.90
    See Turkey No. 3191.

Strawberries — A385

2009, Oct. 9
657 A385 5m multi   8.50 8.50

Franciscan Theological College,
Sarajevo, Cent. — A386

2009, Dec. 7   Litho.
658 A386 1m multi   1.50 1.50
   Printed in sheets of 8 + label.

Franciscan
Order, 800th
Anniv.
A387

2009, Dec. 7
659 A387 1.50m multi   2.25 2.25
   Printed in sheets of 8 + label.

Sign
Language
A388

2009, Dec. 7   *Perf. 13¼x13*
660 A388 1.50m multi   2.50 2.50

Souvenir Sheet

2010 Winter Olympics,
Vancouver — A389

   No. 661: a, 1.50m, Skier, ski jumper, speed
skater, ice hockey players, biathlete. b, 2m,
Figure skater, snowboarder, ice hockey player,
bobsledders.

2010, Feb. 12   *Perf. 13x13¼*
661 A389   Sheet of 2, #a-b   6.00 6.00

Old City,
Srebrenik
A390

Ostrozac
Castle
A391

2010, Mar. 22   *Perf. 13*
662 A390 70pf multi   1.25 1.25
663 A391 1m multi   1.75 1.75
   Nos. 662-663 each were printed in sheets of
8 + label.

Taxus
Baccata
A392

Aesculus Hippocastanum — A393

Cygnus Olor — A394

2010, Apr. 12　　Litho.　　Perf. 13
664　A392　1m multi　　　　　1.75　1.75
665　A393　1m multi　　　　　1.75　1.75
Souvenir Sheet
666　A394　2m multi　　　　　3.50　3.50
Nos. 664-665 each were printed in sheets of 8 + label.

Folk Ballad "Hasanaganica" — A395

2010, Apr. 26　　　　Perf. 13¼x13
667　A395　1m multi　　　　　1.50　1.50
Printed in sheets of 8 + label.

Europa — A396

No. 668: a, 1m, Dragon. b, 1.50m, Little Blu (knight).

2010, Apr. 26　　　　Perf. 13x13¼
668　A396　Horiz. pair, #a-b　　4.50　4.50
c.　　Souvenir sheet #668a-668b　4.50　4.50
d.　　Booklet pane, 3 each #668a-
　　　668b, perf. 13x13¼ on 2 or
　　　3 sides　　　　　　　　13.50　—
　　　Complete booklet, #668d　14.00

Ajvatovica, 500th Anniv. — A397

2010, June 15　　　　Perf. 13
669　A397　1.50m multi　　　2.50　2.50

Robert Schumann (1810-56), Composer — A398

Frédéric Chopin (1810-49), Composer — A399

2010, Oct. 18　Litho.　Perf. 13¼x13
670　A398　1m multi　　　　　1.50　1.50
671　A399　1.50m multi　　　2.50　2.50
Nos. 670-671 each were printed in sheets of 8 + label.

Europa — A400

No. 672 — Tree with denomination at: a, Upper left. b, Upper right.

2011, May 9　　　　Perf. 13x13¼
672　A400　2.50m Horiz. pair,
　　　　　#a-b　　　　　　　7.00　7.00
c.　　Souvenir sheet, #672a-672b　7.00　7.00
d.　　Booklet pane of 6, 3 each
　　　#672a-672b, perf. 13x13¼
　　　on 2 or 3 sides　　　　21.00　—
Intl. Year of Forests. No. 672d was sold with, but not attached to, a booklet cover.

Gentiana
Jasnae
A401

Passer Domesticus — A402

2011, May 26　　　　Perf. 13
673　A401　2m multi　　　　　3.25　3.25
Souvenir Sheet
674　A402　2.50m multi　　　4.00　4.00
No. 673 was printed in sheets of 8 + label.

Apparition of the Virgin Mary at Medjugorje, 30th Anniv. — A403

Litho. With Foil Application
2011, May 26
675　A403　2.50m multi　　　3.75　3.75
Printed in sheets of 8 + label.

Souvenir Sheet

First Man in Space, 50th Anniv. — A404

2011, May 26　　　　Litho.
676　A404　2m multi　　　　　3.00　3.00

Arms of Duke Stjepan Vukcic Kosaca (1404-66)
A405

2011, June 6　Litho.　Perf. 13¼x13
677　A405　1m multi　　　　　1.40　1.40
Printed in sheets of 8 + label.

Campaign Against AIDS, 30th Anniv. — A406

2011, June 6　　　　Litho.　　Perf. 13
678　A406　70pf multi　　　　1.00　1.00

Hutovo Blato Nature Park — A407

2011, Sept. 20
679　A407　70pf multi　　　　.90　.90
No. 679 was printed in sheets of 8 + label.

Astacus
Astacus
A408

2011, Sept. 20
680　A408　1.50m multi　　　2.10　2.10
No. 680 was printed in sheets of 8 + label.

Writers
A409

Designs: 1m, Skender Kulenovic (1910-78). 1.50m, Mesa Selimovic (1910-82).

2011, Oct. 7　　　　Perf. 13¼x13
681-682　A409　Set of 2　　　3.50　3.50
Nos. 681-682 each were printed in sheets of 8 + label.

Fridtjof Nansen (1861-1930), Polar Explorer and Diplomat — A410

2011, Oct. 25　　　　Perf. 13x13¼
683　A410　1.50m multi　　　2.25　2.25
Souvenir Sheet

Sinking of the Titanic, Cent. — A411

2012, May 29　　Litho.　　Perf. 13
684　A411　2.50m multi　　　3.75　3.75
Souvenir Sheet

Locomotives — A412

No. 685: a, 1m, Locomotive 55-99. b, 1.50m, Locomotive 83-180.

2012, May 29　　　　Perf. 13¼x13
685　A412　Sheet of 2, #a-b　3.75　3.75

Europa — A413

No. 686: a, Sarajevo. b, Mountains, waterfalls, rowboat, monument.

2012, May 29　　　　Perf. 13x13¼
686　A413　2.50m Horiz. pair, #a-
　　　　　b　　　　　　　　7.50　7.50
c.　　Souvenir sheet of 2, #686a-
　　　686b　　　　　　　　7.50　7.50
d.　　Booklet pane of 6, 3 each
　　　#686a-686b, perf. 13x13¼
　　　on 2 or 3 sides　　　　22.50　—
　　　Complete booklet, #686d　22.50

Miniature Sheet

Flowers — A414

No. 687: a, Three Viola odorata. b, Two Primula veris. c, Two Helleborus. d, Two Galanthus. e, Two Crocus sativa. f, Viola odorata and bubbles. g, Cluster of Primula veris and leaves. h, Two Helleborus and leaves. i, Two Galanthus and rock crystal. j, Crocus sativa and rock crystal.

2012, June 7   *Perf. 13*
687   A414 70pf Sheet of 10,
    #a-j   10.00 10.00

Rustempasic Castle, Bugojno — A415

2012, June 22
688   A415 2m multi   3.00 3.00
   Printed in sheets of 8 + label.

Old Sections of Cities
A416

No. 689: a, Tesanj. b, Buzim.

2012, June 25   *Perf. 13¼x13*
689   A416 20pf Vert. pair, #a-b   .70 .70

Sports
A417

2012, July 10   *Perf. 13x13¼*
690   A417 2.50m multi   3.75 3.75
   Printed in sheets of 8 + label.

La Benevolencia Jewish Organization, 120th Anniv. — A418

2012, Sept. 10   *Perf. 13*
691   A418 70pf multi   1.10 1.10
   No. 691 was printed in sheets of 8 + label.

Snakes — A419

Designs: 1m, Vipera ammodytes. 1.50m, Vipera berus bosniensis.

2012, Sept. 10
692-693 A419   Set of 2   4.00 4.00
   Nos. 692-693 each were printed in sheets of 8 + label.

Children's Week
A420

2012, Oct. 1
694   A420 70pf multi   1.10 1.10
   Printed in sheets of 8 + label.

Intorduction of Euro Currency in Europe, 10th Anniv. — A421

2012, Oct. 1
695   A421 2m multi   3.00 3.00

Marine Life
A422

No. 696: a, Various fish. b, Seahorse and fish. c, Sstarfish. d, Crab and fish. e, Jellyfish and fish.

2012, Nov. 27
696   Horiz. strip of 5   5.75 5.75
   a.-e. A422 70pf Any single   1.10 1.10

Souvenir Sheet

Insects — A423

No. 697: a, Chorthippus brunneus. b, Tibicen linnei.

2013, Mar. 15
697   A423 2.50m Sheet of 2, #a-b 7.50 7.50

Old City, Kljuc — A424

2013, Mar. 20
698   A424 70pf multi   1.50 1.50

Europa — A425

No. 699 — Postal van: a, Facing left. b, Facing right.

2013, May 9   *Perf. 13¼x13*
699   A425 2.50m Horiz. pair, #a-b   7.50 7.50
   c.   Souvenir sheet of 2, #699a-699b   7.50 7.50
   d.   Booklet pane of 6, 3 each #699a-699b, perf. 13¼x13 on 2 or 3 sides   22.50

No. 699d was sold with, but unattached to, a booklet cover.

Composers
A426

Designs: No. 700, 2m, Giuseppe Verdi (1813-1901). No. 701, 2m, Richard Wagner (1813-83).

2013, May 22   *Serpentine Die Cut 11 Self-Adhesive*
700-701 A426   Set of 2   6.00 6.00
   Nos. 700-701 were printed in sheets of 8 + central label.

17th Mediterranean Games, Mersin, Turkey — A427

2013, June 20   *Perf. 13*
702   A427 1m multi   1.50 1.50

Friends of Nature Postal Workers Lodge, 60th Anniv.
A428

2013, July 29   *Litho.*   *Perf. 13*
703   A428 70pf multi   .95 .95

Architecture — A429

No. 704: a, Velagicevina guest house, Blagaj. b, Guest house, Fojnica.

2013, July 29   *Litho.*   *Perf. 13*
704   A429 90pf Horiz. pair, #a-b 2.50 2.50

Souvenir Sheet

Seventh World Paragliding Accuracy Championships, Bjelasnica — A430

2013, July 29   *Litho.*   *Perf. 13*
705   A430 1.50m multi   2.10 2.10

Flowers — A431

No. 706: a, Sage (kadulja). b, Acacia (bagrem). c, Dandelion (maslacak). d, Linden (lipa). e, Heather (vrijesak).

2013, Sept. 25   *Litho.*   *Perf. 13¼x13*
706   Horiz. strip of 5   .70 .70
   a.-e. A431 10pf Any single   .25 .25

Winning Design in Children's Art Contest on Theme of Water Conservation
A432

2013, Oct. 9   *Litho.*   *Perf. 13x13¼*
707   A432 1.50m multi   2.10 2.10

QR Code — A433

2013, Oct. 9   *Litho.*   *Perf. 13*
708   A433 1.70m multi   2.40 2.40
   Bosnia & Herzegovina Postal Service, 20th anniv.

Statute for First Automobile Club in Bosnia & Herzegovina, Cent. — A434

2013, Nov. 25   *Litho.*   *Perf. 13*
709   A434 1.50m multi   2.10 2.10

Reconstruction of Sarajevo City Hall — A435

2014, May 9   *Litho.*   *Perf. 13x13¼*
710   A435 1.70m multi   2.40 2.40

William Shakespeare (1564-1616), Writer — A436

2014, May 9   *Litho.*   *Perf. 13*
711   A436 2m multi   2.75 2.75
   No. 711 was printed in sheets of 8 + central label.

Sarajevo in Winter, by Fuad Arifhodzic (1914-2008) — A437

2014, May 9   Litho.   Perf. 13¼x13
712 A437 2.50m multi   3.50 3.50
No. 712 was printed in sheets of 8 + central label.

Souvenir Sheet

Paeonia Officinalis — A438

2014, May 9   Litho.   Perf. 13
713 A438 1.50m multi   2.10 2.10

Europa — A439

No. 714 — Sheet music and: a, Accordion. b, Violin and tambourine.

2014, May 9   Litho.   Perf. 13¼x13
714 A439 2.50m Horiz. pair, #a-b   7.00 7.00
c.   Souvenir sheet of 2, 714a-714b   7.00 7.00
d.   Booklet pane of 6, 3 each
      #714a-714b, perf. 13¼x13
      on 2 or 3 sides   21.00 —
No. 714d was sold with, but unattached to, a booklet cover.

Houses of Worship — A440

Designs: 5pf, St. Anthony of Padua Church, Bihac. 10pf, Sava Atik Mosque, Brcko. 20pf, Mosque, Velika Kladusa. 30pf, Synagogue, Zenica. 40pf, Temple of Prophet St. Elias, Maglaj. 50pf, Sultan Mehmid Fatih Mosque, Kraljeva Sutjeska. 2.70m, Heart of Jesus Catholic Cathedral, Sarajevo. 4m, Serbian Orthodox Cathedral, Sarajevo.

2014   Litho.   Perf. 13¼x13
715 A440   5pf black & gray   .25   .25
716 A440   10pf multi   .25   .25
717 A440   20pf multi   .30   .30
718 A440   30pf multi   .40   .40
719 A440   40pf multi   .55   .55
720 A440   50pf multi   .70   .70
721 A440   2.70m multi   3.75 3.75
722 A440   4m multi   5.50 5.50
      Nos. 715-722 (8)   11.70 11.70

Issued: 5pf, 5/9; 20pf, 5/26; others, 7/31.

Aleksa Santic (1868-1924), Poet — A441

2014, May 26   Litho.   Perf. 13
723 A441 90c multi   1.25 1.25

Safvet-beg Basagic (1870-1934), Writer — A442

2014, July 31   Litho.   Perf. 13
724 A442 70pf multi   1.00 1.00

Wind Generators A443

2014, July 31   Litho.   Perf. 13
725 A443 1.10m multi   1.50 1.50

Bijambare Cave A444

2014, July 31   Litho.   Perf. 13¼x13
726 A444 3m multi   4.25 4.25

Rubber Duck — A445

2014, Aug. 20   Litho.   Perf. 13
727 A445 1m multi   1.40 1.40
Cinematography in Bosnia & Herzegovina.

Dzebarska Mosque, Zivinice A446

2014, Aug. 20   Litho.   Perf. 13x13¼
728 A446 1.30m multi   1.75 1.75

Cyphonethes Tajanus — A447

2014, Sept. 10   Litho.   Perf. 13
729 A447 90pf multi   1.25 1.25
No. 729 was printed in sheets of 9 + label.

Children's Art A448

2014, Oct. 9   Litho.   Perf. 13¼x13
730 A448 90pf multi   1.25 1.25

Zepce A449

2014, Oct. 14   Litho.   Perf. 13¼x13
731 A449 1m multi   1.40 1.40

Hrustovo Cave A450

2014, Nov. 20   Litho.   Perf. 13
732 A450 1.50m multi   3.00 3.00

National Handball Team A451

2015, Feb. 17   Litho.   Perf. 13
733 A451 2m multi   2.75 2.75

Souvenir Sheet

Coccinellidae — A452

2015, Feb. 27   Litho.   Perf. 13
734 A452 2m multi   2.75 2.75

United Nations Conference on Disaster Risk Reduction — A453

2015, Mar. 13   Litho.   Perf. 13
735 A453 90pf multi   1.25 1.25

First Bosniak High School, 20th Anniv. A454

2015, May 6   Litho.   Perf. 13x13¼
736 A454 1m multi   1.50 1.50

Souvenir Sheet

Pyotr I. Tchaikovsky (1840-93), Composer — A455

2015, May 7   Litho.   Perf. 13
737 A455 2.50m multi   3.50 3.50

Europa — A456

No. 738: a, Wooden airplane. b, Wooden sled.

2015, May 8   Litho.   Perf. 13
738 A456 2.50m Horiz. pair, #a-b   6.50 6.50
c.   Souvenir sheet of 2, #738a-738b   6.50 6.50
d.   Booklet pane of 6, 3 each
      #738a-738b, perf. 13 on 2 or
      3 sides   20.00 —
No. 738d was sold with, but unattached to, a booklet cover.

Visit of Pope Francis — A457

2015, June 6   Litho.   Perf. 12¾x13¼
739 A457 1.50m multi   2.10 2.10

Bosnian Chairmanship of Council of Europe — A458

Perf. 13¼x12¾
2015, June 21   Litho.
740 A458 50pf multi   .70   .70

Publication of *Alice's Adventures in Wonderland*, by Lewis Carroll, 150th Anniv. — A459

2015, July 1   Litho.   Perf. 13x13¼
741 A459 1.50m multi   2.00 2.00
No. 741 was printed in sheets of 8 + central label.

Berries A460

Designs: 10pf, Rubus fruticosus. 20pf, Rubus idaeus. 30pf, Ribes nigrum.

2015, Aug. 4   Litho.   Perf. 13
742 A460 10pf multi + label   .25 .25
743 A460 20pf multi + label   .25 .25
744 A460 30pf multi + label   .35 .35
   Nos. 742-744 (3)   .85 .85

Discovery of Prehistoric Art in Lascaux Caves, 75th Anniv. — A461

Serpentine Die Cut 11
2015, Sept. 10   Litho.
Self-Adhesive
745 A461 1m multi   1.25 1.25

Jewish District in Sarajevo, 450th Anniv. A462

2015, Oct. 1   Litho.   Perf. 13x13¼
746 A462 40pf multi   .50 .50

Children's Drawing by Amina Covrk — A463

2015, Oct. 9   Litho.   Perf. 13x13¼
747 A463 90pf multi   1.20 1.20

Amel Tuka, Bronze Medalist in 800-Meter Race at 2015 World Track and Field Championships — A464

2015, Oct. 9   Litho.   Perf. 13¼x13
748 A464 1.30m multi   1.60 1.60

Victory of Bosnia & Herzegovina Under-16 Men's Basketball Team in 2015 European Championships — A465

2015, Oct. 9   Litho.   Perf. 13
749 A465 2.70m multi   3.50 3.50

Souvenir Sheet

Konjic Woodcarving — A466

Litho. & Embossed
2015, Oct. 9   Perf. 13x13¼
750 A466 1.50m multi   2.00 2.00

Old Town of Maglaj A467

2015, Oct. 22   Litho.   Perf. 13
751 A467 90pf multi   1.20 1.20

Syringa Vulgaris — A468

2015, Nov. 4   Litho.   Perf. 13
752 A468 1m multi   1.40 1.40

Buildings in Mackovac A469

2015, Nov. 24   Litho.   Perf. 13
753 A469 70pf multi   .80 .80
Ethno Tourism.

Festina Lente Bridge, Sarajevo A470

2015, Nov. 27   Litho.   Perf. 13
754 A470 2.50m multi   2.75 2.75

Rug Design — A471

2015, Dec. 20   Litho.   Perf. 13
755 A471 5m multi   5.75 5.75

Old Mosque, Spionica A472

2015, Dec. 22   Litho.   Perf. 13x13½
756 A472 1.10m multi   1.25 1.25

Carved Tablet and Arch Found Near Zenica A473

2015, Dec. 22   Litho.   Perf. 13
757 A473 3m multi   3.50 3.50
Panel of the Great Judge Gradesa.

First Newspaper in Bosnia & Herzegovina, 150th Anniv. — A474

2016, May 9   Litho.   Perf. 13½
758 A474 1.50m multi   1.75 1.75

A475

Europa A476

2016, May 9   Litho.   Perf. 13¼x13¾
759 A475 2.50m multi   3.00 3.00
760 A476 2.50m multi   3.00 3.00
Think Green Issue.

Souvenir Sheet

Miguel de Cervantes (1547-1616), Writer, and Characters Don Quixote and Sancho Panza — A477

2016, May 9   Litho.   Perf. 13¼x13¾
761 A477 2m multi   2.40 2.40

Hum Mountain Relay Tower — A478

2016, May 17   Litho.   Perf. 13
762 A478 70pf multi   .80 .80

Halacsya Sendtneri A479

2016, May 25   Litho.   Perf. 13¼x13¾
763 A479 1m multi   1.25 1.25

Evliya Celebi (1611-82), Explorer A480

2016, May 25   Litho.   Perf. 13
764 A480 2m multi   2.40 2.40
No. 764 was printed in sheets of 8 + central label.

Souvenir Sheet

Butterflies — A481

No. 765: a, Coenonympha tullia. b, Cupido decolorata.

2016, May 25   Litho.   Perf. 13¼x13¾
765 A481 2.50m Sheet of 2, #a-b   5.75 5.75
c. Booklet pane of 6, 3 each #765a-765b, perf. 13¼x13¾ on 2 or 3 sides   17.50 —
No. 765c was sold with, but unattached to, a booklet cover.

Painting by Nasuh Matrakci (1480-c. 1564), Statesman A482

2016, July 6   Litho.   Perf. 13¼x13¾
766   A482   1.50m multi   1.75   1.75

Yellow Fortress, Sarajevo A483

2016, Aug. 5   Litho.   Perf. 13
767   A483   30pf multi + label   .35   .35

Summer Sports and Recreation — A484

2016, Aug. 5   Litho.   Perf. 13¼x13¾
768   A484   2.50m multi   3.00   3.00

Winning Design in Children's Stamp Design Contest A485

2016, Oct. 3   Litho.   Perf. 13¼x13¾
769   A485   90pf multi   1.10   1.10

Tombstone, Durdevic — A486

Perf. 13¾x13¼
2016, Nov. 24   Litho.
770   A486   1m multi   1.10   1.10

Campaign Against Domestic Violence A487

2016, Dec. 8   Litho.   Perf. 13¼x13¾
771   A487   2.50m multi   2.75   2.75

Mosque, Travnik A488

2016, Dec. 15   Litho.   Perf. 13
772   A488   1.70m multi   1.90   1.90

Pliva Lakes Waterfalls A489

2016, Dec. 15   Litho.   Perf. 13½
773   A489   2.70m multi   3.00   3.00

New Year 2017 A490

2016, Dec. 15   Litho.   Perf. 13
774   A490   1.50m multi + label   1.60   1.60

Pannonian Lakes, Tuzla A491

2016, Dec. 21   Litho.   Perf. 13½
775   A491   2m multi   2.25   2.25

Matija Divkovic (1563-1631), and His 1611 Book *Christian Doctrine* — A492

2016, Dec. 23   Litho.   Perf. 13½
776   A492   90pf multi   .95   .95

Karl May (1842-1912), Writer of Novels About American Indians — A493

2017, Apr. 20   Litho.   Perf. 13
777   A493   2m multi   2.25   2.25

Souvenir Sheet

Coffee Grinders — A494

Litho. & Embossed
2017, Apr. 20   Perf. 13
778   A494   2m multi   2.25   2.25

Birds A495

Designs: 90pf, Aquila pomarina. 2.50m, Ardea cinerea.

2017, Apr. 20   Litho.   Perf. 13x13¼
779   A495   90pf multi   1.00   1.00
Souvenir Sheet
780   A495   2.50m multi   3.00   3.00

Europa — A496

No. 781: a, Window at Jajce Castle. b, Jajce Castle.

2017, May 9   Litho.   Perf. 13
781   A496   2.50m Horiz. pair, #a-b   5.75   5.75
   c.   Souvenir sheet of 2, #781a-781b   5.75   5.75
   d.   Booklet pane of 6, 3 each
      #781a-781b, perf. 13 on 2 or
      3 sides   17.50   —

Membership in the Universal Postal Union, 125th Anniv. — A497

Perf. 13¼x12¾
2017, June 27   Litho.
782   A497   1.50m multi   1.75   1.75

Self-portrait, by Mersad Berber (1940-2012) A498

2017, July 6   Litho.   Perf. 12¾x13¼
783   A498   1.70m multi   2.10   2.10

Exhibition of paintings by Berber at Sarajevo City Hall.

BOSNIA & HERZEGOVINA (CROAT ADMIN)

Bosnian Croat Administration Located In Mostar
(Herceg Bosna)

100 Paras = 1 Dinar (1993)
100 Lipa = 1 Kuna (1994)
100 pfennig = 1 Mark (6/22/98)

> **Catalogue values for all unused stamps in this country are for Never Hinged items.**

A1

1993, May 12   Litho.   Perf. 14
1   A1   2000d multicolored   1.00   1.00
Our Lady of Peace Shrine, Medjugorje.

A2

Silvije Kranjcevic (1865-1908), poet: 500d, Waterfall, gate at Jajce. 1000d, Old bridge, Mostar, horiz.

1993
2-4   A2   Set of 3   1.50   1.50
Issued: 200d, 5/20; 500d, 5/18; 1000d, 5/15.

Census in Bosnia & Herzegovina, 250th Anniv. — A3

1993, May 24
5   A3   100d Medieval gravestone   .30   .30

Madonna of the Grand Duke, by Raphael — A4

1993, Dec. 3
6   A4   6000d multicolored   2.00   2.00
Christmas.

Paintings, by Gabrijel Jurkic (1886-1974) — A5

Europa: a, 3500d, Uplands in Bloom. b, 5000d, Wild Poppy.

1993, Dec. 6
7   A5   Pair, #a.-b.   9.00   9.00

Kravica Waterfalls A6

1993, Dec. 7
8   A6   3000d multicolored   1.00   1.00

Grand Duke Hrvoje Vukcic-Hrvatinic (1350-1416) — A7

1993, Dec. 8
9   A7   1500d multicolored   1.25   1.25

Pleham
Monastery
A8

1993, Dec. 15
10   A8 2200d multicolored   1.25 1.25

Formation of
Bosnian Croat
Administration
A9

1994, Feb. 10
11   A9 10,000d multicolored   4.50 4.50

Bronze
Cross,
Rama
A10

1994, Nov. 28
12   A10 2.80k multicolored   1.50 1.50

Flora & Fauna — A11

a, 3.80k, Campanula hercegovina. b, 4k,
Dog.

1994, Nov. 30
13   A11 Pair, #a.-b.   4.00 4.00

Hutovo
Wetlands
A12

1994, Dec. 2
14   A12 80 l multicolored   .90   .90

Europa — A13

Transportation: a, 8k, Bicycles, 1885. b, 10k,
1901 Mercedes.

1994, Dec. 5
15   A13 Pair, #a.-b.   10.00 10.00

City of
Ljubuski,
550th
Anniv. — A14

1994, Dec. 8
16   A14 1k multicolored   .50   .50

Dr. Nikolic
Franciscan
Hospital, Nova
Bila, 2nd
Anniv. — A15

1994, Dec. 12
17   A15 5k multicolored   2.40 2.40

UN, 50th Anniv. — A16

1995, Oct. 24   *Rouletted*
Self-Adhesive
18   A16 1.50k Card of 10   55.00 55.00
Color ranges from pale pink at UL of card to
dark rose at LR of card. Each stamp is numbered at LR.

Christmas — A17

1995, Dec. 4   *Perf. 14*
19   A17 5.40k multicolored   2.25 2.25

Kraljeva
Sutjeska
Monastery
A18

1995, Dec. 7
20   A18 3k multicolored   1.20 1.20

Cities — A19

Monasteries: 2k, Srebrenica. 4k, Mostar.
1995
21-22 A19 Set of 2   3.00 3.00
Issued: 2k, 12/20; 4k, 12/12.

Europa — A20

1995, Dec. 28
23   A20 6.50k multicolored   21.00 21.00

A21

1996, June 24
24   A21 10k multicolored   5.00 5.00
a.   Booklet pane of 4   20.00
       Complete booklet, #24a   20.00
Apparitions at Medugorje, 15th anniv.

Europa — A22

1996, July 20
25   A22 2.40k multicolored   2.00 2.00
Queen Katarina Kosaca Kotromanic.

A23

1996, July 23
26   A23 1.40k multicolored   .65   .65
Franciscan Monastery, Siroki Brijeg, 150th
anniv.

Virgin Mary — A24

1996, Aug. 14   *Rouletted*
Self-Adhesive
27   A24 2k multicolored   2.75 2.75
a.   Card of 10   27.50 27.50
28   A24 9k multicolored   9.25 9.25
a.   Card of 5 + 5 labels   47.50 47.50

Nos. 27-28 Surcharged

1996, Oct. 21   *Rouletted*
Self-Adhesive
29   A24 1.10k on 2k multi   20.00   —
a.   Card of 10   165.00
30   A24 1.10k on 9k multi   45.00   —
a.   Card of 5 + 5 labels   165.00
Taipei '96 Philatelic Exhibition.

Christmas — A25

1996, Dec. 8   Litho.   *Perf. 14*
31   A25 2.20k multicolored   1.00 1.00

Europa — A26

Myths & legends: a, 2k, St. George slaying
the dragon. b, 5k, Zeus coming to Europa dis-
guised as a bull.

1997, Apr. 4
32   A26 Pair, #a.-b.   4.00 4.00
No. 32b is 39x34mm.

A27

1997, Apr. 12
33   A27 3.60k multicolored   1.60 1.60
a.   Pane of 4   6.50
Visit of Pope John Paul II.

Samatorje
Church — A28

1997, Apr. 20
34   A28 1.40k multi   .55   .55

Flora &
Fauna — A29

Designs: 1k, Ardea purpurea. 2.40k,
Symphyandra hofmannii.

1997
35-36 A29 Set of 2   1.60 1.60
Issued: 1k, 11/19. 2.40k, 11/17.

Christmas
A30

1997, Dec. 1
37   A30 1.40k multicolored   .65 .65

World
Animated
Film Festival
A31

1998, Apr. 1
38   A31 6.50k multicolored   3.50 3.50
        Europa.

Hercegovina,
550th
Anniv. — A32

1998, Apr. 8
39   A32 2.30k multicolored   .90 .90

City of Livno,
1100th
Anniv. — A33

1998, Apr. 9
40   A33 1.20k multicolored   .55 .55

Sibiraea
Croatica — A34

1998, Nov. 9
41   A34 1.40k multicolored   .65 .65

Gyps Fulvus — A35

1998, Nov. 16
42   A35 2.40m multicolored   1.10 1.10

Christmas — A36

1998, Dec. 2
43   A36 5.40k multi   2.75 2.75

Native Attire — A37

1999, Mar. 26   Litho.   Perf. 14
44   A37 40pf multi   .55 .55

A. B. Simic (1898-
1925) — A38

1999, Mar. 29
45   A38 30pf multi   .45 .45

Bobovac
Castle — A39

1999, Mar. 30
46   A39 10pf multi   .30 .30

Europa — A40

1999, Mar. 31
47   A40 1.50m Blidinje Park   3.00 3.00

Dianthus
Freynii — A41

1999, Oct. 11   Litho.   Perf. 14
48   A41 80pf multi   1.25 1.25

Martes
Martes — A42

1999, Oct. 15
49   A42 40pf multi   .60 .60

Stolac
Castle — A43

1999, Nov. 3
50   A43 10pf multi   .30 .30

Christmas — A44

1999, Nov. 22
51   A44 30pf multi   .55 .55

Nikola Sop (1904-
82), Writer — A45

2000, Apr. 5   Litho.   Perf. 14
52   A45 40pf multi   .55 .55

World Health
Day — A46

2000, Apr. 7
53   A46 40pf multi   .55 .55

Europa — A47

2000, May 9
54   A47 1.80m multi   5.25 5.25

Brother Lovro
Karaula (1800-
75) — A48

2000, May 19
55   A48 80pf multi   1.00 1.00

Quercus
Sessilis — A49

2000, Aug. 16
56   A49 1.50m multi   2.00 2.00

Anguilla
Anguilla
A50

2000, Aug. 18
57   A50 80pf multi   1.25 1.25

16th
European
Chess Club
Cup — A51

30th Intl.
Chess
Tournament
A52

2000, Sept. 23
58   A51 80pf multi   1.25 1.25
59   A52 80pf multi   1.25 1.25

Tomislavgrad
Monastery
A53

2000, Sept. 26
60   A53 1.50m multi   2.25 2.25

Woman From
Kraljeva
Sutjeska — A54

2000, Sept. 27
61   A54 40pf multi   .60 .60

Fight Against
AIDS — A55

2000, Dec. 1
62   A55 80pf multi   1.25 1.25

Christmas — A56

2000, Dec. 4
63   A56 40pf multi   .60 .60

Fish — A57

Designs: 30pf, Chondrostoma phoxinus.
1.50m, Salmo marmoratus.

2001
64-65   A57   Set of 2   2.50 2.50

Europa — A58

Designs: 1.10m, Tihaljina spring. 1.80m, Pliva waterfall.

2001, Mar. 31
66-67 A58   Set of 2   4.50 4.50

Execution of Zrinski and Frankopan, 330th Anniv. — A59

No. 68: a, Petar Zrinski (1621-71). b, Fran Krsto Frankopan (1643-71).

2001, Apr. 30   Litho.   Perf. 14
68 A59 40pf Vert. pair, #a-b   1.10 1.10

16th Century Galley — A60

2001, June 15
69 A60 1.80m multi   2.25 2.25

Boat From Neretva River Valley — A61

2001, June 20   Perf. 14x14¼
70 A61 80pf multi   1.25 1.25

Souvenir Sheet

Apparition of the Virgin Mary at Medjugorje, 20th Anniv. — A62

2001, June 24
71 A62 3.80m multi   5.00 5.00

Our Lady of Kondzilo — A63

2001, Aug. 15   Perf. 14
72 A63 80pf multi   1.20 1.20

Computers, 50th Anniv. — A64

No. 73: a, Denomination in red. b, Denomination in black and white.

2001, Sept. 9
73 A64 40pf Horiz. pair, #a-b   1.20 1.20

Mars Odyssey Mission — A65

2001, Sept. 9
74 A65 1.50m multi + label   2.00 2.00

Father Slavko Barbaric (1946-2000), Priest at Medjugorje A66

2001, Nov. 24
75 A66 80pf multi   1.20 1.20

Walt Disney (1901-66), Animated Film Producer A67

2001, Dec. 5
76 A67 1.50m multi   2.00 2.00

Christmas A68

2001, Dec. 8
77 A68 40pf multi   .60 .60

Nobel Prizes, Cent. — A69

2001, Dec. 10   Litho.   Perf. 14
78 A69 1.80m multi   2.50 2.50

2002 Winter Olympics, Salt Lake City — A70

2002, Feb. 4   Litho.   Perf. 14
79 A70 80pf multi   1.20 1.20

Intl. Year of Mountains — A71

2002, Mar. 11   Litho.   Perf. 14
80 A71 40pf multi + label   .60 .60

First Written Record of Mostar, 550th Anniv. — A72

2002, Apr. 3
81 A72 30pf multi   .50 .50

Europa — A73

Designs: 80pf, Clown, lion and mouse. 1.50m, Clowns, juggler, circus tent.

2002, Apr. 5
82-83 A73   Set of 2   5.00 5.00

Leonardo da Vinci (1452-1519) — A74

2002, Apr. 15
84 A74 40pf multi   1.00 1.00

2002 World Cup Soccer Championships, Japan and Korea — A75

2002, May 22
85 A75 1.50m multi   2.50 2.50

Father Didak Buntic (1871-1922) — A76

2002, June 5
86 A76 80pf multi   1.20 1.20

Humac Tablet — A77

2002, June 13
87 A77 40pf multi   .60 .60

Marilyn Monroe (1926-62), Actress — A78

2002, Aug. 5
88 A78 40pf multi   1.20 1.20

Elvis Presley (1935-77) — A79

2002, Aug. 16
89 A79 1.50m multi   2.50 2.50

Television, 75th Anniv. — A80

2002, Sept. 7
90 A80 1.50m multi   2.00 2.00

Stamp Day — A81

2002, Sept. 9
91 A81 80pf multi   1.10 1.10

Croatian Cultural Association Napredak, Cent. — A82

2002, Sept. 14
92 A82 40pf multi   .60 .60

European Bocce Championships, Grude — A83

2002, Oct. 8
93 A83 1.50m multi   2.10 2.10

Viola
Beckiana — A84

2002, Oct. 21
94 A84 30pf multi   .60 .60

Vanessa
Atalanta
A85

2002, Oct. 25
95 A85 80pf multi   1.20 1.20

Christmas — A86

2002, Dec. 4
96 A86 40pf multi   .60 .60

Archdiocesan
Gymnasium,
Travnik, 120th
Anniv. — A87

2002, Dec. 14
97 A87 80pf multi   1.20 1.20

A 50pf stamp commemorating Archbishop Josip Stadler was jointly issued
by the post offices of the Croat Administration and the Muslim Government. It is
listed as No. 435 in the listings of the
Muslim Government issues.

Franciscan
Secondary
School, Siroki
Brijeg — A88

2003, Feb. 26   Litho.   Perf. 14
98 A88 40pf multi   .60 .60

Europa — A89

2003, Apr. 5
99 A89 1.80m multi   3.50 3.50
Printed in sheets of 8 stamps + label.

Abjuration of
the Bogomil
Heresy at
Bilino Polje,
800th
Anniv. — A90

2003, Apr. 8
100 A90 50pf multi   .70 .70

Post Office of the
Croat
Administration, 10th
Anniv. — A91

2003, May 12
101 A91 80pf multi   1.20 1.20

World
Wine
Day
A92

2003, May 25
102 A92 1.50m multi   2.00 2.00

Flora &
Fauna — A93

Designs: 50pf, Oxytropis prenja. 2m,
Alectoris graeca.

2003   Litho.   Perf. 14
103 A93 50pf multi   .75 .75
104 A93 2m multi   2.75 2.75
  Issued: 50pf, 6/10; 2m, 6/16.

Visit of
Pope
John Paul
II — A94

2003, June 22   Perf. 13¼x13½
105 A94 1.50m multi   2.10 2.10

Father Matija
Divkovic (1563-
1631), First Bosnian
Writer — A95

2003, June 24   Perf. 14
106 A95 3.80m multi   5.25 5.25

Woman From
Rama — A96

Jewelry From
Neum — A97

2003, Aug. 20   Litho.   Perf. 14
107 A96 50pf multi   .80 .80
108 A97 70pf multi   1.00 1.00

Cross on Mt.
Krizevac, 70th
Anniv. — A98

2003, Sept. 14
109 A98 80pf multi   1.25 1.25

Ban Stjepan II
Kotromanic, 650th
Anniv. of
Death — A99

2003, Sept. 28
110 A99 20pf multi   .35 .35

Teleprinter,
75th Anniv.
A100

2003, Oct. 9   Litho.   Perf. 14
111 A100 1.50m blk & red brn   2.25 2.25
  World Post Day.

Alberto Fortis,
Writer of Dalmatian
Travelogue, 200th
Anniv. of
Death — A101

2003, Oct. 21
112 A101 50pf multi   .75 .75

Intl. Children's
Day — A102

2003, Nov. 20
113 A102 1m multi   1.40 1.40

Christmas
A103

2003, Dec. 4
114 A103 50pf multi   .90 .90

First Flight,
Cent. — A104

2003, Dec. 17
115 A104 2m multi   2.75 2.75

Intl.
Investment
Conference
A105

2004, Jan. 23
116 A105 5m silver   6.75 6.75

St. Valentine's
Day — A106

2004, Feb. 14
117 A106 10pf multi   .40 .40

Albert
Einstein
(1879-1955)
A107

2004, Mar. 14
118 A107 50pf multi   .90 .90

Hand Tattoos
A108

2004, Mar. 20
119 A108 50pf multi   .90 .90

Flora & Fauna Type of 2003

Designs: 1m, Aquilegia dinarica. 1.50m,
Salamandra atra prenjensis.

2004, Mar. 30
120 A93 1m multi   1.25 1.25
121 A93 1.50m multi   2.50 2.50

Europa — A109

No. 122: a, 1.50m, Skis of skier at hill, 2m,
Fins of swimmer at beach.

2004, Apr. 5   Litho.   Perf. 14
122 A109 Horiz. pair, #a-b   8.00 8.00
Printed in sheets of 4 pairs + 2 labels.

Father Andrija Kacic Miosic (1704-60), Poet — A110

2004, Apr. 17
123 A110 70pf dk ol bis & brn   1.00 1.00

A111

2004, June 12
124 A111 2m multi   2.75 2.75
  a.   Miniature sheet of 4   11.00 11.00

European Soccer Championships, Portugal.

A112

2004, June 27
125 A112 70pf multi   1.00 1.00

Kocerin Tablet, 600th anniv.

Moon Landing, 35th Anniv. — A113

2004, July 20
126 A113 1m multi   1.50 1.50

Reconstruction of Old Bridge, Mostar — A114

2004, July 23
127 A114 50pf multi   .90   .90

Buna River Water Wheel A115

2004, Sept. 9   Litho.   *Perf. 14*
128 A115 1m multi   1.50 1.50

World Post Day — A116

2004, Oct. 9
129 A116 1.50m multi   2.25 2.25
  Printed in sheets of 8 + label.

Savings Day — A117

2004, Oct. 31
130 A117 50pf multi   .90   .90
  Printed in sheets of 8 + label.

Karl Benz (1844-1929), Automobile Manufacturer — A118

2004, Nov. 25
131 A118 1.50m multi   2.25 2.25
  Printed in sheets of 8 + label.

Christmas — A119

No. 132: a, 50pf, Journey to Bethlehem. b, 1m, Christmas trees, man with gift.

2004, Dec. 4
132 A119   Horiz. pair, #a-b   2.25 2.25

Woman From Kupres — A120

2005, Feb. 20
133 A120 1.50m multi   2.25 2.25

Birds — A121

No. 134: a, Egretta garzetta. b, Himantopus himantopus. c, Merops apiaster. d, Alcedo atthis.

2005, Mar. 2
134 A121 1m Block of 4, #a-d   6.25 6.25

Flowers — A122

Designs: No. 135, 50pf, Gentiana dinarica. No. 136, 50pf, Petteria ramentacea.

2005, Mar. 2
135-136 A122   Set of 2   1.50 1.50

Zrinjski Soccer Team, Cent. — A123

No. 137: a, Three players, denomination at right. b, Two players, denomination at left.

2005, Mar. 15   Litho.   *Perf. 14*
137 A123 3m Pair, #a-b   9.00 9.00

Easter — A124

2005, Mar. 27
138 A124 50pf multi   .90   .90

Fairy Tales — A125

No. 139: a, Palcica (Thumbelina, by Hans Christian Andersen). b, Tintilinic, by Ivana Brlic Mazuranic.

2005, Apr. 2
139 A125 20pf Pair, #a-b   .90   .90

Europa — A126

No. 140: a, Wine bottle, knife, cutting board, garlic, ham, cheese, and bread. b, Cruet, grapes, bread, nuts and cheese.

2005, Apr. 5
140   Pair   6.00 6.00
  a.-b. A126 2m Either single   3.00 3.00
  c.   Souvenir sheet, 2 each
          #140a-140b   12.00 12.00

One-string Fiddle — A127

2005, May 10   Litho.   *Perf. 14*
141 A127 5m multi   7.50 7.50

Vjetrenica Cave — A128

2005, June 5   Litho.   *Perf. 14*
142 A128 1m multi   1.50 1.50
  World Environment Day.

Metkovic — Mostar Rail Line — A129

2005, June 14
143 A129 50pf multi   .90   .90

Medjugorje Youth Festival A130

2005, July 29   Litho.   *Perf. 14*
144 A130 1m multi   1.50 1.50

Father Grgo Martic (1822-1905), Writer — A131

2005, Aug. 30
145 A131 1m multi   1.50 1.50

Trumpet A132

2005, Oct. 1   Litho.   *Perf. 14*
146 A132 50pf multi   .90   .90
  Printed in sheets of 8 + label.

Dayton Peace Accords, 10th Anniv. — A133

2005, Nov. 21
147 A133 1.50m multi   2.25 2.25
  Printed in sheets of 8 + label.

Brother Slavko Barbaric (1946-2000) A134

2005, Nov. 24
148 A134 1m multi   1.50 1.50
  Printed in sheets of 8 + label.

Christmas — A135

Designs: No. 149, 50pf, Madonna and Child. No. 150, 50pf, Christmas tree.

2005, Dec. 4
149-150 A135   Set of 2   1.50 1.50

Nos. 149-150 each printed in sheets of 8 + label.

Europa Stamps, 50th Anniv. — A136

No. 151: a, Map of Europe, "50." b, Map of Europe in flowers, envelope. c, Map of Europe in examples of #99. d, Flags, flower, "50."

2006, Jan. 15
151   Horiz. strip of 4   12.00 12.00
a.-d.   A136 2m Any single   2.75   2.75
e.   Souvenir sheet, #151a-151d 18.00 18.00

World Wetlands Day — A137

2006, Feb. 2
152 A137 1m multi   1.50 1.50

Printed in sheets of 8 + label.

Europa — A138

No. 153: a, Footprints and "integration." b, Faces.

2006, Apr. 5
153 A138 2m Pair, #a-b   6.00 6.00
c.   Souvenir sheet, 2 each
         #153a-153b   12.00 12.00

No. 153 printed in sheets containing 4 pairs and 2 labels.

Earth Day — A139

2006, Apr. 22
154 A139 1m multi   1.50 1.50

World Press Freedom Day — A140

2006, May 3
155 A140 50pf multi   .90   .90

World Telecommunications Day — A141

2006, May 17
156 A141 1m multi   1.50 1.50

Apparition of the Virgin Mary at Medjugorje, 25th Anniv. — A142

Designs: No. 157, Statue of Virgin Mary, church at night. No. 158, Statue with halo. No. 159, Statue and cross. No. 160, Statue, church and tent. No. 161, People and church.

2006, June 18   Litho.   Perf. 14
Booklet Stamps
157 A142 1m multi   1.50 1.50
158 A142 1m multi   1.50 1.50
159 A142 1m multi   1.50 1.50
160 A142 1m multi   1.50 1.50
161 A142 1m multi   1.50 1.50
a.   Booklet pane, 2 each #157-161 16.00   —
       Complete booklet, #161a   16.00

Parish of Uzdol, 150th Anniv. — A143

2006, June 24
162 A143 50pf multi   .90   .90

Printed in sheets of 8 + label.

Nikola Tesla (1856-1943), Electrical Engineer — A144

2006, July 9
163 A144 2m multi   3.00 3.00

Medieval Tombstones A145

2006, Sept. 9
164 A145 20pf multi   .40   .40

European Car-Free Day — A146

2006, Sept. 22
165 A146 1m multi   1.50 1.50

Printed in sheets of 8 + label.

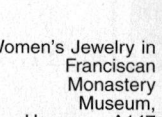

Women's Jewelry in Franciscan Monastery Museum, Humac — A147

2006, Oct. 9
166 A147 5m multi   8.00 8.00

Flowers — A148

No. 167: a, Cerastium dinaricum. b, Papaver kerneri.

2006, Nov. 1
167 A148 20pf Horiz. pair, #a-b   .75   .75

Birds —A148a

Designs: No. 167C, 70pf, Podiceps cristatus. No. 167D, 70pf, Acrocephalus scirpaceus. No. 167E, 70pf, Upupa epops. No. 167F, 70pf, Alauda arvensis.

2006, Nov. 1   Litho.   Perf. 14
167C-167F A148a   Set of 4   4.50 4.50

A148b

Christmas — A148c

2006, Dec. 1   Litho.   Perf. 14
167G A148b 50pf multi   .65   .65
167H A148c 1m multi   1.60 1.60

Nos. 167G-167H each were printed in sheets of 8 + label.

Valentine's Day — A149

2007, Feb. 14   Litho.   Perf. 14
168 A149 10pf multi   .35   .35

Miniature Sheet

Tornjak Dog — A150

No. 169: a, Head of dog facing right. b, Head of dog facing left. c, Entire dog facing right. d, Entire dog facing left.

2007, Feb. 22
169 A150 70pf Sheet of 4, #a-d   4.50 4.50

Mak Dizdar (1917-71), Poet — A151

2007, Mar. 21
170 A151 1m multi   1.50 1.50

Europa — A152

No. 171: a, Clasped hands. b, Knot.

2007, Apr. 5
171 A152 3m Pair, #a-b   9.00 9.00
c.   Miniature sheet, 2 each
         #171a-171b   17.50 17.50

Scouting, cent.

Souvenir Sheet

Arbor Day — A153

2007, Apr. 25
172 A153 2.10m multi   3.50 3.50

Gabela Archaeological Site — A154

2007, May 12
173 A154 1.50m multi   2.25 2.25

Iris — A155

Irises and Ship — A156

2007, May 22
174 A155 2m multi 3.50 3.50
Souvenir Sheet
175 A156 3m multi 5.00 5.00

Apparition of the
Virgin Mary at
Medjugorje, 26th
Anniv. — A157

No. 176: a, Statue of Virgin Mary. b, Hands holding rosary. c, People near statue of Virgin Mary. d, Steeple and statue of Virgin Mary. e, Statue of priest holding crucifix.

2007, June 1   **Booklet Stamps**
176   Horiz. strip of 5   7.50 7.50
a.-e.   A157 1m Any single   1.50 1.50
f.   Booklet pane of 10, 2 each
        #176a-176e   15.00   —
        Complete booklet, #176f   15.00

Bishop Marko
Dobretic (c. 1707-
84) — A158

2007, June 13
177 A158 60pf multi   1.00 1.00

Boljuni Cemetery — A159

2007, Sept. 23   **Litho.**   **Perf. 14**
178 A159 20pf multi   .40 .40
Printed in sheets of 8 + label.

World Bowling
Championships,
Grude — A160

2007, Sept. 24
179 A160 5m black & red   8.50 8.50
Printed in sheets of 8 + label.

Distaff and
Spindle — A161

2007, Oct. 9
180 A161 70pf multi   1.10 1.10
Printed in sheets of 8 + label.

Birds of Hutovo Blato — A162

No. 181: a, Streptopella turtur. b, Anas crecca. c, Anas platyrhynchos. d, Fulica atra.

2007, Nov. 1
181 A162 2m Block of 4, #a-d   14.00 14.00

Flora of
Blidinje
Nature
Park — A163

Designs: No. 182, Gentiana lutea. No. 183, Vaccinium vitis-idaea.

2007, Nov. 1
182 A163 3m multi   5.00 5.00
Souvenir Sheet
183 A163 3m multi   5.00 5.00

Christmas
and New
Year's
Day — A164

Designs: 50pf, Candles and wreath. 70pf, Christmas tree near steps.

2007, Dec. 1
184-185 A164   Set of 2   2.00 2.00
Nos. 184-185 each printed in sheets of 8 + label.

Bishop
Andjeo
Kraljevic
(1807-79)
A165

2007, Dec. 28
186 A165 1m multi   1.50 1.50

Easter — A166

2008, Mar. 23   **Litho.**   **Perf. 14**
187 A166 70pf multi   1.25 1.25

Croatian Cultural
Days — A167

2008, Mar. 25
188 A167 10pf multi   .35 .35

Europa — A168

Designs: No. 189, 3m, Airmail envelope folded into paper airplane. No. 190, 3m, Letter and fountain pen.

2008, Apr. 5
189-190 A168   Set of 2   9.50 9.50
190a   Miniature sheet, 2 each
          #189-190   19.00 19.00

Helmet of Illyrian Warrior — A169

Litho. & Embossed
2008, May 12   **Perf. 14**
191 A169 2.10m multi   3.00 3.00
Printed in sheets of 8 + 2 labels.

Grave of Rabbi Moshe Danon — A170

2008, May 21
192 A170 1.50m multi   2.00 2.00

Souvenir Sheet

Achillea Millefolium and Andrija Simic
(1833-1905), Outlaw — A171

2008, May 22
193 A171 2.90m multi   4.00 4.00

Apparition of the
Virgin Mary at
Medjugorje, 27th
Anniv. — A172

No. 194: a, Dove, cross, cloud. b, Dove, Virgin Mary. c, Bible, crucified Jesus, praying hands. d, Hands, church. e, Virgin Mary, child, dove.

2008, June 1
194   Horiz. strip of 5   8.50 8.50
a.-e.   A172 1m Any single   1.60 1.60

Brotnjo Vintage
Days — A173

Color of grapes: 50pf, Purple. 70pf, Red.

2008, Sept. 9   **Litho.**   **Perf. 14**
195-196 A173   Set of 2   1.90 1.90

Zaostrog Monastery — A174

2008, Oct. 4
197 A174 1m multi   1.50 1.50

Tobacco
Cutter — A175

2008, Oct. 9
198 A175 2m multi   3.00 3.00
Printed in sheets of 8 + label.

Zepce, 550th
Anniv. — A176

2008, Oct. 14
199   A176   1.50m multi   2.25   2.25

Intl. Year of the
Potato — A177

Solanum tuberosum: 60pf, Plant and tubers.
5m, Flower.

2008, Nov. 1
200   A177   60pf multi   .90   .90
     Souvenir Sheet
201   A177   5m multi   7.50   7.50

Birds — A178

No. 202: a, Accipiter gentilis. b, Bubo bubo.
c, Circaetus gallicus. d, Falco tinnunculus.

2008, Nov. 1
202   A178   1.50m Block of 4,
         #a-d   9.50   9.50

Father Leo Petrovic (1883-1945),
Professor — A179

2008, Nov. 15
203   A179   1m multi   2.10   2.10

Christmas
A180

New Year's
Day — A181

2008, Dec. 1
204   A180   70pf multi   1.20   1.20
205   A181   70pf multi   1.20   1.20

Siroki Brijeg Soccer Team, 60th
Anniv. — A182

Players and team emblem: 70pf, Sepia photograph. 2.10m, Full color and black-and-white
photographs.

2008, Dec. 12
206   A182   70pf multi   1.10   1.10
     Souvenir Sheet
207   A182   2.10m multi   3.25   3.25
     No. 207 contains one 35x30mm stamp.

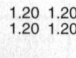

Daffodil Day — A183

2009, Mar. 21   **Litho.**   **Perf. 14**
208   A183   20pf brt pink & yel   .35   .35
     Campaign against breast cancer.

Intl. Water Day — A184

No. 209: a, Waterfall on Pliva River. b, Mills
along river.

2009, Mar. 22
209   A184   70pf Horiz. pair, #a-b   2.00   2.00

Council of Europe,
60th Anniv. — A185

European
Court of
Human
Rights, 50th
Anniv.
A186

2009, Apr. 1
210   A185   1.50m multi   2.25   2.25
211   A186   1.50m multi   2.25   2.25

Europa
A187

No. 212 — Planets and: a, Galileo Galilei
(1564-1642), astronomer. b, Telescope.

2009, Apr. 5   **Litho. & Embossed**
212   A187   3m Vert. pair, #a-b   8.00   9.00
     Intl. Year of Astronomy. Printed in sheets
containing two pairs.

Seal of Duke
Stipan Vukcic
Kosaca — A188

2009, May 12   **Litho.**   **Perf. 14**
213   A188   1.50m multi   2.00   2.00
     Printed in sheets of 8 + label.

Field of Tanacetum
Balsamita — A189

No. 215, Flowers, woman's head.

2009, May 22
214   A189   2.10m shown   2.75   2.75
     Souvenir Sheet
215   A189   2.10m multi   2.75   2.75

Guca Gora
Franciscan
Monastery,
150th Anniv.
A190

2009, May 30
216   A190   70pf multi   1.00   1.00
     Printed in sheets of 8 + central label.

Apparition of the
Virgin Mary at
Medjugorje, 28th
Anniv. — A191

No. 217: a, Virgin Mary. b, Virgin Mary and
church. c, Steeples and hand raising crucifix.
d, Cross and path. e, Church.

2009, June 1   **Perf. 14**
     Booklet Stamps
217   Horiz. strip of 5   6.00   6.00
   a.-e.   A191 1m Any single   1.10   1.10
     f.   Booklet pane of 10, 2 each
        #217a-217e   12.00   —
        Complete booklet, #217f   12.00

10th
Mediterranean
Film Festival
A192

2009, Sept. 1
218   A192   70pf multi   1.00   1.00

Franciscan Order, 800th
Anniv. — A193

No. 219: a, Monk's rope cincture. b, Shrine.

2009, Oct. 4   **Litho.**   **Perf. 14**
219   A193   1m Horiz. pair, #a-b   2.75   2.75

Wooden Hope Chest — A194

2009, Oct. 9
220   A194   70pf multi   1.00   1.00

Gorica Livno Franciscan Monastery,
150th Anniv. — A195

2009, Nov. 1
221   A195   60pf multi   .90   .90

Prunus
Domestica
A196

Prunus domestica: No. 222, Fruit on branch.
No. 223, Blossoms and fruit.

2009, Nov. 1
222   A196   5m multi   6.00   6.00
     Souvenir Sheet
223   A196   5m multi   6.00   6.00

Birds of Hutovo Blato — A197

No. 224: a, Coturnix coturnix. b, Cuculus canorus. c, Rallus aquaticus. d, Nycticorax nycticorax.

2009, Nov. 1
224 A197 1.50m Block or strip of 4, #a-d 7.50 7.50

Christmas A198

New Year's Day — A199

2009, Dec. 1
225 A198 70pf multi 1.00 1.00
226 A199 70pf multi 1.00 1.00

2010 Winter Olympics, Vancouver A200

Designs: 70pf, Shown. 1.50m, Maple leaf on skis.

2010, Feb. 1
227-228 A200 Set of 2 3.00 3.00

Nos. 227-228 each were printed in sheets of 8 + 2 labels.

Intl. Women's Day — A201

2010, Mar. 8
229 A201 20pf multi .30 .30

Friar Martin Nedic (1810-95), Poet — A202

2010, Apr. 1
230 A202 2.10m multi 2.75 2.75

Europa — A203

Stylized child with: No. 231, 3m, Kite. No. 232, 3m, Pinwheel.

2010, Apr. 5
231-232 A203 Set of 2 8.50 8.50
232a Sheet of 4, 2 each #231-232 17.00 17.00

Ravlica Cave Archaeological Site — A204

2010, May 12 Litho. Perf. 14
233 A204 1.50m multi 2.25 2.25

Souvenir Sheet

Linden Tree in Slavic Mythology — A205

2010, May 22
234 A205 5m multi 6.00 6.00

Apparition of the Virgin Mary at Medjugorje, 29th Anniv. A206

No. 235: a, Flags, church and crowd. b, Statue and crowd. c, Hand holding rosary. d, Cross and crowd. e, Statue and crosses on hillside.

2010, June 1 Booklet Stamps
235 Vert. strip of 5 7.50 7.50
a.-e. A206 1m Any single 1.50 1.50
f. Booklet pane of 10, 2 each #235a-235e 15.00 15.00
Complete booklet, #235f 15.00 15.00

Matrix Croatica General Assembly, Citluk — A207

2010, June 19
236 A207 1m red & black 1.25 1.25

Printed in sheets of 8 + 2 labels.

Mother Teresa (1910-97), Humanitarian A208

2010, Aug. 27 Litho. Perf. 14
237 A208 2.10m blue 3.25 3.25

Intl. Day for Habitat Protection — A209

No. 238: a, Lake Prokosko. b, Lake Prokosko and Triturus alpestris reiseri.

2010, Oct. 6
238 A209 1m Horiz. pair, #a-b 3.00 3.00

Peasant's Shoes — A210

2010, Oct. 9
239 A210 70pf multi 1.10 1.10

Worldwide Fund for Nature — A211

No. 240 — Lacerta trilineata: a, With black coloring, on rock. b, Climbing tree. c, With green coloring, on rock. d, Head.

2010, Nov. 1
240 A211 50pf Block of 4, #a-d 2.75 2.75

Mushrooms — A212

No. 241: a, Lycoperdon perlatum. b, Amanita muscaria.

2010, Nov. 1
241 A212 2.10m Horiz. pair, #a-b 6.50 6.50

Father Slavko Barbaric (1946-2000), Investigator of Medjugorje Apparitions — A213

2010, Nov. 24
242 A213 1m multi 1.60 1.60

Christmas A214

New Year 2011 — A215

2010, Dec. 1
243 A214 70pf multi 1.10 1.10
244 A215 70pf multi 1.10 1.10

Printing of First Croatian Book in Bosnia & Herzegovina, 400th Anniv. A216

2011, Feb. 21
245 A216 70pf multi .90 .90

World Meteorological Day — A217

2011, Mar. 23
246 A217 20pf multi .30 .30

Easter A218

2011, Apr. 1
247 A218 70pf multi .90 .90

Europa — A219

No. 248 — Forest with: a, Green panels. b, Red panels.

2011, Apr. 5
248 A219 3m Pair, #a-b 8.50 8.50
c. Souvenir sheet of 4, 2 each #248a-248b 17.00 17.00

Intl. Year of Forests. No. 248 was printed in sheets containing four pairs and two central labels.

First Man in Space, 50th Anniv. — A220

2011, Apr. 12
249 A220 10pf multi .35 .35

Diagram of Early Christian Basilica, Cim — A221

2011, May 12
250 A221 1.50m multi 2.25 2.25

Rudjer Boskovic (1711-87), Astronomer A222

2011, May 18
251 A222 2.10m multi 3.25 3.25

Souvenir Sheet

Hawthorn Branch — A223

2011, May 22
252 A223 5m multi   6.50 6.50

Apparition of the Virgin Mary at Medjugorje, 30th Anniv. — A224

No. 253: a, Wooden cross and rosary beads. b, Church. c, Sculpture of crucified Jesus. d, Statue of Virgin Mary.

Litho. & Embossed
2011, June 1   **Perf. 14x13¾**
253 A224 1m Block of 4, #a-d   6.00 6.00
   e.   Souvenir sheet of 4, #253a-253d   6.00 6.00
   f.   Booklet pane, 2 #253 + 2 labels   12.00 —
    Complete booklet, #253f   12.00

St. Anthony of Padua (1195-1231) A225

2011, June 13   **Litho.**   **Perf. 14**
254 A225 1m multi   1.60 1.60

World Bicycle Day — A226

2011, July 16   **Litho.**   **Perf. 14**
255 A226 70pf green   .90 .90

Skopaljska Gracanica Parish, Cent. — A227

2011, Aug. 13
256 A227 50pf multi   .65 .65

Beatification of the Blessed Martyrs of Drina — A228

2011, Sept. 24
257 A228 70pf multi   .90 .90

Fibulae A229

2011, Oct. 9
258 A229 1m multi   1.25 1.25
World Post Day. No. 258 was printed in sheets of 8 + label.

Fridtjof Nansen (1861-1930), Polar Explorer and Diplomat — A230

2011, Oct. 10
259 A230 1.50m multi   1.90 1.90

Fruit — A231

No. 260: a, Punica granatum. b, Ficus carica.

2011, Nov. 1
260 A231 2m Horiz. pair, #a-b   5.00 5.00

Lynx Lynx — A232

No. 261 — Panel color: a, Green. b, Red. c, Orange. d, Blue violet.

2011, Nov. 1
261 A232 3m Block of 4, #a-d   15.00 15.00

Christmas A233   New Year 2012 A234

2011, Dec. 1
262 A233 70pf multi   .90 .90
263 A234 70pf multi   .90 .90

Latin Grammar Book, by Toma Babic, 300th Anniv. of Publication A235

2012, Feb. 21
264 A235 70pf multi   .90 .90

Cheese Produced at Trappist Monasteries A236

2012, Mar. 21
265 A236 2.10m multi   2.50 2.50

Europa — A237

No. 266 — Sites in Mostar: a, Duke Stjepan Kosaca Lodge. b, Old Bridge.

2012, Apr. 5
266 A237 3m Pair, #a-b   8.00 8.00
   c.   Souvenir sheet of 4, 2 each #266a-266b   16.00 16.00
No. 266 was printed in sheets of 4 pairs + 2 labels.

Intl. Red Cross Day — A238

2012, May 8
267 A238 1m red & black   1.60 1.60

Monument to God Mithra, Konjic A239

2012, May 12
268 A239 70pf multi   1.10 1.10

Souvenir Sheet

Carpinus Betulus — A240

2012, May 22
269 A240 3m multi   3.50 3.50

Nobel Laureates Ivo Andric (1892-1975) and Vladimir Prelog (1906-98) — A241

2012, May 23
270 A241 1.50m multi   1.90 1.90

Apparition of the Virgin Mary at Medjugorje, 31st Anniv. — A242

2012, June 1
271 A242 1m multi   1.50 1.50

Walled Towns — A243

No. 272: a, Visoko. b, Blagaj.

2012, June 22
272 A243 60pf Pair, #a-b   1.50 1.50

Father Nikola Simovic (1839-1912), Vicar General — A244

2012, Sept. 10
273 A244 1m multi   1.40 1.40
Printed in sheets of 8 + central label.

Sargija — A245

2012, Oct. 9
274 A245 20pf multi   .30 .30

3rd Cent. B.C. Coins From Daorson — A246

No. 275 — Obverse and reverse of coin: a, With verdigris (green oxidation). b, Without verdigris.

2012, Oct. 31   **Litho. & Embossed**
275 A246 5m Pair, #a-b   12.00 12.00
Savings Day. No. 275 was printed in sheets containing two pairs.

Prunus Avium — A247

Prunus avium: a, Fruit. b, Blossoms.

2012, Nov. 1   **Litho.**
276 A247 50pf Pair, #a-b   1.40 1.40
   Printed in sheets containing 4 pairs + 2 labels

Snakes — A248

No. 277: a, Natrix natrix. b, Zamenis longissimus. c, Vipera ammodytes. d, Vipera berus.

2012, Nov. 1   **Perf. 14**
277 A248 2m Block of 4, #a-d   10.00 10.00

Christmas
A249

New Year's
Day — A250

2012, Dec. 1
278 A249 70pf multi   .95 .95
279 A250 70pf multi   .95 .95

Edict of Milan,
1700th
Anniv. — A251

2013, Jan. 26
280 A251 90pf multi   1.25 1.25
   Printed in sheets of 8 + central label.

New Year
2013 (Year of
the Snake)
A252

2013, Feb. 10   **Perf. 14**
281 A252 20pf multi   .30 .30

Kulin (1163-1204), Ban of
Bosnia — A253

2013, Mar. 1
282 A253 1.50m multi   2.00 2.00
   Printed in sheets of 8 + 2 labels.

Europa — A254

No. 283: a, Postal van. b, Postal moped.

2013, Apr. 5   **Perf. 14¼x14**
283 A254 3m Horiz. pair, #a-b   8.00 8.00
c.   Souvenir sheet of 4, 2 each
    #283a-283b   16.00 16.00
No. 283 was printed in sheets containing 4 pairs + 2 labels.

Intl. Firefighter's Day — A255

2013, May 4   **Perf. 14**
284 A255 70pf multi   .95 .95

Cemetery Stone,
Monastery of St.
John, Livno — A256

2013, May 12
285 A256 10pf multi   .25 .25

Postage Stamps of Croat
Administration, 20th Anniv. — A257

Litho. With Foil Application
Perf. 13¾x14 Syncopated
2013, May 12
286 A257 2.10m multi   2.75 2.75
   Printed in sheets of 9 + label.

Souvenir Sheet

Quercus Cerris — A258

Perf. 13¾x14 Syncopated
2013, May 22   **Litho.**
287 A258 2m multi   2.50 2.50

Apparition of
the Virgin
Mary at
Medjugorje,
32nd Anniv.
A259

2013, June 1   **Litho.**   **Perf. 14**
288 A259 1m multi   1.40 1.40

Friar Radoslav Glavas
(1867-1913),
Writer — A260

2013, July 20   **Litho.**   **Perf. 14x14¼**
289 A260 1m multi   1.40 1.40

Wooden Plow — A261

2013, Oct. 9   **Litho.**   **Perf. 14x14¼**
290 A261 2.70m multi   3.50 3.50

Giuseppe Verdi (1813-1901),
Composer — A262

2013, Oct. 10   **Litho.**   **Perf. 14x14¼**
291 A262 1.50m multi   1.90 1.90
   No. 291 was printed in sheets of 8 + 2 labels.

Friar Dominik Mandic (1889-1973),
Historian — A263

2013, Oct. 24   **Litho.**   **Perf. 14**
292 A263 1.10m multi   1.50 1.50

Celtis
Australis — A264

No. 293: a, Tree. b, Leaves and fruit on branch.

2013, Nov. 1   **Litho.**   **Perf. 14x14¼**
293 A264 3.10m Vert. pair, #a-b   8.00 8.00

Lutra
Lutra — A265

No. 294 — Otter: a, Head at left, denomination in black. b, Head at right, denomination in white. c, Head at right, denomination in black. d, Head in center, denomination in white.

2013, Nov. 1   **Litho.**   **Perf. 14¼x14**
294 A265 3.10m Vert. strip of
     4, #a-d   16.00 16.00

Christmas and New
Year's Day — A266

No. 295: a, Christmas (blue frame). b, New Year's Day (red frame).

2013, Dec. 1   **Litho.**   **Perf. 14x14¼**
295 A266 90pf Vert. pair, #a-b   2.40 2.40

Friar Mladen Hrkac (1950-2010) A267

2013, Dec. 20   Litho.   Perf. 14
296 A267 2.90m multi   3.75 3.75
  Intl. Human Solidarity Day. No. 296 was printed in sheets of 8 + central label.

Writers — A268

  No. 297: a, Jagoda Truhelka (1864-1957), novelist. b, Anton Gustav Matos (1873-1914), poet. c, Friar Lucijan Kordic (1914-93), historian.

2014, Feb. 21   Litho.   Perf. 14
297 Horiz. strip of 3 +
       flanking label   2.40 2.40
  a.-c. A268 60pf Any single   .75 .75
  Intl. Day of the Mother Tongue.

Snowy Idyll, Painting by Gabrijel Jurkic (1886-1974) — A269

2014, Feb. 25   Litho.   Perf. 14
298 A269 5m multi   6.50 6.50

Europa — A270

  No. 299 — Musical instruments: a, Diple. b, Dvojnice.

2014, Apr. 5   Litho.   Perf. 14
299 A270 3m Pair, #a-b   7.50 7.50
  c.   Souvenir sheet of 4, 2 each
           #299a-299b   15.00 15.00
  No. 299 was printed in sheets of 8 (4 each Nos. 299a-299b) + 2 central labels.

William Shakespeare (1564-1616), Writer, Scene From *Romeo and Juliet* — A271

2014, Apr. 23   Litho.   Perf. 14
300 A271 50pf multi   .70 .70

15th Century Tombstone, Sluzanj — A272

2014, May 12   Litho.   Perf. 14
301 A272 90pf multi   1.25 1.25

Souvenir Sheet

Corylus Avellana Leaves and Nuts — A273

2014, May 22   Litho.   Perf. 14
302 A273 2m multi   2.75 2.75

International Sports Day — A274

2014, May 25   Litho.   Perf. 14x13¾
303 A274 1m multi   1.40 1.40
  Values are for stamps with surrounding selvage. No. 303 was printed in sheets of 8 + central label.

Apparition of the Virgin Mary at Medjugorje, 33rd Anniv. — A275

2014, June 1   Litho.   Perf. 14x13¾
304 A275 1m multi   1.40 1.40
  Values are for stamps with surrounding selvage. No. 304 was impregnated with a rose scent.

Ivan Zovko (1864-1900), Writer and Folklorist — A276

2014, Aug. 20   Litho.   Perf. 14
305 A276 1.50m multi   2.00 2.00
  No. 305 was printed in sheets of 8 + central label.

Victory of Marin Cilic in 2013 U. S. Open Tennis Championships — A277

2014, Sept. 28   Litho.   Perf. 14
306 A277 1.50m multi   2.00 2.00
  No. 306 was printed in sheets of 8 + central label.

Lace A278

2014, Oct. 9   Litho.   Perf. 14x13¾
307 A278 20pf multi   .25 .25
  No. 307 was printed in sheets of 8 + central label. Values are for stamps with surrounding selvage.

Roman Gold Coin Depicting Emperor Nero — A279

Litho. & Embossed
2014, Oct. 31   Perf. 14
308 A279 3m multi   4.00 4.00
  No. 308 was printed in sheets of 6 + 2 labels.

Flowers — A280

  No. 309: a, Helleborus hercegovinus. b, Lilium cattaniae.

2014, Nov. 1   Litho.   Perf. 14
309 A280 1m Pair, #a-b   2.60 2.60

Farm Animals — A281

  No. 310: a, Equus caballus. b, Equus asinus. c, Equus hinnus. d, Equus mulus.

2014, Nov. 1   Litho.   Perf. 14
310 A281 3m Block of 4, #a-d   15.50 15.50

Christmas and New Year's Day — A282

  No. 311: a, Clock and champagne flutes. b, Holy Family, Christmas tree.

2014, Dec. 1   Litho.   Perf. 14
311 A282 90pf Pair, #a-b   2.40 2.40

Persecution of Franciscans at Siroki Brijeg, 70th Anniv. — A283

2015, Feb. 7   Litho.   Perf. 14
312 A283 90pf pur & blk   1.10 1.10
  No. 312 was printed in sheets of 12 + 4 labels.

Ilija Jakovljevic (1898-1948), Writer — A284

2015, Feb. 21   Litho.   Perf. 14
313 A284 1.50m tan & blk   1.75 1.75

Father Mihovila Sucica (1820-65), Physician — A285

2015, Mar. 3   Litho.   Perf. 14
314 A285 1m multi   1.25 1.25

Easter — A286

Litho. With Foil Application
2015, Mar. 25   *Perf. 14*
315 A286 90pf multi   1.10 1.10

No. 315 was printed in sheets of 8 + central label.

Europa — A287

No. 316 — Children and toys: a, Wooden whistle. b, Rocking horse.

2015, Apr. 4   **Litho.**   *Perf. 14*
316 A287 3m Horiz. pair, #a-b   6.75 6.75
   c.   Souvenir sheet of 4, 2 each
      #316a-316b   13.50 13.50

No. 316 was printed in sheets containing 4 pairs + 2 labels.

International Day of Sports for Development and Peace — A288

2015, Apr. 6   **Litho.**   *Perf. 14*
317 A288 5m multi   6.00 6.00

Rivine Archaeological Site — A289

2015, May 12   **Litho.**   *Perf. 14*
318 A289 10pf multi   .25 .25

Souvenir Sheet

Woman Knitting Shirt From Hemp Fibers — A290

2015, May 22   **Litho.**   *Perf. 14*
319 A290 2.90m multi   3.50 3.50

Apparition of the Virgin Mary at Medjugorje, 34th Anniv. — A291

2015, June 1   **Litho.**   *Perf. 14*
320 A291 1m multi   1.25 1.25

Visit of Pope Francis to Bosnia & Herzegovina A292

2015, June 6   **Litho.**   *Perf. 14*
321 A292 90pf multi   1.10 1.10

No. 321 was printed in sheets of 8 + central label.

International Left-Hander's Day — A293

2015, Aug. 13   **Litho.**   *Perf. 14*
322 A293 2m multi   2.40 2.40

Lace — A294

Litho. & Embossed
2015, Oct. 9   *Perf. 14*
323 A294 3.60m multi   4.25 4.25

Intl. Day of Hiking — A295

2015, Oct. 15   **Litho.**   *Perf. 14*
324 A295 1m multi   1.25 1.25

No. 324 was printed in sheets of 8 + central label.

World Food Day — A296

2015, Oct. 16   **Litho.**   *Perf. 14*
325 A296 90pf multi   1.10 1.10

Flowers — A297

No. 326: a, Arum petteri. b, Crocus tommasinianus.

2015, Nov. 1   **Litho.**   *Perf. 14*
326 A297 2m Pair, #a-b   5.00 5.00

Mammals — A298

No. 327: a, Canis lupus. b, Vulpes vulpes. c, Canis aureus. d, Ursus arctos.

2015, Nov. 1   **Litho.**   *Perf. 14*
327 A298 2m Block or vert.
     strip of 4, #a-d   10.00 10.00

Christmas and New Year's Day — A299

No. 328: a, Window and ornaments (New Year's Day). b, Nativity scene (Christmas).

Litho. (#328a), Litho. & Embossed
(#328b)
2015, Dec. 1   *Perf. 14*
328 A299 90pf Pair, #a-b   2.00 2.00

Publication of General Theory of Relativity, by Albert Einstein, Cent. — A300

2016, Mar. 20   **Litho.**   *Perf. 14*
329 A300 90pf multi   1.10 1.10

No. 329 was printed in sheets of 8 + central label.

Europa A301

2016, Apr. 5   **Litho.**   *Perf. 14*
330 A301 3m multi   3.50 3.50
   a.   Souvenir sheet of 2   7.00 7.00
     Think Green Issue.

No. 330 was printed in sheets of 8 + 2 labels.

Runners — A302

2016, Apr. 6   **Litho.**   *Perf. 14*
331 A302 90pf multi   1.10 1.10

International Day of Sport for Development and Peace.

Roman Empire Courier Service A303

2016, May 12   **Litho.**   *Perf. 14*
332 A303 1.50m multi   1.75 1.75

No. 332 was printed in sheets of 8 + central label.

Souvenir Sheet

Cornelian Cherries — A304

2016, May 22   **Litho.**   *Perf. 14*
333 A304 5m multi   5.75 5.75

Father Petar Bakula (1816-73), Theologian — A305

2016, May 24   **Litho.**   *Perf. 14*
334 A305 90pf multi   1.10 1.10

Apparition of the Virgin Mary at Medjugorje, 35th Anniv. — A306

2016, June 1   **Litho.**   *Perf. 14*
335 A306 1m multi   1.25 1.25

Serpentine Die Cut 15¼x14¼
Syncopated
Coil Stamp
Self-Adhesive
336 A306 1m multi   1.25 1.25

World Environment Day — A307

2016, June 5   **Litho.**   *Perf. 14*
337 A307 90pf multi   1.10 1.10

Serpentine Die Cut 15¼x14¼
Syncopated
Coil Stamp
Self-Adhesive
338 A307 90pf multi   1.10 1.10

World
Heart
Day
A308

2016, Sept. 29　Litho.　Perf. 14
339　A308　2.70m multi　　　3.25　3.25
Values are for stamps with surrounding
selvage.

Old Agricultural
Tools — A309

2016, Oct. 9　Litho.　Perf. 14
340　A309　1.10m multi　　　1.25　1.25

Water Lilies — A310

No. 341: a, Nymphaea alba. b, Nymphaea
lutea.

2016, Nov. 1　Litho.　Perf. 14
341　A310　2.70m Pair, #a-b　6.25　6.25

Frogs — A311

No. 342: a, Bombina variegata. b, Bombina
bombina. c, Rana arvalis. d, Rana graeca.

2016, Nov. 1　Litho.　Perf. 14
342　A311　2.10m Block or vert.
　　　　　　strip of 4, #a-d　9.50　9.50

Aristotle (384-
322 B.C.),
Philosopher
A312

2016, Nov. 17　Litho.　Perf. 14
343　A312　90pf multi　　　1.00　1.00

International Men's
Day — A313

Litho. With Foil Application
2016, Nov. 19　　　　　Perf. 14
344　A313　5m multi　　　5.50　5.50

Christmas and New
Year's Day — A314

No. 345: a, Snowman in 2017 snow globe.
b, Holy Family.

2016, Dec. 1　Litho.　Perf. 14
345　A314　90pf Pair, #a-b　2.00　2.00

International
Water
Day — A315

2017, Mar. 22　Litho.　Perf. 14
346　A315　2.70m multi　　　3.00　3.00

Reconstruction
of Franciscan
Monastery,
Humac
A316

2017, May 4　Litho.　Perf. 14
347　A316　60pf multi　　　.70　.70

Europa — A317

No. 348: a, Pocitelj Castle. b, Vranduk
Castle.

2017, May 9　Litho.　Perf. 14
348　A317　3m Pair, #a-b　7.00　7.00
　c.　Souvenir sheet of 4, 2 each
　　　#348a-348b　　　14.00　14.00
Printed in sheets of 8, containing 4 each
Nos. 348a-348b + 2 central labels.

12th Century
Tombstone Epitaph
for Priest
Tjehodraga — A318

2017, May 12　Litho.　Perf. 14
349　A318　90pf black & red　1.10　1.10
Coil Stamp
Self-Adhesive
Serpentine Die Cut 15¼x14¼
Syncopated
350　A318　90pf black & red　1.10　1.10

Souvenir Sheet

Myth of Narcissus and Echo — A319

2017, May 22　Litho.　Perf. 14
351　A319　5m multi　　　5.75　5.75

Apparition of the
Virgin Mary at
Medjugorje, 36th
Anniv. — A320

2017, June 1　Litho.　Perf. 14
352　A320　1m multi　　　1.25　1.25

Invention of
Draisine, by
Karl Drais
(1785-1851)
A321

2017, June 12　Litho.　Perf. 14
353　A321　2.90m multi　　　3.50　3.50

Radoslav Dodig (1954-2016),
Archaeologist — A322

2017, June 17　Litho.　Perf. 14
354　A322　90pf multi　　　1.10　1.10

Friar Branko Maric
(1896-1974),
Ethnomusicologist
A323

2017, June 21　Litho.　Perf. 14
355　A323　2.70m multi　　　3.25　3.25
World Music Day. No. 355 was printed in
sheets of 8 + 2 central labels.

Painting by Milivoj
Uzelac (1897-
1977) — A325

2017, July 23　Litho.　Perf. 14
359　A325　2.90m multi　　　3.50　3.50

BOSNIA & HERZEGOVINA
(SERB ADMIN)

Bosnian Serb Administration
Located In Banja Luka
(Republika Srpska)
100 Paras = 1 Dinar
100 pfennig = 1 mark (6/22/98)

Catalogue values for all unused
stamps in this country are for
Never Hinged items.

Stamps of Yugoslavia Surcharged

No. 3

No. 3a

No. 4

No. 9

No. 11

1992, Oct. 26　Litho.　Perf. 12½
1　A559　5d on 10p
　　　　　#2004　　　1.50　1.50
2　A559　30d on 3d #2015　160.00　160.00
3　A559　50d on 40p
　　　　　#2007a,
　　　　　perf. 13½　　　1.50　1.50
　a.　Thick bars in obliterator　1.50　1.50
　b.　On #2007, perf 12½　100.00　100.00
4　A559　60d on 20p
　　　　　#2005　　　1.75　1.75
5　A559　60d on 30p
　　　　　#2006　　　1.75　1.75
6　A559　100d on 1d #2013　1.75　1.75
7　A559　100d on 2d
　　　　　#2014a,
　　　　　perf. 13½　　　1.75　1.75
　a.　On #2014, perf 12½　75.00　75.00
8　A559　100d on 3d #2015　1.75　1.75
9　A621　300d on 5d
　　　　　#2017a,
　　　　　perf. 13½　　　1.75　1.75
　a.　On #2017, perf 12½　30.00　30.00
10　A620　500d on 50p
　　　　　#2008　　　1.75　1.75
11　A619　500d on 60p
　　　　　#2009　　　1.75　1.75
　a.　On #2009 perf. 13½　110.00　110.00
　　　Nos. 1-11 (11)　　　177.00　177.00
Obliterator on Nos. 1, 3 and 9 has thin bars.

Musical
Instrument — A1

Designs: 10d, 20d, 30d, 5000d, 6000d,
10,000d, Stringed instrument. 50d, 100d,
20,000d, 30,000d, Coat of arms, vert. 500d,
50,000d, Monastery.

1993   *Perf. 13¼, 12½ (#19)*
12	A1	10d blk & org yel	5.25	5.25
13	A1	20d blk & blue	.25	.25
14	A1	30d blk & salmon	.60	.60
15	A1	50d blk & ver	.60	.60
16	A1	100d blk & ver	1.60	1.60
17	A1	500d blk & blue	3.50	3.50
18	A1	5000d blk & lilac	.30	.30
19	A1	6000d blk & yel	.30	.30
20	A1	10,000d blk & vio bl	3.75	3.75
a.		Perf. 12½	2.75	2.75
21	A1	20,000d blk & ver	1.00	1.00
22	A1	30,000d blk & ver	1.60	1.60
23	A1	50,000d blk & lilac	1.60	1.60
		Nos. 12-23 (12)	20.35	20.35

Nos. 12-17 dated 1992, others dated 1993. Issued: Nos. 12-17, 1/11; others 6/8.

Nos. 13 and 21 with an "A" overprint and stamps of type A1 with an "R" overprint are locals.

For surcharges see Nos. 24-26, 34-36, 41-45, F9.

Nos. 15-16 Surcharged

1993, June 15
24	A1	7500d on 50d #15	2.00	2.00
25	A1	7500d on 100d #16	2.00	2.00
26	A1	9000d on 50d #15	3.00	3.00
		Nos. 24-26 (3)	7.00	7.00

Referendum, May 15-16, 1993.

A2

Symbol of St. John, the Evangelist.

1993, Aug. 16   *Perf. 13¼*
27	A2	(A) vermilion	.70	.70

Icon of St. Stefan — A3

1994, Jan. 9   *Perf. 14*
28	A3	1d multicolored	7.00	7.00

King Peter I Karageorge A4

1994, May 28
29	A4	80p sepia	3.00	3.00

City of Banja Luka, 500th Anniv. A5

1994, July 18
30	A5	1.20d multicolored	4.00	4.00

Madonna & Child, Cajnica Church — A6

1994, Sept. 1
33	A6	1d multicolored		3.25 3.25

Nos. 18, 20, 23 Surcharged

1994, Nov. 1   *Perf. 13¼*
34	A1	(A) on 5000d #18	1.60	1.60
35	A1	40p on 10,000d #20	1.60	1.60
a.		On #20a	3.50	3.50
36	A1	2d on 50,000d #23	1.60	1.60
a.		Perf 12½	22.50	22.50
		Nos. 34-36,F9 (4)	6.40	6.40

No. 34 sold for 20p on day of issue.

Mostanica Monastery A7

Designs: 60p, Tavna Monastery, vert. 1.20d, Zitomislic Monastery, vert.

1994   *Perf. 14*
37-39	A7	Set of 3	9.00	9.00

Issued: 60p, 11/11; 1d, 12/31; 1.20d, 12/28.

Flora & Fauna A8

No. 40: a, Shore lark. b, Dinaromys bogdanovi. c, Edraianthus niveus. d, Aquilegia dinarica.

1996, Mar. 1   *Perf. 13¾*
40	A8	1.20d Block of 4, #a.-d.	5.25	5.25

Nos. 14-16, 19, 22 Surcharged

1996, July 1   *Perf. 13¼*
41	A1	70p on 30d #14	.50	.50
42	A1	1d on 100d #16	.70	.70
43	A1	2d on 30,000d #22	1.40	1.40
44	A1	3d on 50d #15	2.25	2.25

           Perf. 12½
45	A1	5d on 6000d #19	3.75	3.75
		Nos. 41-45 (5)	8.60	8.60

Relay Station, Mt. Kozara — A9

1.20d, Drina River Bridge, Srbinje, horiz. 2d, Mt. Romanija relay station. 5d, Stolice relay station, Mt. Maljevica. 10d, Visegrad Bridge, horiz.

1996, Sept. 20   *Perf. 14*
46	A9	(A) multicolored	.25	.25
47	A9	1.20d multicolored	.60	.60
48	A9	2d multicolored	1.20	1.20
49	A9	5d multicolored	2.75	2.75
50	A9	10d multicolored	5.50	5.50
		Nos. 46-50,F10 (6)	11.05	11.05

No. 46 sold for 30p on day of issue.

Church, Bashcharsi A10

1997, July 7   *Perf. 13¾*
51	A10	2.50d multicolored		1.75 1.75

Mihailo Pupin (1848-1935), Electrical Engineer A11

1997, July 14
52	A11	2.50d multicolored		1.75 1.75

A12

Flowers: No. 53, Oxytropis compestris. No. 54, Primula kitaibeliana. No. 55, Pedicularis hoermanniana. No. 56, Knautia sarajevensis.

1997, Sept. 12
53-56	A12	3.20d Set of 4		7.00 7.00

A13

Famous Men: A, Branko Copic (1915-85). 1.50d, Mesa Selimovic (1910-82). 3d, Aleksa Santic (1868-1924). 5d, Peter Kocic (1873-1916). 10d, Ivo Andric (1892-1975).

1997, Nov. 1   *Perf. 13¾*
57	A13	A multicolored	.35	.35
58	A13	1.50d multicolored	.55	.55
59	A13	3d multicolored	1.40	1.40
60	A13	5d multicolored	2.40	2.40
61	A13	10d multicolored	4.50	4.50
		Nos. 57-61,F11 (6)	9.95	9.95

No. 57 sold for 60p on day of issue.

A14

2.50d, Lutra lutra. 4.50d, Capreolus capreolus. 6.50d, Ursus arctos.

1997, Nov. 12
62-64	A14	Set of 3		6.00 6.00

Europa — A15

Stories & legends: 2.50d, Two queens. 6.50d, Prince on horseback.

1997, Nov. 12
65-66	A15	Set of 2		22.50 22.50

Diana, Princess of Wales (1961-97) — A16

"Diana" in: a, Roman letters. b, Cyrillic letters.

1997, Dec. 22
67	A16	3.50d Pair, #a.-b.	15.00	15.00

1998 World Cup Soccer Championships, France — A17

Players, country flags (each 90p) — No. 68: a, Brazil. b, Morocco. c, Norway. d, Scotland. e, Italy. f, Chile. g, Austria. h, Cameroun.

No. 69: a, France. b, Saudi Arabia. c, Denmark. d, South Africa. e, Spain. f, Nigeria. g, Paraguay. h, Bulgaria.

No. 70: a, Netherlands. b, Belgium. c, Mexico. d, South Korea. e, Germany. f, US. g, Yugoslavia. h, Iran.

No. 71: a, Romania. b, England. c, Tunisia. d, Colombia. e, Argentina. f, Jamaica. g, Croatia. h, Japan.

1998, May 5   **Sheets of 8 + label**
68-71	A17	Set of 4	60.00	60.00

Europa — A18

Natl. festivals, each 7.50d: No. 72, Instrument at R. No. 73, Instrument at L.

1998, June 9
72-73	A18	Set of 2	*21.00 21.00*

Icons, Chelandari Monastery A19

Various icons: 50p, 70p, 1.70d, 2d.

1998
74-77	A19	Set of 4		9.00 9.00

Buildings — A20

Designs: 15pf, Bijeljina. 20pf, Sokolac. A, Banja Luka. 75pf, Prijedor. 2m, Brcko, vert. 4.50m, Zvornik, vert. 10m, Doboj.

1999, Mar. 15   Litho.   Perf. 13¾
78-84 A20 Set of 7   27.50 27.50

No. 80 has black "A." It sold for 50pf on day of issue. See No. F12.

Air Srpska Airplanes A21

Airplane: No. 85, 50pf, In clouds. No. 86, 50pf, Over lake. 75pf, Over rocks. 1.50m, Over lake, diff.

1999, Mar. 26   Litho.   Perf. 13¾
85-88 A21 Set of 4   6.00 6.00

World Table Tennis Championships, Belgrade — A22

Designs: 1m, Cracked globe as ball. 2m, Table, paddle, ball.

1999, Apr. 19
89-90 A22 Set of 2   7.50 7.50

Issued in sheets of 8 + label.

Europa — A23

Natl. Parks: 1.50m, Kozara. 2m, Peruchitsa.

1999, May 4
91-92 A23 Set of 2   160.00 160.00

Anniversaries — A24

No. 93, each 50pf: a, Gorazde incorporation document. b, Dobrin Monastery (denomination at UL). c, Illuminated letter. d, Zitomislic Monastery. e, Gomionica Monastery (2 steeples). f, Madonna and Child icon. g, St. Nicholas icon. h, Holy trinity icon.

1999, May 26   Litho.   Perf. 13¾
93 A24 Sheet of 8, #a-h, + label 7.00 7.00

Dabrobosanska and Zahumskohercegovacka Archbishopric, 780th anniv., Gorazde Printing Press, 480th anniv.

Fish — A25

No. 94: a, 50pf, Salmo trutta m. fario. b, 50pf, Salmo trutta m. lacustris. c, 75pf, Hucho hucho. d, 1m, Thymallus thymallus.

1999, June 17
94 A25 Horiz. strip of 4, #a-d, +
         central label   5.25 5.25

Issued in sheets of 5 strips with different labels.

Man on the Moon, 30th Anniv. — A26

Designs: 1m, Equipment on moon. 2m, Astronaut, lunar module.

1999, July 21
95-96 A26 Set of 2   5.25 5.25

Issued in sheets of 8 + 1 label.

UPU, 125th Anniv. — A27

Designs: 75pf, Pencil. 1.25m, Arc and map.

1999, Sept. 9
97-98 A27 Set of 2   3.75 3.75

Issued in sheets of 8 + 1 label.

Icons — A28

No. 99, each 50pf: a, Madonna and Child (black denomination at UL). b, Madonna and Child (white denomination at UL). c, Madonna and Child (white denomination at LR). d, Saint with cross. e, Pieta. f, Christ enters Jerusalem (on donkey). g, St. Jovan (with scroll). h, Sts. Sava and Simeon.

1999, Oct. 29
99 A28 Sheet of 8, #a-h, + label 6.00 6.00

Millennium A29

a, Egyptians, obelisk. b, Hourglass. c, Iron bell. d, Locomotive, steamship. e, Balloon, airplanes, automobiles. f, Man on the moon.

1999, Nov. 22
100   Booklet pane of 6   13.00 13.00
a.-e. A29 50pf Any single   1.75 1.75
f. A29 1m multi   3.00 3.00
     Booklet, #100   14.00 14.00

See No. 126.

Postal Services in Serbian Territory, 135th Anniv. — A30

3m, Postriders on bridge.

1999, Dec. 23
101 A30 50pf shown   .85 .85

Souvenir Sheet
102 A30 3m multi   70.00 70.00

Prince Stephen Nemanja — A31

2000, Feb. 29
103 A31 1.50m multi   2.75 2.75

Issued in sheets of 8 + 1 label.

Flora — A32

1m, Prunus domestica. 2m, Corylus avellana.

2000, Mar. 22
104-105 A32 Set of 2   4.00 4.00

Issued in sheets of 8 + 1 label.

Bridges — A33

No. 106, Brod (deer at left). No. 107, Pavlovica (horses and birds). No. 108, Zepce (bird at right). No. 109, Zvornik (bird at left).

2000, Apr. 12
106-109 A33 1m Set of 4   7.00 7.00

Issued in sheets of 8 + 1 label.

Jovan Ducic (1871-1943), Writer — A34

2000, Apr. 26   Litho.   Perf. 13¾
110 A34 20pf multi   .45 .45

Common Design Type and

Europa — A35

2000, May 5   Litho.   Perf. 13¾
111 CD17 1.50m multi   50.00 50.00
112 A35   2.50m multi   60.00 60.00

Banja Luka Province, Cent. — A36

2000, May 26   Litho.   Perf. 13¾
113 A36 1.50m multi   2.75 2.75

European Soccer Championships A37

Various players. Denominations: 1m, 2m.

2000, June 14
114-115 A37 Set of 2   5.75 5.75

Souvenir Sheet
116 A37 6m Players, map   17.50 17.50

No. 116 contains one 35x42mm stamp.

Nevesinje Rebellion, 125th Anniv. — A38

2000, July 12
117 A38 1.50m multi   2.75 2.75

2000 Summer Olympics, Sydney A39

Map of Australia and: No. 118, 50pf, Handball. No. 119, 50pf, Basketball. No. 120, 50pf, Hurdles. No. 121, 50pf, Volleyball. 2m, Emu, kangaroo, Australian arms.

2000, Sept. 6
118-121 A39 Set of 4   3.50 3.50

Souvenir Sheet
122 A39 2m multi + label   3.50 3.50

No. 122 contains one 42x35mm stamp.

Locomotives A40

No. 123 — Locomotive from: a, 1848. b, 1865. c, 1930. d, 1990.

2000, Oct. 4   Litho.   Perf. 13¾
123   Horiz. strip of 4 +
          central label   8.50 8.50
a.-c. A40 50pf Any single   1.50 1.50
d. A40 1m multi   3.00 3.00

Protected Species — A41

Designs: 1m, Leontopodium alpinum. 2m, Proteus anguinus, horiz.

2000, Oct. 31
124-125 A41 Set of 2 5.50 5.50

Millennium Type of 1999

No. 126: a, Ship. b, Glassblowers. c, Blacksmith. d, Printers. e, James Watt, steam engine, steam-powered vehicle. f, Satellites. g, People on shore, ships (105x55mm).

2000, Nov. 22
126		Booklet pane of 7 + label	10.00	10.00
a.-f.	A29	50pf Any single	1.00	1.00
g.	A29	3m multi	4.00	4.00
		Booklet, #126	11.00	11.00

Icons — A42

Icons from: No. 127, 50pf, 1577-78. No. 128, 50pf, 1607-08. No. 129, 1m, 1577-78. No. 130, 1m, Unknown year.

2000, Dec. 20
127-130 A42 Set of 4 5.00 5.00

Invention of the Telephone, 125th Anniv. — A43

2001, Feb. 27
131 A43 1m multi 1.75 1.75

Manned Space Flight, 40th Anniv. — A44

Designs: 1m, Yuri Gagarin, Vostok 1. 3m, Gagarin, Earth, rocket lift-off.

2001, Mar. 29
132 A44 1m multi 1.75 1.75

Souvenir Sheet
133 A44 3m multi 7.00 7.00

No. 133 contains one 53x35mm stamp.

Vlado Milosevic, Composer — A45

2001, Apr. 11
134 A45 50pf multi .90 .90

Europa — A46

Designs: Nos. 135, 137a, 1m, Skakavac Waterfall. No. 136, 137b, 2m, Turjanica River.

White Border
2001, May 4 **Perf. 13¾**
135-136 A46 Set of 2 6.00 6.00

Light Blue Border
Perf. 13¾ Vert.
137 A46 Vert. pair, #a-b 15.00 15.00

No. 137 printed in panes of 3 pairs which were sold with a booklet cover, but unattached to it.

Butterflies — A47

Designs: No. 138, 50pf, Maniola jurtina. No. 139, 50pf, Pyrgus malvae. No. 140, 1m, Papilio machaon. No. 141, 1m, Lycaena pylaeas.

2001, June 19 **Perf. 13¾**
138-141 A47 Set of 4 5.50 5.50

Kostajnica A48

Srbinje — A49

2001, Sept. 5 **Litho.** **Perf. 13¾**
142 A48 25pf multi .50 .50
143 A49 1m multi 1.60 1.60

Issued: 25pf, 9/5. 1m, 9/20.

Karate Championships A50

2001, Sept. 5
144 A50 1.50m multi 2.50 2.50

A51 A51a

A51b A51c
Costumes

2001, July 17 **Litho.** **Perf. 13¾**
145 A51 50pf multi .75 .75
146 A51a 50pf multi .75 .75
147 A51b 1m multi 1.75 1.75
148 A51c 1m multi 1.75 1.75
Nos. 145-148 (4) 5.00 5.00

A52 A53

A54 A55

A56 A57
Caves

2001, Sept. 20 **Perf. 13¾ Vert.**
149		Booklet pane of 6	5.00	
a.	A52	50pf Rastusha Cave	.80	.80
b.	A53	50pf Vaganska Cave	.80	.80
c.	A54	50pf Pavlova Cave	.80	.80
d.	A55	50pf Orlovacha Cave	.80	.80
e.	A56	50pf Ledana Cave	.80	.80
f.	A57	50pf Pod Jelikom Cave	.80	.80

Building Type of 1999 with Red "A"

2001, Oct. 23 **Litho.** **Perf. 13¾**
150 A20 A Banja Luka .90 .90

No. 150 sold for 50pf on day of issue. "A" on No. 80 is in black.

Nobel Prizes, Cent. — A58

Designs: 1m, Alfred Nobel (1833-96). 2m, Ivo Andric (1892-1975), 1961 Literature laureate.

2001, Oct. 23
151-152 A58 Set of 2 5.00 5.00

Each stamp printed in sheets of 8 + central label.

Bardacha-Srbac — A59

Lake Klinje — A60

2001, Nov. 15
153 A59 1m multi 1.75 1.75
154 A60 1m multi 1.75 1.75

Each stamp printed in sheets of 8 + central label.

Art A61

Designs: No. 155, 50pf, Belgrade Suburb, by Kosta Hakman (1899-1961). No. 156, 50pf, Djerdap, by Todor Shvrakic (1882-1931). No. 157, 50pf, Still Life With Parrot, by Jovan Bijelic (1884-1964), vert. No. 158, 50pf, Adela, by Miodrag Vujacic Mirski (1932-97), vert.

2001, Dec. 5
155-158 A61 Set of 4 3.50 3.50

Each stamp printed in sheets of 8 + central label.

Christmas A62

2001, Dec. 5
159 A62 1m multi 1.75 1.75

Printed in sheets of 8 + central label.

Borac Soccer Team, 75th Anniv. — A63

2001, Dec. 24
160 A63 1.50m multi 2.50 2.50

Printed in sheets of 8 + central label.

Serb Administration, 10th Anniv. — A64

Designs: 50pf, Arms, vert. 1m, Flag.

2002, Jan. 10
161-162　A64　Set of 2　　　2.50　2.50
　Nos. 161-162 were each printed in sheets of 8 + central label. A number has been reserved for an additional item in this set.

Souvenir Sheet

Serb Administration, 10th Anniv. — A65

2002, Jan. 10　**Litho.**　***Perf. 13¾***
163　A65　2m multi　　　　3.50　3.50

War on Terrorism — A66

Designs: 1m, Hand holding snake. 2m, Globe, eyes, guns.

2002, Jan. 29　**Litho.**　***Perf. 13¾***
164　A66　1m multi　　　　1.60　1.60
Souvenir Sheet
165　A66　2m multi　　　　3.50　3.50
　No. 164 printed in sheets of 8 + central label. No. 165 contains one 35x46mm stamp.

2002 Winter Olympics, Salt Lake City — A67

Designs: 50pf, Ski jumper. 1m, Bobsled.

2002, Feb. 13
166-167　A67　Set of 2　　　2.50　2.50
　Each stamp printed in sheets of 8 + label.

Serbian Sarajevo — A68

Serbian Brod — A69

2002
168　A68　50pf multi　　　　.85　.85
169　A69　2m multi　　　　3.50　3.50
　Issued: 50pf, 3/5. 2m, 4/18.

Education, Cent. — A70

2002, Mar. 5
170　A70　1m multi　　　　1.60　1.60
　Printed in sheets of 8 + central label.

Charles Lindbergh's Non-stop Solo Trans-Atlantic Flight, 75th Anniv. — A71

2002, Apr. 11
171　A71　1m multi　　　　1.60　1.60
　Printed in sheets of 8 + central label.

Europa — A72

Designs: 1m, Horses and clown. 1.50m, Elephants and clowns.

2002, Apr. 30　**Litho.**　***Perf. 13¾***
172-173　A72　Set of 2　　　5.00　5.00
Pink Border
173A　Vert. pair　　　　9.00　9.00
　b.　A72 1m Like #172, imperf. at top　2.50　2.50
　c.　A72 1.50m Like #173, imperf. at bottom　5.00　5.00
　No. 173A printed in sheets of 3 pairs which were sold in a booklet cover, but unattached to it.

2002 World Cup Soccer Championships, Japan and Korea — A73

Designs: 50pf, Two players. 1m, Two players, diff.

2002, May 31
174-175　A73　Set of 2　　　2.50　2.50

Resorts — A74

Designs: 25pf, Banja Slatina. 50pf, Banja Mljechanica. 75pf, Banja Vilina Vlas. 1m, Banja Laktashi. 1.50m, Banja Vruchica. 5m, Banja Dvorovi.

2002, July 5
176-181　A74　Set of 6　　　14.00　14.00
　See No. 225. Compare with Nos. 241-242.

Artifacts A75

Designs: No. 182, 50pf, Greco-Illyrian helmet, 4th-5th cent. No. 183, 50pf, Glassware, 14th cent. No. 184, 1m, Silver snake heads, 4th-5th cent. No. 185, 1m, Inscriptions on stone, 12th cent.

2002, Sept. 5
182-185　A75　Set of 4　　　4.50　4.50

Mushrooms A76

　No. 186: a, Boletus regius. b, Macrolepiota procera. c, Amanita caesarea. d, Craterellus cornucopioides.

2002, Oct. 17　**Litho.**　***Perf. 13¾***
186　　Horiz. strip of 4, #a-d, + central label　　4.50　4.50
　a.-b.　A76 50pf Any single　1.00　1.00
　c.-d.　A76 1m Any single　1.40　1.40

Nature Protection — A77

Designs: 50pf, Maglic. 1m, Klekovacha.

2002, Nov. 26　**Litho.**　***Perf. 13¾***
187-188　A77　Set of 2　　　2.50　2.50

Art — A78

Designs: No. 189, 50pf, Crno Jezero pod Durmitorom, by Lazar Drijaca, 1935. No. 190, 50pf, Petar Popovic Pecija, by Spiro Bocaric, 1933, vert. No. 191, 1m, Zembiljeva Ulica, by Branko Sotra, 1937. No. 192, 1m, Ptice u Pejzazu, by Milan Sovilj, 2000.

2002, Dec. 18
189-192　A78　Set of 4　　　5.00　5.00

Souvenir Sheet

Showing of First Film in Bosnia, Cent. — A79

2003, Feb. 13　**Litho.**　***Perf. 13¾***
193　A79　3m multi　　　　5.00　5.00

Alekse Santic (1868-1924), Writer — A80

2003, Mar. 5
194　A80　1m multi　　　　1.60　1.60

Easter — A80a

Designs: 50pf, Crucifixion. 1m, Resurrection of Christ, by Matthias Grünewald.

2003, Mar. 28
195-196　A80a　Set of 2　　　2.50　2.50

Souvenir Sheet

First Ascent of Mt. Everest, 50th Anniv. — A81

　No. 197: a, Mt. Everest. b, Mt. Everest and mountain climber.

2003, Apr. 16　**Litho.**　***Perf. 13¾***
197　A81　1.50m Sheet of 2, #a-b　5.00　5.00

Europa — A82

Designs: 1m, Man affixing poster to wall. 1.50m, Hand and poster.

2003, May 5　　　　***Perf. 13¾***
198　A82　1m multi　　　　2.50　2.50
　a.　Perf. 13¾, imperf. at top　5.50　5.50
　b.　Perf. 13¾, imperf. at bottom　6.00　6.00
199　A82　1.50m multi　　　3.50　3.50
　a.　Perf. 13¾, imperf. at bottom　7.00　7.00
　b.　Perf. 13¾, imperf. at top　8.00　8.00
　A sheet of six containing one each of Nos. 198b and 199b and two each of Nos. 198a and 199a was sold in, but unattached to, a booklet cover.

Horses — A83

Designs: No. 200, 50pf, Arabian. No. 201, 50pf, Two Lippizaners. No. 202, 1m, Bosansko-brdski. No. 203, 1m, Two Posavacs.

2003, June 9　　　　***Perf. 13¾***
200-203　A83　Set of 4　　　5.00　5.00

A84

Visit of Pope John Paul II — A85

2003, June 22 **Perf. 13¾**
204 A84 1.50m multi 4.50 4.50
Perf. 13½x13¾
205 A85 1.50m multi 4.50 4.50
No. 204 was printed in sheets of 8 stamps + central label.

Orders — A86

Different orders with background colors of: 50pf, Brown. 1m, Blue.

2003, July 11 **Perf. 13¾x13**
206-207 A86 Set of 2 2.50 2.50

Fight Against Terrorism — A87

2003, Aug. 14 Litho. Perf. 13¾x13
208 A87 1m multi 1.60 1.60

Leo Tolstoy (1828-1910), Writer — A88

2003, Sept. 25 Litho. Perf. 13¾x13
209 A88 1m multi 1.60 1.60
Printed in sheets of 8 + label.

Nature Protection — A89

Designs: 50pf, Bear eating fish, Ugar River. 1m, Drina River.

2003, Oct. 21
210-211 A89 Set of 2 2.50 2.50
Each stamp printed in sheet of 8 + label.

Icons — A90

No. 212: a, St. Sava and Martyr Barbara (shown). b, St. Lazarus, 1658. c, Crowning of Mary in Heaven, by Dimitrije Bacevic. d, Holy Family.

2003, Nov. 19 **Perf. 13x13¾**
212 Horiz. strip of 4 + central label 5.00 5.00
a.-b. A90 50pf Either single 1.00 1.00
c.-d. A90 1m Either single 1.50 1.50

New Year's Day — A91

Designs: 50pf, Child and snowman. 1m, Santa Claus and reindeer.

2003, Dec. 5 **Perf. 13¾x13**
213-214 A91 Set of 2 2.50 2.50
Each stamp printed in sheet of 8 + label.

Powered Flight, Cent. — A92

Designs: 50pf, Wright Brothers, Wright Flyer. 1m, Count Ferdinand von Zeppelin, Graf Zeppelin.

2003, Dec. 17 **Perf. 13x13¾**
215-216 A92 Set of 2 2.50 2.50

Souvenir Sheet

First Serbian Rebellion, Bicent. — A93

No. 217 — Rebels: a, Denomination at UL. b, Denomination at LR.

2004, Feb. 5 **Perf. 13¾x13**
217 A93 1.50m Sheet of 2, #a-b 5.00 5.00

Souvenir Sheet

2004 Summer Olympics, Athens — A94

No. 218 — Chariot race: a, Denomination at UL. b, Denomination at UR.

2004, Mar. 2 **Perf. 13x13¾**
218 A94 1.50m Sheet of 2, #a-b 5.00 5.00

Albert Einstein (1879-1955) A95

2004, Mar. 12
219 A95 1.50m multi 2.50 2.50
Printed in sheets of 8 + label.

Easter — A96

Paintings by: 50pf, Konstantinos Xenopoulos, 1961. 1m, Eremija Profeta.

2004, Apr. 2
220-221 A96 Set of 2 2.50 2.50

Europa — A97

Designs: Nos. 222, 224a, 224b, 1m, White water rafting. Nos. 223, 224c, 224d, 1.50m, Paragliding.

2004, May 5 Litho. Perf. 13¾x13
White Border
222-223 A97 Set of 2 4.00 4.00
Light Blue Border
Perf. 13¾x13 on 3 Sides
224 Sheet of 6, #224b, 224d, 2 each #224a, 224c 16.00 16.00
a. A97 1m Imperf. at top 2.25 2.25
b. A97 1m Imperf. at bottom 2.25 2.25
c. A97 1.50m Imperf. at bottom 3.00 3.00
d. A97 1.50m Imperf. at top 3.00 3.00
Nos. 222-223 each were printed in sheets of 8 + label. No. 224 was sold in booklet cover but was not attached to it.

Resorts Type of 2002
2004, May 10 **Perf. 13¾**
225 A74 20pf Kulasi .50 .50
a. Dated "2006" .50 .50

Milutin Milankovic (1879-1958), Astronomer — A98

2004, May 28 **Perf. 13¾x13**
226 A98 1m multi 1.60 1.60
Printed in sheets of 8 + label.

European Soccer Championships, Portugal — A99

2004, June 8 **Perf. 13x13¾**
227 A99 1.50m multi 2.50 2.50
Printed in sheets of 8 + label.

2004 Summer Olympics, Athens A100

Athens Olympics emblem and: No. 228, 50pf, Shot put, Greek ruins. No. 229, 50pf, Hurdle, Greek ruins. No. 230, 1m, Runners, Greek ruins. No. 231, 1m, Runners, horses.

2004, July 12
228-231 A100 Set of 4 3.25 3.25
Nos. 228-230 each were printed in sheets of 8 + label. No. 231 was printed in sheet of 3 + 3 labels.

Nature Protection — A101

Designs: 50pf, Arctostaphylos uva-ursi. 1m, Monticola saxatilis.

2004, Aug. 27 Litho. Perf. 13¾x13
232-233 A101 Set of 2 2.50 2.50
Each stamp printed in sheets of 8 + label.

Minerals A102

Designs: No. 234, 50pf, Antimonite (shown). No. 235, 50pf, Pyrite (Prussian blue background). No. 236, 1m, Sphalerite. No. 237, 1m, Quartz, vert.

2004, Sept. 14 **Perf. 13¾**
234-237 A102 Set of 4 4.50 4.50
Each stamp printed in sheets of 8 + label.

Michael Pupin (1858-1935), Physicist — A103

2004, Oct. 9 Litho. Perf. 13¾x13½
238 A103 1m multi 1.60 1.60
Printed in sheets of 8 + label.

Fight Against Terrorism — A104

2004, Oct. 21
239 A104 1m multi 1.60 1.60
Printed in sheets of 8 + label.

Flowers — A105

No. 240: a, Digitalis grandiflora. b, Arnica montana. c, Rosa pendulina. d, Gentiana lutea.

2004, Nov. 18   Litho.   Perf. 13¾x13
240   Horiz. strip of 4 + central label   5.00   5.00
a.-b.   A105 50pf Either single   .80   .80
c.-d.   A105 1m Either single   1.60   1.60

Banja Mljechanica Resort — A106

Banja Laktashi Resort — A107

2004, Dec. 6   Perf. 13¾
241 A106 50pf multi   .75   .75
242 A107 1m multi   1.75   1.75

Compare No. 241 with No. 177, which has red in sky and a black roof. Compare No. 242 with No. 179, which has a blue sky.

Christmas A108

2004, Dec. 7   Perf. 13x13¾
243 A108 1m multi   1.60   1.60
Printed in sheets of 8 + label.

Paintings by Milenko Atanatskovic A109

Designs: 50c, Serbian Farmer, Semberije. 1m, Beledija, Stara Opstina, (house) horiz.

2005, Feb. 7   Perf. 13¾x13, 13x13¾
244-245 A109 Set of 2   2.50   2.50
Each stamp printed in sheets of 8 + label.

Janj River Waterfall A110

Perf. 13¼x13¾
2005, Mar. 22   Litho.
246 A110 1m multi   1.60   1.60
Printed in sheets of 8 + label.

Europa A111

Designs: Nos. 247, 249a, 249b, 1m, Cooking pots near fire. Nos. 248. 249c, 249d, 1.50m, Food on table.

2005, Apr. 4   Perf. 13¼x13¾
Tan Bottom Panel
247-248 A111   Set of 2   4.50   4.50
Green Bottom Panel
Perf. 13¼x13¾ on 3 Sides
249   Sheet of 6, #249b,
                249d, 2 each #249a,
                249c   11.00 11.00
a.   A111 1m Imperf. at top   1.25   1.25
b.   A111 1m Imperf. at bottom   1.25   1.25
c.   A111 1.50m Imperf. at top   2.00   2.00
d.   A111 1.50m Imperf. at bottom   2.00   2.00

Nos. 247-248 each were printed in sheets of 8 + label. No. 249 was issued with, but not attached to, a booklet cover.

Easter — A112

2005, Apr. 18   Perf. 13¾x13¼
250 A112 50pf multi   .80   .80
Printed in sheets of 8 + label.

Pope John Paul II (1920-2005) A113

Pope John Paul II: 1.50m, Praying. 5m, With arms open.

2005, Apr. 21   Litho.   Perf. 13x13¾
251 A113 1.50m multi   2.50   2.50
Souvenir Sheet
252 A113 5m multi   7.50   7.50
No. 251 printed in sheets of 8 + label.

Vipers — A114

No. 253: a, Vipera berus berus. b, Vipera ursinii. c, Vipera berus bosniensis. d, Vipera ammodytes.

Perf. 13¼x13¾
2005, June 23   Litho.
253   Horiz. strip of 4 + central label   5.00   5.00
a.-b.   A114 50pf Either single   .75   .75
c.-d.   A114 1m Either single   1.50   1.50

Disneyland, 50th Anniv. — A115

Designs: 50pf, Sleeping Beauty Castle. 1m, Buildings.

2005, July 15   Perf. 13¾x13¼
254-255 A115   Set of 2   2.50   2.50
Nos. 254-255 each printed in sheets of 8 + label.

Bulls — A116

2005, Aug. 5   Litho.   Perf. 13¼x13¾
256 A116 1.50m multi   2.50   2.50
Printed in sheets of 8 + label.

European Philatelic Cooperation, 50th Anniv. (in 2006) — A117

Designs: No. 257, 1.95m, Perucica (stream). No. 258, 1.95m, Rafters. No. 259, 1.95m, Old Bridge, Mostar. No. 260, 1.95m, Drina River multi-arch stone bridge.

2005, Aug. 30   Perf. 13¾x13¼
257-260 A117   Set of 4   12.00 12.00
260a   Sheet of 4, #257-260   13.00 13.00
Europa stamps, 50th anniv. (in 2006).
Nos. 257-260 each printed in sheets of 8 + label.

2005 European Basketball Championships — A118

No. 261 — Background colors: a, Green. b, Indigo. c, Blue. d, Red. e, Yellow brown.

Perf. 13¼x13¾
2005, Sept. 16   Litho.
261   Strip of 5   4.00   4.00
a.-e.   A118 50pf Any single   .75   .75

Museum of the Serb Republic, 75th Anniv. — A119

National Theater, 75th Anniv. — A120

2005, Sept. 26   Perf. 13¾x13¼
262 A119 1m multi   1.60   1.60
Perf. 13¼x13¾
263 A120 1m multi   1.60   1.60
Nos. 262-263 each printed in sheets of 8 + label.

Souvenir Sheet

Visegrad-Mokra Gora Railroad — A121

No. 264: a, 50pf, Train and tunnel. b, 1m, Train and station.

2005, Oct. 3   Perf. 13¼x13¾
264 A121   Sheet of 2, #a-b   2.50   2.50

Intl. Aeronautics Federation, Cent. — A122

2005, Oct. 14
265 A122 1.50m multi   2.50   2.50
Printed in sheets of 8 + label.

Dayton Peace Accords, 10th Anniv. — A123

2005, Nov. 21   Perf. 13¾x13¼
266 A123 1.50m multi   2.50   2.50
Printed in sheets of 8 + label.

Banja Guber Resort — A124

2005, Nov. 23   Perf. 13¾
267 A124 50pf multi   .80   .80

Nature Protection — A125

Birds: 50pf, Crex crex. 1m, Platalea leucorodia.

2005, Nov. 25   Perf. 13¾x13¼
268-269 A125   Set of 2   2.60   2.60
Nos. 268-269 each printed in sheets of 8 + label.

Liberation of Jasenovac Concentration Camp, 60th Anniv. — A126

2005, Dec. 15   Perf. 13¼x13¾
270 A126 50pf multi   .80   .80
Printed in sheets of 8 + label.

Wolfgang Amadeus Mozart (1756-91), Composer — A127

2006, Jan. 27   Perf. 13¾x13¼
271 A127 1.50m multi   2.50   2.50
Printed in sheets of 8 + label.

Branka Sotre (1906-60), Painter — A128

2006, Jan. 31
272 A128 1m multi   1.60 1.60
Printed in sheets of 8 + label.

2006 Winter Olympics, Turin — A129

Designs: 50pf, Biathlon. 1m, Alpine skier.

2006, Feb. 10   Perf. 13¼x13¾
273-274 A129 Set of 2   2.50 2.50
Nos. 273-274 each printed in sheets of 8 + label.

Flowers A130

No. 275: a, Saxifraga prenja. b, Asperula hercegovina. c, Oxytropis prenja. d, Campanula hercegovina.

Perf. 13¼x13¾
2006, Mar. 14   Litho.
275   Strip of 4 + central label   4.50 4.50
a.-b. A130 50pf Either single   .75 .75
c.-d. A130 1m Either single   1.40 1.40
Printed in sheets of 24 containing six of each stamp + a central label.

Europa A131

Designs: Nos. 276, 278a, 278b, 1m, Person crying. Nos. 277, 2778c, 278d, 1.50m, People holding hands.

2006, Apr. 5   Perf. 13¼x13¾
White Top and Bottom Panel
276-277 A131 Set of 2   4.50 4.50
Yellow Backgrounds
Perf. 13¼x13¾ on 3 Sides
278   Sheet of 6, #278a,
       278d, 2 each #278b,
       278c   14.00 14.00
a. A131 1m Imperf. at top   1.60 1.60
b. A131 1m Imperf. at bottom   1.60 1.60
c. A131 1.50m Imperf. at top   2.75 2.75
d. A131 1.50m Imperf. at bottom 2.75 2.75
Nos. 276-277 each printed in sheets of 8 + label. No. 278 was issued with, but not attached to, a booklet cover.

Easter — A132

2006, Apr. 14   Perf. 13¼x13¾
279 A132 70pf multi   1.25 1.25
Printed in sheets of 8 + label.

2006 World Cup Soccer Championships, Germany — A133

No. 280: a, 50pf, Players and soccer ball. b, 1m, Soccer ball, German flag, stadium. 3m, Player and soccer ball.

2006, June 9
280 A133 Pair, #a-b   2.50 2.50
Souvenir Sheet
281 A133 3m multi   4.50 4.50
No. 280 printed in sheets containing 4 of each stamp + label. No. 281 contains one 35x27mm stamp.

Vidovdan Race, Brcko — A134

2006, June 28
282 A134 1m multi   1.60 1.60
Printed in sheets of 8 + label.

Souvenir Sheet

Nikola Tesla (1856-1943), Inventor — A135

2006, July 10
283 A135 1.50m multi   2.50 2.50
See No. 288A.

Nature Protection A136

Designs: 50pf, Tetrao urogallus. 1m, Rupicapra rupicapra.

2006, Sept. 19
284-285 A136 Set of 2   2.60 2.60

Children's Theater, 50th Anniv. — A137

2006, Oct. 14 Litho. Perf. 13¼x13¾
286 A137 1m multi   1.60 1.60
Printed in sheets of 8 + label.

A138

Jewelry A139

2006, Nov. 28
287 A138 1m multi   1.60 1.60
288 A139 1m multi   1.60 1.60
Each stamp printed in sheets of 8 + label.

Tesla Type of 2006
2006, Dec. 29   Litho.   Perf. 13¾
Size: 25x23mm
288A A135 70pf multi   1.20 1.20

Johann Wolfgang von Goethe (1749-1832), Poet — A140

Perf. 13¼x13¾
2007, Mar. 22   Litho.
289 A140 1.50m multi   2.50 2.50
Printed in sheets of 8 + label.

Easter — A141

2007, Apr. 10   Perf. 13¾x13¼
290 A141 70pf multi   1.20 1.20
Printed in sheets of 8 + label.

Leonardo da Vinci (1452-1519), Painter — A142

No. 291, 70pf — Head of Isabella d'Este with text in: a, Cyrillic letters. b, Latin letters. No. 292, 1m — Sketch of St. Peter with text in: a, Cyrillic letters. b, Latin letters.

2007, Apr. 16   Perf. 13¾x13¼
Pairs, #a-b
291-292 A142 Set of 2   5.50 5.50
Nos. 291-292 each printed in sheets of 4 pairs + label.

Europa A143

Designs: Nos. 293, 295a, 295b, 1m, Scouts and tents. Nos. 294, 295c, 295d, 1.50m, Scouts on expedition.

2007, May 3   Perf. 13¼x13¾
Green Background
293-294 A143 Set of 2   4.50 4.50
Rose Violet Background
Perf. 13¼x13¾ on 3 Sides
295   Sheet of 6, #295a,
       295d, 2 each #295b,
       295c   15.00 15.00
a. A143 1m Imperf. at top   2.00 2.00
b. A143 1m Imperf. at bottom   2.00 2.00
c. A143 1.50m Imperf. at top   3.00 3.00
d. A143 1.50m Imperf. at bottom 3.00 3.00
Scouting, cent. Nos. 293-294 were each printed in sheets of 8 + label. No. 295 was issued with, but not attached to, a booklet cover.

Monasteries A144

Designs: 70pf, Liplje Monastery. 1m, Dobricevo Monastery.

2007, June 5   Perf. 13¼x13¾
296-297 A144 Set of 2   2.75 2.75
Nos. 296-297 were each printed in sheets of 8 + label.

Post Office and Church, Obudovac A145

Municipal Building, Prijedor A146

Fire House, Kozarac
A147

Town Square, Bijeljina
A148

Deventa
A149

Foca
A150

Cultural Club, Laktasi
A151

Building, Srebrenica
A152

Cultural Club, Sipovo — A153

Municipal Building, Mrkonjic Grad — A154

Old City, Trebinje
A155

Zvornik
A156

2007   **Litho.**   **Perf. 13¾**

298	A145	10pf multi	.50	.50
299	A146	20pf multi	.50	.50
300	A147	20pf multi	.50	.50
301	A148	20pf multi	.50	.50
302	A149	20pf multi	.50	.50
303	A150	20pf multi	.50	.50
304	A151	20pf multi	.50	.50
305	A152	70pf multi	1.20	1.20
306	A153	1.50m multi	2.00	2.00
307	A154	1.50m multi	2.00	2.00
308	A155	2m multi	3.00	3.00
309	A156	5m multi	8.50	8.50
	Nos. 298-309 (12)		20.20	20.20

Issued: 10pf, 7/7; 70pf, 6/20; others, 6/9.

A157

A158

Dogs — A160

2007, July 5   **Perf. 13¼x13¾**
310   Horiz. strip of 4 + central label   4.50   4.50
   a.   A157 70pf multi   1.00   1.00
   b.   A158 70pf multi   1.00   1.00
   c.   A159 70pf multi   1.00   1.00
   d.   A160 70pf multi   1.00   1.00

Ban Svetislav Milosavljevic (1882-1960)
A161

2007, Sept. 7   **Perf. 13¾x13¼**
311   A161 1.50m multi   2.50   2.50

Souvenir Sheet

Tennis in Banja Luka, Cent. — A162

No. 312: a, Wooden racquet, old balls. b, Modern racquet and ball.

2007, Sept. 14   **Perf. 13¾**
312   A162 1m Sheet of 2, #a-b   3.00   3.00

Launch of Sputnik 1, 50th Anniv. — A163

2007, Oct. 4   **Litho.**   **Perf. 13¾x13¼**
313   A163 1.50m multi   2.50   2.50
   Printed in sheets of 8 + label.

Pine Cones — A164

Designs: 70pf, Picea abies. 1m, Picea omorica.

2007, Nov. 9
314-315   A164   Set of 2   2.75   2.75
   Nos. 314-315 each printed in sheets of 8 + label.

Dogs — A160

2007, July 5

Filip Visnjic Library, 75th Anniv. — A165

2007, Nov. 26   **Perf. 13¼x13¾**
316   A165 70pf multi   1.20   1.20
   Printed in sheets of 8 + label.

New Year 2008 — A166

Designs: No. 317, 70pf, Snowman. No. 318, 70pf, Christmas tree.

    Perf. 13¾x13¼
2007, Dec. 10   **Litho.**
317-318   A166   Set of 2   2.25   2.25
   Nos. 317-318 were each printed in sheets of 8 + label.

Serb Republic Adminstrative Center — A167

2007, Dec. 20
319   A167 70pf multi   1.20   1.20

Samac Post Office, 125th Anniv. — A168

2008, Feb. 28   **Litho.**   **Perf. 14**
320   A168 1.40m multi   2.25   2.25
   Printed in sheets of 8 + label.

Self-Portrait of Vincent Van Gogh (1853-90), Painter — A169

2008, Mar. 28   **Litho.**   **Perf. 14x14¼**
321   A169 1.50m multi   2.50   2.50
   Printed in sheets of 8 + label.

Souvenir Sheet

UEFA Euro 2008 Soccer Championships, Austria and Switzerland — A170

No. 322: a, Foot to left of soccer ball. b, Foot to right of soccer ball.

2008, Apr. 18   **Perf. 13x13½**
322   A170 1.40m Sheet of 2, #a-b   4.50   4.50

Europa — A171

Letter and: Nos. 323, 325a, 325b, 1m, Quill pen and inkwell. Nos. 324, 325c, 325d, 2m, Hand with pencil.

2008, Apr. 24   **Perf. 14**
Stamps With White Frames
323-324   A171   Set of 2   5.00   5.00
   Stamps With Tan Frames
   Perf. 13x13½ on 3 Sides
325   Sheet, #325a, 325d, 2
     each #325b-325c   15.00   15.00
   a.   A171 1m Imperf. at top   1.50   1.50
   b.   A171 1m Imperf. at bottom   1.50   1.50
   c.   A171 2m Imperf. at top   3.00   3.00
   d.   A171 2m Imperf. at bottom   3.00   3.00
   Nos. 323-324 each were printed in sheets of 8 + label.

Djurdjevdan Festival
A172

2008, May 8   **Litho.**   **Perf. 13**
326   A172 1.50m multi   2.50   2.50
   Printed in sheets of 8 + label.

A173

A174

A175

Personalized Stamps
A176

2008, May 13 *Serpentine Die Cut 10*
Self-Adhesive
327	A173 70pf multi	1.10	1.10
328	A174 70pf multi	1.10	1.10
329	A175 70pf multi	1.10	1.10
330	A176 70pf multi	1.10	1.10
	Nos. 327-330 (4)	4.40	4.40

Images shown in frames of Nos. 327-330 are generic and could be personalized.

Banja Luka Carnival — A177

2008, May 15 **Perf. 13**
331	A177 1.50m multi	2.50	2.50

Mushrooms A178

No. 332: a, Gyromitra esculenta. b, Amanita muscaria. c, Amanita pantherina. d, Amanita phalloides.

2008, May 26 **Perf. 13x13¼**
332	Horiz. strip of 4 + central label	4.50	4.50
a.-d.	A178 70pf Any single	1.10	1.10

Charles Darwin (1809-82), Naturalist, and Birds — A179

2008, July 1 **Perf. 13**
333	A179 1.50m multi	2.50	2.50

Development by Darwin of theory of evolution, 150th anniv.

Flowers
A180   A181

Designs: 50pf, Gentiana verna. 1.50m, Galanthus nivalis. 2m, Viola odorata. 5m, Centaurea cyanus.

2008, July 7 **Litho.** **Perf. 13**
334	A180 50pf multi	.80	.80
335	A181 1.50m multi	2.25	2.25
336	A180 2m multi	3.25	3.25
337	A180 5m multi	8.00	8.00
	Nos. 334-337 (4)	14.30	14.30

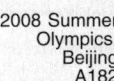

2008 Summer Olympics, Beijing A182

Map of China and: 70pf, High jump, National Stadium. 2.10m, Swimmer on starting platform, Aquatics Center. 3.10m, Gymnast.

2008, July 16
338-339	A182 Set of 2	4.50	4.50

Souvenir Sheet

340	A182 3.10m multi	4.50	4.50

Nos. 338 and 339 were printed in sheets of 8 + label.

Birds — A183

Designs: No. 341, 1m, Strix aluco. No. 342, 1m, Ciconia ciconia.

2008, Aug. 12
341-342	A183 Set of 2	3.00	3.00

Nos. 341 and 342 each were printed in sheets of 8 + label.

Monasteries A184

Monastery at: No. 343, 1m, Gracanica (shown). No. 344, 1m, Tvrdos.

2008, Sept. 10
343-344	A184 Set of 2	3.00	3.00

Nos. 343 and 344 each were printed in sheets of 8 + label.

Souvenir Sheet

Bosnian Serb Pres. Milan Jelic (1956-2007) — A185

2008, Sept. 20
345	A185 2.10m multi	3.25	3.25

Orient Express, 125th Anniv. — A186

2008, Oct. 3 **Litho.** **Perf. 13**
346	A186 1.40m multi	2.25	2.25

Printed in sheets of 8 + label.

Alfred Nobel (1833-96), Inventor and Philanthropist A187

2008, Oct. 21
347	A187 1.50m multi	2.50	2.50

Printed in sheets of 8 + label.

Jovan Jovanovich Zmaj (1833-1904), Poet — A188

2008, Nov. 24
348	A188 1.50m multi	2.50	2.50

Printed in sheets of 8 + label.

Christmas A189

2008, Dec. 26
349	A189 1m multi	1.60	1.60

Printed in sheets of 8 + label.

1984 Sarajevo Winter Olympics, 25th Anniv. — A190

2009, Feb. 13
350	A190 1.50m multi	2.50	2.50

Printed in sheets of 8 + label.

Explorers and Ships — A191

Designs: 70pf, Amerigo Vespucci (1454-1512). 1.50m, Marco Polo (1254-1324).

2009, Mar. 7
351-352	A191 Set of 2	3.50	3.50

Nos. 351-352 each were printed in sheets of 8 + label.

Buildings A192

Designs; 1m, European Court of Human Rights. 1.50m, Council of Europe Building.

2009, Mar. 25
353-354	A192 Set of 2	4.00	4.00

European Court of Human Rights, 50th anniv., Council of Europe, 60th anniv. Nos. 353-354 each were printed in sheets of 8 + label.

Animals — A193

Designs: 20pf, Meles meles. 70pf, Sciurus vulgaris. 1m, Vulpes vulpes.

2009, Apr. 15
355	A193 20pf multi	.40	.40
a.	Perf. 13¾	.40	.40
356	A193 70pf multi	1.75	1.75
357	A193 1m multi	1.10	1.10
	Nos. 355-357 (3)	3.25	3.25

Issued: No. 355a, 12/10.

Dinosaurs A194

Designs: 70pf, Triceratops. 1.50m, Diplodocus.

2009, Mar. 13 **Litho.** **Perf. 13**
358-359	A194 Set of 2	3.50	3.50

Nos. 358-359 each were printed in sheets of 8 + label.

Europa A195

Designs: Nos. 360, 362a, 362b, 362c, 1m, Observatory. Nos. 361, 362d, 362e, 362f, 2m, Telescope and star chart.

2009, Apr. 23 **Perf. 13**
Stamp Size: 35x26mm
360-361	A195 Set of 2	5.00	5.00

Souvenir Sheet
Stamp Size: 38x27mm
Perf. 13¼x13 on 2 or 3 Sides
362	Sheet of 6	16.00	16.00
a.	A195 1m Imperf. at right	1.75	1.75
b.	A195 1m Imperf. at left	1.75	1.75
c.	A195 1m Imperf. at right and bottom	1.75	1.75
d.	A195 2m Imperf. at left	3.50	3.50
e.	A195 2m Imperf. at right	3.50	3.50
f.	A195 2m Imperf. at left and bottom	3.50	3.50

Intl. Year of Astronomy. Nos. 360-361 each were printed in sheets of 8 + label.

Souvenir Sheet

World Rafting Championships, Banja Luka — A196

No. 363 — Rafters with: a, All paddles in water. b, Two paddles out of water.

2009, May 15 **Perf. 13¾**
363	A196 1.50m Sheet of 2, #a-b	5.00	5.00

Paja Jovanovic (1859-1957), Painter — A197

2009, June 16 **Perf. 13¾x13¼**
364	A197 1.40m multi	2.25	2.25

Printed in sheets of 8 + label.

Portraits of Amedeo Modigliani (1884-1920) A198

2009, July 11 **Perf. 13¼x13¾**
365	A198 1.50m multi	2.25	2.25

Printed in sheets of 8 + label.

Cats — A199

No. 366: a, Siamese (shown). b, Tabby (broom in background). c, Russian blue (flower pot with flowers in background). d, Persian (large pot in background).

2009, Aug. 19
366   Horiz. strip of 4 + cen-
            tral label   4.50   4.50
a.-d. A199 70pf Any single   1.00   1.00

Forts — A200

Fort at: 20pf, Doboj. 70pf, Zvornik. 1m, Kastel.

2009   Litho.   Perf. 13¾
367 A200 20pf multi   .30   .30
368 A200 70pf multi   1.10   1.10
369 A200 1m multi   1.60   1.60
       Nos. 367-369 (3)   3.00   3.00
    Issued: 20pf, 7/23; 70pf, 1m, 9/25.

Insects
A201

Designs: No. 370, 1m, Coccinellidae. No. 371, 1m, Odonata. No. 372, 1m, Lucanus cervus.

2009, Sept. 9 Litho. Perf. 13¼x13¾
370-372 A201   Set of 3   4.50   4.50
    Nos. 370-372 each were printed in sheets of 8 + label.

Skoda 1937
Locomotive
A202

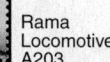

Rama
Locomotive
A203

UNRRA 22
Locomotive
A204

JZ 83-056
Locomotive
A205

2009, Nov. 10
373 A202 70pf multi   1.10   1.10
374 A203 70pf multi   1.10   1.10
375 A204 80pf multi   1.20   1.20
376 A205 80pf multi   1.20   1.20
       Nos. 373-376 (4)   4.60   4.60
    Nos. 373-376 each were printed in sheets of 8 + label.

Automobiles
A206

Designs: No. 377, 70pf, Red Citroen 2CV. No. 378, 70pf, Yellow Fiat 500. 80pf, Volkswagen Beetle.

2009, Nov. 17
377-379 A206   Set of 3   3.50   3.50
    Nos. 377-379 each were printed in sheets of 8 + label.

Christmas and
New Year's
Day — A207

Designs: No. 380, 60pf, Santa Claus. No. 381, 60pf, Snowman.

2009, Dec. 4   Perf. 13¾x13¼
380-381 A207   Set of 2   2.00   2.00
    Nos. 380-381 each were printed in sheets of 8 + label.

Zvornik, 600th
Anniv. — A208

2010, Jan. 26   Perf. 13¼x13¾
382 A208 70pf multi   1.10   1.10
    Printed in sheets of 8 + label.

2010 Winter
Olympics,
Vancouver
A209

Designs: 70pf, Luge. 1.50m, Figure skating.

2010, Feb. 5
383-384 A209   Set of 2   3.50   3.50
    Nos. 383-384 each were printed in sheets of 8 + label.

Frédéric Chopin
(1810-49),
Composer — A210

2010, Mar. 1   Perf. 13¾x13¼
385 A210 1.50m multi   2.50   2.50
    Printed in sheets of 8 + label.

Mesa Selimovic
(1910-82),
Writer — A211

2010, Apr. 20
386 A211 1m multi   1.50   1.50
    Printed in sheets of 8 + label.

Europa
A212

Children's books: Nos. 387, 389a, 389b, 389c, 1m, Flying. Nos. 388, 389d, 389e, 389f, 2m, On tree.

2010, May 7   Litho.   Perf. 13x13¾
387-388 A212   4.00   4.00
    Perf. 13x13¾ on 2 or 3 Sides
389   Sheet of 6   12.00 12.00
a. A212 1m Imperf. at top   1.40   1.40
b. A212 1m Imperf. at bottom   1.40   1.40
c. A212 1m Imperf. at bottom and
            right   1.40   1.40
d. A212 2m Imperf. at top   2.60   2.60
e. A212 2m Imperf. at top and
            right   2.60   2.60
f. A212 2m Imperf. at bottom   2.60   2.60
    Nos. 387-388 each were printed in sheets of 8 + label. No. 389 was sold with, but unattached to, a booklet cover.

2010 World Cup Soccer
Championships, South Africa — A213

Designs: No. 390, 1.50m, Player with arms raised. No. 391, 1.50m, Player dribbling ball.

2010, May 25   Perf. 13x13¾
390-391 A213   Set of 2   4.50   4.50
    Nos. 390-391 each were printed in sheets of 8 + label.

Animals — A214

2010, May 28   Perf. 13¾
392 A214 10pf Hedgehog   .35   .35
393 A214 50pf Boar   .80   .80
394 A214 90pf Wolf   1.40   1.40
395 A214 1m Bear   1.60   1.60
       Nos. 392-395 (4)   4.15   4.15

Old
Weapons — A215

2010, June 15
396 A215 1.80m Knives   2.75   2.75
397 A215 2m Guns   3.00   3.00
398 A215 5m Iron mace   7.25   7.25
       Nos. 396-398 (3)   13.00 13.00
    Nos. 396-398 each were printed in sheets of 8 + label.

Endangered
Flora — A216

No. 399: a, Rhododendron hirsutum. b, Edrainthus sutjeske. c, Trollius europaeus. d, Pancicia serbica.

2010, June 17   Perf. 13x13¾
399   Horiz. strip of 4 + cen-
            tral label   4.50   4.50
a.-d. A216 70pf Any single   1.00   1.00

Fragments of
Roman
Monuments
A217

Monument fragment showing: 70pf, People. 1.50m, Text.

2010, June 30
400-401 A217   Set of 2   3.50   3.50
    Nos. 400-401 each were printed in sheets of 8 + label.

50th Trumpet
Festival, Guca,
Serbia — A218

2010, Aug. 13 Litho. Perf. 13x13¾
402 A218 1.50m multi   2.25   2.25
    Printed in sheets of 8 + label. See Serbia No. 516.

Day of Fallen and
Missing
Persons — A219

2010, Sept. 15   Perf. 13¾x13
403 A219 90pf multi   1.50   1.50
    Printed in sheets of 8 + label.

A220

Fish — A221

2010, Sept. 23   Perf. 13¼x13¾
404 A220 1m multi   1.50   1.50
405 A221 1m multi   1.50   1.50
    Nos. 404-405 each were printed in sheets of 8 + label.

Serb Republic Museum, Banja Luka, 80th Anniv. — A222

2010, Sept. 24   *Perf. 13¾x13*
406 A222 90pf multi   1.40 1.40
Printed in sheets of 8 + label.

Banja Luka Gymnasium, 115th Anniv. — A223

2010, Oct. 4   *Perf. 13x13¾*
407 A223 90pf multi   1.40 1.40
Printed in sheets of 8 + label.

Souvenir Sheet

World Post Day — A224

No. 408: a, 70pf, Detail from Bosnia & Herzegovina #41. b, 1.40m, Marija Zvijezda Trappist Monastery, Banja Luka, detail from Bosnia & Herzegovina #41.

2010, Oct. 9   *Litho.*
408 A224   Sheet of 2, #a-b   3.50 3.50

St. Nicholas and Christmas Stocking A225

2010, Nov. 24
409 A225 1m multi   1.50 1.50
Printed in sheets of 8 + label.

Souvenir Sheet

St. Basil of Ostrog (1610-71) — A226

No. 410: a, 70pf, Ostrog Monastery. b, 1.40m, St. Basil of Ostrog.

2010, Dec. 28   *Perf. 13¾*
410 A226   Sheet of 2, #a-b   3.25 3.25

Women's Beaded Headdresses A227

Various headdresses with denomination at: No. 411, 90pf, UR. No. 412, 90pf, UL.

2011, Jan. 24   *Perf. 13x13¾*
411-412 A227   Set of 2   2.75 2.75
Nos. 411-412 each were printed in sheets of 8 + label.

Milan Budimir (1891-1975), Philosopher A228

2011, Feb. 11   *Perf. 13¾x13*
413 A228 90pf multi   1.50 1.50
Printed in sheets of 8 + label.

Awarding of Nobel Prize in Chemistry to Marie Curie, Cent. — A229

2011, Mar. 8   *Litho.*   *Perf. 13¾x13¼*
414 A229 1.50m multi   2.25 2.25
Printed in sheets of 8 + central label.

Europa A230

Forest scene with: Nos. 415, 417a, 417b, 417c, 1m, Deer and rabbit. Nos. 416, 417d, 417e, 417f, 2m, Fox and bear.

2011, Apr. 6   *Perf. 13x13¾*
415-416 A230   Set of 2   4.50 4.50
   Perf. 13x13¾ on 2 or 3 Sides
417   Sheet of 6   18.00 18.00
  a.   A230 1m Imperf. at top   2.00 2.00
  b.   A230 1m Imperf. at bottom   2.00 2.00
  c.   A230 1m Imperf. at bottom and right   2.00 2.00
  d.   A230 2m Imperf. at top   4.00 4.00
  e.   A230 2m Imperf. at top and right   4.00 4.00
  f.   A230 2m Imperf. at bottom   4.00 4.00

Intl. Year of Forests. Nos. 415-416 each were printed in sheets of 8 + label. No. 417 was sold with, but unattached to, a booklet cover.

Animals — A231

2011, Apr. 20   *Litho.*   *Perf. 13¾*
418 A231 10pf Rabbit   .25 .25
419 A231 20pf Weasel   .35 .35
420 A231 50pf Otter   .80 .80
421 A231 90pf Lynx   1.60 1.60
   Nos. 418-421 (4)   3.00 3.00

Birds — A232

No. 422: a, Aythya ferina. b, Alcedo atthis. c, Cygnus olor. d, Podiceps nigricollis

2011, May 10   *Perf. 13¼x13¾*
422   Horiz. strip of 4 + central label   5.50 5.50
  a.-d.   A232 90pf Any single   1.25 1.25

National and University Library, 75th Anniv. — A233

2011, May 17   *Perf. 13¾x13¼*
423 A233 90pf multi   1.40 1.40
Printed in sheets of 8 + label.

Souvenir Sheet

European Kayak and Canoe Championships, Banja Luka. — A234

No. 424: a, 1.50m, Canoeist. b, 2.30m, Kayaker.

2011, June 7   *Perf. 13¾*
424 A234   Sheet of 2, #a-b   5.50 5.50

Book Illuminations A235

Various book illuminations.

2011, June 15   *Perf. 13¾*
   Denomination Color
425 A235 1.50m brown   2.25 2.25
426 A235 2.30m blue green   3.50 3.50
427 A235 5m buff   7.25 7.25
  a.   Dated "2013"   5.50 5.50
   Nos. 425-427 (3)   13.00 13.00
   Issued: No. 427a, 12/5/13.

Intl. Youth Year — A236

2011, June 30   *Perf. 13¾x13¼*
428 A236 90pf multi   1.40 1.40
Printed in sheets of 8 + label.

Locomotives A237

Designs: No. 429, 90pf, DMV 801. No. 430, 90pf, DMV 802. No. 431, 90pf, DHL 720-001. No. 432, 90pf, DHL 740-108. 3m, DHL L458-096.

2011, July 1   *Perf. 13¼x13¾*
429-432 A237   Set of 4   5.25 5.25
   Souvenir Sheet
   Perf. 13¾
433 A237 3m multi   4.50 4.50
Nos. 429-432 each were printed in sheets of 8 + label. No. 433 contains one 35x29mm stamp.

Birds — A238

Designs: 90pf, Buteo buteo. 1.50m, Accipiter gentilis.

2011, Sept. 15   *Perf. 13¼x13¾*
434-435 A238   Set of 2   3.50 3.50

Fridtjof Nansen (1861-1930), Polar Explorer and Diplomat — A239

2011, Oct. 10   *Perf. 13¾x13¼*
436 A239 1.50m multi   2.25 2.25
No. 436 was printed in sheets of 8 + central label.

Franz Liszt (1811-86), Composer A240

2011, Oct. 22
437 A240 1.50m multi   2.25 2.25
No. 437 was printed in sheets of 8 + central label.

Novak Djokovic, Tennis Player, and Wimbledon Singles Trophy — A241

2011, Nov. 30
438 A241 90pf multi   3.50 3.50
No. 438 was printed in sheets of 8 + central label.

Ivo Andric (1892-1975), 1961 Nobel Literature Laureate A242

2011, Dec. 10   *Perf. 13¼x13¾*
439 A242 90pf multi   1.40 1.40
No. 439 was printed in sheets of 8 + central label.

Roald
Amundsen's
Expedition to
South Pole,
Cent. — A243

Amundsen and: 1.50m, Expedition member
Helmer Hanssen near Norwegian flag at South
Pole. 2m, Dog sled, Norwegian flag and map
of expedition's route.

2011, Dec. 14   *Perf. 13¼x13¾*
440 A243 1.50m multi   2.25 2.25

Souvenir Sheet
Perf. 13¾
441 A243 2m multi   3.00 3.00

No. 440 was printed in sheets of 8 + central
label. No. 441 contains one 35x29mm stamp.

New Year 2012
(Year of the
Dragon)
A244

2012, Feb. 14   *Perf. 13¼x13¾*
442 A244 90pf multi   2.50 2.50

No. 442 was printed in sheets of 8 + central
label.

Postal Service
of the Serbian
Administration
of Bosnia &
Herzegovina,
15th Anniv.
A245

2012, Feb. 23
443 A245 90pf multi   1.40 1.40

No. 443 was printed in sheets of 8 + central
label.

A246

A247

A248

Architecture
A249

2012, Mar. 9   *Perf. 13x13¼*
444   Horiz. strip of 4 + central
    label   5.50 5.50
   a.   A246 90pf multi   1.25 1.25
   b.   A247 90pf multi   1.25 1.25
   c.   A248 90pf multi   1.25 1.25
   d.   A249 90pf multi   1.25 1.25

Transportation
Disasters
A250

Designs: No. 445, 1.50m, Titanic. No. 446,
1.50m, Hindenburg.

2012, Apr. 23   *Perf. 13¼x13¾*
445-446 A250 Set of 2   4.50 4.50

Sinking of the Titanic, cent.; Burning of the
Hindenburg, 75th anniv. Nos. 445-446 each
were printed in sheets of 8 + central label.

Europa
A251

Forest scene with: Nos. 447, 449a, 449b,
449c, 1m, River rafters. Nos. 448, 449d, 449e,
449f, 2m, Hikers.

2012, Apr. 26   *Perf. 13x13¾*
447-448 A251 Set of 2   4.00 4.00

Perf. 13x13¾ on 2 or 3 Sides
449   Sheet of 6   12.00 12.00
   a.   A251 1m Imperf. at top   1.40 1.40
   b.   A251 1m Imperf. at bottom   1.40 1.40
   c.   A251 1m Imperf. at top and
     right   1.40 1.40
   d.   A251 2m Imperf. at top   2.60 2.60
   e.   A251 2m Imperf. at bottom   2.60 2.60
   f.   A251 2m Imperf. at bottom and
     right   2.60 2.60

Nos. 447-448 each were printed in sheets of
8 + label. No. 449 was sold with, but unattached to, a booklet cover.

Musical
Instruments — A252

2012, May 17   *Perf. 13¾*
450 A252 10pf Dvojnice   .35 .35
451 A252 20pf Rognjaca   .35 .35
452 A252 35pf Gusle   .45 .45
    Nos. 450-452 (3)   1.15 1.15

European
Nature
Protection
A253

No. 453: a, 90pf, Stone pinnacles. b, 1.50m,
Janja River waterfalls.

2012, May 29   *Perf. 13x13¾*
453 A253 Vert. pair, #a-b   4.00 4.00

Printed in sheets containing 4 pairs + 2
labels

Animals — A254

2012, June 12   *Perf. 13¾*
454 A254 50pf Otter   .75 .75
455 A254 90pf Lynx   1.50 1.50

Trees — A255

No. 456: a, Quercus (oak). b, Fraxinus
(ash). c, Tilia (linden). d, Betula (birch).

2012, June 13   *Perf. 13x13¼*
456   Horiz. strip of 4 +
    flanking label   5.50 5.50
   a.-d.   A255 90pf Any single   1.25 1.25

Slavija Boxing
Club, 50th
Anniv. — A256

2012, Sept. 15   *Litho.*
457 A256 90pf multi   1.40 1.40

Printed in sheets of 8 + central label.

Airplanes
A257

Designs: 90pf, Fizir FN biplane. 1.50m,
Ikarus IK-2.

2012, Sept. 19   *Perf. 13x13¾*
458-459 A257 Set of 2   3.50 3.50

Nos. 458-459 each were printed in sheets of
8 + central label.

Souvenir Sheet

Amateur Film Making in Banja Luka,
75th Anniv. — A258

2012, Oct. 26   *Perf. 13¾*
460 A258 2.30m multi   3.50 3.50

Vuk Karadzic
(1787-1864),
Linguist
A259

2012, Nov. 7   *Perf. 13x13¼*
461 A259 1.50m multi   2.25 2.25

Printed in sheets of 8 + central label.

Sub-machine
Guns — A260

Designs: 10pf, MP 40. 20pf, PPSh-41. 35pf,
Sten Mk II.

2013, Jan. 10   *Perf. 13¾*
462 A260 10pf multi   .25 .25
463 A260 20pf multi   .30 .30
464 A260 35pf multi   .50 .50
    Nos. 462-464 (3)   1.05 1.05

Chess Pieces — A261

Designs: 50pf, Black rook, White bishop.
90pf, Black knight, White pawn. 2.30m, Black
queen, White king.

2013, Jan. 10
465 A261 50pf multi   .60 .60
466 A261 90pf multi   1.10 1.10
467 A261 2.30m multi   2.75 2.75
    Nos. 465-467 (3)   4.45 4.45

JZ 73 Steam
Locomotive
A262

JZ 85 Steam
Locomotive
A263

JZ 92 Steam
Locomotive
A264

Kloze Steam
Locomotive
A265

2013, Feb. 7   *Perf. 13¼x13¾*
468 A262 90pf multi   1.25 1.25
469 A263 90pf multi   1.25 1.25
470 A264 90pf multi   1.25 1.25
471 A265 90pf multi   1.25 1.25
    Nos. 468-471 (4)   5.00 5.00

Nos. 468-471 each were printed in sheets of
8 + central label.

Banja Luka
Brewery, 140th
Anniv. — A266

2013, Mar. 6   *Perf. 13¾x13¼*
472 A266 90pf multi   1.40 1.40

No. 472 was printed in sheets of 8 + central
label.

Europa
A267

Old postal truck: Nos. 473, 475a, 475b, 475c, 1m, Facing right. Nos. 474, 475d, 475e, 475f, 2m, Facing left.

2013, July 12   *Perf. 13x13¾*
473-474 A267   Set of 2   4.50   4.50
     Perf. 13x13¾ on 2 or 3 Sides
475   Sheet of 6   13.00 13.00
   a.   A267 1m Imperf. at top   1.50   1.50
   b.   A267 1m Imperf. at bottom   1.50   1.50
   c.   A267 1m Imperf. at top and
       right   1.50   1.50
   d.   A267 2m Imperf. at top   2.75   2.75
   e.   A267 2m Imperf. at bottom   2.75   2.75
   f.   A267 2m Imperf. at bottom and
       right   2.75   2.75

Nos. 473-474 each were printed in sheets of 8 + central label.

Giuseppe Verdi (1813-1901), Composer A268

Richard Wagner (1813-83), Composer A269

2013, July 17   *Perf. 13x13¾*
476 A268 1.50m multi   2.10   2.10
477 A269 1.50m multi   2.10   2.10

Nos. 476-477 each were printed in sheets of 8 + central label.

Souvenir Sheet

Edict of Milan, 1700th Anniv. — A270

No. 478: a, Bust of Emperor Constantine. b, Chrismon and wreath.

2013, July 19   *Perf. 13¾*
478 A270 1.50m Sheet of 2, #a-b   4.25   4.25

Glas Newspaper, 70th Anniv. — A271

2013, July 30   *Perf. 13¾x13*
479 A271 90pf multi   1.40   1.40

No. 479 was printed in sheets of 8 + central label.

Souvenir Sheet

Nevesinje Olympics — A272

No. 480: a, Horse racing. b, Shot put.

2013, Aug. 29   Litho.   *Perf. 13¾*
480 A272 1.50m Sheet of 2, #a-b   4.25   4.25

Amphibians A273

Designs: 90pf, Salamandra salamandra. 1.50m, Rana dalmatina.

     Perf. 13¼x13¾
2013, Sept. 12   Litho.
481-482 A273   Set of 2   3.50   3.50
482a   Vert. pair, #481-482   3.50   3.50

Nos. 481-482 were printed in sheets of 8 (4 of each stamp) + 2 labels

Bats — A274

No. 483: a, Rhinolophus ferrumequinum. b, Myotis myotis. c, Rhinolophus euryale. d, Miniopterus schreibersii.

     Perf. 13¼x13¾
2013, Sept. 20   Litho.
483   Horiz. strip of 4 +
     flanking label   5.25   5.25
   a.-d.   A274 90pf Any single   1.25   1.25

Traditional Handicrafts A275

No. 484: a, Lid with handle. b, Saddle. c, Harness. d, Knife.

2013, Oct. 18   Litho.   *Perf. 13¼x13¾*
484   A275   Vert. strip of 4 +
       flanking label   5.25   5.25
   a.-d.   90pf Any single   1.25   1.25

Petar II Petrovic-Njegos (1813-51), Prince of Montenegro A276

2013, Nov. 13   *Perf. 13¾x13¼*   Litho.
485 A276 1.50m multi   2.10   2.10

No. 485 was printed in sheets of 8 + central label.

Patenting of Turbine Invented by Nikola Tesla, Cent. — A277

2013, Nov. 29   *Perf. 13¼x13¾*   Litho.
486 A277 90pf multi   1.40   1.40

No. 486 was printed in sheets of 8 + central label.

William Shakespeare (1564-1616), Writer — A278

Galileo Galilei (1564-1642), Astronomer A279

2014, Feb. 5   Litho.   *Perf. 13¼x13¾*
487 A278 1.70m multi   2.50   2.50
488 A279 1.70m multi   2.50   2.50

Nos. 487-488 each were printed in sheets of 8 + central label.

Butterflies — A280

Designs: 1.10m, Erebia medusa. 1.70m, Aglais urticae. 2.70m, Melanargia galathea. 4m, Nymphalis antiopa. 5.10m, Iphiclides podalirius.

2014, Feb. 25   Litho.   *Perf. 13¾*
489 A280 1.10m multi   1.60   1.60
490 A280 1.70m multi   2.40   2.40
491 A280 2.70m multi   3.75   3.75
492 A280   4m multi   5.75   5.75
493 A280 5.10m multi   7.25   7.25
     Nos. 489-493 (5)   20.75 20.75

Borik Sports Arena, Banja Luka, 40th Anniv. — A281

2014, Mar. 20   *Perf. 13¼x13¾*   Litho.
494 A281 90pf multi   1.40   1.40

No. 494 was printed in sheets of 8 + central label.

Nature Protection A282

Flora: 90pf, Fagus moesiaca. 1.70m, Adiantum capillis-veneris.

     Perf. 13¼x13¾
2014, Mar. 20   Litho.
495-496 A282   Set of 2   3.75   3.75

Nos. 495-496 were each printed in sheets of 8 + central label.

Europa A283

Designs: Nos. 497, 499a, 499b, 499c, 1m, Dvojnice (flute). Nos. 498, 499d, 499e, 499f, 2m, Fiddle.

2014, Apr. 25   Litho.   *Perf. 13x13¼*
497-498 A283   Set of 2   4.25   4.25
     Perf. 13x13¾ on 2 or 3 Sides
499   Sheet of 6   13.00 13.00
   a.   A283 1m Imperf. at top   1.40   1.40
   b.   A283 1m Imperf. at bottom   1.40   1.40
   c.   A283 1m Imperf. at top and
       right   1.40   1.40
   d.   A283 2m Imperf. at top   2.75   2.75
   e.   A283 2m Imperf. at bottom   2.75   2.75
   f.   A283 2m Imperf. at bottom and
       right   2.75   2.75

Nos. 497-498 were each printed in sheets of 8 + central label.

Souvenir Sheet

2014 World Cup Soccer
Championships, Brazil — A284

2014, May 12   Litho.   Perf. 13¾
500 A284 5.10m multi   7.25 7.25

Dr. Vaso
Butozan
Veterinary
Institute, 80th
Anniv. — A285

2014, May 15   Litho.   Perf. 13x13¾
501 A285 90pf multi   1.40 1.40
No. 501 was printed in sheets of 8 + central
label.

National
Library,
Srebrenica,
55th
Anniv. — A286

2014, June 2   Litho.   Perf. 13x13¾
502 A286 90pf multi   1.40 1.40
No. 502 was printed in sheets of 8 + central
label.

Zmijanje Embroidery — A287

No. 503 — Embroidery designs: a, 90pf. b,
1.70m.

2014, June 5   Litho.   Perf. 13¾x13
503 A287 Horiz. pair, #a-b   3.75 3.75
No. 503 was printed in sheets of 4 pairs + 2
labels, with stamps of the same denomination
arranged tete-beche in relation to each other.

Wooden
Churches — A288

Designs: 10pf, Church of the Ascension,
Omarska. 20pf, St. Nicholas Church, Roma-
novci. 75pf, St. Nicholas Church, Jelicka.

2014, July 17   Litho.   Perf. 13¾
504 A288 10pf multi   .25 .25
505 A288 20pf multi   .30 .30
506 A288 75pf multi   1.00 1.00
     Nos. 504-506 (3)   1.55 1.55

Insects — A289

Designs: 90pf, Mosquito. 1.10m, Ant.
2.70m, Wasp.

2014, July 17   Litho.   Perf. 13¾
507 A289 90pf   multi   1.25 1.25
508 A289 1.10m multi   1.50 1.50
509 A289 2.70m multi   3.75 3.75
     Nos. 507-509 (3)   6.50 6.50

Prijedorska
Zelenika
Apples — A290

Ilinjaca
Apples — A291

Bijelica
Apples — A292

Krompirusa
Apples — A293

Perf. 13¼x13¾
2014, Sept. 10   Litho.
510   Horiz. strip of 4 + flank-
          ing label   5.25 5.25
   a. A290 90pf multi   1.25 1.25
   b. A291 90pf multi   1.25 1.25
   c. A292 90pf multi   1.25 1.25
   d. A293 90pf multi   1.25 1.25

Branislav Nusic
(1864-1938),
Writer — A294

2014, Oct. 20   Litho.   Perf. 13¼x13¾
511 A294 90pf multi   1.40 1.40
No. 511 was printed in sheets of 8 + central
label.

Sword and
Spearheads
A295

Ceramic
Cup — A296

Perf. 13¼x13¾
2014, Nov. 20   Litho.
512 A295 90pf   multi   1.25 1.25
513 A296 1.70m multi   2.50 2.50
Items from Donja Dolina archaeological site.
Nos. 512-513 were printed in sheets of 8 (4 of
each stamp) + 2 labels.

Milan
Kovacevic
(1915-85),
Sports
Television
Broadcaster
A297

Branko Copic
(1915-84),
Writer — A298

2015, Jan. 23   Litho.   Perf. 13¼x13¾
514 A297 90pf   multi   1.25 1.25
515 A298 1.70m multi   2.50 2.50
Nos. 514-515 were each printed in sheets of
8 + central label.

International
Year of
Light — A299

Perf. 13¼x13¾
2015, Feb. 16   Litho.
516 A299 1.70m multi   2.50 2.50
No. 516 was printed in sheets of 8 + central
label.

Liberation of
Jasenovac
Concentration
Camp, 70th
Anniv. — A300

2015, Apr. 15   Litho.   Perf. 13¾x13¼
517 A300 90pf multi   1.40 1.40
No. 517 was printed in sheets of 8 + central
label.

Europa
A301

Old toys: Nos. 518, 520a, 520b, 520c, 90pf,
Robot. Nos. 519, 520d, 520e, 520f, 1.70m,
Tractor.

2015, Apr. 17   Litho.   Perf. 13¼x13¾
518-519 A301   Set of 2   4.00 4.00
Perf. 13¼x13¾ on 2 or 3 Sides
520   Sheet of 6   12.00 12.00
   a. A301 90pf Imperf. at top   1.00 1.00
   b. A301 90pf Imperf. at bottom 1.00 1.00
   c. A301 90pf Imperf. at top and
                    right   1.00 1.00
   d. A301 1.70m Imperf. at top   2.00 2.00
   e. A301 1.70m Imperf. at bottom 2.00 2.00
   f. A301 1.70m Imperf. at bottom
                    and right   2.00 2.00
Nos. 518-519 were each printed in sheets of
8 + central label.

Victory in
World War II,
70th
Anniv. — A302

2015, May 8   Litho.   Perf. 13¼x13¾
521 A302 90pf multi   1.40 1.40
No. 521 was printed in sheets of 8 + central
label.

Doboj, 600th
Anniv. — A303

2015, May 20   Litho.   Perf. 13x13¾
522 A303 90pf multi   1.40 1.40
No. 522 was printed in sheets of 8 + central
label.

Monument to Petar
Kocic (1877-1916),
Writer — A304

2015, Aug. 21   Litho.   Perf. 13¾x13
523 A304 2.70m multi   4.00 4.00
50th Kocic Assembly. No. 523 was printed
in sheets of 8 + label.

Nuts — A305   Farm
                     Animals — A306

Designs: 10pf, Castanea sativa. 20pf, Corylus avellana. 90pf, Juglans. 1.10m, Bos taurus
taurus. 1.70m, Capra hircus. 2.70m, Ovis
aries. 5.10m, Equus caballus.

Perf. 13¾x13¼
2015, Aug. 28   Litho.
524 A305 10pf   multi   .25   .25
525 A305 20pf   multi   .25   .25
526 A305 90pf   multi   1.20 1.20
527 A306 1.10m multi   1.40 1.40
528 A306 1.70m multi   2.25 2.25
529 A306 2.70m multi   3.50 3.50
530 A306 5.10m multi   6.50 6.50
     Nos. 524-530 (7)   15.35 15.35

Souvenir Sheet

2015 World Fly Fishing
Championships, Jajce — A307

No. 531: a, 1.70m, Fisherman and Thymallus thymallus. b, 2.70m, Salmo trutta morpah
fario.

2015, Sept. 2   Litho.   Perf. 13¾
531 A307 Sheet of 2, #a-b   6.50 6.50

Birds — A308

No. 532: a, Alauda arvensis. b, Carduelis
carduelis. c, Luscinia megarhynchos. d,
Turdus merula.

2015, Sept. 3 Litho. *Perf. 13¼x13¾*
532   Horiz. strip of 4   5.25 5.25
a.-d. A308 90pf Any single   1.25 1.25
   Printed in sheets containing 5 strips + 5 labels at right.

Dayton Peace Accords, 20th Anniv. — A309

Perf. 13¾x13¼
2015, Sept. 17   Litho.
533 A309 90pf multi   1.40 1.40
   No. 533 was printed in sheets of 8 + central label.

Nature Protection A310

   No. 534: a, 90pf, Nuphar luteum (yellow water lily). b, 1.70m, Urtica kioviensis (swamp nettle).

2015, Sept. 23 Litho. *Perf. 13x13¾*
534 A310   Vert. pair, #a-b   3.75 3.75
   No. 534 was printed in sheets containing 4 pairs + 2 labels.

Jovan Cvijic (1865-1927), Geologist A311

2015, Oct. 12 Litho. *Perf. 13¼x13¾*
535 A311 1.70m multi   2.50 2.50
   No. 535 was printed in sheets of 8 + central label.

Waterfall and Bridge — A312

Millstone A313

Water Wheel — A314

Mill Exterior A315

Perf. 13¼x13¾
2015, Nov. 27   Litho.
536   Horiz. strip of 4 + label
          at right   4.00 4.00
a. A312 90pf multi   1.00 1.00
b. A313 90pf multi   1.00 1.00
c. A314 90pf multi   1.00 1.00
d. A315 90pf multi   1.00 1.00

Diana Budisavljevic (1891-1978), Rescuer of Children in Concentration Camps — A316

2016, Jan. 25 Litho. *Perf. 13¾x13¼*
537 A316 1.70m multi   1.90 1.90
   No. 537 was printed in sheets of 8 + central label.

Death of Serbian King Stefan Dragutin, 700th Anniv. — A317

Perf. 13¾x13¼
2016, Feb. 10   Litho.
538 A317 90pf multi   1.00 1.00
   No. 538 was printed in sheets of 8 + central label.

Fruit — A318

   Designs: 90pf, Prunus spinosa. 1.10m, Rubus fruticosus.

2016, Apr. 6 Litho. *Perf. 13¾x13¼*
539-540 A318   Set of 2   2.40 2.40
               See No. 549.

A319

Europa A320

2016, Apr. 25 Litho. *Perf. 13¼x13¾*
541 A319 1.50m multi   1.75 1.75
542 A320 1.50m multi   1.75 1.75
Perf. 13¼x13¾ on 2 or 3 Sides
543   Sheet of 4   7.00 7.00
a. A319 1.50m Imperf. at top   1.75 1.75
b. A320 1.50m Imperf. at top and
          right   1.75 1.75

c. A320 1.50m Imperf. at bottom   1.75 1.75
d. A319 1.50m Imperf. at bottom and
          right   1.75 1.75
          Think Green Issue.

Nature Protection — A321

   No. 544: a, 90pf, Ciconia nigra. b, 1.70m, Helichrysum arenarium.

2016, May 16 Litho. *Perf. 13¼x13¾*
544 A321   Pair, #a-b   3.00 3.00
   Printed in sheets containing 4 each Nos. 544a-544b + 2 labels.

Children's Day — A322

2016, June 1 Litho. *Perf. 13¾x13¼*
545 A322 1.70m multi   2.00 2.00
   No. 545 was printed in sheets of 8 + label.

Souvenir Sheet

Soccer Player and Ball — A323

2016, June 10   Litho.   *Perf. 13¾*
546 A323 5.10m multi   6.00 6.00

Miniature Sheet

Summer Sports — A324

   No. 547: a, Shot put. b, Judo. c, Running. d, Swimming.

2016, July 7   Litho.   *Perf. 13¾*
547 A324 1.70m Sheet of 4, #a-d 7.75 7.75

Miniature Sheet

Gyps Fulvus — A325

   No. 548: Bird: a, 90pf, Perched on rock. b, 90pf, In flight at angle. c, 1.70m, In flight, feet down. d, 1.70m, Perched on tree stump.

2016, Sept. 14   Litho.   *Perf. 13¾*
548 A325   Sheet of 4, #a-d   6.00 6.00

Fruit Type of 2016
Perf. 13¾x13¼
2016, Sept. 16   Litho.
549 A318 50pf Comus mas   .60   .60

River Fauna — A326

   Designs: 10pf, Castor fiber. 20pf, Anas platyrhynchos. 1m, Astacus astacus. 1.70m, Esox lucius. 2.70m, Mauremys rivulata.

2016, Oct. 14 Litho. *Perf. 13¾x13¼*
550-554 A326   Set of 5   6.50 6.50

National Assembly, 25th Anniv. — A327

2016, Oct. 21 Litho. *Perf. 13¼x13¾*
555 A327 90pf multi   1.10 1.10
   No. 555 was printed in sheets of 8 + central label.

Mushrooms — A328

   No. 556: a, Pleurotus ostreatus (Oyster). b, Cantharellus cibarius (Chanterelle). c, Ganoderma lucidum (Reishi). d, Trametes versicolor (Turkey tail).

Perf. 13¼x13¾
2016, Nov. 25   Litho.
556 A328 90pf Block of 4, #a-d   4.00 4.00
   No. 556 was printed in sheets containing 4 each Nos. 556a-556d + 9 labels.

A329

A330

A331

Household
Objects
A332

2016, Dec. 2   Litho.   *Perf. 13¼x13¾*
557   Horiz. strip of 4 + flank-
       ing label   4.00 4.00
  a.   A329 90pf multi   1.00 1.00
  b.   A330 90pf multi   1.00 1.00
  c.   A331 90pf multi   1.00 1.00
  d.   A332 90pf multi   1.00 1.00

Composers — A333

No. 558: a, Sergei Prokofiev (1891-1953). b,
Erik Satie (1866-1925). c, Antonín Dvořák
(1841-1904).

2016, Dec. 9   Litho.   *Perf. 13¾x13¼*
558   A333 1.70m Block of 3, #a-c,
       + label   5.50 5.50
  Printed in sheets of 12 (4 each Nos. 558a-
558c) + 4 central labels.

Radio in Banja
Luka, 50th
Anniv. — A334

2017, Feb. 2   Litho.   *Perf. 13¾x13¼*
559   A334 90pf multi   1.00 1.00
  No. 559 was printed in sheets of 8 + central
label.

Coronation of
King Stefan
Nemanjic (c.
1165-1228),
800th
Anniv. — A335

2017, Mar. 9   Litho.   *Perf. 13¼x13¾*
560   A335 1.70m multi   1.90 1.90
  No. 560 was printed in sheets of 8 + central
label.

Stuplje
Monastery
A336

Mostanica
Monastery
A337

Krupa
Monastery
A338

Gomionica
Monastery
A339

Perf. 13¾x13¼
2017, Mar. 23   Litho.
561   A336   90pf multi   1.00 1.00
562   A337   1.10m multi   1.25 1.25
563   A338   2m multi   2.25 2.25
564   A339   4m multi   4.50 4.50
       Nos. 561-564 (4)   9.00 9.00

Jovan Ducic (1871-
1943),
Writer — A340

2017, Apr. 5   Litho.   *Perf. 13¾x13¼*
565   A340 90pf multi   1.00 1.00
  No. 565 was printed in sheets of 8 + central
label.

Elektrokrajina,
70th
Anniv. — A341

2017, Apr. 19   Litho.   *Perf. 13¼x13¾*
566   A341 90pf multi   1.00 1.00
  No. 566 was printed in sheets of 8 + central
label.

A342

Kastel
Fortress, Banja
Luka — A343

2017, Apr. 28   Litho.   *Perf. 13¼x13¾*
567   A342 1.70m multi   1.90 1.90
568   A343 1.70m multi   1.90 1.90
Perf. 13¼x13¾ on 2 or 3 Sides
569   Sheet of 4   7.75 7.75
  a.   A342 1.70m Imperf. at top   1.90 1.90
  b.   A343 1.70m Imperf. at top and
       right   1.90 1.90
  c.   A343 1.70m Imperf. at bottom   1.90 1.90
  d.   A342 1.70m Imperf. at bottom and
       right   1.90 1.90
  Europa. Nos. 567-568 were each printed in
sheets of 8 + central label.

Petar Kocic Theater
Festival, 20th
Anniv. — A344

2017, May 11   Litho.   *Perf. 13¾x13¼*
570   A344 90pf multi   1.10 1.10
  No. 570 was printed in sheets of 8 + central
label.

International
Family
Day — A345

2017, May 15   Litho.   *Perf. 13¾x13¼*
571   A345 1.70m multi   2.00 2.00
  No. 571 was printed in sheets of 8 + central
label.

Filip Visnjic (1767-
1834), Poet and
Musician — A346

2017, May 29   Litho.   *Perf. 13¾x13¼*
572   A346 90pf multi   1.10 1.10
  No. 572 was printed in sheets of 8 + label.

Battle of Kozara, 75th Anniv. — A347

No. 573: a, Kozara Memorial. b, Woman,
children, soldiers.

Perf. 13¾x13¼
2017, June 10   Litho.
573   A347 1.70m Horiz. pair, #a-b   4.00 4.00

Flowers — A348

Designs: 20pf, Cyclamen purpurascens.
1.50m, Scrophularia scopolii. 1.70m, Lilium
martagon. 2.70m, Limodorum abortivum.
5.10m, Convallaria majalis.

Perf. 13¾x13¼
2017, June 15   Litho.
574-578 A348   Set of 5   13.00 13.00

Souvenir Sheet

Dayak Boats — A349

2017, July 5   Litho.   *Perf. 13¾*
579   A349 5.10m multi   6.25 6.25

REGISTRATION STAMPS

No. 19 Surcharged

1994, Nov. 1   Litho.   *Perf. 13¼*
F9   A1 (P) on 6,000d #19   1.60 1.60
  No. F9 sold for 40p on day of issue.

Relay Station Type of 1996
Kraljica relay station, Mt. Ozren.

1996, Sept. 20   *Perf. 14*
F10   A9 (R) multicolored   .75   .75
  No. F10 sold for 90p on day of issue.

Famous Men Type of 1997
1997, Nov. 1   *Perf. 13¾*
F11   A13 (R) Jovan Ducic (1871-
      1943)   .75   .75
  No. F11 sold for 90p on day of issue.

Building Type of 1999
1999, Mar. 15   Litho.   *Perf. 13¾*
F12   A20 (R) Trebinje   2.00 2.00
  No. F12 sold for 1m on day of issue.

POSTAL TAX STAMPS

Robert Koch (1843-
1910) — PT1

**1997, Sept. 14   Litho.   *Imperf.*
Self-Adhesive**
RA1   PT1 15p red & blue   1.00 1.00
  Obligatory on mail 9/14-21.

Red Cross — PT2

1998, May 5   Self-Adhesive
RA2   PT2 90p multicolored   1.00 1.00
  Obligatory on mail 5/5-15.

Fight Against
Tuberculosis
PT3

1998, Sept. 14 *Perf. 10¾*
RA3 PT3 75pf multicolored 1.00 1.00
Obligatory on mail 9/14-21.

Red
Cross — PT4

1999, May 8 **Litho.** *Perf. 10¾*
RA4 PT4 10pf multi 1.00 1.00
Obligatory on mail 5/8-5/15.

Red Cross — PT5

1999, Sept. 14 **Litho.** *Perf. 10¾*
RA5 PT5 10pf multi .60 .60
Obligatory on mail 9/14-21.

Red
Cross — PT6

2000, May 8 **Litho.** *Perf. 10¾*
RA6 PT6 10pf multi 1.00 1.00
Obligatory on mail 5/8-5/15.

Red Cross — PT7

2000, Sept. 14 **Litho.** *Perf. 10¾*
RA7 PT7 10pf multi 1.00 1.00
Obligatory on mail 9/14-21.

Red Cross — PT8

2001, May 8 **Litho.** *Perf. 10¾*
RA8 PT8 10pf multi 1.00 1.00
Obligatory on mail 5/8-5/15.

Anti-Tuberculosis
Week — PT9

2001, Sept. 14 **Litho.** *Perf. 10½*
RA9 PT9 10pf multi 1.00 1.00
Obligatory on mail 9/14-9/21.

Red
Cross — PT10

2002, May 8 **Litho.** *Perf. 10¾*
RA10 PT10 10pf multi .90 .90
Obligatory on mail 5/8-5/15.

Fight Against
Tuberculosis — PT11

2002, Sept. 14 **Litho.** *Perf. 10¾*
RA11 PT11 10pf multi .90 .90
Obligatory on mail 9/14-9/21.

Red Cross — PT12

2003, May 8 **Litho.** *Perf. 10¾*
RA12 PT12 10pf multi .90 .90
Obligatory on mail 5/8-5/15.

Fight Against
Tuberculosis
PT13

2003, Sept. 14 **Litho.** *Perf. 10¾*
RA13 PT13 10pf multi .90 .90
a. Imperf. 1.90 1.90
Obligatory on mail 9/14-9/21.

Red Cross — PT14

2004, May 8 **Litho.** *Perf. 10¾*
RA14 PT14 10pf multi .75 .75
a. Imperf. 1.75 1.75
Obligatory on mail 5/8-5/15.

Fight Against
Tuberculosis
PT15

2004, Sept. 14 **Litho.** *Perf. 10¾*
RA15 PT15 10pf multi .75 .75
a. Imperf. 1.75 1.75
Obligatory on mail 9/14-9/21.

Red
Cross — PT16

2005, May 8 **Litho.** *Imperf.*
Self-Adhesive
RA16 PT16 10pf red & black .80 .80
Obligatory on mail 5/8-5/15.

Fight Against
Tuberculosis
PT17

Rouletted 16½
2005, Sept. 14 **Litho.**
RA17 PT17 10pf multi .50 .50
a. Imperf. .75 .75
Obligatory on mail 9/14-9/21.

PT18

2006, May 8 **Litho.** *Perf. 10*
RA18 PT18 20pf multi .50 .50
a. Imperf. .75 .75
Red Cross. Obligatory on mail 5/8-5/15.

PT19

2006, Sept. 14 *Perf. 10¾*
RA19 PT19 20pf multi .50 .50
a. Imperf. .75 .75
Fight against tuberculosis. Obligatory on
mail 9/14-9/21.

PT20

2007, May 8 **Litho.** *Perf. 10*
RA20 PT20 20pf multi .50 .50
a. Imperf. .75 .75
Red Cross. Obligatory on mail May 8-15.

PT21

2007, Sept. 14 *Perf. 10*
RA21 PT21 20pf multi .60 .60
a. Imperf. 1.40 1.40
Fight against tuberculosis. Obligatory on
mail Sept. 14-21.

Hands — PT22

2008, May 8 **Litho.** *Perf. 10*
RA22 PT22 20pf multi .60 .60
a. Imperf. .60 .60
Red Cross. Obligatory on mail May 8-15.

PT23

2008, Sept. 14 **Litho.** *Perf. 10*
RA23 PT23 20pf multi .60 .60
a. Imperf. .60 .60
Fight against tuberculosis. Obligatory on
mail Sept. 14-21.

PT24

2009, May 8 *Perf. 10¾*
RA24 PT24 20pf multi .60 .60
a. Imperf. .60 .60
Red Cross. Obligatory on mail May 8-15.

Fight Against
Tuberculosis
PT25

2009, Sept. 14 **Litho.** *Perf. 10¾x11*
RA25 PT25 20pf multi .60 .60
a. Imperf. .60 .60
Obligatory on mail Sept. 14-21.

Red Cross — PT26

2010, May 8   **Litho.**   *Perf. 10¾*
RA26 PT26 20pf multi   .60   .60
   a.   Imperf.   .60   .60
   Obligatory on mail May 8-15.

Fight Against
Tuberculosis
PT27

2010, Sept. 14   **Litho.**   *Perf. 10¾*
RA27 PT27 20pf multi   .60   .60
   a.   Imperf.   .60   .60
   Obligatory on mail Sept. 14-21.

Red Cross — PT28

2011, May 8   *Perf. 10*
RA28 PT28 20pf multi   .60   .60
   a.   Perf. 10 horiz.   .60   .60
   Obligatory on mail May 8-15.

Fight Against
Tuberculosis — PT29

2011, Sept. 14
RA29 PT29 20pf multi   .60   .60
   a.   Imperf.   .60   .60
   Obligatory on mail Sept. 14-21.

Red Cross — PT30

2012, May 8   *Perf. 9*
RA30 PT30 20pf multi   .60   .60
   a.   Imperf.   .60   .60
   Obligatory on mail May 8-15.

Fight Against
Tuberculosis
PT31

2012, Sept. 14   **Litho.**   *Perf. 9*
RA31 PT31 20pf multi   .60   .60
   a.   Imperf.   .60   .60
   Obligatory on mail Sept. 14-21.

Red Cross, 150th
Anniv. — PT32

2013, May 8   **Litho.**   *Perf. 9*
RA32 PT32 20pf multi   .60   .60
   a.   Imperf.   .60   .60
   Obligatory on mail May 8-15.

Fight Against
Tuberculosis — PT33

2013, Sept. 14   **Litho.**   *Perf. 9*
RA33 PT33 20pf multi   .60   .60
   a.   Imperf.   .60   .60
   Obligatory on mail Sept. 14-21.

Red Cross — PT34

2014, May 8   **Litho.**   *Perf. 9*
RA34 PT34 20pf red & silver   .60   .60
   a.   Imperf.   .60   .60
   Obligatory on mail May 8-15.

Fight Against
Tuberculosis
PT35

2014, Sept. 14   **Litho.**   *Perf. 9*
RA35 PT35 20pf multi   .60   .60
   a.   Imperf.   .60   .60
   Obligatory on mail Sept. 14-21.

Red Cross — PT36

2015, May 8   **Litho.**   *Perf. 9*
RA36 PT36 20pf red & black   .60   .60
   a.   Imperf.   .60   .50
   Obligatory on mail May 8-15.

Fight Against
Tuberculosis
PT37

2015, Sept. 14   **Litho.**   *Perf. 9*
RA37 PT37 20pf multi   .60   .60
   a.   Imperf.   .60   .60
   Obligatory on mail Sept. 14-21.

Red
Cross — PT38

2016, May 8   **Litho.**   *Perf. 9*
RA38 PT38 20pf red & blue   .25   .25
   a.   Imperf.   .25   .25
   Obligatory on mail May 8-15.

Fight Against
Tuberculosis
PT39

2016, Sept. 14   **Litho.**   *Perf. 9*
RA39 PT39 20pf multi   .25   .25
   a.   Imperf.   .25   .25
   Obligatory on mail Sept. 14-21.

Red Cross — PT40

2017, May 8   **Litho.**   *Perf. 9*
RA40 PT40 20pf grnsh blue &
     red   .25   .25
   a.   Imperf.   .25   .25
   Obligatory on mail May 8-15.

BOTSWANA

bä-'swä-nə

LOCATION — In central South Africa,
north of the Republic of South Africa,
east of Namibia and bounded on the
north by the Caprivi Strip of Namibia
and on the east by Zimbabwe.
GOVT. — Independent republic
AREA — 222,000 sq. mi.
POP. — 1,561,973 (July 2004 est.)
CAPITAL — Gaborone

The former Bechuanaland Protector-
ate became an independent republic,
September 30, 1966, taking the name
Botswana.

100 Cents = 1 Rand
100 Thebe = 1 Pula (1976)

**Catalogue values for all unused
stamps in this country are for
Never Hinged items.**

National Assembly Building — A1

Designs: 5c, Abattoir, Lobatsi. 15c, Dakota
plane. 35c, State House, Gaborone.

1966, Sept. 30   **Photo.**   *Perf. 14*
1   A1   2½c multicolored   .25   .25
   a.   Imperf., pair   425.00
2   A1   5c multicolored   .25   .25
3   A1   15c multicolored   .80   .25
4   A1   35c multicolored   .50   .40
   Nos. 1-4 (4)   1.80   1.15

Establishment of Republic of Botswana.

Bechuanaland
Protectorate Nos.
180-193 Overprinted

Perf. 14x14½, 14½x14
1966, Sept. 30   **Wmk. 314**

5	A15	1c multicolored	.45	.25
6	A15	2c multicolored	.50	1.75
7	A15	2½c multicolored	.50	.25
8	A15	3½c yel, blk, sep & pink	1.75	.25
9	A15	5c multicolored	2.25	1.50
10	A15	7½c multicolored	.75	1.75
11	A15	10c multicolored	1.50	.25
12	A15	12½c multicolored	2.75	4.00
13	A15	20c gray & brown	.35	2.00
14	A15	25c yel & dk brn	.35	2.50
15	A15	35c dp org & ultra	.55	3.00
16	A15	50c lt ol grn & sep	.55	.95
17	A15	1r ocher & black	.75	1.25
18	A15	2r blue & brown	1.75	3.25
		Nos. 5-18 (14)	14.75	22.95

European Golden
Oriole — A2

Birds: 2c, African hoopoe. 3c, Ground-
scraper thrush. 4c, Blue waxbill. 5c, Secretary
bird. 7c, Yellow-billed hornbill. 10c, Crimson-
breasted shrike. 15c, Malachite kingfisher.
20c, Fish eagle. 25c, Gray lourie. 35c, Scimitar bill. 50c, Knob-billed duck. 1r, Crested bar-
bet. 2r, Didrio cuckoo.

Perf. 14x14½
1967, Jan. 3   **Photo.**   *Unwmk.*

19	A2	1c gray & multi	.40	.25
20	A2	2c lt blue & multi	.60	.25
21	A2	3c yel green & multi	.75	.25
22	A2	4c salmon & multi	.75	.35
23	A2	5c pink & multi	.75	.40
24	A2	7c slate & multi	.80	.70
25	A2	10c emerald & multi	.80	.80
26	A2	15c lt green & multi	9.00	2.75
27	A2	20c ultra & multi	9.00	1.50
28	A2	25c green & multi	6.50	1.50
29	A2	35c multicolored	9.00	3.00
30	A2	50c dl yel & multi	3.50	3.00
31	A2	1r dl grn & multi	7.50	3.50
32	A2	2r org brn & multi	9.50	17.50
		Nos. 19-32 (14)	58.85	35.75

No. 19 exists with Maltese Cross watermark
(error). Value, used $1,100.
Nos. 19, 20, 22, 24 and 25 exist with gum
Arabic and PVA gum.

University Buildings and
Graduates — A3

1967, Apr. 7   *Perf. 14x14½*

33	A3	3c yel, sepia & dp blue	.25	.25
34	A3	7c blue, sepia & dp bl	.25	.25
35	A3	15c dull rose, sepia & dp bl	.25	.25
36	A3	35c lt vio, sepia & dp bl	.25	.25
		Nos. 33-36 (4)	1.00	1.00

1st conferment of degrees by the University
of Botswana, Lesotho and Swaziland at Roma,
Lesotho.

Chobe
Bush
Bucks
A4

Designs: 7c, Sable antelopes. 35c, Fishing
on the Chobe River.

1967, Oct. 2   Photo.   Perf. 14

37 A4	3c multicolored	.25	.25
38 A4	7c multicolored	.25	.25
39 A4	35c multicolored	1.35	1.40
	Nos. 37-39 (3)	1.85	1.90

Publicity for Chobe Game Reserve.

Human Rights Flame and Arms of Botswana — A5

Design elements rearranged on 15c, 25c.

1968, Apr. 8   Litho.   Perf. 13½x13

40 A5	3c brown red & multi	.25	.25
41 A5	15c emerald & multi	.30	.45
42 A5	25c yellow & multi	.30	.55
	Nos. 40-42 (3)	.85	1.25

International Human Rights Year.

Rock Painting A6

Girl Wearing Ceremonial Beads — A7

Designs: 10c, Baobab Trees, by Thomas Baines (34x25mm). 15c, National Museum and Art Gallery (71½x19mm).

Perf. 13x13½ (3c, 10c); Perf. 12½ (7c); Perf. 12½x13 (15c)

1968, Sept. 30   Litho.

43 A6	3c multicolored	.25	.25
44 A7	7c multicolored	.35	.40
45 A6	10c multicolored	.35	.35
46 A6	15c multicolored	.55	1.60
a.	Souv. sheet of 4, #43-46, perf. 13½	2.00	3.00
	Nos. 43-46 (4)	1.50	2.60

Opening of the National Museum and Art Gallery, Gaborone, Sept. 30, 1968.

African Nativity Scene A8

1968, Nov. 11   Unwmk.   Perf. 13x14

47 A8	1c car & multi	.25	.25
48 A8	2c brown & multi	.25	.25
49 A8	5c green & multi	.25	.25
50 A8	25c dp violet & multi	.25	.50
	Nos. 47-50 (4)	1.00	1.25

Christmas.

Boy Scout, Botswana Scout Emblem and Lion — A9

Botswana Boy Scout emblem, lion and: 15c, Boy Scouts cooking, vert. 25c, Boy Scouts around campfire.

1969, Aug. 21   Litho.   Perf. 13½

51 A9	3c emerald & multi	.60	.30
52 A9	15c lt brown & multi	.70	1.10
53 A9	25c dk brown & multi	.70	1.10
	Nos. 51-53 (3)	2.00	2.50

22nd World Scouting Conf., Helsinki, Finland, Aug. 21-27.

Mother, Child and Star of Bethlehem — A10

1969, Nov. 6   Perf. 14½x14

54 A10	1c dk brn & lt blue	.25	.25
55 A10	2c dk brn & apple grn	.25	.25
56 A10	4c dk brn & dull yel	.25	.25
57 A10	35c dk brn & vio blue	.25	.25
a.	Souv. sheet, #54-57, perf 14½	1.00	1.00
	Nos. 54-57 (4)	1.00	1.00

Christmas.

Diamond Treatment Plant, Orapa — A11

Designs: 7c, Copper and nickel mining, Selebi-Pikwe. 10c, Copper and nickel mining and metal bars, Selebi-Pikwe, horiz. 35c, Orapa diamond mine and diamonds, horiz.

1970, Mar. 23   Perf. 14½x14, 14x14½

58 A11	3c multicolored	1.00	.30
59 A11	7c multicolored	1.30	.30
60 A11	10c multicolored	1.75	.25
61 A11	35c multicolored	3.75	1.75
	Nos. 58-61 (4)	7.80	2.60

Botswana development program.

Mr. Micawber and Charles Dickens A12

Charles Dickens (1812-70), English novelist and: 7c, Scrooge. 15c, Fagin. 25c, Bill Sykes.

1970, July 7   Litho.   Perf. 11

62 A12	3c gray green & multi	.30	.25
63 A12	7c multicolored	.30	.25
64 A12	15c brown & multi	.55	.50
65 A12	25c dp violet & multi	.85	.75
a.	Souvenir sheet of 4, #62-65	4.00	4.00
	Nos. 62-65 (4)	2.00	1.75

UN Headquarters, Emblem — A13

1970, Oct. 24   Litho.   Perf. 11

66 A13	15c ultra, red & silver	.90	.40

United Nations' 25th anniversary.

Toys A14

1970, Nov. 3   Litho.   Perf. 14

67 A14	1c Crocodile	.25	.25
68 A14	2c Giraffe	.25	.25
69 A14	7c Elephant	.25	.25
70 A14	25c Rhinoceros	.75	.90
a.	Souvenir sheet of 4, #67-70	1.80	1.80
	Nos. 67-70 (4)	1.50	1.65

Christmas.

Sorghum A15

1971, Apr. 6   Litho.   Perf. 14

71 A15	3c shown	.25	.25
72 A15	7c Millet	.25	.25
73 A15	10c Corn	.25	.25
74 A15	35c Peanuts	1.00	1.00
	Nos. 71-74 (4)	1.75	1.75

Ox Head and Botswana Map — A16

Map of Botswana and: 4c, Cogwheels and waves. 7c, Zebra rampant. 10c, Tusk and corn. 20c, Coat of arms of Botswana.

1971, Sept. 30   Perf. 14½x14

75 A16	3c yel grn, blk & brn	.25	.25
76 A16	4c lt blue, blk & bl	.25	.25
77 A16	7c orange & blk	.25	.25
78 A16	10c yellow & multi	.25	.25
79 A16	20c blue & multi	.70	2.40
	Nos. 75-79 (5)	1.70	3.40

5th anniversary of independence.

King Bringing Gift — A17

Christmas: 2c, King bringing gift. 7c, Kneeling King with gift. 20c, Three Kings and star.

1971, Nov. 11   Perf. 14

80 A17	2c brt rose & multi	.25	.25
81 A17	3c lt blue & multi	.25	.25
82 A17	7c brt pink & multi	.25	.25
83 A17	20c vio blue & multi	.25	.60
a.	Souvenir sheet of 4, #80-83	1.25	1.25
	Nos. 80-83 (4)	1.00	1.35

Constellation Orion — A18

Night sky over Botswana: 7c, Scorpio. 10c, Centaur. 20c, Southern Cross.

1972, Apr. 24   Litho.   Perf. 14

84 A18	3c dp org, bl grn & blk	1.15	.45
85 A18	7c org, blue & blk	1.40	1.00
86 A18	10c org, green & blk	1.60	1.15
87 A18	20c emer, vio bl & blk	2.25	4.00
	Nos. 84-87 (4)	6.40	6.60

Gubulawayo Cancel and Map of Trail — A19

Sections of Mafeking-Gubulawayo Trail and: 4c, Bechuanaland Protectorate No. 65. 7c, Mail runners. 20c, Mafeking 638 killer cancellation.

1972, Aug. 21   Perf. 13½x13

88 A19	3c cream & multi	.30	.25
89 A19	4c cream & multi	.30	.30
90 A19	7c cream & multi	.45	.45
91 A19	20c cream & multi	1.10	1.40
a.	Souvenir sheet of 4	16.00	16.00
	Nos. 88-91 (4)	2.15	2.40

84th anniv. of Mafeking to Gubulawayo runner post. No. 91a contains one each of Nos. 88-91, arranged vertically to show map of trail. No. 91a exists with pale buff background omitted. Value, $700.
Compare with design A89.

Cross, Map of Botswana, Bells — A20

Cross, map of Botswana and: 3c, Candle. 7c, Christmas tree. 20c, Star and holly.

1972, Nov. 6   Litho.   Perf. 14

92 A20	2c yellow & multi	.25	.25
93 A20	3c pale lilac & multi	.25	.25
94 A20	7c yel green & multi	.25	.25
95 A20	20c pink & multi	.25	.25
a.	Souvenir sheet of 4, #92-95	1.80	1.80
	Nos. 92-95 (4)	1.00	1.00

Christmas.

Chariot of the Sun, Trundholm, Denmark — A21

WMO Emblem and: 3c, Thor, Norse thunder god, vert. 7c, Ymir, Icelandic frost giant, vert. 20c, Odin on 8-legged horse Sleipnir.

1973, Mar. 23   Litho.   Perf. 14

96 A21	3c orange & multi	.25	.25
97 A21	4c yellow & multi	.35	.25
98 A21	7c ultra & multi	.40	.25
99 A21	20c gold & multi	1.10	1.05
	Nos. 96-99 (4)	2.10	1.80

Intl. meteorological cooperation, cent.

Livingstone and Boat on Lake Ngwami — A22

Design: 20c, Livingstone and his meeting with Henry Stanley.

1973, Sept. 10   Litho.   Perf. 13½x14

100 A22	3c gray & multi	.25	.25
101 A22	20c yel green & multi	1.20	1.20

Dr. David Livingstone (1813-1873), medical missionary and explorer.

Shepherd and Flock — A23

Christmas: 3c, Ass and foal, African huts, vert. 7c, African mother, child and star, vert. 20c, Tribal meeting (kgotla), symbolic of Wise Men.

1973, Nov. 12 Litho. Perf. 14½
102	A23	3c multicolored	.25	.25
103	A23	4c multicolored	.25	.25
104	A23	7c multicolored	.25	.25
105	A23	20c multicolored	.25	.75
		Nos. 102-105 (4)	1.00	1.50

Gaborone Campus, Botswana A24

Designs: 7c, Kwaluseni Campus, Swaziland. 20c, Roma Campus, Lesotho. 35c, Map and flags of Botswana, Swaziland & Lesotho.

1974, May 8 Litho. Perf. 14
106	A24	3c lt blue & multi	.25	.25
107	A24	7c yel green & multi	.25	.25
108	A24	20c yel green & multi	.25	.25
109	A24	35c brt blue & multi	.25	.25
		Nos. 106-109 (4)	1.00	1.00

10th anniversary of the University of Botswana, Lesotho and Swaziland.

UPU Emblem, Mail Vehicles — A25

UPU, cent.: 3c, Post Office, Palapye, c. 1889. 7c, Bechuanaland police camel post, 1900. 20c, 1920 and 1974 planes.

1974, May 22 Litho. Perf. 13½x14
110	A25	2c car & multi	.65	.40
111	A25	3c green & multi	.65	.40
112	A25	7c brown & multi	1.10	.80
113	A25	20c blue & multi	3.00	2.75
		Nos. 110-113 (4)	5.40	4.35

Gems and Minerals A26

1c, Amethyst. 2c, Agate Botswana pink. 3c, Quartz. 4c, Niccolite. 5c, Moss agate. 7c, Agate. 10c, Stilbite. 15c, Moshaneng banded marble. 20c, Gem diamonds. 25c, Chrysotile. 35c, Jasper. 50c, Moss quartz. 1r, Citrine. 2r, Chalcopyrite.

1974, July 1 Photo. Perf. 14x13
114	A26	1c multi	.65	2.50
115	A26	2c multi	.65	2.50
116	A26	3c multi	.70	.80
117	A26	4c multi	.80	.60
118	A26	5c multi	.80	1.00
119	A26	7c multi	.90	1.25
120	A26	10c multi	1.75	.65
121	A26	15c multi	2.25	4.00
122	A26	20c multi	4.50	4.00
123	A26	25c multi	5.50	2.50
124	A26	35c multi	5.50	4.75
125	A26	50c multi	5.00	5.50
126	A26	1r multi	8.25	10.00
127	A26	2r multi	22.00	20.00
		Nos. 114-127 (14)	59.25	60.05

For surcharges see Nos. 155-168.

Stapelia Variegata — A27

Flowers of Botswana: 7c, Hibiscus lunarifolius. 15c, Ceratotheca triloba. 20c, Nerine laticoma.

1974, Nov. 4 Litho. Perf. 14
128	A27	2c multicolored	.40	.45
129	A27	7c multicolored	.55	.25
130	A27	15c multicolored	.85	1.00
131	A27	20c multicolored	1.15	1.25
a.		Souvenir sheet of 4, #128-131	4.00	4.00
		Nos. 128-131 (4)	2.95	2.95

Pres. Sir Seretse Khama — A28

1975, Mar. 24 Photo. Perf. 13½x13
132	A28	4c olive & multi	.25	.25
133	A28	10c yellow & multi	.25	.25
134	A28	20c ultra & multi	.25	.25
135	A28	35c brown & multi	.40	.40
a.		Souvenir sheet of 4, #132-135	1.10	1.25
		Nos. 132-135 (4)	1.15	1.15

10th anniv. of self-government.

Ostrich and Rock Painting A29

Paintings and animals: 10c, Rhinoceros. 25c, Hyena. 35c, Scorpion.

1975, June 23 Litho. Perf. 14x14½
136	A29	4c yel green & multi	1.00	.25
137	A29	10c buff & multi	1.60	.25
138	A29	25c blue & multi	3.25	.60
139	A29	35c lilac & multi	3.25	1.25
a.		Souvenir sheet of 4, #136-139	17.00	17.00
		Nos. 136-139 (4)	9.10	2.35

Rock paintings from Tsodilo Hills.

Map of British Bechuanaland A30

Chiefs Sebele, Bathoen and Khama A31

Design: 10c, Khama the Great, antelope.

Perf. 14½x14, 14x14½
1975, Oct. 31 Litho.
140	A30	6c buff & multi	.45	.25
141	A30	10c rose & multi	.55	.25
142	A31	25c lt green & multi	1.15	.80
		Nos. 140-142 (3)	2.15	1.30

Establishment of Protectorate, 90th anniv. (6c); Khama the Great (1828-1923), centenary of his accession as chief (10c); visit of the

chiefs of the Bakwena, Bangwaketse and Bamangwato tribes to London, 80th anniv. (25c).

Aloe Marlothii — A32

Christmas: 10c, Aloe lutescens. 15c, Aloe zebrina. 25c, Aloe littoralis.

1975, Nov. 3 Litho. Perf. 14½x14
143	A32	3c multicolored	.40	.25
144	A32	10c multicolored	.80	.25
145	A32	15c multicolored	1.20	1.75
146	A32	25c multicolored	1.50	2.75
		Nos. 143-146 (4)	3.90	5.00

Traditional Musical Instruments — A33

Designs: 4c, Drum. 10c, Hand piano. 15c, Segankuru (violin). 25c, Kudu signal horn.

1976, Mar. 1 Litho. Perf. 14
147	A33	4c yellow & multi	.25	.25
148	A33	10c lilac & multi	.25	.25
149	A33	15c dull yel & multi	.35	.55
150	A33	25c lt blue & multi	.40	1.25
		Nos. 147-150 (4)	1.25	2.30

1-pula Bank Note with Seretse Khama A34

Reverse of Bank Notes: 10c, Basket weaver, hut builder. 15c, Antelopes. 25c, National Assembly building.

1976, June 28 Litho. Perf. 14
151	A34	4c rose & multi	.25	.25
152	A34	10c brt green & multi	.25	.25
153	A34	15c yel green & multi	.35	.25
154	A34	25c blue & multi	.45	.45
a.		Souvenir sheet of 4, #151-154	2.40	3.50
		Nos. 151-154 (4)	1.30	1.20

First national currency.

Nos. 114-127 Surcharged in Black or Gold

Type I

Type II

Type I surcharge: Thick numerals and "t."
Type II surcharge: Thin numerals and "t."

Type I

1976, Aug. 23 Photo. Perf. 14x13
155	A26	1t on 1c multi	2.30	.70
156	A26	2t on 2c multi	2.30	1.00
157	A26	3t on 3c multi (G)	1.75	.60
158	A26	4t on 4c multi	2.75	.45
159	A26	5t on 5c multi	2.75	.45

160	A26	7t on 7c multi	1.45	2.50
161	A26	10t on 10c multi	1.45	.80
162	A26	15t on 15c multi (G)	5.00	2.75
163	A26	20t on 20c multi	8.50	.80
164	A26	25t on 25c multi	5.75	1.25
165	A26	35t on 35c multi	4.75	4.75
166	A26	50t on 50c multi	6.25	9.00
167	A26	1p on 1r multi	7.00	9.50
168	A26	2p on 2r multi (G)	9.25	11.50
		Nos. 155-168 (14)	61.25	46.05

1977, July 15 Type II
155a	A26	1t on 1c multi	2.25	.80
156a	A26	2t on 2c multi	2.25	.80
158a	A26	4t on 4c multi	2.60	.80
159a	A26	5t on 5c multi	2.60	.80
162a	A26	15t on 15c multi (G)	6.00	1.50
163a	A26	20t on 20c multi (G)	7.75	1.50
		Nos. 155a-163a (6)	23.45	6.20

The government printer in Pretoria applied the typographed type I surcharge. Enschede applied the lithographed type II surcharge.

1977, Aug. 3 - Oct. 17 Type I
Surcharge at Bottom Right
157b	A26	3t on 3c multi	60.00	17.50
160b	A26	7t on 7c multi	70.00	22.50
166b	A26	50t on 50c multi	300.00	75.00
167b	A26	1p on 1r multi	90.00	45.00
		Nos. 157b-167b (4)	520.00	160.00

Cattle Industry A35

Designs: 10t, Antelope, tourism, vert. 15t, Schoolhouse and children, education. 25t, Rural weaving, vert. 35t, Mining industry, vert.

1976, Sept. 30 Litho. Perf. 14x14½
Textured Paper
169	A35	4t multicolored	.25	.25
170	A35	10t multicolored	.25	.25
171	A35	15t multicolored	.25	.50
172	A35	25t multicolored	.25	.65
173	A35	35t multicolored	.95	1.00
		Nos. 169-173 (5)	1.95	2.65

10th anniversary of independence.

Colophospermum Mopane — A36

Trees: 4t, Baikiaea plurijuga. 10t, Sterculia rogersii. 25t, Acacia nilotica. 40t, Kigelia africana.

1976, Nov. 1 Litho. Perf. 13
174	A36	3t multicolored	.30	.25
175	A36	4t multicolored	.30	.25
176	A36	10t multicolored	.40	.25
177	A36	25t multicolored	.90	.90
178	A36	40t multicolored	1.50	1.50
		Nos. 174-178 (5)	3.40	3.15

Christmas.

Pres. Seretse Khama and Elizabeth II — A37

Designs: 25t, Coronation coach in procession. 40t, Recognition scene.

1977, Feb. 7 Litho. Perf. 12
179	A37	4t multicolored	.25	.25
180	A37	25t multicolored	.25	.25
181	A37	40t multicolored	.35	.50
		Nos. 179-181 (3)	.85	1.00

Reign of Queen Elizabeth II, 25th anniv.

Clawless Otter — A38

World Wildlife Fund Emblem and: 4t, Serval. 10t, Bat-eared foxes. 25t, Pangolins. 40t, Brown hyena.

1977, June 6 Litho. *Perf. 14*

182	A38	3t multicolored	6.75	.70
183	A38	4t multicolored	6.75	.70
184	A38	10t multicolored	7.75	.70
185	A38	25t multicolored	17.50	3.25
186	A38	40t multicolored	21.00	12.00
		Nos. 182-186 (5)	59.75	17.35

Endangered wildlife.

Khama Memorial A39

Designs: 4t, Gcwihaba Caverns. 15t, Green's (expedition) tree. 20t, Mmajojo ruins. 25t, Ancient morabaraba board. 35t, Matsieng's footprints.

1977, Aug. 22 Litho. *Perf. 14*

187	A39	4t multicolored	.30	.25
188	A39	5t multicolored	.30	.25
189	A39	15t multicolored	.50	.40
190	A39	20t multicolored	.50	.50
191	A39	25t multicolored	.50	.50
192	A39	35t multicolored	.65	.65
a.		Souvenir sheet of 6, #187-192	3.75	3.75
		Nos. 187-192 (6)	2.75	2.55

Historical sites and national monuments.

Lilies — A40

Designs: 3t, Hypoxis Itida. 5t, Haemanthus magnificus. 10t, Boophane disticha. 25t, Vellozia retinervis. 40t, Ammocharis coranica.

1977, Nov. 7 Litho. *Perf. 14*

193	A40	3t sepia & multi	.25	.25
194	A40	5t gray & multi	.25	.25
195	A40	10t multicolored	.25	.25
196	A40	25t multicolored	.50	*.65*
197	A40	40t multicolored	.90	*1.25*
		Nos. 193-197 (5)	2.15	2.65

Christmas.

Birds — A41

1t, Black korhaan. 2t, Marabou storks. 3t, Red-billed hoopoe. 4t, Carmine bee-eaters. 5t, African jacana. 7t, Paradise flycatcher. 10t, Bennett's woodpecker. 15t, Red bishop. 20t, Crowned plovers. 25t, Giant kingfishers. 30t, White-faced ducks. 35t, Green-backed heron. 45t, Black-headed herons. 50t, Spotted eagle owl. 1p, Gabar goshawk. 2p, Martial eagle. 5p, Saddlebill storks.

1978, July 3 Photo. *Perf. 14*

198	A41	1t multicolored	.90	*1.20*
199	A41	2t multicolored	1.20	1.20
200	A41	3t multicolored	.90	.90
201	A41	4t multicolored	2.60	*1.00*
202	A41	5t multicolored	1.30	.40
203	A41	7t multicolored	1.30	*2.75*
204	A41	10t multicolored	2.60	.60
205	A41	15t multicolored	2.00	*2.75*
206	A41	20t multicolored	2.25	2.00
207	A41	25t multicolored	.90	*3.00*
208	A41	30t multicolored	.90	.90
209	A41	35t multicolored	.90	*3.00*
210	A41	45t multicolored	1.30	*2.75*
211	A41	50t multicolored	6.50	4.50
212	A41	1p multicolored	3.25	*4.50*
213	A41	2p multicolored	4.00	*8.00*
214	A41	5p multicolored	7.25	*16.00*
		Nos. 198-214 (17)	40.05	55.45

For surcharges see Nos. 289-290.

Tawana Making Kaross (Garment) A42

Designs: 5t, Map of Okavango Delta. 15t, Bushman collecting roots. 20t, Herero woman milking cow. 25t, Yei pulling mokoro (boat). 35t, Mbukushu fishing.

1978, Sept. 11 Litho. *Perf. 14*

Textured Paper

215	A42	4t multicolored	.25	*.30*
216	A42	5t multicolored	.25	.25
217	A42	15t multicolored	.25	*.40*
218	A42	20t multicolored	.30	*.65*
219	A42	25t multicolored	.35	*.60*
220	A42	35t multicolored	.60	*1.50*
a.		Souvenir sheet of 6, #215-220	2.25	*3.50*
		Nos. 215-220 (6)	2.00	*3.70*

People of the Okavango Delta.

Caralluma Lutea — A43

Flowers: 10t, Hoodia lugardii. 15t, Ipomoea transvaalensis. 25t, Ansellia gigantea.

1978, Nov. 6

221	A43	5t multicolored	.40	.25
222	A43	10t multicolored	.50	.25
223	A43	15t multicolored	1.10	.60
224	A43	25t multicolored	1.25	.80
		Nos. 221-224 (4)	3.25	1.90

Christmas.

Boy at Sip Well — A44

Water Development: 5t, Watering pit. 10t, Hand-dug well and goats. 25t, Windmill, well and cattle. 40t, Modern drilling rig.

1979, Mar. 30 Litho. *Perf. 14*

225	A44	3t multicolored	.25	.25
226	A44	5t multicolored	.25	.25
227	A44	10t multicolored	.25	.25
228	A44	25t multicolored	.25	.25
229	A44	40t multicolored	.30	.30
		Nos. 225-229 (5)	1.30	1.30

Botswana Pot — A45

Handicrafts: 10t, Clay buffalo. 25t, Woven covered basket. 40t, Beaded bag.

1979, June 11 Litho. *Perf. 14*

230	A45	5t multicolored	.25	.25
231	A45	10t multicolored	.25	.25
232	A45	25t multicolored	.25	.25
233	A45	40t multicolored	.50	.50
a.		Souvenir sheet of 4, #230-233	1.50	1.50
		Nos. 230-233 (4)	1.25	1.25

Bechuanaland No. 6, Rowland Hill — A46

Sir Rowland Hill (1795-1879), originator of penny postage, and: 25t, Bechuanaland Protectorate No. 107. 45t, Botswana No. 20.

1979, Aug. 27 Litho. *Perf. 13½*

234	A46	5t rose & black	.25	.25
235	A46	25t multicolored	.35	.35
236	A46	45t multicolored	.50	.50
		Nos. 234-236 (3)	1.10	1.10

Children Playing A47

Design: 10t, Child playing with rag doll, and IYC emblem, vert.

1979, Sept. 24 *Perf. 14*

237	A47	5t multicolored	.25	.25
238	A47	10t multicolored	.25	.25

International Year of the Child.

Ximenia Caffra — A48

Christmas: 10t, Sclerocarya caffra. 15t, Hexalobus monopetalus. 25t, Ficus soldanella.

1979, Nov. 12 Litho. *Perf. 14*

239	A48	5t multicolored	.25	.25
240	A48	10t multicolored	.25	.25
241	A48	15t multicolored	.45	.45
242	A48	25t multicolored	.60	.60
		Nos. 239-242 (4)	1.55	1.55

Flap-Necked Chameleon A49

10t, Leopard tortoise. 25t, Puff adder. 40t, White-throated monitor.

1980, Mar. 3 Litho. *Perf. 14*

243	A49	5t shown	.80	.25
244	A49	10t multicolored	.80	.30
245	A49	25t multicolored	1.30	1.25
246	A49	40t multicolored	1.60	*3.00*
		Nos. 243-246 (4)	4.50	4.80

Rock Breaking (Early Mining) A50

1980, July 7 Litho. *Perf. 13½x14*

247	A50	5t shown	.35	.25
248	A50	10t Ore hoisting	.45	.25
249	A50	15t Ore transport	1.00	.80
250	A50	20t Ore crushing	1.10	1.10
251	A50	25t Smelting	1.15	1.10
252	A50	35t Tools, products	1.45	*1.50*
		Nos. 247-252 (6)	5.50	5.00

Chiwele and the Giant — A51

Folktales: 10t, Kgori Is Not Deceived. 30t, Nyambi's Wife and Crocodile. 45t, Clever Hare, horiz.

Perf. 14, 14½ (10t, 30t)

1980, Sept. 8

253	A51	5t multicolored	.25	.25

Size: 28x36mm

254	A51	10t multicolored	.25	.25
255	A51	30t multicolored	.50	.50

Size: 44x26mm

256	A51	45t multicolored	.65	.65
		Nos. 253-256 (4)	1.65	1.65

Game Watching — A52

1980, Oct. 6 Litho. *Perf. 14*

257	A52	5t multicolored	.70	.40

World Tourism Conf., Manila, Sept. 27.

Christmas — A53

10t, Acacia nilotica. 25t, Acacia erubescens. 40t, Dichrostachys cinerea.

1980, Nov. 3 Litho. *Perf. 14*

258	A53	5t shown	.25	.25
259	A53	10t multicolored	.25	.25
260	A53	25t multicolored	.60	.35
261	A53	40t multicolored	.95	.70
		Nos. 258-261 (4)	2.05	1.55

Heinrich von Stephan, Bechuanaland Protectorate No. 150, Botswana No. 111 — A55

Design: 20t, Von Stephan, Bechuanaland Protectorate No. 151, Botswana No. 112.

1981, Jan. 7 *Perf. 14*

266	A55	6t multicolored	.65	.35
267	A55	20t multicolored	1.75	*2.25*

Von Stephan (1831-1897), founder of UPU.

Emperor Dragonfly — A56

7t, Praying mantis. 10t, Elegant grasshopper. 20t, Dung beetle. 30t, Citrus swallowtail butterfly. 45t, Mopane worm.

1981, Feb. 23 Litho. *Perf. 14*

268	A56	6t shown	.40	.25
269	A56	7t multicolored	.40	.25
270	A56	10t multicolored	.40	.25
271	A56	20t multicolored	.75	.55
272	A56	30t multicolored	1.00	.75

273 A56 45t multicolored   1.25 1.25
   a. Souv. sheet of 6, #268-273   7.00 7.00
     Nos. 268-273 (6)   4.20 3.30

Blind
Basket
Weaver
A57

1981, Apr. 6   Litho.   *Perf. 14*
274 A57 6t Seamstress   .25   .25
275 A57 20t shown   .65   .35
276 A57 30t Carpenter   .85   .45
     Nos. 274-276 (3)   1.75 1.05

International Year of the Disabled.

Woman Reading
Letter (Literacy
Campaign) — A58

7t, Man sending telegram. 20t, Boy, newspaper. 30t, Father and daughter reading.

1981, June 8
277 A58 6t shown   .25   .25
278 A58 7t multicolored   .25   .25
279 A58 20t multicolored   .45   .35
280 A58 30t multicolored   .65   .45
     Nos. 277-280 (4)   1.60 1.30

Pres.
Seretse
Khama
(1921-80)
and Flag
A59

Portrait and various local buildings: 6t, 10t, 45t..

1981, July 13
281 A59 6t multicolored   .25   .25
282 A59 10t multicolored   .25   .25
283 A59 30t multicolored   .45   .45
284 A59 45t multicolored   .55   .55
     Nos. 281-284 (4)   1.50 1.50

Cattle in Agricultural Show — A60

1981, Sept. 21   Litho.   *Perf. 14½*
285 A60 6t Plowing   .25   .25
286 A60 20t shown   .35   .25
287 A60 30t Meat Commission   .50   .40
288 A60 45t Vaccine Institute   .70   .60
     Nos. 285-288 (4)   1.80 1.50

Nos. 204, 209
Surcharged

1981, Sept. 1   Photo.   *Perf. 14*
289 A41 25t on 35t multicolored   4.75 3.50
290 A41 30t on 10t multicolored   4.75 3.50

Christmas — A61

Designs: Water lilies.

1981, Nov. 11   Litho.
291 A61 6t Nymphaea caerulea   .30   .25
292 A61 10t Nymphoides indica   .35   .25
293 A61 25t Nymphaea lotus   .80   .90
294 A61 40t Ottelia kunenensis   1.05 2.25
     Nos. 291-294 (4)   2.50 3.65

Children's Drawings — A62

1982, Feb. 15   Litho.   *Perf. 14½x14*
295 A62 6t Cattle   .50   .25
296 A62 10t Kgotla meeting   .65   .25
297 A62 30t Village   2.25 1.50
298 A62 45t Huts   2.25 2.25
     Nos. 295-298 (4)   5.65 4.25

Traditional Houses — A63

1982, May 3   Litho.   *Perf. 14*
299 A63 6t Common type   .50   .25
300 A63 10t Kgatleng   .60   .25
301 A63 30t Northeastern   2.25 1.25
302 A63 45t Sarwa   2.25 3.00
     Nos. 299-302 (4)   5.60 4.75

Red-billed
Teals — A64

1t, Masked weaver. 2t, Lesser double-collared sunbirds. 3t, White-fronted bee-eaters. 4t, Ostriches. 5t, Grey-headed gulls. 6t, Pygmy geese. 7t, Cattle egrets. 8t, Lanner falcon. 10t, Yellow-billed storks. 20t, Barn owls. 25t, Hamerkops. 30t, Stilts. 35t, Blacksmith plovers. 45t, Wattled plover. 50t, Crowned guinea-fowl. 1p, Cape vultures. 2p, Augur bustards.

Perf. 14x14½, 14½x14
1982, Aug. 2   Photo.
303 A64 1t multicolored   .95 *1.75*
304 A64 2t multicolored   1.15 *1.75*
305 A64 3t multicolored   1.40 *1.75*
306 A64 4t multicolored   1.40 *1.75*
307 A64 5t multicolored   1.40 *1.75*
308 A64 6t multicolored   1.40   .45
309 A64 7t multicolored   1.40   .25
310 A64 8t multicolored   3.25 1.60
311 A64 10t multicolored   1.40   .25
312 A64 15t shown   3.25   .30
313 A64 20t multicolored   6.50 3.75
314 A64 25t multicolored   3.75   .85
315 A64 30t multicolored   4.50 1.00
316 A64 35t multicolored   4.50   .90
317 A64 45t multicolored   4.50 2.00
318 A64 50t multicolored   5.50 2.75
319 A64 1p multicolored   10.50 12.00
320 A64 2p multicolored   13.00 17.00
     Nos. 303-320 (18)   69.75 51.85

Nos. 303-311 vert.
For surcharges see Nos. 401-403.

Christmas — A65

Designs: Mushrooms.

1982, Nov. 2   Litho.   *Perf. 14½*
321 A65 7t Shaggy mane   2.75   .25
322 A65 15t Orange milk   4.25   .75
323 A65 35t Panther   6.75 2.25
324 A65 50t King boletus   8.50 9.00
     Nos. 321-324 (4)   22.25 12.25

A66

7t, Pres. Quett Masire. 15t, Dancers. 35t, Melbourne Conference Center. 45t, Heads of State meeting.

1983, Mar. 14   Litho.   *Perf. 14*
325 A66 7t multicolored   .25   .25
326 A66 15t multicolored   .25   .25
327 A66 35t multicolored   .60   *.65*
328 A66 45t multicolored   .70 *1.00*
     Nos. 325-328 (4)   1.80 2.15

Commonwealth Day.

Endangered
Species — A67

7t, Wattle crane. 15t, Aloe lutescens. 35t, Roan antelope. 50t, Hyphaene ventricosa.

1983, Apr. 19   Litho.   *Perf. 14x14½*
329 A67 7t multi   4.00   .50
330 A67 15t multi   3.50   .90
331 A67 35t multi   4.00 3.00
332 A67 50t multi   4.50 5.75
     Nos. 329-332 (4)   16.00 10.15

Wooden
Spoons — A68

1983, June 18   Litho.   *Perf. 14*
333 A68 7t shown   .40   .25
334 A68 15t Jewelry   .75   .30
335 A68 35t Ox-hide milk bag   1.25   .75
336 A68 50t Decorated knives   1.65 1.10
   a. Souvenir sheet of 4, #333-336 8.25 8.25
     Nos. 333-336 (4)   4.05 2.40

Christmas
A69

Dragonflies: 6t, Pantala flavescens. 15t, Anax imperator. 25t, Trithemis arteriosa. 45t, Chlorolestes elegans.

1983, Nov. 7   Litho.   *Perf. 14½x14*
337 A69 6t multicolored   1.00   .25
338 A69 15t multicolored   2.25   .40
339 A69 25t multicolored   2.50   .80
340 A69 45t multicolored   3.25 *4.75*
     Nos. 337-340 (4)   9.00 6.20

Mining
Industry — A70

7t, Diamonds. 15t, Lime. 35t, Copper, nickel, vert. 50t, Coal, vert.

1984, Mar. 19   Litho.   *Perf. 14½*
341 A70 7t multi   3.00   .60
342 A70 15t multi   3.00   .85
343 A70 35t multi   4.75 3.50
344 A70 50t multi   5.50 10.00
     Nos. 341-344 (4)   16.25 14.95

Traditional
Transport
A71

1984, June 16   Litho.   *Perf. 14½x14*
345 A71 7t Man riding ox   .30   .25
346 A71 25t Sled   1.00   .75
347 A71 35t Wagon   1.30 *1.40*
348 A71 50t Cart   1.90 2.25
     Nos. 345-348 (4)   4.50 4.65

Intl. Civil
Aviation Org.,
40th
Anniv. — A72

7t, Avro 504. 10t, Westland Wessex. 15t, Junkers 52-3M. 25t, Dragon Rapide. 35t, DC-3. 50t, F27 Fokker Friendship.

1984, Oct. 8   Litho.   *Perf. 14x13½*
349 A72 7t multi   .95   .25
350 A72 10t multi   1.25   .40
351 A72 15t multi   1.75 1.00
352 A72 25t multi   2.50 2.00
353 A72 35t multi   3.00 3.75
354 A72 50t multi   3.25 *7.00*
     Nos. 349-354 (6)   12.70 14.40

Butterflies
A73

7t, Papilio demodocus. 25t, Byblia acheloia. 35t, Hypolimnas missipus. 50t, Graphium taboranus.

1984, Nov. 5   Litho.   *Perf. 14½x14*
355 A73 7t multicolored   2.75   .30
356 A73 25t multicolored   4.25 1.75
357 A73 35t multicolored   4.75 3.25
358 A73 50t multicolored   6.25 *11.00*
     Nos. 355-358 (4)   18.00 16.30

Christmas 1984.

Traditional & Exotic
Foods — A74

7t, Man preparing seswaa. 15t, Woman preparing bogobe. 25t, Girl eating madilla. 50t, Woman collecting caterpillars.

1985, Mar. 18   Litho.   Perf. 14½

359	A74	7t multicolored	.65	.30
360	A74	15t multicolored	.90	.55
361	A74	25t multicolored	1.25	1.00
362	A74	50t multicolored	2.10	2.10
a.		Souvenir sheet of 4, #359-362	10.50	10.50
		Nos. 359-362 (4)	4.90	3.95

Southern African Development Coordination Conference, 5th anniv.

Bechuanaland No. 4 — A75

Postage stamp cent.: 15t, Bechuanaland Protectorate No. 72. 25t, Bechuanaland Protectorate No. 106. 35t, Bechuanaland No. 199, 50t, Botswana No. 1, horiz.

1985, June 24

363	A75	7t multicolored	1.25	.25
364	A75	15t multicolored	2.25	.60
365	A75	25t multicolored	2.75	.85
366	A75	35t multicolored	3.25	2.25
367	A75	50t multicolored	3.50	4.50
		Nos. 363-367 (5)	13.00	8.45

Police Centenary A76

Designs: 7t, Bechuanaland Border Police, 1885-95. 10t, Bechuanaland Mounted Police, 1894-1902. 25t, Bechuanaland Protectorate Police, 1903-66. 50t, Botswana Motorcycle Police, 1966-85.

1985, Aug. 5   Perf. 14½x14

368	A76	7t multicolored	2.75	.60
369	A76	10t multicolored	3.25	.60
370	A76	25t multicolored	4.50	1.25
371	A76	50t multicolored	7.00	5.75
		Nos. 368-371 (4)	17.50	8.20

Edible Wild Cucumbers A77

7t, Cucumis metuliferus. 15t, Acanthosicyos naudinianus. 25t, Coccinia sessilifolia. 50t, Momordica balsamina.

1985, Nov. 4

372	A77	7t multicolored	2.00	.65
373	A77	15t multicolored	2.00	1.00
374	A77	25t multicolored	3.25	1.90
375	A77	50t multicolored	6.00	6.00
		Nos. 372-375 (4)	13.25	9.55

Christmas.

Declaration of Protectorate, Cent. — A78

7t, Heads of state meet. 15t, Declaration reading, 1885. 25t, Mackenzie and Khama. 50t, Map.

1985, Dec. 30   Litho.   Perf. 14x14½

376	A78	7t multicolored	.50	.25
377	A78	15t multicolored	1.00	.50
378	A78	25t multicolored	1.75	1.25
379	A78	50t multicolored	4.00	5.25
a.		Souvenir sheet of 4, #376-379	18.00	18.00
		Nos. 376-379 (4)	7.25	7.25

Halley's Comet — A79

7t, Comet over Serowe. 15t, Over Bobonong. 35t, Over Gomare swamps. 50t, Over Thamaga, Letlhakeng.

1986, Mar. 24   Perf. 14½x14

380	A79	7t multicolored	1.10	.25
381	A79	15t multicolored	2.00	.90
382	A79	35t multicolored	2.75	1.75
383	A79	50t multicolored	3.00	3.75
		Nos. 380-383 (4)	8.85	6.65

Milk Containers — A80

1986, June 23   Perf. 14½

384	A80	8t Leather bag	.40	.25
385	A80	15t Ceramic pots	.50	.40
386	A80	35t Wood pot	1.00	1.00
387	A80	50t Woman, pots	1.40	1.40
		Nos. 384-387 (4)	3.30	3.05

Souvenir Sheet

20th Anniversary of Independence

Natl. Independence, 20th Anniv. — A81

No. 388: a, Map of natl. parks and reserves. b, Morupule Power Station. c, Cattle, Kgalagadi. d, Natl. Assembly.

1986, Sept. 30   Litho.   Perf. 14½x14

388	A81	Sheet of 4	6.00	6.00
a.-d.		20t any single	1.50	1.50

Flowers of the Okavango Swamps — A82

8t, Ludwigia stogonifera. 15t, Sopubia mannii. 35t, Commelina diffusa. 50t, Hibiscus diversifolius.

1986, Nov. 3   Litho.   Perf. 14x14½

389	A82	8t multicolored	1.50	.25
390	A82	15t multicolored	2.75	1.35
391	A82	35t multicolored	4.50	3.75
392	A82	50t multicolored	5.00	8.00
		Nos. 389-392 (4)	13.75	13.35

Christmas.

Traditional Medicine A83

8t, Professional diviners. 15t, Lightning prevention. 35t, Rainmaker. 50t, Bloodletting.

1987, Mar. 2   Litho.   Perf. 14½x14

393	A83	8t multicolored	1.00	.25
394	A83	15t multicolored	1.90	.75
395	A83	35t multicolored	2.75	2.75
396	A83	50t multicolored	3.50	5.00
		Nos. 393-396 (4)	9.15	8.75

UN Child Survival Campaign — A84

1987, June 1

397	A84	8t Oral rehydration therapy	.50	.25
398	A84	15t Growth monitoring	.80	.60
399	A84	35t Immunization	1.70	2.00
400	A84	50t Breast-feeding	2.00	3.00
		Nos. 397-400 (4)	5.00	5.85

Nos. 308, 311 and 318 Surcharged

Perf. 14x14½,14½x14

1987, Apr. 1   Photo.

401	A64	3t on 6t No. 308	2.60	1.25
402	A64	5t on 10t No. 311	2.60	1.75
403	A64	20t on 50t No. 318	4.75	1.60
		Nos. 401-403 (3)	9.95	4.60

Wildlife Conservation — A85

1t, Cape fox. 2t, Lechwe. 3t, Zebra. 4t, Duiker. 5t, Banded mongoose. 6t, Rusty-spotted genet. 8t, Hedgehog. 10t, Scrub hare. 12t, Hippopotamus. 15t, Suricate. 20t, Caracal. 25t, Steenbok. 30t, Gemsbok. 35t, Square-lipped rhino. 40t, Mountain reedbuck. 50t, Rock dassie. 1p, Giraffe. 2p, Tsessebe. 3p, Side-striped jackal. 5p, Hartebeest.

1987, Aug. 3   Perf. 14

404	A85	1t multicolored	.25	1.25
405	A85	2t multicolored	.75	1.75
406	A85	3t multicolored	.25	1.50
407	A85	4t multicolored	.25	1.75
408	A85	5t multicolored	.30	1.75
409	A85	6t multicolored	.30	1.75
410	A85	8t multicolored	.45	.25
411	A85	10t multicolored	.45	.25
412	A85	12t multicolored	5.75	4.00
413	A85	15t multicolored	3.50	2.50
414	A85	20t multicolored	1.00	.75
415	A85	25t multicolored	1.00	1.50
416	A85	30t multicolored	2.10	2.00
417	A85	35t multicolored	3.50	3.50
418	A85	40t multicolored	2.50	2.00
419	A85	50t multicolored	1.30	2.00
420	A85	1p multicolored	3.50	3.25
421	A85	2p multicolored	3.50	5.50
422	A85	3p multicolored	5.50	8.50
423	A85	5p multicolored	8.50	10.00
		Nos. 404-423 (20)	44.65	55.75

For surcharges see Nos. 480-482, 506-509.

Wetland Grasses — A86

8t, Cyperus articulatus. 15t, Miscanthus junceus. 30t, Cyperus alopecuroides. 1p, Typha latifolia.

1987, Oct. 26   Perf. 14x14½

424	A86	8t multicolored	.50	.25
425	A86	15t multicolored	.80	.50
426	A86	30t multicolored	1.60	.80
427	A86	1p multicolored	3.25	5.75
a.		Souvenir sheet of 4, #424-427	8.00	8.00
		Nos. 424-427 (4)	6.15	7.30

Christmas, preservation of the Okavango and Kuando-Chobe River wetlands.

Early Cultivation Techniques A87

8t, Digging stick. 15t, Iron hoe. 35t, Wooden plow. 50t, Communal planting, Lesotla.

1988, Mar. 14   Litho.   Perf. 14½x14

428	A87	8t multicolored	.55	.25
429	A87	15t multicolored	.80	.40
430	A87	35t multicolored	1.40	1.40
431	A87	50t multicolored	2.00	2.00
		Nos. 428-431 (4)	4.75	4.05

World Wildlife Fund — A88

Designs: WWF emblem and various red lechwe, Kobus leche.

1988, June 6   Litho.   Perf. 14½x14

432	A88	10t Adult wading	1.20	.25
433	A88	15t Adult, sun	2.40	.75
434	A88	35t Cow, calf	3.25	2.00
435	A88	75t Herd	5.00	8.50
		Nos. 432-435 (4)	11.85	11.50

Runner Post, Cent. — A89

Routes and: 10t, Gubulawayo, Bechuanaland, cancellation dated Aug. 21 '88. 15t, Bechuanaland Protectorate No. 65. 30t, Pack traders. 60t, Mafeking killer cancel No. 638.

1988, Aug. 22   Litho.   Perf. 14½

436	A89	10t multicolored	.50	.25
437	A89	15t multicolored	.80	.35
438	A89	30t multicolored	1.40	.85
439	A89	60t multicolored	2.25	2.75
a.		Souvenir sheet of 4, #436-439	13.50	13.50
		Nos. 436-439 (4)	4.95	4.20

Printed in a continuous design picturing the Mafeking-Gubulawayo route and part of the Shoshong runner post route.

State Visit of Pope John Paul II, Sept. 13 — A90

1988, Sept. 13 Litho.   Perf. 14x14½
440	A90	10t Map, portrait	2.25	.25
441	A90	15t Portrait	2.50	.35
442	A90	30t Map, portrait, diff.	3.25	.85
443	A90	80t Portrait, diff.	4.00	5.00
		Nos. 440-443 (4)	12.00	6.45

Natl. Museum and Art Gallery, Gaborone, 20th Anniv. — A91

8t, Museum. 15t, Pottery, c. 400-1300. 30t, Buffalo bellows. 60t, Children, mobile museum.

1988, Sept. 30   Perf. 14½
444	A91	8t multicolored	.35	.25
445	A91	15t multicolored	.45	.45
446	A91	30t multicolored	.80	.80
447	A91	60t multicolored	1.60	1.60
		Nos. 444-447 (4)	3.20	3.10

Flowering Plants of Southeastern Botswana — A92

8t, Grewia flava. 15t, Cienfuegosia digitata. 40t, Solanum seaforthianum. 75t, Carissa bispinosa.

1988, Oct. 31 Litho.   Perf. 14x14½
448	A92	8t multicolored	.35	.25
449	A92	15t multicolored	.50	.35
450	A92	40t multicolored	1.00	.75
451	A92	75t multicolored	1.75	1.75
		Nos. 448-451 (4)	3.60	3.10

Christmas.

Traditional Grain Storage — A93

8t, Sesigo basket granary. 15t, Letlole daga granary. 30t, Sefalana bisque granary. 60t, Serala granaries.

1989, Mar. 13 Litho.   Perf. 14x14½
452	A93	8t multicolored	.95	.25
453	A93	15t multicolored	1.50	.50
454	A93	30t multicolored	2.10	.75
455	A93	60t multicolored	3.25	3.00
		Nos. 452-455 (4)	7.80	4.50

Slaty Egrets A94

1989, July 5   Perf. 15x14
456	A94	8t Nesting	.80	.25
457	A94	15t Young	1.10	.45
458	A94	30t Adult in flight	1.50	.80
459	A94	60t Two adults	2.10	3.00
a.		Souvenir sheet of 4, #456-459	5.50	5.50
		Nos. 456-459 (4)	5.50	4.50

Children's Drawings A95

10t, Ephraim Seeletso. 15t, Neelma Bhatia, vert. 30t, Thabo Habana. 1p, Thabo Olesitse.

1989, Sept. 4   Perf. 14½x14, 14x14½
460	A95	10t multicolored	.55	.25
461	A95	15t multicolored	.75	.55
462	A95	30t multicolored	1.15	1.10
463	A95	1p multicolored	3.00	3.50
		Nos. 460-463 (4)	5.45	5.40

Star and Orchids — A96

8t, Eulophia angolensis. 15t, Eulophia heroensis. 30t, Eulophia speciosa. 60t, Eulophia petersii.

1989, Oct. 30 Litho.   Perf. 14x14½
464	A96	8t multicolored	1.15	.25
465	A96	15t multicolored	2.00	.65
466	A96	30t multicolored	2.50	1.15
467	A96	60t multicolored	4.25	7.75
		Nos. 464-467 (4)	9.90	9.80

Christmas.

Anniversaries — A97

Designs: 8t, Bechuanaland Protectorate #201. 15t, Voter at ballot box. 30t, Map & flags of nations at SADCC conference. 60t, Great Britain #1.

1990, Mar. 5 Litho.   Perf. 14½
468	A97	8t multicolored	1.75	.25
469	A97	15t multicolored	1.75	.85
470	A97	30t multicolored	3.50	2.40
471	A97	60t multicolored	4.50	8.00
		Nos. 468-471 (4)	11.50	11.50

25th anniv. of self government (8t); 1st elections, 25th anniv. (15t); Southern African Development Coordination Conference (SADCC), 10th anniv. (30t); and Penny Black, 150th anniv. (60t).

Stamp World London '90 — A98

Aspects of the telecommunications industry.

1990, May 3
472	A98	8t Training	.65	.25
473	A98	15t Transmission	1.10	.60
474	A98	30t Public telephone	1.80	1.00
475	A98	2p Testing circuitry	4.75	6.25
		Nos. 472-475 (4)	8.30	8.10

Traditional Dress — A99

1990, Aug. 1 Litho.   Perf. 14
476	A99	8t Children	.60	.25
477	A99	15t Young woman	1.10	.40
478	A99	30t Man	2.00	.75
479	A99	2p Adult woman	5.00	7.00
a.		Souvenir sheet of 4, #476-479	11.25	11.25
		Nos. 476-479 (4)	8.70	8.40

Nos. 404 & 412 Surcharged

No. 409 Surcharged

1990, Apr. 27
480	A85	10t on 1t No. 404	1.00	.25
481	A85	20t on 6t No. 409	1.75	1.00
482	A85	50t on 12t No. 412	5.50	5.50
		Nos. 480-482 (3)	8.25	6.75

Flowering Trees — A100

8t, Acacia nigrescens. 15t, Peltophorum africanum. 30t, Burkea africana. 2p, Pterocarpus angolensis.

1990, Oct. 30 Litho.   Perf. 14
483	A100	8t multicolored	.80	.25
484	A100	15t multicolored	1.25	.45
485	A100	30t multicolored	2.25	1.00
486	A100	2p multicolored	5.00	7.50
		Nos. 483-486 (4)	9.30	9.20

Christmas.

Natl. Road Safety Day A101

8t, Children playing on road. 15t, Accident. 30t, Livestock on road.

1990, Dec. 7 Litho.   Perf. 14½
487	A101	8t multicolored	3.25	.50
488	A101	15t multicolored	3.75	1.50
489	A101	30t multicolored	4.75	3.75
		Nos. 487-489 (3)	11.75	5.75

Petroglyphs A102

Various petroglyphs.

1991, Mar. 4 Litho.   Perf. 14x14½
Textured Paper
490	A102	8t multicolored	3.00	.50
491	A102	15t multicolored	3.50	1.00
492	A102	30t multicolored	4.25	1.75
493	A102	2p multicolored	7.50	13.00
		Nos. 490-493 (4)	18.25	16.25

Natl. Census — A103

8t, Children playing. 15t, Houses. 30t, Children in schoolyard. 2p, Children, hospital.

1991, June 3 Litho.   Perf. 14
494	A103	8t multicolored	1.50	.25

Perf. 14½
495	A103	15t multicolored	2.10	.70

Perf. 14x14½
496	A103	30t multicolored	2.40	1.30
497	A103	2p multicolored	9.50	12.50
		Nos. 494-497 (4)	15.50	14.75

African Tourism Year A104

8t, Tourists, elephants. 15t, Birds, crocodiles. 35t, Airplane, fish eagles. 2p, Okavango Delta.

1991, Sept. 30 Litho.   Perf. 14
498	A104	8t multicolored	3.25	1.15
499	A104	15t multicolored	3.75	1.30
500	A104	35t multicolored	7.25	4.75

Size 26x43mm
501	A104	2p multicolored	9.50	12.00
		Nos. 498-501 (4)	23.75	19.20

No. 501 incorporates designs of Nos. 498-500.

Christmas — A105

Seed pods: 8t, Harpagophytum procumbens. 15t, Tylosema esculentum. 30t, Abrus precatorius. 2p, Kigelia africana.

1991, Nov. 4 Litho.   Perf. 14
502	A105	8t multicolored	.75	.25
503	A105	15t multicolored	1.25	.50
504	A105	30t multicolored	2.25	1.00
505	A105	2p multicolored	5.50	8.00
		Nos. 502-505 (4)	9.75	9.75

Nos. 406, 409 & 412 Surcharged

1992, Mar. 9 Litho.   Perf. 14
506	A85	8t on 12t No. 412	2.75	1.00
507	A85	10t on 12t No. 412	2.75	1.00
508	A85	25t on 6t No. 409	2.00	2.25
509	A85	40t on 3t No. 406	3.50	6.00
		Nos. 506-509 (4)	11.00	10.25

Climbing Frogs — A106

Designs: 8t, Cacosternum boettgeri, horiz. 10t, Hyperolius marmoratus angolensis. 40t, Bufo fenoulheti, horiz. 1p, Hyperolius.

1992, Mar. 23 Perf. 14½x14, 14x14½
510	A106	8t multicolored	1.00	.30
511	A106	10t multicolored	1.00	.30
512	A106	40t multicolored	3.00	1.50
513	A106	1p multicolored	6.00	8.50
		Nos. 510-513 (4)	11.00	10.60

Botswana Railways A107

Designs: 10t, Deluxe air-conditioned coaches. 25t, BD1 locomotive. 40t, Deluxe coach interio. 2p, Locomotive pulling air-conditioned coaches.

1992, June 29   Litho.   Perf. 14

514	A107	10t multi	1.75	.50
515	A107	25t multi, vert.	2.25	1.00
516	A107	40t multi, vert.	2.50	1.25
517	A107	2p multi	3.75	8.50
a.		Souv. sheet of 4, #514-517 + label	17.00	17.00
		Nos. 514-517 (4)	10.25	11.25

Wild Animals
A108

1t, Cheetah. 2t, Spring hares. 4t, Blackfooted cat. 5t, Striped mouse. 10t, Oribi. 12t, Pangolin. 15t, Aardwolf. 20t, Warthog. 25t, Ground squirrels. 35t, Honey badger. 40t, Common mole rat. 45t, Wild dogs. 50t, Water mongoose. 80t, Klipspringer. 1p, Lesser bushbaby. 2p, Bushveld elephant shrew. 5p, Zorilla. 10p, Vervet monkey.

1992, Aug. 3   Litho.   Perf. 14½

518	A108	1t multicolored	.45	2.00
519	A108	2t multicolored	.45	2.00
520	A108	4t multicolored	.80	2.00
521	A108	5t multicolored	.80	1.75
522	A108	10t multicolored	1.10	.30
523	A108	12t multicolored	1.75	3.00
524	A108	15t multicolored	1.75	.60
525	A108	20t multicolored	1.75	.50
526	A108	25t multicolored	1.75	.30
527	A108	35t multicolored	2.00	.45
528	A108	40t multicolored	2.00	.45
529	A108	45t multicolored	2.00	.45
530	A108	50t multicolored	2.00	.55
531	A108	80t multicolored	3.50	2.75
532	A108	1p multicolored	3.50	2.75
533	A108	2p multicolored	5.50	5.50
534	A108	5p multicolored	8.00	8.50
535	A108	10p multicolored	10.00	12.00
		Nos. 518-535 (18)	49.10	45.85

For surcharges see Nos. 594A-597.

A109

1992, Aug. 7   Perf. 14x15

536	A109	10t Boxer	.75	.25
537	A109	50t Four sprinters	1.75	.65
538	A109	1p Two boxers	2.50	3.00
539	A109	2p Three runners	3.00	4.25
a.		Souvenir sheet of 4, #536-539	8.50	8.50
		Nos. 536-539 (4)	8.00	8.15

1992 Summer Olympics, Barcelona.

Ferns — A110

10t, Adiantum incisum. 25t, Actiniopteris radiata. 40t, Ceratopteris cornuta. 1.50p, Pellaea calomelanos.

1992, Nov. 23   Litho.   Perf. 14½

540	A110	10t multicolored	.70	.25
541	A110	25t multicolored	1.10	.45
542	A110	40t multicolored	1.45	.70
543	A110	1.50p multicolored	4.50	6.25
		Nos. 540-543 (4)	7.75	7.65

Christmas.

Organizations
A111

10t, Lions Intl., conquering blindness. 15t, Red Cross Society. 25t, Ecumenical Decade, churches in solidarity with women. 35t, Round Table supporting the deaf. 40t, Rotary Intl. 50t, Botswana Christian Council.

1993, Mar. 29   Litho.   Perf. 14

544	A111	10t multi, vert.	1.00	.25
545	A111	15t multi	1.10	.50
546	A111	25t multi, vert.	1.10	.60
547	A111	35t multi	1.50	1.75
548	A111	40t multi, vert.	1.50	2.00
549	A111	50t multi	2.00	3.00
		Nos. 544-549 (6)	8.20	8.10

Botswana Railway, Cent.
A112

Designs: 10t, Engine No. 1, 6th class 4-6-0, Bechuanaland Railways. 40t, Engine No. 317, 19th class 4-8-2. 50t, Engine No. 256, 12th class 4-8-2. 1.50p, Engine No. 71, 7th class 4-8-0, Rhodesia Railways.

1993, May 24   Litho.   Perf. 15x14

550	A112	10t multicolored	1.10	.60
551	A112	40t multicolored	2.10	.85
552	A112	50t multicolored	2.10	1.10
553	A112	1.50p multicolored	3.00	5.00
a.		Souvenir sheet of 4, #550-553	8.25	8.25
		Nos. 550-553 (4)	8.30	7.55

Eagles — A113

10t, Long crested eagle. 25t, Snake eagle. 50t, Bateleur eagle. 1.50p, Secretary bird.

1993, Aug. 30   Litho.   Perf. 14½

554	A113	10t multicolored	1.00	.50
555	A113	25t multicolored	2.00	1.00
556	A113	50t multicolored	2.50	2.50
557	A113	1.50p multicolored	4.00	5.50
		Nos. 554-557 (4)	9.50	9.50

Christmas
A114

12t, Aloe zebrina. 25t, Croton megalobotrys. 50t, Boophane disticha. 1p, Euphorbia davyi.

1993, Oct. 25   Litho.   Perf. 14x14½

558	A114	12t multicolored	.60	.25
559	A114	25t multicolored	.90	.30
560	A114	50t multicolored	1.25	.70
561	A114	1p multicolored	1.90	3.50
		Nos. 558-561 (4)	4.65	4.75

Traditional Children's Toys
A115

10t, Mantadile. 40t, Dikgomo tsa mimopa. 50t, Sefuu-fuu. 1p, Mantlwane.

1994, Mar. 28   Litho.   Perf. 14½

562	A115	10t multicolored	.45	.25
563	A115	40t multicolored	.85	.45
564	A115	50t multicolored	.95	.70
565	A115	1p multicolored	1.75	2.60
		Nos. 562-565 (4)	4.00	4.00

ICAO, 50th Anniv.
A116

10t, Inside control tower. 25t, Fire engine. 40t, Baggage carts, vert. 50t, Control tower, vert.

Perf. 14½x14, 14x14½

1994, June 30   Litho.

566	A116	10t multicolored	.45	.25
567	A116	25t multicolored	.85	.45
568	A116	40t multicolored	.95	.70
569	A116	50t multicolored	1.75	2.60
		Nos. 566-569 (4)	4.00	4.00

A117

Environmental Protection: 10t, Flamingos, Sua Pan, vert. 35t, Makgadikgadi Pan trees. 50t, Zebra, Makgadikgadi Palm trees, vert. 2p, Map of Makgadikgadi Pans.

1994, Sept. 26   Litho.   Perf. 14

570	A117	10t multicolored	1.90	.50
571	A117	35t multicolored	.85	.50
572	A117	50t multicolored	1.30	1.00
573	A117	2p multicolored	4.50	6.50
		Nos. 570-573 (4)	8.55	8.50

Christmas
A118

Edible fruits: 10t, Ziziphus mucronata. 25t, Strychnos cocculoides. 40t, Bauhinia petersiana. 50t, Schinziphyton rautaneii.

1994, Oct. 24

574	A118	10t multicolored	.45	.25
575	A118	25t multicolored	.65	.50
576	A118	40t multicolored	1.00	1.10
577	A118	50t multicolored	1.15	1.40
		Nos. 574-577 (4)	3.25	3.25

See Nos. 587-590.

Traditional Fishing
A119

1995, Apr. 3   Litho.   Perf. 14

578	A119	15t Spear	.60	.30
579	A119	40t Hook	1.15	.60
580	A119	65t Net	1.50	1.60
581	A119	80t Basket	2.00	2.75
		Nos. 578-581 (4)	5.25	5.25

UN, 50th Anniv. — A120

20t, FAO. 50t, World Food Program. 80t, Development Plan. 1p, UNICEF.

1995, Oct. 16   Litho.   Perf. 14

582	A120	20t multicolored	.30	.25
583	A120	50t multicolored	.55	.45
584	A120	80t multicolored	1.50	1.05
585	A120	1p multicolored	1.15	1.75
		Nos. 582-585 (4)	3.50	3.50

World Wildlife Fund — A121

No. 586 — Hyaena brunnea: a, 20t, Adult walking right. b, 50t, Two young. c, 80t, Adult finding eggs. d, 1p, Two young, adult resting.

1995, Nov. 6

586	A121	Strip of 4, #a.-d.	5.50	5.50

No. 586 was printed in sheets of 16 containing 4 strips each of 4 stamps.

Christmas Type of 1994

20t, Adenia glauca. 50t, Pterodiscus ngamicus. 80t, Sesamothamnus lugardii. 1p, Fockea multiflora.

1995, Nov. 27   Litho.   Perf. 14

587	A118	20t multicolored	.50	.25
588	A118	50t multicolored	.90	.45
589	A118	80t multicolored	1.50	1.50
590	A118	1p multicolored	1.60	2.25
		Nos. 587-590 (4)	4.50	4.45

Traditional Weapons
A122

20t, Spears. 50t, Axes. 80t, Shield, knobkerries. 1p, Knives, cases.

1996, Mar. 25   Litho.   Perf. 14

591	A122	20t multicolored	.35	.25
592	A122	50t multicolored	.65	.55
593	A122	80t multicolored	1.00	1.00
594	A122	1p multicolored	1.10	1.30
		Nos. 591-594 (4)	3.10	3.10

No. 523 Surcharged

Nos. 518-520 Surcharged

1994-96   Litho.   Perf. 14½

594A	A108	10t on 12t No. 523	18.00	3.00
595	A108	20t on 2t No. 519	1.90	.80
596	A108	20t on 1t No. 518	2.10	1.40
597	A108	70t on 4t No. 520	3.25	7.00
		Nos. 594A-597 (4)	25.25	12.20

Issued: No. 594A, 8/1/94; others, 2/12/96.

Radio, Cent. — A123

Designs: 20t, Child listening to early radio. 50t, Mobile unit, transmitter. 80t, Local police. 1p, Radio Botswana at the Kgotila.

1996, June 3　　Litho.　　Perf. 14

598	A123	20t multicolored	.30	.25
599	A123	50t multicolored	.50	.45
600	A123	80t multicolored	2.50	1.45
601	A123	1p multicolored	.85	2.00
		Nos. 598-601 (4)	4.15	4.15

Modern Olympic Games, Cent. — A124

Designs: 20t, Hand holding torch, laurel wreath, Olympic rings. 50t, Pierre de Coubertin. 80t, Map, flag of Botswana, athletes. 1p, Ruins of original Olympic Stadium, Olympia.

1996, July 19　　Litho.　　Perf. 14

602	A124	20t multicolored	.60	.25
603	A124	50t multicolored	.80	.35
604	A124	80t multicolored	2.25	1.50
605	A124	1p multicolored	1.25	2.00
		Nos. 602-605 (4)	4.90	4.10

Worthy Causes — A125

Designs: 20t, Family planning education, Welfare Association. 30t, Skills for the blind, Pudulogong Rehabilitation Center. 50t, Collection of seeds, Forestry Association. 70t, Secretarial class, YWCA. 80t, Day care center, Council of Women. 1p, SOS Children's Village, Tlokweng.

1996, Sept. 23　　Litho.　　Perf. 14

606	A125	20t multicolored	.35	.25
607	A125	30t multicolored	.35	.25
608	A125	50t multicolored	.50	.50
609	A125	70t multicolored	.70	.90
610	A125	80t multicolored	.85	1.10
611	A125	1p multicolored	1.00	1.90
		Nos. 606-611 (6)	3.75	4.90

Adansonia Digitata — A126

1996, Nov. 4　　Litho.　　Perf. 14

612	A126	20t Leaf, flower	.40	.25
613	A126	50t Fruit	.65	.40
614	A126	80t Tree in leaf	.95	1.10
615	A126	1p Tree without leaves	1.10	1.75
		Nos. 612-615 (4)	3.10	3.50

Christmas.

Francistown, Cent. — A127

Designs: 20t, Tati Hotel. 50t, Railway station. 80t, Company manager's house. 1p, Monarch Mine.

1997, Apr. 21　　Litho.　　Perf. 14

616	A127	20t multicolored	.70	.30
617	A127	50t multicolored	.75	.65
618	A127	80t multicolored	1.25	1.25
619	A127	1p multicolored	1.40	2.00
		Nos. 616-619 (4)	4.10	4.20

Birds — A128

Designs: 5t, Pel's fishing owl. 10t, Gymnogene. 15t, Meyers parrot. 20t, Harlequin quail. 25t, Marico sunbird. 30t, Kurrichane thrush. 40t, Redheaded finch. 50t, Buffalo weaver. 60t, Sacred ibis. 70t, Cape shoveller. 80t, Greater honeyguide. 1p, Woodland kingfisher. 1.25p, Purple heron. 1.50p, Yellowbilled oxpecker. 2p, Shafttailed whydah. 2.50p, White stork. 5p, Ovambo sparrowhawk. 10p, Spotted crake.

1997, Aug. 4　　Litho.　　Perf. 13½

620	A128	5t multi, vert.	.70	1.20
621	A128	10t multi	.70	1.20
622	A128	15t multi, vert.	.85	1.20
623	A128	20t multi	.85	1.20
624	A128	25t multi	.85	1.20
625	A128	30t multi	.85	1.20
626	A128	40t multi	1.10	.70
627	A128	50t multi, vert.	1.10	.45
628	A128	60t multi	1.30	.85
629	A128	70t multi	1.30	.85
630	A128	80t multi	1.30	.85
631	A128	1p multi	1.50	.85
632	A128	1.25p multi, vert.	2.10	1.70
633	A128	1.50p multi	2.10	2.40
634	A128	2p multi, vert.	2.60	2.60
635	A128	2.50p multi, vert.	3.25	3.25
636	A128	5p multi, vert.	6.00	6.00
637	A128	10p multi, vert.	8.25	8.25
		Nos. 620-637 (18)	36.70	35.95

For surcharge, see No. 935A.

Botswana Railway, Cent. — A129

Designs: 35t, Bechuanaland Rail, 1897. 50t, Elephants on the tracks. 80t, First locomotives in Bechuanaland, Cape of Good Hope 4-6-0. 1p, 4-6-4+4-6-4 Beyer Garratt. 2p, New BD3 locomotive. 2.50p, Fantuzzi Container Stacker.

1997, July 12　　Litho.　　Perf. 14x14½

638	A129	35t multicolored	.60	.35
639	A129	50t multicolored	1.00	.50
640	A129	80t multicolored	1.10	.70
641	A129	1p multicolored	1.10	.95
642	A129	2p multicolored	1.40	1.75
643	A129	2.50p multicolored	1.50	2.10
		Nos. 638-643 (6)	6.70	6.35

A130

Queen Elizabeth II and Prince Philip, 50th wedding anniv.: No. 644, Prince in casual attire. No. 645, Queen wearing white & blue hat. No. 646, Queen with horse. No. 647, Prince with horse. No. 648, Prince, Queen. No. 649, Princess Anne in riding attire.
10p, Queen, Prince riding in open carriage.

Wmk. 373

1997, Sept. 22　　Litho.　　Perf. 13

644	A130	35t multicolored	.30	.30
645	A130	35t multicolored	.30	.30
a.		Pair, #644-645	.60	.60
646	A130	2p multicolored	1.50	1.50
647	A130	2p multicolored	1.50	1.50
a.		Pair, #646-647	3.00	3.00
648	A130	2.50p multicolored	1.60	1.60
649	A130	2.50p multicolored	1.60	1.60
a.		Pair, #648-649	3.25	3.25
		Nos. 644-649 (6)	6.80	6.80

Souvenir Sheet

650	A130	10p multicolored	6.00	6.00

A131

Christmas (Combretum):, 35t, Zeyheri. 1p, Apiculatum. 2p, Molle. 2.50p, Imberbe.

1997, Nov. 10　　Unwmk.　　Perf. 14

651	A131	35t multicolored	.45	.25
652	A131	1p multicolored	1.10	.50
653	A131	2p multicolored	2.25	2.25
654	A131	2.50p multicolored	2.75	2.75
		Nos. 651-654 (4)	6.55	5.75

Tourism A132

1998, Mar. 23

655	A132	35t Baobab trees	.35	.25
656	A132	1p Crocodile	.75	.50
657	A132	2p Stalactites, vert.	1.25	1.25
658	A132	2.50p Tourists, vert.	1.75	2.00
		Nos. 655-658 (4)	4.10	4.00

Diana, Princess of Wales (1961-97)
Common Design Type

Portraits: 35t, No. 663a, Wearing red (without hat). 1p, No. 663b, Wearing red with hat. 2p, No. 663c, Wearing white (hand on face). No. 662, Greeting people.

1998, June 1　　Wmk. 373　　Perf. 13

659	CD355	35t multicolored	.30	.25
660	CD355	1p multicolored	.50	.45
661	CD355	2p multicolored	1.00	1.25
662	CD355	2.50p multicolored	1.20	1.60
		Nos. 659-662 (4)	3.00	3.55

Souvenir Sheet

663	CD355	2.50p Sheet of 4, #662, 663a-663c	5.25	5.25

Textiles — A133

Designs: 35t, Tapestry of a village. 55t, Woman arranging materials on ground. 1p, Tapestry of African map, animals, huts, people. 2p, Woman seated at loom.
2.50p, Tapestry of elephants and trees, horiz.

Perf. 14x13½

1998, Sept. 28　　Litho.　　Unwmk.

664	A133	35t multicolored	.55	.30
665	A133	55t multicolored	.75	.40
666	A133	1p multicolored	1.50	1.40
667	A133	2p multicolored	1.75	2.60
		Nos. 664-667 (4)	4.55	4.70

Souvenir Sheet
Perf. 13½

668	A133	2.50p multicolored	3.75	3.75

Christmas — A134

Berries: 35t, Ficus ingens. 55t, Ficus pygmaea. 1p, Ficus abutilifolia. 2.50p, Ficus sycomorus.

1998, Nov. 30　　Litho.　　Perf. 13x13½

669	A134	35t multicolored	.65	.25
670	A134	55t multicolored	.80	.25
671	A134	1p multicolored	1.50	.70
672	A134	2.50p multicolored	2.50	3.50
		Nos. 669-672 (4)	5.45	4.70

Tourism A135

Designs: 35t, Rock paintings. 55t, Salt pan. 1p, Rock paintings, diff. 2p, Baobab tree.

1999, May 24　　Litho.　　Perf. 13½x14

673	A135	35t multi	1.00	.25
674	A135	55t multi	1.50	.40

Perf. 14x13½

675	A135	1p multi, vert.	1.75	1.50
676	A135	2p multi, vert.	1.90	2.75
		Nos. 673-676 (4)	6.15	4.90

Souvenir Sheet

Southern African Development Community Day — A136

1999, Aug. 17　　Litho.　　Perf. 14¼

677	A136	5p multi	5.75	5.75

UPU, 125th Anniv. A137

1999, Oct. 9　　Litho.　　Perf. 14¼

678	A137	2p multicolored	2.60	2.60

Mpule Kwelagobe, Miss Universe 1999 — A138

35t, With crown, vert. 1p, With headdress. 2p, In swimsuit, vert. 2.50p, With Botswana sash. 15p, With leopard.

1999, Dec. 1　　Perf. 14½

679	A138	35t multi	.60	.25
680	A138	1p multi	1.25	.40
681	A138	2p multi	1.75	.95
682	A138	2.50p multi	1.90	1.00
683	A138	15p multi	10.50	13.00
a.		Souvenir sheet of 5, #679-683	16.50	16.50
		Nos. 679-683 (5)	16.00	15.60

River Scenes A139

Designs: 35t, Bird over river. 1p, Hippopotami in river, vert. 2p, Bird, man in canoe. 2.50p, Elephant on shore, vert.

2000, Apr. 5   *Litho.*   *Perf. 14*
684	A139	35t multi	.70	.25
685	A139	1p multi	1.05	.75
686	A139	1.75p multi	1.75	1.25
687	A139	2.50p multi	2.00	2.25
	Nos. 684-687 (4)		5.50	4.50

Moths
A140

Designs: 35t, Mopane. 70t, Wild silk. 1p, Crimson-speckled footman. 2p, African lunar. 15p, Speckled emperor.

2000, July 19   *Litho.*   *Perf. 12½*
688-692	A140	Set of 5	10.00	11.00
692a	Souvenir sheet, #688-692		13.00	15.00

Literacy
Decade
A141

Designs: 35t, Mother and child. 70t, Old men learning to read. 2p, Man unaware of fire danger. 2.50p, Man at ATM machine.

2000, Aug. 23   *Perf. 12*
693-696	A141	Set of 4 + labels	3.25	3.25

Kings and
Presidents
A142

Designs: 35t, Sebele I of Bakwena, Bathoen I of Bangwaketse, Khama III of Bangwato (60x40mm). 1p, Sir Seretse Khama. 2p, Sir Ketumile J. Masire. 2.50p, Festus G. Mogae.

Litho. & Embossed

2000, Sept. 29   *Perf. 14*
697-700	A142	Set of 4	4.00	4.00

Botswana Flying
Mission — A143

Designs: 35t, Two men, plane with yellow stripes. 1.75p, Plane, nurses, people. 2p, Plane in air, natives in boats. 2.50p, Plane, donkey cart.

2000, Nov. 3   *Litho.*   *Perf. 13½*
701-704	A143	Set of 4	4.50	4.50
704a	Horiz. strip of 4, #701-704, + central label		5.75	5.75

Wetlands
Fauna
A144

Designs: 35t, Hippopotamus. 1p, Tiger fish, tilapia. 1.75p, Wattled crane, painted reed frog, vert. 2p, Vervet monkey, Pels fishing owl, vert. 2.50p, Sitatunga, Nile crocodile, red lechwe.

2000, Dec. 6   *Litho.*   *Perf. 13¾*
705-709	A144	Set of 5	7.00	7.00
709a	Souvenir sheet, #705-709, perf. 13½		7.50	7.50
709b	As "a," with emblem of Hong Kong 2001 Stamp Exhibition in margin		7.75	7.75

Issued: No. 709b, 1/2/01.
See Nos. 726-730, 761-765, 775-779.

Diamonds — A145

Cut diamond and: 35t, Uncut diamonds. 1.75p, Mine. 2p, Diamond grader. 2.50p, Pendant and ring.

Serpentine Die Cut 10

2001, Feb. 1   *Litho.*

Self-Adhesive
710-713	A145	Set of 4	8.00	8.50

Unused value is for stamps with surrounding selvage. See No. 1013.

Kgalagadi
Transfrontier
Park
A146

Designs: 35t, Pygmy falcons. 1p, Leopard. 2p, Gemsboks, flags of Botswana and South Africa. 2.50p, Bat-eared fox.

2001, May 12   *Litho.*   *Perf. 13x13¼*
714-717	A146	Set of 4	7.50	7.50
717a	Souvenir sheet #715, 717		4.00	4.00

See South Africa Nos. 1252-1255.

Basketry
A147

Designs: 35t, Shown. 1p, Tall basket with triangles and chevrons. 2p, Basket weaver. 2.50p, Spherical basket.

2001, July 30   *Perf. 13¼*
718-721	A147	Set of 4	3.75	3.75
721a	Souvenir sheet, #718-721		3.75	3.75

Sky
Views
A148

Natives and pictures of sun on horizon: 50t, 1p, 2p, 10p.

2001, Sept. 28   *Perf. 13½*
722-725	A148	Set of 4	6.75	6.75

Wetlands Fauna Type of 2000

Designs: 50t, Water monitor, carmine bee-eaters. 1.75p, Buffalos. 2p, Savanna baboons, vert. 2.50p, Lion, vert. 3p, African elephants.

2001, Dec. 12   *Litho.*   *Perf. 13¾*
726-730	A144	Set of 5	6.50	6.50
730a	Souvenir sheet, #726-730, perf. 13½		6.75	6.75

Snakes
A149

Designs: 50t, Black mamba. 1.75p, Spitting cobra, vert. 2.50p, Puff adder. 3p, Boomslang, vert.

2002, Mar. 22   *Perf. 14x13¼, 13¼x14*
731-734	A149	Set of 4	4.25	4.50

Pottery
A150

Pots: 50t, Mbukushu. 2p, Sekgatla. 2.50p, Setswana. 3p, Kalanga.

2002, May 31   *Litho.*   *Perf. 13¾*
735-738	A150	Set of 4	3.75	3.75

Reign of Queen
Elizabeth II, 50th
Anniv. — A151

Queen Elizabeth II: 55t, Wearing crown, horiz. 2.75p, Holding flowers.

2002, July 25   *Perf. 13x13¼, 13¼x13*
739-740	A151	Set of 2	3.00	3.25

Mammals — A152

Designs: 5t, Tree squirrel. 10t, Black-backed jackal. 20t, African wild cat. 30t, Slender mongoose, horiz. 40t, African civet, horiz. 55t, Elephant. 90t, Reedbuck. 1p, Kudu. 1.45p, Waterbuck. 1.95p, Sable, horiz. 2.20p, Sitatunga, horiz. 2.75p, Porcupine, horiz. 3.30p, Serval, horiz. 4p, Antbear, horiz. 5p, Bush pig, horiz. 15p, Chakma baboon.

Perf. 13½x13¼, 13¼x13½

2002, Aug. 5   **Photo.**
741	A152	5t multi	.25	.25
742	A152	10t multi	.25	.25
743	A152	20t multi	.35	.35
744	A152	30t multi	.45	.45
745	A152	40t multi	.60	.50
746	A152	55t multi	1.90	.50
747	A152	90t multi	.85	.50
748	A152	1p multi	.85	.50
749	A152	1.45p multi	1.25	.85
750	A152	1.95p multi	1.75	1.50
751	A152	2.20p multi	2.00	1.50
752	A152	2.75p multi	2.00	1.50
753	A152	3.30p multi	2.10	1.90
754	A152	4p multi	2.50	2.75
755	A152	5p multi	2.75	3.00
756	A152	15p multi	5.75	8.25
	Nos. 741-756 (16)		25.60	24.55

For surcharges see Nos. 813A-813B.

2002-03 AIDS
Campaign — A153

Designs: 55t, Voluntary counseling and testing centers. 1.10p, Prevention of mother to child transmission. 2.75p, Stigma and discrimination. 3.30p, Orphan care.

2002, Dec. 1   *Litho.*   *Perf. 14x14¼*
757-760	A153	Set of 4	5.00	5.00

Wetlands Fauna Type of 2000

Wildlife in the Makgadikgadi Pans: 55t, Aardwolf. 1.10p, Blue wildebeest. 2.50p, Zebras, vert. 2.75p, Flamingos, vert. 3.30p, Pelican.

2002, Dec. 18   *Perf. 13¾*
761-765	A144	Set of 5	6.75	6.75
765a	Souvenir sheet, #761-765, perf. 13½		7.00	7.00

Tourist
Attractions
A154

Designs: 55t, Hill of Lovers. 2.20p, Sand dunes, Bokspits. 2.75p, Moremi Waterfalls, vert. 3.30p, Entrance of Gcwihaba Cave.

2003, Mar. 27   *Litho.*   *Perf. 13¾*
766-769	A154	Set of 4	4.25	4.25

Beetles — A155

Designs: 55t, Ngwale. 2.20p, Kgomo-ya-buru. 2.75p, Kgomo-ya-pula. 3.30p, Lebitse. 5.50p, Kgaladuwa.

2003, Nov. 12   *Litho.*   *Perf. 13*
770-773	A155	Set of 4	5.00	5.00

Souvenir Sheet
774	A155	5.50p multi	5.50	5.75

Wetlands Fauna Type of 2000

Fauna of the Limpopo River Valley: 55t, Giraffe. 1.45p, Black eagle, Nile crocodile, vert. 2.50p, Ostrich, vert. 2.75p, Klipspringer. 3.30p, Serval cat.

2003, Dec. 23   *Litho.*   *Perf. 13¾*
775-779	A144	Set of 5	7.25	7.25
779a	Souvenir sheet, #775-779, perf. 13½		7.25	7.25

Contemporary
Art — A156

Designs: 55t, People and Birds. 1.45p, Stylized trees. 2.75p, Stylized tree. 3.30p, Snake.

2004, Apr. 29   *Perf. 13¾*
780-783	A156	Set of 4	5.00	5.00

Traditional Lifestyles — A157

Designs: 80t, Masimo. 2.10p, Kgotla. 3.90p, Moraka. 4.70p, Legae.

2004, June 30   Litho.   Perf. 14
784-787 A157   Set of 4   6.50 6.50

World Post Day — A158

Designs: 80t, Child placing letter in mail box. 2.10p, Children reading letter. 3.90p, Mailman and car. 4.70p, Woman reading letter.

2004, Oct. 9   Litho.   Perf. 14x14¾
788-791 A158   Set of 4   6.50 6.50

Birds A159

Designs: 5p, Cattle egrets, national bird of Botswana.

No. 793: a, 40t, Peregrine falcons, national bird of Angola. b, 50t, African fish eagles, national bird of Zambia. c, 60t, African fish eagles, national bird of Zimbabwe. d, 70t, Bar-tailed trogons. e, 80t, Purple-crested louries, national bird of Swaziland. f, 1p, African fish eagles, national bird of Namibia. g, 2p, Blue cranes, national bird of South Africa.

2004, Oct. 9   Litho.   Perf. 14
792 A159   5p multi   2.75 2.75
Miniature Sheet
793 A159   Sheet of 8, #a-g, #792   7.00 7.00

See Namibia No. 1052, South Africa No. 1342, Swaziland Nos. 727-735, Zambia No. 1033, and Zimbabwe No. 975.

Christmas A160

Flowers: 80t, Pterodiscus speciosus. 2.10p, Bulbine narcissifolia. 3.90p, Babiana hypogea. 4.70p, Hibiscus micranthus.

2004, Dec. 8   Perf. 13
794-797 A160   Set of 4   7.00 7.00

Historic Buildings A161

Designs: 80t, Blackbeard's Store, Phalat-swe, 1899. 2.10p, Primary School, 1899.

3.90p, Telegraph Office, Phalatswe, 1899. 4.70p, Magistrate's Court, Phalatswe, 1899.

2005, Mar. 21   Litho.   Perf. 14¾x14
798-801 A161   Set of 4   6.50 6.50

Food Crops — A162

Designs: 80t, Beans. 2.10p, Millet. 3.90p, Sorghum. 4.70p, Watermelon.

2005, June 15   Litho.   Perf. 13¾
802-805 A162   Set of 4   4.75 4.75

Worldwide Fund for Nature (WWF) — A163

Black-footed cat: 80t, With dead bird. 2.10p, Looking left. 3.90p, Adult and kitten. 4.70p, Close-up of head.

2005, Oct. 25   Litho.   Perf. 13¼x13½
806-809 A163   Set of 4   5.00 5.00
809a   Sheet, 2 each #806-809   10.00 10.00

Christmas A164

Doves and pigeons: 80t, Namaqua dove. 2.10p, Red-eyed dove. 3.90p, Laughing doves. 4.70p, Green pigeons.

2005, Dec. 20   Perf. 14x14¾
810-813 A164   Set of 4   5.25 5.25

No. 747 Surcharged

No. 750 Surcharged

Methods and Perfs As Before
2006, Apr. 26
813A A152   80t on 90t #747   5.25 —
813B A152   2.10p on 1.95p #750   5.25 —

Fish A165

Nembwe - Dolye
BOTSWANA   2006   Tim Liversedge

Designs: 80t, Nembwe. 2.10p, Tiger fish. 3.90p, Pike. 4.70p, Spotted squeaker.

2006, May 30   Litho.   Perf. 13¼x13¾
814-817 A165   Set of 4   5.25 5.25

Tswana Cattle — A166

Designs: 1.10p, Oxen. 2.60p, Cows and calves. 4.10p, Bulls. 4.90p, Horn shapes.

2006, Sept. 4   Litho.   Perf. 13¾x13¼
818-821 A166   Set of 4   5.25 5.25

Independence, 40th Anniv. — A167

Maps of Botswana showing: 1.10p, Primary and secondary roads. 2.60p, Population distribution. 4.10p, Mines and coal resources. 4.90p, National parks and reserves.

Perf. 13¼x13¾
2006, Sept. 29   Litho.
822-825 A167   Set of 4   4.00 4.00
825a   Souvenir sheet, #822-825   4.00 4.00

Christmas A168

Flora: 1.10p, Hyphaene petersiana tree. 2.60p, Phoenix reclinata tree. 4.10p, Hyphaene petersiana fruit. 4.90p, Phoenix reclinata fruit.

2006, Dec. 1   Perf. 13¾x13¼
826-829 A168   Set of 4   4.00 4.00

Kingfishers A169

Designs: 1.10p, Pied kingfisher. 2.60p, Malachite kingfisher. 4.10p, Woodland kingfisher. 4.90p, Brown-hooded kingfisher.

Perf. 13¾x13¼
2007, Mar. 31   Litho.
830-833 A169   Set of 4   4.00 4.00

Mushrooms — A170

Designs: 1.10p, False parasols. 2.60p, Bushveld bolete. 4.10p, Lacquered bracket fungus. 4.90p, Collared earthstars.

2007, July 30   Litho.   Perf. 13½x13¾
834-837 A170   Set of 4   4.00 4.00

Miniature Sheet

National Animals — A171

No. 838: a, 1.10p, Nyala (Malawi). b, 2.60p, Nyala (Zimbabwe). c, 4.10p, Oryx (Namibia). d, 4.90p, Buffalo (Zambia). e, 5.50p, Bruschell's zebra (Botswana).

Litho. With Foil Application
2007, Oct. 9   Perf. 13¾
838 A171   Sheet of 5, #a-e   6.00 6.00

See Malawi No. 752, Namibia Nos. 1141-1142, Zambia Nos. 1097-1101, Zimbabwe Nos. 1064-1068.

University of Botswana, 25th Anniv. A172

Anniversary emblem and: 1.10p, Library. 2.60p, Campus appeal. 4.10p, Okavango research. 4.90p, Old and new infrastructure.

2007, Oct. 13   Litho.   Perf. 14
839-842 A172   Set of 4   4.50 4.50

Butterflies A173

Designs: 10t, Mimosa sapphire. 20t, Bushveld orange-tip. 30t, African monarch. 40t, Common black-eye. 50t, Brown playboy. 1p, Sapphire. B, Dwarf blue. 2p, Large blue emperor. A, Scarlet tip. 3p, Apricot playboy. 4p, Blue pansy. 5p, Black-striped hairtail. 10p, Natal barred blue. 20p, Foxy charaxes.

2007, Nov. 1   Litho.   Perf. 13½x13¾
843	A173	10t multi	.30 .30
844	A173	20t multi	.30 .30
845	A173	30t multi	.30 .30
846	A173	40t multi	.30 .30
847	A173	50t multi	.30 .30
848	A173	1p multi	.45 .45
849	A173	B multi	.55 .55
850	A173	2p multi	.90 .90
851	A173	A multi	1.20 1.20
852	A173	3p multi	1.30 1.30
853	A173	4p multi	1.90 1.90
854	A173	5p multi	2.25 2.25
855	A173	10p multi	4.50 4.50
856	A173	20p multi	9.00 9.00

Nos. 843-856 (14)   23.55 23.55

On day of issue, No. 849 sold for 1.10p; No. 851 for 2.60p.

Art — A174

Designs: 1.10p, Dancer, by Boitshepo Lesego. 2.60p, Baobab Tree, by Philip Huebsch. 4.10p, Child Playing with Dolls, by Giel Kgamane. 4.90p, Donkeys Tired After Hard Work, by Tineni Kepaletswe, horiz. 5.50p, Donkeys in the City, by Andrew Jones, horiz.

2008, Mar. 28   *Perf. 14*
857-861 A174   Set of 5   6.00 6.00

Elephants
A175

Elephants and: 1.10p, Hunters. 2.60p, Tourists in boat. 4.10p, Botswana villagers. 4.90p, Riders.

2008, June 20   Litho.   *Perf. 14*
862-865 A175 Set of 4   4.00 4.00

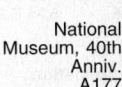

2008 Summer
Olympics,
Beijing — A176

Designs: 1.10p, Runners. 2.60p, Boxing.

2008, Aug. 8   *Perf. 14¼*
866-867 A176   Set of 2   1.25 1.25

National
Museum, 40th
Anniv.
A177

Designs: 1.10p, Launch of Pitse Ya Naga (mobile museum), 1978. 2.60p, Opening of Botanical Garden, 1988, vert. 4.10p, Opening of new museum galleries, 2008. 4.90p, Tsodilo Hills rock drawings, 1998. 5.50p, Official opening, 1968, vert.

2008, Sept. 29
868-872 A177   Set of 5   5.50 5.50

Events of
2008 — A178

Designs: 4.10p, Premiere of movie filmed in Botswana, *The No. 1 Ladies Detective Agency.* 4.90p, Launch of Heart Foundation of Botswana, vert. 5.50p, Launch of Diamond Trading Company.

2008, Oct. 30
873-875 A178   Set of 3   3.75 3.75

Beetles
A179

Designs: 1.10p, Small green dung beetle. 2.60p, Lunate ladybird. 4.10p, Garden fruit chafer. 4.90p, Darkling beetle.

2008, Dec. 1   *Perf. 14x13¼*
876-879 A179   Set of 4   3.25 3.25

Endangered
Birds — A180

Designs: 1.10p, Lesser flamingos. 2.60p, Gray crowned cranes, horiz. 4.10p, Wattled cranes, horiz. 4.90p, Blue cranes, horiz.

2009, June 5   Litho.   *Perf. 14*
880-883 A180   Set of 4   3.75 3.75

Children
A181

Inscriptions: 1.10p, Education. 2.60p, Sanitation, vert. 4.10p, Inoculation, vert. 4.90p, Orphan care.

2009, Sept. 11   Litho.   *Perf. 14*
884-887 A181   Set of 4   4.00 4.00

Night Sky Over Botswana — A182

Botswana landscapes and: 1.10p, Southern Cross constellation, giraffes. 2.60p, Meteorite, native hunters. 4.10p, Moon, native dancers. 4.90p, Solar eclipse, lions.

2009, Nov. 18   *Perf. 13½x13¾*
888-891 A182   Set of 4   4.00 4.00

Honey
Bees
A183

Apis mellifera: 1.10p, Bee at flower. 2.60p, Bees on honeycomb. 4.10p, Beehive. 4.90p, Bees at flower.

2010, Mar. 25   Litho.   *Perf. 14x13¼*
892-895 A183   Set of 4   3.75 3.75

2010 World Cup Soccer
Championships, South Africa — A184

Soccer players, ball, 2010 World Cup mascot and flag of: Nos. 896, 905a, 1.10p, Botswana. Nos. 897, 905b, 2.60p, Namibia. Nos. 898, 905c, 3p, South Africa. Nos. 899, 905d, 4p, Zimbabwe. Nos. 900, 905e, 4.10p, Malawi. Nos. 901, 905f, 4.90p, Swaziland. Nos. 902, 905g, 5.50p, Mauritius. Nos. 903, 905h, 6.60p, Lesotho. Nos. 904, 905i, 8.20p, Zambia.

2010, Apr. 9   *Perf. 13¾*
On Plain Paper With Olive Brown Background
896-904 A184   Set of 9   12.00 12.00
On Gold-faced Paper
905 A184   Sheet of 9, #a-i   14.00 14.00

No. 905 exists imperf. Value $800.
See Lesotho No. , Malawi No. 753, Mauritius No. , Namibia No. 1188, South Africa No. 1403, Swaziland Nos. 794-803, Zambia Nos. 1115-1118, and Zimbabwe Nos. 1112-1121.
A single sheetlet of 9 omnibus issues exist containing 905a. See footnote under Namibia 1188.

Energy — A185

Designs: 2.60p, Family watching television. 4.10p, Botswanan with cell phone, solar panel outside of house. 5.50p, Man on locomotive. 6.10p, People and compact fluorescent lightbulb, horiz.

2010, Oct. 8   *Perf. 14*
906-909 A185   Set of 4   6.00 6.00

Nocturnal Animals
— A185a

Designs: 2.60p, Spring hare. 3p, Fruit bat. 4.10p, Pearl spotted owl. 5.50p, Aardwolf, horiz. 5.60p, Porcupine. 6.10p, Civet, horiz.

     Perf. 13¼x13, 13x13¼
2010, Dec. 1   Litho.
Granite Paper
909A-909F A185a   Set of 6   8.25 8.25
909g   Souvenir sheet of 6, #909A-
       909F   8.00 8.00

Flowers — A186

Designs: 2.60p, Ipomoea obscura. 4.10p, Xenostegia tridentata. 5.50p, Ipomoea magnusiana. 6.10p, Ipomoea bolusiana.

2011, Mar. 11   *Perf. 13¼x13¾*
910-913 A186   Set of 4   6.00 6.00

Worldwide
Fund for
Nature
(WWF)
A187

Southern white rhinoceros: 2.60p, One rhinoceros facing left. 4.10p, Two rhinoceroses facing forward. 5.50p, Two rhinoceroses facing left. 6.10p, One rhinoceros facing forward, another facing right.

2011, Nov. 21   *Perf. 14x13¼*
914-917 A187   Set of 4   5.25 5.25
917a   Souvenir sheet of 4, #914-
       917   5.75 5.75

No. 917a is in the shape of a rhinoceros.

2011
Census
A188

Emblem of 2011 Census and: 2.60p, Map of Botswana showing population density. 4.10p, Graduates, road, communications tower. 5.50p, Bar graph showing males and females in age groupings, vert. 6.20p, Population growth graph, vert.

2011, Sept. 9   *Perf. 14x13¼, 13¼x14*
918-921 A188   Set of 4   5.25 5.25

Malaria
Prevention
A189

Inscriptions: 2.60p, Spraying of houses. 4.10p, Using anti-malaria medicines. 5.50p, Keeping surroundings clean. 6.10p, Sleeping under treated mosquito nets.

2011, Oct. 25   *Perf. 13¼x14*
922-925 A189   Set of 4   5.25 5.25

Wild Dogs
A190

Designs: 2.60p, One dog. 4.10p, Two dogs. 5.50p, Four dogs. 6.10p, Six dogs.

2011, Dec. 18   Litho.   *Perf. 14x13½*
926-929 A190   Set of 4   8.00 8.00

Myths and
Legends
A191

Designs: 3.20p, Matsieng. 4p, All the Stars in Heaven. 4.10p, Turntumbolosa, horiz. 4.90p,

Kgwanyape, horiz. 5.50p, Nonyane, horiz. 6.60p, How Death Came to the World.

Perf. 13¾x13¼, 13¼x13¾

2012			Litho.
930-935	A191	Set of 6	7.75 7.75

No. 625 Surcharged

Method and Perf. As Before

2013, Jan. 11			
935A	A128	7.30p on 30t #625	3.25 3.25

Save Water — A192

No. 936, 3.20p: a, Water flowing from spigot to bucket. b, Woman carrying water bucket.
No. 937, 4.90p: a, Water flowing from bowl to jar. b, Water cistern.
No. 938, 7.30p: a, Hands collecting water droplets over jar. b, Water pipe and pumping plant.

2013, Apr. 8   Litho.   Perf. 14
Horiz. pairs, #a-b

936-938	A192	Set of 3	7.75 7.75

Birds A193

Designs: 10t, Harlequin quail. 20t, Burchell's sandgrouse. 50t, Purple gallinule, vert. 1p, Pied avocet, vert. 2p, Kori bustard, vert. 3p, African spoonbill, vert. (3.50p), Southern red bishops, vert. 5p, African skimmer. (5.40p), Blue waxbill. (8p), Paradise flycatcher, vert. 10p, Secretary bird, vert. 20p, Bradfield's hornbill. 30p, Spotted eagle owl, vert. 50p, Southern red bishop, vert.

Perf. 14x13½, 13½x14

2014, May 13				Litho.
939	A193	10t multi	.25	.25
940	A193	20t multi	.25	.25
941	A193	50t multi	.25	.25
942	A193	1p multi	.25	.25
943	A193	2p multi	.45	.45
944	A193	3p multi	.70	.70
945	A193	(3.50p) multi	.80	.80
946	A193	5p multi	1.10	1.10
947	A193	(5.40p) multi	1.25	1.25
948	A193	(8p) multi	1.90	1.90
949	A193	10p multi	2.25	2.25
950	A193	20p multi	4.50	4.50
951	A193	30p multi	6.75	6.75
952	A193	50p multi	11.50	11.50
	Nos. 939-952 (14)		32.20	32.20

Lions of the Chobe A194

Designs: 3.50p, Male lion facing left. 5.40p, Pride of lions. 7.30p, Lioness facing right. 8p, Two lionesses and cub.

2014, June 20		Litho.	Perf. 13½
953-956	A194	Set of 4	5.50 5.50
956a		Souvenir sheet of 4, #953-956, perf. 14	5.50 5.50
956b		As "a," with PhilaKorea 2014 emblem in sheet margin	5.50 5.50

Issued: No. 956b, 8/7.

Domesticated Animals — A195

Designs: 30t, Dogs. 40t, Goats. 3.50p, Cattle. 5.40p, Donkeys. 7.30p, Chickens. 8p, Cats.

2014, Aug. 1		Litho.	Perf. 14
957-962	A195	Set of 6	5.75 5.75

World Post Day A196

Map of Botswana and: 3.50p, People and stack of papers. 5.40p, Airplane and globe. 7.30p, Elderly people and card reader. 8p, Letter and people in canoe.

Litho. With Foil Application

2014, Oct. 9			Perf. 14
963-966	A196	Set of 4	5.25 5.25

National Flora A197

Designs: 3.50p, Morula tree, Motshikiri grass, Sengaparile flowers. 5.40p, Morula tree and people (44x30mm). 7.30p, Motshikiri grass, grass harvesters (44x30mm). 8p, Sengaparile flowers, hand with seeds (44x30mm).

2014, Nov. 27		Litho.	Perf. 14
967-970	A197	Set of 4	5.25 5.25

Naming of Okavango Delta as 1000th UNESCO World Heritage Site — A198

Various Okavango Delta animals and inscription: 3.50p, Pristine freshwater systems and biodiversity. 5.40p, Exceptional natural and untouched beauty. 7.30p, Protecting places for posterity. 8p, Significant natural habitat for conservation.

2015, Mar. 10		Litho.	Perf. 14½x14
971-974	A198	Set of 4	5.00 5.00
974a		Souvenir sheet of 4, #971-974	5.00 5.00

Nos. 971-974, 974a have printing on back.

Abstract Art — A199

Designs: 4p, The Drum, by Modirwa Kekwaletswe. 5.90p, Hut, by Reginald Bakwena, horiz. 8p, Untitled, by Isaac Chibua, horiz. 10p, Come Together, by Prince Marokane.

Perf. 14x14¼, 14¼x14

2015, May 20		Litho.	
975-978	A199	Set of 4	5.75 5.75

Buffalos A200

Designs: 4p, Head of adult buffalo. 5.90p, Two young bulls jousting. 7.80p, Lion and buffalos (The Wall of Horns). 10p, Cow and calf, vert.

Perf. 13¾x13¼, 13¼x13¾

2015, July 22		Litho.	
979-982	A200	Set of 4	5.50 5.50
982a		Souvenir sheet of 4, #979-982, perf. 14	5.50 5.50

Vultures A201

Designs: 4p, Lappet-faced vultures. 5p, White-headed vultures. 5.90p, White-backed vultures. 7.80p, Hooded vultures. 10p, Hooded vultures (60x30mm).

Perf. 13¾x13¼, 14 (10p)

2015, Sept. 28		Litho.	
983-987	A201	Set of 5	6.25 6.25
987a		Souvenir sheet of 5, #983-987, perf. 14	6.25 6.25

Vervet Monkeys — A202

Designs: 4p, Vervet monkey, drawing and paint brush. 5.90p, Vervet monkeys grooming, horiz. 7.80p, Vervet monkeys in trees, horiz. 10p, Mother vervet monkey nurturing juvenile.

2015, Nov. 20		Litho.	Perf. 14
988-991	A202	Set of 4	5.25 5.25
991a		Souvenir sheet of 4, #988-991	5.25 5.25
991b		As "a," with Thailand 2016 emblem in sheet margin	5.25 5.25
991c		As "a," with Hong Kong 2015 emblem in sheet margin	5.25 5.25

Elephants A203

Elephants: 4p, Foraging. 5.90p, Mother and calf. 7.80p, Cooling down in Okavango Delta. 10p, Herd seeking water.

Perf. 13¾x13½

2016, Mar. 14			Litho.
992-995	A203	Set of 4	5.25 5.25
995a		Souvenir sheet of 4, #992-995	5.25 5.25
995b		As #995a, with Thailand 2016 emblem in sheet margin	5.25 5.25

Issued: No. 995b, 8/10.

Dances A204

Dances: 4p, Diware. 5.90p, Tsutsube. 7.80p, Setapa. 10p, Hosana.

Litho. & Embossed

2016, May 1		Perf. 13¾x13½
996-999	A204	Set of 4	5.25 5.25

50 Years of Progress — A205

Inscriptions: 30t, Health. 40t, Education. 50t, Sports development. 4p, Access to clean water. 5p, Infrastructure communications. 5.90p, Rural development. 7.80p, Infrastructure roads & buildings, vert. 10p, Gender equity, vert.

Perf. 14½x14, 14x14½

2016, Aug. 1		Litho.	
1000-1007	A205	Set of 8	6.50 6.50

Independence, 50th anniv.

Diamonds Type of 2001 and

Favorite Botswana Stamps — A206

Designs: 50t, Botswana #132. 4p, Botswana #359. 5.90p, Botswana #831. 7.80p, Botswana #490. No. 1012, 10p, Botswana #710. No. 1013, Cut and uncut diamonds.

2016, Oct. 1		Litho.	Perf. 14x14½
1008-1012	A206	Set of 5	5.25 5.25

Souvenir Sheet
Self-Adhesive

Litho. With Foil Application
Serpentine Die Cut 10

1013	A145	10p multi	1.90 1.90

People Participating in Kgotlas — A207

Various people participating in kgotla and inscription: 50t, Traditional adjudication. 4p, Information dissemination. 5.90p, Coronation of a chief. 10p, Dikgafela Harvest Celebration.

2016, Dec. 1		Litho.	Perf. 14x13¼
1014-1017	A207	Set of 4	4.00 4.00

Leopards — A208

Designs: 4p, Female leopard and cub. 5.90p, Male leopard in tree (45x30mm). 8p,

Leopard returning from the hunt (45x30mm).
10p, Head of leopard.

Perf. 14¾, 14¼x14 (#1019-1020)

2017, Feb. 28   **Litho.**
1018-1021   A208   Set of 4   5.50   5.50
1021a   Souvenir sheet of 4,
         #1018-1021, perf. 14   5.50   5.50

2017 Netball
World Youth
Cup, Gaborone
A209

Various netball players with frame color of:
40t, Orange. 50t, Red. 4p, Blue. 5.90p, Green.
10p, Magenta (35x70mm).

Perf. 14¼, 14x14¼ (10p)

2017, May 1   **Litho.**
1022-1026   A209   Set of 5   4.00   4.00
1026a   Souvenir sheet of 1   1.90   1.90

Endangered Birds — A210

Designs: 50t, Kori bustard and chick. 5p,
Black-bellied bustard, vert. 7p, Red-crested
korhaan and Northern black korhaan, vert. 9p,
Denham's bustard, vert. 10p, Ludwig's bustard, vert.

Perf. 14¼x14, 14x14¼

2017, Aug. 7   **Litho.**
1027-1031   A210   Set of 5   6.25   6.25
1031a   Souvenir sheet of 5,
         #1027-1031   6.25   6.25

POSTAGE DUE STAMPS

Bechuanaland
Protectorate Nos. J10-
J12 Overprinted

Perf. 14

1967, Mar. 1   **Wmk. 4**   **Typo.**
J1   D2   1c carmine rose   .30   3.00
J2   D2   2c dull violet   .30   3.00
J3   D2   5c olive green   .40   3.00
     Nos. J1-J3 (3)   1.00   9.00

Elephant — D1

Perf. 13½

1971, June 9   **Litho.**   **Unwmk.**
J4   D1   1c carmine rose   1.75   4.50
J5   D1   2c violet blue   2.25   5.00
J6   D1   6c sepia   2.75   7.50
J7   D1   14c green   3.25   10.00
     Nos. J4-J7 (4)   10.00   27.00

Zebra — D2

1978   *Perf. 12½*
J8   D2   1t red orange & black   1.00   1.75
J9   D2   2t emerald & black   1.00   1.75
J10   D2   4t red & black   1.00   1.75
J11   D2   10t dark blue & black   1.00   1.75
J12   D2   16t brown & black   1.00   1.75
     Nos. J8-J12 (5)   5.00   8.75

1984   *Perf. 14½x14*
J8a   D2   1t   1.30   2.00
J9a   D2   2t   1.30   2.00
J10a   D2   4t   1.30   2.00
J11a   D2   10t   1.30   2.00
J12a   D2   16t   1.30   2.00
     Nos. J8a-J12a (5)   6.50   10.00

1989, Apr. 1   *Perf. 14½*
J8b   D2   1t   .50   .65
J9b   D2   2t   .50   .65
J10b   D2   4t   .50   .65
J11b   D2   10t   .50   1.00
J12b   D2   16t   .75   1.00
     Nos. J8b-J12b (5)   2.75   3.60

The design is the same size on the 1984
and 1989 issues, but the grass of Nos. J8b-
J12b is lower and less defined than on previous issues. The paper is wider on the 1989
issue.

1994, Dec. 1   *Perf. 14*
J8c   D2   1t   1.00   1.00
J9c   D2   2t   1.00   1.00
J10c   D2   4t   1.00   1.00
J11c   D2   10t   1.00   1.00
J12c   D2   16t   1.00   1.00
     Nos. J8c-J12c (5)   5.00   5.00

See note after No. J12b.

BRAZIL

brə-ˈzil

Brasil (after 1918)

LOCATION — On the north and east coasts of South America, bordering on the Atlantic Ocean.

GOVT. — Republic

AREA — 3,286,000 sq. mi.

POP. — 157,070,163 (1996)

CAPITAL — Brasilia

Brazil was an independent empire from 1822 to 1889, when a constitution was adopted and the country became officially known as The United States of Brazil.

1000 Reis = 1 Milreis

100 Centavos = 1 Cruzeiro (1942)

100 Centavos = 1 Cruzado (1986)

100 Centavos = 1 Cruzeiro (1990)
(Cruzeiro Real 8/2/93-7/1/94)

100 Centavos = 1 Real (7/1/94)

Catalogue values for unused stamps in this country are for Never Hinged items, beginning with Scott 680 in the regular postage section, Scott B12 in the semi-postal section, Scott C66 in the airpost section, Scott RA2 in the postal tax section, and Scott RAB1 in the postal tax semi-postal section.

Values for unused stamps are for examples with original gum as defined in the catalogue introduction except for Nos. 1-98, which are valued without gum. Nos. 1-52 with original gum command a substantial premium (up to 100%). Nos. 53-78 with original gum command a premium of up to 50%. Nos. 79-98 with original gum command a premium of 10%-25%.

Watermarks

Wmk. 97 — "CORREIO FEDERAL REPUBLICA DOS ESTADOS UNIDOS DO BRAZIL" in Sheet

Wmk. 98 — "IMPOSTO DE CONSUMO REPUBLICA DOS ESTADOS UNIDOS DO BRAZIL" in Sheet

Wmk. 99 — "CORREIO"

Wmk. 100 — "CASA DA MOEDA" in Sheet

Because of the spacing of this watermark, a few stamps in each sheet may show no watermark. Variations of this watermark occur in some stamps reading 'CASA MOEDA ENTRE ESTRELAS', 'CASA DA MOEDA ENTRE ESTRELAS', or 'CASACASA DA MOEDA ENTRE ESTRALAS.'

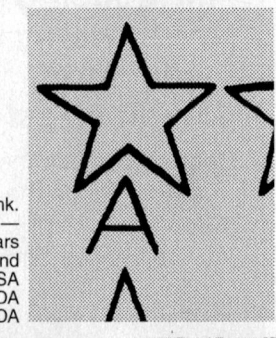

Wmk. 101 — Stars and CASA DA MOEDA

Wmk. 116 — Crosses and Circles

Wmk. 127 — Quatrefoils

Wmk. 193 — ESTADOS UNIDOS DO BRASIL

Wmk. 206 — Star-framed CM, Multiple

Wmk. 218 — E U BRASIL Multiple, Letters 8mm High

Wmk. 221 — ESTADOS UNIDOS DO BRASIL, Multiple, Letters 6mm High

Wmk. 222 — CORREIO BRASIL and 5 Stars in Squared Circle

Wmk. 236 — Coat of Arms in Sheet

Watermark (reduced illustration) covers 22 stamps in sheet.

Wmk. 245 — Multiple "CASA DA MOEDA DO BRASIL" and Small Formee Cross

Wmk. 249 — "CORREIO BRASIL" multiple

Wmk. 256 — "CASA+DA+MOEDA+DO+BRAZIL" in 8mm Letters

Wmk. 264 — "*CORREIO*BRASIL*" Multiple, Letters 7mm High

Wmk. 267 — "*CORREIO*BRASIL*" Multiple in Small Letters 5mm High

Wmk. 268 — "CASA+DA+MOEDA+DO+BRASIL" in 6mm Letters

Wmk. 270 — Wavy Lines and Seal

Wmk. 271 — Wavy Lines

Wmk. 281 — Wavy Lines

ISSUES OF THE EMPIRE

A1

Fine Impressions
Grayish or Yellowish Paper
Unwmk.

			Engr.	Imperf.
1843, Aug. 1				
1	A1	30r black	4,500.	550.
c.		Pair, #1-2		950,000.
2	A1	60r black	825.	275.
3	A1	90r black	4,000.	1,300.

Nos. 1-3 were issued with gum, but very few unused examples retain even a trace of their original gum. Stamps with original gum command substantial premiums.

Fine impressions are true black and have background lathework complete. Intermediate impressions are grayish black and have weaker lathework in the background. These sell for somewhat less than fine impressions. Worn impressions have white areas in the background surrounding the numerals due to plate wear affecting especially the lathework. These examples sell for somewhat less than intermediate impressions.

Most examples of Nos. 1-3 also exist on white paper, usually thin and somewhat translucent. Such examples are scarce and command premiums. For detailed listings, see the Scott Classic Specialized catalogue

A2

Grayish or Yellowish Paper
1844-46

7	A2	10r black	125.00	25.00
8	A2	30r black	145.00	35.00
9	A2	60r black	125.00	25.00
10	A2	90r black	1,000.	120.00
11	A2	180r black	4,500.	1,800.
12	A2	300r black	6,500.	2,000.
13	A2	600r black	6,000.	2,200.

Nos. 8, 9 and 10 exist on thick paper and are considerably scarcer.

A3

Grayish or Yellowish Paper
1850, Jan. 1

21	A3	10r black	30.00	35.00
22	A3	20r black	92.50	120.00
23	A3	30r black	12.00	3.50
24	A3	60r black	12.00	3.00
25	A3	90r black	110.00	14.50
26	A3	180r black	115.00	65.00
27	A3	300r black	400.00	72.50
28	A3	600r black	500.00	110.00

No. 22 used is generally found precanceled with a single horizontal line in pen or blue crayon or with two diagonal pen lines. Value precanceled without gum, $75.

All values except the 90r were reprinted in 1910 on very thick paper.

1854

37	A3	10r blue	14.50	12.00
c.		Double impression	2,000.	650.00
38	A3	30r blue	40.00	65.00

For more complete listings, see Scott *Classic Specialized Catalogue of Stamps and Covers 1840-1940.*

A4

1861

39	A4	280r red	160.00	110.00
40	A4	430r yellow	200.00	160.00

Nos. 39-40 have been reprinted on thick white paper with white gum. They are printed in aniline inks and the colors are brighter than those of the originals.

1866   *Perf. 13½*

42	A3	10r blue	300.00	150.00
43	A3	20r black	1,100.	500.00
44	A3	30r black	350.00	400.00
45	A3	30r blue	800.00	925.00
46	A3	60r black	300.00	30.00
47	A3	90r black	725.00	350.00
48	A3	180r black	925.00	350.00
49	A4	280r red	800.00	850.00
50	A3	300r black	1,100.	425.00
51	A4	430r yellow	725.00	425.00
52	A3	600r black	725.00	300.00

Fraudulent perforations abound. Purchases should be accompanied by certificates of authenticity.

A 10r black is questioned.

A5

A6

A7

A8

A8a

A9

Emperor Dom Pedro — A9a

Types of 100 reis:
Type I — Left frameline weak and incomplete and composed of a single line that never touches the upper or lower ornaments. The upper left ornament is broken. The lower left ornament is vestigial.
Type Ia — Left frameline is incomplete and composed of a single line that does not touch the upper ornaments. The lower left ornament is complete.
Type II — Left frameline incomplete and composed of a double outer line that does not touch the upper ornaments. The lower left ornament is slightly broken.
Type III — Left frameline complete and composed of two continuous outer lines that meet the upper ornaments. The lower left ornament is complete.

Thick or Thin White Wove Paper
1866, July 1   *Perf. 12*

53	A5	10r vermilion	14.50	5.00
54	A6	20r red lilac	25.00	3.50
56	A7	50r blue	35.00	2.50
57	A8	80r slate violet	92.50	6.00
58	A8a	100r blue green	35.00	1.90
59	A9	200r black	120.00	12.00
a.		Half used as 100r on cover		1,750.
60	A9a	500r orange	250.00	35.00
		Nos. 53-60 (7)	572.00	65.90

The 10r and 20r exist imperf. on both white and bluish paper. Some authorities consider them proofs.
Nos. 58 and 65 are found in four types.

1868   **Bluish Paper**

53a	A5	10r	600.00	500.00
54b	A6	20r	190.00	35.00
56a	A7	50r	225.00	30.00
57a	A8	80r	300.00	35.00
58b	A8a	100r Type II	960.00	140.00

1876-77   **Rouletted**

61	A5	10r vermilion ('77)	72.50	35.00
62	A6	20r red lilac ('77)	85.00	30.00
63	A7	50r blue ('77)	85.00	8.50
64	A8	80r violet ('77)	210.00	20.00
65	A8a	100r green (III)	50.00	1.50
66	A9	200r black ('77)	100.00	9.25
a.		Half used as 100r on cover		1,000.
67	A9a	500r orange	225.00	42.50
		Nos. 61-67 (7)	827.50	146.75

A10

A11

A12

A13

A14

A15

A16

A17

A18

A19

A20

1878-79   **Rouletted**

68	A10	10r vermilion	14.50	3.50
69	A11	20r violet	19.00	3.00
70	A12	50r blue	30.00	2.00
71	A13	80r lake	35.00	10.00
72	A14	100r green	35.00	1.50
73	A15	200r black	175.00	17.50
a.		Half used as 100r on cover		1,000.
74	A16	260r dk brown	100.00	27.50
75	A18	300r bister	100.00	7.25
a.		One-third used as 100r on cover		10,000.
76	A19	700r red brown	190.00	100.00
77	A20	1000r gray lilac	225.00	47.50
		Nos. 68-77 (10)	923.50	219.75

1878, Aug. 21   *Perf. 12*

78	A17	300r orange & grn	100.00	25.00

Nos. 68-78 exist imperforate.

A21

A22

A23

Small Heads
Laid Paper
Perf. 13, 13½ and Compound
1881, July 15

79	A21	50r blue	150.00	24.00
80	A22	100r olive green	600.00	47.50
81	A23	200r pale red brn	600.00	140.00
a.		Half used as 100r on cover		2,100.

On Nos. 79 and 80 the hair above the ear curves forward. On Nos. 83 and 88 it is drawn backward. On the stamps of the 1881 issue the beard is smaller than in the 1882-85 issues and fills less of the space between the neck and the frame at the left.
See No. 88.

A24

A25

A26

A27

100 REIS:
Type I — Groundwork formed of diagonal crossed lines and horizontal lines.
Type II — Groundwork formed of diagonal crossed lines and vertical lines.
200 REIS:
Type I — Groundwork formed of diagonal and horizontal lines.
Type II — Groundwork formed of diagonal crossed lines.

Larger Heads
Laid Paper
Perf. 12½ to 14 and Compound
1882-84

82	A24	10r black	12.00	25.00
83	A25	100r ol grn, type I	50.00	4.50
b.		100r dark green, type II	425.00	14.50
84	A26	200r pale red brn, type I	100.00	30.00
a.		Half used as 100r on cover		1,300.
85	A27	200r pale rose, type II	55.00	5.50
a.		Diag. half used as 100r on cover		950.00
		Nos. 82-85 (4)	217.00	65.00

See No. 86.

A28

A29

A30

TYPES OF A29
Type I — Groundwork of horizontal lines.
Type II — Groundwork of diagonal crossed lines.
Type III — Groundwork solid.

Perf. 13, 13½, 14 and Compound
1884-85

86	A24	10r orange	3.00	3.25
87	A28	20r slate green	35.00	3.50
a.		20r olive green	35.00	3.50
b.		Half used as 10r on newspaper		3,500.
88	A21	50r bl, head larger	35.00	3.50
90	A29	100r lilac, type I	150.00	3.00
a.		100r lilac, type II	450.00	75.00
b.		100r lilac, type III	325.00	55.00
91	A30	100r lilac	200.00	5.00
		Nos. 86-91 (5)	423.00	18.25

A31

Perf. 13, 13½, 14 and Compound
1885

92	A31	100r lilac	140.00	3.00

Design A31 has a value tablet the color of the stamp. Design A35 has a white value tablet.

A32

Southern Cross — A33

Crown — A34

1887

93	A32	50r chalky blue	35.00	5.00
94	A33	300r gray blue	230.00	30.00
95	A34	500r olive	140.00	14.00
		Nos. 93-95 (3)	405.00	49.00

A35

A36

Entrance to Bay of Rio de Janeiro — A37

1888

96	A35	100r lilac	72.50	1.90
a.		Imperf., pair	150.00	175.00
97	A36	700r violet	80.00	110.00
98	A37	1000r dull blue	275.00	110.00
		Nos. 96-98 (3)	427.50	221.90

Issues of the Republic

Southern Cross — A38

Wove Paper, Thin to Thick
Perf. 12½ to 14, 11 to 11½, and 12½ to 14x11 to 11½, Rough or Clean-Cut

Engraved; Typographed (#102)

1890-91

99	A38	20r gray green	2.50	1.90
a.		20r blue green	2.50	1.90
b.		20r emerald	19.00	7.00
100	A38	50r gray green	6.25	1.90
a.		50r olive green	14.00	7.00
b.		50r yellow green	14.00	7.00
c.		50r dark slate green	8.25	4.00
d.		Horiz. pair, imperf. btwn.	—	
101	A38	100r lilac rose	475.00	6.00
102	A38	100r red lil, redrawn	30.00	1.90
a.		Tete beche pair	25,000.	19,000.
103	A38	200r purple	10.00	1.90
a.		200r violet	12.00	2.50
b.		200r violet blue	27.50	3.50
c.		Half used as 100r on cover		875.00
104	A38	300r dark violet	90.00	6.00
a.		300r gray	90.00	10.00
b.		300r gray blue	100.00	10.00
c.		300r slate violet	175.00	30.00
105	A38	500r olive bister	21.00	9.50
a.		500r olive gray	21.00	11.50
106	A38	500r slate	21.00	13.50
107	A38	700r fawn	19.00	19.00
a.		700r chocolate	24.00	26.00
108	A38	1000r bister	17.50	3.50
a.		1000r yellow buff	35.00	8.50
		Nos. 99-108 (10)	692.25	65.10

The redrawn 100r may be distinguished by the absence of the curved lines of shading in the left side of the central oval. The pearls in the oval are not well aligned and there is less shading at right and left of "CORREIO" and "100 RÉIS."

A 100 reis stamp of type A38 but inscribed "BRAZIL" instead of "E. U. DO BRAZIL" was not placed in issue but postmarked copies are known. A reprint on thick paper was made in 1910.

No. 101 exists imperf., not regularly issued.

For surcharges see Nos. 151-158.

Liberty Head — A39

Perf. 12½ to 14, 11 to 11½ and 12½ to 14x11 to 11½

1891, May 1   Typo.

109	A39	100r blue & red	42.50	1.75
a.		Frame inverted	175.00	110.00
b.		Tete beche pair	850.00	925.00
c.		100r ultra & red	42.50	1.90

Liberty Head — A40

Perf. 11, 11½, 13, 13½, 14 and Compound

1893, Jan. 18   Litho.

111	A40	100r rose	75.00	1.75

A41

A41a

Sugarloaf Mountain

A42

A42a

Liberty Head

Hermes — A43

Perf. 11 to 11½, 12½ to 14 and 12½ to 14x11 to 11½

1894-97   Unwmk.

112	A41	10r rose & blue	2.50	.90
113	A41a	10r rose & blue	2.50	.90
114	A41a	20r orange & bl ('97)	1.40	.40
115	A41a	50r dk blue & blue	13.00	1.60
116	A42	100r carmine & blk	5.00	.50
118	A42a	200r orange & blk	1.25	.50
d.		Half used as 100r on cover		850.00
119	A42a	300r green & blk	19.00	.70
120	A42a	500r blue & blk	30.00	2.00
121	A42a	700r light lilac & blk	20.00	2.00
122	A43	1000r green & vio	72.50	2.00
124	A43	2000r blk & gray lil	85.00	20.00
		Nos. 112-124 (11)	252.15	31.50

The head of No. 116 exists in five types. See Nos. 140-150A, 159-161, 166-171d.

1889 Issue of Newspaper Stamps Surcharged (Type N1)

a

b

c

1898   **Green Surcharge**   *Rouletted*

125	(b)	700r on 500r yel	8.50	12.00
126	(c)	1000r on 700r yel	42.50	35.00
a.		Surcharged "700r"	850.00	1,000.
127	(c)	2000r on 1000r yel	35.00	18.00
128	(c)	2000r on 1000r brn	25.00	7.25

Violet Surcharge

129	(a)	100r on 50r brn yel	2.50	55.00
130	(c)	100r on 50r brn yel	90.00	75.00
131	(c)	300r on 200r blk	4.00	1.40
a.		Double surcharge	190.00	325.00

The surcharge on No. 130 is handstamped. The impression is blurred and lighter in color than on No. 129. The two surcharges differ most in the shapes and serifs of the figures "1."

Counterfeits exist of No. 126a.

Black Surcharge

132	(b)	200r on 100r vio	4.00	1.40
a.		Double surcharge	95.00	200.00
b.		Inverted surcharge	95.00	200.00
132C	(b)	500r on 300r car	6.50	3.50
133	(b)	700r on 500r grn	9.50	2.40

Blue Surcharge

134	(b)	500r on 300r car	7.50	6.25

Red Surcharge

135	(c)	1000r on 700r ultra	27.50	17.00
a.		Inverted surcharge	240.00	

Surcharged on 1890-94 Issues

d

e

Perf. 11 to 14 and Compound

Black Surcharge

136	N3(e)	20r on 10r blue	3.75	7.00
137	N2(d)	200r on 100r red lilac	25.00	17.00
a.		Double surcharge	275.00	300.00

Surcharge on No. 137 comes blue to deep black.

Blue Surcharge

138	N3(e)	50r on 20r grn	9.50	11.50

Red Surcharge

139	N3(e)	100r on 50r grn	21.00	24.00
a.		Blue surcharge	15.00	

The surcharge on 139a exists inverted, and in pair, one without surcharge.

Types of 1894-97

1899   *Perf. 5½-7 and 11-11½x5½-7*

140	A41a	10r rose & bl	6.00	14.00
141	A41a	20r orange & bl	9.25	9.25
142	A41a	50r dk bl & lt bl	12.00	37.50
143	A42	100r car & blk	20.00	5.50
144	A42a	200r org & blk	12.00	3.50
145	A42a	300r green & blk	75.00	8.75
		Nos. 140-145 (6)	134.25	78.50

Perf. 8½-9½, 8½-9½x11-11½

146	A41a	10r rose & bl	6.00	3.50
147	A41a	20r orange & bl	19.00	3.50
147A	A41a	50r dk bl & bl	160.00	35.00
148	A42	100r car & blk	37.50	1.75
149	A42a	200r org & blk	19.00	1.25
150	A42a	300r green & blk	75.00	6.00
150A	A43	1000r green & vio	160.00	15.00
		Nos. 146-150A (7)	476.50	66.00

Nos. 140-150A are valued with perfs just cut into the design on one or two sides. Expect some irregularity of the perforations.

Issue of 1890-93 Surcharged in Violet or Magenta

Perf. 11 to 11½, 12½ to 14 and Compound

1899, June 25

151	A38	50r on 20r gray grn	2.50	3.50
a.		Double surcharge	150.00	150.00
152	A38	100r on 50r gray grn	2.50	3.50
b.		Double surcharge	125.00	125.00
153	A38	300r on 200r pur	9.25	14.50
a.		Double surcharge	300.00	
b.		Pair, one without surcharge	500.00	—
154	A38	500r on 300r ultra, perf. 13	22.50	8.75
a.		500r on 300r gray lilac	35.00	10.00
b.		Pair, one without surcharge	500.00	575.00
c.		500r on 300r slate violet	45.00	17.00
155	A38	700r on 500r ol bis	30.00	7.00
a.		Pair, one without surcharge	500.00	—
156	A38	1000r on 700r choc	22.50	7.00
157	A38	1000r on 700r fawn	22.50	7.00
a.		Pair, one without surcharge	500.00	575.00
158	A38	2000r on 1000r bister (perf 11-11½)	37.50	5.25
a.		2000r on 1000r yel buff (perf 13)	60.00	5.25
b.		Pair, one without surcharge	500.00	575.00
		Nos. 151-158 (8)	149.25	56.50

Types of 1894-97
Perf. 11, 11½, 13 and Compound

1900

159	A41a	50r green	13.00	.70
160	A42	100r rose	25.00	.35
a.		Frame around inner oval	125.00	4.75
161	A42a	200r blue	14.50	.40
		Nos. 159-161 (3)	52.50	1.45

Three types exist of No. 161, all of which have the frame around inner oval.

Cabral Arrives at Brazil — A44

Independence Proclaimed — A45

"Emancipation of Slaves" — A46

Allegory, Republic of Brazil — A47

1900, Jan. 1   Litho.   *Perf. 12½*

162	A44	100r red	7.25	4.50
a.		Imperf., pair	400.00	500.00
163	A45	200r green & yel	7.25	4.50
164	A46	500r blue	7.25	4.50
165	A47	700r emerald	7.25	4.50
		Nos. 162-165 (4)	29.00	18.00
		Set, never hinged	75.00	

Discovery of Brazil, 400th anniversary.

Types of 1894-97
Wmk. (97? or 98?)

1905   *Perf. 11, 11½*

166	A41a	10r rose & bl	7.00	4.75
167	A41a	20r org & bl	12.50	2.40
168	A41a	50r green	25.00	3.50
169	A42	100r rose	32.50	1.25
170	A42a	200r dark blue	19.00	1.25
171	A42a	300r grn & blk	65.00	2.40
		Nos. 166-171 (6)	161.00	15.55

Positive identification of Wmk. 97 or 98 places stamp in specific watermark groups below.

Wmk. 97

166b	A41a	10r rose & blue	37.50	19.00
167b	A41a	20r org & blue	37.50	9.50
168b	A41a	50r green	72.50	9.50
169b	A42	100r rose	250.00	35.00
170b	A42a	200r dark blue	150.00	4.75
171b	A42a	300r green & blk	450.00	35.00
171A	A43	1000r grn & vio	350.00	35.00
		Nos. 166b-171A (7)	1,348.	147.75

Issue of 1890-93 Surcharged in Violet or Magenta

1899
50 RÉIS

Wmk. 98

166c	A41a	10r rose & blue	50.00	50.00
167c	A41a	20r org & blue	100.00	24.00
168c	A41a	50r green	200.00	35.00
169c	A42	100r rose	100.00	4.75
170c	A42a	200r dark blue	150.00	4.75
171d	A42a	300r green & blk	350.00	35.00
		Nos. 166c-171d (6)	950.00	153.50

Allegory, Pan-American Congress
A48

1906, July 23   Litho.   Unwmk.

172	A48	100r carmine rose	28.00	22.00
173	A48	200r blue	65.00	8.00

Third Pan-American Congress.

Aristides Lobo
A48a

Benjamin Constant
A49

Pedro Alvares Cabral
A50

Eduardo Wandenkolk
A51

Manuel Deodoro da Fonseca
A52

Floriano Peixoto
A53

Prudente de Moraes
A54

Manuel Ferraz de Campos Salles
A55

Francisco de Paula Rodrigues Alves — A56

Liberty Head — A57

A58

A59

1906-16   Engr.   Perf. 12

174	A48a	10r bluish slate ('15)	1.10	.25
175	A49	20r aniline violet ('15)	1.50	.25
176	A50	50r green	1.10	.25
a.		Booklet pane of 6 ('08)	50.00	120.00
177	A51	100r anil rose	2.50	.25
a.		Imperf. vert., coil ('16)	5.50	.40
b.		Booklet pane of 6 ('08)	120.00	120.00

178	A52	200r blue	2.50	.25
a.		Booklet pane of 6 ('08)	85.00	120.00
179	A52	200r ultra ('15)	2.50	.25
a.		Imperf. vert., coil ('16)	3.00	.40
180	A53	300r gray blk	4.75	.80
181	A54	400r olive grn	50.00	2.40
182	A55	500r dk violet	7.50	.80
183	A56	600r ol grn ('10)	3.50	1.20
184	A56	700r red brown	7.50	3.50
185	A57	1000r vermilion	45.00	1.25
186	A58	2000r yellow grn	35.00	.80
187	A58	2000r Prus blue ('15)	24.00	1.25
188	A59	5000r car rose	16.50	2.40
		Nos. 174-188 (15)	204.95	15.90

Allegorical Emblems: Liberty, Peace, Industry, etc. — A60

1908, July 14

189	A60	100r carmine	5.00	2.00

National Exhibition, Rio de Janeiro.

Emblems of Peace Between Brazil and Portugal A61

1908, July 14

190	A61	100r red	13.00	1.50

Opening of Brazilian ports to foreign commerce, cent. Medallions picture King Carlos I of Portugal and Pres. Affonso Penna of Brazil.

Bonifacio, Bolivar, Hidalgo, O'Higgins, San Martin, Washington — A62

1909

191	A62	200r deep blue	12.00	1.50

For surcharge see No. E1.

Nilo Peçanha — A63

1910, Nov. 15

192	A63	10,000r brown	10.00	2.50

Baron of Rio Branco — A64

1913-16

193	A64	1000r deep green	4.75	.40
194	A64	1000r slate ('16)	37.50	.80

Cabo Frio — A65

Perf. 11½

1915, Nov. 13   Litho.   Wmk. 99

195	A65	100r dk grn, *yelsh*	6.00	4.50

Founding of the town of Cabo Frio, 300th anniversary.

Bay of Guajara
A66

1916, Jan. 5

196	A66	100r carmine	8.00	6.00

City of Belem, 300th anniversary.

Revolutionary Flag — A67

1917, Mar. 6

197	A67	100r deep blue	16.00	8.00

Revolution of Pernambuco, Mar. 6, 1817.

Rodrigues Alves — A68

Unwmk.

1917, Aug. 31   Engr.   Perf. 12

198	A68	5000r red brown	100.00	12.00

Liberty Head
A69   A70

Perf. 12½, 13, 13x13½.

1918-20   Typo.   Unwmk.

200	A69	10r orange brn	.80	.30
201	A69	20r slate	.80	.30
202	A69	25r ol gray ('20)	.80	.30
203	A69	50r green	170.00	4.00
204	A70	100r rose	2.25	.30
a.		Imperf., pair	350.00	
205	A70	300r red orange	40.00	4.00
206	A70	500r dull violet	40.00	4.00
		Nos. 200-206 (7)	254.65	13.20

1918-20   Wmk. 100

207	A69	10r red brown	8.00	2.00
a.		Imperf., pair	—	
207B	A69	20r slate	2.00	1.90
c.		Imperf., pair	350.00	
208	A69	25r ol gray ('20)	1.00	.60
209	A69	50r green	1.90	.60
210	A70	100r rose	100.00	.60
a.		Imperf., pair	—	
211	A70	200r dull blue	8.00	.60
212	A70	300r orange	90.00	5.00
213	A70	500r dull violet	90.00	10.00
214	A70	600r orange	3.75	10.00
		Nos. 207-214 (9)	304.65	31.30

Because of the spacing of this watermark, a few stamps in each sheet may show no watermark, these are worth considerably more.

The editors would like to see evidence of the existence of Nos. 207a and 210a.

"Education" — A72

1918   Engr.   Perf. 11½

215	A72	1000r blue	9.00	.30
216	A72	2000r red brown	45.00	13.00
217	A72	5000r dark violet	9.00	9.00
		Nos. 215-217 (3)	63.00	22.30

Watermark note below No. 257 also applies to Nos. 215-217.

See Nos. 233-234, 283-285, 404, 406, 458, 460. For surcharge see No. C30.

Railroad
A73

"Industry"
A74

"Aviation"
A75

Mercury
A76

"Navigation" — A77

Perf. 13½x13, 13x13½

1920-22   Typo.   Unwmk.

218	A73	10r red violet	1.50	.50
219	A73	20r olive green	1.50	.50
220	A74	25r brown violet	.50	.50
221	A74	50r blue green	2.00	.50
222	A74	50r org brn ('22)	4.50	.50
223	A75	100r rose red	4.50	.50
224	A75	100r orange ('22)	10.00	.50
225	A75	150r violet ('21)	2.00	.50
226	A75	200r blue	6.00	.50
227	A75	200r rose red ('22)	9.00	.50
228	A76	300r olive gray	17.00	.50
229	A76	400r dull blue ('22)	30.00	3.75
230	A76	500r red brown	24.00	.50
		Nos. 218-230 (13)	112.50	9.75

See Nos. 236-257, 265-266, 268-271, 273-274, 276-281, 302-311, 316-322, 326-340, 357-358, 431-434, 436-441, 461-463B, 467-470, 472-474, 488-490, 492-494. For surcharges see Nos. 356-358, 376-377.

Nos. 218, 219, and 227 exist on experimental chalky paper. Value $300 each.

Perf. 11, 11½

Engr.   Wmk. 100

231	A77	600r red orange	2.40	.50
232	A77	1000r claret	4.75	.30
a.		Perf. 8½	150.00	15.00
233	A72	2000r dull violet	27.50	.50
234	A72	5000r brown	21.00	11.00
		Nos. 231-234 (4)	55.65	12.30

Nos. 233 and 234 are inscribed "BRASIL CORREIO." Watermark note below No. 257 also applies to Nos. 231-234.

See No. 282.

King Albert of Belgium and President Epitacio Pessoa
A78

1920, Sept. 19   Engr.   Perf. 11½x11

235	A78	100r dull red	1.00	1.75

Visit of the King and Queen of Belgium.

Types of 1920-22 Issue

Perf. 13x13½, 13x12½

1922-29   Typo.   Wmk. 100

236	A73	10r red violet	.75	.35
237	A73	20r olive green	.75	.35
238	A75	20r gray vio ('29)	.50	.50
239	A74	25r brown violet	.75	6.00
240	A74	50r blue grn	4.25	80.00
241	A74	50r org brn ('23)	.75	1.50
242	A75	100r rose red	30.00	.50
243	A75	100r orange ('26)	2.00	.50
244	A75	100r turq grn ('28)	1.50	.25
245	A75	150r violet	4.00	.30
246	A75	200r blue	400.00	12.00
247	A75	200r rose red	2.50	.35
248	A75	200r ol grn ('28)	7.00	9.00
249	A76	300r olive gray	4.00	.50
250	A76	300r rose red ('29)	2.00	.50
251	A76	400r blue	4.00	.35
252	A76	400r orange ('29)	1.50	6.00
253	A76	500r red brown	10.00	.50
254	A76	500r ultra ('29)	16.00	1.40
255	A76	600r brn org ('29)	12.00	3.00

256 A76 700r dull vio ('29) 16.00 1.60
257 A76 1000r turq bl ('29) 16.00 .50
Nos. 236-257 (22) 536.25 125.95

Because of the spacing of the watermark, a few stamps in each sheet show no watermark.

A booklet exists with panes of 6 (2x3), created from the left margin blocks of sheet stamps of Nos. 241, 243, 247, 249 and 253. Once removed from the booklet, they cannot be separately identified.

"Agriculture" — A79

1922 Unwmk. Perf. 13x13½
258 A79 40r orange brown .70 .50
259 A79 80r grnsh blue .50 3.00

See Nos. 263, 267, 275.

No. 259 exists with watermark 100. Value $2500.

Declaration of Ypiranga — A80

Dom Pedro I and Jose Bonifacio — A81

National Exposition and President Pessoa — A82

Unwmk.
1922, Sept. 7 Engr. Perf. 14
260 A80 100r ultra 2.40 .75
261 A81 200r red 5.00 .50
262 A82 300r green 5.00 .50
Nos. 260-262 (3) 12.40 1.75
Set, never hinged 72.00

Cent. of independence and Natl. Exposition of 1922.

Agriculture Type of 1922
Perf. 13½x12
1923 Wmk. 100 Typo.
263 A79 40r orange brown .75 10.00

Brazilian Army Entering Bahia — A83

Unwmk.
1923, July 12 Litho. Perf. 13
264 A83 200r rose 11.00 7.50

Centenary of the taking of Bahia from the Portuguese.

Types of 1920-22 Issue
Perf. 13x13½
1924 Typo. Wmk. 193
265 A73 10r red violet 10.00 7.00
266 A73 20r olive green 14.00 7.00
267 A79 40r orange brown 8.50 3.00
268 A74 50r orange brown 13.00 30.00
269 A75 100r orange 8.50 .75
270 A75 200r rose 13.00 .75
271 A76 400r blue 10.00 6.00
Nos. 265-271 (7) 77.00 54.50

Arms of Equatorial Confederation, 1824 — A84

Unwmk.
1924, July 2 Litho. Perf. 11
272 A84 200r bl, blk, yel, & red 3.25 1.75
a. Red omitted 350.00 350.00

Centenary of the Equatorial Confederation. Chemically bleached fakes of No. 272a are more common than the genuine error. Expertization is advised.

Types of 1920-22 Issue
Perf. 9½ to 13½ and Compound
1924-28 Typo. Wmk. 101
273 A73 10r red violet .50 .35
274 A73 20r olive gray .50 .35
275 A79 40r orange brn .50 .35
276 A74 50r orange brn .75 .30
277 A75 100r red orange 2.25 .35
278 A75 200r rose 1.00 .35
279 A76 300r ol gray ('25) 12.00 .50
280 A76 400r blue 6.00 .50
281 A76 500r red brown 25.00 .50

Engr.
282 A77 600r red org ('26) 2.50 .35
283 A72 2000r dull vio ('26) 8.00 .75
284 A72 5000r brown ('26) 22.50 12.50
285 A72 10,000r rose ('28) 30.00 2.00
Nos. 273-285 (13) 111.50 19.15

Nos. 283-285 are inscribed "BRASIL CORREIO."

Ruy Barbosa — A85

1925 Wmk. 100 Perf. 11½
286 A85 1000r claret 10.00 5.00

1925-27 Wmk. 101 Perf. 11½-11¾
287 A85 1000r claret 4.00 2.00
a. Perf. 11-11½ ('25) 100.00 6.50

Watermark of no. 287 reads 'CASA MOEDA ENTRE ESTRELAS' vertically or horizontally. Watermark on Np. 287a reads 'CASA DA MOEDA ENTRE ESTRELAS' or 'CASACACA DA MOEDA ENTRE ESTRELAS' horizontally. See note below watermark 100.

"Justice" — A86

Scales of Justice and Map of Brazil — A87

Perf. 13½x13
1927, Aug. 11 Typo. Wmk. 206
288 A86 100r deep blue 1.10 .65
289 A87 200r rose 1.05 .65

Founding of the law courses, cent.

Liberty Holding Coffee Leaves — A88

1928, Feb. 5
290 A88 100r blue green 2.00 1.00
291 A88 200r carmine 1.50 .75
292 A88 300r olive black 9.00 .60
Nos. 290-292 (3) 12.50 2.35

Introduction of the coffee tree in Brazil, bicent.

Official Stamps of 1919 Surcharged in Red or Black

Perf. 11, 11½
1928 Wmk. 100 Engr.
293 O3 700r on 500r org 12.00 12.00
a. Inverted surcharge 450.00 450.00
294 O3 1000r on 100r rose red (Bk) 6.00 .60
295 O3 2000r on 200r dull bl 7.50 1.40
296 O3 5000r on 50r grn 7.50 2.00
a. Inverted surcharge 450.00 450.00
297 O3 10,000r on 10r ol grn 30.00 2.50
Nos. 293-297 (5) 63.00 18.50

Nos. 293-297 were used for ordinary postage.

Stamps in the outer rows of the sheets are often without watermark.

Ruy Barbosa — A89

1929 Wmk. 101 Perf. 11¼x11¾
300 A89 5000r blue violet 20.00 .50
300a Perf. 9-9½ 30.00 .50

See Nos. 405, 459. For surcharge see No. C29.

Types of 1920-22 Issue
Perf. 13½x12½
1929 Typo. Wmk. 218
302 A75 20r gray violet .50 .30
303 A75 50r red brown .50 .30
304 A75 100r turq green .50 .30
305 A75 200r olive green 30.00 6.00
306 A76 300r rose red 1.50 .30
307 A76 400r orange 1.50 4.00
308 A76 500r ultra 15.00 .65
309 A76 600r brown org 20.00 1.50
310 A76 700r dp violet 3.25 .30
311 A76 1000r turq blue 8.00 .30
Nos. 302-311 (10) 80.75 13.95

Wmk. 218 exists both in vertical alignment and in echelon.

Wmk. in echelon
302a A75 20r .50 .40
303a A75 50r 375.00 240.00
306a A76 300r 1.50 1.00
308a A76 500r 450.00 150.00
311a A76 1000r 17.50 20.00

Architectural Fantasies A90 A91

Architectural Fantasy — A92

Perf. 13x13½
1930, June 20 Wmk. 206
312 A90 100r turq blue 2.00 1.75
313 A91 200r olive gray 4.25 1.00
314 A92 300r rose red 7.00 1.75
Nos. 312-314 (3) 13.25 4.50

Fourth Pan-American Congress of Architects and Exposition of Architecture.

Types of 1920-22 Issue
1930 Wmk. 221 Perf. 13x12½
316 A75 20r gray violet .60 .35
317 A75 50r red brown .60 .35
318 A75 100r turq blue 1.50 .35
319 A75 200r olive green 5.00 .75

320 A76 300r rose red 1.25 .35
321 A76 500r ultra 2.50 .35
322 A76 1000r turq blue 35.00 2.00
Nos. 316-322 (7) 46.45 4.50

A stamp, design A89, 5000r, perforated 11, watermark 221 was prepared but not issued. Value $3750. One is known with a favor cancel.

Imperforates

From 1930 to 1947, imperforate or partly perforated sheets of nearly all commemoratives were obtainable. Additionally many definitive issues were available imperforate between 1920 and 1947.

Types of 1920-22 Issue
Perf. 11, 13½x13, 13½x12½, 13x12½
1931-34 Typo. Wmk. 222
326 A75 10r deep brown .25 .25
327 A75 20r gray violet .25 .25
328 A74 25r brn vio ('34) .25 1.00
330 A75 50r blue green .25 .25
331 A75 50r red brown .25 .25
332 A75 100r orange .40 .25
334 A76 200r dp carmine 1.00 .40
335 A76 300r olive green .60 .25
336 A76 400r ultra 2.00 .25
337 A76 500r red brown 4.75 .25
338 A76 600r brown org 12.50 .25
339 A76 700r deep violet 7.50 .25
340 A76 1000r turq blue 18.00 .25
Nos. 326-340 (13) 48.00 4.15

Getulio Vargas and Joao Pessoa A93

Vargas and Pessoa A94

Oswaldo Aranha A95 A96

Antonio Carlos A97

Pessoa A98

Vargas — A99

Unwmk.
1931, Apr. 29 Litho. Perf. 14
342 A93 10r + 10r lt bl .25 20.00
343 A93 20r + 20r yel brn .25 14.00
344 A95 50r + 50r bl grn, red & yel .25 .25
a. Red missing at left 1.60 1.60
345 A93 100r + 50r orange .70 .45
346 A93 200r + 100r green .55 .45
347 A94 300r + 150r multi .55 .45
348 A93 400r + 200r dp rose 1.00 1.00
349 A93 500r + 250r dk bl 1.00 .50
350 A93 600r + 300r brn vio .95 17.00
351 A94 700r + 350r multi .80 .30
352 A96 1000r + 500r brt grn, red & yel 2.00 .30
353 A97 2000r + 1000r gray blk & red 6.00 .80
354 A98 5000r + 2500r blk & red 32.50 13.50

355 A99 10000r + 5000r brt
grn & yel 65.00 24.00
Nos. 342-355 (14) 111.80 93.00
Set, Never hinged 210.00

Revolution of Oct. 3, 1930. Prepared as semi-postal stamps, Nos. 342-355 were sold as ordinary postage stamps with stated surtax ignored.

Nos. 306, 320 and 250
Surcharged

Perf. 13½x12½
1931, July 20 **Wmk. 218**
356 A76 200r on 300r rose red 2.50 1.40
a. Wmk. in echelon 30.00 30.00
b. Inverted surcharge 95.00 95.00

Perf. 13x12½
Wmk. 221
357 A76 200r on 300r rose red .50 .25
a. Inverted surcharge 95.00 95.00
b. Double surcharge 80.00 80.00

Perf. 13½x12½
Wmk. 100
358 A76 200r on 300r rose red 120.00 120.00
a. Inverted surcharge 1,200. —

Map of South America Showing Meridian of Tordesillas — A100

Joao Ramalho and Tibiriça A101

Martim Affonso de Souza A102

King John III of Portugal A103

Disembarkation of M. A. de Souza at Sao Vicente — A104

Wmk. 222
1932, June 3 **Typo.** **Perf. 13**
359 A100 20r dk violet .40 .40
360 A101 100r black .40 .40
361 A102 200r purple .40 .40
362 A103 600r red brown 1.60 2.00

Engr.
Wmk. 101
Perf. 9½, 11, Compound
363 A104 700r ultra 3.00 2.50
Nos. 359-363 (5) 5.80 5.70

1st colonization of Brazil at Sao Vicente, in 1532, under the hereditary captaincy of Martim Affonso de Souza.
Values for No. 363 are for perf. 9½, other varieties are worth more. All nine perforation varieties can be found in a single block of nine. Value $225.

Revolutionary Issue

Map of Brazil — A105

Soldier and Flag — A106

Allegory: Freedom, Justice, Equality A107

Soldier's Head A108

"LEX" and Sword A109

Symbolical of Law and Order — A110

Symbolical of Justice — A111

Perf. 11½
1932, Sept. **Litho.** **Unwmk.**
364 A105 100r brown org .60 2.00
365 A106 200r dk car .50 .80
366 A107 300r gray green 1.25 3.75
367 A108 400r dark blue 3.50 6.00
368 A105 500r blk brn 3.50 6.00
369 A107 600r red 3.50 6.00
370 A106 700r violet 2.50 6.00
371 A108 1000r orange 1.60 6.00
372 A109 2000r dark brn 22.00 30.00
373 A110 5000r yellow grn 30.00 55.00
374 A111 10000r plum 35.00 60.00
Nos. 364-374 (11) 103.95 181.55

Issued by the revolutionary forces in the state of Sao Paulo during the revolt of September, 1932. Subsequently the stamps were recognized by the Federal Government and placed in general use.
Excellent counterfeits of Nos. 373 and 374 exist. Favor cancels, applied at a later date, abound.

City of Vassouras and Illuminated Memorial — A112

Wmk. 222
1933, Jan. 15 **Typo.** **Perf. 12**
375 A112 200r rose red 1.00 .60
City of Vassouras founding, cent.

Nos. 306, 320 Surcharged

Perf. 13½x12½
1933, July 28 **Wmk. 218**
376 A76 200r on 300r rose red 2.50 2.50
a. Wmk. 218 in echelon (No. 306a) 30.00 30.00
b. Wmk. 100 (No. 250) 350.00 350.00
d. As "b," inverted surcharge 1,350. —

Perf. 13x12½
Wmk. 221
377 A76 200r on 300r rose red .75 .75
a. Inverted surcharge 100.00 100.00
b. Double surcharge 100.00 100.00

Religious Symbols and Inscriptions — A113

Wmk. 222
1933, Sept. 3 **Typo.** **Perf. 13**
378 A113 200r dark red 1.00 .80
1st Natl. Eucharistic Congress in Brazil.

"Flag of the Race" A114

1933, Aug. 18
379 A114 200r deep red 1.25 .80
The raising of the "Flag of the Race" and the 441st anniv. of the sailing of Columbus from Palos, Spain, Aug. 3, 1492.

Republic Figure, Flags of Brazil and Argentina — A115

Wmk. 101
1933, Oct. 7 **Engr.** **Perf. 11½**
380 A115 200r blue .25 .25

Thick Laid Paper
1933, Dec. **Wmk. 236** **Perf. 11, 11½**
381 A115 400r green .60 .60
382 A115 600r brt rose 3.00 3.50
383 A115 1000r lt violet 3.50 3.00
Nos. 380-383 (4) 7.35 7.35

Visit of President Justo of the Argentina to Brazil, Oct. 2-7, 1933.

Allegory: "Faith and Energy" — A116

1933 **Typo.** **Wmk. 222**
384 A116 200r dark red .50 .25
385 A116 200r dark violet 1.50 .25

See Nos. 435, 471, 491.

Allegory of Flight — A117

Wmk. 236
1934, Apr. 15 **Engr.** **Perf. 12**
386 A117 200r blue .80 .25
1st Natl. Aviation Congress at Sao Paulo.

A118

Wmk. 222
1934, May 12 **Typo.** **Perf. 11**
387 A118 200r dark olive .25 .25
388 A118 400r carmine 1.00 1.25
a. Double impression 1,500.
389 A118 700r ultra 1.60 1.60
390 A118 1000r orange 4.75 .80
Nos. 387-390 (4) 7.60 3.90

7th Intl. Fair at Rio de Janeiro.

Christ of Corcovado A119

1934, Oct. 20
392 A119 300r dark red, I 4.25 4.25
a. Tete beche pair 17.00 17.00
393 A119 700r ultra, I 17.00 17.00
a. Tete beche pair 60.00 60.00

The three printings of Nos. 392-393, distinguishable by shades, sell for different prices.

José de Anchieta A120

Thick Laid Paper
Perf. 11, 12, Compound
1934, Nov. 8 **Wmk. 236**
394 A120 200r yellow brown .90 .40
395 A120 300r violet .90 .40
396 A120 700r blue 2.00 2.50
397 A120 1000r lt green 4.00 1.25
Nos. 394-397 (4) 7.80 4.55

Jose de Anchieta, S.J. (1534-1597), Portuguese missionary and "father of Brazilian literature."

A121

"Brazil" and "Uruguay" — A122

Wmk. 222
1935, Jan. 8 **Typo.** **Perf. 11**
398 A121 200r orange .80 .25
399 A122 300r yellow .80 1.25
400 A122 700r ultra 4.50 10.00
401 A121 1000r dk violet 12.00 8.00
Nos. 398-401 (4) 18.10 19.50

Visit of President Terra of Uruguay.

View of
Town of
Igarassu
A123

1935, July 1
402 A123 200r maroon & brn   1.60 .75
403 A123 300r vio & olive brn 1.60 .60
  Captaincy of Pernambuco founding, 400th anniv.

Types of 1918-29
Thick Laid Paper
Perf. 11, 12, Compound
1934-36   Engr.   Wmk. 236
404 A72 2000r violet   50.00 .80
405 A89 5000r blue vio ('36) 100.00 .80
406 A72 10000r claret ('36)   85.00 .80
  Nos. 404-406 (3)   235.00 2.40
  No. 404 is inscribed "BRASIL CORREIO."

Revolutionist
A124

Bento Gonçalves da Silva — A125

Duke
of
Caxias
A126

1935, Sept. 20-1936, Jan.
407 A124 200r black   1.00   .50
408 A124 300r rose lake   1.00   .50
409 A125 700r dull blue   3.25 4.50
410 A126 1000r light violet 4.75 1.75
  Nos. 407-410 (4)   10.00 7.25
  Centenary of the "Ragged" Revolution.

Federal
District
Coat of
Arms
A127

Wmk. 222
1935, Oct. 19   Typo.   Perf. 11
411 A127 200r blue   3.25 3.25
  8th Intl. Sample Fair held at Rio de Janeiro.

Coutinho's Ship — A128

Arms of Fernandes
Coutinho — A129

1935, Oct. 25
412 A128 300r maroon   2.50 1.25
413 A129 700r turq blue   5.50 3.75
  400th anniversary of the establishment of the first Portuguese colony at Espirito Santo by Vasco Fernandes Coutinho.

Gavea,
Rock near
Rio de
Janeiro
A130

1935, Oct. 12   Wmk. 245   Perf. 11
414 A130 300r brown & vio   2.50 1.25
415 A130 300r blk & turq bl 2.50 1.25
416 A130 300r Prus bl & ultra 2.50 1.25
417 A130 300r crimson & blk 2.50 1.25
  Nos. 414-417 (4)   10.00 5.00
  "Child's Day," Oct. 12.

Viscount of
Cairu — A131

Perf. 11, 12x11
1936, Jan. 20   Engr.   Wmk. 236
418 A131 1200r violet   7.50 6.00
  Jose da Silva Lisboa, Viscount of Cairu (1756-1835).

View of
Cametá
A132

1936, Feb. 26   Perf. 11, 12
419 A132 200r brown orange   1.25 1.00
420 A132 300r green   1.25   .85
  300th anniversary of the founding of the city of Cameta, Dec. 24, 1635.

Coining
Press
A133

Thick Laid Paper
1936, Mar. 24   Perf. 11
421 A133 300r pur brn, *cr* 1.00 1.00
  1st Numismatic Cong. at Sao Paulo, Mar., 1936.

Carlos Gomes — A134

"Il Guarany" — A135

Thick Laid Paper
1936, July 11   Perf. 11, 11x12
422 A134 300r dull rose   .75   .25
423 A134 300r black brown   .75   .25
424 A135 700r ocher   3.25 1.50
425 A135 700r blue   4.00 2.50
  Nos. 422-425 (4)   8.75 4.50
  Birth cent. of Antonio Carlos Gomes, who composed the opera "Il Guarany."

Scales of
Justice — A136

Wmk. 222
1936, July 4   Typo.   Perf. 11
426 A136 300r rose   1.00   .65
  a. Double impression   525.00   —
  First National Judicial Congress.

Federal
District
Coat of
Arms
A137

1936, Nov. 13   Typo.   Wmk. 249
427 A137 200r rose red   1.25   .50
  Ninth International Sample Fair held at Rio de Janeiro.

Eucharistic
Congress
Seal — A138

1936, Dec. 17   Wmk. 245   Perf. 11½
428 A138 300r grn, yel, bl & blk 1.00 .50
  2nd Natl. Eucharistic Congress in Brazil.

Botafogo
Bay
A139

Thick Laid Paper
Wmk. 236
1937, Jan. 2   Engr.   Perf. 11
429 A139 700r blue   1.25   .65
430 A139 700r black   1.25   .65
  Birth cent. of Francisco Pereira Passos, engineer who planned the modern city of Rio de Janeiro.

Types of 1920-22, 1933
Perf. 11, 11½ and Compound
1936-37   Typo.   Wmk. 249
431 A75   10r deep brown   .35   .25
432 A75   20r dull violet   .35   .25
433 A75   50r blue green   .35   .25
434 A75 100r orange   1.00   .25
435 A116 200r dk violet   2.75   .25
436 A76 300r olive green   .75   .25
437 A76 400r blue   1.75   .25
438 A76 500r lt brown   2.40   .25
439 A76 600r brn org ('37) 12.00 .25
440 A76 700r deep violet 4.75   .25
441 A76 1000r turq blue   8.00   .25
  Nos. 431-441 (11)   34.45 2.75

Massed Flags
and Star of
Esperanto
A140

1937, Jan. 19
442 A140 300r green   1.00   .75
  Ninth Brazilian Esperanto Congress.

Bay of
Rio de
Janeiro
A141

1937, June 9   Unwmk.   Perf. 12½
443 A141 300r orange red & blk 1.00 .75
444 A141 700r blue & dk brn   2.00 1.00
  2nd South American Radio Communication Conf. held in Rio, June 7-19.

Globe — A142

Perf. 11, 12
1937, Sept. 4   Wmk. 249
445 A142 300r green   1.00   .65
  50th anniversary of Esperanto.

Monroe
Palace, Rio
de Janeiro
A143

Botanical Garden,
Rio de
Janeiro — A144

1937, Sept. 30   Unwmk.   Perf. 12½
446 A143   200r lt brn & bl   .75   .50
447 A144   300r org & ol grn   .75   .50
448 A143 2000r grn & cerise   8.00 12.00
449 A144 10000r lake & indigo 65.00 57.50
  Nos. 446-449 (4)   74.50 70.50

Brig. Gen. Jose
da Silva
Paes — A145

1937, Oct. 11   Wmk. 249   Perf. 11½
450 A145 300r blue   .75 .50
Bicentenary of Rio Grande do Sul.

Eagle and
Shield — A146

1937, Dec. 2   Typo.   Perf. 11
451 A146 400r dark blue   .85 .25
150th anniversary of the US Constitution.

Bags of
Brazilian
Coffee
A147

**Frame Engraved, Center
Typographed**
1938, Jan. 17   Unwmk.   Perf. 12½
452 A147 1200r multicolored   6.00 .60

Arms of
Olinda
A148

Perf. 11, 11x11½
1938, Jan. 24   Engr.   Wmk. 249
453 A148 400r violet   .80 .25
4th cent. of the founding of the city of Olinda.

Independence
Memorial,
Ypiranga
A149

1938, Jan. 24   Typo.   Perf. 11
454 A149 400r brown olive   .80 .25
Proclamation of Brazil's independence by
Dom Pedro, Sept. 7, 1822.

Iguaçu
Falls — A150

Perf. 12½
1938, Jan. 10   Unwmk.   Engr.
455 A150 1000r sepia & yel
                brn   2.50 1.00
456 A150 5000r ol blk & grn   30.00 25.00

Couto de
Magalhaes
A151

Perf. 11, 11x11½
1938, Mar. 17   Wmk. 249
457 A151 400r dull green   .80 .25
General Couto de Magalhaes (1837-1898),
statesman, soldier, explorer, writer, developer.

Types of 1918-38
Perf. 11, 12x11, 12x11½, 12
1938   Engr.   Wmk. 249
458 A72 2000r blue violet   17.50 .30
459 A89 5000r violet blue   55.00 1.50
460 A72 10000r rose lake   90.00 2.25
    Nos. 458-460 (3)   162.50 4.05
No. 458 is inscribed "BRASIL CORREIO."

Types of 1920-22
1938   Wmk. 245   Typo.   Perf. 11
461 A75 50r blue green   1.40 1.10
462 A75 100r yellow   4.75 1.10
463 A76 300r olive green   1.40 2.50
463A A76 400r ultra   425.00 200.00
463B A76 500r red brown   1.40 80.00
    Nos. 461-463B (5)   433.95 284.70

National
Archives
Building
A152

1938, May 20   Wmk. 249
464 A152 400r brown   .75 .25
Centenary of National Archives.

Souvenir Sheets

Sir Rowland Hill — A153

1938, Oct. 22   Imperf.
465 A153   Sheet of 10   18.00 18.00
    a.   400r dull green, single stamp   1.70 1.70
Brazilian Intl. Philatelic Exposition (Brapex).
Issued in sheets measuring 106x118mm. A
few perforated sheets exist.

President Vargas — A154

1938, Nov. 10
Without Gum   Perf. 11
466 A154   Sheet of 10   35.00 35.00
    a.   400r slate blue, single stamp   1.75 1.75
Constitution of Brazil, set up by President
Vargas, Nov. 10, 1937. Size: 113x135½mm.

Types of 1920-33
1939   Typo.   Wmk. 256   Perf. 11
467 A75 10r red brown   1.50 1.50
468 A75 20r dull violet   2.75 .30
469 A75 50r blue green   2.25 .30
470 A75 100r yellow org   2.25 .30
471 A116 200r dk violet   3.25 .30
472 A76 400r ultra   4.25 .30
473 A76 600r dull orange   6.00 .30
474 A76 1000r turq blue   25.00 .30
    Nos. 467-474 (8)   47.25 3.60

View of Rio de
Janeiro — A155

1939, June 14   Engr.   Wmk. 249
475 A155 1200r dull violet   2.00 .25

View of
Santos — A156

1939, Aug. 23
476 A156 400r dull blue   .50 .40
Centenary of founding of Santos.

Chalice Vine and
Blossoms — A157

1939, Aug. 23
477 A157 400r green   1.00 .35
1st South American Botanical Congress
held in January, 1938.

Eucharistic
Congress
Seal — A158

1939, Sept. 3
478 A158 400r rose red   .60 .45
Third National Eucharistic Congress.

Duke of Caxias,
Army
Patron — A159

1939, Sept. 12   Photo.   Rouletted
479 A159 400r deep ultra   .60 .45
Issued for Soldiers' Day.

A159a

A159b

A159c

A159d

Designs: 400r, George Washington. 800r,
Emperor Pedro II. 1200r, Grover Cleveland.
1600r, Statue of Friendship, given by US.

1939, Oct. 7   Engr.   Perf. 12
Unwmk.
480 A159a 400r yellow orange   .40 .25
481 A159b 800r dark green   .35 .25
482 A159c 1200r rose car   .40 .25
483 A159d 1600r dark blue   .40 .25
    Nos. 480-483 (4)   1.55 1.00
New York World's Fair.

Benjamin
Constant
A160

Fonseca on
Horseback
A162

Manuel
Deodoro da
Fonseca and
President
Vargas
A161

Wmk. 249
1939, Nov. 15   Photo.   Rouletted
484 A160 400r deep green   .85 .25
485 A161 1200r chocolate   .65 .25

Engr.   Perf. 11
486 A162 800r gray black   .80 .25
    Nos. 484-486 (3)   2.30 .75
Proclamation of the Republic, 50th anniv.
No. 484 was issued without gum.

President
Roosevelt,
President
Vargas
and Map
of the
Americas
A163

1940, Apr. 14
487 A163 400r slate blue   .60 .25
Pan American Union, 50th anniversary.

Types of 1920-33

1940-41	**Typo.**	**Wmk. 264**	***Perf. 11***	
488	A75	10r red brown	.80	.80
489	A75	20r dull violet	.80	*1.50*
489A	A75	50r blue grn		
		('41)	1.50	2.25
490	A75	100r yellow org	2.50	.50
491	A116	200r violet	5.00	.50
492	A76	400r ultra	13.00	.50
493	A76	600r dull org	13.00	.50
494	A76	1000r turq blue	27.50	.50
		Nos. 488-494 (8)	64.10	7.05

Map of
Brazil — A164

1940, Sept. 7   **Engr.**

495	A164	400r carmine	.50	.25
a.		Unwmkd.	160.00	100.00
b.		Wmk. 249	1,500.	—

9th Brazilian Congress of Geography held at Florianopolis.
No. 495 exists with papermaker's watermark of a large globe and "American Bank" in sheet. Value $350.
Nos. 495a-b were issued without gum.

Victoria Regia Water Lily — A165   President Vargas — A166

Relief Map of
Brazil — A167

1940, Oct. 30   **Wmk. 249**   ***Perf. 11***
Without Gum

496	A165	1000r dull violet	2.25	2.25
a.		Sheet of 10	24.00	24.00
497	A166	5000r red	15.00	18.00
a.		Sheet of 10	150.00	200.00
498	A167	10,000r slate blue	30.00	15.00
a.		Sheet of 10	225.00	250.00
		Nos. 496-498 (3)	47.25	35.25

New York World's Fair.
All three sheets exist unwatermarked and also with papermaker's watermark of large globe and "AMERICA BANK" in sheet. Value $600 per sheet. A few imperforate sheets also exist.
Nos. 496-498 were issued without gum.

Joaquim Machado
de Assis — A168

1940, Nov. 1

499	A168	400r black	.65	.25

Birth centenary of Joaquim Maria Machado de Assis, poet and novelist.

Pioneers and
Buildings of Porto
Alegre — A169

1940, Nov. 2   **Wmk. 264**

500	A169	400r green	.45	.25

Colonization of Porto Alegre, bicent.

Proclamation of King John IV of
Portugal — A173

1940, Dec. 1   **Wmk. 249**

501	A173	1200r blue black	1.75	.50

800th anniv. of Portuguese independence and 300th anniv. of the restoration of the monarchy.
No. 501 was also printed on paper with papermaker's watermark of large globe and "AMERICA BANK." Value $375. Unwatermarked stamps are from these sheets. Value of unwatermarked stamps, $150.

Brazilian Flags
and Head of
Liberty — A175

1940, Dec. 18   **Wmk. 256**   ***Perf. 11***

502	A175	400r dull violet	.45	.25
b.		Unwmkd.	225.00	225.00

Wmk. 245

502A	A175	400r dull violet	62.50	40.00

10th anniv. of the inauguration of President Vargas.

Calendar Sheet
and Inscription
"Day of the Fifth
General Census
of Brazil" — A176

Wmk. 256

1941, Jan. 14   **Typo.**   ***Perf. 11***

503	A176	400r blue & red	.40	.25
		Never hinged	.80	

Wmk. 245

504	A176	400r blue & red	2.00	.75
		Never hinged	8.00	

Fifth general census of Brazil.

King Alfonso
Henriques
A177   Father Antonio
Vieira
A178

Salvador Corrêia de
Sa e
Benevides — A179

President Carmona of Portugal and
President Vargas
A180

Wmk. 264

1940-41		**Photo.**	***Rouletted***	
504A	A177	200r pink	.35	.25
505	A178	400r ultra	.35	.25
506	A179	800r brt violet	.40	.25
506A	A180	5400r slate grn	2.50	.40

Wmk. 249

507	A177	200r pink	7.25	2.50
507A	A178	400r ultra	50.00	30.00
508	A180	5400r slate grn	7.25	3.75
		Nos. 504A-508 (7)	68.10	37.40
		Set, never hinged	160.00	

Portuguese Independence, 800th anniv.
For surcharge & overprint see nos. C45, C47.

Jose de
Anchieta — A181

Wmk. 264

1941, Aug. 1   **Engr.**   ***Perf. 11***

509	A181	1000r gray violet	1.00	.50
		Never hinged	4.00	

Society of Jesus, 400th anniversary.

Amador Bueno — A182

1941, Oct. 20   ***Perf. 11½***

510	A182	400r black	.75	.25
		Never hinged	1.25	

300th anniv. of the acclamation of Amador Bueno (1572-1648) as king of Sao Paulo.

Air Force
Emblem
A183

1941, Oct. 20   ***Perf. 11***

511	A183	5400r slate green	3.50	1.00
		Never hinged	12.00	

Issued in connection with Aviation Week, as propaganda for the Brazilian Air Force.

Petroleum
A184   Agriculture
A185

Steel Industry
A186   Commerce
A187

Marshal
Peixoto
A188   Count of Porto
Alegre
A189

Admiral J. A.
C. Maurity
A190   "Armed
Forces"
A191

Vargas — A192

1941-42   **Wmk. 264**   **Typo.**   ***Perf. 11***

512	A184	10r yellow brn	.50	.40
513	A184	20r olive grn	.50	.40
514	A184	50r olive bis	.50	.40
515	A184	100r blue grn	.50	.40
516	A185	200r brown org	2.00	.40
517	A185	300r lilac rose	.50	.40
518	A185	400r grnsh blue	2.40	.40
519	A185	500r salmon	.50	.40
520	A186	600r violet	2.00	.40
521	A186	700r brt rose	.50	.40
522	A186	1000r gray	3.75	.40
523	A186	1200r dl blue	4.75	.40
524	A187	2000r gray vio	5.50	.40

Engr.

525	A188	5000r blue	15.00	.40
526	A189	10,000r rose red	18.00	.40
527	A190	20,000r dp brown	22.50	2.00
528	A191	50,000r red ('42)	47.50	13.50
529	A192	100,000r blue ('42)	1.25	*13.50*
		Nos. 512-529 (18)	128.15	35.00

Nos. 512 to 527 and later issues come on thick or thin paper. The stamps on both papers also exist with three vertical green lines printed on the back, a control mark.
See Nos. 541-587, 592-593, 656-670.

Bernardino de
Campos
A193   Prudente de
Morais
A194

1942, May 25

533	A193	1000r red	1.60	.40
		Never hinged	20.00	
534	A194	1200r blue	6.00	.25
		Never hinged	60.00	

100th anniversary of the birth of Bernardino de Campos and Prudente de Morais, lawyers and statesmen of Brazil.

Head of Indo-Brazilian Bull — A195

1942, May 1   Wmk. 264   Perf. 11½
535	A195	200r blue	.40	.25
		Never hinged	1.50	
536	A195	400r orange brn	.40	.25
		Never hinged	1.50	
a.		Wmk. 267	85.00	85.00
		Never hinged	175.00	

2nd Agriculture and Livestock Show of Central Brazil held at Uberaba.

Outline of Brazil and Torch of Knowledge — A196

Wmk. 264
1942, July 5   Typo.   Perf. 11
537	A196	400r orange brn	.60	.25
		Never hinged	1.50	

8th Brazilian Congress of Education.

Map of Brazil Showing Goiania — A197

1942, July 5
538	A197	400r lt violet	.60	.25
		Never hinged	1.50	

Founding of Goiania city.

Seal of Congress A198

1942, Sept. 20   Wmk. 264
539	A198	400r olive bister	.60	.25
		Never hinged	1.25	
a.		Wmk. 267	30.00	30.00
		Never hinged	70.00	

4th Natl. Eucharistic Cong. at Sao Paulo.

Types of 1941-42
1942-47   Wmk. 245   Perf. 11
541	A184	20r olive green	.60	2.00
542	A184	50r ol bis	.60	.45
543	A184	100r blue grn	3.75	3.75
544	A185	200r brown org	2.00	.50
545	A185	400r grnsh blue	2.00	.50
546	A186	600r lt violet	5.50	.50
547	A186	700r brt rose	.60	2.00
548	A186	1200r dl blue	5.50	.50
549	A187	2000r gray vio ('47)	14.00	.50

Engr.
550	A188	5000r blue	25.00	.50
551	A189	10,000r rose red	22.50	.75
552	A190	20,000r dp brn ('47)	15.00	2.00
553	A192	100,000r blue	18.00	22.50
		Nos. 541-553 (13)	115.05	36.45

Types of 1941-42
1941-47   Typo.   Wmk. 268   Perf. 11
554	A184	20r olive grn	.80	.90
555	A184	50r ol bis ('47)	2.00	1.50
556	A184	100r bl grn ('43)	1.25	.45
557	A185	200r brn org ('43)	.80	.40

558	A185	300r lil rose ('43)	1.25	.40
559	A185	400r grnsh bl ('42)	1.25	.45
560	A185	500r sal ('43)	1.25	.40
561	A186	600r violet	2.00	.40
562	A186	700r brt rose ('45)	1.25	5.50
563	A186	1000r gray	2.40	.40
564	A186	1200r dp bl ('44)	4.00	.45
565	A187	2000r gray vio ('43)	15.00	.40

Engr.
566	A188	5000r blue ('43)	15.00	.40
567	A189	10,000r rose red ('43)	22.50	1.25
568	A190	20,000r dp brn ('42)	60.00	.40
569	A191	50,000r red ('42)	30.00	4.00
a.		50,000r dark brown ('47)	30.00	15.00
570	A192	100,000r blue	2.00	5.50
		Nos. 554-570 (17)	162.75	23.20

Nos. 554-570 exist with horizontal and vertical watermarks, coming in two varieties, 'CASA+DA+MOEDA+DO+BRAZIL' and 'CASA+DA+MOEDA.'

Types of 1941-42
1942-47   Typo.   Wmk. 267
573	A184	20r ol grn ('43)	.60	.40
574	A184	50r ol bis ('43)	.60	.40
575	A184	100r bl grn ('43)	.60	.40
576	A185	200r brn org ('43)	2.00	.40
577	A185	400r grnsh blue	.60	.40
578	A185	500r sal ('43)	175.00	45.00
579	A186	600r violet ('43)	30.00	4.50
580	A186	700r brt rose ('47)	1.25	45.00
581	A186	1000r gray ('44)	4.00	.40
582	A186	1200r dl bl	4.00	.40
583	A187	2000r gray vio	7.50	.40

Engr.
584	A188	5000r blue	7.50	.40
585	A189	10,000r rose red ('44)	15.00	2.00
586	A190	20,000r dp brn ('45)	20.00	.90
587	A191	50,000r red ('43)	75.00	18.00
		Nos. 573-587 (15)	343.65	119.00

1942   Typo.   Wmk. 249
592	A184	100r bl grn	15.00	20.00
593	A186	600r violet	4.50	4.50

Map Showing Amazon River — A199

1943, Mar. 19   Wmk. 267   Perf. 11
607	A199	40c orange brown	.60	.25
		Never hinged	1.50	

Discovery of the Amazon River, 400th anniv.

Reproduction of Brazil Stamp of 1866 — A200

1943, Mar. 28   Wmk. 267
608	A200	40c violet	.60	.60
		Never hinged	2.00	
a.		Wmk. 268	1,100.	
		Never hinged	1,900.	

Centenary of city of Petropolis.

Adaptation of 1843 "Bull's-eye" A201

1943, Aug. 1   Engr.   Imperf.
609	A201	30c black	.70	.30
610	A201	60c black	.85	.25
611	A201	90c black	.70	.30
		Nos. 609-611 (3)	2.25	.85
		Set, never hinged	7.00	

Cent. of the 1st postage stamp of Brazil. Nos. 609-611 exist unwatermarked. Values $200, $400, and $200 respectively.
Nos. 610 and 611 exist with Globe watermark. See note below No. 501. Value $400 each.

Souvenir Sheet

A202

Wmk. 281 Horizontally or Vertically
1943   Engr.   Imperf.
Without Gum
612	A202	Sheet of 3	20.00	20.00
a.		30c black	6.00	6.00
b.		60c black	6.00	6.00
c.		90c black	6.00	6.00

No. 612 exists unwatermarked. Value $600. Exists in two sizes. Sheets over 100mm vertically are worth more. Value $250 unused and $35 used.

Ubaldino do Amaral — A203

Perf. 11, 12, Compound
1943, Aug. 27   Typo.   Wmk. 264
613	A203	40c dull slate green	.30	.25
		Never hinged	2.00	
a.		Wmk. 267	50.00	30.00
		Never hinged	100.00	

Birth centenary of Ubaldino do Amaral, banker and statesman.

"Justice" — A204

1943, Aug. 30   Wmk. 267
614	A204	2cr bright rose	.85	.85
		Never hinged	3.50	

Centenary of Institute of Brazilian Lawyers.

Indo-Brazilian Bull — A205

1943, Aug. 30   Engr.
615	A205	40c dk red brn	.55	.30
		Never hinged	2.00	

9th Livestock Show at Bahia.

José Barbosa Rodrigues — A206

1943, Nov. 13   Typo.
616	A206	40c bluish grn	.40	.25
		Never hinged	2.00	

Birth cent. of Jose Barbosa Rodrigues, botanist.

Charity Hospital, Santos A207

1943, Nov. 7   Engr.
617	A207	1cr blue	.55	.35
		Never hinged	2.00	

400th anniv. of Charity Hospital, Santos.

Pedro Americo de Figueiredo e Melo (1843-1905), Artist-hero and Statesman — A208

Wmk. 267
1943, Dec. 16   Typo.   Perf. 11
618	A208	40c brown orange	.40	.25
		Never hinged	2.00	

Gen. A. E. Gomes Carneiro A209

1944, Feb. 9   Engr.
619	A209	1.20cr rose	1.00	.25
		Never hinged	2.40	

50th anniversary of the Lapa siege.

Statue of Baron of Rio Branco — A210

1944, May 13   Typo.
620	A210	1cr blue	.45	.25
		Never hinged	2.40	

Statue of the Baron of Rio Branco unveiling.

Duke of Caxias A211

1944, May 13   Unwmk.   *Perf. 12*
Granite Paper
621 A211 1.20cr bl grn & pale org   .60   .25
Never hinged   2.40

Centenary of pacification of Sao Paulo and Minas Gerais in an independence movement in 1842.

YMCA Seal — A212

1944, June 7   Litho.   *Perf. 11*
Granite Paper
622 A212 40c dp bl, car & yel   .25   .25
Never hinged   1.60

Centenary of Young Men's Christian Assn.

Chamber of Commerce Rio Grande — A213

Wmk. 268
1944, Sept. 25   Engr.   *Perf. 12*
623 A213 40c lt yellow brn   .25   .25
Never hinged   1.60

Centenary of the Chamber of Commerce of Rio Grande.

Martim F. R. de Andrada A214

1945, Jan. 30   *Perf. 11*
624 A214 40c blue   .30   .25
Never hinged   1.60

Centenary of the death of Martim F. R. de Andrada, statesman.

Meeting of Duke of Caxias and David Canabarro A215

1945, Mar. 19   Photo.
625 A215 40c ultra   .30   .25
Never hinged   1.60

Pacification of Rio Grande do Sul, cent.

Globe and "Esperanto" — A216

1945, Apr. 16
626 A216 40c lt blue grn   .40   .35
Never hinged   1.60

10th Esperanto Congress, Rio, Apr. 14-22.

Baron of Rio Branco's Bookplate A217

1945, Apr. 20   Wmk. 268   *Perf. 11*
627 A217 40c violet   .40   .25
Never hinged   1.00

Cent. of the birth of Jose Maria da Silva Paranhos, Baron of Rio Branco.

Nostalgia A218

Glory — A219

Victory A220

Peace A221

Cooperation — A222

Rouletted 7
1945, May 8   Engr.   Wmk. 268
628 A218 20c dk rose vio   .25   .25
629 A219 40c dk carmine   .25   .25
630 A220 1cr dull orange   3.00   3.00

---

631 A221 2cr steel blue   .55   .45
632 A222 5cr green   2.00   .35
Nos. 628-632 (5)   6.05   4.30
Set, never hinged   17.00

Victory of the Allied Nations in Europe.
Nos. 628-632 exist on thin card, imperf. and unwatermarked.

Francisco Manoel da Silva (1795-1865), Composer (in 1831) of the National Anthem — A223

Wmk. 245
1945, May 30   Typo.   *Perf. 12*
633 A223 40c brt rose   .40   .25
Never hinged   1.50
a.   Wmk. 268   15.00   15.00
Never hinged   35.00

Bahia Institute of Geography and History A224

1945, May 30   Wmk. 268   *Perf. 11*
634 A224 40c lt ultra   .30   .25
Never hinged   2.25

50th anniv. of the founding of the Institute of Geography and History at Bahia.

Emblems of 5th Army and B.E.F.
A225   A226

U.S. Flag and Shoulder Patches A227

Brazilian Flag and Shoulder Patches A228

Victory Symbol and Shoulder Patches — A229

1945, July 18   Litho.
635 A225 20c multicolored   .30   .25
636 A226 40c multicolored   .30   .25
637 A227 1cr multicolored   1.15   .25
638 A228 2cr multicolored   1.60   .50
639 A229 5cr multicolored   2.75   .65
Nos. 635-639 (5)   6.10   2.00
Set, never hinged   18.00

Honoring the Brazilian Expeditionary Force and the US 5th Army Battle against the Axis in Italy.

Radio Tower and Map — A230

1945, Sept. 3   Engr.
640 A230 1.20cr gray   .30   .25
Never hinged   2.00

Third Inter-American Conference on Radio Communications.
No. 640 was reproduced on a souvenir card with blue background and inscriptions. Size: 145x116mm.

A 40c lilac stamp, picturing the International Bridge between Argentina and Brazil and portraits of Presidents Justo and Vargas, was prepared late in 1945. It was not issued, but later was sold, without postal value, to collectors. Value, 30 cents.

Admiral Luiz Felipe Saldanha da Gama (1846-1895) — A231

1946, Apr. 7
641 A231 40c gray black   .30   .95
Never hinged   1.20

Exists unwatermarked. Value $120.

Princess Isabel d'Orleans-Braganca Birth Cent. — A232

1946, July 29   Unwmk.
642 A232 40c black   .30   5.00
Never hinged   1.20

Post Horn, V and Envelope — A233

Post Office, Rio de Janeiro A234

Bay of Rio de Janeiro and Plane A235

Wmk. 268
1946, Sept. 2   Litho.   *Perf. 11*
643 A233 40c blk & pale org   .25   .25

Perf. 12½
Engr.   Unwmk.
Center in Ultramarine
644 A234 2cr slate   .40   .40
645 A234 5cr orange brn   .60   .40
646 A234 10cr dk violet   1.00   .40
Center in Brown Orange
647 A235 1.30cr dk green   .60   .40
648 A235 1.70cr car rose   2.75   .75
649 A235 2.20cr dp ultra   4.00   .55
     Nos. 643-649 (7)   9.60 3.15
     Set, never hinged   24.00

5th Postal Union Congress of the Americas and Spain.
No. 643 was reproduced on a souvenir card. Size: 188x239mm. Sold for 10cr.

Liberty — A236

Perf. 11x11½
1946, Sept. 18   Wmk. 268
650 A236 40c blk & gray   .25   .25
     Never hinged   .40
  a.   Unwmkd.   150.00
     Never hinged   300.00

Adoption of the Constitution of 1946.

Columbus Lighthouse, Dominican Republic — A237

1946, Sept. 14   Litho.   *Perf. 11*
651 A237 5cr Prus grn   4.00 1.60
     Never hinged   20.00

Orchid — A238

1946, Nov. 8   Wmk. 268
652 A238 40c ultra, red & yel   .25   .25
     Never hinged   1.20
  a.   Unwmkd.   150.00

4th National Exhibition of Orchids, Rio de Janeiro, November, 1946.

Gen. A. E. Gomes Carneiro — A239

Perf. 10½x12
1946, Dec. 6   Engr.   Unwmk.
653 A239 40c deep green   .25   .25
     Never hinged   .40

Centenary of the birth of Gen. Antonio Ernesto Gomes Carneiro.

Brazilian Academy of Letters A240

1946, Dec. 14   *Perf. 11*
654 A240 40c blue   .25   .25
     Never hinged   .60

50th anniv. of the foundation of the Brazilian Academy of Letters, Rio de Janeiro.

Antonio de Castro Alves (1847-1871), Poet — A241

1947, Mar. 14   Litho.   Wmk. 267
655 A241 40c bluish green   .25   .25
     Never hinged   .60

Types of 1941-42, Values in Centavos or Cruzeiros
1947-54   Wmk. 267   Typo.   *Perf. 11*
656 A184   2c olive   .30   .25
657 A184   5c yellow brn   .30   .25
658 A184   10c green   .55   .25
659 A185   20c brown org   .55   .25
660 A185   30c dk lil rose   1.25   .25
661 A185   40c blue   .55   .25
  b.   Wmk. 268   3,000. 225.00
661A A185 50c salmon   1.25   .25
662 A186   60c lt violet   1.75   .25
663 A186   70c brt rose
           ('54)   .55   .25
664 A186   1cr gray   3.75   .25
665 A186   1.20cr dull blue   6.00   .25
  a.   Wmk. 268   300.00 75.00
666 A187   2cr gray violet   7.50   .25
Engr.
667 A188   5cr blue   22.50   .25
  a.   Perf. 11¾   70.00 1.75
668 A189   10cr rose red   35.00   .25
669 A190   20cr deep brn   30.00   .25
  a.   Perf. 13-13½   60.00 1.75
670 A191   50cr red   60.00   .25
  a.   Perf. 14-14½   60.00 7.50
     Nos. 656-670 (16)   171.80 4.00

Pres. Gonzalez Videla of Chile A242

1947, June 26 Unwmk. *Perf. 12x11*
671 A242 40c dk brown orange   .25   .25
     Never hinged   .40

Visit of President Gabriel Gonzalez Videla of Chile, June 1947.
A souvenir folder contains four impressions of No. 671, and measures 6½x8¼ inches.

"Peace" and Western Hemisphere A243

1947, Aug. 15   *Perf. 11x12*
672 A243 1.20cr blue   .30   .25
     Never hinged   1.20

Inter-American Defense Conference at Rio de Janeiro, August-September, 1947.

Pres. Harry S. Truman, Map and Statue of Liberty A244

1947, Sept. 1   Typo.   *Perf. 12x11*
673 A244 40c ultra   .25   .25
     Never hinged   .80

Visit of US President Harry S Truman to Brazil, Sept. 1947.

Pres. Eurico Gaspar Dutra — A245

Wmk. 268
1947, Sept. 7   Engr.   *Perf. 11*
674 A245 20c green   .25   .25
675 A245 40c rose carmine   .25   .25
676 A245 1.20cr deep blue   .25   .25
     Nos. 674-676 (3)   .75   .75
     Set, never hinged   2.25

The souvenir sheet containing Nos. 674-676 is listed as No. C73A. See No. 679.

Mother and Child — A246

1947, Oct. 10   Typo.   Unwmk.
677 A246 40c brt ultra   .25   .25
     Never hinged   .80

Issued to mark Child Care Week, 1947.

Arms of Belo Horizonte — A247

1947, Dec. 12   Engr.   Wmk. 267
678 A247 1.20cr rose carmine   .25   .25
     Never hinged   .80

50th anniversary of the founding of the city of Belo Horizonte.

Dutra Type of 1947
1948   Engr.   Wmk. 267
679 A245 20c green   3.75 3.75
     Never hinged   8.00

Catalogue values for unused stamps in this section, from this point to the end of the section, are for Never Hinged items.

Globe — A248

1948, July 10   Litho.
680 A248 40c dl grn & pale lil   .65   .25

International Exposition of Industry and Commerce, Petropolis, 1948.

Arms of Paranagua A249

1948, July 29
681 A249 5cr bister brown   7.50   .65

300th anniversary of the founding of the city of Paranagua, July 29, 1648.

Child Reading Book — A250

1948, Aug. 1
682 A250 40c green   .60   .25

National Education Campaign.
No. 682 was reproduced on a souvenir card. Size: 124x157mm.

Tiradentes — A251

1948, Nov. 12
683 A251 40c brown orange   .40   .25

200th anniversary of the birth of Joaquim José da Silva Xavier (Tiradentes).

Symbolical of Cancer Eradication A252

1948, Dec. 14
684 A252 40c claret   .60   .25

Anti-cancer publicity.

Adult Student A253

1949, Jan. 3   Wmk. 267   *Perf. 12x11*
685   A253   60c red vio & pink   .60   .25
   Campaign for adult education.

"Battle of Guararapes," by Vitor Meireles — A254

1949, Feb. 15   *Perf. 11½x12*
686   A254   60c lt blue   2.50   .30
   2nd Battle of Guararapes, 300th anniv.

Church of Sao Francisco de Paula — A255

Perf. 11x12
1949, Mar. 8   Unwmk.   Engr.
687   A255   60c dark brown   .60   .25
a.   Souvenir sheet   75.00   75.00
   Bicentenary of city of Ouro Fino, state of Minas Gerais.
   No. 687a contains one imperf. stamp similar to No. 687, with dates in lower margin. Size: 70x89mm. Issued without gum.

Manuel de Nobrega — A256

1949, Mar. 29   *Imperf.*
688   A256   60c violet   .60   .25
   Founding of the City of Salvador, 400th anniv.

Emblem of Brazilian Air Force and Plane A257

1949, June 18
689   A257   60c blue violet   .60   .25
   Issued to honor the Brazilian Air Force.

Star and Angel — A258

1949   Wmk. 267   Litho.   *Perf. 11x12*
690   A258   60c pink   .60   .25
   1st Ecclesiastical Cong., Salvador, Bahia.

Globe A259

1949, Oct. 31   Typo.   *Perf. 12x11*
691   A259   1.50cr blue   .75   .25
   75th anniv. of the UPU.

Ruy Barbosa A260

Unwmk.
1949, Dec. 14   Engr.   *Perf. 12*
692   A260   1.20cr rose carmine   1.00   .25
   Centenary of birth of Ruy Barbosa.

Joaquim Cardinal Arcoverde A. Cavalcanti, Birth Centenary — A261

Perf. 11x12
1950, Feb. 27   Litho.   Wmk. 267
693   A261   60c rose   .65   .25

Grapes and Factory — A262

1950, Mar. 15   *Perf. 12x11*
694   A262   60c rose lake   .60   .25
   75th anniversary of Italian immigration to the state of Rio Grande do Sul.

Virgin of the Globe — A263

1950, May 31   *Perf. 11x12*
695   A263   60c blk & lt bl   .60   .25
   Establishment in Brazil of the Daughters of Charity of St. Vincent de Paul, cent.

Globe and Soccer Players — A264

1950, June 24
696   A264   60c ultra, bl & gray   1.50   .30
   4th World Soccer Championship.

Symbolical of Brazilian Population Growth A265

1950, July 10   Typo.   *Perf. 12x11*
697   A265   60c rose lake   .60   .25
   Issued to publicize the 6th Brazilian census.

Dr. Oswaldo Cruz — A266

1950, Aug. 23   Litho.   *Perf. 11x12*
698   A266   60c orange brown   .65   .25
   5th International Congress of Microbiology.

View of Blumenau and Itajai River A267

Perf. 12x11
1950, Sept. 9   Wmk. 267
699   A267   60c bright pink   .65   .25
   Centenary of the founding of Blumenau.

Amazonas Theater, Manaus A268

1950, Sept. 27
700   A268   60c light brn red   .60   .25
   Centenary of Amazonas Province.

Arms of Juiz de Fora — A269

1950, Oct. 24   *Perf. 11x12*
701   A269   60c carmine   .60   .25
   Centenary of the founding of Juiz de Fora.

Post Office at Recife A270

1951, Jan. 10   Typo.   *Perf. 12x11*
702   A270   60c carmine   .60   .25
703   A270   1.20cr carmine   .60   .25
   Opening of the new building of the Pernambuco Post Office.

Arms of Joinville — A271

1951, Mar. 9   *Perf. 11x12*
704   A271   60c orange brown   .80   .25
   Centenary of the founding of Joinville.

Jean-Baptiste de La Salle — A272

1951, Apr. 30   Litho.
705   A272   60c blue   .80   .25
   Birth of Jean-Baptiste de La Salle, 300th anniv.

Heart and Flowers — A273

1951, May 13   Engr.
706   A273   60c deep plum   .90   .25
   Mother's Day, May 14, 1951.

Sylvio Romero — A274

1951, Apr. 21   **Litho.**
707 A274 60c dl vio brn   .60   .25
  Romero (1851-1914), poet and author.

Joao Caetano, Stage and Masks A275

1951, July 9   **Perf. 12x11**
708 A275 60c lt gray bl   .60   .25
  1st Brazilian Theater Cong., Rio, July 9-13, 1951.

Orville A. Derby — A276

1951, July 23   **Perf. 11x12**
709 A276 2cr slate   .70   .25
  Centenary of the birth (in New York State) of Orville A. Derby, geologist.

First Mass Celebrated in Brazil — A277

1951, July 25
710 A277 60c dl brn & buff   .60   .25
  4th Inter-American Congress on Catholic Education, Rio de Janeiro, 1951.

Euclides Pinto Martins A278

1951, Aug. 16   **Perf. 12x11**
711 A278 3.80cr brn & citron   3.50   .30
  1st flight from NYC to Rio, 29th anniv.

Monastery of the Rock A279

1951, Sept. 8
712 A279 60c dl brn & cream   .60   .25
  Founding of Vitoria, 4th centenary.

Santos-Dumont and Model Plane Contest — A280   Dirigible and Eiffel Tower — A281

Perf. 11x12
1951, Oct. 19   **Wmk. 267**   **Litho.**
713 A280 60c salmon & dk brn   .80   .25

Unwmk.   **Engr.**
714 A281 3.80cr dark purple   2.40   .25
  Week of the Wing and 50th anniv. of Santos-Dumont's flight around the Eiffel Tower.
  In December 1951, Nos. 713 and 714 were privately overprinted: "Exposicao Filatelica Regional Distrito Federal 15-XII-1951 23-XII-1951." These were attached to souvenir sheets bearing engraved facsimiles of Nos. 38, 49 and 51, which were sold by Clube Filatelico do Brasil to mark its 20th anniversary. The overprinted stamps on the sheets were canceled, but 530 "unused" sets were sold by the club.

Farmers and Ear of Wheat — A282

1951, Nov. 10   **Litho.**   **Wmk. 267**
715 A282 60c dp grn & gray   .60   .25
  Festival of Grain at Bage, 1951.

Map and Open Bible A283

1951, Dec. 9   **Perf. 12x11**
716 A283 1.20cr brn org   1.25   .25
  Issued to publicize the Day of the Bible.

Queen Isabella — A284

1952, Mar. 10   **Perf. 11x12**
717 A284 3.80cr lt bl   2.00   .30
  500th anniversary of the birth of Queen Isabella I of Spain.

Henrique Oswald — A285

1952, Apr. 22
718 A285 60c brown   .60   .25
  Oswald (1852-1931), composer.

Vicente Licinio Cardoso — A286

1952, May 2
719 A286 60c gray blue   .75   .25
  4th Brazilian Homeopathic Congress.

Map and Symbol of Labor — A287

1952, Apr. 30
720 A287 1.50cr brnsh pink   .75   .25
  5th International Labor Organization Conference for American Countries.

Gen. Polidoro da Fonseca — A288

  Portraits: 5cr, Baron de Capanema. 10cr, Minister Eusebio de Queiros.

Unwmk.
1952, May 11   **Engr.**   **Perf. 11**
721 A288 2.40cr lt car   .60   .25
722 A288 5cr blue   4.00   .25
723 A288 10cr dk bl grn   4.00   .25
    Nos. 721-723 (3)   8.60   .75
  Centenary of telegraph in Brazil.

Luiz de Albuquerque M. P. Caceres — A289

Perf. 11x12
1952, June 8   **Litho.**   **Wmk. 267**
724 A289 1.20cr vio bl   .60   .25
  200th anniversary of the founding of the city of Mato Grosso.

Symbolizing the Glory of Sports — A290

1952, July 21   **Perf. 12x11**
725 A290 1.20cr dp bl & bl   1.50   .40
  Fluminense Soccer Club, 50th anniversary.

José Antonio Saraiva — A291

1952, Aug. 16   **Perf. 11x12**
726 A291 60c lil rose   .75   .25
  Centenary of the founding of Terezina, capital of Piaui State.

Emperor Dom Pedro — A292

1952, Sept. 3   **Wmk. 267**
727 A292 60c lt bl & blk   .75   .25
  Issued for Stamp Day and the 2nd Philatelic Exhibition of Sao Paulo.

Flag-encircled Globe — A293

1952, Oct. 24   **Perf. 13½**
728 A293 3.80cr blue   2.50   .40
  Issued to publicize United Nations Day.

View of Sao Paulo, Sun and Compasses — A294

1952, Nov. 8   **Litho.**   **Perf. 12x11**
729 A294 60c dl bl, yel & gray grn   .75   .25
  City Planning Day.

Father Diogo Antonio Feijo — A295

1952, Nov. 9   *Perf. 11x12*
730 A295 60c fawn   .60   .25

Rodolpho Bernardelli and His "Christ and the Adultress" A297

1952, Dec. 18   *Perf. 12x11*
732 A297 60c gray blue   .75   .25
   Bernardelli, sculptor and painter, birth cent.

Map of Western Hemisphere and View of Rio de Janeiro — A298

1952, Sept. 20
733 A298 3.80cr vio brn & lt grn   2.00   .35
   2nd Congress of American Industrial Medicine, Rio de Janeiro, 1952.

Arms and Head of Pioneer A299

Coffee, Cotton and Sugar Cane — A300

   Designs: 2.80cr, Jesuit monk planting tree. 3.80cr, 5.80cr, Spiral, symbolizing progress.

1953, Jan. 25   **Litho.**   *Perf. 11*
734 A299 1.20cr ol brn & blk brn   2.00   .25
735 A300 2cr olive grn & yel   3.50   .25
736 A300 2.80cr red brn & dp org   2.25   .25
737 A300 3.80cr dk brn & yel grn   1.90   .25
738 A300 5.80cr int bl & yel grn   1.75   .25
     Nos. 734-738 (5)   11.40   1.25
   400th anniversary of Sao Paulo. Used copies of No. 734 exist with design inverted. Value $6,000.

Ledger and Winged Cap A301

1953, Feb. 22   *Perf. 12x11*
739 A301 1.20cr dl brn & fawn   1.00   .25
   6th Brazilian Accounting Congress.

Joao Ramalho — A302

     Wmk. 264
1953, Apr. 8   **Engr.**   *Perf. 11½*
740 A302 60c blue   .25   .25
   Founding of the city of Santo Andre, 4th cent.

Aarao Reis and Plan of Belo Horizonte A303

1953, May 6   **Photo.**
741 A303 1.20cr red brn   .25   .25
   Aarao Leal de Carvalho Reis (1853-1936), civil engineer.

Almirante Saldanha — A304

1953, May 16
742 A304 1.50cr royal blue   .30   .30
   4th globe-circling voyage of the training ship Almirante Saldanha.

A305

   Joaquim Jose Rodrigues Torres, Viscount of Itaborai.

1953, July 5   **Photo.**
743 A305 1.20cr violet   .25   .25
   Centenary of the Bank of Brazil.

Lamp and Rio-Petropolis Highway — A306

1953, July 14
744 A306 1.20cr gray   .25   .25
   10th Intl. Congress of Nursing, Petropolis, 1953.

Bay of Rio de Janeiro A307

1953, July 15
745 A307 3.80cr dk bl grn   .40   .25
   Issued to publicize the fourth World Congress of Baptist Youth, July 1953.

Arms of Jau and Map A308

1953, Aug. 15   **Engr.**
746 A308 1.20cr purple   .25   .25
   Centenary of the city of Jau.

Ministry of Health and Education Building, Rio — A309

1953, Aug. 1
747 A309 1.20cr dp grn   .25   .25
   Day of the Stamp and the first Philatelic Exhibition of National Education.

Maria Quiteria de Jesus Medeiros — A310

1953, Aug. 21   **Photo.**
748 A310 60c vio bl   .25   .25
   Centenary of the death of Maria Quiteria de Jesus Medeiros (1792-1848), independence heroine.

Pres. Odria of Peru — A311

1953, Aug. 25
749 A311 1.40cr rose brn   .25   .25
   Issued to publicize the visit of Gen. Manuel A. Odria, President of Peru, Aug. 25, 1953.

Duke of Caxias Leading his Troops — A312

   Designs: 1.20cr, Caxias' tomb. 1.70cr, 5.80cr, Portrait of Caxias. 3.80cr, Arms of Caxias.

     Engr. (60c, 5.80cr); Photo.
1953, Aug. 25
750 A312 60c dp grn   .30   .25
751 A312 1.20cr dp claret   .30   .25
752 A312 1.70cr slate grn   .30   .25
753 A312 3.80cr rose brn   .50   .25
754 A312 5.80cr gray vio   .50   .25
     Nos. 750-754 (5)   1.90   1.25
   150th anniversary of the birth of Luis Alves de Lima e Silva, Duke of Caxias.

Quill Pen, Map and Tree — A313

1953, Sept. 12   **Photo.**
755 A313 60c ultra   .25   .25
   5th National Congress of Journalism.

Horacio Hora — A314

1953, Sept. 17   **Litho.**   **Wmk. 267**
756 A314 60c org & dp plum   .25   .25
   Horacio Pinto de Hora (1853-1890), painter.

Pres. Somoza of Nicaragua — A315

1953, Sept. 24   **Photo.**   **Wmk. 264**
757 A315 1.40cr dk vio brn   .25   .25
   Issued to publicize the visit of Gen. Anastasio Somoza, president of Nicaragua.

Auguste de Saint-Hilaire A316

1953, Sept. 30
758 A316 1.20cr dk brn car   .25   .25
   Centenary of the death of Auguste de Saint-Hilaire, explorer and botanist.

Jose Carlos do Patrocinio — A317

1953, Oct. 9   **Photo.**
759 A317 60c dk slate gray   .25   .25

Jose Carlos do Patrocinio, (1853-1905), journalist and abolitionist.

Clock Tower, Crato — A318

1953, Oct. 17
760 A318 60c blue green   .25   .25

Centenary of the city of Crato.

Joao Capistrano de Abreu — A319

1953, Oct. 23
761 A319 60c dull blue   .25   .25
762 A319 5cr purple   1.30   .25

Joao Capistrano de Abreu (1853-1927), historian.

Allegory: "Justice" — A320

1953, Nov. 17
763 A320 60c indigo   .25   .25
764 A320 1.20cr dp magenta   .25   .25

50th anniv. of the Treaty of Petropolis.

Farm Worker in Wheat Field — A321

1953, Nov. 29   **Photo.**   **Perf. 11½**
766 A321 60c dk green   .25   .25

3rd Natl. Wheat Festival, Erechim, 1953.

Teacher and Pupils — A322

1953, Dec. 14
767 A322 60c red   .25   .25

First National Conference of Primary School Teachers, Salvador, 1953.

Zacarias de Gois e Vasconsellos A323

Porters With Trays of Coffee Beans — A323a

1953-54   **Photo.**
768 A323 2cr org brn & blk, *buff* ('54)   1.30   .50
   a.   White paper   2.00   1.00
769 A323a 5cr dp org & blk   1.00   .40

Centenary of the state of Parana.

Alexandre de Gusmao — A324

1954, Jan. 13
770 A324 1.20cr brn vio   .25   .25

Gusmao (1695-1753), statesman, diplomat and writer.

Symbolical of Sao Paulo's Growth — A325

Arms and View of Sao Paulo A326

Designs: 2cr, Priest, settler and Indian. 2.80cr, José de Anchieta.

1954, Jan. 25   **Perf. 11½x11**
771 A325 1.20cr dk vio brn   .50   .25
   a.   Buff paper   2.50   1.00

         Engr.
772 A325 2cr lilac rose   .70   .25
773 A325 2.80cr pur gray   1.00   .25
      Perf. 11x11½
774 A326 3.80cr dl grn   1.15   .25
   a.   Buff paper   4.00   .80
775 A326 5.80cr dl red   1.50   .25
   a.   Buff paper   8.00   .75
     Nos. 771-775 (5)   4.85   1.25

400th anniversary of Sao Paulo.

J. Fernandes Vieira, A. Vidal de Negreiros, A. F. Camarao and H. Dias — A327

     Perf. 11x11½
1954, Feb. 18   **Photo.**   **Unwmk.**
776 A327 1.20cr ultra   .25   .25

300th anniversary of the recovery of Pernambuco from the Dutch.

Sao Paulo and Minerva A328

1954, Feb. 24
777 A328 1.50cr dp plum   .25   .25

10th International Congress of Scientific Organizations, Sao Paulo, 1954.

Stylized Grapes, Jug and Map — A329

1954, Feb. 27   **Photo.**   **Perf. 11½x11**
778 A329 40c dp claret   .25   .25

Grape Festival, Rio Grande do Sul.

Monument of the Immigrants — A330

1954, Feb. 28
779 A330 60c dp vio bl   .25   .25

Unveiling of the Monument to the Immigrants of Caxias do Sul.

First Brazilian Locomotive — A331

     Perf. 11x11½
1954, Apr. 30   **Unwmk.**
781 A331 40c carmine   .35   .25

Centenary of the first railroad engine built in Brazil.

Pres. Chamoun of Lebanon — A332

1954, May 12   **Photo.**   **Perf. 11½x11**
782 A332 1.50cr maroon   .25   .25

Visit of Pres. Camille Chamoun of Lebanon.

Sao Jose College, Rio de Janeiro A333

J. B. Champagnat Marcelin — A334

1954, June 6   **Perf. 11x11½, 11½x11**
783 A333 60c purple   .25   .25
784 A334 120cr vio blue   .25   .25

50th anniversary of the founding of the Marist Brothers in Brazil.

Apolonia Pinto — A335

1954, June 21   **Photo.**
785 A335 1.20cr bright green   .40   .25

Apolonia Pinto (1854-1937), actress.

Adm. Marques Tamandare — A336

Portraits: 2c, 5c, 10c, Admiral Marques Tamandare. 20c, 30c, 40c, Oswaldo Cruz. 50c, 60c, 90c, Joaquim Murtinho. 1cr, 1.50cr, 2cr, Duke of Caxias. 5cr, 10cr, Ruy Barbosa. 20cr, 50cr, Jose Bonifacio.

1954-60   **Wmk. 267**   **Perf. 11x11½**
786 A336 2c vio blue   .30   .25
787 A336 5c org red   .30   .25
788 A336 10c brt green   .30   .25
789 A336 20c magenta   .50   .25
790 A336 30c dk gray grn   .50   .25
791 A336 40c rose red   1.00   .30
792 A336 50c violet   1.50   .30
793 A336 60c gray grn   1.00   .30
794 A336 90c orange ('55)   1.00   .30
795 A336 1cr brown   1.50   .25
796 A336 1.50cr blue   .30   .25
   a.   Wmk. 264   50.00   12.50
797 A336 2cr dk bl grn ('56)   2.75   .30
798 A336 5cr rose lil ('56)   9.00   .30
799 A336 10cr lt grn ('60)   4.50   .30
800 A336 20cr crim rose ('59)   9.00   .30
801 A336 50cr ultra ('59)   17.50   .30
     Nos. 786-801 (16)   50.45   4.40

See Nos. 890, 930-933.

Boy Scout Waving Flag (Statue) — A337

1954, Aug. 2   Unwmk.   *Perf. 11½x11*
802 A337 1.20cr vio bl   .50 .25
    Intl. Boy Scout Encampment, Sao Paulo.

Baltasar Fernandes, Explorer — A338

1954, Aug. 15
803 A338 60c dk red   .25 .25
    300th anniversary of city of Sorocaba.

Adeodato Giovanni Cardinal Piazza — A339

1954, Sept. 2
804 A339 4.20cr red org   .50 .35
    Visit of Adeodato Cardinal Piazza, papal legate to Brazil.

Our Lady of Aparecida, Map of Brazil — A340   Virgin Standing on Globe — A340a

1954
805 A340   60c claret   .30 .30
806 A340a 1.20cr vio bl   .30 .30
    No. 805 was issued for the 1st Cong. of Brazil's Patron Saint (Our Lady of Aparecida); No. 806, the cent. of the proclamation of the dogma of the Immaculate Conception. Both stamps also for the Marian Year.
    Issue dates: 60c, Sept. 6; 1.20cr, Sept. 8.

Benjamin Constant and Hand Reading Braille A341

1954, Sept. 27   Photo.   Unwmk.
807 A341 60c dk grn   .25 .25
    Centenary of the founding of the Benjamin Constant Institute.

River Battle of Riachuelo — A342

Admiral F. M. Barroso — A343

1954, Oct. 6   *Perf. 11x11½, 11½x11*
808 A342 40c redsh brown   .25 .25
809 A343 60c violet   .25 .25
    Admiral Francisco Manoel Barroso da Silva (1804-82).

Dr. Christian F. S. Hahnemann — A344

1954, Oct. 8   *Perf. 11½x11*
810 A344 2.70cr dk green   .50 .25
    1st World Cong. of Homeopathic Medicine.

Nizia Floresta — A345

1954, Oct. 12
811 A345 60c lilac rose   .25 .25
    Reburial of the remains of Nizia Floresta (Dio Nizia Pinto Lisboa), writer and educator.

Ears of Wheat — A346

1954, Oct. 22
812 A346 60c olive   .25 .25
    4th National Wheat Festival, Carazinho.

Basketball Player and Ball-Globe — A347

1954, Oct. 23   Photo.
813 A347 1.40cr orange red   .50 .25
    Issued to publicize the second World Basketball Championship Matches, 1954.

Allegory of the Spring Games — A348

Perf. 11½x11
1954, Nov. 6   Wmk. 267
814 A348 60c red brown   .45 .25
    Issued to publicize the 6th Spring Games.

San Francisco Hydroelectric Plant — A349

1955, Jan. 15   *Perf. 11x11½*
815 A349 60c brown org   .25 .25
    Issued to publicize the inauguration of the San Francisco Hydroelectric Plant.

Itutinga Hydroelectric Plant — A350

1955, Feb. 3
816 A350 40c blue   .25 .25
    Issued to publicize the inauguration of the Itutinga Hydroelectric Plant at Lavras.

Rotary Emblem and Bay of Rio de Janeiro — A351

1955, Feb. 23   *Perf. 12x11½*
817 A351 2.70cr dp turq grn & dp
               bluish grn   1.20 .35
    Rotary International, 50th anniversary.

Fausto Cardoso Palace A352

1955, Mar. 17   *Perf. 11x11½*
818 A352 40c henna brown   .25 .25
    Centenary of Aracaju.

Aviation Symbols A353

1955, Mar. 13   Photo.   *Perf. 11½*
819 A353 60c dark gray green   .25 .25
    Issued to publicize the third National Aviation Congress at Sao Paulo, Mar. 6-13.

Arms of Botucatu A354

1955, Apr. 14
820 A354 60c orange brn   .25 .25
821 A354 1.20cr brt green   .25 .25
    Centenary of Botucatu.

Young Racers at Starting Line A355

Perf. 11½
1955, Apr. 30   Photo.   Unwmk.
823 A355 60c orange brn   .30 .25
    5th Children's Games.

Marshal Hermes da Fonseca — A356

1955, May 12   Wmk. 267
824 A356 60c purple   .25 .25
    Marshal Hermes da Fonseca, birth cent.

Congress Altar, Sail and Sugarloaf Mountain — A357

    Designs: 2.70cr, St. Pascoal. 4.20cr, Aloisi Benedetto Cardinal Masella.

Granite Paper
Engraved; Photogravure (2.70cr)
1955, July 17   Unwmk.   *Perf. 11½*
825 A357 1.40cr green   .30   .25
826 A357 2.70cr deep claret   .30   .40
827 A357 4.20cr blue   .80   .30
    Nos. 825-827 (3)   1.40   .95

36th World Eucharistic Cong. in Rio de Janeiro.

Girl
Gymnasts
A358

1955, Nov. 12   Engr.
Granite Paper
828 A358 60c rose lilac   .30   .25

Issued to publicize the 7th Spring Games.

José B.
Monteiro
Lobato,
Author
A359

1955, Dec. 8   Granite Paper
829 A359 40c dark green   .25   .25

Adolfo
Lutz — A360

1955, Dec. 18   Granite Paper
830 A360 60c dk green   .25   .25

Centenary of the birth of Adolfo Lutz, public health pioneer.

Lt. Col. Vilagran
Cabrita — A361

1955, Dec. 22   Photo.   Wmk. 267
831 A361 60c violet blue   .25   .25

First Battalion of Engineers, cent.

Salto
Grande
Hydroelectric
Dam
A362

1956, Jan. 15   Unwmk.   *Perf. 11½*
Granite Paper
832 A362 60c brick red   .25   .25

Arms of
Mococa — A363

Wmk. 256
1956, Apr. 17   Photo.   *Perf. 11½*
833 A363 60c brick red   .25   .25

Centenary of Mococa, Sao Paulo.

"G" and
Globe — A364

1956, Apr. 14   Unwmk.
Granite Paper
834 A364 1.20cr violet blue   .25   .25

18th Intl. Geographic Cong., Rio, Aug. 1956.

Girls' Foot
Race
A365

1956, Apr. 28   Photo.
Granite Paper
835 A365 2.50cr brt blue   .30   .25

6th Children's Games.

Plane over Map of
Brazil — A366

1956, June 12   Wmk. 267   *Perf. 11½*
836 A366 3.30cr brt vio bl   .30   .25

National Airmail Service, 25th anniv.

Fireman
Rescuing
Child
A367

1956, July 2   Wmk. 264
837 A367 2.50cr crimson   .40   .25
    a.   Buff paper   .80   .25

Centenary of the Fire Brigade.

Map of
Brazil and
Open Book
A368

1956, Sept. 8   Wmk. 267
838 A368 2.50cr brt vio bl   .25   .25

50th anniversary of the arrival of the Marist Brothers in Northern Brazil.

Church and
Monument,
Franca — A369

1956, Sept. 7   Engr.
839 A369 2.50cr dk blue   .25   .25

Centenary of city of Franca, Sao Paulo.

Woman
Hurdler
A370

1956, Sept. 22   Photo.   Unwmk.
Granite Paper
840 A370 2.50cr dk car   .60   .30

Issued to publicize the 8th Spring Games.

Forest and Map of
Brazil — A371

1956, Sept. 30   Wmk. 267   *Perf. 11½*
841 A371 2.50cr dk green   .30   .25

Issued to publicize education in forestry.

Baron da
Bocaina
A372

1956, Oct. 8   Engr.   Wmk. 268
842 A372 2.50cr reddish brown   .30   .30

Centenary of the birth of Baron da Bocaina, who introduced the special delivery mail system to Brazil.

Marbleized Paper
Paper with a distinct wavy-line or marbleized watermark (which Brazilians call *marmorizado* paper) has been found on many stamps of Brazil, 1956-68, including Nos. 843-845, 847, 851-854, 858-858A, 864, 878, 880, 882, 884, 886-887, 896, 909, 918, 920-921, 925-928, 936-939, 949, 955-958, 960, 962-964, 978-979, 983, 985-987, 997-998, 1002-1003, 1005, 1009-1012, 1017, 1024, 1026, 1055, 1075, 1078, 1082, C82, C82a, C83-C87, C96, C99, C109.
Quantities are much less than those of stamps on regular paper.

Panama Stamp
Showing Pres.
Juscelino
Kubitschek
A373

1956, Oct. 12   Photo.   Wmk. 267
843 A373 3.30cr green & blk   .30   .25

Issued on America Day, Oct. 12, to commemorate the meeting of the Presidents and the Pan-American Conference at Panama City, July 21-22.

Symbolical of Steel
Production — A374

Wmk. 267
1957, Jan. 31   Photo.   *Perf. 11½*
844 A374 2.50cr chocolate   .30   .25

2nd expansion of the National Steel Company at Volta Redonda.

Joaquim E.
Gomes da
Silva — A375

1957, Mar. 1   Photo.   Unwmk.
Granite Paper
845 A375 2.50cr dk bl grn   .30   .25

Centenary of the birth (in 1856) of Joaquim E. Gomes da Silva.

Allan
Kardec
A376

Wmk. 268
1957, Apr. 18   Engr.   *Perf. 11½*
846 A376 2.50cr dk brown   .25   .25

Issued in honor of Allan Kardec, pen name of Leon Hippolyto Denizard Rivail, and for the centenary of the publication of his "Codification of Spiritism."

Boy
Gymnast
A377

1957, Apr. 27   Photo.   Unwmk.
Granite Paper
847 A377 2.50cr lake   .40   .25

7th Children's Games.

Pres. Craveiro Lopes — A378

1957, June 7   Engr.   Wmk. 267
848 A378 6.50cr blue   .30 .25
Visit of Gen. Francisco Higino Craveiro Lopes, President of Portugal.

Stamp of 1932 — A379

1957, July 9   Photo.
849 A379 2.50cr rose   .30 .25
25th anniv. of the movement for a constitution.

St. Antonio Monastery, Pernambuco — A380

1957, Aug. 24   Engr.   Wmk. 267
850 A380 2.50cr deep magenta   .25 .25
300th anniv. of the emancipation of the Franciscan province of St. Antonio in Pernambuco State.

Volleyball — A381

1957, Sept. 28 Photo. Perf. 11½
851 A381 2.50cr dull org red   .50 .30
Issued for the 9th Spring Games.

Basketball — A382

1957, Oct. 12
852 A382 3.30cr org & brt grn   .40 .30
2nd Women's International Basketball Championship, Rio de Janeiro.

Count of Pinhal and Sao Carlos A383

1957, Nov. 4   Wmk. 267   Perf. 11½
853 A383 2.50cr rose   .30 .30
Centenary of the city of Sao Carlos and honoring the Count of Pinhal, its founder.

Auguste Comte — A384

1957, Nov. 15
854 A384 2.50cr dk red brn   .25 .25
Centenary of the death of Auguste Comte, French mathematician and philosopher.

Radio Station A385

1957, Dec. 10   Wmk. 268
855 A385 2.50cr dk green   .25 .25
Opening of Sarapui Central Radio Station.

Admiral Tamandare and Warship — A386

Aircraft Carrier — A386a

1957-58   Photo.
856 A386   2.50cr light blue   .25 .25
Engr.
857 A386a 3.30cr green ('58)   .25 .25
150th anniversary of the birth of Admiral Joaquin Marques de Tamandare, founder of the Brazilian navy.

Coffee Plant and Symbolic "R" — A387

**   Wmk. 267**
1957-58   Photo.   Perf. 11½
858   A387 2.50cr magenta   .30 .25

Unwmk.
Granite Paper
858A A387 2.50cr magenta ('58)   .30 .25
Centenary (in 1956) of the city of Ribeirao Preto in Sao Paulo state.

Dom John VI — A388

1958, Jan. 28   Engr.   Wmk. 268
859 A388 2.50cr magenta   .25 .25
150th anniversary of the opening of the ports of Brazil to foreign trade.

Bugler A389

1958, Mar. 18   Wmk. 267
860 A389 2.50cr red   .25 .25
Brazilian Marine Corps, 150th anniv.

Station at Rio and Locomotive of 1858 — A390

**   Wmk. 267**
1958, Mar. 29 Photo.   Perf. 11½
861 A390 2.50cr red brn   .25 .25
Central Railroad of Brazil, cent.

Court House — A391

1958, Apr. 1   Engr.   Wmk. 256
862 A391 2.50cr green   .25 .25
150th anniv. of the Military Superior Court.

Emblem and Brazilian Pavilion A392

1958, Apr. 17   Wmk. 267
863 A392 2.50cr dk blue   .25 .25
World's Fair, Brussels, Apr. 17-Oct. 19.

High Jump — A393

1958, Apr. 20   Photo.   Unwmk.
Granite Paper
864 A393 2.50cr crimson rose   .40 .30
8th Children's Games.

Marshal Mariano da Silva Rondon A394

1958, Apr. 19   Engr.   Wmk. 267
865 A394 2.50cr magenta   .25 .25
Issued to honor Marshal Mariano da Silva Rondon and the "Day of the Indian."

Hydroelectric Station — A395

1958, Apr. 28   Wmk. 267   Perf. 11½
866 A395 2.50cr magenta   .25 .25
Opening of Sao Paulo State power plant.

National Printing Plant A396

1958, May 22   Photo.
867 A396 2.50cr redsh brn   .25 .25
150th anniversary of the founding of the National Printing Plant.

Marshal Osorio — A397

1958, May 24
868 A397 2.50cr brt violet   .25 .25
150th anniversary of the birth of Marshal Manoel Luiz Osorio.

Pres. Ramon Villeda Morales — A398

1958, June 7 Engr. Perf. 11½
869 A398 6.50cr dk green 2.00 .40
a. Wmk. 268 12.00 1.25
Visit of Pres. Ramon Villeda Morales of Honduras.

Fountain — A399

1958, June 13
870 A399 2.50cr dk green .25 .25
Botanical Garden, Rio de Janeiro, 150th anniv.

Symbols of Agriculture A400

1958, June 18 Photo.
871 A400 2.50cr rose carmine .25 .25
50th anniv. of Japanese immigration to Brazil.

Prophet Joel — A401

1958, June 21 Engr.
872 A401 2.50cr dk blue .25 .25
Bicentenary of the Cathedral of Bom Jesus at Matosinhos.

Stylized Globe A402

1958, July 10 Photo.
873 A402 2.50cr dk brown .25 .25
Intl. Investment Conference, Belo Horizonte.

Julio Bueno Brandao — A403

1958, Aug. 1 Wmk. 268 Perf. 11½
874 A403 2.50cr red brown .25 .25
Centenary of the birth of Julio Bueno Brandao, President of Minas Gerais.

Palacio Tiradentes (House of Congress) A404

1958, July 24 Engr.
875 A404 2.50cr sepia .25 .25
47th Interparliamentary Conference, Rio de Janeiro, July 24-Aug. 1.

Presidential Palace, Brasilia — A405

1958, Aug. 8 Photo. Wmk. 267
876 A405 2.50cr ultra .25 .25
Issued to publicize the construction of Brazil's new capital, Brasilia.

Freighters A406

1958, Aug. 22
877 A406 2.50cr blue .25 .25
Brazilian merchant marine.

Joaquim Caetano da Silva A407

1958, Sept. 2 Unwmk.
Granite Paper
878 A407 2.50cr redsh brn .25 .25
Joaquim Caetano da Silva, scientist & historian.

Giovanni Gronchi — A408

1958, Sept. 4 Engr. Wmk. 268
879 A408 7cr dk blue .50 .25
Visit of Italy's President Giovanni Gronchi to Brazil.

Archers — A409

Perf. 11½
1958, Sept. 21 Photo. Unwmk.
Granite Paper
880 A409 2.50cr red org .50 .25
Issued to publicize the 10th Spring Games.

Elderly Couple — A410

1958, Sept. 27 Wmk. 267
881 A410 2.50cr magenta .25 .25
Day of the Old People, Sept. 27.

Machado de Assis — A411

1958, Sept. 28 Unwmk.
882 A411 2.50cr red brn .25 .25
50th anniversary of the death of Joaquim Maria Machado de Assis, writer.

Pres. Vargas and Oil Derrick A412

1958, Oct. 6 Wmk. 268
883 A412 2.50cr blue .25 .25
5th anniv. of Pres. Getulio D. Vargas' oil law.

Globe — A413

Wmk. 267
1958, Nov. 14 Photo. Perf. 11½
884 A413 2.50cr blue .30 .25
7th Inter-American Congress of Municipalities.

Gen. Lauro Sodré — A414

1958, Nov. 15 Engr.
885 A414 3.30cr green .25 .25
Cent. of the birth of Gen. Lauro Sodré.

UN Emblem — A415

1958, Dec. 26 Photo. Perf. 11½
886 A415 2.50cr brt blue .25 .25
10th anniv. of the signing of the Universal Declaration of Human Rights.

Soccer Player — A416

1959, Jan. 20
887 A416 3.30cr emer & red brn .50 .30
World Soccer Championships of 1958.

Railroad Track and Map — A417

1959, Apr. Wmk. 267 Perf. 11½
888 A417 2.50cr dp orange .25 .25
Centenary of the linking of Patos and Campina Grande by railroad.

Pres. Sukarno of Indonesia — A418

1959, May 20
889 A418 2.50cr blue .25 .25
Visit of President Sukarno of Indonesia.

Dom John VI — A419

Perf. 10½x11½
1959, June 12 Wmk. 267
890 A419 2.50cr crimson .30 .25

Boy Polo
Players — A420

1959, June 13   *Perf. 11½*
891 A420 2.50cr orange brn   .30 .25
9th Children's Games.

Loading
Freighter — A421

1959, July 10
892 A421 2.50cr dk green   .25 .25
Honoring the merchant marine.

Organ and
Emblem — A422

1959, July 16   **Photo.**
893 A422 3.30cr magenta   .25 .25
Bicentenary of the Carmelite Order in Brazil.

Joachim Silverio
de Souza — A423

1959, July 20   *Perf. 11½*
894 A423 2.50cr red brown   .25 .25
Birth centenary of Joachim Silverio de
Souza, first bishop of Diamantina, Minas
Gerais.

Symbolic
Road — A424

1959, Sept. 27   **Wmk. 267**
895 A424 3.30cr bl grn & ultra   .25 .25
11th International Roadbuilding Congress.

Woman
Athlete — A425

1959, Oct. 4
896 A425 2.50cr lilac rose   .30 .25
11th Spring Games.

Map of
Parana
A426

1959, Sept. 27
897 A426 2.50cr dk green   .25 .25
Founding of Londrina, Parana, 25th anniv.

Globe and
Snipes — A427

1959, Oct. 22   *Perf. 11½*
898 A427 6.50cr dull grn   .30 .25
World Championship of Snipe Class Sailboats, Porto Alegre, won by Brazilian
yachtsmen.

Cross of
Lusitania — A428

1959, Oct. 24   **Engr.**
899 A428 6.50cr dull blue   .25 .25
4th Intl. Conf. on Brazilian-Portuguese Studies, University of Bahia, Aug. 10-20.

Factory Entrance
and Order of
Southern
Cross — A429

1959, Nov. 19   **Photo.**
900 A429 3.30cr orange red   .25 .25
Pres. Vargas Gunpowder Factory, 50th
anniv.

Corcovado Christ,
Globe and
Southern
Cross — A430

1959, Nov. 26   *Perf. 11½*
901 A430 2.50cr blue   .30 .25
Universal Thanksgiving Day.

Burning
Bush
A431

1959, Dec. 24   **Wmk. 267**
902 A431 3.30cr lt grn   .25 .25
Centenary of Presbyterian work in Brazil.

Piraja da Silva and Schistosoma
Mansoni — A432

1959, Dec. 28
903 A432 2.50cr rose violet   .25 .25
25th anniv. of the discovery and identification of schistosoma mansoni, a parasite of the
fluke family, by Dr. Piraja da Silva.

Luiz de
Matos
A433

1960, Jan. 3   **Photo.**
904 A433 3.30cr red brown   .25 .25
Birth centenary of Luiz de Matos.

Zamenhof — A434

1960, Mar. 10 Wmk. 267 *Perf. 11½*
905 A434 6.50cr emerald   .25 .25
Lazarus Ludwig Zamenhof (1859-1917),
Polish oculist who invented Esperanto in 1887.

Adél Pinto — A435

1960, Mar. 19 Engr. Wmk. 268
906 A435 11.50cr rose red   .25 .25
Centenary of the birth of Adél Pinto, civil
engineer and railroad expert.

Presidential Palace,
Colonnade — A436

Design: 27cr, Plan of Brasilia (like No.
C98).

              Perf. 11x11½
1960   **Photo.**   **Wmk. 267**
907 A436 2.50cr brt green   .25 .25
          Size: 105x46½mm
908 A436 27cr salmon   1.75 .60
   Nos. 907-908,C95-C98 (6)   3.15 1.85
No. 907 for the inauguration of Brazil's new
capital, Brasilia, Apr. 21, 1960.
No. 908 for the birthday of Pres. Juscelino
Kubitschek and has a 27cr in design of No.
C98, flanked by the chief design features of
Nos. 907, C95-C97, with Kubitschek signature
below. Issued in sheets of 4 with wide horizon-
tal gutter.
Issued: 2.50cr, 4/21; 27cr, 9/12.

Grain, Coffee,
Cotton and
Cacao — A437

              Perf. 11½x11
1960, July 28   **Wmk. 267**
909 A437 2.50cr brown   .25 .25
Centenary of Ministry of Agriculture.

Paulo de
Frontin — A438

1960, Oct. 12   **Wmk. 268**
910 A438 2.50cr orange red   .25 .25
Cent. of the birth of Paulo de Frontin,
engineer.

Woman Athlete Holding Torch — A439

1960, Oct. 18		**Perf. 11½x11**
911 A439 2.50cr blue grn			.25 .25
12th Spring Games.

Volleyball and Net — A440

Perf. 11½x11
1960, Nov. 12		**Wmk. 268**
912 A440 11cr blue			.30 .25
International Volleyball Championships.

Locomotive Wheels — A441

1960, Oct. 15		**Perf. 11½x11**
913 A441 2.50cr ultra			.30 .25
10th Pan-American Railroad Congress.

Symbols of Flight A442

1960, Dec. 16	**Photo.**	**Perf. 11½**
914 A442 2.50cr brn & yel		.25 .25
Intl. Fair of Industry and Commerce, Rio.

Emperor Haile Selassie — A443

1961, Jan. 31		**Perf. 11½x11**
915 A443 2.50cr dk brown		.25 .25
Visit of Emperor Haile Selassie of Ethiopia to Brazil, Dec. 1960.

Map of Brazil, Open Book and Sacred Heart Emblem A444

Perf. 11x11½
1961, Mar. 13		**Wmk. 268**
916 A444 2.50cr blue			.25 .25
50th anniv. of the operation in Brazil of the Order of the Blessed Heart of Mary.

Map of Guanabara — A445

1961, Mar. 27		**Wmk. 267**
917 A445 7.50cr org brn			.35 .25
Promulgation of the constitution of the state of Guanabara.

Arms of Agulhas Negras — A446

Design: 3.30cr, Dress helmet and sword.

Perf. 11½x11
1961, Apr. 23		**Wmk. 267**
918 A446 2.50cr green			.25 .25
919 A446 3.30cr rose car			.25 .25
Sesquicentennial of the Agulhas Negras Military Academy.

Brazil and Senegal Linked on Map — A447

1961, Apr. 28		**Photo.**
920 A447 27cr ultra			.30 .25
Visit of Afonso Arinos, Brazilian foreign minister, to Senegal to attend its independence ceremonies.

View of Ouro Preto, 1711 A448

1961, June 6		**Perf. 11x11½**
921 A448 1cr orange			.25 .25
250th anniversary of Ouro Preto.

War Arsenal A449

1961, June 20		**Wmk. 256**
924 A449 5cr dk red brn			.30 .25
War Arsenal, Rio de Janeiro, 150th anniv.

Coffee Bean and Branch — A450

Perf. 11½x11
1961, June 26		**Wmk. 267**
925 A450 20cr redsh brn			.60 .25
8th Directorial Committee meeting of the Intl. Coffee Convention, Rio, June 26.

Rabindranath Tagore — A451

1961, July 28	**Photo.**	**Wmk. 267**
926 A451 10cr rose car			.30 .25
Rabindranath Tagore, Indian poet, birth cent.

Stamp of 1861 and Map of English Channel A452

Design: 20cr, 430r stamp of 1861 and map of Netherlands.

1961, Aug. 1		**Perf. 11x11½**
927 A452 10cr rose			.40 .25
928 A452 20cr salmon pink		1.60 .25
Centenary of 1861 stamp issue.

Portrait Type of 1954-60
Designs as Before

1961	Wmk. 268	Perf. 11x11½	
930	A336	1cr brown	1.20	.60
931	A336	2cr dk bl grn	1.80	.60
932	A336	5cr red lilac	5.50	.35
933	A336	10cr emerald	10.00	.35
	Nos. 930-933 (4)		18.50	1.90

1cr, 5cr, 10cr have patterned background.

Sun, Clouds, Rain and Weather Symbols — A453

1962, Mar. 23		**Perf. 11½x11**
936 A453 10cr red brown			.50 .25
World Meteorological Day, Mar. 23.

Dedo de Deus Peak — A454

1962, Apr. 14	**Photo.**	**Wmk. 267**
937 A454 8cr emerald			.25 .25
50th anniversary of the climbing of Dedo de Deus (Finger of God) peak.

Dr. Gaspar Vianna and Leishmania Protozoa — A455

1962, Apr. 24		**Perf. 11x11½**
938 A455 8cr blue			.25 .25
Discovery by Gaspar Oliveiro Vianna (1885-1914) of a cure for leishmaniasis, 50th anniv.

Henrique Dias A456

1962, June 18		**Wmk. 267**
939 A456 10cr dk vio brn			.25 .25
300th anniversary of the death of Henrique Dias, Negro military leader who fought against the Dutch and Spaniards.

Millimeter Gauge — A457

1962, June 26		**Perf. 11½x11**
940 A457 100cr car rose			.50 .25
Centenary of the introduction of the metric system in Brazil.

Sailboats, Snipe Class — A458

1962, July 21	**Photo.**	**Wmk. 267**
941 A458 8cr Prus green			.30 .25
Commemorating the 13th Brazilian championships for Snipe Class sailing.

Julio Mesquita A459

1962, Aug. 18   *Perf. 11x11½*
942 A459 8cr dull brown   2.50 .25
   Julio Mesquita, journalist and founder of a
Sao Paulo newspaper, birth cent.

Empress Leopoldina — A460

1962, Sept. 7   *Perf. 11½x11*
943 A460 8cr rose claret   .25 .25
   140th anniversary of independence.

Buildings, Brasilia — A461

Perf. 11x11½
1962, Oct. 24   **Wmk. 267**
944 A461 10cr orange   .25 .25
   51st Interparliamentary Conf., Brasilia.

Pouring Ladle — A462

1962, Oct. 26   *Perf. 11½x11*
945 A462 8cr orange   .25 .25
   Inauguration of the Usiminas State Iron and
Steel Foundry at Belo Horizonte, Minas
Gerais.

UPAE Emblem A463

1962, Nov. 19   *Perf. 11x11½*
946 A463 8cr bright magenta   .25 .25
   Founding of the Postal Union of the Americas and Spain, UPAE, 50th anniv.

Chimney and Cogwheel Forming "10" — A464

1962, Nov. 26   *Perf. 11½x11*
947 A464 10cr lt blue grn   .25 .25
   Natl. Economic and Development Bank,
10th anniv.

Quintino Bocaiuva — A465

Perf. 11½x11
1962, Dec. 27   **Photo.**   **Wmk. 267**
948 A465 8cr brown org   .25 .25
   Bocaiuva, journalist, 50th death anniv.

Soccer Player and Globe — A466

1963, Jan. 14
949 A466 10cr blue grn   1.00 .25
   World Soccer Championship of 1962.

Carrier Pigeon — A467

1963, Jan. Unwmk. Litho. Perf. 14
950 A467   8cr yel, dk bl, red &
             grn   .30   .25

Souvenir Sheet
Imperf
951 A467 100cr yel, dk bl, red &
             grn   6.00 1.75

   300 years of Brazilian postal service.
Issue dates: 8cr, Jan. 25; 100cr, Jan. 31.

Severino Neiva — A468

Perf. 10½x11½
1963, Jan. 31   Photo.   Wmk. 267
952 A468 8cr brt vio   .50 .25

Radar Tracking Station and Rockets — A469

Perf. 11½x11
1963, Mar. 15   **Wmk. 268**
953 A469 21cr lt ultra   .25 .25
   International Aeronautics and Space Exhibition, Sao Paulo.

"Cross of Unity" — A470

1963   Wmk. 267   Perf. 11½x11
954 A470 8cr red lilac   .25 .25
   Vatican II, the 21st Ecumenical Council of
the Roman Catholic Church.

"ABC" in Geometric Form — A471

1963, Apr. 22   Photo.   Wmk. 267
955 A471 8cr brt bl & lt bl   .25 .25
   Education Week, Apr. 22-27, 3-year alpha-
betization program.

Basketball Player — A472

1963, May 15
956 A472 8cr dp lilac rose   .40 .25
   4th International Basketball Championships,
Rio de Janeiro, May 10-25, 1963.

Games Emblem — A473

1963, May 22   *Perf. 11½x11*
957 A473 10cr car rose   .40 .25
   4th Pan American Games, Sao Paulo.

"OEA" and Map of the Americas — A474

1963, June 6
958 A474 10cr org & dp org   .30 .25
   15th anniversary of the charter of the
Organization of American States.

José Bonifacio de Andrada — A475

1963, June 13
959 A475 8cr dk brown   .25 .25
   Bicentenary of the birth of José Bonifacio de
Andrada e Silva, statesman.

Wheat A476

Perf. 11x11½
1963, June 18   Photo.   Wmk. 267
960 A476 10cr blue   .30 .25
   FAO "Freedom from Hunger" campaign.

Centenary Emblem — A477

1963, Aug. 19   *Perf. 11½x11*
961 A477 8cr yel org & red   .25 .25
   Centenary of International Red Cross.

Joao Caetano — A478

1963, Aug. 24   *Perf. 11½x11*
962 A478 8cr slate   .25 .25
   Death centenary of Joao Caetano, actor.

Symbols of Agriculture, Industry and Atomic Energy — A479

1963, Aug. 28
963 A479 10cr car rose   .30 .25
Atomic Development Law, 1st anniv.

Hammer Thrower — A480

1963, Sept. 13
964 A480 10cr gray   .40 .25
Intl. College Students' Games, Porto Alegre.

Marshal Tito — A481

1963, Sept. 19
965 A481 80cr sepia   .75 .25
Visit of Marshal Tito of Yugoslavia.

Compass Rose, Map of Brazil and View of Rio — A482

1963, Sept. 20
966 A482 8cr lt blue grn   .25 .25
8th International Leprology Congress.

Oil Derrick and Storage Tank A483

1963, Oct. 3   Perf. 11x11½
967 A483 8cr dk slate grn   .25 .25
Petrobras, the natl. oil company, 10th anniv.

"Spring Games" A484

1963, Nov. 5   Photo.   Wmk. 267
968 A484 8cr yel & org   .40 .25
1963 Spring Games.

Dr. Borges de Medeiros (1863-1962), Governor of Rio Grande do Sul — A485

1963, Nov. 29   Perf. 11½x11
969 A485 8cr red brown   .25 .25

Sao Joao del Rei A486

1963, Dec. 8   Perf. 11x11½
970 A486 8cr violet blue   .25 .25
250th anniversary of Sao Joao del Rei.

Dr. Alvaro Alvim A487

1963, Dec. 19
971 A487 8cr dk gray   .25 .25
Alvaro Alvim (1863-1928), X-ray specialist and martyr of science.

Viscount de Mauá — A488

1963, Dec. 28   Perf. 11½x11
972 A488 8cr rose car   .25 .25
Sesquicentennial of the birth of Viscount de Mauá, founder of first Brazilian railroad.

Mandacaru Cactus and Emblem — A489

1964, Jan. 23   Photo.   Wmk. 267
973 A489 8cr dull green   .25 .25
Bank of Northeast Brazil, 10th anniv.

Coelho Netto — A490

1964, Feb. 21   Perf. 11½x11
974 A490 8cr brt violet   .25 .25
Birth centenary of Coelho Netto, writer.

Lauro Müller — A491

1964, Mar. 8   Wmk. 267
975 A491 8cr dp orange   .25 .25
Lauro Siverino Müller, politician and member of the Brazilian Academy of Letters, birth cent.

Child Holding Spoon A492

1964, Mar. 25   Perf. 11x11½
976 A492 8cr yel brn & yel   .25 .25
Issued for "School Meals Week."

Chalice Rock — A493

1964, Apr. 9   Engr.   Perf. 11½x11
977 A493 80cr red orange   .25 .25
Issued for tourist publicity.

Allan Kardec — A494

1964, Apr. 18   Photo.
978 A494 30cr slate green   .50 .25
Cent. of "O Evangelho" (Gospel) of the codification of Spiritism.

Heinrich Lübke — A495

Perf. 11½x11
1964, May 8   Photo.   Wmk. 267
979 A495 100cr red brown   .35 .25
Visit of President Heinrich Lübke of Germany.

Pope John XXIII — A496

1964, June 29   Wmk. 267
980 A496 20cr dk car rose   .25 .25
a.   Unwmkd.   2.00 .25
Issued in memory of Pope John XXIII.

Pres. Senghor of Senegal — A497

1964, Sept. 19   Wmk. 267
981 A497 20cr dk brown   .25 .25
Visit of Leopold Sedar Senghor, President of Senegal.

Botafogo Bay and Sugarloaf Mountain — A498

Designs: 100cr, Our Lady of Penha Church, vert. 200cr, Copacabana beach.

Perf. 11x11½, 11½x11
1964-65   Photo.
983 A498 15cr org & bl   .25 .25
984 A498 100cr brt grn & red brn, yel   .30 .25
985 A498 200cr black & red   1.60 .25
a.   Souvenir sheet of 3 ('65)   17.50 17.50
     Nos. 983-985 (3)   2.15 .75
4th cent. of Rio de Janeiro.
No. 985a contains three imperf. stamps similar to Nos. 983-985, but printed in brown. Sold for 320cr. Issued Dec. 30, 1965.
A souvenir card containing one lithographed facsimile of No. 984, imperf., exists, but has no franking value. Size: 100x125mm. Sold by P.O. for 250cr.

Pres. Charles de
Gaulle — A499

1964, Oct. 13 *Perf. 11½x11*
986 A499 100cr orange brn .30 .25
Visit of Charles de Gaulle, President of
France, Oct. 13-15.

Pres. John F.
Kennedy — A500

1964, Oct. 24 Photo. Wmk. 267
987 A500 100cr slate .25 .25

"Prophet" by
Lisboa — A501

1964, Nov. 18 *Perf. 11½x11*
988 A501 10cr slate .25 .25
150th death anniv. of the sculptor Antonio
Francisco Lisboa, "O Aleijadinho" (The
Cripple).

Antonio Goncalves
Dias — A502

Designs: 30cr, Euclides da Cunha. 50cr,
Prof. Angelo Moreira da Costa Lima. 200cr,
Tiradentes. 500cr, Dom Pedro I. 1000cr, Dom
Pedro II.

1965-66 Wmk. 267 *Perf. 11x11½*
989 A502 30cr brt bluish
grn ('66) 4.00 .25
989A A502 50cr dull brn
('66) 3.50 .25
990 A502 100cr blue 1.50 .25
991 A502 200cr brown org 7.00 .25
992 A502 500cr red brown 30.00 .45
992A A502 1000cr sl bl ('66) 60.00 1.60
Nos. 989-992A (6) 106.00 3.05

Statue of St.
Sebastian,
Guanataro
Bay — A503

The
Arches
A504

Design: 35cr, Estacio de Sa (1520-67),
founder of Rio de Janeiro.

1965 Photo. *Perf. 11½*
Size: 24x37mm
993 A503 30cr bl & rose red .25 .25

Lithographed and Engraved
Perf. 11x11½
994 A504 30cr lt bl & blk .25 .25

Photo. *Perf. 11½*
Size: 21x39mm
995 A503 35cr blk & org .25 .25
a. Souvenir sheet of 3 5.75 5.75
Nos. 993-995 (3) .75 .75
4th cent. of Rio de Janeiro.
No. 995a contains three imperf. stamps similar to Nos. 993-995, but printed in deep
orange. Size: 130x79mm. Sold for 100cr.
Issued: No. 993, 3/5; No. 994, 11/30; No.
995, 7/28; No. 995a, 12/30.

Sword and
Cross — A505

1965, Apr. 15 Wmk. 267 *Perf. 11½*
996 A505 120cr gray .25 .25
1st anniv. of the democratic revolution.

Vital
Brazil — A506

1965, Apr. 28 Wmk. 267 *Perf. 11½*
997 A506 120cr deep orange .40 .25
Centenary of birth of Vital Brazil, M.D.
A souvenir card containing one impression
similar to No. 997, imperf., exists, printed in
dull plum. Sold by P.O. for 250cr. Size:
114x180mm.

Shah of
Iran — A507

1965, May 5 Photo.
998 A507 120cr rose claret .30 .25
Commemorating the visit of Shah Mohammed Riza Pahlavi of Iran.

Marshal Mariano
da Silva
Rondon — A508

1965, May 7 Engr.
999 A508 30cr claret .30 .25
Marshal Mariano da Silva Rondon (1865-
1958), explorer and expert on Indians.

Lions'
Emblem — A509

1965, May 14 Photo.
1000 A509 35cr pale vio & blk .25 .25
12th convention of the Lions Clubs of Brazil,
Rio de Janeiro, May 11-16.

ITU Emblem, Old and New
Communication Equipment — A510

1965, May 21 *Perf. 11½*
1001 A510 120cr yellow & grn .30 .25
Centenary of the ITU.

Epitácio
Pessoa — A511

1965, May 23 Photo.
1002 A511 35cr blue gray .25 .25
Epitácio da Silva Pessoa (1865-1942), jurist,
president of Brazil, 1919-22.

Statue of Admiral
Barroso — A512

1965, June 11
1003 A512 30cr blue .25 .25
Cent. of the naval battle of Riachuelo.
A souvenir card containing one lithographed
facsimile of No. 1003, imperf., exists. Size:
100x139½mm.

José de Alencar and
Indian
Princess — A513

1965, June 24 *Perf. 11½x11*
1004 A513 30cr deep plum .25 .25
Centenary of the publication of "Iracema" by
Joséde Alencar.
A souvenir card containing one lithographed
facsimile of No. 1004, printed in rose red and
imperf., exists. Size: 100x141½mm.

Winston
Churchill
A514

1965, June 25 *Perf. 11x11½*
1005 A514 200cr slate .35 .25

Scout Jamboree
Emblem — A515

1965, July 17 Photo. *Perf. 11¾*
1006 A515 30cr dull bl grn .35 .25
1st Pan-American Boy Scout Jamboree,
Fundao Island, Rio de Janeiro, July 15-25.

ICY
Emblem
A516

1965, Aug. 25 Wmk. 267 *Perf. 11½*
1007 A516 120cr dl bl & blk .50 .25
International Cooperation Year, 1965.

Leoncio
Correias — A517

1965, Sept. 1 *Perf. 11½x11*
1008 A517 35cr slate grn .25 .25
Leoncio Correias, poet, birth cent.

Emblem — A518

1965, Sept. 4
1009 A518 30cr brt rose .25 .25
Eighth Biennial Fine Arts Exhibition, Sao
Paulo, Nov.-Dec., 1965.

Pres. Saragat of Italy — A519

1965, Sept. 11   Photo.   Wmk. 267
1010 A519 100cr slate grn, *pink*   .25 .25
· Visit of Pres. Giuseppe Saragat of Italy.

Grand Duke and Duchess of Luxembourg — A520

1965, Sept. 17   Perf. 11x11½
1011 A520 100cr brn olive   .25 .25
Visit of Grand Duke Jean and Grand Duchess Josephine Charlotte of Luxembourg.

Biplane — A521

1965, Oct. 8   Photo.   Perf. 11½x11
1012 A521 35cr ultra   .25 .25
3rd Aviation Week Philatelic Exhibition, Rio.
A souvenir card carries one impression of this 35cr, imperf. Size: 102x140mm. Sold for 100cr.

Flags of OAS Members A522

1965, Nov. 17   Perf. 11x11½
1013 A522 100cr brt bl & blk   .25 .25
2nd meeting of OAS Foreign Ministers, Rio.

King Baudouin and Queen Fabiola of Belgium — A523

1965, Nov. 18
1014 A523 100cr gray   .25 .25
Visit of King and Queen of Belgium.

"Coffee Beans" — A524

Perf. 11½x11
1965, Dec. 21   Photo.   Wmk. 267
1015 A524 30cr brown   .30 .25
Brazilian coffee publicity.

Conveyor and Loading Crane A525

1966, Apr. 1   Perf. 11x11½
1016 A525 110cr tan & dk sl grn   .30 .25
Opening of the new terminal of the Rio Doce Iron Ore Company at Tubarao.

Pouring Ladle and Steel Beam — A526

Perf. 11½x11
1966, Apr. 16   Photo.   Wmk. 267
1017 A526 30cr blk, *dp org*   .25 .25
25th anniv. of the National Steel Company (nationalization of the steel industry).

Prof. de Rocha Dissecting Cadaver — A527

1966, Apr. 26
1018 A527 30cr brt bluish grn   .30 .25
50th anniv. of the discovery and description of Rickettsia Prowazeki, the cause of typhus fever, by Prof. Henrique de Rocha Lima.

Battle of Tuiuti A528

Perf. 11x11½
1966, May 24   Photo.   Wmk. 267
1019 A528 30cr gray grn   .30 .25
Centenary of the Battle of Tuiuti.

Symbolic Water Cycle — A529

1966, July 1   Perf. 11½x11
1020 A529 100cr lt brn & bl   .25 .25
Hydrological Decade (UNESCO), 1965-74.

Pres. Shazar of Israel — A530

1966, July 18   Photo.   Wmk. 267
1021 A530 100cr ultra   .30 .25
Visit of Pres. Zalman Shazar of Israel.

Imperial Academy of Fine Arts — A531

Perf. 11x11½
1966, Aug. 12   Engr.   Wmk. 267
1022 A531 100cr red brown   1.00 .25
150th anniversary of French art mission.

Military Service Emblem A532

1966, Sept. 6   Photo.   Perf. 11x11½
1023 A532 30cr yel, ultra & grn   .25 .25
a.   With commemorative border   3.25 3.25
New Military Service Law.
No. 1023a issued in sheets of 4. It carries at left a 30cr, design A532, in deeper tones of yellow and ultramarine, Wmk. 264. Without gum. Sold for 100cr.

Ruben Dario — A533

Perf. 11½x11
1966, Sept. 20   Photo.   Wmk. 267
1024 A533 100cr brt rose lilac   .25 .25
Ruben Dario (pen name of Felix Ruben Garcia Sarmiento (1867-1916), Nicaraguan poet, newspaper correspondent and diplomat.

Ceramic Candlestick from Santarém — A534

1966, Oct. 6   Perf. 11x11½
1025 A534 30cr dk brn, *salmon*   .25 .25
Centenary of Goeldi Museum at Belem.

Arms of Santa Cruz — A535

Perf. 11½x11
1966, Oct. 15   Photo.   Wmk. 267
1026 A535 30cr slate grn   .25 .25
1st Natl. Tobacco Exposition, Santa Cruz.

UNESCO Emblem A536

1966, Oct. 24   Engr.   Perf. 11½
1027 A536 120cr black   .40 .25
a.   With commemorative border   8.00 8.00
20th anniv. of UNESCO. No. 1027a issued in sheets of 4. It carries at right a design similar to No. 1027. Unwatermarked granite paper, without gum. Sold for 150cr.

Captain Antonio Correia Pinto and Map of Lages — A537

Perf. 11½x11
1966, Nov. 22   Photo.   Wmk. 267
1028 A537 30cr salmon pink   .25 .25
Arrival of Capt. Antonio Correia Pinto, bicent.

Cross of Lusitania and Southern Cross — A538

1966, Dec. 4   Perf. 11½
1029 A538 100cr blue green   .30 .25
LUBRAPEX 1966 philatelic exhibition at the National Museum of Fine Arts, Rio.

A539

A540

Madonna and Child — A540a

Perf. 11½x11

1966, Dec.　Photo.　Wmk. 267
1030 A539 30cr blue green　.25　.25
　　　　　Perf. 11½
1031 A540 35cr salmon & ultra　.25　.25
　　a.　A540a 150cr salmon & ultra　4.00　5.50
　　　　　Christmas 1966.
No. 1031a measures 46x103mm and is
printed in sheets of 4. Issued without gum.
Issued: 30cr, 12/8; 35cr, 12/22; 150cr,
12/28.

Arms of
Laguna
A541

1967, Jan. 4　Engr.　Perf. 11x11½
1032 A541 60cr sepia　　　.25　.25
　Centenary of the Post and Telegraph
Agency of Laguna, Santa Catarina.

Railroad
Bridge
A542

1967, Feb. 16　Photo.　Wmk. 267
1033 A542 50cr deep orange　.35　.25
　Centenary of the Santos-Jundiai railroad.

Black Madonna of Czestochowa,
Polish Eagle and Cross — A543

1967, Mar. 12　　　Perf. 11x11½
1034 A543 50cr yel, bl & rose red　.35　.25
　Adoption of Christianity in Poland, 1,000th
anniv.

Research
Rocket — A544

1967, Mar. 23　　　Perf. 11½x11
1035 A544 50cr blk & brt bl　　.35　.25
　World Meteorological Day, March 23.

Anita Garibaldi — A545

　Portraits: 1c, Mother Joana Angelica. 2c,
Marilia de Dirceu. 3c, Dr. Rita Lobato. 6c, Ana
Neri. 10c, Darcy Vargas.

　　　Perf. 11x11½
1967-69　　　Photo.　　Wmk. 267
1036 A545　1c dp ultra　　　.25　.25
1037 A545　2c red brn　　　.25　.25
1038 A545　3c brt grn　　　.25　.25
1039 A545　5c black　　　.25　.25
1040 A545　6c brown　　　.25　.25
1041 A545 10c dk slate grn　1.25　.25
　　Nos. 1036-1041 (6)　2.50　1.50
　Issued: 1c, 5/3; 2c, 8/14; 3c, 6/7; 5c, 4/14;
6c, 5/14/67; 10c, 6/18/69.

VARIG
Airlines — A546

1967, May 8　　　Perf. 11½x11
1046 A546 6c brt bl & blk　　.25　.25
　40th anniversary of VARIG Airlines.

Lions
Emblem
and
Globes
A547

1967, May 9　Engr.　Perf. 11x11½
1047 A547 6c green　　　.25　.25
　　a.　Souvenir sheet　　7.50　7.50
　50th anniv. of Lions Intl. No. 1047a contains
one imperf. stamp similar to No. 1047. Sold for
15c.

Madonna and Child,
by Robert
Feruzzi — A548

1967, May 14　Photo.　Perf. 11½x11
1048 A548 5c violet　　　.25　.25
　　a.　15c Souvenir sheet　5.50　2.75
　Mother's Day. No. 1048a contains one 15c
imperf. stamp in design of No. 1048.

Prince
Akihito
and
Princess
Michiko
A549

1967, May 25　　　Perf. 11x11½
1049 A549 10c black & pink　.55　.25
　Visit to Brazil of Crown Prince Akihito and
Princess Michiko of Japan.

Carrier Pigeon and
Radar
Screen — A550

1967, June 20　Photo.　Wmk. 267
1050 A550 10c sl & brt pink　.25　.25
　Commemorating the opening of the Communications Ministry in Brasilia.

Brother Vicente do
Salvador — A551

1967, June 28　　　　　Engr.
1051 A551 5c brown　　　.25　.25
　400th birth anniv. of Brother Vicente do Salvador (1564-1636), founder of Franciscan convent in Rio de Janeiro, and historian.

Boy, Girl
and 4-S
Emblem
A552

1967, July 12　Photo.　Perf. 11½
1052 A552 5c green & blk　.25　.25
　National 4-S (4-H) Day.

Möbius
Strip
A553

1967, July 21　　　Perf. 11x11½
1053 A553 5c brt bl & blk　　.25　.25
　6th Brazilian Mathematical Congress.

Fish
A554

1967, Aug. 1　　　　Perf. 11½
1054 A554 5c slate　　　　.30　.25
　Bicentenary of city of Piracicaba.

Golden Rose and Papal Arms — A555

1967, Aug. 15
1055 A555 20c mag & yel　　.50　.25
　Offering of a golden rose by Pope Paul VI to
the Virgin Mary of Fatima (Our Lady of Peace),
Patroness of Brazil.

General
Sampaio — A556

1967, Aug. 25　Engr.　Perf. 11½x11
1056 A556 5c blue　　　　.25　.25
　Honoring General Antonio de Sampaio,
hero of the Battle of Tutui.

King Olaf of
Norway — A557

1967, Sept. 8　　　　　Photo.
1057 A557 10c brown org　　.25　.25
　Visit of King Olaf of Norway.

Sun over Sugar
Loaf, Botafogo
Bay — A558

Photogravure and Embossed
1967, Sept. 25 Wmk. 267 *Perf. 11½*
1058 A558 10c blk & dp org .35 .25
22nd meeting of the Intl. Monetary Fund, Intl. Bank for Reconstruction and Development, Intl. Financial Corporation and Intl. Development Assoc.

Nilo
Peçanha — A559

Perf. 11½x11
1967, Oct. 1 Photo. Wmk. 267
1059 A559 5c brown violet .25 .25
Peçanha (1867-1924), Pres. of Brazil 1909-10.

Virgin of the
Apparition and
Basilica of
Aparecida — A560

1967, Oct. 11 *Perf. 11½*
1060 A560 5c ultra & dl yel .25 .25
a. Souvenir sheet of 2 20.00 14.00
250th anniv. of the discovery of the statue of Our Lady of the Apparition, now in the National Basilica of the Apparition at Aparecida do Norte.
No. 1060a contains imperf. 5c and 10c stamps similar to No. 1060. Issued Dec. 27, 1967, for Christmas.

Cockerel, Festival
Emblem — A561

Engraved and Photogravure
1967, Oct. 16 *Perf. 11½x11*
1061 A561 20c black & multi .35 .25
Second International Folksong Festival.

Balloon,
Plane
and
Rocket
A562

Perf. 11x11½
1967, Oct. 18 Photo. Unwmk.
1062 A562 10c blue .35 .25
a. 15c souvenir sheet 37.50 20.00
Week of the Wing, Oct. 18-23. No. 1062a contains one imperf. 15c stamp similar to No. 1062 and was issued Oct. 23.

Pres. Arthur
Bernardes — A563

Portraits of Brazilian Presidents: 20c, Campos Salles. 50c, Wenceslau Pereira Gomes Braz. 1cr, Washington Pereira de Souza Luiz. 2cr, Castello Branco.

Perf. 11x11½
1967-68 Photo. Wmk. 267
1063 A563 10c blue .35 .25
1064 A563 20c dk red brn 2.50 .25
Engr.
1065 A563 50c black ('68) 12.00 .25
1066 A563 1cr lil rose ('68) 18.00 .25
1067 A563 2cr emerald ('68) 3.00 .25
Nos. 1063-1067 (5) 35.85 1.25

Carnival of
Rio — A564

1967, Nov. 22 *Perf. 11½x11*
1070 A564 10c lem, ultra &
pink .25 .25
a. 15c souvenir sheet 13.00 8.00
Issued for International Tourist Year, 1967. No. 1070a contains a 15c imperf. stamp in design of No. 1070. Issued Nov. 24.

Ships, Anchor and
Sailor — A565

1967, Dec. 6
1071 A565 10c ultra .35 .25
Issued for Navy Week.

Christmas
Decorations
A566

1967, Dec. 8 *Perf. 11½*
1072 A566 5c car, yel & bl .25 .25
Christmas 1967.

Olavo
Bilac,
Planes,
Tank and
Aircraft
Carrier
A567

Perf. 11x11½
1967, Dec. 16 Photo. Wmk. 267
1073 A567 5c brt blue & yel .25 .25
Issued for Reservists' Day and to honor Olavo Bilac, sponsor of compulsory military service.

Rodrigues de
Carvalho — A568

1967, Dec. 18 Engr. *Perf. 11½x11*
1074 A568 10c green .40 .25
Cent. of the birth of Rodrigues de Carvalho, poet and lawyer.

Orlando
Rangel
A569

1968, Feb. 29 Photo. *Perf. 11x11½*
1075 A569 5c lt grnsh bl & blk .30 .25
Orlando de Fonseca Rangel, pioneer of pharmaceutical industry in Brazil, birth cent.

Virgin of Paranagua
and Diver — A570

1968, Mar. 9 *Perf. 11½x11*
1076 A570 10c dk sl grn & brt yel
grn .25 .25
250th anniversary of the first underwater explorations at Paranagua.

Map of Brazil
Showing
Manaus — A571

1968, Mar. 13 Photo. Wmk. 267
1077 A571 10c yel, grn & red .30 .25
Free port of Manaus on the Amazon River.

Human Rights
Flame — A572

1968, Mar. 21 *Perf. 11½x11*
1078 A572 10c blue & salmon .25 .25
International Human Rights Year.

Paul Harris and
Rotary
Emblem — A573

1968, Apr. 19 Litho. Unwmk.
Without Gum
1079 A573 20c grn & org brn .40 .30
Paul Percy Harris (1868-1947), founder of Rotary International.

Pedro Alvares Cabral and his
Fleet — A574

Design: 20c, First Mass celebrated in Brazil.

1968 Without Gum *Perf. 11½*
1080 A574 10c multicolored .25 .25
1081 A574 20c multicolored .40 .25
500th anniversary of the birth of Pedro Alvares Cabral, navigator, who took possession of Brazil for Portugal.
Issue dates: 10c, Apr. 22; 20c, July 11.

College Arms — A575

1968, Apr. 22 Photo. Wmk. 267
1082 A575 10c vio bl, red & gold .25 .25
Centenary of St. Luiz College, Sao Paulo.

Motherhood,
by Henrique
Bernardeli
A576

1968, May 12 Litho. Unwmk.
Without Gum
1083 A576 5c multicolored .30 .25
Issued for Mother's Day.

Harpy Eagle A577

Photogravure and Engraved
1968, May 28 **Wmk. 267**
1084 A577 20c brt bl & blk 1.25 .25
Sesquicentennial of National Museum.

Brazilian and Japanese Women — A578

1968, June 28 **Litho.** **Unwmk.**
Without Gum
1085 A578 10c yellow & multi .30 .25
Commemorating the inauguration of Varig's direct Brazil-Japan airline.

Horse Race A579

Perf. 11x11½
1968, July 16 **Litho.** **Unwmk.**
Without Gum
1086 A579 10c multicolored .30 .25
Centenary of the Jockey Club of Brazil.

Musician Wren A580

Designs: 10c, Red-crested cardinal, vert. 50c, Royal flycatcher, vert.

Perf. 11½x11, 11x11½
1968-69 **Engr.** **Wmk. in Sheet**
Without Gum
1087 A580 10c multi ('69) .35 .25
1088 A580 20c multicolored .50 .25
1089 A580 50c multicolored 1.00 .25
Nos. 1087-1089 (3) 1.85 .75

Some stamps in each sheet of Nos. 1087-1089 show parts of a two-line papermaker's watermark: "WESTERPOST / INDUSTRIA BRASILEIRA" with diamond-shaped emblem between last two words. Entire watermark appears in one sheet margin. Value, set $45.
Issued: 10c, 8/20/69; 20c, 7/9/68; 50c, 8/2/68.

Mailbox and Envelope — A581

Photogravure and Engraved
1968, Aug. 1 **Wmk. 267** **Perf. 11**
1091 A581 5c tan, blk & grn .25 .25
Stamp Day, 1968 and for 125th anniv. of the 1st Brazilian postage stamps.

Emilio Luiz Mallet — A582

Perf. 11½x11
1968, Aug. 25 **Engr.** **Wmk. 267**
1092 A582 10c pale purple .25 .25
Honoring Marshal Emilio Luiz Mallet, Baron of Itapevi, patron of the marines.

Map of South America — A583

1968, Sept. 5 **Photo.**
1093 A583 10c deep orange .25 .25
Visit of President Eduardo Frei of Chile.

Seal of Portuguese Literary School — A584

Photogravure and Engraved
1968, Sept. 10 **Perf. 11½**
1094 A584 5c pink & grn .25 .25
Centenary of Portuguese Literary School.

Map of Brazil and Telex Tape A585

1968, Sept. **Photo.** **Perf. 11x11½**
1095 A585 20c citron & brt grn .50 .25
Linking of 25 Brazilian cities by teletype.

Soldiers' Heads on Medal — A586

Perf. 11½x11
1968, Sept. 24 **Litho.** **Unwmk.**
Without Gum
1096 A586 5c blue & gray .25 .25
8th American Armed Forces Conference.

Clef, Notes and Sugarloaf Mountain A587

1968, Sept. 30 **Perf. 11½**
Without Gum
1097 A587 6c blk, yel & red .25 .25
Third International Folksong Festival.

Catalytic Cracking Plant A588

1968, Oct. 4 **Without Gum**
1098 A588 6c blue & multi .40 .25
Petrobras, the natl. oil company, 15th anniv.

Child Protection — A589

Whimsical Girl — A590

5c, School boy walking toward the sun.

Perf. 11½x11, 11x11½
1968, Oct. 16 **Litho.** **Unwmk.**
Without Gum
1099 A590 5c gray & lt bl .25 .25
1100 A589 10c brt bl, dk red & blk .25 .25
1101 A590 20c multicolored .35 .25
Nos. 1099-1101 (3) .85 .75
22nd anniv. of UNICEF.

Children with Books A591

1968, Oct. 23 **Perf. 11x11½**
Without Gum
1102 A591 5c multicolored .25 .25
Book Week.

UN Emblem and Flags — A592

1968, Oct. 24 **Perf. 11½x11**
Without Gum
1103 A592 20c black & multi .35 .25
20th anniv. of WHO.

Jean Baptiste Debret, Self-portrait — A593

Perf. 11x11½
1968, Oct. 30 **Litho.** **Unwmk.**
Without Gum
1104 A593 10c dk gray & pale yel .25 .25
Jean Baptiste Debret, (1768-1848), French painter who worked in Brazil (1816-31). Design includes his "Burden Bearer."

Queen Elizabeth II A594

1968, Nov. 4 **Perf. 11½**
Without Gum
1105 A594 70c lt bl & multi .60 .40
Visit of Queen Elizabeth II of Great Britain.

Francisco Braga — A595

Perf. 11½x11
1968, Nov. 19 **Wmk. 267**
1106 A595 5c dull red brn .35 .25
Cent. of the birth of Antonio Francisco Braga, composer of the Hymn of the Flag.

Brazilian Flag — A596

1968, Nov. 19 **Unwmk.** **Perf. 11½**
Without Gum
1107 A596 10c multicolored .30 .25
Issued for Flag Day.

Clasped Hands and Globe A597

Perf. 11x11½
1968, Nov. 25   Typo.   Unwmk.
Without Gum
1108 A597 5c multicolored   .25 .25
Issued for Voluntary Blood Donor's Day.

Old Locomotive — A598

1968, Nov. 28   Litho.   *Perf. 11½*
Without Gum
1109 A598 5c multicolored   1.00 .35
Centenary of the Sao Paulo Railroad.

Bell — A599

Santa Claus and Boy — A599a

1968   Without Gum   *Perf. 11½x11*
1110 A599 5c multicolored   .25 .25
1111 A599a 6c multicolored   .25 .25
Christmas 1968.
Issue dates: 5c, Dec. 12; 6c, Dec. 20.

Francisco Caldas, Jr. — A600

1968, Dec. 13   Without Gum
1112 A600 10c crimson & blk   .25 .25
Cent. of the birth of Francisco Caldas, Jr., journalist and founder of Correio de Povo, newspaper.

Map of Brazil, War Memorial and Reservists' Emblem — A601

Perf. 11x11½
1968, Dec. 16   Photo.   Wmk. 267
1113 A601 5c bl grn & org brn   .25 .25
Issued for Reservists' Day.

Radar Antenna — A602

Perf. 11½x11
1969, Feb. 28   Litho.   Unwmk.
Without Gum
1114 A602 30c ultra, lt bl & blk   .35 .25
Inauguration of EMBRATEL, satellite communications ground station bringing US television to Brazil via Telstar.

Viscount of Rio Branco — A603

1969, Mar. 16   Without Gum
1115 A603 5c black & buff   .25 .25
José Maria da Silva Paranhos, Viscount of Rio Branco (1819-1880), statesman.

St. Gabriel — A604

1969, Mar. 24   Without Gum
1116 A604 5c multicolored   .25 .25
Honoring St. Gabriel as patron saint of telecommunications.

Shoemaker's Last and Globe — A605

Perf. 11x11½
1969, Mar. 29   Litho.   Unwmk.
Without Gum
1117 A605 5c multicolored   .25 .25
4th Intl. Shoe Fair, Novo Hamburgo.

Allan Kardec A606

1969, Mar. 31   Photo.   Wmk. 267
1118 A606 5c brt grn & org brn   .35 .25
Allan Kardec (pen name of Leon Hippolyto Denizard Rivail, 1803-1869), French physician and spiritist.

Men of 3 Races and Arms of Cuiabá A607

1969, Apr. 8   Litho.   Unwmk.
Without Gum
1119 A607 5c black & multi   .25 .25
250th anniversary of the founding of Cuiabá, capital of Matto Grosso.

State Mint — A608

1969, Apr. 11   *Perf. 11½*
Without Gum
1120 A608 5c olive bister & org   .30 .25
Opening of the state money printing plant.

Brazilian Stamps and Emblem A609

Perf. 11x11½
1969, Apr. 30   Litho.   Unwmk.
Without Gum
1121 A609 5c multicolored   .30 .25
Sao Paulo Philatelic Society, 50th anniv.

St. Anne, Baroque Statue A610

1969, May 8   *Perf. 11½*
Without Gum
1122 A610 5c lemon & multi   .25 .25
Issued for Mother's Day.

ILO Emblem A611

Perf. 11x11½
1969, May 13   Photo.   Wmk. 267
1123 A611 5c dp rose red & gold   .25 .25
50th anniv. of the ILO.

Diving Platform and Swimming Pool — A612

Lithographed and Photogravure
Perf. 11½x11
1969, June 13   Unwmk.
Without Gum
1124 A612 20c bis brn, blk & bl grn   .35 .25
40th anniversary of the Cearense Water Sports Club, Fortaleza.

Mother and Child at Window — A613

Sculpture, by Felicia Leirner — A613a

"The Sun Sets in Brasilia," by Danilo di Prete — A613b

Angelfish, by Aldemir Martins — A613c

Size: 24x36mm
1969   Litho.   *Perf. 11½*
1125 A613 10c orange & multi   .35 .25
Size: 33x34mm
1126 A613a 20c red & multi   .35 .25
Size: 33x53mm
1127 A613b 50c yellow & multi   1.50 .50
Without Gum
1128 A613c 1cr gray & multi   2.00 .75
Nos. 1125-1128 (4)   4.20 1.75
10th Biennial Art Exhibition, Sao Paulo, Sept.-Dec. 1969.

Angelfish A614

No. 1130: 10c, Tetra. 15c, Piranha. 20c, Megalamphodus megalopterus. 30c, Black tetra.

Wmk. 267
1969, July 21   Litho.   *Perf. 11½*
1129 A614 20c multicolored   .35 .25

Souvenir Sheet

Fish — A615

1969, July 24   Unwmk.   Imperf.
1130 A615   Sheet of 4   5.75   5.75
  a. 10c yellow & multi   1.25   1.25
  b. 15c bright blue & multi   1.25   1.25
  c. 20c green & multi   1.25   1.25
  d. 30c orange & multi   1.25   1.25

Issued to publicize the work of ACAPI, an organization devoted to the preservation and development of fish in Brazil.

No. 1130 contains four 38½x21mm stamps.

L. O. Teles de Menezes — A616

Perf. 11½x11
1969, July 26   Photo.   Wmk. 267
1131 A616 50c dp org & bl grn   .75   .75

Centenary of Spiritism press in Brazil.

Mailman — A617

1969, Aug. 1
1132 A617 30c blue   .60   .25

Issued for Stamp Day.

Map of Brazil A618

Railroad Bridge A619

Gen. Tasso Fragoso — A620

Without Gum

Perf. 11½
1969, Aug. 25   Unwmk.   Litho.
1133 A618 10c lt ultra, grn & yel   .25   .25
Perf. 11x11½
1134 A619 20c multicolored   .30   .25

With Gum

Perf. 11½x11
Engr.   Wmk. 267
1135 A620 20c green   .50   .25
  Nos. 1133-1135 (3)   1.05   .75

No. 1133 honors the Army as guardian of security; No. 1134, as promoter of development. No. 1135 the birth centenary of Gen. Tasso Fragoso.

Jupia Dam, Parana River A621

Perf. 11½
1969, Sept. 10   Litho.   Unwmk.
Without Gum
1136 A621 20c lt blue & multi   .35   .25

Inauguration of the Jupia Dam, part of the Urubupunga hydroelectric system serving Sao Paulo.

Gandhi and Spinning Wheel A622

1969, Oct. 2   Perf. 11x11½
1137 A622 20c yellow & blk   .60   .30

Mohandas K. Gandhi (1869-1948), leader in India's fight for independence.

Santos Dumont, Eiffel Tower and Module Landing on Moon — A623

1969, Oct. 17   Perf. 11½
Without Gum
1138 A623 50c dk bl & multi   1.00   1.00

Man's first landing on the moon, July 20, 1969. See note after US No. C76.

Smelting Plant A624

1969, Oct. 26   Unwmk.   Perf. 11½
Without Gum
1139 A624 20c multicolored   .30   .25

Expansion of Brazil's steel industry.

Steel Furnace A625

1969, Oct. 31   Litho.
Without Gum
1140 A625 10c yellow & multi   .30   .25

25th anniversary of Acesita Steel Works.

Water Vendor, by J. B. Debret — A626

Design: 30c, Street Scene, by Debret.

1969-70   Without Gum
1141 A626 20c multicolored   .70   .25
1141A A626 30c multicolored   .50   .30

Jean Baptiste Debret (1768-1848), painter. Issued: 20c, 11/5/69; 30c, 5/19/70.

Exhibition Emblem — A627

1969, Nov. 15   Perf. 11½x11
Without Gum
1142 A627 10c multicolored   .25   .25

ABUEXPO 69 Philatelic Exposition, Sao Paulo, Nov. 15-23.

Plane — A628

1969, Nov. 23   Without Gum
1143 A628 50c multicolored   1.00   .35

Publicizing the year of the expansion of the national aviation industry.

Pelé Scoring A629

1969-70   Without Gum
1144 A629 10c multicolored   .50   5.00
Souvenir Sheet
Imperf
1145 A629 75c multi ('70)   6.00   5.00

Commemorating the 1,000th goal scored by Pele, Brazilian soccer player.

No. 1145 contains one imperf. stamp with simulated perforations.

Issued: 10c, 11/28/69; 75c, 1/23/70.

Madonna and Child from Villa Velha Monastery A630

Perf. 11½
1969, Dec.   Unwmk.   Litho.
1146 A630 10c gold & multi   .30   .25
Souvenir Sheet
Imperf
1147 A630 75c gold & multi   30.00 30.00

Christmas 1969.

No. 1147 has simulated perforations.

Issue dates: 10c, Dec. 8; 75c, Dec. 18.

Destroyer and Submarine — A631

Perf. 11x11½
1969, Dec. 9   Engr.   Wmk. 267
1148 A631 5c bluish gray   .35 .25

Issued for Navy Day.

Dr. Herman Blumenau A632

1969, Dec. 26   Perf. 11½
1149 A632 20c gray grn   .70   .25

Dr. Herman Blumenau (1819-1899), founder of Blumenau, Santa Catarina State.

Carnival Scene — A633

Sugarloaf Mountain, Mask, Confetti and Streamers A634

Designs: 5c, Jumping boy and 2 women, vert. 20c, Clowns. 50c, Drummer.

1969-70 Litho. Unwmk.
Without Gum
1150 A633 5c multicolored .50 .25
1151 A633 10c multicolored .50 .25
1152 A633 50c multicolored .50 .25
1153 A634 30c multicolored 1.50 .50
1154 A634 50c multicolored 3.00 .50
Nos. 1150-1154 (5) 6.00 1.75

Carioca Carnival, Rio de Janeiro.
Issued: nos. 1150-1152, 12/29; others, 2/5/70.

Opening Bars of "Il Guarani" with Antonio Carlos Gomes Conducting — A635

1970, Mar. 19 Litho. Perf. 11½
Without Gum
1155 A635 20c blk, yel, gray & brn .35 .25
Centenary of the opera Il Guarani, by Antonio Carlos Gomes.

Church of Penha A636

1970, Apr. 6 Unwmk. Perf. 11½
Without Gum
1156 A636 20c black & multi .30 .25
400th anniversary of the Church of Penha, State of Espirito Santo.

Assembly Building A637

10th anniv. of Brasilia: 50c, Reflecting Pool. 1cr, Presidential Palace.

1970, Apr. 21 Without Gum
1157 A637 20c multicolored .35 .25
1158 A637 50c multicolored 1.20 1.00
1159 A637 1cr multicolored 1.45 1.00
Nos. 1157-1159 (3) 3.00 2.25

Symbolic Water Design A638

1970, May 5 Unwmk. Perf. 11½
Without Gum
1161 A638 50c multicolored .60 .25
Publicizing the Rondon Project for the development of the Amazon River basin.

Marshal Manoel Luiz Osorio and Osorio Arms — A639

1970, May 8 Without Gum
1162 A639 20c multicolored .60 .30
Commemorating the inauguration of the Marshal Osorio Historical Park.

Madonna, from San Antonio Monastery, Rio de Janeiro A640

1970, May 10 Without Gum
1163 A640 20c multicolored .35 .25
Issued for Mother's Day.

Detail from Brasilia Cathedral — A641

1970, May 27 Engr. Wmk. 267
1164 A641 20c lt yellow grn .30 .25
8th National Eucharistic Congress, Brasilia.

Census Symbol — A642

Perf. 11½
1970, June 22 Unwmk. Litho.
Without Gum
1165 A642 20c green & yel .35 .25
Publicizing the 8th general census.

Soccer Cup, Maps of Brazil and Mexico A643

Swedish Flag and Player Holding Rimet Cup — A644

Designs: 2cr, Chilean flag and soccer. 3cr, Mexican flag and soccer.

1970 Without Gum
1166 A643 50c blk, lt bl & gold .70 .30
1167 A644 1cr pink & multi 2.00 .60
1168 A644 2cr gray & multi 3.50 1.00
1169 A644 3cr multicolored 3.00 .50
Nos. 1166-1169 (4) 9.20 2.40

9th World Soccer Championships for the Jules Rimet Cup, Mexico City, May 30-June 21. No. 1166 honors Brazil's victory.
Issued: No. 1166, 6/24; Nos. 1167-1169, 8/4.

Corcovado Christ and Map of South America A645

1970, July 18 Without Gum
1170 A645 50c brn, dk red & bl .50 .25
6th World Cong. of Marist Brothers' Alumni.

Pandia Calogeras, Minister of War — A646

Perf. 11½x11
1970, Aug. 25 Photo. Unwmk.
1171 A646 20c blue green .40 .25

Brazilian Military Emblems and Map — A647

Perf. 11x11½
1970, Sept. 8 Litho. Unwmk.
Without Gum
1172 A647 20c gray & multi .30 .25
25th anniv. of victory in World War II.

Annunciation (Brazilian Primitive Painting) A648

1970, Sept. 29 Perf. 11½
Without Gum
1173 A648 20c multicolored .40 .25
Issued for St. Gabriel's (patron saint of communications) Day.

Boy in Library — A649

1970, Oct. 23 Without Gum
1174 A649 20c multicolored .25 .25
Issued to publicize Book Week.

UN Emblem — A650

1970, Oct. 24 Without Gum
1175 A650 50c dk bl, lt bl & sil .40 .25
25th anniversary of the United Nations.

Rio de Janeiro, 1820 — A651

Designs: 50c, LUBRAPEX 70 emblem. 1cr, Rio de Janeiro with Sugar Loaf Mountain, 1970. No. 1179, like 20c.

1970, Oct. Without Gum
1176 A651 20c multicolored .60 .25
1177 A651 50c yel brn & blk 2.50 .60
1178 A651 1cr multicolored 3.00 1.00
Nos. 1176-1178 (3) 6.10 1.85

Souvenir Sheet
Imperf
1179 A651 1cr multicolored 16.00 12.00
LUBRAPEX 70, 3rd Portuguese-Brazilian Phil. Exhib., Rio de Janeiro, Oct. 24-31.
Issued: Nos. 1176-1178, 10/27; No. 1179, 10/31.

Holy Family by Candido Portinari A652

1970, Dec. Litho. Perf. 11½
Without Gum
1180 A652 50c multicolored .50 .30
Souvenir Sheet
Imperf
1181 A652 1cr multicolored 37.50 5.00
Christmas 1970. No. 1181 contains one stamp with simulated perforations.
Issue dates: 50c, Dec. 1; 1cr, Dec. 8.

Battleship — A653

1970, Dec. 11　　Litho.　　Perf. 11½
Without Gum
1182　A653　20c multicolored　　.50　.30
Navy Day.

CIH
Emblem — A654

1971, Mar. 28　　Litho.　　Perf. 11½
Without Gum
1183　A654　50c black & red　　.50　.25
3rd Inter-American Housing Cong., 3/27-4/3.

Links Around
Globe — A655

1971, Mar. 31　　Litho.　　Perf. 12½x11
Without Gum
1184　A655　20c grn, yel, blk & red　　.30　.25
Intl. year against racial discrimination.

Morpho Melacheilus — A656

Design: 1cr, Papilio thoas brasiliensis.

Perf. 11x11½
1971, Apr. 28　　Litho.　　Unwmk.
Without Gum
1185　A656　20c multicolored　　.75　.25
1186　A656　1cr multicolored　　3.50　1.00

Madonna and
Child — A657

1971, May 9　　Litho.　　Perf. 11½
Without Gum
1187　A657　20c multicolored　　.40　.25
Mother's Day, 1971.

Basketball
A658

1971, May 19　　　　Without Gum
1188　A658　70c multicolored　　.75　.40
6th World Women's Basketball Championship.

Map of Trans-Amazon
Highway — A659

Perf. 11½
1971, July 1　　Unwmk.　　Litho.
Without Gum
1189　　40c multicolored　　5.00　1.00
1190　　1cr multicolored　　5.00　1.75
　a.　A659　Pair, #1189-1190　　20.00　10.00

Trans-Amazon Highway. No. 1190a printed in sheets of 28 (4x7). Horizontal rows contain 2 No. 1190a with a label between. Each label carries different inscription.

Man's Head,
by Victor
Mairelles de
Lima
A661

Stamp Day: 1cr, Arab Violinist, by Pedro Américo.

1971, Aug. 1
1191　A661　40c pink & multi　　.90　.25
1192　A661　1cr gray & multi　　2.50　.80

Duke of
Caxias and
Map of
Brazil
A662

1971, Aug. 23　　　　Photo.
1193　A662　20c yel grn & red brn　　.45　.25
Army Week.

Anita
Garibaldi — A663

1971, Aug. 30　　　　　　Litho.
Without Gum
1194　A663　20c multicolored　　.50　.25
Anita Garibaldi (1821-1849), heroine in liberation of Brazil.

Xavante Jet and Santos Dumont's
Plane, 1910 — A664

1971, Sept. 6　　　　Without Gum
1195　A664　40c yellow & multi　　.70　.25
First flight of Xavante jet plane.

Flags and Map of
Central American
Nations — A665

1971, Sept. 15　　　　Without Gum
1196　A665　40c ocher & multi　　.60　.25
Sesquicentennial of the independence of Central American nations.

"71" in French Flag
Colors — A666

1971, Sept. 16　　　　Without Gum
1197　A666　1.30cr ultra & multi　　.40　.25
French Exhibition.

Black Mother, by
Lucilio de
Albuquerque
A667

1971, Sept. 28　　　　Without Gum
1198　A667　40c multicolored　　.30　.25
Centenary of law guaranteeing personal freedom starting at birth.

Archangel
Gabriel — A668

1971, Sept. 29　　　　Perf. 11½x11
Without Gum
1199　A668　40c multicolored　　.50　.25
St. Gabriel's Day.

Bridge over
River
A669

Children's Drawings: 35c, People crossing bridge. 60c, Woman with hat.

1971, Oct. 25　　　　Perf. 11½
Without Gum
1200　A669　35c pink, bl & blk　　.60　.25
1201　A669　45c black & multi　　.60　.25
1202　A669　60c olive & multi　　.60　.25
　Nos. 1200-1202 (3)　　1.80　.75
Children's Day.

Werkhäuserii Superba — A670

1971, Nov. 16　　　　Without Gum
1203　A670　40c blue & multi　　.70　.25
In memory of Carlos Werkhauser, botanist.

Greek Key Pattern "25" — A671

1971, Dec. 3　　　　Without Gum
1204　　20c black & blue　　1.25　.25
1205　　40c black & org　　1.25　.25
　a.　A671　Pair, #1204-1205　　3.50　3.50

25th anniversary of SENAC (national apprenticeship system) and SESC (commercial social service).

Gunboat
A672

1971, Dec. 8　　　　Perf. 11
Without Gum
1206　A672　20c blue & multi　　.30　.25
Navy Day.

Cross and
Circles — A673

1971, Dec. 11
1207　A673　20c car & blue　　.60　.25
1208　A673　75c silver & gray　　.60　.25
1209　A673　1.30cr blk, yel, grn & bl　　1.60　.60
　Nos. 1207-1209 (3)　　2.80　1.10
Christmas 1971.

Washing of Bonfim Church, Salvador, Bahia — A674

Designs: 40c, Grape Festival, Rio Grande do Sul. 75c, Festival of the Virgin of Nazareth, Belém. 1.30cr, Winter Arts Festival, Ouro Preto.

1972, Feb. 18   Litho.   Perf. 11½x11
Without Gum

1210	A674	20c silver & multi	.55	.25
1211	A674	40c silver & multi	.70	.25
1212	A674	75c silver & multi	.90	.25
1213	A674	1.30cr silver & multi	3.50	1.10
		Nos. 1210-1213 (4)	5.65	2.10

Pres. Lanusse and Flag of Argentina A675

1972, Mar. 13   Perf. 11x11½
Without Gum

1214	A675	40c blue & multi	.70	.50

Visit of Lt. Gen. Alejandro Agustin Lanusse, president of Argentina.

Presidents Castello Branco, Costa e Silva and Garrastazu Medici — A676

1972, Mar. 29   Without Gum

1215	A676	20c emerald & multi	.70	.25

Anniversary of 1964 revolution.

Post Office Emblem — A677

Perf. 11½x11½

1972, Apr. 10   Photo.   Unwmk.

1216	A677	20c red brown	1.50	.25

No. 1216 is luminescent.

Pres. Thomaz and Portuguese Flag — A678

1972, Apr. 22   Litho.   Perf. 11
Without Gum

1217	A678	75c ol brn & multi	.85	.50

Visit of Pres. Americo Thomaz of Portugal to Brazil, Apr. 22-27.

Soil Research (CPRM) A679

40c, Offshore oil rig. 75c, Hydroelectric dam. 1.30cr, Iron ore production.

1972, May 3   Perf. 11½
Without Gum

1218	A679	20c shown	.50	.25
1219	A679	40c multi	.70	.25
1220	A679	75c multi	.70	.60
1221	A679	1.30cr multi	1.45	.35
		Nos. 1218-1221 (4)	3.35	1.45

Industrial development. Stamps are inscribed with names of industrial firms. See Nos. 1228-1229.

Souvenir Sheet

Poster for Modern Art Week 1922 — A680

1972, May 5

1222	A680	1cr black & car	50.00	40.00

50th anniversary of Modern Art Week.

Mailman, Map of Brazil and Letters A681

Designs: 45c, "Telecommunications", vert. 60c, Tropospheric scatter system. 70c, Road map of Brazil and worker.

1972, May 26   Without Gum

1223	A681	35c blue & multi	.70	.25
1224	A681	45c silver & multi	.70	.30
1225	A681	60c black & multi	.70	.25
1226	A681	70c multicolored	1.00	.25
		Nos. 1223-1226 (4)	3.10	1.05

Unification of communications in Brazil.

Development Type of 1972 and

Automobiles — A682

Perf. 11x11½, 11½x11

1972, June 21   Photo.

1227	A682	35c shown	.60	.25

Litho.

1228	A679	45c Ships	.60	.25
1229	A679	70c Ingots	.60	.25
		Nos. 1227-1229 (3)	1.80	.75

Industrial development. The 35c is luminescent.

Soccer — A683

75c, Folk music. 1.30cr, Plastic arts.

Perf. 11½x11

1972, July 7   Photo.   Unwmk.

1230	A683	20c black & yel	.40	.25
1231	A683	75c black & ver	.80	.40
1232	A683	1.30cr black & ultra	1.60	.80
		Nos. 1230-1232 (3)	2.80	1.45

150th anniv. of independence. No. 1230 publicizes the 1972 sports tournament, a part of independence celebrations. Luminescent.

Souvenir Sheet

Shout of Independence, by Pedro Americo de Figueiredo e Melo — A684

1972, July 19   Litho.   Perf. 11½
Without Gum

1233	A684	1cr multicolored	6.00	7.00

4th Interamerican Philatelic Exhibition, EXFILBRA, Rio de Janeiro, Aug 26-Sept. 2.

Figurehead A685

Brazilian folklore: 60c, Gauchos dancing fandango. 75c, Acrobats (capoeira). 1.15cr, Karajá (ceramic) doll. 1.30cr, Mock bullfight (bumba meu boi).

1972, Aug. 6   Without Gum

1234	A685	45c multicolored	.40	.25
1235	A685	60c org & multi	.80	.40
1236	A685	75c gray & multi	.40	.25
1237	A685	1.15cr multicolored	.40	.25
1238	A685	1.30cr yellow & multi	2.50	.60
		Nos. 1234-1238 (5)	4.50	1.75

Map of Brazil, by Diego Homem, 1568 A686

Designs: 1cr, Map of Americas, by Nicholas Visscher, 1652. 2cr, Map of Americas, by Lopo Homem, 1519.

1972, Aug. 26   Litho.   Perf. 11½
Without Gum

1239	A686	70c multicolored	.80	.25
1240	A686	1cr multicolored	6.00	.70
1241	A686	2cr multicolored	1.50	.60
		Nos. 1239-1241 (3)	8.30	1.55

4th Inter-American Philatelic Exhibition, EXFILBRA, Rio de Janeiro, Aug. 26-Sept. 2.

Dom Pedro Proclaimed Emperor, by Jean Baptiste Debret — A687

Designs: 30c, Founding of Brazil (people with imperial flag), vert. 1cr, Coronation of Emperor Dom Pedro, vert. 2cr, Dom Pedro commemorative medal. 3.50cr, Independence Monument, Ipiranga.

1972, Sept. 4   Litho.   Perf. 11½x11

1242	A687	30c yellow & grn	.60	.25
1243	A687	70c pink & rose lil	.60	.25
1244	A687	1cr buff & red brn	3.00	.25
1245	A687	2cr pale yel & blk	2.00	.25
1246	A687	3.50cr gray & blk	2.00	.70
		Nos. 1242-1246 (5)	8.20	1.70

Sesquicentennial of independence.

Souvenir Sheet

"Automobile Race" — A688

1972, Nov. 14   Perf. 11½

1247	A688	2cr multicolored	8.50	10.00

Emerson Fittipaldi, Brazilian world racing champion.

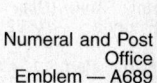

Numeral and Post Office Emblem — A689

Möbius Strip A689a

Perf. 11½x11

1972-75   Unwmk.   Photo.

1248	A689	5c orange ('74)	.25	.25
a.		Wmk. 267	.35	.25
1249	A689	10c brown ('73)	.25	.25
a.		Wmk. 267	1.50	.25
1250	A689	15c brt blue ('75)	.35	.25
1251	A689	20c ultra	2.00	.25
1252	A689	25c sepia ('75)	.35	.25
1253	A689	30c dp carmine	1.20	.25
1254	A689	40c dk grn ('73)	.35	.25
1255	A689	50c olive ('74)	1.00	.25
1256	A689	70c red lilac ('75)	.50	.25

Engr.   Perf. 11½

1257	A689a	1cr lilac ('74)	.75	.25
1258	A689a	2cr grnsh bl ('74)	1.20	.25
1259	A689a	4cr org & vio ('75)	4.50	.25
1260	A689a	5cr brn, car & buff ('74)	3.50	.25
1261	A689a	10cr grn, blk & buff ('74)	6.00	.25
		Nos. 1248-1261 (14)	21.95	3.50

The 5cr and 10cr have beige lithographed multiple Post Office emblem underprint. Nos. 1248-1261 are luminescent. Nos. 1248a and 1249a are not.

No. 1257 exists unwatermarked. Value $150.
No. 1258 exists with watermark 267. Value $250.

Hand Writing "Mobral"
A690

Designs: 20c, Multiracial group and population growth curve. 1cr, People and hands holding house. 2cr, People, industrial scene and upward arrow.

1972, Nov. 28 Litho. Perf. 11½
Without Gum

1262	A690	10c black & multi	.40	.25
1263	A690	20c black & multi	.40	.25
1264	A690	1cr black & multi	1.20	.25
1265	A690	2cr black & multi	5.00	.50
		Nos. 1262-1265 (4)	7.00	1.25

Publicity for: "Mobral" literacy campaign (10c); Centenary of census (20c); Housing and retirement fund (1cr); Growth of gross national product (2cr).

Congress Building, Brasilia, by Oscar Niemeyer, and "Os Guerreiros," by Bruno Giorgi — A691

1972, Dec. 4 Without Gum
1266 A691 1cr blue, blk & org 6.00 3.50
Meeting of Natl. Cong., Brasilia, Dec. 4-8.

Holy Family (Clay Figurines) — A692

1972, Dec. 13 Photo. Perf. 11½x11
1267 A692 20c ocher & blk .40 .25
Christmas 1972. Luminescent.

Retirement Plan — A693

Designs: No.1269, School children and traffic lights, horiz. 70c, Dr. Oswaldo Cruz with Red Cross, caricature. 2cr, Produce, fish and cattle, horiz.

Perf. 11½x11, 11x11½
1972, Dec. 20 Litho.
Without Gum

1268	A693	10c blk, bl & dl org	.60	.25
1269	A693	10c orange & multi	.60	.25
1270	A693	70c blk, red & brn	2.25	1.50
1271	A693	2cr green & multi	6.00	3.00
		Nos. 1268-1271 (4)	9.45	5.00

Publicity for: Agricultural workers' assistance program (No. 1268); highway and transportation development (No. 1269); centenary of the birth of Dr. Oswaldo Cruz (1872-1917),

Director of Public Health Institute (70c); agricultural and cattle export (2cr). Nos. 1268-1271 are luminescent.

Sailing Ship, Navy A694

Designs: 10c, Monument, Brazilian Expeditionary Force. No. 1274, Plumed helmet, Army. No. 1275, Rocket, Air Force.

Lithographed and Engraved
1972, Dec. 28 Perf. 11x11½
Without Gum

1272	A694	10c brn, dk brn & blk	.60	.60
1273	A694	30c lt ultra, grn & blk	.60	.60
1274	A694	30c yel grn, bl grn & blk	.60	.60
1275	A694	30c lilac, mar & blk	.60	.60
a.		Block of 4, #1272-1275	3.50	3.50

Armed Forces Day.

Rotary Emblem and Cogwheels A695

Perf. 11½
1973, Mar. 21 Litho. Unwmk.
1276 A695 1cr ultra, grnsh bl & yel 1.25 .60
Rotary International serving Brazil 50 years.

Swimming — A696

Designs: No. 1278, Gymnastics. No. 1279, Volleyball, vert.

1973 Photo. Perf. 11x11½, 11½x11

1277	A696	40c brt bl & red brn	.55	.25
1278	A696	40c green & org brn	1.00	.25
1279	A696	40c violet & org brn	.55	.25
		Nos. 1277-1279 (3)	2.10	.75

Issued: No. 1277, 4/19; No. 1278, 5/22; No.1279, 10/15.

Flag of Paraguay A697

Perf. 11½
1973, Apr. 27 Litho. Unwmk.
1280 A697 70c multicolored .85 .35
Visit of Pres. Alfredo Stroessner of Paraguay, Apr. 25-27.

"Communications" — A698

Designs: 1cr, Neptune, map of South America and Africa.

1973, May 5 Perf. 11x11½
1281 A698 70c multicolored 1.00 .25
1282 A698 1cr multicolored 2.50 .70

Inauguration of the Ministry of Communications Building, Brasilia (70c); and of the first underwater telephone cable between South America and Europe, Bracan 1 (1cr).

Congress Emblem — A699

1973, May 19 Perf. 11½x11
1283 A699 1cr orange & pur 2.50 .70

24th Congress of the International Chamber of Commerce, Rio de Janeiro, May 19-26.

Swallowtailed Manakin — A700

Birds: No. 1285, Orange-backed oriole. No. 1286, Brazilian ruby (hummingbird).

1973 Litho. Perf. 11x11½

1284	A700	20c multicolored	1.25	.25
1285	A700	20c multicolored	1.25	.25
1286	A700	20c multicolored	1.25	.25
		Nos. 1284-1286 (3)	3.75	.75

Issued: No. 1284, 5/26; No. 1285, 6/6; No. 1286, 6/19.

Tourists A701

1973, June 28 Litho. Perf. 11x11½
1287 A701 70c multicolored .50 .25

National Tourism Year.

Conference at Itu — A702

1973 Perf. 11½x11

1288	A702	20c shown	.60	.25
1289	A702	20c Decorated wagon	.60	.25
1290	A702	20c Indian	.60	.25
1291	A702	20c Graciosa Road	.60	.25
		Nos. 1288-1291 (4)	2.40	1.00

Centenary of the Itu Convention (No. 1288); sesquicentennial of the July 2 episode (No. 1289); 400th anniversary of the founding of Niteroi (No. 1290); centenary of Graciosa Road (No. 1291).
Issue dates: No. 1291, July 29; others July 2.

Satellite and Multi-spectral Image A703

Designs: 70c, Official opening of Engineering School, 1913. 1cr, Möbius strips and "IMPA."

1973, July 11 Perf. 11½

1292	A703	20c black & multi	.40	.25
1293	A703	70c dk blue & multi	1.25	.25
1294	A703	1cr lilac & multi	1.75	.25
		Nos. 1292-1294 (3)	3.40	.75

Institute for Space Research (20c); School of Engineering, Itajubá, 60th anniversary (70c); Institute for Pure and Applied Mathematics (1cr).

Santos-Dumont and 14-Bis Plane — A704

Santos-Dumont and: 70c, No. 6 Balloon and Eiffel Tower. 2cr Demoiselle plane.

Lithographed and Engraved
1973, July 20 Perf. 11x11½

1295	A704	20c lt grn, brt grn & brn	.60	.25
1296	A704	70c yel, rose red & brn	1.25	.50
1297	A704	2cr bl, vio bl & brn	2.50	.50
		Nos. 1295-1297 (3)	4.35	1.25

Centenary of the birth of Alberto Santos-Dumont (1873-1932), aviation pioneer.

Mercator Map — A705

Designs: No. 1298, "BRASIL" within white background. No. 1299, Right half of "0" in "40" overlays red border. No. 1299A, "B" in "BRASIL" touches red. No. 1299B, Top edge of "0" in "40" overlays red border.

Photogravure and Engraved
1973, Aug. 1 Wmk. 267

1298		40c red & black	2.50	2.50
1299		40c red & black	.60	.60
1299A		40c red & black	12.00	7.00
1299B		40c red & black	3.50	3.50
c.	A705	Block of 4, #1298-1299B	25.00	20.00

Stamp Day. Nos. 1298-1299B are printed se-tenant horizontally and tête bêche vertically in sheets of 55.

Gonçalves Dias (1823-1864), Poet — A706

Perf. 11½x11
1973, Aug. 10 Wmk. 267
1300 A706 40c violet & blk .40 .20

Souvenir Sheet

Copernicus and Sun — A707

Perf. 11x11½
1973, Aug. 15   Litho.   Unwmk.
1301 A707 1cr multicolored   12.50 12.50
500th anniversary of the birth of Nicolaus Copernicus (1473-1543), Polish astronomer.

Folklore Festival Banner — A708

1973, Aug. 22   Perf. 11½
1302 A708 40c ultra & multi   .40 .25
Folklore Day, Aug. 22.

Masonic Emblem A709

1973, Aug. 24   Photo.   Perf. 11x11½
1303 A709 1cr Prus blue   1.50 .65
Free Masons of Brazil, 1822-1973.

Nature Protection — A710

Designs: No. 1305, Fire protection. No. 1306, Aviation safety. No. 1307, Safeguarding cultural heritage.

1973, Sept. 20   Litho.   Perf. 11x11½
1304 A710 40c brt grn & multi   .45 .45
1305 A710 40c dk blue & multi   .45 .45
1306 A710 40c lt blue & multi   .45 .45
1307 A710 40c pink & multi   .45 .45
    Nos. 1304-1307 (4)   1.80 1.80

Souvenir Sheet

St. Gabriel and Proclamation of Pope Paul VI — A711

Lithographed and Engraved
1973, Sept. 29   Unwmk.   Perf. 11½
1308 A711 1cr bister & blk   12.50 5.75
1st National Exhibition of Religious Philately, Rio de Janeiro, Sept. 29-Oct. 6.

St. Teresa — A712

Photogravure and Engraved
Perf. 11½x11
1973, Sept. 30   Wmk. 267
1309 A712 2cr dk org & brn   1.25 .75
St. Teresa of Lisieux, the Little Flower (1873-1897), Carmelite nun.

Monteiro Lobato and Emily A713

No. 1311, Aunt Nastacia. No. 1312, Snubnose, Peter and Rhino. No. 1313, Viscount de Sabugosa. No. 1314, Dona Benta.

Perf. 11½
1973, Oct. 12   Litho.   Unwmk.
1310 A713 40c shown   .65 .60
1311 A713 40c multicolored   .65 .60
1312 A713 40c multicolored   .65 .60
1313 A713 40c multicolored   .65 .60
1314 A713 40c multicolored   .65 .60
   a.   Block of 5 + label   3.25 3.25
Monteiro Lobato, author of children's books.

Soapstone Sculpture of Isaiah (detail) A714

Baroque Art in Brazil: No. 1316, Arabesque, gilded wood carving, horiz. 70c, Father José Mauricio Nuñes Garcia and music score. 1cr, Church door, Salvador, Bahia. 2cr, Angels, church ceiling painting by Manoel da Costa Athayde, horiz.

1973, Nov. 5
1315 A714 40c multicolored   .55 .25
1316 A714 40c multicolored   .55 .25
1317 A714 70c multicolored   1.25 .65
1318 A714 1cr multicolored   5.00 .90
1319 A714 2cr multicolored   5.00 1.10
    Nos. 1315-1319 (5)   12.35 3.15

Old and New Telephones — A715

1973, Nov. 28   Perf. 11x11½
1320 A715 40c multicolored   .40 .25
50th anniv. of Brazilian Telephone Co.

Symbolic Angel A716

1973, Nov. 30   Perf. 11½
1321 A716 40c ver & multi   .40 .25
Christmas 1973.

River Boats A717

1973, Nov. 30   Litho.   Perf. 11x11½
1322 A717 40c "Gaiola"   .40 .25
1323 A717 70c "Regatao"   .65 .45
1324 A717 1cr "Jangada"   3.00 1.50
1325 A717 2cr "Saveiro"   2.50 1.05
    Nos. 1322-1325 (4)   6.55 3.25
Nos. 1322-1325 are luminescent.

Scales of Justice A718

1973, Dec. 5   Perf. 11½
1326 A718 40c magenta & vio   .45 .25
To honor the High Federal Court, created in 1891. Luminescent.

José Placido de Castro — A719

Lithographed and Engraved
Perf. 11½x11
1973, Dec. 12   Wmk. 267
1327 A719 40c lilac rose & blk   .65 .25
Centenary of the birth of Jose Placido de Castro, liberator of the State of Acre.

Scarlet Ibis and Victoria Regia — A720

Designs: 70c, Jaguar and spathodea campanulata. 1cr, Scarlet macaw and carnauba palm. 2cr, Rhea and coral tree.

Perf. 11½x11
1973, Dec. 28   Litho.   Unwmk.
1328 A720 40c brown & multi   .65 .25
1329 A720 70c brown & multi   1.60 .75
1330 A720 1cr bister & multi   1.60 .25
1331 A720 2cr bister & multi   6.25 1.90
    Nos. 1328-1331 (4)   10.10 3.15
Nos. 1328-1331 are luminescent.

Saci Perere, Mocking Goblin — A721

Characters from Brazilian Legends: 80c, Zumbi, last chief of rebellious slaves. 1cr, Chico Rei, African king. 1.30cr, Little Black Boy of the Pasture. 2.50cr, Iara, Queen of the Waters.

Perf. 11½x11
1974, Feb. 28   Litho.   Unwmk.
Size: 21x39mm
1332 A721 40c multicolored   .55 .25
1333 A721 80c multicolored   1.00 .25
1334 A721 1cr multicolored   1.25 .25
Perf. 11½
Size: 32½x33mm
1335 A721 1.30cr multicolored   2.75 .50
1336 A721 2.50cr multicolored   7.25 1.90
    Nos. 1332-1336 (5)   12.80 3.15
Nos. 1332-1336 are luminescent.

Pres. Costa e Silva Bridge A722

1974, Mar. 11
1337 A722 40c multicolored   .65 .25
Inauguration of the Pres. Costa e Silva Bridge, Rio Niteroi, connecting Rio de Janeiro and Guanabara State.

"The Press" A723

1974, Mar. 25   Perf. 11½
1338 A723 40c shown   .40 .25
1339 A723 40c "Radio"   .40 .25
1340 A723 40c "Television"   .40 .25
    Nos. 1338-1340 (3)   1.20 .75
Communications Commemorations: No. 1338, bicentenary of first Brazilian newspaper, published in London by Hipolito da Costa; No. 1339, founding of the Radio Sociedade do Rio de Janeiro by Roquette Pinto; No. 1340, installation of first Brazilian television station by Assis Chateaubriand. Luminescent.

"Reconstruction" — A724

1974, Mar. 31
1341 A724 40c multicolored   .45 .25
10 years of progress. Luminescent.

Corcovado Christ, Marconi, Colors of Brazil and Italy — A725

1974, Apr. 25 Litho. Perf. 11½
1342 A725 2.50cr multi 5.25 2.75
Guglielmo Marconi (1874-1937), Italian physicist and inventor. Luminescent.

Stamp Printing Press, Stamp Designing A726

1974, May 6
1343 A726 80c multicolored .55 .25
Brazilian mint.

World Map, Indian, Caucasian and Black Men — A727

World Map and: No. 1345, Brazilians. No. 1346, Cabin & German horseback rider. No. 1347, Italian farm wagon. No. 1348, Japanese woman & torii.

1974, May 3 Unwmk.
1344 A727 40c multicolored .45 .25
1345 A727 40c multicolored .45 .25
1346 A727 2.50cr multicolored 2.25 .40
1347 A727 2.50cr multicolored 4.75 .40
1348 A727 2.50cr multicolored 2.25 .40
Nos. 1344-1348 (5) 10.15 1.70
Ethnic and migration influences in Brazil.

Sandstone Cliffs, Sete Cidades National Park — A728

Tourist publicity: 80c, Ruins of Cathedral of Sao Miguel das Missões.

Lithographed and Engraved
1974, June 8 Perf. 11x11½
1349 A728 40c multicolored .55 .25
1350 A728 80c multicolored .55 .25

Souvenir Sheet

Soccer — A729

1974, June 20 Litho. Perf. 11½
1351 A729 2.50cr multi 12.50 12.50
World Cup Soccer Championship, Munich, June 13-July 7.

Church and College, Caraça A730

1974, July 6 Litho. Perf. 11x11½
1352 A730 40c multicolored .55 .25
College (Seminary) of Caraça, bicent.

Wave on Television Screen A731

1974, July 15 Perf. 11½
1353 A731 40c black & blue .30 .25
TELEBRAS, Third Brazilian Congress of Telecommunications, Brasilia, July 15-20.

Fernao Dias Paes A732

1974, July 21 Perf. 11½
1354 A732 20c green & multi .30 .25
3rd centenary of the expedition led by Fernao Dias Paes exploring Minas Gerais and the passage from South to North in Brazil.

Mexican Flag — A733

1974, July 24 Litho. Perf. 11½
1355 A733 80c multicolored 1.10 .55
Visit of Pres. Luis Echeverria Alvares of Mexico, July 24-29.

Flags of Brazil and Germany A734

1974, Aug. 5 Perf. 11x11½
1356 A734 40c multicolored .55 .30
World Cup Soccer Championship, 1974, victory of German Federal Republic.

Souvenir Sheet

Congress Emblem — A735

1974, Aug. 7 Perf. 11½
1357 A735 1.30cr multi 1.75 1.75
5th World Assembly of the World Council for the Welfare of the Blind, Sao Paulo, Aug. 7-16. Stamp and margin inscribed in Braille with name of Assembly.
Exists imperforate. Value $1300. Exists with the braile missing or duplicated in the margin. Value $600 and $65 respectively.

Raul Pederneiras (1874-1953, Journalist, Professor of Law and Fine Arts), Caricature by J. Carlos — A736

Lithographed and Engraved
1974, Aug. 15 Perf. 11½x11
1358 A736 40c buff, blk & ocher .35 .25

Society Emblem and Landscape — A737

1974, Aug. 19 Litho. Perf. 11x11½
1359 A737 1.30cr multi .50 .30
13th Congress of the International Union of Building and Savings Societies.

Souvenir Sheet

Five Women, by Di Cavalcanti — A738

1974, Aug. 26 Litho. Perf. 11½
1360 A738 2cr multicolored 5.25 5.25
LUBRAPEX 74, 5th Portuguese-Brazilian Phil. Exhib., Sao Paulo, Nov. 26-Dec. 4.

"UPU" and World Map A739

1974, Oct. 9 Litho. Perf. 11½
1361 A739 2.50cr blk & brt bl 4.75 2.50
Centenary of Universal Postal Union.

Hammock (Antillean Arawak Culture) A740

Bilro Lace — A741

Singer of "Cord" Verses — A742

Ceramic Figure by Master Vitalino — A743

1974, Oct. 16 Litho. Perf. 11½
1362 A740 50c deep rose lilac .75 .25
1363 A741 50c lt & dk blue 1.10 .25
1364 A742 50c yel & red brn .65 .25
1365 A743 50c brt yel & dk brn .65 .25
Nos. 1362-1365 (4) 3.15 1.00
Popular Brazilian crafts.

Branch of Coffee A744

1974, Oct. 27 Unwmk. Perf. 11
1366 A744 50c multicolored .40 .25
Centenary of city of Campinas.

Hornless Tabapua A745

Animals of Brazil: 1.30cr, Creole horse. 2.50cr, Brazilian mastiff.

1974, Nov. 10   *Perf. 11½*
1367	A745	80c multi	.75	.30
1368	A745	1.30cr multi	.75	.30
1369	A745	2.50cr multi	5.50	1.00
	Nos. 1367-1369 (3)		7.00	1.60

Christmas — A746

1974, Nov. 18   *Perf. 11½x11*
1370	A746	50c Angel	.25	.25

Solteira Island Hydroelectric
Dam — A747

1974, Nov. 11   *Perf. 11½*
1371	A747	50c black & yellow	.35	.25

Inauguration of the Solteira Island Hydroelectric Dam over Parana River.

The Girls, by
Carlos
Reis — A748

1974, Nov. 26
1372	A748	1.30cr multi	.25	.25

LUBRAPEX 74, 5th Portuguese-Brazilian Phil. Exhib., Sao Paulo, Nov. 26-Dec. 4.

Youths,
Judge,
Scales
A749

1974, Dec. 20   **Litho.**   *Perf. 11½*
1373	A749	90c yel, red & bl	.25	.25

Juvenile Court of Brazil, 50th anniversary.

Long Distance
Runner — A750

1974, Dec. 23
1374	A750	3.30cr multi	.55	.30

Sao Silvestre long distance running, 50th anniversary.

News
Vendor,
1875,
Masthead,
1975
A751

1975, Jan. 4
1375	A751	50c multicolored	.35	.25

Newspaper "O Estado de S. Paulo," cent.

Sao
Paulo
Industrial
Park
A752

Designs: 1.40cr, Natural rubber industry, Acre. 4.50cr, Manganese mining, Amapá.

1975, Jan. 24   **Litho.**   *Perf. 11x11½*
1376	A752	50c vio bl & yel	.50	.25
1377	A752	1.40cr yellow & brn	.30	.25
1378	A752	4.50cr yellow & blk	1.50	.25
	Nos. 1376-1378 (3)		2.30	.75

Economic development.

Fort of the
Holy Cross
A753

Colonial forts: No. 1380, Fort of the Three Kings. No. 1381, Fort of Monteserrat. 90c, Fort of Our Lady of Help.

Litho. & Engr.
1975, Mar. 14   *Perf. 11½*
1379	A753	50c yel & red brn	.35	.25
1380	A753	50c yel & red brn	.35	.25
1381	A753	50c yel & red brn	.35	.25
1382	A753	90c yel & red brn	.35	.25
	Nos. 1379-1382 (4)		1.40	1.00

House on
Stilts,
Amazon
Region
A754

Designs: 50c, Modern houses and plan of Brasilia. 1.40cr, Indian hut, Rondonia. 3.30cr, German-style cottage (Enxaimel), Santa Catarina.

1975, Apr. 18   **Litho.**   *Perf. 11½*
1383	A754	50c yel & multi	1.25	.75
1384	A754	50c yel & multi	11.00	5.25
a.	Pair, #1383-1384		12.50	6.50
1385	A754	1cr yel & multi	.40	.30
1386	A754	1.40cr yel & multi	7.00	1.90
1387	A754	1.40cr yel & multi	.40	.30
a.	Pair, #1386-1387		8.00	2.75
1388	A754	3.30cr yel & multi	.40	.30
1389	A754	3.30cr yel & multi	7.00	1.25
a.	Pair, #1388-1389		8.00	1.90
	Nos. 1383-1389 (7)		27.45	10.05

Brazilian architecture. Nos. 1383, 1386, 1388 have yellow strip at right side, others at left.

Fish — A755

No. 1390, Astronotus ocellatus. No. 1391, Colomesus psitacus. No. 1392, Phallocerus

---

caudimaculatus. No. 1393, Symphysodon discus.

1975, May 2   **Litho.**   *Perf. 11½*
1390	A755	50c multicolored	.40	.25
1391	A755	50c multicolored	.40	.25
1392	A755	50c multicolored	.40	.25
1393	A755	50c multicolored	.40	.25
	Nos. 1390-1393 (4)		1.60	1.00

Soldier's Head in
Brazil's Colors,
Plane, Rifle and
Ship — A756

1975, May 8   *Perf. 11½x11*
1394	A756	50c vio bl & multi	.35	.25

In honor of the veterans of World War II, on the 30th anniversary of victory.

Brazilian
Otter — A757

Nature protection: 70c, Brazilian pines, horiz. 3.30cr, Marsh cayman, horiz.

1975, June 17   **Litho.**   *Perf. 11½*
1395	A757	70c bl, grn & blk	.75	.40
1396	A757	1cr multi	.55	.30
1397	A757	3.30cr multi	.55	.30
	Nos. 1395-1397 (3)		1.85	1.00

Petroglyphs, Stone
of Ingá — A758

Marjoara Vase,
Pará — A759

Vinctifer
Comptoni,
Petrified
Fish
A760

1975, July 8   **Litho.**   *Perf. 11½*
1398	A758	70c multicolored	.55	.25
1399	A759	1cr multicolored	.30	.25
1400	A760	1cr multicolored	.30	.25
	Nos. 1398-1400 (3)		1.15	.75

Archaeological discoveries.

Immaculate
Conception,
Franciscan
Monastery,
Vitoria — A761

1975, July 15
1401	A761	3.30cr blue & multi	.55	.30

Holy Year 1975 and 300th anniv. of establishment of the Franciscan Province in Southern Brazil.

Post and
Telegraph
Ministry — A762

1975, Aug. 8   **Engr.**   *Perf. 11½*
1402	A762	70c dk carmine	.30	.25

Stamp Day 1975.

Dances
A763

Designs: No. 1403, Sword Dance, Minas Gerais. No. 1404, Umbrella Dance, Pernambuco. No. 1405, Warrior's Dance, Alagoas.

1975, Aug. 22   **Litho.**   *Perf. 11½*
1403	A763	70c pale blue & multi	.35	.25
1404	A763	70c pink & multi	.35	.25
1405	A763	70c yellow & multi	.35	.25
	Nos. 1403-1405 (3)		1.05	.75

Trees
A764

1975, Sept. 15   *Perf. 11x11½*
1406	A764	70c multicolored	.25	.25

Annual Tree Festival.

Globe, Radar and
Satellite — A765

1975, Sept. 16   *Perf. 11½*
1407	A765	3.30cr multi	.50	.30

Inauguration of 2nd antenna of Tangua Earth Station, Rio de Janeiro State.

Woman Holding Flowers and Globe
A766

1975, Sept. 23
1408 A766 3.30cr multi   .55 .30
International Women's Year 1975.

Tile, Railing and Column, Alcantara
A767

Cross and Monastery, Sao Cristovao — A768

Historic cities: No. 1411, Jug and Clock Tower, Goiás, vert.

1975, Sept. 27   **Litho.**   **Perf. 11½**
1409 A767 70c multicolored   .30 .25
1410 A768 70c multicolored   .30 .25
1411 A768 70c multicolored   .30 .25
   Nos. 1409-1411 (3)   .90 .75

"Books teach how to live"
A769

1975, Oct. 23   **Litho.**   **Perf. 11½**
1412 A769 70c multicolored   .25 .25
Day of the Book.

ASTA Congress Emblem
A770

1975, Oct. 27   **Perf. 11x11½**
1413 A770 70c multicolored   .25 .25
American Society of Travel Agents, 45th World Congress, Rio, Oct. 27-Nov. 1.

Angels
A771

1975, Nov. 11
1414 A771 70c red & brown   .25 .25
Christmas 1975.

Map of Americas, Waves — A772

1975, Nov. 19   **Perf. 11½x12**
1415 A772 5.20cr gray & multi   1.50 .75
2nd Interamerican Conference of Telecommunications (CITEL), Rio, Nov. 19-27.

Dom Pedro II — A773

1975, Dec. 2   **Engr.**   **Perf. 12**
1416 A773 70c violet brown   .55 .25
Dom Pedro II (1825-1891), emperor of Brazil, birth sesquicentennial.

People and Cross
A774

1975, Nov. 27   **Litho.**   **Perf. 11x11½**
1417 A774 70c lt bl & dp bl   .25 .25
National Day of Thanksgiving.

Tourism
A775

Designs: No. 1418, Guarapari Beach, Espirito Santo. No. 1419, Salt Stone beach, Piaui. No. 1420, Cliffs, Rio Grande Do Sul.

1975, Dec. 19   **Litho.**   **Perf. 11½**
1418 A775 70c multicolored   .25 .25
1419 A775 70c multicolored   .25 .25
1420 A775 70c multicolored   .35 .25
   Nos. 1418-1420 (3)   .85 .75

Triple Jump, Games Emblem
A776

1975, Dec. 22   **Perf. 11x11½**
1421 A776 1.60cr bl grn & blk   .25 .25
Triple jump world record by Joao Carlos de Oliveira in 7th Pan-American Games, Mexico City, Oct. 12-26.

UN Emblem and Headquarters — A777

1975, Dec. 29   **Perf. 11½**
1422 A777 1.30cr dp bl & vio bl   .25 .25
United Nations, 30th anniversary.

Light Bulbs, House and Sun
A778

Energy conservation: No. 1424, Gasoline drops, car and sun.

1976, Jan. 16
1423 A778 70c multicolored   .25 .25
1424 A778 70c multicolored   .25 .25

Concorde
A779

1976, Jan. 21   **Litho.**   **Perf. 11x11½**
1425 A779 5.20cr bluish black   .30 .25
First commercial flight of supersonic jet Concorde from Paris to Rio, Jan. 21.

Souvenir Sheet

Nautical Map of South Atlantic, 1776 — A780

1976, Feb. 2   **Perf. 11½**
1426 A780 70c salmon & multi   .75 .75
Centenary of the Naval Hydrographic and Navigation Institute.

Telephone Lines, 1876
Telephone — A781

1976, Mar. 10   **Litho.**   **Perf. 11x11½**
1427 A781 5.20cr orange & blue   .30 .25
Centenary of first telephone call by Alexander Graham Bell, March 10, 1876.

Eye and Exclamation Point — A782

1976, Apr. 7   **Litho.**   **Perf. 11½x11**
1428 A782 1cr vio red brn & brn   .25 .55
World Health Day: "Foresight prevents blindness."

Kaiapo Body Painting — A783

Designs: No. 1430, Bakairi ceremonial mask. No. 1431, Karajá feather headdress.

1976, Apr. 19   **Litho.**   **Perf. 11½**
1429 A783 1cr light violet & multi   .25 .25
1430 A783 1cr light violet & multi   .25 .25
1431 A783 1cr light violet & multi   .25 .25
   Nos. 1429-1431 (3)   .75 .75
Preservation of indigenous culture.

Itamaraty Palace, Brasilia
A784

1976, Apr. 20
1432 A784 1cr multicolored   .25 .55
Diplomats' Day. Itamaraty Palace, designed by Oscar Niemeyer, houses the Ministry of Foreign Affairs.

Watering Can over Stones, by José Tarcisio
A785

Fingers and Ribbons, by Pietrina Checcacci
A786

1976, May 14   **Litho.**   **Perf. 11½**
1433 A785 1cr multi   .25 .25
1434 A786 1.60cr multi   .25 .25
Modern Brazilian art.

Basketball — A787

Olympic Rings and: 1.40cr, Yachting. 5.20cr, Judo.

1976, May 21   **Litho.**   **Perf. 11½**
1435 A787   1cr emerald & blk   .25 .25
1436 A787 1.40cr dk blue & blk   .25 .25
1437 A787 5.20cr orange & blk   .25 .25
   Nos. 1435-1437 (3)   .75 .75
21st Olympic Games, Montreal, Canada, July 17-Aug. 1.

Orchid — A788

Nature protection: No. 1439, Golden-faced lion monkey.

1976, June 4   *Perf. 11½x11*
1438 A788 1cr multicolored   .25 .25
1439 A788 1cr multicolored   .25 .25

Film Camera, Brazilian Colors — A789

1976, June 19
1440 A789 1cr vio bl, brt grn & yel   .25 .25

Brazilian film industry.

Bahia Woman — A790

Designs: 10c, Oxcart driver, horiz. 20c, Raft fishermen, horiz. 30c, Rubber plantation worker. 40c, Cowboy, horiz. 50c, Gaucho. 80c, Gold panner. 1cr, Banana plantation worker. 1.10cr, Grape harvester. 1.30cr, Coffee picker. 1.80cr, Farmer gathering wax palms. 2cr, Potter. 5cr, Sugar cane cutter. 7cr, Salt mine worker. 10cr, Fisherman. 15cr, Coconut seller. 20cr, Lacemaker.

Perf. 11½x11, 11x11½
1976-78   **Photo.**
1441 A790 10c red brn ('77)   .25 .25
1442 A790 15c brown   .25 .25
1443 A790 20c violet blue   .25 .25
1444 A790 30c lilac rose   .25 .25
1445 A790 40c orange ('77)   .25 .25
1446 A790 50c citron   .40 .25
1447 A790 80c slate green   1.25 .25
1448 A790 1cr black   .25 .25
1449 A790 1.10cr magenta ('77)   .25 .25
1450 A790 1.30cr red ('77)   .25 .25
1451 A790 1.80cr dk vio bl ('78) .25 .25
                  Engr.
1452 A790 2cr brown ('77)   2.75 .25
1453 A790 5cr dk pur ('77)   3.75 .25
1454 A790 7cr violet   7.25 .25
1455 A790 10cr yel grn ('77)   5.25 .25
1456 A790 15cr gray grn ('78)   2.25 .25
1457 A790 20cr blue   4.75 .25
        Nos. 1441-1457 (17)   29.90 4.25

See Nos. 1653-1657.

Fish A791

Designs: No. 1460, Hyphessobrycon innesi. No. 1461, Copeina arnoldi. No. 1462, Prochilodus insignis. No. 1463, Crenicichla lepidota. No. 1464, Ageneiosus. No. 1465, Corydoras reticulatus.

1976, July 12 Litho.   Perf. 11x11½
1460 A791 1cr multi   .40 .35
1461 A791 1cr multi   .40 .35
1462 A791 1cr multi   .40 .35
1463 A791 1cr multi   .40 .35
1464 A791 1cr multi   .40 .35
1465 A791 1cr multi   .40 .35
a.   Block of 6, #1460-1465   2.50 2.50

Santa Marta Lighthouse A792

1976, July 29 Engr.   Perf. 12x11½
1466 A792 1cr blue   .25 .35

300th anniversary of the city of Laguna.

Children on Magic Carpet A793

1976, Aug. 1 Litho.   Perf. 11½x12
1467 A793 1cr multicolored   .25 .25

Stamp Day.

Nurse's Lamp and Head A794

1976, Aug. 12 Litho.   Perf. 11½
1468 A794 1cr multicolored   .25 .25

Brazilian Nurses' Assoc., 50th anniv.

Puppet, Soldier — A795

Designs: 1.30cr, Girl's head. 1.60cr, Hand with puppet head on each finger, horiz.

1976, Aug. 20
1469 A795 1cr multi   .25 .25
1470 A795 1.30cr multi   .25 .25
1471 A795 1.60cr multi   .25 .25
        Nos. 1469-1471 (3)   .75 .75

Mamulengo puppet show.

Winner's Medal — A796

1976, Aug. 21
1472 A796 5.20cr multi   .30 .30

27th International Military Athletic Championships, Rio de Janeiro, Aug. 21-28.

Family Protection — A797

1976, Sept. 12
1473 A797 1cr lt & dk blue   .25 .25

National organizations SENAC and SESC helping commercial employees to improve their living standard, both commercially and socially.

Dying Tree — A798

1976, Sept. 20 Litho.   Perf. 11½
1474 A798 1cr gray & multi   .25 .25

Protection of the environment.

Atom Symbol, Electron Orbits A799

1976, Sept. 21
1475 A799 5.20cr multi   .25 .25

20th General Conference of the International Atomic Energy Agency, Rio de Janeiro, Sept. 21-29.

Train in Tunnel A800

1976, Sept. 26
1476 A800 1.60cr multi   .25 .25

Sao Paulo subway, 1st in Brazil.

St. Francis and Birds A801

1976, Oct. 4
1477 A801 5.20cr multi   .30 .25

St. Francis of Assisi, 750th death anniv.

Ouro Preto School of Mining — A802

1976, Oct. 12 Engr.   Perf. 12x11½
1478 A802 1cr dk vio   .25 .75

Ouro Preto School of Mining, centenary.

Three Kings A803

Children's drawings — No. 1480, Santa Claus on donkey. No. 1481, Virgin and Child and Angels. No. 1482, Angels with candle. No. 1483, Nativity.

1976, Nov. 4 Litho.   Perf. 11½
1479 A803 80c shown   .50 .25
1480 A803 80c multicolored   .50 .25
1481 A803 80c multicolored   .50 .25
1482 A803 80c multicolored   .50 .25
1483 A803 80c multicolored   .50 .25
a.   Strip of 5, #1479-1483 2.50 2.50

Christmas 1976.

Souvenir Sheet

30,000 Reis Banknote — A804

1976, Nov. 5 Litho.   Perf. 11½
1484 A804 80c multicolored   .30 .75

Opening of 1000th branch of Bank of Brazil, Barra do Bugres, Mato Grosso. Exists imperforate. Value $10,000.

Virgin of Monte Serrat, by Friar Agostinho A805

St. Joseph, 18th Century Wood Sculpture — A806

5.60cr, The Dance, by Rodolfo Bernadelli, 19th cent. 6.50cr, The Caravel, by Bruno Giorgi, 20th cent. abstract sculpture.

1976, Nov. 5
1485 A805 80c multi   .25 .25
1486 A806 5cr multi   .30 .30
1487 A805 5.60cr multi   .30 .30
1488 A806 6.50cr multi   .30 .30
        Nos. 1485-1488 (4)   1.15 1.15

Development of Brazilian sculpture.

Praying
Hands
A807

1976, Nov. 25
1489 A807 80c multicolored   .25 .25
National Day of Thanksgiving.

Sailor, 1840 — A808

Design: 2cr, Marine's uniform, 1808.

1976, Dec. 13   Litho.   Perf. 11½x11
1490 A808 80c multicolored   .25 .25
1491 A808 2cr multicolored   .30 .25
Brazilian Navy.

"Natural Resources and
Development" — A809

1976, Dec. 17   Perf. 11½
1492 A809 80c multicolored   .25 .25
Brazilian Bureau of Standards, founded 1940.

Wheel of
Life — A810

Designs: 5.60cr, Beggar, sculpture by Agnaldo dos Santos. 6.50cr, Benin mask.

1977, Jan. 14
1493 A810 5cr multi   .30 .25
1494 A810 5.60cr multi   .30 .25
1495 A810 6.50cr multi   .30 .25
    Nos. 1493-1495 (3)   .90 .75
FESTAC '77, 2nd World Black and African Festival, Lagos, Nigeria, Jan. 15-Feb. 12.

A811

1977, Jan. 20   Litho.   Perf. 11½
1496 A811 6.50cr bl & yel grn   .30 .30
Rio de Janeiro International Airport.

Seminar Emblem
with Map of
Americas — A812

1977, Feb. 6
1497 A812 1.10cr gray, vio bl & bl .25 .25
6th Inter-American Budget Seminar.

Salicylate,
Microphoto
A813

1977, Apr. 10   Litho.   Perf. 11½
1498 A813 1.10cr multi   .25 .25
International Rheumatism Year.

Lions
International
Emblem
A814

1977, Apr. 16
1499 A814 1.10cr multi   .25 .25
25th anniv. of Brazilian Lions Intl.

Heitor
Villa
Lobos
A815

No. 1501, Chiquinha Gonzaga. No. 1502, Noel Rosa.

1977, Apr. 26   Perf. 11x11½
1500 A815 1.10cr shown   .25 .25
1501 A815 1.10cr multicolored .25 .25
1502 A815 1.10cr multicolored .25 .25
    Nos. 1500-1502 (3)   .75 .75
Brazilian composers.

Farmer and
Worker — A816

Medicine Bottles
and Flask — A817

1977, May 8   Litho.   Perf. 11½
1503 A816 1.10cr grn & multi   .25 .25
1504 A817 1.10cr lt & dk grn   .25 .25
Support and security for rural and urban workers (No. 1503) and establishment in 1971 of Medicine Distribution Center (CEME) for low-cost medicines (No. 1504).

Churchyard Cross, Porto
Seguro — A818

Views, Porto Seguro: 5cr, Beach and boats. 5.60cr, Our Lady of Pena Chapel. 6.50cr, Town Hall.

1977, May 25   Litho.   Perf. 11½
1505 A818 1.10cr multi   .25 .25
1506 A818 5cr multi   .40 .25
1507 A818 5.60cr multi   .30 .25
1508 A818 6.50cr multi   .30 .25
    Nos. 1505-1508 (4)   1.25 1.00
Cent. of Brazil's membership in UPU.

Diario de
Porto
Alegre
A819

1977, June 1
1509 A819 1.10cr multi   .25 .25
Diario de Porto Alegre, newspaper, 150th anniv.

Blue Whale
A820

1977, June 3
1510 A820 1.30cr multi   .30 .25
Protection of marine life.

"Life and
Development"
A821

1977, June 20
1511 A821 1.30cr multi   .25 .25
National Development Bank, 25th anniv.

Train
Leaving
Tunnel
A822

1977, July 8   Engr.   Perf. 11½
1512 A822 1.30cr black   .25 .25
Centenary of Sao Paulo-Rio de Janeiro railroad.

Shells — A823

Designs: No. 1513, Vasum cassiforme. No. 1514, Strombus goliath. No. 1515, Murex tenuivaricosus.

1977, July 14   Litho.
1513 A823 1.30cr blue & multi   .30 .25
1514 A823 1.30cr brown & multi .30 .25
1515 A823 1.30cr green & multi .30 .25
    Nos. 1513-1515 (3)   .90 .75

Caduceus, Formulas
for Water and
Fluoride — A824

1977, July 15   Perf. 11½x11
1516 A824 1.30cr multi   .25 .25
3rd Intl. Odontology Congress, Rio, 7/15-21.

Masonic Emblem,
Map of
Brazil — A825

1977, July 18   Perf. 11½
1517 A825 1.30cr bl, lt bl & blk   .30 .25
50th anniversary of the founding of the Brazilian Grand Masonic Lodge.

"Stamps Don't
Sink or Lose their
Way" — A826

1977, Aug. 1
1518 A826 1.30cr multi   .25 .25
Stamp Day 1977.

Dom Pedro's
Proclamation
A827

1977, Aug. 11   Litho.   Perf. 11½
1519 A827 1.30cr multi   .25 .25
150th anniversary of Brazilian Law School.

Horses and Bulls — A828

Brazilian folklore: No. 1521, King on horseback. No. 1522, Joust, horiz.

Perf. 11½x11, 11x11½

1977, Aug. 20   **Litho.**

1520	A828	1.30cr ocher & multi	.25	.25
1521	A828	1.30cr blue & multi	.25	.25
1522	A828	1.30cr yel & multi	.25	.25
		Nos. 1520-1522 (3)	.75	.75

Brazilian Colonial Coins A829

Designs: No. 1523, 2000-reis doubloon. No. 1524, 640r pataca. No. 1525, 20r copper "vintem."

1977, Aug. 31   **Perf. 11½**

1523	A829	1.30cr vio bl & multi	.25	.25
1524	A829	1.30cr dk red & multi	.25	.25
1525	A829	1.30cr yel & multi	.25	.25
		Nos. 1523-1525 (3)	.75	.75

Pinwheel — A830

1977, Sept. 1

1526	A830	1.30cr multi	.25	.25

National Week.

Neoregelia Carolinae — A831

1977, Sept. 21   **Litho.**   **Perf. 11½**

1527	A831	1.30cr multi	.25	.25

Nature preservation.

Pen, Pencil, Letters — A832

1977, Oct. 15   **Litho.**   **Perf. 11½**

1528	A832	1.30cr multi	.25	.25

Primary education, sesquicentennial.

Dome and Telescope A833

1977, Oct. 15

1529	A833	1.30cr multi	.25	.25

National Astrophysics Observatory, Brasópolis, sesquicentennial.

"Jahu" Hydroplane (Savoia Marchetti S-55) — A834

Design: No. 1531, PAX, dirigible.

1977, Oct. 17

1530	A834	1.30cr multi	.25	.25
1531	A834	1.30cr multi	.25	.25

50th anniv. of crossing of South Atlantic by Joao Ribeiro de Barros, Genoa-Sao Paulo (No. 1530) and 75th anniv. of the PAX airship (No. 1531).

Il'Guarani — A835

1977, Oct. 24

1532	A835	1.30cr multi	.25	.25

Book Day and to honor Jose Martiniano de Alencar, writer, jurist.

Amateur Radio Operators' Day — A836

1977, Nov. 5   **Litho.**   **Perf. 11½**

1533	A836	1.30cr Waves	.25	.25

Christmas A837

Folk art: 1.30cr, Nativity. 2cr, Annunciation. 5cr, Nativity.

1977, Nov. 10

1534	A837	1.30cr bister & multi	.25	.25
1535	A837	2cr bister & multi	.25	.25
1536	A837	5cr bister & multi	.35	.35
		Nos. 1534-1536 (3)	.85	.85

A838

1977, Nov. 19

1537	A838	1.30cr Emerald	.25	.25
1538	A838	1.30cr Topaz	.25	.25
1539	A838	1.30cr Aquamarine	.25	.25
		Nos. 1537-1539 (3)	.75	.75

PORTUCALE 77, 2nd International Topical Exhibition, Porto, Nov. 19-20.

Angel, Cornucopia A839

1977, Nov. 24   **Litho.**   **Perf. 11½**

1540	A839	1.30cr multicolored	.25	.25

National Thanksgiving Day.

Army's Railroad Construction Battalion — A840

Civilian services of armed forces: No. 1542, Navy's Amazon flotilla. No. 1543, Air Force's postal service (plane).

1977, Dec. 5

1541	A840	1.30cr multi	.25	.25
1542	A840	1.30cr multi	.25	.25
1543	A840	1.30cr multi	.25	.25
		Nos. 1541-1543 (3)	.75	.75

Varig Emblem, Jet A841

1977, Dec.   **Perf. 11x11½**

1544	A841	1.30cr bl & blk	.25	.25

50th anniversary of Varig Airline.

Brazilian Architecture A842

Designs: 2.70cr, Sts. Cosme and Damiao Church, Igaracu. 7.50cr, St. Bento Monastery Church, Rio de Janeiro. 8.50cr, Church of St. Francis of Assisi, Ouro Preto. 9.50cr, St. Anthony Convent Church, Joao Pessoa.

1977, Dec. 8

1545	A842	2.70cr multi	.30	.25
1546	A842	7.50cr multi	.50	.25
1547	A842	8.50cr multi	.55	.25
1548	A842	9.50cr multi	.55	.30
		Nos. 1545-1548 (4)	1.90	1.05

Woman Holding Sheaf — A843

1977, Dec. 19   **Perf. 11½**

1549	A843	1.30cr multi	.25	.25

Brazilian diplomacy.

Soccer Ball and Foot — A844

Designs: No. 1551, Soccer ball in net. No. 1552, Symbolic soccer player.

1978, Mar. 1   **Litho.**   **Perf. 11½**

1550	A844	1.80cr multi	.25	.25
1551	A844	1.80cr multi	.25	.25
1552	A844	1.80cr multi	.25	.25
		Nos. 1550-1552 (3)	.75	.75

11th World Cup Soccer Championship, Argentina, June 1-25.

"La Fosca" on La Scala Stage and Carlos Gomes A845

1978, Feb. 9

1553	A845	1.80cr multi	.25	.25

Bicentenary of La Scala in Milan, and to honor Carlos Gomes (1836-1893), Brazilian composer.

Symbols of Postal Mechanization — A846

1978, Mar. 15   **Litho.**   **Perf. 11½**

1554	A846	1.80cr multi	.25	.25

Opening of Postal Staff College.

Hypertension Chart — A847

1978, Apr. 4

1555	A847	1.80cr multi	.25	.25

World Health Day, fight against hypertension.

Waves from Antenna Uniting World — A848

1978, May 17 Litho. Perf. 12x11½
1556 A848 1.80cr multi   .25 .25
10th World Telecommunications Day.

Brazilian Canary A849

Birds: 8.50cr, Cotinga. 9.50cr, Tanager fastuosa.

1978, June 5 Perf. 11½x12
1557 A849 7.50cr multi   .55 .40
1558 A849 8.50cr multi   .55 .40
1559 A849 9.50cr multi   .55 .40
  Nos. 1557-1559 (3)   1.65 1.20

Inocencio Serzedelo Correa and Manuel Francisco Correa, 1893 — A850

1978, June 20 Litho. Perf. 11x11½
1560 A850 1.80cr multi   .25 .25
85th anniversary of Union Court of Audit.

Post and Telegraph Building A851

1978, June 22 Perf. 11½
1561 A851 1.80cr multi   .25 .25

Souvenir Sheet
Imperf
1562 A851 7.50cr multi   .65 1.50
Inauguration of Post and Telegraph Building (ECT), Brasilia, and for BRAPEX, 3rd Brazilian Philatelic Exhibition, Brasilia, June 23-28 (No. 1562).

Ernesto Geisel, President of Brazil — A852

1978, June 22 Engr. Perf. 11½
1563 A852 1.80cr dull green   .25 .25

Savoia-Marchetti S-64, Map of South Atlantic — A853

1978, July 3 Litho.
1564 A853 1.80cr multi   .25 .25
50th anniv. of 1st crossing of South Atlantic by Carlos del Prete and Arturo Ferrarin.

Symbolic of Smallpox Eradication A854

1978, July 25
1565 A854 1.80cr multi   .25 .25
Eradication of smallpox.

Brazil No. 68 — A855

1978, Aug. 1
1566 A855 1.80cr multi   .25 .25
Stamp Day, centenary of the "Barba Branca" (white beard) issue.

Stormy Sea, by Seelinger A856

1978, Aug. 4
1567 A856 1.80cr multi   .25 .25
Helios Seelinger, painter, birth centenary.

Musicians and Instruments A857

Designs: No. 1568, Guitar players. No. 1569, Flutes. No. 1570, Percussion instruments.

1978, Aug. 22 Litho. Perf. 11½
1568 A857 1.80cr multi   .25 .25
1569 A857 1.80cr multi   .25 .25
1570 A857 1.80cr multi   .25 .25
  Nos. 1568-1570 (3)   .75 .75

Children at Play A858

1978, Sept. 1 Litho. Perf. 11½
1571 A858 1.80cr multi   .25 .25
National Week.

Collegiate Church A859

1978, Sept. 6 Engr.
1572 A859 1.80cr red brn   .25 .25
Restoration of patio of Collegiate Church, Sao Paulo.

Justice by A. Geschiatti A860

1978, Sept. 18 Litho.
1573 A860 1.80cr blk & olive   .25 .25
Federal Supreme Court, sesquicentennial.

Iguacu National Park — A861

Design: No. 1574, Iguacu Falls. No. 1575, Yellow ipe.

1978, Sept. 21
1574 A861 1.80cr multi   .25 .25
1575 A861 1.80cr multi   .25 .25

Stages of Intelsat Satellite A862

1978, Oct. 9 Litho. Perf. 11½
1576 A862 1.80cr multi   .25 .25

Brazilian Flags A863

Designs: No. 1577, Flag of the Order of Christ. No. 1578, Principality of Brazil. No. 1579, United Kingdom. No. 1580, Imperial Brazil. No. 1581, National flag (current).

1978, Oct. 13
1577 A863 1.80cr multi   .30 .30
1578 A863 1.80cr multi   .30 .30
1579 A863 1.80cr multi   .30 .30
1580 A863 8.50cr multi   .30 .30
1581 A863 8.50cr multi   .30 .30
  a. Block of 5, #1577-1581 + label 1.50 1.50
  Nos. 1577-1581 (5)   1.50 1.50
7th LUBRAPEX Philatelic Exhibition, Porto Alegre.

Mail Transportation — A864

Designs: No. 1582, Mail street car. No. 1583, Overland mail truck. No. 1584, Mail delivery truck. 7.50cr. Railroad mail car. 8.50cr, Mail coach. 9.50cr, Post riders.

1978, Oct. 21 Perf. 11x11½
1582 A864 1.80cr multi   .30 .25
1583 A864 1.80cr multi   .30 .25
1584 A864 1.80cr multi   .30 .25
1585 A864 7.50cr multi   .30 .25
1586 A864 8.50cr multi   .30 .25
1587 A864 9.50cr multi   .30 .25
  a. Block of 6, #1582-1587 2.00 2.00
18th UPU Congress, Rio de Janeiro, 1979.

Gaucho Herding Cattle, and Cactus — A865

1978, Oct. 23 Perf. 11½x11
1588 A865 1.80cr multi   .25 .25
Joao Guimaraes Rosa, poet and diplomat, 70th birthday.

Landscape Paintings A866

Designs: No. 1589, St. Anthony's Hill, by Nicholas A. Taunay. No. 1590, Castle Hill, by Victor Meirelles. No. 1591, View of Sabara, by Alberto da Veiga Guignard. No. 1592, View of Pernambuco, by Frans Post.

1978, Nov. 6 Litho. Perf. 11½
1589 A866 1.80cr multi   .25 .25
1590 A866 1.80cr multi   .25 .25
1591 A866 1.80cr multi   .25 .25
1592 A866 1.80cr multi   .25 .25
  Nos. 1589-1592 (4)   1.00 1.00

Christmas A867

Angel with: No. 1593, Harp. No. 1594, Lute. No. 1595, Oboe.

1978, Nov. 10
1593 A867 1.80cr multi   .25 .25
1594 A867 1.80cr multi   .25 .25
1595 A867 1.80cr multi   .25 .25
  Nos. 1593-1595 (3)   .75 .75

Symbolic
Candles — A868

1978, Nov. 23
1596 A868 1.80cr blk, gold & car   .25 .25
National Thanksgiving Day.

Red
Crosses
and
Activities
A869

1978, Dec. 5 Litho. Perf. 11x11½
1597 A869 1.80cr blk & red   .25 .25
70th anniversary of Brazilian Red Cross.

Paz Theater,
Belem
A870

Designs: 12cr, José de Alencar Theater,
Fortaleza. 12.50cr, Municipal Theater, Rio de
Janeiro.

1978, Dec. 6   Perf. 11½
1598 A870 10.50cr multi   .55 .30
1599 A870 12cr multi   .55 .30
1600 A870 12.50cr multi   .55 .30
    Nos. 1598-1600 (3)   1.65 .90

Subway
Trains — A871

1979, Mar. 5 Litho. Perf. 11½
1601 A871 2.50cr multi   .25 .25
Inauguration of Rio subway system.

Old and
New Post
Offices
A872

Designs: No. 1603, Old and new mail boxes.
No. 1604, Manual and automatic mail sorting.
No. 1605, Old and new planes. No. 1606, Tel-
egraph and telex machine. No. 1607,
Mailmen's uniforms.

1979, Mar. 20 Litho. Perf. 11x11½
1602 A872 2.50cr multi   .35 .25
1603 A872 2.50cr multi   .35 .25
1604 A872 2.50cr multi   .35 .25
1605 A872 2.50cr multi   .35 .25
1606 A872 2.50cr multi   .35 .25
1607 A872 2.50cr multi   .35 .25
  a. Block of 6, #1602-1607   2.10 2.10

10th anniv. of the new Post and Telegraph
Dept., and 18th Universal Postal Union Cong.,
Rio de Janeiro, Sept.-Oct., 1979.

O'Day 23
Class
Yacht
A873

Yachts and Stamp Outlines: 10.50cr, Penguin Class. 12cr, Hobie Cat Class. 12.50cr,
Snipe Class.

1979, Apr. 18 Litho. Perf. 11x11½
1608 A873 2.50cr multi   .25 .25
1609 A873 10.50cr multi   .25 .25
1610 A873 12cr multi   .25 .25
1611 A873 12.50cr multi   .25 .25
    Nos. 1608-1611 (4)   1.00 1.00

Brasiliana '79, 3rd World Thematic Stamp
Exhibition, Sao Conrado, Sept. 15-23.

Children, IYC
Emblem — A874

1979, May 23 Litho. Perf. 11½
1612 A874 2.50cr multi   .25 .25
Intl. Year of the Child & Children's Book Day.

Giant Water
Lily — A875

Designs: 12cr, Amazon manatee. 12.50cr,
Arrau (turtle).

1979, June 5 Litho. Perf. 11½
1613 A875 10.50cr multi   .35 .25
1614 A875 12cr multi   .35 .25
1615 A875 12.50cr multi   .35 .25
    Nos. 1613-1615 (3)   1.05 .75

Amazon National Park, nature conservation.

Bank
Emblem
A876

1979, June 7
1616 A876 2.50cr multi   .25 .25
Northwest Bank of Brazil, 25th anniversary.

Physician
Tending
Patient
15th Cent.
Woodcut
A877

1979, June 30
1617 A877 2.50cr multi   .25 .25
Natl. Academy of Medicine, 150th anniv.

Flower made of
Hearts — A878

1979, July 8 Litho. Perf. 11½
1618 A878 2.50cr multi   .25 .25
35th Brazilian Cardiology Congress.

Souvenir Sheet

Hotel Nacional, Rio de
Janeiro — A879

1979, July 16
1619 A879 12.50cr multi   .65 1.00
Brasiliana '79 comprising 1st Inter-American
Exhibition of Classical Philately and 3rd World
Topical Exhibition, Rio de Janeiro, Sept. 15-
23.

Cithaerias
Aurora
A880

Moths: 10.50cr, Evenus regalis. 12cr, Caligo
eurilochus. 12.50cr, Diaethria clymena janeira.

1979, Aug. 1
1620 A880 2.50cr multi   .30 .25
1621 A880 10.50cr multi   .55 .30
1622 A880 12cr multi   .55 .30
1623 A880 12.50cr multi   .75 .40
    Nos. 1620-1623 (4)   2.15 1.25
Stamp Day 1979.

EMB-121
Xingo
A881

1979, Aug. 19 Litho. Perf. 11½
1624 A881 2.50cr vio blue   .25 .25
Embraer, Brazilian aircraft comp., 10th anniv.

National
Week — A882

Natl. emblem over landscape.

1979, Sept. 12
1625 A882 3.20cr multi   .25 .25

A883

1979, Sept. 8 Litho. Perf. 11½
1626 A883 2.50cr multi   .25 .25
Statue of Our Lady of the Apparition, 75th
anniversary of coronation.

"UPU,"
Envelope
and Mail
Transport
A884

"UPU" and: No. 1628, Post Office emblems.
10.50cr, Globe. 12cr, Flags of Brazil and UN.
12.50cr, UPU emblem.

1979, Sept. 12   Perf. 11x11½
1627 A884 2.50cr multi   .25 .25
1628 A884 2.50cr multi   .25 .25
1629 A884 10.50cr multi   .25 .25
1630 A884 12cr multi   .25 .25
1631 A884 12.50cr multi   .25 .25
    Nos. 1627-1631 (5)   1.25 1.25
18th UPU Cong., Rio, Sept.-Oct. 1979.

Pyramid Fountain,
Rio de
Janeiro — A885

Fountains: 10.50cr, Facade, Marilia, Ouro
Preto, horiz. 12cr, Boa Vista, Recife.

**   Perf. 12x11½, 11½x12**
1979, Sept. 15
1632 A885 2.50cr multi   .25 .25
1633 A885 10.50cr multi   .30 .25
1634 A885 12cr multi   .30 .25
    Nos. 1632-1634 (3)   .85 .75
Brasiliana '79, 1st Interamerican Exhibition
of Classical Philately.

Church of
the Glory
A886

Landscapes by Leandro Joaquim: 12cr,
Whale hunting on Guanabara Bay. 12.50cr,
Boqueirao Lagoon and Carioca Aqueduct.

1979, Sept. 15 *Perf. 11½*
1635 A886 2.50cr multi .25 .25
1636 A886 12cr multi .30 .25
1637 A886 12.50cr multi .30 .25
　　Nos. 1635-1637 (3) .85 .75

Brasiliana '79, 3rd World Topical Exhibition, Sao Conrado, Sept. 15-23.

World Map
A887

1979, Sept. 20
1638 A887 2.50cr multi .25 .25

3rd World Telecommunications Exhibition, Geneva, Sept. 20-26.

"UPU" and UPU
Emblem — A888

1979, Oct. 9 Litho. *Perf. 11½x11*
1639 A888 2.50cr multi .25 .25
1640 A888 10.50cr multi .25 .25
1641 A888 12cr multi .25 .25
1642 A888 12.50cr multi .25 .25
　　Nos. 1639-1642 (4) 1.00 1.00

Universal Postal Union Day.

IYC
Emblem,
Feather
Toy
A889

IYC Emblem and Toys: No. 1644, Bumble bee, ragdoll. No. 1645, Flower, top. No. 1646, Wooden acrobat.

1979, Oct. 12 *Perf. 11½*
1643 A889 2.50cr multi .25 .25
1644 A889 3.20cr multi .25 .25
1645 A889 3.20cr multi .25 .25
1646 A889 3.20cr multi .25 .25
　　Nos. 1643-1646 (4) 1.00 1.00

International Year of the Child.

Christmas
A890

Designs: No. 1647, Adoration of the Magi. No. 1648, Nativity. No. 1649 Jesus and the Elders in the Temple.

1979, Nov. 12 Litho. *Perf. 11½*
1647 A890 3.20cr multi .25 .25
1648 A890 3.20cr multi .25 .25
1649 A890 3.20cr multi .25 .25
　　Nos. 1647-1649 (3) .75 .75

Souvenir Sheet

Hands Reading Braille — A891

Lithographed and Embossed
1979, Nov. 20. *Perf. 11½*
1650 A891 3.20cr multi .55 .75

Publication of Braille script, 150th anniversary. Margin shows extension of stamp design with Braille printed and embossed.

Thanksgiving
A892

1979, Nov. 22
1651 A892 3.20cr Wheat harvester .25 .25

Steel Mill — A893

1979, Nov. 23
1652 A893 3.20cr multi .25 .25

COSIPA Steelworks, Sao Paulo, 25th anniversary.

Type of 1976

Designs: 70c, Women grinding coconuts. 2.50cr, Basket weaver. 3.20cr, River boatman. 21cr, Harvesting ramie (China grass). 27cr, Man leading pack mule. 3.20cr, 27cr, horiz.

Photogravure, Engraved (21cr)
1979 *Perf. 11x11½, 11½x11*
1653 A790 70c gray green .25 .25
1654 A790 2.50cr sepia .25 .25
1655 A790 3.20cr blue .25 .25
1656 A790 21cr purple 1.50 .25
1657 A790 27cr sepia 1.75 .25
　　Nos. 1653-1657 (5) 4.00 1.25

A894

Designs: 2cr, Coconuts. 3cr, Mangoes. 4cr, Corn. 5cr, Onions. 7cr, Oranges. 10cr, Maracuja. 12cr, Pineapple. 15cr, Bananas. 17cr, Guarana. 20cr, Sugar cane. 24cr, Beekeeping. 30cr, Silkworm. 34cr, Cacao. 38cr, Coffee. 42cr, Soybeans. 45cr, Mandioca. 50cr, Wheat. 57cr, Peanuts. 66cr, Grapes. 100cr, Cashews. 140cr, Tomatoes. 200cr, Mamona. 500cr, Cotton.

1980-83 **Photo.** *Perf. 11½x11*
1658 A894 2cr yel brn ('82) .25 .25
1659 A894 3cr red ('82) .25 .25
1660 A894 4cr orange .30 .25
1661 A894 5cr dk pur ('82) .25 .25
1662 A894 7cr org ('81) .25 .25
1663 A894 10cr bl grn ('82) .25 .25
1664 A894 12cr dk grn ('81) .25 .25
1665 A894 15cr gldn brn
　　　　　　　　('83) .25 .25
1666 A894 17cr brn org ('82) .40 .25
1667 A894 20cr olive ('82) .25 .25
1668 A894 24cr bis ('82) .75 .25
1669 A894 30cr blk ('82) .75 .25

1670 A894 34cr brown 5.50 .55
1671 A894 38cr red ('83) 2.75 .25
1672 A894 42cr green 13.00 .65
1673 A894 45cr sepia ('83) .25 .25
1674 A894 50cr yel org ('82) .30 .25
1675 A894 57cr brn ('83) 2.75 .25
1676 A894 66cr pur ('81) 7.50 .30
1677 A894 100cr dk red brn
　　　　　　　　('81) .35 .25
1678 A894 140cr red ('82) 7.50 1.60
Engr.
1678A A894 200cr grn ('82) 1.25 .25
1679 A894 500cr brn ('82) 2.00 .25
　　Nos. 1658-1679 (23) 47.35 7.85

See Nos. 1934-1941.

Plant Inside
Raindrop — A896

Light bulb containing: 17cr+7cr, Sun. 20cr+8cr, Windmill. 21cr+9cr, Dam.

1980, Jan. 2 Litho. *Perf. 12*
1680 A896 3.20cr multi .25 .25
1681 A896 24cr (17 + 7) .25 .25
1682 A896 28cr (20 + 8) .60 .30
1683 A896 30cr (21 + 9) .75 .40
　　Nos. 1680-1683 (4) 1.85 1.20

Nos. 1681-1683 were originally intended to be sold as semi-postal stamps but were actually issued as regular postage stamps, sold and valid for the combined denominations appearing on each stamp.

Anthracite
Industry
A897

1980, Mar. 19 Litho. *Perf. 11½*
1684 A897 4cr multi .25 .25

Map of Americas, Symbols of
Development — A898

1980, Apr. 14 Litho. *Perf. 11x11½*
1685 A898 4cr multi .25 .25

21st Assembly of Inter-American Development Bank Governors, Rio, Apr. 14-16.

Tapirape
Mask,
Mato
Grosso
A899

No. 1687, Tukuna mask, Amazonas, vert. No. 1688, Kanela mask, Maranhao, vert.

1980, Apr. 18 *Perf. 11½*
1686 A899 4cr shown .25 .25
1687 A899 4cr multicolored .25 .25
1688 A899 4cr multicolored .25 .25
　　Nos. 1686-1688 (3) .75 .75

Brazilian
Television,
30th
Anniversary
A900

1980, May 5 Litho. *Perf. 11½*
1689 A900 4cr multicolored .25 .25

Duke of Caxias,
by
Miranda — A901

1980, May 7
1690 A901 4cr multicolored .25 .25

Duke of Caxias, death centenary.

The Worker, by
Candido
Portinari — A902

Paintings: 28cr, Mademoiselle Pogany, by Constantin Brancusi. 30cr, The Glass of Water, by Francisco Aurelio de Figueiredo.

1980, May 18
1691 A902 24cr multi .30 .30
1692 A902 28cr multi .40 .30
1693 A902 30cr multi .65 .40
　　Nos. 1691-1693 (3) 1.35 1.00

Graf Zeppelin, 50th Anniversary of
Atlantic Crossing
A903

1980, June Litho. *Perf. 11x11½*
1694 A903 4cr multicolored .25 .25

Pope John
Paul II, St.
Peter's,
Rome,
Congress
Emblem
A904

Pope, Emblem and Brazilian Churches: No. 1696, Fortaleza, vert. 24cr, Apericida 28cr, Rio de Janeiro. 30cr, Brasilia.

1980, June 24 *Perf. 12*
1695 A904 4cr multi .25 .25
1696 A904 4cr multi .25 .25
1697 A904 24cr multi .30 .30
1698 A904 28cr multi .30 .30
1699 A904 30cr multi .55 .40
　　Nos. 1695-1699 (5) 1.65 1.50

Visit of Pope John Paul II to Brazil, June 30-July 12; 10th National Eucharistic Congress, Fortaleza, July 9-16.

1st Airmail Flight across the South
Atlantic, 50th Anniv.
A905

1980, June   Litho.   Perf. 11x11½
1700 A905 4cr multicolored   .25 .25

Souvenir Sheet

Yacht Sail, Exhibition Emblem — A906

1980, June   Perf. 11½
1701 A906 30cr multi   .60 .60
Brapex IV Stamp Exhib., Fortaleza, June
13-21.

Rowing,
Moscow '80
Emblem
A907

1980, June 30
1702 A907 4cr shown   .35 .25
1703 A907 4cr Target shooting   .35 .25
1704 A907 4cr Bicycling   .35 .25
      Nos. 1702-1704 (3)   1.05 .75
22nd Summer Olympic Games, Moscow,
July 19-Aug. 3.

Rondon
Community
Works
Project
A908

1980, July 11
1705 A908 4cr multicolored   .25 .25

Helen Keller
and Anne
Sullivan
A909

1980, July 28
1706 A909 4cr multicolored   .25 .25
Helen Keller (1880-1968), blind deaf writer
and lecturer taught by Anne Sullivan (1867-
1936).

Souvenir Sheet

São Francisco River Canoe — A910

1980, Aug. 1   Litho.   Perf. 11½
1707 A910 24cr multi   .65 .65
Stamp Day.

Microscope, Red
Cross, Insects, Brick
and Tile
Houses — A911

1980, Aug. 5   Perf. 11½x11
1708 A911 4cr multi   .25 .25
National Health Day.

EMBRATEL, 15th Anniversary — A912

1980, Sept. 16   Litho.   Perf. 12
1709 A912 5cr multi   .25 .25

Souvenir Sheet

A913

1980, Sept. 29   Perf. 11½x12
1710 A913 30cr multi   .60 .60
St. Gabriel World Union, 6th congress.

Orchids
A914

Designs: No. 1711, Cattleya amethys-
toglossa. No. 1712, Laelia cinnabarina. 24cr,
Zygopetalu, crinitum. 28cr, Laelia tenebrosa.

1980, Oct. 3   Perf. 11½
1711 A914 5cr multi   .25 .25
1712 A914 5cr multi   .25 .25
1713 A914 24cr multi   .90 .40
1714 A914 28cr multi   .90 .40
      Nos. 1711-1714 (4)   2.30 1.30
Espamer 80, American-European Philatelic
Exhibition, Madrid, Oct. 3-12.

Parrots — A915

Designs: No. 1715, Amazona brazilensis.
No. 1716, Amazona Vinacea. No. 1717, Touit
melanonota. No. 1718, Amazona pretrei.

1980, Oct. 18   Litho.   Perf. 12
1715 A915 5cr multi   .40 .25
1716 A915 5cr multi   .40 .25
1717 A915 28cr multi   .90 .40
1718 A915 28cr multi   .90 .40
      Nos. 1715-1718 (4)   2.60 1.30
Lubrapex '80 Stamp Exhib., Lisbon, Oct. 18-
26.

Captain Rodrigo,
Hero of Erico
Verissimo's "O
Continento"
A916

1980, Oct. 23
1719 A916 5cr multi   .25 .25
Book Day.

Christmas
A917

1980, Nov. 5
1720 A917 5cr Flight into Egypt   .25 .25

Sound
Waves and
Oscillator
Screen
A918

1980, Nov. 7
1721 A918 5cr multi   .25 .25
Telebras Research Center inauguration.

Carvalho Viaduct, Paranagua-Curitiba
Railroad — A919

1980, Nov. 10
1722 A919 5cr multi   .25 .25
Engineering Club centenary.

Postal Chess
Contest
A920

5cr, Portable chess board.

1980, Nov. 18   Litho.   Perf. 11½
1723 A920 5cr multicolored   .25 .25

Thanksgiving
A921

1980, Nov. 27   Perf. 11½x11
1724 A921 5cr Sun, wheat   .25 .25

Father Anchieta
Writing "Virgin
Mary, Mother of
God" on Sand of
Iperoig
Beach — A922

1980, Dec. 8   Perf. 12
1725 A922 5cr multi   .25 .25

Antonio Francisco Lisboa (O
Aleijadinho), 250th Birth
Anniv. — A923

No. 1726 — Paintings of the life of Christ: a,
Mount of Olives. b, Arrest in the Garden. c,
Flagellation. d, Crown of Thorns. e, Christ
Carrying the Cross (shown). f, Crucifixion.

1980, Dec. 29
1726   Block of 6   3.50 6.50
a.-f. A923 5cr any single   .55 .25

Agricultural Productivity — A924

35cr, Domestic markets. 40cr, Exports.

1981, Jan. 2   Litho.   Perf. 11x11½
1727 A924 30cr shown   .60 .25
1728 A924 35cr multicolored   .60 .25
1729 A924 40cr multicolored   .60 .25
      Nos. 1727-1729 (3)   1.80 .75

Boy
Scout
and
Campfire
A925

1981, Jan. 22   Litho.   Perf. 11x11½
1730 A925 5cr shown   .30 .25
1731 A925 5cr Scouts cooking   .30 .25
1732 A925 5cr Scout, tents   .30 .25
      Nos. 1730-1732 (3)   .90 .75
4th Pan-American Scout Jamboree.

Souvenir Sheet

Dept. of Posts & Telegraphs, 50th anniv. — A926

1981, Mar. 11   **Litho.**   **Perf. 11**
1733 A926   Sheet of 3   5.00 5.00
   a.   30cr Mailman, 1930   1.25 1.25
   b.   35cr Mailman, 1981   1.25 1.25
   c.   40cr Telegram messenger,   1.25 1.25
      1930

Souvenir Sheet

The Hunter and the Jaguar, by Felix Taunay (1795-1881) — A927

1981, Apr. 10   **Litho.**   **Perf. 11**
1734 A927 30cr multi   1.25 1.25

Lima Barreto and Rio de Janeiro, 1900 A928

1981, May 13   **Litho.**   **Perf. 11½**
1735 A928 7cr multi   .25 .25
Lima Barreto, writer, birth centenary.

Maraca Indian Funerary Urn — A929

No. 1737, Marajoara triangular jug. No. 1738, Tupi-Guarani bowl.

1981, May 18
1736 A929 7cr shown   .25 .25
1737 A929 7cr multicolored   .25 .25
1738 A929 7cr multicolored   .25 .25
    Nos. 1736-1738 (3)   .75 .75

Hummingbirds — A930

Designs: No. 1739, Lophornis magnifica. No. 1740, Phaethornis pretrei. No. 1741, Chrysolampis mosquitus. No. 1742, Heliactin cornuta.

1981, May 22   **Perf. 11½**
1739 A930 7cr multi   .50 .35
1740 A930 7cr multi   .50 .35
1741 A930 7cr multi   .50 .35
1742 A930 7cr multi   .50 .35
    Nos. 1739-1742 (4)   2.00 1.40

Rotary Emblem and Faces A931

1981, May 31
1743 A931   7cr Emblem, hands   .35 .25
1744 A931 35cr shown   .70 .40
72nd Convention of Rotary Intl., Sao Paulo.

Environmental Protection — A932

1981, June 5   **Perf. 12**
1745 A932 7cr Fish   .40 .25
1746 A932 7cr Forest   .40 .25
1747 A932 7cr Clouds (air)   .40 .25
1748 A932 7cr Village (soil)   .40 .25
   a.   Block of 4, #1745-1748   2.50 2.50

Biplane, 1931 (Airmail Service, 50th Anniv.) A933

1981, June 10   **Perf. 11½**
1749 A933 7cr multi   .25 .25

Madeira-Mamore Railroad, 50th Anniv. of Nationalization — A934

1981, July 10   **Litho.**   **Perf. 11x11½**
1750 A934 7cr multi   .25 .25

66th Intl. Esperanto Congress, Brasilia A935

1981, July 26   **Perf. 12**
1751 A935 7cr green & blk   .25 .25

No. 79 A936

1981, Aug. 1
1752 A936 50cr shown   .75 .50
1753 A936 55cr No. 80   .75 .50
1754 A936 60cr No. 81   .75 .50
    Nos. 1752-1754 (3)   2.25 1.50
Stamp Day; cent. of "small head" stamps.

Institute of Military Engineering, 50th Anniv. — A937

1981, Aug. 11   **Litho.**   **Perf. 11½**
1755 A937 12cr multi   .25 .25

Reisado Dancers A938

1981, Aug. 22
1756 A938 50cr Dancers, diff.   .75 .35
1757 A938 55cr Sailors   .75 .35
1758 A938 60cr shown   .75 .35
    Nos. 1756-1758 (3)   2.25 1.05

Intl. Year of the Disabled A939

1981, Sept. 17   **Litho.**   **Perf. 11½**
1759 A939 12cr multi   .25 .25

Flowers of the Central Plateau A940

No. 1760, Palicourea rigida. No. 1761, Dalechampia caperonioides. No. 1762, Cassia clausseni, vert. No. 1763, Eremanthus sphaerocephalus, vert.

1981, Sept. 21   **Litho.**   **Perf. 12**
1760 A940 12cr multicolored   .30 .25
1761 A940 12cr multicolored   .30 .25
1762 A940 12cr multicolored   .30 .25
1763 A940 12cr multicolored   .30 .25
    Nos. 1760-1763 (4)   1.20 1.00

Virgin of Nazareth Statue — A941

1981, Oct. 10   **Litho.**   **Perf. 12**
1764 A941 12cr multi   .25 .25
Candle Festival of Nazareth, Belem.

Christ the Redeemer Statue, Rio de Janeiro, 50th Anniv. — A942

1981, Oct. 12
1765 A942 12cr multi   .25 .25

World Food Day A943

1981, Oct. 16
1766 A943 12c multi   .25 .25

75th Anniv. of Santos-Dumont's First Flight — A944

1981, Oct. 23   **Litho.**   **Perf. 12**
1767 A944 60cr multi   1.25 .40

Father José de Santa Rita Durao, Titlepage of his Epic Poem Caramuru, Diego Alvares Correia (Character) — A945

1981, Oct. 29
1768 A945 12cr multi   .25 .25
Caramuru publication 200th anniv.; World Book Day.

Christmas A946

Designs: Creches and figurines.

1981, Nov. 10   **Litho.**   **Perf. 12**
1769 A946 12cr multi   .30 .25
1770 A946 50cr multi   .40 .25
1771 A946 55cr multi, vert.   .40 .25
1772 A946 60cr multi, vert.   .65 .25
    Nos. 1769-1772 (4)   1.75 1.00

State Flags A947

No. 1773: a, Alagoas. b, Bahia. c, Federal District. d, Pernambuco. e, Sergipe.

1981, Nov. 19
1773   Block of 5 + label   1.50 2.25
   a.-e.   A947 12cr, any single   .30 .25
    Label shows arms of Brazil.
    See Nos. 1830, 1892, 1962, 2037, 2249, 2726-2727.

Thanksgiving
A948

1981, Nov. 26   Litho.   Perf. 11½
1776 A948 12cr multi   .30 .25

Ministry of
Labor,
50th Anniv.
A949

1981, Nov. 26
1777 A949 12cr multi   .25 .25

School of Engineering, Itajuba — A950

1981, Nov. 30   Perf. 11x11½
1778 A950 15cr lt grn & pur   .25 .25
Theodomiro C. Santiago, founder, birth
centenary.

Sao Paulo State
Police
Sesquicentennial
A951

No. 1779, Policeman with saxophone. No.
1780, Mounted policemen.

1981, Dec. 15   Litho.   Perf. 12
1779 A951 12cr multicolored   .25 .25
1780 A951 12cr multicolored   .25 .25

Army Library
Centenary
A952

1981, Dec. 17
1781 A952 12cr multi   .25 .25

Souvenir Sheet

A953

1981, Dec. 18   Perf. 11
1782 A953 180cr multi   3.75 3.75
Philatelic Club of Brazil, 50th anniv.

Brigadier
Eduardo
Gomes
A954

1982, Jan. 20   Litho.   Perf. 11x11½
1783 A954 12cr blue & blk   .25 .25

Birth Centenary of Henrique Lage,
Industrialist — A956

1982, Mar. 14   Litho.   Perf. 11½
1785 A956 17cr multi   .25 .25

1982 World
Cup Soccer
A957

Designs: Various soccer players.

1982, Mar. 19
1786 A957 75cr multi   1.25 .60
1787 A957 80cr multi   1.25 .60
1788 A957 85cr multi   1.25 .60
  Nos. 1786-1788 (3)   3.75 1.80
Souvenir Sheet
Imperf
1789   Sheet of 3   7.50 7.50
  a.   A957 100cr like #1786   2.00 1.50
  b.   A957 100cr like #1787   2.00 1.50
  c.   A957 100cr like #1788   2.00 1.50

TB Bacillus
Cent. — A958

90cr, Microscope, lung. 100cr, Lung, pills.

1982, Mar. 24   Perf. 12
1790 A958 90cr multicolored   2.75 1.25
1791 A958 100cr multicolored   2.75 1.25
  a.   Pair, #1790-1791   6.00 2.50

Souvenir Sheet

A959

1982, Apr. 17   Litho.   Perf. 11
1792 A959   Sheet of 3   9.00 9.00
  a.   75cr Laelia Purpurata   2.75 2.75
  b.   80cr Oncidium flexuosum   2.75 2.75
  c.   85cr Cleistes revoluta   2.75 2.75
BRAPEX V Stamp Exhibition, Blumenau.

Oil Drilling
Centenary
A960

1982, Apr. 18   Perf. 11½
1793 A960 17cr multi   .25 .25

400th Birth
Anniv. of
St. Vincent
de Paul
A961

1982, Apr. 24   Litho.   Perf. 11½
1794 A961 17cr multi   .25 .25

Seven
Steps of
Guaira
(Waterfalls)
A962

1982, Apr. 29
1795 A962 17cr Fifth Fall   .25 .25
1796 A962 21cr Seventh Fall   .25 .25

Ministry of Communications, 15th
Anniv. — A963

1982, May 15
1797 A963 21cr multi   .25 .25

Museology
Course,
Natl.
Historical
Museum,
50th Anniv.
A964

1982, May 18
1798 A964 17cr blk & sal pink   .25 .25

Vale de Rio
Doce Mining
Co. — A965

1982, June 1
1799 A965 17cr Gears   .25 .25

Martin
Afonso de
Souza
Reading
Charter to
Settlers
A966

1982, June 3   Litho.   Perf. 11½
1800 A966 17cr multi   .25 .25
Town of Sao Vincente, 450th anniv.

Armadillo
A967

1982, June 4
1801 A967 17cr shown   .35 .25
1802 A967 21cr Wolves   .55 .25
1803 A967 30cr Deer   1.50 .25
  Nos. 1801-1803 (3)   2.40 .75

Film Strip
and Award
A968

1982, June 19
1804 A968 17cr multi   .25 .25
20th anniv. of Golden Palm award for The
Promise Keeper, Cannes Film Festival.

Souvenir Sheet

50th Anniv. of Constitutionalist
Revolution — A969

1982, July 9   Litho.   Perf. 11
1805 A969 140cr multi   3.25 3.25

Church of Our
Lady of
O'Sabara — A970

Baroque Architecture, Minas Gerais State:
No. 1807, Church of Our Lady of the Rosary,
Diamantina. No. 1808, Town Square, Mariana.

1982, July 16   Perf. 11½
1806 A970 17cr multi   .35 .25
1807 A970 17cr multi, horiz.   .35 .25
1808 A970 17cr multi, horiz.   .35 .25
  Nos. 1806-1808 (3)   1.05 .75

St. Francis of
Assisi, 800th Birth
Anniv. — A971

1982, July 24
1809 A971 21cr multi   .25 .25

Stamp Day
and
Centenary of
Pedro II
"Large
Head"
Stamps
A972

1982, Aug. 1
1810 A972 21cr No. 82 .25 .25

Port of
Manaus
Free
Trade
Zone
A973

1982, Aug. 15   Perf. 11x11½
1811 A973 75cr multi .50 .30

Scouting Year — A974

1982, Aug. 21   Litho.   Perf. 11
1812 A974 Sheet of 2 7.75 7.75
  a.   185cr Scout 3.75 3.75
  b.   85cr Baden-Powell 3.75 3.75

Orixas Folk
Costumes of
African
Origin
A975

1982, Aug. 21   Perf. 11½
1813 A975 20cr Iemanja .45 .25
1814 A975 20cr Xango .45 .25
1815 A975 20cr Oxumare .45 .25
  Nos. 1813-1815 (3) 1.35 .75

10th Anniv.
of Central
Bank of
Brazil
Currency
Museum
A976

Designs: No. 1816, 1645 12-florin coin,
obverse and reverse. No. 1817, 1822 Emperor
Pedro 6.40-reis coronation coin.

1982, Aug. 31
1816 A976 25cr multi .25 .25
1817 A976 25cr multi .25 .25

Dom Pedro Proclaiming
Independence — A977

1982, Sept. 1
1818 A977 25cr multi .25 .25

National Week.

Portrait — A978

1982, Oct. 4
1819 A978 85cr multicolored .75 .40

St. Theresa of Avila (1515-1582).

A979

1982, Oct. 15   Litho.   Perf. 11½x11
1820 A979 75cr Instruments .75 .40
1821 A979 80cr Dancers .75 .40
1822 A979 85cr Musicians .75 .40
  Nos. 1820-1822 (3) 2.25 1.20

Souvenir Sheet
Perf. 11
1822A A979 Sheet of 3, 4.75 4.75
    #1820-1822
  b.   75cr Instruments 1.25 1.25
  c.   80cr Dancers 1.25 1.25
  d.   85cr Musicians 1.25 1.25

Lubrapex 82, 4th Portuguese-Brazilian
Stamp Exhibition. Stamps in No. 1822A are
without "LUBRAPEX 82".

Aviation
Industry
Day
A980

24cr, Embraer EMB-312 trainer plane.

1982, Oct. 17   Perf. 12
1823 A980 24cr multicolored .25 .25

Bastos
Tigre,
Poet, Birth
Centenary,
and
"Saudade"
Text
A981

1982, Oct. 29
1824 A981 24cr multi .25 .25

Book Day.

10th Anniv. of Brazilian
Telecommunications Co. — A982

1982, Nov. 9   Litho.   Perf. 11½
1825 A982 24cr multi .25 .25

Christmas
A983

Children's Drawings.

1982, Nov. 10
1826 A983 24cr Nativity .75 .25
1827 A983 24cr Angels .75 .25
1828 A983 30cr Nativity, diff. .75 .25
1829 A983 30cr Flight into Egypt .75 .25
  Nos. 1826-1829 (4) 3.00 1.00

State Flags Type of 1981
No. 1830: a, Ceara. b, Espirito Santo. c,
Paraiba. d, Grande de Norte. e, Rondonia.

1982, Nov. 19
1830   Block of 5 + label 5.50 10.00
  a.-e. A947 24cr any single 1.10 .30

Thanksgiving — A985

1982, Nov. 25
1835 A985 24cr multi .25 .25

Homage to the
Deaf — A986

1982, Dec. 1
1836 A986 24cr multi .25 .25

Naval
Academy
Bicentenary
A987

Training Ships: No. 1837, Brazil. No. 1838,
Benjamin Constant. No. 1839, Almirante
Saldanha.

1982, Dec. 14
1837 A987 24cr multi .40 .25
1838 A987 24cr multi .40 .25
1839 A987 24cr multi .40 .25
  Nos. 1837-1839 (3) 1.20 .75

Souvenir Sheet

No. 12 — A988

1982, Dec. 18   Litho.   Perf. 11
1840 A988 200cr multi 3.75 3.75

BRASILIANA '83 Intl. Stamp Exhibition, Rio
de Janeiro, July 29-Aug. 7.

Brasiliana
'83 Carnival
A989

24cr, Samba drummers. 130cr, Street
parade. 140cr, Dancer. 150cr, Male dancer.

1983, Feb. 9   Litho.   Perf. 11½
1841 A989 24cr multi .65 .25
1842 A989 130cr multi 2.50 .80
1843 A989 140cr multi 2.50 .80
1844 A989 150cr multi 2.50 .80
  Nos. 1841-1844 (4) 8.15 2.65

Antarctic
Expedition
A990

150cr, Support ship Barano de Teffe.

1983, Feb. 20   Litho.   Perf. 11½
1845 A990 150cr multi 1.10 .55

50th Anniv. of
Women's
Rights — A991

1983, Mar. 8
1846 A991 130cr multi .90 .55

Itaipu Hydroelectric Power Station
Opening — A992

1983, Mar.   Litho.   Perf. 12
1847 A992 140cr multi .90 .50

Cancer Prevention
A993

Designs: 30cr, Microscope. 38cr, Antonio
Prudente, Paulista Cancer Assoc. founder,
Camargo Hospital.

1983, Apr. 18
1848 A993 30cr multi .85 .50
1849 A993 38cr multi .85 .50
  a.   Pair, #1848-1849 1.75 1.25

Martin Luther (1483-1546) A994

1983, Apr. 18
1850 A994 150cr pale grn & blk   1.25 .50

Agricultural Research A995

No. 1851, Chestnut tree. No. 1852, Genetic research. No. 1853, Tropical soy beans.

1983, Apr. 26   Litho.   Perf. 11½
1851 A995 30cr multi   .30 .25
1852 A995 30cr multi   .30 .25
1853 A995 38cr multi   .30 .25
    Nos. 1851-1853 (3)   .90 .75

Father Rogerio Neuhaus (1863-1934), Centenary of Ordination — A996

1983, May 3   Perf. 11½x11
1854 A996 30cr multi   .30 .25

30th Anniv. of Customs Cooperation Council — A997

1983, May 5   Perf. 11x11½
1855 A997 30cr multi   .30 .25

World Communications Year — A998

1983, May 17   Litho.   Perf. 11½
1856 A998 250cr multi   2.50 .75

Toucans A999

30cr, Tucanucu. 185cr, White-breasted. 205cr, Green-beaked. 215cr, Black-beaked.

1983, May 21
1857 A999 30cr multicolored   .85 .40
1858 A999 185cr multicolored   3.25 .65
1859 A999 205cr multicolored   3.25 .65
1860 A999 215cr multicolored   3.25 .65
    Nos. 1857-1860 (4)   10.60 2.35

Souvenir Sheet

Resurrection, by Raphael (1483-1517) — A1000

1983, May 25   Perf. 11
1861 A1000 250cr multi   3.75 3.75

Hohenzollern 980 Locomotive, 1875 — A1001

Various locomotives: No. 1863, Baldwin #1, 1881. No. 1864, Fowler #1, 1872.

1983, June 12   Perf. 11½
1862 A1001 30cr shown   .65 .30
1863 A1001 30cr multicolored   .65 .30
1864 A1001 38cr multicolored   .65 .30
    Nos. 1862-1864 (3)   1.95 .90

9th Women's Basketball World Championship A1002

1983, July 24   Litho.   Perf. 11½x11
1865 A1002 30cr Players, front view .40 .25
1866 A1002 30cr Players, rear view .40 .25

Simon Bolivar (1783-1830) — A1003

1983, July 24   Perf. 12
1867 A1003 30cr multi   .25 .25

Children's Polio and Measles Vaccination Campaign — A1004

1983, July 25
1868 A1004 30cr Girl, measles   .25 .25
1869 A1004 30cr Boy, polio   .25 .25

Goddess Minerva, Computer Tape — A1005

1983, July 28   Perf. 11½x11
1870 A1005 30cr multicolored   .25 .25
    20th Anniv. of Master's program in engineering.

A1006

Guanabara Bay.

1983, July 29   Engr.
1871 A1006 185cr No. 1   1.10 .55
1872 A1006 205cr No. 2   1.25 .55
1873 A1006 215cr No. 3   1.60 .55
    Nos. 1871-1873 (3)   3.95 1.65
Souvenir Sheet
Perf. 11
1874   Sheet of 3   9.00 9.00
  a.   A1006 185cr No. 1   2.75 2.75
  b.   A1006 205cr No. 2   2.75 2.75
  c.   A1006 215cr No. 3   2.75 2.75
BRASILIANA '83 Intl. Stamp Show, Rio de Janeiro, July 29-Aug. 7.
Stamps in No. 1874 have unframed denomination at bottom of the stamps. The background scene is enlarged to cover all 3 stamps in a continuous design.

Souvenir Sheets
    A set of five 2000cr souvenir sheets also exist for BRASILIANA '83. These picture early flying attempts, Ademar Ferreira da Silva, Olympic gold medal winner, Soccer, Formula 1 auto racing, and Gold medal winners in Olympic sailing. Value $30 each.

Souvenir Sheet

The First Mass in Brazil, by Vitor Meireles (1833-1903) — A1007

1983, Aug. 18   Perf. 11
1875 A1007 250cr multi   3.75 3.75

EMB-120 Brasilia Passenger Plane A1008

1983, Aug. 19   Perf. 12
1876 A1008 30cr multi   .35 .30

Vision of Don Bosco Centenary A1009

1983, Aug. 30
1877 A1009 130cr multi   .65 .30

Independence Week — A1010

1983, Sept. 1   Litho.   Perf. 11½
1878 A1010 50cr multi   .30 .25

National Steel Corp., 10th Anniv. A1011

1983, Sept. 17   Litho.   Perf. 11½
1879 A1011 45cr multi   .30 .25

Cactus A1012

No. 1880, Pilosocereus gounellei. No. 1881, Melocactus bahiensis. No. 1882, Cereus jamacaru.

1983, Sept. 12   Litho.   Perf. 11½
1880 A1012 45cr multicolored   .50 .25
1881 A1012 45cr multicolored   .50 .25
1882 A1012 57cr multicolored   .65 .25
    Nos. 1880-1882 (3)   1.65 .75

50th Anniv. of the 1st National Eucharistic Congress A1013

1983, Oct. 12   Litho.   Perf. 11½
1883 A1013 45cr multi   .25 .25

World Food Program A1014

1983, Oct. 14   Litho.   Perf. 11½
1884 A1014 45cr Mouth, grain   .25 .25
1885 A1014 57cr Fish, sailboat   .25 .25

Souvenir Sheet

Louis Breguet, Death
Centenary — A1015

376cr, Telegraph transmitter.

1983, Oct. 27　Litho.　Perf. 11
1886 A1015 376cr multi　　　7.50 7.50

Christmas
1983
A1016

17th-18th Cent. Statues: 45cr, Our Lady of
the Angels. 315cr, Our Lady of the Parturition.
335cr, Our Lady of Joy. 345cr, Our Lady of
the Presentation.

1983, Nov. 10　Litho.　Perf. 11½
1887 A1016 45cr multi　　　.40 .30
1888 A1016 315cr multi　　　2.00 .75
1889 A1016 335cr multi　　　2.00 .75
1890 A1016 345cr multi　　　2.00 .75
　　　Nos. 1887-1890 (4)　　　6.40 2.55

Marshal Mascarenhas Birth
Centenary — A1017

1983, Nov. 13　Litho.　Perf. 11½
1891 A1017 45cr Battle sites　　.30 .25

Commander of Brazilian Expeditionary
Force in Italy.

State Flags Type of 1981

No. 1892: a, Amazonas. b, Goias. c, Rio. d,
Mato Grosso Do Sol. e, Parana.

1983, Nov. 17　Litho.　Perf. 11½
1892　Block of 5 + label　6.00 12.00
a.-e. A947 45cr any single　1.00 .40

Thanksgiving — A1018

1983, Nov. 24　Litho.　Perf. 12
1896 A1018 45cr Madonna, wheat　.30 .30

Manned Flight
Bicentenary
A1019

345cr, Montgolfiere balloon, 1783.

1983, Dec. 15　Litho.　Perf. 12
1897 A1019 345cr multi　　　2.75 1.25

Ethnic
Groups
A1020

1984, Jan. 20　Litho.　Perf. 12
1898 A1020 45cr multi　　　.25 .25

50th anniv. of publication of Masters and
Slaves, sociological study by Gilberto Freyre.

Centenary
of Crystal
Palace,
Petropolis
A1021

1984, Feb. 2
1899 A1021 45cr multi　　　.25 .25

Souvenir Sheet

Flags (Sculpture with 40 Figures), by
Victor Brecheret (b. 1894) — A1022

1984, Feb. 22　Litho.　Perf. 11
1900 A1022 805cr multi　　　2.75 2.75

Naval
Museum
Centenary
A1023

620cr, Figurehead, frigate, 1847.

1984, Mar. 23　Litho.　Perf. 11½
1901 A1023 620cr multi　　　.90 .25

Slavery
Abolition
Centenary
A1024

585cr, Broken chain, raft. 610cr, Freed
slave.

1984, Mar. 25
1902 A1024 585cr multi　　　.75 .30
1903 A1024 610cr multi　　　.75 .30

Souvenir Sheet

Visit of King Carl XVI Gustaf of
Sweden — A1025

1984, Apr. 2　　　Perf. 11
1904 A1025 2105cr multi　　6.00 6.00

1984
Summer
Olympics
A1026

No. 1905, Long jump. No. 1906, 100-meter
race. No. 1907, Relay race. 585cr, Pole vault.
610cr, High jump. 620cr, Hurdles.

1984, Apr. 13　　　Perf. 11½
1905 A1026 65cr multi　　　.85 .30
1906 A1026 65cr multi　　　.85 .30
1907 A1026 65cr multi　　　.85 .30
1908 A1026 585cr multi　　　.85 .30
1909 A1026 610cr multi　　　.85 .30
1910 A1026 620cr multi　　　.85 .30
a.　Block of 6, #1905-1910　5.25 5.25

Voters
Casting
Ballots,
Symbols of
Labor
A1027

Pres. Getulio Vargas Birth Centenary —
Symbols of Development: No. 1912, Oil rig,
blast furnace. No. 1913, High-tension towers.

1984, Apr. 19　　　Perf. 11½
1911 A1027 65cr shown　　　.25 .25
1912 A1027 65cr multi　　　.25 .25
1913 A1027 65cr multi　　　.25 .25
　　　Nos. 1911-1913 (3)　　　.75 .75

Columbus, Espana
'84
Emblem — A1028

1984, Apr. 27
1914 A1028　65cr Pedro Cabral　.30 .25
1915 A1028 610cr shown　　　.75 .30

Map of Americas,
Heads — A1029

1984, May 7　Litho.　Perf. 11½
1916 A1029 65cr multi　　　.25 .25

Pan-American Association of Finance and
Guarantees, 8th Assembly.

Lubrapex
'84 — A1030

18th Century Paintings, Mariana Cathedral:
65cr, Hunting scene. 585cr, Pastoral scene.
610cr, People under umbrellas. 620cr,
Elephants.

1984, May 8　　　Perf. 11½x11
1917 A1030　65cr multi　　　.65 .25
1918 A1030 585cr multi　　　1.25 .40
1919 A1030 610cr multi　　　1.25 .40
1920 A1030 620cr multi　　　1.25 .40
　　　Nos. 1917-1920 (4)　　　4.40 1.45

Souvenir Sheet

Intl. Fedn. of Soccer Associations,
80th Anniv. — A1031

1984, May 21　　　Perf. 11
1921 A1031 2115cr Globe　　6.00 6.00

Exists imperforate. Value $800.

Matto
Grosso
Lowland
Fauna
A1032

1984, June 5　Litho.　Perf. 11½
1922　Strip of 3　　　1.25 1.25
a.　A1032 65cr Deer　　　.40 .30
b.　A1032 65cr Jaguar　　　.40 .30
c.　A1032 80cr Alligator　　　.40 .30

First Letter Mailed
in Brazil, by Guido
Mondin — A1033

1984, June 8　　　Perf. 12x11½
1923 A1033 65cr multi　　　.25 .25

Postal Union of Americas and Spain, first
anniv. of new headquarters.

Brazil-Germany Air Service, 50th
Anniv. — A1034

610cr, Dornier-Wal seaplane. 620cr,
Steamer Westfalen.

1984, June 19
1924 610cr multi   1.50 .40
1925 620cr multi   1.50 .40
  a. A1034 Pair, #1924-1925   3.00 .80

Woolly Spider Monkey, World Wildlife Fund Emblem — A1036

1984, July 2   *Perf. 11½*
1926 A1036 65cr Mother, baby   .35 .30
1927 A1036 80cr Monkey   .35 .30

Agriculture Type of 1980

Designs: 65cr, Rubber tree. 80cr, Brazil nuts. 120cr, Rice. 150cr, Eucalyptus. 300cr, Pinha da Parana. 800cr, Carnauba. 1000cr, Babacu. 2000cr, Sunflower.

Photogravure (65, 80, 120, 150cr), Engraved

1984-85   *Perf. 11x11½*
1934 A894   65cr lilac   .25 .25
1935 A894   80cr brn red   .55 .25
1936 A894 120cr dk sl bl   .25 .25
1937 A894 150cr green   .25 .25
1938 A894 300cr rose mag   2.75 .25
1939 A894 800cr grnsh bl   1.25 .25
1940 A894 1000cr lemon   1.25 .25
1941 A894 2000cr yel org ('85) 2.25 .30
  Nos. 1934-1941 (8)   8.80 2.05

Marajo Isld. Buffalo A1037

1984, July 9   Litho.   *Perf. 12*
1942 A1037 Strip of 3   1.25 1.25
  a. 65cr Approaching stream   .40 .30
  b. 65cr Standing on bank   .40 .30
  c. 80cr Drinking   .40 .30

Continuous design.

Banco Economico Sesquicentenary — A1038

1984, July 13   *Perf. 11½*
1943 A1038 65cr Bank, coins   .25 .25

Historic Railway Stations A1039

No. 1944, Japeri. No. 1945, Luz, vert. No. 1946, Sao Joao del Rei.

1984, July 23   Litho.   *Perf. 11½*
1944 A1039 65cr multi   .25 .25
1945 A1039 65cr multi   .25 .25
1946 A1039 80cr multi   .25 .25
  Nos. 1944-1946 (3)   .75 .75

Souvenir Sheet

A1040

1984, Aug. 13   *Perf. 11*
1947 A1040 585cr Girl scout   5.50 5.50

Girl Scouts in Brazil, 65th anniv.

Couple Sheltered From Rain — A1041

1984, Aug. 21   Litho.   *Perf. 11½*
1948 A1041 65cr multicolored   .25 .25

Housing project bank, 20th anniv.

Independence Week — A1042

Children's Drawings: No. 1949, Explorer & ship. No. 1950, Sailing ships. No. 1951, "BRASIL" mural. No. 1952, Children under rainbow.

1984, Sept. 3
1949 A1042 100cr multi   .30 .25
1950 A1042 100cr multi   .30 .25
1951 A1042 100cr multi   .30 .25
1952 A1042 100cr multi   .30 .25
  Nos. 1949-1952 (4)   1.20 1.00

Rio de Janeiro Chamber of Commerce Sesquicentenary — A1043

100cr, Monument, worker silhouette.

1984, Sept. 10
1953 A1043 100cr multi   .25 .25

Death Sesquicentenary of Don Pedro I (IV of Portugal) — A1044

1984, Sept. 23   *Perf. 12x11½*
1954 A1044 1000cr Portrait   2.75 .75

Local Mushrooms A1045

120cr, Pycnoporus sanguineus. 1050cr, Calvatia sp. 1080cr, Pleurotus sp, horiz.

1984, Oct. 22   *Perf. 11½*
1955 A1045 120cr multi   .30 .25
1956 A1045 1050cr multi   1.90 .55
1957 A1045 1080cr multi   1.90 .55
  Nos. 1955-1957 (3)   4.10 1.35

Book Day — A1046

120cr, Girl in open book.

1984, Oct. 23   *Perf. 11½*
1958 A1046 120cr multi   .25 .25

New State Mint Opening — A1047

1984, Nov. 1
1959 A1047 120cr multi   .25 .25

Informatics Fair & Congress A1048

120cr, Eye, computer terminal.

1984, Nov. 5   Litho.   *Perf. 12*
1960 A1048 120cr multi   .25 .25

Org. of American States, 14th Assembly A1049

1984, Nov. 14
1961 A1049 120cr Emblem, flags .25 .25

State Flags Type of 1981

No. 1962: a, Maranhaio. b, Mato Grosso. c, Minas Gerais. d, Piaui. e, Santa Catarina.

1984, Nov. 19   *Perf. 11½*
1962   Block of 5 + label   3.25 3.25
  a.-e. A947 120cr, any single .55 .40

Thanksgiving 1984 — A1051

120cr, Bell tower, Brasilia.

1984, Nov. 22
1963 A1051 120cr multicolored   .25 .25

Christmas 1984 A1052

Paintings: No. 1964, Nativity, by Djanira. No. 1965, Virgin and Child, by Glauco Rodrigues. No. 1966, Flight into Egypt, by Paul Garfunkel. No. 1967, Nativity, by Di Cavalcanti.

1984, Dec. 3   Litho.   *Perf. 12*
1964 A1052 120cr multi   .30 .30
1965 A1052 120cr multi   .30 .30
1966 A1052 1050cr multi   1.50 .55
1967 A1052 1080cr multi   1.50 .55
  Nos. 1964-1967 (4)   3.60 1.70

40th Anniv., International Civil Aviation Organization — A1053

120cr, Aircraft, Earth globe.

1984, Dec. 7   Litho.   *Perf. 12*
1968 A1053 120cr multi   .25 .25

25th Anniv., North-Eastern Development — A1054

1984, Dec. 14   Litho.   *Perf. 12*
1969 A1054 120cr Farmer, field .25 .25

Emilio Rouede A1055

Painting: Church of the Virgin of Safe Travels, by Rouede.

1985, Jan. 22   Litho.   *Perf. 12*
1970 A1055 120cr multi   .25 .25

BRASILSAT — A1056

1985, Feb. 8   Litho.   *Perf. 11½x12*
1971 A1056 150cr Satellite, Brazil .25 .25

Metropolitan Railways — A1057

1985, Mar. 2   Litho.   Perf. 11x11½
1972 A1057 200cr Passenger trains .25 .25

Brasilia
Botanical
Gardens
A1058

200cr, Caryocar brasiliense.

1985, Mar. 8   Litho.   Perf. 11½x12
1973 A1058 200cr multi   .25 .25

40th Anniv.,
Brazilian
Paratroops
A1059

1985, Mar. 8   Litho.   Perf. 11½x12
1974 A1059 200cr Parachute drop .25 .25

Natl. Climate Awareness
Program — A1060

1985, Mar. 18   Litho.   Perf. 11½x12
1975 A1060 500cr multi   .25 .25

Pure Bred
Horses
A1061

No. 1976, Campolina. No. 1977, Marajoara.
No. 1978, Mangalarga marchador.

1985, Mar. 19   Litho.   Perf. 12
1976 A1061 1000cr multi   1.10 .55
1977 A1061 1500cr multi   1.10 .55
1978 A1061 1500cr multi   1.10 .55
    Nos. 1976-1978 (3)   3.30 1.65

Ouro Preto — A1062

No. 1980, St. Miguel des Missoes. No.
1981, Olinda.

1985, Apr. 18   Litho.   Perf. 11½x12
1979 A1062 220cr shown   .25 .25
1980 A1062 220cr multi   .25 .25
1981 A1062 220cr multi   .25 .25
    Nos. 1979-1981 (3)   .75 .75

Polivolume, by Mary
Vieira — A1063

1985, Apr. 20   Litho.
1982 A1063 220cr multi   .25 .25
    Rio Branco Inst., 40th anniv.

Natl. Capital, Brasilia, 25th
Anniv. — A1064

No. 1983, Natl. Theater, acoustic shell. No.
1984, Catetinho Palace, JK Memorial.

1985, Apr. 22   Litho.
1983 A1064 220cr multi   .25 .25
1984 A1064 220cr multi   .25 .25

A1065

A1065a

1985-86   Photo.   Perf. 11½
1985 A1065   50cr lake   .25 .25
1986 A1065   100cr dp vio   .25 .25
1987 A1065   150cr violet   .25 .25
1988 A1065   200cr ultra   .25 .25
1989 A1065   220cr green   .35 5.00
1990 A1065   300cr royal bl   .25 .25
1991 A1065   500cr olive blk   .25 .25
1992 A1065a 1000cr brn ol ('86)   .25 .25
1993 A1065a 2000cr brt grn ('86)   .25 .25
1994 A1065a 3000cr dl vio   .25 .25
1995 A1065a 5000cr brown   1.25 .25
    Nos. 1985-1995 (11)   3.85 7.50

Marshal
Rondon,
120th
Birth
Anniv.
A1066

1985, May 5   Perf. 11x11½
1996 A1066 220cr multi   .25 .25
    Educator, protector of the Indians, building
superintendent of telegraph lines.

Candido Fontoura
(1885-1974)
A1067

1985, May 14   Perf. 12x11½
1997 A1067 220cr multi   .25 .25
    Pioneer of the Brazilian pharmaceutical
industry.

Brapex VI — A1068

Cave paintings: No. 1998, Deer, Cerca
Grande. No. 1999, Lizards, Lapa do Caboclo.
No. 2000, Running deer, Grande Abrigo de
Santana do Riacho.

1985, May 18   Perf. 11½x11
1998 A1068   300cr multi   .25 .25
1999 A1068   300cr multi   .25 .25
2000 A1068   2000cr multi   .65 .65
    Nos. 1998-2000 (3)   1.15 1.15
Souvenir Sheet
Perf. 10½x11
2000A A1068   Sheet of 3, #1998-
    2000   3.50 3.50
    b.   300cr multi   .80 .80
    c.   300cr multi   .80 .80
    d.   2000cr multi   .80 .80

Wildlife Conservation — A1069

Birds in Marinho dos Abrolhos National
Park: No. 2001, Fregata magnificens. No.
2002, Sula dactylatra. No. 2003, Anous
stolidus. No. 2004, Pluvialis squatarola.

1985, June 5   Perf. 11½x12
2001 A1069   220cr multi   .30 .30
2002 A1069   220cr multi   .30 .30
2003 A1069   220cr multi   .35 .30
2004 A1069   2000cr multi   1.00 .35
    Nos. 2001-2004 (4)   1.95 1.25

A1070

UN infant survival campaign: No. 2005,
Mother breastfeeding infant. No. 2006, Hand,
eyedropper, children.

1985, June 11   Perf. 12x11½
2005 A1070   220cr multi   .35 .35
2006 A1070   220cr multi   .35 .35
    a.   Pair, #2005-2006   .70 .70

Sea Search &
Rescue — A1071

1985, June 22   Litho.   Perf. 11½x11
2007 A1071 220cr multi   .25 .25

World Cup Soccer, Mexico,
1986 — A1072

1985, June 23   Perf. 11
2008 A1072 2000cr multi   5.50 5.50

Intl. Youth
Year — A1073

1985, June 28   Perf. 12
2009 A1073 220cr Circle of children .25 .25

11th Natl.
Eucharistic
Congress
A1074

2000cr, Mosaic, Priest raising host.

1985, July 16   Perf. 12x11½
2010 A1074 2000cr multi   .55 .30

Director Humberto Mauro, Scene from
Sangue Mineiro, 1929 — A1075

1985, July 27
2011 A1075 300cr multi   .25 .25
    Cataguases Studios, 60th anniv.

Escola e Sacro Museum, Convent St.
Anthony, Joao Pessoa, Paraiba
A1076

1985, Aug. 5   Perf. 11½x12
2012 A1076 330cr multi   .25 .25
    Paraiba State 400th anniv.

Inconfidencia Museum
A1077

No. 2014, Museum of History & Diplomacy.

1985, Aug. 11   **Perf. 12x11½**
2013 A1077 300cr shown   .25 .25
2014 A1077 300cr multi   .25 .25

Revolutionary, by Guido Mondin — A1078

1985, Aug. 14
2015 A1078 330cr multi   .25 .25

Cabanagem Insurrection, 150th anniv.

AMX Subsonic Air Force Fighter Plane
A1079

1985, Aug. 19   **Perf. 11½x12**
2016 A1079 330cr multi   .25 .25

AMX Project, joint program with Italy.

16th-17th Century Military Uniforms
A1080

No. 2017, Captain, crossbowman. No. 2018, Harquebusier, sergeant. No. 2019, Musketeer, pikeman. No. 2020, Fusilier, pikeman.

1985, Aug. 26   **Perf. 12x11½**
2017 A1080 300cr multi   .25 .25
2018 A1080 300cr multi   .25 .25
2019 A1080 300cr multi   .25 .25
2020 A1080 300cr multi   .25 .25
    Nos. 2017-2020 (4)   1.00 1.00

Bento Goncalves and Insurrectionist Cavalry on Southern Battlefields, by Guido Mondin — A1081

1985, Sept. 20   **Perf. 11½x12**
2021 A1081 330cr multi   .25 .25

Farrouphilha Insurrection, 150th anniv.

Aparados da Serra National Park
A1082

3100cr, Ravine. 3320cr, Mountains. 3480cr, Forest, waterfall.

1985, Sept. 23
2022 A1082 3100cr multi   1.10 .30
2023 A1082 3320cr multi   1.10 .30
2024 A1082 3480cr multi   1.50 .45
    Nos. 2022-2024 (3)   3.70 1.05

President-elect Tancredo Neves, Natl. Congress, Alvorada Palace, Supreme Court — A1083

1985, Oct. 10   **Litho.**   **Perf. 11x11½**
2025 A1083 330cr multi   .25 .25

FEB, Postmark
A1084

1985, Oct. 10   **Perf. 11½x12**
2026 A1084 500cr multi   .25 .25

Brazilian Expeditionary Force Postal Service, 41st anniv.

Rio de Janeiro-Niteroi Ferry Service, 150th Anniv. — A1085

1985, Oct. 14   **Perf. 11½x12**
2027 A1085 500cr Segunda   .30 .25
2028 A1085 500cr Terceira   .30 .25
2029 A1085 500cr Especuladora   .30 .25
2030 A1085 500cr Urca   .30 .25
    Nos. 2027-2030 (4)   1.20 1.00

Muniz M-7 Inaugural Flight, 50th Anniv. — A1086

1985, Oct. 22
2031 A1086 500cr multi   .25 .25

UN 40th Anniv. — A1087

1985, Oct. 24   **Perf. 11½x11**
2032 A1087 500cr multi   .25 .25

Natl. Press System — A1088

1985, Nov. 7
2033 A1088 500cr multi   .25 .25

Diario de Pernambuco, newspaper, 160th anniv.

Christmas 1985
A1089

No. 2034, Christ in Manger. No. 2035, Adoration of the Magi. No. 2036, Flight to Egypt.

1985, Nov. 11   **Perf. 11½x12**
2034 A1089 500cr multi   .30 .25
2035 A1089 500cr multi   .30 .25
2036 A1089 500cr multi   .30 .25
    Nos. 2034-2036 (3)   .90 .75

State Flags Type of 1981

No. 2037: a, Para. b, Rio Grande do Sul. c, Acre. d, Sao Paulo.

1985, Nov. 19   **Perf. 12**
2037   Block of 4   2.25 4.00
a.-d.   A947 500cr, any single   .55 .30

Thanksgiving Day — A1091

500cr, Child gathering wheat.

1985, Nov. 28   **Perf. 12x11½**
2038 A1091 500cr multi   .25 .25

Economic Development of Serra dos Carajas Region — A1092

1985, Dec. 11   **Litho.**   **Perf. 11½x12**
2039 A1092 500cr multi   .25 .25

Fr. Bartholomeu Lourenco de Gusmao (1685-1724), Inventor, the Aerostat — A1093

1985, Dec. 19   **Litho.**   **Perf. 11x11½**
2040 A1093 500cr multi   .25 .25

A1094

The Trees, by Da Costa E Silva (b. 1885), poet.

1985, Dec. 20   **Litho.**   **Perf. 12x11½**
2041 A1094 500cr multi   .25 .25

Values for used commemoratives issued after 1985 and for used souvenir sheets are for favor-canceled examples. Postally used examples are worth more.

Souvenir Sheet

A1095

1986, Mar. 3   **Litho.**   **Perf. 11**
2042 A1095 10000cr multi   6.00 6.00

1986 World Cup Soccer Championships, Mexico. LUBRAPEX '86, philatelic exhibition.

Halley's Comet — A1096

1986, Apr. 11   **Litho.**   **Perf. 11½x12**
2043 A1096 50c multi   .25 .25

Commander Ferraz Antarctic Station, 2nd Anniv. — A1097

1986, Apr. 25
2044 A1097 50c multi   .30 .25

Labor
Day — A1098

1986, May 1   Litho.   Perf. 12x11½
2045 A1098 50c multi   .25 .25

Maternity, by
Henrique
Bernardelli (1858-
1936)
A1099

1986, May 8
2046 A1099 50c multi   .25 .25

Amnesty
Intl., 25th
Anniv.
A1100

1986, May 28   Litho.   Perf. 11½x12
2047 A1100 50c multi   .25 .25

Butterflies
A1101

No. 2048, Pyrrhopyge ruficauda. No. 2049,
Prepona eugenes diluta. No. 2050, Pierriballia
mandel molione.

1986, June 5   Perf. 12x11½
2048 A1101 50c multi   .40 .25
2049 A1101 50c multi   .40 .25
2050 A1101 50c multi   .40 .25
    Nos. 2048-2050 (3)   1.20 .75

Score from Opera "Il Guarani" and
Antonio Carlos Gomes (1836-1896),
Composer — A1102

1986, July 11   Perf. 11½x12
2051 A1102 50c multi   .25 .25

Natl. Accident
Prevention
Campaign — A1103

1986, July 30   Litho.   Perf. 11½x11
2052 A1103 50c Lineman   .25 .25

Souvenir Sheet

Stamp Day — A1104

1986, Aug. 1   Perf. 11
2053 A1104 5cz No. 53   2.00 2.00
    Brazilian Phil. Soc., 75th anniv., and Dom
Pedro II issue, Nos. 53-60, 120th anniv.

Architecture
A1105

Designs: 10c, House of Garcia D'Avila,
Nazare de Mata, Bahia. 20c, Church of Our
Lady of the Assumption, Anchieta Village. 50c,
Fort Reis Magos, Natal. 1cz, Pilgrim's Col-
umn, Alcantara Village, 1648. 2cz, Cloisters,
St. Francis Convent, Olinda. 5cz, St. Anthony's
Chapel, Sao Roque. 10cz, St. Lawrence of the
Indians Church, Niteroi. 20cz, Principe da
Beiro Fort, Mato Dentro. 50cz, Jesus of
Matozinhos Church, vert. 100cz, Church of
our Lady of Sorrow, Campanha. 200cz, Casa
dos Contos, Ouro Preto. 500cz, Antiga
Alfandega, Belem, Para.

Perf. 11x10½, 10½x11
1986-88   Photo.
2055 A1105 10c sage grn   .25   .25
2057 A1105 20c brt blue   .25   .25
2059 A1105 50c orange   .25   .25
  a.   Litho., perf. 13 ('88)   5.50   .30
2064 A1105 1cz golden brn   .25   .25
  a.   Litho., perf. 11½x11 ('88) 4.50   .30
2065 A1105 2cz dull rose   .25   .25
  a.   Litho., perf. 13 ('88)   .75   .25
  b.   Litho., perf. 11½x11 ('88) 1.90   .25
2067 A1105 5cz lt olive grn   .25   .25
  a.   Litho., perf. 13 ('88)   2.25   .25
  b.   Litho., perf. 11½x11 ('88) 6.00   .25
2068 A1105 10cz slate blue   .25   .25
  a.   Litho., perf. 13 ('88)   3.75   .40
  b.   Litho., perf. 11½x11 ('88) 4.50   .40
2069 A1105 20cz lt red brn   .25   .25
2070 A1105 50cz brn org   .25   .25
2071 A1105 100cz dull grn   .25   .25
2072 A1105 200cz deep blue   .25   .25
2073 A1105 500cz dull red brn   .25   .25
    Nos. 2055-2073 (12)   3.00   3.00

Nos. 2065-2070 exist in multiple shades.
    Issued: 10c, 8/11; 20c, 12/8; 50c, 8/19; 1cz,
11/19; 2cz, 11/9; 5cz, 12/30; 10cz, 6/2/87;
20cz, 50cz, 9/18/87; 100cz, 12/21/87; 200cz,
5/9/88; 500cz, 11/22/88.

A1106

Famous
Men —
A1106a

Designs: No. 2074, Juscelino Kubitschek
de Oliveira, president 1956-61, and Alvorado
Palace, Brasilia. No. 2075, Octavio Man-
gabeira, statesman, and Itamaraty Palace, Rio
de Janeiro, horiz.

1986   Perf. 12x11½, 11½x12
2074 A1106 50c multi   .25 .25
2075 A1106a 50c multi   .25 .25
    Issued: No. 2074, Aug. 21; No. 2075, Aug.
27.

World Gastroenterology Congress,
Sao Paulo — A1107

1986, Sept. 7   Perf. 11½x12
2076 A1107 50c multi   .25 .25

Federal
Broadcasting
System, 50th
Anniv. — A1108

1986, Sept. 15   Perf. 12x11½
2077 A1108 50c multi   .25 .25

Intl. Peace
Year — A1109

Painting (detail): War and Peace, by
Candido Portinari.

1986, Sept. 16
2078 A1109 50c multi   .25 .25

Ernesto
Simoes
Filho (b.
1886),
Publisher of
A Tarde
A1110

1986, Oct. 4   Litho.   Perf. 11½x12
2079 A1110 50c multi   .25 .25

Famous
Men — A1111

Designs: No. 2080, Title page from manu-
script, c. 1683-94, by Gregorio Mattos e
Guerra (b. 1636), author. No. 2081, Manuel
Bandeira (1886-1968), poet, text from I'll Go
Back to Pasargada.

1986, Oct. 29   Perf. 11½x11
2080 A1111 50c lake & beige   .25 .25
2081 A1111 50c lake & dl grn   .25 .25

Federal Savings
Bank, 125th
Anniv. — A1112

1986, Nov. 4   Perf. 12x11½
2082 A1112 50c multi   .25 .25

Flowering
Plants — A1113

50c, Urera mitis. 6.50cz, Couroupita
guyanensis. 6.90cz, Bauhinia variegata, horiz.

Perf. 12x11½, 11½x12
1986, Sept. 23
2083 A1113   50c multi   .25 .25
2084 A1113 6.50cz multi   .55 .30
2085 A1113 6.90cz multi   .65 .30
    Nos. 2083-2085 (3)   1.45 .85

Glauber Rocha, Film
Industry
Pioneer — A1114

1986, Nov. 20   Perf. 12x11½
2086 A1114 50c multi   .25 .25

LUBRAPEX '86 — A1115

Cordel Folk Tales: No. 2087, Romance of
the Mysterious Peacock. No. 2088, History of
the Empress Porcina.

1986, Nov. 21   Perf. 11x12
2087 A1115 6.90cz multi   .55 .25
2088 A1115 6.90cz multi   .55 .25
    Souvenir Sheet
    Perf. 11
2088A A1115 Sheet of 2, #2087-
              2088   2.75 2.75
  b.   6.90cz multi   1.00 1.00
  c.   6.90cz multi   1.00 1.00

Christmas
A1116

Birds: 50c, And Christ child. 6.50cz, And
tree. 7.30cz, Eating fruit.

1986, Nov. 10   *Perf. 11½x12*
2089 A1116   50c multi   .30   .25
2090 A1116   6.50cz multi   .55   .30
2091 A1116   7.30cz multi   .65   .30
    Nos. 2089-2091 (3)   1.50   .85

Military Uniforms,
c. 1930 — A1117

Designs: No. 2092, Navy lieutenant commander, dreadnought Minas Gerais. No. 2093, Army flight lieutenant, WACO S.C.O. biplane, Fortaleza Airport.

1986, Dec. 15   *Perf. 12x11½*
2092 A1117   50c multi   .25   .25
2093 A1117   50c multi   .25   .25
   Fortaleza Air Base, 50th anniv. (No. 2093).

Bartolomeu de
Gusmao Airport,
50th
Anniv. — A1118

1986, Dec. 26
2094 A1118   1cz multi   .30   .25

Heitor Villa Lobos
(1887-1959),
Conductor
A1119

1987, Mar. 5   Litho.   *Perf. 12x11½*
2095 A1119   1.50cz multi   .25   .25

Natl. Air Force C-130 Transport
Plane, Flag, the Antarctic
A1120

1987, Mar. 9   *Perf. 11x11½*
2096 A1120   1cz multi   .30   .25
     Antarctic Project.

Special Mail
Services
A1121

1987, Mar. 20   *Perf. 12x11½*
2097 A1121   1cz Rural delivery   .25   .25
2098 A1121   1cz Intl. express   .25   .25

TELECOM
'87,
Geneva
A1122

    2cz, Brasilsat, wave, globe.

1987, May 5   *Perf. 11½x12*
2099 A1122   2cz multi   .25   .25

10th Pan American
Games,
Indianapolis, Aug. 7-
25 — A1123

1987, May 20   *Perf. 12x11½*
2100 A1123   18cz multi   .25   .25

Natl. Fine
Arts
Museum,
150th Anniv
A1124

1987, Jan. 13   *Perf. 11½x12*
2101 A1124   1cz multi   .25   .25

Marine Conservation — A1125

   No. 2102, Eubalaena australis. No. 2103, Eretmochelys imbricata.

1987, June 5
2102 A1125   2cz multi   .30   .25
2103 A1125   2cz multi   .30   .25

Federal
Court of
Appeal,
40th Anniv.
A1126

1987, June 15
2104 A1126   2cz multi   .25   .25

Military Club,
Cent. — A1127

1987, June 26   *Perf. 12x11½*
2105 A1127   3cz multi   .25   .25

Agriculture
Institute of
Campinas,
Cent.
A1128

1987, June 27   *Perf. 11½x12*
2106 A1128   2cz multi   .25   .25

Entomological Society, 50th
Anniv. — A1129

1987, July 17
2107 A1129   3cz Zoolea lopiceps   .25   .25
2108 A1129   3cz Fulgora servillei   .25   .25

Natl.
Tourism
Year
A1130

   Designs: No. 2109, Monuments and Sugarloaf Mountain, Rio de Janeiro. No. 2110, Colonial church, sailboats, parrot, cashews.

1987, Aug. 4
2109 A1130   3cz multicolored   .25   .25
2110 A1130   3cz multicolored   .25   .25

Royal Portuguese
Cabinet of
Literature, 150th
Anniv. — A1131

1987, Aug. 27   *Perf. 12x11½*
2111 A1131   30cz ver & brt grn   .50   .40

Sport Club Intl. — A1132

   Championship soccer clubs, Brazil's Gold Cup: b, Sao Paulo. c, Guarani. d, Regatas do Flamengo.

1987, Aug. 29   *Perf. 11½x12*
2112 A1132   Block of 4   1.10   2.00
  a.-d.   3cz any single   .25   .25

St. Francis
Convent,
400th
Anniv.
A1133

1987, Oct. 4
2113 A1133   4cz multi   .25   .25

Jose
Americo
de
Almeida,
Author
A1134

   Design: Characters from romance novel, "A Bagaceira," 1928, and portrait of author.

1987, Oct. 23   Litho.   *Perf. 11x11½*
2114 A1134   4cz multi   .25   .25

Spanish
Galleons
Anchored
in Recife
Port, 1537
A1135

1987, Nov. 12   Litho.   *Perf. 11½x12*
2115 A1135   5cz Harbor entrance   .25   .25
    Recife City, 450th anniv.

Thanksgiving
A1136

1987, Nov. 26   *Perf. 12x11½*
2116 A1136   5cz multi   .25   .25

Christmas
1987
A1137

   No. 2117, Shepherd and flock. No. 2118, Christmas pageant. No. 2119, Six angels.

1987, Nov. 30   *Perf. 11½x12*
2117 A1137   6cz multi   .25   .25
2118 A1137   6cz multi   .25   .25
2119 A1137   6cz multi   .25   .25
    Nos. 2117-2119 (3)   .75   .75

Pedro II College, 150th
Anniv. — A1138

   Gold pen Emperor Pedro II used to sign edict establishing the school, and Senator Bernardo Pereira de Vasconcellos, founder.

1987, Dec. 2
2120 A1138   6cz multi   .25   .25

Natl. Orchid
Growers'
Soc., 50th
Anniv.
A1139

No. 2121, Laelia lobata veitch. No. 2122,
Cattleya guttata lindley.

1987, Dec. 3
2121 A1139 6cz multi .30 .25
2122 A1139 6cz multi .30 .25

Marian
Year — A1140

Statue of Our Lady and Basilica at Fatima,
Portugal.

1987, Dec. 20 **Perf. 12x11½**
2123 A1140 50cz multi .45 .25

Exhibit of the Statue of Our Lady of Fatima
in Brazil.

Descriptive Treatise of Brazil, by
Gabriel S. de Sousa, 400th
Anniv. — A1141

1987, Dec. 21 Litho. Perf. 11x11½
2124 A1141 7cz multi .25 .25

Natl.
Archives,
150th
Anniv.
A1142

Design: Text from illuminated Gregorian
canticle and computer terminal.

1988, Jan. 5 **Perf. 11½x12**
2125 A1142 7cz multi .25 .25

Opening of Brazilian Ports to Ships of
Friendly Nations, 180th Anniv.
A1143

1988, Jan. 28 **Perf. 11x11½**
2126 A1143 7cz multi .25 .25

Souvenir Sheet

Antarctic Research — A1144

1988, Feb. 9 Litho. Perf. 11
2127 A1144 80cz multi 1.10 1.10

Energy
Resources
A1145

1988, Mar. 15 Litho. Perf. 12x11½
2128 A1145 14cz Electricity .25 .25
2129 A1145 14cz Fossil fuels .25 .25

Souvenir Sheet

Brazilians as Formula 1 World
Champions in 1981, 1983,
1987 — A1146

1988, Mar. 30 **Perf. 11**
2130 A1146 300cz multi 3.75 3.75

Jose Bonifacio,
Armorial and
Masonic Emblems
A1147

1988, Apr. 6 **Perf. 12x11½**
2131 A1147 20cz multi .25 .25

Jose Bonifacio de Andrada e Silva (c. 1763-
1838), geologist and prime minister under
Pedro I who supported the movement for independence from Portugal and was exiled for
opposing the emperor's advisors.

Abolition of
Slavery,
Cent. — A1148

Designs: 20cz, Declaration and quill pen.
50cz, Slave ship and maps of African coastline
and slave trade route between Africa and
South America.

1988, May 12 Litho. Perf. 12x11½
2132 A1148 20cz multi .25 .25
2133 A1148 50cz multi .25 .25

Telecom
'88 — A1149

1988, May 16 **Perf. 11½x11**
2134 A1149 50cz multi .25 .25

Jesus of
Matosinhos
Sanctuary
A1150

50cz, Pilot plan of Brasilia. 100cz, Salvador
historic district.

1988, May 16 **Perf. 11½x12**
2135 A1150 20cz shown .25 .25
2136 A1150 50cz multi .25 .25
2137 A1150 100cz multi .25 .25
 Nos. 2135-2137 (3) .75 .75

LUBRAPEX '88. World heritage list.

Japanese
Immigrants in Brazil,
80th
Anniv. — A1151

1988, June 18 Litho. Perf. 11½x11
2138 A1151 100cz multi .35 .25

A1152

1988, July 1 Photo. Perf. 13
2139 A1152 (A) brt blue 1.50 .25
 a. Perf 11x11½ 1.50 .25

No. 2139 met the first class domestic letter
postage rate (28cz).
See Nos. 2201, 2218.

Judo — A1153

1988, July 14 Litho. Perf. 12x11½
2140 A1153 20cz multi .35 .25

1988 Summer Olympics, Seoul.

Wildlife Conservation — A1154

20cz, Myrmecophaga tridactyla. 50cz,
Chaetomys subspinosus. 100cz, Speothos
venaticus.

1988, July 24 **Perf. 11½x12**
2141 A1154 20cz multi .30 .25
2142 A1154 50cz multi .30 .25
2143 A1154 100cz multi .45 .25
 Nos. 2141-2143 (3) 1.05 .75

Souvenir Sheet

The Motherland, 1919 by Pedro
Bruno — A1155

1988, Aug. 1 Litho. Perf. 11
2144 A1155 250cz multi 3.75 3.75

Stamp Day, BRASILIANA '89.

Natl. Confederation of Industries, 50th
Anniv. — A1156

1988, Aug. 12 **Perf. 11½x12**
2145 A1156 50cz multi .25 .25

Soccer
Clubs
A1157

No. 2146, Recife, Pernambuco. No. 2147,
Coritiba, Parana. 100cz, Gremio, Porto Alegre,
Rio Grando do Sul. 200cz, Fluminense, Rio de
Janeiro.

1988, Sept. 29 **Perf. 11½x12**
2146 A1157 50cz multi .35 .35
2147 A1157 50cz multi .35 .35
2148 A1157 100cz multi .35 .35
2149 A1157 200cz multi .35 .35
 a. Block of 4, #2146-2149 1.50 3.00

Poems,
1888
A1158

Portraits and text: 50cz, O Ateneu, by Raul
Pompeia. 100cz, Poesias, by Olavo Bilac.

1988, Oct. 28 **Perf. 11x11½**
2150 A1158 50cz multi .25 .25
2151 A1158 100cz multi .25 .25

Souvenir Sheet

1988 Democratic Constitution for the
Union of the People and the
State — A1159

550cz, Government building.

1988, Oct. 5 Litho. Perf. 11
2152 A1159 550cz multi 2.25 2.25

Origami Art
A1160

50cz, Abbey, nuns. 100cz, Nativity. 200cz, Santa Claus, presents.

1988, Nov. 11 Litho. *Perf. 11½x12*
2153	A1160	50cz multi	.25 .25
2154	A1160	100cz multi	.25 .25
2155	A1160	200cz multi	.30 .30
	Nos. 2153-2155 (3)		.80 .80

Christmas.

ARBRAFEX Philatelic Exhibition of
Argentina and Brazil — A1161

1988, Nov. 26
2156 A1161 400cz multi   1.50 .75

Fresh-water Fish — A1162

Designs: a, Gasteropelecus. b, Osteoglossum ferreirai. c, Moenkhausia. d, Xavantei. e, Ancistrus hoplogenys. f, Brochis splendens. Se-tenant in a continuous design.

1988, Nov. 29 Litho. *Perf. 11½x12*
2157   Block of 6   1.25 2.50
a.-f. A1162 55cz any single   .25 .25

Souvenir Sheet

BRAPEX '88, Ecological
Preservation — A1163

1988, Dec. 10   *Perf. 11*
2158	A1163	Sheet of 3	4.00 4.00
a.		100cz Parrot	.50 .50
b.		250cz Plant	1.25 1.25
c.		400cz Egret	2.00 2.00

Satellite
Dishes — A1164

1988, Dec. 20   *Perf. 12x11½*
2159 A1164 70cz multi   .25 .25

Ansat 10, Earth satellite station communication.

Performing
Arts — A1165

1988, Dec. 21
2160 A1165 70cz multi   .25 .25

Court of
Justice,
Bahia,
380th
Anniv.
A1166

1989, Mar. 10 Litho. *Perf. 11½x12*
2161 A1166 25c multi   .25 .25

Public
Library Year
A1167

25c, Library, Bahia, 1811.

1989, Mar. 13   *Perf. 11½*
2162 A1167 25c multi   .25 .25

Brazilian
Post &
Telegraph
Enterprise,
20th Anniv.
A1168

No. 2163 — Intl. and domestic postal services: a, Facsimile transmission (Post-Grama). b, Express mail (EMS). c, Parcel post (Sedex). d, Postal savings (CEFPostal).

1989, Mar. 20   *Perf. 11½x12*
2163   Block of 4   .85 1.60
a.-d. A1168 25c any single   .25 .25

Souvenir Sheet

Ayrton Senna, 1988 Formula 1 World
Champion — A1169

1989, Mar. 23
2164 A1169 2cz multi   12.00 12.00

Environmental
Conservation
A1170

1989, Apr. 6 Litho. *Perf. 12x11½*
2165 A1170 25c multi   .25 .25

Mineira Inconfidencia Independence
Movement, Bicent. — A1171

Designs: a, Pyramid, hand. b, Figure of a man, houses. c, Destruction of houses.

1989, Apr. 21   *Perf. 11½x12*
2166	A1171	Strip of 3	.65 .50
a.-b.		30c any single	.25 .25
c.		40c multi	.25 .25

First rebellion against Portuguese dominion.

Military
School, Rio
de Janeiro,
Cent.
A1172

1989, May 6 Litho. *Perf. 11½x12*
2167 A1172 50c multi   .25 .25

Flowering
Plants
A1173

Designs: 50c, Pavonia alnifolia. 1cz, Worsleya rayneri. 1.50cz, Heliconia farinosa.

1989, June 5 *Perf. 11½x12, 12x11½*
2168	A1173	50c multi	.30 .25
2169	A1173	1cz multi	.40 .25
2170	A1173	1.50cz multi	.50 .25
	Nos. 2168-2170 (3)		1.20 .75

Nos. 2169-2170 vert.

Barreto and Recife Law School, Pedro
II Square
A1174

1989, June 7   *Perf. 11x11½*
2171 A1174 50c multi   .25 .25

Tobias Barreto (b. 1839), advocate of Germanization of Brazil.

Cultura Broadcasting System, 20th
Anniv. — A1175

1989, June 27 Litho. *Perf. 11½x12*
2172 A1175 50c multi   .25 .25

Aviation
A1176

50c, Ultra-light aircraft. 1.50cz, Eiffel Tower, Demoiselle.

1989, July 7
2173 A1176 50c multi   .35 .25
2174 A1176 1.50cz multi   .35 .25

Flight of Santos-Dumont's *Demoiselle,* 80th anniv (1.50cz).

Indigenous
Flora — A1177

Designs: 10c, Dichorisandra, vert. 20c, Quiabentia zehnteri. 50c, Bougainvillea glabra. 1cz, Impatiens specie. 2cz, Chorisia crispiflora. 5cz, Hibiscus trilineatus.

1989 Photo. *Perf. 11x11½, 11½x11*
2176	A1177	10c multi	.25 .25
2177	A1177	20c multi	.25 .25
2178	A1177	50c multi	.25 .25
2179	A1177	1cz multi	.25 .25
2180	A1177	2cz multi	.25 .25
2181	A1177	5cz multi	.25 .25
	Nos. 2176-2181 (6)		1.50 1.50

Issued: 10c, July 4; 20c, June 21; 50c, June 26; 1cz, June 19; 2cz, 5cz, Dec. 4.
No. 2181 vert.
See Nos. 2259-2273.

Souvenir Sheet

Largo da Carioca, by Nicolas Antoine
Taunay — A1179

1989, July 7 Litho. *Perf. 11*
2197 A1179 3cz multi   3.25 3.25

PHILEXFRANCE '89, French revolution bicent.
Exists imperforate. Value $550.

Cut and Uncut
Gemstones
A1180

1989, July 12 Litho. *Perf. 12x11½*
2198 A1180 50c Tourmaline   .30 .25
2199 A1180 1.50cz Amethyst   .30 .25

Souvenir Sheet

Paco Imperial, Rio de Janeiro, and Map — A1181

1989, July 28   *Perf. 11*
2200 A1181 5cz multi   5.00 5.00

BRASILANA '89.

Type of 1988 Redrawn
1989, July 26   Photo.   *Perf. 13*
Size: 17x21mm
2201 A1152 (A) org & brt blue   1.25 .25
       Complete booklet, strip of 10
       #2201   12.50

Size of type and postal emblem are smaller on No. 2201; "1e PORTE" is at lower left. No. 2201 met the first class domestic letter postage rate (cz).

Pernambuco Commercial Assoc., 150th Anniv. — A1182

1989, Aug. 1   Litho.   *Perf. 11½x12*
2202 A1182 50c multi   .25 .25

Photography, 150th Anniv. — A1183

1989, Aug. 14
2203 A1183 1.50cz multi   .25 .25

1st Hydroelecric Power Station in South America, Marmelos-o, Cent. — A1184

1989, Sept. 5   Litho.   *Perf. 11½x12*
2204 A1184 50c multi   .25 .25

Conchs Endemic to the Brazilian Coast A1185

Designs: 50c,Voluta ebraea. 1cz, Morum matthewsi. 1.50cz, Agaronia travassosi.

1989, Sept. 8
2205 A1185 50c multi   .30 .30
2206 A1185 1cz multi   .40 .30
2207 A1185 1.50cz multi   .50 .30
       Nos. 2205-2207 (3)   1.20 .90

Wildlife conservation.

America Issue A1186

UPAE emblem and pre-Columbian stone carvings: 1cz, Muiraquita ritual statue, vert. 4cz, Ceramic brazier under three-footed votive urn.

Perf. 12x11½, 11½x12
1989, Oct. 12   *Litho.*
2208 A1186 1cz multicolored   .25 .25
2209 A1186 4cz multicolored   .25 .30

Discovery of America 500th anniv. (in 1992).

A1187

Hologram and: a. *Lemons*, by Danilo di Prete. b. *O Indio E A Suacuapara*, by sculptor Victor Brecheret. c. Francisco Matarazzo.

1989, Oct. 14   *Perf. 11*
Souvenir Sheet
2210 A1187 Sheet of 3   2.50 2.50
       a.   2cz multicolored   .75 .75
       b.   3cz multicolored   .75 .75
       c.   5cz multicolored   .75 .75

Sao Paulo 20th intl. art biennial.

A1188

Writers, residences and quotes: No. 2211, Casimiro de Abreu (b. 1839). No. 2212, Cora Coralina (b. 1889). No. 2213, Joaquim Machado de Assis (b. 1839).

1989, Oct. 26   *Perf. 11½x11*
2211 A1188 1cz multicolored   .25 .25
2212 A1188 1cz multicolored   .25 .25
2213 A1188 1cz multicolored   .25 .25
       Nos. 2211-2213 (3)   .75 .75

Federal Police Department, 25th Anniv. — A1189

1989, Nov. 9   *Perf. 11½x12*
2214 A1189 1cz multicolored   .25 .25

Christmas A1190

1989, Nov. 10   *Perf. 12x11½*
2215 A1190 70c Heralding angel   .25 .25
2216 A1190 1cz Holy family   .25 .25

Thanksgiving Day — A1191

1989, Nov. 23
2217 A1191 1cz multicolored   .25 .25

Type of 1988 Redrawn
Size: 22x26mm

1989, Nov. 6   Photo.   *Perf. 13x13½*
2218 A1152 (B) org & dark red   1.60 .55

Size of type and postal emblem are smaller on No. 2218; "1e PORTE" is at lower left. No. 2218 met the first class intl. letter postage rate, initially at 9cz.

Souvenir Sheet

Proclamation of the Republic, Cent. — A1192

1989, Nov. 19   Litho.   *Perf. 11*
2225 A1192 15cz multicolored   2.50 2.50

Bahia Sports Club, 58th Anniv. A1193

1989, Nov. 30   *Perf. 11½x12*
2226 A1193 50c Soccer   .30 .25

Yellow Man, by Anita Malfatti (b. 1889) A1194

1989, Dec. 2   *Perf. 12x11½*
2227 A1194 1cz multicolored   .25 .25

Bahia State Public Archives, Cent. — A1195

1990, Jan. 16   Litho.   *Perf. 11½x12*
2228 A1195 2cz multicolored   .25 .25

Brazilian Botanical Soc., 40th Anniv. A1196

2cz, Sabia, Caatinga. 13cz, Pau, Brazil.

1990, Jan. 21
2229 A1196 2cz multi   .25 .25
2230 A1196 13cz multi   .25 .25

Churches A1197

Designs: 2cz, St. John the Baptist Cathedral, Santa Cruz do Sul, vert. 3cz, Our Lady of Victory Church, Oeiras. 5cz, Our Lady of the Rosary Church, Ouro Preto, vert.

1990, Feb. 5   *Perf. 12x11½, 11½x12*
2231 A1197 2cz multicolored   .25 .25
2232 A1197 3cz multicolored   .25 .25
2233 A1197 5cz multicolored   .25 .25
       Nos. 2231-2233 (3)   .75 .75

Lloyd's of London in Brazil, Cent. A1198

1990, Feb. 19   Litho.   *Perf. 11½x12*
2234 A1198 3cz multicolored   .25 .25

Souvenir Sheet

Antarctic Research Program — A1199

1990, Feb. 22   Litho.   *Perf. 11*
2235 A1199 20cz Fauna, map   2.50 2.50

Vasco da Gama Soccer Club A1200

1990, Mar. 5
2236 A1200 10cz multicolored   .25 .25

Lindolfo Collor (b. 1890), Syndicated Columnist, and Labor Monument A1201

1990, Mar. 7
2237 A1201 20cz multicolored   .25 .25

Pres. Jose Sarney — A1202

1990, Mar. 8   *Perf. 12x11½*
2238 A1202 20cz chalky blue   .25   .25

AIDS Prevention A1203

1990, Apr. 6   *Perf. 12x11½*
2239 A1203 20cz multicolored   .25   .25

Souvenir Sheet

Penny Black, 150th Anniv. — A1204

No. 2240: 20cr, Dom Pedro, Brazil No. 1. 100cr, Queen Victoria, Great Britain No. 1.

1990, May 3   Litho.   *Perf. 11*
2240 A1204   Sheet of 2   2.50 2.50
   a.   20cr multicolored   .65   .65
   b.   100cr multicolored   1.75 1.75

Central Bank, 25th Anniv. A1205

1990, Mar. 30   Litho.   *Perf. 11½x12*
2241 A1205 20cr multicolored   .25   .25

Amazon River Postal Network, 21st Anniv. A1207

1990, Apr. 20   *Perf. 11x11½*
2243 A1207 20cr multicolored   .25   .25

Souvenir Sheet

World Cup Soccer Championships, Italy — A1208

1990, May 12   Litho.   *Perf. 12x11½*
2244 A1208 120cr multicolored   2.50 2.50

22nd Congress of the Intl. Union of Highway Transportation — A1209

1990, May 14   *Perf. 11½x12*
2245 A1209   20cr multicolored   .55   .55
2246 A1209   80cr multicolored   .55   .55
   a.   Pair, #2245-2246   1.10 1.10

No. 2246a has a continuous design.

Imperial Crown, 18th Cent. — A1210

Designs: No. 2248, Our Lady of Immaculate Conception, 18th cent.

1990, May 18   *Perf. 12x11½*
2247 A1210 20cr shown   .25   .25
2248 A1210 20cr multicolored   .25   .25
Imperial Museum, 50th anniv.(No. 2247). Mission Museum, 50th anniv. (No. 2248).

State Flags Type of 1981
1990, May 20   *Perf. 11½x12*
2249 A947 20cr Tocantins   .25   .25

Army Geographical Service, Cent. — A1212

1990, May 30   *Perf. 11x11½*
2250 A1212 20cr multicolored   .25   .25

Film Personalities — A1213

No. 2251, Adhemar Gonzaga. No. 2252, Carmen Miranda. No. 2253, Carmen Santos. No. 2254, Oscarito.

1990, June 19   *Perf. 11½x12*
2251 A1213 25cr multi   1.50 1.50
2252 A1213 25cr multi   1.50 1.50
2253 A1213 25cr multi   1.50 1.50
2254 A1213 25cr multi   1.50 1.50
   a.   Block of 4, #2251-2254   6.00 12.00

France-Brazil House, Rio de Janeiro — A1214

1990, July 14   Litho.   *Perf. 11½x11*
2255 A1214 50cr multicolored   .55   .55
See France No. 2226.

World Men's Volleyball Chmpships. A1215

1990, July 28   Litho.   *Perf. 12x11½*
2256 A1215 10cr multicolored   .25   .25

CBA 123 A1216

1990, July 30   *Perf. 11½x12*
2257 A1216 10cr multicolored   .25   .25

Intl. Literacy Year — A1217

1990, Aug. 22   *Perf. 12x11½*
2258 A1217 10cr multicolored   .25   .25

Flora Type of 1989
Designs: 1cr, Like #2179. 2cr, Like #2180. 5cr, Like #2181. 10cr, Tibouchina granulosa. 20cr, Cassia macranthera. No. 2264, Clitoria fairchildiana. No. 2265, Tibouchina mutabilis. 100cr, Erythrina crista-galli. 200cr, Jacaranda mimosifolia. 500cr, Caesalpinia peltophoroides. 1000, Pachira aquatica. 2000, Hibiscus

---

pernambucensis. 5000, Triplaris surinamensis. 10,000, Tabebuia heptaphylla. 20,000, Erythrina speciosa.

Perf. 11x11½, 11½x11

				1989-93		**Photo.**
2259	A1177	1cr multi			.25	.25
2260	A1177	2cr multi			.25	.25
2261	A1177	5cr multi			.25	.25
2262	A1177	10cr multi			.25	.25
2263	A1177	20cr multi			.25	.25
2264	A1177	50cr multi			.25	.25
2265	A1177	50cr multi			.40	.25
2266	A1177	100cr multi, perf. 13			.25	.25
2267	A1177	200cr multi			.30	.25
2268	A1177	500cr multi			.30	.25
2269	A1177	1000cr multi			.25	.25
2270	A1177	2000cr multi			.25	.25
2271	A1177	5000cr multi			.30	.25
2272	A1177	10,000cr multi			.40	.25
2273	A1177	20,000cr multi			.30	.25
	Nos. 2259-2273 (15)				4.25	3.75

Issued: 1cr, 11/8/90; 2cr, 11/12/90; 5cr, 11/16/90; No. 2264, 6/1/89; 10cr, 4/18/90; 20cr, 5/4/90; 100cr, 8/24/90; 200cr, 6/16/91; 500cr, 5/14/91; 1000cr, 9/2/92; 2000cr, 9/8/92; 5000cr, 10/16/92; 10,000cr, 11/16/92; 20,000cr, 4/25/93; No. 2265, 10/20/93.

Granbery Institute, Cent. A1218

1990, Sept. 8   Litho.   *Perf. 11½x12*
2279 A1218 13cr multicolored   .25   .25

18th Panamerican Railroad Congress — A1219

1990, Sept. 9
2280 A1219 95cr multicolored   .75   .75

Embratel, 25th Anniv. — A1220

1990, Sept. 21
2281 A1220 13cr multicolored   .25   .25

LUBRAPEX '90 A1221

Statues by Ceschiatti and Giorgi (No. 2283): No. 2282, As Banhistas. No. 2283, Os Candangos. No. 2284, Evangelista Sao Joao. No. 2285, A Justica.

1990, Sept. 22
2282 A1221 25cr multi   1.10 1.10
2283 A1221 25cr multi   1.10 1.10
2284 A1221 100cr multi   1.60 1.60
2285 A1221 100cr multi   1.60 1.60
   a.   Block of 4, #2282-2285   6.00 6.00
   b.   Souv. sheet of 4, #2282-2285   7.00 7.00

Praia Do Sul Wildlife Reserve A1222

1990, Oct. 12
2286 A1222 15cr Flowers .30 .30
2287 A1222 105cr Shoreline 1.00 1.00
  a. Pair, #2286-2287 1.40 1.40
Discovery of America, 500th anniv. (in 1992).

Natl. Library, 180th Anniv. A1223

Writers: No. 2289, Guilherme de Almeida (1890-1969). No. 2290, Oswald de Andrade (1890-1954).

1990, Oct. 29 Litho. Perf. 11x11½
2288 A1223 15cr multicolored .25 .25
2289 A1223 15cr multicolored .25 .25
2290 A1223 15cr multicolored .25 .25
    Nos. 2288-2290 (3) .75 .75

Natl. Tax Court, Cent. A1224

1990, Nov. 7 Litho. Perf. 11½x12
2291 A1224 15cr multicolored .25 .25

Christmas A1225

Architecture of Brasilia: No. 2292, National Congress. No. 2293, Television tower.

1990, Nov. 20
2292 A1225 15cr multicolored .25 .25
2293 A1225 15cr multicolored .25 .25

A1226

1990, Dec. 13 Litho. Perf. 12x11½
2294 A1226 15cr multicolored .25 .25
Organization of American States, cent.

A1227

1990, Dec. 14
2295 A1227 15cr multicolored .25 .25
First Flight of Nike Apache Missile, 25th anniv.

Colonization of Sergipe, Founding of Sao Cristovao, 400th Anniv. — A1228

1990, Dec. 18 Litho. Perf. 11½x12
2296 A1228 15cr multicolored .25 .25

World Congress of Physical Education A1229

1991, Jan. 7 Perf. 11½x12
2297 A1229 17cr multicolored .25 .25

Rock in Rio II — A1230

1991, Jan. 9 Perf. 12x11½
2298 A1230 25cr Cazuza .35 .35
2299 A1230 185cr Raul Seixas .35 .35
  a. Pair, #2298-2299 .75 .75
    Complete booklet, pane of 12 5.00 5.00
Printed in panes of 12.

Ministry of Aviation, 50th Anniv. A1231

1991, Jan. 20 Perf. 11x11½
2300 A1231 17cr multicolored .25 .25

Carnivals A1232

1991, Feb. 8 Litho. Perf. 12x11½
2301 A1232 25cr Olinda .25 .25
2302 A1232 30cr Salvador .25 .25
2303 A1232 280cr Rio de Janeiro .30 .30
    Nos. 2301-2303 (3) .80 .80

Visit to Antarctica by Pres. Collor — A1233

1991, Feb. 20
2304 A1233 300cr multicolored .75 .75

Hang Gliding World Championships — A1234

1991, Feb. 24 Perf. 11½x12
2305 A1234 36cr multicolored .25 .25

11th Pan American Games, 25th Summer Olympics A1235

1991, Mar. 30 Litho. Perf. 11½x12
2306 A1235 36cr Sailing .55 .55
2307 A1235 36cr Rowing .55 .55
2308 A1235 300cr Swimming .55 .55
  a. Block of 3, #2306-2308 + label 1.75 1.75

Fight Against Drugs — A1236

1991, Apr. 7 Litho. Perf. 12x11½
2309 A1236 40cr Drugs .25 .25
2310 A1236 40cr Alcohol .25 .25
2311 A1236 40cr Smoking .25 .25
    Nos. 2309-2311 (3) .75 .75

Yanomami Indian Culture — A1237

1991, Apr. 19 Perf. 11½x11, 11x11½
2312 A1237 40cr shown .25 .25
2313 A1237 400cr Indian, horiz. .65 .65

Journal of Brazil, Cent. A1238

1991, Apr. 8 Litho. Perf. 11x11½
2314 A1238 40cr multicolored .25 .25

Neochen Jubata (Orinoco Goose) — A1239

1991, June 5 Litho. Perf. 12x11½
2315 A1239 45cr multi .25 .25
UN Conference on Development.

Snakes & Dinosaurs A1240

No. 2316, Bothrops jararaca. No. 2317, Corallus caninus. No. 2318, Teropods. No. 2319, Sauropods.

1991, June 6 Perf. 11½x12
2316 A1240 45cr multi .25 .25
2317 A1240 45cr multi .25 .25
  a. Pair, #2316-2317 .50 .50
2318 A1240 45cr multi .25 .25
2319 A1240 350cr multi .40 .40
  a. Pair, #2318-2319 .65 .65
    Nos. 2316-2319 (4) 1.15 1.15

Flag of Brazil — A1241

Perf. 13x13½
1991, June 10-1992, Oct. Photo.
2320 A1241 A multicolored 1.00 .25
Valued at domestic letter rate on day of issue.
No. 2320 exists with a printer's marking on lower right.

Fire Pumper A1242

1991, July 2 Litho. Perf. 11½x12
2321 A1242 45cr multicolored .25 .25

Tourism A1243

Map location and: 45cr, Painted stones, Roraima. 350cr, Dedo de Deus Mountain, Rio De Janeiro.

1991, July 6 Perf. 11x11½
2322 A1243 45cr multicolored .25 .25
2323 A1243 350cr multicolored .55 .55

Labor Laws, 50th Anniv. A1244

1991, Aug. 11 Perf. 11½x12
2324 A1244 45cr multicolored .25 .25

Leonardo Mota, Birth Cent. A1245

1991, Aug. 22
2325 A1245 45cr buff, blk & red .25 .25
Folklore Festival.

Jose Basilio da Gama (1741-1795),
Poet — A1246

Designs: No. 2327, Fagundes Varela (b. 1841), poet. No. 2328, Jackson de Figueiredo (b. 1891), writer.

1991, Aug. 29
2326	A1246	45cr multicolored	.25	.25
2327	A1246	50cr multicolored	.25	.25
2328	A1246	50cr multicolored	.25	.25
		Nos. 2326-2328 (3)	.75	.75

12th Natl.
Eucharistic
Congress
A1247

50cr, Pope John Paul II. 400cr, Map, crosses.

1991, Oct. 6   Litho.   Perf. 12x11½
2329	A1247	50cr multi	.85	.85
2330	A1247	400cr multi	1.40	1.40
a.		Pair, #2329-2330	2.50	2.50

Visit by Pope John Paul II.

First Brazilian Constitution,
Cent. — A1248

1991, Oct. 7   Perf. 11½x12
| 2331 | A1248 | 50cr multicolored | .25 | .25 |

Telecom
'91 — A1249

1991, Oct. 8   Perf. 12x11½
| 2332 | A1249 | 50cr multicolored | .25 | .25 |

Sixth World Forum and Exposition on Telecommunications, Geneva, Switzerland.

America
Issue
A1250

UPAEP emblem and explorers: 50cr, Ferdinand Magellan (c. 1480-1521). 400cr, Francisco de Orellana (c. 1490-c. 1546).

1991, Oct. 12   Perf. 11½x12
| 2333 | A1250 | 50cr multicolored | .25 | .25 |
| 2334 | A1250 | 400cr multicolored | .55 | .55 |

Discovery of America, 500th anniv. (in 1992).

A1251

BRAPEX VIII (Orchids and Hummingbirds): 50cr, Colibri serrirostris, Cattleya warneri. No. 2336, Chlorostilbon aureoventris, Rodriguezia venusta. No. 2337, Clytolaema rubricauda, Zygopetalum intermedium. No. 2338a, 50cr, Colibri serrirostris. b, 50cr, Chlorostilbon aureoventris. c, 500cr, Clytolaema rubricauda.

1991, Oct. 29   Litho.   Perf. 12x11½
2335	A1251	50cr multicolored	.25	.25
2336	A1251	65cr multicolored	.25	.25
2337	A1251	65cr multicolored	.25	.25
		Nos. 2335-2337 (3)	.75	.75

Souvenir Sheet
| 2338 | A1251 | Sheet of 3, #a.-c. | 8.00 | 8.00 |

A1252

1991, Oct. 29   Litho.   Perf. 11½x11
| 2339 | A1252 | 400cr multicolored | .40 | .40 |

Lasar Segall, artist, birth cent.

Bureau of
Agriculture and
Provision of Sao
Paulo,
Cent. — A1253

1991, Nov. 11   Perf. 12x11½
| 2340 | A1253 | 70cr multicolored | .25 | .25 |

First Civilian Presidents, Birth
Sesquicentennials — A1254

Designs: 70cr, Manuel de Campos Salles. 90cr, Prudente de Moraes Barros.

1991, Nov. 14   Perf. 11½x12
2341	A1254	70cr multi	.25	.25
2342	A1254	90cr multi	.25	.25
a.		Pair, #2341-2342	.50	.50

Christmas
A1255

1991, Nov. 20   Perf. 12x11½
| 2343 | A1255 | 70cr multicolored | .25 | .25 |

Thanksgiving
A1256

1991, Nov. 28
| 2344 | A1256 | 70cr multicolored | .25 | .25 |

Military
Police
A1257

1991, Dec. 1   Perf. 11½x12
| 2345 | A1257 | 80cr multicolored | .25 | .25 |

Souvenir Sheet

Emperor Dom Pedro (1825-1891) — A1258

No. 2346: a, 80cr, Older age. b, 800cr, Wearing crown.

Litho. & Engr.
1991, Nov. 29   Perf. 11
| 2346 | A1258 | Sheet of 2, #a.-b. | 3.50 | 3.50 |

BRASILIANA 93.

Churches
A1259

Designs: No. 2347, Presbyterian Church, Rio de Janeiro. No. 2348, First Baptist Church, Niteroi.

1992, Jan. 12   Litho.   Perf. 12x11½
| 2347 | A1259 | 250cr multicolored | .25 | .25 |
| 2348 | A1259 | 250cr multicolored | .25 | .25 |

1992
Summer
Olympics,
Barcelona
A1260

Medalists in shooting, Antwerp, 1920: 300cr, Afranio Costa, silver. 2500cr, Guilherme Paraense, gold.

1992, Jan. 28   Perf. 11½x12
| 2349 | A1260 | 300cr multicolored | .25 | .25 |
| 2350 | A1260 | 2500cr multicolored | 1.00 | 1.00 |

Port of
Santos,
Cent.
A1261

1992, Feb. 3   Litho.   Perf. 11½
| 2351 | A1261 | 300cr multicolored | .25 | .25 |

Fauna of
Fernando
de Noronha
Island
A1262

400cr, White-tailed tropicbirds. 2500cr, Dolphins.

1992, Feb. 25   Litho.   Perf. 11½x12
| 2352 | A1262 | 400cr multi | .25 | .25 |
| 2353 | A1262 | 2500cr multi | .75 | .75 |

Earth Summit, Rio de Janeiro.

Yellow
Amaryllis — A1263

1992, Feb. 27   Photo.   Perf. 13½
| 2354 | A1263 | (A) multicolored | 3.00 | .25 |

No. 2354 met the second class domestic letter postage rate of 265cr on date of issue.

ARBRAFEX '92, Argentina-Brazil
Philatelic Exhibition — A1264

Designs: No. 2355, Gaucho throwing bola at rhea. No. 2356, Man playing accordion, couple dancing. No. 2357, Couple in horse-drawn cart, woman. 1000cr, Gaucho throwing lasso at steer.

No. 2358c, 250cr, like No. 2356. d, 500cr, like No. 2355. e, 1500cr, like No. 2358.

1992, Mar. 20   Litho.   Perf. 11½x12
2355	A1264	250cr multi	.25	.25
2356	A1264	250cr multi	.25	.25
2357	A1264	250cr multi	.25	.25
2358	A1264	1000cr multi	.55	.55
a.		Block of 4, Nos. 2355-2358	1.40	1.40

Souvenir Sheet
| 2358B | A1264 | Sheet of 4, #2357, 2358c-2358e | 12.00 | 12.00 |

1992 Summer
Olympics,
Barcelona
A1265

1992, Apr. 3   Perf. 12x11½
| 2359 | A1265 | 300cr multicolored | .25 | .25 |

Discovery of America, 500th Anniv. A1266

500cr, Columbus' fleet. 3500cr, Columbus, map.

1992, Apr. 24   **Perf. 11½x12**
2360	A1266	500cr multi	.30	.30
2361	A1266	3500cr multi	.65	.65
a.		Pair, #2360-2361	1.00	1.00

Telebras Telecommunications System — A1267

1992, May 5   **Perf. 11x11½**
2362 A1267 350cr multicolored   .25   .25

Installation of 10 million telephones.

Langsdorff Expedition to Brazil, 170th Anniv. A1268

Designs: No. 2363, Aime-Adrien Taunay, natives. No. 2364, Johann Moritz Rugendas, monkey. No. 2365, Hercule Florence, flowering plant. 3000cr, Gregory Ivanovitch Langsdorff, map.

1992, June 2   **Perf. 11½x12**
2363	A1268	500cr multicolored	.25	.25
2364	A1268	500cr multicolored	.25	.25
2365	A1268	500cr multicolored	.25	.25
2366	A1268	3000cr multicolored	.55	.55
		Nos. 2363-2366 (4)	1.30	1.30

UN Conf. on Environmental Development, Rio.

UN Conference on Environmental Development, Rio de Janeiro — A1269

Globe and: No. 2367, Flags of Sweden and Brazil. No. 2368, City, grain, mountain and tree. 3000cr, Map of Brazil, parrot, orchid.

1992, June 3   **Litho.**   **Perf. 11x11½**
2367	A1269	450cr multicolored	.25	.25
2368	A1269	450cr multicolored	.25	.25
2369	A1269	3000cr multicolored	.75	.75
		Nos. 2367-2369 (3)	1.25	1.25

Ecology A1270

Designs: No. 2370, Flowers, waterfall, and butterflies. No. 2371, Butterflies, canoe, and hummingbirds. No. 2372, Boy taking pictures of tropical birds. No. 2373, Armadillo, girl picking fruit.

1992, June 4   **Perf. 11½x12**
2370	A1270	500cr multicolored	.30	.30
2371	A1270	500cr multicolored	.30	.30
2372	A1270	500cr multicolored	.30	.30
2373	A1270	500cr multicolored	.30	.30
a.		Strip of 4, #2370-2373	1.25	1.25
		Complete booklet, #2373a	1.25	

UN Conf. on Environmental Development, Rio.

Floral Paintings by Margaret Mee — A1271

No. 2374, Nidularium innocentii. No. 2375, Canistrum exiguum. No. 2376, Canistrum cyathiforme. No. 2377, Nidularium rubens.

1992, June 5   **Perf. 12x11½**
2374	A1271	600cr multicolored	.30	.25
2375	A1271	600cr multicolored	.30	.25
2376	A1271	700cr multicolored	.30	.25
2377	A1271	700cr multicolored	.30	.25
		Nos. 2374-2377 (4)	1.20	1.00

UN Conf. on Environmental Development, Rio.

Souvenir Sheet

Joaquim Jose da Silva Xavier (1748-1792), Patriot — A1272

Litho. & Engr.   **Perf. 11**
1992, Apr. 21
2378 A1272 3500cr multicolored   2.75   2.75

Souvenir Sheet

A1273

Expedition of Alexandre Rodrigues Ferreira, Bicent.: a, 500cr, Sailing ships, gray and green hulls. b, 1000cr, Sailing ships, red hulls. c, 2500cr, Sailing ship at shore.

1992, May 9   **Litho.**   **Perf. 11½x12**
2379 A1273 Sheet of 3, #a.-c.   2.75   2.75

Lubrapex '92.

Diabetes Day — A1274

1992, June 5   **Litho.**   **Perf. 12x11½**
2380 A1274 600cr Hummingbird   .25   .25

Volunteer Firemen of Joinville — A1275

1992, July 13   **Litho.**   **Perf. 11½x11**
2381 A1275 550cr multicolored   .30   .25

A1276

Serra da Capivara National Park: No. 2382, Leopard, animals, map of park. No. 2383, Canyon, map of Brazil.

1992, July 17   **Perf. 12x11½**
2382		550cr multicolored	.30	.30
2383		550cr multicolored	.30	.30
a.	A1276	Pair, #2382-2383	.65	.65

A1277

1992, July 24
2384 A1277 550cr multicolored   .25   .25

Financing for studies and projects.

Natl. Service for Industrial Training, 50th Anniv. — A1278

1992, Aug. 5   **Perf. 11½x12**
2385 A1278 650cr multicolored   .25   .25

Fortresses A1279

650cr, Santa Cruz. 3000cr, Santo Antonio.

1992, Aug. 19   **Litho.**   **Perf. 11½x12**
| 2386 | A1279 | 650cr multi | .25 | .25 |
| 2387 | A1279 | 3000cr multi | .55 | .55 |

Masonic Square, Compass and Lodge A1280

1992, Aug. 20
2388 A1280 650cr multicolored   .30   .30

Brazilian Assistance Legion, 50th Anniv. — A1281

1992, Aug. 28   **Perf. 12x11½**
2389 A1281 650cr multicolored   .25   .25

Hospital of Medicine and Orthopedics A1282

1992, Sept. 11
2390 A1282 800cr multicolored   .25   .25

Merry Christmas A1283

1992, Nov. 20   **Perf. 11½**
2391 A1283 (1) multicolored   1.50   1.50

No. 2391 met the first class domestic letter postage rate of 1090cr on day of issue.

Writers A1284

Designs: No. 2392, Graciliano Ramos (1892-1953). No. 2393, Menotti del Picchia (1892-1988). 1000cr, Assis Chateaubriand (1892-1968).

Perf. 12x11½, 11½x12
1992, Oct. 29   **Litho.**
2392	A1284	900cr multi, vert.	.25	.25
2393	A1284	900cr multi, vert.	.25	.25
2394	A1284	1000cr multi	.25	.25
		Nos. 2392-2394 (3)	.75	.75

Expedition of Luis Cruls, Cent. A1285

1992, Nov. 11   **Perf. 11½x12**
2395 A1285 900cr multicolored   .25   .25

Brazillian Program for Quality and Productivity A1286

1992, Nov. 12
2396 A1286 1200cr multicolored   .25   .25

Souvenir Sheet

Tourism Year in the
Americas — A1287

a, 1200cr, Mountains, coastline. b, 9000cr,
Sugarloaf Mt., aerial tram, Rio de Janeiro.

1992, Nov. 18 Litho. Perf. 11½x12
2397 A1287 Sheet of 2, #a.-b. 1.60 1.60

Brasiliana '93.

Sister Irma
Dulce
A1288

1993, Mar. 13 Litho. Perf. 11½x12
2398 A1288 3500cr multicolored .25 .25

Souvenir Sheet

Water Sports Championships of South
America — A1289

Designs: a, 3500cr, Diver. b, 3500cr, Synchronized swimmers. c, 25,000cr, Water polo.

1993, Mar. 21 Litho. Perf. 11
2399 A1289 Sheet of 3, #a.-c. 2.25 2.25

Curitiba,
300th
Anniv.
A1290

1993, Mar. 29
2400 A1290 4500cr multicolored .25 .25

Health and
Preservation of
Life — A1291

Red Cross emblem and: No. 2401, Bleeding
heart, flowers. No. 2402, Cancer symbol,
breast. No. 2403, Brain waves, rainbow
emerging from head.

1993, Apr. 7 Litho. Perf. 12x11½
2401 A1291 4500cr multicolored .40 .40
2402 A1291 4500cr multicolored .40 .40
2403 A1291 4500cr multicolored .40 .40
   a. Strip of 3, #2401-2403 1.25 1.25

Pedro Americo,
150th Birth
Anniv. — A1292

Paintings: 5500cr, A Study of Love, 1883.
No. 2405, David and Abizag, 1879, horiz. No.
2406, Seated Nude, 1882.

1993, Apr. 29 Perf. 12x11½, 11½x12
2404 A1292 5500cr multi .25 .25
2405 A1292 36,000cr multi .55 .55
2406 A1292 36,000cr multi .55 .55
   Nos. 2404-2406 (3) 1.35 1.35

Natl. Flag —
A1292a

1993, May 26 Litho. Die Cut
Self-adhesive
2407 A1292a A multicolored 1.90 .35

No. 2407 valued at first class domestic letter
rate of 9570cr on day of issue.

Beetles
A1293

8000cr, Dynastes hercules. 55,000cr, Batus
barbicornis.

1993, June 5 Litho. Perf. 11½x12
2408 A1293 8000cr multi .25 .25
2409 A1293 55,000cr multi .55 .55

3rd Iberian-American Conference of
Chiefs of State and Heads of
Government, Salvador — A1294

1993, July 15 Litho. Perf. 11x11½
2410 A1294 12,000cr multi .25 .25

1st Brazilian
Postage Stamps,
150th
Anniv. — A1295

Litho. & Engr.
1993, July 30 Perf. 12x11½
2411 A1295 30,000cr No. 1 .55 .55
2412 A1295 60,000cr No. 2 .55 .55
2413 A1295 90,000cr No. 3 1.25 1.25
   a. Souvenir sheet of 3, #2411-
       2413, wmk. 268 16.00 16.00
   Nos. 2411-2413 (3) 2.35 2.35

No. 2413a sold for 200,000cr and was
issued without gum. Stamps in No. 2413a do
not have imprint at bottom.

Union of
Portuguese
Speaking
Capitals
A1296

No. 2414: a, 15,000cr, Brasilia. b, 71,000cr,
Rio de Janeiro.

1993, July 30 Litho. Perf. 11½x12
2414 A1296 Pair, #a.-b. 1.00 1.00

No. 2414 printed in continuous design.

Monica & Friends, by Mauricio de
Sousa — A1297

Monica, Cebolinha, Cascao, Magali, and
Bidu: a, Engraving die. b, Reading proclama-
tion, king, No. 1. c, Writing and sending letter,
No. 2. d, Receiving letter, No. 3.

1993, Aug. 1
2415 A1297 (1) Strip of 4, #a.-d. 6.00 6.00
   Complete booklet, #2415 6.00

First Brazilian postage stamps, 150th anniv.
Nos. 2415a-2415d paid the first class rate
(9600cr) on day of issue.

Brazilian Post, 330th Anniv. — A1298

No. 2416 — Postal buildings: a, Imperial
Post Office, Rio de Janeiro. b, Petropolis. c,
Central office, Rio de Janeiro. d, Niteroi.

1993, Aug. 3 Litho. Perf. 11½x12
2416 A1298 20,000cr Block of 4,
        #a.-d. 1.10 1.10

Brazilian Engineering
Schools — A1299

Designs: No. 2417, School of Engineering,
Federal University, Rio de Janeiro. No. 2418,
Polytechnical School, University of Sao Paulo.

1993, Aug. 24 Litho. Perf. 11x11½
2417 A1299 17cr multicolored .25 .25
2418 A1299 17cr multicolored .25 .25

Preservation of
Sambaquis
Archaelogical
Sites — A1300

1993, Sept. 19 Perf. 12x11½
2419 A1300 17cr Two artifacts .25 .25
2420 A1300 17cr Six artifacts .25 .25

Ulysses Guimaraes, Natl.
Congress — A1301

1993, Oct. 6 Litho. Perf. 11x11½
2421 A1301 22cr multicolored .25 .25

A1302

1993, Oct. 8 Litho. Perf. 12x11½
2422 A1302 22cr multicolored .25 .25

Virgin of Nazare Religious Festival, bicent.

A1303

Endangered birds (America Issue): 22cr,
Anodorhynchus hyacinthinus, anodorhynchus
glaucus, anodorhynchus leari. 130cr, Cyanop-
sitta spixii.

1993, Oct. 13 Litho. Perf. 11½x11
2423 A1303 22cr multicolored .30 .30
2424 A1303 130cr multicolored .75 .75

Composers
A1304

No. 2425, Vinicius de Moraes. No. 2426,
Pixinguinha.

1993, Oct. 19 Litho. Perf. 12x11½
2425 A1304 22cr multi .25 .25
2426 A1304 22cr multi .25 .25

Poets — A1307

No. 2427, Mario de Andrade (1893-1945). No. 2428, Alceu Amoroso Lima (Tristao de Athayde) (1893-1983). No. 2429, Gilka Machado (1893-1980).

1993, Oct. 29   Litho.   Perf. 12x11½
2427 A1307 30cr multicolored   .25   .25
2428 A1307 30cr multicolored   .25   .25
2429 A1307 30cr multicolored   .25   .25
         Nos. 2427-2429 (3)   .75   .75

Natl. Book Day.

Brazil-Portugal Treaty of Consultation and Friendship, 40th Anniv. — A1308

1993, Nov. 3   Litho.   Perf. 11½x12
2430 A1308 30cr multicolored   .25   .25

See Portugal No. 1980.

Image of the Republic — A1309

Photo. & Engr.
1993, Nov. 3   Perf. 13
2431 A1309 (B) multicolored   3.75   1.50

Valued at first class international letter rate (178.70 cr) on day of issue.

2nd Intl. Biennial of Comic Strips A1310

Cartoon drawings: No. 2432, Nho-Quim. No. 2433, Benjamin. No. 2434, Lamparina. No. 2435, Reco-Reco, Bolao, Azeitona.

1993, Nov. 11   Litho.   Perf. 11½x12
2432 A1310 (1) multicolored   1.25   1.25
2433 A1310 (1) multicolored   1.25   1.25
2434 A1310 (1) multicolored   1.25   1.25
2435 A1310 (1) multicolored   1.25   1.25
  a.   Block of 4, #2432-2435   5.00   5.00

Valued at first class domestic letter rate (30.20 cr) on day of issue.

Launching of First Brazilian-Built Submarine — A1311

1993, Nov. 18   Perf. 11½
2436 A1311 240cr multicolored   .60   .60

Christmas A1312

1993, Nov. 20
2437 A1312 (1) multicolored   1.60   1.60

Valued at first class domestic letter rate (30.20 cr) on day of issue.

First Fighter Group, 50th Anniv. A1313

1993, Dec. 18   Litho.   Perf. 11½
2438 A1313 42cr multicolored   .30   .30

Convent of Merces, 340th Anniv. A1314

1994, Jan. 31   Litho.   Perf. 11½x12
2439 A1314 58cr multicolored   .25   .25

Mae Menininha of Gantois, Birth Cent. — A1315

1994, Feb. 10   Litho.   Perf. 11x11½
2440 A1315 80cr multicolored   .25   .25

Intl. Olympic Committee, Cent. A1316

1994, Feb. 17   Perf. 11½x12
2441 A1316 (1) multicolored   2.25   2.25

No. 2441 valued at first class international letter rate (446.30 cr) on day of issue.

Natl. Flag — A1317

1994, Jan. 31   Litho.   Die Cut
Self-Adhesive
2442 A1317 (1) multicolored   1.25   .25

No. 2442 valued at first class domestic letter rate (55.90 cr) on day of issue.

Birds — A1318

Designs: 10cr, Notiochelidon cyanoleuca. 20cr, Buteo magnirostris. 50cr, Turdus rufiventris. 100cr, Columbina talpacoti. 200cr, Vanellus chilensis. 500cr, Zonotrichia capensis.

1994   Photo.   Perf. 11x11½
2443 A1318 10cr multi   .25   .25
2444 A1318 20cr multi   .25   .25
2445 A1318 50cr multi   .25   .25
2446 A1318 100cr multi   .25   .25
2447 A1318 200cr multi   .30   .25
2448 A1318 500cr multi   .40   .25
      Nos. 2443-2448 (6)   1.70   1.50

Issued: 10cr, 3/17; 20cr, 3/9; 50cr, 3/1; 100cr, 200cr, 4/4; 500cr, 4/13. See Nos. 2484-2494.

Image of the Republic — A1318a

Self-Adhesive
Die Cut

1994, May 10   Litho.
2449 A1318a (1) blue   .80   .25
2450 A1318a (3) claret   1.25   .35

Size: 25x35mm
Perf. 12x11½
2451 A1318a (4) green   1.25   .40
2452 A1318a (5) henna brown   1.50   .65
      Nos. 2449-2452 (4)   4.80   1.65

Nos. 2449, 2450, 2451, 2452 valued 131.37cr, 321.14cr, 452.52cr, 905.05cr on day of issue.

Prince Henry the Navigator (1394-1460) — A1319

1994, Mar. 4   Litho.   Perf. 11½x12
2463 A1319 635cr multicolored   .55   .55

See Macao No. 719, Portugal No. 1987.

America Issue A1320

Postal vehicles: 110cr, Bicycle, country scene. 635cr, Motorcycle, city scene.

1994, Mar. 18
2464 A1320 110cr multicolored   .35   .35
2465 A1320 635cr multicolored   1.00   1.00

Father Cicero Romao Batista, 150th Birth Anniv. A1321

1994, Mar. 24   Perf. 11x11½
2466 A1321 (1) multicolored   .80   .75

No. 2466 valued at first class domestic letter rate (98.80 cr) on day of issue.

Albert Sabin, Campaign Against Polio A1322

1994, Apr. 7   Perf. 11½x12
2467 A1322 160cr multicolored   .35   .35

Carlos Castello Branco, Journalist A1323

1994, Apr. 14
2468 A1323 160cr multicolored   .35   .35

Karl Friedrich Phillip von Martius, Naturalist A1324

Flowers: No. 2469, Euterpe oleracea. No. 2470, Jacaranda paucifoliolata. No. 2471, Barbacernia tomentosa.

1994, Apr. 24   Perf. 12x11½
2469 A1324 (1) multicolored   .90   .90
2470 A1324 (1) multicolored   .90   .90
2471 A1324 (1) multicolored   1.50   1.50
      Nos. 2469-2471 (3)   3.30   3.30

Nos. 2469-2470 were valued at first class domestic letter rate (144 cr) on day of issue. No. 2471 valued at first class intl. letter rate (860 cr) on day of issue.

Monkeys — A1326

No. 2474, Leontopithecus rosalia. No. 2475, Saguinus imperator. No. 2476, Saguinus bicolor.

1994, May 24
2474 A1326 (1) multicolored   .80   .80
2475 A1326 (1) multicolored   .80   .80
2476 A1326 (1) multicolored   .80   .80
      Nos. 2474-2476 (3)   2.40   2.40

Nos. 2474-2476 were valued at first class domestic letter rate (207.03 cr) on day of issue.

1994 World Cup Soccer Championships, US — A1327

1994, May 19   Perf. 11½x12
2477 A1327 (1) multicolored   1.75   1.75

No. 2477 was valued at first class intl. rate (1378.32 cr) on day of issue. Soccer in Brazil, cent.

Souvenir Sheet

46th Frankfurt Intl. Book Fair — A1328

1994, May 27
2478 A1328 (1) multicolored   2.75   2.75

No. 2478 was valued at first class intl. rate (1523.83 cr) on day of issue.

Natl. Literacy Program — A1329

Designs: No. 2479, Pencil, buildings. No. 2480, Pencil, people on television, people watching. No. 2481, Classroom, pencil. No. 2482, Pencils crossed over fingerprint, map of Brazil.

1994, June 3 Litho. ***Perf. 12x11½***

2479 A1329 (1) multicolored .80 .80
2480 A1329 (1) multicolored .80 .80
2481 A1329 (1) multicolored .80 .80
2482 A1329 (1) multicolored .80 .80
Nos. 2479-2482 (4) 3.20 3.20

Nos. 2479-2482 were valued at first class domestic letter rate (233.05 cr) on day of issue.

Souvenir Sheet

Treaty of Tordesillas, 500th Anniv. — A1330

1994, June 7

2483 A1330 (1) multicolored 3.50 3.50

No. 2483 was valued at first class intl. letter rate (1689.02 cr) on day of issue.

Bird Type of 1994 and

A1330a

Designs: 1c, Like No. 2443. 2c, Like No. 2444. 5c, Like No. 2445. 10c, Like No. 2446. 15c, Sicalis flaveola. 20c, Like No. 2447. No. 2490, Tyrannus savana. 50c, Like No. 2448. 1r, Fumarius rufus.

No. 2498, Myiozetestes similis. No. 2499, Volantia jacarina.

Perf. 11x11½, 13 (15c), 12½13 (22c)

1994-2001 **Photo.**

2484 A1318 1c multi .25 .25
2485 A1318 2c multi .25 .25
2486 A1318 5c multi .25 .25
2487 A1318 10c multi .25 .25
2488 A1330a 15c multi .75 .35
2489 A1318 20c multi .50 .40
2490 A1318 22c multi .40 .40
a. Inscribed "1999" 1.00 .45
2491 A1318 50c multi 1.10 1.00
2494 A1318 1r multi 2.00 2.00
Nos. 2484-2494 (9) 5.75 5.15

Size: 21x27mm

Self-Adhesive

Serpentine Die Cut 5¾

2498 A1318 22c multi .85 .30
2499 A1318 (22c) multi 1.25 .55
a. Inscribed "2000" 1.10 1.10

No. 2499 is inscribed "1o PORTE NATIONAL" and was valued at 22c on day of issue.

No. 2490 has 1998 year date; No. 2499 has 1997 year date.

Issued: 1c, 2c, 5c, 20c, 20c, 50c, 1r, 7/1/94; 11/16/95; No. 2490, 10/13/97; No. 2498, 2/16/98; No. 2499, 7/22/97; No. 2490a, 11/99; No. 2499a, 1/01.

Prominent Brazilians A1331

Designs: No. 2504, Edgard Santos (1894-1962), surgeon, educator. No. 2505, Oswaldo Aranha (1894-1960), politician. No. 2507, Otto Lara Resende (1922-92), writer, educator.

1994, July 5 Litho. ***Perf. 11½x12***

2504 A1331 (1) multicolored .75 .60
2505 A1331 (1) multicolored .75 .60
2506 A1331 (1) multicolored .75 .60
Nos. 2504-2506 (3) 2.25 1.80

Nos. 2504-2506 were valued at first class domestic letter rate (12c) on day of issue.

Petrobras, 40th Anniv. — A1332

1994, July 15 ***Perf. 12x11½***

2507 A1332 12c multicolored .25 .25

Brazilian State Mint, 300th Anniv. — A1333

Litho. & Engr.

1994, July 26 ***Perf. 11½***

2508 A1333 12c multicolored .25 .25

Campaign Against Famine & Misery A1334

1994, July 27 Litho. ***Perf. 11½x12***

2509 A1334 (1) Fish .80 .35
2510 A1334 (1) Bread .80 .35

Nos. 2509-2510 were valued at first class domestic letter rate (12c) on day of issue.

Institute of Brazilian Lawyers, 150th Anniv. A1335

1994, Aug. 11

2511 A1335 12c multicolored .25 .25

Intl. Year of the Family A1336

1994, Aug. 16 ***Perf. 11½***

2512 A1336 84c multicolored 1.10 1.10

Maternity Hospital of Sao Paulo, Cent. A1337

1994, Aug. 26 ***Perf. 11½x12***

2513 A1337 12c multicolored .25 .25

Vincente Celestino (1894-1968), Singer — A1338

1994, Sept. 12

2514 A1338 12c multicolored .25 .25

"Contos da Carochinha," First Brazilian Children's Book, Cent. — A1339

No. 2515: Fairy tales: a, Joao e Maria (Hansel & Gretel). b, Dona Baratinha. c, Puss 'n Boots. d, Tom Thumb.

1994, Oct. 5 Litho. ***Perf. 11½x12***

2515 Block of 4 3.00 3.00
a.-b. A1339 12c any single .30 .30
c.-d. A1339 84c any single 1.00 1.00

Brazilian Literature A1340

Portraits: No. 2516, Tomas Antonio Gonzaga (1744-1809?), poet. No. 2517, Fernando de Azevedo (1894-1974), author.

1994, Oct. 5 ***Perf. 11½***

2516 A1340 12c multicolored .25 .25
2517 A1340 12c multicolored .25 .25

St. Clare of Assisi (1194-1253) A1341

1994, Oct. 19 ***Perf. 12x11½***

2518 A1341 12c multicolored .25 .25

Ayrton Senna (1960-1994), Race Car Driver — A1342

No. 2519: a, McClaren Formula 1 race car, Brazilian flag. b, Fans, Senna. c, Flags, race cars, Senna.

1994, Oct. 24 ***Perf. 11½x12***

2519 Triptych 1.75 1.75
a.-b. A1342 12c any single .30 .30
c. A1342 84c multicolored 1.10 1.10

Institute of History & Geography of Sao Paulo, Cent. A1343

1994, Nov. 1

2520 A1343 12c multicolored .25 .25

Popular Music A1344

Designs: No. 2521, Music from "The Sea," by Dorival Caymmi. No. 2522, Adoniran Barbosa (1910-82), samba composer.

1994, Nov. 5 ***Perf. 11½***

2521 A1344 12c multicolored .25 .25
2522 A1344 12c multicolored .25 .25

Christmas A1345

No. 2523 — Folk characters: a, Boy wearing Santa coat, pot on head. b, Worm in apple. c, Man, animals singing. d, Shoe on tree stump, man with pipe holding pen.

1994, Dec. 1 Litho. ***Perf. 11½***

2523 Block of 4 1.75 1.75
a. A1345 84c multicolored 1.10 1.10
b.-d. A1345 12c any single .35 .35
e. Booklet pane, #2523 + 4 labels 17.50
Complete booklet, #2523e 20.00

Souvenir Sheet

Brazil, 1994 World Cup Soccer Champions — A1346

1994, Dec. 5 ***Perf. 12x11½***

2524 A1346 2.14r multicolored 6.00 6.00

Louis Pasteur (1822-95) A1347

1995, Feb. 19   Litho.   *Perf. 11½x12*
2525 A1347 84c multicolored   1.25 1.25

Historical Events A1348

Designs: No. 2526, Capture of Monte Castello, 50th anniv. No. 2527, End of the Farroupilha Revolution, 150th anniv.

1995, Feb. 21
2526 A1348 12c multicolored   .25   .25
2527 A1348 12c multicolored   .25   .25

Pres. Itamar Franco — A1349

1995, Mar. 22   Litho.   *Perf. 12x11½*
2528 A1349 12c multicolored   .25   .25

FAO, 50th Anniv. — A1350

1995, Apr. 3   *Perf. 11½x11*
2529 A1350 84c multicolored   1.25 1.25

Famous Men A1351

Designs: No. 2530, Alexandre de Gusmao (1695-1753), diplomat. No. 2531, Francisco Brandao, Viscount of Jequitinhonha (1794-1870), lawyer, abolitionist. 15c, Jose da Silva Paranhos, Jr., Baron of Rio Branco (1845-1912), politician, diplomat.

1995, Apr. 28   *Perf. 11½x12*
2530 A1351 12c multicolored   .25   .25
2531 A1351 12c multicolored   .25   .25
2532 A1351 15c multicolored   .25   .25
       Nos. 2530-2532 (3)   .75   .75

Guglielmo Marconi (1874-1937), Radio Transmitting Equipment — A1352

1995, May 5   Litho.   *Perf. 11½x12*
2533 A1352 84c multicolored   1.25 1.25
       Radio, cent.

Friendship Between Brazil & Japan A1353

1995, May 29
2534 A1353 84c multicolored   1.25 1.25

Endangered Birds — A1354

No. 2535, Tinamus solitarius. No. 2536, Mitu mitu.

1995, June 5   *Perf. 12x11½*
2535 A1354 12c multicolored   .50   .30
2536 A1354 12c multicolored   .50   .30

June Festivals — A1355

Designs: No. 2537, Couples dancing at Campina Grande, "Greatest St. John's Party of the World." No. 2538, Bride, bridegroom, festivities, Caruaru.

1995, June 11   *Perf. 11½x12*
2537 A1355 12c multicolored   .30   .30
2538 A1355 12c multicolored   .30   .30

St. Anthony of Padua (1195-1231) — A1356

1995, June 13
2539 A1356 84c multicolored   1.25 1.25
       See Portugal No. 2054.

Souvenir Sheet

Louis and Auguste Lumiere, Camera — A1357

1995, June 21
2540 A1357 2.14r multicolored   6.50 6.50
       Motion pictures, cent.

New Currency, The Real, 1st Anniv. — A1358

1995, July 1   Litho.   *Perf. 12x11½*
2541 A1358 12c multicolored   .30   .30

Volleyball, Cent. — A1359

1995, July 8
2542 A1359 15c multicolored   .30   .30

Dinosaurs A1360

15c, Angaturama limai. 1.50r, Titanosaurus.

1995, July 23   *Perf. 11½x12*
2543 A1360 15c multi   .30   .30
2544 A1360 1.50r multi   1.50 1.50

Traffic Safety Program A1361

Designs: 12c, Test dummy without seat belt hitting windshield. 71c, Auto hitting alcoholic beverage glass.

1995, July 25
2545 A1361 12c multicolored   .30   .30
2546 A1361 71c multicolored   1.25 1.25

Souvenir Sheet

Roberto Burle Marx, Botanist — A1362

No. 2547: a, 15c, Calathea burle-marxii. b, 15c, Vellozia burle-marxii. c, 1.50r, Heliconia aemygdiana.

1995, Aug. 4   Litho.   *Perf. 12x11½*
2547 A1362 Sheet of 3, #a.-c.   6.00 6.00
       Singapore '95.

Parachute Infantry Brigade, 50th Anniv. — A1363

1995, Aug. 23
2548 A1363 15c multicolored   .30   .30

Paulista Museum, Cent. A1364

1995, Sept. 5   *Perf. 11½*
2549 A1364 15c multicolored   .30   .30

Lighthouses A1365

No. 2550, Olinda. No. 2551, Sao Joao. No. 2552, Santo Antonio da Barra.

1995, Sept. 28
2550 A1365 15c multi   1.00   .35
2551 A1365 15c multi   1.00   .35
2552 A1365 15c multi   1.00   .35
       Nos. 2550-2552 (3)   3.00 1.05

Wilhelm Röntgen (1845-1923), Discovery of the X-Ray, Cent. A1366

1995, Sept. 30
2553 A1366 84c multicolored   1.25 1.25

Lubrapex '95, 15th Brazilian-Portuguese Philatelic Exhibition — A1367

Wildlife scene along Tiete River: 15c, No. 2556a, Bird, otter with fish. 84c, No. 2556b, Birds, river boat.

1995, Sept. 30   *Perf. 12x11½*
2554 A1367 15c multicolored   .55   .55
2555 A1367 84c multicolored   1.50   1.50
              Souvenir Sheet
2556 A1367 1.50r Sheet of 2,
              #a.-b.   12.00 12.00

No. 2556 is a continuous design.

Flamengo Regatta Soccer Club — A1368

1995, Oct. 6   *Perf. 11x11½*
2557 A1368 15c multicolored   .55   .35

America Issue — A1369

Outdoor scenes: 15c, Trees, mushrooms, alligator, lake. 84c, Black-neck swans on lake, false swans in air.

1995, Oct. 12 Litho.   *Perf. 11½x12*
2558 A1369 15c multicolored   .30   .30
2559 A1369 84c multicolored   1.25   1.25
  a. A1369 Pair, #2558-2559   1.75   1.75

UN, 50th Anniv. — A1370

1995, Oct. 24   *Perf. 12x11½*
2560 1.05r multicolored   1.75   1.75
2561 1.05r multicolored   1.75   1.75
  a. A1370 Pair, No. 2560-2561 4.00   4.00

Writers — A1372

Designs: No. 2562, Eca de Queiroz (1845-1900), village. No. 2563, Rubem Braga (1913-90), beach, Rio de Janeiro. 23c, Carlos Drummond de Andrade (1902-87), letters.

1995, Oct. 27   *Perf. 12x11*
2562 A1372 15c multicolored   .40   .40
2563 A1372 15c multicolored   .40   .40
2564 A1372 23c multicolored   .60   .60
     Nos. 2562-2564 (3)   1.40   1.40

Souvenir Sheet

Death of Zumbi Dos Palmares, Slave Resistance Leader, 300th Anniv. — A1373

1995, Nov. 20   *Perf. 12x11½*
2565 A1373 1.05r multicolored   6.00   6.00

2nd World Short Course Swimming Championships — A1374

No. 2566: a, Freestyle. b, Backstroke. c, Butterfly. d, Breaststroke.

1995, Nov. 30   *Perf. 11½x12*
2566 A1374 23c Block of 4, #a.-
              d.   3.25   3.25

Christmas — A1375

No. 2567: a, 23c, Cherub looking right, stars. b, 15c, Cherub looking left, stars.

1995, Dec. 1   *Perf. 11½*
2567 A1375 Pair, #a.-b.+2 labels 1.75 1.75

Botafogo Soccer and Regatta Club A1376

1995, Dec. 8   *Perf. 11x11½*
2568 A1376 15c multicolored   .40   .35

Diário de Pernambuco Newspaper, 170th Anniv. — A1377

1995, Dec. 14 Litho.   *Perf. 12x11½*
2569 A1377 23c multicolored   .60   .60

Souvenir Sheet

Amazon Theatre, Cent. — A1378

1996, Feb. 27
2570 A1378 1.23r multicolored   6.00   6.00

Francisco Prestes Maia, Politician, Birth Cent. A1379

1996, Mar. 19   *Perf. 11½x12*
2571 A1379 18c multicolored   .60   .40

Irineu Bornhausen, Governor of Santa Catarina, Birth Cent. — A1380

1996, Mar. 25   *Perf. 11x11½*
2572 A1380 27c multicolored   .60   .55

Paintings A1381

Designs: No. 2573, Boat with Little Flags and Birds, by Alfredo Volpi. No. 2574, Ouro Preto Landscape, by Alberto da Veiga Guignard.

1996, Apr. 15   *Perf. 12x11½*
2573 A1381 15c multicolored   .75   .30
2574 A1381 15c multicolored   .75   .30

UNICEF, 50th Anniv. A1382

1996, Apr. 16   *Perf. 11½*
2575 A1382 23c multicolored   .75   .50

Portuguese Discovery of Brazil, 500th Anniv. (in 2000) — A1383

1996, Apr. 22   *Perf. 12x11½*
2576 A1383 1.05r multicolored   2.75   2.25
     See No. 2626.

Israel Pinheiro da Silva, Politician, Business Entrepeneur, Birth Cent. — A1384

1996, Apr. 23   *Perf. 11½x12*
2577 A1384 18c multicolored   .75   .40

Tourism A1385

Designs: No. 2578, Amazon River. No. 2579, Swampland area. No. 2580, Sail boat, northeastern states. No. 2581, Sugarloaf, Guanabara Bay. No. 2582, Iguacu Falls.

1996, Apr. 24   *Die Cut*
              Self-Adhesive
2578 A1385 23c multicolored   .75   .30
2579 A1385 23c multicolored   .75   .30
2580 A1385 23c multicolored   .75   .30
2581 A1385 23c multicolored   .75   .30
2582 A1385 23c multicolored   .75   .30
  a.   Strip of 5, #2578-2582 4.00

Hummingbirds — A1386

Espamer '96: 15c, Topaza pella. 1.05r, Stephanoxis lalandi. 1.15r, Eupetomena macroura.

1996, May 4 Litho.   *Perf. 11½*
2583 A1386 15c multicolored   .75   .50
2584 A1386 1.05r multicolored   4.00   3.00
2585 A1386 1.15r multicolored   4.00   3.00
     Nos. 2583-2585 (3)   8.75   6.50

1996 Summer Olympic Games, Atlanta A1387

No. 2586, Marathon. No. 2587, Gymnastics. No. 2588, Swimming. No. 2589, Beach volleyball.

1996, May 21
2586 A1387 18c multi   .75   .40
2587 A1387 23c multi   1.00   .50
2588 A1387 1.05r multi   3.75   2.00
2589 A1387 1.05r multi   3.75   2.00
     Nos. 2586-2589 (4)   9.25   4.90

              Souvenir Sheet

Brazilian Caverns — A1388

1996, June 5   *Perf. 11½x12*
2590 A1388 2.68r multicolored   8.00   8.00

Americas Telecom '96 — A1389

1996, June 10 **Perf. 11½**
2591 A1389 1.05r multicolored   2.75 2.75

Souvenir Sheet

World Day to Fight Desertification — A1390

1996, June 17 **Perf. 12x11½**
2592 A1390 1.23r multicolored   6.00 6.00

Fight Against Drug Abuse A1391

1996, June 26 **Perf. 11½x12**
2593 A1391 27c multicolored   1.25 .65

Year of Education A1392

1996, July 10 **Perf. 12x11½**
2594 A1392 23c multicolored   1.25 .55

Princess Isabel, 150th Birth Anniv. A1393

1996, July 29 **Perf. 11½x12**
2595 A1393 18c multicolored   .75 .40

Carlos Gomes (1836-96), Composer A1394

1996, Sept. 16 **Perf. 11½**
2596 A1394 50c multicolored   1.25 1.25

15th World Orchid Conference A1395

Designs: No. 2597, Promenaea stape-lioides. No. 2598, Cattleya eldorado. No. 2599, Cattleya loddigesii.

1996, Sept. 17
2597 A1395 15c multicolored   1.50 .60
2598 A1395 15c multicolored   1.50 .60
2599 A1395 15c multicolored   1.50 .60
  Nos. 2597-2599 (3)   4.50 1.80

Apparition of Virgin Mary at La Salette, 150th Anniv. A1396

1996, Sept. 19
2600 A1396 1r multicolored   2.75 2.25

Souvenir Sheet

Popular Legends — A1397

No. 2601: a, 23c, "Cuca" walking from house. b, 1.05r, "Boitatá," snake of life. c, 1.15r, "Caipora," defender of ecology.

1996, Sept. 28 **Perf. 11x10½**
2601 A1397 Sheet of 3, #a.-c.   7.50 7.50
  BRAPEX '96.

23rd Sao Paulo Intl. Biennial Exhibition — A1398

No. 2602: a, Marilyn Monroe by Andy Warhol, vert. b, The Scream, by Edvard Munch, vert. c, Abstract, by Louise Bourgeois, vert. d, Woman Drawing, by Pablo Picasso.

1996, Oct. 5 **Perf. 12x11½**
2602 A1398 55c Block of 4,
         #a.-d.   22.50 22.50

Traditional Costumes A1400

America issue: 50c, Man dressed as cowboy. 1r, Woman dressed in baiana clothes.

1996, Oct. 12 **Litho.** **Perf. 11½**
2604 A1400 50c multicolored   1.00 1.00
2605 A1400 1r multicolored   3.50 3.50

Christmas A1401

1996, Nov. 4 **Litho.** **Perf. 12x11½**
2606 A1401 1st multicolored   1.25 .60
No. 2606 was valued at 23c on day of issue.

José Carlos (1884-1950), Caricaturist A1402

1996, Nov. 22
2607 A1402 1st multicolored   1.25 .60
No. 2607 was valued at 23c on day of issue.

Tourism A1403

Designs: No. 2608, Ipiranga Monument, Sao Paulo. No. 2609, Hercílio Luz Bridge, Florianópolis. No. 2610, Natl. Congress Building,

Brasília. No. 2611, Pelourinho, Salvador. No. 2612, Ver-o-Peso Market, Belém.

Serpentine Die Cut
1996, Dec. 9 **Photo.**
         Self-Adhesive
2608 A1403 1st multicolored   .80 .30
2609 A1403 1st multicolored   .80 .30
2610 A1403 1st multicolored   .80 .30
2611 A1403 1st multicolored   .80 .30
2612 A1403 1st multicolored   .80 .30
  a.   Strip of 5, #2608-2612   4.00

Nos. 2608-2612 are inscribed "1o PORTE NACIONAL," and were valued 23c on day of issue. Selvage surrounding each stamp in No. 2612a is rouletted.

Rio de Janeiro, Candidate for 2004 Summer Olympic Games A1404

1997, Jan. 17 **Litho.** **Perf. 11½**
2613 A1404 1st multicolored   2.75 2.25
No. 2613 is inscribed "1o PORTE INTER-NACIONAL" and was valued at 1.05r on day of issue.

The Postman A1405

1997, Jan. 25
2614 A1405 1st multicolored   .80 .75
America issue. No. 2614 is inscribed "1o PORTE NACIONAL" and was valued at 23c on day of issue.

Antonio de Castro Alves (1847-71), Poet A1406

1997, Mar. 14
2615 A1406 15c multicolored   .60 .50

Marquis of Tamandaré, Naval Officer, Death Cent. — A1407

1997, Mar. 19 **Perf. 11x11½**
2616 A1407 23c multicolored   .65 .50

Stamp Design Contest Winner A1408

1997, Mar. 20 **Perf. 11½x12**
2617 A1408 15c "Joy Joy"   .75 .35

World Day of
Water — A1409

1997, Mar. 22   *Perf. 12x11½*
2618 A1409 1.05r multicolored   1.90 1.90

Brazilian
Airplanes
A1410

Designs: No. 2619, EMB-145. No. 2620,
AMX. No. 2621, EMB-312 H Super Tucano.
No. 2622, EMB-120 Brasilia. No. 2623, EMB-
312 Tucano.

1997, Mar. 27   **Litho.**   *Die Cut*
Self-Adhesive
2619 A1410 15c multicolored   .75 .30
2620 A1410 15c multicolored   .75 .30
2621 A1410 15c multicolored   .75 .30
2622 A1410 15c multicolored   .75 .30
2623 A1410 15c multicolored   .75 .30
  a.   Strip of 5, #2619-2623   4.00 4.00

Campaign
Against
AIDS — A1411

1997, Apr. 7   **Litho.**   *Perf. 12x11½*
2624 A1411 23c multicolored   .65 .50

Souvenir Sheet

Indian Culture — A1412

Weapons of the Xingu Indians.

1997, Apr. 16   *Perf. 11x11½*
2625 A1412 1.15r multicolored   3.00 3.00

**Portuguese Discovery of Brazil,
500th Anniv. Type**
1997, Apr. 22   *Perf. 12x11½*
2626 A1383 1.05r like #2576   2.25 2.25

No. 2576 has green background and blue in
lower right corner. No. 2626 has those colors
reversed and is inscribed "BRASIL 97" at top.

Pixinguinha (1897-
1973), Composer,
Musician — A1413

1997, Apr. 23
2627 A1413 15c multicolored   .60 .35

Souvenir Sheet

Brazilian Claim to Trindade Island,
Cent. — A1414

1997, May 7   *Perf. 11½x11*
2628 A1414 1.23r multicolored   6.00 6.00

Human
Rights — A1415

1997, May 13   *Perf. 12x11½*
2629 A1415 18c multicolored   .60 .35

Souvenir Sheet

Brazilian Antarctic Program — A1416

1997, May 13
2630 A1416 2.68r multicolored   6.50 6.50

Fruits and
Nuts — A1417

Designs: 1c, Oranges. 2c, Bananas. 5c,
Papayas. 10c, Pineapple. Nos. 2635, 2636L,
Cashews. Nos. 2636, 2636Q, Sugar apple.
No. 2636A, Grapes. Nos. 2636B, 2636M,

2636R, Watermelon. 50c, Surinam cherry
(pitanga), 51c, Coconuts. 80c, Apples. 82c,
Lemons. 1r, Strawberries.

1997-99   **Litho.**   *Serpentine Die Cut*
Self-Adhesive
2631 A1417   1c multi   .65 .30
2632 A1417   2c multi   .65 .30
2633 A1417   5c multi   .65 .30
2634 A1417   10c multi, vert.   1.50 .65
2635 A1417   20c multi, vert.   3.00 1.50
2636 A1417   20c multi, vert.   1.50 .65
2636A A1417   22c multi   .65 .30
2636B A1417   (22c) multi   2.75 .35
2636C A1417   50c multi   .90 .45
2636D A1417   51c multi, vert.   2.00 1.50
2636E A1417   80c multi, vert.   5.00 3.00
2636F A1417   82c multi, vert.   6.50 5.00
2636G A1417   1r multi, vert.   2.00 .65
   Nos. 2631-2636G (13)   27.75 14.95

Issued: (22c), 5/28; 1c, 6/97; 2c, 10c, No.
2635, 7/97; 5c, 8/97; 1r, 8/3; 22c, 10/3; No.
2636, 51c, 80c, 82c, 1/15/98; 50c, 11/26/99.
No. 2636B is inscribed "1o PORTE
NATIONAL" and was valued at 22c on day of
issue.

Fruits and Nuts Type of 1997-99

1998-99   **Litho.**   *Die Cut*
Self-Adhesive
2636H A1417   1c multi   .35 .35
2636I A1417   2c multi   .50 .50
2636J A1417   5c multi   .65 .65
2636K A1417   10c multi,
         vert.   1.50 .65
2636L A1417   20c multi,
         vert.   2.00 .65
2636M A1417   (22c) multi   3.25 .35
   Nos. 2636H-2636M (6)   8.25 3.15

Microperfed
Without Gum
2636N A1417   1c multi   1.75 1.75
2636O A1417   5c multi   8.00 8.00
2636P A1417   10c multi,
         vert.   12.00 12.00
2636Q A1417   20c multi,
         vert.   12.00 12.00
2636R A1417   (31c) multi   6.00 6.00
2636S A1417   51c multi,
         vert.   12.00 12.00
2636T A1417   80c multi,
         vert.   20.00 20.00
2636U A1417   1r multi,
         vert.   20.00 20.00
   Nos. 2636N-2636U (8)   91.75 91.75

Issued: 2636H-2636L, 1998. No. 2636M,
1999.
Issued: Nos. 2636N-2636Q, 9/28/99; No.
2636R, 9/12/99; No. 2636S, 9/22/99; Nos.
2636T, 2636U, 9/15/99.

A1418

Amazon Flora and Fauna — A1419

Designs: No. 2637, Swietenia macropylla.
No. 2638, Arapaima gigas.

1997, June 5   **Litho.**   *Perf. 11½x12*
2637 A1418 27c multicolored   .75 .40
2638 A1419 27c multicolored   .75 .40

Fr. José de
Anchieta (1534-
97), Missionary in
Brazil — A1420

Design: No. 2640, Fr. António Vieira (1608-
97), missionary in Brazil, diplomat.

1997, June 9   *Perf. 12*
2639 A1420 1.05r multicolored   1.75 1.75
2640 A1420 1.05r multicolored   1.75 1.75

See Portugal Nos. 2168-2169.

Tourism
A1421

Designs: No. 2641, Parnaíba River Delta.
No. 2642, Lençóis Maranhenses Park.

1997, June 20   *Perf. 11½x12*
2641 A1421 1st multicolored   2.25 2.00
2642 A1421 1st multicolored   2.25 2.00

Nos. 2641-2642 are inscribed "1o PORTE
INTERNACIONAL TAXE PERCUE" and were
each valued at on day of issue.

Brazilian
Academy of
Literature,
Cent.
A1422

1997, July 20
2643 A1422 22c multicolored   .55 .50

Emiliano de
Cavalcanti
(1897-1976),
Painter
A1423

1997, Sept. 16   **Litho.**   *Perf. 11½*
2644 A1423 31c multicolored   .55 .50

2nd World
Meeting of
the Pope
with
Families,
Rio de
Janeiro
A1424

1997, Sept. 22   *Perf. 11½x12*
2645 A1424 1.20r multicolored   1.75 1.75

A1425

1997, Sept. 26   *Perf. 12x11½*
2646 A1425 80c multicolored   1.25 1.25

MERCOSUR (Common Market of Latin
America). See Argentina #1975, Bolivia
#1019, Paraguay #2565, Uruguay #1681.

A1426

1997, Sept. 27
2647 A1426 22c multicolored　　　.75　.75
End of Canudos War, cent.

Integration of MERCOSUR
Communications by Telebras, 25th
Anniv. — A1427

1997, Oct. 6　　　　　**Perf. 11½**
2648 A1427 80c multicolored　　1.25　1.25

Composers — A1428

Designs: No. 2649, Oscar Lorenzo Fernandez (1897-1948). No. 2650, Francisco Mignone (1897-1986).

1997, Oct. 7　　　　　**Perf. 11x11½**
2649 A1428 22c multicolored　　.65　.45
2650 A1428 22c multicolored　　.65　.45

Marist
Brothers
Presence
in Brazil,
Cent.
A1429

1997, Oct. 22
2651 A1429 22c multicolored　　.65　.45

Christmas
A1430

1997, Nov. 5　　　　　**Perf. 12x11½**
2652 A1430 22c multicolored　　.65　.45

Education and Citizenship — A1431

1997, Dec. 10　　　　**Perf. 11x11½**
2653 A1431 31c blue & yellow　　.65　.65

City of Belo
Horizonte,
Cent.
A1432

1997, Dec. 12　　　　**Perf. 11½x12**
2654 A1432 31c multicolored　　.65　.65

Citzenship
A1433

Map of Brazil and: No. 2655, Education, stack of books. No. 2656, Employment, worker's papers. No. 2657, Agriculture, oranges. No. 2658, Health, stethoscope, vert. No. 2659, Culture, clapboard with musical notes, artist's paint brush, vert.

1997, Dec. 20　　　　　**Die Cut**
Self-Adhesive
Booklet Stamps
2655 A1433 22c multicolored　　.90　.45
2656 A1433 22c multicolored　　.90　.45
2657 A1433 22c multicolored　　.90　.45
2658 A1433 22c multicolored　　.90　.45
2659 A1433 22c multicolored　　.90　.45
　a.　Bkkt. pane, 2 ea #2655-2659　10.00

The peelable paper backing of No. 2659a serves as a booklet cover.

Gems — A1434

No. 2660, Alexandrite. No. 2661, Cat's eye chrysoberyl. No. 2662, Indicolite.

1998, Jan. 22　　　　　**Perf. 12x11½**
2660 A1434 22c multicolored　　1.50　.60
2661 A1434 22c multicolored　　1.50　.60
2662 A1434 22c multicolored　　1.50　.60
　a.　Strip of 3, #2660-2662　4.50　2.75

Famous
Brazilian
Women
A1435

America Issue: No. 2663, Elis Regina, singer. No. 2664, Clementina de Jesus, singer. No. 2665, Dulcina de Moraes, actress. No. 2666, Clarice Lispector, writer.

1998, Mar. 11　　　　　**Perf. 11½**
2663 A1435 22c multicolored　　.70　.45
2664 A1435 22c multicolored　　.70　.45
2665 A1435 22c multicolored　　.70　.45
2666 A1435 22c multicolored　　.70　.45
　a.　Block of 4, #2663-2666　3.00　3.00

Education — A1436

1998, Mar. 19　　　　　**Perf. 12x11½**
2667　31c Children at desks　　.65　.65
2668　31c Teacher at blackboard　.65　.65
　a.　A1436 Pair, #2667-2668　1.40　1.40

Cruz e
Sousa
(1861-98),
Poet
A1437

1998, Mar. 19 Litho. Perf. 11½x12
2669 A1437 36c multicolored　　.65　.65

Discovery of Brazil, 500th
Anniv. — A1438

Designs: No. 2670, 1519 map showing natives, vegetation, fauna. No. 2671, Caravel from Cabral's fleet.

1998, Apr. 22　　　　　**Perf. 12x11½**
2670　1.05r multicolored　　　2.75　1.40
2671　1.05r multicolored　　　2.75　1.40
　a.　A1438 Pair, #2670-2671　5.50　5.50

Volunteer Work — A1439

Designs: a, Caring for sick man. b, Caring for sick child. c, Fighting forest fire. c, Child's hand holding adult's finger.

1998, May 5　　　　　**Perf. 11½x12**
2672 A1439 31c Block of 4, #a.-
　　　　　　　　　d.　　　2.25　2.25

Brazilian Circus — A1440

No. 2673 — Piolin the clown: a, Looking through circle. b, Standing in ring. c, With outside of tent to the left. d, With inside of tent to the right.

1998, May 18　　　　　**Perf. 12x11½**
2673 A1440 31c Block of 4, #a.-
　　　　　　　　　d.　　　2.25　2.25

Intl. Year of the Ocean — A1441

No. 2674 — Pictures, drawings of marine life: a, Turtle. b, Tail fin of whale. c, Barracuda. d, Jellyfish, school of fish. e, School of fish, diver. f, Dolphins. g, Yellow round fish. h, Two whales. i, Two black-striped butterfly fish. j, Orange & yellow fish. k, Manatee. l, Yellow-striped fish. m, Blue & yellow fish. n, Several striped fish. o, Fish with wing-like fins. p, Manta ray. q, Two fish swimming in opposite directions. r, Long, thin fish, coral. s, Moray eel. t, Yellow & black butterfly fish, coral. u, Starfish, fish. v, Crab, coral. w, Black & orange fish, coral. x, Sea horse, coral.

1998, May 22　　　　　**Perf. 11½x12**
Sheet of 24
2674 A1441 31c #a.-x.　　22.00　22.00
Expo '98.

1998 World Cup Soccer
Championships, France — A1442

No. 2675 — Paintings by: a, Gregorio Gruber. b, Mario Gruber. c, Maciej Babinski. d, Cildo Meireles, vert. e, Claudio Tozzi, vert. f, Antonio Henrique Amaral, vert. g, Jose Roberto Aguilar. h, Nelson Leirner. i, Wesley Duke Lee. j, Mauricio Nogueira Lima, vert. k, Zelio Alves Pinto, vert. l, Aldemir Martins, vert. m, Ivald Granato. n, Carlos Vergara. o, Joao Camara, vert. p, Roberto Magalhaes, vert. q, Guto Lacaz, vert. r, Glauco Rodrigues, vert. s, Leda Catunda. t, Tomoshige Kusuno. u, Jose Zaragoza. v, Luiz Zerbine, vert. w, Antonio Peticov, vert. x, Marcia Grostein, vert.

1998, May 28 Perf. 11½x12, 12x11½
2675 A1442 22c Sheet of 24,
　　　　　#a.-x.　　　22.00　22.00

Feijoada,
Traditional
Cuisine
A1443

1998, June 1　　　　　**Perf. 11½**
2676 A1443 31c multicolored　　.55　.50

Preservation of Flora and
Fauna — A1444

Designs: No. 2677, Araucaria angustifolia. No. 2678, Cyanocorax caeruleus.

1998, June 5　　　　　**Perf. 11½x12**
2677　22c multicolored　　　.60　.60
2678　22c multicolored　　　.60　.60
　a.　A1444 Pair, #2677-2678　1.40　1.40

Launching of Submarine Tapajó A1445

1998, June 5
2679 A1445 51c multicolored .75 .75

Luiz de Queiroz (1849-98), Founder of Agricultural School A1446

1998, June 6 *Perf. 11½*
2680 A1446 36c multicolored .60 .60

Benedictine Monastery, Sao Paulo, 400th Anniv. A1447

1998, July 10 *Litho.* *Perf. 11½x12*
2681 A1447 22c multicolored .60 .60

Alberto Santos-Dumont (1873-1932), Aviation Pioneer — A1448

Designs: No. 2682, Balloon "Brazil." No. 2683, Dirigible Nr. 1, Santos-Dumont at controls.

1998, July 18
2682 A1448 31c multicolored .80 .40
2683 A1448 31c multicolored .80 .40
a. Pair, #2682-2683 1.75 1.10

Brazilian Cinema, Cent. (in 1997) — A1449

No. 2684: a, Guanabara Bay, by Lumière, 1897. b, Taciana Reiss in "Limite," by Mário Peixoto, 1931. c, Actors in (Chanchada), from "A Dupla do Barulho," by Carlos Manga, 1953. d, Films produced by Vera Cruz pictures, caricature of Mazzaropi from "The Dream Factory." e, Glauber Rocha's "New Cinema". f, International film festival awards won by Brazilian films.

1998, July 24 *Perf. 11½*
2684 A1449 31c Block of 6,
 #a.-f. 3.50 3.50

Rodrigo Melo Franco de Andrade (1898-1969), and Church of Our Lady of the Rosary, Ouro Preto — A1450

1998, Aug. 17 *Perf. 11x11½*
2685 A1450 51c multicolored .75 .65

Luís da Camara Cascudo (1898-1986), Writer — A1451

1998, Aug. 22
2686 A1451 22c multicolored .55 .40

42nd Aeronautical Pentathlon World Championship — A1452

No. 2687: a, Fencing. b, Running. c, Swimming. d, Shooting. e, Basketball.

1998, Aug. 22 *Perf. 12x11½*
2687 A1452 22c Strip of 5, #a.-e. 3.50 3.50

Missionary Cross, Ruins of the Church of Sao Miguel das Missoes — A1453

1998, Sept. 17 *Perf. 11½x12*
2688 A1453 80c multicolored 1.25 1.00

24th Sao Paulo Art Biennial — A1454

No. 2689: a, Biennial emblem, by José Leonilson. b, Tapuia Dance, by Albert von Eckhout. c, The Schoolboy, by Vincent van Gogh. d, Portrait of Michel Leiris, by Francis Bacon. e, The King's Museum, by René Magritte. f, Urutu, by Tarsila do Amaral. g, Facade with Arcs, Circle and Fascia, by Alfredo Volpi. h, The Raft of the Medusa, by Asger Jorn.

1998, Sept. 22
2689 A1454 31c Block of 8,
 #a.-h. 4.50 4.50
Nos. 2689b, 2689h have horiz. designs placed vert. on stamps.

Child and Citizenship Stamp Design Contest Winner A1455

1998, Oct. 9
2690 A1455 22c multicolored .35 .30

Reorganization of Maritime Mail from Portugal to Brazil, Bicent. — A1456

1998, Oct. 9
2691 A1456 1.20r multicolored 1.75 1.50
 See Portugal Nos. 2271-2272.

Dom Pedro I (1798-1834) A1457

1998, Oct. 13 *Perf. 11½*
2692 A1457 22c multicolored .55 .25

Frisco's Mango Refreshment Promotional Stamp — A1458

Serpentine Die Cut
1998, Oct. 15 *Photo.*
Self-Adhesive
2693 A1458 36c multicolored 2.75 2.75
 No. 2693 is valid on all mail, but must be used on mail entries to Frisco on Faustao's Truck raffle.

Flowers — A1459

No. 2694: a, Solanum lycocarpum. b, Cattleya walkeriana. c, Kielmeyera coriacea.

1998, Oct. 23 *Litho.* *Perf. 11½*
2694 A1459 31c Strip of 3, #a.-c. 1.75 1.75

Humanitarians — A1460

No. 2695: a, Mother Teresa (1910-97). b, Friar Galvao (1739-1822). c, Herbert José de Souza "Betinho" (b. 1935). d, Friar Damiao (1898-1997).

1998, Oct. 25
2695 A1460 31c Block of 4, #a.-
 d. 2.25 2.25

A1461

31c, Sergio Motta, Former Minister of Communications, Natl. Telecommunications Agency Headquarters, Brasilia.

1998, Nov. 5 *Perf. 12x11½*
2696 A1461 31c multicolored .60 .35

Christmas — A1462

1998, Nov. 19 *Perf. 11½x12*
2697 A1462 22c multicolored .60 .30

Domestic Animals A1463

Designs: No. 2698, Moxotó goat. No. 2699, Brazilian donkey. No. 2700, Junqueira ox. No. 2701, Brazilian terrier. No. 2702, Brazilian shorthair cat.

1998, Nov. 20 *Die Cut*
Booklet Stamps
Self-Adhesive
2698 A1463 22c multi .60 .60
2699 A1463 22c multi .60 .60
2700 A1463 22c multi .60 .60
2701 A1463 22c multi, vert. .60 .60
2702 A1463 22c multi, vert. .60 .60
a. Bklt. pane, 2 ea #2698-2702 6.50

No. 2702a is a complete booklet.

Universal Declaration of Human Rights, 50th Anniv. — A1464

1998, Dec. 9 *Perf. 12x11½*
2703 A1464 1.20r multicolored 1.25 1.25

Natal, 400th Anniv. A1465

No. 2704, Wise Men's Fortress. No. 2705, Mother Luiza Lighthouse, vert.

Perf. 11x11½, 11½x11
1999, Jan. 6 *Litho.*
2704 A1465 31c multicolored .45 .40
2705 A1465 31c multicolored .45 .40

Program for Evaluating Resources in Brazil's Exclusive Economic Zone — A1466

No. 2706: a, Satellite, St. Peter and St. Paul Archipelago. b, Bird on buoy. c, Fishing boat. d, Sea turtle. e, Dolphin. f, Diver.

1999, Mar. 5   *Perf. 11½x12*
2706 A1466 31c Block of 6,
     #a.-f.   2.50   2.50

Australia '99 World Stamp Expo.

UPU, 125th Anniv. — A1467

No. 2707: a, Stamp vending machines from 1940s and 1998. b, Vending machines, 1906, 1998. c, Collection boxes, 1870, 1973. d, Federal Government's 1998 Quality Award.

1999, Mar. 19   *Perf. 11½*
2707 A1467 31c Block of 4, #a.-
     d.   1.75   1.75

Reorganization of Brazilian Posts and Telegraphs, 30th anniv.

City of Salvador, 450th Anniv. — A1468

1999, Mar. 29   **Litho.**   *Perf. 11½x12*
2708 A1468 1.05r multi   1.50   1.50

Dinosaurs' Valley
A1469

1999, Apr. 17   **Litho.**   *Perf. 11½x12*
2709 A1469 1.05r multicolored   1.25   1.25

Fort of Santo Amaro da Barra Grande — A1470

1999, Apr. 21   **Litho.**   *Perf. 11½x12*
2710 A1470 22c multicolored   .45   .25

Souvenir Sheet

Discovery of Brazil, 500th Anniv. (in 2000) — A1471

1999, Apr. 22   **Litho.**   *Perf. 11½x11*
2711 A1471 2.68r multi   4.50   4.50

Lubrapex 2000.

6th Air Transportation Squadron, 30th Anniv. — A1472

1999, May 12   **Litho.**   *Perf. 11x11½*
2712 A1472 51c multicolored   .65   .50

Holy Spirit Feast, Planaltina — A1473

1999, May 21   *Perf. 12x11½*
2713 A1473 22c multicolored   .45   .25

Historical and Cultural Heritage — A1474

No. 2714 — Views of cities: a, Ouro Preto. b, Olinda. c, Sao Luís.

1999, June 2   *Perf. 11½x11*
2714 A1474 1.05r Sheet of 3,
     #a.-c.   3.75   3.75

PhilexFrance '99, World Philatelic Exhibition.

Sao Paolo State Institute for Technological Research, Cent. — A1475

1999, June 24   **Litho.**   *Perf. 11½x12*
2715 A1475 36c multicolored   .60   .40

Flight of Alberto Santos-Dumont's Dirigible No. 3, Cent. — A1476

1999, July 20
2716 A1476 1.20r multicolored   1.75   1.75

Forest Fire Prevention A1477

No. 2717: a, Anteater. b, Flower. c, Leaf. d, Burnt trunk.

Serpentine Die Cut 6
1999, Aug. 1   **Litho.**
         Self-Adhesive
2717   Block of 4   3.25   3.25
   a.-d. A1477 51c Any single   .75   .75

No. 2717 is printed on recycled paper impregnated with burnt wood odor.

Souvenir Sheet

America Issue, A New Millennium Without Arms — A1478

No. 2718: a, Hands of adult and child drawing dove. b, Overturned tank.

1999, Aug. 6   **Litho.**   *Perf. 12x11½*
2718 A1478 90c Sheet of 2, #a.-
     b.   1.75   1.75

Issued with rouletted tab at right showing Universal Product Code.

Political Amnesty, 20th Anniv. — A1479

1999, Aug. 18
2719 A1479 22c multicolored   .45   .25

Famous Brazilians — A1480

Designs: 22c, Joaquim Nabuco (1849-1910), politician and diplomat. 31c, Ruy Barbosa (1849-1923), politician and justice for International Court.

1999, Aug. 19   **Litho.**   *Perf. 11½x12*
2720 A1480 22c multicolored   .45   .25
2721 A1480 31c multicolored   .45   .35

Fish — A1481

No. 2722: a, 22c, Salminus maxillosus. b, 31c, Brycon microlepsus. c, 36c, Acestrorhynchus pantaneiro. d, 51c, Hyphessobrycon eques. e, 80c, Rineloricaria. f, 90c, Leporinus macrocephalus. g, 1.05r, Abramites. h, 1.20r, Ancistrus.

1999, Aug. 20   **Litho.**   *Perf. 11½x12*
2722 A1481 Sheet of 8, #a.-h.   8.00   8.00

China 1999 World Philatelic Exhibition. No. 2722h has a holographic image. Soaking in water may affect hologram.

Mercosur Cultural Heritage Day A1482

1999, Sept. 17   **Litho.**   *Perf. 11½x12*
2723 A1482 80c multi   .75   .75

Water Resources — A1483

No. 2724: a, Ecological station, Aguas Emendadas. b, House on water's edge, boat. c, Cedro Dam. d, Orós Dam.

1999, Oct. 21
2724 A1483 31c Block of 4,
     #a.-d.   1.75   1.75

National Library
of Rio de Janeiro
Bookplate
A1484

1999, Oct. 29   Litho.   Perf. 12x11½
2725 A1484 22c multi   .45 .25

State Flag Type of 1981
1999, Nov. 19   Litho.   Perf. 11½x12
2726 A947 31c Amapá   .45 .35
2727 A947 36c Roraima   .45 .35

Antonio
Carlos
Jobim
(1927-94),
Composer
A1485

1999, Nov. 22
2728 A1485 31c multi   .45 .35

Christianity, 2000th Anniv. — A1486

No. 2729: a, The Annunciation. b, Birth of
Jesus and adoration of the Magi. c, Presenta-
tion of Jesus in the temple. d, Baptism of
Jesus by John the Baptist. e, Evangelization of
Jesus and Apostles. f, Death of Jesus and
resurrection.

1999, Nov. 26   Litho.   Perf. 11½
2729 A1486 22c Block of 6, #a-f 2.50 2.50

New Middle School Education
System — A1487

1999, Dec. 2   Perf. 11x11½
2730 A1487 31c multi   .45 .35

Itamaraty
Palace, Rio
A1488

Litho. & Engr.
1999, Dec. 6   Perf. 11½x12
2731 A1488 1.05r pale yel & brn 1.25 1.25

New Year 2000 — A1489

2000, Jan. 1   Litho.
2732 A1489 90c multi   .75 .75

National
School
Book
Program
A1490

2000, Feb. 7   Perf. 11x11½
2733 A1490 31c multi   .45 .35

Aviatrixes — A1491

No. 2734: a, Ada Rogato (1920-86). b, Ther-
eza de Marzo (1903-86). c, Anésia Pinheiro
(1904-99).

2000, Mar. 8   Perf. 11½x12
2734 A1491 22c Horiz. strip of 3,
                 #a-c   .80 .80

Regional Cuisine — A1492

a, Moqueca Capixaba. b, Moqueca Baiana.

2000, Mar. 24
2735 A1492 1.05r Pair, #a-b   2.00 2.00

Gilberto Freyre (1900-87),
Sociologist — A1493

2000, Mar. 24
2736 A1493 36c multi   .45 .40

UIT Telecom
A1494

2000, Apr. 9   Litho.   Perf. 11½
2737 A1494 51c multi   .60 .55
      Discovery of Brazil, 500th anniv.

Discovery of Brazil, 500th
Anniv. — A1495

No. 2738: a, Two sailors, three natives, parrot. b, Sailor, ships, four natives. c, Sailors,
natives, sails. d, Sailor and natives inspecting
tree.

2000, Apr. 11   Litho.   Perf. 11½x12
2738 A1495 31c Block of 4, #a-d 2.25 2.25
      See Portugal Nos. 2354-2357.

Discovery of Brazil, 500th
Anniv. — A1496

2000, Apr. 11   Litho.   Perf. 11½
2739 A1496 31c multi + label   8.00 8.00
      Printed in sheets of 9 stamps + 9 labels that
could be personalized. Sheets sold for 5r.

Discovery of Brazil, 500th
Anniv. — A1497

No. 2740: a, Brazilian flag as sails of ship. b,
Man with pineapple, telephone dial, horn. c,
Parrot and ships. d, Ship, map of Brazil, children. e, Race car driver Ayrton Senna. f, Flora
and fauna. g, Map of Brazil, compass roses. h,
Dove. i, Native with decorated face. j, Stylized
"500." k, Native with feathered headdress. l,
Children's drawing. m, Aviator Alberto Santos
Dumont. n, Ship, manuscript. o, World Cup
trophies, soccer player and ball, map. p, Fiber
optic cables, street lights. q, Bull with Brazilian
flag. r, Parrot. s, Native masks. t, Ship, Brazil
highlighted on globe.

2000, Apr. 22   Litho.   Perf. 11½
2740 A1497 45c Sheet of 20,
                 #a-t, + 4 la-
                 bels   22.50 22.50

Brazil Trade
Net Website,
2nd Anniv.
A1498

2000, May 11   Litho.   Perf. 11½
2741 A1498 27c multi   .45 .30

National Coastal Management
Program — A1499

2000, May 16   Litho.   Perf. 11½
2742 A1499 40c multi   .45 .40

Souvenir Sheet

Expo 2000, Hanover — A1500

No. 2743: a, Map of Western Brazil. b, Map
of Eastern Brazil. c, Gold and gemstones.

2000, May 19   Litho.   Perf. 10¾x11
2743 A1500 1.30r #a-c   5.00 5.00

Oswaldo Cruz Foundation,
Cent. — A1501

2000, May 25   Perf. 11½x12
2744 A1501 40c multicolored   .45 .40

Africa Day
A1502

2000, May 25   Perf. 11½
2745 A1502 1.10r multi   .75 .75

Sailing Feats
of Amyr
Klink
A1503

No. 2746: a, First crossing of South Atlantic
by rowboat, 1984. b, Solo circumnavigation of
Antarctica, 1999.

2000, May 27
2746 A1503 1r Vert. pair, #a-b 2.75 2.75

Juiz de Fora, 150th Anniv. — A1504

2000, May 31 *Perf. 11½x12*
2747 A1504 60c multi .60 .60

Sports — A1505

No. 2748, Hanggliding. No. 2749, Surfing. No. 2750, Mountain climbing. No. 2751, Skateboarding.

Serpentine Die Cut 5¾
2000 Self-Adhesive Photo.
2748 A1505 27c multi .35 .25
2749 A1505 27c multi .30 .25
2750 A1505 40c multi .50 .25
2751 A1505 40c multi .45 .25
Nos. 2748-2751 (4) 1.60 1.00

Issued: Nos. 2748, 2750, 6/1; No. 2749, 8/1; No. 2751, 7/1.

Environmental Protection — A1506

No. 2752: a, Trees. b, Trees, Felis tigrina in background. c, Heads of two Felis tigrina, two white flowers. d, Felis tigrina, one white flower.

2000, June 5 *Perf. 11½*
2752 A1506 40c Block of 4, #a-d 3.00 3.00

Ships — A1507

No. 2753: a, Cisne Branco. b, Brasil.

2000, June 11 Litho. Perf. 11x11½
2753 A1507 27c Pair, #a-b .85 .60

Souvenir Sheets

Military Presence in Amazonia — A1508

2000, June 11 Litho. Perf. 11½x11
2754 A1508 1.50r multi 1.25 1.25

Barcode is separated from the sheet margin by a row of microperfs.

America Issue — A1509

No. 2755: a, Campaign against AIDS. b, Natl. anti-drug week.

2000, June 19 *Perf. 12x11½*
2755 A1509 1.10r Sheet of 2, #a-
b 2.25 2.25

Barcode is separated from the sheet margin by a row of microperfs.

Anísio Teixeira (1900-71), Educator — A1510

2000, July 12 Litho. Perf. 11½x12
2756 A1510 45c multi .45 .45

Children's and Teenagers Statute, 10th Anniv. — A1511

2000, July 13 *Perf. 12x11½*
2757 A1511 27c multi .30 .30

Natl. Movement of Street Boys and Girls, 15th Anniv. — A1512

2000, July 13
2758 A1512 40c multi .45 .45

Gustavo Capanema (1900-54), Politician — A1513

2000, Aug. 10 Litho. Perf. 11½x12
2759 A1513 60c multi .60 .60

Milton Campos, Politician — A1514

2000, Aug. 16
2760 A1514 1r multi .75 .75

World Ozone Layer Protection Day — A1515

2000, Sept. 16 *Perf. 12x11½*
2761 A1515 1.45r multi 1.25 1.25

Fruit — A1516

Serpentine Die Cut 5¾
2000, Sept. 21 Litho.
Self-Adhesive
2762 A1516 27c Cupuacu .65 .35
2763 A1516 40c Soursop 1.00 .55

2000 Summer Olympics, Sydney — A1517

No. 2764: a, Pommel horse. b, Weight lifting. c, Discus. d, Men's rings. e, Sprinting. f, Javelin. g, Rhythmic gymnastics. h, Field hockey. i, Volleyball. j, Synchronized swimming. k, Judo. l, Wrestling. m, Cycling. n, Rowing. o, Parallel bars. p, Equestrian. q, Pole vault. r, Fencing. s, Shooting. t, Taekwondo.
No. 2765: a, Archery. b, Beach volleyball. c, Boxing. d, Soccer. e, Canoeing. f, Handball. g, Diving. h, Rhythmic gymnastics. i, Badminton. j, Swimming. k, Hurdles. l, Pentathlon. m, Basketball. n, Tennis. o, Marathon. p, High jump. q, Long jump. r, Triple jump. s, Triathlon. t, Yachting.

2000, Sept. 23 Litho. Perf. 11½x12
2764 Sheet of 20 + 4 labels 26.00 26.00
a.-t. A1517 40c Any single 1.25 1.25
2765 Sheet of 20 + 4 labels 26.00 26.00
a.-t. A1517 40c Any single 1.25 1.25

Organ Donation and Transplantation — A1519

No. 2766: a, Doctor holding heart. b, Heart, hands, body with organs outlined.

2000, Sept. 27
2766 A1519 1.50r Horiz. pair, #a-b 2.50 2.50

Masks and Puppets A1520

Designs: No. 2767, 27c, Chinese puppet. No. 2768, 27c, Brazilian mask.

2000, Oct. 9
2767-2768 A1520 Set of 2 .60 .60

Brazil-People's Republic of China diplomatic relations, 25th anniv. See People's Republic of China Nos. 3053-3054.

Race Car Drivers A1521

Designs: 1.30r, Francisco "Chico" Landi (1907-89). 1.45r, Ayrton Senna (1960-94).

2000, Oct. 12 *Perf. 11x11½*
2769-2770 A1521 Set of 2 2.50 2.50

Telecourse 2000 Project A1522

2000, Oct. 13 Litho. Perf. 11½x12
2771 A1522 27c multi .30 .30

Airplanes A1523

No. 2772: a, EMB 145 AEW. b, Super Tucano. c, AMX-T. d, ERJ 135. e, ERJ 170. f, ERJ 145. g, ERJ 190. h, EMB 145 RS/MP. i, ERJ 140. j, EMB 120.

2000, Oct. 23 Litho. Die Cut
Self-Adhesive
2772 Pane of 10 6.00 6.00
a.-j. A1523 27c Any single .30 .30

Christmas — A1524

No. 2773: a, Hand of Jesus, star of Bethlehem. b, Mary, baby Jesus. c, Hand of Jesus, fish, boats on Sea of Galilee. d, Jesus, Sea of Galilee. e, Hand of Jesus, mountain, trees, Earth. f, Jesus, Earth.

2000, Nov. 23 *Perf. 11½*
2773 A1524 Block of 6 2.25 2.25
a.-f. 27c Any single .35 .35

Light and Sound Project — A1525

2000, Dec. 2   **Perf. 12x11½**
2774 A1525 1.30r multi   1.00 1.00

Settlement of Brazil-French Guiana Border Dispute, Cent. — A1526

2000, Dec. 12   **Perf. 11½x12**
2775 A1526 40c multi   .40 .40

Advent of New Millennium — A1527

Designs: Nos. 2776, 2779a, 40c, Chalice and eucharist. Nos. 2777, 2779b, 1.30r, Star of David, menorah, Torah, tablets. Nos. 2778, 2779c, 1.30r, Minaret, dome of mosque, Holy Ka'aba.

2001, Jan. 1   **Perf. 11x11½**
2776-2778 A1527 Set of 3   2.50 2.50
Souvenir Sheet
2779 A1527 Sheet of 3, #a-c   3.25 3.25

Nos. 2779a-2779c lack white border. On No. 2779, barcode is separated from sheet margin by a row of rouletting.

Pan-American Scout Jamboree, Foz do Iguaçu — A1528

No. 2780: a, Flags, map, emblems. b, Scouts in canoe, waterfall.

2001, Jan. 7   **Perf. 12x11½**
2780 A1528 1.10r Horiz. pair, #a-b   1.90 1.90

New Year 2001 (Year of the Snake) — A1529

Litho. & Embossed
2001, Jan. 24   **Perf. 11½**
2781 A1529 1.45r multi   1.25 1.25

Hong Kong 2001 Stamp Exhibition.

Venomous Animals A1530

No. 2782: a, Dirphya sp. b, Megalopyge sp. c, Phoneutria sp. d, Tityus bahiensis. e, Crotalus durissus. f, Micrurus corallinus. g, Lachesis muta. h, Bothrops jararaca.

2001, Feb. 23   **Litho.**   **Perf. 11½x12**
2782   Sheet of 8   4.50 4.50
a.-h A1530 40c Any single   .55 .40

Butantan Institute, cent.

Brazilian Publishing Industry — A1531

2001, Mar. 5   **Perf. 11x11½**
2783 A1531 27c multi   .30 .30

Special Exports Program — A1532

2001, Mar. 5   **Perf. 11½x12**
2784 A1532 1.30r multi   1.00 1.00

National Library, 190th Anniv. — A1533

Litho. & Engr.
2001, Mar. 26   **Perf. 11½x12**
2785 A1533 27c multi   .30 .25

Council for Scientific and Technical Development — A1534

2001, Apr. 17
2786 A1534 40c blue   .40 .40

Soccer Teams — A1535

Designs: No. 2787, Regatas Vasco da Gama. No. 2788, Palmeiras. No. 2789, Gremio. No. 2790, Sao Paolo. No. 2791, Santos. No. 2792, Regatas do Flamengo.

2001   **Litho.**   **Perf. 12x11½**
2787 A1535 70c multi   1.10 1.10
2788 A1535 70c multi   1.10 1.10
2789 A1535 70c multi   1.10 1.10
2790 A1535 70c multi   1.10 1.10

2791 A1535 1r multi   1.10 1.10
2792 A1535 1r multi   1.10 1.10
  Nos. 2787-2792 (6)   6.60 6.60
Issued: No. 2787, 8/21; No. 2788, 8/26; No. 2789, 9/10; No. 2790, 12/16; No. 2791, 4/20. No. 2792, 11/28.

Intl. Culture of Peace — A1536

2001, May 3   **Litho.**   **Perf. 12x11½**
2794 A1536 1.10r multi   .90 .90

Murilo Mendes (1901-75), Poet — A1537

2001, May 13   **Perf. 11x11½**
2795 A1537 40c multi   .40 .35

Minas Commercial Association, Cent. A1538

2001, May 16   **Perf. 11½**
2796 A1538 40c multi   .40 .35

World Tobacco-free Day — A1539

2001, May 31   **Perf. 12x11½**
2797 A1539 40c multi   .40 .35

José Lins do Rego (1901-87), Writer — A1540

2001, May 31   **Perf. 11x11½**
2798 A1540 60c multi   .45 .45

Worldwide Fund for Nature (WWF) — A1541

Parrots: a, Anodorhynchus hyacinthinus. b, Aratinga solstitialis auricapilla. c, Pyrrhura cruentata. d, Amazona xanthops.

2001, June 3   **Perf. 11½**
2799 A1541 1.30r Sheet of 4, #a-d   6.50 6.50

Barbosa Lima Sobrinho (1897-2000), Journalist A1542

2001, June 6
2800 A1542 40c multi   .35 .35

Beaches A1543

No. 2801: a, Jericoacoara. b, Ponta Negra. c, Rosa.

2001, June 13   **Perf. 11x11½**
2801   Horiz. strip of 3   1.40 1.40
a.-c. A1543 40c Any single   .45 .45

Issued in sheets of 25 stamps containing 10 each of Nos. 2801a-2801b and 5 of No. 2801c.

Souvenir Sheet

Automobiles — A1544

No. 2802: a, 1959 Romi Isetta. b, 1965 DKW Vemag. c, 1962 Renault Gordini. d, 1959 Volkswagen 1200. e, 1964 Simca Chambord. f, 1961 Aero-Willys.

2001, June 16   **Perf. 11½x12**
2802 A1544 1.10r Sheet of 6, #a-f   7.25 7.25

Bernardo Sayao (1901-59), Politician A1545

2001, June 18 *Perf. 11½*
2803 A1545 60c multi .55 .50

Eleazar de Carvalho (1912-96), Composer A1546

2001, July 1
2804 A1546 45c multi .35 .35

Souvenir Sheet

Third French Tennis Open Victory of Gustavo Kuerten — A1547

2001, July 10
2805 A1547 1.30r multi 1.75 1.75

Academic Qualifications Coordinating Institution, 50th Anniv. — A1548

2001, July 11 *Perf. 11x11½*
2806 A1548 40c multi .35 .35

Pedro Aleixo, Politician, Cent. of Birth A1549

2001, Aug. 1 *Perf. 11½*
2807 A1549 55c multi .55 .50

Solidarity Community Programs — A1550

No. 2808: a, Map on man. b, Man on map.

2001, Aug. 25
2808 A1550 55c Horiz. pair, #a-b .60 .60

World Conference Against Racism, Durban, South Africa — A1551

2001, Aug. 30 *Perf. 12x11½*
2809 A1551 1.30r multi 1.00 1.00
See South Africa Nos. 1261-1262.

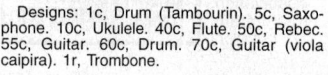

Musical Instruments A1552

Designs: 1c, Drum (Tambourin). 5c, Saxophone. 10c, Ukulele. 40c, Flute. 50c, Rebec. 55c, Guitar. 60c, Drum. 70c, Guitar (viola caipira). 1r, Trombone.

2001 Litho. *Serpentine Die Cut 5¾*
Self-Adhesive
2810 A1552 1c multi .30 .25
2811 A1552 5c multi .45 .25
2812 A1552 10c multi .45 .25
2813 A1552 40c multi .60 .25
2814 A1552 50c multi .60 .25
2815 A1552 55c multi .60 .25
2816 A1552 60c multi .80 .30
2817 A1552 70c multi .80 .30
2818 A1552 1r multi 1.25 .30
Nos. 2810-2818 (9) 5.85 2.40
Booklet Stamp
Self-Adhesive
Die Cut
2818A A1552 40c multi .65 .65
b. Booklet pane of 5 6.50
Issued: Nos. 2810-2818, 9/20. No. 2818A, 10/15.

Clóvis Beviláqua (1859-1944), Writer of Civil Law Code A1553

2001, Oct. 4 Litho. *Perf. 11½*
2819 A1553 55c multi .50 .50

Year of Dialogue Among Civilizations A1554

2001, Oct. 9 *Perf. 12x11½*
2820 A1554 1.30r multi 1.00 1.00

Souvenir Sheet

Commercial Aircraft — A1555

No. 2821: a, Junkers F-13. b, Douglas C-47. c, Dornier Wal. d, Lockheed Constellation. e, Convair 340. f, Caravelle.

2001, Oct. 23 Litho. *Perf. 11½x12*
2821 A1555 55c Sheet of 6, #a-f 4.75 4.75
Barcode is separated from sheet margin by a row of rouletting.

Cecília Meireles (1901-64), Poet — A1556

2001, Nov. 7 Litho. *Perf. 11x11½*
2822 A1556 55c multi .75 .50

America Issue - Bom Jesus de Matosinhos Sanctuary, UNESCO World Heritage Site — A1557

2001, Nov. 9 *Perf. 11½x12*
2823 A1557 1.30r multi 1.00 1.00

Madalena Caramuru, First Literate Woman in Brazil A1558

2001, Nov. 14
2824 A1558 55c multi .50 .50

National Day of Black Consciousness — A1559

2001, Nov. 20
2825 A1559 40c multi .35 .35

Pantanal Flora A1560

No. 2826: a, Caiman crocodilus yacare, Plataleia ajaja. b, Anhinga anhinga. c, Ardea cocoi. d, Jabiru mycteria. e, Pseudoplatystoma fasciatum. f, Leporinus macrocephalus. g, Hydrochoerus hydrochoeris. h, Nasua nasua, Casmerodius albus. i, Eichornia crassipes. j, Porphyrula martinica.

2001, Nov. 20 *Die Cut Perf. 6¼*
Self-Adhesive
2826 Booklet of 10 7.50
a.-j. A1560 55c Any single .50 .50
See No. 2832.

Christmas A1561

2001, Nov. 23 *Perf. 11½x12*
2827 A1561 40c multi .35 .35

Souvenir Sheet

Minerals — A1562

No. 2828: a, Topaz jewelry. b, Garnet ring.

2001, Nov. 30 *Perf. 12x11½*
2828 A1562 1.30r Sheet of 2, #a-b 2.75 2.75

Intl. Day of Disabled Persons — A1563

2001, Dec. 3 *Perf. 11½*
2829 A1563 1.45r multi 1.25 1.25

Coffee A1564

2001, Dec. 7 *Perf. 11½x12*
2830 A1564 1.30r multi 1.00 1.00
No. 2830 is impregnated with a coffee scent.

Merchant Ships — A1565

No. 2831: a, Copacabana. b, Flamengo.

2001, Dec. 13 *Perf. 11x11½*
2831 A1565 55c Horiz. pair, #a-b 1.50 1.50

Pantanal Flora Type of 2001 With "MERCOSUR" Inscription Added

1r, Eichornia crassipes.

2001, Dec. 21   *Perf. 11½x12*
2832 A1560 1r multi   .75 .75

Kahal Zur Israel, First Synagogue in the Americas A1566

2001, Oct. 21   **Litho.**   *Perf. 11½x12*
2833 A1566 1.30r multi   1.00 1.00

New Year 2002 (Year of the Horse) — A1567

Litho. With Foil Application
2002, Jan. 25   *Perf. 11½*
2834 A1567 1.45r multi   1.25 1.25

2002 Winter Olympics, Salt Lake City — A1568

No. 2835: a, Alpine skiing. b, Cross-country skiing. c, Luge. d, Bobsled.

2002, Feb. 4   **Litho.**   *Perf. 11½x12*
2835 A1568 1.10r Block of 4, #a-d   3.50 3.50

Lucio Costa (1902-98), Architect A1569

2002, Feb. 27
2836 A1569 55c multi   .50 .50

Intl. Women's Day — A1570

2002, Mar. 8   *Perf. 11½*
2837 A1570 40c multi   .35 .35

Sao José do Rio Preto, 150th Anniv. A1571

2002, Mar. 19   *Perf. 11½x12*
2838 A1571 40c multi   .35 .35

Pres. Juscelino Kubitschek (1902-76) — A1572

2002, Apr. 21   **Litho.**
2839 A1572 55c multi   .50 .45

2002 World Cup Soccer Championships, Japan and Korea — A1573

No. 2840: a, Flags, soccer ball, and field (28mm diameter). b, Soccer players, years of Brazilian championships.

2002, Apr. 22   **Photo.**   *Perf. 13¾*
2840 A1573 55c Horiz. pair, #a-b   1.10 1.10

See Argentina No. 2184, France No. 2891, Germany No. 2163, Italy No. 2526, and Uruguay No. 1946.

Progress in Brazilian Education — A1574

No. 2841: a, Children in classroom, globe, letters "a-d." b, Computer, globe, letters "e-h."

2002, Apr. 28   **Litho.**   *Perf. 11½x12*
2841 A1574 40c Horiz. pair, #a-b   .75 .70

St. Josemaría Escrivá de Balaguer (1902-75) — A1575

2002, May 1
2842 A1575 55c multi   .50 .45

Souvenir Sheet

Brazilian Air Force's Esquadrilha da Fumaça Aerobatics Team — A1576

No. 2843: a, T-6 North American. b, T-24 Super Fouga Magister. c, T-25 Universal. d, Two T-27 Tucanos, one flying upside-down. e, T-27 Tucanos, heart-shaped smoke design. f, Blue, green and yellow T-27 Tucano.

2002, May 17
2843 A1576 55c Sheet of 6, #a-f   3.75 3.75

Barcode is separated from sheet margin by a row of rouletting.

Children's Cavalhadinha of Pirenópolis — A1577

No. 2844: a, Procession of virgins and stick-pony riders. b, Stick-pony combat. c, Children wearing masks. d, Musicians and vendor.

2002, May 19   *Perf. 11x11½*
2844 A1577 40c Block of 4, #a-d   2.25 2.25

Couroupita Guianensis A1578

Serpentine Die Cut 12¾x13
2002, May 20   **Photo.**
Coil Stamp
Self-Adhesive
2845 A1578 55c multi   1.10 1.00

Souvenir Sheet

Coral Reefs — A1579

No. 2846 — Coral and: a, Orange fish, school of fish. b, Seahorse. c, Orange fish. d, Orange fish, starfish.

2002, June 5   *Perf. 11½*
2846 A1579 40c Sheet of 4, #a-d   2.75 2.75

Philakorea 2002 World Stamp Exhibition, Seoul. Barcode is separated from sheet margin by a row of rouletting.

Charity Hospital of Curitiba, 150th Anniv. A1580

2002, June 9   **Litho.**   *Perf. 11x11½*
2847 A1580 70c multi   .60 .50

Brazil's Fifth World Cup Soccer Championship A1581

2002, July 2   **Litho.**   *Perf. 12x11½*
2848 A1581 55c multi   .60 .50

Souvenir Sheet

Preservation of Caatinga Nordestina — A1582

2002, July 14   **Litho.**   *Perf. 10¾x11*
2849 A1582 1.10r multi   1.75 1.75

Fluminense
Soccer Team,
Cent. — A1583

2002, July 17   Litho.   Perf. 12x11½
2850 A1583 55c multi   .60   .40

Souvenir Sheet

Alberto Santos-Dumont's House,
Encantada — A1584

No. 2851: a, House. b, Santos-Dumont and
stairway.
2002, July 19   Litho.   Perf. 11¾
2851 A1584 1r Sheet of 2, #a-b   2.75 2.75

System for the Vigilance of the
Amazon Project — A1585

2002, July 27   Perf. 11½x12
2852 A1585 1.10r multi   1.00   .75

Jorge Amado (1912-2001),
Writer — A1586

2002, Aug. 5   Perf. 11x11½
2853 A1586 40c multi   .40   .30

Plácido de
Castro and
Rio Branco
Palace
A1587

2002, Aug. 6   Litho.   Perf. 11½x12
2854 A1587 50c multi   .40   .35

Acre Revolution, cent.

Souvenir Sheet

Protected Area for Whales — A1588

2002, Sept. 14   Litho.   Perf. 12x11½
2855 A1588 1.30r multi   1.75 1.75

Confluence
of Rio
Solimoes and
Rio Negro
A1589

2002, Sept. 27   Perf. 11½
2856 A1589 45c multi   .40   .25

Adhemar Ferreira da Silva (1927-
2001), 1952 and 1956 Olympic Triple
Jump Gold Medalist — A1590

2002, Sept. 28   Perf. 11x11½
2857 A1590 40c multi   .40   .25

Motorcycles — A1591

No. 2858: a, YZF-R1. b, CG125 Titan. c,
GSX-R1000. d, Daytona 955i Centennial Edition. e, BMW R32 and BMW R 1200 C. f, V-
ROD.
2002, Sept. 29   Litho.   Perf. 11½x12
2858 A1591 60c Sheet of 6, #a-f   8.00 8.00

Locomotives — A1592

No. 2859, Zezé Leoni. 2860, Baroneza.

2002, Sept. 30
2859   55c multicolored   .65   .65
2859A   55c multicolored   .65   .65
  a.   A1592 Pair, #2859-2859A   3.75 3.75

Tourism in
Bonito
A1593

2002, Oct. 2   Litho.   Perf. 11½x12
2860 A1593 1r multi   .75   .55

Carlos Drummond de Andrade (1902-
87), Writer — A1594

2002, Oct. 25   Perf. 11x11½
2861 A1594 55c multi   .50   .30

America Issue - Youth, Education and
Literacy — A1595

2002, Nov. 14   Litho.   Perf. 11½x12
2862 A1595 1.30r multi   1.00   .95

National Archives — A1596

2002, Nov. 20
2863 A1596 40c multi   .40   .30

Sergio
Motta
Cultural
Center
A1597

2002, Nov. 24
2864 A1597 45c multi   .45   .30

Christmas
A1598

2002, Nov. 29
2865 A1598 45c multi   .45   .30

Social
Security in
Brazil, 80th
Anniv.
A1599

2002, Dec. 3
2866 A1599 45c multi   .45   .30

Ethnographic Paintings of Albert
Eckhout — A1600

No. 2867: a, Group of natives. b, Woman
with basket of flowers. c, Native man with
headdress and spears. d, Man with bow and
arrows. e, Man with spears. f, Woman with
child and basket. g, Woman with headdress
and child. h, Man with gun.

2002, Dec. 3   Perf. 11½
2867 A1600 45c Block of 8, #a-h   8.00 8.00

Brazil —
Iran
Diplomatic
Relations,
Cent.
A1601

Flags of Brazil and Iran, and pottery and rug
from: No. 2868, 60c, Brazil. No. 2869, 60c,
Iran.

2002, Dec. 15   Perf. 11½x12
2868-2869 A1601   Set of 2   1.25   .80
        See Iran No. 2844.

Musical
Instruments — A1602

Designs: 1c, Drum (Atabaque). 5c, Snare
drum (Caixa clara). 10c, Trumpet. 20c, Clarinet. 45c, Mandolin (Bandolim). 50c, Tambourine (Pandeiro). 60c, Accordion. 70c, Maraca
(Cholcalho). 80c, Xylophone. 1r, Berimbau.

Serpentine Die Cut 5¾
2002-05   **Photo.**
            Self-Adhesive
2869A A1602 1c multi   .25   .25
2870   A1602 5c multi   .25   .25
2871   A1602 10c multi   .25   .25
2872   A1602 20c multi   .25   .25
2873   A1602 45c multi   .50   .25

2874	A1602	50c multi	.50	.25
2875	A1602	60c multi	.55	.25
2876	A1602	70c multi	.60	.25
2877	A1602	80c multi	.80	.25
2877A	A1602	1r multi	1.10	.55

Die Cut Perf. 12x12¼

2877B	A1602	1c like #2869A	1.00	.30
2877C	A1602	5c like #2870	.30	.30
2877D	A1602	10c like #2871	.30	.30
2877E	A1602	20c like #2872	.30	.30
2877K	A1602	1r like #2877A	.90	.60

Nos. 2869A-2877K (14) 7.55 4.30

Issued: Nos. 2869A-2877A, 2002; Nos. 2877B-2877D, 2877K, 5/2005; 2877E, 2005.

Rotary Intl. in Brazil, 80th Anniv. — A1603

2003, Feb. 26   Litho.   *Perf. 12x11½*
| 2878 | A1603 | 60c multi | .60 | .35 |

Waterfalls A1604

Waterfalls: No. 2879, Itiquira. No. 2880, Rio Preto.

2003, Mar. 22
2879	A1604	45c multi	.40	.40
2880	A1604	45c multi	.40	.40
a.		Pair, #2879-2880	1.25	1.25

Souvenir Sheet

Coffee Plantations — A1605

No. 2881: a, Pau d'Alho. b, Ponte Alta.

2003, Apr. 15   *Perf. 11½*
| 2881 | A1605 | 1r Sheet of 2, #a-b | 2.75 | 2.75 |

Independence of East Timor — A1606

2003, May 20   *Perf. 11½x12*
| 2882 | A1606 | 1.45r multi | 1.40 | 1.10 |

America Issue — Medicinal Plants — A1607

No. 2883: a, Macrosiphonia velame. b, Lychnophora ericoides. c, Lafoensia pacari. d, Tabebuia impetiginosa. e, Xylopia aromatica. f, Himatanthus obovatus.

2003, June 2   *Perf. 11½*
| 2883 | A1607 | 60c Sheet of 6, #a-f | 4.75 | 4.75 |

Art Made From Recycled Material — A1608

No. 2884: a, Glass bottles. b, Paper. c, Plastic. d, Metal.

2003, June 5
| 2884 | A1608 | 60c Block of 4, #a-d | 4.00 | 4.00 |

Santo Inácio College, Cent. A1609

2003, July 1   *Perf. 11½x12*
| 2885 | A1609 | 60c multi | .60 | .45 |

Pluft, the Ghost, and Maribel A1610

2003, July 12
| 2886 | A1610 | 80c multi | .70 | .55 |

Ceará State, 400th Anniv. A1611

2003, July 15
| 2887 | A1611 | 70c multi | .70 | .50 |

Souvenir Sheet

Stamp Collecting — A1612

No. 2888: a, Collector's album, Brazil #2 in tongs. b, Portugal #2 in tongs.

2003, Aug. 1   *Perf. 11½*
| 2888 | A1612 | 1.30r Sheet of 2, #a- | | |
| | | b | 3.25 | 3.25 |

First Portuguese stamp, 150th anniv., Lubrapex 2003 Philatelic Exhibition.

Souvenir Sheet

Dolphins — A1613

Litho. with Hologram Applied
2003, Aug. 10   *Perf. 11½*
| 2889 | A1613 | 2.90r multi | 3.75 | 3.75 |

Bangkok 2003 Intl. Philatelic Exhibition.

Barnabite Order in Brazil, Cent. A1614

2003, Aug. 22   Litho.   *Perf. 11½x12*
| 2890 | A1614 | 45c multi | .50 | .35 |

A1615

60c, Luis Alves de Lima y Silva, Duque de Caxias (1803-80), Soldier and Politician.

2003, Aug. 25
| 2891 | A1615 | 60c multi | .60 | .45 |

Self-Portrait, by Candido Portinari (1903-62) A1616

2003, Sept. 4   Litho.   *Perf. 12x11½*
| 2892 | A1616 | 80c multi | .75 | .55 |

Courtesy on Mass Transit — A1617

Designs: No. 2893, "No Drinking." No. 2894, "Be Peaceful" (dove in triangle).

Serpentine Die Cut 5¾
2003, Sept. 5   Photo.
Self-Adhesive
2893	A1617	(50c) multi	.55	.25
2894	A1617	(74c) multi	.85	.25

Grémio Soccer Team, Cent. — A1618

2003, Sept. 18   Litho.   *Perf. 12x11½*
| 2895 | A1618 | 60c multi | .55 | .45 |
| a. | | Sheet of 12 + 12 labels | 65.00 | 65.00 |

No. 2895a sold for 21r. Labels could be personalized.

Antonina - Morretes Railway A1619

2003, Sept. 30   Litho.   *Perf. 11½*
| 2896 | A1619 | 74c multi | .75 | .75 |

Children's Games — A1620

No. 2897: a, Kite flying (Pipa). b, Cricket (Bete). c, Rope jumping (Pula corda). d, Hula hoop (Bambole).

2003, Oct. 4
| 2897 | A1620 | 50c Block of 4, #a-d | 4.00 | 4.00 |

Program Against Hunger A1621

2003, Oct. 9   *Perf. 11½x12*
2898 A1621 50c multi   .50 .50

Souvenir Sheet

Export Products — A1622

2003, Oct. 29   *Perf. 11½*
2899 A1622 1.30r multi   1.75 1.75

Christmas — A1623

Frame color: No. 2900, 50c, Green. No. 2901, 50c, Gold.

2003, Oct. 31   *Die Cut Perf. 12*
Self-Adhesive
2900-2901 A1623   Set of 2   1.50 1.50

Marcantonio Vilaça Cultural Space — A1624

2003, Nov. 5   *Litho.*   *Perf. 11½x12*
2902 A1624 74c multi   .75 .75

Ary Barroso (1903-64), Songwriter, Television Personality — A1625

2003, Nov. 7
2903 A1625 1.50r multi   1.25 1.25

Congress, 180th Anniv. A1626

2003, Nov. 13
2904 A1626 74c multi   .75 .75

Brazil — Lebanon Diplomatic and Cultural Relations A1627

2003, Nov. 21   *Litho.*   *Perf. 12x11½*
2905 A1627 1.75r multi   1.25 1.25

Fight Against AIDS A1628

2003, Dec. 1   *Litho.*   *Perf. 11*
2906 A1628 74c multi   .75 .75
Values are for stamps with surrounding selvage.

Paragliding A1629

2003, Dec. 6   *Perf. 11½x12*
2907 A1629 75c multi   .65 .65

Capistrano de Abreu (1853-1927), Ethnographer — A1630

2003, Dec. 9
2908 A1630 50c multi   .40 .40

Fernando Henrique Cardoso, President from 1995-2002 A1631

2003, Dec. 20   *Perf. 11½*
2909 A1631 74c multi   .65 .65

Paintings by Candido Portinari — A1632

Designs: 74c, Boy from Brodowski. 75c, Cowboy.

2003   *Litho.*   *Die Cut Perf. 12x12¼*
Self-Adhesive
2910 A1632 74c black   .75 .75
2911 A1632 75c black   .75 .75

Festivals — A1633

Cats — A1634

Romance — A1635

Wedding Rings — A1636

Mata Atlantica — A1637

2003-04   *Litho.*   *Perf. 12x11½*
2912 A1633   45c multi + label   6.00 6.00
2913 A1634   (50c) multi + label   1.75 1.75
2914 A1635   (50c) multi + label   2.50 2.50
2915 A1636   (50c) multi + label   1.75 1.75
2916 A1637   60c multi + label   1.75 1.75
   Nos. 2912-2916 (5)   18.00 18.00

Issued: Nos. 2912, 2916, 2003; Nos. 2913-2915, 2004. Nos. 2912-2916 each were printed in sheets of 12 stamps + 12 labels that could be personalized. Each sheet sold for 21r.

Souvenir Sheet

Sao Miguel Arcanjo Chapel, Sao Paolo — A1638

2004, Jan. 17   *Litho.*   *Perf. 12x11½*
2917 A1638 1.50r multi   1.50 1.50

Sao Paolo, 450th Anniv. — A1639

No. 2918: a, Faces. b, Buildings, road. c, Buildings, trees. d, "450."

2004, Jan. 23   *Perf. 11½x12*
2918   Block of 4   2.50 2.50
a.-d.   A1639 74c Any single   .60 .50

Vicente Scherer (1903-96), Monk, Educator A1640

2004, Feb. 5
2919 A1640 50c multi   .40 .40

Bairro da Lapa — A1641

2004, Feb. 19   *Perf. 12x11½*
2920 A1641 75c multi   .60 .60

Eudocimus Ruber A1642

2004, Feb. 20   *Perf. 11½x12*
2921 A1642 74c multi   .60 .60
2921a   Sheet of 12 + 12 labels   37.50 37.50

No. 2921a sold for 21r. Labels could be personalized.

Potable Water — A1643

2004, Mar. 22   *Perf. 12x11½*
2922 A1643 1.20r multi   1.00 1.00

Orlando Villas Bôas (1914-2002), Advocate of Indian Rights — A1644

2004, Apr. 19
2923 A1644 74c multi   .60 .60

FIFA
(Fédération
Internationale
de Football
Association),
Cent.
A1645

2004, May 21   *Perf. 11½*
2924 A1645 1.60r multi   1.25 1.25

92nd Intl. Labor Organization
Conference — A1646

2004, June 1   *Perf. 11½x12*
2925 A1646 50c multi   .40 .40

Preservation of Mangrove Swamps
and Tidal Zones — A1647

No. 2926: a, Ajaja ajaja. b, Pitangus sulphuratus. c, Chasmagnathus granulata. d, Aramides mangle. e, Goniopsis cruentata.

2004, June 5
2926 A1647 1.60r Sheet of 5, #a-e   7.50 7.50

2004 Summer Olympics,
Athens — A1648

No. 2927: a, Torch bearer, Rio de Janeiro. b, 2004 Athens Olympics emblem. c, Sailing. d, Track and field.

2004, June 12   *Perf. 11½*
2927 A1648 1.60r Block of 4, #a-d   2.25 2.25

Bonfim
Basilica,
250th
Anniv.
A1649

2004, June 18   *Perf. 11½x12*
2928 A1649 74c multi   .60 .60

Folk Festivals — A1650

No. 2929: a, Caprichoso. b, Garantido.

2004, June 28
2929 A1650 74c Horiz. pair, #a-b   .85 .85

Brazilian
Inventions
A1651

Designs: No. 2930, Telephone card. No. 2931, Artificial heart valve. No. 2932, Caller identification system for telephones.

2004, July 15   *Perf. 11½*
2930 A1651 50c multi   .40 .40
2931 A1651 50c multi   .40 .40
2932 A1651 50c multi   .40 .40
   a.   Strip of 3, #2930-2932   3.00 3.00

Nos. 2930-2932 were printed in sheets containing eight of each stamp.

CBERS-2
Satellite
A1652

2004, Aug. 9   Litho.   *Perf. 11½x12*
2933 A1652 1.75r multi   1.40 1.40

Masonic Traditions — A1653

No. 2934 — Masonic emblem and: a, Pillars. b, Mason with hammer and chisel. c, Book, ladder and symbols. d, Tools.

2004, Aug. 20   Litho.   *Perf. 11½*
2934 A1653 50c Block of 4, #a-d 3.50 3.50

Paintings by
Candido
Portinari — A1654

Designs: 55c, Negrinha. 80c, Duas Crianças. 95c, Seated Child with Sheep. 1.15r, Group of Women and Child. 1.50r, Marcel Gontrau.

2004, May 26   *Die Cut Perf. 12x12¼*
Self-Adhesive
2935 A1654   55c multi   .40 .25
2936 A1654   80c multi   .55 .25
2937 A1654   95c multi   .70 .30
2938 A1654   1.15r black   .85 .30

2939 A1654 1.50r multi   1.10 .40
   a.   Die cut perf. 12x12¼ syncopated ('11)   .65 .65
    Nos. 2935-2939 (5)   3.60 1.50

Flag and Sculptures — A1655

Chiroxiphia Caudata — A1656

Tourism — A1657

2004   Litho.   *Perf. 11½x12*
2940 A1655 (80c) multi + label   2.25 2.25
2941 A1656 (80c) multi + label   2.25 2.25
2942 A1657 (80c) multi + label   2.25 2.25
    Nos. 2940-2942 (3)   6.75 6.75

Issued: No. 2940, 8/3; No. 2941, 9/22; No. 2942, 10/15. Labels could be personalized.

Nelson Rodrigues (1912-80),
Playwright — A1658

2004, Aug. 23   Litho.   *Perf. 11½x12*
2943 A1658 50c multi   .60 .60

Brazil in World War II — A1659

No. 2944: a, Airplane. b, Ship. c, Troops in action. d, Soldier reading letter.

2004, Aug. 25   *Perf. 11½*
2944 A1659 50c Block of 4, #a-d 3.50 3.50

Coronation of
Our Lady of
Aparecida,
Cent. — A1660

2004, Sept. 8   *Perf. 12x11½*
2945 A1660 74c multi   .60 .60

Allan
Kardec
(1804-69),
Writer
A1661

2004, Oct. 3   *Perf. 11½x12*
2946 A1661 1.60r multi   1.25 1.25

Christmas
A1662

2004, Oct. 28   *Die Cut*
Self-Adhesive
2947 A1662 (55c) multi   .75 .75
   a.   Booklet pane of 10   12.00

Porto
Alegre
Post Office
A1663

2004, Oct. 29   *Perf. 11½x12*
2948 A1663 50c multi   .40 .40

Cyperus
Articulatus
A1664

2004, Nov. 23   *Perf. 12x11½*
2949 A1664 1.60r multi   1.40 1.40

Pampulha Architectural
Complex — A1665

2004, Dec. 12   *Perf. 11½x12*
2950 A1665 80c multi   .65 .65

Nise da Silveira (1905-99),
Psychiatrist — A1666

2005, Feb. 15   Litho.
2951 A1666 55c multi   .45 .45

Rotary International, Cent. — A1667

2005, Mar. 23 **Perf. 11½**
2952 A1667 1.45r multi 1.10 1.10

Souvenir Sheet

Cupuaçu

Theobroma Grandiflorum — A1668

No. 2953: a, Fruit on tree. b, Fruit cut open.

2005, Mar. 15
2953 A1668 1.90r Sheet of 2, #a-
  b 3.25 3.25
Pacific Explorer 2005 World Stamp Expo, Sydney.

Lebanese Immigration to
Brazil — A1669

2005, Mar. 31 **Perf. 11½x12**
2954 A1669 1.75r multi 1.50 1.50

Oscar
Niemeyer
Museum
A1670

2005, Apr. 25
2955 A1670 80c multi .65 .65

Pope John Paul II
(1920-2005)
A1671

2005, May 18 **Perf. 11½x11**
2956 A1671 80c multi .70 .70

Souvenir Sheet

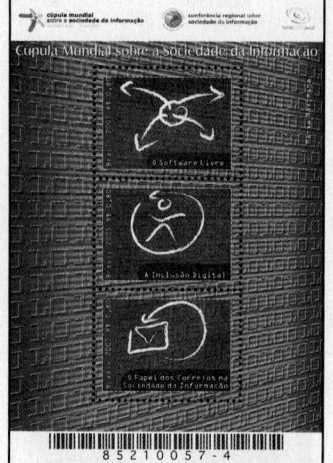

Cúpula Mundial sobre a Sociedade da Informação

World Summit on the Information
Society, Tunis — A1672

No. 2957: a, Circle and arrows. b, Stick figure of person in circle. c, Envelope and arrow.

2005, June 8 **Litho.**
2957 A1672 80c Sheet of 3, #a-c 2.50 2.50

Brazil Year
in France
A1673

No. 2958, 80c: a, Pankararu Indians. b,
Musicians.
No. 2959, 80c: a, Contemporary Dance. b,
Vivaldo Lima Stadium.
No. 2960, 80c: a, "String" literature. b, Pato
na Tucupi and Açai.

2005, June 15 **Perf. 11½x12**
Pairs, #a-b
2958-2960 A1673 Set of 3 4.25 4.25

Erico Veríssimo
(1905-75),
Writer — A1674

2005, July 9 **Perf. 11½x11**
2961 A1674 1.25r multi 1.25 1.25

Mario
Quintana
(1906-94),
Poet
A1675

2005, July 30 **Engr.** **Perf. 11½**
2962 A1675 80c green .80 .80

America Issue —
Fight Against
Poverty — A1676

2005, Aug. 10 **Litho.** **Perf. 12x11½**
2963 A1676 80c multi .80 .80

19th Congress of
the Postal Union of
the Americas, Spain
and
Portugal — A1677

2005, Aug. 10 **Die Cut Perf. 12x12¼**
Self-Adhesive
2964 A1677 (85c) multi .75 .75

Royal Road — A1678

No. 2965: a, Map, miner. b, Hikers and
cyclist. c, People on horseback, hills and food.

Litho., Litho. & Embossed (#2965a)
2005, Aug. 13 **Perf. 11½**
2965 A1678 80c Horiz. strip of 3,
  #a-c 2.25 2.25

Samba
Dancer
A1679

2005, Aug. 15 **Litho.** **Perf. 11½x12**
2966 A1679 55c multi .60 .60

Dances — A1680

Parrot and: No. 2967, 80c, Son dancers and
Cuban flag. No. 2968, 80c, Samba dancers
and Brazilian flag.

2005, Aug. 16 **Litho.** **Perf. 12x11½**
2967 A1680 80c multi .50 .50
2968 A1680 80c multi .50 .50
  a. Pair, #2967-2968 1.45 1.45

See Cuba No. 4497-4498.

Sao
Francisco
River
Basin
A1681

2005, Sept. 2 **Perf. 11½x12**
2969 A1681 80c multi .70 .70

Army Staff
and
Command
School,
Cent.
A1682

2005, Sept. 22
2970 A1682 80c multi .70 .70

Teacher's
Day — A1683

Die Cut Perf. 12x12¼
2005, Oct. 15 **Litho.**
Self-Adhesive
2971 A1683 (55c) multi .50 .50

Christmas
A1684

2005, Oct. 25 **Litho.** **Die Cut**
2972 A1684 (55c) multi .50 .50

Souvenir Sheet

Adoration of the Shepherds, by Oscar
Pereira da Silva — A1685

2005, Nov. 24 **Litho.** **Perf. 12x11½**
2973 A1685 2.90r multi 2.75 2.75
  Christmas.

Women's
Soccer
A1686

2005, Oct. 30 **Litho.** **Perf. 11½x12**
2974 A1686 85c multi .90 .90

Souvenir Sheet

Salminus Maxillosus — A1687

Litho. & Embossed
2005, Nov. 3   *Perf. 11¾*
2975 A1687 3.10r multi   3.25 3.25

Brazilian Furniture and Furnishings Design — A1688

No. 2976: a, Ceiling light fixtures, by Fernando Prado. b, Ceiling fan, by Indio da Costa Design. c, Chair, by Humberto and Fernando Campana. d, Desk, by Ivan Rezende.

2005, Dec. 12   **Litho.**   *Perf. 11¾*
2976 A1688 85c Block of 4, #a-d 3.25 3.25

Hans Christian Andersen (1805-75), Author A1689

2005, Dec. 14   *Perf. 11½x12*
2977 A1689 55c multi   .70 .70

Occupations A1690

Die Cut Perf. 12x12¼
2005, Dec. 19   **Photo.**
Self-Adhesive
2978 A1690 5c Seamstress .25 .25
  a. Die cut perf. 12x12¼ syncopated ('11) .25 .25
2979 A1690 20c Shoemaker .25 .25
  a. Die cut perf. 12x12¼ syncopated ('11) .25 .25
2980 A1690 85c Shoe polisher .70 .70
  Nos. 2978-2980 (3) 1.20 1.20

See Nos. 2997-2998, 3020A-3020B.

Graffiti Artists — A1691

Designs: No. 2981, Man with paint sprayer. No. 2982, Man wearing hat, wavy lines. No. 2983, Man with cap and spray paint can, horiz.

Perf. 12x11½, 11½x12
2006, Mar. 27   **Litho.**
2981 A1691 55c multi .35 .35
2982 A1691 55c multi .35 .35
2983 A1691 55c multi .35 .35
  a. Strip of 3, #2981-2983 1.75 1.75

Lubrapex 2006, Rio. See No. 2993.

Brazilian Space Agency — A1692

No. 2984: a, Alberto Santos-Dumont's 14bis airplane. b, Soyuz spacecraft. c, Intl. Space Station.

2006, Apr. 3   *Perf. 11½*
2984 A1692 85c Horiz. strip of 3, #a-c 2.50 2.50
  Brazilians in flight, cent.

2006 World Cup Soccer Championships, Germany — A1693

2006, Apr. 19
2985 A1693 85c multi .90 .90

Bidu Sayao (1902-99), Opera Singer A1694

2006, May 11
2986 A1694 55c multi .60 .60

World Day of Cultural Diversity for Dialogue and Development A1695

2006, May 21   *Perf. 11½x11*
2987 A1695 1.90r multi 2.00 2.00

2007 Pan American Games, Rio — A1696

2006-07   *Serpentine Die Cut 10¾*
Self-Adhesive
2988 A1696 (85c) multi .90 .90
   Perf. 12x11½
2988A A1696 60c multi + label 2.75 2.75

Issued: No. 2988, 8/8/06, No. 2988A, 2007. No. 2988A was issued in sheets of 12 + 12 labels that could be personalized. Sheets sold for 25r.

Brazilian Paralympic Committee, 11th Anniv. — A1697

2006, Aug. 16   *Perf. 11½x12*
2989 A1697 55c multi .80 .80

Viola de Cocho A1698

2006, Aug. 22
2990 A1698 1.35r multi 1.50 1.50

National Parks and Reserves — A1699

No. 2991: a, Emas National Park. b, Mamirauá Reserve. c, Chapada dos Veadeiros National Park. d, Itatiaia National Park.

Litho. & Embossed
2006, Sept. 4   *Perf. 11½*
2991 A1699 85c Block of 4, #a-d 3.50 3.50

Souvenir Sheet

Cashews — A1700

2006, Sept. 11   **Litho.**   *Die Cut*
2992 A1700 2.90r multi 3.25 3.25

Graffiti Type of 2006
Souvenir Sheet
No. 2993: a, Like #2981. b, Like #2982.

2006, Sept. 11   *Perf. 12x11½*
2993 A1691 1.60r Sheet of 2, #a-b 3.50 3.50

Lubrapex 2006, Rio.

Fernando de Noronha Archipelago A1701

2006, Sept. 27   *Perf. 11½*
2994 A1701 2.50r multi 3.25 3.25

First Flight of Alberto Santos-Dumont's 14bis Airplane, Cent. — A1702

2006, Oct. 23   **Litho.**   *Perf. 11½x12*
2995 A1702 (90c) multi .90 .90

Christmas A1703

2006, Oct. 27   **Litho.**   *Die Cut*
Self-Adhesive
2996 A1703 (60c) multi .65 .65
Glitter was applied to portions of the stamp.

Occupation Type of 2005
Die Cut Perf. 12x12¼
2006, Nov. 6   **Photo.**
Self-Adhesive
2997 A1690 1c Popcorn vendor .30 .30
  a. Die cut perf. 12x12¼ syncopated ('11) .25 .25
2998 A1690 1r Manicurist 1.10 1.10
  a. Die cut perf. 12x12¼ syncopated ('11) 1.10 1.10

Souvenir Sheet

Christmas — A1704

No. 2999: a, Shepherds and sheep (25x35mm). b, Angel with horn (36x41mm). c, Holy Family (25x35mm).

Serpentine Die Cut 11½x11
2006, Nov. 9   **Litho.**
2999 A1704 1.60r Sheet of 3, #a-c 5.00 5.00

A shiny varnish was applied to portions of the design.

America Issue, Energy Conservation — A1705

2006, Nov. 22   *Perf. 11½x12*
3000 A1705 1.75r multi 1.90 1.90

Souvenir Sheet

Sharks — A1706

No. 3001: a, Isurus oxyrinchus and Sphyrna lewini. b, Mustelus schmitti.

Litho., Litho. & Embossed (#3001b)
2006, Nov. 26   **Perf. 11½**
3001 A1706 1.90r Sheet of 2, #a-
      b   3.75 3.75

Christmas — A1707

2006, Oct. 30   **Litho.**   **Perf. 12x11½**
3002 A1707 (55c) multi + label   6.50 6.50

No. 3002 was printed in sheets of 12 stamps + 12 labels that could be personalized. Sheets sold for 21r.

A1708

Flag and Map of Brazil — A1708a

2007   **Litho.**   **Perf. 11½x12**
3003 A1708 (90c) multi + label 6.50 6.50
      Perf. 12x11½
3003A A1708a (90c) multi + label 6.50 6.50

Issued: No. 3003, 2/14; No. 3003A, 10/30. Nos. 3003 and 30003A each were printed in sheets of 12 stamps + 12 labels that could be personalized. Each sheet sold for 25r. See Nos. 3080M-3080N for similar stamps without year date.

Praia Vermelha (Red Beach) — A1708b

Cable Car, Sugarloaf Mountain — A1708c

Guanabara Bay, Sugarloaf Mountain — A1708d

Candelária Church — A1708e

Christ the Redeemer Statue — A1708f

Arcos da Lapa (Carioca Aqueduct) — A1708g

2007, Sept. 24   **Litho.**   **Perf. 12x12¾**
3003B   Block of 6 + 6 la-
     bels   13.00 13.00
  c.   A1708b (90c) multi + label   2.10 2.10
  d.   A1708c (90c) multi + label   2.10 2.10
  e.   A1708d (90c) multi + label   2.10 2.10
  f.   A1708e (90c) multi + label   2.10 2.10
  g.   A1708f (90c) multi + label   2.10 2.10
  h.   A1708g (90c) multi + label   2.10 2.10

Rio de Janeiro tourist attractions. No. 3003B was printed in sheets containing 12 stamps +12 labels, two of each stamp, that could be personalized. Sheets sold for 25r.

2007 Pan American Games, Rio A1709

Designs: No. 3004, (85c), Indoor soccer, bright blue background. No. 3005, (85c), Diving, orange background. No. 3006, (85c), Water polo, blue violet background. No. 3007, (85c), Swimming, yellow orange background. No. 3008, (85c), Synchronized swimming, green background.

Serpentine Die Cut 11
2007, Jan. 19   **Litho.**
        Self-Adhesive
3004 A1709 (85c) multi   .75 .75
3005 A1709 (85c) multi   .75 .75
3006 A1709 (85c) multi   .75 .75
3007 A1709 (85c) multi   .75 .75
3008 A1709 (85c) multi   .75 .75
  a.   Strip of 5, #3004-3008   20.00 20.00

Dances A1710

No. 3009: a, Carimbo. b, Frevo.

2007, Feb. 8   **Perf. 11½**
3009 A1710   Vert. pair, #a-b 1.50 1.50
  a.   (55c) multi   .55 .55
  b.   (55c) multi   .55 .55

Intl. Polar Year — A1711

No. 3010: a, Ship Ary Rongel. b, Commander Ferraz Antarctic Station. c, Emperor penguin, map of Antarctica.

2007, Mar. 13   **Perf. 11½x12**
3010 A1711 (90c) Horiz. strip of
     3, #a-c   3.00 3.00

Path of Father José de Anchieta — A1712

No. 3011: a, Our Lady of the Assumption Church. b, Father José de Anchieta. c, Metropolitan Cathedral, Vitória.

2007, Mar. 19   **Perf. 12x11½**
3011 A1712 90c Horiz. strip of 3,
     #a-c   3.00 3.00

Soccer Stadiums — A1713

Designs: 60c, Mangueirao Stadium, Belem. 90c, Serra Dourada Stadium, Goiania. No. 3014, 2.60r, Maracana Stadium, Rio. No. 3015, 2.60r, Pacaembu Stadium, Sao Paulo.

2007, Mar. 25   **Perf. 11x11½**
3012-3015 A1713   Set of 4   7.00 7.00

Juscelino Kubitschek Bridge, Brasilia A1714

2007, Apr. 21   **Perf. 11½x12**
3016 A1714 (90c) multi   1.10 1.10

Scouting, Cent. — A1715

2007, Apr. 23   **Perf. 12x11½**
3017 A1715 2r multi   2.25 2.25

Pope Benedict XVI A1716

2007, May 9   **Perf. 11½x12**
3018 A1716 90c multi   1.25 1.25

Souvenir Sheet

Shells — A1717

No. 3019: a, Cochlespira elongata. b, Charonia variegata. c, Chicoreus beauii.

Litho. & Embossed
2007, June 5   **Perf. 12x11½**
3019 A1717 2r Sheet of 3, #a-c   6.75 6.75

Portions of the design were applied by a thermographic process producing a shiny, raised effect.

Diplomatic Relations Between Brazil and Canada, 140th Anniv. — A1718

2007, June 27   **Litho.**   **Perf. 12¾x12**
3020 A1718 90c multi   .95 .95

Occupations Type of 2005
Die Cut Perf. 12x12¼
2007, July 4   **Photo.**
       Self-Adhesive
3020A A1690 60c Barber   .65 .65
3020B A1690 90c Carpenter   .95 .95

Giuseppe Garibaldi (1807-82), Italian Leader A1719

Designs: No. 3021, 1.40r, Ship, Garibaldi on horseback. No. 3022, 1.40r, Garibaldi, ship.

2007, July 4   **Perf. 12x12¾**
3021-3022 A1719   Set of 2   3.25 3.25
3022a   Horiz. pair, #3021-3022   3.25 3.25

See Uruguay Nos. 2196-2197.

Rail Transport A1720

Designs: 1.40r, Rio de Janeiro Metro car. 1.45r, Baroneza steam locomotive. 1.60r, Tram, Santa Teresa.

2007, July 6

3023-3025 A1720 Set of 3 4.75 4.75

Teófilo Ottoni (1807-69), Leader of 1842 Uprising A1721

2007, Aug. 23 Litho. ***Perf. 12x12¾***

3026 A1721 60c multi .75 .75

America Issue, Education for All A1722

2007, Sept. 8

3027 A1722 60c multi .75 .75

Souvenir Sheet

Rose Varieties — A1723

No. 3028: a, High & Magic. b, Caballero. c, Avalanche.

2007, Sept. 29 ***Perf. 12¾x12***

3028 A1723 2.60r Sheet of 3, #a-c 8.75 8.75

Zoo Animals A1724

No. 3029: a, African elephant. b, Tiger. c, Giraffes. d, Parrot. e, African lion. f, Chimpanzee.

2007, Oct. 5 Litho. ***Perf. 12x12¾***

3029 Block or horiz. strip of 6 4.25 4.25

a.-f. A1724 60c Any single .65 .65

Christmas

A1725 A1726

Die Cut Perf. 12x12¼

2007, Oct. 11 **Photo.**

Self-Adhesive

3030 A1725 (60c) multi .70 .70

3031 A1726 (90c) multi 1.00 1.00

Arrival of Portuguese Royal Family in Brazil, 200th Anniv. — A1727

No. 3032: a, King John VI and ships. b, Royal family and ship.

2008, Jan. 22 Litho. ***Perf. 12x12¾***

3032 A1727 2r Horiz. pair, #a-b 4.50 4.50

See Portugal No. 2973.

Bank of Brazil, 200th Anniv. A1728

2008, Jan. 28

3033 A1728 (90c) multi 1.10 1.10

Opening of Brazilian Ports to Friendly Nations, 200th Anniv. A1729

2008, Jan. 28

3034 A1729 (90c) multi 1.10 1.10

Foreign Trade, 200th Anniv. A1730

2008, Jan. 28

3035 A1730 (90c) multi 1.10 1.10

America Issue - Dancer and Musicians A1731

Die Cut Perf. 12¼x12

2008, Feb. 1 **Photo.**

Self-Adhesive

3036 A1731 (60c) multi .75 .75

Medical Faculty Bicentenaries — A1732

Buildings at: No. 3037, (90c), Federal University of Bahia. No. 3038, (90c), Federal University of Rio de Janeiro.

2008, Feb. 18 Litho. ***Perf. 12x12¾***

3037-3038 A1732 Set of 2 2.25 2.25

First National Youth Conference, Brasilia — A1733

Die Cut Perf. 12x12¼

2008, Feb. 27 **Photo.**

Self-Adhesive

3039 A1733 (90c) multi 1.10 1.10

Naval Fusiliers Corps, 200th Anniv. A1734

2008, Mar. 7 Litho. ***Perf. 12x12¾***

3040 A1734 (90c) multi 1.10 1.10

Souvenir Sheet

Architecture of Oscar Niemeyer — A1735

No. 3041: a, Museum of Contemporary Art, Niterói. b, Latin America Memorial, Sao Paolo.

Litho. & Embossed

2008, Mar. 18 ***Perf. 12x11½***

3041 A1735 2.60r Sheet of 2, #a-b 6.25 6.25

Independent Judiciary, 200th Anniv. — A1736

2008, Mar. 27 Litho. ***Perf. 12¾x12***

3042 A1736 (90c) multi 1.10 1.10

Military Justice in Brazil, 200th Anniv. A1737

2008, Apr. 1 ***Perf. 12x12¾***

3043 A1737 (90c) multi 1.10 1.10

Brazilian Press Association, Cent. — A1738

2008, Apr. 7

3044 A1738 (90c) multi 1.10 1.10

Brazilian Heroes — A1739

No. 1739: a, Dom Pedro I (1798-1834). b, Marshal Manuel Deodoro da Fonseca (1827-92). c, Duque de Caxias (1803-80), soldier and politician. d, Admiral Francisco Manuel Barroso (1804-82). e, Admiral Joaquim Marques de Tamandaré (1807-97). f, José Bonifácio (1763-1838), statesman. g, Alberto Santos-Dumont (1873-1932), aviation pioneer. h, Zumbi dos Palmares (1655-95), fugitive slave leader. i, Tiradentes (1746-92), Brazilian independence leader. j, José Plácido de Castro (1873-1908), Acrean Army leader.

2008, Apr. 21 ***Perf. 12x11½***

3045 A1739 (90c) Block of 10, #a-j 11.00 11.00

Police, 200th Anniv. A1740

2008, May 10 ***Perf. 12x12¾***

3046 A1740 (90c) multi 1.10 1.10

Independence Dragoons, 200th Anniv. — A1741

2008, May 10 ***Perf. 12¾x12***

3047 A1741 (90c) multi 1.10 1.10

National Printing Office, 200th Anniv. — A1742

2008, May 10

3048 A1742 (90c) multi 1.10 1.10

Souvenir Sheet

Fauna of Serra do Japi
Region — A1743

No. 3049: a, Tangara cayana cayana. b, Consul fabius drurii.

2008, May 16   *Perf. 11½x12*
3049 A1743 2r Sheet of 2, #a-b   5.00 5.00

Rio de Janeiro
Botanical
Gardens, 200th
Anniv. — A1744

2008, June 13   *Perf. 12¾x12*
3050 A1744 (60c) multi   .75 .75

Souvenir Sheet

Japanese Immigration to Brazil,
Cent. — A1745

No. 3051: a, Map of Brazil, ship Kasato-Maru. b, Flags of Brazil and Japan, origami crane.

Litho. With Foil Application
2008, June 18   *Perf. 12x11½*
3051 A1745 3.50r multi   8.75 8.75
     See Japan No. 3028.

French and Brazilian
Landscapes — A1746

No. 3052: a, Glacier, France. b, Amazonian forest, Brazil.

2008, June 21 Litho.   *Perf. 11½x12*
3052   Horiz. pair   5.00 5.00
a.-b. A1746 2r Either single   2.50 2.50

Joao Guimaraes
Rosa (1908-67),
Novelist — A1747

Litho. & Embossed
2008, June 27   *Perf. 12x11½*
3053 A1747 60c multi   .75 .75

Agriculture
Ministry, 200th
Anniv. — A1748

2008, June 30 Litho.   *Perf. 12¾x12*
3054 A1748 (90c) multi   1.10 1.10

2008 Summer Olympics,
Beijing — A1749,

No. 3055: a, Mascot Beibei, rhythmic gymnastics. b, Mascot Jingjing, equestrian. c, Mascot Huanhuan, swimming. d, Mascots Nini and Yingying, emblem of 2008 Summer Olympics.

Litho. & Embossed
2008, July 4   *Perf. 11½*
3055 A1749 65c Block of 4, #a-d   3.25 3.25

Brazilian
Cuisine
A1750

2008, Aug. 8 Litho.   *Perf. 11½x12*
3056 A1750 90c multi   1.10 1.10

Endangered Animals of the Amazon
Region — A1751

   Designs: No. 3057, 1r, Pteronura brasiliensis. No. 3058, 1r, Lontra longicaudis. No. 3059, 1r, Trichechus inunguis.

2008, Sept. 5   *Perf. 11½x12*
3057-3059 A1751   Set of 3   3.50 3.50

Birds — A1752

   Designs: No. 3060, Strix virgata. No. 3060A, Celeus obrieni.

2008, Oct. 10   *Perf. 12x11½*
3060   A1752 1.40r multi   1.25 1.25
3060A A1752 1.40r multi   1.25 1.25

Christmas
A1753   A1754
Die Cut Perf. 12x12¼
2008, Oct. 17   **Photo.**
Self-Adhesive
3061 A1753 (65c) multi   .60 .60
3062 A1754 (1r) multi   .95 .95
   Convent of St. Anthony, 400th anniv. (No. 3061), Franciscan Movement, 800th anniv. (in 2009) (No. 3062).

Provisional Regulations of General
Administration of the Posts, 200th
Anniv. — A1755

2008, Nov. 22 Litho.   *Perf. 11½x12*
3063 A1755 1r multi   .85 .85

Louis Braille (1809-52), Educator of
the Blind — A1756

2009, Jan. 4   **Litho. & Embossed**
3064 A1756 2.20r multi   2.00 2.00

Brazilian
Leadership in
Production of
Fuels From
Renewable
Resources
A1757

Serpentine Die Cut 4¾x5
2009, Jan. 13   **Litho.**
Self-Adhesive
3065 A1757 1r multi   .85 .85

New Year 2009 (Year of the
Ox) — A1758

Litho. & Embossed With Foil
Application
2009, Jan. 15   *Perf. 11½x12*
3066 A1758 2.35r multi   2.00 2.00

Souvenir Sheets

Rivers — A1759

   Designs: No. 3067, 2.60r, Sao Simao Hydroelectric Plant, Paranaíba River. No. 3068, 3.85r, Cichla mirianae, Sao Benedito River.

2009, Jan. 27   **Litho.**
3067-3068 A1759   Set of 2   5.75 5.75

Archbishop
Helder
Camara
(1909-99)
A1760

2009, Feb. 7 Litho.   *Perf. 11½x12*
3069 A1760 1r multi   .85 .85

Map, Flag and Scenes of
Pernambuco — A1761

2009, Feb. 21
3070 A1761   (1r) multi + label   2.60 2.60
   No. 3070 was printed in sheets of 12 stamps + 12 labels that could be personalized. Sheets sold for 26r.

Intl. Polar Year — A1762

   No. 3071: a, Hydrurga leptonyx. b, Ursus maritimus.

     Perf. 11½x11¾
2009, Mar. 18   **Litho.**
3071 A1762 1r Horiz. pair, #a-b   1.90 1.90

Postman
A1763

Die Cut Perf. 12¼x12
2009, Mar. 20   **Photo.**
Self-Adhesive
3072 A1763 65c multi   .60 .60

Sport Club
Internacional
Soccer Team,
Cent. — A1764

2009, Apr. 4 Litho.   *Perf. 12x11½*
3073 A1764 1r multi   .95 .95

Diplomatic
Relations
Between Brazil
and Thailand
A1765

Flowers and buildings: No. 3074, 2.35r, Rhynchostylis gigantea, Grand Palace, Bangkok. No. 3075, 2.35r, Aechmea disticantha, Sao Pedro de Alcântara Cathedral, Petrópolis, Brazil.

2009, Apr. 17
3074-3075 A1765   Set of 2   4.50 4.50

Hercílio Luz Bridge,
Florianópolis — A1766

Serra do Rio do Rastro — A1766a

Blumenau — A1766b

Balneário Camboriú — A1766c

Santa Marta Lighthouse, Laguna —
A1766d

Windmill, Joinville — A1766e

2009, Apr. 17 Litho.   Perf. 11½x12
3076   Block of 6 + 6 labels   32.50 32.50
a. A1766 (1r) multi + label   5.25   5.25
b. A1766a (1r) multi + label   5.25   5.25
c. A1766b (1r) multi + label   5.25   5.25
d. A1766c (1r) multi + label   5.25   5.25
e. A1766d (1r) multi + label   5.25   5.25
f. A1766e (1r) multi + label   5.25   5.25

Santa Catarina tourist attractions. No. 3076 was printed in sheets containing 12 stamps +12 labels, two of each stamp, that could be personalized. Sheets sold for 26r.

Miniature Sheet

Zebu Expo — A1767

No. 3077: a, Bos taurus indicus Indubrasil. b, Bos taurus indicus Nelore Mocho. c, Bos taurus indicus Sindi. d, Bos taurus indicus Tabapua. e, Bos taurus indicus Brahman. f, Bos taurus indicus Nelore. g, Bos taurus indicus Guzerá. h, Bos taurus indicus Gir Leiteiro. i, Zebu Breeders Association of Brazil Headquarters (Sede ABCZ). j, Bos taurus indicus Gir Mocho. k, Bos taurus indicus Gir Dupla Aptidao. l, Zebu Breeders Association of Brazil Exposition Park.

2009, May 3
3077   A1767   Sheet of 12 +
                12 labels   65.00 65.00
a.-l. (1r) Any single + label   5.25   5.25
No. 3077 sold for 26r. Labels could be personalized.

Miniature Sheet

Tocantins Tourist Attractions — A1768

No. 3078: a, Morro da Catedral, Jalapao. b, Our Lady of Mercy Cathedral, Porto Nacional. c, Registro Waterfall, Natividade. d, Matriz Church, Natividade. e, Owl, Palmas. f, Araguatins Quay, Araguatins. g, Flower, Palmas. h, Tartaruga Beach, Peixe. i, Velha Waterfall, Jalapao. j, Rafting on Rio Novo, Jalapao. k, Jalapao. l, Graciosa Beach, Palmas.

2009, May 14
3078   A1768   Sheet of 12 +
                12 labels   26.00 26.00
a.-l. (1r) Any single + label   2.10   2.10
No. 3078 sold for 26r. Labels could be personalized.

Planes and Coastline — A1769

Two Planes — A1769a

Plane and Smoke — A1769b

Plane and Sun — A1769c

Plane Over Water — A1769d

Planes Over Forest — A1769e

2009, May 15 Litho.   Perf. 11½x12
3079   Block of 6 + 6 labels   13.00 13.00
a. A1769 (1r) multi + label   2.10   2.10
b. A1769a (1r) multi + label   2.10   2.10
c. A1769b (1r) multi + label   2.10   2.10
d. A1769c (1r) multi + label   2.10   2.10
e. A1769d (1r) multi + label   2.10   2.10
f. A1769e (1r) multi + label   2.10   2.10

Aerobatics Squadron. No. 3079 was printed in sheets containing 12 stamps +12 labels, two of each stamp, that could be personalized. Sheets sold for 26r.

Miniature Sheet

Rio Grande do Norte Tourist
Attractions — A1770

No. 3080: a, Genipabu Beach, Natal. b, Castelo Zé dos Montes, Sítio Novo. c, Pipa Beach, Tibau do Sul. d, Fortalez dos Reis Magos, Natal. e, Rodolfo Fernandes Square, Mossoró. f, Alberto Maranhao Theater, Natal. g, Mae Luiza Lighthouse, Natal. h, Newton Navarro Bridge, Natal. i, Three Wise Men Statue, Natal. j, Ponta Negra Beach, Natal. k, Barra de Cunhaú Beach, Canguaretama. l, Matriz Church, Martins.

2009, July 27
3080   A1770   Sheet of 12 +
                12 labels   26.00 26.00
a.-l. (1r) Any single + label   2.10   2.10
No. 3080 sold for 26r. Labels could be personalized.

A1770a

Flag and Map of Brazil — A1770b

2009, Aug. 6   Perf. 11½x12
3080M A1770a (1r) multi + label 2.60 2.60
         Perf. 12x11½
3080N A1770b (1r) multi + label 2.60 2.60
Nos. 3080M and 3080N each were printed in sheets of 12 stamps + 12 labels that could be personalized. Each sheet sold for 26r.

Miniature Sheet

Ceará Tourist Attractions — A1771

No. 3081: a, West Coast, Lagoinha. b, Ipú Waterfall. c, Dragao do Mar Arts and Culture Center, Fortaleza. d, José de Alencar Theater, Fortaleza. e, Iracema Statue, Fortaleza. f, Ubajara National Park. g, Statue of Padre Cícero, Juazerio do Norte. h, West Coast, Jericoacara. i, Beira Mar Avenue, Fortaleza. j, Fortim. k, Cedro Dam and Galinha Choco rock, Quixadá. l, Canoa Quebrada.

2009, Aug. 18   Perf. 11½x12
3081   A1771   Sheet of 12 +
                12 labels   26.00 26.00
a.-l. (1r) Any single + label   2.10   2.10
No. 3081 sold for 26r. Labels could be personalized.

Books, Khalil Gibran (1883-1931),
Poet, and His House in Beirut,
Lebanon — A1772

2009, May 5   Litho.   Perf. 11½x12
3082   A1772 2.35r multi   2.40 2.40

Telegram
A1773

Die Cut Perf. 12¼x12
2009, Mar. 20   Photo.
          Self-Adhesive
3083   A1773 1r multi   .90   .90
a.   With blue outline of denomination, year and country name
       ('10)   1.25 1.25

Brazilian
Kickboxing
A1774

Die Cut Perf. 12
2009, May 25   Litho.
          Self-Adhesive
3084   A1774 65c multi   .70   .70

Edésio
Fernandes
School of
Justice — A1775

2009, May 29   Perf. 12x11½
3085   A1775 1r multi   1.10 1.10

Cooperation in Space Projects With Russia — A1776

2009, June 12   *Perf. 11½x12*
3086 A1776 2.35r multi   2.50 2.50

Municipal Theater, Rio de Janeiro, Cent. A1777

Litho. With Foil Application
2009, July 14   *Perf. 11½x11¾*
3087 A1777 (1r) multi   1.10 1.10

Commercial Association of Rio de Janeiro, Bicent. A1778

2009, July 15 Litho.   *Perf. 11½x12*
3088 A1778 1r multi   1.10 1.10

Fruit — A1779

No. 3092: a, Vitis labrusca (purple). b, Prunus persica. c, Prunus salicina. d, Malpighia glabra. e, Vitis labrusca (green). f, Fragaria x ananassa. g, Passiflora edulis. h, Vitis spp. i, Ficus carica. j, Diospyros kaki.

2009, July 23 Litho.   *Perf. 12x11½*
3089   Block of 10   11.00 11.00
a.-j.   A1779 (1r) Any single   1.10 1.10

Miniature Sheet

Dutch Presence in Brazil — A1780

No. 3090: a, Prince John Maurice of Nassau-Siegen ("The Brazilian") (1604-79), governor general of Dutch possessions in Brazil. b, Dutch ship Zutphen. c, Dutch pipes. d, Palácio de Friburgo, Recife. e, Palácio do Campo das

Princesas, Recife. f, Dutch houses on Rua Aurora, Recife.

2009, Aug. 4 Litho.   *Perf. 12x11½*
3090 A1780 2.20r Sheet of 6, #a-f   14.50 14.50

America Issue, Traditional Games — A1781

No. 3091: a, Marbles (bola-de-gude). b, Dominoes. c, Checkers. d, Paddleball.

Litho. & Embossed
2009, Aug. 18   *Perf. 11½*
3091 A1781 1r Block of 4, #a-d   4.25 4.25

A1782

Minas Gerais Flag and Map, Church in Serro — A1783

2009, Aug. 21   *Perf. 11½x12*
3092 A1782 (1r) multi + label   2.60 2.60
       Perf. 12x11½
3093 A1783 (1r) multi + label   2.60 2.60
Nos. 3092 and 3093 each were printed in sheets of 12 samps + 12 labels that could be personalized. Each sheet sold for 26r.

Miniature Sheet

A1784

Sao Paulo Tourist Attractions — A1785

Nos. 3094 and 3095: a, Pateo do Collegio. b, Paulista Avenue. c, Ipiranga Museum. d, Luz Station. e, Santa Ifigênia Viaduct. f, Post Office (Palácio dos Correios). g, Mercado Municipal Paulistano. h, Altino Arantes Building. i, Sao Paulo Cathedral (Catedral da Sé). j, Sao Paulo Museum of Art (MASP). k, Latin America Memorial. l, Octávio Frias de Oliveira

Bridge. Stamps from No. 3094 are vertical and from No. 3095, horizontal.

2009, Aug. 29   *Perf. 12x11½*
3094 A1784   Sheet of 12 + 12 labels   26.00 26.00
a.-l.   (1r) Any single + label   2.10 2.10
       Perf. 11½x12
3095 A1785   Sheet of 12 + 12 labels   26.00 26.00
a.-l.   (1r) Any single + label   2.10 2.10
Nos. 3094 and 3095 each sold for 26r. Labels could be personalized.

Federal Educational, Professional and Technological Network, Cent. — A1786

Litho. & Embossed
2009, Sept. 23   *Perf. 11½x12*
3096 A1786 (1r) multi   1.10 1.10
Redrawn With White Border
3096A A1786 (1r) multi + label   6.50 6.50
No. 3096A was printed in sheets of 12 stamps + 12 labels that could be personalized. Sheets sold for 26r.

Buildings, Historic Center of Sao Luís UNESCO World Heritage Site — A1787

2009, Sept. 25   Litho.
3097 A1787 (1r) multi   1.10 1.10

Miniature Sheet

Birds — A1788

No. 3098: a, Paroaria coronata. b, Rupicola rupicola. c, Chlorophonia cyanea. d, Porphyrospiza caerulescens. e, Tangara cyanocephala. f, Amblyramphus holosericeus.

2009, Oct. 2
3098 A1788 1r Sheet of 6, #a-f   6.75 6.75
Lubrapex 2009, Evora, Portugal; Birdpex 2010, Antwerp, Belgium.

Carmen Miranda (1909-55), Actress — A1789

2009, Oct. 6   *Perf. 12x11½*
3099 A1789 2.20r multi   2.60 2.60

Souvenir Sheet

France Year in Brazil — A1790

No. 3100: a, Le Corbusier (1887-1965), architect. b, Brazilian Indian.

Litho. & Engr. (#3100a), Litho. & Embossed (#3100b)
2009, Oct. 7   *Perf. 11½*
3100 A1790 2.20r Sheet of 2, #a-b   5.25 5.25

Postman on Motorcycle A1791

Mail Bag — A1792

Die Cut Perf. 12¼x12
2009, Oct. 9   Photo.
Self-Adhesive
3101 A1791 (65c) multi   .75 .75
a.   Die cut perf. 12¼x12 syncopated ('11)   .70 .70
Die Cut Perf. 12x12¼
3102 A1792 (1r) multi   1.25 1.25
a.   Die cut perf. 12x12¼ syncopated ('11)   1.10 1.10

Coritiba Soccer Club, Cent. — A1793

2009, Oct. 12 Litho.   *Perf. 12x11½*
3103 A1793 1.05r multi   1.25 1.25

Sport Club International Soccer Team, Cent. — A1794

2009, Oct. 13
3104 A1794 (1r) multi + label   2.60 2.60
No. 3104 was printed in sheets of 12 stamps + 12 labels that could be personalized. Sheets sold for 26r.

Souvenir Sheet

Christmas — A1795

No. 3105 — Angel with denomination at: a, UR. b, UL.

Litho. & Engr.
2009, Oct. 16   *Perf. 11½*
3105 A1795 2.70r Sheet of 2, #a-
     b   6.50 6.50

A1796

A1797

A1798

A1799

A1800

A1801

Christmas A1802

Die Cut Perf. 12
2009, Oct. 16   **Litho.**
Self-Adhesive
3106 A1796 (65c) multi   .75 .75
3107 A1797 (65c) multi   .75 .75
3108 A1798 (65c) multi   .75 .75
3109 A1799 (65c) multi   .75 .75
3110 A1800 (65c) multi   .75 .75

3111 A1801 (65c) multi   .75 .75
   a.   Horiz. strip of 6, #3106-3111   4.50
Die Cut
3112 A1802 (1r) multi   1.25 1.25
   Nos. 3106-3112 (7)   5.75 5.75

Bridges — A1803

No. 3113: a, Incheon Bridge, South Korea (denomination at UR). b, Octavio Frias de Oliveira Bridge, Brazil (denomination at UL).

2009, Oct. 30   *Perf. 11½x11*
3113 A1803 1.05r Horiz. pair, #a-
     b   2.50 2.50

See South Korea No. 2324.

Soccer — A1804

No. 3114 — Soccer player from: a, Brazil, denomination at UR. b, Brazil, denomination at UL. c, Hong Kong, denomination at LR. d, Hong Kong, denomination at LL.

2009, Nov. 5
3114 A1804 1.05r Block of 4, #a-
     d   5.00 5.00

See Hong Kong Nos. 1372-1375.

Flag, Map and Scenes of Rondônia — A1805

2009, Dec. 29   **Litho.**   *Perf. 11½x12*
3115 A1805 (1.05r) multi + label   2.60 2.60

No. 3115 was printed in sheets of 12 stamps + 12 labels that could be personalized. Sheets sold for 26r.

Miniature Sheet

Rio de Janeiro Beach Scenes — A1806

No. 3116 — Flag of Brazil and: a, Praia Vermelha (Red Beach). b, Barra da Tijuca. c, Copacabana. d, Leblon. e, Botafogo. f, Flamengo. g, Ipanema. h, Arpoador. i, Recreio dos Bandeirantes. j, Praia da Reserva. k, Leme. l, Sao Conrado.

2009, Dec. 29
3116 A1806   Sheet of 12 +
     12 labels   26.00 26.00
   a.-l.   (1.05r) Any single + label   2.10 2.10

No. 3116 sold for 26r. Labels could be personalized.

Corrida de Reis Race, Cuiabá — A1807

2010, Jan. 10   **Litho.**   *Perf. 11½x12*
3117 A1807 70c multi   .75 .75

Miniature Sheet

Brasília Tourist Attractions — A1808

No. 3118: a, Cathedral. b, Palácio da Justiça (Palace of Justice. c, Palácio do Planalto (Palace of the Highlands). d, National Congress. e, Our Lady of Fátima Church. f, Federal Supreme Tribunal Building. g, Museum of the Republic. h, Dois Candangos sculpture. i, Juscelino Kubitschek Bridge. j, Ipé tree on the Esplenade. k, Juscelino Kubitschek Memorial. l, Interior of Cathedral.

2010, Feb. 5
3118 A1808   Sheet of 12 +
     12 labels   26.00 26.00
   a.-l.   (1.05r) Any single + label   2.10 2.10

No. 3118 sold for 26r. Labels could be personalized.

Pres. Tancredo de Almeida Neves (1910-85) — A1809

2010, Mar. 10   **Litho.**   *Perf. 11x11½*
3119 A1809 1.05r multi   1.25 1.25

Zilda Arns (1934-2010), Pediatrician and Aid Worker — A1810

2010, Mar. 25   *Perf. 11½x12*
3120 A1810 1.45r multi   1.75 1.75

Francisco Cândido Xavier (1910-2002), Medium and Writer — A1811

2010, Apr. 2   *Perf. 12x11½*
3121 A1811 (1.05r) multi   1.25 1.25

Architecture and Monuments of Brasília — A1812

No. 3122: a, Juscelino Kubitschek Memorial. b, Dois Candangos Monument. c, Cathedral of Brasília, horiz. d, Our Lady of Fatima Chapel (Igrejinha), horiz. e, Sculpture at Alvorada Palace. f, National Congress Buildings and ipê tree blossoms.

Perf. 12x11½, 11½x12 (#3122c, 3122d)
2010, Apr. 21
3122   Strip of 6   7.50 7.50
   a.-f. A1812 (1.05r) Any single   1.25 1.25

St. Benedict's Monastery, Sorocaba, Paintign by Sonia Vrubleski A1813

2010, Apr. 23   *Perf. 12x11½*
3123 A1813 (1.05r) multi   1.25 1.25

St. Benedict's Monastery, 350th Anniv.

Souvenir Sheet

Amerigo Vespucci (1454-1512), Navigator — A1814

No. 3124 — Map and ship with: a, Vespucci. b, Vespucci and silhouette of building.

2010, May 10   *Perf. 11½x12*
3124 A1814 2.40r Sheet of 2, #a-
     b   5.25 5.25

Fifth World Military Games, Rio A1815

2010, May 12
3125 A1815 2r multi   2.25 2.25

Souvenir Sheet

16th National Eucharistic Congress, Brasília — A1816

No. 3126: a, Congress emblem, Cathedral of Brasília, half of Dois Candangos Monument. b, Half of Dois Candangos Monument, Juscelino Kubitschek Moument, Catetinho (first home of Pres. Kubitschek and first building in Brasília).

2010, May 13
3126 A1816 2.70r Sheet of 2, #a-
b   6.00 6.00

Church of Our Lady of the Rosary and St. Benedict's Chapel, Cuiabá — A1817

2010, June 4   Litho.
3127 A1817 1.10r multi   1.25 1.25

Feast of the Divine Eternal Father, Trinidade A1818

2010, June 6   Perf. 12x11½
3128 A1818 70c multi   .80 .80

2010 World Cup Soccer Championships, South Africa — A1819

2010, June 11   Perf. 11½
3129 A1819 2.55r multi   3.00 3.00
    Values are for stamps with surrounding selvage.

Miniature Sheet

Brasília Tourist Attractions — A1820

No. 3130: a, Juscelino Kubitschek Memorial. b, Brazilian flag on flagpole. c, Catetinho Building. d, Dois Candangos sculpture. e, National Museum. f, Wall of tiles of Athos Bulcao. g, National Congress. h, Television tower. i, Juscelino Kubitschek Bridge. j, Palácio de Alvorada (President's residence). k, Panteao da Pátria (Pantheon of the Fatherland). l, Cathedral.

2010, June 11
3130 A1820 Sheet of 12 +
    12 labels   26.00 26.00
 a.-l. (1.10r) Any single + label 2.10 2.10
    No. 3130 sold for 26r. Labels could be personalized.

Peter Lund (1801-80), Paleontologist — A1821

2010, June 14   Litho.   Perf. 11½x12
3131 A1821 1.05r multi   1.25 1.25

Historical and Tourism Sites of Brazil and Syria — A1822

2010, June 28   Perf. 11½x12
3132 A1822 2r multi   2.25 2.25
    See Syria No. 1677.

Iguaçu Falls and Flags of Brazil and State of Paraná — A1823

2010, June 29
3133 A1823 (1.10r) multi + label 2.60 2.60
    No. 3133 was printed in sheets of 12 stamps + 12 labels that could be personalized. Sheets sold for 26r.

Miniature Sheet

Pará Tourist Attractions — A1824

No. 3134: a, Atalaia Dunes, Salinópolis. b, Buildings, Belém. c, Mosqueiro Beach Entranceway, Belém. d, Ver-o-Peso Market Complex, Belém. e, Mangal das Garças Park, Belém. f, Docks Station (Estaçao das Docas), Belém. g, Antônio Lemos Palace, Belém. h, Paz Theater, Belém. i, Açai berries and paste. j, House of Eleven Windows (Casa das Onze Janelas), Belém. k, Hangar, Convention Center and Amazon Fair, Belém. l, Our Lady of Nazareth Basilica, Belém.

2010, June 29   Litho.   Perf. 11½x12
3134 A1824 Sheet of 12 +
    12 labels   26.00 26.00
 a.-l. (1.10r) Any single + label 2.10 2.10
    No. 3134 sold for 26r. Labels could be personalized.

Souvenir Sheet

Fish of Lake Malawi, Africa — A1825

No. 3135: a, Nimbochromis venustus. b, Ajacobfreibergi eureka. c, Cynotilapia sp.

2010, July 6
3135 A1825 2r Sheet of 3, #a-c   7.00 7.00

English Village in Paranapiacaba — A1826

2010, July 17
3136 A1826 1.05r multi   1.25 1.25

Temple of Abu Simbel, Egypt A1827

2010, July 22
3137 A1827 1.05r multi   1.25 1.25

Ministry of Agriculture, Livestock and Food Supply, 150th Anniv. — A1828

2010, July 28   Perf. 12x11½
3138 A1828 1.05r multi   1.25 1.25

Irineu Evangelista de Sousa, Viscount of Mauá (1813-89), Railroad Entrepreneur — A1829

2010, July 28   Perf. 11½x12
3139 A1829 1.05r multi   1.25 1.25
    Ministry of Transportation, 150th anniv.

Victoria Regia — A1830

Victoria Regia Flower — A1831

Parrots — A1832

Jaguar — A1833

Ipé Tree — A1834

Caiman — A1835

Jabiru — A1836

2010, June 26   Litho.   Perf. 11½x12
3140   Sheet of 12, #a-b, 2
    each #c-g, + 12 la-
    bels   26.00 26.00
 a. A1830 (1.05r) multi   2.10 2.10
 b. A1831 (1.05r) multi   2.10 2.10
 c. A1832 (1.05r) multi   2.10 2.10
 d. A1833 (1.05r) multi   2.10 2.10
 e. A1834 (1.05r) multi   2.10 2.10
 f. A1835 (1.05r) multi   2.10 2.10
 g. A1836 (1.05r) multi   2.10 2.10
    Pantanal flora and fauna. No. 3140 sold for 30r. Labels could be personalized.

Textile Crops — A1837

No. 3141: a, Gossypium hirsutum (cotton). b, Cocos nucifera (coir). c, Corchorus capsularis (jute).d, Agave sisalana (sisal).

2010, Aug. 12   Litho. & Engr.
3141 A1837 2r Block of 4, #a-d   9.25 9.25

Miniature Sheet

Espírito Santo Tourist
Attractions — A1838

No. 3142: a, O Frade e a Freira rock formations. b, Moqueca Capixaba (seafood stew). c, Itaúnas Dunes. d, Ponte da Passagem, Vitória. e, Palácio Anchieta. f, Penha Convent, Vila Velha. g, Caparaó National Park. h, Pedra Azul. i, Pedra da Cebola. j, Guarapari Beach. k, Port of Vitória. l, Curva da Jurema Beach.

2010, Aug. 16   Litho.   Perf. 11½x12
3142   A1838   Sheet of 12 +
             12 labels   26.00 26.00
  a.-l.   (1.05r) Any single + label   2.10 2.10
No. 3142 sold for 30r. Labels could be personalized.

A1839

A1840

A1841

Corinthians Paulista Sport Club, Cent. A1842

2010, Sept. 1   Litho.   Perf. 11½x12
3143   A1839   1.05r multi   1.25 1.25
3144   A1840   (1.05r) multi + label 2.10 2.10
           Perf. 12x11½
3145   A1841   (1.05r) multi + label 2.10 2.10
        Embroidered
       Self-Adhesive
    Die Cut Perf. 11¾x11½
3146   A1842   8.30r multi   9.75 9.75
Nos. 3144-3145 each were printed in sheets of 12 stamps + 12 labels that sold for 30r. Labels could be personalized.

America Issue, National
Symbols — A1843

No. 3147: a, National coat of arms. b, National flag. c, National seal. d, National anthem.

2010, Sept. 7   Litho.   Perf. 11½
3147   A1843   1.05r Block of 4, #a-
              d   5.00 5.00

13th Conference of Government Postage Stamp Printers' Association, Rio de Janeiro A1844

Litho. & Embossed
2010, Sept. 20   Perf. 11½
3148   A1844   2r multi   2.40 2.40

Souvenir Sheet

Intl. Year of Biodiversity — A1845

No. 3149: a, Tomatoes on vine. b, Organic green vegetables.

2010, Sept. 21   Litho.   Perf. 11½x12
3149   A1845   2.40r Sheet of 2, #a-
             b   5.75 5.75
Portugal 2010 World Philatelic Exhibition, Lisbon.

Miniature Sheet

Rio de Janeiro Tourist
Attractions — A1846

No. 3150: a, Arcos de Lapa (Lapa Arches), Rio de Janeiro. b, Ponte Estalada (Estalada Bridge), Rio des Ostras. c, Imperial Museum, Petrópolis. d, Monumento dos Pracinhas (World War II Soldier's Monument), Rio de Janeiro. e, Santa Rita Church, Paraty. f, Christ the Redeemer Statue, Rio de Janeiro. g, Serra dos Oragaos, Teresópolis. h, Ponte Rio Niterói (Niterói River Bridge), Rio de Janeiro. i, Crystal Palace, Petrópolis. j, Museum of Contemporary Art, Niterói. k, Sao Tomé Lighthouse, Campos dos Goytacazes. l, Metropolitan Cathedral, Rio de Janeiro.

2010, Sept. 27   Perf. 12x11½
3150   A1846   Sheet of 12 +
             12 labels   26.00 26.00
  a.-l.   (1.05r) Any single + label   2.10 2.10
No. 3150 sold for 30r. Labels could be personalized.

A1847

 A1848

Christmas
A1849

2010, Oct. 22   Perf. 11½
    Souvenir Sheet
3151   A1847   2.70r multi   3.25 3.25
    Self-Adhesive
   Die Cut Perf. 12
3152   A1848   (75c) multi   .90 .90
3153   A1849   (1.05r) multi   1.25 1.25

Diplomatic Relations Between Brazil
and Zambia — A1850

No. 3154 — Animals and sites in Zambia: a, Leopard. b, Victoria Falls. c, Lion. d, Buffalo. e, Black rhinoceros. f, African elephant.

2010, Oct. 24   Perf. 11½
3154   A1850   1.05r Block of 6, #a-f 7.50 7.50

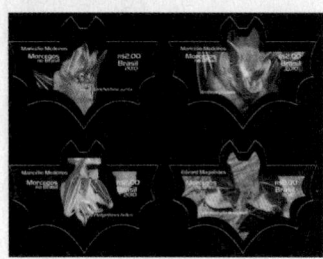

Bats — A1851

No. 3155: a, Lonchorhina aurita. b, Artibeus gnomus. c, Platyrrhinus helleri. d, Lonchophylla dekeyseri.

2010, Oct. 30   Die Cut
    Self-Adhesive
3155   A1851   Block of 4   9.75
  a.-d. 2r Any single   2.40 2.40

A1852

Christmas — A1853

2010, Nov. 30   Litho.   Perf. 11½x12
3156   A1852   (1.05r) multi + label 2.40 2.40
         Perf. 12x11½
3157   A1853   (1.05r) multi + label 2.40 2.40
Nos. 3156-3157 each were printed in sheets of 12 stamps + 12 labels that sold for 30r. Labels could be personalized.

Miniature Sheet

Goias Tourist Attractions — A1854

No. 3158: a, Vaca Brava Park, Goiânia. b, Waterfalls near Cavalcante. c, Pools, Caldas Novas. d, Rio Quente. e, Praça do Trabalhador (Worker's Square), Goiânia. f, Rio Araguala. g, Mask from Pirenópolis. h, Bosque dos Buritis, Goiânia. i, Waterfalls, Chapada dos Veadeiros National Park. j, Waterfalls, Pirenópolis. k, Basilica, Trinidade. l, Casa de Cora (House of Cora Coralina), Cidade de Goiás.

2010, Dec. 23   Perf. 11½x12
3158   A1854   Sheet of 12 +
             12 labels   24.00 24.00
  a.-l.   (1.05r) Any single + label   2.00 2.00
No. 3158 sold for 30r. Labels could be personalized.

End of Term of Pres. Luiz Inácio Lula da Silva — A1855

2011, Jan. 1   Perf. 12x11½
3159   A1855   2r mulyi   2.40 2.40

Federal Savings Bank, 150th Anniv. A1856

2011, Jan. 12   Litho.   Perf. 11½x12
3160   A1856   (1.05r) multi   1.25 1.25

Federal Savings Bank, 150th
Anniv. — A1857

2011, Jan. 12   *Perf. 12x11½*
3161 A1857 (1.05r) multi + label   3.00 3.00

No. 3161 was printed in sheets of 12
stamps + 12 labels that sold for 30r. Labels
could be personalized.

Father Roberto Landell de Moura
(1861-1928), Radio Pioneer — A1858

2011, Jan. 21   *Perf. 11½x12*
3162 A1858 (1.05r) multi   1.25 1.25

Postal
Union of the
Americas,
Spain and
Portugal
(UPAEP),
Cent.
A1859

2011, Mar. 23   *Perf. 11½*
3163 A1859 1.25r multi   1.60 1.60

Guarani Soccer
Team,
Cent. — A1860

2011, Apr. 2   *Perf. 12x11½*
3164 A1860 (1.10r) multi   1.40 1.40

Mariana, 300th Anniv. — A1861

2011, Apr. 8   *Perf. 11½x12*
3165 A1861 1.10r multi   1.40 1.40

Military
Academy of
Agulhas
Negras,
200th
Anniv.
A1862

2011, Apr. 15
3166 A1862 1.10r multi   1.40 1.40

Railway
Stations
A1863

Designs: No. 3167, Luz Station, Sao Paolo.
No. 3168, Júlio Prestes Station, Sao Paolo.
No. 3169, Central do Brasil Station, Rio de
Janeiro, vert.

2011, Apr. 30   *Perf. 11½x12*
3167 A1863 1.10r multi   1.40 1.40
3168 A1863 1.10r multi   1.40 1.40

Self-Adhesive
Die Cut Perf. 12

3169 A1863 1.10r multi   1.40 1.40

Itaipu Dam
A1864

2011, May 6   *Perf. 11½x12*
3170 A1864 1.10r multi   1.40 1.40

Paraguayan independence, bicent.

Miniature Sheet

Marine Life — A1865

No. 3171: a, Pelagia sp., Phyllorhiza
punctata. b, Sepioteuthis sepioidea. c, Octopus insularis. d, Oreaster reticulatus.

2011, June 5
3171 A1865 2.70r Sheet of 4,
      #a-d   13.50 13.50

PhilaNippon 2011 Intl. Philatelic Exhibition,
Yokohama, Japan.

Intl. Elder Abuse
Awareness
Day — A1866

2011, June 15   *Perf. 12x11½*
3172 A1866 1.10r multi   1.40 1.40

Assembly of God Churches in Brazil,
Cent. — A1867

2011, June 18   *Perf. 11½x12*
3173 A1867 (1.10r) multi + label   3.25 3.25

No. 3173 was printed in sheets of 12
stamps + 12 labels that sold for 30r. Labels
could be personalized.

Souvenir Sheet

Flora and Fauna of Tijuca National
Park — A1868

No. 3174: a, Tangara seledon, Hadrolaelia
lobata. b, Thalurania glaucopis, Coendou
insidiosus.

2011, July 6   **Litho.**
3174 A1868   5r Sheet of 2,
      #a-b   13.00 13.00

Intl. Year of Forests, Brasiliana 2013 Intl.
Philatelic Exhibition, Rio de Janeiro.

Ouro Preto, 300th Anniv. — A1869

2011, July 8
3175 A1869 1.10r multi   1.40 1.40

Regional Labor Court,
Fortaleza — A1870

2011, July 11   *Perf. 11½x12*
3176 A1870 (1.10r) multi + label   3.25 3.25

No. 3176 was printed in sheets of 12
stamps + 12 labels that sold for 30r. Labels
could be personalized.

Bahia
Commercial
Association,
200th
Anniv. — A1871

2011, July 15   *Perf. 12x11½*
3177 A1871 1.10r multi   1.40 1.40

Paulo Gracindo (1911-95),
Actor — A1872

2011, July 16   *Perf. 11½x12*
3178 A1872 1.85r multi   2.40 2.40

Sabará, 300th Anniv. — A1873

2011, July 17
3179 A1873 1.10r multi   1.40 1.40

Brazilian Folklore — A1874

Nos. 3180 and 3181: a, Curupira on boar,
logger with chainsaw. b, Mother-of-gold (mae-
do-ouro), gold panner. c, Dolphin (boto), pregnant woman. d, Headless mule (mula-sem-
cabeça), church.

2011, July 23   *Perf. 11½*
3180 A1874 (1.10r) Block of 4,
      #a-d   5.50 5.50

Souvenir Sheet

3181 A1874   1.10r Sheet of 4,
      #a-d   5.50 5.50

Nos. 3180a-3180d are each inscribed "1
Porte Carta Nao Comercial." Brapex 2011,
Recife (No. 3181).

Stylized People and
Envelope — A1875

Die Cut Perf. 12¼x12 Syncopated
2011, Aug. 5   **Self-Adhesive**
3182 A1875 (1c) dk blue & org
      brn   .25 .25

No. 3182 was for use by impoverished people in the Bolsa Família program on a maximum of five hand-addressed domestic letters
weighing no more than 10 grams. Stamps
were applied to letters by postal clerks upon
verification of the sender's involvement in the
program and were not intended for direct sale
to customers. The stamp was valid until Sept.
30, 2011.

Diplomatic Relations Between Brazil
and Ukraine — A1876

2011, Aug. 24   *Perf. 11x11½*
3183 A1876 2.55r multi   3.00 3.00

Mogi das Cruzes, 400th
Anniv. — A1877

2011, Sept. 1   *Perf. 11½x12*
3184 A1877 1.10r multi   1.25 1.25

Delivery of Registered Letter — A1878

Die Cut Perf. 12 Syncopated
2011, Sept. 2   **Self-Adhesive**
3185 A1878 (2.80r) multi   3.25 3.25

Sao Paolo Municipal Theater, Cent. — A1879

2011, Sept. 12   **Perf. 11½x12**
3186 A1879 2r multi   2.40 2.40

Miniature Sheet

Piauí Tourist Attractions — A1880

No. 3187: a, Parnaíba River Delta. b, Rock arch, Serra da Capivara National Park, Sao Raimundo Nonato. c, Metálica Bridge, Teresina. d, Our Lady of Victory Church, Oeiras. e, Carved wooden statues, Teresina. f, Ferry approaching dock, Parnaiba. g, Master Isidoro França Bridge, Teresina. h, Opal jewelry, Pedro II. i, Rio Poty Canyon, Buriti dos Montes. j, Sete Cidades National Park, Piracuruca. k, Barra Grande Beach, Cajueiro da Praia. l, Monument to the Battle of Jenipapo, Campos Maior.

2011, Sept. 12
3187 A1880   Sheet of 12 + 12 labels   35.00 35.00
   a.-l.   (1.10r) Any single + label   2.75 2.75
No. 3187 sold for 30r. Labels could be personalized.

Coelho Rodrigues Court House, Teresina — A1881

2011, Oct. 1   **Perf. 11½x12**
3188 A1881 (1.10r) multi + label   2.75 2.75
No. 3188 was printed in sheets of 12 stamps + 12 labels that sold for 30r. Labels could be personalized.

Trees of Brazil — A1882

Nos. 3189 and 3190: a, Tree with small branches and few leaves, text above tree starting with "As árvores nascem." b, Larger tree, text above tree starting with "copas abertas." c, Larger tree, text above tree starting with "devolvendo." d, No text above large tree.

2011, Oct. 3   **Perf. 11½**
Stamps With White Frames
3189 A1882 (1.10r) Block of 4, #a-d   5.00 5.00
Miniature Sheet
Stamps Without White Frames
3190 A1882   2.70r Sheet of 4, #a-d, + 5 labels   12.50 12.50

On No. 3190, a square of cedar wood is affixed to the back of the central label. The four numbered corner labels illustrate how the stamps can be folded to show the square of cedar wood through the die cut openings replacing the tree trunks that were made in Nos. 3190a-3190c. Two of the corner labels depict stamps from No. 3190, but these labels are not valid for postage.

Mail Recipient Signing for Registered Letter — A1883

Die Cut Perf. 12 Syncopated
2011, Oct. 7   **Self-Adhesive**
3191 A1883 (5.60r) multi   6.50 6.50

America Issue — A1884

No. 3192: a, Imperial era mailbox. b, Republic era mailbox. c, Department of Mail and Telegraphs (DCT) mailbox. d, Mailbox in current use.

Litho. & Engr., Litho. & Embossed (#3192d)
2011, Oct. 9   **Perf. 11½**
3192 A1884 2r Block of 4, #a-d   9.25 9.25

Diplomatic Relations Between Brazil and Italy — A1885

2011, Oct. 12   **Litho.**   **Perf. 12x11½**
3193 A1885 2.10r multi   2.40 2.40

A1886

A1887

Christmas
A1888

No. 3194: a, Open Bible. b, Closed Bible.
No. 3196 — Ornament color: a, Dark red. b, Purple. c, Green. d, Yellow. e, Blue. f, Red violet.

2011, Oct. 21   **Perf. 11½**
3194 A1886 2.70r Souvenir sheet of 2, #a-b   6.25 6.25
Self-Adhesive
Die Cut
3195 A1887 (75c) multi   .85 .85
3196   Block of 6   7.50
   a.-f.   A1888 (1.10r) Any single   1.25 1.25

People and Postal Direct Marketing Emblem — A1889

Die Cut Perf. 12 Syncopated
2011, Oct. 24   **Self-Adhesive**
3197 A1889 2r multi   2.25 2.25

Writers — A1890

No. 3198: a, Ivo Andric (1892-1975), Yugoslavian writer, and Nobel medal. b, Rachel de Queiroz (1910-2003), Brazilian writer.

2011, Oct. 26   **Perf. 11½x12**
3198 A1890 2.55r Horiz. pair, #a-b   6.00 6.00
See Serbia Nos. 570-571.

Diplomatic Relations Between Belgium and Brazil — A1891

Designs: Nos, 3199, 3201a, 2.55r, Flag bearer and master of ceremonies at Carnaval. Nos. 3200, 3201b, 2.55r, Acarajé de Lansan, No Ilê Oxumarê, painting by Carybé.

2011, Oct. 29   **Perf. 11x11½**
Stamps With White Frames
3199-3200 A1891   Set of 2   5.75 5.75
Souvenir Sheet
Stamps With Gray Frames
3201 A1891 2.55r Sheet of 2, #a-b   5.75 5.75

Brazilian Philatelic Society, Cent. — A1893

Litho. & Engr.
2011, Nov. 18   **Perf. 12x11½**
3202 A1893 2.55r copper & black 3.00 3.00
No. 3202 was printed in sheets of 28 stamps + 2 labels.

Dawn in Parana Area, Cyanocorax Caeruleus — A1894

Tree and Cyanocorax Caeruleus — A1895

2011, Nov. 25   **Litho.**   **Perf. 11½x12**
3203 A1894 (1.10r) multi + label   2.75 2.75
Perf. 12x11½
3204 A1895 (1.10r) multi + label   2.75 2.75
Nos. 3203-3204 each were printed in sheets of 12 stamps + 12 labels that sold for 30r. Labels could be personalized.

Mário Lago (1911-2002), Actor — A1896

Litho. & Engr.
2011, Nov. 26   **Perf. 11½x12**
3205 A1896 1.85r black & bronze 2.10 2.10

Campaign for Prevention of
AIDS — A1897

No. 3206: a, Heart, condom, man and
woman. b, Condom. c, Hypodermic needle. d,
Man and woman looking up. e, Condom, man
and woman embracing. f, Heart in hourglass
frame. g, AIDS ribbons. h, Condoms and
hearts.

2011, Dec. 1   Litho.   Perf. 11½
3206 A1897 (1.10r) Block of 8,
#a-h   10.00 10.00

Diplomatic
Relations
Between Brazil
and
Qatar — A1898

Litho. & Embossed
2011, Dec. 19   Perf. 12x11½
3207 A1898 2.70r multi   3.00 3.00

Rio de Janeiro
Presbyterian Church,
150th
Anniv. — A1899

2012, Jan. 12
3208 A1899 1.60r multi   1.90 1.90

Lula Oil
Field — A1900

2012, Jan. 17   Litho.
3209 A1900 (1.10r) multi   1.25 1.25

Bahia Medical Faculty, 200th
Anniv. — A1901

2012, Jan. 19   Perf. 11½x12
3210 A1901 (1.10r) multi + label   2.75 2.75

No. 3210 was printed in sheets of 12
stamps + 12 labels that sold for 30r. Labels
could be personalized.

Minas Gerais Flag — A1902

Minas Gerais Flag — A1903

2012, Jan. 19   Perf. 12x11½
3211 A1902 (1.10r) multi + label   2.75 2.75
**   Perf. 11½x12**
3212 A1903 (1.10r) multi + label   2.75 2.75

Nos. 3211-3212 each were printed in sheets
of 12 stamps + 12 labels that sold for 30r.
Labels could be personalized.

Miniature Sheet

Santa Catarina Tourist
Attractions — A1904

No. 3213: a, Hercílio Luz Bridge, Florianóp-
olis. b, Rock arch, Pedra Furada, Urubici. c,
Rua des Palmeiras, Joinville. d, Morro dos
Conventos, Araranguá. e, Sao Francisco do
Sul. f, Monument to Explorers, Chapecó. g,
Whale near Siriú Beach, Garopaba. h, Santa
Paulina Sanctuary, Nova Trento. i, Balneário
Camboriú. j, German Village, Blumenau. k,
Port of Itajaí. l, Railroad Museum, Tubarao.

2012, Jan. 19   Perf. 11½x12
3213 A1904   Sheet of 12 +
             12 labels   35.00 35.00
a.-l.   (1.10r) Any single + label   2.75 2.75

No. 3213 sold for 30r. Labels could be
personalized.

Souvenir Sheet

Dorina Nowill Foundation for the
Blind — A1905

No. 3214: a, Blind boy. b, Nowill (1919-
2010), philantropist.

Litho., Litho. & Embossed (#3214b)
2012, Mar. 11   Perf. 12x11½
Without Gum
3214 A1905 2.80r Sheet of 2, #a-
             b   6.25 6.25

Santos Soccer
Team,
Cent. — A1906

2012, Apr. 14   Litho.   Perf. 12x11½
3215 A1906 (1.10r) black & gold   1.25 1.25

América Soccer
Team,
Cent. — A1907

2012, Apr. 30
3216 A1907 (1.10r) multi   1.25 1.25

Traditional Foods of Brazil and
Mexico — A1908

No. 3217: a, Milho e mandioca. b, Pozole.

2012, June 1   Perf. 11½
3217 A1908 2.30r Horiz. pair, #a-
             b   4.75 4.75
See Mexico Nos. 2784-2785.

A1909

Rio + 20 United Nations Conference
on Sustainable Development, Rio de
Janeiro — A1910

No. 3218: a, Monkey, crocodile, birds, butterflies and armadillo in forest. b, Irrigation of
fields near house and water tanks. c, People
and dog approaching school building. d, Rio +
20 conference emblem. e, Bird, ecotourists,
guide, kayaker. f, Farmers harvesting crops
from irrigated field, house, water tank, truck. g,
Truck at produce market. h, Garbage truck
near apartment buildings and park. i, Bulldozer, logs, man planting saplings. j, Dam,
dyanmo, electric power lines and towers. k,
Cars at gas station and electric recharging station. l, Train, cable cars, bicycles. m, Green
factory, electric train, forklift and crates. n,
Swimmer in river, scientists testing water. o,
Bus on road, electric train on bridge. p, Handicapped people at telephone, bus stop and
crosswalk. q, Indigenous people, boar, fish. r,
Garbage trucks at recycling center. s, Birds
and crabs in mangrove swamp. t, People on
beach, solar panels. u, Wind generators. v,
Electric train, ship and shipping containers at
port. w, Wildlife warden and fishermen in
boats. x, Scuba diver, whale, turtle, jellyfish
and marine life.

No. 3219: a, City in droplet, sun, birds, tree,
ship, whale, shark and dolphins. b, Bird, fish,
bicycle, windmill and hand. c, Earth and city in
flower.

2012, June 1   Perf. 11½x12
3218   Sheet of 24   26.50 26.50
a.-x.   A1909 (1.10r) Any single   1.10 1.10
Souvenir Sheet
Self-Adhesive
Die Cut Perf. 12
3219 A1910 2r Sheet of 3, #a-
             c   6.00 6.00

Wild Cats
A1911

No. 3220: a, Puma yagouaroundi. b,
Leopardus pardalis.

2012, June 5   Perf. 11½
3220 A1911 (1.10r) Pair, #a-b   2.25 2.25

Wind
Turbines
A1912

2012, June 15   *Perf. 11x11½*
3221 A1912 1.85r multi   1.90 1.90

21st LUBRAPEX
Philatelic
Exhibition, Sao
Paolo — A1913

Litho. & Engr.
2012, Aug. 1   *Perf. 12x11½*
3222 A1913 2.75r silver & blk   2.75 2.75

Medicinal Plants — A1914

No. 3223: a, Carapa guianensis. b,
Copaifera martii. c, Ptychopetalum olacoides.
d, Uncaria guianensis.

2012, Aug. 5   **Litho.**   *Perf. 11½*
3223 A1914 (1.20r) Block of 4,
     #a-d   4.75 4.75

America
Issue
A1915

No. 3224 — Legend of origin of: a,
Guaraná. b, Cassava.

2012, Aug. 22
3224 A1915 1.85r Vert. pair, #a-b 3.75 3.75

A1916

Poets — A1917

No. 3225: a, Fernando Pessoa (1888-1935).
b, Poetry by Pessoa, ship.
No. 3226: a, Joao da Cruz e Sousa (1861-
98). b, Poetry by Cruz e Sousa, bird in flight.

2012, Sept. 7   *Perf. 12x11½*
3225 A1916 2r Horiz. pair, #a-b   4.00 4.00
3226 A1917 2r Horiz. pair, #a-b   4.00 4.00

LUBRAPEX 2012, Sao Paolo. See Portugal
Nos. 3437-3438.

Sao Luís Cathedral, Palace of the
Lions, Sao Luís — A1918

2012, Sept. 8   *Perf. 11½x12*
3227 A1918 1.20r multi   1.25 1.25
   Sao Luís, 400th anniv.

Holy Family — A1919

Choir — A1920

Gifts in Post
Office
Box — A1921

No. 3228: a, Jesus and Virgin Mary. b, St.
Joseph.

Litho. With Foil Application
2012, Oct. 17   *Perf. 12x11½*
   Souvenir Sheet
3228 A1919 3.85r Sheet of 2,
     #a-b   7.75 7.75

   Litho.
   Die Cut
   Self-Adhesive
3229 A1920 (80c) multi   .80 .80
3230 A1921 (1.20r) multi   1.25 1.25
   Christmas.

Emblems of
Postal Bank,
Bank of Brazil
and Brazilian
Postal
Service — A1922

Die Cut Perf. 12 Syncopated
2012, Oct. 22   **Litho.**
   Self-Adhesive
3231 A1922 (1.20r) multi   1.25 1.25

    Souvenir Sheet

Sugarloaf Mountain Aerial Cable Car,
Cent. — A1923

No. 3232: a, Sugarloaf Mountain. b, Cable
car.

2012, Oct. 27   *Perf. 11½*
3232 A1923 2.40r Sheet of 2, #a-
     b   4.75 4.75

   Brasiliana 2013 Intl. Philatelic Exhibition,
Rio de Janeiro.

Jorge
Amado
(1912-2001),
Writer
A1924

2012, Nov. 10
3233 A1924 1.20r multi   1.25 1.25
   LUBRAPEX 2012, Sao Paolo.

Quilombo dos Palmares Memorial
Park, Uniao dos Palmares — A1925

2012, Nov. 19   *Perf. 11x11½*
3234 A1925 (1.20r) multi   1.25 1.25

Chinese Immigration to Brazil, 200th
Anniv. — A1926

No. 3235: a, Dragon and ship. b, Dragon
dancers.

2012, Dec. 10   *Perf. 11½x12*
3235 A1926 2.90r Horiz. pair, #a-
     b   5.75 5.75

Luiz
Gonzaga
(1912-89),
Musician
A1927

   Litho. & Embossed
2012, Dec. 13   *Perf. 11½*
3236 A1927 (1.20r) multi   1.25 1.25

Sports and
Their Venues
A1928

No. 3237: a, Horse racing, Gávea Horse
Racing Track, Rio de Janeiro. b, Go-karting,
Ayrton Senna Kart Track, Interlagos. c, Volley-
ball, Journalist Felipe Drummond Stadium,
Belo Horizonte. d, Auto racing, Nelson Piquet
International Racetrack, Brasilia. e, Cycling,
Velodrome, Maringá.

2012, Dec. 14   **Litho. & Engr.**
3237   Horiz. strip of 5   10.00 10.00
a.-e.   A1928 2r Any single   2.00 2.00

Federal University of Paraná,
Cent. — A1929

2012, Dec. 19   **Litho.**   *Perf. 11x11½*
3238 A1929 1.20r multi   1.25 1.25

    Miniature Sheet

Brazilian Postal Services, 350th
Anniv. — A1930

No. 3239: a, Ship (first postal activities in
Brazil, 1663). b, Mail delivery by horseback. c,
Building (first postal administration in Brazil,
1798). d, Court postman making delivery,
1835. e, Issuance of Brazil #1, 2 and 3, 1843.
f, Issuance of Brazil #7, 8, 9, 10 and 13, 1844.
g, Mail collection box, 1845, Brazil #3192a and
3192b. h, Baron Capanema (1824-1908),
installer of first electric telegraph system in
Brazil, 1852. i, Dial of Bréguet telegraph. j,
Workers constructing telegraph line. k, Equipment in telegraph office. l, Issuance of Brazil
#59, 1866. m, Construction of first post office
in Rio de Janeiro, 1878. n, Pneumatic post
mail, 1910. o, Sao Paolo Post Office, 1922. p,
Badges (creation of Department of Posts and
Telegraphs,1931). q, Mechanical sorting of
mail, 1940. r, Postman with bicycle, emblem of
Brazil Posts and Telegraphs Company (creation of Brazilian Posts and Telegraphs Company, 1969). s, Postal workers at electronic
sorting equipment, 1972. t, Brazil Postal Headquarters, 1978. u, Participation of postal workers in social and environmental projects. v,
Mail sorters, postmen, motorcycle, ship. w,
Mail deliverers, postal truck (presence of postal service in all towns, 2001). x, 350th anniv.
emblem, Brazil Post emblem (2013).

2013, Jan. 25   **Litho.**   *Perf. 11½x12*
3239 A1930   Sheet of 24   30.00 30.00
a.-x.   (1.20r) Any single   1.25 1.25

Campaign Against Racial
Discrimination — A1931

2013, Mar. 21   **Litho.**   *Perf. 11½x12*
3240 A1931 2r multi   2.00 2.00
    America issue.

Souvenir Sheet

Intl. Year of Water Cooperation — A1932

No. 3241 — Half of stylized globe, water stream and: a, Hand. b, Open mouth.

Litho. & Embossed
2013, Mar. 22   *Perf. 12x11½*
3241 A1932 2.75r Sheet of 2, #a-
b   5.50 5.50

World Youth Day, Rio de Janeiro — A1933

2013, Mar. 23   Litho.   *Perf. 12x11½*
3242 A1933 1.20r multi   1.25 1.25

Telegraph Key, Smartphone and Map of South America — A1934

2013, May 17   Litho.   *Perf. 11x11½*
3243 A1934 2r multi   1.90 1.90

Diplomatic Relations Between Brazil and Georgia — A1935

No. 3244: a, Woodcutter, by Antonio Rafael Pinto Bandeira, Brazilian flag. b, Fisherman in a Red Shirt, by Pirosmani, Georgian flag.

2013, May 26   Litho.   *Perf. 11½*
3244 A1935 2.90r Horiz. pair, #a-b
b   5.50 5.50

Ants — A1936

No. 3245: a, Camponotus senex textor. b, Odontomachus bauri. c, Atta sexdens. d, Solenopsis saevissima.

2013, June 5   Litho.   *Perf. 11x11½*
3245 A1936 (1.20r) Block of 4,
#a-d   4.50 4.50

Souvenir Sheet

2013 FIFA Confederations Cup Soccer Tournament, Brazil — A1937

No. 3246: a, 2013 Confederations Cup Tournament emblem. b, Confederations Cup trophy.

2013, June 6   Litho.   *Perf. 11½*
3246 A1937 2.75r Sheet of 2, #a-
b   5.25 5.25

Diplomatic Relations Between Brazil and Czech Republic — A1938

No. 3247 — Scene from final match of 1962 World Cup soccer tournament: a, Players. b, Players, Brazilian and Czech flags.

2013, June 13   Litho.   *Perf. 11½*
3247 A1938 2.75r Horiz. pair, #a-
b   5.25 5.25

The Flotilla Commanded by Jerônimo de Albuquerque, by Carlos Kirovsky — A1939

2013, June 26   Litho.   *Perf. 11½x12*
3248 A1939 (1.20r) multi   1.10 1.10
Albuquerque's command of flotilla, 400th anniv,

Ilê Axé Opô Afonjá, Brazilian-African Religious Cult — A1940

2013, July 13   Litho.   *Perf. 11½x12*
3249 A1940 (1.20r) multi   1.10 1.10

Pope Francis A1941

2013, July 23   Litho.   *Perf. 11½x12*
3250 A1941 1.80r multi   1.60 1.60
2013 World Youth Day, Rio de Janeiro.

Brasiliana 2013 Intl. Philatelic Exhibition, Rio de Janeiro — A1942

Brazilian Postage Stamps, 170th Anniv. — A1943

No. 3252: a, Brazil #1. b, Brazil #2. c, Brazil #3.

Litho. & Engr.
2013, Aug. 1   *Perf. 12x11½*
3251 A1942 2.90r gold & blk   2.50 2.50
Souvenir Sheet
3252 A1943 3.15r Sheet of 3, #a-
c   8.25 8.25

No. 3251 was printed in sheets of 28 + 2 labels. Under magnification, "170" can be seen in the stamp engravings of Brazil #1-3 on Nos. 3252a-3252c.

Serra da Lua Rock Art A1944

2013, Aug. 12   Litho.   *Perf. 11½x12*
3253 A1944 (1.20r) multi   1.10 1.10

Cemeteries — A1945

No. 3254: a, Gateway to Arez Cemetery. b, Santa Isabel Cemetery, Mucugê. c, Batalho Cemetery, Campo Maior. d, Head of statue, Soledade Cemetery, Belém.

2013, Aug. 17   Litho.   *Perf. 11½*
3254 A1945 2r Block of 4, #a-d   7.00 7.00

Equatorial Monument, Macapá — A1946

2013, Sept. 22   Litho.   *Perf. 12x11½*
3255 A1946 (1.20r) multi   1.10 1.10

Miniature Sheet

Diplomatic Relations Between Brazil and Germany — A1947

No. 3256: a, German architecture in Bosque do Alemao Park, Curitiba, Our Lady of Lourdes Cathedral, Canela. b, Wind generators, solar panels, computer, woman reading book. c, Ship, gears, Volkswagen Beetle. d, Hermann Blumenau (1819-99), founder of city of Blumenau, bridge and building in Blumenau. e, Performer on stage, Bertolt Brecht (1898-1956), playwright.

2013, Oct. 3   Litho.   *Perf. 11½x12*
3256 A1947 2.75r Sheet of 5,
#a-e   13.00 13.00

Souvenir Sheet

Brazilian Postal Services, 350th Anniv. — A1948

No. 3257: a, Caravel, map of coast of Brazil, 1663. b, Telegraph office, 1852. c, Child in doorway, postal sorting machinery, 2013.

2013, Nov. 19   Litho.   *Perf. 12x11½*
3257 A1948 3r Sheet of 3, #a-c   7.75 7.75

Personalized Stamp A1949

2013, Nov. 20   Litho.   *Perf. 11½*
3258 A1949 (1.20r) multi   2.75 2.75

No. 3258 was printed in sheets of 12 that sold for 38r. The image portion of the stamp could be personalized, as shown in the illustration. Numerous stamps with generic images were also printed and sold by Brazil Post.

Vinicius de Moraes (1913-80), Composer A1950

2013, Nov. 20   Litho.   *Perf. 11½*
3259 A1950 2.75r blk & gold   2.40 2.40
a.   Tete-beche pair   4.80 4.80

A1951

A1952

Christmas — A1953

No. 3260: a, Woman with white blouse and red skirt in center of front row of people. b, Man with light green shirt in center of front row of people.

Litho., Sheet Margin Litho. With Foil Application

2013, Dec. 2 *Perf.*
Souvenir Sheet
3260 A1951 4.15r Sheet of 2,
#a-b 7.25 7.25
Litho.
Self-Adhesive
Die Cut
3261 A1952 (80c) multi .70 .70
3262 A1953 (1.20r) multi 1.10 1.10

Diplomatic Relations Between Brazil and Kenya — A1954

No. 3263: a, Ipu Fallus, Brazil. b, Grevy's zebras, Kenya.

2013, Dec. 12 Litho. *Perf. 11½*
3263 A1954 2.90r Horiz. pair, #a-
b 5.00 5.00

Souvenir Sheet

Mauritia Flexuosa — A1955

No. 3264: a, Palm crown and fruit. b, Parrots and grove of trees.

2013, Dec. 19 Litho. *Perf. 11½*
3264 A1955 2.45r Sheet of 2, #a-
b 4.25 4.25

Official Posters for Host Cities of the 2014 World Cup Soccer Tournament A1956

No. 3265 — Poster for: a, Belo Horizonte. b, Brasília. c, Cuiabá. d, Curitiba. e, Fortaleza. f, Manaus. g, Natal. h, Porto Alegre. i, Recife. j, Rio de Janeiro. k, Salvador. l, Sao Paolo.

2014, Jan. 30 Litho. *Perf. 11½*
3265 Block of 12 12.00 12.00
a.-l. A1956 1.20r Any single 1.00 1.00

Paysandú Sports Club, Cent. — A1957

2014, Feb. 2 Litho. *Perf. 12x11½*
3266 A1957 (1.20r) multi 1.00 1.00

Autism Awareness — A1958

2014, Apr. 2 Litho. *Perf. 12x11½*
3267 A1958 2r multi 1.75 1.75

Souvenir Sheet

2014 World Cup Soccer Tournament, Brazil — A1959

No. 3268: a, Mascot. b, World Cup trophy. c, Emblem.

2014, Apr. 21 Litho. *Perf. 12x11½*
3268 A1959 2.75r Sheet of 3, #a-
c 7.50 7.50

Miniature Sheet

Monica's Gang, Comic Strip by Mauricio de Sousa — A1960

No. 3269 — Various comic book covers depicting: a, Monica, turtle, man in car. b, Monica playing drum and elephant. c, Monica with rabbits in holsters. d, Monica and stars. e, Monica on ground, Jimmy standing above Her with fists clenched. f, Monica holding rabbit by

ears. g, Monica, other characters, man with birthday cake. h, Monica on swing. i, Monica wearing dress inscribed "10 anos," holding rabbit by ears. j, Monica holding rabbit, elephant, stacks of comic books. k, Monica, other characters banner. l, 50th anniv. emblem ("5" with teeth, "0" as rabbit's head).

2014, Apr. 21 Litho. *Perf. 12x11½*
3269 A1960 Sheet of 12 +
12 labels 30.00 30.00
a.-l. (1.20r) Any single + label 2.50 2.50
No. 3269 sold for 33r. Labels could be personalized.

Child With Soccer Ball A1961

No. 3270 — Various depictions of child and soccer ball with name of 2014 World Cup host city at bottom: a, Belo Horizonte. b, Fortaleza. c, Recife. d, Brasília. e, Manaus. f, Rio de Janeiro. g, Cuiabá. h, Natal. i, Salvador. j, Curitiba. k, Porto Alegre. l, Sao Paolo.

Die Cut Perf. 12 Syncopated
2014, Apr. 29 *Litho.*
Self-Adhesive
3270 Block of 12 13.50
a.-l. A1961 (1.20r) Any single 1.10 1.10

Dorival Caymmi (1914-2008), Singer — A1962

2014, Apr. 30 Litho. *Perf. 12x11½*
3271 A1962 1.20r black 1.10 1.10

Portuguese Language, 800th Anniv. A1963

2014, May 5 Litho. *Perf. 11½x12*
3272 A1963 3r multi 2.75 2.75

New Emblem of Brazilian Post A1964

2014, May 6 Litho. *Perf. 11½x12*
3273 A1964 (1.20r) multi 1.10 1.10

Zélio Fernandino de Moraes (1891-1975), Founder of Umbanda Branca Religion — A1965

2014, May 13 Litho. *Perf. 11½x12*
3274 A1965 (1.20r) multi 1.10 1.10

Ceará Sporting Club, Cent. A1966

2014, June 2 Litho. *Perf. 11½x12*
3275 A1966 (1.20r) black 1.10 1.10

Intl. Year of Family Farming — A1967

No. 3276: a, Farmers with basket of harvested crops, farmer on tractor. b, House, farmers with livestock and wheelbarrow of harvested crops.

2014, June 3 Litho. *Perf. 11½*
3276 A1967 1.50r Horiz. pair, #a-
b 2.75 2.75

Brazilian Olympic Committee, Cent. — A1968

2014, June 8 Litho. *Perf. 12x11½*
3277 A1968 2.30r multi 2.10 2.10

Diplomatic Relations Between Brazil and the Philippines — A1969

No. 3278: a, Urubitinga coronata, part of Brazilian flag. b, Pithecophaga jeffreyi, part of Philippines flag.

2014, June 10 Litho. *Perf. 11½x11*
3278 A1969 2.90r Horiz. pair, #a-
b 5.25 5.25

Brazilian National Soccer Team, Cent. — A1970

No. 3279: a, 1914 team, emblem inscribed "FBS." b, Brazilian flag, player, goalie making save, emblem inscribed "CBD." c, Brazilian flag, player dribbling ball, emblem inscribed "CBF."

2014, July 21 Litho. *Perf. 12x11½*
3279 A1970 2r Horiz. strip of 3,
#a-c 5.50 5.50

Diplomatic Relations Between Brazil and Peru — A1971

No. 3280: a, Machu Picchu, Peru. b, Rio de Janeiro, Brazil.

2014, July 29   Litho.   Perf. 11½
3280 A1971 2.20r Horiz. pair, #a-
b   4.00 4.00

Sergio Vieira de Mello (1948-2003), United Nations Special Representative for Iraq — A1972

2014, Aug. 19   Litho.   Perf. 12x11½
3281 A1972 2.45r multi   2.25 2.25

Sociedade Esportiva Palmeiras Soccer Team, Cent. A1973

2014, Aug. 26   Litho.   Perf. 11½
3282 A1973 (1.30r) multi   1.25 1.25

Syngonanthus Nitens — A1974

No. 3283: a, Map of State of Tocantins, field of Syngonanthus nitens grass. b, Grass harvester. c, Hands making table mat from grass. d, Brazilian flag, hat, vase of Syngonanthus nitens.

Litho., Litho. & Embossed With Foil Application (#3283d)
2014, Sept. 12   Perf. 12x11½
3283 A1974 1.80r Block of 4, #a-
d   6.00 6.00

People of Kalunga Community, Santa Barbara Waterfall — A1975

2014, Sept. 27   Litho.   Perf. 11½x12
3284 A1975 1.30r multi   1.10 1.10

Prehistoric Animals — A1976

No. 3285: a, Prionosuchus plummeri, vert. b, Oxalaia quilomboensis, vert. c, Pycnonemosaurus nevesi. d, Eremotherium laurillardi.

2014, Oct. 12   Litho.   Perf. 11½x12
3285 A1976 1.30r Block of 4, #a-
d   4.25 4.25

The prehistoric animals were covered with a smooth varnish on Nos. 3285a and 3285d, and a rough varnish on Nos. 3285b and 3285c.

Diplomatic Relations Between Brazil and Croatia — A1977

No. 3286: a, Map of Brazil, Mario Schenberg (1914-90), physicist. b, Map of Croatia, Nikola Tesla (1856-1943), inventor.

2014, Oct. 28   Litho.   Perf. 11½
3286 A1977 2.95r Horiz. pair, #a-
b   4.75 4.75

Kusiwa Wajapi Indigenous Art — A1978

2014, Nov. 3   Litho.   Perf. 11½
3287 A1978 (1.30r) multi   1.00 1.00

A1979

A1980

Christmas
A1981

No. 3288 — St. Nicholas and: a, Shoes filled with coins. b, People in tub.

2014   Litho.   Perf. 11½
Souvenir Sheet
3288 A1979 3r Sheet of 2,
#a-b   4.50 4.50
Self-Adhesive
Die Cut Perf. 12 Syncopated
3289 A1980 (90c) multi   .70 .70
3290 A1981 (1.30r) multi   1.00 1.00

Issued: No. 3288, 12/5; Nos. 3289-3290, 11/7.

Souvenir Sheet

Saints Peter and Paul Archipelago — A1982

No. 3291: a, Belmonte Island Scientific Station (denomination at UR). b, Belmonte Island Lighthouse (denomination at LL).

2014, Dec. 12   Litho.   Perf. 11½x12
3291 A1982 2.50r Sheet of 2, #a-
b   3.75 3.75

Souvenir Sheet

Oscar Niemeyer (1907-2012), Architect — A1983

No. 3292: a, Niemeyer holding pen. b, Design for Palacio do Planalto.

2014, Dec. 12   Litho.   Perf. 11½x12
3292 A1983 3.50r Sheet of 2, #a-
b   5.25 5.25

Transition from 2012 Olympics to 2016 Olympics — A1984

Transition from 2012 Paralympics to 2016 Paralympics — A1985

No. 3293 — Olympic Rings and: a, London skyline, Tower Bridge, Union Jack. b, Tower Bridge, Sugarloaf Mountain and birds. c, Christ the Redeemer statue, Brazilian flag.
No. 3294 — Paralympics emblem and: a, London skyline, Tower Bridge, Union Jack. b, Tower Bridge, Sugarloaf Mountain and birds. c, Christ the Redeemer statue, Brazilian flag.

2015, Jan. 30   Litho.   Perf. 11½x12
3293   Horiz. strip of 3   3.00 3.00
a.-c. A1984 (1.30r) Any single   1.00 1.00
3294   Horiz. strip of 3   3.00 3.00
a.-c. A1985 (1.30r) Any single   1.00 1.00

Though Nos. 3293-3294 are dated "2012" and first day covers bearing these stamps have July 27, 2012 cancels, the strips were not put on sale until Jan. 30, 2015.

Souvenir Sheets

Transition from 2012 Olympics to 2016 Olympics — A1985a

Transition from 2012 Paralympics to 2016 Paralympics — A1985b

No. 3294D — Olympic rings and: f, Big Ben, Tower Bridge, London. g, Sugarloaf Mountain and cable car, Rio de Janeiro.
No. 3294E — Paralympics emblem and: h, London Eye. i, Christ the Redeemer Statue, Rio de Janeiro.

2015, Feb. 2   Litho.   Perf. 11½
3294D A1985a 2.60r Sheet of 2,
#f-g   4.00 4.00
3294E A1985b 2.60r Sheet of 2,
#h-i   4.00 4.00

Though Nos. 3294D-3294E are dated "2012" and first day covers bearing the stamps are dated Dec. 28, 2012, the stamps were not put on sale until Feb. 2, 2015.

2015 WorldSkills Professional Education Competition, Sao Paulo — A1986

2015, Feb. 3   Litho.   Perf. 11½x12
3295 A1986 3.15r multi   2.10 2.10

Rio de Janeiro, 450th Anniv. — A1987

No. 3296 — Stylized head with: a, Musical symbols and hat. b, Streamers and dots. c, Green, blue and yellow hair. d, Hair of black curved lines.

2015, Mar. 1   Litho.   Perf. 11½
3296 A1987 (1.30r) Block of 4,
#a-d   3.50 3.50

World Summit on Disaster Risk
Reduction, Sendai, Japan — A1988

No. 3297: a, Desertification, tornado, rain
storms. b, Flood, forest fire, landslide.

2015, Mar. 14   Litho.   Perf. 11½
3297 A1988 1.80r Horiz. pair, #a-
b   2.40 2.40

Miniature Sheet

Sports of the 2016 Summer Olympics
and Paralympics, Rio de
Janeiro — A1989

No. 3298: a, Basketball (orange area at LL).
b, Paralympic racing (orange areas at LL and
UR). c, Basketball (light green area at LL). d,
Paralympic racing (dark orange area at LL,
light green area at UR). e, Rugby (green area
at LL). f, Archery (dark orange area at LL, light
green area at UR). g, Rugby (deep orange
area at LL). h, Archery (light green areas at LL
and UR). i, Weight lifting (dark blue area at
LL). j, Cycling (deep orange across top). k,
Weight lifting (light green area at LL). l, Cycling
(light green area at UL). m, Rowing (dark blue
in central area). n, Badminton (green and blue
background colors). o, Rowing (light green
area at UL). p, Badminton (orange in central
area). q, Aquatic sports (dark blue in central
area). r, Wrestling (blue area across bottom).
s, Aquatic sports (light green behind symbol).
t, Wrestling (light green area at LR).

2015, Mar. 24   Litho.   Perf. 11x11½
3298 A1989 (1.30r) Sheet of
20, #a-t   17.00 17.00

World Games of
Indigenous
Peoples,
Palmas — A1990

2015, Apr. 16   Litho.   Perf. 12x11½
3299 A1990 (1.40r) multi   .95   .95

Intl. Association of Portuguese-
Speaking Countries, 25th
Anniv. — A1991

2015, Apr. 27   Litho.   Perf. 12x11½
3300 A1991 3.15r multi   2.10 2.10

See Angola No. , Cape Verde No. 1004,
Guinea-Bissau No. , Macao No. 1440,
Mozambique No. , Portugal Nos. 3694-3695,
St. Thomas & Prince Islands No. 2954, and
Timor No.

Sustainable Minimum Wages — A1992

2015, Apr. 30   Litho.   Perf. 11x11½
3301 A1992 (1.40r) multi   .95   .95

Marshal Cândido Mariano da Silva
Rondon (1865-1958), First Director of
Indian Protection Bureau — A1993

No. 3302 — Rondon and: a, Birthplace. b,
Surveyor's transit, Praia Vermelha Military
School. c, Margarida Telegraph Office. d, Boat
and map. e, Indigenous people. f, Automobile
used to inspect borders and military badge.

2015, May 5   Litho.   Perf. 11½x12
3302 A1993 (1.40r) Block of 6,
#a-f   5.50 5.50

International Telecommunication
Union, 150th Anniv. — A1994

No. 3303 — Background color: a, Blue. b,
Green. c, Orange brown. d, Red orange.

2015, May 17   Litho.   Perf. 11½x12
3303 A1994 3.25r Block of 4, #a-
d   8.25 8.25

Miniature Sheet

Bees — A1995

No. 3304: a, Paratrigona lineata. b, Plebeia
flavocincta. c, Melipona rufiventris. d, Melipona subnitida. e, Melipona quinquefasciata. f,
Nannotrigona testaceicornis.

2015, May 27   Litho.   Perf. 11½x12
3304 A1995 2.50r Sheet of 6, #a-
f   9.50 9.50

Diplomatic Relations Between Brazil
and Azerbaijan — A1996

No. 3305: a, Três Poderes Square, Brasília,
arms of Brazil. b, National Flag Square, Baku,
arms of Azerbaijan.

2015, May 27   Litho.   Perf. 11½x12
3305 A1996 3.45r Horiz. pair, #a-
b   4.50 4.50

Quadrilha Dancers — A1997

No. 3306 — Dancers and fire with: a, Triangle player, inset of saint at UL. b, Flautist, decorated pole. c, Accordion player, inset of saint
at top center. d, Inset of saint at UR.

2015, June 1   Litho.   Perf. 12¾
3306 A1997 1.80r Block of 4, #a-
d   4.75 4.75

Miniature Sheet

Sports of the 2016 Summer Olympics
and Paralympics, Rio de
Janeiro — A1998

No. 3307: a, Boxing (green area at LR). b,
Paralympic judo (green area at LL). c, Boxing
(blue area at LR). d, Paralympic judo (violet
blue area at LL). e, Fencing (green area at
UR). f, Soccer (green area at LL). g, Fencing
(light blue area at UR). h, Soccer (light blue
area at LL). i, Kayaking (violet blue stripe at LR
corner). j, Golf (light blue area at UR). k,
Kayaking (two violet blue arcs across stamp).
l, Golf (green area at UR). m, Triathlon (green
area at LR). n, Table tennis (green area at LL).
o, Triathlon (bright purple and blue areas at
LR). p, Table tennis (bright purple and violet
blue areas at LL). q, Taekwondo (green area
at LL). r, Handball (blue area at LL). s,
Taekwondo (light blue area at LL). t, Handball
(orange area at LL).

2015, June 8   Litho.   Perf. 11x11½
3307 A1998 (1.40r) Sheet of
20, #a-t   18.00 18.00

Young
Apprentice
A1999

Campaign to
Reduce Carbon
Dioxide Emissions
A2000

Die Cut Perf. 12 Syncopated
2015, June 10   Photo.
Self-Adhesive
3308 A1999 (95c) multi   .60   .60
3309 A2000 (1.40r) multi   .90   .90

Campaign Against
Human
Trafficking — A2001

2015, July 30   Litho.   Perf. 12x11½
3310 A2001 3.25r blue   1.90 1.90
America Issue.

St. John Bosco (1815-88) — A2002

No. 3311 — Inscription at top: a, Presença
Salesiana no Brasil. b, Santuário Dom Bosco
Brasília. c, Cultura e Arte. d, Ressocializaçao.
e, Amazônia. f, Sonho de Brasília.

2015, Aug. 16   Litho.   Perf. 11½x12
3311 A2002 (95c) Block of 6, #a-f 3.25 3.25

A2003

Christmas
A2004

No. 3312: a, Bird, woman, child, horse, blind
man, guide dog and puppy. b, Family. c, People with gifts.
No. 3313, (95c), Elderly man and girl hugging. No. 3314 (1.40r), Woman and child with
gift hugging.

2015, Oct. 1   Litho.   Perf. 11½x11
Souvenir Sheet
3312 A2003 2.50r Sheet of 3, #a-
c   4.00 4.00
Self-Adhesive
Die Cut Perf. 12 Syncopated
3313-3314 A2004   Set of 2   1.25 1.25

Pepper Varieties — A2005

No. 3315: a, Malagueta peppers (denomination at LL). b, Dedo-de-moça peppers (denomination at LR). c, Bode peppers and flower (denomination at UL). d, Biquinho peppers (denomination at UR).

Litho. & Embossed
2015, Oct. 16   *Perf. 12¾*
3315   A2005   1.95r Block of 4, #a-d   4.00   4.00

Waters of Minas Gerais — A2006

No. 3316 — Views of: a, Baependi. b, Cambuquira. c, Campanha. d, Carmo de Minas. e, Caxambu. f, Conceiçao do Rio Verde. g, Lambari. h, Maria da Fé. i, Soledade de Minas. j, Três Coraçoes.

2015, Nov. 9   Litho.   *Perf. 11½x12*
3316   A2006   (1.40r) Block of 10, #a-j   7.25   7.25

Sports and Emblems of the 2016 Summer Olympics and Paralympics — A2007

Sports, Emblems and Mascots of the 2016 Summer Olympics — A2008

Vinicius, Mascot of 2016 Summer Olympics — A2009

Tom, Mascot of 2016 Summer Paralympics — A2010

No. 3317: a, Women's tennis, dark blue background. b, Paralympic swimming, dark blue background. c, Field hockey, dark blue background. d, Equestrian, dark blue background. e, Women's beach volleyball, dark blue backgrouund. f, Sailing, dark blue background at top. g, Men's rings, dark blue background at top. h, Rio 2016 Summer Olympics emblem. i, Shooting, dark blue background at top. j, Modern pentathlon, blue background at top. k, Judo, curved bister lines at UL, UR and bottom. l, Women's high jump, one curved bister line. m, "Rio 2016." n, As "l," curved bister lines at top and lower corners. o, As "k," bifurcating bister lines connected in middle. p, As "j," green blue background at bottom. q, As "i," green blue background at bottom. r, Rio 2016 Summer Paralympics emblem. s, As "g," green blue background at bottom. t, As "f," green blue background at bottom. u, As "e," green blue background. v, As "d," green blue background. w, As "c," green blue background. x, As "b," green blue background. y, As "a," green blue background.

No. 3318 — Brazilian flag and: a, Mascot Vinicius. b, Boxing. c, Wrestling. e, Rugby. f, Judo. g, Fencing. h, Field hockey. i, Women's tennis. j, Weight lifting. k, Basketball. l, Modern pentathlon. m, Cycling. n, Handball. o, Men's rings. p, Table tennis. q, Taekwondo. r, Sailing. s, Shooting. t, Badminton. u, Rowng. v, Equestrian. w, Soccer. x, Archery. y, Women's beach volleyball. z, Women's high jump. aa, Triathlon. ab, Golf. ac, Aquatic sports. ad, Rio 2016 Summer Olympics emblem.

No. 3319 — Vinicius with: a, Arm extended to left. b, Arm raised.

No. 3320 — Tom: a, Holding tambourine. b, Dancing.

2015   Litho.   *Perf. 11x11½*
3317   A2007   (1.40r) Sheet of 25, #a-y   17.50 17.50
3318   A2008   1.40r Sheet of 30, #a-ad 21.00 21.00

Souvenir Sheets
Litho. & Embossed
Perf. 11½
3319   A2009   3.25r Sheet of 2, #a-b   3.25   3.25
3320   A2010   3.25r Sheet of 2, #a-b   3.25   3.25

Issued: Nos. 3317, 3319, 3320, 12/12; No. 3318, 12/15.

Sculptures Depicting Eve — A2011

No. 3321 — Sculpture by: a, Victor Brecheret, Brazil. b, Gheorghe Leonida, Romania.

2015, Dec. 21   Litho.   *Perf. 11½*
3321   A2011   3.25r Horiz. pair, #a-b   3.25   3.25

See Romania Nos. 5743-5744.

Miniature Sheet

Belém, 400th Anniv. — A2012

No. 3322: a, 400th anniv. emblem. b, Theatro da Paz. c, Círio de Nazaré. d, Ver o Peso. e, Açaí berries. f, Forte do Castelo. g, Costumed Carimbó dancers. h, Estaçao das Docas.

2016, Jan. 12   Litho.   *Perf. 11½x12*
3322   A2012   (1.50r) Sheet of 8, #a-h   6.00   6.00

Poets — A2013

No. 3323: a, Rubén Darío (1867-1916), Nicaraguan poet. b, Manoel de Barros (1916-2014), Brazilian poet.

2016, Feb. 25   Litho.   *Perf. 11½*
3323   A2013   2.95r Horiz. pair, #a-b   3.00   3.00

French Artistic Mission in Brazil, 200th Anniv. — A2014

No. 3324: a, Joachim Lebreton (1760-1819), leader of mission. b, Auguste-Henri-Victor Grandjean de Montigny (1776-1850), architect. c, Nicholas Antoine Taunay (1755-1830), landscape painter. d, Jean-Baptiste Debret (1768-1848), painter.

2016, Mar. 26   Litho.   *Perf. 11x11½*
3324   A2014   3.55r Block of 4, #a-d   8.00   8.00

Souvenir Sheet

Lubrapex Philatelic Exhibitions, 50th Anniv. — A2015

No. 3325: a, Feathered headdress. b, Heart-shaped pendant.

2016, Apr. 26   Litho.   *Perf. 11½x12*
3325   A2015   3.55r Sheet of 2, #a-b   4.25   4.25

Brazilian Sciences Academy, Cent. — A2016

2016, May 3   Litho.   *Perf. 11½x12*
3326   A2016   (1.50r) multi   .85   .85

Consumption of Water and Electricity — A2017

Consumption of: No. 3327, 2.10r, Electricity. No. 3328, 2.10r, Water.

Die Cut Perf. 12 Syncopated
2016, June 15   Litho.
Self-Adhesive
3327-3328   A2017   Set of 2   2.60   2.60

Horses — A2018

No. 3329, 3.55r: a, Mangalarga Marchador horse, Brazil. b, Lipicanec horse, Slovenia.

2016, June 21   Litho.   *Perf. 12x11½*
3329   A2018   Vert. pair, #a-b   4.50   4.50

Souvenir Sheet

2013 World Championship Trophy of Brazilian Women's Handball Team — A2019

Litho. & Embossed
2016, June 26   *Perf. 11x11½*
3330   A2019   4.25r multi   2.75   2.75

Miniature Sheet

Olympic Sports and Values — A2020

No. 3331 — Winning art in stamp design contest by: a, Alicia Teberga. b, André Paiva. c, Anne Beth. d, Athos Spilborghs. e, Danielle Martins. f, Fernando Degrossi. g, Gabriel Trindade. h, Girlan Quidute. i, Hegildo Alencar. j, Hemilly Pereira. k, Ivan Mola (torch bearer). l, Mola (wheelchair athlete). m, Larissa Mazza. n, Mateus Kuwer. o, Samara Brum. p, Valéria Boelter.

Die Cut Syncopated
2016, June 27   Litho.
Self-Adhesive
3331   A2020   Sheet of 16   15.50
   a.-p.   (1.50r) Any single   .95   .95

Serro do Mar Paranaense
Railway — A2021

No. 3332: a, Train on Carvalho Viaduct. b, Train approaching Sao Joao Viaduct. c, Train in Marumbi State Park. d, Train on bridge in Serra do Mar Mountains.

2016, July 26   Litho.   Perf. 11½x11¾
3332 A2021 (1.70r) Block of 4,
              #a-d   4.25 4.25

Stadiums Used For 2016 Summer
Olympics and Paralympics — A2022

No. 3333: a, Estádio Olímpico (Olympic Stadium). b, Velódromo Olímpico do Rio (Olympic Velodrome). c, Arena da Juventude (Youth Arena). d, Maracana Stadium. e, Sambódromo. f, Estádio da Lagoa (Lagoa Stadium).

Litho. & Embossed
2016, Aug. 1   Perf. 11½x12
3333 A2022 3.75r Sheet of 6,
              #a-f   14.00 14.00
  g. As No. 3333, with 2016
      Paralympics emblem and
      text in sheet margin   14.00 14.00

America issue. No. 3333 has 2016 Summer Olympics emblem and text in sheet margin.

Souvenir Sheets

Torch and Emblems of 2016 Summer
Olympics — A2023

Torch and Emblems of 2016 Summer
Paralympics — A2024

No. 3334 — Olympics: a, Torch. b, Opening ceremony emblem. c, Closing ceremony emblem.
No. 3335 — Paralympics: a, Torch. b, Opening ceremony emblem. c, Closing ceremony emblem.

2016, Aug. 5   Litho.   Perf. 11½x11
3334 A2023 2.65r Sheet of 3, #a-
              c   5.00 5.00
3335 A2024 2.65r Sheet of 3, #a-
              c   5.00 5.00

School of Fine Arts, Rio de Janeiro,
200th Anniv. — A2025

No. 3336: a, School building. b, Head of David.

2016, Aug. 12   Litho.   Perf. 12x11½
3336 A2025 1.70r Horiz. pair, #a-
              b   2.10 2.10

Brazilian
Naval
Aviation,
Cent.
A2026

Perf. 10¾x11½
2016, Aug. 23   Litho.
3337 A2026 (1.70r) multi   1.10 1.10

A2027

A2028

A2029

A2030

Dolls Made by
Izabel Mendes da
Cunha (1924-
2014)
A2031

2016, Aug. 31   Litho.   Perf. 12x11½
3338   Horiz. strip of 5   5.50 5.50
  a. A2027 1.70r multi   1.10 1.10
  b. A2028 1.70r multi   1.10 1.10

  c. A2029 1.70r multi   1.10 1.10
  d. A2030 1.70r multi   1.10 1.10
  e. A2031 1.70r multi   1.10 1.10

A2032

Fruit — A2033

No. 3339: a, Ananas ananassoides. b, Pouteria ramiflora. c, Miconia albicans. d, Byrsonima verbascifolia. e, Alibertia edulis. f, Hancornia speciosa.
No. 3340: a, Anacardium humile. b, Campomanesia adamantium. c, Eugenia klotzschiana. d, Eugenia dysenterica. e, Passiflora setacea. f, Salacia crassifolia. g, Annona crassiflora. h, Dipteryx alata. i, Caryocar brasiliense.

2016, Sept. 11   Litho.   Perf. 11½
3339 A2032 (1.70r) Block of 6   6.75 6.75
  a.-f.   (1.70r) Any single   1.10 1.10
Miniature Sheet
Self-Adhesive

Die Cut Perf. 11¼x11½ Syncopated
3340 A2033   Sheet of 9   13.50
  a.-i.   (2.35r) Any single   1.50 1.50

Employee's
Severence
Indemnity Fund,
50th
Anniv. — A2034

2016, Sept. 13   Litho.   Perf. 12x11½
3341 A2034 (1.70r) multi   1.10 1.10

Sustainable
Transportation
A2035

No. 3342: a, Train, bus, people with skateboard, wheelchair, stroller. b, Car, bicycle, people walking, entrance to Metro station.

2016, Sept. 22   Litho.   Perf. 11½x11
3342 A2035 1.70r Vert. pair, #a-b 2.10 2.10

A2036

Christmas
A2037

**Litho. & Embossed With Foil
Application**
2016, Oct. 4   Perf. 12x11½
3343 A2036 2.40r gold & multi 1.50 1.50
Litho.
Self-Adhesive
Die Cut Perf. 12¼ Syncopated
3344 A2037 (1.70r) multi   1.10 1.10

João Carlos de
Oliveira (1954-99),
Olympic Triple Jump
Bronze
Medalist — A2038

2016, Oct. 15   Litho.   Perf. 11½x11
3345 A2038 (1.70r) multi   1.10 1.10

Miniature Sheets

A2039

Butterflies — A2040

No. 3346: a, Aricoris middletoni. b, Evenus gabriela. c, Parides bunichus bunichus. d, Melete lycimnia. e, Myscelia orsis. f, Mimoniades versicolor.

No. 3347: a, Udranomia spitzi. b, Marpesia petreus. c, Emesis fatimella. d, Protesilaus sp. e, Junonia evarete. f, Anartia amathea. g, Heliconius sara apseudes. h, Lasaia agesilas. i, Vanessa myrinna. j, Crocozona coecias. k, Siproeta stelenes. l, Urbanus esmeraldus. m, Phocides sp. n, Echydna punctata. o, Chorinea licursis. p, Chamaelimnas briola.

2016, Oct. 20	Litho.	Perf. 11½	
3346	A2039	Sheet of 6	6.75 6.75
a.-f.		1.70r Any single	1.10 1.10
		Perf. 11x11½	
3347	A2040	Sheet of 16	18.00 18.00
a.-p.		(1.70r) Any single	1.10 1.10

Miniature Sheet

Tattoos — A2041

No. 3348: a, Tattoo on man's chest, shoulders and arms, horiz. b, Man's tattooed face, map and tattooing tools. c, Tattoo depicting split face of woman wearing hat. d, Tattoo depicting helmeted man with spear and chain. e, Tattoo depicting flowers and woman wearing mask.

Perf. 11½x12 (#3348a), 12x11½			
2016, Nov. 11		Litho.	
3348	A2041	Sheet of 5	5.00 5.00
a.-e.		(1.70r) Any single	1.00 1.00

Fossils of Insects From Araripe Geopark — A2042

No. 3349 — Fossil of: a, Dragonfly (libélula). b, Emperor moth (mariposa).

2016, Nov. 21	Litho.	Perf. 11½x12	
3349	A2042	(1.70r) Horiz. pair,	
		#a-b	2.00 2.00

Miguel Arraes (1916-2005), Politician A2043

2016, Dec. 14	Litho.	Perf. 12x11½	
3350	A2043	(1.70r) multi	1.10 1.10

Martin Luther (1483-1546), Religious Reformer — A2044

2017, Apr. 13	Litho.	Perf. 11x11½	
3351	A2044	4.15r multi	2.60 2.60

Protestant Reformation, 500th anniv. See Germany No. 2962.

A2045

Birds A2046

Nos. 3352 and 3353: a, Pararu-espelho (purple-winged ground dove). b, Rolinha-do-planalto (blue-eyed ground dove). c, Soldadinho-do-araripe (Araripe manakin).

2017, June 19	Litho.	Perf. 12x11½	
3352		Horiz. strip of 3	2.25 2.25
a.-c.		A2045 1.25r Any single	.75 .75
		Self-Adhesive	
		Die Cut Perf. 12¼ Syncopated	
3353		Horiz. strip of 3	2.25
a.-c.		A2046 (1.25r) Any single	.75 .75

Souvenir Sheet

First Samba Recording, Cent. — A2047

2017, June 23	Litho.	Perf. 12½	
3354	A2047	(1.80r) multi	1.10 1.10

Salvador Metro Train A2048

2017, July 28	Litho.	Perf. 11x11½	
3355	A2048	1.50r multi	1.00 1.00

Statues — A2049

No. 3356: a, O Laçador (The Lassoer), Porto Alegre. b, Equestrian Statue of Dom Pedro I, Rio de Janeiro. c, Abertura dos Portos (Monument to the Opening of the Amazon Province Ports to Foreign Nations), Manaus.

2017, Aug. 11	Litho.	Perf. 11½	
3356		Horiz. strip of 3	3.75 3.75
a.-c.		A2049 1.80r Any single	1.25 1.25

Tourist Attractions A2056

No. 3363: a, Mt. Roraima. b, Maragogi. c, Waterfall, Chapada dos Veadeiros National Park. d, Iguaçu Falls. e, Armação dos Búzios.

2017, Sept. 27	Litho.	Perf. 12¾	
3363		Horiz. strip of 5	7.00 7.00
a.-e.		A2056 2r Any single	1.40 1.40

Miniature Sheet

Brasilia as UNESCO World Heritage Site, 30th Anniv. — A2058

No. 3365: a, Playground at Sarah Kubitschek Park. b, National Museum of Brazil. c, Dom Bosco Sanctuary. d, Brazilian Army Headquarters (QG). e, Television tower and fountain. f, Cruzeiro Square (Praça do Cruzeiro). g, Brasilia Palace Hotel. h, Mané Garrincha Stadium. i, Cloverleaf in residential neighborhood (Tesourinha). j, Structural details on apartment building (Cobogó).

2017, Oct. 24	Litho.	Perf. 11½x12	
3365	A2058	2r Sheet of 10,	
		#a-j	12.50 12.50

Miniature Sheet

Plays by William Shakespeare (1564-1616) — A2059

No. 3366: a, Romeo and Juliet. b, A Midsummer Night's Dream (Sonho de uma Noite de Verao). c, Hamlet. d, Othello. e, King Lear. f, Macbeth.

	Litho. & Embossed		
2017, Oct. 26		Perf. 12x11½	
3366	A2059	4.20r Sheet of 6,	
		#a-f	15.50 15.50

SEMI-POSTAL STAMPS

National Philatelic Exhibition Issue

SP1

Thick Paper

Wmk. Coat of Arms in Sheet (236)

1934, Sept. 16	Engr.	Imperf.	
B1	SP1	200r + 100r dp claret	.40 2.00
B2	SP1	300r + 100r ver	.40 2.00
B3	SP1	700r + 100r brt bl	4.00 24.00
B4	SP1	1000r + 100r blk	5.00 24.00
		Nos. B1-B4 (4)	9.80 52.00

The surtax was to help defray the expenses of the exhibition. Issued in sheets of 60, inscribed "EXPOSICAO FILATELICA NACIONAL."

Red Cross Nurse and Soldier SP2

Wmk. 222

1935, Sept. 19   Typo.   Perf. 11

B5	SP2	200r + 100r pur & red	1.20	.40
B6	SP2	300r + 100r ol brn & red	1.60	.40
B7	SP2	700r + 100r turq bl & red	10.00	5.00
		Nos. B5-B7 (3)	12.80	5.80

3rd Pan-American Red Cross Conf. Exist imperf.

Three Wise Men and Star of Bethlehem — SP3

Angel and Child — SP4

Southern Cross and Child — SP5

Mother and Child — SP6

Wmk. 249

1939-40   Litho.   Perf. 10½

B8	SP3	100r + 100r chlky bl & bl blk	.60	.25
a.		Horiz. or vert. pair, imperf. between	40.00	
B9	SP4	200r + 100r brt grnsh bl	.80	.40
a.		Horizontal pair, imperf. between	40.00	
B10	SP5	400r + 200r ol grn & ol	.60	.25
B11	SP6	1200r + 400r crim & brn red	2.00	.25
a.		Vertical pair, imperf. between	40.00	
		Nos. B8-B11 (4)	4.00	1.15

Dates of issue: #B8, 12/20/39; #B9-B11, 2/26/40.

Surtax for charitable institutions.
For surcharges see Nos. C55-C59.

Catalogue values for unused stamps in this section, from this point to the end of the section, are for Never Hinged items.

In 1980 three stamps that were intended to be semi-postals were issued as postage stamps at the total combined face value. See Nos. 1681-1683.

Children and Citizenship — SP7

Designs: a, Cutouts of children forming pyramid. b, Man and woman's hands holding onto girl. c, Children going into school. d, Pregnant woman in front of house. e, Children flying paper doves. f, Parent working in garden, child writing letters, doves. g, Breastfeeding. h, Father holding birth certificate, mother holding infant. i, Disabled child on wheelchair ramp. j, Mother, father with sick child. k, Stylized child, pencil, letters. l, Hands above and below pregnant woman. m, Two families of different races. n, Small child playing large guitar. o, People looking to baby on pedestal. p, Children, book, "Statute of Children and Adolescent."

1997, Nov. 20   Litho.   Perf. 12x11½

B12		Sheet of 16	12.50	12.50
a.-p.		SP7 22c +8c any single	.70	.70

Surcharge for Natl. Fund for Children and Adolescents.

Stampin' the Future Children's Stamp Design Contest Winners — SP8

Art by: a, Jonas Sampaio de Freitas. b, Clarissa Cazane. c, Caio Ferreira Guimaraes de Oliveira. d, Milena Karoline Ribeiro Reis.

2000, Jan. 1   Litho.   Perf. 11½x12

B13	SP8	22c + 8c Block of 4, #a-d	6.00	6.00

Children's Hope SP9

Designs: No. B14, Child and family activities. No. B15, Children reading, painting, dancing.

2002, July 26   Litho.   Perf. 11½x12

B14	SP9	(80c) +10c multi	.85	.85
B15	SP9	(80c) +10c multi	.85	.85
a.		Pair, #B14-B15	3.75	3.75

AIR POST STAMPS

Nos. O14-O29 Surcharged

1927, Dec. 28   Unwmk.   Perf. 12

C1	O2	50r on 10r	.40	.25
a.		Inverted surcharge	250.00	225.00
b.		Top ornaments missing	60.00	40.00
C2	O2	200r on 1000r	2.25	4.25
a.		Double surcharge	250.00	
C3	O2	200r on 2000r	1.25	9.50
a.		Double surcharge	575.00	
b.		Double surcharge, one inverted	575.00	
C4	O2	200r on 5000r	1.60	1.20
a.		Double surcharge	250.00	225.00
b.		Double surcharge, one inverted	250.00	
c.		Triple surcharge	350.00	
C5	O2	300r on 500r	1.60	2.00
a.		Double surcharge	275.00	—
C6	O2	300r on 600r	.80	.60
b.		Pair, one without surch.	3,750.	
c.		Double surcharge	1,000.	
C6A	O2	500r on 10r	400.00	425.00
C7	O2	500r on 50r	1.60	.60
a.		Double surcharge	225.00	—
b.		Red surcharge	80.00	—
c.		Inverted surcharge	1,200.	
C8	O2	1000r on 20r	1.20	.25
a.		Double surcharge	250.00	250.00
C9	O2	2000r on 100r	2.50	1.75
a.		Pair, one without surcharge	2,000.	
b.		Double surcharge	250.00	
C10	O2	2000r on 200r	2.75	1.75
C11	O2	2000r on 10,000r	2.50	.60
C12	O2	5000r on 20,000r	8.75	4.00
C13	O2	5000r on 50,000r	8.75	4.00
C14	O2	5000r on 100,000r	24.00	30.00
C15	O2	10,000r on 500,000r	27.50	10.00
C16	O2	10,000r on 1,000,000r	25.00	25.00
		Nos. C1-C6,C7-C16 (16)	112.45	105.75

Nos. C1, C1b, C6A, C7, C8 and C9 have small diamonds printed over the numerals in the upper corners.

Monument to de Gusmao — AP1

Santos-Dumont's Airship — AP2

Augusto Severo's Airship "Pax" — AP3

Santos-Dumont's Biplane "14 Bis" — AP4

Ribeiro de Barros's Seaplane "Jahu" — AP5

Perf. 12½x13, 13x13½

1929   Typo.   Wmk. 206

C17	AP1	50r blue grn	.35	.25
C18	AP2	200r red	.40	.25
C19	AP3	300r brt blue	.40	.25
C20	AP4	500r red violet	1.60	.25
C21	AP5	1000r orange brn	9.50	.25
		Nos. C17-C21 (5)	12.25	1.25

Perf. 11

C17a	AP1	50r blue grn	1.00	.25
C18a	AP2	200r red	1.60	.25
C19a	AP3	300r brt blue	2.00	1.60

C20a	AP4	500r red violet	2.00	.25
C21a	AP5	1000r orange brn	7.50	.40
		Nos. C17a-C21a (5)	14.10	2.75

See Nos. C32-C36. For surcharges see Nos. C26-C27.

Bartholomeu de Gusmao — AP6

Augusto Severo — AP7

Alberto Santos-Dumont AP8

Perf. 11-12

1929-30   Engr.   Wmk. 101

C22	AP6	2000r lt green ('30)	7.50	.40
C23	AP7	5000r carmine	10.00	.60
C24	AP8	10,000r olive grn	10.00	.80
		Nos. C22-C24 (3)	27.50	1.80

Perf. 9

C22a	AP6	2000r lt green	20.00	.80
C23a	AP7	5000r carmine	40.00	6.25
C24a	AP8	10,000r olive grn	40.00	1.60
		Nos. C22a-C24a (3)	100.00	9.80

Perf. 11x9, 9x11

C23b	AP7	5000r carmine	100.00	47.50
C24b	AP8	10,000r olive grn	200.00	25.00

Nos. C23-C24 exist imperf.
See Nos. C37, C40.

Allegory: Airmail Service between Brazil and the US — AP9

1929   Typo.   Wmk. 206   Perf. 11-12

C25	AP9	3000r violet	10.00	2.00
a.		Perf. 9	10.00	2.00
b.		Perf. 9x11, 11x9	10.00	1.60
c.		Perf. 9, 11, compound	10.00	1.60

Exists imperf. See Nos. C38, C41. For surcharge see No. C28.

Nos. C18-C19 Surcharged in Blue or Red

ZEPPELIN 2$500

1931, Aug. 16   Perf. 12½x13½

C26	AP2	2500r on 200r (Bl)	16.00	18.00
C27	AP3	5000r on 300r (R)	20.00	24.00

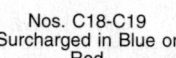

No. C25 Surcharged

2.500 REIS

1931, Sept. 2   Perf. 11

C28	AP9	2500r on 3000r vio	20.00	20.00
a.		Inverted surcharge	160.00	425.00
b.		Surch. on front and back	160.00	

Regular Issues of 1928-29 Surcharged

ZEPPELIN 3$500

1932, May　　　　　　　**Wmk. 101**
C29 A89 3500r on 5000r gray
　　lil　　　　　　　　12.00 14.00
C30 A72 7000r on 10,000r
　　rose　　　　　　　12.00 14.00
　b. Horiz. pair, imperf. between　750.00
　c. Perf. 11½　　　　　30.00 40.00

Imperforates

Since 1933, imperforate or partly per-forated sheets of nearly all of the airmail issues have become available.

Flag and
Airplane
AP10

1933, June 7　Wmk. 222　Typo.
C31 AP10 3500r grn, yel & dk bl 4.75 1.25
　　　See Nos. C39, C42.

1934　　　　　　　　　**Wmk. 222**
C32 AP1　50r blue grn　　1.25 1.25
C33 AP2　200r red　　　　.80 .25
C34 AP3　300r brt blue　　2.40 .60
C35 AP4　500r red violet　.80 .25
C36 AP5 1000r orange brn　5.00 .25
　　Nos. C32-C36 (5)　　10.25 2.60

1934 Wmk. 236 Engr. Perf. 12x11
Thick Laid Paper
C37 AP6 2000r lt green　　2.50 1.25

Types of 1929, 1933
Perf. 11-12
1937-40　　**Typo.**　　**Wmk. 249**
C38 AP9 3000r violet　　25.00 2.25
C39 AP10 3500r grn, yel & dk bl 2.50 1.25
Engr.
C40 AP7 5000r ver ('40)　9.00 2.00
　　Nos. C38-C40 (3)　　36.50 5.50

Watermark note after No. 501 also applies to No. C40.

Types of 1929-33
Perf. 11, 11½x12
1939-40　　**Typo.**　　**Wmk. 256**
C41 AP9 3000r violet　　1.25 1.25
C42 AP10 3500r bl, dl grn & yel
　　('40)　　　　　　　1.25 .75

Map of the Western Hemisphere
Showing Brazil — AP11

1941, Jan. 14　Engr.　Perf. 11
C43 AP11 1200r dark brown　2.50 .40
　Never hinged　　　　　8.00

5th general census of Brazil.

No. 506A Overprinted in Carmine

1941, Nov. 10　Wmk. 264　Rouletted
C45 A180 5400r slate grn　3.75 1.20
　Never hinged　　　　10.00
　a. Overprint inverted　100.00 100.00
　　Never hinged　　　200.00
　b. Wmk. 249　　　　1,200. 1,650.
　　Never hinged　　　2,200.
　c. Pair, one without overprint 1,000.
　　Never hinged　　　1,500.
　d. Double overprint　600.00
　e. Dbl. ovpt., one inverted 215.00 215.00
　　Never hinged　　　470.00
　f. As "c," wmk. 249　1,500.
　　Never hinged　　　3,000.

President Varges' new constitution, 4th anniv.

Nos. 506A and 508 Surcharged in Black

1942, Nov. 10　　　　　**Wmk. 264**
C47 A180 5.40cr on 5400r sl
　　grn　　　　　　4.50 2.25
　　Never hinged　　13.00
　a. Wmk. 249　　130.00 130.00
　　Never hinged　225.00
　b. Surcharge inverted 80.00 80.00
　　Never hinged　175.00
　c. Double surcharge 110.00 110.00
　　Never hinged　220.00

President Vargas' new constitution, 5th anniv.

Southern
Cross and
Arms of
Paraguay
AP12

Wmk. 270
1943, May 11　Engr.　Perf. 12½
C48 AP12 1.20cr lt gray blue　.80 .25
　Never hinged　　　　8.00

Issued in commemoration of the visit of President Higinio Morinigo of Paraguay.

Map of South
America — AP13

1943, June 30　Wmk. 271　Perf. 12½
C49 AP13 1.20cr multi　　.80 .25
　Never hinged　　　　4.00

Visit of President Penaranda of Bolivia.

Numeral of
Value
AP14

1943, Aug. 7
C50 AP14 1cr blk & dull yel　1.00 .50
　a. Double impression　30.00
C51 AP14 2cr blk & pale grn　2.00 .50
　a. Double impression　40.00
C52 AP14 5cr blk & pink　2.75 .80
　　Nos. C50-C52 (3)　5.75 1.80
　Set, never hinged　19.50

Centenary of Brazil's first postage stamps.

Souvenir Sheet

AP15

Without Gum　Imperf.
C53 AP15　Sheet of 3　50.00 50.00
　a. 1cr black & dull yellow 15.00 15.00
　b. 2cr black & pale green 15.00 15.00
　c. 5cr black & pink　15.00 15.00

100th anniv. of the 1st postage stamps of Brazil and the 2nd Phil. Exposition (Brapex). Printed in panes of 6 sheets, perforated 12½ between. Each sheet is perforated on two or three sides. Size approximately 155x155mm. Issued without gum.

Law
Book — AP16

1943, Aug. 13　　　　　**Perf. 12½**
C54 AP16 1.20cr rose & lil rose　.60 .25
　Never hinged　　　　2.25

2nd Inter-American Conf. of Lawyers.

No. B10
Surcharged in
Red, Carmine or
Black

1944, Jan. 3　Wmk. 249　Perf. 10½
C55 SP5　20c on 400r+200r
　　　(R)　　　　　2.00 .50
C56 SP5　40c on 400r+200r
　　　(Bk)　　　　2.75 .50
C57 SP5　60c on 400r+200r
　　　(C)　　　　　3.50 .50
C58 SP5　1cr on 400r+200r
　　　(Bk)　　　　4.75 .50
C59 SP5 1.20cr on 400r+200r
　　　(C)　　　　　9.50 .50
　　Nos. C55-C59 (5)　22.50 2.50
　Set, never hinged　75.00

No. C59 is known with surcharge in black but its status is questioned.

Bartholomeu de
Gusmao and the
"Aerostat" — AP17

Wmk. 268
1944, Oct. 23　Engr.　Perf. 12
C60 AP17 1.20cr rose carmine　.40 .25
　Never hinged　　　　2.00

Week of the Wing.

L. L.
Zamenhof
AP18

1945, Apr. 16　Litho.　Perf. 11
C61 AP18 1.20cr dull brown　.45 .30
　Never hinged　　　　2.00

Esperanto Congress held in Rio, Apr. 14-22.

Map of South
America — AP19

Baron of Rio
Branco — AP20

1945, Apr. 20
C62 AP19 1.20cr gray brown　.75 .30
　Never hinged　　　　3.00
C63 AP20　5cr rose lilac　1.75 .30
　Never hinged　　　　5.00

Centenary of the birth of José Maria de Silva Paranhos, Baron of Rio Branco. Nos. C62-C63 exist without watermark and gum. Value $75 each.

Dove and
Flags of
American
Republics
AP21

Perf. 12x11
1947, Aug. 15　　　　　**Unwmk.**
C64 AP21 2.20cr dk blue green　.35 .25
　Never hinged　　　　1.50

Inter-American Defense Conference at Rio de Janeiro August-September, 1947.

Santos-Dumont
Monument, St.
Cloud,
France — AP22

1947, Nov. 15　Typo.　Perf. 11x12
C65 AP22 1.20cr org brn & ol　.50 .30
　Never hinged　　　　1.60

Issued to commemorate the Week of the Wing and to honor the Santos-Dumont monument which was destroyed in World War II.

> **Catalogue values for unused stamps in this section, from this point to the end of the section, are for Never Hinged items.**

Bay of Rio de
Janeiro and
Rotary
Emblem — AP23

1948, May 16　Engr.　Perf. 11
C66 AP23 1.20cr deep claret　1.25 .30
C67 AP23 3.80cr dull violet　3.75 .30

39th convention of Rotary Intl., Rio.

Hotel Quitandinha, Petropolis — AP24

1948, July 10 Litho. Wmk. 267
C68 AP24 1.20cr org brn   .75 .30
C69 AP24 3.80cr violet   2.00 .30
International Exposition of Industry and
Commerce, Petropolis, 1948.

Musician
and
Singers
AP25

1948, Aug. 13 Engr. Unwmk.
C70 AP25 1.20cr blue   1.75 .30
National School of Music, cent.

Luis Batlle
Berres
AP26

1948, Sept. 2 Typo.
C71 AP26 1.70cr blue   .75 .25
Visit of President Luis Batlle Berres of Uru-
guay, September, 1948.

Merino
Ram
AP27

Perf. 12x11
1948, Oct. 10 Wmk. 267
C72 AP27 1.20cr dp orange   2.00 .40
Intl. Livestock Exposition at Bagé.

Eucharistic
Congress
Seal — AP28

Unwmk.
1948, Oct. 23 Engr. Perf. 11
C73 AP28 1.20cr dk car rose   .75 .25
5th Natl. Eucharistic Cong., Porto Alegre,
Oct. 24-31.

Souvenir Sheet

AP28a

1948, Dec. 14 Engr. Imperf.
Without Gum
C73A AP28a Sheet of 3   90.00 150.00
No. C73A contains one each of Nos. 674-
676. Issued in honor of President Eurico
Gasper Dutra and the armed forces. Exists
both with and without number on back. Mea-
sures 130x75mm. Issued without gum.

Church of Prazeres,
Guararapes — AP29

Perf. 11½x12
1949, Feb. 15 Litho. Wmk. 267
C74 AP29 1.20cr pink   5.00 .80
Second Battle of Guararapes, 300th anniv.

Thomé de Souza
Meeting
Indians — AP30

Perf. 11x12
1949, Mar. 29 Engr. Unwmk.
C75 AP30 1.20cr blue   1.25 .30
Founding of the City of Salvador, 400th
anniv.
A souvenir folder, issued with No. C75, has
an engraved 20cr red brown postage stamp
portraying John III printed on it, and a copy of
No. C75 affixed to it and postmarked. Paper is
laid, and size of folder front is 100x150mm.
Value, $5. Also exists on parchment paper in
blue, black and red. Value, each $500.

Franklin D.
Roosevelt
AP31

1949, May 20 Unwmk. Imperf.
C76 AP31 3.80cr deep blue   2.50 .60
  a. Souvenir sheet   35.00 35.00
No. C76a measures 85x110mm, with deep
blue inscriptions in upper and lower margins. It
also exists unwatermarked or with
papermaker's watermark. Value, $25. Souve-
nir sheet issued without gum.

Joaquim Nabuco
(1849-1910),
Lawyer and
Writer — AP32

1949, Aug. 30 Perf. 12
C77 AP32 3.80cr rose lilac   2.00 .25
  a. Wmk. 256, imperf.   25.00

Maracaná
Stadium
AP33

Soccer Player and
Flag — AP34

Perf. 11x12, 12x11
1950, June 24 Litho. Wmk. 267
C78 AP33 1.20cr ultra & salmon 2.00 .40
C79 AP34 5.80cr bl, yel grn & yel 7.50 .55
4th World Soccer Championship, Rio.

AP35

Symbolical of Brazilian population growth.

1950, July 10 Perf. 12x11
C80 AP35 1.20cr red brown   1.25 .25
Issued to publicize the 6th Brazilian census.

AP36

Design: J. B. Marcelino Champagnat.

1956, Sept. 8 Engr. Perf. 11½
C81 AP36 3.30cr rose lilac   .25 .25
50th anniversary of the arrival of the Marist
Brothers in Northern Brazil.

Santos-Dumont's 1906 Plane — AP37

1956   **Photo.**
C82 AP37   3cr dk blue grn   .80 .25
C83 AP37   3.30cr brt ultra   .35 .25
C84 AP37   4cr dp claret   .50 .25
C85 AP37   6.50cr red brown   .35 .25
C86 AP37   11.50cr orange red   1.25 .35
    Nos. C82-C86 (5)   3.25 1.35
Souvenir Sheet
C86A AP37   Sheet of 4   22.50 5.75
  b.   3cr dark carmine   2.50 .40
1st flight by Santos-Dumont, 50th anniv.
Issued: No. C86A, 10/14; others 10/16.

Lord Baden-Powell
AP38

1957, Aug. 1 Unwmk.
Granite Paper
C87 AP38 3.30cr deep red lilac   .50 .25
Centenary of the birth of Lord Baden-Pow-
ell, founder of the Boy Scouts.

UN
Emblem,
Soldier and
Map of
Suez
Canal Area
AP39

Wmk. 267
1957, Oct. 24 Engr. Perf. 11½
C88 AP39 3.30cr dark blue   .25 .25
Brazilian contingent of the UN Emergency
Force.

Basketball
Player — AP40

1959, May 30 Photo. Perf. 11½
C89 AP40 3.30cr brt red brn & bl .50 .30
Brazil's victory in the World Basketball
Championships of 1959.

Symbol of
Flight
AP41

1959, Oct. 21 Wmk. 267
C90 AP41 3.30cr deep ultra   .25 .25
Issued to publicize Week of the Wing.

Caravelle
AP42

1959, Dec. 18 Perf. 11½
C91 AP42 6.50cr ultra   .25 .25
Inauguration of Brazilian jet flights.

Pres. Adolfo
Lopez
Mateos — AP43

1960, Jan. 19 Photo. Wmk. 267
C92 AP43 6.50cr brown   .25 .25
Issued to commemorate the visit of Presi-
dent Adolfo Lopez Mateos of Mexico.
Exists unwatermarked. Value $150.

Pres. Dwight D. Eisenhower AP44

1960, Feb. 23   *Perf. 11½*
C93 AP44 6.50cr deep orange   .25 .25
Visit of Pres. Dwight D. Eisenhower.

World Refugee Year Emblem — AP45

1960, Apr. 7   **Wmk. 268**
C94 AP45 6.50cr blue   .25 .25
WRY, July 1, 1959-June 30, 1960.

Type of Regular Issue and

Tower at Brasilia — AP46

Designs: 3.30cr, Square of the Three Entities. 4cr, Cathedral. 11.50cr, Plan of Brasilia.

Perf. 11x11½, 11½x11
1960, Apr. 21   **Photo.**   **Wmk. 267**
C95 A436 3.30cr violet   .25 .25
C96 A436 4cr blue   .30 .25
C97 AP46 6.50cr rose carmine   .30 .25
C98 A436 11.50cr brown   .30 .25
   Nos. C95-C98 (4)   1.15 1.00
Inauguration of Brazil's new capital, Brasilia, Apr. 21, 1960.

Chrismon and Oil Lamp AP47

1960, May 16   *Perf. 11x11½*
C99 AP47 3.30cr lilac rose   .25 .25
7th Natl. Eucharistic Congress at Curitiba.

Cross, Sugarloaf Mountain and Emblem — AP48

1960, July 1   **Wmk. 267**
C100 AP48 6.50cr brt blue   .25 .25
10th Cong. of the World Baptist Alliance, Rio.

Boy Scout — AP49

1960, July 23   *Perf. 11½x11*
C101 AP49 3.30cr orange ver   .30 .25
Boy Scouts of Brazil, 50th anniversary.

Caravel — AP50

1960, Aug. 5   **Engr.**   **Wmk. 268**
C102 AP50 6.50cr black   .25 .25
Prince Henry the Navigator, 500th death anniv.

Maria E. Bueno AP51

1960, Dec. 15   **Photo.**   *Perf. 11x11½*
C103 AP51 60cr pale brown   .30 .25
Victory at Wimbledon of Maria E. Bueno, women's singles tennis champion.

War Memorial, Sugarloaf Mountain and Allied Flags — AP52

1960, Dec. 22   **Wmk. 268**
C104 AP52 3.30cr lilac rose   .25 .25
Reburial of Brazilian servicemen of WW II.

Power Line and Map — AP53

1961, Jan. 20   *Perf. 11½x11*
C105 AP53 3.30cr lilac rose   .25 .25
Inauguration of Three Marias Dam and hydroelectric station in Minas Gerais.

Malaria Eradication Emblem — AP54

1962, May 24   **Wmk. 267**   **Engr.**
C106 AP54 21cr dark blue   .25 .25
WHO drive to eradicate malaria.

F. A. de Varnhagen — AP55

1966, Feb. 17   **Photo.**   **Wmk. 267**
C107 AP55 45cr red brown   .25 .25
Francisco Adolfo de Varnhagen, Viscount of Porto Seguro (1816-1878), historian and diplomat.

Map of the Americas and Alliance for Progress Emblem AP56

1966, Mar. 14   *Perf. 11x11½*
C108 AP56 120cr grnsh bl & vio bl   .30 .25
5th anniv. of the Alliance for Progress.
A souvenir card contains one impression of No. C108, imperf. Size: 113x160mm.

Nun and Globe — AP57

1966, Mar. 25   **Photo.**   *Perf. 11½x11*
C109 AP57 35cr violet   .25 .25
Centenary of the arrival of the teaching Sisters of St. Dorothea.

Face of Jesus from Shroud of Turin — AP58

1966, June 3   **Photo.**   **Wmk. 267**
C110 AP58 45cr brown org   .30 .25
Issued to commemorate Vatican II, the 21st Ecumenical Council of the Roman Catholic Church, Oct. 11, 1962-Dec. 8, 1965.
A souvenir card contains one impression of No. C110, imperf. Size: 100x39mm.

Admiral Mariz e Barros — AP59

1966, June 13   **Photo.**   **Wmk. 267**
C111 AP59 35cr red brown   .25 .25
Death centenary of Admiral Antonio Carlos Mariz e Barros, who died in the Battle of Itaperu.

"Youth" by Eliseu Visconti — AP60

1966, July 31   *Perf. 11½x11*
C112 AP60 120cr red brown   .55 .25
Birth centenary of Eliseu Visconti, painter.

SPECIAL DELIVERY STAMPS

No. 191 Surcharged

1930   **Unwmk.**   *Perf. 12*
E1   A62 1000r on 200r dp blue   6.50 1.25
  a.   Inverted surcharge   700.00
  b.   Red surcharge   450.00

POSTAGE DUE STAMPS

D1

1889   **Unwmk.**   **Typo.**   *Rouletted*
J1   D1   10r carmine   2.00 1.40
J2   D1   20r carmine   2.40 2.00
J3   D1   50r carmine   4.00 4.00
J4   D1   100r carmine   2.00 1.40
J5   D1   200r carmine   60.00 20.00
J6   D1   300r carmine   5.25 *7.25*
J7   D1   500r carmine   5.25 *7.25*
J8   D1   700r carmine   8.75 *12.00*
J9   D1   1000r carmine   8.75 8.75
   Nos. J1-J9 (9)   98.40 64.05

   Counterfeits are common.

1890
J10   D1   10r orange   .65 .25
J11   D1   20r ultra   .65 .25
J12   D1   50r olive   1.40 .25
J13   D1   200r magenta   5.25 .60
J14   D1   300r blue green   2.75 1.50
J15   D1   500r slate   4.00 2.75
J16   D1   700r purple   4.00 *8.00*
J17   D1   1000r dk violet   5.25 4.75
   Nos. J10-J17 (8)   23.95 18.35

   Counterfeits are common.

D2

1895-1901   *Perf. 11x11½*

J18	D2	10r dk blue ('01)	2.00	1.25
J19	D2	20r yellow grn	21.00	2.75
J20	D2	50r yellow grn ('01)	8.75	5.25
J21	D2	100r brick red	5.50	1.25
a.		Double impression	1,200.	1,200.
J22	D2	200r violet	5.50	.60
J23	D2	300r dull blue	2.75	2.25
J24	D2	2000r brown	13.00	13.00
		Nos. J18-J24 (7)	58.50	26.35

Perf. 13

J18c	D2	10r dk blue	20.00	2.50
J19c	D2	20r yellow grn	10.00	2.50
J20c	D2	50r yellow grn	15.00	11.00
J21c	D2	100r brick red	10.00	4.50
J22c	D2	200r gray lilac	20.00	4.50

Perf. 13x11

J19d	D2	20r yellow grn	11.00	10.00
J20d	D2	50r yellow grn	10.00	10.00
J23d	D2	300r bluish gray	37.50	14.00
J24d	D2	2000r brn, perf.	37.50	37.50
		13x11x11x11		

Perf. 11

Thick Paper

J21e	D2	100r brick red	8.00	2.75
J22e	D2	200r gray lilac	5.25	1.75

1906   **Wmk. 97**

J25	D2	100r brick red	4.75	2.00

Wmk. (97? or 98?)

J26	D2	200r violet	8.75	15.00
a.		Wmk. 97	350.00	125.00
b.		Wmk. 98	15.00	47.50

D3

1906-10   **Unwmk.**   **Engr.**   *Perf. 12*

J28	D3	10r slate	.25	.25
J29	D3	20r brt violet	.25	.25
J30	D3	50r dk green	.30	.25
J31	D3	100r carmine	1.40	.60
J32	D3	200r dp blue	1.00	.25
J33	D3	300r gray blk	.75	1.25
J34	D3	400r olive grn	1.40	.60
J35	D3	500r dk violet	35.00	35.00
J36	D3	600r violet ('10)	1.40	2.50
J37	D3	700r red brown	35.00	35.00
J38	D3	1000r red	2.25	3.25
J39	D3	2000r green	4.75	5.50
J40	D3	5000r choc ('10)	1.50	37.50
		Nos. J28-J40 (13)	85.25	122.20

D4

1919-23   **Typo.**   *Perf. 12½*

J41	D4	5r red brown	.60	.45
J42	D4	10r violet	.60	.45
J43	D4	20r olive gray	3.00	3.00
J44	D4	50r green ('23)	.25	.25
J45	D4	100r red	5.00	2.00
J46	D4	200r blue	15.00	2.10
J47	D4	400r brown ('23)	1.75	1.60
		Nos. J41-J47 (7)	26.20	9.85

Perf. 11x10½

J43a	D4	20r olive gray	.25	.25
J44a	D4	50r green	.25	.25
J45a	D4	100r red	1.60	.25
J46a	D4	200r blue	7.50	2.00

Perf. 12½ (J48-J49), 12½x13½

1924-35   **Wmk. 100**

J48	D4	5r red brown	.25	.25
J49	D4	100r carmine	.85	1.50
J50	D4	200r slate bl ('29)	1.25	.50
J51	D4	400r dp brn ('29)	1.25	1.25
J52	D4	600r dk vio ('29)	1.40	1.25
J53	D4	600r orange ('35)	.60	.60
		Nos. J48-J53 (6)	5.60	5.35

1924   **Wmk. 193**   *Perf. 11x10½*

J54	D4	100r red	55.00	55.00
J55	D4	200r slate blue	6.00	6.00

1925-27   **Wmk. 101**   *Perf. 11x10½*

J56	D4	20r olive gray	.25	.25
J57	D4	100r red, perf. 13x13½	1.25	1.25
J58	D4	200r slate blue	10.00	3.75
a.		Perf. 13x13½	3.75	1.75

J59	D4	400r brown	3.25	2.00
J60	D4	600r dk violet	5.50	5.50
		Nos. J56-J60 (5)	20.25	12.75

Wmk. E U BRASIL Multiple (218)

1929-30   *Perf. 12½x13½*

J61	D4	100r light red	.50	.50
J62	D4	200r blue black	1.75	1.75
J63	D4	400r brown	1.75	1.75
J64	D4	1000r myrtle green	1.75	1.75
		Nos. J61-J64 (4)	5.75	5.75

1931-36   **Wmk. 222**   *Perf. 11*

J65	D4	10r lt violet ('35)	.25	.25
J66	D4	20r black ('33)	.75	.75
a.		Perf. 12½x13½	.25	.25
J67	D4	50r blue grn ('35)	.75	.50
J68	D4	100r rose red ('35)	.75	.50
J69	D4	200r sl blue ('35)	2.00	1.25
J70	D4	400r blk brn ('35)	3.25	1.50
J71	D4	600r dk violet	.75	.50
J72	D4	1000r myrtle grn	1.25	1.00
a.		Perf. 12½x13½	.65	.85
J73	D4	2000r brown ('36)	1.25	1.25
J74	D4	5000r indigo ('36)	1.75	1.75
		Nos. J65-J74 (10)	12.75	9.25

1938   **Wmk. 249**   *Perf. 11*

J75	D4	200r slate blue	2.75	1.25

1940   **Typo.**   **Wmk. 256**

J76	D4	10r light violet	1.10	1.10
J77	D4	20r black	1.10	1.10
J79	D4	100r rose red	1.10	1.10
J80	D4	200r myrtle green	2.40	1.10
		Nos. J76-J80 (4)	5.70	4.40

1942   **Wmk. 264**

J81	D4	10r lt violet	.25	.25
J82	D4	20r olive blk	.25	.25
J83	D4	50r lt blue grn	.25	.25
J84	D4	100r vermilion	1.10	1.00
J85	D4	200r gray blue	1.75	1.75
J86	D4	400r claret	1.10	1.10
J87	D4	600r rose vio	.75	.50
J88	D4	1000r dk bl grn	.75	.50
J89	D4	2000r dp yel brn	1.75	1.75
J90	D4	5000r indigo	.90	.90
		Nos. J81-J90 (10)	8.85	8.35

1949   **Wmk. 268**

J91	D4	10c pale rose lilac	1.40	1.40
J92	D4	20r black	20.00	20.00

No. J92 exists in shades of gray ranging to gray olive.

OFFICIAL STAMPS

Pres. Affonso Penna — O1

Unwmk.

1906, Nov. 15   **Engr.**   *Perf. 12*

O1	O1	10r org & grn	1.00	.25
O2	O1	20r org & grn	1.25	.25
O3	O1	50r org & grn	1.90	.25
O4	O1	100r org & grn	1.00	.25
O5	O1	200r org & grn	1.25	.25
O6	O1	300r org & grn	4.00	.40
O7	O1	400r org & grn	7.25	2.00
O8	O1	500r org & grn	4.00	1.40
O9	O1	700r org & grn	4.75	2.75
O10	O1	1000r org & grn	4.75	.80
O11	O1	2000r org & grn	6.50	1.60
O12	O1	5000r org & grn	12.00	1.40
O13	O1	10,000r org & grn	12.00	1.00
		Nos. O1-O13 (13)	61.65	12.60

The portrait is the same but the frame differs for each denomination of this issue.

Pres. Hermes da Fonseca — O2

1913, Nov. 15   **Center in Black**

O14	O2	10r gray	.25	.40
O15	O2	20r ol grn	.25	.40
O16	O2	50r gray	.25	.40
O17	O2	100r ver	.60	.25
O18	O2	200r blue	1.40	.25
O19	O2	500r orange	2.75	.60
O20	O2	600r violet	4.00	2.50
O21	O2	1000r blk brn	4.00	1.75
O22	O2	2000r red brn	7.00	2.00
O23	O2	5000r brown	8.75	3.50

O24	O2	10,000r black	14.00	7.25
O25	O2	20,000r blue	26.00	26.00
O26	O2	50,000r green	50.00	50.00
O27	O2	100,000r org red	200.00	200.00
O28	O2	500,000r brown	325.00	325.00
O29	O2	1,000,000r dk brn	325.00	325.00
		Nos. O14-O29 (16)	969.25	945.30

The portrait is the same on all denominations of this series but there are eight types of the frame.

Pres. Wenceslau Braz — O3

Perf. 11, 11½

1919, Apr. 11   **Wmk. 100**

O30	O3	10r olive green	.40	5.50
O31	O3	50r green	1.00	1.00
O32	O3	100r rose red	2.00	.60
O33	O3	200r dull blue	2.50	.60
O34	O3	500r orange	7.00	40.00
		Nos. O30-O34 (5)	12.90	47.70

The official decree called for eleven stamps in this series but only five were issued.
For surcharges see Nos. 293-297.

NEWSPAPER STAMPS

N1

Rouletted

1889, Feb. 1   **Unwmk.**   **Litho.**

P1	N1	10r yellow	5.00	5.00
a.		Pair, imperf. between	180.00	180.00
P2	N1	20r yellow	12.00	12.00
P3	N1	50r yellow	18.00	15.00
P4	N1	100r yellow	7.50	3.00
P5	N1	200r yellow	3.00	3.00
P6	N1	300r yellow	3.00	3.00
P7	N1	500r yellow	60.00	15.00
P8	N1	700r yellow	6.00	24.00
P9	N1	1000r yellow	6.00	24.00
		Nos. P1-P9 (9)	120.50	104.00

For surcharges see Nos. 125-127.

1889, May 1

P10	N1	10r olive	3.00	1.50
P11	N1	20r green	3.00	1.50
P12	N1	50r brn yel	3.00	1.50
P13	N1	100r violet	4.50	3.00
P14	N1	200r black	4.50	3.00
P15	N1	300r carmine	21.00	21.00
P16	N1	500r green	82.50	90.00
P17	N1	700r pale blue	50.00	55.00
P18	N1	1000r brown	21.00	82.50
		Nos. P10-P18 (9)	192.50	259.00

For surcharges see Nos. 128-135.

N2

White Wove Paper Thin to Thick

1890   **Typo.**   *Perf. 12½-14*

P19	N2	10r blue	22.50	12.00
P20	N2	20r emerald	70.00	21.00
P21	N2	100r violet	22.50	22.50
		Nos. P19-P21 (3)	115.00	55.50

Perf. 11-11½

P19b	N2	10r blue	50.00	20.00
P20b	N2	20r emerald	425.00	125.00
P21b	N2	100r violet	135.00	37.50

Perf. 11-11½x12½-14

P19c	N2	10r blue	—	1,500.
P20c	N2	20r emerald	300.00	27.50
P21c	N2	100r violet	20.00	20.00

For surcharge see No. 137.
No. P19-P21 exist on medium and thick papers.

N3

1890-93   *Perf. 11-11½*

P22	N3	10r ultramarine	7.50	5.50
P23	N3	10r ultra, buff	7.50	3.00
P24	N3	20r green	10.00	3.00
f.		20r grn, perf. 13	50.00	20.00
h.		20r grn, perf. 13	50.00	22.00
j.		20r grn, perf. 11x13	40.00	15.00
P25	N3	50r yel grn ('93)	40.00	15.00
		Nos. P22-P25 (4)	65.00	26.50

Perf. 12½-14

P22e	N3	10r ultra	3.00	2.00
P23e	N3	10r blue, buff	3.00	2.00
P24e	N3	20r blue green	8.00	4.00

For surcharges see Nos. 136, 138-139.

POSTAL TAX STAMPS

Icarus from the Santos-Dumont Monument at St. Cloud, France — PT1

Perf. 13½x12½

1933, Oct. 1   **Typo.**   **Wmk. 222**

RA1	PT1	100r deep brown	.75	.25
a.		Perf. 11	1.30	.25

Honoring the Brazilian aviator, Santos-Dumont. Its use was obligatory as a tax on all correspondence sent to countries in South America, the US and Spain. Its use on correspondence to other countries was optional. The funds obtained were used for the construction of airports throughout Brazil.

Catalogue values for unused stamps in this section, from this point to the end of the section, are for Never Hinged items.

Father Joseph Damien and Children PT2

Perf. 12x11

1952, Nov. 24   **Litho.**   **Wmk. 267**

RA2	PT2	10c yellow brown	1.00	.25

1953, Nov. 30

RA3	PT2	10c yellow green	1.00	.25

Father Bento Dias Pacheco — PT3

1954, Nov. 22   **Photo.**   *Perf. 11½*

RA4	PT3	10c violet blue	.25	.25

1955-69, Nov. 24

RA5	PT3	10c dk car rose	.25	.25
RA6	PT3	10c org red ('57)	.25	.25
RA7	PT3	10c dp emer ('58)	.25	.25
RA8	PT3	10c red lilac ('61)	.25	.25
RA9	PT3	10c choc ('62)	.25	.25
RA10	PT3	10c slate ('63)	.25	.25
RA11	PT3	2cr dp mag ('64)	.25	.25
RA12	PT3	2cr violet ('65)	.25	.25
RA13	PT3	2cr orange ('66)	.30	.25
RA14	PT3	5c brt yel grn ('68)	4.00	1.20
RA15	PT3	5c deep plum ('69)	.80	.30

Issued: 11/25, No. RA14; 11/28, No. RA15; others, 11/24.

Eunice Weaver — PT4

1971-73, Nov. 24
RA16 PT4 10c slate green .35 .25
RA17 PT4 10c brt rose lil ('73) .50 .30

Father Nicodemos — PT5

1975, Nov. 24   Litho.   Unwmk.
RA18 PT5 10c sepia .40 .40

Father Vicente Borgard (1888-1977) — PT6

1983, Nov. 24   Photo.   Perf. 11½
RA19 PT6 10cr brown 2.75 2.00

Father Bento Dias Pacheco — PT7

1984, Nov. 24   Photo.   Perf. 11½
RA20 PT7 30cr deep blue .60 .40

1985, Nov. 24   Litho.
RA21 PT7 100cr lake .40 .25

1986, Nov. 24   Litho.
RA22 PT7 10c gray brown .30 .25

1987, Nov. 24   Photo.
RA23 PT7 30c sage green .30 .25

Father Santiago Uchoa — PT8

1988, Nov. 24   Litho.
RA24 PT8 1.30cz dull red brn .40 .35
See Nos. RA29-RA30.

Fr. Joseph Damien — PT9

1989-92   Photo.   Perf. 11½
RA25 PT9 2c deep lilac rose .30 .25
RA26 PT9 50c blue .25 .25
Perf. 12½
RA27 PT9 3cr green .25 .25
RA28 PT9 30cr brown .25 .25
Nos. RA25-RA28 (4) 1.05 1.00

Issued: 2c, Nov. 24; 50c, Nov. 24, 1990; 3cr, Nov. 24, 1991; 30cr, Nov. 24, 1992.

Father Santiago Uchoa Type of 1988
1993, Nov. 24   Photo.   Perf. 12½
RA29 PT8 50c blue .25 .25

1994, Nov. 24
RA30 PT8 1c dull lake .25 .25

The tax was for the care and treatment of lepers.
Use of Nos. RA2-RA30 was required for one week.

POSTAL TAX SEMI-POSTAL STAMP

Catalogue values for unused stamps in this section are for Never Hinged items.

Icarus — PTSP1

Wmk. 267
1947, Nov. 15   Typo.   Perf. 11
RAB1 PTSP1 40c + 10c brt red .80 .50
a.   Pair, imperf. between   350.00
Aviation Week, November 15-22, 1947, and compulsory on all domestic correspondence during that week.

BRITISH ANTARCTIC TERRITORY

'bri-tish „ant-'ärk-tik 'ter-ə-,tōr-ē

LOCATION — South Atlantic Ocean between 20-80 degrees longitude and south of 60 degrees latitude
GOVT. — British territory
POP. — About 300 scientific staff at research stations.

This territory includes Graham Land (Palmer Peninsula), South Shetland Islands and South Orkney Islands. Formerly part of Falkland Islands Dependency.

12 Pence = 1 Shilling
20 Shillings = 1 Pound
100 Pence = 1 Pound (1971)

Catalogue values for all unused stamps in this country are for Never Hinged items.

M. V. Kista Dan — A1

1p, Skiers hauling load. 1½p, Muskeg (tractor). 2p, Skiers. 2½p, Beaver seaplane. 3p, R.R.S. John Biscoe. 4p, Camp scene. 6p, H.M.S. Protector. 9p, Dog sled. 1sh, Otter skiplane. 2sh, Huskies & aurora australis. 2sh6p, Helicopter. 5sh, Snocat (truck). 10sh, R.R.S. Shackleton. £1, Map of Antarctica.

Perf. 11x11½
1963, Feb. 1   Engr.   Wmk. 314
1 A1 ½p dark blue 1.00 1.75
2 A1 1p brown 1.25 .85
3 A1 1½p plum & red 1.40 1.40
4 A1 2p rose violet 1.50 .85
5 A1 2½p dull green 2.75 1.30
6 A1 3p Prus blue 2.75 1.40
7 A1 4p sepia 2.25 1.50
8 A1 6p dk blue & olive 4.00 2.25
9 A1 9p olive 3.00 2.00
10 A1 1sh steel blue 3.25 1.25
11 A1 2sh dl vio & bis 20.00 9.00
12 A1 2sh6p deep 19.00 12.00
13 A1 5sh rose red & org 22.50 17.50
14 A1 10sh grn & vio bl 42.50 24.00
15 A1 £1 black & blue 45.00 45.00
Nos. 1-15 (15) 172.15 122.05

See No. 24. For surcharges see Nos. 25-38.

Common Design Types pictured following the introduction.

Churchill Memorial Issue
Common Design Type
1966, Jan. 24   Photo.   Perf. 14
16 CD319 ½p bright blue .85 3.25
17 CD319 1p green 3.50 3.25
18 CD319 1sh brown 16.00 5.50
19 CD319 2sh violet 17.50 6.00
Nos. 16-19 (4) 37.85 18.00

Lemaire Channel, Iceberg and Adelie Penguins A2

Designs: 6p, Weather sonde and operator. 1sh, Muskeg (tractor) pulling tent equipment. 2sh, Surveyors with theodolite.

1969, Feb. 6   Litho.
20 A2 3½p blue, vio bl & blk 3.25 2.75
21 A2 6p emer, blk & dp org 1.00 2.00
22 A2 1sh ultra, blk & ver 1.00 1.75
23 A2 2sh grnsh bl, blk & och 1.00 2.50
Nos. 20-23 (4) 6.25 9.00

25 years of continuous scientific work in the Antarctic.

Type of 1963
£1, H.M.S. Endurance and helicopter.
1969, Dec. 1   Engr.   Perf. 11x11½
24 A1 £1 black & rose red 160.00 150.00

Nos. 1-14 Surcharged in Decimal Currency; Three Bars Overprinted
1971, Feb. 15   Wmk. 314
25 A1 ½p on ½p .65 3.50
26 A1 1p on 1p 1.00 1.00
27 A1 1½p on 1½p 1.25 .80
28 A1 2p on 2p 1.25 .50
29 A1 2½p on 2½p 3.25 2.50
30 A1 3p on 3p 2.25 .80
31 A1 4p on 4p 2.50 .80
32 A1 5p on 6p 4.50 3.50
33 A1 6p on 9p 16.00 8.00
34 A1 7½p on 1sh 17.00 9.25
35 A1 10p on 2sh 17.00 12.00
36 A1 15p on 2sh6p 17.00 12.00
37 A1 25p on 5sh 20.00 15.00
38 A1 50p on 10sh 30.00 30.00
Nos. 25-38 (14) 133.65 99.65

Map of Antarctica, Aurora Australis, Explorers — A3

Map of Antarctica, Aurora Australis and: 4p, Sea gulls. 5p, Seals. 10p, Penguins.

Litho. & Engr.
1971, June 23   Perf. 14x13
39 A3 1½p multicolored 6.00 2.00
40 A3 4p multicolored 15.00 5.00
41 A3 5p multicolored 10.00 8.00
42 A3 10p multicolored 22.50 10.00
Nos. 39-42 (4) 53.50 25.50

10th anniv. of the Antarctic Treaty pledging peaceful uses of and scientific cooperation in Antarctica.

Silver Wedding Issue, 1972
Common Design Type
Design: Queen Elizabeth II, Prince Philip, seals and emperor penguins.
1972, Dec. 13   Photo.   Perf. 14x14½
43 CD324 5p rose brn & multi 3.25 2.60
44 CD324 10p olive & multi 4.50 3.50

Capt. Cook and "Resolution" — A4

Polar Explorers and their Crafts: 1p, Thaddeus von Bellingshausen and "Vostok." 1½p, James Weddell and "Jane." 2p, John Biscoe and "Tula." 2½p, J. S. C. Dumont d'Urville and "Astrolabe." 3p, James Clark Ross and "Erebus." 4p, C. A. Larsen and "Jason." 5p, Adrien

---

de Gerlache and "Belgica." 6p, Otto Nordenskjöld and "Antarctic." 7½p, W. S. Bruce and "Scotia." 10p, Jean-Baptiste Charcot and "Pourquoi Pas?" 15p, Ernest Shackleton and "Endurance." 25p, Hubert Wilkins and airplane "San Francisco." 50p, Lincoln Ellsworth and airplane "Polar Star." £1, John Rymill and "Penola."

Wmk. 373
1975-80   Litho.   Perf. 14½
45 A4 ½p multi .90 2.90
46 A4 1p multi ('78) .75 2.50
47 A4 1½p multi ('78) .75 2.50
48 A4 2p multi ('79) 2.50 3.50
49 A4 2½p multi ('79) 2.50 3.50
50 A4 3p multi ('79) 3.00 3.75
52 A4 5p multi ('79) 3.00 4.00
55 A4 10p multi ('79) 2.25 3.75
56 A4 15p multi ('79) 1.50 2.50
57 A4 25p multi ('79) 1.50 1.60
58 A4 50p multi ('79) 2.40 3.25
59 A4 £1 multi ('78) 5.00 2.50
Nos. 45-59 (12) 26.05 36.25

1973, Feb. 14   Wmk. 314
45a A4 ½p multi 1.50 2.75
46a A4 1p multi 2.75 4.25
47a A4 1½p multi 11.50 5.50
48a A4 2p multi 2.50 2.25
49a A4 2½p multi 2.00 2.25
50a A4 3p multi 1.10 2.25
51a A4 4p multi 1.10 2.25
52a A4 5p multi 1.25 2.25
53a A4 6p multi 1.50 2.25
54a A4 7½p multi 1.75 3.00
55a A4 10p multi 3.00 3.50
56a A4 15p multi 6.00 5.00
57a A4 25p multi 3.75 5.00
58a A4 50p multi 3.00 5.50
59a A4 £1 multi 5.25 9.50
Nos. 45a-59a (15) 47.95 57.50

1980   Wmk. 373   Perf. 12
51 A4 4p multi .65 2.00
53 A4 6p multi 1.00 3.50
54 A4 7½p multi 1.50 4.00
55b A4 10p multi .75 3.50
56b A4 15p multi .75 3.50
57b A4 25p multi 1.25 3.00
58b A4 50p multi 2.40 2.90
59b A4 £1 multi 4.75 4.50
Nos. 51-59b (8) 13.05 26.90

Princess Anne's Wedding Issue
Common Design Type
1973, Nov. 14   Wmk. 314   Perf. 14
60 CD325 5p ocher & multi .30 .30
61 CD325 15p blue grn & multi .80 .80

Wedding of Princess Anne and Capt. Mark Phillips, Nov. 14, 1973. Nos. 60-61 were not available locally until Dec. 23, 1973, and first-day covers bear that date.

Churchill and Map of Churchill Peninsula A5

Design: 15p, Churchill and "Trepassey" of Operation Tabarin, 1943.

1974, Nov. 30   Litho.   Perf. 14
62 A5 5p multicolored 1.75 1.75
63 A5 15p multicolored 3.00 3.00
a.   Souvenir sheet of 2, #62-63   15.00 15.00
Sir Winston Churchill (1874-1965).

Humpback Whale — A6

Wmk. 373
1977, Jan. 4   Litho.   Perf. 14
64 A6 2p Sperm whale 6.50 4.50
65 A6 8p Fin whale 7.50 5.00
66 A6 11p shown 7.75 5.00
67 A6 25p Blue whale 8.50 6.75
Nos. 64-67 (4) 30.25 21.25
Conservation of whales.

Prince Philip in Antarctica, 1956-57 — A7

Designs: 11p, Coronation oath. 33p, Queen before taking oath.

1977, Feb. 7   Perf. 13½x14

68	A7	6p multicolored	.70	.50
69	A7	11p multicolored	.80	.60
70	A7	33p multicolored	2.10	.80
		Nos. 68-70 (3)	3.60	1.90

25th anniv. of the reign of Elizabeth II.

Elizabeth II Coronation Anniversary Issue
Common Design Types
Souvenir Sheet
Unwmk.

1978, June 2   Litho.   Perf. 15

71	Sheet of 6	6.00	6.00
a.	CD326 25p Black bull of Clarence	1.00	1.00
b.	CD327 25p Elizabeth II	1.00	1.00
c.	CD328 25p Emperor penguin	1.00	1.00

No. 71 contains 2 se-tenant strips of Nos. 71a-71c, separated by horizontal gutter with commemorative and descriptive inscriptions and showing central part of coronation procession with coach.

Macaroni Penguins — A8

Perf. 13½x14
1979, Jan. 14   Litho.   Wmk. 373

72	A8	3p shown	11.00	11.00
73	A8	8p Gentoo	3.25	3.25
74	A8	11p Adelie	3.50	3.50
75	A8	25p Emperor	4.75	4.75
		Nos. 72-75 (4)	22.50	22.50

John Barrow, Tula, Society Emblem — A9

Royal Geographical Society Sesquicentennial (Past Presidents and Expedition Scenes): 7p, Clement Markham 11p, Lord Curzon. 15p, William Goodenough. 22p, James Wordie. 30p, Raymond Priestley.

Wmk. 373
1980, Dec. 1   Litho.   Perf. 13½

76	A9	3p multicolored	.25	.25
77	A9	7p multicolored	.25	.25
78	A9	11p multicolored	.35	.35
79	A9	15p multicolored	.45	.45
80	A9	22p multicolored	.65	.65
81	A9	30p multicolored	.85	.85
		Nos. 76-81 (6)	2.80	2.80

20th Anniv. of Antarctic Treaty — A10

10p, Map. 13p, Conservation research. 25p, Satellite image mapping. 26p, Global geophysics.

1981, Dec. 1   Perf. 13½x14

82	A10	10p multicolored	.25	.65
83	A10	13p multicolored	.35	.75
84	A10	25p multicolored	.60	.80
85	A10	26p multicolored	.65	.80
		Nos. 82-85 (4)	1.85	3.00

Continental Drift and Climatic Change — A11

1982, Mar. 8   Litho.   Perf. 13½x14

86	A11	3p Land, water	.30	.35
87	A11	6p Shrubs	.35	.45
88	A11	10p Dinosaur	.35	.55
89	A11	13p Volcano	.50	.65
90	A11	25p Trees	.65	.75
91	A11	26p Penguins	.65	.75
		Nos. 86-91 (6)	2.80	3.50

Princess Diana Issue
Common Design Type

5p, Arms. 17p, Diana, by Bryan Organ. 37p, Wedding. 50p, Portrait.

1982, July 1   Litho.   Perf. 14½x14

92	CD333	5p multi	.40	.25
93	CD333	17p multi	.90	.70
94	CD333	37p multi	1.50	1.00
95	CD333	50p multi	2.50	1.50
		Nos. 92-95 (4)	5.30	3.45

10th Anniv. of Convention for Conservation of Antarctic Seals — A12

1983, Jan. 3   Litho.

96	A12	5p shown	.35	.35
97	A12	10p Weddell seals	.50	.50
98	A12	13p Elephant seals	.60	.60
99	A12	17p Fur seals	.75	.75
100	A12	25p Ross seal	.80	.80
101	A12	34p Crabeater seals	1.40	1.40
		Nos. 96-101 (6)	4.40	4.40

Corethron Criophilum — A13

1p, shown. 2p, Desmonema gaudichaudi. 3p, Tomopteris carpenteri. 4p, Pareuchaeta antarctica. 5p, Antarctomysis maxima. 6p, Antarcturus signiensis. 7p, Serolis comuta. 8p, Parathemisto gaudichaudii. 9p, Bovallia gigantea. 10p, Euphausia superba. 15p, Colossendeis australis. 20p, Todarodes sagittatus. 25p, Notothenia neglecta. 50p, Chaenocephalus aceratus. £1, Lobodon carcinophagus. £3, Antarctic marine food chain.

1984, Mar. 15   Litho.   Perf. 14

102	A13	1p multicolored	.85	1.60
103	A13	2p multicolored	.90	1.60
104	A13	3p multicolored	.90	1.60
105	A13	4p multicolored	1.00	1.60
106	A13	5p multicolored	1.00	1.60
107	A13	6p multicolored	1.00	1.60
108	A13	7p multicolored	1.00	1.60
109	A13	8p multicolored	1.00	1.60
110	A13	9p multicolored	1.00	1.60
110A	A13	10p multicolored	1.00	1.60
111	A13	15p multicolored	1.00	1.60
112	A13	20p multicolored	1.10	1.60
113	A13	25p multicolored	1.10	1.60
114	A13	50p multicolored	1.75	2.00
115	A13	£1 multicolored	2.25	2.50
116	A13	£3 multicolored	6.50	6.50
		Nos. 102-116 (16)	23.35	31.80

Manned Flight Bicentenary — A14

5p, De Havilland Twin Otter. 13p, De Havilland Single Otter. 17p, Consolidated Canso. 50p, Lockheed Vega.

1983, Dec. 17   Wmk. 373

117	A14	5p multicolored	.30	.30
118	A14	13p multicolored	.55	.55
119	A14	17p multicolored	.70	.70
120	A14	50p multicolored	1.90	1.90
		Nos. 117-120 (4)	3.45	3.45

British-Graham Land Expedition, 1934-1937 — A15

Designs: 7p, M. Y. Penola in Stella Creek. 22p, Northern base, Winter Island. 27p, D. H. Fox Moth at southern base, Barry Island. 54p, Dog team near Ablation Point, George VI Sound.

1985, Mar. 23   Litho.   Perf. 14½

121	A15	7p multicolored	.50	.50
122	A15	22p multicolored	.80	.80
123	A15	27p multicolored	1.00	1.00
124	A15	54p multicolored	1.90	1.90
		Nos. 121-124 (4)	4.20	4.20

A16

Naturalists, fauna and flora: 7p, Robert McCormick (1800-1890), Catharacta Skua Maccormicki. 22p, Sir Joseph Dalton Hooker (1817-1911), Deschampsea antarctica. 27p, Jean Rene C. Quoy (1790-1869), Lagenorhynchus cruciger. 54p, James Weddell (1787-1834), Leptonychotes weddelli.

1985, Nov. 4   Litho.   Perf. 14½

125	A16	7p multicolored	1.75	1.75
126	A16	22p multicolored	2.25	3.25
127	A16	27p multicolored	2.50	3.25
128	A16	54p multicolored	3.25	4.50
		Nos. 125-128 (4)	9.75	12.75

A17

Halley's comet: 7p, Edmond Halley. 22p, Halley Station. 27p, Trajectory, 1531. 54p, Giotto space probe.

1986, Jan. 6   Wmk. 373   Perf. 14

129	A17	7p multi	1.75	1.50
130	A17	22p multi	2.25	2.75
131	A17	27p multi	2.50	3.25
132	A17	54p multi	3.25	5.25
		Nos. 129-132 (4)	9.75	12.75

Intl. Glaciological Society, 50th Anniv. — A18

Different snowflakes.

1986, Dec. 6   Wmk. 384   Perf. 14½

133	A18	10p dp blue & lt bl	.65	1.00
134	A18	24p blue grn & lt bl grn	.85	1.50
135	A18	29p dp rose lil & lt lil	.95	1.75
136	A18	58p dp vio & pale vio blue	2.10	2.75
		Nos. 133-136 (4)	4.55	7.00

Capt. Robert Falcon Scott, CVO RN (1868-1912) — A19

Designs: 24p, The Discovery at Hut Point, 1902-1904. 29p, Cape Evans Hut, 1911-1913. 58p, South Pole, 1912.

1987, Mar. 19   Litho.   Wmk. 373

137	A19	10p multicolored	.80	.95
138	A19	24p multicolored	1.40	2.00
139	A19	29p multicolored	1.60	2.40
140	A19	58p multicolored	2.25	3.25
		Nos. 137-140 (4)	6.05	8.60

Intl. Geophysical Year, 30th Anniv. — A20

1987, Dec. 25   Wmk. 384

141	A20	10p Emblem	.55	.70
142	A20	24p Port Lockroy	.85	1.40
143	A20	29p Argentine Islands	1.10	1.60
144	A20	58p Halley Bay	2.00	2.60
		Nos. 141-144 (4)	4.50	6.30

Commonwealth Trans-Antarctic Expedition — A21

10p, Aurora over South Ice. 24p, Otter aircraft. 29p, Seismic ice-depth sounding. 58p, Sno-cat over crevasse.

1988, Mar. 19   Perf. 14

145	A21	10p multicolored	.35	.35
146	A21	24p multicolored	.80	.80
147	A21	29p multicolored	.95	.95
148	A21	58p multicolored	1.90	1.90
		Nos. 145-148 (4)	4.00	4.00

Lichens — A22

10p, Xanthoria elegans. 24p, Usnea aurantiaco-atra. 29p, Cladonia chlorophaea. 58p, Umbilicaria antarctica.

1989, Mar. 25 — Wmk. 373

149	A22	10p multicolored	1.15	1.15
150	A22	24p multicolored	2.25	2.25
151	A22	29p multicolored	2.60	3.00
152	A22	58p multicolored	4.00	4.50
		Nos. 149-152 (4)	10.00	10.90

Fossils
A23

1p, Archaeocyath. 2p, Brachiopod. 3p, Trilobite (Triplagnostus). 4p, Trilobite (Lyriaspis). 5p, Gymnosperm. 6p, Fern. 7p, Belemnite. 8p, Ammonite (Sanmartinoceras). 9p, Bivalve (Pinna). 10p, Bivalve (Aucellina). 20p, Bivalve (Trigonia). 25p, Gastropod. 50p, Ammonite (Ainoceras). £ 1, Ammonite (Gunnarites). £ 3, Crayfish.

1990, Apr. 2 — Litho. — Wmk. 384

153	A23	1p multicolored	1.50	1.50
154	A23	2p multicolored	1.50	1.50
155	A23	3p multicolored	1.60	1.60
156	A23	4p multicolored	1.75	1.75
157	A23	5p multicolored	1.75	1.75
158	A23	6p multicolored	1.75	1.75
159	A23	7p multicolored	1.75	1.90
160	A23	8p multicolored	1.75	1.90
161	A23	9p multicolored	1.75	1.90
162	A23	10p multicolored	1.75	1.90
163	A23	20p multicolored	3.00	3.50
164	A23	25p multicolored	3.00	3.50
165	A23	50p multicolored	4.00	5.00
166	A23	£1 multicolored	7.00	9.00
167	A23	£3 multicolored	10.00	12.00
		Nos. 153-167 (15)	43.85	50.45

Queen Mother, 90th Birthday
Common Design Types

26p, Wedding portrait, 1923. £ 1, Family portrait, 1940.

1990, Aug. 4 — Wmk. 384 — Perf. 14x15

170	CD343	26p multicolored	1.50	1.50

Perf. 14½

171	CD344	£1 multicolored	5.25	5.25

Age of
Dinosaurs
A24

12p, Late Cretaceous forest. 26p, Hypsilophodont dinosaur. 31p, Frilled shark. 62p, Mosasaur, plesiosaur.

1991, Mar. 27 — Wmk. 373 — Perf. 14

172	A24	12p multicolored	1.50	1.50
173	A24	26p multicolored	2.50	2.50
174	A24	31p multicolored	2.75	2.75
175	A24	62p multicolored	4.75	4.75
		Nos. 172-175 (4)	11.50	11.50

Antarctic
Ozone
Hole — A25

12p, Launching weather balloon. 26p, Measuring ozone. 31p, Ozone hole over Antarctica. 62p, Airplane, chemical studies.

1991, Mar. 30 — Perf. 14½x14

176	A25	12p multicolored	1.10	1.90
177	A25	26p multicolored	1.75	3.00
178	A25	31p multicolored	2.25	3.25
179	A25	62p multicolored	4.00	5.00
		Nos. 176-179 (4)	9.10	13.15

Antarctic Treaty,
30th
Anniv. — A26

12p, Dry valley. 26p, Mapping ice sheet. 31p, BIOMASS emblem. 62p, Ross seal.

1991, June 24 — Perf. 14½

180	A26	12p multicolored	1.50	1.50
181	A26	26p multicolored	2.25	2.25
182	A26	31p multicolored	2.75	2.75
183	A26	62p multicolored	4.50	4.50
		Nos. 180-183 (4)	11.00	11.00

Royal
Research
Ship James
Clark
Ross — A27

Designs: 12p, HMS Erebus and Terror in Antarctic by John W. Carmichael. 26p, Launch of RRS James Clark Ross. 62p, Scientific research.

1991, Dec. 10 — Perf. 14x14½

184	A27	12p multicolored	1.25	1.75
185	A27	26p multicolored	2.25	3.00
186	A27	31p shown	2.75	3.50
187	A27	62p multicolored	4.50	5.25
		Nos. 184-187 (4)	10.75	13.50

Inscribed in
Blue

1991, Dec. 24

188	A27	12p like #184	1.75	2.25
189	A27	26p like #185	2.25	3.25
190	A27	31p like #186	2.75	4.25
191	A27	62p like #187	4.75	5.25
		Nos. 188-191 (4)	11.50	15.00

Seals
and
Penguins
A28

4p, Ross seal. 5p, Adelie penguin. 7p, Weddell seal. 29p, Emperor penguin. 34p, Crabeater seal. 68p, Chinstrap penguin.

1992, Oct. 20 — Perf. 13½

192	A28	4p multi	1.50	1.75
193	A28	5p multi	1.50	1.75
194	A28	7p multi	1.50	1.75
195	A28	29p multi	3.25	3.75
196	A28	34p multi	3.00	3.75
197	A28	68p multi	3.75	4.25
		Nos. 192-197 (6)	14.50	17.00

World Wildlife Fund.

Lower
Atmospheric
Phenomena
A29

14p, Sun pillar at Faraday. 29p, Halo with iceberg. 34p, Lee wave cloud. 68p, Nacreous clouds.

Perf. 14x14½

1992, Dec. 22 — Litho. — Wmk. 373

198	A29	14p multi	1.10	1.75
199	A29	29p multi	2.00	2.25
200	A29	34p multi	2.50	3.00
201	A29	68p multi	4.00	5.00
		Nos. 198-201 (4)	9.60	12.00

Research
Ships
A30

1p, SS Fitzroy. 2p, HMS William Scoresby. 3p, SS Eagle. 4p, MV Trepassey. 5p, RRS John Biscoe (I). 10p, MV Norsel. 20p, HMS Protector. 30p, MV Oluf Sven. 50p, RRS John Biscoe (II), RRS Shackleton. £ 1, MV Tottan. £ 3, MV Perla Dan. £ 5, HMS Endurance (I).

Wmk. 373

1993, Dec. 13 — Litho. — Perf. 14

202	A30	1p multi	1.75	2.50
203	A30	2p multi	2.50	2.50
204	A30	3p multi	2.50	2.50
205	A30	4p multi	2.50	2.50
206	A30	5p multi	2.50	2.50
207	A30	10p multi	3.00	3.25
208	A30	20p multi	3.75	4.00
209	A30	30p multi	4.25	4.75
210	A30	50p multi	5.25	6.00
a.		Souvenir sheet of 1	5.00	5.25
211	A30	£1 multi	7.00	7.25
a.		Souvenir sheet of 1	8.00	8.00
212	A30	£3 multi	15.00	17.00
213	A30	£5 multi	27.50	29.00
		Nos. 202-213 (12)	77.50	83.75

No. 210a for Hong Kong '97. Issued 2/3/97.
No. 211a for return of Hong Kong to China. Issued 7/1/97.

Operation
Taberin, 50th
Anniv. — A31

Designs: 15p, Bransfield House and Post Office, Port Lockroy. 31p, Survey team, Hope Bay. 36p, Dog team, Hope Bay. 72p, SS Fitzroy, HMS William Scoresby at sea.

Wmk. 373

1994, Mar. 19 — Litho. — Perf. 14

214	A31	15p multicolored	1.75	2.25
215	A31	31p multicolored	3.00	3.25
216	A31	36p multicolored	3.50	3.75
217	A31	72p multicolored	4.75	5.00
		Nos. 214-217 (4)	13.00	14.25

Old and New Transportation — A32

Designs: 15p, Huskies. 24p, DeHavilland DHC-2 Turbo Beaver, British Antarctic Survey. 31p, Dogs, cargo being taken from aircraft. 36p, DHC-6 Twin Otter, sled team. 62p, DHC-6 in flight. 72p, DHC-6 taxiing down runway.

1994, Mar. 21

218	A32	15p multicolored	1.25	1.25
219	A32	24p multicolored	1.75	1.75
220	A32	31p multicolored	2.00	2.25
221	A32	36p multicolored	2.25	2.50
222	A32	62p multicolored	3.00	3.50
223	A32	72p multicolored	3.75	4.00
		Nos. 218-223 (6)	14.00	15.25

Ovptd. with Hong Kong '94 Emblem

1994, Feb. 18

224	A32	15p on #218	1.50	1.50
225	A32	24p on #219	2.00	2.00
226	A32	31p on #220	2.25	2.50
227	A32	36p on #221	2.50	2.75
228	A32	62p on #222	3.50	3.75
229	A32	72p on #223	4.25	4.50
		Nos. 224-229 (6)	16.00	17.00

Antarctic
Food
Chain — A33

a, Crabeater seals. b, Blue whale. c, Wandering albatross. d, Mackeral icefish. e, Krill. f, Squid.

1994, Nov. 29

230	A33	35p Sheet of 6, #a-f	16.00	16.00

Geological
Structures
A34

Designs: 17p, Hauberg Mountains, folded sedimentary rocks. 35p, Arrowsmith Peninsula, dikes cross-cutting granite. 40p, Colbert Mountains, columnar jointing in volcanic rocks. 76p, Succession Cliffs, flat-lying sedimentary rocks.

Perf. 14x14½

1995, Nov. 28 — Litho. — Wmk. 373

231	A34	17p multicolored	2.00	2.00
232	A34	35p multicolored	3.25	3.25
233	A34	40p multicolored	3.50	4.00
234	A34	76p multicolored	5.25	6.00
		Nos. 231-234 (4)	14.00	15.25

Scientific Committee on Antarctic
Research (SCAR) — A35

Designs: 17p, World map showing SCAR member countries. 35p, Earth sciences. 40p, Atmospheric sciences. 76p, Life sciences. £1, Cambridge, August 1996.

Wmk. 384

1996, Mar. 23 — Litho. — Perf. 14

235	A35	17p multicolored	1.75	1.75
236	A35	35p multicolored	2.75	2.75
237	A35	40p multicolored	3.00	3.00
238	A35	76p multicolored	4.50	4.50
		Nos. 235-238 (4)	12.00	12.00

Souvenir Sheet

239	A35	£1 multicolored	9.00	9.00

Queen Elizabeth II, 70th Birthday
Common Design Type

Various portraits of Queen: 17p, Pink outfit. 35p, In formal dress, tiara. 40p, Blue outfit. 76p, Red coat.

Wmk. 384

1996, Nov. 25 — Litho. — Perf. 14½

240	CD354	17p multicolored	1.75	.90
241	CD354	35p multicolored	2.25	1.50
242	CD354	40p multicolored	2.50	2.50
243	CD354	76p multicolored	4.00	4.00
		Nos. 240-243 (4)	10.50	8.90

Whales
A36

Wmk. 373

1996, Nov. 25 — Litho. — Perf. 14

244	A36	17p Killer whale	1.50	1.00
245	A36	35p Sperm whale	2.25	1.50
246	A36	40p Minke whale	3.75	2.50
247	A36	76p Blue whale	4.75	4.00
		Nos. 244-247 (4)	12.25	9.00

Souvenir Sheet

248	A36	£1 Humpback whale	11.00	11.00

Christmas — A37

Penguins in snow: 17p, Sledding. 35p, Caroling. 40p, Throwing snowballs. 76p, Ice skating.

Wmk. 384

1997, Dec. 22   Litho.   Perf. 14½
249 A37 17p multicolored   3.50   2.25
250 A37 35p multicolored   5.50   3.75
251 A37 40p multicolored   6.25   5.50
252 A37 76p multicolored   8.00   8.50
    Nos. 249-252 (4)   23.25 20.00

History of
Mapping — A38

Maps of Antarctic and: 16p, Surveyor looking through theodolite, 1902-03. 30p, Cartographer, 1949. 35p, Man using radar rangefinder, 1964. 40p, Satellite, 1981. 65p, Tripod, hand held remote control device, 1993.

Wmk. 373

1998, Mar. 19   Litho.   Perf. 14
253 A38 16p multicolored   2.50   2.25
254 A38 30p multicolored   3.00   2.50
255 A38 35p multicolored   3.75   3.00
256 A38 40p multicolored   4.00   4.25
257 A38 65p multicolored   5.00   5.50
    Nos. 253-257 (5)   18.25 17.50

Diana, Princess of Wales (1961-97)
Common Design Type

a, Wearing sun glasses. b, In white top. c, Up close. d, Wearing blue-green blazer.

1998, Mar. 31   Perf. 14½x14
258 CD355 35p Sheet of 4, #a-d 6.25 6.25

No. 258 sold for £1.40 + 20p, with surtax and 50% of profit from total sales being donated to the Princess Diana Memorial Fund.

Antarctic Clothing
Through the
Ages — A39

Man outfitted for cold weather: 30p, Holding shovel, sailing ship, 1843. 35p, With dog, sailing ship, 1900. 40p, With sketch pad, tripod, dog, steamer ship, 1943. 65p, Wearing red suit, penguins, ship, 1998.

Perf. 14½x14
1998, Nov. 30   Litho.   Wmk. 373
259 A39 30p multicolored   4.75   3.50
260 A39 35p multicolored   5.00   3.75
261 A39 40p multicolored   5.25   5.00
262 A39 65p multicolored   7.50   7.25
    Nos. 259-262 (4)   22.50 19.50

Birds
A40

Designs: 1p, Sheathbill. 2p, Antarctic prion. 5p, Adelie penguin. 10p, Emperor penguin. 20p, Antarctic tern. 30p, Black bellied storm petrel. 35p, Antarctic fulmar. 40p, Blue eyed

shag. 50p, McCormick's skua. £1, Kelp gull. £3, Wilson's storm petrel. £5, Brown skua.

1998   Perf. 14
263 A40 1p multicolored   1.40   1.40
264 A40 2p multicolored   1.40   1.40
265 A40 5p multicolored   1.60   1.60
266 A40 10p multicolored   1.75   1.75
267 A40 20p multicolored   2.00   2.00
268 A40 30p multicolored   2.50   2.50
269 A40 35p multicolored   2.75   2.75
270 A40 40p multicolored   3.25   3.25
271 A40 50p multicolored   4.50   4.50
272 A40 £1 multicolored   5.50   5.50
273 A40 £3 multicolored   11.00 11.00
274 A40 £5 multicolored   17.50 17.50
    Nos. 263-274 (12)   55.15 55.15

Fish — A41

Wmk. 373
1999, Nov. 14   Litho.   Perf. 13½
275 A41 10p Mackerel icefish   2.40   1.75
276 A41 20p Toothfish   3.50   2.40
277 A41 25p Borch   4.00   2.75
278 A41 50p Marbled notothen   6.00   4.00
279 A41 80p Bernach   7.00   7.00
    Nos. 275-279 (5)   22.90 17.90

Survey Discoveries — A42

15p, Map of crustal microplates of West Antarctica. 30p, Lead levels in ice. 35p, Gigantism in marine invertebrates. 40p, Ozone hole. 70p, Electric field associated with aurora.

Wmk. 373
1999, Dec. 18   Litho.   Perf. 14
280 A42 15p multi, vert.   4.25   2.00
281 A42 30p multi, vert.   4.75   2.75
282 A42 35p multi   5.00   3.00
283 A42 40p multi   5.25   3.25
284 A42 70p multi   6.75   6.00
    Nos. 280-284 (5)   26.00 17.00

Sir Ernest Shackleton (1874-1922),
Polar Explorer — A43

Designs: 35p, Wreck of the Endurance. 40p, Ocean Camp on ice floe. 65p, Launching the James Caird from Elephant Island.

2000, Feb. 10   Wmk. 373
285 A43 35p multi   7.00   3.50
286 A43 40p multi   7.50   3.50
287 A43 65p multi   8.50   5.50
    Nos. 285-287 (3) 23.00 12.50

See Falkland Islands Nos. 758-760, South Georgia and South Sandwich Islands Nos. 254-256.

The Stamp Show 2000,
London — A44

Commonwealth Trans-Antarctic Exhibition of 1955-58: a, Map of route. b, Expedition at South Pole, 1958. c, MV Magga Dan. d, Sno-

cat repair camp. e, Sno-cat over crevasse. f, Seismic explosion.

Perf. 13¼x13¾
2000, May 22   Litho.   Wmk. 373
288 A44 37p Sheet of 6, #a-f   70.00 70.00

Survey
Ships
A45

Designs: 20p, RRS Bransfield unloading near Halley, vert. 33p, Supply boat Tula and RRS Ernest Shackleton, vert. 37p, RRS Bransfield. 43p, RRS Ernest Shackleton.

Wmk. 373
2000, Nov. 30   Litho.   Perf. 14
289-292 A45 Set of 4   27.50 27.50

Composing of Antarctic Symphony, by
Sir Peter Maxwell Davies — A46

Designs: No. 293, 37p, RRS James Clark Ross and track cut through ice. No. 294, 37p, Iceberg. No. 295, 43p, Camp on Jones Ice Shelf. No. 296, 43p, Iceberg, diff.

2000, Dec. 4
293-296 A46 Set of 4   24.00 24.00

Port Lockroy — A47

Designs: 33p, Visitors near building, penguins, flagpole, 2001. 37p, Visitors on rocks below building, ship in water, 2001. 43p, Port Lockroy building, 1945. 65p, Laboratory interior, 1945.

Perf. 13¾x14
2001, Nov. 29   Litho.   Wmk. 373
297-300 A47 Set of 4   28.00 28.00

British
National
Antarctic
Expedition
of 1901-
04, Cent.
A48

Designs: 33p, Map of expedition's route, vert. 37p, Capt. Robert Falcon Scott (1868-1912), vert. 43p, First Antarctic balloon ascent, 1902. 65p, Emperor penguin chick, vert. 70p, Ernest Shackleton, Scott, Edward Adrian Wilson, sleds at southernmost point of expedition. 80p, Discovery trapped in ice.

2001, Dec. 5   Wmk. 384   Perf. 14
301-306 A48 Set of 6   26.00 26.00

Reign Of Queen Elizabeth II, 50th Anniv. Issue
Common Design Type

Designs: Nos. 307, 311a, 20p, Princess Elizabeth making first broadcast. Nos. 308, 311b, 37p, At Garter ceremony, 1998. Nos. 309, 311c, 43p, In 1952. Nos. 310, 311d, 50p, In 1996. No. 311e, 50p, 1955 portrait by Annigoni (38x50mm).

Perf. 14¼x14½, 13¾ (#311e)
2002, Feb. 6   Litho.   Wmk. 373
With Gold Frames
307 CD360 20p multicolored   1.50   1.50
308 CD360 37p multicolored   2.75   2.75

309 CD360 43p multicolored   3.00   3.00
310 CD360 50p multicolored   3.75   3.75
    Nos. 307-310 (4)   11.00 11.00
Souvenir Sheet
Without Gold Frames
311 CD360 Sheet of 5, #a-e   14.00 14.00

Queen Mother Elizabeth (1900-2002)
Common Design Type

Designs: 40p, Without hat (sepia photograph). 45p, Wearing blue green hat. No. 314: a, 70p, Wearing feathered hat (black and white photograph). b, 95p, Wearing dark blue hat.

Wmk. 373
2002, Aug. 5   Litho.   Perf. 14¼
With Purple Frames
312 CD361 40p multicolored   3.00   3.00
313 CD361 45p multicolored   3.25   3.25
Souvenir Sheet
Without Purple Frames
Perf. 14½x14¼
314 CD361 Sheet of 2, #a-b   13.00 13.00

Commission for the Conservation of
Antarctic Marine Living Resources,
20th Anniv. — A49

No. 315: a, Map of Antarctica, vessel monitoring satellite. b, Wandering albatross, fishing boat. c, Icefish, toothfish and crabeater seal. d, Krill and phytoplankton.

Perf. 13½x13¾
2002, Oct. 22   Litho.   Wmk. 373
315 Vert. strip of 4   13.00 13.00
  a.-d. A49 37p Any single   3.00   3.00

Scottish National Antarctic Expedition,
1902-04 — A50

Designs: 30p, Map of oceanographic cruises of the Scotia, vert. 40p, Bagpiper Gilbert Kerr and Emperor penguin. 45p, SY Scotia, vert. 70p, Meteorological observations, cent. 95p, William Speirs Bruce, vert. £1, Omond House, Laurie Island.

Wmk. 373
2002, Dec. 5   Litho.   Perf. 14
316-321 A50 Set of 6   35.00 35.00

Head of Queen Elizabeth II
Common Design Type

Wmk. 373
2003, June 2   Litho.   Perf. 13¾
322 CD362 £2 multi   10.00 10.00

Coronation of Queen Elizabeth II, 50th Anniv.
Common Design Type

Designs: Nos. 323, 40p, 325a, Queen in carriage. Nos. 324, 45p, 325b, Queen and family on Buckingham Palace balcony.

Perf. 14¼x14½
2003, June 2   Litho.   Wmk. 373
Vignettes Framed, Red Background
323 CD363 40p multicolored   4.25   4.25
324 CD363 45p multicolored   4.75   4.75
Souvenir Sheet
Vignettes Without Frame, Purple Panel
325 CD363 95p Sheet of 2, #a-b   17.00 17.00

Worldwide Fund for Nature (WWF) A51

Blue whale: 40p, Underwater. No. 327, 45p, Tail above water. No. 328, 50p, Two whales underwater. 70p, Two whales at surface.

Wmk. 373

2003, Dec. 5		**Litho.**		**Perf. 14**
326-329	A51	Set of 4	10.00	10.00
329a		Sheet, 4 each #326-329	42.50	42.50

Bases and Postmarks A52

Bases: 1p, G, Admiralty Bay. 2p, B, Deception Island. 5p, D, Hope Bay. 22p, F, Argentine Islands. 25p, E, Stonington Island. 40p, A, Port Lockroy. 45p, H, Signy. 50p, N, Anvers Island. 95p, R, Rothera. £1, T, Adelaide Island. £3, Y, Horseshoe Island. £5, Z, Halley Bay.

2003, Dec. 8		**Wmk. 373**		**Perf. 14**
330	A52	1p multi	.40	.40
331	A52	2p multi	.50	.50
332	A52	5p multi	.60	.60
333	A52	22p multi	1.00	1.00
334	A52	25p multi	1.10	1.10
335	A52	40p multi	1.75	1.75
336	A52	45p multi	2.00	2.00
337	A52	50p multi	2.10	2.10
338	A52	95p multi	4.00	4.00
339	A52	£1 multi	4.25	4.25
340	A52	£3 multi	12.50	12.50
341	A52	£5 multi	20.00	20.00
		Nos. 330-341 (12)	50.20	50.20

Climate Change A53

No. 342, 24p: a, Map of Antarctica showing annual temperature trends since 1950. b, Larsen Ice Shelf.
No. 343, 42p: a, Graph of ice core age and warmth. b, Ice core drilling.
No. 344, 50p: a, Graph of rise of mean summer air temperatures at Faraday Station. b, Pearlwort.

Wmk. 373

2004, Dec. 9		**Litho.**		**Perf. 14**
		Vert. Pairs, #a-b		
342-344	A53	Set of 3	20.00	20.00

Petrels A54

Designs: 25p, Cape petrel. 42p, Snow petrel. 75p, Wilson's storm petrel. £1, Antarctic petrel.
No. 349 — Southern giant petrel: a, In flight, name at right. b, In flight, name at left. c, Close-up of head, bird in flight. d, With wings extended above nest. e, Adult and chick. f, Chick.

2005, Jan. 23			**Perf. 13¾**
345-348	A54	Set of 4	21.00 21.00
		Souvenir Sheet	
349	A54	50p Sheet of 6, #a-f	25.00 25.00

Ships Named Endurance A55

Designs: 42p, Endurance, 1914-15. 50p, HMS Endurance, 1968-90. £1, HMS Endurance, 1991-present.

2005, Jan. 24			**Perf. 14¾x14**
350-352	A55	Set of 3	17.50 17.50

Falkland Islands and Dependencies Aerial Survey Expedition, 50th Anniv. — A56

Designs: 45p, Deception Island. 55p, Hunting Lodge. 80p, Bell 47 helicopter. £1, Canso Flying Boat.

Wmk. 373

2005, Dec. 19		**Litho.**		**Perf. 14**
353-356	A56	Set of 4	18.00	18.00

Halley VI Research Station Design Competition — A57

Designs: No. 357, 45p, Concept of Faber Maunsell. No. 358, 45p, Concept of Buro Happold. 55p, Concept by Hopkins. 80p, Laws Building of Halley V Research Station.

Wmk. 373

2005, Dec. 22		**Litho.**		**Perf. 14**
357-360	A57	Set of 4	16.00	16.00

Dogs of Sir Ernest Shackleton — A58

Designs: No. 361, 45p, Shackleton and puppies. No. 362, 45p, Samson, Shakespeare and Surley, horiz. 55p, Ice kennels around ship, Endurance, horiz. £1, Training on sea ice.

2005, Dec. 22			
361-364	A58	Set of 4	13.00 13.00

Antarctic Treaty Consultative Meeting Scottish Children's Stamp Design Competition A59

Winning designs by: No. 365, 45p, Erica Currie. No. 366, 45p, Meghan Joyce. 55p, Lorna MacDonald. £1, Danielle Dalgleish.

2006, Feb. 26			
365-368	A59	Set of 4	17.00 17.00

Queen Elizabeth II, 80th Birthday A60

Queen: 45p, As child. Nos. 370, 373a, 55p, Wearing crown. Nos. 371, 373b, 80p, Wearing red hat. £1, Without head covering.

Wmk. 373

2006, Apr. 21		**Litho.**		**Perf. 14**
		With White Frames		
369-372	A60	Set of 4	19.00	19.00
		Souvenir Sheet		
		Without White Frames		
373	A60	Sheet of 2, #a-b	11.00	11.00

Seals A61

Designs: 25p, Elephant seals. 50p, Crabeater seals. 60p, Weddell seals. £1.05, Leopard seal.

Perf. 14¼x14¾

2006, Dec. 16		**Litho.**		**Wmk. 373**
374-377	A61	Set of 4	20.00	20.00

Icebergs A62

Various icebergs: 25p, 50p, 60p, £1.05.

Wmk. 373

2007, Nov. 14		**Litho.**		**Perf. 13¾**
378-381	A62	Set of 4	14.50	14.50

Marine Invertebrates — A63

Designs: 25p, Sea lemon. 50p, Antarctic sea anemone. 60p, Sea spider. £1.05, Sea star.

2007, Nov. 14			**Perf. 14**
382-385	A63	Set of 4	14.00 14.00

Souvenir Sheet

Intl. Polar Year — A64

2007, Nov. 14			**Perf.**
386	A64	£2 multi	11.00 11.00

Explorers and Ships A65

Designs: 1p, James Weddell (1787-1834), Jane and Beaufoy. 2p, Sir James Clark Ross (1800-62), Erebus and Terror. 5p, Neil Alison Mackintosh (1900-74), Discovery II. 27p, Sir Douglas Mawson (1882-1958), Discovery. 55p, Captain James Cook (1728-79), Resolution. Nos. 392, 399a, Captain Egeberg Borchgrevink (1864-1934), Southern Cross. Nos. 393, 399b, Dr. William Speirs Bruce (1867-1921), Scotia. Nos. 394, 399c, Captain Robert Falcon Scott (1868-1912), Discovery. Nos. 395, 399d, Sir Ernest Shackleton (1874-1922), Endurance. £1.10, John Riddoch Rymill (1905-68), Penola. £2.50, Captain Victor Marchesi (1914-2006), William Scoresby. £5, Sir Vivian Fuchs (1908-99), Magga Dan.

Wmk. 406

2008, Nov. 17		**Litho.**		**Perf. 14**
387	A65	1p multi	.25	.25
388	A65	2p multi	.25	.25
389	A65	5p multi	.25	.25
390	A65	27p multi	.90	.90
391	A65	55p multi	1.75	1.75
392	A65	65p multi	2.10	2.10
393	A65	65p multi	2.10	2.10
394	A65	65p multi	2.10	2.10
395	A65	65p multi	2.10	2.10
396	A65	£1.10 multi	4.25	4.25
397	A65	£2.50 multi	8.25	8.25
398	A65	£5 multi	16.50	16.50
		Nos. 387-398 (12)	40.80	40.80
		Souvenir Sheet		
399		Sheet of 4	7.75	7.75
a.-d.	A65	(65p) Any single	1.90	1.90

Nos. 399a-399d are inscribed "Airmail Letter."

A66

A67

A68

A69

Aurora Australis A70

2008, Nov. 17		**Wmk. 373**
400		Horiz. strip of 5	17.50 17.50
a.	A66	65p multi	3.50	3.50
b.	A67	65p multi	3.50	3.50
c.	A68	65p multi	3.50	3.50
d.	A69	65p multi	3.50	3.50
e.	A70	65p multi	3.50	3.50

Fossil
Ferns
A71

Map of Antarctica and: 55p, Lophosoria
cupulatus. 65p, Cladophlebis oblonga. No.
403, £1.10, Pachypteris indica. No. 404,
£1.10, Aculea acicularis.

2008, Nov. 17   *Perf. 14*
401-404 A71   Set of 4   14.00 14.00

Naval
Aviation,
Cent.
A72

Designs: No. 405, 10p, Fairey Seafox. No.
406, 10p, Westland Lynx helicopter. No. 407,
90p, Supermarine Walrus. No. 408, 90p,
Westland Wasp helicopter.
£2, HMA No. 1 Mayfly airship.

Wmk. 406
2009, Jan. 1   **Litho.**   *Perf. 14*
405-408 A72   Set of 4   8.00 8.00
Souvenir Sheet
409 A72   £2 multi   9.50 9.50

Worldwide Fund for Nature
(WWF) — A73

Crabeater seal: 27p, On ice. 65p, Head pok-
ing through hole in ice. £1.10, Two seals on
ice. £1.50, Underwater.

Wmk. 406
2009, Nov. 6   **Litho.**   *Perf. 14*
410-413 A73   Set of 4   13.00 13.00
413a   Sheet of 16, 4 each
   #410-413   52.00 52.00

Antarctic Treaty, 50th Anniv. — A74

No. 414, 27p: a, Antarctic fur seal. b, Hump-
back whale.
No. 415, 55p: a, Southern giant petrel. b,
Gentoo penguins.
No. 416, 65p: a, Giant squid. b, Jellyfish.

2009, Nov. 6   *Perf. 14*
Horiz. Pairs, #a-b
414-416 A74   Set of 3   12.00 12.00

Miniature Sheet

Effects of Climate Change — A75

No. 417 — Maps showing present day and
1950 extents of: a, George VI Ice Shelf
(South). b, Larsen B Ice Shelf. c, Wilkins Ice
Shelf. d, Larsen C Ice Shelf.

2009, Nov. 26   *Perf. 13¼x13½*
417 A75   £1.10 Sheet of 4,
   #a-d   17.50 17.50

Marine
Life
A76

Designs: No. 418, 27p, Polychaete worm.
No. 419, 27p, Button worm. No. 420, 27p,
Sponge. No. 421, 27p, Amphipod.
No. 422: a, Solitary coral. b, Amphipod, diff.
c, Comb jellyfish. d, Basket star.

Wmk. 406
2010, Dec. 3   **Litho.**   *Perf. 14*
418-421 A76   Set of 4   4.50 4.50
Souvenir Sheet
   Perf. 13¼
422 A76   £1.15 Sheet of 4,
   #a-d   17.00 17.00
No. 422 contains four 36x36mm stamps.

Birds — A77

No. 423, 27p: a, South polar skua. b, Adélie
penguin.
No. 424, 70p: a, Gray-headed albatross. b,
Emperor penguin.
No. 425, £1.15: a, Kelp gull. b, Antarctic
petrel.

2010, Dec. 3   *Perf. 14*
Horiz. Pairs, #a-b
423-425 A77   Set of 3   20.00 20.00

Miniature Sheets

Photographs of 1910-13 British
Antarctic Expedition — A78

No. 426, 27p: a, Ship, Terra Nova, on hori-
zon. b, Ponies. c, Cavern in iceberg. d, "Tene-
ments" bunks in Winterquarters hut. e, Capt.
Robert Falcon Scott's birthday dinner. f,
Observing at the weather station. g, Capt.
Scott writing in his journal. h, Terra Nova in the
ice.
No. 427, 60p: a, Terra Nova in harbor. b,
Lieutenant Rennick leading pony. c, Matter-
horn Berg. d, Nelson at work in the lab. e,
Capt. Scott on skis. f, Chris (dog) and gramo-
phone. g, Motorized tractor and load passing
Inaccessible Island. h, Polar party at the South
Pole.

2010, Dec. 3   *Perf. 13¼*
Sheets of 8, #a-h
426-427 A78   Set of 2   24.00 24.00

Miniature Sheets

A79

Filming in British Antarctic Territrory of
Frozen Planet Television Series — A80

No. 428: a, Close-up of head of seal. b, Seal
with head on rock. c, Head of seal on back in
snow. d, Seal in water. e, Dorsal fin of killer
whales. f, Head of killer whale and four other
killer whales with heads below water. g, Two
killer whales with heads abovve water. h, Dorsal fins of two killer whales.
No. 429: a, Adult and juvenile penguin. b,
Three penguins walking. c, Four penguins,
one with beak open. d, Adult penguin feeding
juvenile. e, Juvenile penguin on rock facing
left. f, Penguin and ship. g, Group of penguins
jumping from water to ice. h, Chinstrap penguin facing forward.

2011, Nov. 17
428 A79   27p Sheet of 8, #a-h   6.75 6.75
429 A80   60p Sheet of 8, #a-h   15.00 15.00

Miniature Sheets

A81

A82

Science in the Antarctic — A83

No. 430: a, Building (sepia-toned). b, Building (color). c, Scientists preparing weather balloon for flight (sepia-toned), vert. d, Scientist
preparing weather ballon for flight (color), vert.
e, Two scientists on boat preparing equipment
(sepia-toned), vert. f, Scientific equipment on
cable (color), vert. g, Two skiers, iceberg
(sepia-toned). h, Scientists in small boat
(color).
No. 431 (color images): a, Airplane. b, Scientist spraying water into air. c, Scientist opening weather station. d, British Antarctic Survey
Advanced Ionospheric Sounder.
No. 432 (sepia-toned images): a, Scientist,
microscope and bottles. b, Scientist at weather
station. c, Equipment in storage. d, Scientist
looking through telescope.

2011, Nov. 17   *Perf. 14*
430 A81   27p Sheet of 8,
   #a-h   6.75 6.75
431 A82   70p Sheet of 4,
   #a-d   8.75 8.75
432 A83   £1.15 Sheet of 4,
   #a-d   14.50 14.50
  Nos. 430-432 (3)   30.00 30.00

A84

A85

A86

A87

A88

A89

A90

A91

A92

Glaciers and
Icesheets
A93

2012, Dec. 21   *Perf. 13¾*
433	Horiz. strip of 5	10.00	10.00
a.	A84 65p multi	2.00	2.00
b.	A85 65p multi	2.00	2.00
c.	A86 65p multi	2.00	2.00
d.	A87 65p multi	2.00	2.00
e.	A88 65p multi	2.00	2.00
434	Horiz. strip of 5	12.00	12.00
a.	A89 75p multi	2.40	2.40
b.	A90 75p multi	2.40	2.40
c.	A91 75p multi	2.40	2.40
d.	A92 75p multi	2.40	2.40
e.	A93 75p multi	2.40	2.40

British Graham Land Expedition, 75th Anniv. — A94

No. 435, 40p: a, Boat on shore with three crew members. b, Two boats on dock.
No. 436, 40p: a, Dog. b, Dog and expedition member.
No. 437, 50p: a, Airplane, dog, expedition members. b, Airplane on water.
No. 438, 50p: a, Ship, denomination in white at LR. b, Ship, denomination in black at UR. £1.20, Ship "Penola."

2012, Dec. 21   **Perf. 13¾**
Horiz. Pairs, #a-b
435-438 A94 Set of 4   12.00 12.00
Souvenir Sheet
Perf. 14x14¾
439 A94 £1.20 multi   4.50 4.50
No. 439 contains one 49x33mm stamp.

Souvenir Sheet

HMS Protector — A95

2012, Dec. 21   **Perf. 14¼x15**
440 A95 £3.50 multi   11.50 11.50

Souvenir Sheet

Naming of Queen Elizabeth Land — A96

2013, Mar. 18   **Perf. 14¾x14**
441 A96 £3 multi   9.25 9.25

British Antarctic Territory Postage Stamps, 50th Anniv. A97

British Antarctic Territory stamps issued from 1963-69: 1p, #1. 1p, #2. 2p, #3. 5p, #4. 30p, #5. 40p, #6. 50p, #7. 65p, #8. 75p, #9. 85p, #10. 95p, #11. £1, #12. £1.20, #13. £2, #14. £3.50, #15. £5, #24.

Wmk. 406
2013, Nov. 27   Litho.   **Perf. 14**
442 A97 1p multi   .25 .25
443 A97 2p multi   .25 .25
444 A97 5p multi   .25 .25
445 A97 10p multi   .35 .35
446 A97 30p multi   1.00 1.00
447 A97 40p multi   1.40 1.40
448 A97 50p multi   1.60 1.60
449 A97 65p multi   2.10 2.10
450 A97 75p multi   2.50 2.50
451 A97 85p multi   2.75 2.75
452 A97 95p multi   3.00 3.00
453 A97 £1 multi   3.25 3.25
454 A97 £1.20 multi   4.00 4.00
455 A97 £2 multi   6.50 6.50
456 A97 £3.50 multi   11.50 11.50
457 A97 £5 multi   16.50 16.50
Nos. 442-457 (16)   57.20 57.20

Bransfield House, 70th Anniv. A98

Designs: 65p, Penguins outside of Bransfield House. 75p, Laboratory. 85p, Bransfield House and storage building. £1.20, Kitchen.

Wmk. 406
2013, Nov. 27   Litho.   **Perf. 14**
458-461 A98 Set of 4   11.50 11.50

Halley VI Research Station A99

Station: 75p, In daylight. 85p, At night. 95p, In daylight, diff. £1.20, At night, diff.

Wmk. 406
2013, Nov. 27   Litho.   **Perf. 14**
462-465 A99 Set of 4   12.50 12.50

Penguins — A100

No. 466, 40p: a, Adult Gentoo penguin (denomination at UR). b, Juvenile Gentoo penguin (denomination at UL).
No. 467, 50p: a, Adult Adélie penguin (denomination at UR). b, Juvenile Adélie penguins (denomination at UL).
No. 468, 75p: a, Adult Chinstrap penguin (denomination at UR). b, Juvenile Chinstrap penguins (denomination at UL).
No. 469, £1.20: a, Adult Emperor penguins (denomination at UR). b, Juvenile Emperor penguins (denomination at UL).

Wmk. 406
2013, Nov. 27   Litho.   **Perf. 13¾**
Horiz. Pairs, #a-b
466-469 A100 Set of 4   19.00 19.00

Miniature Sheet

Imperial Trans-Antarctic Expedition, Cent. (in 2014) — A101

No. 470: a, 65p, Sir Ernest Shackleton and his wife. b, 65p, Expedition members How, Barr, Irvine, Macleod, and Macaulay. c, 65p, Lieutenant A. E. Mackintosh and Frank Wild. d, 75p, Departure from Millwall Docks. e, 75p, Shackleton on board the Endurance. f, 75p, SS Endurance setting sail.

Wmk. 406
2013, Nov. 27   Litho.   **Perf. 14**
470 A101 Sheet of 6, #a-f   14.00 14.00
See Nos. 471-476, 490-495.

Imperial Trans-Antarctic Expedition
Type of 2013

Designs: No. 471, 65p, Endurance in full sail in ice. No. 472, 65p, Endurance trapped in ice and capsizing. No. 473, 75p, Ernest Shackleton and Frank Wild at Ocean Camp. No. 474, 75p, Shackleton and Frank Hurley at Patience Camp. No. 475, £1, Expedition members dragging the James Caird across the ice. No. 476, £1, Expedition members landing on Elephant Island.

2014, Nov. 19   Litho.   **Perf. 14**
471-476 A101 Set of 6   15.00 15.00

iStar Ice Stability Program A102

Designs: 65p, Twin Otter airplane in flight. 75p, Surface radar. £1, RRS James Clark Ross. £1.20, Autosub.

2014, Nov. 19   Litho.   **Perf. 14**
477-480 A102 Set of 4   11.50 11.50

Antarctic Marine Food Web A103

Designs (without arrows): No. 481, 65p, Phytoplankton. 75p, Krill and squid. £1, Penguins and flying birds. £1.20, Leopard seal.
No. 485, 65p — Designs with arrows: a, Penguins and flying birds. b, Fish. c, Smaller toothed whale. d, Leopard seal. e, Krill and squid. f, Seals. g, Baleen whale. h, Zooplankton. i, Phytoplankton.

2014, Nov. 19   Litho.   **Perf. 14**
481-484 A103 Set of 4   11.50 11.50
Miniature Sheet
485 A103 65p Sheet of 9, #a-i   18.50 18.50

Queen Elizabeth II, Longest-Reigning British Monarch — A104

Queen Elizabeth II and events during her reign: 66p, Publications reporting on her coronation, 1953. 76p, Satellite that discovered hole in ozone layer over Antarctica, 1985. £1.01, RSS James Clark Ross, 1990. £1.22, Map of Queen Elizabeth Land, 2012.

2015, Sept. 9   Litho.   **Perf. 14**
486-489 A104 Set of 4   11.00 11.00

Imperial Trans-Antarctic Expedition
Type of 2013

Designs: No. 490, 66p, Launching the James Caird. No. 491, 66p, Digging a cave for shelter, Elephant Island. No. 492, 76p, The Snuggery, Elephant Island. No. 493, 76p, Crossing the South Georgia Mountains. No. 494, £1.01, The Yelcho rescuing the crew from Elephant Island. No. 495, £1.01, The Yelcho with crew arrives in Chile.

2015, Nov. 17   Litho.   **Perf. 14**
490-495 A101 Set of 6   15.00 15.00

Wildlife and Huts — A105

Designs: No. 496, 66p, Weddell seals, Damoy Hut, Dorian Bay. No. 497, 66p, Adélie penguins, Base W, Detaille Island. 76p, Skua, Base Y, Horseshoe Island. £1.01, Blue-eyed shag, Base E, Stonington Island. £1.22, Orca, Base F, Wordie House, Winter Island.

2015, Nov. 17   Litho.   **Perf. 14**
496-500 A105 Set of 5   13.00 13.00

Whales — A106

Designs: No. 501, 66p, Antarctic minke whale. No. 502, 66p, Blue whale. No. 503, 66p, Sperm whales. No. 504, 66p, Killer whale. No. 505, 66p, Southern bottlenose whales. No. 506, 66p, Humpback whales.

Perf. 13¼x13½
2015, Nov. 17   Litho.
501-506 A106 Set of 6   12.00 12.00

Queen Elizabeth II, 90th Birthday — A107

Photographs of Queen Elizabeth from: 66p, 1948. 76p, 1972. £1.01, 1962. £1.22, 2009. £3, Queen Elizabeth II in 2008.

2016, Apr. 21   Litho.   **Perf. 14**
507-510 A107 Set of 4   11.00 11.00
Souvenir Sheet
511 A107 £3 multi   9.00 9.00

International Association of Antarctic Tour Operators, 25th Anniv. — A108

Emblem and: 66p, Zodiac boat and icebergs. 76p, Tents lit at night. £1.01, Kayakers. £1.22, Penguins and ship.

2016, Nov. 13   Litho.   **Perf. 13¼**
512-515 A108 Set of 4   9.25 9.25

Protocol on Environmental Protection to the Antarctic Treaty, 25th Anniv. — A109

Designs: No. 516, 66p, Krill. No. 517, 66p, Emperor penguin. No. 518, 76p, Weddell seal. No. 519, 76p, Humpback whale. No. 520,

£1.01, Halley VI Station. No. 521, £1.01, South Pole.

2016, Nov. 13   Litho.   Perf. 14
516-521 A109 Set of 6   12.50 12.50

A110

Marine Life of Antarctic Ocean Zones — A111

Designs: No. 522, 66p, Antarctic silverfish. 76p, Glacial squid. £1.01, Anglerfish. £1.22, Cirrate octopus.
No. 526: a, Antarctic silverfish, diff. b, Antarctic krill, diff. c, Weddell seal. d, Antarctic lanternfish. e, Glacial squid, diff. f, Pram bug. g, Anglerfish, diff. h, Colossal squid. i, Scaly dragonfish. j, Dogtooth grenadier. k, Alarm jellyfish. l, Cirrate octopus, diff.

Perf. 13¼x13½
2016, Nov. 13   Litho.
522-525 A110 Set of 4   9.25 9.25
Miniature Sheet
526 A111 66p Sheet of 12, #a-l   20.00 20.00

SEMI-POSTAL STAMPS

Antarctic Heritage SP1

Designs: 17p+3p, Capt. James Cook, HMS Resolution. 35p+15p, Sir James Clark Ross, HMS Erebus, HMS Terror. 40p+10p, Capt. Robert Falcon Scott. 76p+4p, Sir Ernest Shackleton, HMS Endurance trapped in ice.

Wmk. 384
1994, Nov. 23   Litho.   Perf. 14½
B1 SP1 17p + 3p multi   2.50 2.50
B2 SP1 35p + 15p multi   3.50 3.50
B3 SP1 40p + 10p multi   3.50 3.50
B4 SP1 76p + 4p multi   6.50 6.50
    Nos. B1-B4 (4)   16.00 16.00
Surtax for United Kingdom Antarctic Heritage Trust.

AIR POST STAMPS

Penguins — AP1

No. C1: a, Two Emperors. b, Macaroni. c, Adult Gentoo. d, Two Adelies. e, Adult Chinstrap. f, Juvenile Gentoo. g, Two emperors,

horizon. h, Juvenile Chinstrap. i, Seven Adelies. j, Adult and juvenile Gentoos. k, Two Macaronis. l, Emperor.

Wmk. 373
2003, Dec. 8   Litho.   Perf. 13¼
C1 AP1 (40p) Sheet of 12, #a-l   42.50 42.50

Penguins — AP2

Nos. C2 and C3: a, Chinstrap chick. b, Head of Emperor. c, Adelie with wings extended. d, Head of Chinstrap. e, Head of Macaroni, red country name. f, Gentoo adult feeding juvenile. g, Emperor chick. h, Adelie on nest. i, Two Emperors and mountain. j, Gentoo. k, Two Adelies. l, Two Emperor juveniles.

Wmk. 373
2006, Nov. 8   Litho.   Perf. 13¼
C2 AP2 (50p) Sheet of 12, #a-l 29.00 29.00
Self-Adhesive
Unwmk.
Die Cut Perf. 9x9½
C3 AP2 (50p) Booklet pane of 12, #a-l   29.00 29.00

Miniature Sheet

Penguins — AP3

No. C4: a, Head of Chinstrap. b, Adult Gentoo and two chicks. c, Macaroni with open beak. d, Chinstrap with open beak and wings extended. e, Two Emperors. f, Adelie chicks. g, Chinstrap with wings extended. h, Gentoo with open beak. i, Macaroni. j, Adult Emperor and chick. k, Two Adelies. l, Emperor chick.

Wmk. 373
2008, Nov. 17   Litho.   Perf. 13¼
C4 AP3 (55p) Sheet of 12, #a-l 25.00 25.00

RRS James Clark Ross — AP4

RRS James Clark Ross — AP5

RRS Bransfield — AP6

RRS Bransfield — AP7

RRS Ernest Shackleton — AP8

RRS Ernest Shackleton — AP9

Design: £1.15, RRS James Clark Ross and penguin.

Perf. 14¼x14¾
2011, Nov. 17   Wmk. 406
C5 AP4 (60p) multi   1.90 1.90
C6 AP5 (60p) multi   1.90 1.90
C7 AP6 (60p) multi   1.90 1.90
C8 AP7 (60p) multi   1.90 1.90
C9 AP8 (60p) multi   1.90 1.90
C10 AP9 (60p) multi   1.90 1.90
    Nos. C5-C10 (6)   11.40 11.40
Souvenir Sheet
Perf. 13¼
C11 AP4 £1.15 multi   3.75 3.75
Coil Stamps
Self-Adhesive
Size: 33x22mm
Unwmk.
Die Cut Perf. 13¼x12¾
C12 AP4 (60p) multi   1.90 1.90
C13 AP5 (60p) multi   1.90 1.90
C14 AP6 (60p) multi   1.90 1.90
C15 AP7 (60p) multi   1.90 1.90
C16 AP8 (60p) multi   1.90 1.90
C17 AP9 (60p) multi   1.90 1.90
a. Horiz. coil strip of 6, #C12-C17   11.50
    Nos. C12-C17 (6)   11.40 11.40

Gentoo Penguins AP10

Chinstrap Penguin AP12

Gentoo Penguin — AP14

Adelie Penguin AP11

Adelie Penguin AP13

Die Cut Perf. 13¼x13½
2012, Nov. 16   Self-Adhesive
Coil Stamps
C18 AP10 (65p) multi   2.10 2.10
C19 AP11 (65p) multi   2.10 2.10
C20 AP12 (65p) multi   2.10 2.10
C21 AP13 (65p) multi   2.10 2.10
C22 AP14 (65p) multi   2.10 2.10
a. Vert. strip of 5, #C18-C22   10.50
    Nos. C18-C22 (5)   10.50 10.50

Penguins AP15

Designs: Nos. C23, C28, Macaroni penguins. Nos. C24, C29, Adelie penguins. Nos. C25, C30, Chinstrap penguins. Nos. C26, C31, Gentoo penguins. Nos. C27, C32, Emperor penguins.

2014, Nov. 19   Litho.   Perf. 13¾
Inscribed "Airmail Letter"
C23 AP15 (75p) multi   2.40 2.40
C24 AP15 (75p) multi   2.40 2.40
C25 AP15 (75p) multi   2.40 2.40
C26 AP15 (75p) multi   2.40 2.40
C27 AP15 (75p) multi   2.40 2.40
    Nos. C23-C27 (5)   12.00 12.00
Coil Stamps
Self-Adhesive
Size: 22x28mm
Inscribed "Airmail Postcard"
Die Cut Perf. 13½
C28 AP15 (65p) multi   2.10 2.10
C29 AP15 (65p) multi   2.10 2.10
C30 AP15 (65p) multi   2.10 2.10
C31 AP15 (65p) multi   2.10 2.10
C32 AP15 (65p) multi   2.10 2.10
a. Horiz. strip of 5, #C28-C32   10.50
    Nos. C28-C32 (5)   10.50 10.50

AP16

AP17

AP18

AP19

AP20

Gentoo Penguins
AP21

Perf. 13½x13¾

2016, Nov. 13			**Litho.**	
C33	AP16	(76p) multi	2.00	2.00
C34	AP17	(76p) multi	2.00	2.00
C35	AP18	(76p) multi	2.00	2.00

Perf. 13¾x13½

C36	AP19	(76p) multi	2.00	2.00
C37	AP20	(76p) multi	2.00	2.00
C38	AP21	(76p) multi	2.00	2.00
	Nos. C33-C38 (6)		12.00	12.00

Coil Stamps
Self-Adhesive
Country Name in Purple
Inscribed "Airmail Postcard"
Size: 25x21mm

Die Cut Perf. 13½

C39	AP17	(66p) multi	1.75	1.75
C40	AP18	(66p) multi	1.75	1.75

Size: 21x25mm

C41	AP19	(66p) multi	1.75	1.75
C42	AP20	(66p) multi	1.75	1.75
C43	AP21	(66p) multi	1.75	1.75
a.	Coil strip of 5, #C39-C43		8.75	
	Nos. C39-C43 (5)		8.75	8.75

BRITISH CENTRAL AFRICA

'bri-tish 'sen-trəl 'a-fri-kə

LOCATION — Central Africa, on the west shore of Lake Nyassa
GOVT. — British territory, under charter to the British South Africa Company
AREA — 37,800 sq. mi.
POP. — 1,639,329
CAPITAL — Zomba

In 1907 the name was changed to Nyasaland Protectorate, and stamps so inscribed replaced those of British Central Africa.

12 Pence = 1 Shilling
20 Shillings = 1 Pound

Rhodesia Nos. 2, 4-19
Overprinted in Black

1891-95		**Unwmk.**	**Perf. 14**	
1	A1	1p black	12.00	14.00
2	A2	2p gray green & ver	13.00	5.00
a.	Half used as 1p on cover ('95)			7,000.
3	A2	4p red brn & blk	17.00	7.50
4	A1	6p ultramarine	60.00	24.00
5	A1	6p dark blue	21.00	12.00
6	A2	8p rose & blue	20.00	35.00
7	A1	1sh bis brown	32.50	19.00
8	A1	2sh vermilion	50.00	60.00
9	A1	2sh6p gray lilac	90.00	105.00
10	A2	3sh brn & grn ('95)	90.00	90.00
11	A2	4sh gray & ver ('93)	100.00	110.00
12	A1	5sh yellow	110.00	120.00
13	A1	10sh green	200.00	230.00
14	A3	£1 blue	1,300.	800.00
15	A3	£2 rose red	1,400.	1,600.
16	A3	£5 yel green	2,250.	
17	A3	£10 red brown	4,500.	5,500.
	Nos. 1-13 (13)		815.50	831.50

High values with fiscal cancellation are fairly common and can be purchased at a small fraction of the above values. This applies to subsequent issues also. The most common fiscal marking consists of an undated double-circle cancel with the words "BRITISH CENTRAL AFRICA" between the circles, and a town name in the center. This cancel exists in various sizes and is usually applied in black.
For surcharge see No. 20.

Rhodesia Nos. 13-14
Surcharged in Black

1892-93				
18	A2	3sh on 4sh gray & ver ('93)	400.00	400.00
19	A1	4sh on 5sh yellow	100.00	110.00

No. 2 Surcharged in
Black, with Bar

1895				
20	A2	1p on 2p	42.50	65.00
a.	Double surcharge		11,000.	8,000.

A double surcharge, without period after "Penny," and measuring 16mm instead of 18mm, is from a trial printing made at Blantyre. Value, $650.

A4

Coat of Arms of
the
Protectorate — A5

1895		**Unwmk.**	**Typo.**	**Perf. 14**
21	A4	1p black	22.50	17.50
22	A4	2p grn & blk	55.00	14.50
23	A4	4p org & blk	90.00	52.50
24	A4	6p ultra & blk	95.00	10.00
25	A4	1sh rose & blk	120.00	42.50
26	A5	2sh6p vio & blk	375.00	375.00
27	A5	3sh yel & blk	225.00	65.00
28	A5	5sh ol & blk	300.00	275.00
29	A5	£1 org & blk	1,200.	800.00
30	A5	£10 ver & blk	8,000.	5,500.
31	A5	£25 bl grn & blk	16,000.	16,000.
	Nos. 21-28 (8)		1,283.	852.00
1896			**Wmk. 2**	
32	A4	1p black	4.25	10.00
33	A4	2p green & black	24.00	6.00
34	A4	4p org brown & blk	42.50	21.00
35	A4	6p ultra & black	50.00	17.50
36	A4	1sh rose & black	50.00	25.00
	Wmk. 1 Sideways			
37	A5	2sh6p vio rose & blk	200.00	160.00
38	A5	3sh yel & black	180.00	75.00
39	A5	5sh olive & blk	275.00	275.00
40	A5	£1 blue & blk	1,200.	650.00
41	A5	£10 ver & blk	11,000.	6,000.
42	A5	£25 bl grn & blk	26,000.	—
	Nos. 32-39 (8)		825.75	589.50

A6

A7

1897-1901			**Wmk. 2**	
43	A6	1p ultra & blk	4.00	1.50
44	A6	1p rose & vio ('01)	3.50	.80
45	A6	2p yel & black	4.25	2.50
46	A6	4p car rose & blk	8.00	2.25
47	A6	4p ol grn & vio ('01)	16.00	13.50
48	A6	6p grn & blk	60.00	5.25

49	A6	6p red brn & vio ('01)	14.00	6.50
50	A6	1sh gray lil & blk	13.50	8.50
		Wmk. 1		
51	A7	2sh6p ultra & blk	100.00	50.00
52	A7	3sh gray grn & blk	350.00	375.00
53	A7	4sh car rose & blk	130.00	100.00
54	A7	10sh ol & blk	325.00	325.00
55	A7	£1 dp vio & blk	500.00	275.00
56	A7	£10 org & black	8,500.	2,750.
	Nos. 43-54 (12)		1,028.	890.00

No. 52
Surcharged in Red

1897				
57	A7	1p on 3sh	11.00	20.00
a.	"PNNEY"		9,500.	7,000.
b.	"PENN"		4,500.	3,750.
c.	Double surcharge		800.00	1,300.

A8

Type I — The vertical framelines are not continuous between stamps.
Type II — The vertical framelines are continuous between stamps.

1898, Mar. 11		**Unwmk.**	**Imperf.**	
		Type I		
		Control on Reverse		
58	A8	1p ver & ultra	—	145.00
a.	1p ver & deep ultra		5,500.	150.00
b.	No control on reverse		6,500.	220.00
c.	Control double			525.00
d.	Control on front			3,900.
e.	Pair, one without oval		32,500.	
		Type II		
		Control on Reverse		
f.	1p ver & ultra		—	800.00
		No Control on Reverse		
g.	1p grayish blue & ver, initials on back		16,000.	1,100.
h.	No initials		7,500.	
i.	Oval inverted		32,500.	
j.	Oval double			
k.	Pair, with 3 ovals		—	
		Perf. 12		
		Type I		
		Control on Reverse		
59	A8	1p ver & ultra	6,000.	35.00
a.	1p ver & deep ultra		—	47.50
b.	Two diff. controls on reverse			850.00
		No Control on Reverse		
d.	1p ver & ultra		5,500.	115.00

There are 30 types of each setting of Nos. 58-59.
No. 58 issued without gum.
Control consists of figures or letters.
Initials are of Postmaster General (J.G. or J.T.G.).

A9

King Edward
VII — A10

1903-04			**Wmk. 2**	
60	A9	1p car & black	9.50	2.25
61	A9	2p vio & dull vio	4.50	2.25
62	A9	4p blk & gray green	3.25	11.00
63	A9	6p org brn & blk	4.00	4.00
64	A9	1sh pale blue & blk ('04)	5.00	16.00

			Wmk. 1	
65	A10	2sh6p gray green	70.00	110.00
66	A10	4sh vio & dl vio	115.00	105.00
67	A10	10sh blk & gray green	200.00	300.00
68	A10	£1 scar & blk	360.00	250.00
69	A10	£10 ultra & blk	8,000.	4,750.
	Nos. 60-68 (9)		771.25	800.50

1907			**Wmk. 3**	
70	A9	1p car & black	12.00	3.50
71	A9	2p vio & dull vio	19,000.	
72	A9	4p blk & gray grn	19,000.	
73	A9	6p org brn & blk	52.50	60.00

Nos. 71-72 were not issued.
British Central Africa stamps were replaced by those of Nyasaland Protectorate in 1908.

BRITISH EAST AFRICA

'bri-tish 'ēst 'a-fri-kə

LOCATION — East coast of Africa; modern Kenya. Included all of the territory in East Africa under British control.

Postage stamps were issued by the Imperial British East Africa Company (IBEAC) in May 1900. Transferred to the Crown as a Protectorate July 1, 1895. Postal administration amalgamated with Uganda in 1901 with new stamps issued in July 1903 inscribed 'East Africa and Uganda Protectorates.'

16 Annas = 1 Rupee

BRITISH EAST AFRICA COMPANY
HALF ANNA
A1

BRITISH EAST AFRICA COMPANY
1 ANNA
A2

BRITISH EAST AFRICA COMPANY
4 ANNAS
A3

Queen Victoria — A3

1890   Wmk. 30   Perf. 14

1	A1	½a on 1p lilac	350.00	240.00

Beware of forgeries.

2	A2	1a on 2p grn & car rose	575.00	350.00
3	A3	4a on 5p lilac & bl	600.00	375.00

A4

Sun and Crown Symbolical of "Light and Liberty" — A5

1890-94   Unwmk.   Litho.   Perf. 14

14	A4	½a bister brown	1.25	15.00
b.		½a deep brown	1.00	10.00
c.		As "b," horiz. pair, imperf. btwn.	1,925.	775.00
d.		As "b," vert. pair, imperf. btwn.	1,400.	600.00
15	A4	1a blue green	9.50	15.00
16	A4	2a vermilion	5.00	6.50
17	A4	2½a black, yel ('93)	6.25	9.50
a.		Horiz. pair, imperf. btwn.	8,000.	
18	A4	3a black, red ('91)	5.50	12.00
b.		Horiz. pair, imperf. btwn.	1,400.	525.00
c.		Vert. pair, imperf. btwn.	1,400.	600.00
19	A4	4a yellow brown	3.00	14.00
20	A4	4½a brn vio ('91)	3.00	24.00
b.		4½a gray violet ('91)	42.50	22.50
c.		Horiz. pair, imperf. btwn.	2,100.	1,200.
d.		Vert. pair, imperf. btwn.	1,200.	600.00
21	A4	5a blk, blue ('94)	1.50	13.00
22	A4	7½a black ('94)	1.50	19.00
23	A4	8a blue	6.75	11.50
24	A4	8a gray	350.00	350.00
25	A4	1r rose	7.50	11.00
26	A4	1r gray	275.00	275.00
27	A5	2r brick red	17.00	50.00
28	A5	3r gray violet	14.00	60.00
29	A5	4r ultra	15.00	60.00
30	A5	5r gray green	37.50	85.00
		Nos. 14-30 (17)	759.25	1,031.

Some of the paper used for this issue had a papermaker's watermark and parts of it often can be seen on the stamps.

Values for Nos. 14c, 14d, 18b, 18c, 20c, 20d, unused, are for examples with little or no original gum. Stamps with natural straight edges are almost as common as fully perforated stamps from the early printings of Nos. 14-30, and for all printings of the rupee values. Values about the same.

For surcharges and overprints see Nos. 31-53.

1890-93   Imperf.

Values for Pairs except No. 19b.

14a	A4	½a bister brown	1,200.	450.
14e	A4	½a deep brown	1,700.	725.
15a	A4	1a blue green	4,750.	1,200.
16a	A4	2a vermilion	4,500.	1,300.
17d	A4	2½a blk, brt yel	1,200.	550.
18a	A4	3a black, red	1,200.	500.
19a	A4	4a yel brown	4,750.	1,600.
19b	A4	4a gray	1,500.	1,700.
20a	A4	4½a dull violet	2,000.	550.
23a	A4	8a blue	10,000.	1,400.
25a	A4	1r rose	15,000.	1,600.

½ Anna
A6

Handstamped Surcharges

1891   Perf. 14

31	A6	½a on 2a ver ("A.D.")	14,000.	1,100.
a.		Double surcharge		13,000.
32	A6	1a on 4a yel brn ("A.B.")	21,000.	2,300.

Validation initials are shown in parentheses. See note below No. 35.

Manuscript Surcharges

1891-95

33	A6	½a on 2a ver ("A.B.")	17,000.	1,100.
a.		"½ Annas" ("A.B.")		1,200.
b.		Initialed "A.D."		6,500.
34	A6	½a on 3a blk, red ("T.E.C.R.")	700.	60.
b.		Initialed "A.B."	18,000.	2,750.
34A	A6	1a on 3a blk, red ("V.H.M.")	16,000.	2,250.
c.		Initialed "T.E.C.R."	23,000.	3,250.
35	A6	1a on 4a yel brn ("A.B.")	12,000.	2,200.

The manuscript initials on Nos. 31-35, given in parentheses, stand for Andrew Dick, Archibald Brown, Victor H. Mackenzie (1891) and T.E.C. Remington (1895).

Three persons applied the surcharge to No. 33, and two persons applied the surcharge to No. 35, resulting in different types.

5 ANNAS
A7

1894   Printed Surcharges

36	A7	5a on 8a blue	85.00	110.00
37	A7	7½a on 1r rose	85.00	110.00

BRITISH EAST AFRICA

Stamps of 1890-94 Handstamped in Black

1895

38	A4	½a deep brown	90.00	35.00
b.		Inverted overprint		6,000.
39	A4	1a blue green	200.00	135.00
40	A4	2a vermilion	220.00	115.00
41	A4	2½a black, yel	220.00	67.50
42	A4	3a black, dull red	105.00	60.00
43	A4	4a yel brown	72.50	47.50
44	A4	4½a gray violet	250.00	120.00
a.		4½a brown violet	1,450.	1,150.
45	A4	5a black, blue	300.00	170.00
b.		Inverted overprint		5,000.
46	A4	7½a black	150.00	100.00
47	A4	8a blue	115.00	90.00
b.		Inverted overprint		8,000.
48	A4	1r rose	67.50	60.00
49	A5	2r brick red	550.00	325.00
50	A5	3r gray violet	275.00	160.00
		Inverted overprint		
51	A5	4r ultra	250.00	200.00
52	A5	5r gray green	525.00	325.00
		Nos. 38-52 (15)	3,390.	2,010.

Forgeries exist.

Double Overprints

38a	A4	½a	550.	525.
39a	A4	1a	750.	550.
40a	A4	2a	850.	575.
41a	A4	2½a	850.	525.
43a	A4	4a	600.	550.
44b	A4	4½a gray violet	900.	675.
44c	A4	4½a brown violet	3,300.	2,400.
45a	A4	5a	1,100.	1,000.
46a	A4	7½a	850.	675.
47a	A4	8a	750.	725.
48a	A4	1r	700.	675.
50a	A5	3r	1,200.	1,100.
51a	A5	4r	1,100.	1,000.
52a	A5	5r	1,600.	1,600.

Surcharged in Red

1895

53	A4	2½a on 4½a gray vio	225.00	90.00
a.		Double overprint (#44b)	1,200.	1,050.

Stamps of India 1874-95 Overprinted or Surcharged

British East Africa
a

British 2⅟₂
b

British 2⅟₂
c

1895   Wmk. Star (39)

54	A17	½a green	8.50	6.75
55	A19	1a maroon	8.00	7.25
56	A20	1a6p bister brn	5.25	5.00
57	A21	2a ultra	10.00	3.75
58	A28	2a6p green	17.50	3.25
59	A20(a)	2½a on 1a6p bis brn	120.00	57.50
a.		"½" without fraction line	135.00	
d.		As "a," "1" of "½" invtd.	1,200.	725.00
62	A22	3a orange	26.00	13.50
63	A23	4a ol grn	50.00	42.50
a.		4a slate green	32.00	26.00
64	A24	8a red violet	35.00	60.00
a.		8a red lilac	110.00	85.00
65	A26	12a vio, red	27.50	40.00
66	A27	1r gray	115.00	80.00
67	A29	1r car & grn	55.00	160.00
a.		Dbl. ovpt., one sideways	525.00	1,100.
68	A30	2r bis & rose	120.00	180.00
69	A30	3r grn & brn	170.00	200.00
70	A30	5r vio & ultra	175.00	240.00
a.		Double overprint	2,750.	

Wmk. Elephant's Head (38)

71	A14	6a bister	50.00	60.00
		Nos. 54-59,62-71 (16)	992.75	1,160.

Varieties of the overprint include "Brit1sh," "Br1tish," "Afr1ca," inverted "a" for "t," "Eas" for "East," and letter "B" handstamped. See the Scott Specialized Catalogue of Stamps and Covers for detailed listings.

No. 59 is surcharged in bright red; surcharges in brown red were prepared for the UPU, but not regularly issued as stamps. See note following No. 93.

BRITISH EAST AFRICA
HALF ANNA
PROTECTORATE

Queen Victoria and British Lions — A8

1896-1901   Engr.   Wmk. 2   Perf. 14

72	A8	½a yel green	6.50	1.00
73	A8	1a carmine	17.50	.50
a.		1a red	16.00	.50
74	A8	1a dp rose ('01)	32.50	5.00
75	A8	2a chocolate	13.00	8.50
76	A8	2½a dark blue	18.00	2.50
77	A8	3a gray	10.00	15.00
78	A8	4a deep green	8.50	9.00
79	A8	4½a orange	17.50	20.00
80	A8	5a dk ocher	9.25	8.00
81	A8	7½a lilac	11.00	27.00
82	A8	8a olive gray	11.00	7.00
83	A8	1r ultra	140.00	80.00
a.		1r pale blue	80.00	30.00
84	A8	2r red orange	80.00	35.00
85	A8	3r deep violet	80.00	40.00
86	A8	4r lake	72.50	85.00
87	A8	5r dark brown	70.00	50.00
		Nos. 72-87 (16)	597.25	389.50

Zanzibar Nos. 38-40, 44-46 Overprinted in Black

British East Africa ½ ANNA

1897   Wmk. Rosette (71)

88	A2	½a yel grn & red	67.50	55.00
89	A2	1a indigo & red	115.00	110.00
90	A2	2a red brn & red	50.00	26.00
91	A2	4½a org & red	60.00	37.50
92	A2	5a bister & red	67.50	50.00
93	A2	7½a lilac & red	70.00	50.00
a.		Ovptd. on front and back		
		Nos. 88-93 (6)	430.00	328.50

The 1a with red overprint, which includes a period after "Africa," was sent to the UPU, but never placed in use. Nos. 88, 90-93 and 95-100 also exist with period (in black) in sets sent to the UPU. Some experts consider these essays.

Black Ovpt. on Zanzibar #39, 42 New Value Surcharged in Red

1897

95	A2(a)	2½a on 1a	135.00	80.00
a.		Black overprint double	7,800.	
96	A2(b)	2½a on 1a	325.00	130.00
97	A2(c)	2½a on 1a	160.00	90.00
a.		Black overprint double	7,800.	
98	A2(a)	2½a on 3a	135.00	67.50
99	A2(b)	2½a on 3a	325.00	120.00
100	A2(c)	2½a on 3a	160.00	75.00
		Nos. 95-100 (6)	1,240.	562.50

A special printing of the 2½a surcharge on the 1a and 3a stamps was made for submission to the U.P.U. Stamps have a period after "Africa" in the overprint, and the surcharges included a "2" over "1" error in the fraction of the surcharge. These stamps were never placed in use. The fraction error appears on both the 1a and 3a stamps. Value, each, $1,500.

BRITISH EAST AFRICA
FIVE RUPEES
PROTECTORATE
A10

1898   Wmk. 1   Engr.

102a	A10	1r 1r dull blue ('01)	120.00	50.00
103	A10	2r orange	140.00	150.00
104	A10	3r dk violet	180.00	190.00
105	A10	4r carmine	500.00	550.00
106	A10	5r black brown	450.00	550.00
107	A10	10r bister	450.00	600.00
108	A10	20r yel green	1,200.	2,500.
109	A10	50r lilac	2,500.	9,000.
		Nos. 102a-107 (6)	1,840.	2,090.

Nos. 102-109 are often found with fiscal or Court Fee cancels. Stamps with these cancels can be purchased at a fraction of these values.

The stamps of this country were superseded by the stamps of East Africa and Uganda Protectorate.

BRITISH GUIANA

'bri-tish gē-'a-nə, -'ä-nə

LOCATION — On the northeast coast of South America
GOVT. — British Crown Colony
AREA — 83,000 sq. mi.
POP. — 628,000 (estimated 1964)
CAPITAL — Georgetown

British Guiana became the independent state of Guyana May 26, 1966.

100 Cents = 1 Dollar

Catalogue values for unused stamps in this country are for Never Hinged items, beginning with Scott 242 in the regular postage section and Scott J1 in the postage due section.

Values for unused stamps are for examples with original gum except for Nos. 6-12 and 35-53, which are valued without gum. Very fine examples of all stamps from No. 6 on will have four clear margins. Inferior examples sell at much reduced prices, depending on the condition of the individual stamp.

A1

1850-51 Typeset Unwmk. Imperf.
1	A1	2c blk, *pale rose*, cut to shape ('51)	325,000.
2	A1	4c black, *orange*	100,000.
		Cut to shape	16,000.
a.		4c black, *yellow*	130,000.
		Cut to shape	22,500.
3	A1	4c blk, *yellow* (pelure)	135,000.
		Cut to shape	26,000.
4	A1	8c black, *green*	70,000.
		Cut to shape	16,000.
5	A1	12c black, *blue*	35,000.
		Cut to shape	11,000.
a.		12c black, *pale blue*	40,000.
		Cut to shape	14,000.
b.		12c black, *indigo*	45,000.
		Cut to shape	13,000.
c.		"1" of "12" omitted, cut to shape	250,000.

These stamps were initialed before use by the Deputy Postmaster General or by one of the clerks of the Colonial Postoffice at Georgetown. The following initials are found: — E. T. E. D(alton); E. D. W(ight); G. B. S(mith); H. A. K(illikelley); W. H. L(ortimer). As these stamps are type-set there are several types of each value.

Ship and Motto of Colony — A2

1852 Litho.
6	A2	1c black, *magenta*	15,000.	7,000.
7	A2	4c black, *blue*	25,000.	13,000.

Both 1c and 4c are found in two types. Examples with paper cracked or rubbed sell for much less.
Some examples are initialed E. D. W(ight).
The reprints are on thicker paper and the colors are brighter. They are perforated 12½ and imperforate. Value $20 each.

Seal of the Colony — A3

Without Line above Value
1853-59 **Imperf.**
8	A3	1c vermilion	8,000.	1,750.

A proof of No. 8 exists in reddish brown, value about $1,600.

Full or Partial White Line Above Value
1853-59
9	A3	1c red (I)	7,750.	2,250.
10	A3	4c blue	3,250.	850.
a.		4c dark blue	6,000.	1,200.
b.		4c pale blue	2,250.	750.

On No. 9, "ONE CENT" varies from 11 to 13mm in width.

No. 10 Retouched; White Line above Value Removed
11	A3	4c blue	4,750.	1,100.
a.		4c dark blue	8,500.	1,750.
b.		4c pale blue	3,500.	1,100.

Reprints of Nos. 8 and 10 are on thin paper, perf. 12½ or imperf. The 1c is orange red, the 4c sky blue.

1860
Numerals in Corners Framed
12	A3	4c blue	7,500.	850.

A4

1856 Typeset Imperf.
13	A4	1c black, *mag*	9,500,000.
14	A4	4c black, *mag*	100,000.	25,000.
a.		4c black, *rose carmine*	50,000.	40,000.
15	A4	4c black, *blue*	150,000.
16	A4	4c black, *blue*, paper colored through		225,000.

These stamps were initialed before being issued and the following initials are found: — E. T. E. D.; E. D. W.; W. H. L.; C. A. W. No. 13 is unique.

A5

1862 Typeset Rouletted
35	A6	1c black, *rose*	5,750.	850.
		Unsigned		650.
36	A7	1c black, *rose*	7,500.	1,400.
		Unsigned		750.
37	A8	1c black, *rose*	9,750.	1,500.
		Unsigned		1,300.
38	A6	2c black, *yellow*	5,750.	450.
		Unsigned		2,600.
39	A7	2c black, *yellow*	7,500.	575.
		Unsigned		3,000.
40	A8	2c black, *yellow*	9,750.	925.
		Unsigned		3,750.
41	A9	4c black, *blue*	8,000.	1,400.
		Unsigned		1,400.

Wide space between value and "Cents"
1860-61 Litho. Perf. 12
Thick Paper
17	A5	1c brown red ('61)	500.00	125.00
18	A5	1c pink	3,500.	300.00
19	A5	2c orange	350.00	65.00
20	A5	8c rose	825.00	130.00
21	A5	12c gray	750.00	55.00
a.		12c lilac	850.00	55.00
22	A5	24c green	1,700.	85.00

All denominations of type A5 above four cents are expressed in Roman numerals.
Bisects and trisects are found on covers. These were not officially authorized.
The reprints of the 1c pink are perforated 12½; the other values have not been reprinted.

1862-65 Thin Paper
23	A5	1c brown	950.00	275.00
24	A5	1c black ('63)	175.00	65.00
25	A5	2c orange	165.00	65.00
26	A5	8c rose ('63)	340.00	85.00
27	A5	12c lilac	450.00	55.00
28	A5	24c green	1,850.	110.00

Perf. 12½ and 13
29	A5	1c black	80.00	25.00
30	A5	2c orange	95.00	27.50
31	A5	8c rose	350.00	97.50
32	A5	12c lilac	1,200.	150.00
33	A5	24c green	875.00	80.00

Medium Paper
33A	A5	1c black ('64)	70.00	55.00
33B	A5	2c dp org ('64)	90.00	32.50
33C	A5	8c pink ('64)	300.00	80.00
33D	A5	12c lilac ('65)	1,250.	130.00
33E	A5	24c green ('64)	375.00	65.00
f.		24c deep green	450.00	90.00

Perf. 10
34	A5	12c gray lilac	875.00	97.50

Imperfs. are proofs. See Nos. 44-62.

A6

A7

A8

A9

A10

A11

42	A10	4c black, *blue*	11,000.	2,000.
		Unsigned		
a.		Without inner lines	8,000.	1,400.
		As "a," unsigned	1,300.	
43	A11	4c black, *blue*	6,500.	1,100.
		Unsigned	1,300.	

Nos. 35-43 were typeset, in sheets of 24 each. They were initialed before use "R. M. Ac. R. G.," being the initials of Robert Mather, Acting Receiver General.
The initials are in black on the 1c and in red on the 2c. An alkali was used on the 4c stamps, which, destroying the color of the paper, caused the initials to appear to be written in white.
Uninitialed stamps are remainders, few sheets having been found.
Stamps with roulette on all sides are valued higher.

Narrow space between value and "Cents"
1860 Thick Paper Litho. Perf. 12
44	A5	4c blue	450.00	80.00
c.		4c deep blue	800.00	120.00

Thin Paper
44A	A5	4c pale blue	150.00	42.50
d.		4c blue	175.00	55.00

Perf. 12½ and 13
44B	A5	4c blue	115.00	32.50

Medium Paper
1863-68 Perf. 12½ and 13
45	A5	1c black ('66)	80.00	40.00
46	A5	2c orange	85.00	10.00
47	A5	4c gray blue ('64)	100.00	25.00
48	A5	8c rose ('68)	425.00	27.50
49	A5	12c lilac ('67)	650.00	50.00
		Nos. 45-49 (5)	1,340.	152.50

1866-71 Perf. 10
50	A5	1c black	25.00	8.50
51	A5	2c orange	65.00	5.00
52	A5	4c blue	130.00	11.00
a.		Half used as 2c on cover		7,500.
53	A5	8c rose	300.00	37.50
a.		Diagonal half used as 4c on cover		—
54	A5	12c lilac	300.00	27.50
a.		Third used as 4c on cover		—
		Nos. 50-54 (5)	820.00	89.50

1875-76 Perf. 15
58	A5	1c black	65.00	9.00
59	A5	2c orange	195.00	17.00
60	A5	4c blue	350.00	120.00
61	A5	8c rose	400.00	110.00
62	A5	12c lilac	925.00	100.00
		Nos. 58-62 (5)	1,935.	356.00

Seal of Colony — A12

1863 Perf. 12
63	A12	24c yellow green	275.00	15.50
a.		24c green	350.00	25.00

Perf. 12½ to 13
64	A12	6c blue	200.00	72.50
65	A12	24c green	275.00	16.00
66	A12	48c deep red	425.00	80.00
a.		48c rose	450.00	80.00
		Nos. 63-66 (4)	1,175.	184.00

1866 Perf. 10
67	A12	6c blue	200.00	40.00
a.		6c ultramarine	215.00	67.50
68	A12	24c yellow green	275.00	9.00
a.		24c green	375.00	11.00
69	A12	48c rose red	425.00	37.50
		Nos. 67-69 (3)	900.00	86.50

For surcharges see Nos. 83-92.

1875   Perf. 15

70	A12	6c ultra	1,150.	150.00
71	A12	24c yellow green	850.	42.50
a.		24c deep green	1,600.	120.00

Seal of Colony — A13

1876   Typo.   Wmk. 1   Perf. 14

72	A13	1c slate	3.25	1.75
a.		Perf. 14x12½		225.00
73	A13	2c orange	92.50	4.00
74	A13	4c ultra	150.00	15.00
a.		Perf. 12½	1,450.	250.00
75	A13	6c chocolate	110.00	14.00
76	A13	8c rose	160.00	1.00
77	A13	12c lilac	80.00	2.50
78	A13	24c green	90.00	4.00
79	A13	48c red brown	160.00	50.00
80	A13	96c bister	575.00	325.00
		Nos. 72-80 (9)	1,421.	417.25

See Nos. 107-111. For surcharges see Nos. 93-95, 98-101.

Stamps Surcharged by Brush-like Pen Lines

Type a   Type b

Type c   Type d

Surcharge Types:
Type a — Two horiz. lines.
Type b — Two lines, one horiz., one vert.
Type c — Three lines, two horiz., one vert.
Type d — One horiz. line.

On Nos. 75 and 67

1878   Perf. 10, 14

82	A13(a)	(1c) on 6c choc	52.50	150.00
83	A12(b)	(1c) on 6c blue	250.00	90.00
84	A13(b)	(1c) on 6c choc	450.00	135.00

On Nos. O3, O8-O10

85	A13(c)	(1c) on 4c ultra	425.00	120.00
a.		Type b	50,000.	6,000.
86	A13(c)	(1c) on 6c choc	725.00	135.00
87	A5(c)	(2c) on 8c rose	5,250.	400.00
88A	A13(b)	(2c) on 8c rose	600.00	240.00

On Nos. O1, O3, O6-O7

89	A5(d)	(1c) on 1c blk	325.00	90.00
89A	A5(d)	(2c) on 8c rose		
90	A13(d)	(1c) on 1c sl	220.00	80.00
91	A13(d)	(2c) on 2c org	450.00	80.00

The provisional values of Nos. 82 to 91 were established by various official decrees. The horizontal lines crossed out the old value, "OFFICIAL," or both.

The existence of No. 89A has been questioned by specialists. The editors would like to see authenticated evidence of its existence.

Nos. 69 and 80 Surcharged with New Values in Black

No. 92   No. 93

No. 94   No. 95

1881

92	A12	1c on 48c red	55.00	7.00
93	A13	1c on 96c bister	6.00	14.00
94	A13	2c on 96c bister	24.00	27.50
95	A13	2c on 96c bister	85.00	160.00
		Nos. 92-95 (4)	170.00	208.50

Nos. O4, O5 and Unissued Official Stamps Surcharged with New Values

No. 96   No. 97

Nos. 98, 100   Nos. 99, 101

No. 102

1881

96	A5	1c on 12c lilac (#O4)	155.00	85.00
97	A13	1c on 48c red brn	225.00	140.00
98	A13	2c on 12c lilac	750.00	500.00
99	A13	2c on 12c lilac	110.00	70.00
a.		"2" inverted	950.00	550.00
b.		"2" double		
100	A13	2c on 24c green	1,000.	950.00
101	A13	2c on 24c green	110.00	70.00
a.		"2" inverted		
d.		Double surcharge	1,325.	
102	A12	2c on 24c green (#O5)	400.00	200.00

A27

Typeset

ONE AND TWO CENTS.
Type I — Ship with three masts.
Type II — Brig with two masts.

"SPECIMEN"
Perforated Diagonally across Stamp

1882   Unwmk.   Perf. 12

103	A27	1c black, lil rose, I	80.00	35.00
a.		Horiz. pair, imperf between		10,000.
104	A27	1c black, lil rose, II	80.00	35.00
a.		Without "Specimen"	1,500.	600.00
105	A27	2c black, yel, I	115.00	60.00
a.		Without "Specimen"	1,300.	700.00
b.		Diagonal half used as 1c on cover		—
106	A27	2c black, yel, II	110.00	65.00
a.		Without "Specimen"	1,300.	700.00
		Nos. 103-106 (4)	385.00	195.00

Nos. 103-106 were typeset, 12 to a sheet, and, to prevent fraud on the government, the word "Specimen" was perforated across them before they were issued. There were 2 settings of the 1c and 3 settings of the 2c, thus there are 24 types of the former and 36 of the latter.

Type of 1876

1882   Typo.   Wmk. 2   Perf. 14

107	A13	1c slate	20.00	.50
108	A13	2c orange	60.00	.35
a.		"2 CENTS" double		11,500.

109	A13	4c ultra	110.00	6.50
110	A13	6c brown	6.00	8.00
111	A13	8c rose	140.00	1.00
		Nos. 107-111 (5)	336.00	16.35

"INLAND REVENUE" Overprint and Surcharged in Black

A28

Type I   Type II

4 CENTS and $4
Type I — Figure "4" is 3mm high.
Type II — Figure "4" is 3½mm high.
6 CENTS
Type I — Top of "6" is flat.
Type II — Top of "6" turns downward.

1889

112	A28	1c lilac	3.00	.55
113	A28	2c lilac	3.50	3.50
114	A28	3c lilac	2.25	.40
115	A28	4c lilac, I	13.00	.45
116	A28	4c lilac, II	24.00	7.50
117	A28	6c lilac, I	23.00	8.50
118	A28	6c lilac, II	15.00	6.50
119	A28	8c lilac	2.75	.65
120	A28	10c lilac	8.50	3.25
121	A28	20c lilac	27.50	22.50
122	A28	40c lilac	52.50	35.00
123	A28	72c lilac	85.00	72.50
124	A28	$1 green	575.00	650.00
125	A28	$2 green	275.00	300.00
126	A28	$3 green	275.00	300.00
127	A28	$4 green, I	650.00	775.00
127A	A28	$4 green, II	2,400.	3,000.
128	A28	$5 green	400.00	450.00
		Nos. 112-128 (18)	4,835.	5,636.

For surcharges see Nos.129, 148-151B.

No. 113 Surcharged in Red

1889

129	A29	2c on 2c lilac	6.50	.55

Inverted and double surcharges of "2" were privately made.

A30

1889-1903   Typo.

130	A30	1c lilac & gray	11.00	3.50
131	A30	1c green ('90)	1.10	.25
131A	A30	1c gray grn ('00)	2.10	6.75
132	A30	2c lilac & org	8.50	.25
133	A30	2c lil & rose ('00)	4.00	.40
134	A30	2c vio & blk, red ('01)	2.00	.25
135	A30	4c lilac & ultra	5.50	4.00
a.		4c lilac & blue	25.00	4.00
136	A30	5c ultra ('91)	4.50	.25
137	A30	6c lilac & mar	8.50	25.00
a.		6c lilac & brown	42.50	27.50
138	A30	6c gray blk & ultra ('02)	8.00	13.50
139	A30	8c lilac & rose	24.00	4.00
140	A30	8c lil & blk ('90)	13.00	3.25
141	A30	12c lilac & vio	10.00	4.00
142	A30	24c lilac & grn	7.50	4.00
143	A30	48c lilac & ver	42.50	13.00
144	A30	48c dk gray & lil brn ('01)	35.00	35.00
a.		48c gray & purple brown	60.00	50.00
145	A30	60c gray grn & car ('03)	75.00	250.00
146	A30	72c lil & org brn	34.00	55.00
a.		72c lilac & yellow brown	77.50	90.00
147	A30	96c lilac & carmine	80.00	85.00
a.		96c lilac & rose	90.00	100.00
		Nos. 130-147 (19)	376.20	507.40

Stamps of the 1889-1903 issue with pen or revenue cancellation sell for a small fraction of the above quotations.
See Nos. 160-177.

A31

1890   Red Surcharge

148	A31	1c on $1 grn & blk	3.50	.50
a.		Double surcharge	300.00	170.00
149	A31	1c on $2 grn & blk	2.50	1.40
a.		Double surcharge	120.00	
150	A31	1c on $3 grn & blk	4.00	1.40
a.		Double surcharge	160.00	—
151	A31	1c on $4 grn & blk, type I	7.50	17.50
a.		Double surcharge	150.00	
151B	A31	1c on $4 grn & blk, type II	15.00	50.00
c.		Double surcharge		
		Nos. 148-151B (5)	32.50	70.80

Mt.
Roraima
A32

Kaieteur (Old
Man's)
Falls — A33

1898   **Wmk. 1**   **Engr.**
152	A32	1c car & gray blk	10.00	2.50
153	A33	2c indigo & brn	40.00	4.75
a.		Horiz. pair, imperf. between	16,500.	
b.		2c blue & brown	45.00	4.75
154	A32	5c brown & grn	57.50	6.50
155	A33	10c red & blue blk	30.00	32.50
156	A32	15c blue & red brn	37.50	26.00
		Nos. 152-156 (5)	175.00	72.25

60th anniv. of Queen Victoria's accession to
the throne.

Nos. 154-
156
Surcharged
in Black

1899
157	A32	2c on 5c brn & grn	4.00	3.25
a.		Without period	185.00	140.00
158	A33	2c on 10c red & bl	4.50	2.75
		black		
a.		"GENTS"	70.00	92.50
b.		Inverted surcharge	750.00	875.00
c.		Without period	25.00	65.00
159	A32	2c on 15c bl & red	4.50	1.50
		brown		
a.		Without period	80.00	80.00
b.		Double surcharge	1,100.	1,500.
c.		Inverted surcharge	875.00	1,100.
		Nos. 157-159 (3)	13.00	7.50

There are many slight errors in the setting of
this surcharge, such as: small "E" in "CENTS";
no period and narrow "C"; comma between "T"
and "S"; dash between "TWO" and "CENTS";
comma between "N" and "T."

Ship Type of 1889-1903
1905-10   **Wmk. 3**
Chalky Paper
160	A30	1c gray green	12.00	1.35
a.		Booklet pane of 6		
161	A30	2c vio & blk, red	6.50	.25
162	A30	4c lilac & ultra	9.00	15.00
163	A30	5c lil & blue, bl	4.25	8.00
164	A30	6c gray black &		
		ultra	18.00	50.00
165	A30	12c lilac & vio	27.50	55.00
166	A30	24c lil & grn ('06)	4.50	5.50
167	A30	48c gray & vio brn	17.00	27.50
168	A30	60c gray grn & car		
		rose	17.00	110.00
169	A30	72c lil & org brn		
		('07)	42.50	85.00
170	A30	96c blk & red,		
		yel('06)	42.50	55.00
		Nos. 160-170 (11)	200.75	412.60

The 2c-60c exist on ordinary paper. See
*Scott Classic Specialized Catalogue of
Stamps and Covers.*

A34

Black Overprint
171	A34	$2.40 grn & vio	210.00	500.00

Ship Type of 1889-1903

Type I   Type II

TWO CENTS
Type I — Only the upper right corner of the
flag touches the mast.
Type II — The entire right side of the flag
touches the mast.

1907-10   **Ordinary Paper**
171A	A30	1c blue green		
		('10)	16.00	3.00
172	A30	2c red, type I	21.00	1.10
b.		2c red, type II	10.50	.25
174	A30	4c brown & vio	3.50	1.35
175	A30	5c blue	18.50	6.00
176	A30	6c gray & black	16.00	8.50
177	A30	12c orange & vio	5.00	6.50
		Nos. 171A-177 (6)	80.00	26.45

George V — A35

1913-17   **Perf. 14**
178	A35	1c green	5.00	1.00
a.		bl grn ('17)	2.25	.30
179	A35	2c scarlet	3.75	.25
a.		2c carmine	1.60	.25
180	A35	4c brn & red vio	7.50	.40
181	A35	5c ultra	2.25	1.25
182	A35	6c gray & black	3.75	2.75
183	A35	12c org & vio	1.75	1.25

Chalky Paper
184	A35	24c dl vio & grn	4.25	5.00
185	A35	48c blk & vio brn	30.00	21.00
186	A35	60c grn & car	20.00	60.00
187	A35	72c dl vio & org		
		brn	60.00	100.00

Surface Colored Paper
188	A35	96c blk & red, yel	32.50	65.00

Paper Colored Through
189	A35	96c blk & red, yel		
		('16)	22.50	65.00
		Nos. 178-189 (12)	193.25	322.90

The 72c and late printings of the 2c and 5c
are from redrawn dies. The ruled lines behind
the value are thin and faint, making the tablet
appear lighter than before. The shading lines
in other parts of the stamps are also lighter.
Several paper shades of No. 189 exist.

1921-27   **Wmk. 4**
191	A35	1c green	5.75	.40
192	A35	2c rose red	7.75	.30
193	A35	2c dp vio ('23)	3.00	.25
194	A35	4c brn & vio	5.75	.25
195	A35	6c ultra	3.75	.40
196	A35	12c org & vio	3.50	2.00

Chalky Paper
197	A35	24c dl vio & grn	2.75	5.50
198	A35	48c blk & vio brn		
		('26)	12.00	4.50
199	A35	60c grn & car ('26)	12.50	57.50
200	A35	72c dl vio & brn		
		org	37.50	80.00
201	A35	96c blk & red, yel		
		('27)	35.00	55.00
		Nos. 191-201 (11)	129.25	206.10

Plowing a Rice
Field — A36

Indian Shooting   Kaieteur
Fish — A37   Falls — A38

Georgetown,
Public
Buildings
A39

1931, July 21   **Engr.**   **Perf. 12½**
205	A36	1c blue green	3.00	1.75
206	A37	2c dk brown	2.75	.25
207	A38	4c car rose	2.50	.60
208	A39	6c ultra	3.00	1.50
209	A38	$1 violet	60.00	70.00
		Nos. 205-209 (5)	71.25	74.10
		Set, never hinged	100.00	

Cent. of the union of Berbice, Demerara and
Essequibo to form the Colony of British
Guiana.

A40

A41   Gold
Mining — A42

Kaieteur
Falls — A43

Shooting Logs
over
Falls — A44

Stabroek
Market — A45

Sugar Cane in
Punts — A46

Forest
Road — A47

Victoria Regia
Lilies — A48

Mt.
Roraima — A49

Sir Walter Raleigh
and Son — A50

Botanical
Gardens
A51

1934, Oct. 1   **Perf. 12½**
210	A40	1c green	.75	2.25
211	A41	2c brown	1.75	1.90
212	A42	3c carmine	.50	.25
b.		Perf. 12½x13½ ('43)	1.10	1.10
c.		Perf. 13x13½ ('49)	.75	.25
213	A43	4c vio black	2.50	3.75
a.		Vert. pair, imperf. horiz.	20,000.	20,000.
214	A44	6c dp ultra	8.00	7.50
215	A45	12c orange	.50	.35
a.		Perf. 13½x13 ('51)	.70	1.25
216	A46	24c rose violet	4.50	15.00
217	A47	48c black	13.00	10.00
218	A43	50c green	18.00	25.00
219	A48	60c brown	32.50	32.00
220	A49	72c rose violet	2.25	3.50
221	A45	96c black	42.50	47.50
222	A51	$1 violet	52.50	50.00
		Nos. 210-222 (13)	179.25	199.00
		Set, never hinged	290.00	

See Nos. 236, 238, 240.

Common Design Types
pictured following the introduction.

Silver Jubilee Issue
Common Design Type
1935, May 6   **Perf. 13½x14**
223	CD301	2c gray blk & ul-		
		tra	.35	.25
224	CD301	6c blue & brown	1.50	5.50
225	CD301	12c indigo & grn	6.50	9.75
226	CD301	24c brt vio & ind	10.00	20.00
		Nos. 223-226 (4)	18.35	35.50
		Set, never hinged	27.50	

Coronation Issue
Common Design Type
1937, May 12   **Perf. 13½x14**
227	CD302	2c brown	.25	.25
228	CD302	4c gray black	.65	.65
229	CD302	6c bright ultra	.55	2.15
		Nos. 227-229 (3)	1.45	3.05
		Set, never hinged	1.60	

A52

A53   A54

A55

A56

A57

A58

Victoria Regia
Lilies and
Jacanas — A59

1938-52		Engr.	Wmk. 4	Perf. 12½	
230	A52	1c green		.25	.25
b.		Perf. 14x13 ('49)		.65	1.00
231	A53	2c violet blk, perf. 13x14 ('49)		.40	.25
b.		Perf. 12½		.50	.25
232	A54	4c black & rose, perf. 13x14 ('52)		.65	.25
a.		Perf. 12½		.90	.40
c.		Vert. pair, imperf. between		35,000.	35,000.
233	A55	6c deep ultra, perf. 13x14 ('49)		1.50	.40
a.		Perf. 12½		1.00	.25
234	A56	24c deep green		2.75	.25
a.		Wmk. upright		20.00	12.50
235	A53	36c purple		3.50	.25
a.		Perf. 13x14 ('51)		3.00	.40
236	A47	48c orange yel		.90	.60
a.		Perf. 14x13 ('51)		1.25	2.25
237	A57	60c brown		13.50	10.00
238	A50	96c brown vio		8.00	3.25
a.		Perf. 12½x13½ ('44)		8.75	13.00
239	A58	$1 deep violet		17.50	.55
a.		Perf. 14x13 ('51)		300.00	700.00
240	A49	$2 rose vio ('45)		12.50	27.50
a.		Perf. 14x13 ('50)		16.00	37.50
241	A59	$3 org brn ('45)		27.50	40.00
a.		Perf. 14x13 ('52)		29.50	55.00
		Nos. 230-241 (12)		88.95	83.55
		Set, never hinged		135.00	

The watermark on No. 234 is sideways.

Catalogue values for unused stamps in this section, from this point to the end of the section, are for Never Hinged items.

Peace Issue
Common Design Type

1946, Oct. 21			Perf. 13½x14	
242	CD303	3c carmine	.25	.45
243	CD303	6c deep blue	.80	.95

Silver Wedding Issue
Common Design Types

1948, Dec. 20	Photo.	Perf. 14x14½	
244	CD304 3c scarlet	.25	.45

Engr.
Perf. 11½x11

245	CD305 $3 orange brown	24.00	28.00

UPU Issue
Common Design Types
Engr.; Name Typo. on 6c and 12c
Perf. 13½, 11x11½

1949, Oct. 10			Wmk. 4	
246	CD306	4c rose carmine	.25	.55
247	CD307	6c indigo	2.00	2.00
248	CD308	12c orange	.25	.75
249	CD309	24c blue green	.25	.90
		Nos. 246-249 (4)	2.75	4.20

University Issue
Common Design Types

1951, Feb. 16	Engr.	Perf. 14x14½	
250	CD310 3c carmine & black	.55	.55
251	CD311 6c dp ultra & black	.55	.70

Coronation Issue
Common Design Type

1953, June 2		Perf. 13½x13	
252	CD312 4c car & blk	.45	.25

G. P. O.,
Georgetown
A60

Victoria Regia
Lilies and
Jacanas —
A60a

Indian Shooting
Fish — A60b

Map — A60c

Felling Greenheart
Tree — A60d

Bauxite Mining
— A60e

Mt. Roraima —
A60f

Kaieteur Falls —
A60g

Arapaima, Fish —
A60h

Toucan — A60i

Coat of Arms —
A60j

Designs: 2c, Botanical gardens. 6c, Rice combine. 8c, Sugar cane entering factory. $2, Dredging gold.

Engr., Center Litho. on $1
Perf. 12½x13, 13

1954, Dec. 1			Wmk. 4	
253	A60	1c black	.25	.25
254	A60	2c dark green	.25	.25
255	A60a	3c red brn & ol	3.75	.25
256	A60b	4c violet	1.50	.25
257	A60c	5c black & red	1.75	.25
258	A60	6c yellow green	1.00	.25
259	A60	8c ultramarine	.40	.25
260	A60d	12c brown & black	1.25	.30
261	A60e	24c orange & black	4.50	.25
262	A60f	36c black & rose	6.00	1.00
263	A60g	48c red brn & ultra	1.00	1.25
264	A60h	72c emerald & rose	14.00	3.00
265	A60i	$1 blk, yel, grn & sal	17.00	2.50
266	A60	$2 magenta	22.50	7.00
267	A60j	$5 black & ultra	21.00	30.00
		Nos. 253-267 (15)	96.15	47.05

See Nos. 279-287.

Clasped
Hands — A62

Perf. 14½x14

1961, Oct. 23		Photo.	Wmk. 314	
268	A62	5c sal pink & brown	.25	.25
269	A62	6c lt blue grn & brown	.25	.25
270	A62	30c lt orange & brown	.45	.40
		Nos. 268-270 (3)	.95	.90

Fourth annual History and Culture Week.

Freedom from Hunger Issue
Common Design Type

1963, July 22		Perf. 14x14½	
271	CD314 20c lilac	.45	.25

Red Cross Centenary Issue
Common Design Type
Wmk. 314

1963, Sept. 2	Litho.	Perf. 13	
272	CD315 5c black & red	.25	.25
273	CD315 20c ultra & red	.80	.55

Queen Types of 1954
Engr.; Center Litho. on $1
Perf. 12½x13, 13

1963-65			Wmk. 314	
279	A60	3c red brn & ol ('65)	4.00	2.50
280	A60	5c black & red ('64)	.40	.25
281	A61	12c brown & blk ('64)	.50	.25
282	A60	24c orange & black	4.50	.25
283	A60	36c black & rose	.80	.25
284	A61	48c red brn & ultra	1.75	3.00
285	A61	72c emerald & rose	5.00	22.50
286	A60	$1 blk, yel, grn & sal	8.25	1.50
287	A60	$2 magenta	13.50	15.00
		Nos. 279-287 (9)	38.70	45.50

Weight
Lifter
A63

1964, Oct. 1		Photo.	Perf. 13x13½	
290	A63	5c orange	.25	.25
291	A63	8c blue	.25	.25
292	A63	25c carmine rose	.45	.45
		Nos. 290-292 (3)	.95	.95

18th Olympic Games, Tokyo, Oct. 10-25.

ITU Issue
Common Design Type
Perf. 11x11½

1965, May 17	Litho.	Wmk. 314	
293	CD317 5c emerald & olive	.25	.25
294	CD317 25c lt blue & brt pink	.35	.30

Intl. Cooperation Year Issue
Common Design Type

1965, Oct. 25	Wmk. 314	Perf. 14½	
295	CD318 5c blue grn & claret	.25	.25
296	CD318 25c lt vio & green	.40	.35

Winston Churchill and St. George's
Cathedral, Georgetown — A64

1966, Jan. 24		Photo.	Perf. 14x14½	
297	A64	5c multicolored	.75	.25
298	A64	25c dp blue, blk & gold	2.40	.70

Sir Winston Leonard Spencer Churchill (1874-1965), statesman and WWII leader.

Royal Visit Issue
Common Design Type

1966, Feb. 4	Litho.	Perf. 11x12	
299	CD320 3c violet blue	.95	.80
300	CD320 25c dark car rose	2.40	.80

POSTAGE DUE STAMPS

Catalogue values for unused stamps in this section are for Never Hinged items.

D1

Perf. 13½x14

1940-55		Typo.	Wmk. 4	
J1	D1	1c green, chalky paper ('52)	1.50	22.50
a.		Wmk. 4a (error)	150.00	
J2	D1	2c black, chalky paper ('52)	4.00	10.00
a.		Wmk. 4a (error)	145.00	
J3	D1	4c ultra ('52)	.35	14.00
a.		Wmk. 4a (error)	145.00	
J4	D1	12c carmine, chalky paper ('55)	17.50	45.00
		Nos. J1-J4 (4)	23.35	91.50

The 1940 printings of Nos. J1-J2 and J4 are on ordinary paper. For detailed listings, see the Scott Classic Specialized catalogue.

WAR TAX STAMP

Regular Issue No. 179 Overprinted

1918, Jan. 4   Wmk. 3   Perf. 14
MR1 A35 2c scarlet   1.90 .25
The relative positions of "War" and "Tax" vary throughout the sheet.

OFFICIAL STAMPS

Counterfeit overprints exist.

No. 50 Overprinted in Red

1875   Unwmk.   Perf. 10
O1 A5 1c black   75.00 26.00
a. Horiz. pair, imperf btwn.   22,500.

Nos. 51, 53-54, 68 Overprinted in Black

O2 A5 2c orange   300.00 17.50
O3 A5 8c rose   375.00 150.00
O4 A5 12c lilac   3,500. 600.00
O5 A12 24c green   2,750. 325.00
For surcharges see Nos. 87, 89, 89A, 96, 102.

Nos. 72-76 Overprinted "OFFICIAL" Similar to #O2-O5
1877   Wmk. 1   Perf. 14
O6 A13 1c slate   350.00 70.00
a. Vert. pair, imperf btwn.   27,500.
O7 A13 2c orange   160.00 18.00
O8 A13 4c ultramarine   140.00 35.00
O9 A13 6c chocolate   6,600. 725.00
O10 A13 8c rose   2,400. 550.00
The type A13 12c lilac, 24c green and 48c red brown overprinted "OFFICIAL" were never placed in use. A few examples of the 12c and 24c have been seen but the 48c is only known surcharged with new value for provisional use in 1881. See Nos. 97-101.
For surcharges see #85-86, 88A, 90-91.

BRITISH HONDURAS

'bri-tish hän-'dur-əs

LOCATION — Central America bordering on Caribbean on east, Mexico on north and Guatemala on west.
GOVT. — British Crown Colony
AREA — 8,867 sq. mi.
POP. — 130,000 (est. 1972)
CAPITAL — Belmopan

Before British Honduras became a colony (subordinate to Jamaica) in 1862, it was a settlement under British influence. In 1884 it became an independent colony. In 1973 the colony changed its name to Belize.

12 Pence = 1 Shilling
100 Cents = 1 Dollar (1888)

Catalogue values for unused stamps in this country are for Never Hinged items, beginning with Scott 127 in the regular postage section, Scott J1 in the postage due section.

Values for unused stamps are for examples with original gum as defined in the catalogue introduction. Very fine examples of Nos. 1-37 will have perforations touching the design on at least one side due to the narrow spacing of the stamps on the plates. Stamps with perfs clear of the design on all four sides are extremely scarce and will command higher prices.

Queen Victoria — A1

1866   Unwmk.   Typo.   Perf. 14
1 A1 1p pale blue   72.50 72.50
a. Horiz. pair, imperf. btwn.
2 A1 6p rose   425.00 195.00
3 A1 1sh green   400.00 145.00
The 6p and 1sh were printed only in a sheet with the 1p. The 1p was later printed in sheets without the 6p and 1sh. The 1sh is known in se-tenant gutter pairs with the 1p and the 6p.

1872   Wmk. 1   Perf. 12½
4 A1 1p pale blue   100.00 30.00
5 A1 3p reddish brn   180.00 90.00
6 A1 6p rose   450.00 55.00
7 A1 1sh green   550.00 32.50
a. Horiz. pair, imperf. btwn.   27,500.
For surcharges see Nos. 18-19.
No. 7a is unique and has faults.

1877-79   Perf. 14
8 A1 1p blue   87.50 32.50
a. Horiz. strip of 3, imperf. btwn.   28,000.
9 A1 3p brown   170.00 32.50
10 A1 4p violet ('79)   300.00 10.00
11 A1 6p green ('78)   500.00 225.00
12 A1 1sh green   325.00 14.50
For surcharges see Nos. 20-21, 29.

1882-87   Wmk. 2
13 A1 1p blue ('84)   75.00 25.00
14 A1 1p rose ('84)   25.00 16.00
a. Diagonal half used as ½p on cover
b. 1p carmine   60.00 32.50
15 A1 4p violet   100.00 5.75
16 A1 6p yellow ('85)   325.00 240.00
17 A1 1sh gray ('87)   300.00 200.00
For surcharges see Nos. 22-26, 28-35.

Stamps of 1872-87 Surcharged in Black

2 CENTS

1888   Wmk. 1   Perf. 12½
18 A1 2c on 6p rose   350.00 275.00
19 A1 3c on 3p brown   20,000. 6,500.

Perf. 14
20 A1 2c on 6p rose   190.00 180.00
a. Diagonal half used as 1c on cover   300.00
b. Double surcharge   2,700.
c. "2" with curved tail   3,500.
21 A1 3c on 3p brown   110.00 110.00

Wmk. 2
22 A1 2c on 1p rose   15.00 50.00
a. Diagonal half used as 1c on cover   220.00
b. Double surcharge   1,100. 1,100.
c. Inverted surcharge   9,000. 5,500.
23 A1 10c on 4p violet   70.00 20.00
a. Inverted surcharge
24 A1 20c on 6p yellow   32.50 50.00
25 A1 50c on 1sh gray   475.00 725.00

No. 25 with Additional Surcharge in Red or Black

TWO CENTS

26 A1 2c (R) on 50c on 1sh gray   60.00 115.00
a. "TWO" in black   18,750. 15,000.
b. "TWO" double (Blk + R)   18,750. 16,000.
c. Diagonal half used as 1c on cover   350.00

Stamps of 1872-87 Srchd. in Black — c

2 CENTS

1888-89
28 A1 2c on 1p rose   1.25 1.75
a. Diagonal half used as 1c on cover   110.00
29 A1 3c on 3p brown   6.25 1.75
30 A1 10c on 4p violet   27.50 1.00
a. Double surcharge   3,500.
31 A1 20c on 6p yel ('89)   19.00 15.00
32 A1 50c on 1sh gray   40.00 105.00
Nos. 28-32 (5)   94.00 124.50
For other examples of this surcharge see Nos. 36, 47. For overprint see No. 51.

No. 30 with Additional Surcharge in Black or Red

6 10 CENTS

1891
33 A1 6c (Blk) on 10c on 4p   3.00 2.25
a. "6" and bar inverted   4,500. 1,200.
b. "6" only inverted   6,500.
34 A1 6c (R) on 10c on 4p   1.90 2.50
a. "6" and bar inverted   725.00 725.00
b. "6" only inverted   6,500.
Stamps similar to No. 33 but with "SIX" instead of "6," both with and without bar, were prepared but not regularly issued.
See No. 37.

No. 29 with Additional Surcharge in Black

FIVE CENTS

35 A1 5c on 3c on 3p brown   1.60 2.00
a. Double surcharge of "Five" and bar   450.00 850.00

Black Surcharge, Type "c"
36 A1 6c on 3p blue   6.00 25.00

No. 36 with Additional Surcharge like Nos. 33-34 in Red
1891
37 A1 15c (R) on 6c on 3p blue   18.00 35.00
a. Double surcharge

A8   2c

1891-98   Wmk. 2   Perf. 14
38 A8 1c green   2.75 1.50
39 A8 2c carmine rose   4.25 .25
40 A8 3c brown   10.00 4.75
41 A8 5c ultra ('95)   12.00 1.25
42 A8 6c ultramarine   15.00 2.00
43 A8 10c vio & grn ('95)   14.00 19.00
44 A8 12c vio & green   2.50 3.50
45 A8 24c yellow & blue   7.00 23.00
46 A8 25c red brn & grn ('98)   95.00 150.00
Nos. 38-46 (9)   162.50 205.25
Numeral tablet on Nos. 43-46 has lined background with colorless value and "c."
For overprints see Nos. 48-50.

Type of 1866 Surcharged Type "c"
1892
47 A1 1c on 1p green   1.00 1.90

REVENUE 5c
Regular Issue Overprinted in Black

1899   Overprint 12mm Long
48 A8 5c ultramarine   28.00 3.00
a. "BEVENUE"   180.00 175.00
49 A8 10c lilac & green   19.00 21.00
a. "BEVENUE"   350.00 425.00
c. "REVENU"   725.00
50 A8 25c red brn & grn   4.25 42.50
a. "BEVENUE"   200.00 425.00
c. "REVE UE"   2,700.
51 A1 50c on 1sh gray (No. 32)   275.00 450.00
a. "BEVENUE"   5,500. 6,500.
Nos. 48-51 (4)   326.25 516.50
Two lengths of the overprint are found on the same pane: 12mm (43 to the pane) and 11mm (17 to the pane). The "U" is found in both a tall, narrow type and the more common small type. The tall variety is found in row 1, position 5. The BEVENUE vaiety is found in row 6, position 4.

A9   5c

1899-1901
52 A9 5c gray blk & ultra, bl ('00)   22.50 3.50
53 A9 10c vio & grn ('01)   11.00 10.00
54 A9 50c grn & car rose   30.00 72.50
55 A9 $1 grn & car rose   95.00 155.00
56 A9 $2 green & ultra   150.00 200.00
57 A9 $5 green & black   325.00 475.00
Nos. 52-57 (6)   633.50 916.00
Numeral tablet on Nos. 53-54 has lined background with colorless value and "c."

2c   King Edward VII — A10

1902-04   Typo.   Wmk. 2
58 A10 1c gray grn & grn ('04)   2.00 27.50
59 A10 2c vio & blk, red   2.25 .30
60 A10 5c gray blk & ultra, blue   19.00 .35
61 A10 20c dl vio & vio ('04)   14.00 18.00
Nos. 58-61 (4)   37.25 46.15

1904-06   Chalky Paper   Wmk. 3
62 A10 1c green   4.00 2.75
63 A10 2c vio & blk, red   2.75 .40
64 A10 5c blk & ultra, bl ('05)   2.25 .25
65 A10 10c vio & grn ('06)   5.25 18.00
67 A10 25c vio & org ('06)   12.00 60.00
68 A10 50c grn & car rose ('06)   30.00 100.00
69 A10 $1 grn & car rose ('06)   75.00 120.00
70 A10 $2 grn & ultra ('06)   160.00 275.00
71 A10 $5 grn & blk ('06)   375.00 450.00
Nos. 62-71 (9)   666.25 1,026.
The 1c and 2c exist also on ordinary paper.

1909   Ordinary Paper
72 A10 2c carmine   16.00 .25
73 A10 5c ultramarine   2.75 .25

1911
74 A10 25c black, green   7.50 50.00
Numeral tablet on Nos. 61, 65-68, 74 has lined background with colorless value and "c."

1c   25c
King George V
A11   A12

1913-17   Wmk. 3   Perf. 14
75 A11 1c green   5.00 1.75
76 A11 2c scarlet   6.50 1.75
Complete booklet of 100 #76, in blocks of 10 (5x2)   4,500.
a. 2c carmine   6.50 1.25
77 A11 3c orange ('17)   2.00 .25
Complete booklet of 100 #77, in blocks of 10 (5x2)   —
78 A11 5c ultra   3.50 1.10

Chalky Paper

79	A12	10c dl vio & ol grn	6.50	8.00
80	A12	25c blk, gray grn	1.50	14.50
a.		25c black, emerald	2.10	35.00
b.		25c blk, bl grn, olive back	6.00	13.50
81	A12	50c vio & ultra, bl	30.00	17.50
82	A11	$1 black & scar	32.50	70.00
83	A11	$2 grn & dull vio	90.00	120.00
84	A11	$5 vio & blk, red	290.00	350.00
		Nos. 75-84 (10)	467.50	584.85

See No. 91. For overprints see Nos. MR2-MR5.

With Moire Overprint in Violet

1915

85	A11	1c green	4.75	24.00
a.		1c yellow green	.65	21.00
86	A11	2c carmine	4.25	.50
87	A11	5c ultramarine	.40	6.00
		Nos. 85-87 (3)	9.40	30.50

For 'War' overprint see No. MR1.

Peace Commemorative Issue

Seal of Colony and George V A13

1921, Apr. 28 Engr.

89	A13	2c carmine	5.50	.80
		Never hinged	11.50	

Similar to A13 but without "Peace"

1922 Wmk. 4

90	A13	4c dark gray	12.00	1.25
		Never hinged	25.00	

Type of 1913-17

1921 Typo. Wmk. 4

91	A11	1c green	9.00	13.00

A14

1922-33 Typo. Wmk. 4

92	A14	1c green ('29)	19.00	6.50
93	A14	2c dark brown	2.00	2.00
		Complete booklet of 100 #93, in blocks of 10 (5x2)	—	
94	A14	2c rose red ('27)	12.00	2.00
		Complete booklet of 100 #94, in blocks of 10 (5x2)	—	
95	A14	3c orange ('33)	37.50	5.00
96	A14	4c gray ('29)	22.50	1.00
97	A14	5c ultramarine	2.00	.70

Chalky Paper

98	A14	10c olive grn & lil	4.00	.40
99	A14	25c black, emerald	3.25	9.00
100	A14	50c ultra & vio, bl	8.00	16.00
101	A14	$1 scarlet & blk	22.50	30.00
102	A14	$2 red vio & blk	50.00	130.00

Wmk. 3

103	A14	25c black, emerald	8.50	55.00
104	A14	$5 blk & vio, red	225.00	300.00
		Nos. 92-104 (13)	416.25	557.60

For surcharges see Nos. B1-B5.

Common Design Types pictured following the introduction.

Silver Jubilee Issue
Common Design Type
Perf. 11x12

1935, May 6 Engr. Wmk. 4

108	CD301	3c black & ultra	2.00	.60
109	CD301	4c indigo & grn	4.50	4.25
110	CD301	5c ultra & brn	2.25	2.50
111	CD301	25c brn vio & ind	6.50	9.00
		Nos. 108-111 (4)	15.25	16.35
		Set, never hinged	24.00	

Coronation Issue
Common Design Type

1937, May 12 *Perf. 13½x14*

112	CD302	3c deep orange	.25	.25
113	CD302	4c gray black	.35	.25
114	CD302	5c bright ultra	.60	1.90
		Nos. 112-114 (3)	1.20	2.40
		Set, never hinged	2.00	

Mayan Figures A15

Chicle Tapping — A16

Cohune Palm — A17

Local Products A18

Grapefruit Industry A19

Mahogany Logs in River — A20

Sergeant's Cay — A21

Dory — A22

Chicle Industry A23

Court House, Belize — A24

Mahogany Cutting — A25

Seal of Colony — A26

1938 *Perf. 11x11½, 11½x11*

115	A15	1c green & violet	.25	1.00
116	A16	2c car & black	.50	.70
a.		Perf. 12 ('47)	1.90	1.25
117	A17	3c brown & dk vio	.80	1.25
118	A18	4c green & black	.75	.50
119	A19	5c slate bl & red vio	1.25	1.25
120	A20	10c brown & yel grn	1.60	.45
121	A21	15c blue & brown	3.00	1.00
122	A22	25c green & ultra	1.75	1.40
123	A23	50c dk vio & blk	13.50	3.25
124	A24	$1 ol green & car	18.00	7.00
125	A25	$2 rose lake & ind	20.00	28.00
126	A26	$5 brn & carmine	19.00	42.50
		Nos. 115-126 (12)	80.40	88.30
		Set, never hinged	180.00	

Issued: 3c-5c, 1/10; 1c, 2c, 10c-50c, 2/14; $1-$5, 2/28.

> Catalogue values for unused stamps in this section, from this point to the end of the section, are for Never Hinged items.

Peace Issue
Common Design Type
Perf. 13½x14

1946, Sept. 9 Engr. Wmk. 4

127	CD303	3c brown	.25	.25
128	CD303	5c deep blue	.25	.25

Silver Wedding Issue
Common Design Types

1948, Oct. 1 Photo. *Perf. 14x14½*

129	CD304	4c dark green	.25	.70

Engraved; Name Typographed
Perf. 11½x11

130	CD305	$5 light brown	25.00	52.50

St. George's Cay — A27

H.M.S. Merlin — A28

1949, Jan. 10 Engr. *Perf. 12½*

131	A27	1c green & ultra	.25	1.25
132	A27	3c yel brn & dp blue	.25	1.50
133	A27	4c purple & brn ol	.25	1.75
134	A28	5c dk blue & brown	2.00	.75
135	A28	10c vio brn & blue grn	2.00	.45
136	A28	15c ultra & emerald	2.00	.45
		Nos. 131-136 (6)	6.75	6.15

Battle of St. George's Cay, 150th anniv.

UPU Issue
Common Design Types
Perf. 13½, 11x11½

1949, Oct. 10 Engr. Wmk. 4

137	CD306	4c blue green	.40	1.25
138	CD307	5c indigo	1.60	.60
139	CD308	10c chocolate	.55	3.75
140	CD309	25c blue	.75	.75
		Nos. 137-140 (4)	3.30	6.35

University Issue
Common Design Types

1951, Feb. 16 Engr. *Perf. 14x14½*

141	CD310	3c choc & purple	.70	1.75
142	CD311	10c choc & green	.70	.45

Coronation Issue
Common Design Type

1953, June 2 *Perf. 13½x13*

143	CD312	4c dk green & black	.60	.40

Arms — A29

Maya — A30

Designs: 2c, Tapir. 3c, Legislative Council Chamber and mace. 4c, Pine industry. 5c, Spiny lobster. 10c, Stanley Field Airport. 15c, Mayan frieze. 25c, Blue butterfly. $1, Armadillo. $2, Hawkesworth Bridge. $5, Pine Ridge orchid.

1953-57 Engr. *Perf. 13½*

144	A29	1c gray blk & green	.25	.35
a.		Perf. 13½	2.75	2.25
145	A29	2c gray blk & brn, perf. 14 ('57)	2.50	.50
a.		Perf. 13½	1.50	2.75
b.		Perf. 13½x13	2.75	1.75
146	A29	3c mag & rose lil, perf. 14 ('57)	.25	.25
a.		Perf. 13½	.40	.40
b.		Perf. 13½x13	13.00	24.00
147	A29	4c grn & dk brn	1.30	.30
148	A29	5c car & ol brn, perf. 14 ('57)	2.00	.25
a.		Perf. 13½	.85	.25
149	A29	10c ultra & bl gray	1.75	.25
a.		Perf. 13½x13	1.75	.25
150	A29	15c vio & yel grn	.60	.25
151	A29	25c brown & ultra	6.50	3.50
152	A30	50c purple & brown	17.50	3.50
153	A29	$1 red brn & sl bl	9.50	4.50
154	A29	$2 gray & car	9.50	4.00
155	A30	$5 blue gray & pur	42.50	15.00
		Nos. 144-155 (12)	94.15	32.65

Issued: 5c, 5/15; 2c, 3c, 9/18, perf. 13½, 9/2. For overprints see Nos. 159-166.

View of Belize, 1842 — A31

Designs: 10c, Public seals, 1860 and 1960. 15c, Tamarind Tree, Newtown Barracks.

Perf. 11½x11

1960, July 1 Wmk. 314

156	A31	2c green	.55	1.10
157	A31	10c carmine	.55	.25
158	A31	15c blue	.55	.30
		Nos. 156-158 (3)	1.65	1.65

Cent. of the establishment of a local PO.

Nos. 145-146, 149-150 Overprinted

1961, Mar. 1 Wmk. 4 *Perf. 14, 13*

159	A29	2c gray black & brn	.30	.50
160	A29	3c mag & rose lilac	.40	.50
161	A29	10c ultra & blue gray	.40	.25
162	A29	15c violet & yel green	.40	.25
		Nos. 159-162 (4)	1.50	1.50

Nos. 144, 149, 151-152 Overprinted

1962, Jan. 15   *Perf. 13*
163	A29	1c gray black & green	.25	1.10
164	A29	10c ultra & blue gray	.30	.25
165	A29	25c brown & ultra	1.90	.60
166	A30	50c purple & brown	.75	1.10
		Nos. 163-166 (4)	3.20	3.05

Hurricane Hattie struck Belize, Oct. 31, 1961.

Great Curassow A32

Birds: 2c, Red-legged honeycreeper. 3c, American jacana. 4c, Great kiskadee. 5c, Scarlet-rumped tanager. 10c, Scarlet macaw. 15c, Massena trogon. 25c, Redfooted booby. 50c, Keel-billed toucan. $1, Magnificent frigatebird. $2, Rufous-tailed jacamar. $5, Montezuma oropendola.

Perf. 14x14½

1962, Apr. 2   **Photo.**   **Wmk. 314**
Birds in Natural Colors; Black Inscriptions
167	A32	1c yellow	1.25	.60
168	A32	2c gray	1.60	.25
a.		Green omitted	850.00	
169	A32	3c lt yel green	3.75	2.50
a.		Dark grn (legs) omitted	850.00	
170	A32	4c lt gray	3.00	3.25
171	A32	5c buff	2.25	.25
172	A32	10c beige	3.75	.25
a.		Blue omitted	900.00	
173	A32	15c pale lemon	1.25	.25
174	A32	25c bluish gray & pink	3.75	.25
175	A32	50c pale blue	5.00	.30
b.		Blue (beak & claw) omitted	1,250.	1,250.
176	A32	$1 blue	7.50	1.75
177	A32	$2 pale gray	19.50	5.75
178	A32	$5 light blue	23.00	15.00
		Nos. 167-178 (12)	75.60	30.40

For overprints see Nos. 182-186, 195-199.

1967   **Wmk. 314 Sideways**
Colors as 1962 Issue
167a	A32	1c	.25	.50
168b	A32	2c	.25	1.00
170a	A32	4c	2.75	2.75
171a	A32	5c	.45	.25
172b	A32	10c	.30	.25
173a	A32	15c	.30	.25
175a	A32	50c	2.25	3.50
		Nos. 167a-175a (7)	6.55	8.50

Issued: 1, 4, 5, 50c, 2/16; 2, 10, 15c, 11/28.

Freedom from Hunger Issue
Common Design Type
1963, June 4   *Perf. 14x14½*
179	CD314	22c green	.60	.25

Red Cross Centenary Issue
Common Design Type
Wmk. 314
1963, Sept. 2   **Litho.**   *Perf. 13*
180	CD315	4c black & red	.25	1.25
181	CD315	22c ultra & red	.75	1.25

Nos. 167, 169, 170, 172 and 174 Overprinted

1964   **Photo.**   *Perf. 14x14½*
182	A32	1c multicolored	.25	.40
a.		Yellow omitted	300.00	
183	A32	3c multicolored	.75	.40
184	A32	4c multicolored	.75	.40
185	A32	10c multicolored	.75	.25
186	A32	25c multicolored	1.00	.75
		Nos. 182-186 (5)	3.50	2.20

Attainment of self-government.

ITU Issue
Common Design Type
Perf. 11x11½
1965, May 17   **Litho.**   **Wmk. 314**
187	CD317	2c ver & green	.25	.25
188	CD317	50c yel & red lilac	.50	.50

Intl. Cooperation Year Issue
Common Design Type
1965, Oct. 25   *Perf. 14½*
189	CD318	1c bl grn & claret	.25	.25
190	CD318	22c lt violet & green	.35	.30

Churchill Memorial Issue
Common Design Type
1966, Jan. 24   **Photo.**   *Perf. 14*
Design in Black, Gold and Carmine Rose
191	CD319	1c bright blue	.25	.50
192	CD319	4c green	.50	.25
193	CD319	22c brown	.80	.25
194	CD319	25c violet	.90	.30
		Nos. 191-194 (4)	2.45	1.30

Bird Type of 1962 Overprinted

Wmk. 314 Sideways
1966, July 1   *Perf. 14x14½*
195	A32	1c multicolored	.25	.45
a.		Yellow omitted	400.00	
196	A32	3c multicolored	.60	.45
197	A32	4c multicolored	.60	.45
198	A32	10c multicolored	.60	.30
199	A32	25c multicolored	.90	.40
		Nos. 195-199 (5)	2.95	2.05

Citrus Grove — A33

10c, Half Moon Cay & Lighthouse Reef. 22c, Hidden Valley Falls & Mountain Pine Ridge. 25c, Xunantunich Mayan ruins in Cayo district.

1966, Oct. 1   **Photo.**   **Wmk. 314**
200	A33	5c multicolored	.25	.25
201	A33	10c multicolored	.25	.25
202	A33	22c multicolored	.25	.25
203	A33	25c multicolored	.25	.50
		Nos. 200-203 (4)	1.00	1.25

1st British Honduras stamp issue, cent.

International Tourist Year — A34

1967, Dec. 4   *Perf. 12½*
204	A34	5c Sailfish	.25	.30
205	A34	10c Deer	.25	.25
206	A34	22c Jaguar	.40	.25
207	A34	25c Tarpon	.40	.50
		Nos. 204-207 (4)	1.30	1.30

Schomburgkia Tibicinis — A35

Orchids: 10c, Maxillaria tenuifolia. 22c, Bletia purpurea. 25c, Sobralia macrantha.

Inscribed: "20th Anniversary of E.C.L.A."
Perf. 14½x14
1968, Apr. 16   **Photo.**   **Wmk. 314**
208	A35	5c violet & multi	.60	.55
209	A35	10c green & multi	.75	.35
210	A35	22c multicolored	.90	.35
211	A35	25c olive & multi	1.20	.75
		Nos. 208-211 (4)	3.45	2.00

20th anniv. of the Economic Commission for Latin America. See Nos. 226-229, 255-258.

Belizean Patriots' Memorial, Belize City, and Human Rights Flame — A36

Design: 50c, Mayan motif stele, monument at new capital site and Human Rights flame.

Perf. 13x13½
1968, July 15   **Litho.**   **Wmk. 314**
212	A36	22c multicolored	.25	.25
213	A36	50c multicolored	.25	.25

International Human Rights Year.

Jewfish A37

Designs: 2c, White-lipped peccary. 3c, Grouper (sea bass). 4c, Collared anteater. 5c, Bonefish. 10c, Paca. 15c, Dolphinfish. 25c, Kinkajou. 50c, Yellow-and-green-banded muttonfish. $1, Tayra. $2, Great barracudas. $5, Mountain lion.

Perf. 13x12½
1968, Oct. 15   **Litho.**   **Unwmk.**
214	A37	1c yellow & multi	.40	.25
215	A37	2c brt yel & multi	.25	.25
216	A37	3c pink & multi	.25	.25
217	A37	4c brt grn & multi	.25	1.25
218	A37	5c brick red & multi	.25	1.25
219	A37	10c lilac & multi	.25	.25
220	A37	15c org yel & multi	2.00	.25
221	A37	25c multicolored	.40	.50
222	A37	50c bl grn & multi	.85	1.25
223	A37	$1 ocher & multi	2.75	1.50
224	A37	$2 violet & multi	2.75	2.50
225	A37	$5 ultra & multi	14.00	7.00
		Nos. 214-225 (12)	24.40	16.50

See Nos. 234-240, Belize 327-339.
For overprints see Nos. 251-254, 281-282.

Orchid Type of 1968
Inscribed "Orchids of Belize"

Designs: 5c, Rhyncholaetia digbyana. 10c, Cattleya bowringiana. 22c, Lycaste cochleatum. 25c, Coryanthes speciosum.

Perf. 14½x14
1969, Apr. 9   **Wmk. 314**
226	A35	5c Prus blue & multi	.90	.30
227	A35	10c olive bis & multi	1.00	.25
228	A35	22c yellow grn & multi	1.50	.25
229	A35	25c violet blue & multi	1.60	1.75
		Nos. 226-229 (4)	5.00	2.55

Hardwood Trees — A38

1969, Sept. 1   **Litho.**   *Perf. 14*
230	A38	5c Ziricote	.25	.25
231	A38	10c Rosewood	.25	.25
232	A38	22c Mayflower	.25	.25
233	A38	25c Mahogany	.35	.35
		Nos. 230-233 (4)	1.10	1.10

Timber industry of British Honduras. Issued in sheets of 9 (3x3) on simulated wood background.

Fish-Animal Type of 1968
Designs: ½c, Crana (fish). Others as before.

Wmk. 314 Sideways (½c, 2c, $5),
Upright (3c, 5c, 10c)
1969-72   **Litho.**   *Perf. 13x12½*
234	A37	½c vio bl, yel & blk	.25	.25
235	A37	½c citron, blk & bl ('71)	2.00	2.00

236	A37	2c brt yel, blk & grn ('72)	5.25	3.75
237	A37	3c pink & multi ('72)	5.25	3.75
a.		Wmk. sideways ('72)	4.00	6.00
238	A37	5c brick red & multi ('72)	5.25	3.75
239	A37	10c lilac & multi ('72)	5.25	3.75
a.		Wmk. sideways ('72)	4.00	7.00
240	A37	$5 ultra & multi ('70)	2.00	6.00
		Nos. 234-240 (7)	25.25	23.25

For overprints see Nos. 251-252.

Virgin and Child, by Giovanni Bellini — A39

Christmas: 22c, 25c, Adoration of the Kings, by Veronese.

1969, Nov. 1   **Litho.**   *Perf. 14*
247	A39	5c multicolored	.25	.25
248	A39	15c dp orange & multi	.25	.25
249	A39	22c lilac rose & multi	.25	.25
250	A39	25c emerald & multi	.25	.25
		Nos. 247-250 (4)	1.00	1.00

Nos. 238-239 and Type of 1968 Overprinted

Wmk. 314 Sideways
1970, Feb. 2   **Photo.**   *Perf. 13x12½*
251	A37	5c brick red & multi	.25	.25
252	A37	10c lilac & multi	.25	.25
253	A37	15c org yel & multi	.30	.25
254	A37	25c multicolored	.30	.25
		Nos. 251-254 (4)	1.10	1.00

Orchid Type of 1968
Inscribed: "Orchids of Belize"
Wmk. 314
1970, Apr. 2   **Litho.**   *Perf. 14*
255	A35	5c Black	.65	.25
256	A35	15c White butterfly	1.00	.25
257	A35	22c Swan	1.30	.25
258	A35	25c Butterfly	1.30	.75
		Nos. 255-258 (4)	4.25	1.50

Santa Maria Tree and Wood (Calophyllum Brasiliense) — A40

Hardwood Trees and Woods: 15c, Nargusta (terminalia amazonia). 22c, Cedar (cedrela mexicana). 25c, Sapodilla (achras sapota).

1970, Sept. 7   *Perf. 14*
259	A40	5c multicolored	.40	.25
260	A40	15c multicolored	.65	.25
261	A40	22c multicolored	.80	.25
262	A40	25c multicolored	.80	.65
		Nos. 259-262 (4)	2.65	1.40

Nativity, by Arthur Hughes — A41

Christmas: 5c, 15c, 50c, Mystic Nativity, by Botticelli.

1970, Nov. 2   **Perf. 14**
263	A41	½c black & multi	.25	.25
264	A41	5c brown & multi	.25	.25
265	A41	10c multicolored	.25	.25
266	A41	15c slate bl & multi	.25	.25
267	A41	22c dk green & multi	.30	.25
268	A41	50c black & multi	.40	.40
		Nos. 263-268 (6)	1.70	1.65

Legislative
Assembly
House
A42

Designs: 5c, View of South Side of Belize. 10c, Government Plaza, Belmopan. 22c, Magistrates' Court. 25c, Police Headquarters. 50c, New General Post Office.

1971, Jan. 30   **Litho.**   **Perf. 13½x14**
Size: 59x22mm
269	A42	5c multicolored	.25	.25
270	A42	10c multicolored	.25	.25

Size: 37x21½mm
271	A42	15c multicolored	.25	.25
272	A42	22c multicolored	.30	.25
273	A42	25c multicolored	.35	.25
274	A42	50c multicolored	.40	.40
		Nos. 269-274 (6)	1.80	1.65

New capital at Belmopan.

Tabebuia Chrysantha — A43

Flowers: 5c, 22c, Hymenocallis littoralis. 10c, 25c, Hippeastrum equestre. 15c, like ½c.

1971, Mar. 27   **Litho.**   **Perf. 14**
275	A43	½c vio blue & multi	.25	.25
276	A43	5c olive & multi	.25	.25
277	A43	10c violet & multi	.25	.25
278	A43	15c multicolored	.25	.25
279	A43	22c multicolored	.25	.25
280	A43	25c lt brown & multi	.25	.25
		Nos. 275-280 (6)	1.50	1.50

Easter.

Type of 1968 Overprinted: "RACIAL EQUALITY / YEAR — 1971"
Perf. 13x12½
1971, June 14   **Litho.**   **Wmk. 314**
281	A37	10c lilac & multi	.45	
282	A37	50c blue green & multi	1.30	.30

Intl. year against racial discrimination.

Tubroos
(Enterolobium
Cyclocarpum)
A44

Hardwood Trees of Belize: 15c, Yemeri (Vochysia hondurensis). 26c, Billyweb (Sweetia panamensis). 50c, Logwood (Haematoxylum campechiaum).

Queen's Head in Silver
1971, Aug. 16   **Perf. 14**
283	A44	5c green, brn & blk	.80	.25
284	A44	15c multicolored	1.10	.35
285	A44	26c multicolored	1.50	.35
286	A44	50c multicolored	2.40	4.75
a.		Souvenir sheet of 4, #283-286	7.00	7.00
		Nos. 283-286 (4)	5.80	5.70

Verrazano-Narrows Bridge, New York, and Quebec Bridge, Canada — A45

Bridges of the World: ½c, Hawksworth Bridge connecting San Ignacio and Santa Helena and Belcan Bridge, Belize, Br. Honduras. 26c, London Bridge in 1871, and at Lake Havasu City, Ariz., in 1971. 50c, Belize-Mexico Bridge and Belize Swing Bridge.

1971, Sept. 23   **Litho.**
287	A45	½c multicolored	.25	.35
288	A45	5c multicolored	.40	.25
289	A45	26c multicolored	1.10	.25
290	A45	50c multicolored	1.25	1.50
		Nos. 287-290 (4)	3.00	2.35

Petrae
Volubis — A46

Wild Flowers: 15c, Vochysia hondurensis. 26c, Tabebuia pentaphylla. 50c, Erythrina americana.

1972, Feb. 28
Flowers in Natural Colors; Black Inscriptions
292	A46	6c lilac & yellow	.25	.25
293	A46	15c lt blue & pale grn	.40	.30
294	A46	26c pink & lt blue	.70	.50
295	A46	50c orange & lt grn	1.10	1.40
		Nos. 292-295 (4)	2.45	2.45

Easter.

Seated Jade
Figure — A47

Mayan Carved Jade, 4th-8th centuries: 6c, Dancing priest. 16c, Sun god's head, horiz. 26c, Priest on throne and sun god's head. 50c, Figure and mask.

Perf. 14x13½, 13½x14
1972, May 22   **Unwmk.**
296	A47	3c rose red & multi	.35	.25
297	A47	6c vio bl & multi	.35	.25
298	A47	16c brown & multi	.60	.25
299	A47	26c ol grn & multi	.85	.25
300	A47	50c purple & multi	1.60	2.50
		Nos. 296-300 (5)	3.75	3.50

Black inscription with details of designs on back of stamps.

Banak (Virola
Koschnyi) — A48

Hardwood Trees of Belize: 5c, Quamwood (Schizolobium parahybum). 16c, Waika chewstick (Symphonia globulifera). 26c, Mammee-

apple (Mammea americana). 50c, My lady (Aspidosperma megalocarpon).

1972, Aug. 21   **Wmk. 314**   **Perf. 14**
Queen's Head in Gold
301	A48	3c brt pink & multi	.25	.25
302	A48	5c gray & multi	.25	.25
303	A48	16c green & multi	.60	.25
304	A48	26c lemon & multi	.80	.25
305	A48	50c lt violet & multi	1.75	2.00
		Nos. 301-305 (5)	3.65	3.00

Silver Wedding Issue, 1972
Common Design Type

Design: Queen Elizabeth II, Prince Philip and Belize orchids.

1972, Nov. 20   **Photo.**   **Perf. 14x14½**
306	CD324	26c slate grn & multi	.30	.30
307	CD324	50c violet & multi	.50	.50

Baron
Bliss Day
A49

Festivals of Belize: 10c, Labor Day boat race. 26c, Carib Settlement Day dance. 50c, Pan American Day parade.

1973, Mar. 9   **Litho.**   **Perf. 14½**
308	A49	3c dull blue & black	.25	.25
309	A49	10c red & multi	.25	.25
310	A49	26c ver & multi	.50	.40
311	A49	50c black & multi	1.00	1.00
		Nos. 308-311 (4)	2.00	1.90

SEMI-POSTAL STAMPS

Regular Issue of 1921-29 Surcharged in Black or Red

1932   **Wmk. 4**   **Perf. 14**
B1	A14	1c + 1c green	3.00	15.00
B2	A14	2c + 2c rose red	3.00	15.00
B3	A14	3c + 3c orange	3.00	32.50
B4	A14	4c + 4c gray (R)	10.00	35.00
B5	A14	5c + 5c ultra	7.50	15.00
		Nos. B1-B5 (5)	26.50	112.50

The surtax was for a fund to aid sufferers from the destruction of the city of Belize by a hurricane in Sept. 1931.

POSTAGE DUE STAMPS

> **Catalogue values for unused stamps in this section are for Never Hinged items.**

D1

1923-64   **Typo.**   **Wmk. 4**   **Perf. 14**
J1	D1	1c black	3.25	15.00
J2	D1	2c black	3.25	8.00
J3	D1	4c black	2.50	7.00
		Nos. J1-J3 (3)	9.00	30.00

Nos. J1-J3 were re-issued on chalky paper in 1956. Values shown are for the 1956 issue. The 1923 issue, on yellowish thin ordinary paper, sells for $7.25 unused, $42.50 used. The 1c was reprinted in 1964 on white, ordinary paper. Value, $37.50 unused, $45 used.

Perf. 13½x13, 13½x14
1965-72   **Wmk. 314**
J4	D1	2c black ('72)	4.00	7.50
J5	D1	4c black	2.00	7.50

WAR TAX STAMPS

Nos. 85, 75 and 77
Overprinted

1916-17   **Wmk. 3**   **Perf. 14**
With Moire Overprint
MR1	A11	1c green	.25	3.00
a.		"WAR" inverted	300.00	*350.00*

Without Moire Overprint
MR2	A11	1c green ('17)	1.75	*5.50*
MR3	A11	3c orange ('17)	5.50	*14.00*
a.		Double overprint	425.00	425.00
		Nos. MR1-MR3 (3)	7.50	22.50

Nos. 75 and 77
Overprinted

1918
MR4	A11	1c green	.25	*.40*
MR5	A11	3c orange	1.00	*4.00*

BRITISH INDIAN OCEAN TERRITORY

'bri-tish 'in-dēan 'ō-chən

'ter-ə-ˌtōr-ē

LOCATION — Indian Ocean
GOVT. — British Dependency
POP. — 0

B.I.O.T. was established Nov. 8, 1965. This island group lies 1,180 miles north of Mauritius. It consisted of Chagos Archipelago (chief island: Diego Garcia), Aldabra, Farquhar and Des Roches Islands until June 23, 1976, when the last three named islands were returned to Seychelles.

There is no permanent population on the islands. There are military personnel located there.

100 Cents = 1 Rupee
100 Pence = 1 Pound (1990)

Catalogue values for all unused stamps in this country are for Never Hinged items.

Seychelles Nos. 198-202, 204-212 Overprinted

Perf. 14½x14, 14x14½
1968, Jan. 17 Photo. Wmk. 314
Size: 24x31, 31x24mm

1	A17	5c multicolored	1.40	1.75
2	A17	10c multicolored	.25	.25
3	A17	15c multicolored	.25	.25
4	A17	20c multicolored	.25	.25
5	A17	25c multicolored	.25	.25
6	A18	40c multicolored	.35	.25
7	A18	45c multicolored	.35	.35
8	A17	50c multicolored	.35	.35
9	A17	75c multicolored	.85	.45
10	A18	1r multicolored	1.00	.45
11	A18	1.50r multicolored	2.50	1.75
12	A18	2.25r multicolored	4.00	4.50
13	A18	3.50r multicolored	4.00	5.25
14	A18	5r multicolored	14.00	8.00

Perf. 13x14
Size: 22½x39mm

15	A17	10r multicolored	26.00	20.00
		Nos. 1-15 (15)	55.80	44.10

Lascar
A1

Marine Fauna: 10c, Hammerhead shark, vert. 15c, Tiger shark. 20c, Sooty eagle ray. 25c, Butterflyfish, vert. 30c, Robber crab. 40c, Green carangue. 45c, Needlefish, vert. 50c, Barracuda. 60c, Spotted pebble crab. 75c, Parrotfish. 85c, Rainbow runner (fish). 1r, Giant hermit crab. 1.50r, Humphead. 2.25r, Rock cod. 3.50r, Black marlin. 5r, Whale shark, vert. 10r, Lionfish.

Perf. 14x13½, 13½x14; 14 (30c, 60c, 85c)

1968-73 Litho. Wmk. 314

16	A1	5c multicolored	1.00	2.25
a.		Wmk. upright ('73)	1.40	5.50
17	A1	10c multicolored	.40	1.10
18	A1	15c multicolored	.40	1.60
19	A1	20c multicolored	.40	.90
20	A1	25c multicolored	.90	.90
21	A1	30c multi ('70)	4.25	3.75
22	A1	40c multicolored	1.10	.25
23	A1	45c multicolored	2.50	2.50
24	A1	50c multicolored	1.10	.65
25	A1	60c multi ('70)	4.25	4.25
26	A1	75c multicolored	2.75	2.50
27	A1	85c multi ('70)	5.25	4.25
28	A1	1r multicolored	1.75	.65
29	A1	1.50r multicolored	2.75	2.75
30	A1	2.25r multicolored	13.50	11.00
31	A1	3.50r multicolored	4.25	4.00

32	A1	5r multicolored	13.50	15.00
33	A1	10r multicolored	10.00	7.50
		Nos. 16-33 (18)	70.05	65.80

No. 16 has watermark sideways.

Aldabra Atoll and Sacred Ibis — A2

1969, July 10 Litho. Perf. 13½x13

34	A2	2.25r vio blue & multi	2.25	1.75

Outrigger Canoe — A3

75c, Beaching canoe. 1r, Merchant ship Nordvaer. 1.50r, Yacht, Isle of Farquhar.

Perf. 13½x14

1969, Dec. 15 Litho. Wmk. 314

35	A3	45c multicolored	.35	.35
36	A3	75c multicolored	.65	.65
37	A3	1r multicolored	1.00	1.00
38	A3	1.50r multicolored	1.50	1.50
		Nos. 35-38 (4)	3.50	3.50

Giant Land Tortoise — A4

Designs: 75c, Aldabra lily. 1r, Aldabra tree snail. 1.50r, Dimorphic egrets.

1971, Feb. 1 Litho. Wmk. 314

39	A4	45c multicolored	2.75	2.50
40	A4	75c multicolored	3.25	2.50
41	A4	1r multicolored	3.75	2.50
42	A4	1.50r multicolored	13.00	11.00
		Nos. 39-42 (4)	22.75	18.50

Aldabra Nature Reserve.

Society Coat of Arms and Flightless Rail — A5

1971, June 30 Litho. Perf. 13½

43	A5	3.50r multicolored	16.50	11.00

Opening of Royal Society Research Station at Aldabra.

Acropora Formosa
A6

Corals: 60c, Goniastrea pectinata. 1r, Fungia fungites. 1.75r, Tubipora musica.

1972, Mar. 1

44	A6	40c blue & multi	3.75	3.75
45	A6	60c brt pink & multi	4.25	4.25
46	A6	1r blue & multi	4.25	4.25
47	A6	1.75r brt pink & multi	5.75	5.75
		Nos. 44-47 (4)	18.00	18.00

Common Design Types pictured following the introduction.

**Silver Wedding Issue, 1972
Common Design Type**

Design: Queen Elizabeth II, Prince Philip, flightless rail and sacred ibis.

1972, Nov. 20 Photo. Perf. 14x14½

48	CD324	95c multicolored	1.00	.50
49	CD324	1.50r violet & multi	1.00	.50

Crucifixion, 17th Century — A7

Paintings, Ethiopian Manuscripts, 17th Century: 75c, 1.50r, Joseph and Nicodemus burying Jesus. 1r, Like 45c.

1973, Apr. 9 Litho. Perf. 14

50	A7	45c buff & multi	.25	.40
51	A7	75c buff & multi	.30	.55
52	A7	1r buff & multi	.35	.60
53	A7	1.50r buff & multi	.65	.70
a.		Souvenir sheet of 4, #50-53	2.40	3.50
		Nos. 50-53 (4)	1.55	2.25

Easter.

Upsidedown Jellyfish — A8

1973, Nov. 12 Litho. Wmk. 314

54	A8	50c shown	3.75	3.50
55	A8	1r Butterflies	4.25	3.50
56	A8	1.50r Spider	4.50	3.50
		Nos. 54-56 (3)	12.50	10.50

Nordvaer and July 14, 1969 Cancel — A9

2.50r, Nordvaer offshore and cancel.

1974, July 14

57	A9	85c multicolored	1.00	.85
58	A9	2.50r multicolored	2.00	1.50

Nordvaer traveling post office, 5th anniv.

Terebra Maculata and Terebra Subulata — A10

Sea Shells: 75c, Turbo marmoratus. 1r, Drupa rubusidaeus. 1.50r, Cassis rufa.

1974, Nov. 12 Litho. Perf. 13½x14

59	A10	45c multicolored	2.50	1.40
60	A10	75c multicolored	2.75	1.60
61	A10	1r multicolored	3.00	1.90
62	A10	1.50r multicolored	3.25	2.10
		Nos. 59-62 (4)	11.50	7.00

Aldabra Drongo — A11

Birds: 10c, Malagasy coucal. 20c, Red-headed forest fody. 25c, Fairy tern. 30c, Crested tern. 40c, Brown booby. 50c, Noddy tern. 60c, Gray heron. 65c, Blue-faced booby. 95c, Malagasy white-eye. 1r, Green-backed heron. 1.75r, Lesser frigate bird. 3.50r, White-tailed tropic bird. 5r, Souimanga sunbird. 10r, Malagasy turtledove. Nos. 69, 71-77 horiz.

1975, Feb. 28 Wmk. 314 Perf. 14

63	A11	5c buff & multi	1.50	3.25
64	A11	10c lt ultra & multi	1.50	3.25
65	A11	20c dp yel & multi	1.50	3.25
66	A11	25c ultra & multi	1.50	3.25
67	A11	30c dl yel & multi	1.50	3.25
68	A11	40c bis & multi	1.50	3.25
69	A11	50c lt blue & multi	1.50	3.50
70	A11	60c yel & multi	1.50	3.50
71	A11	65c yel grn & multi	1.50	3.50
72	A11	95c citron & multi	1.50	3.50
73	A11	1r bister & multi	1.50	3.50
74	A11	1.75r yel & multi	2.50	8.50
75	A11	3.50r blue & multi	3.25	8.50
76	A11	5r pale sal & multi	4.50	7.50
77	A11	10r brt yel & multi	8.50	13.00
		Nos. 63-77 (15)	35.25	74.50

Grewia Salicifolia — A12

Native Plants: 65c, Cassia aldabrensis. 1r, Hypoestes aldabrensis. 1.60r, Euphorbia pyrifolia.

1975, July 10 Litho. Wmk. 314

78	A12	50c multicolored	.65	1.10
79	A12	65c multicolored	.70	1.25
80	A12	1r multicolored	.85	1.25
81	A12	1.60r multicolored	1.10	1.75
		Nos. 78-81 (4)	3.30	5.35

Nature protection.

Aldabra and Compass Rose — A13

Maps of Islands: 1r, Desroches. 1.50r, Farquhar. 2r, Diego Garcia.

1975, Nov. 8 Litho. Perf. 13½x14

82	A13	50c blk, blue & grn	1.00	1.00
83	A13	1r green & multi	1.10	1.10
84	A13	1.50r blk, ultra & grn	1.40	1.40
85	A13	2r blk, lilac & grn	1.50	1.50
a.		Souvenir sheet of 4, #82-85	9.50	14.00
		Nos. 82-85 (4)	5.00	5.00

British Indian Ocean Territory, 10th anniv.

Crimson Speckled Moth — A14

Insects: 1.20r, Dysdercus fasciatus. 1.50r, Sphex torridus. 2r, Oryctes rhinoceros.

1976, Mar. 22		**Litho.**		**Wmk. 373**
86	A14	65c multicolored	1.25	1.25
87	A14	1.20r multicolored	1.50	1.50
88	A14	1.50r multicolored	1.75	1.75
89	A14	2r multicolored	1.75	1.75
		Nos. 86-89 (4)	6.25	6.25

Exhibition
Emblem
and No.
37 — A15

1990, May 3		**Wmk. 373**		**Perf. 14**
90	A15	15p No. 62	6.25	5.75
91	A15	20p No. 89	6.75	6.00
92	A15	34p No. 85	10.00	8.25
93	A15	54p shown	12.00	10.00
		Nos. 90-93 (4)	35.00	30.00

Stamp World London '90.

Birds — A16

15p, White-tailed tropic birds. 20p, Turtle doves. 24p, Greater frigate birds. 30p, Little green herons. 34p, Greater sand plovers. 41p, Crab plovers. 45p, Crested terns. 54p, Lesser crested terns. 62p, Fairy terns. 71p, Red-footed boobies. 80p, Indian mynahs. £ 1, Madagascar fodies.

1990, May 3		**Wmk. 384**		**Perf. 14**
94	A16	15p multicolored	1.30	2.25
95	A16	20p multicolored	1.40	2.25
96	A16	24p multicolored	2.50	2.25
97	A16	30p multicolored	1.90	2.50
98	A16	34p multicolored	2.10	2.50
99	A16	41p multicolored	2.10	2.50
100	A16	45p multicolored	4.00	3.00
101	A16	54p multicolored	3.00	3.75
102	A16	62p multicolored	3.00	3.75
103	A16	71p multicolored	3.25	3.75
104	A16	80p multicolored	3.25	4.50
105	A16	£1 multicolored	4.50	4.75
		Nos. 94-105 (12)	32.30	37.75

For overprints see Nos. 145-146.

Queen Mother, 90th Birthday
Common Design Types

Designs: 24p, Lady Elizabeth Bowes-Lyon, 1923. £1, Queen, Princesses Elizabeth & Margaret, 1940.

1990, Aug. 4		**Wmk. 384**		**Perf. 14x15**
106	CD343	24p multicolored	7.00	6.50
		Perf. 14½		
107	CD344	£1 brown & black	11.00	12.00

British Indian
Ocean Territory,
25th
Anniv. — A17

1990, Nov. 8		**Litho.**		**Perf. 14**
108	A17	20p Flag	5.75	5.75
109	A17	24p Coat of arms	5.75	5.75
Souvenir Sheet				
110	A17	£1 Map	13.50	13.50

Govt.
Services
A18

20p, Postal service. 24p, Royal Marines. 34p, Police station, officers. 54p, Customs service.

		Wmk. 373		
1991, June 3		**Litho.**		**Perf. 14**
111	A18	20p multi	2.25	2.25
112	A18	24p multi	3.50	2.50
113	A18	34p multi	4.00	4.00
114	A18	54p multi	5.50	5.50
		Nos. 111-114 (4)	15.25	14.25

Visiting
Ships
A19

20p, Survey ship Experiment, 1786. 24p, US Brig Pickering, 1819. 34p, SMS Emden, 1914. 54p, HMS Edinburgh, 1988.

1991, Nov. 8				
115	A19	20p multicolored	3.00	3.00
116	A19	24p multicolored	3.25	3.25
117	A19	34p multicolored	4.25	4.25
118	A19	54p multicolored	5.25	5.25
		Nos. 115-118 (4)	15.75	15.75

Queen Elizabeth II's Accession to the Throne, 40th Anniv.
Common Design Type

		Wmk. 373		
1992, Feb. 6		**Litho.**		**Perf. 14**
119	CD349	15p multicolored	3.25	2.75
120	CD349	20p multicolored	4.00	3.00
121	CD349	24p multicolored	5.50	4.00
122	CD349	34p multicolored	5.00	4.75
123	CD349	54p multicolored	5.00	4.75
		Nos. 119-123 (5)	22.75	19.25

Aircraft
A20

		Wmk. 384		
1992, Oct. 23		**Litho.**		**Perf. 14**
124	A20	20p Catalina	1.75	2.50
125	A20	24p Nimrod	2.25	2.50
126	A20	34p P-3 Orion	2.75	3.25
127	A20	54p B-52	3.75	4.50
		Nos. 124-127 (4)	10.50	12.75

Christmas — A21

Paintings: 5p, The Mystical Marriage of St. Cathrin, by Correggio. 24p, Madonna and Child by unknown artist. 34p, Madonna and Child by unknown artist, diff. 54p, The Birth of Jesus, by Kaspar Jele.

1992, Nov. 27				**Perf. 14½**
128	A21	5p multicolored	.75	.75
129	A21	24p multicolored	1.50	1.50
130	A21	34p multicolored	2.00	2.00
131	A21	54p multicolored	2.50	2.50
		Nos. 128-131 (4)	6.75	6.75

Coconut
Crab
A22

No. 132, Crab, coconut. No. 133, Large crab. No. 134, Two crabs. No. 135, Crab on tree trunk.

		Wmk. 384		
1993, Mar. 3		**Litho.**		**Perf. 14**
132	A22	10p multi	2.10	2.10
133	A22	10p multi	2.10	2.10
134	A22	10p multi	2.10	2.10
135	A22	15p multi	2.50	2.50
		Nos. 132-135 (4)	8.80	8.80

World Wildlife Fund.

Royal Air Force, 75th Anniv.
Common Design Type

Airplanes: No. 136, Vickers Virginia. 24p, Bristol Bulldog. 34p, Short Sunderland. 54p, Bristol Blenheim IV.
No. 140: a, Douglas Dakota. b, Gloster Javelin. c, Blackburn Beverley. d, Vickers VC10.

1993, Apr. 1		**Wmk. 373**		
136	CD350	20p multicolored	1.10	1.10
137	CD350	24p multicolored	1.40	1.40
138	CD350	34p multicolored	1.60	1.60
139	CD350	54p multicolored	3.00	3.00
		Nos. 136-139 (4)	7.10	7.10
Souvenir Sheet of 4				
140	CD350	20p #a.-d.	9.00	9.00

Flowers — A23

Christmas: 20p, Stachytarpheta urticifolia. 24p, Ipomea pes-caprae. 34p, Sida pusilla. 54p, Catharanthus roseus.

		Wmk. 373		
1993, Nov. 22		**Litho.**		**Perf. 14½**
141-144	A23	Set of 4	7.00	7.00

Nos. 96, 105 Ovptd. with Hong Kong '94 Emblem

		Wmk. 384		
1994, Feb. 18		**Litho.**		**Perf. 14**
145	A16	24p multicolored	5.50	3.00
146	A16	£1 multicolored	8.00	8.50

A24

18th Cent. Maps and Charts: a, 20p, Sketch of Diego Garcia. b, 24p, Plan of harbor, Chagos Island or Diego Garcia, by Lt. Archibald Blair. c, 34p, Chart of Chagos Archipelago, by Lt. Blair. d, 44p, Plan of part of Chagos Island or Diego Garcia, from survey made by the Drake. e, 54p, Plan of Chagos Island or Diego Garcia, by M. Aa Fontaine.

1994, June 1		**Wmk. 373**		
147	A24	Strip of 5, #a.-e.	6.75	6.75

Butterflies — A25

24p, Junonia villida. 30p, Petrelaea dana. 56p, Hypolimnas misippus.

1994, Aug. 16		**Wmk. 384**		
148	A25	24p multi	2.50	2.50
149	A25	30p multi	3.00	3.00
150	A25	56p multi	4.00	4.00
		Nos. 148-150 (3)	9.50	9.50

Sharks
A26

15p, Nurse. 20p, Silver tip. 24p, Black tip reef. 30p, Oceanic white tip. 35p, Black tip. 41p, Smooth hammerhead. 46p, Lemon. 55p, White tip reef. 65p, Tiger. 74p, Indian sand tiger. 80p, Great hammerhead. £ 1, Great white.

1994, Nov. 1		**Wmk. 373**		
151	A26	15p multicolored	4.75	3.50
152	A26	20p multicolored	4.75	3.50
153	A26	24p multicolored	5.50	3.75
154	A26	30p multicolored	6.25	4.75
155	A26	35p multicolored	7.50	6.00
156	A26	41p multicolored	7.50	6.00
157	A26	46p multicolored	7.50	6.00
158	A26	55p multicolored	9.00	6.25
159	A26	65p multicolored	9.00	6.25
a.		Souvenir sheet of 1	5.25	5.25
160	A26	74p multicolored	9.25	7.25
a.		Souvenir sheet of 1	7.25	7.25
161	A26	80p multicolored	10.50	8.00
162	A26	£1 multicolored	11.50	9.00
		Nos. 151-162 (12)	93.00	70.25

No. 159a for Hong Kong '97. Issued 2/3/97. No. 160a for return of Hong Kong to China. Issued 7/1/97.

End of World War II, 50th Anniv.
Common Design Types

20p, War graves, memorial cross, Diego Garcia. 24p, 6-inch naval gun, Cannon Point. 30p, Sunderland flying boat, 230 Squadron. 56p, HMIS Clive.
£1, Reverse of War Medal 1939-45.

		Wmk. 373		
1995, May 8		**Litho.**		**Perf. 14**
163	CD351	20p multicolored	2.00	2.00
164	CD351	24p multicolored	2.25	2.25
165	CD351	30p multicolored	2.75	2.75
166	CD351	56p multicolored	3.75	3.75
		Nos. 163-166 (4)	10.75	10.75
Souvenir Sheet				
167	CD352	£1 multicolored	5.50	5.50

Game
Fish
A27

1995, Oct. 6		**Wmk. 384**		
168	A27	20p Dolphinfish	2.10	2.10
169	A27	24p Sailfish	2.10	2.10
170	A27	30p Wahoo	3.00	3.00
171	A27	56p Striped marlin	4.25	4.25
		Nos. 168-171 (4)	11.45	11.45

Sea Shells
A28

20p, Terebra crenulata. 24p, Bursa bufonia. 30p, Nassarius papillosus. 56p, Lopha cristagalli.

1996, Jan. 8   Wmk. 373   Perf. 14

172	A28	20p multicolored	2.00	2.00
173	A28	24p multicolored	2.10	2.10
174	A28	30p multicolored	2.50	2.50
175	A28	56p multicolored	4.50	4.50
		Nos. 172-175 (4)	11.10	11.10

Queen Elizabeth II, 70th Birthday
Common Design Type

Various portraits of Queen, scenes of British Indian Ocean Territory: 20p, View to north from south end of lagoon. 24p, Manager's House, Peros Banhos. 30p, Wireless station, Peros Banhos. 56p, Sunset scene. £1, Wearing crown, formal dress.

Perf. 14x14½

1996, Apr. 22   Wmk. 384

176	CD354	20p multicolored	.95	.95
177	CD354	24p multicolored	1.10	1.10
178	CD354	30p multicolored	1.20	1.20
179	CD354	56p multicolored	2.00	2.00
		Nos. 176-179 (4)	5.25	5.25

Souvenir Sheet

180	CD354	£1 multicolored	6.25	6.25

Turtles
A29

1996, Sept. 2   Wmk. 373

181	A29	20p Loggerhead	1.90	1.90
182	A29	24p Leatherback	2.00	2.00
183	A29	30p Hawksbill	2.75	2.75
184	A29	56p Green	3.50	3.50
		Nos. 181-184 (4)	10.15	10.15

Uniforms — A30

Designs: 20p, British representative. 24p, Royal Marine officer. 30p, Royal Marine in camouflage. 56p, Police dog handler, female police officer.

1996, Dec.   Perf. 14

185	A30	20p multicolored	1.40	1.40
186	A30	24p multicolored	1.90	1.90
187	A30	30p multicolored	2.25	2.25
188	A30	56p multicolored	3.00	3.00
		Nos. 185-188 (4)	8.55	8.55

Queen Elizabeth II and Prince Philip, 50th Wedding Anniv. — A31

No. 189, Queen up close. No. 190, 4-horse team fording river. No. 191, Queen riding in open carriage. No. 192, Prince Philip up close. No. 193, Prince driving 4-horse team, Prince, Queen near jeep. No. 194, Queen on horseback, castle in distance. £1.50, Queen, Prince riding in open carriage.

1997, July 10   Perf. 14½x14

189	A31	20p multicolored	1.75	1.75
190	A31	20p multicolored	1.75	1.75
a.		Pair, #189-190	3.50	3.50
191	A31	24p multicolored	1.75	1.75
192	A31	24p multicolored	1.75	1.75
a.		Pair, #191-192	3.50	3.50
193	A31	30p multicolored	1.75	1.75
194	A31	30p multicolored	1.75	1.75
a.		Pair, #193-194	3.50	3.50
		Nos. 189-194 (6)	10.50	10.50

Souvenir Sheet

195	A31	£1.50 multicolored	11.50	11.50

Ocean Wave '97, Naval Exercise — A32

Designs: a, HMS Richmond, HMS Beaver. b, HMS Illustrious. c, HMS Beaver. d, RFA Sir Percivale, HMY Britannia, HMS Beaver. e, HMY Britannia. f, HMS Richmond, HMS Beaver, HMS Gloucester. g, HMS Richmond. h, HMS Illustrious (aerial view). i, HMS Sheffield. j, RFA Diligence, HMS Trenchant. k, HMS Illustrious, RFA Fort George, HMS Gloucester. l, HMS Richmond, HMS Beaver, HMS Gloucester.

1997, Dec. 1   Litho.   Perf. 14x14½
196 A32 24p Sheet of 12, #a.-l.   22.50 22.50

Diana, Princess of Wales (1961-97)
Common Design Type

Various portraits: a, 26p, shown. b, 26p, Close-up. c, 34p. d, 60p.

1998, Mar. 31   Perf. 14½x14
197 CD355 Sheet of 4, #a.-d.   5.50 5.50

No. 197 sold for £1.46 + 20p, with surtax and 50% of profits from total sale being donated to the Princess Diana Memorial Fund.

Royal Air Force, 80th Anniv.
Common Design Type of 1993
Re-inscribed

Designs: 26p, Blackburn Iris, 1930-34. 34p, Gloster Gamecock, 1926-33. 60p, North American Sabre F86, 1953-56. 80p, Avro Lincoln, 1945-55.
No. 202: a, Sopwith Baby, 1915-19. b, Martinsyde Elephant, 1916-19. c, De Havilland Tiger Moth, 1932-55. d, North American Mustang III, 1943-47.

1998, Apr. 1   Wmk. 384   Perf. 14

198	CD350	26p multicolored	1.60	1.60
199	CD350	34p multicolored	1.90	1.90
200	CD350	60p multicolored	3.25	3.25
201	CD350	80p multicolored	4.25	4.25
		Nos. 198-201 (4)	11.00	11.00

Souvenir Sheet

202	CD350	34p Sheet of 4, #a.-d.	10.50	10.50

Intl. Year of the Ocean A33

Dolphins and whales: No. 203, Striped dolphin. No. 204, Bryde's whale. No. 205, Pilot whale. No. 206, Spinner dolphin.

Wmk. 373

1998, Dec. 7   Litho.   Perf. 14

203	A33	26p multicolored	4.00	4.00
204	A33	26p multicolored	4.00	4.00
205	A33	34p multicolored	4.00	4.00
206	A33	34p multicolored	4.00	4.00
		Nos. 203-206 (4)	16.00	16.00

Sailing Ships — A34

2p, Bark "Westminster," 1837. 15p, "Sao Cristovao," Spain, 1589. 20p, Clipper ship "Sea Witch," US, 1849. 26p, HMS "Royal George," 1778. 34p, Clipper ship "Cutty Sark," 1883. 60p, British East India Co. ship "Mentor," 1789. 80p, HM brig "Trinculo," 1809. £1, Paddle steamer "Enterprise," 1825. £1.15, Privateer "Confiance," France, 1800. £2, British East India Co. ship "Kent," 1820.

Wmk. 373

1999, Feb. 1   Litho.   Perf. 14

207	A34	2p multicolored	.65	.65
208	A34	15p multicolored	1.25	1.25
209	A34	20p multicolored	1.50	1.50
210	A34	26p multicolored	1.75	1.75
211	A34	34p multicolored	2.25	2.25
212	A34	60p multicolored	3.50	3.50
213	A34	80p multicolored	4.25	4.25
214	A34	£1 multicolored	5.25	5.25
215	A34	£1.15 multicolored	5.75	5.75
216	A34	£2 multicolored	9.00	9.00
		Nos. 207-216 (10)	35.15	35.15

Tea Race, 1872
A35

a, Cutty Sark (up close). b, Thermopylae (in distance).

Wmk. 384

1999, Mar. 19   Litho.   Perf. 14
217 A35 60p Sheet of 2, #a.-b.   11.00 11.00

Australia '99 World Stamp Expo.

The Stamp Show 2000, London — A36

Winning photos in photography contest: a, 26p, Field vole by Colin Sargent. b, 34p, Puffin, by P. J. Royal. c, 55p, Red fox, by Jim Wilson. d, £1, Robin, by Harry Smith.

Perf. 14½x14¼

2000, May 22   Litho.   Wmk. 373
218 A36 Sheet of 4, #a-d.   13.00 13.00

Satellite Images A37

Designs: 15p, Salomon Atoll. 20p, Egmont Atoll. 60p, Blenheim Reef. 80p, Diego Garcia.

Wmk. 373

2000, July 3   Litho.   Perf. 14
219-222 A37 Set of 4   11.00 11.00

Queen Mother, 100th Birthday — A38

Designs: 26p, Blue hat. 34p, Blue green hat. No. 225: a, 55p, Blue hat. £1, Yellow hat.

2000, Aug. 4   Wmk. 373   Perf. 13¾
223-224 A38 Set of 2   4.50 4.50

Souvenir Sheet
225 A38 Sheet of 2, #a-b   9.00 9.00

Flowers — A39

Designs: 26p, Delonix regia. 34p, Barringtonia asiatica. 60p, Zephyranthes rosea.

2000, Dec. 4   Perf. 14½x14¼
226-228 A39 Set of 3   10.00 10.00

Souvenir Sheet

New Year 2001 (Year of the Snake) — A40

Butterflies: a, 26p, Precis orithya. b, 34p, Junonia villida chagoensis.

Perf. 14 ¼

2001, Feb. 1   Litho.   Wmk. 373
229 A40 Sheet of 2, #a-b   6.50 6.50

Hong Kong 2001 Stamp Exhibition.

Souvenir Sheet

Royal Navy Submarines, Cent. — A41

No. 230: a, 26p, HMS Turbulent. b, 26p, HMS Churchill. c, 34p, HMS Resolution. d, 34p, HMS Vanguard. e, 60p, HMS Otter. f, 60p, HMS Oberon. Size of Nos. 230e-230f: 75x30mm.

Perf. 14¼x14½

2001, May 28   Litho.   Wmk. 373
230 A41 Sheet of 6, #a-f   17.00 17.00

Worldwide Fund for Nature (WWF) A42

Starfish: 15p, Cushion star. 26p, Azure sea star. 34p, Crown-of-thorns. 56p, Banded bubble star.

Wmk. 373

2001, Aug. 1   Litho.   Perf. 13¾

231-234	A42	Set of 4	9.00	9.00
234a		Strip, #231-234	10.00	10.00

Plants — A43

Designs: 10p, Catharanthus roseus, horiz. 26p, Scadoxus mutiflora. 34p, Striga asiatica. 60p, Argusia argentia, horiz. 70p, Euphorbia cyathophora, horiz.

2001, Sept. 24   *Perf. 13¾x14¼*
235 A43 26p multi   3.00 3.00
   a.   Perf. 14½   3.00 3.00
236 A43 34p multi   3.25 3.25
   a.   Perf. 14½   3.25 3.25

Souvenir Sheet
Perf. 14½
237   Sheet, #a-c, 235a,
    236a   12.00 12.00
   a.   A43 10p multi   .70 .70
   b.   A43 60p multi   3.00 3.00
   c.   A43 70p multi   3.50 3.50

Souvenir Sheet

Birdlife International World Bird Festival — A44

Crab plover: a, Resting. b, Eating crab, vert. c, Close-up of head, vert. d, In flight. e, Standing on one leg.

2001, Oct. 1   *Perf. 14½*
238 A44 50p Sheet of 5, #a-e   13.00 13.00

Reign Of Queen Elizabeth II, 50th Anniv. Issue
Common Design Type
Designs: Nos. 239, 243a, 10p, Princess Elizabeth, 1943. Nos. 240, 243b, 25p, In 1967. Nos. 241, 243c, 35p, With Prince Philip, 1947. Nos. 242, 243d, 55p, Wearing tiara. No. 243e, 75p, 1955 portrait by Annigoni (38x50mm).

Perf. 14¼x14½, 13¾ (#243e)
2002, Feb. 6   Litho.   **Wmk. 373**
With Gold Frames
239 CD360 10p multicolored   .65 .65
240 CD360 25p multicolored   1.75 1.75
241 CD360 35p multicolored   2.50 2.50
242 CD360 55p multicolored   4.00 4.00
   Nos. 239-242 (4)   8.90 8.90

Souvenir Sheet
Without Gold Frames
243 CD360   Sheet of 5, #a-e   10.50 10.50

Souvenir Sheet

Red-footed Booby — A45

No. 244: a, Head of bird with brown feathers. b, Bird in flight, vert. c, Bird on nest, vert. d, Close-up of bird with white and black feathers. e, Chick.

Wmk. 373
2002, June 17   Litho.   *Perf. 14½*
244 A45 50p Sheet of 5, #a-e   14.50 14.50

Queen Mother Elizabeth (1900-2002)
Common Design Type
Designs: 26p, Wearing hat (sepia photograph). No. 246, £1, Wearing blue green hat. No. 247: a, £1, Wearing feathered hat (black and white photograph). b, £1, Wearing dark blue hat.

Wmk. 373
2002, Aug. 5   Litho.   *Perf. 14¼*
With Purple Frames
245 CD361 26p multicolored   1.10 1.10
246 CD361 £1 multicolored   4.75 4.75

Souvenir Sheet
Without Purple Frames
Perf. 14½x14¼
247 CD361   Sheet of 2, #a-b   11.50 11.50

Friends of the Chagos, 10th Anniv. — A46

Various reef fish: 2p, 15p, 26p, 34p, 58p, £1. £1.90, Fish.

Perf. 14¼x14½
2002, Oct. 3   Litho.   **Wmk. 373**
248-253 A46   Set of 6   14.50 14.50

Souvenir Sheet
254 A46 £1.90 multi   12.00 12.00
No. 254 is a parcel post stamp.

Sea Slugs — A47

Designs: 2p, Halgerda tesselata. 15p, Notodoris minor. 26p, Nembrotha lineolata. 50p, Chromodoris quadricolor. 76p, Glossodoris cincta. £1.10, Chromodoris cf. leopardus.

Wmk. 373
2003, Mar. 17   Litho.   *Perf. 13¼*
255-260 A47   Set of 6   14.50 14.50

Head of Queen Elizabeth II
Common Design Type
Wmk. 373
2003, June 2   Litho.   *Perf. 13¾*
261 CD362 £2.50 multi   11.00 11.00

Coronation of Queen Elizabeth II, 50th Anniv.
Common Design Type
Designs: Nos. 262, 264a, £1, Queen wearing crown. Nos. 263, 264b, £2, Queen with family.

Perf. 14¼x14½
2003, June 2   Litho.   **Wmk. 373**
Vignettes Framed, Red Background
262 CD363 £1 multicolored   5.00 5.00
263 CD363 £2 multicolored   9.00 9.00

Souvenir Sheet
Vignettes Without Frame, Purple Panel
264 CD363   Sheet of 2, #a-b   14.00 14.00

Prince William, 21st Birthday
Common Design Type
No. 265: a, William on polo pony at right. b, William with Prince Charles at left.

Wmk. 373
2003, June 21   Litho.   *Perf. 14¼*
265   Horiz. pair   8.00 8.00
   a.   CD364 50p multi   3.00 3.00
   b.   CD364 £1 multi   4.50 4.50

Powered Flight, Cent. — A48

Designs: No. 266, 34p, De Havilland Mosquito. No. 267, 34p, Avro Lancaster Dambuster. No. 268, 58p, Supermarine Spitfire. No. 269, 58p, Hawker Hurricane. No. 270,

76p, Lockheed C-130 Hercules. No. 271, 76p, Vickers Armstrong Wellington.
No. 272: a, Boeing E-3A Sentry AWACS. b, Boeing B-17 Flying Fortress. c, Lockheed P3 Orion. d, Consolidated B-24 Liberator. e, Lockheed C-141 Starlifter. f, Supermarine Walrus. g, Short Sunderland. h, Supermarine Stranraer. i, PBY Catalina. j, Supermarine Sea Otter.
Illustration reduced.

Wmk. 373
2003, July 18   Litho.   *Perf. 14*
Stamp + Label
266-271 A48   Set of 6   15.00 15.00
Miniature Sheet
272 A48 26p Sheet of 10, #a-j   15.00 15.00

Fisheries Patrol — A49

No. 273: a, 34p, M. V. Pacific Marlin. b, 34p, Marlin. c, 58p, Skipjack tuna. d, 58p, Yellowfin tuna. e, 76p, Swordfish. f, 76p, Bigeye tuna.

Wmk. 373
2004, Feb. 16   Litho.   *Perf. 14¼*
273 A49   Sheet of 6, #a-f   17.00 17.00

Birds A50

Designs: 2p, Madagascar fody. 14p, Barred ground dove. 20p, Indian mynah. 26p, Cattle egret. 34p, Fairy tern. 58p, Masked booby. 76p, Greater frigatebird. 80p, White-tailed tropicbird. £1.10, Little green heron. £1.34, Pacific golden plover. £1.48, Garganey teal. £2.50, Bar-tailed godwit.

Wmk. 373
2004, June 21   Litho.   *Perf. 14*
274 A50 2p multi   .30 .30
275 A50 14p multi   .65 .65
276 A50 20p multi   .95 .95
277 A50 26p multi   1.10 1.10
278 A50 34p multi   1.50 1.50
279 A50 58p multi   2.50 2.50
280 A50 76p multi   3.25 3.25
281 A50 80p multi   3.50 3.50
282 A50 £1.10 multi   5.00 5.00
283 A50 £1.34 multi   6.00 6.00
284 A50 £1.48 multi   7.25 7.25
285 A50 £2.50 multi   11.00 11.00
   Nos. 274-285 (12)   43.00 43.00

Crabs A51

Designs: 26p, Coconut crab. 34p, Land crab. 76p, Rock crab. £1.10, Ghost crab.

Wmk. 373
2004, Dec. 20   Litho.   *Perf. 14*
286-289 A51   Set of 4   13.00 13.00

Turtles A52

Designs: No. 290, 26p, Green turtle hatchling. No. 291, 26p, Hawksbill turtle hatchlings. No. 292, 34p, Hawksbill turtle's head. No. 293,

34p, Green turtle's head. 76p, Hawksbill turtle swimming. £1.10, Green turtle swimming. £1.70, Like £1.10.

2005, Feb. 14
290-295 A52   Set of 6   14.00 14.00
Souvenir Sheet
296 A52 £1.70 multi   9.00 9.00

Battle of Trafalgar, Bicent. — A53

Designs: No. 297, 26p, HMS Phoebe. No. 298, 26p, Tower Sea Service pistol, 1796. No. 299, 34p, HMS Harrier. No. 300, 34p, Royal Navy Boatswain, 1805. No. 301, 76p, Portrait of Adm. Horatio Nelson. No. 302, 76p, HMS Victory, horiz.
No. 303: a, HMS Minotaur, ship in distance. b, HMS Spartiate.

Wmk. 373, Unwmkd. (#302)
2005, May 6   *Perf. 13¼*
297-302 A53   Set of 6   18.00 18.00
Souvenir Sheet
303 A53 £1.10 Sheet of 2,
     #a-b   12.00 12.00
No. 302 has particles of wood from the HMS Victory embedded in the areas covered by a thermographic process that produces a raised, shiny effect.

Miniature Sheet

End of World War II, 60th Anniv. — A54

No. 304: a, 26p, HMAS Wollongong. b, 26p, Dutch tanker Ordina, HMIS Bengal attacked by Japanese surface raiders. c, 26p, HMS Pathfinder arrives at Diego Garcia. d, 26p, HMS Lossie rescues 112 survivors from Australian freighter Nellore. e, 26p, US Liberty Ship Jean Nicolet sunk by HIJMS I-8. f, 34p, Gen. Douglas MacArthur. g, 34p, Gen. Bernard L. Montgomery. h, 34p, Gen. George S. Patton. i, 34p, British Prime Minister Winston Churchill. j, 34p, Pres. Franklin D. Roosevelt.

Wmk. 373
2005, June 26   Litho.   *Perf. 13¾*
304 A54   Sheet of 10, #a-j   18.00 18.00

Sharks and Rays A55

Designs: No. 305, 26p, Blacktip reef shark. No. 306, 26p, Gray reef shark. No. 307, 34p, Silvertip shark. No. 308, 34p, Spotted eagle ray. No. 309, 34p, Tawny nurse shark. No. 310, 34p, Manta ray. 76p, Porcupine ray. £2, Feathertail stingray.

2005, Aug. 15   *Perf. 13½x13¾*
305-312 A55   Set of 8   26.00 26.00

Battle of Trafalgar, Bicent. — A56

Designs: 26p, HMS Victory. 34p, Ships in battle, horiz. £2, Admiral Horatio Nelson.

Perf. 13¼

2005, Oct. 18   Litho.   Unwmk.
313-315 A56   Set of 3   13.00 13.00

Miniature Sheet

British Indian Ocean Territory, 40th Anniv. — A57

No. 316: a, Crab, palm fronds. b, Two crabs. c, White birds. d, Black bird, map of Indian Ocean area. e, Fish, blue starfish. f, Two triggerfish, corals. g, Angelfish, corals. h, Turtle, map of British Indian Ocean Territory.

Perf. 14¾x14¼

2005, Nov. 8   Wmk. 373
316 A57 34p Sheet of 8, #a-h 17.00 17.00

Queen Elizabeth II, 80th Birthday A58

Queen: 26p, As young woman, wearing military cap. 34p, As young woman, diff. 76p, Wearing tiara. £1.10, Wearing kerchief. No. 321: a, Like 34p. b, Like 76p.

Wmk. 373

2006, Apr. 21   Litho.   Perf. 14
317-320 A58   Set of 4   13.00 13.00
Souvenir Sheet
321 A58   £1 Sheet of 2, #a-b   10.00 10.00

Miniature Sheet

Angelfish — A59

No. 322: a, 26p, Dusky angelfish. b, 26p, Twospined angelfish. c, 26p, Bicolor angelfish. d, 34p, Orangeback angelfish. e, 34p, Emperor angelfish. £2, Threespot angelfish.
No. 323: a, 26p, Melon butterflyfish. b, 26p, Raccoon butterflyfish. c, 26p, Scrawled butterflyfish. d, 34p, Longnose butterflyfish. e, 34p, Threadfin butterflyfish. f, £2, Masked bannerfish.
No. 324: a, 54p, Common parrotfish. b, 54p, Daisy parrotfish. c, 54p, Bicolor parrotfish. d, 54p, Bridled parrotfish. e, 90p, Indian Ocean steephead parrotfish. f, 90p, Male and female ember parrotfish.

2006-07
322 A59   Sheet of 6, #a-f   19.00 19.00
323 A59   Sheet of 6, #a-f   15.00 15.00
324 A59   Sheet of 6, #a-f   18.00 18.00

Issued: No. 322, 5/29; No. 323, 7/31; No. 324, 3/29/07.

Miniature Sheet

BirdLife International — A60

No. 325: a, 26p, Great frigatebird. b, 26p, Black-naped terns. c, 26p, Yellow-billed tropicbirds. d, 26p, White terns. e, 26p, Brown noddies. f, £2, Red-footed boobies.

2006, Oct. 6   Perf. 13¾
325 A60   Sheet of 6, #a-f   16.00 16.00

Wedding of Queen Elizabeth II and Prince Philip, 60th Anniv. — A61

Designs: No. 326, 54p, Couple. No. 327, 54p, Coach in procession. No. 328, 90p, Couple, diff. No. 329, 90p, Wedding ceremony. £2.14, Couple, diff.

Wmk. 373

2007, June 1   Litho.   Perf. 13¾
326-329 A61   Set of 4   12.00 12.00
Souvenir Sheet
Perf. 14
330 A61   £2.14 multi   9.00 9.00
No. 330 contains one 43x58mm stamp.

Charles Darwin (1809-82), Naturalist A62

Designs: No. 331, 54p, Darwin and wildlife. No. 332, 54p, HMS Beagle. No. 333, 90p, Coral reef. No. 334, 90p, Turtles.

Wmk. 373

2007, July 23   Litho.   Perf. 13¼
331-334 A62   Set of 4   14.00 14.00

BirdLife International — A63

Designs: No. 335, 54p, Pomarine skua chasing white-tailed tropic bird. No. 336, 54p, Two Pomarine skuas in flight. No. 337, 54p, Two Pomarine skuas on beach. No. 338, 54p, Pomarine skua attacking red-footed booby in flight, boobies on land. No. 339, 90p, Pomarine skua attacking black-necked terns in flight. No. 340, Pomarine skua on water.

2007, Oct. 1   Perf. 12½x13
335-340 A63   Set of 6   19.00 19.00

Miniature Sheet

Damselfish — A64

No. 341: a, 54p, One-spot demoiselle. b, 54p, Banded sergeant. c, 54p, Johnston Island damsel. d, 54p, Chagos anemonefish. e, 90p, Black-axil chromis. f, 90p, Caerulean damsel.

Wmk. 373

2008, Jan. 30   Litho.   Perf. 14
341 A64   Sheet of 6, #a-f   18.00 18.00

Military Uniforms — A65

Designs: No. 342, 27p, Royal Marines. No. 343, 27p, Royal Engineers. No. 344, 54p, Officer, East India Company Army. No. 345, 54p, Sepoys, East India Company Army. No. 346, 54p, Sergeant, Royal Military Police. No. 347, 54p, Artillery Corps.

2008, Mar. 3
342-347 A65   Set of 6   11.00 11.00

A66

Royal Air Force, 90th Anniv. — A67

Designs: No. 348, 27p, Avro 504. No. 349, 27p, Short Sunderland. No. 350, 27p, Vickers VC10. No. 351, 27p, De Havilland Mosquito. 54p, English Electric Canberra. £1.72, King George V, Marshal of the Royal Air Force.

Wmk. 373

2008, Apr. 1   Litho.   Perf. 14
348-352 A66   Set of 5   7.50 7.50
Souvenir Sheet
353 A67   £1.72 black   9.00 9.00

Nos. 348-352 each were printed in sheets of 8 + central label. Value, set of five singles with labels $9.50.

End of World War I, 90th Anniv. — A68

Soldiers and their letters home: No. 354, 50p, Sergeant Major Francis Proud. No. 355, 50p, Second Lieutenant Eric Heaton. No. 356, 50p, Private Dennis Harry Wilson. No. 357, 50p, Second Lieutenant Eric Rose. No. 358, 50p, Second Lieutenant Charles Roberts. No. 359, 50p, Private Harry Lamin. £1, Wreath of Remembrance.

Wmk. 406

2008, Sept. 16   Litho.   Perf. 14
354-359 A68   Set of 6   14.00 14.00
Souvenir Sheet
360 A68   £1 multi   5.00 5.00

Worldwide Fund For Nature (WWF) — A69

Designs: No. 361, 54p, Ocellated sea cucumber. No. 362, 54p, Pineapple sea cucumber. No. 363, 90p, Graeffe's sea cucumber. No. 364, 90p, Dark green sea cucumber.

Wmk. 373

2008, Dec. 1   Litho.   Perf. 14
361-364 A69   Set of 4   11.00 11.00
  a.   Sheet of 16, 4 each
        #361-364   44.00 44.00

Ships A70

 (Seafaring & Exploration / Vasco da Gama)

Vasco da Gama (c. 1460-1524), Explorer — A71

Designs: No. 365, 54p, HMS Victory. No. 366, 54p, HMS Endeavour. No. 367, 54p, HMS Beagle. No. 368, 54p, SS Windsor Castle. No. 369, 54p, HMS Edinburgh. No. 370, 54p, SMS Fürst Bismarck.

Wmk. 406

2009, Mar. 9   Litho.   Perf. 14
365-370 A70   Set of 6   13.00 13.00
Souvenir Sheet
371 A71   £1.30 multi   5.25 5.25

Naval Aviation, Cent. A72

Royal Navy aircraft: No. 372, 27p, Short S.38 and ship. No. 373, 27p, Sopwith Pup. No. 374, 54p, Supermarine Scimitar and ship. No. 375, 54p, Westland Wessex helicopter and ship.

£1.72, Squadron Commander E. H. Dunning landing airplane on HMS Furious, 1917.

2009, Apr. 17
372-375 A72 Set of 4 7.50 7.50
Souvenir Sheet
376 A72 £1.72 multi 7.50 7.50

Nos. 372-375 each were printed in sheets of 8 + central label. Value, set of four singles with labels $10.

Space Exploration A73

Designs: No. 377, 54p, Early rockets Corporal and Private. No. 378, 54p, Flying Bedstead, 1964. No. 379, 54p, Apollo launch site, 1969. No. 380, 54p, Space Shuttle STS-71 launch, 1995. 90p, ESA Columbus laboratory, STS-122, 2008.
£1.50, Astronaut on Moon, painting by Capt. Alan Bean, vert.

2009, July 20 *Perf. 13¼*
377-381 A73 Set of 5 15.00 15.00
Souvenir Sheet *Perf. 13x13¼*
382 A73 £1.50 multi 7.75 7.75

No. 382 contains one 40x60mm stamp. Nos. 377-381 each were printed in sheets of 6.

Flora, Fauna and Sites — A74

Designs: 1p, Two-band anemonefish. 2p, Angelfish. 5p, Royal poinciana flowers. 12p, Beach morning glories. 27p, Bay cedar flowers. 45p, Scaevola bush flowers. 54p, Madagascan red fodies. 90p, Greater frigatebirds. £1.30, Sharks Cove. £1.72, Turtle Cove. £2.64, Hawksbill turtles. £3.02 Sticklefin lemon sharks.

Wmk. 406
2009, Oct. 5 **Litho.** *Perf. 13¾*
383	A74	1p multi	.30	.30
384	A74	2p multi	.30	.30
385	A74	5p multi	.30	.30
386	A74	12p multi	.50	.50
387	A74	27p multi	1.10	1.10
388	A74	45p multi	1.75	1.75
389	A74	54p multi	2.10	2.10
390	A74	90p multi	3.50	3.50
391	A74	£1.30 multi	5.25	5.25
392	A74	£1.72 multi	7.00	7.00
393	A74	£2.64 multi	10.50	10.50
394	A74	£3.02 multi	12.00	12.00
a.		Sheet of 12, #383-394	45.00	45.00
		Nos. 383-394 (12)	44.60	44.60

Fungi — A75

Designs: No. 395, 54p, Entoloma sp. No. 396, 54p, Lentinus sp. No. 397, 90p, Leucocoprinus sp. No. 398, 90p, Pycnoporus sp.

2009, Dec. 7 *Perf. 13¼*
395-398 A75 Set of 4 14.50 14.50

Battle of Britain, 70th Anniv. — A76

British leaders and aces: No. 399, 50p, Mike Crossley. No. 400, 50p, Bob Doe. No. 401, 50p, Sir Hugh Dowding. No. 402, 50p, Ginger Lacey. No. 403, 50p, Eric Lock. No. 404, 50p, Bob Stanford Tuck.
£1.50, Sir Douglas Bader.

2010, Mar. 18 **Litho.** **Wmk. 406** *Perf. 12¾x13*
399-404 A76 Set of 6 11.00 11.00
Souvenir Sheet
405 A76 £1.50 black & gray 7.00 7.00

Nos. 399-405 each were printed in sheets of 6.

Souvenir Sheet

Great Britain No. 161 — A77

2010, May 8 *Perf. 14*
406 A77 £1.50 multi 7.00 7.00

Accession to throne of King George V, cent.; London 2010 Intl. Stamp Exhibition.

Battles and Sieges A78

Designs: No. 407, 50p, Battle of Hastings, 1066. No. 408, 50p, Battle of Agincourt, 1415. No. 409, 50p, Battle of Bosworth, 1485. No. 410, 50p, Battle of Naseby, 1645. No. 411, 50p, Battle of Culloden, 1746. No. 412, 50p, Battle of Waterloo, 1815. No. 413, 50p, Battle of the Alma, 1854. No. 414, 50p, Battle of Rorke's Drift, 1879. No. 415, 50p, Siege of Mafeking, 1899. No. 416, 50p, Battle of the Somme, 1916. No. 417, 50p, Battle of El Alamein, 1942. No. 418, 50p, Normandy Landings, 1944.

Wmk. 406
2010, Sept. 30 **Litho.** *Perf. 13¼*
407-418 A78 Set of 12 24.00 24.00

Service of Queen Elizabeth II and Prince Philip — A79

Designs: No. 419, 54p, Queen Elizabeth II. No. 420, 54p, Queen and Prince Philip, black-and-white photograph, Queen at left. No. 421, 54p, Queen and Prince Philip, black-and-white photograph, Queen at right. No. 422, 54p, Queen and Prince Philip, color photograph, Queen at left. No. 423, 54p, Queen and Prince

Philip, color photograph, Queen at right. No. 424, 54p, Prince Philip.
£3.02, Queen and Prince Philip, diff.

Perf. 13¼
2011, Mar. 1 **Litho.** **Unwmk.**
419-424 A79 Set of 6 12.00 12.00
424a Sheet of 6, #419-424, + 3 labels 12.00 12.00
Souvenir Sheet
425 A79 £3.02 multi 11.00 11.00

Souvenir Sheet

Wedding of Prince William and Catherine Middleton — A80

Perf. 14¾x14
2011, Apr. 29 **Wmk. 406**
426 A80 £3 multi 11.00 11.00

Wedding of Prince William and Catherine Middleton — A81

Designs: No. 427, 54p, Couple in carriage waving. No. 428, 54p, Couple kissing, vert. No. 429, 90p, Couple in car after wedding. No. 430, 90p, Couple holding hands, vert.

Wmk. 406
2011, Aug. 1 **Litho.** *Perf. 12½*
427-430 A81 Set of 4 9.50 9.50

Royal British Legion, 90th Anniv. A82

Poppy at left and: No. 431, 50p, Poppies on crosses. No. 432, 50p, Lines from poem "In Flanders Fields," poppy field. No. 433, 50p, Shadow of soldier, Glorious Dead Cenotaph, London. No. 434, 50p, War graves. No. 435, 50p, Poppy drop. No. 436, 50p, Poppy appeal. No. 437, 50p, Ex-servicemen. No. 438, 50p, Festival of Remembrance. £1.50, Soldiers and sailors at attention.

Perf. 13¼x13½
2011, Nov. 11 **Wmk. 406**
431-438 A82 Set of 8 12.50 12.50
Souvenir Sheet
439 A82 £1.50 multi 4.75 4.75

Reign of Queen Elizabeth II, 60th Anniv. — A83

Queen Elizabeth II wearing: No. 440, 54p, Pearl necklace, no tiara (black-and-white photograph). No. 441, 54p, Blue hat (color photograph). No. 442, 54p, Red dress (color photograph). No. 443, 54p, Tiara and necklace

(color photograph). No. 444, 54p, Tiara (black-and-white photograph). No. 445, 54p, Eyeglasses (color photograph).
£3.02, Queen Elizabeth II wearing red dress, diff.

2012, Feb. 6 *Perf. 13¼*
440-445 A83 Set of 6 10.50 10.50
445a Souvenir sheet of 6, #440-445 10.50 10.50
Souvenir Sheet
446 A83 £3.02 multi 9.75 9.75

Coronation of Queen Elizabeth II, 60th Anniv. — A84

Various photographs of Queen Elizabeth II with panel colors of: 34p, Dark red. 54p, Green. 90p, Purple. £1.10, Dark blue.

Wmk. 406
2013, Dec. 2 **Litho.** *Perf. 13½*
447-450 A84 Set of 4 9.50 9.50

Coat of Arms A85

No. 451: a, Left half of coat of arms (denomination at left). b, Right half of coat of arms (denomination at right).
£2, Entire coat of arms.

Wmk. 406
2014, June 9 **Litho.** *Perf. 13¼*
451 A85 54p Horiz. pair, #a-b 3.75 3.75
Souvenir Sheet
452 A85 £2 multi 7.00 7.00

No. 452 contains one 45x45mm stamp.

Miniature Sheet

Sharks — A86

No. 453: a, Tiger shark. b, Silvertip shark. c, Silky shark. d, Gray reef shark. e, Shortfin mako shark. f, Tawny nurse shark.

Wmk. 406
2016, Feb. 12 **Litho.** *Perf. 14*
453 A86 50p Sheet of 6, #a-f 8.50 8.50

Queen Elizabeth II, 90th Birthday A87

Photograph of Queen Elizabeth II in: No. 454, 54p, Black-and-white, as child. No. 455, 54p, Color, as adult. No. 456, 90p, Black-and-white, as adult. No. 457, 90p, Color, as adult, diff.

Wmk. 406

2016, Apr. 21   Litho.   Perf. 13¼
454-457 A87   Set of 4   8.50 8.50

Writers and Characters from Their Works — A88

Designs: No. 458, 54p, William Shakespeare (1564-1616), Romeo and Juliet. No. 459, 54p, Beatrix Potter (1866-1943), Peter Rabbit. No. 460, 90p, Charlotte Bronte (1816-55), Jane Eyre. No. 461, 90p, Roald Dahl (1916-90), Fantastic Mr. Fox.

Wmk. 406

2016, July 28   Litho.   Perf. 14
458-461 A88   Set of 4   7.75 7.75

Sea Turtles A89

Designs: No. 462, 60p, Green turtle hatchling. No. 463, 60p, Hawksbill turtle hatchling. No. 464, £1, Green turtle swimming. No. 465, £1, Hawksbill turtle swimming. £3, Green turtle on sea floor. £5, Hawksbill turtle eating.

2016, Nov. 15   Litho.   Wmk. 406   Perf. 13¼x13½
462-467 A89   Set of 6   28.50 28.50
467a   Souvenir sheet of 1 #467   13.00 13.00

World War I Aircraft A90

Designs: No. 468, 60p, Royal Aircraft Factory F. E. 2b. No. 469, 60p, Nieuport 11 (Bébé). No. 470, 60p, Sopwith Camel. No. 471, £1, Bristol F.2B. No. 472, £1, Royal Aircraft Factory S. E. 5a. £1.50, Handley Page H.P. O/400.

Perf. 13¼x13½
2017, Mar. 6   Litho.   Wmk. 406
468-473 A90   Set of 6   13.50 13.50

BRUNEI

'brü-,nī

LOCATION — On the northwest coast of Borneo
GOVT. — Independent state sultanate
AREA — 2,226 sq. mi.
POP. — 422,675 (2014 est.)
CAPITAL — Bandar Seri Begawan

Brunei became a British protectorate in 1888. A treaty between the sultan and the British Government in 1979 provided for independence in 1983.

100 Cents (Sen) = 1 Dollar

Catalogue values for unused stamps in this country are for Never Hinged items, beginning with Scott 62.

See the *Scott Classic Specialized Catalogue of Stamps and Covers* for the 1895 issue.

Watermarks

Wmk. 385 — CARTOR

Wmk. 388 — Multiple "SPM"

Syncopated Perforation

Type A (first stamp #555): On 2 longer sides, oval holes equal in width to 3 holes which are the 11th hole from the top and 10th hole from the bottom.

Labuan Stamps of 1902-03 Overprinted or Surcharged in Red

1906   Unwmk.   Perf. 12 to 16
1	A38	1c violet & blk	50.00	65.00
a.		Black overprint	2,500.	3,000.
2	A38	2c on 3c brn & blk	7.00	21.00
a.		"BRUNEI." double	4,500.	3,000.
b.		"TWO CENTS." double	6,500.	
3	A38	2c on 8c org & blk	32.50	80.00
a.		"TWO CENTS." double	14,000.	
b.		"TWO CENTS." omitted, in pair with normal	15,000.	
4	A38	3c brown & blk	38.50	100.00
5	A38	4c on 12c yel & black	8.50	6.00
6	A38	5c on 16c org brn & green	55.00	90.00
7	A38	8c orange & blk	15.00	37.50
8	A38	10c on 16c org brn & green	7.75	26.00
9	A38	25c on 16c org brn & green	125.00	150.00
10	A38	30c on 16c org brn & green	125.00	150.00
11	A38	50c on 16c org brn & green	125.00	150.00
12	A38	$1 on 8c org & blk	125.00	150.00
		Nos. 1-12 (12)	714.25	1,026.

The 25c surcharge reads: "25 CENTS."

Scene on Brunei River — A1

Type I   Type II

Two Types of 1908 1c, 3c:
Type I — Dots form bottom line of water shading. (Double plate.)
Type II — Dots removed. (Single plate.)

1907-21   Engr.   Wmk. 3   Perf. 14
13	A1	1c yel green & blk	2.75	13.00
14	A1	1c green (II) ('11)	.70	2.50
a.		Type I ('19)	1.00	2.75
15	A1	2c red & black	3.25	4.25
16	A1	2c brn & blk ('11)	4.75	1.50
17	A1	3c red brn & blk	12.50	26.00
18	A1	3c car (I) ('08)	8.00	1.50
a.		Type II ('17)	130.00	45.00
19	A1	4c lilac & blk	9.00	8.00
20	A1	4c claret ('12)	8.00	.90
21	A1	5c ultra & blk	60.00	110.00
22	A1	5c org & blk ('08)	8.50	8.50
23	A1	5c orange ('16)	26.00	25.00
24	A1	8c orange & blk	9.00	27.50
25	A1	8c blue & indigo blue ('08)	8.50	13.00
26	A1	8c ultra ('16)	8.00	32.50
27	A1	10c dk green & blk	5.25	5.00
28	A1	10c violet, *yel* ('12)	10.00	2.10
29	A1	25c yel brn & blue	37.50	57.50
30	A1	25c violet ('12)	11.00	30.00
31	A1	30c black & grn	30.00	25.00
32	A1	30c org & red vio ('12)	17.50	20.00
33	A1	50c brown & grn	18.00	25.00
34	A1	50c blk, *grn* ('12)	40.00	75.00
35	A1	50c blk, *grnsh bl* ('21)	11.00	42.50
36	A1	$1 slate & red	72.50	110.00
37	A1	$1 red & blk, *bl* ('12)	30.00	57.50
38	A1	$5 lake, *grn* ('08)	200.00	350.00
39	A1	$25 blk, *red* ('08)	650.00	1,350.
		Nos. 13-38 (26)	651.70	1,074.
		Set, never hinged		1,500.

Used value for No. 39 is for a canceled-to-order example dated before December 1941. CTOs dated later are worth about half the value given.

Some stamps in this set exist with watermark reversed or inverted; values are two to five times those shown.

Stamps of 1908-21 Overprinted in Four Lines in Black

1922
14b	A1	1c green	12.00	55.00
16a	A1	2c brown & black	13.00	50.00
18b	A1	3c carmine	14.00	60.00
20a	A1	4c claret	20.00	60.00
23a	A1	5c orange	27.50	65.00
28a	A1	10c violet, *yellow*	12.00	65.00
30a	A1	25c violet	16.00	85.00
35a	A1	50c greenish blue	47.50	160.00
37a	A1	$1 red & black, *blue*	80.00	200.00
		Nos. 14b-37a (9)	242.00	800.00
		Set, never hinged		600.00

Industrial fair, Singapore, Mar. 31-Apr. 15

Type of 1907 Issue

1924-37   Wmk. 4
43	A1	1c black ('26)	1.25	.90
44	A1	2c deep brown	1.25	11.00
45	A1	2c green ('33)	2.40	1.25
46	A1	3c green	2.00	7.75
47	A1	4c claret brown	3.25	1.50
48	A1	4c orange ('29)	2.40	1.25
49	A1	5c orange	16.00	2.00
50	A1	5c lt gray ('31)	25.00	14.00
51	A1	5c brown ('33)	25.00	1.20
52	A1	8c ultra ('27)	7.25	6.00
53	A1	8c gray ('33)	19.00	.90
54	A1	10c violet, *yel* ('37)	40.00	32.50
55	A1	25c dk violet ('31)	24.00	15.00
56	A1	30c org & red vio ('31)	25.00	19.00
57	A1	50c black, *grn* ('31)	20.00	17.50
58	A1	$1 red & blk, *bl* ('31)	29.00	90.00
		Nos. 43-58 (16)	242.80	221.75

For overprints see Nos. N1-N20.

Dwellings in Town of Brunei A2

1924-31
59	A2	6c black	17.00	12.00
60	A2	6c red ('31)	13.00	12.50
61	A2	12c blue	5.50	11.00
		Nos. 59-61 (3)	35.50	35.50

See note after Nos. N1-N19.

Catalogue values for unused stamps in this section, from this point to the end of the section, are for Never Hinged items.

Types of 1907-24

1947-51   Engr.   Perf. 14
62	A1	1c brown	.65	2.50
63	A1	2c gray	.75	6.00
a.		Perf. 14½x13½ ('50)	2.40	5.25
64	A2	3c dark green	1.50	8.00
65	A1	5c deep orange	1.00	1.75
a.		Perf. 14½x13½ ('50)	4.75	22.00
66	A2	6c gray black	1.25	6.75
67	A1	8c scarlet	.60	1.50
a.		Perf. 13 ('51)	.65	13.00
68	A1	10c violet	2.25	.40
a.		Perf. 14½x13½ ('50)	3.75	6.50
69	A1	15c brt ultra	2.10	.90
70	A1	25c red violet	3.25	1.25
a.		Perf. 14½x13½ ('51)	4.50	16.00
71	A1	30c dp org & gray blk	3.00	1.25
a.		Perf. 14½x13½ ('51)	3.50	22.00
72	A1	50c black	6.50	1.00
a.		Perf. 13 ('50)	2.10	22.00
73	A1	$1 scar & gray blk	16.00	2.50
74	A1	$5 red org & grn ('48)	22.50	25.00
75	A1	$10 dp claret & gray blk ('48)	110.00	35.00
		Nos. 62-75 (14)	171.35	93.80

Sultan Ahmed and Pile Dwellings A3

1949, Sept. 22   Wmk. 4   Perf. 13
76	A3	8c car & black	1.50	1.50
77	A3	25c red orange & pur	1.50	2.10
78	A3	50c blue & black	1.50	2.10
		Nos. 76-78 (3)	4.50	5.70

25th anniv. of the reign of Sultan Ahmed Tajudin Akhazul Khair Wad-din.

Common Design Types pictured following the introduction.

UPU Issue
Common Design Types
Engr.; Name Typo. on 15c and 25c

1949, Oct. 10   Perf. 13½, 11x11½
79	CD306	8c rose car	1.40	1.75
80	CD307	15c indigo	3.50	2.10
81	CD308	25c red lilac	2.00	2.00
82	CD309	50c slate	2.60	2.60
		Nos. 79-82 (4)	9.50	8.45

Sultan Omar Ali Saifuddin — A4

River Kampong A5

Perf. 13½x13
1952, Mar. 1   Engr.   Wmk. 4
Center in Black
83	A4	1c black	.25	.25
84	A4	2c red orange	.25	.25
85	A4	3c red brown	.25	.25
86	A4	4c green	.25	.25
87	A4	6c gray	.25	.25
88	A4	8c carmine	.30	.25
89	A4	10c olive brown	.25	.25
90	A4	12c violet	4.25	.25
91	A4	15c blue	3.00	.25
92	A4	25c purple	3.00	.25

93	A4	50c ultramarine	3.00	.30

Perf. 13

94	A5	$1 dull green	4.00	1.20
95	A5	$2 red	6.75	3.00
96	A5	$5 deep plum	28.00	12.00
		Nos. 83-96 (14)	53.80	19.00

See Nos. 101-114.

Mosque and Sultan Omar A6

1958, Sept. 24 Wmk. 314 Perf. 13

Center in Black

97	A6	8c dull green	.30	.45
98	A6	15c carmine rose	.45	.45
99	A6	35c rose violet	.60	.65
		Nos. 97-99 (3)	1.35	1.55

Opening of the Brunei Mosque.

Freedom from Hunger Issue

Common Design Type with Portrait of Sultan Omar

1963, June 4 Photo. Perf. 14x14½

| 100 | CD314 | 12c sepia | 3.25 | 2.25 |

Types of 1952
On Ordinary Paper

Wmk. 314 Upright

1964-70 Engr. Perf. 13½x13

Center in Black

101	A4	1c black	.25	.25
102	A4	2c red orange	.25	.25
103	A4	3c red brown	.25	.25
104	A4	4c green	.45	.25
105	A4	6c gray	1.10	.25
c.		6c black ('69)	3.50	1.20
106	A4	8c dk carmine	.75	.25
107	A4	10c olive brown	.50	.25
108	A4	12c violet	1.75	.25
109	A4	15c blue	1.30	.25
110	A4	25c purple	2.60	.25
111	A4	50c ultramarine	3.00	.50
b.		50c bright ultra ('69)	10.50	1.00

Perf. 13

| 112 | A5 | $1 dull green ('68) | 12.00 | 4.00 |
| | | Nos. 101-112 (12) | 24.20 | 7.00 |

On Whiter, Glazed Paper

Wmk. 314 Upright

1969-72 Perf. 13½x13

Center in Black

101a	A4	1c black ('69)	.70	.70
c.		1c slate gray ('72)	.25	.25
102a	A4	2c red org ('70)	.30	.25
103a	A4	3c red brn ('70)	.30	.25
104a	A4	4c green ('70)	.45	.25
c.		4c emerald & black ('71)	1.00	.35
105a	A4	6c gray ('69)	.55	.25
106a	A4	8c dk carmine ('70)	.70	.25
c.		8c brownish red & black ('71)	2.25	.75
107a	A4	10c olive brn ('70)	2.25	.25
c.		10c pale brn & gray ('71)	3.00	.35
108a	A4	12c violet ('70)	8.50	.30
109a	A4	15c blue ('70)	.75	.25
110a	A4	25c purple ('70)	10.00	.85
c.		Reddish violet & black ('71)	13.00	2.00
111a	A4	50c br ultra ('70)	10.00	.25
c.		50c indigo & gray ('71)	11.00	1.00

Perf. 13

112a	A5	$1 dull green ('70)	7.00	4.25
113	A5	$2 red ('70)	37.50	22.50
114	A5	$5 deep plum ('70)	42.50	35.00
		Nos. 101a-114 (14)	121.50	65.60

Wmk. 314 Sideways

1972-73 Perf. 13½x13

Center in Black

102b	A4	2c red orange	1.75	.85
103b	A4	3c red brown	2.00	.25
104b	A4	4c green	.60	.25
105b	A4	6c black	3.25	.30
106b	A4	8c dark carmine	3.00	2.50
107b	A4	10c olive brown	1.00	.25
108b	A4	12c violet	1.75	1.00
109b	A4	15c blue	2.00	1.00
		Nos. 102b-109b (8)	15.35	6.40

Issue dates: 2c, 8c, May 9, 1973, others, Nov. 17, 1972.

The following six sets are Common Design Types but with the portrait of Sultan Omar.

ITU Issue

Perf. 11x11½

1965, May 17 Litho. Wmk. 314

| 116 | CD317 | 4c red lil & org brn | .35 | .35 |
| 117 | CD317 | 75c orange & emer | 1.40 | 1.40 |

Intl. Cooperation Year Issue

1965, Oct. 25 Perf. 14½

| 118 | CD318 | 4c blue grn & claret | .25 | .25 |
| 119 | CD318 | 15c lt violet & grn | .60 | .60 |

Churchill Memorial Issue

1966, Jan. 24 Photo. Perf. 14

120	CD319	3c multicolored	.25	.25
121	CD319	15c multicolored	1.00	.80
122	CD319	25c multicolored	1.90	1.50
123	CD319	75c multicolored	4.50	4.00
		Nos. 120-123 (4)	7.65	6.55

World Cup Soccer Issue

1966, July 4 Litho. Perf. 14

| 124 | CD321 | 4c multicolored | .30 | .30 |
| 125 | CD321 | 75c multicolored | 1.00 | .95 |

WHO Headquarters Issue

1966, Sept. 20 Litho. Perf. 14

| 126 | CD322 | 12c multicolored | .45 | .45 |
| 127 | CD322 | 25c multicolored | .90 | .90 |

UNESCO Anniversary Issue

1966, Dec. 1 Litho. Wmk. 314

128	CD323	4c "Education"	.40	.40
129	CD323	15c "Science"	1.00	1.00
130	CD323	75c "Culture"	3.25	4.00
		Nos. 128-130 (3)	4.65	5.40

State Religious Building and Sultan Hassanal Bolkiah A7

1967, Dec. 19 Photo. Perf. 12½

131	A7	4c violet & multi	.25	.25
132	A7	10c red & multi	.25	.25
133	A7	25c orange & multi	.30	.30
134	A7	50c lt violet & multi	.45	.45
		Nos. 131-134 (4)	1.25	1.25

A three-stamp set (12c, 25c, 50c) showing views of the new Language and Communications Headquarters was prepared and announced for release in April, 1968. The Crown Agents distributed sample sets, but the stamps were not issued. Later, Nos. 144-146 were issued instead.

Sultan Hassanal Bolkiah, Brunei Mosque and Flags A8

Sultan Hassanal Bolkiah Installation: 12c, Sultan, Mosque and flags, horiz.

Perf. 13x14, 14x13

1968, July 9 Photo. Unwmk.

135	A8	4c green & multi	.25	.25
136	A8	12c dp bister & multi	.50	.50
137	A8	25c violet & multi	.65	.75
		Nos. 135-137 (3)	1.40	1.50

Sultan Hassanal Bolkiah A9

Wmk. 314

1968, July 15 Litho. Perf. 12

138	A9	4c multicolored	.25	.25
139	A9	12c multicolored	.25	.25
140	A9	25c multicolored	.50	.50
		Nos. 138-140 (3)	1.00	1.00

Sultan Hassanal Bolkiah's birthday.

Coronation of Sultan Hassanal Bolkiah, Aug. 1, 1968 — A10

1968, Aug. 1 Photo. Perf. 14½x14

141	A10	4c Prus blue & multi	.25	.25
142	A10	12c rose lilac & multi	.25	.25
143	A10	25c multicolored	.50	.50
		Nos. 141-143 (3)	1.00	1.00

A11

Hall of Language and Culture — A12

Perf. 13½, 12½x13½ (A12)

1968, Sept. 29 Photo. Wmk. 314

144	A11	10c blue grn & multi	.25	.25
145	A12	15c ocher & multi	.25	.25
146	A12	30c ultra & multi	.60	.60
		Nos. 144-146 (3)	1.10	1.10

Opening of the Hall of Language and Culture and of the Broadcasting and Information Department Building. Nos. 144-146 are overprinted "1968" and 4 bars over the 1967 date. They were not issued without this overprint.

Human Rights Flame and Struggling Man — A13

Unwmk.

1968, Dec. 16 Litho. Perf. 14

147	A13	12c green, yel & blk	.25	.25
148	A13	25c ultra, yel & blk	.30	.30
149	A13	75c dk plum, yel & blk	.60	.60
		Nos. 147-149 (3)	1.15	1.15

International Human Rights Year.

Sultan and WHO Emblem A14

1968, Dec. 19 Litho. Perf. 14

150	A14	4c lt blue, org & blk	.30	.30
151	A14	15c brt purple, org & blk	.45	.45
152	A14	25c olive, org & blk	.90	.90
		Nos. 150-152 (3)	1.65	1.65

20th anniv. of the WHO.

Sultan Hassanal Bolkiah, Pengiran Shahbandar and Oil Rig — A15

Perf. 14x13

1969, July 10 Photo. Wmk. 314

153	A15	12c green & multi	.75	.75
154	A15	40c dk rose brn & multi	1.00	1.00
155	A15	50c violet & multi	1.90	1.90
		Nos. 153-155 (3)	3.65	3.65

Installation of Pengiran Shahbandar as Second Minister (Di-Galong Sahibol Mal).

Royal Assembly Hall and Council Chamber — A16

Design: 50c, Front view of buildings.

Unwmk.

1969, Sept. 23 Litho. Perf. 15

156	A16	12c multicolored	.25	.25
157	A16	25c multicolored	.35	.35
158	A16	50c violet & pink	.70	.70
		Nos. 156-158 (3)	1.30	1.30

Opening of the Royal Assembly Hall and Council Chamber.

Youth Center — A17

1969, Dec. 20 Litho. Wmk. 314

159	A17	6c lt org, blk & dull vio	.25	.25
160	A17	10c cit, blk & dl Prus grn	.25	.25
161	A17	30c yel green, blk & brn	.70	.70
		Nos. 159-161 (3)	1.20	1.20

Opening of Youth Center, Mar. 15, 1969.

Helicopter and Emblem — A18

Designs: 10c, Soldier and emblem, vert. 75c, Patrol boat and emblem.

1971, May 31 Litho. Perf. 14

162	A18	10c green & multi	.75	.75
163	A18	15c Prus blue & multi	1.80	1.80
164	A18	75c lt ultra & multi	4.75	4.75
		Nos. 162-164 (3)	7.30	7.30

10th anniv. of Royal Brunei Malay Reg.

50th Anniv. of
the Royal Brunei
Police
Force — A19

1971, Aug. 14   **Perf. 14½**
165 A19 10c Superintendent .50 .50
166 A19 15c Constable .75 .75
167 A19 50c Traffic policeman 2.75 2.75
   Nos. 165-167 (3) 4.00 4.00

Sultan, Heir Apparent and View of
Brunei — A20

Portraits and: 25c, View of Brunei with
Mosque. 50c, Mosque and banner.

1971, Aug. 27   **Litho.**   **Wmk. 314**
168 A20 15c multicolored .75 .60
169 A20 25c multicolored 1.00 .85
170 A20 50c multicolored 2.00 2.75
   Nos. 168-170 (3) 3.75 4.20

Installation of Sultan Hassanal Bolkiah's
brother Muda Omar Ali Saifuddin as heir
apparent (Perdana Wazir).

Brass and
Copper
Goods
A21

Designs: 12c, Basketware. 15c, Leather
goods. 25c, Silverware. 50c, Brunei Museum.

1972, Feb. 29   **Perf. 13½x14**
   Size: 37x21mm
   Portrait in Black
171 A21 10c brn, sal & yel grn .30 .30
172 A21 12c org, yel & green .50 .50
173 A21 15c dk grn, emer & org .65 .65
174 A21 25c brown, org & slate 1.60 1.60
   Size: 58x21mm
175 A21 50c dull blue & multi 2.90 2.90
   Nos. 171-175 (5) 5.95 5.95

Opening of Brunei Museum.

Queen Elizabeth II, Sultan and
View — A22

Queen Elizabeth II, Sultan Hassanal Bolkiah
and: 15c, View of Brunei. 25c, Mosque and
barge. 50c, Royal Assembly Hall.

1972, Feb. 29   **Photo.**   **Perf. 13x13½**
176 A22 10c lt brown & multi .35 .35
177 A22 15c lt blue & multi 1.40 1.40
178 A22 25c lt green & multi 2.40 2.40
179 A22 50c dull purple & multi 4.00 4.00
   Nos. 176-179 (4) 8.15 8.15

Visit of Queen Elizabeth II, Feb. 29.

Bangunan Secretariat (Government
Buildings) — A23

Sultans Omar Ali Saifuddin and Hassanal
Bolkiah: 15c, Istana Darul Hana (Sultan's resi-
dence). 25c, View of capital. 50c, View of new
Mosque.

1972, Oct. 4   **Litho.**   **Perf. 13½**
180 A23 10c org, blk & green .30 .30
181 A23 15c green & multi .45 .45
182 A23 25c ultra & multi .90 .90
183 A23 50c rose red & multi 1.35 1.35
   Nos. 180-183 (4) 3.00 3.00

Change of capital's name from Brunei to
Bandar Seri Begawan, Oct. 4, 1970.

Beverley Plane Landing — A24

Design: 25c, Blackburn Beverley plane
dropping supplies by parachute, vert.

   Perf. 14x13½, 13½x14
1972, Nov. 15   **Litho.**
184 A24 25c blue & multi 2.25 2.25
185 A24 75c ultra & multi 4.50 4.50

Opening of Royal Air Force Museum, Hen-
don, London.

Silver Wedding Issue, 1972
Common Design Type

Design: Queen Elizabeth II, Prince Philip;
girl and boy with traditional gifts.

1972, Nov. 20   **Photo.**   **Perf. 14x14½**
186 CD324 12c multi .25 .25
187 CD324 75c multi .45 .45

INTERPOL Emblem and
Headquarters, Paris — A25

Design: 50c, similar to 25c.

1973, Sept. 7   **Litho.**   **Perf. 14x14½**
188 A25 25c emerald & multi 1.90 1.90
189 A25 50c multicolored 1.90 1.90

50th anniv. of Intl. Criminal Police Org.
(INTERPOL).

Princess Anne and Mark
Phillips — A26

1973, Nov. 14   **Perf. 13½**
190 A26 25c vio blue & multi .25 .25
191 A26 50c red lilac & multi .40 .40

Wedding of Princess Anne and Capt. Mark
Phillips, Nov. 14, 1973.

Churchill Painting
Outdoors — A27

Design: 50c, Churchill making "V" sign.

   Perf. 14x13½
1973, Dec. 31   **Litho.**   **Wmk. 314**
192 A27 12c car rose & multi .35 .35
193 A27 50c dk green & multi .50 .50

Winston Churchill Memorial Exhibition.

Sultan Hassanal
Bolkiah — A28

Wmk. 314 Sideways
1974, July 15   **Photo.**   **Perf. 13x15**
194 A28 4c blue grn & multi .25 .25
195 A28 5c dull blue & multi .25 .25
196 A28 6c olive grn & multi .75 .75
197 A28 10c lt violet & multi .25 .25
  b.   Watermark upright ('76) 3.00 .50
198 A28 15c brown & multi .25 .25
199 A28 20c buff & multi .25 .25
  b.   Watermark upright ('76) 2.50 .75
200 A28 25c olive & multi .25 .25
  b.   Watermark upright ('76) 3.50 1.00
201 A28 30c multicolored .30 .25
202 A28 35c gray & multi .40 .25
203 A28 40c multicolored .40 .25
204 A28 50c yel brn & multi .45 .25
205 A28 75c multicolored .90 1.00
206 A28 $1 dull org & multi 1.50 1.25
207 A28 $2 multicolored 3.00 1.25
208 A28 $5 silver & multi 4.00 6.25
209 A28 $10 gold & multi 11.00 10.00
   Nos. 194-209 (16) 24.20 23.00

Issue date: Nos. 197b-200b, Apr. 12.

1975, Aug. 13   **Wmk. 373**
194a A28 4c .25 .25
195a A28 5c .25 .25
196a A28 6c 6.00 1.00
197a A28 10c .25 .25
   Complete booklet, 4 x
   #195a, 8 x #197a 7.25
198a A28 15c .60 .25
199a A28 20c .60 .25
200a A28 25c .65 .25
201a A28 30c .35 .25
202a A28 35c .45 .30
203a A28 40c .55 .25
204a A28 50c .90 .25
205a A28 75c .85 1.10
206a A28 $1 1.75 1.10
207a A28 $2 4.75 4.75
208a A28 $5 6.50 17.50
209a A28 $10 24.00 35.00
   Nos. 194a-209a (16) 48.70 63.00

For surcharge see No. 225.
CTO examples of Nos. 208a and 209a sell
for less. Values: $6.50 and $24, respectively.

Brunei
Airport
A29

Design: 75c, Sultan Hassanal Bolkiah in
uniform and jet over airport.

   Perf. 14x14½, 12½x13 (75c)
1974, July 18   **Litho.**   **Wmk. 314**
   Size: 44x28mm
215 A29 50c multicolored 1.60 1.60
   Size: 47x36mm
216 A29 75c multicolored 1.90 1.90

Opening of Brunei Airport.

UPU
Emblem
A30

1974, Oct. 28   **Perf. 14½**
217 A30 12c orange & multi .30 .30
218 A30 50c blue & multi .70 .70
219 A30 75c emerald & multi 1.00 1.00
   Nos. 217-219 (3) 2.00 2.00

Centenary of Universal Postal Union.

Winston
Churchill
A31

Design: 75c, Churchill smoking cigar.

1974, Nov. 30   **Wmk. 373**   **Perf. 14**
220 A31 12c vio blue, blue &
       gold .40 .40
221 A31 75c dk grn, blk & gold 1.00 1.00

Sir Winston Churchill (1874-1965).

Boeing
737
Planes at
Airport
A32

Designs: 35c, Boeing 737 over Bandar Seri
Begawan Mosque. 75c, Boeing 737 in flight.
All planes with crest of Royal Brunei Airlines.

   Perf. 12½x12
1975, May 14   **Unwmk.**
222 A32 12c multicolored .60 .60
223 A32 35c multicolored 1.50 1.50
224 A32 75c multicolored 3.50 3.50
   Nos. 222-224 (3) 5.60 5.60

Inauguration of Royal Brunei Airlines.

No. 196a
Surcharged in Silver

   Perf. 13x15
1976, Aug. 16   **Photo.**   **Wmk. 373**
225 A28 10c on 6c multicolored 3.00 3.00
  a.   10c on 6c, wmk 314 sideways
      (#196) 3.25 3.25

British Royal
Coat of
Arms — A33

20c, Imperial State Crown. 75c, Elizabeth II.

   Wmk. 373
1977, June 7   **Litho.**   **Perf. 14**
226 A33 10c dk blue & multi .25 .25
227 A33 20c purple & multi .25 .25
228 A33 75c yellow & multi .65 .65
   Nos. 226-228 (3) 1.15 1.15

25th anniv. of the reign of Elizabeth II.

Coronation of Elizabeth II
A34

20c, Elizabeth II with coronation regalia. 75c, Departure from Westminster Abbey (coach).

1978, June 2   Litho.   Perf. 13½x13
229 A34 10c multicolored   .25   .25
230 A34 20c multicolored   .25   .25
231 A34 75c multicolored   .60   .60
      Nos. 229-231 (3)   1.10   1.10

25th anniv. of coronation of Elizabeth II.

Sultan's Coat of Arms — A35

Coronation of Sultan Hassanal Bolkiah, 10th Anniv.: 20c, Ceremony. 75c, Royal crown.

1978, Aug. 1   Wmk. 373   Perf. 12
232 A35 10c multicolored   .25   .25
233 A35 20c multicolored   .30   .30
234 A35 75c multicolored   1.25   1.25
  a. Souvenir sheet of 3, #232-234   19.00 19.00
      Nos. 232-234 (3)   1.80   1.80

Struggling Man, Human Rights Flame — A36

1978, Dec. 10   Litho.   Perf. 14
235 A36 10c red, black & yel   .25   .25
236 A36 20c violet, black & yel .25   .25
237 A36 75c olive, black & yel   1.00   1.00
      Nos. 235-237 (3)   1.50   1.50

Universal Declaration of Human Rights, 30th anniversary.

Children and IYC Emblem A37

1979, June 30   Wmk. 373   Perf. 14
238 A37 10c shown   .25   .25
239 A37 $1 IYC emblem   1.40   1.40

Telisai Earth Satellite Station A38

Designs: 20c, Radar screen and satellite. 75c, Cameraman, telex operator, telephone.

1979, Sept. 23   Litho.   Perf. 14½x14
240 A38 10c multicolored   .25   .25
241 A38 20c multicolored   .30   .30
242 A38 75c multicolored   1.00   1.00
      Nos. 240-242 (3)   1.55   1.55

Hajeer Emblem — A39

1979, Nov. 21
243 A39 10c multicolored   .25   .25
244 A39 20c multicolored   .25   .25
245 A39 75c multicolored   1.10   1.10
  a. Souvenir sheet of 3, #243-245   5.75   5.75
      Nos. 243-245 (3)   1.60   1.60

Hegira, 1400th anniversary.

A set of four depicting the opening of ports and harbors was prepared for use but not issued. A small number of sets exist in collector hands.

A40

No. 246, Installation ceremony. No. 247, Ceremony, diff. No. 248, Jefri Bolkiah. No. 249, Sufri Bolkiah.

1980   Litho.   Perf. 14
Color of Panels at Top and Bottom
246 A40 10c brt blue   .25   .25
247 A40 10c dark green   .25   .25
248 A40 75c brt blue   1.00   1.00
249 A40 75c dark green   1.00   1.00
      Nos. 246-249 (4)   2.50   2.50

Installation of Jefri Bolkiah and Sufri Bolkiah as Wizars (Ministers of State for Royalty) 1st anniv. Issued: Nos. 246, 248, 11/8; others, 12/6.

A41

1981, Jan. 19   Litho.   Perf. 12x11½
255 A41 10c Umbrella   .25   .25
256 A41 15c Dagger, shield .35   .35
257 A41 20c Spears   .45   .45
258 A41 30c Gold pouch   .60   .60
      Size: 22½x40mm
      Perf. 14x13½
259 A41 50c Headdress   1.15   1.15
  a. Souvenir sheet of 5, #255-259   6.00   6.00
      Nos. 255-259 (5)   2.80   2.80

A42

1981, May 17   Litho.   Perf. 13x13½
260 A42 10c car rose & black   .35   .35
261 A42 75c dp violet & black   2.50   2.50

13th World Telecommunications Day.

A43

Perf. 12½x12, 12 (75c)
1981, July 15   Litho.
Deep Rose Lilac Background
262 A43 10c Dagger, case   .25   .25
263 A43 15c Rifle, powder pouch .25   .25
264 A43 20c Spears   .25   .25
265 A43 30c Sword, tunic, shield .50   .50
266 A43 50c Horns   1.00   1.00
      Size: 28½x45mm
267 A43 75c Gold bowl, table   1.50   1.50
      Nos. 262-267 (6)   3.75   3.75

      See Nos. 278-289.

Royal Wedding Issue
Common Design Type
1981, July 29   Perf. 14
268 CD331 10c Bouquet   .25   .25
269 CD331 $1 Charles   .65   1.50
270 CD331 $2 Couple   1.25   2.75
      Nos. 268-270 (3)   2.15   4.50

World Food Day — A44

1981, Oct. 16   Litho.   Perf. 12
271 A44 10c Fishermen   .75   .75
272 A44 $1 Produce   6.00   6.00

Intl. Year of the Disabled — A45

1981, Dec. 16   Wmk. 373   Perf. 12
273 A45 10c Blind man   .60   .60
274 A45 20c Sign language   1.10   1.10
275 A45 75c Man in wheelchair 4.00   4.00
      Nos. 273-275 (3)   5.70   5.70

TB Bacillus Centenary — A46

1982, Mar. 24   Perf. 12, 13½ (75c)
276 A46 10c Lungs   .45   .45
277 A46 75c Bacillus, microscope 3.50   3.50

Type of 1981

1982, May 31   Litho.   Perf. 12½x12
Deep Magenta Background
278 A43 10c shown   .25   .25
279 A43 15c Pedestal urn   .25   .25
280 A43 20c Silver bowl   .25   .25
281 A43 30c Candle   .50   .50
282 A43 50c Gold pipe   1.00   1.00
      Size: 28x44mm
      Perf. 13½
283 A43 75c Silver pointer 1.50   1.50
      Nos. 278-283 (6)   3.75   3.75

1982, July 15   Litho.   Perf. 12½x12
Violet Background
284 A43 10c Urn   .30   .30
285 A43 15c Crossed banners .35   .35
286 A43 20c Golden fan   .50   .50
287 A43 30c Lid   1.00   1.00
288 A43 50c Sword, sheath 1.50   1.50
      Size: 28x44mm
      Perf. 12
289 A43 75c Golden chalice pole 2.00   2.00
      Nos. 284-289 (6)   5.65   5.65

A47

10c, Flag. 20c, Omar Ali Saifuddin Mosque. 75c, Oil well. $2, Sultan Bolkiah.

1983, Mar. 14   Litho.   Perf. 13½
290 A47 10c multi   .25   .25
291 A47 20c multi   .25   .25
292 A47 75c multi   1.20   1.20
293 A47 $2 multi   3.00   3.00
  a. Block or strip of 4, #290-293   4.50   4.50

      Commonwealth Day.

World Communications Year — A48

10c, Mail delivery. 75c, Teletype, phone. $2, Dish antenna, satellite, TV.

1983, July 15   Litho.   Perf. 13½
294 A48 10c multi   .25   .25
295 A48 75c multi   1.15   1.15
296 A48 $2 multi   2.75   2.75
      Nos. 294-296 (3)   4.15   4.15

Opening of Hassanal Bolkiah National Stadium — A49

1983, Sept. 23   Litho.   Perf. 12
297 A49 10c Soccer, vert.   .40   .40
298 A49 75c Runners, vert. 2.00   2.00
299 A49 $1 shown   4.00   4.00
      Nos. 297-299 (3)   6.40   6.40

      Size, Nos. 297-298: 26x33mm.

Fishing Industry — A50

1983, Sept. 23   **Litho.**   *Perf. 13½*
300	A50	10c Shrimp, lobster	.50	.50
301	A50	50c Pacific jacks	3.00	3.00
302	A50	75c Parrotfish, flatfish	4.75	4.75
303	A50	$1 Tuna	5.75	5.75
		Nos. 300-303 (4)	14.00	14.00

State Assembly Building — A51

Map of Southeast Asia, Flag — A52

Sultan Hassanal Bolkiah — A53

20c, State Secretariat building. 35c, New Law Court. 50c, Liquid natural gas well. 75c, Omar Ali Saifuddin Mosque. $1, Sultan's Palace.

1984, Jan. 1   **Litho.**   *Perf. 13*
304	A51	10c shown	.25	.25
305	A51	20c multicolored	.40	.40
306	A51	35c multicolored	.75	.75
307	A51	50c multicolored	1.50	1.50
308	A51	75c multicolored	2.00	2.00
309	A51	$1 multicolored	2.75	2.75
310	A52	$3 shown	7.75	7.75
a.		Souvenir sheet of 7, #304-310	16.50	16.50
		Nos. 304-310 (7)	15.40	15.40

Souvenir Sheets
311	A53	Sheet of 4, Constitution signing, 1959	3.50	3.50
a.-d.		25c any single	.75	.75
312	A53	Sheet of 4, Brunei U.K. Friendship Agreement, 1979	3.50	3.50
a.-d.		25c any single	.75	.75

Forestry Resources — A54

10c, Forests, enrichment planting. 50c, Water resources. 75c, Recreation forest. $1, Wildlife.

1984, Apr. 21   **Litho.**   *Perf. 13½*
313	A54	10c multi	1.50	1.50
314	A54	50c multi	3.00	3.00
315	A54	75c multi	4.50	4.50
316	A54	$1 multi	6.00	6.00
		Nos. 313-316 (4)	15.00	15.00

Philakorea 1984 — A55

Litho. & Engr.
1984, Oct. 22   *Perf. 13*
317	A55	10c No. 93	.75	.75
a.		Souvenir sheet of 1	.90	.90
318	A55	75c No. 27	2.00	2.00
a.		Souvenir sheet of 1	2.25	2.25
319	A55	$2 1895 local stamp	4.00	4.00
a.		Souvenir sheet of 1	4.50	4.50
		Nos. 317-319 (3)	6.75	6.75

Brunei Admission to Intl. Organizations — A56

1985, Sept. 23   **Litho.**   *Perf. 13*
320	A56	50c UN	1.00	1.00
321	A56	50c Commonwealth	1.00	1.00
322	A56	50c ASEAN	1.00	1.00
323	A56	50c OIC	1.00	1.00
a.		Souv. sheet, #320-323 + label	6.25	6.25
		Nos. 320-323 (4)	4.00	4.00

Intl. Youth Year A57

75c, Industry, education. $1, Public Service.

1985, Oct. 17   *Perf. 12*
324	A57	10c shown	1.25	1.25
325	A57	75c multi	5.50	5.50
326	A57	$1 multi	6.75	6.75
		Nos. 324-326 (3)	13.50	13.50

Intl. Day of Solidarity with the Palestinian People A58

1985, Nov. 29   *Perf. 12x12½*
327	A58	10c lt blue & multi	1.50	1.50
328	A58	50c pink & multi	4.75	4.75
329	A58	$1 lt green & multi	7.75	7.75
		Nos. 327-329 (3)	14.00	14.00

Natl. Scout Jamboree, Dec. 14-20 — A59

1985, Dec. 14   *Perf. 13½*
330	A59	10c Scout handshake	.45	.45
331	A59	20c Semaphore	.90	.90
332	A59	$2 Jamboree emblem	4.50	4.50
		Nos. 330-332 (3)	5.85	5.85

Sultan Hassanal Bolkiah — A60

1985-86   **Wmk. 233**   *Perf. 13½x14½*
333	A60	10c multi	.25	.25
334	A60	15c multi	.25	.25
		Complete booklet, 4 ea. #333, 334	3.00	
335	A60	20c multi	.25	.25
336	A60	25c multi	.30	.30
337	A60	35c multi ('86)	.40	.40
338	A60	40c multi ('86)	.45	.45
339	A60	50c multi ('86)	.55	.55
340	A60	75c multi ('86)	.75	.75

Size: 35x42mm
Perf. 14
341	A60	$1 multi ('86)	1.25	1.25
342	A60	$2 multi ('86)	2.75	2.75
343	A60	$5 multi ('86)	6.50	6.50
344	A60	$10 multi ('86)	12.00	12.00
		Nos. 333-344 (12)	25.70	25.70

Issued: Nos. 333-336, Dec. 23; Nos. 337-340, Jan. 15; Nos. 341-343, Feb. 23; No. 344, Mar. 29.

Admission to Intl. Organizations A61

Wmk. Cartor (385)
1986, Apr. 30   **Litho.**   *Perf. 13*
345	A61	50c WMO	.75	.75
346	A61	50c ITU	.75	.75
347	A61	50c UPU	.75	.75
348	A61	50c ICAO	.75	.75
a.		Souv. sheet, #345-348 + label	6.00	6.00
		Nos. 345-348 (4)	3.00	3.00

Royal Brunei Armed Forces, 25th Anniv. A62

1986, May 31   **Unwmk.**   *Perf. 13½*
349		Strip of 4	25.00	25.00
a.	A62	10c In combat	4.75	4.75
b.	A62	20c Communications	5.25	5.25
c.	A62	50c Air and sea defense	6.75	6.75
d.	A62	75c On parade, Royal Palace	8.25	8.25

Royal Ensigns — A63

No. 350, Tunggul charok buritan, Pisang-pisang, Alam bernaga, Sandaran. No. 351, Dadap, Tunggul kawan, Ambal, Payong ubor-ubor, Sapu-sapu ayeng and Rawai lidah. No. 352, Ula-ula besar, Payong haram, Sumbu layang. No. 353, Payong ubor-ubor tiga ringkat and Payong tinggi. No. 354, Panji-panji, Chogan istiadat, Chogan ugama. No. 355, Lambang duli yang maha mulia and Mahligai.

1986   **Litho.**   *Perf. 12½*
350	A63	10c multicolored	.35	.35
351	A63	10c multicolored	.35	.35
352	A63	75c multicolored	1.75	1.75
353	A63	75c multicolored	1.75	1.75
354	A63	$2 multicolored	3.00	3.00
355	A63	$2 multicolored	3.00	3.00
		Nos. 350-355 (6)	10.20	10.20

Intl. Peace Year — A64

1986, Oct. 24   **Litho.**   *Perf. 12*
356	A64	50c Peace doves	1.00	1.00
357	A64	75c Hands	1.50	1.50
358	A64	$1 Peace symbols	2.00	2.00
		Nos. 356-358 (3)	4.50	4.50

Natl. Anti-Drug Campaign Posters — A65

1987, Mar. 15   **Litho.**   *Perf. 12*
359	A65	10c Jail	1.35	1.35
360	A65	75c Noose	4.50	4.50
361	A65	$1 Execution	6.50	6.50
		Nos. 359-361 (3)	12.35	12.35

Brass Artifacts — A66

1987, July 15
362	A66	50c Kiri (kettle)	.90	.90
363	A66	50c Langguai (bowl)	.90	.90
364	A66	50c Badil (cannon)	.90	.90
365	A66	50c Pelita (lamp)	.90	.90
		Nos. 362-365 (4)	3.60	3.60

See Nos. 388-391.

Dewan Bahasa Dan Pustaka, 25th Anniv. — A67

1987, Sept. 29   *Perf. 13½x13*
366	A67	Strip of 3	3.75	3.75
a.		10c multicolored	.25	.25
b.		50c multicolored	.75	.75
c.		$2 multicolored	2.75	2.75

Language and Literature Bureau.

ASEAN, 20th Anniv. — A68

1987, Aug. 8   **Litho.**   *Perf. 14x13½*
367	A68	20c Map	.55	.55
368	A68	50c Year dates	.80	.80
369	A68	$1 Flags, emblem	1.90	1.90
		Nos. 367-369 (3)	3.25	3.25

World Food Day A70

Fruit: a, Artocarpus odoratissima. b, Canarium odontophyllum mig. c, Litsea garciae. d, Mangifera foetida lour.

1987, Oct. 31   *Perf. 12½*
370   Strip of 4   4.50   4.50
   a.-d. A70 50c any single   1.10   1.10
    See Nos. 374, 405, 423, 457-460.

Intl. Year of
Shelter for
the
Homeless
A71

Various houses.

1987, Nov. 28   Litho.   *Perf. 13*
371   A71 50c multi   .65   .65
372   A71 75c multi, diff.   .95   .95
373   A71 $1 multi, diff.   1.90   1.90
    Nos. 371-373 (3)   3.50   3.50

**Fruit Type of 1987
Without FAO Emblem, Dated 1988**

Fruit: a, Durio. b, Durio oxleyanus. c, Durio graveolens (cross section at L). d, Durio graveolens (cross section at R).

1988, Jan. 30   Litho.   *Perf. 12*
374   Strip of 4   4.50   4.50
   a.-d. A70 50c, any single   1.10   1.10

Opening of Malay
Technology
Museum — A72

10c, Wooden lathe. 75c, Water wheel, buffalo. $1, Bird caller in blind.

1988, Feb. 29   *Perf. 12½x12*
375   A72 10c multi   .25   .25
376   A72 75c multi   1.10   1.10
377   A72 $1 multi   2.25   2.25
    Nos. 375-377 (3)   3.60   3.60

Handwoven Cloth — A73

Designs: 10c, Kain Beragi Bunga Sakah-Sakah Dan Bunga Cengkih. 20c, Kain Jong Sarat. 25c, Kain Si Pugut. 40c, Kain Si Pugut Bunga Berlapis. 75c, Kain Si Lobang Bangsi Bunga Belitang Kipas.

1988, Apr. 30   Litho.   *Perf. 12*
378   A73 10c multicolored   .25   .25
379   A73 20c org brown & blk   .25   .25
380   A73 25c multicolored   .25   .25
381   A73 40c multicolored   .55   .55
382   A73 75c multicolored   1.40   1.40
   a.   Souvenir sheet of 5, #378-382 +
     label   4.25   4.25
    Nos. 378-382 (5)   2.70   2.70

1988, Sept. 29   Litho.   *Perf. 12*
Designs: 10c, Kain Beragi. 20c, Kain Bertabur. 25c, Kain Sukma Indra. 40c, Kain Si Pugut Bunga Bersusup. 75c, Kain Beragi Si Lobang Bangsi Bunga Cendera Kesuma.

383   A73 10c multicolored   .25   .25
384   A73 20c multicolored   .25   .25
385   A73 25c multicolored   .55   .55
386   A73 40c multicolored   .80   .80
387   A73 75c multicolored   1.10   1.10
   a.   Souvenir sheet of 5, #383-387   4.25   4.25
    Nos. 383-387 (5)   2.95   2.95

Brass Artifacts Type of 1987

No. 388, Celapa (repousse box). No. 389, Gangsa (footed plate). No. 390, Periok (lidded pot). No. 391, Lampong (candlestick).

1988, June 30   Litho.   *Perf. 12*
388   A66 50c multicolored   .80   .80
389   A66 50c multicolored   .80   .80
390   A66 50c multicolored   .80   .80
391   A66 50c multicolored   .80   .80
    Nos. 388-391 (4)   3.20   3.20

Coronation of
Sultan Hassanal
Bolkiah, 20th
Anniv. — A74

75c, Reading from the Koran. $2, In full regalia.

1988, Aug. 1   Litho.   *Perf. 14*
392   A74 20c shown   .30   .30
393   A74 75c multicolored   1.10   1.10

    Size: 26x62mm
      Perf. 12½x13
394   A74 $2 multicolored   2.50   2.50
   a.   Souvenir sheet of 3, #392-394   4.50   4.50
    Nos. 392-394 (3)   3.90   3.90

Eradicate Malaria, WHO 40th
Anniv. — A75

25c, Mosquito. 35c, Extermination. $2, Microscope, infected blood cells.

1988, Dec. 17   Litho.   *Perf. 14x13½*
395   A75 25c multicolroed   1.20   1.20
396   A75 35c multicolored   1.60   1.60
397   A75 $2 multicolored   4.00   4.00
    Nos. 395-397 (3)   6.80   6.80

Natl. Day
A76

20c, Sultan Bolkiah, officials. 30c, Honor guard. 60c, Fireworks, palace, vert. $2, Religious ceremony.

1989, Feb. 23   Litho.   *Perf. 12*
    Size of 60c: 22x54½mm
398   A76 20c multicolored   .25   .25
399   A76 30c multicolored   .50   .50
400   A76 60c multicolored   1.00   1.00
401   A76 $2 multicolored   2.50   2.50
   a.   Souvenir sheet of 4, #398-401   6.25   6.25
    Nos. 398-401 (4)   4.25   4.25

Independence from Britain, 5th anniv.

Solidarity with the Palestinians — A77

1989, Apr. 1   Litho.   *Perf. 13½*
402   A77 20c shown   .75   .75
403   A77 75c Map, flag   2.25   2.25
404   A77 $1 Dome of the Rock   3.00   3.00
    Nos. 402-404 (3)   6.00   6.00

**Fruit Type of 1987
Without FAO Emblem, Dated 1989**

Designs: a, Daemonorops fissa. b, Eleiodoxa conferia. c, Salacca zalacca. d, Calamus ornatus.

1989, Oct. 31   Litho.   *Perf. 12*
405   Strip of 4   9.75   9.75
   a.-d. A70 60c any single   2.25   2.25

Oil and
Gas
Industry,
60th Anniv.
A79

1989, Dec. 28   *Perf. 13½*
406   A79 20c Oil well pump   1.50   1.50
407   A79 60c Tanker   4.00   4.00
408   A79 90c Offshore rig   4.00   4.00
409   A79 $1 Rail transport   7.75   7.75
410   A79 $2 Offshore platform   11.00   11.00
    Nos. 406-410 (5)   28.25   28.25

Brunei
Museum,
25th
Anniv.
A80

30c, Exhibits. 60c, Official opening, 1965. $1, Museum exterior.

1990, Jan. 1   Litho.   *Perf. 12x12½*
411   A80 30c multicolored   1.75   1.75
412   A80 60c multicolored   3.25   3.25
413   A80 $1 multicolored   4.50   4.50
    Nos. 411-413 (3)   9.50   9.50

Intl.
Literacy
Year
A81

1990, July 15   Litho.   *Perf. 12x12½*
414   A81 15c multicolored   1.00   1.00
415   A81 90c multicolored   3.00   3.00
416   A81 $1 multicolored   4.00   4.00
    Nos. 414-416 (3)   8.00   8.00

Tarsier — A82

1990, Sept. 29   Litho.   *Perf. 12*
417   A82 20c shown   1.20   1.20
418   A82 60c Eating leaves   3.50   3.50
419   A82 90c Climbing tree   4.75   4.75
    Nos. 417-419 (3)   9.45   9.45

Fight Against
AIDS — A83

30c, AIDS transmission. 90c, Tombstone, skulls.

1990, Dec. 1   Litho.   *Perf. 13*
420   A83 20c shown   2.50   2.50
421   A83 30c multicolored   6.00   6.00
422   A83 90c multicolored   11.00   11.00
    Nos. 420-422 (3)   19.50   19.50

**Fruit Type of 1987
Without FAO Emblem, Dated 1990**

Fruit: a, Willoughbea (uncut core). b, Willoughbea (core cut in half). c, Willoughbea angustifolia.

1990, Dec. 31   *Perf. 12½*
423   Strip of 3   9.50   9.50
   a.-c. A70 60c any single   3.00   3.00

Proboscis Monkey,
World Wildlife
Fund — A84

1991, Mar. 30   Litho.   *Perf. 13½x14*
424   A84 15c shown   1.50   1.50
425   A84 20c Head, facing   1.75   1.75
426   A84 50c Sitting on branch   3.75   3.75
427   A84 60c Adult with young   5.25   5.25
    Nos. 424-427 (4)   12.25   12.25

Teacher's
Day
A85

Design: 90c, Teacher at blackboard.

1991, Sept. 23   Litho.   *Perf. 13½x14*
428   A85 60c multicolored   3.25   3.25
429   A85 90c multicolored   3.75   3.75

Brunei
Beauty
A86

1991, Oct. 1   Litho.   *Perf. 13*
430   A86 30c Three immature   1.50   1.50
431   A86 60c Female   3.00   3.00
432   A86 $1 Adult male   4.25   4.25
    Nos. 430-432 (3)   8.75   8.75

Happy Family
Campaign — A87

20c, Family, graduating son. 60c, Mothers, children. 90c, Adults, children, heart.

1991, Nov. 30   Litho.   *Perf. 13*
433   A87 20c multicolored   .90   .90
434   A87 60c multicolored   2.25   2.25
435   A87 90c multicolored   3.50   3.50
    Nos. 433-435 (3)   6.65   6.65

World Health
Day — A88

1992, Apr. 7   Litho.   *Perf. 13*
436   A88 20c multicolored   1.25   1.25
437   A88 50c multi, diff.   3.50   3.50
    Size: 48x28mm
438   A88 75c multi, diff.   5.25   5.25
    Nos. 436-438 (3)   10.00   10.00

Brunei-Singapore and Brunei-
Malaysia-Philippines Fiber Optic
Submarine Cables — A89

1992, Apr. 28   Litho.   Perf. 12
439 A89 20c Map   1.75   1.75
440 A89 30c Diagram   2.25   2.25
441 A89 90c Submarine cable   7.00   7.00
    Nos. 439-441 (3)   11.00 11.00

Visit ASEAN Year — A90

Designs: a, 20c, Sculptures. b, 60c, Judo
exhibition. c, $1, Sculptures, diff.

1992, June 30 Litho.   Perf. 13½x14
442 A90 Strip of 3, #a.-c.   8.25   8.25

ASEAN, 25th
Anniv. — A91

60c, Building. 90c, Views of member states.

1992, Aug. 8   Litho.   Perf. 14
443 A91 20c shown   1.25   1.25
444 A91 60c multicolored   3.50   3.50
445 A91 90c multicolored   3.50   3.50
    Nos. 443-445 (3)   8.25   8.25

A92

Sultan in various forms of dress and: No.
446a, Coronation procession. b, Airport. c,
New Law Court, Sultan's Palace. d, Ship and
Brunei University. e, Mosque, buildings.

1992, Oct. 5   Perf. 14x13½
446 A92 25c Strip of 5, #a.-e.   8.50   8.50

Sultan Hassanal Bolkiah's Accession to the
Throne, 25th Anniv.

Birds
A93

Designs: No. 447, Crested wood partridge,
vert. No. 448, Long-tailed parakeet, vert. No.
449, Chestnut-breasted malkoha. No. 450,
Asian paradise flycatcher, vert. No. 451, Magpie robin, vert. No. 452, White-rumped shama.
No. 453, Great argus pheasant, vert. No. 454,
Malay lorikeet, vert. No. 455, Black and red
broadbill, vert.

Perf. 14x13½, 13½x14
1992-93   Litho.
447 A93 30c multicolored   1.20   1.20
448 A93 30c multicolored   1.20   1.20
449 A93 30c multicolored   1.20   1.20
450 A93 60c multicolored   2.40   2.40
451 A93 60c multicolored   2.40   2.40
452 A93 60c multicolored   2.40   2.40

453 A93 $1 multicolored   2.75   2.75
454 A93 $1 multicolored   2.75   2.75
455 A93 $1 multicolored   2.75   2.75
    Nos. 447-455 (9)   19.05 19.05

Issued: Nos. 447, 450, 453, 12/30/92; Nos.
448, 451, 454, 1/27/93; others, 5/3/93.

Natl. Day, 10th
Anniv. — A94

10th anniv. emblem and: a, 10c, Natl. flag.
b, 20c, Hands supporting inscription. c, 30c,
Natl. day emblems, 1985-93. d, 60c, Emblem
with star, crossed swords.

1994, June 16   Litho.   Perf. 13
456 A94 Strip of 4, #a.-d.   5.50   5.50

Fruit Type of 1987
Without FAO Emblem, Dated 1994

No. 457, Nephelium mutabile. No. 458,
Nephelium xerospermoides. No. 459, Nephelium spp. No. 460, Nephelium macrophyllum.

1994, Aug. 8   Litho.   Perf. 13½x13
457 A70 60c multicolored   1.40   1.40
458 A70 60c multicolored   1.40   1.40
459 A70 60c multicolored   1.40   1.40
460 A70 60c multicolored   1.40   1.40
    Nos. 457-460 (4)   5.60   5.60

A95

World Stop Smoking Day: 10c, Cigarette,
lung, fetus over human figure. 15c, People
throwing away tobacco, cigarettes, pipe. $2,
Arms around world crushing out cigarettes.

1994, Sept. 1   Litho.   Perf. 13½x13
461 A95 10c multicolored   .50   .50
462 A95 15c multicolored   1.00   1.00
463 A95 $2 multicolored   4.75   4.75
    Nos. 461-463 (3)   6.25   6.25

A96

Girl Guides in Brunei, 40th anniv.: a,
Leader. b, Girl receiving award. c, Girl reading.
d, Girls in various costumes. e, Girls camping
out.

1994, Oct. 7   Perf. 13½
464 A96 40c Strip of 5, #a.-e.   10.00 10.00

Royal
Brunei
Airlines,
20th Anniv.
A97

Airplanes: 10c, Twin-engine propeller. 20c,
Passenger jet attached to tow bar. $1, Passen-
ger jet in air.

1994, Nov. 18   Litho.   Perf. 13½
465 A97 10c multicolored   .85   .85
466 A97 20c multicolored   1.40   1.40
467 A97 $1 multicolored   3.50   3.50
    Nos. 465-467 (3)   5.75   5.75

Intl. Day Against
Drug Abuse — A98

Healthy people wearing traditional costumes: 20c, 60c, $1.

1994, Dec. 30   Litho.   Perf. 13½
468 A98 Strip of 3, #a.-c.   6.25   6.25

No. 468 is a continuous design.

City of
Bandar
Seri
Begawan,
25th Anniv.
A100

Aerial view of city: 30c, In 1970. 50c, In
1980, with details of significant buildings. $1,
In 1990.

1995, Oct. 4   Litho.   Perf. 13½
481 A100 30c multicolored   1.00   1.00
482 A100 50c multicolored   2.00   2.00
483 A100 $1 multicolored   2.75   2.75
    Nos. 481-483 (3)   5.75   5.75

A101

UN headquarters: 20c, Delegates in General Assembly. 60c, Security Council. 90c,
Exterior.

1995, Oct. 24   Perf. 14½x14
484 A101 20c multicolored   .35   .35
485 A101 60c multicolored   1.40   1.40

Size: 27x44mm
486 A101 90c multicolored   2.00   2.00
    Nos. 484-486 (3)   3.75   3.75

UN, 50th anniv.

A102

University of Brunei, 10th Anniv.: 30c, Students in classroom. 50c, Campus buildings.
90c, Sultan in procession.

1995, Oct. 28   Perf. 13x13½
487 A102 30c multicolored   1.00   1.00
488 A102 50c multicolored   1.00   1.00
489 A102 90c multicolored   1.60   1.60
    Nos. 487-489 (3)   3.60   3.60

A103

Royal Brunei Police, 75th Anniv.: 25c,
Policemen in various uniforms. 50c, Various
tasks performed by police. 75c, Sultan reviewing police.

1996, Feb. 10   Litho.   Perf. 13½x13
490 A103 25c multicolored   1.00   1.00
491 A103 50c multicolored   2.00   2.00
492 A103 75c multicolored   3.00   3.00
    Nos. 490-492 (3)   6.00   6.00

A104

World Telecommunications Day: 20c, Cartoon telephone, cordless telephone. 35c,
Globe, telephone dial surrounded by communication devices. $1, Signals transmitting from
earth, people communicating.

1996, May 17   Litho.   Perf. 13½
493 A104 20c multicolored   1.00   1.00
494 A104 35c multicolored   1.50   1.50
495 A104 $1 multicolored   2.50   2.50
    Nos. 493-495 (3)   5.00   5.00

A105

Sultan: No. 496, Among people, in black
attire. No. 497, Waving, in yellow attire. No.
498, In blue shirt. No. 499, Among people,
wearing cream-colored robe.
$1, Hand raised in yellow attire.

1996, July 15   Litho.   Perf. 13
496 A105 50c multicolored   1.50   1.50
497 A105 50c multicolored   1.50   1.50
498 A105 50c multicolored   1.50   1.50
499 A105 50c multicolored   1.50   1.50
    Nos. 496-499 (4)   6.00   6.00

Souvenir Sheet
500 A105 $1 multicolored   3.75   3.75

Sultan Paduka Seri Baginda, 50th birthday.
A souvenir sheet of five $50 stamps exists.
Value $650.

Terns — A106

20c, Black-naped tern. 30c, Roseate tern.
$1, Bridle tern.

1996, Nov. 11   Litho.   Perf. 13½
501	A106	20c multi	1.10	1.10
502	A106	30c multi	1.10	1.10
503	A106	$1 multi	2.75	2.75
		Nos. 501-503 (3)	4.95	4.95

No. 502 is spelled "Roslate" on stamp.

Sultan Hassanal Bolkiah
A107   A108

Perf. 14x13½

1996, Oct. 9   Litho.   Wmk. 387
Background Color
504	A107	10c yellow green	.25	.25
505	A107	15c pale pink	.25	.25
506	A107	20c lilac pink	.30	.25
507	A107	30c salmon	.35	.25
508	A107	50c yellow	.60	.25
509	A107	60c pale green	.65	.25
510	A107	75c blue	.90	.30
511	A107	90c lilac	1.00	.65
512	A108	$1 pink	1.25	.65
513	A108	$2 orange yellow	3.00	.65
514	A108	$5 light blue	7.50	2.25
515	A108	$10 bright yellow	13.50	9.75
		Nos. 504-515 (12)	29.55	15.75

Flowers
A109

20c, Acanthus ebracteatus. 30c, Lumnitzera littorea. $1, Nypa fruticans.

1997, May 29   Litho.   Perf. 12
516	A109	20c multicolored	.45	.45
517	A109	30c multicolored	.70	.70
518	A109	$1 multicolored	1.90	1.90
		Nos. 516-518 (3)	3.05	3.05

Marine Life
A110

Designs: No. 519, Bohadschia argus. No. 520, Oxycomanthus bennetti. No. 521, Heterocentrotus mammillatus. No. 522, Linckia laevigata.

1997, Dec. 15   Litho.   Perf. 12
519	A110	60c multicolored	.95	.95
520	A110	60c multicolored	.95	.95
521	A110	60c multicolored	.95	.95
522	A110	60c multicolored	.95	.95
		Nos. 519-522 (4)	3.80	3.80

Asian and Pacific Decade of Disabled Persons (1993-2002) — A111

Designs: 20c, Silhouettes of people, hands finger spelling "Brunei," children. 50c, Fireworks over city, blind people participating in arts, crafts, music. $1, Handicapped people playing sports.

1998, Mar. 31   Litho.   Perf. 13x13½
523	A111	20c multicolored	.45	.45
524	A111	50c multicolored	1.10	1.10
525	A111	$1 multicolored	2.00	2.00
		Nos. 523-525 (3)	3.55	3.55

ASEAN, 30th Anniv. — A112

Designs: No. 526, Night scene of Sultan's Palace, buildings, map of Brunei. No. 527, Flags of ASEAN nations. No. 528, Daytime scenes of Sultan's Palace, transportation methods, buildings in Brunei.

1998, Aug. 8   Litho.   Perf. 13½
526	A112	30c multicolored	1.25	1.25
527	A112	30c multicolored	1.25	1.25
528	A112	30c multicolored	1.25	1.25
		Nos. 526-528 (3)	3.75	3.75

Sultan Hassanal Bolkiah, 30th Anniv. of Coronation — A113

Designs: 60c, In procession, saluting, on throne. 90c, Sultan Omar Ali Saifuddin standing, Sultan Hassanal Bolkiah on throne. $1, Procession.

1998, Aug. 1   Litho.   Perf. 12
529	A113	60c multicolored	1.00	1.00
530	A113	90c multicolored	1.50	1.50
531	A113	$1 multicolored	1.50	1.50
a.		Souvenir sheet, #529-531	5.00	5.00
		Nos. 529-531 (3)	4.00	4.00

A114

Investiture of Crown Prince Al-Muhtadee Billah: $1, Signing document. $2, Formal portrait. $3, Arms of the Crown Prince.

1998, Aug. 10
532	A114	$1 multicolored	1.25	1.25
533	A114	$2 multicolored	2.50	2.50
534	A114	$3 multicolored	3.75	3.75
a.		Souvenir sheet, #532-534	8.00	8.00
		Nos. 532-534 (3)	7.50	7.50

30c, Hands clasped, woman, man. 60c, Dollar sign over book, arrows, "7.45AM." 90c, Silhouettes of people seated at table, standing, scales.

1998, Sept. 29   Perf. 13x13½
535	A115	30c multicolored	.70	.70
536	A115	60c multicolored	1.05	1.05
537	A115	90c multicolored	1.75	1.75
		Nos. 535-537 (3)	3.50	3.50

Civil Sevice Day, 5th anniv.

Kingfishers
A116

20c, Blue-eared. 30c, Common. 60c, White-collared. $1, Stork-billed.

1998, Nov. 11   Litho.   Perf. 13½x13
538	A116	20c multi	.75	.75
539	A116	30c multi	1.10	1.10
540	A116	60c multi	1.75	1.75
541	A116	$1 multi	3.00	3.00
		Nos. 538-541 (4)	6.60	6.60

A117

National Day, 15th Anniv.: 20c, Boat docks, residential area. 60c, Methods of communications. 90c, Buildings, roadways, tower, oil rig.

1999, Feb. 23   Litho.   Perf. 13
542	A117	20c multicolored	.35	.35
543	A117	60c multicolored	1.25	1.25
544	A117	90c multicolored	2.00	2.00
a.		Souvenir sheet, #542-544	4.25	4.25
		Nos. 542-544 (3)	3.60	3.60

20th Sea Games, 1999 — A119

No. 549, 20c: a, Field hockey, cycling. b, Basketball, soccer. c, Tennis, track and field. d, Billiards. e, Bowling.
No. 550, 20c: a, Shooting. b, Golf, squash. c, Boxing. d, Kick fighting, badminton, ping pong. e, Swimming, rowing.
$1, Shooting, tennis, running, soccer, cycling, basketball.

1999, Aug. 7   Litho.   Perf. 14¼
Strips of 5, #a.-e.
549-550	A119	Set of 2	6.00	6.00

Souvenir Sheet
551	A119	$1 multicolored	3.50	3.50

No. 551 contains one 35x35mm stamp.

UPU, 125th Anniv. — A120

20c, Handshake, globe, letters. 30c, Emblems of UPU, Brunei Post. 75c, Postal workers & services.

1999, Oct. 9   Litho.   Perf. 14
552	A120	20c multicolored	.35	.35
553	A120	30c multicolored	.70	.70
554	A120	75c multicolored	1.75	1.75
		Nos. 552-554 (3)	2.80	2.80

Millennium — A121

No. 555: a, Building with clock, children at computer. b, Building with red roof, man and woman at computer. c, Building with gray roof, mosque. d, Map of park. e, Airplane and ships. f, Satellite dishes.

Perf. 13¾x13½ Syncopated Type A
2000, Feb. 1   Litho.
555	A121	20c Strip of 6, #a-f	3.75	3.75
g.		Souvenir sheet, #555	4.25	4.25

Flowers
A122

Designs: 30c, Rafflesia pricei. 50c, Rhizanthes lowi. 60c, Nepenthes rafflesiana.

2000, Oct. 2   Litho.   Perf. 14¼x14
556-558	A122	Set of 3	3.50	3.50

Asia-Pacific Economic Cooperation
A123

Designs: 20c, Satellite dish, people at computers. 30c, Food processing enterprises. 60c, Eco-tourism (flower and bridge).

2000, Nov. 15   Perf. 13½x13
559	A123	20c multi	.50	.50
a.		Booklet pane of 1	.50	
560	A123	30c multi	1.00	1.00
a.		Booklet pane of 1	1.00	
561	A123	60c multi	1.50	1.50
a.		Booklet pane of 1	1.50	
		Booklet, #559a-561a	3.00	
b.		Souvenir sheet, #559-561	3.50	3.50

The 20th Century — A124

No. 562 — Scenes from: a, 1901-20. b, 1921-40. c, 1941-60. d, 1961-80. e, 1981-99.

Perf. 13¾x13½ Syncopated Type A
2000, Feb. 23   Litho.
562		Strip of 5	5.00	5.00
a.-e.	A124	30c Any single	.90	.90

Turtles
A125

No. 563: a, Green turtle. b, Hawksbill turtle. c, Olive Ridley turtle.

2000, Nov. 16   Perf. 13¼x13
563		Strip of 3	4.00	4.00
a.-c.	A125	30c Any single	.75	.75

Sultans — A126

No. 564: a, Hashim Jalilul Alam. b, Muhammad Jamalul Alam II. c, Ahmed Tajudin. d, Haji Omar Ali Saifuddin. e, Haji Hassanal Bolkiah.

2000, July 15	Litho.	Perf. 13¾	
564	Horiz. strip of 5	8.00	8.00
a.-e.	A126 60c Any single	1.40	1.40
f.	Souvenir sheet, #564, perf. 14¼x14	7.50	7.50
g.	Booklet pane of 1, #564a	2.75	
h.	Booklet pane of 1, #564b	2.75	
i.	Booklet pane of 1, #564c	2.75	
j.	Booklet pane of 1, #564d	2.75	
k.	Booklet pane of 1, #564e	2.75	
	Booklet, #564g-564k	24.00	

Visit Brunei Year — A127

Designs: 20c, People in boat. 30c, Houses on pilings. 60c, Shown.

2001, Mar. 14		Perf. 14¼x13¾
565-567	A127	Set of 3	4.25 4.25

Sultan Hassanal Bolkiah, 55th Birthday — A128

No. 568: a, Navy blue uniform. b, Light blue uniform. c, Robes. d, Camouflage uniform. e, White uniform.
No. 569, Casual shirt.

	Perf. 12¼		
2001, July 15	Litho.	Unwmk.	
568	Horiz. strip of 5	4.00	4.00
a.-e.	A128 55c Any single	.75	.75

Souvenir Sheet
Perf. 12

| 569 | A128 55c multi | 4.00 4.00 |

No. 569 contains one 40x70mm stamp.

International Youth Camp 2001 — A129

No. 570: a, Scout, administering first aid. b, Girls, tents. c, Scouts and leader.

2001, Aug. 5	Wmk. 388	Perf. 12¼
570	Horiz. strip of 3	2.75 2.75
a.-c.	A129 30c Any single	.75 .75
d.	Souvenir sheet, #570	4.25 4.25

First Intl. Islamic Expo A130

No. 571: a, Jewelry, cane. b, Mosque exterior. c, Computer, satellite dishes. d, Mosque interior.

2001, Aug. 18	Wmk. 388	Perf. 12
571	Horiz. strip of 4	2.40 2.40
a.-d.	A130 20c Any single	.60 .60

Visit Brunei Year A131

No. 572: a, Bridge. b, Waterfall. c, Aerial view of city. d, Dock.

	Perf. 13¼x13½
2001, Sept. 1	Unwmk.
572	Horiz. strip of 4	3.00 3.00
a.-d.	A131 20c Any single	.80 .80

Year of Dialogue Among Civilizations A132

No. 573: a, Emblem. b, Two abstract heads. c, Cubist-style head, native. d, Multicolored leaves.

2001, Oct. 9	Unwmk.	Perf. 12
573	Horiz. strip of 4	3.50 3.50
a.-d.	A132 30c Any single	.80 .80

Worldwide Fund for Nature (WWF) — A133

No. 574 — Bulwer's pheasant: a, Male and female. b, Male. c, Female and chicks. d, Female.

2001, Nov. 1	Wmk. 388	Perf. 12
574	Horiz. strip of 4	3.50 3.50
a.-d.	A133 30c Any single	.80 .70

Jabatan Telekom Brunei, 50th Anniv. — A134

No. 575: a, People, old telecommunications equipment. b, Anniversary emblem. c, Women, computer, new services.

2002	Litho.	Perf. 12¼
575	A134 50c Horiz. strip of 3, #a-c	3.00 3.00
a.-c.	50c Any single	.90 .90

Survey Department, 50th Anniv. — A135

No. 576: a, "50." b, Headquarters. c, Surveyor.

2002, July	Litho.	Perf. 12¼
576	Horiz. strip of 3	3.00 3.00
a.-c.	A135 50c Any single	.90 .90

Yayasan Sultan Haji Hassanal Bolkiah, 10th Anniv. — A136

No. 577: a, Stilt house community. b, Mosque. c, School and children. d, Buildings.

2002, Oct. 5		Perf. 12¾x12½
577	Horiz. strip of 4	2.00 2.00
a.-d.	A136 10c Any single	.45 .45

Anti-Corruption Bureau, 20th Anniv. — A137

No. 578: a, Anti-Corruption Bureau buildings. b, City skyline. c, Posters.

2002, Nov. 19	Litho.	Perf. 13
578	Horiz. strip of 3	2.25 2.25
a.-c.	A137 20c Any single	.65 .65

Medicinal Plants — A138

No. 579: a, Melastoma malabathricum. b, Etlingera solaris. c, Dillenia suffruticosa. d, Costus speciosus.

2003		Perf. 12¾x12½
579	Horiz. strip of 4	3.25 3.25
a.-d.	A138 20c Any single	.75 .75

ASEAN - Japan Exchange Year — A139

No. 580: a, Drums. b, Tops. c, Kites.

2003, Dec. 13	Litho.	Perf. 13
580	Horiz. strip of 3	2.00 2.00
a.-c.	A139 20c Any single	.45 .45

National Day, 20th Anniv. — A140

No. 581: a, Sultan Hassanal Bolkiah at UN. b, Military officer. c, Man reading from scroll. d, Emblem.

2004, Feb. 23		Perf. 12¼
581	Horiz. strip of 4	2.25 2.25
a.-d.	A140 20c Any single	.65 .65
e.	Souvenir sheet, #581	3.00 3.00

Brunei National Philatelic Society — A141

No. 582: a, Magnifying glass, #A1. b, Magnifying glass, tongs, perforation gauge, stamps. c, Brunei stamps and cancels

2004, Mar. 27		Perf. 12¾x12½
582	Horiz. strip of 3	2.00 2.00
a.-c.	A141 25c Any single	.45 .45

Wedding of Crown Prince Haji al-Muhtadee Billah and Sarah Salleh — A142

No. 583: a, Dark shadows on background below and to right of Sultan Bolkiah's picture and between picture frames. b, Dark shadows on background below "Darussalam" and to left of Crown Prince's picture frame.

2004, Sept. 9	Litho.	Perf. 12
583	A142 99c Horiz. pair, #a-b, + central label	3.00 3.00

Sultan Hassanal Bolkiah, 60th Birthday — A143

No. 584 — Photographs of Sultan at various activities with panel color of: a, Red violet. b, Rose (women at LL). c, Orange. d, Red (men at LL). e, Green. b, Prussian blue. $60, Sultan at activities.

2006, July 15		Perf. 12½
584	Horiz. strip of 6	5.25 5.25
a.-f.	A143 60c Any single	.85 .85
g.	Souvenir sheet, #584	5.25 5.25

Souvenir Sheet
Perf. 13¾x13½

| 585 | A143 $60 black | 150.00 150.00 |

No. 585 contains one 100x91mm stamp.

100 sen

A144

BRUNEI DARUSSALAM

ONE HUNDRED YEARS OF POSTAL SERVICES DEPARTMENT

Brunei Postal Service, Cent. — A145

No. 586: a, General Post Office, Bandar Seri Begawan. b, Kuala Belait Post Office. c, Tutong Post Office. d, Bangar Post Office, Temburong.

No. 587 — Children's drawings: a, Airplane, mailbox, letters, packages, globe. b, Postal worker, Postal Service, emblem, post office scenes. c, Cycle of mail delivery. d, Postal worker, letters, buildings, mailbox. e, Globe, letter with wings, children. f, Globe, flags, airplane.

2006, Oct. 11   Litho.   Perf. 13¾x13¼

586	Horiz. strip of 4	5.75	5.75
a.-d.	A144 100c Any single	1.40	1.40
e.	Souvenir sheet, #586a-586d	6.00	6.00
587	A145 100c Sheet of 6, #a-f	9.50	9.50

Marine Life — A146

Designs: No. 588, 60c, Orange-striped triggerfish. No. 589, 60c, Leaf scorpionfish.

No. 590: a, Chambered nautilus. b, Spotted boxfish.

Perf. 13½x12x13½x13½

2007, Feb. 6

| 588-589 | A146 | Set of 2 | 2.50 | 2.50 |

Souvenir Sheet

Perf. 13½x13¼

| 590 | A146 $1 Sheet of 2, #a-b | 3.25 | 3.25 |

Dated 2006. See Malaysia Nos. 1139-1141.

Sultan Hassanal Bolkiah

A147   A148

2007, Feb. 23   Perf. 13¼

Background Color

591	A147 10c light blue	.25	.25
592	A147 15c bright green	.25	.25
593	A147 20c lilac	.25	.25
594	A147 30c blue	.35	.25
595	A147 50c orange	.60	.30
596	A147 60c red	.70	.55
597	A147 75c green	1.00	.75

| 598 | A147 90c brt yel grn | 1.40 | .90 |

Perf. 13¼x13¾

599	A148 $1 blue	1.75	.55
600	A148 $2 purple	3.50	1.90
601	A148 $5 green	6.75	6.25
602	A148 $10 yellow	17.00	12.00
	Nos. 591-602 (12)	33.80	24.20

30 SEN

Bubungan Dua Belas (House of 12 Roofs), Bukit Subok, Cent. — A149

Designs: 30c, House from foot of hill. 60c, Aerial view of house. $1, Early black-and-white picture of house.

2007, July 23   Litho.   Perf. 13½x13¼

| 603-605 | A149 | Set of 3 | 3.25 | 3.25 |
| 605a | | Souvenir sheet of 3, #603-605 | 3.50 | 3.50 |

Bubungan Dua Belas was the residence of the British High Commissioner.

Public Works Department, Cent. — A150

No. 606: a, Modern building. b, Riverfront building. c, Centenary emblem.

2007, Aug. 30   Perf. 13¼

| 606 | A150 75c Horiz. strip of 3, #a-c | 3.50 | 3.50 |

Miniature Sheet

ASEAN Joint Stamp Issue

Association of South East Asian Nations (ASEAN), 40th Anniv. — A151

No. 607: a, Secretariat Building, Bandar Seri Begawan, Brunei. b, Yangon Post Office, Myanmar. c, National Museum of Cambodia. d, Malacañang Palace, Philippines. e, Fatahillah Museum, Jakarta, Indonesia. f, National Museum of Singapore. g, Typical house, Laos. h, Vimanmek Mansion, Bangkok, Thailand. i, Malayan Railway Headquarters Building, Kuala Lumpur, Malaysia. j, Presidential Palace, Hanoi, Viet Nam.

2007, Nov. 21

| 607 | A151 20c Sheet of 10, #a-j | 3.25 | 3.25 |

See Burma No. 370, Cambodia No. 2339, Indonesia Nos. 2120-2121, Laos Nos. 1717-1718, Malaysia No. 1170, Philippines Nos. 3103-3105, Singapore No. 1265, Thailand No. 2315, and Viet Nam Nos. 3302-3311.

Movement of Capital From Kampong Air to Bandar Seri Begawan, Cent. — A152

Designs: 20c, Istana Majlis. 30c, Istana Kota. 60c, Bandar Brunei. 100c, Bandar Seri Begawan.

2008, Apr. 24   Litho.   Perf. 13¼

| 608-611 | A152 | Set of 4 | 3.25 | 3.25 |

40 SEN

Coronation of Sultan Hassanal Bolkiah, 40th Anniv. — A153

No. 612 — Coronation ceremony: a, Sultan with hand raised. b, Parade. c, Crowning of Sultan. d, Sultan wearing crown.

$40, Parade, diff.

2008, Aug. 1   Perf. 12¾x12½

| 612 | Horiz. strip of 4 | 2.40 | 2.40 |
| a.-d. | A153 40c Any single | .60 | .60 |

Souvenir Sheet

Perf. 12

| 613 | A153 $40 multi | 55.00 | 55.00 |

No. 613 contains one 45x70mm stamp.

50 sen

Omar Ali Saifuddien Mosque, 50th Anniv. — A154

No. 614: a, Opening ceremony (green panels). b, Sultan Hassanal Bolkiah (blue panels). c, Worshipers (orange panels). d, Aerial view of mosque (red violet panels).

$50, Mosque, diff.

2008, Sept. 26   Perf. 14½x14

614	Horiz. strip of 4	2.75	2.75
a.-d.	A154 50c Any single	.65	.65
e.	Souvenir sheet of 4, #614a-614d	2.75	2.75

Souvenir Sheet

Litho. With Foil Application

Perf. 13¾x13½

| 615 | A154 $50 multi | 60.00 | 60.00 |

No. 615 contains one 44x72mm stamp.

10

Health Services, Cent. — A155

Designs: No. 616, 10c, Pediatric examination. No. 617, 10c, Magnetic resonance imaging machine, operating room. $1, First government hospital in Brunei town.

2008, Oct. 9   Litho.   Perf. 13¼

| 616-618 | A155 | Set of 3 | 1.75 | 1.75 |

25th National Day — A156

Nos. 619 and 620: a, Buildings, blue sky. b, Buildings, green sky. c, Buildings, military parade, red sky. d, Buildings, buff sky. e, Oil facilities, blue violet sky. f, People with flags, red violet sky. g, Buildings, airplane, satellite dish, brown orange sky. h, Emblem.

$25, Sultans Hassanal Bolkiah and Omar Ali Saifuddin, horiz.

2009, Feb. 23   Perf. 13¼

Stamps With Blue Frames

| 619 | A156 25c Sheet of 8, #a-h | 2.60 | 2.60 |

Stamps With White Frames

| 620 | A156 25c Sheet of 8, #a-h | 2.60 | 2.60 |

Souvenir Sheet

| 621 | A156 $25 multi | 35.00 | 35.00 |

No. 621 contains one 102x72mm stamp.

10

Orchids — A157

No. 622: a, Dendrobium secundum. b, Bulbophyllum sp. c, Phalaenopsis cornucervi. No. 623: a, Bulbophyllum beccarii. b, Vanda hastifera. c, Corybas pictus.

Litho. & Embossed

2009, Dec. 9   Perf. 14

622	Horiz. strip of 3	1.90	1.90
a.	A157 10c multi	.25	.25
b.	A157 20c multi	.30	.30
c.	A157 $1 multi	1.40	1.40
623	Horiz. strip of 3	1.90	1.90
a.	A157 10c multi	.25	.25
b.	A157 20c multi	.30	.30
c.	A157 $1 multi	1.40	1.40

Modern Land Administration, Cent. — A158

No. 624: a, People at Land Administration office. b, Surveyors at construction site. c, Two men, house.

2010, June 23   Litho.   Perf. 13½

624	Horiz. strip of 3	1.90	1.90
a.	A158 10c multi	.25	.25
b.	A158 20c multi	.30	.30
c.	A158 $1 multi	1.40	1.40

40 SEN

Liquid Natural Gas, 40th Anniv. of Production (in 2009) — A159

No. 625: a, Tanker in harbor. b, Control rooms. c, Workers and pipelines.

2010, July 7   Perf. 13½x14

| 625 | Horiz. strip of 3 | 1.75 | 1.75 |
| a.-c. | A159 40c Any single | .55 | .55 |

Miniature Sheet

Sultan Hassanal Bolkiah, 65th Birthday — A160

No. 626 — Sultan and other people with panel color of: a, Dull violet. b, Golden brown. c, Green. d, Blue green. e, Dark brown. f, Rose.

2011, July 15   **Perf. 14x14¼**
626 A160 65c Sheet of 6, #a-f   6.50 6.50

A $65 souvenir sheet was sold only with special packaging for more than face value.

Dewan Bahasa Dan Pustaka Library, 50th Anniv. A161

2011, Sept. 17   **Perf. 12¾**
627   Horiz. strip of 3   2.75 2.75
    a.   A161 20c Books   .35 .35
    b.   A161 50c Libraries   .80 .80
    c.   A161 $1 Men   1.60 1.60
    d.   Souvenir sheet of 3, #627a-627c   2.75 2.75

Farmers and Fishermen Day — A162

No. 628: a, Fishermen at work. b, Farm products.

2011, Nov. 1
628 A162 20c Horiz. pair, #a-b   .65 .65

A163

Rice Production A164

No. 629 — Inscription "Towards Self-Sufficiency In Rice Production 20%" and: a, Rice plants, arrow with "20%." b, Sultan Hassanal Bolkiah. c, Sultan in rice field.
No. 630 — Inscription "To Commemorate Large Scale Rice Planting" and: a, Sultan driving motorized farm equipment. b, Rice field. c, Sultan planting rice.

2011, Nov. 1   **Perf. 12¾**
629   Horiz. strip of 3   1.10 1.10
    a.-c.   A163 20c Any single   .35 .35
630   Horiz. strip of 3   1.10 1.10
    a.-c.   A164 20c Any single   .35 .35

Royal Brunei Armed Forces, 50th Anniv. (in 2011) — A165

No. 631 — Sultan Hassanal Bolkiah in various uniforms with frame color of: a, Golden brown. b, Dark gray. c, Red. d, Light gray. e, Blue.
$50, Sultan Hassanal Bolkiah and soldiers.

2012, May 31   **Perf. 13¼**
631   Horiz. strip of 5   4.00 4.00
    a.-e.   A165 50c Any single   .80 .80

Souvenir Sheet
Litho., Margin Litho. With Foil Application
Perf. 14½x14¼
632 A165 $50 multi   80.00 80.00

No. 632 contains one 40x72mm stamp dated "2011."

Currency Interchangeability Agreement Between Brunei and Singapore, 45th Anniv. — A166

Designs: $1, Images from Brunei banknotes issued in 1967, 1989, 1996 and 2007. $2, Singapore skyline, and mosque, Brunei.

2012, Nov. 27   **Litho.**   **Perf. 12¾**
633-634 A166   Set of 2   5.00 5.00

See Singapore Nos. 1585-1587.

Butterflies — A167

Designs: 10c, Trogonoptera troides brookiana. 20c, Graphium macareus. $1, Graphium delesserti.

2012, Dec. 24   **Litho.**   **Perf. 14**
635-637 A167   Set of 3   2.25 2.25
    Complete booklet, #635-637   2.25

A souvenir sheet was issued in this set. The editors would like to examine any example of it.

See Nos. 639-641, 645-648, 651-654.

Butterflies Type of 2012

Designs: 10c, Papilio helenus. 20c, Ideopsis juventa. $1, Charaxes solon echo.

2013, Feb. 28   **Litho.**   **Perf. 14**
639-641 A167   Set of 3   2.10 2.10

A souvenir sheet was issued in this set. The editors would like to examine any example of it.

ASEAN Summit, Bandar Seri Begawan A168

No. 643 — Summit emblem and: a, Brunei Prime Minister's Office. b, Flags of ASEAN member nations. c, International Convention Center, Bandar Seri Begawan.
$23, Buildings in Bandar Seri Begawan, vert.

2013, Oct. 9   **Litho.**   **Perf. 12¾**
643   Horiz. strip of 3   4.80 4.80
    a.-c.   A168 $1 Any single   1.60 1.60
    Complete booklet, #643   4.80

Souvenir Sheet
Perf. 13¾
644 A168 $23 multi   37.00 37.00

No. 644 contains one 57x78mm stamp.

Butterflies Type of 2012

Designs: 10c, Hypolimnas misippus. 20c, Paduca fasciata. $1, Junonia orithya. $2, Graphium delesserti.

2013, Dec. 12   **Litho.**   **Perf. 14**
645-647 A167   Set of 3   2.10 2.10

Souvenir Sheet
648 A167 $2 multi   3.25 3.25

30th National Day — A169

No. 649: a, Ship, combine, fishermen and crates of fish, finished products (light blue stripes). b, Soldiers, police (lilac pink stripes). c, People and mosques (light green stripes). d, Emblem (orange stripes).
$30, Sultan Hassanal Bolkiah and National Day emblems, horiz.

2014, Feb. 23   **Litho.**   **Perf. 12¾**
649   Horiz. strip of 4   4.25 4.25
    a.-b.   A169 30c Either single   .50 .50
    c.-d.   A169 $1 Either single   1.60 1.60

Litho. & Embossed
Souvenir Sheet
650 A169 $30 multi   47.50 47.50

No. 650 contains one 150x74mm stamp.

Butterflies Type of 2012

Designs: 10c, Chilasa paradoxa telesicles. 20c, Hypolimnas anomala. $1, Parthenos sylvia. $2, Troides andromacha.

2014, Apr. 20   **Litho.**   **Perf. 14**
651-653 A167   Set of 3   2.10 2.10
    Complete booklet, #651-653   2.10

Souvenir Sheet
654 A167 $2 multi   3.25 3.25

Formal Education in Brunei, Cent. A170

No. 655: a, Students of 2014. b, Schools. c, Students and teacher in black-and-white photograph. d, Centenary emblem.

2014, Oct. 9   **Litho.**   **Perf. 13¼**
655   Horiz. strip of 4   3.75 3.75
    a.   A170 10c multi   .25 .25
    b.   A170 20c multi   .30 .30
    c.-d.   A170 $1 Either single   1.60 1.60
    e.   Souvenir sheet of 4, #655a-655d   3.75 3.75

ASEAN, 48th Anniv. A171

60c, Flags and Emblem of Association of Southeast Asian Nations.

2015, Aug. 8   **Litho.**   **Perf. 13**
656 A171 60c multi   .85 .85
    Complete booklet, #656   .85

See Burma Nos. 417-418, Cambodia No. , Indonesia No. 2428, Laos No. , Malaysia No. , Philippines No. 3619, Singapore No. 1742, Thailand No. 2875, Viet Nam No. 3529.

United Nations, 70th Anniv. A172

No. 657: a, 70th anniv. emblem. b, United Nations emblem. c, United Nations Headquarters.

2015, Oct. 24   **Litho.**   **Perf. 13¼**
657   Horiz. strip of 3   3.00 3.00
    a.-c.   A172 70c Any single   1.00 1.00
    d.   Souvenir sheet of 3, #657a-657c   3.00 3.00

Royal Brunei Navy, 50th Anniv. — A173

No. 658: a, Ceremony, docked ship and sailors, Sultan Hassanal Bolkiah saluting. b, Sailors, flag of Brunei, Sultan Hassanal Bolkiah wearing white uniform. c, Ships at sea, Sultan Hassanal Bolkiah wearing beret.

2015, Oct. 30   **Litho.**   **Perf. 12¾**
658 A173 50c Horiz. strip of 3, #a-c   2.25 2.25

A174

A175

A176

A177

Sultan Hassanal Bolkiah, 70th Birthday A178

2016, July 15   **Litho.**   **Perf. 13¾**
659   Vert. strip of 5   5.50 5.50
    a.   A174 70c multi   1.10 1.10
    b.   A175 70c multi   1.10 1.10
    c.   A176 70c multi   1.10 1.10

d.	A177 70c multi	1.10	1.10
e.	A178 70c multi	1.10	1.10
f.	Souvenir sheet of 5, #659a-659e	5.50	5.50
	Complete booklet, #659	5.50	

OCCUPATION STAMPS

Issued under Japanese Occupation

Stamps and Types of 1908-37 Hstmpd. in Violet, Red Violet, Blue or Red

Perf. 14, 14x11½ (#N7)

			Wmk. 4	
1942-44				
N1	A1	1c black	11.00	28.00
N2	A1	2c green	65.00	125.00
N3	A1	2c dull orange	9.50	10.00
N4	A1	3c green	37.50	60.00
N5	A1	4c orange	6.00	16.50
N6	A1	5c brown	8.75	16.00
N7	A2	6c slate gray	60.00	300.00
N8	A2	6c red	800.00	775.00
N9	A1	8c gray (RV)	1,000.	950.00
N10	A2	8c carmine	12.50	13.50
N11	A1	10c violet, *yel*	11.00	20.00
N12	A2	12c blue	35.00	20.00
N13	A2	15c ultra	25.00	20.00
N14	A1	25c dk violet	25.00	55.00
N15	A1	30c org & red vio	105.00	200.00
N16	A1	50c blk, *green*	42.50	65.00
N17	A1	$1 red & blk, *bl*	75.00	70.00
			Wmk. 3	
N18	A1	$5 lake, *green*	1,050.	3,500.
N19	A1	$25 black, *red*	1,050.	3,500.

Overprints vary in shade. Nos. N3, N7, N10 and N13 without overprint are not believed to have been regularly issued.

No. N1 Surcharged in Red

1944	**Wmk. 4**		**Perf. 14**
N20	A1 $3 on 1c black	7,500.	7,500.
a.	On No. 43	9,000.	

BULGARIA

ˌbəl-ˈgar-ē-ə

LOCATION — Southeastern Europe bordering on the Black Sea on the east and the Danube River on the north

GOVT. — Republic

AREA — 42,855 sq. mi.

POP. — 8,194,772 (1999 est.)

CAPITAL — Sofia

In 1885 Bulgaria, then a principality under the suzerainty of the Sultan of Turkey, was joined by Eastern Rumelia. Independence from Turkey was obtained in 1908.

100 Centimes = 1 Franc
100 Stotinki = 1 Lev (1881)

Catalogue values for unused stamps in this country are for Never Hinged items, beginning with Scott 293 in the regular postage section, Scott B1 in the semipostal section, Scott C15 in the airpost section, Scott CB1 in the airpost semi-postal section, Scott E1 in the special delivery section, Scott J47 in the postage due section, Scott O1 in the officials section, and Scott Q1 in the parcel post section.

Watermarks

Wmk. 145 — Wavy Lines

Wmk. 168 — Wavy Lines and EZGV in Cyrillic

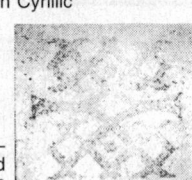

Wmk. 275 — Entwined Curved Lines

Lion of Bulgaria
A1   A2   A3

Perf. 14½x15

1879, May 1		**Wmk. 168**	**Typo.**	
		Laid Paper		
1	A1	5c black & orange	150.00	40.00
2	A1	10c black & green	650.00	150.00
3	A1	25c black & violet	400.00	35.00
a.		Imperf.	5,600.	
4	A1	50c black & blue	575.00	120.00
5	A2	1fr black & red	100.00	35.00
1881, Apr. 10				
6	A3	3s red & silver	27.50	5.50
7	A3	5s black & orange	27.50	5.50
a.		Background inverted	2,100.	2,100.
8	A3	10s black & green	160.00	17.50
9	A3	15s dp car red & green	175.00	17.50
10	A3	25s black & violet	650.00	75.00
11	A3	30s blue & fawn	27.50	14.00
1882, Dec. 4				
12	A3	3s orange & yel	1.40	.70
a.		Background inverted	3,500.	2,500.
13	A3	5s green & pale green	10.50	1.00
a.		5s rose & pale rose (error)	2,500.	2,500.
14	A3	10s rose & pale rose	14.00	1.00
15	A3	15s red vio & pale lil	14.00	1.00
16	A3	25s blue & pale blue	12.50	1.40
17	A3	30s violet & grn	12.50	1.00
18	A3	50s blue & pink	12.50	1.00
		Nos. 12-18 (7)	77.40	7.10

See Nos. 207-210, 286.

Surcharged in Black, Carmine or Vermilion

A4   A5

1884, May 1			**Typo. Surcharge**	
19	A4	3s on 10s rose (Bk)	210.00	70.00
20	A4	5s on 30s blue & fawn (C)	140.00	90.00
20A	A4	5s on 30s bl & fawn (Bk)	2,800.	2,250.
21	A5	15s on 25s blue (C)	175.00	100.00

On some values the surcharge may be found inverted or double.

1885, Apr. 5			**Litho. Surcharge**	
21B	A4	3s on 10s rose (Bk)	70.00	70.00
21C	A4	5s on 30s bl & fawn (V)	70.00	70.00
21D	A5	15s on 25s blue (V)	125.00	90.00
22	A5	50s on 1fr blk & red (Bk)	500.00	325.00

Forgeries of Nos. 19-22 are plentiful.

Word below left star in oval has 5 letters
A6

Third letter below left star is "A"
A7

1885, May 25				
23	A6	1s gray vio & pale gray	25.00	8.50
24	A7	2s sl grn & pale gray	25.00	5.50

Word below left star has 4 letters
A8

Third letter below left star is "b" with cross-bar in upper half
A9

A10

1886-87				
25	A8	1s gray vio & pale gray	1.75	.35
26	A9	2s sl grn & pale gray	1.75	.35
27	A10	1 l black & red ('87)	50.00	6.50
		Nos. 25-27 (3)	53.50	7.20

For surcharge see No. 40.

A11

Perf. 10½, 11, 11½, 13, 13½

1889		**Wove Paper**	**Unwmk.**	
28	A11	1s lilac	1.40	.35
29	A11	2s gray	2.10	1.00
30	A11	3s bister brown	.70	.35
31	A11	5s yellow green	17.50	.30
a.		Vert. pair, imperf. btwn.		
32	A11	10s rose	10.00	.70
33	A11	15s orange	60.00	.70
34	A11	25s blue	10.00	.70
35	A11	30s dk brown	12.00	.70
36	A11	50s green	.70	.35
37	A11	1 l orange red	.70	.70
		Nos. 28-37 (10)	115.10	5.85

The 10s orange is a proof.
Nos. 28-34 exist imperforate. Value, set $350.
See Nos. 39, 41-42. For overprints and surcharges see Nos. 38, 55-56, 77-81, 113.

No. 35 Surcharged in Black

1892, Jan. 26				
38	A11	15s on 30s brn	35.00	1.40
a.		Inverted surcharge	70.00	52.50
1894			***Perf. 10½, 11, 11½***	
			Pelure Paper	
39	A11	10s red	5.25	1.75
a.		Imperf.	57.50	

No. 26 Surcharged in Red

		Wmk. Wavy Lines (168)		
1895, Oct. 25			**Perf. 14½x15**	
		Laid Paper		
40	A9	1s on 2s	1.00	.35
a.		Inverted surcharge	8.00	6.50
b.		Double surcharge	62.50	62.50
c.		Pair, one without surcharge	250.00	210.00

The surcharge on No. 24 is a proof. Value, $400.

		Wmk. Coat of Arms in the Sheet		
1896, Apr. 30			**Perf. 11½, 13**	
		Wove Paper		
41	A11	2 l rose & pale rose	2.75	2.10
42	A11	3 l black & buff	4.25	5.00

Coat of Arms — A14

1896, Feb. 2			**Perf. 13**	
43	A14	1s blue green	.35	.25
44	A14	5s dark blue	.35	.25
45	A14	15s purple	.35	.40
46	A14	25s red	5.75	2.00
		Nos. 43-46 (4)	6.80	2.90

Baptism of Prince Boris.
Examples of Nos. 41-46 from sheet edges show no watermark.
Nos. 43, 45-46 were also printed on rough unwatermarked paper.

Cherry Wood Cannon — A15

1901, Apr. 20		**Litho.**	**Unwmk.**	
53	A15	5s carmine	1.00	1.25
54	A15	15s yellow green	1.00	1.25

Insurrection of Independence in April, 1876, 25th anniversary.
Exist imperf. Forgeries exist.

Nos. 30 and 36 Surcharged in Black

1901, Mar. 24			**Typo.**	
55	A11	5s on 3s bister brn	2.00	1.25
a.		Inverted surcharge	45.00	45.00
b.		Pair, one without surcharge	70.00	70.00
56	A11	10s on 50s green	2.00	1.25
a.		Inverted surcharge	50.00	50.00
b.		Pair, one without surcharge	72.50	72.50

Tsar Ferdinand — A17

Type I   Type II

ONE LEV:

Type I — The numerals in the upper corners have, at the top, a sloping serif on the left side and a short straight serif on the right.

Type II — The numerals in the upper corners are of ordinary shape without the serif at the right.

1901, Oct. 1-1905   Typo.   Perf. 12½

57	A17	1s vio & gray blk	.25	.25
58	A17	2s brnz grn & ind	.35	.25
a.		Imperf.		
59	A17	3s orange & ind	.35	.25
60	A17	5s emerald & brn	1.40	.25
61	A17	10s rose & blk	2.00	.25
62	A17	15s claret & gray blk	1.00	.25
63	A17	25s blue & blk	1.00	.25
64	A17	30s bis & gray blk	22.50	.30
65	A17	50s dk blue & brn	1.40	.25
66	A17	1 l red org & brnz grn, type I	3.50	.30
67	A17	1 l brn red & brnz grn, II ('05)	75.00	3.00
68	A17	2 l carmine & blk	7.00	1.00
69	A17	5 l slate & red brn	7.00	5.00
		Nos. 57-69 (13)	122.75	11.60

For surcharges see Nos. 73, 83-85, 87-88.

Fighting at Shipka Pass — A18

1902, Aug. 29   Litho.   Perf. 11½

70	A18	5s lake	2.10	.70
71	A18	10s blue green	2.10	.70
72	A18	15s blue	8.00	3.50
		Nos. 70-72 (3)	12.20	4.90

Battle of Shipka Pass, 1877.
Imperf. copies are proofs.
Excellent forgeries of Nos. 70 to 72 exist.

No. 62 Surcharged in Black

1903, Oct. 1   Perf. 12½

73	A17	10s on 15s	3.50	.70
a.		Inverted surcharge	57.50	50.00
b.		Double surcharge	57.50	50.00
c.		Pair, one without surcharge	100.00	100.00
d.		10s on 10s rose & black	700.00	700.00

Ferdinand in 1887 and 1907 — A19

1907, Aug. 12   Litho.   Perf. 11½

74	A19	5s deep green	15.00	1.40
75	A19	10s red brown	21.00	1.40
76	A19	25s deep blue	60.00	3.00
		Nos. 74-76 (3)	96.00	5.80

Accession to the throne of Ferdinand I, 20th anniversary.

Nos. 74-76 imperf. are proofs. Nos. 74-76 exist in pairs imperforate between. Values: 5s, $70; 10s, $100; 25s, $140.

Stamps of 1889 Overprinted

1909

77	A11	1s lilac	.65	.60
a.		Inverted overprint	21.00	17.50
b.		Double overprint, one inverted	24.00	24.00
78	A11	5s yellow green	1.60	.60
a.		Inverted overprint	25.00	25.00
b.		Double overprint	25.00	25.00

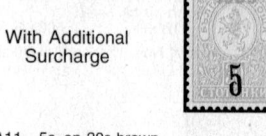

With Additional Surcharge

79	A11	5s on 30s brown (Bk)	2.00	.50
a.		"5" double	700.00	550.00
b.		"1990" for "1909"		
80	A11	10s on 15s org (Bk)	2.00	.60
a.		Inverted surcharge	17.50	17.50
b.		"1909" omitted	27.50	27.50
81	A11	10s on 50s dk grn (R)	2.00	.60
a.		"1990" for "1909"	100.00	100.00
b.		Black surcharge	52.50	52.50

Nos. 62 & 64 Surcharged with Value Only

83	A17	5s on 15s (Bl)	1.50	.65
a.		Inverted surcharge	21.00	21.00
84	A17	10s on 15s (Bl)	4.00	.55
a.		Inverted surcharge	21.00	21.00
85	A17	25s on 30s (R)	8.00	1.25
a.		Double surcharge	75.00	75.00
b.		"2" of "25" omitted	87.50	87.50
c.		Blue surcharge	650.00	450.00

Nos. 59 and 62 Surcharged in Blue

1910, Oct.

87	A17	1s on 3s	3.00	1.25
a.		"1910" omitted	21.00	
88	A17	5s on 15s	3.00	1.00

Tsar Assen's Tower (Crown over lion) A20

Tsar Ferdinand A21

City of Trnovo A22

Tsar Ferdinand A23

Ferdinand A24

Isker River A25

Ferdinand A26

Rila Monastery (Crown at UR) A27

Tsar and Princes — A28

Ferdinand in Robes of Ancient Tsars — A29

Monastery of Holy Trinity — A30

View of Varna — A31

1911, Feb. 14   Engr.   Perf. 12

89	A20	1s myrtle green	.25	.25
90	A21	2s car & blk	.25	.25
91	A22	3s lake & blk	.35	.25
92	A23	5s green & blk	1.00	.25
93	A24	10s dp red & blk	1.60	.25
94	A25	15s brown bister	4.75	.25
95	A26	25s ultra & blk	.35	.25
96	A27	30s blue & blk	4.75	.25
97	A28	50s ocher & blk	26.00	.25
a.		Center inverted	4,250.	
98	A29	1 l chocolate	8.00	.25
99	A30	2 l dull pur & blk	2.25	.50
100	A31	3 l blue vio & blk	13.00	4.75
		Nos. 89-100 (12)	62.55	7.75

See Nos. 114-120, 161-162. For overprints and surcharges see Nos. 104-112, 188, B8, Greece N167-N178, N182-N187, Thrace 16-21, Romania 2N1-2N4.

Tsar Ferdinand — A32

1912, Aug. 2   Typo.   Perf. 12½

101	A32	5s olive green	3.00	1.00
a.		5s pale green	975.00	225.00
102	A32	10s claret	4.00	1.75
103	A32	25s slate	5.00	3.00
		Nos. 101-103 (3)	12.00	5.75

25th year of reign of Tsar Ferdinand.

Nos. 89-95 Overprinted in Various Colors

1913, Aug. 6   Engr.

104	A20	1s myrtle grn (C)	.35	.25
105	A21	2s car & blk (Bl)	1.25	.25
107	A22	3s lake & blk (Bl Bk)	1.25	.25
108	A23	5s grn & blk (R)	.35	.25
109	A24	10s dp red & blk (Bk)	.35	.25
110	A25	15s brown bis (G)	1.50	1.00
111	A26	25s ultra & blk (R)	4.50	1.75
		Nos. 104-111 (7)	9.55	4.00

Victory over the Turks in Balkan War of 1912-1913.

No. 95 Surcharged in Red

1915, July 6

112	A26	10s on 25s	.75	.25
a.		Pair, one without surcharge	160.00	160.00

No. 28 Surcharged in Green

113	A11	3s on 1s lilac	4.50	3.00

Types of 1911 Re-engraved

1915, Nov. 7   Perf. 11½, 14

114	A20	1s dk bl grn	.25	.25
115	A23	5s grn & brn vio	2.75	.25
116	A24	10s red brn & brnsh blk	.25	.25
117	A25	15s olive green	.25	.25
118	A26	25s indigo & blk	.25	.25
119	A27	30s ol grn & red brn	.25	.25
120	A31	1 l dark brown	.35	.25
		Nos. 114-120 (7)	4.35	1.75

Widths: No. 114 is 19½mm; No. 89, 18½mm. No. 118 is 19¼mm; No. 95, 18¼mm. No. 120 is 20mm; No. 98, 19mm. The re-engraved stamps also differ from the 1911 issue in many details of design. Nos. 114-120 exist imperforate. Values, each $11-$22.50.

The 5s exists in two types: I, 20x29.3mm, green and brown violet; II, 19.5x29mm, dark green and brown. There are a number of minor design differences between the two types. The editors would welcome any information that Bulgarian specialists can provide on this and similar varieties on stamps of this period.

The 5s and 10s exist perf. 14x11½.

For Nos. 114-116 and 118 overprinted with Cyrillic characters and "1916-1917," see Romania Nos. 2N1-2N4.

Coat of Arms — A33

Peasant and Bullock — A34

Soldier and Mt. Sonichka — A35   View of Nish — A36

Town and Lake Okhrida — A37

Demir-Kapiya (Iron Gate) — A37a

View of
Gevgeli — A38

Perf. 11½, 12½x13, 13x12½

1917-19				Typo.	
122	A33	5s green		.40	.25
123	A34	15s slate		.25	.25
124	A35	25s blue		.25	.25
125	A36	30s orange		.25	.25
126	A37	50s violet		.75	.60
126A	A37a	2 l brn org ('19)		.75	.50
127	A38	3 l claret		1.25	1.25
		Nos. 122-127 (7)		3.90	3.35

Liberation of Macedonia. A 1 l dark green was prepared but not issued. Value $1.65.
For surcharges see Nos. B9-B10, B12.

View of
Veles — A39

Monastery of
St. Clement at
Okhrida — A40

1918			Perf. 13x14	
128	A39	1s gray	.35	.25
129	A40	5s green	.35	.25

Tsar
Ferdinand — A41

1918, July 1			Perf. 12½x13	
130	A41	1s dark green	.70	.25
131	A41	2s dark brown	.70	.25
132	A41	3s indigo	1.40	.35
133	A41	10s brown red	.70	.25
		Nos. 130-133 (4)	3.50	1.20

Ferdinand's accession to the throne, 30th anniv. Nos. 131-133 exist on a thin gray paper.

Plowing with
Oxen — A42

1919			Perf. 13½x13	
134	A42	1s gray	.25	.25

Sobranye
Palace — A43

1919			Perf. 11½x12, 12x11½	
135	A43	1s black	.25	.25
137	A43	2s olive green	.25	.25

For surcharges see Nos. 186, B1.

Tsar Boris III — A44

1919, Oct. 3

138	A44	3s orange brn	.30	.25
139	A44	5s green	.30	.25
140	A44	10s rose red	.30	.25
141	A44	15s violet	.30	.25
142	A44	25s deep blue	.30	.25

143	A44	30s chocolate	.30	.25
144	A44	50s yellow brn	.30	.25
		Nos. 138-144 (7)	2.10	1.75

1st anniv. of enthronement of Tsar Boris III.
Nos. 135-144 exist imperforate.
For surcharges see Nos. 187, B2-B7.

Birthplace of Vazov at Sopot and
Cherrywood Cannon — A47

"The Bear
Fighter"-a
Character from
"Under the
Yoke" — A48

Ivan Vazov
in 1870
and 1920
A49

Vazov — A50

Homes of
Vazov at
Plovdiv and
Sofia
A51

The Monk
Paisii — A52

1920, Oct. 20		Photo.	Perf. 11½	
147	A47	30s brown red	.25	.25
148	A48	50s dark green	.35	.25
149	A49	1 l drab	.50	.35
150	A50	2 l light brown	1.25	.60
151	A51	3 l black violet	2.00	.90
152	A52	5 l deep blue	2.50	1.50
		Nos. 147-152 (6)	6.85	3.85

70th birthday of Ivan Vazov (1850-1921), Bulgarian poet and novelist.
Several values of this series exist imperforate and in pairs imperforate between.

Tsar Ferdinand
A53   A54

Mt. Shar — A55

Bridge over Vardar
River — A56

View of
Ohrid — A57

1921, June 11			Typo.	
153	A53	10s claret	.25	.25
154	A54	10s claret	.25	.25
155	A55	10s claret	.25	.25
156	A56	10s rose lilac	.25	.25
157	A57	20s blue	.50	.25
		Nos. 153-157 (5)	1.50	1.25

Nos. 153-157 were intended to be issued in 1915 to commemorate the liberation of Macedonia. They were not put in use until 1921. A 50s violet was prepared but never placed in use. Value $1.75.

View of
Sofia — A58

"The Liberator,"
Monument to
Alexander II
A59

Monastery at Shipka
Pass — A62

Tsar Boris
III — A63

Harvesting
Grain — A64

Tsar Assen's
Tower (No
crown over
lion) — A65

Rila Monastery
(Rosette at
upper
right) — A66

1921-23		Engr.	Perf. 12	
158	A58	10s blue gray	.25	.25
159	A59	20s deep green	.25	.25
160	A63	25s blue grn ('22)	.25	.25
161	A22	50s orange	.25	.25
162	A22	50s dk blue ('23)	3.00	1.75
163	A62	75s dull vio	.25	.25
164	A62	75s dp blue ('23)	.25	.25
165	A63	1 l carmine	.25	.25
166	A63	1 l dp blue ('22)	.30	.25
167	A64	2 l brown	.30	.25
168	A65	3 l brown vio	.60	.25
169	A66	5 l lt blue	2.75	.30
170	A63	10 l violet brn	7.00	1.75
		Nos. 158-170 (13)	15.70	6.30

For surcharge see No. 189.

Bourchier in
Bulgarian
Costume
A67

James David
Bourchier
A68

View of Rila
Monastery
A69

1921, Dec. 31

171	A67	10s red orange	.25	.25
172	A67	20s orange	.25	.25
173	A68	30s dp gray	.25	.25
174	A68	50s bluish gray	.25	.25
175	A68	1 l dull vio	.25	.25
176	A69	1½ l olive grn	.25	.25
177	A69	2 l deep green	.25	.25
178	A69	3 l Prus blue	.50	.25
179	A69	5 l red brown	.80	.50
		Nos. 171-179 (9)	3.05	2.50

Death of James D. Bourchier, Balkan correspondent of the London Times.
For surcharges see Nos. B13-B16.

Postage Due Stamps
of 1919-22
Surcharged — a

1924

182	D6	10s on 20s yellow	.25	.25
183	D6	20s on 5s gray grn	.25	.25
a.		20s on 5s emerald	30.00	30.00
184	D6	20s on 10s violet	.25	.25
185	D6	20s on 30s orange	.25	.25
		Nos. 182-185 (4)	1.00	1.00

Nos. 182 to 185 were used for ordinary postage.

**Regular Issues of 1919-23
Surcharged in Blue or Red**

b   c

186	A43 (a)	10s on 1s black (R)	.25	.25
187	A44 (b)	1 l on 5s emer (Bl)	.25	.25
188	A22 (c)	3 l on 50s dk bl (R)	.25	.25
189	A63 (b)	6 l on 1 l car (Bl)	.60	.25
		Nos. 186-189 (4)	1.35	1.00

The surcharge of No. 188 comes in three types: normal, thick and thin.
Nos. 182, 184-189 exist with inverted surcharge.

Lion of Bulgaria
A70   A71

686 BULGARIA

Tsar Boris
III — A72

New Sofia
Cathedral — A73

Harvesting
A74

1925 **Typo.** **Perf. 13, 11½**
191 A70 10s red & bl, *pink* .30 .25
192 A70 15s car & org, *blue* .30 .25
193 A70 30s blk & buff .30 .25
  a. Cliche of 15s in plate of 30s
194 A71 50s choc, *green* .30 .25
195 A72 1 l dull green .70 .25
196 A73 2 l dk grn & buff 1.50 .25
197 A74 4 l lake & yellow 1.50 .25
  Nos. 191-197 (7) 4.90 1.75

Several values of this series exist imperforate and in pairs imperforate between.
See Nos. 199, 201. For overprint see No. C2.

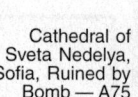

Cathedral of
Sveta Nedelya,
Sofia, Ruined by
Bomb — A75

1926 **Perf. 11½**
198 A75 50s gray black .25 .25

A76 A77

**Type A72 Re-engraved. (Shoulder at
left does not touch frame)**

1926
199 A76 1 l gray .45 .25
  a. 1 l green .45 .25
201 A76 2 l olive brown .70 .25

Center Embossed
202 A77 6 l dp bl & pale lemon 1.50 .25
203 A77 10 l brn blk & brn org 3.50 1.75
  Nos. 199-203 (4) 6.15 2.50

For overprints see Nos. C1, C3-C4.

Christo
Botev — A78

1926, June 2
204 A78 1 l olive green .55 .30
205 A78 2 l slate violet 1.20 .30
206 A78 4 l red brown 1.20 1.60
  Nos. 204-206 (3) 2.95 2.20

Botev (1847-76), Bulgarian revolutionary, poet.

Lion Type of 1881 Redrawn
1927-29 **Perf. 13**
207 A3 10s dk red & drab .25 .25
208 A3 15s blk & org ('29) .25 .25
209 A3 30s dk bl & bis brn ('28) .25 .25
  a. 30s indigo & buff .25
210 A3 50s blk & rose red ('28) .25 .25
  Nos. 207-210 (4) 1.00 1.00

Scott 207-210 have less detailed scrollwork surrounding the central lion, which is also less detailed than Scott 1-18.

Tsar Boris III — A79

1928, Oct. 3 **Perf. 11½**
211 A79 1 l olive green .90 .25
212 A79 2 l deep brown 1.00 .25

St. Clement
A80

Konstantin
Miladinov
A81

George S.
Rakovski
A82

Drenovo
Monastery
A83

Paisii — A84

Tsar
Simeon — A85

Lyuben
Karavelov
A86

Vassil Levski
A87

Georgi
Benkovski
A88

Tsar Alexander II
A89

1929, May 12
213 A80 10s dk violet .25 .25
214 A81 15s violet brn .25 .25
215 A82 30s red .25 .25
216 A83 50s olive grn .30 .25
217 A84 1 l orange brn .80 .25
218 A85 2 l dk blue .80 .25
219 A86 3 l dull green 2.00 .60
220 A87 4 l olive brown 3.50 .25
221 A88 5 l brown 3.00 .75
222 A89 6 l Prus green 3.50 1.50
  Nos. 213-222 (10) 14.65 4.60

Millenary of Tsar Simeon and 50th anniv. of the liberation of Bulgaria from the Turks.

Royal Wedding Issue

Tsar Boris
and Fiancee,
Princess
Giovanna
A90

Queen
Ioanna and
Tsar
Boris — A91

1930, Nov. 12 **Perf. 11½**
223 A90 1 l green .35 .40
224 A91 2 l dull violet .35 .40
225 A90 4 l rose red .35 .40
226 A91 6 l dark blue .35 .40
  Nos. 223-226 (4) 1.40 1.60

Fifty-five copies of a miniature sheet incorporating one each of Nos. 223-226 were printed and given to royal, governmental and diplomatic personages.

Tsar Boris III
A92 A93

Perf. 11½, 12x11½, 13
1931-37 **Unwmk.**
227 A92 1 l blue green .25 .25
228 A92 2 l carmine .40 .25
229 A92 4 l red org ('34) .75 .25
230 A92 4 l yel org ('37) .25 .25
231 A92 6 l deep blue .70 .25
232 A92 7 l dp bl ('37) .25 .25
233 A92 10 l slate blk 8.75 .70
234 A92 12 l lt brown .40 .25
235 A92 14 l lt brn ('37) .30 .25
236 A93 20 l claret & org brn 1.00 .25
  Nos. 227-236 (10) 13.05 3.15

Nos. 230-233 and 235 have outer bars at top and bottom as shown on cut A92; Nos. 227-229 and 234 are without outer bars.
See Nos. 251, 279-280, 287. For surcharge see No. 252.

Balkan Games Issues

Gymnast
A95

Soccer — A96 Riding — A97

Swimmer
A100

"Victory"
A101

Designs: 6 l, Fencing. 10 l, Bicycle race.

1931, Sept. 18 **Perf. 11½**
237 A95 1 l lt green 1.25 1.00
238 A96 2 l garnet 1.75 1.40
239 A97 4 l carmine 3.25 1.60
240 A95 6 l Prus blue 7.50 4.50
241 A95 10 l red org 17.50 7.00
242 A100 12 l dk blue 55.00 20.00
243 A101 50 l olive brn 60.00 45.00
  Nos. 237-243 (7) 146.25 80.50

1933, Jan. 5
244 A95 1 l blue grn 1.60 2.75
245 A96 2 l blue 2.50 3.00
246 A97 4 l brn vio 4.00 4.00
247 A95 6 l brt rose 8.00 7.00
248 A95 10 l olive brn 65.00 45.00
249 A100 12 l orange 110.00 70.00
250 A101 50 l red brown 300.00 375.00
  Nos. 244-250 (7) 491.10 506.75

Nos. 244-250 were sold only at the philatelic agency.

Boris Type of 1931
**Outer Bars at Top and Bottom
Removed**
1933 **Perf. 13**
251 A92 6 l deep blue .80 .25

Type of 1931
Surcharged in Blue

1934
252 A92 2 (l) on 3 l ol brn 6.00 .60

Soldier
Defending
Shipka Pass
A102

Shipka Battle
Memorial
A103

Color-Bearer
A104

Veteran of the
War of
Liberation,
1878 — A105

Widow and
Orphans — A106

Perf. 10½, 11½

1934, Aug. 26   **Wmk. 145**

253	A102	1 l green	.70	.70
254	A103	2 l pale red	.55	.35
255	A104	3 l bister brn	1.75	2.00
256	A105	4 l dk carmine	1.25	.70
257	A104	7 l dk blue	2.50	2.50
258	A106	14 l plum	9.00	12.50
		Nos. 253-258 (6)	15.75	18.75

Shipka Pass Battle memorial unveiling.

An unwatermarked miniature sheet incorporating one each of Nos. 253-258 was put on sale in 1938 in five cities at a price of 8,000 leva. Printing: 100 sheets. Value: $1,500.

1934, Sept. 21

259	A102	1 l bright green	.70	.70
260	A103	2 l dull orange	.55	.35
261	A104	3 l yellow	1.75	2.00
262	A105	4 l rose	1.25	.70
263	A104	7 l blue	2.50	2.50
264	A106	14 l olive bister	9.00	12.50
		Nos. 259-264 (6)	15.75	18.75

An unwatermarked miniature sheet incorporating one each of Nos. 259-263 was issued. Value: $1,500.

Velcho A.
Djamjiyata
A108

Capt. G. S.
Mamarchev
A109

1935, May 5   **Perf. 11½**

265	A108	1 l deep blue	1.50	.60
266	A109	2 l maroon	1.50	.90

Bulgarian uprising against the Turks, cent.

Soccer
Game — A110

Cathedral of
Alexander
Nevski — A111

Soccer
Team — A112

Symbolical of
Victory — A113

Player and
Trophy — A114

The Trophy — A115

1935, June 14

267	A110	1 l green	8.00	7.00
268	A111	2 l blue gray	8.00	7.00
269	A112	4 l crimson	8.00	7.00
270	A113	7 l brt blue	8.00	7.00
271	A114	14 l orange	8.00	7.00
272	A115	50 l lilac brn	175.00	200.00
		Nos. 267-272 (6)	215.00	235.00

5th Balkan Soccer Tournament.

Gymnast on
Parallel Bars
A116

Youth in "Yunak"
Costume
A117

Girl in "Yunak"
Costume
A118

Pole Vaulting
A119

Stadium,
Sofia — A120

Yunak
Emblem — A121

1935, July 10

273	A116	1 l green	4.00	7.00
274	A117	2 l lt blue	4.00	7.00
275	A118	4 l carmine	4.00	7.00
276	A119	7 l dk blue	4.00	7.00
277	A120	14 l dk brown	4.00	7.00
278	A121	50 l red	125.00	140.00
		Nos. 273-278 (6)	145.00	175.00

8th tournament of the Yunak Gymnastic Organization at Sofia, July 12-14.

Boris Type of 1931

1935   **Wmk. 145**   **Perf. 12½, 13**

279	A92	1 l green	.55	.25
280	A92	2 l carmine	20.00	.25

Janos Hunyadi
A122

King Ladislas
Varnenchik
A123

Varna
Memorial
A124

King Ladislas
III — A125

Battle of
Varna,
1444 — A126

1935, Aug. 4   **Perf. 10½, 11½**

281	A122	1 l brown org	2.00	1.50
282	A123	2 l maroon	2.00	1.50
283	A124	4 l vermilion	12.50	6.00
284	A125	7 l dull blue	2.00	1.50
285	A126	14 l green	2.00	1.50
		Nos. 281-285 (5)	20.50	12.00

Battle of Varna, and the death of the Polish King, Ladislas Varnenchik (1424-44). Nos. 281-285 exist imperf. Value, set $50.

Lion Type of 1881

1935   **Wmk. 145**   **Perf. 13**

286	A3	10s dk red & drab	.40	.25

Boris Type of 1933
Outer Bars at Top and Bottom Removed

1935

287	A92	6 l gray blue	.65	.25

Dimitr Monument
A127

Haji
Dimitr — A128

Haji Dimitr
and Stefan
Karaja
A129

Taking the
Oath — A130

Birthplace of
Dimitr
A131

1935, Oct. 1   **Unwmk.**   **Perf. 11½**

288	A127	1 l green	1.75	1.10
289	A128	2 l brown	2.75	1.75
290	A129	4 l car rose	6.75	4.00
291	A130	7 l blue	9.00	7.00
292	A131	14 l orange	11.00	7.00
		Nos. 288-292 (5)	31.25	20.85

67th anniv. of the death of the Bulgarian patriots, Haji Dimitr and Stefan Karaja. Nos. 288-292 exist imperf.

> **Catalogue values for unused stamps in this section, from this point to the end of the section, are for Never Hinged items.**

A132

A133

1936-39   **Perf. 13x12½, 13**

293	A132	10s red org ('37)	.35	.25
294	A132	15s emerald	.35	.25
295	A133	30s maroon	.35	.25
296	A133	30s yel brn ('37)	.35	.25
297	A133	30s Prus bl ('37)	.35	.25
298	A133	50s ultra	.35	.25
299	A133	50s dk car ('37)	.35	.25
300	A133	50s slate grn ('39)	.35	.25
		Nos. 293-300 (8)	2.80	2.00

Meteorological
Station, Mt.
Moussalla
A134

Peasant Girl
A135

Town of
Nessebr
A136

1936, Aug. 16   **Photo.**   **Perf. 11½**

301	A134	1 l purple	3.00	1.50
302	A135	2 l ultra	3.00	1.50
303	A136	7 l dark blue	6.00	3.00
		Nos. 301-303 (3)	12.00	6.00

4th Geographical & Ethnographical Cong., Sofia, Aug. 1936.

Sts. Cyril and
Methodius
A137

Displaying the
Bible to the
People
A138

1937, June 2

304	A137	1 l dk green	.55	.25
305	A137	2 l dk plum	.55	.25
306	A138	4 l vermilion	.55	.25
307	A137	7 l dk blue	3.00	1.60
308	A138	14 l rose red	3.00	1.90
		Nos. 304-308 (5)	7.65	4.25

Millennium of Cyrillic alphabet.

Princess Marie
Louise — A139

1937, Oct. 3

310	A139	1 l yellow green	.50	.25
311	A139	2 l brown red	.50	.25
312	A139	4 l scarlet	.50	.40
		Nos. 310-312 (3)	1.50	.90

Issued in honor of Princess Marie Louise.

Tsar Boris III — A140

1937, Oct. 3
313 A140 2 l brown red   .80 .35
19th anniv. of the accession of Tsar Boris III to the throne. See No. B11.

National Products Issue

Peasants Bundling Wheat A141   Sunflower A142

Wheat — A143   Chickens and Eggs — A144

Cluster of Grapes — A145

Rose and Perfume Flask — A146

Strawberries A147   Girl Carrying Grape Clusters A148

Rose — A149   Tobacco Leaves — A150

1938   *Perf. 13*
316 A141 10s orange   .25 .25
317 A141 10s red org   .25 .25
318 A142 15s brt rose   .35 .25
319 A142 15s deep plum   .35 .25
320 A143 30s golden brn   .30 .25
321 A143 30s copper brn   .30 .25
322 A144 50s black   .75 .25
323 A144 50s indigo   .75 .25
324 A145 1 l yel grn   .75 .25
325 A145 1 l green   .75 .25
326 A146 2 l rose pink   .75 .25

327 A146 2 l rose brn   .75 .25
328 A147 3 l dp red lil   1.40 .65
329 A147 3 l brn lake   1.40 .65
330 A148 4 l plum   1.00 .35
331 A148 4 l golden brn   1.00 .35
332 A149 7 l vio blue   2.10 .65
333 A149 7 l dp blue   2.10 .65
334 A150 14 l dk brown   3.50 1.40
335 A150 14 l red brn   3.50 1.40
   Nos. 316-335 (20)   22.30 9.10
Several values of this series exist imperforate.

Crown Prince Simeon
A151   A153

Designs: 2 l, Same portrait as 1 l, value at lower left. 14 l, similar to 4 l, but no wreath.

1938, June 16
336 A151 1 l brt green   .25 .25
337 A151 2 l rose pink   .25 .25
338 A153 4 l dp orange   .30 .25
339 A151 7 l ultra   1.00 .50
340 A153 14 l dp brown   1.00 .50
   Nos. 336-340 (5)   2.80 1.75
First birthday of Prince Simeon. Nos. 336-340 exist imperf. Value, set $15.

Tsar Boris III
A155   A156
Various Portraits of Tsar.

1938, Oct. 3
341 A155 1 l lt green   .25 .25
342 A156 2 l rose brown   .85 .25
343 A156 4 l golden brn   .30 .25
344 A156 7 l brt ultra   .45 .45
345 A156 14 l deep red lilac .45 .45
   Nos. 341-345 (5)   2.30 1.65
Reign of Tsar Boris III, 20th anniv. Nos. 341-345 exist imperf. Value, set $40.

Early Locomotive A160

Designs: 2 l, Modern locomotive. 4 l, Train crossing bridge. 7 l, Tsar Boris in cab.

1939, Apr. 26
346 A160 1 l yel green   .35 .25
347 A160 2 l copper brn   .35 .25
348 A160 4 l red orange 2.00 1.00
349 A160 7 l dark brown 6.50 3.00
   Nos. 346-349 (4)   9.20 4.50
50th anniv. of Bulgarian State Railways.

Post Horns and Arrows — A164

Central Post Office, Sofia — A165

1939, May 14   *Typo.*
350 A164 1 l yellow grn   .35 .25
351 A165 2 l brt carmine .35 .25
Establishment of the postal system, 60th anniv.

Gymnast on Bar — A166   Yunak Emblem — A167

Discus Thrower — A168   Athletic Dancer — A169

Weight Lifter — A170

1939, July 7   *Photo.*
352 A166 1 l yel grn & pale grn .35 .35
353 A167 2 l brt rose   .35 .35
354 A168 4 l brn & gldn brn .75 .35
355 A169 7 l dk bl & bl   2.00 1.00
356 A170 14 l plum & rose vio 10.50 8.50
   Nos. 352-356 (5)   13.95 10.55
9th tournament of the Yunak Gymnastic Organization at Sofia, July 4-8.

Tsar Boris III — A171

1940-41   *Typo.*
356A A171 1 l dl grn ('41) .70 .25
357 A171 2 l brt crimson .70 .25

Bulgaria's First Stamp — A172

20 l, Similar design, scroll dated "1840-1940."

1940, May 19 *Photo.* *Perf. 13*
358 A172 10 l olive black 2.25 1.75
359 A172 20 l indigo   2.25 1.75
Cent. of 1st postage stamp. Nos. 358-359 exist imperf. Value, set $100.

Peasant Couple and Tsar Boris — A174   Flags over Wheat Field and Tsar Boris — A175

Tsar Boris and Map of Dobrudja A176

1940, Sept. 20
360 A174 1 l slate green   .25 .25
361 A175 2 l rose red   .25 .25
362 A176 4 l dark brown   .35 .25
363 A176 7 l dark blue   .75 .60
   Nos. 360-363 (4)   1.60 1.35
Return of Dobrudja from Romania.

Fruit A177   Bees and Flowers A178

Plowing A179   Shepherd and Sheep A180

Tsar Boris III — A181

1940-44 *Typo.* *Unwmk.* *Perf. 13*
364 A177 10s red orange   .25 .25
365 A178 15s blue   .25 .25
366 A179 30s olive brn ('41) .25 .25
367 A180 50s violet   .25 .25
368 A181 1 l brt green   .25 .25
  a. Perf 10¼ ('44)   1.75 .50
  b. Perf 10¼x11½ ('44)   .25 .25
  c. Perf 11½x10¼   35.00 35.00
  d. Perf 11½ ('44)   .25 .25
369 A181 2 l rose car   .25 .25
  a. Perf 10¼ ('44)   1.10 .25
  b. Perf 10¼x11½ ('44)   .25 .25
  c. Perf 11½x10¼   25.00 25.00
  d. Perf 11½ ('44)   .25 .25
370 A181 4 l red orange   .25 .25
  a. Perf 11½ ('41)   3.50 3.00
371 A181 6 l red vio ('44) .35 .25
372 A181 7 l blue   .25 .25
373 A181 10 l blue grn ('41) .35 .25
   Nos. 364-373 (10)   2.70 2.50
See Nos. 373A-377, 440. For overprints see Nos. 455-463, C31-C32.

1940-41 *Wmk. 145* *Perf. 13*
373A A180 50s violet ('41) .25 .25
374 A181 1 l brt grn   1.00 .25
375 A181 2 l rose car   .35 .25
376 A181 7 l dull blue   .35 .25
377 A181 10 l blue green .35 .25
   Nos. 373A-377 (5)   2.30 1.25
Watermarked vertically or horizontally. Nos. 374-375 exist imperf. Value, each $15.

P. R. Slaveikov
A182

Sofronii, Bishop
of Vratza
A183

Saint Ivan
Rilski — A184

Martin S.
Drinov — A185

Hrabar The
Monk — A186

Kolio
Ficheto — A187

1940, Sept. 23   Photo.   Unwmk.

378	A182	1 l	brt bl grn	.25	.25
379	A183	2 l	brt carmine	.25	.25
380	A184	3 l	dp red brn	.25	.25
381	A185	4 l	red orange	.25	.25
382	A186	7 l	deep blue	1.60	1.60
383	A187	10 l	red brn	2.40	1.60
	Nos. 378-383 (6)			5.00	4.20

Liberation of Bulgaria from the Turks in 1878.

Johannes
Gutenberg
A188

N. Karastoyanov,
1st Bulgarian
Printer
A189

1940, Dec. 16

384	A188	1 l	slate green	.35	.25
385	A189	2 l	orange brown	.35	.25

500th anniv. of the invention of the printing press and 100th anniv. of the 1st Bulgarian printing press.

Christo
Botev — A190

Monument to
Botev — A192

Botev with his
Insurgent
Band — A191

1941, May 3

386	A190	1 l	dark blue green	.25	.25
387	A191	2 l	crimson rose	.35	.25
388	A192	3 l	dark brown	.90	.70
				1.50	1.20

Christo Botev, patriot and poet.

Palace of
Justice,
Sofia — A193

20 l, Workers' hospital. 50 l, National Bank.

1941-43   Engr.   Perf. 11½

389	A193	14 l	lt gray brn ('43)	.60	.35
390	A193	20 l	gray grn ('43)	.60	.35
391	A193	50 l	lt bl gray	2.60	1.50
	Nos. 389-391 (3)			3.80	2.20

Macedonian
Woman — A196

City of
Okhrida — A200

Outline of
Macedonia
and Tsar
Boris III
A197

View of
Aegean
Sea — A198

Poganovski
Monastery
A199

1941, Oct. 3   Photo.   Perf. 13

392	A196	1 l	slate grn	.25	.25
393	A197	2 l	crimson	.25	.25
394	A198	2 l	red org	.25	.25
395	A199	4 l	org brn	.25	.25
396	A200	7 l	dp gray bl	.65	.45
	Nos. 392-396 (5)			1.65	1.45

Issued to commemorate the acquisition of Macedonian territory from neighboring countries.

Peasant
Working in a
Field — A201

Designs: 15s, Plowing. 30s, Apiary. 50s, Women harvesting fruit. 3 l, Shepherd and sheep. 5 l, Inspecting cattle.

1941-44

397	A201	10s	dk violet	.25	.25
398	A201	10s	dk blue	.25	.25
399	A201	15s	Prus blue	.25	.25
400	A201	15s	dk ol brn	.25	.25
401	A201	30s	red orange	.25	.25
402	A201	30s	dk slate grn	.25	.25
403	A201	50s	blue vio	.25	.25
404	A201	50s	red lilac	.25	.25
405	A201	3 l	henna brn	.35	.25
406	A201	3 l	dk brn ('44)	1.25	.75
407	A201	5 l	sepia	1.00	.50
408	A201	5 l	vio bl ('44)	1.25	.75
	Nos. 397-408 (12)			5.85	4.25

Girls
Singing — A207

Boys in
Camp — A208

Raising
Flag — A209

Folk
Dancers — A211

Camp Scene
A210

1942, June 1   Photo.

409	A207	1 l	dk bl grn	.25	.25
410	A208	2 l	scarlet	.25	.25
411	A209	4 l	olive gray	.30	.25
412	A210	7 l	deep blue	.40	.25
413	A211	14 l	fawn	.45	.25
	Nos. 409-413 (5)			1.65	1.25

National "Work and Joy" movement.

Wounded
Soldier — A212

Soldier's
Farewell
A213

4 l, Aiding wounded soldier. 7 l, Widow & orphans at grave. 14 l, Tomb of Unknown Soldier. 20 l, Queen Ioanna visiting wounded.

1942, Sept. 7

414	A212	1 l	slate grn	.30	.25
415	A213	2 l	brt rose	.30	.25
416	A213	4 l	yel org	.30	.25
417	A213	7 l	dark blue	.30	.25
418	A213	14 l	brown	.30	.25
419	A213	20 l	olive blk	.65	.25
	Nos. 414-419 (6)			2.15	1.50

Issued to aid war victims. No. 419 was printed in sheets of 50, alternating with 50 labels.

Legend of
Kubrat — A218

Cavalry
Charge — A219

Designs: 30s, Rider of Madara. 50s, Christening of Boris I. 1 l, School, St. Naum. 2 l, Crowning of Tsar Simeon by Boris I. 3 l, Golden era of Bulgarian literature. 4 l, Sentencing of the Bogomil Basil. 5 l, Proclamation of 2nd Bulgarian Empire. 7 l, Ivan Assen II at

Trebizond. 10 l, Deporting the Patriarch Jeftimi. 14 l, Wandering minstrel. 20 l, Monk Paisii. 30 l, Monument, Shipka Pass.

1942, Oct. 12

420	A218	10s	bluish blk	.25	.25
421	A219	15s	Prus grn	.25	.25
422	A219	30s	dk rose vio	.25	.25
423	A219	50s	indigo	.25	.25
424	A219	1 l	slate grn	.25	.25
425	A219	2 l	crimson	.25	.25
426	A219	3 l	brown	.25	.25
427	A219	4 l	orange	.25	.25
428	A219	5 l	grnsh blk	.25	.25
429	A219	7 l	dk blue	.25	.25
430	A219	10 l	brown blk	.25	.25
431	A219	14 l	olive blk	.25	.25
432	A219	20 l	henna brn	.70	.50
433	A219	30 l	black	1.25	.75
	Nos. 420-433 (14)			4.95	4.25

Tsar Boris III
A234

Designs: Various portraits of Tsar.

Perf. 13, Imperf.

1944, Feb. 28   Photo.   Wmk. 275

Frames in Black

434	A234	1 l	olive grn	.25	.40
435	A234	2 l	red brown	.25	.40
436	A234	4 l	brown	.25	.40
437	A234	5 l	gray vio	.50	1.00
438	A234	7 l	slate blue	.60	1.25
	Nos. 434-438 (5)			1.85	3.45

Tsar Boris III (1894-1943).

Tsar Simeon II — A239

Unwmk.

1944, June 12   Typo.   Perf. 13

439	A239	3 l	red orange	.25	.25
a.	Perf 11½			.35	.25

Shepherd Type of 1940

1944

440	A180	50s	yellow green	.25	.25

Parcel Post Stamps
of 1944 Overprinted
in Black or Orange

1945, Jan. 25   Perf. 11½

448	PP5	1 l	dk carmine	.25	.25
449	PP5	7 l	rose lilac	.25	.25
450	PP5	20 l	org brn	.25	.25
451	PP5	30 l	dk brn car	.30	.25
452	PP5	50 l	red orange	.50	.25
453	PP5	100 l	blue (O)	.75	.25

Overprint reads: "Everything for the Front."

No. 448 with Additional Surcharge of New Value in Black

454	PP5	4 l on 1 l	dk car	.25	.25
	Nos. 448-454 (7)			2.55	1.75

Nos. 368 to 370
Overprinted in Black

1945, Mar. 15 — Perf. 11½, 13

455	A181	1 l brt green, perf 13	.30	.30
456	A181	2 l rose carmine, perf 11½	1.10	.30
a.		Perf 10¾	2.50	3.50
b.		Perf 11½x10¾	35.00	17.50
457	A181	4 l red orange, perf 13	.75	.30

Overprint reads: "Collect old iron."

Overprinted in Black

458	A181	1 l brt green, perf 13	.25	.30
a.		Perf 11½	.25	.30
459	A181	2 l rose carmine, perf 11½	.65	.30
a.		Perf 10¾	12.00	9.00
460	A181	4 l red orange, perf. 13	.95	.30
a.		Perf 11½	4.50	3.00

Overprint reads: "Collect discarded paper."

Overprinted in Black

461	A181	1 l brt green, perf 11½	.25	.25
a.		Perf 13	.30	.30
462	A181	2 l rose carmine, perf 11½	1.10	.25
a.		Perf 10¾	12.00	9.00
b.		Perf 11½x10¾	30.00	18.00
463	A181	4 l red orange, perf 13	.95	.25
		Nos. 455-463 (9)	6.30	2.55

Overprint reads: "Collect all kinds of rags."

Oak Tree — A245

Imperf., Perf. 11½.

1945 — Litho. — Unwmk.

464	A245	4 l vermilion	.25	.25
465	A245	10 l blue	.25	.25

Imperf

466	A245	50 l brown lake	.35	.35
		Nos. 464-466 (3)	.85	.85

Slav Congress, Sofia, March, 1945.

A246 — A247

A248 — A249

A251 — A252

A253

A254

2 l and 4 l:
Type I. Large crown close to coat of arms.
Type II. Smaller crown standing high.

1945-46 — Photo. — Perf. 13

469	A246	30s yellow grn	.25	.25
470	A247	50s peacock grn	.25	.25
471	A248	1 l dk green	.25	.25
472	A249	2 l choc (I)	.25	.25
a.		Type II	.25	.25
473	A249	4 l dk blue (I)	.25	.25
a.		Type II	.25	.25
475	A251	5 l red violet	.25	.25
476	A251	9 l slate gray	.25	.25
477	A252	10 l Prus blue	.25	.25
478	A253	15 l brown	.25	.25
479	A254	20 l carmine	.35	.25
480	A254	20 l gray blk	.35	.25
		Nos. 469-480 (11)	2.95	2.75

Breaking Chain — A255

1 Lev Coin — A256

Water Wheel — A257

Coin and Symbols of Agriculture and Industry — A258

1945, June 4 — Litho. — Imperf.
Unwmk. — Laid Paper

481	A255	50 l brn red, *pink*	.25	.25
482	A255	50 l org, *pink*	.25	.25
483	A256	100 l gray bl, *pink*	.25	.25
484	A256	100 l brn, *pink*	.25	.25
485	A257	150 l dk ol gray, *pink*	.85	.25
486	A257	150 l dl car, *pink*	.85	.25
487	A258	200 l dp bl, *pink*	1.25	.70
488	A258	200 l ol grn, *pink*	1.25	.70
		Nos. 481-488 (8)	5.20	2.90

Souvenir Sheets

489		Sheet of 4	6.00	9.00
a.	A255	50 l violet blue	.60	.25
b.	A256	100 l violet blue	.60	.25
c.	A257	150 l violet blue	.60	.25
d.	A258	200 l violet blue	.60	.25

490		Sheet of 4	6.00	9.00
a.	A255	50 l brown orange	.60	.25
b.	A256	100 l brown orange	.60	.25
c.	A257	150 l brown orange	.60	.25
d.	A258	200 l brown orange	.60	.25

Publicizing Bulgaria's Liberty Loan.

Olive Branch — A260

1945, Sept. 1 — Typo. — Perf. 13

491	A260	10 l org brn & yel grn	.25	.25
492	A260	50 l dull red & dp grn	.40	.25

Victory of Allied Nations, World War II.

September 9, 1944 — A261

Numeral, Broken Chain — A262

1945, Sept. 7

493	A261	1 l gray green	.25	.25
494	A261	4 l deep blue	.25	.25
495	A261	5 l rose lilac	.25	.25
496	A262	10 l lt blue	.25	.25
497	A262	20 l brt car	.25	.25
498	A261	50 l brt bl grn	.70	.25
499	A261	100 l orange brn	.80	.50
		Nos. 493-499 (7)	2.75	2.00

1st anniv. of Bulgaria's liberation.

Old Postal Savings Emblem — A263

Child Putting Coin in Bank — A265

First Bulgarian Postal Savings Stamp A264

Postal Savings Building, Sofia — A266

1946, Apr. 12

500	A263	4 l brown org	.25	.25
501	A264	10 l dk olive	.25	.25
502	A265	20 l ultra	.25	.25
503	A266	50 l slate gray	.90	.90
		Nos. 500-503 (4)	1.65	1.65

50th anniv. of Bulgarian Postal Savings.

Refugee Children A267

Nurse Assisting Wounded Soldier A269

Wounded Soldier A268

35 l, 100 l, Red Cross hospital train.

1946, Apr. 4 — Cross in Carmine

504	A267	2 l dk olive	.25	.25
505	A268	4 l violet	.25	.25
506	A267	10 l plum	.25	.25
507	A268	20 l ultra	.25	.25
508	A269	30 l brown org	.25	.25
509	A268	35 l gray blk	.25	.25
510	A269	50 l violet brn	.45	.35
511	A268	100 l gray brn	1.10	1.40
		Nos. 504-511 (8)	3.05	3.25

See Nos. 553-560.

Advancing Troops A271

Grenade Thrower — A272

Attacking Planes — A274

Designs: 5 l, Horse-drawn cannon. 9 l, Engineers building pontoon bridge. 10 l, 30 l, Cavalry charge. 40 l, Horse-drawn supply column. 50 l, Motor transport column. 60 l, Infantry, tanks and planes.

1946, Aug. 9 — Typo. — Unwmk.

512	A271	2 l dk red vio	.25	.25
513	A272	4 l dk gray	.25	.25
514	A271	5 l dk org red	.25	.25
515	A271	6 l black brn	.25	.25
516	A271	9 l rose lilac	.25	.25
517	A271	10 l dp violet	.25	.25
518	A271	20 l dp blue	.45	.25
519	A271	30 l red org	.45	.25
520	A271	40 l dk ol bis	.50	.25
521	A271	50 l dk green	.55	.25
522	A271	60 l red brown	.85	.50
		Nos. 512-522 (11)	4.30	3.00

Bulgaria's participation in World War II.

Arms of Russia and Bulgaria — A279

1946, May 23

523	A279	4 l red orange	.25	.25
525	A279	20 l turq green	.30	.30

Congress of the Bulgarian-Soviet Association, May 1946. The 4 l exists in dk car rose and 20 l in blue. Value, set $12.

Lion
Rampant — A280

1946, May 25   *Imperf.*
526 A280 20 l blue   .60 .30

Day of the Postage Stamp, May 26, 1946.

Alekandr
Stamboliski — A281

1946, June 13   *Perf. 12*
527 A281 100 l red orange   6.25 6.25

23rd anniversary of the death of Alekandr Stamboliski, agrarian leader.

Flags of Albania,
Romania, Bulgaria
and
Yugoslavia — A282

1946, July 6   *Perf. 11½*
528 A282 100 l black brown   1.20 1.20

1946 Balkan Games.
Sheet of 100 arranged so that all stamps are tete beche vert. and horiz., except 2 center rows in left pane which provide 10 vert. pairs that are not tete beche vert.

St. Ivan
Rilski — A283

A286

A284

A285

Views of Rila
Monastery
A287

1946, Aug. 26
529 A283 1 l red brown   .25 .25
530 A284 4 l black brn   .25 .25
531 A285 10 l dk green   .25 .25
532 A286 20 l dp blue   .35 .25
533 A287 50 l dk red   1.25 .80
    Nos. 529-533 (5)   2.35 1.80

Millenary of Rila Monastery.

People's Republic

A288

1946, Sept. 15   *Typo.*
534 A288 4 l brown lake   .25 .25
535 A288 20 l dull blue   .25 .25
536 A288 50 l olive bister   .35 .35
    Nos. 534-536 (3)   .85 .85

No. 535 is inscribed "BULGARIA" in Latin characters.
Referendum of Sept. 8, 1946, resulting in the establishment of the Bulgarian People's Republic.

Partisan
Army — A289

Snipers — A290

Soldiers: Past
and
Present — A291

Design: 30 l, Partisans advancing.

1946, Dec. 2
537 A289 1 l violet brn   .25 .25
538 A290 4 l dull grn   .25 .25
539 A291 5 l chocolate   .25 .25
540 A290 10 l crimson   .25 .25
541 A289 20 l ultra   .30 .25
542 A290 30 l olive bister   .35 .25
543 A291 50 l black   .50 .35
    Nos. 537-543 (7)   2.15 1.85

Relief Worker
and
Children — A294

Child with Gift
Parcels — A295

Waiting for Food
Distribution
A296

Mother and
Child
A297

1946, Dec. 30
545 A294 1 l dk vio brn   .25 .25
546 A295 4 l brt red   .25 .25
547 A295 9 l olive bis   .25 .25
548 A294 10 l slate gray   .25 .25
549 A296 20 l ultra   .25 .25
550 A297 30 l dp brn org   .25 .25
551 A296 40 l maroon   .25 .25
552 A294 50 l peacock grn   .50 .50
    Nos. 545-552 (8)   2.25 2.25

"Bulgaria" is in Latin characters on No. 548.

Red Cross Types of 1946

1947, Jan. 31   **Cross in Carmine**
553 A267 2 l olive bister   .25 .25
554 A268 4 l olive black   .25 .25
555 A267 10 l blue grn   .25 .25
556 A268 20 l brt blue   .25 .25
557 A269 30 l yellow grn   .50 .50
558 A269 35 l grnsh gray   .50 .50
559 A269 50 l henna brn   .85 .85
560 A268 100 l dark blue   1.25 1.25
    Nos. 553-560 (8)   4.10 4.10

Laurel Branch,
Allied and
Bulgarian
Emblems
A298

Dove of Peace
A299

1947, Feb. 28
561 A298 4 l olive   .25 .25
562 A299 10 l brown red   .25 .25
563 A299 20 l deep blue   .25 .25
    Nos. 561-563 (3)   .75 .75

Return to peace at the close of World War II. "Bulgaria" in Latin characters on No. 563.

A302

Guerrilla Fighters
A303   A304

1947, Jan. 21   *Perf. 11½*
567 A302 10 l choc & brn org   .55 .40
568 A303 20 l dk bl & bl   .55 .40
569 A304 70 l dp claret & rose   42.50 40.00
    Nos. 567-569 (3)   43.60 40.80

Issued to honor the anti-fascists.

Hydroelectric
Station
A305

Miner — A306

Symbols of
Industry — A307

Tractor
A308

1947, Aug. 6
570 A305 4 l olive green   .25 .25
571 A306 9 l red brown   .25 .25
572 A307 20 l deep blue   .30 .25
573 A308 40 l olive brown   .75 .55
    Nos. 570-573 (4)   1.55 1.30

Exhibition
Building
A309

Former Home of
Alphonse de
Lamartine
A310

Symbols of
Agriculture and
Horticulture
A311

Perf. 11x11½, 11½x11
1947, Aug. 31   *Litho.*   *Unwmk.*
574 A309 4 l scarlet   .25 .25
575 A310 9 l brown lake   .25 .25
576 A311 20 l brt ultra   .30 .30
    Nos. 574-576 (3)   .80 .80

Plovdiv Intl. Fair, 1947. See No. C54.

Basil Evstatiev
Aprilov — A312

1947, Oct. 19   *Photo.*   *Perf. 11*
577 A312 40 l brt ultra   .60 .30

Cent. of the death of Basil Evstatiev Aprilov, educator and historian. See No. 603.

Bicycle
Race — A313

Basketball
A314

Chess
A315

Balkan Games: 20 l, Soccer players. 60 l, Four flags of participating nations.

1947, Sept. 29   *Typo.*   *Perf. 11½*
578 A313 2 l plum   .25 .25
579 A314 4 l dk olive grn   .25 .25
580 A315 9 l orange brn   1.00 .45
581 A315 20 l brt ultra   1.25 1.00
582 A315 60 l violet brn   3.00 1.50
    Nos. 578-582 (5)   5.75 2.95

People's Theater, Sofia A316

National Assembly A317

Central Post Office, Sofia A318

Presidential Mansion A319

1947-48   **Typo.**   *Perf. 12½*

583	A316	50s yellow grn	.25	.25
584	A317	50s yellow grn	.25	.25
585	A318	1 l green	.25	.25
586	A316	1 l green	.25	.25
587	A316	2 l brown lake	.25	.25
588	A317	2 l lt brown	.25	.25
589	A316	4 l deep blue	.25	.25
590	A317	4 l deep blue	.25	.25
591	A316	9 l carmine	.35	.25
592	A317	20 l deep blue	.75	.30
		Nos. 583-592 (10)	3.10	2.55

On Nos. 583-592 inscription reads "Bulgarian Republic." No. 592 is inscribed in Latin characters.

Redrawn

Added to inscription

593	A318	1 l green	.25	.25
594	A318	2 l brown lake	.25	.25
595	A318	4 l deep blue	.25	.25
		Nos. 593-595 (3)	.75	.75

Cyrillic inscription beneath design on Nos. 593-595 reads "Bulgarian People's Republic."

Geno Kirov — A320

Actors' Portraits: 1 l, Zlatina Nedeva. 2 l, Ivan Popov. 3 l, Athanas Kirchev. 4 l, Elena Snejina. 5 l, Stoyan Bachvarov.

Perf. 10½

1947, Dec. 8   **Unwmk.**   **Litho.**

596	A320	50s bister brn	.25	.25
597	A320	1 l lt blue grn	.25	.25
598	A320	2 l slate green	.25	.25
599	A320	3 l dp blue	.25	.25
600	A320	4 l scarlet	.25	.25
601	A320	5 l red brown	.25	.25
		Nos. 596-601,B22-B26 (11)	3.80	3.25

National Theater, 50th anniversary.

Merchant Ship "Fatherland" — A321

1947, Dec. 19

602	A321	50 l Prus bl, *cream*	.80	.60

B. E. Aprilov — A322

1948, Feb. 19   *Perf. 11*

603	A322	4 l brn car, *cream*	.25	.25

Centenary of the death of Basil Evstatiev Aprilov, educator and historian.

Worker — A323

1948, Feb. 29   **Photo.**   *Perf. 11½x12*

604	A323	4 l dp blue, *cream*	.25	.25

2nd Bulgarian Workers' Congress.

Self-education A324

Accordion Player — A325

Factory Recess — A326

Girl Throwing Basketball — A327

1948, Mar. 31   **Photo.**

605	A324	4 l red	.25	.25
606	A325	20 l deep blue	.25	.25
607	A326	40 l dull green	.50	.25
608	A327	60 l brown	.85	.60
		Nos. 605-608 (4)	1.85	1.35

Nicholas Vaptzarov — A328

Portraits: 9 l, P. K. Iavorov. 15 l, Christo Smirnenski. 20 l, Ivan Vazov. 45 l, P. R. Slaveikov.

1948, May 18   **Litho.**   *Perf. 11*
Cream Paper

611	A328	4 l brt ver	.25	.25
612	A328	9 l lt brown	.25	.25
613	A328	15 l claret	.25	.25
614	A328	20 l deep blue	.30	.30
615	A328	45 l green	.40	.40
		Nos. 611-615 (5)	1.45	1.45

Soviet Soldier — A329

Civilians Offering Gifts to Soldiers A330

Designs: 20 l, Soldiers, 1878 and 1944. 60 l, Stalin and Spasski Tower.

1948, July 5   **Photo.**   **Cream Paper**

616	A329	4 l brown org	.25	.25
617	A330	10 l olive grn	.25	.25
618	A330	20 l dp blue	.25	.25
619	A329	60 l olive brn	1.00	.85
		Nos. 616-619 (4)	1.75	1.60

The Soviet Army.

Demeter Blagoev — A331

Monument to Bishop Andrey A332

9 l, Gabriel Genov. 60 l, Marching youths.

1948, Sept. 6   **Litho.**   **Cream Paper**

620	A331	4 l dk brown	.25	.25
621	A331	9 l brown org	.25	.25
622	A332	20 l dp blue	.25	.25
623	A332	60 l brown	.80	.60
		Nos. 620-623 (4)	1.55	1.35

No. 623 is inscribed in Cyrillic characters. Natl. Insurrection of 1923, 25th anniv.

Christo Smirnenski — A333

1948, Oct. 2   **Photo.**   *Perf. 11½*
Cream Paper

624	A333	4 l blue	.25	.25
625	A333	16 l red brown	.25	.25

Christo Smirnenski, poet, 1898-1923.

Battle of Grivitza, 1877 — A334

1948, Nov. 1

626	A334	20 l blue	.25	.25
		Nos. 626,C56-C57 (3)	1.50	1.45

Romanian-Bulgarian friendship.

Bath, Gorna Banya — A335

Mineral Bath, Sofia A337

Bath, Bankya — A336

Maliovitza A338

1948-49   **Typo.**   *Perf. 12½*

627	A335	2 l red brown	.25	.25
628	A336	3 l red orange	.25	.25
629	A337	4 l deep blue	.25	.25
630	A338	5 l violet brown	.25	.25
631	A336	10 l red violet	.30	.25
632	A338	15 l olive grn ('49)	.75	.25
633	A335	20 l deep blue	1.40	.25
		Nos. 627-633 (7)	3.45	1.75

Latin characters on No. 633. See No. 653.

Emblem of the Republic — A339

1948-50

634	A339	50s red orange	.25	.25
634A	A339	50s org brn ('50)	.25	.25
635	A339	1 l green	.25	.25
636	A339	9 l black	.40	.25
		Nos. 634-636 (4)	1.15	1.00

Botev's Birthplace, Kalofer A340

Christo Botev — A341

Designs: 9 l, Steamer "Radetzky." 15 l, Kalofer village. 20 l, Botev in uniform. 40 l, Botev's mother. 50 l, Pen, pistol and wreath.

Cream Paper

Perf. 11x11½, 11½

1948, Dec. 21   **Photo.**

638	A340	1 l dk green	.25	.25
639	A341	4 l violet brn	.25	.25
640	A340	9 l violet	.25	.25
641	A340	15 l brown	.25	.25
642	A341	20 l blue	.25	.25
643	A340	40 l red brown	.50	.25
644	A341	50 l olive blk	.65	.50
		Nos. 638-644 (7)	2.40	2.00

Botev, Bulgarian natl. poet, birth cent.

Lenin — A342

Lenin Speaking — A343

1949, Jan. 24   Unwmk.   Perf. 11½
Cream Paper
645 A342   4 l brown   .35 .25
646 A343 20 l brown red   .50 .25

25th anniversary of the death of Lenin.

Road
Construction
A344

Designs: 5 l, Tunnel construction. 9 l, Locomotive. 10 l, Textile worker. 20 l, Female tractor driver. 40 l, Workers in truck.

1949, Apr. 6   Perf. 10½
Inscribed: "CHM"
Cream Paper
647 A344   4 l dark red   .25 .25
648 A344   5 l dark brown   .25 .25
649 A344   9 l dk slate grn   .50 .25
650 A344 10 l violet   .50 .25
651 A344 20 l dull blue   .85 .65
652 A344 40 l brown   1.75 .85
   Nos. 647-652 (6)   4.10 2.50

Honoring the Workers' Cultural Brigade.

Type of 1948 Redrawn
Country Name and "POSTA" in
English Characters
1949   Typo.   Perf. 12½
653 A337 20 l deep blue   2.00 .25

Miner — A345

1949   Perf. 11x11½
654 A345   4 l dark blue   .25 .25

A347

Prime Minister
George
Dimitrov, 1882-
1949
A348

1949, July 10   Photo.
656 A347   4 l red brown   .25 .25
657 A348 20 l dark blue   1.00 .25

Power   Grain
Station — A349   Towers — A350

Farm
Machinery — A351

Tractor Parade
A352

Agriculture
and Industry
A353

1949, Aug. 5   Perf. 11½x11, 11x11½
658 A349   4 l olive green   .25 .25
659 A350   9 l dark red   .25 .25
660 A351 15 l purple   .35 .25
661 A352 20 l blue   1.00 .65
662 A353 50 l orange brn   3.00 1.40
   Nos. 658-662 (5)   4.85 2.80

Bulgaria's Five Year Plan.

Grenade and Javelin
Throwers — A354

Hurdlers
A355

Motorcycle
and Tractor
A356

Boy and Girl
Athletes — A357

1949, Sept. 5
663 A354   4 l brown orange   .50 .25
664 A355   9 l olive green   1.40 .45
665 A356 20 l violet blue   2.00 1.10
666 A357 50 l red brown   5.25 2.25
   Nos. 663-666 (4)   9.15 4.05

A358

Frontier
Guards — A359

1949, Oct. 31
667 A358   4 l chestnut brn   .35 .35
668 A359 20 l gray blue   1.10 .55
   See No. C60.

George
Dimitrov — A360

Allegory of
Labor — A361

Laborers of Both   Workers and
Sexes — A362   Flags of Bulgaria
                  and
                  Russia — A363

Perf. 11½
1949, Dec. 13   Photo.   Unwmk.
669 A360   4 l orange brn   .25 .25
670 A361   9 l purple   .75 .45
671 A362 20 l dull blue   .75 .45
672 A363 50 l red   .75 .45
   Nos. 669-672 (4)   2.50 1.60

Joseph V.   Stalin and
Stalin — A364   Dove — A365

1949, Dec. 21
673 A364   4 l deep orange   .35 .25
674 A365 40 l rose brown   1.10 .80

70th anniv. of the birth of Joseph V. Stalin.

Kharalamby
Stoyanov — A366

Railway
Strikers
A367

Communications
Strikers — A368

1950, Feb. 15
675 A366   4 l yellow brown   .35 .25
676 A367 20 l violet blue   .35 .25
677 A368 60 l brown olive   1.10 .70
   Nos. 675-677 (3)   1.80 1.20

30th anniv. (in 1949) of the General Railway
and Postal Employees' Strike of 1919.

Miner — A369

Locomotive
A370

Shipbuilding — A371

Tractor
A372

Stalin Central   Textile
Heating   Worker — A375
Plant — A374

Farm
Machinery
A373

1950-51   Perf. 11½, 13
678 A369   1 l olive   .25 .25
679 A370   2 l gray blk   .25 .25
680 A371   3 l gray blue   .25 .25
681 A372   4 l dk blue grn   2.25 .60
682 A373   5 l henna brn   .45 .25
682A A373   9 l gray blk ('51)   .25 .25
683 A374 10 l dp plum ('51)   .30 .25
684 A375 15 l dk car ('51)   .50 .25
685 A375 20 l dk blue ('51)   .80 .25
   Nos. 678-685 (9)   5.30 2.60

No. 685 is inscribed in Latin characters.
See Nos. 750-751A.

Vassil Kolarov
(1877-1950) — A377

1950, Mar. 6   *Perf. 11½*
Size: 21½x31½mm
686 A377   4 l red brown   .25   .25
Size: 27x39½mm
687 A377   20 l violet blue   .70   .70

No. 687 has altered frame and is inscribed in Latin characters.

Stanislav Dospevski, Self-portrait A378

King Kaloyan and Desislava A379

Plowman Resting, by Christo Stanchev A380

Statue of Dimtcho Debelianov, by Ivan Lazarov — A381

"Harvest," by V. Dimitrov — A382

Design: 9 l, Nikolai Pavlovich, self-portrait.

1950, Apr. 15   *Perf. 11½*
688 A378   1 l dk olive grn   .30   .25
689 A379   4 l dk red   1.25   .45
690 A378   9 l chocolate   1.75   .45
691 A380   15 l brown   2.50   .60
692 A380   20 l deep blue   4.00   1.75
693 A381   40 l red brown   5.00   1.25
694 A382   60 l deep orange   4.00   2.00
    Nos. 688-694 (7)   18.80   6.75

Latin characters on No. 692.

Ivan Vazov (1850-1921), Poet and Birthplace A383

1950, June 26
695 A383   4 l olive green   .25   .25

Road Building A384

Men of Three Races and "Stalin" Flag — A385

Perf. 11½x11, 11x11½
1950, Sept. 19
696 A384   4 l brown red   .25   .25
697 A385   20 l violet blue   .65   .25

2nd National Peace Conference.

Molotov, Kolarov, Stalin and Dimitrov A386

Spasski Tower and Flags — A387

Russian and Bulgarian Women — A388

Loading Russian Ship — A389

Perf. 11½
1950, Oct. 10   Unwmk.   **Photo.**
698 A386   4 l brown   .25   .25
699 A387   9 l rose carmine   .25   .25
700 A388   20 l gray blue   .35   .30
701 A389   50 l dk grnsh blue   1.75   .75
    Nos. 698-701 (4)   2.60   1.55

2nd anniversary of the Soviet-Bulgarian treaty of mutual assistance.

St. Constantine Sanatorium — A390

2 l, 10 l, Children at seashore. 5 l, Rest home.

1950   **Typo.**
702 A390   1 l dark green   .25   .25
703 A390   2 l carmine   .25   .25
704 A390   5 l deep orange   .25   .25
705 A390   10 l deep blue   .40   .25
    Nos. 702-705 (4)   1.15   1.00

Originally prepared in 1945 as "Sunday Delivery Stamps," this issue was released for ordinary postage in 1950. Compare with Nos. RA16-RA18.

Runners — A393

1950, Aug. 21   **Photo.**   *Perf. 11½*
706 A393   4 l shown   .70   .40
707 A393   9 l Cycling   .70   .50
   a.   Perf 10¾   1.75   1.40

708 A393   20 l Shot put   1.00   .85
   a.   Perf 10¾   2.00   1.75
   b.   Perf 11½x10¾   3.50   3.00
709 A393   40 l Volleyball   2.00   2.00
   a.   Perf 10¾   4.25   3.50
    Nos. 706-709 (4)   4.40   3.75

Marshal Fedor I. Tolbukhin — A394

Natives Greeting Tolbukhin A395

Perf. 11½x11, 11x11½
1950, Dec. 10   **Photo.**   **Unwmk.**
710 A394   4 l claret   .30   .25
711 A395   20 l dk blue   1.10   .25

The return of Dobrich and part of the province of Dobruja from Romania to Bulgaria.

Dimitrov's Birthplace A396

George Dimitrov A397

A398

Various Portraits, Inscribed

Design: 2 l, Dimitrov Museum, Sofia.

1950, July 2   *Perf. 10½*
712 A396   50s olive grn   .30   .25
713 A397   50s brown   .30   .25
714 A397   1 l redsh brn   .30   .25
715 A396   2 l gray   .30   .25
716 A397   4 l claret   .60   .25
717 A397   9 l red brown   1.00   .50
718 A398   10 l brown red   1.50   .70
719 A397   15 l olive gray   1.50   .70
720 A398   20 l dark blue   2.50   .80
    Nos. 712-720,C61 (10)   13.80   6.70

1st anniversary of the death of George Dimitrov, statesman. No. 720 is inscribed in Latin characters.

A. S. Popov — A400

1951, Feb. 10
722 A400   4 l red brown   .40   .25
723 A400   20 l dark blue   .90   .25

No. 723 is inscribed in Latin characters.

Arms of Bulgaria
A401   A402

1950   Unwmk.   Typo.   *Perf. 13*
724 A401   2 l dk brown   .25   .25
725 A401   3 l rose   .25   .25
726 A402   5 l carmine   .25   .25
727 A402   9 l aqua   .25   .25
    Nos. 724-727 (4)   1.00   1.00

Nos. 724-727 were prepared in 1947 for official use but were issued as regular postage stamps Oct. 1, 1950.

Heroes Chankova, Antonov-Malchik, Dimitrov and Dimitrova — A403

Stanke Dimitrov-Marek A404

George Kirkov A405

George Dimitrov at Leipzig A406

Natcho Ivanov and Avr. Stoyanov A407

9 l, Anton Ivanov. 15 l, Christo Michailov.

1951, Mar. 25   **Photo.**   *Perf. 11½*
728 A403   1 l red violet   .25   .25
729 A404   2 l dk red brn   .25   .25
730 A405   4 l car rose   .25   .25
731 A405   9 l orange brn   .80   .25
732 A405   15 l olive brn   1.75   .65
733 A406   20 l dark blue   1.75   .90
734 A407   50 l olive gray   4.25   1.50
    Nos. 728-734 (7)   9.30   4.05

First Bulgarian Tractor A408

First Steam Roller — A409

First Truck — A410

Bulgarian Embroidery — A411

15 l, Carpet. 20 l, Tobacco & roses. 40 l, Fruits.

Perf. 11x10½

			Unwmk.	
1951, Mar. 30		**Photo.**		
735	A408	1 l olive brn	.25	.25
736	A409	2 l violet	.30	.25
737	A410	4 l red brown	.50	.25
738	A411	9 l purple	.75	.25
739	A409	15 l deep plum	1.60	.55
740	A411	20 l violet blue	3.00	.55
741	A410	40 l deep green	4.25	1.25

Perf. 13
Size: 23x18½mm

742	A408	1 l purple	.25	.25
743	A409	2 l Prus green	.25	.25
744	A410	4 l red brown	.25	.25
		Nos. 735-744 (10)	11.40	4.10

For surcharges, see Nos. 894, 973.

Turkish Attack on Mt. Zlee Dol A412

Designs: 4 l, Georgi Benkovski speaking to rebels. 9 l, Cherrywood cannon of 1876 and Russian cavalry, 1945. 20 l, Rebel, 1876 and partisan, 1944. 40 l, Benkovski and Dimitrov.

1951, May 3 **Perf. 10½**
Cream Paper

745	A412	1 l redsh brown	.45	.25
746	A412	4 l dark green	.50	.25
747	A412	9 l violet brown	.75	.60
748	A412	20 l deep blue	1.10	1.00
749	A412	40 l dark red	1.50	1.25
		Nos. 745-749 (5)	4.30	3.35

75th anniv. of the "April" revolution.

Industrial Types of 1950

1951			**Perf. 13**	
750	A369	1 l violet	.25	.25
a.		Perf 10¾	35.00	17.50
b.		Perf 11½	25.00	11.00
751	A370	2 l dk brown	.35	.35
a.		Perf 10¾	42.50	11.00
b.		Perf 11½	17.50	7.00
c.		Perf 11½x10¾	42.50	21.00
751A	A372	4 l dk yel grn	.55	.25
a.		Perf 10¾	27.50	8.50
c.		Perf 11½	35.00	11.00
		Nos. 750-751A (3)	1.15	.85

Demeter Blagoev Addressing 1891 Congress at Busludja — A413

1951		**Photo.**	**Perf. 11**	
752	A413	1 l purple	.40	.25
753	A413	4 l dark green	.70	.25
754	A413	9 l deep claret	1.40	.60
		Nos. 752-754 (3)	2.50	1.10

60th anniversary of the first Congress of the Bulgarian Social-Democratic Party. See Nos. 1174-1176.

Day Nursery A414

Designs: 4 l, Model building construction. 9 l, Playground. 20 l, Children's town.

			Unwmk.	
1951, Oct. 10				
755	A414	1 l brown	.25	.25
756	A414	4 l deep plum	.45	.25
757	A414	9 l blue green	1.00	.90
758	A414	20 l deep blue	2.00	1.25
		Nos. 755-758 (4)	3.70	2.15

Children's Day, Sept. 25, 1951.

Order of Labor
A415 A416

1952, Feb. 1 **Perf. 13**
Reverse of Medal

759	A415	1 l red brown	.25	.25
760	A415	4 l blue green	.25	.25
761	A415	9 l dark blue	.45	.25

Obverse of Medal

762	A416	1 l carmine	.25	.25
763	A416	4 l green	.25	.25
764	A416	9 l purple	.45	.25
		Nos. 759-764 (6)	1.90	1.50

No. 764 has numeral at lower left and different background.

Workers and Symbols of Industry — A417

Design: 4 l, Flags, Dimitrov, Chervenkov.

Inscribed: "16 XII 1951"

1951, Dec. 29 **Perf. 11**

765	A417	1 l olive black	.25	.25
766	A417	4 l chocolate	.35	.25

Third Congress of Bulgarian General Workers' Professional Union.

Dimitrov and Chemical Works — A418

George Dimitrov and V. Chervenkov — A419

Portrait: 80s, Dimitrov.

		Unwmk.		
1952, June 18		**Photo.**	**Perf. 11**	
767	A418	16s brown	.60	.35
768	A419	44s brown carmine	1.00	.55
769	A418	80s brt blue	1.75	1.00
		Nos. 767-769 (3)	3.35	1.90

70th anniv. of the birth of George Dimitrov.

Vassil Kolarov Dam — A420

1952, May 16 **Perf. 13**

770	A420	4s dark green	.25	.25
771	A420	12s purple	.25	.25
772	A420	16s red brown	.25	.25
773	A420	44s rose brown	.65	.25
774	A420	80s brt blue	2.75	.35
		Nos. 770-774 (5)	4.15	1.35

No. 774 is inscribed in Latin characters.

Republika Power Station — A421

1952, June 30 **Perf. 13, Pin Perf.**

775	A421	16s dark brown	.40	.25
a.		Perf 10¾	25.00	10.00
b.		Perf 11½	32.50	20.00
776	A421	44s magenta	1.25	.95
a.		Perf 10¾	25.00	10.00
b.		Perf 11½	32.50	20.00

Nikolai I. Vapzarov A422

Designs: Various portraits.

1952, July 23 **Perf. 10½**

777	A422	16s rose brown	.25	.25
778	A422	44s dk red brn	1.75	.95
779	A422	80s dk olive brn	3.75	1.25
		Nos. 777-779 (3)	5.75	1.75

10th anniversary of the death of Nikolai I. Vapzarov, poet and revolutionary.

Dimitrov and Youth Conference — A423

16s, Resistance movement incident. 44s, Frontier guards & industrial scene. 80s, George Dimitrov & young workers.

1952, Sept. 1 **Perf. 11x11½**

780	A423	2s brown carmine	.25	.25
781	A423	16s purple	.25	.25
782	A423	44s dark green	.85	.55
783	A423	80s dark brown	1.75	1.10
		Nos. 780-783 (4)	3.10	2.15

40th anniv. of the founding conference of the Union of Social Democratic Youth.

Assault on the Winter Palace — A424

Designs: 8s, Volga-Don Canal. 16s, Symbols of world peace. 44s, Lenin and Stalin. 80s, Himlay hydroelectric station.

Perf. 11½

1952, Nov. 6 **Unwmk.** **Photo.**
Dated: "1917-1952"

784	A424	4s red brown	.35	.25
785	A424	8s dark green	.35	.25
786	A424	16s dark blue	1.00	.35
787	A424	44s brown	1.00	.35
788	A424	80s olive brown	2.00	1.60
		Nos. 784-788 (5)	4.70	2.80

35th anniv. of the Russian revolution.

Vassil Levski — A425

Design: 44s, Levski and comrades.

1953, Feb. 19 **Perf. 11**
Cream Paper

789	A425	16s brown	.25	.25
790	A425	44s brown blk	.45	.25

80th anniv. of the death of Levski, patriot.

Ferrying Artillery and Troops into Battle A426

Soldier — A427

Designs: 44s, Victorious soldiers. 80s, Soldier welcomed. 1 l, Monuments.

1953, Mar. 3 **Perf. 10½**

791	A426	8s Prus green	.25	.25
792	A427	16s dp brown	.30	.25
793	A426	44s dk slate grn	.70	.25
794	A426	80s dull red brn	2.00	1.00
795	A426	1 l black	2.25	2.00
		Nos. 791-795 (5)	5.50	3.75

Bulgaria's independence from Turkey, 75th anniv.

Mother and Children — A428

1953, Mar. 9

796	A428	16s slate green	.25	.25
797	A428	16s bright blue	.25	.25

Women's Day.

Woodcarvings at Rila Monastery
A429 A430

Designs: 12s, 16s, 28s, Woodcarvings, Rila Monastery. 44s, Carved Ceilings, Trnovo. 80s, 1 l, 4 l, Carvings, Pasardjik.

		Unwmk.	**Photo.**	**Perf. 13**
1953				
798	A429	2s gray brown	.25	.25
799	A430	8s dk slate grn	.25	.25
800	A430	12s brown	.25	.25
801	A430	16s rose lake	.50	.25
802	A429	28s dk olive grn	.70	.25
803	A430	44s dk brown	1.00	.25
804	A430	80s ultra	1.20	.25
805	A430	1 l violet blue	2.50	.40
806	A430	4 l rose lake	3.25	1.50
		Nos. 798-806 (9)	9.90	3.65

For surcharge see No. 1204.

Karl Marx — A431

"Das Kapital" — A432

1953, Apr. 30   **Perf. 10½**
807 A431 16s bright blue   .35 .25
808 A432 44s deep brown   .70 .50

70th anniversary of the death of Karl Marx.

Labor Day Parade — A433

1953, Apr. 30   **Perf. 13**
809 A433 16s brown red   .35 .35

Labor Day, May 1, 1953.

Joseph V. Stalin — A434

1953, May 23   **Perf. 13x13½**
810 A434 16s dark gray   .65 .25
811 A434 16s dark brown   .35 .25

Death of Joseph V. Stalin, Mar. 5, 1953.

Georgi Delchev — A435   Battle Scene — A436

Peasants Attacking Turkish Troops A437

1953, Aug. 8   **Perf. 13**
812 A435 16s dark brown   .25 .25
813 A436 44s purple   .55 .35
814 A437 1 l deep claret   .80 .60
    Nos. 812-814 (3)   1.60 1.20

50th anniv. of the Ilinden Revolt (Nos. 812, 814) and the Preobrazhene Revolt (No. 813).

Soldier and Rebels A438

44s, Soldier guarding industrial construction.

1953, Sept. 18
815 A438 16s deep claret   .35 .25
816 A438 44s greenish blue   .75 .25

Army Day.

George Dimitrov and Vassil Kolarov A439

Designs: 16s, Citizens in revolt. 44s, Attack.

1953, Sept. 22
817 A439   8s olive gray   .25 .25
818 A439 16s dk red brn   .30 .25
819 A439 44s cerise   1.00 .25
    Nos. 817-819 (3)   1.55 .75

September Revolution, 30th anniversary.

Demeter Blagoev — A440

Portraits: 44s, G. Dimitrov and D. Blagoev.

1953, Sept. 21
820 A440 16s brown   .35 .25
821 A440 44s red brown   1.00 .25

50th anniversary of the formation of the Social Democratic Party.

Railway Viaduct A441

Pouring Molten Metal — A442

Designs: 16s, Welder and storage tanks. 80s, Harvesting machine.

1953, Oct. 17
826 A441   8s brt blue   .25 .25
827 A441 16s grnsh blk   .25 .25
828 A442 44s brown red   .70 .25
829 A441 80s orange   .70 .50
    Nos. 826-829 (4)   1.90 1.25

Month of Bulgarian-Russian friendship.

Belladonna — A443

Medicinal Flowers: 4s, Jimson weed. 8s, Sage. 12s, Dog rose. 16s, Gentian. 20s, Poppy. 28s, Peppermint. 40s, Bear grass. 44s, Coltsfoot. 80s, Cowslip. 1 l, Dandelion. 2 l, Foxglove.

1953   Unwmk.   Photo.   Perf. 13
White or Cream Paper
830 A443   2s dull blue   .25 .25
831 A443   4s brown org   .25 .25
832 A443   8s blue grn   .25 .25
833 A443 12s brown org   .25 .25
834 A443 12s blue grn   .25 .25
835 A443 16s violet blue   .35 .25
836 A443 16s dp red brn   .35 .25
837 A443 20s car rose   .70 .25
838 A443 28s dk gray grn   .55 .25

---

839 A443 40s dark blue   .35 .35
840 A443 44s brown   1.00 .45
841 A443 80s yellow brn   1.40 .80
842 A443   1 l henna brn   2.75 1.40
843 A443   2 l purple   5.50 2.75
    a.   Souvenir sheet   40.00 40.00
    Nos. 830-843 (14)   14.20 8.00

No. 843a contains 12 stamps, one of each denomination above, printed in dark green. Size: 161x172mm. Sold for 6 leva.
Nos. 830-843 exist perf 10¾, 10¾x11½, 12¾, 12¾x10¾, 13¼x12½ and 13¼.

Kolarov Library, Sofia — A444

1953, Dec. 16
854 A444 44s brown   .45 .25

75th anniversary of the founding of the Kolarov Library, Sofia.

Singer and Accordionist A445

1953, Dec. 26
855 A445 16s shown   .25 .25
856 A445 44s Dancers   .50 .30

Lenin and Stalin — A446

Designs: 44s, Lenin statue. 80s, Lenin mausoleum, Moscow. 1 l, Lenin.

1954, Mar. 13   **Cream Paper**
857 A446 16s brown   .25 .25
858 A446 44s rose brown   .50 .25
859 A446 80s blue   .70 .30
860 A446   1 l dp olive grn   1.40 1.00
    Nos. 857-860 (4)   2.85 1.80

30th anniversary of the death of Lenin.

Demeter Blagoev and Followers A447

Design: 44s, Blagoev at desk.

1954, Apr. 28   **Cream Paper**
861 A447 16s dp red brn   .25 .25
862 A447 44s black brn   .50 .25

30th anniv. of the death of Demeter Blagoev.

George Dimitrov — A448

Dimitrov and Refinery A449

1954, June 11
863 A448 44s lake, *cream*   .35 .25
864 A449 80s brown, *cream*   .75 .50

5th anniv. of the death of George Dimitrov.

Train Leaving Tunnel — A450

1954, July 30
865 A450 44s dk grn, *cream*   1.00 .50
866 A450 44s blk brn, *cream*   1.00 .50

Day of the Railroads, Aug. 1, 1954.

Miner at Work — A451

1954, Aug. 19
867 A451 44s grnsh blk, *cream*   .35 .25

Miners' Day.

Academy of Science A452

1954, Oct. 27
868 A452 80s black, *cream*   1.00 .55

85th anniversary of the foundation of the Bulgarian Academy of Science.

Horsemanship — A454

16s, 44s, 2 l, vert.

1954, Dec. 21
869 A454 16s Gymnastics   1.00 .30
870 A454 44s Wrestling   1.20 .65
871 A454 80s shown   2.50 1.25
872 A454   2 l Skiing   4.00 2.75
    Nos. 869-872 (4)   8.70 4.95

Welcoming Liberators A455

Soldier's Return — A456

28s, Refinery. 44s, Dimitrov & Workers. 80s, Girl & boy. 1 l, George Dimitrov.

1954, Oct. 4   **Cream Paper**
873 A455 12s brown car   .25 .25
874 A456 16s dp carmine   .25 .25
875 A455 28s indigo   .25 .25
876 A456 44s redsh brn   .40 .25
877 A456 80s deep blue   .90 .35
878 A456   1 l dark green   1.00 .45
    Nos. 873-878 (6)   3.05 1.80

10th anniversary of Bulgaria's liberation.

Recreation at Workers' Rest Home — A457

Metal Worker and Furnace — A458

80s, Dimitrov, Blagoev, Kirkov.

Unwmk.
1954, Dec. 28   **Photo.**   ***Perf. 13***
Cream Paper

879	A457	16s dark green	.25	.25
880	A458	44s brown orange	.35	.25
881	A457	80s dp violet blue	.85	.25
		Nos. 879-881 (3)	1.45	.75

50th anniversary of Bulgaria's trade union movement.

Geese — A459

Designs: 4s, Chickens. 12s, Hogs. 16s, Sheep. 28s, Telephone building. 44s, Communist party headquarters. 80s, Apartment buildings. 1 l, St. Kiradgieff Mills.

1955-56

882	A459	2s dk blue grn	.25	.25
883	A459	4s olive green	.25	.25
884	A459	12s dk red brn	.45	.25
885	A459	16s brown orange	.75	.25
886	A459	28s violet blue	.45	.25
887	A459	44s lil red, *cream*	3.50	.25
a.		44s brown red	6.75	2.50
888	A459	80s dk red brown	1.10	.35
889	A459	1 l dk blue green	1.50	.75
		Nos. 882-889 (8)	8.25	3.10

Issued: No. 887, 4/20/56; others, 2/19/55.
Nos. 882-889 exist perf 10¾, 11½, 10¾x13, 12¾, 13½ and 13x11½.

Textile Worker A460

Mother and Child — A461

Design: 16s, Woman feeding calf.

1955, Mar. 5

890	A460	12s dark brown	.25	.25
891	A460	16s dark green	.25	.25
892	A461	44s dk car rose	.85	.25
893	A461	44s blue	.85	.25
		Nos. 890-893 (4)	2.20	1.00

Women's Day, Mar. 8, 1955.

No. 744 Surcharged in Blue

Type I   Type II

Two overprint types: I, overprint in blue-black, "16" 4mm high, thin font; II, overprint in blue, "16" 5mm high, thick font.

1955, Mar. 8   ***Perf. 13***

894	A410	16s on 4 l red brown, Type I	1.50	.35
a.		Type II	1.50	.35

May Day Demonstration of Workers — A462

Design: 44s, Three workers and globe.

1955, Apr. 23   **Photo.**

895	A462	16s car rose	.25	.25
896	A462	44s blue	.50	.25

Labor Day, May 1, 1955.

Sts. Cyril and Methodius A463

Designs: 8s, Paisii Hilendarski. 16s, Nicolas Karastoyanov's printing press. 28s, Christo Botev. 44s, Ivan Vazov. 80s, Demeter Blagoev and socialist papers. 2 l, Blagoev printing plant, Sofia.

1955, May 21   **Cream Paper**

897	A463	4s deep blue	.25	.25
898	A463	8s olive	.25	.25
899	A463	16s black	.25	.25
900	A463	28s henna brn	.25	.25
901	A463	44s brown	.60	.25
902	A463	80s rose red	1.10	.25
903	A463	2 l black	3.00	.95
		Nos. 897-903 (7)	5.70	2.45

Creation of the Cyrillic alphabet, 1100th anniv. Latin lettering at bottom on Nos. 901-903.

Sergei Rumyantzev — A464

16s, Christo Jassenov. 44s, Geo Milev.

1955, June 30   **Unwmk.**   ***Perf. 13***
Cream Paper

904	A464	12s orange brn	.30	.25
905	A464	16s lt brown	.30	.25
906	A464	44s grnsh blk	1.10	.70
		Nos. 904-906 (3)	1.70	1.20

30th anniv. of the deaths of Sergei Rumyanchev, Christo Jassenov and Geo Milev. Latin lettering at bottom of No. 906.

Mother and Children — A465

1955, July 30

907	A465	44s brn car, *cream*	.75	.25

World Congress of Mothers in Lausanne, 1955.

Young People of Three Races — A466

1955, July 30

908	A466	44s blue, *cream*	.75	.25

5th World Festival of Youth in Warsaw, July 31-Aug. 14.

Friedrich Engels and Book — A467

1955, July 30

909	A467	44s brown	.75	.25

60th anniv. of the death of Friedrich Engels.

Entrance to Fair, 1892 — A468

Statuary Group at Fair, 1955 — A469

Designs: 44s, "Fruit of our Land." 80s, Woman holding Fair emblem.

1955, Aug. 31   **Cream Paper**

910	A468	4s deep brown	.25	.25
911	A469	16s dk car rose	.25	.25
912	A468	44s olive blk	.35	.25
913	A469	80s deep blue	.90	.30
		Nos. 910-913 (4)	1.75	1.05

16th International Plovdiv Fair. Latin lettering on Nos. 912-913.

Friedrich von Schiller — A470

44s, Adam Mickiewicz. 60s, Hans Christian Andersen. 80s, Baron de Montesquieu. 1 l, Miguel de Cervantes. 2 l, Walt Whitman.

1955, Oct. 31   **Cream Paper**

914	A470	16s brown	.40	.25
915	A470	44s brown red	.80	.25
916	A470	60s Prus blue	1.00	.25
917	A470	80s black	1.40	.45
918	A470	1 l rose violet	2.75	1.10
919	A470	2 l olive green	3.50	2.50
		Nos. 914-919 (6)	9.85	4.80

Various anniversaries of famous writers. Nos. 918 and 919 are issued in sheets alternating with labels without franking value. The labels show title pages for Leaves of Grass and Don Quixote in English and Spanish, respectively. Latin lettering on Nos. 915-919.

A471

A472   A473

2s, Karl Marx Industrial Plant. 4s, Alekandr Stamboliski Dam. 16s, Bridge over Danube. 44s, Friendship Monument. 80s, I. V. Michurin. 1 l, Vladimir V. Mayakovsky.

1955, Dec. 1   **Unwmk.**

920	A471	2s slate blk	.25	.25
921	A471	4s deep blue	.25	.25
922	A471	16s dk blue grn	.25	.25
923	A472	44s red brown	.25	.25
924	A473	80s dark green	.85	.25
925	A473	1 l gray blk	.90	.40
		Nos. 920-925 (6)	2.75	1.65

Russian-Bulgarian friendship.

Library Seal — A474

Krusto Pishurka A475

Portrait: 44s, Bacho Kiro.

1956, Feb. 10   ***Perf. 11x10½***

926	A474	12s car lake, *cream*	.25	.25
927	A475	16s dp brn, *cream*	.25	.25
928	A475	44s slate blk, *cream*	.85	.25
		Nos. 926-928 (3)	1.35	.75

100th anniversary of the National Library. Latin lettering at bottom of No. 928.

Canceled to Order

Beginning about 1956, some issues were sold in sheets canceled to order. Values in second column when much less than unused are for "CTO" examples. Postally used stamps are valued at slightly less than, or the same as, unused.

Quinces — A476

8s, Pears. 16s, Apples. 44s, Grapes.

1956   **Photo.**   ***Perf. 13***

929	A476	4s carmine	1.60	.25
930	A476	8s blue green	.75	.25
931	A476	16s lilac rose	1.25	.25
932	A476	44s deep violet	1.50	.45
		Nos. 929-932 (4)	5.10	1.20

Latin lettering on No. 932. See Nos. 964-967. For surcharge see No. 1364.

Cherrywood Cannon A477

1956, Apr. 28   *Perf. 11x10½*
933 A477 16s shown   .35 .25
934 A477 44s Cavalry attack   .35 .25

April Uprising against Turkish rule, 80th anniv.

Demeter Blagoev (1856-1924), Writer, Birthplace
A478

1956, May 30   *Perf. 11*
935 A478 44s Prus blue   1.00 .50

Cherries — A479

1956   **Unwmk.**   *Perf. 13*
936 A479   2s shown   .25 .25
937 A479 12s Plums   .25 .25
938 A479 28s Peaches   .25 .25
939 A479 80s Strawberries   1.00 .25
      Nos. 936-939 (4)   1.75 1.00

Latin lettering on No. 939.

Gymnastics A480

Pole Vaulting A481

Designs: 12s, Discus throw. 44s, Soccer, 80s, Basketball. 1 l, Boxing.

Perf. 11x10½, 10½x11
1956, Aug. 29
940 A480   4s brt ultra   .40 .25
941 A480 12s brick red   .50 .25
942 A481 16s yellow brn   .55 .25
943 A481 44s dark green   1.00 .45
944 A480 80s dark red brn   1.60 .85
945 A481   1 l deep magenta   2.25 1.00
      Nos. 940-945 (6)   6.30 3.05

Latin lettering on Nos. 943-945.
16th Olympic Games at Melbourne, Nov. 22-Dec. 8, 1956.

Tobacco, Rose and Distillery — A482

1956, Sept. 1   *Perf. 13*
946 A482 44s deep carmine   1.00 .40
947 A482 44s olive green   1.00 .40

17th International Plovdiv Fair.

People's Theater A483

Design: 44s, Dobri Woinikoff and Sawa Dobroplodni, dramatists.

1956, Nov. 16   **Unwmk.**
948 A483 16s dull red brown   .25 .25
949 A483 44s dark blue green   .50 .25

Bulgarian Theater centenary.

Benjamin Franklin — A484

Portraits: 20s, Rembrandt. 40s, Mozart. 44s, Heinrich Heine. 60s, Shaw. 80s, Dostoevski. 1 l, Ibsen. 2 l, Pierre Curie.

1956, Dec. 29
950 A484 16s dark olive grn   .25 .25
951 A484 20s brown   .25 .25
952 A484 40s dark car rose   .25 .25
953 A484 44s dark violet brn   .60 .25
954 A484 60s dark slate   .75 .25
955 A484 80s dark brown   1.10 .25
956 A484   1 l bluish grn   1.75 .75
957 A484   2 l Prus green   4.00 1.25
      Nos. 950-957 (8)   8.95 3.50

Great personalities of the world.

Cyclists, Palms and Pyramids — A485

1957, Mar. 6   **Photo.**   *Perf. 10½*
958 A485 80s henna brown   1.00 .50
959 A485 80s Prus green   1.00 .50

Fourth Egyptian bicycle race.

Woman Technician A486

Designs: 16s, Woman and children. 44s, Woman feeding chickens.

1957, Mar. 8
960 A486 12s deep blue   .25 .25
961 A486 16s henna brown   .25 .25
962 A486 44s slate green   .45 .25
      Nos. 960-962 (3)   .95 .75

Women's Day. Latin lettering on 44s.

"New Times" Review — A487

1957, Mar. 8   **Unwmk.**
963 A487 16s deep carmine   .35 .35

60th anniversary of the founding of the "New Times" review.

Fruit Type of 1956
4s, Quinces. 8s, Pears. 16s, Apples. 44s, Grapes.

1957   **Photo.**   *Perf. 13*
964 A476   4s yellow green   .25 .25
965 A476   8s brown orange   .25 .25
966 A476 16s rose red   .25 .25
967 A476 44s orange yellow   .90 .25
      Nos. 964-967 (4)   1.65 1.00

Latin lettering on No. 967. For surcharge see No. 1364.

Sts. Cyril and Methodius — A488

1957, May 22   *Perf. 11*
968 A488 44s olive grn & buff   .90 .25

Centenary of the first public veneration of Sts. Cyril and Methodius, inventors of the Cyrillic alphabet.

Basketball A489

1957, June 20 Photo. *Perf. 10½x11*
969 A489 44s dark green   1.50 .50

10th European Basketball Championship at Sofia.

Dancer and Spasski Tower, Moscow — A490

1957, July 18   *Perf. 13*
970 A490 44s blue   .60 .25

Sixth World Youth Festival in Moscow.

George Dimitrov (1882-1949) — A491

1957, July 18
971 A491 44s deep carmine   1.10 .25

Vassil Levski — A492

1957, July 18   *Perf. 11*
972 A492 44s grnsh black   .75 .25

120th anniversary of the birth of Vassil Levski, patriot and national hero.

No. 742 Surcharged in Carmine

1957   **Unwmk.**   *Perf. 13*
973 A408 16s on 1 l purple   .25 .25

Trnovo and Lazarus L. Zamenhof A493

1957, July 27
974 A493 44s slate green   1.00 .25

50th anniv. of the Bulgarian Esperanto Society and the 70th anniv. of Esperanto. For surcharge see No. 1235.

Bulgarian Veteran of 1877 War and Russian Soldier — A494

Design: 44s, Battle of Shipka Pass.

1957, Aug. 13
975 A494 16s dk blue grn   .25 .25
976 A494 44s brown   .50 .25

80th anniversary of Bulgaria's liberation from the Turks. Latin lettering on No. 976.

Woman Planting Tree — A495

Red Deer in Forest — A496

16s, Dam, lake and forest. 44s, Plane over forest. 80s, Fields on edge of forest.

1957, Sept. 16   **Photo.**   *Perf. 13*
977 A495   2s deep green   .25 .25
978 A496 12s dark brown   .25 .25
979 A496 16s Prus blue   .25 .25
980 A496 44s Prus green   .50 .25
981 A496 80s yellow green   .85 .25
      Nos. 977-981 (5)   2.10 1.25

Latin lettering on Nos. 980 and 981.

Lenin — A497

Designs: 16s, Cruiser "Aurora." 44s, Dove over map of communist area. 60s, Revolutionaries and banners. 80s, Chemical plant.

1957, Oct. 29   *Perf. 11*
982 A497 12s chocolate   .85 .25
983 A497 16s Prus green   1.75 .55
984 A497 44s deep blue   2.40 1.10

985 A497 60s dk car rose 4.00 1.50
986 A497 80s dark green 6.25 2.00
    Nos. 982-986 (5) 15.25 5.40

40th anniv. of the Communist Revolution. Latin lettering on Nos. 984-985.

Globes
A498

1957, Oct. 4   *Perf. 13*
987 A498 44s Prus blue .60 .25

4th Intl. Trade Union Cong., Leipzig, 10/4-15.

Vassil Kolarov Hotel A499

Bulgarian Health Resorts: 4s, Skis and Pirin Mountains. 8s, Old house at Koprivspitsa. 12s, Rest home at Velingrad. 44s, Momin-Prochod Hotel. 60s, Nesebr Hotel, shoreline and peninsula. 80s, Varna beach scene. 1 l, Hotel at Varna.

1958   **Photo.**   *Perf. 13*
988 A499 4s blue .25 .25
989 A499 8s orange brn .25 .25
990 A499 12s dk green .25 .25
991 A499 16s green .25 .25
992 A499 44s dk blue grn .25 .25
993 A499 60s deep blue .25 .25
994 A499 80s fawn .60 .25
995 A499 1 l dk red brn .25 .25
    Nos. 988-995 (8) 2.90 2.00

Latin lettering on 44s, 60s, 80s, and 1 l. Issue dates: Nos. 991-994, 1/20; others, 7/5.

For surcharges see Nos. 1200, 1436.

Mikhail I. Glinka — A500

Portraits: 16s, Jan A. Komensky (Comenius). 40s, Carl von Linné. 44s, William Blake. 60s, Carlo Goldoni. 80s, Auguste Comte.

1957, Dec. 30
996 A500 12s dark brown .50 .25
997 A500 16s dark green .50 .25
998 A500 40s Prus blue 1.25 .30
999 A500 44s maroon 1.25 .35
1000 A500 60s orange brown 1.40 .50
1001 A500 80s deep plum 2.00 2.00
    Nos. 996-1001 (6) 6.90 3.65

Famous men of other countries. Latin lettering on Nos. 999-1001.

Young Couple, Flag, Dimitrov — A501

1957, Dec. 28   *Perf. 11*
1002 A501 16s carmine rose .25 .25

10th anniversary of Dimitrov's Union of the People's Youth.

People's Front Salute — A502

1957, Dec. 28
1003 A502 16s dk violet brn .25 .25

15th anniversary of the People's Front.

Hare A503

12s, Red deer (doe), vert. 16s, Red deer (stag). 44s, Chamois. 80s, Brown bear. 1 l, Wild boar.

    Perf. 10½
1958, Apr. 5   **Unwmk.**   **Photo.**
1004 A503 2s lt & dk ol grn .45 .25
1005 A503 12s sl grn & red brn .65 .25
1006 A503 16s bluish grn & dk
    red brn 1.00 .30
1007 A503 44s blue & brown 1.20 .55
1008 A503 80s bis & dk brn 1.40 .50
1009 A503 1 l stl bl & dk brn 1.75 1.50
    Nos. 1004-1009 (6) 6.45 3.35

Value, imperf. set $11.

Marx and Lenin A504

Designs: 16s, Marchers and flags. 44s, Lenin blast furnaces.

1958, July 2   *Perf. 11*
1010 A504 12s dark brown .30 .25
1011 A504 16s dark carmine .50 .25
1012 A504 44s dark blue 1.00 .65
    Nos. 1010-1012 (3) 1.80 1.15

Bulgarian Communist Party, 7th Congress.

Wrestlers — A505

1958, June 20   *Perf. 10½*
1013 A505 60s dk carmine rose 1.40 1.00
1014 A505 80s deep brown 1.60 1.40

World Wrestling Championship, Sofia.

Chessmen and Globe A506

    Perf. 10½
1958, July 18   **Unwmk.**   **Photo.**
1015 A506 80s grn & yel grn 9.00 7.50
    a. Horiz. pair, imperf. btwn. 80.00

5th World Students' Chess Games, Varna.

Conference Emblem A507

1958, Sept. 24
1016 A507 44s blue .65 .25

World Trade Union Conference of Working Youth, Prague, July 14-20.

Swimmer A508

1958 Students' Games: 28s, Dancer, vert. 44s, Volleyball, vert.

1958, Sept. 19   *Perf. 11x10½*
1017 A508 16s bright blue .25 .25
1018 A508 28s brown orange .40 .25
1019 A508 44s bright green .65 .25
    Nos. 1017-1019 (3) 1.30 .75

Onions — A509

Vegetables: 12s, Garlic. 16s, Peppers. 44s, Tomatoes. 80s, Cucumbers. 1 l, Eggplant.

1958, Sept. 20   *Perf. 13*
1020 A509 2s orange brown .25 .25
1021 A509 12s Prus blue .25 .25
1022 A509 16s dark green .25 .25
1023 A509 44s deep carmine .30 .25
1024 A509 80s deep green .80 .25
1025 A509 1 l brt purple 1.10 .30
    Nos. 1020-1025 (6) 2.95 1.55

Value, imperf. set $7.
See No. 1072. For surcharge see No. 1201.

Plovdiv Fair Building A510

1958, Sept. 14   **Unwmk.**   *Perf. 11*
1026 A510 44s deep carmine .65 .25

18th International Plovdiv Fair.

Attack — A511

44s, Fighter dragging wounded man.

1958, Sept. 23   **Photo.**   *Perf. 11*
1027 A511 16s orange ver .25 .25
1028 A511 44s lake .60 .25

35th anniv. of the September Revolution.

Emblem, Brussels Fair — A512

1958, Oct. 13   *Perf. 11*
1029 A512 1 l blk & brt blue 7.50 7.50

Brussels World's Fair, Apr. 17-Oct. 19.
Exists imperf. Value, $55.

Runner at Finish Line — A513

Woman Throwing Javelin A514

60s, High jumper. 80s, Hurdler. 4 l, Shot putter.

1958, Nov. 30
1030 A513 16s red brn, *pnksh* .60 .30
1031 A514 44s olive, *yelsh* .65 .40
1032 A514 60s dk bl, *bluish* 1.10 .50
1033 A514 80s dp grn, *grnsh* 1.40 .65
1034 A513 4 l dp rose cl,
    pnksh 8.00 5.50
    Nos. 1030-1034 (5) 11.75 7.35

1958 Balkan Games.
Latin lettering on Nos. 1032-1033.

Christo Smirnenski A515

1958, Dec. 22
1035 A515 16s dark carmine .30 .25

Christo Smirnenski (1898-1923), poet.

Girls Harvesting — A516

Girl Tending Calves A517

16s, Boy & girl laborers. 40s, Boy pushing wheelbarrow. 44s, Headquarters building.

1959, Nov. 29   **Photo.**
1036 A516 8s dk olive green .25 .25
1037 A517 12s redsh brown .25 .25
1038 A516 16s violet brown .25 .25

1039 A517 40s Prus blue .25 .25
1040 A516 44s deep carmine .75 .25
   Nos. 1036-1040 (5) 1.75 1.25

4th Congress of Dimitrov's Union of People's Youth.

UNESCO
Building,
Paris
A518

1959, Mar. 28   **Unwmk.**   **Perf. 11**
1041 A518 2 l dp red lilac, *cream* 2.25 1.50

Opening of UNESCO Headquarters, Paris, Nov. 3, 1958. Value imperf. $5.

Skier — A519

1959, Mar. 28   **Perf. 11**
1042 A519 1 l blue, *cream* 1.50 .75

Forty years of skiing in Bulgaria.

Soccer
Players — A520

1959, Mar. 25
1043 A520 2 l chestnut, *cream* 2.50 1.50

1959 European Youth Soccer Championship.

Russian Soldiers
Installing Telegraph
Wires — A521

First
Bulgarian
Postal
Coach
A522

Designs: 60s, Stamp of 1879. 80s, First Bulgarian automobile. 1 l, Television tower. 2 l, Strike of railroad and postal workers, 1919.

1959, May 4
1044 A521 12s dk grn & cit .25 .25
1045 A522 16s deep plum .35 .25
1046 A521 60s dk brn & yel .65 .35
1047 A522 80s hn brn & sal .65 .35
1048 A521 1 l blue 1.60 .40
1049 A522 2 l dk red brown 3.25 1.50
   Nos. 1044-1049 (6) 6.75 3.10

80th anniv. of the Bulgarian post. Latin lettering on Nos. 1046-1049.

Two imperf. souvenir sheets exist with olive borders and inscriptions. One contains one copy of No. 1046 in black & ocher, and measures 92x121mm. The other sheet contains one copy each of Nos. 1044-1045 and 1047-1048 in changed colors: 12s, olive green & ocher; 16s, deep claret & ocher; 80s, dark red & ocher; 1 l, olive & ocher. Each sheet sold for 5 leva. Value, each $45.

Great Tits
A523

Birds: 8s, Hoopoe. 16s, Great spotted woodpecker, vert. 45s, Gray partridge, vert. 60s, Rock partridge. 80s, European cuckoo.

1959, June 30   **Photo.**
1050 A523 2s olive & sl grn .25 .25
1051 A523 8s dp orange & blk .55 .25
1052 A523 16s chestnut & dk
          brn .55 .25
1053 A523 45s brown & blk 1.25 .60
1054 A523 60s dp blue & gray 2.25 .85
1055 A523 80s dp bl grn & gray 3.25 1.50
   Nos. 1050-1055 (6) 8.10 3.70

Bagpiper — A524

12s, Acrobats. 16s, Girls exercising with hoops. 20s, Male dancers. 80s, Ballet dancers. 1 l, Ceramic pitcher. 16s, 20s, 80s are horiz.

1959, Aug. 29   **Unwmk.**   **Perf. 11**
Surface-colored Paper
1056 A524 4s dk olive .25 .25
1057 A524 12s scarlet .25 .25
1058 A524 16s maroon .25 .25
1059 A524 20s dk blue .35 .25
1060 A524 80s brt green 1.10 .45
1061 A524 1 l brown org 1.10 .70
   Nos. 1056-1061 (6) 3.30 2.15

7th International Youth Festival, Vienna. Latin inscriptions on Nos. 1060-1061.

Partisans
in Truck
A525

Designs: 16s, Partisans and soldiers shaking hands. 45s, Steel mill. 60s, Tanks. 80s, Harvester. 1.25 l, Children with flag, vert.

1959, Sept. 8
1062 A525 12s red & Prus grn .25 .25
1063 A525 16s red & dk pur .25 .25
1064 A525 45s red & int bl .25 .25
1065 A525 60s red & ol grn .25 .25
1066 A525 80s red & brn .60 .25
1067 A525 1.25 l red & dp brn 1.20 .50
   Nos. 1062-1067 (6) 2.80 1.75

15th anniversary of Bulgarian liberation.

Soccer
A526

1959, Oct. 10   **Unwmk.**   **Perf. 11**
1068 A526 1.25 l dp green, *yel* 5.25 5.25

50 years of Bulgarian soccer.
Stamp exists imperf in changed colors. Value $15 unused or used.

Batak
Defenders
A527

1959, Aug. 8
1069 A527 16s deep claret .35 .25

300th anniv. of the settlement of Batak.

Post Horn and
Letter — A528

Design: 1.25 l, Dove and letter.

1959, Nov. 23
1070 A528 45s emerald & blk .45 .25
1071 A528 1.25 l lt blue, red &
          blk .85 .25

Intl. Letter Writing Week Oct. 5-11.

Type of 1958
Surcharged in Dark
Blue

Design: Tomatoes.

1959   **Photo.**   **Perf. 13**
1072 A509 45s on 44s scarlet 1.00 .25

Bird-shaped
Lyre — A529

1960, Feb. 23   **Unwmk.**   **Perf. 10½**
1073 A529 80s shown .65 .25
1074 A529 1.25 l Lyre 1.00 .25

50th anniv. of Bulgaria's State Opera.

N. I.
Vapzarov — A530

1959, Dec. 14   **Perf. 11**
1075 A530 80s yel grn & red brn .65 .25

Vapzarov, poet and patriot, 50th birth anniv.

Parachute and
Radio
Tower — A531

1959, Dec. 3   **Photo.**
1076 A531 1.25 l dp grnsh bl &
          yel 2.25 1.10

3rd Cong. of Voluntary Participants in Defense.

Cotton
Picker — A532

Harvester
Combine
A533

Designs: 2s, Kindergarten. 4s, Woman doctor and child. 10s, Woman milking cow. 12s, Woman holding tobacco leaves. 15s, Woman working loom. 16s, Industrial plants, Dimitrovgrad. 25s, Rural electrification. 28s, Woman picking sunflowers. 40s, "Cold-well" hydroelectric dam. 45s, Miner. 60s, Foundry worker. 80s, Woman harvesting grapes. 1 l, Worker and peasant with cogwheel. 1.25 l, Industrial worker. 2 l, Party leader.

1959-61   **Photo.**   **Perf. 13**
1077 A533 2s brn org ('60) .25 .25
1077A A532 4s gldn brn
          ('61) .25 .25
1078 A532 5s dk green .25 .25
1079 A532 10s red brn ('61) .25 .25
1080 A532 12s red brown .25 .25
1081 A532 15s red lil ('60) .25 .25
1082 A533 16s dp vio ('60) .25 .25
1083 A533 20s orange .25 .25
1084 A532 25s brt blue ('60) .25 .25
1085 A533 28s brt green .25 .25
1086 A533 40s brt grnsh bl .35 .25
1087 A532 45s choc ('60) .25 .25
1088 A533 60s scarlet .65 .25
1089 A532 80s olive ('60) 1.20 .25
1090 A532 1 l maroon .65 .25
1090A A533 1.25 l dull bl ('61) 2.00 .50
1091 A532 2 l dp car ('60) 1.25 .40
   Nos. 1077-1091 (17) 8.85 4.65

Early completion of the 5-year plan (in 1959). For surcharges see Nos. 1192-1199, 1202-1203.

L. L. Zamenhof
A534

1959, Dec. 5   **Unwmk.**   **Perf. 11**
1092 A534 1.25 l dk grn & yel
          grn 1.00 .65

Lazarus Ludwig Zamenhof (1859-1917), inventor of Esperanto.

Path of Lunik
3 — A535

1960, Mar. 28   **Perf. 11**
1093 A535 1.25 l Prus bl & brt
          yel 6.50 4.75

Flight of Lunik 3 around moon. Value, imperf. $9

Skier
A536

1960, Apr. 15 **Litho.**
1094 A536 2 l ultra, blk & brn   1.00 1.00

8th Winter Olympics, Squaw Valley, CA, Feb. 18-29. Value, imperf. $2.75 unused or used.

Vela Blagoeva
A537

Portraits: 28s, Anna Maimunkova. 45s, Vela Piskova. 60s, Rosa Luxemburg. 80s, Klara Zetkin. 1.25 l, N. K. Krupskaya.

1960, Apr. 27 **Photo.** **Perf. 11**
1095 A537 16s rose & red brn   .25 .25
1096 A537 28s citron & olive   .25 .25
1097 A537 45s ol grn & sl grn .25 .25
1098 A537 60s lt bl & Prus bl .35 .25
1099 A537 80s red org & dp brn .55 .25
1100 A537 1.25 l dull yel & olive .70 .25
   Nos. 1095-1100 (6)   2.35 1.50

International Women's Day, Mar. 8, 1960.

Lenin — A538

1960, May 12
1101 A538 16s shown   1.50 .45
1102 A538 45s Lenin sitting 2.75 1.00

90th anniversary of the birth of Lenin.

A539

1960, June 3 **Perf. 11**
1103 A539 1.25 l yel & slate grn 1.40 .65

Seventh European Women's Basketball championships.

A541

1960, June 29 **Litho.**
1105 A541 16s Parachutist   .35 .35
1106 A541 1.25 l Parachutes 2.25 .65

5th International Parachute Championships.

Yellow
Gentian — A542

5s, Tulips. 25s, Turk's-cap lily. 45s, Rhododendron. 60s, Lady's-slipper. 80s, Violets.

1960, July 27 **Photo.** **Perf. 11**
1107 A542 2s beige, grn & yel .25 .25
1108 A542 5s yel grn, grn & car rose .60 .25
1109 A542 25s pink, grn & org .75 .25
1110 A542 45s pale lil, grn & rose lil .75 .25
1111 A542 60s yel, grn & org 1.50 .25
1112 A542 80s gray, grn & vio bl 1.50 .85
   Nos. 1107-1112 (6)   5.35 2.10

Soccer
A543

12s, Wrestling. 16s, Weight lifting. 45s, Woman gymnast. 80s, Canoeing. 2 l, Runner.

1960, Aug. 29 **Unwmk.** **Perf. 11**
Athletes' Figures in Pink
1113 A543 8s brown   .25 .25
1114 A543 12s violet .25 .25
1115 A543 16s Prus blue .25 .25
1116 A543 45s deep plum .35 .25
1117 A543 80s blue   .85 .25
1118 A543 2 l deep green 1.10 .60
   Nos. 1113-1118 (6)   3.05 1.85

17th Olympic Games, Rome, 8/25-9/11. Value, set imperf. in changed colors, $8.50.

Globes — A544

Unwmk.
1960, Oct. 12 **Photo.** **Perf. 11**
1125 A544 1.25 l blue & ultra .75 .25

15th anniversary of the World Federation of Trade Unions.

Alexander
Popov
A545

1960, Oct. 12
1126 A545 90s blue & blk 1.10 .25

Centenary of the birth of Alexander Popov, radio pioneer.

Bicyclists
A546

1960, Sept. 22
1127 A546 1 l yel, red org & blk 1.50 .85

The 10th Tour of Bulgaria Bicycle Race.

Jaroslav
Vésin
A547

1960, Nov. 22 **Unwmk.** **Perf. 11**
1128 A547 1 l brt citron & ol grn 3.50 1.10

Birth centenary of Jaroslav Vesin, painter.

UN Headquarters
A548

1961, Jan. 14 **Photo.** **Perf. 11**
1129 A548 1 l brown & yel 1.75 1.00
 a. Souvenir sheet   12.00 12.00

15th anniv. of the UN. No. 1129 sold for 2 l. Value, imperf. $6.
No. 1129a sold for 2.50 l and contains one copy of No. 1129, imperf, in dark olive and pink.

Costume of
Kyustendil — A549

Regional Costumes: 16s, Pleven. 28s, Sliven. 45s, Sofia. 60s, Rhodope. 80s, Karnobat.

1961, Jan. 28
1130 A549 12s sal, sl grn & yel .25 .25
1131 A549 16s pale lil, brn vio & buff .25 .25
1132 A549 28s pale grn, sl grn & rose .30 .25
1133 A549 45s blue & red .45 .25
1134 A549 60s grnsh bl, Prus bl & yel 1.00 .25
1135 A549 80s yel, sl grn & pink 1.00 .45
   Nos. 1130-1135 (6)   3.25 1.70

Theodor
Tiro
(Fresco)
A550

Designs: 60s, Boyana Church. 1.25 l, Duchess of Dessislava (fresco).

1961, Jan. 28 **Photo.**
1136 A550 60s yel grn, blk & grn .75 .35
1137 A550 80s yel, sl grn & org 1.10 .35
1138 A550 1.25 l yel grn, hn brn & buff 1.50 .75
   Nos. 1136-1138 (3)   3.35 1.45

700th anniv. of murals in Boyana Church.

Clock Tower,
Vratsa — A551

Wooden
Jug — A552

Designs: 12s, Clock tower, Bansko. 20s, Anguchev House, Mogilitsa. 28s, Oslekov House, Koprivspitsa, horiz. 40s, Pasha's house. Melnik, horiz. 45s, Lion sculpture. 60s, Man on horseback, Madara. 80s, Fresco, Bratchkovo monastery. 1 l, Tsar Assen coin.

1961, Feb. 25 **Unwmk.** **Perf. 11**
Denomination and Stars in Vermilion
1139 A551 8s olive grn   .25 .25
1140 A551 12s lt violet .25 .25
1141 A552 16s dk red brn .25 .25
1142 A551 20s brt blue   .25 .25
1143 A551 28s grnsh blue .25 .25
1144 A551 40s red brown .30 .25
1145 A552 45s olive gray .35 .25
1146 A552 60s slate   .50 .25
1147 A552 80s dk olive gray .90 .25
1148 A552 1 l green   .50 .25
   Nos. 1139-1148 (10)   3.80 2.50

Capercaillie
A553

Birds: 4s, Dalmatian pelican. 16s, Ring-necked pheasant. 80s, Great bustard. 1 l, Lammergeier. 2 l, Hazel hen.

1961, Mar. 31
1149 A553 2s blk, sal & Prus grn .25 .25
1150 A553 4s blk, yel grn & org .25 .25
1151 A553 16s brn, lt grn & org .35 .25
1152 A553 80s brn, bluish grn & yel 2.40 1.85
1153 A553 1 l blk, lt bl & yel 3.00 1.40
1154 A553 2 l brn, bl & yel 3.50 1.50
   Nos. 1149-1154 (6)   9.75 5.50

Radio Tower
and Winged
Anchor
A554

1961, Apr. 1 **Unwmk.** **Perf. 11**
1155 A554 80s brt green & blk .75 .25

50th anniv. of the Transport Workers' Union.

T. G.
Shevchenko
A555

1961, Apr. 27
1156 A555 1 l olive & blk 4.75 3.50

Centenary of the death of Taras G. Shevchenko, Ukrainian poet.

Water Polo — A556

Designs: 5s, Tennis. 16s, Fencing. 45s, Throwing the discus. 1.25 l, Sports Palace. 2 l, Basketball. 5 l, Sports Palace, different view. 5s, 16s, 45s and 1.25 l, are horizontal.

1961, May 15   Black Inscriptions
1157	A556	4s lt ultra	.25	.25
1158	A556	5s orange ver	.25	.25
1159	A556	16s olive grn	.25	.25
1160	A556	45s dull blue	.40	.25
1161	A556	1.25 l yellow brn	1.50	.25
1162	A556	2 l lilac	1.50	.85
	Nos. 1157-1162 (6)		4.15	2.10

Souvenir Sheet
Imperf
1163	A556	5 l yel grn, dl bl & yel	12.50	12.50

1961 World University Games, Sofia, Aug. 26-Sept. 3.

Value, Nos. 1157-1162 in changed colors, imperf. $7.50.

Monk Seal
A557

Black Sea Fauna: 12s, Jellyfish. 16s, Dolphin. 45s, Black Sea sea horse, vert. 1 l, Starred sturgeon. 1.25 l, Thornback ray.

1961, June 19   Perf. 11
1164	A557	2s green & blk	.25	.25
1165	A557	12s Prus grn & pink	.25	.25
1166	A557	16s ultra & vio bl	.25	.25
1167	A557	45s lt blue & brn	1.00	.70
1168	A557	1 l yel grn & Prus grn	2.75	1.10
1169	A557	1.25 l lt vio bl & red brn	3.00	1.50
	Nos. 1164-1169 (6)		7.50	4.05

Hikers — A558

Designs: 4s, "Sredetz" hostel, horiz. 16s, Tents. 1.25 l, Mountain climber.

1961, Aug. 25   Litho.   Perf. 11
1170	A558	4s yel grn, yel & blk	.25	.25
1171	A558	12s lt bl, cr & blk	.25	.25
1172	A558	16s green, cr & blk	.25	.25
1173	A558	1.25 l bister, cr & blk	.65	.25
	Nos. 1170-1173 (4)		1.40	1.00

"Know Your Country" campaign.

Demeter Blagoev Addressing 1891 Congress at Busludja — A559

1961, Aug. 5   Photo.
1174	A559	45s dk red & buff	.25	.25
1175	A559	80s blue & pink	.55	.25
1176	A559	2 l dk brn & pale cit	1.20	1.00
	Nos. 1174-1176 (3)		2.00	1.00

70th anniversary of the first Congress of the Bulgarian Social-Democratic Party.

The Golden Girl
A560

Fairy Tales: 8s, The Living Water. 12s, The Golden Apple. 16s, Krali-Marko, hero. 45s, Samovila-Vila, Witch. 80s, Tom Thumb.

1961, Oct. 10   Unwmk.   Perf. 11
1177	A560	2s blue, blk & org	.25	.25
1178	A560	8s rose lil, blk & gray	.25	.25
1179	A560	12s bl grn, blk & pink	.25	.25
1180	A560	16s red, blk, bl & gray	.75	.25
1181	A560	45s ol grn, blk & pink	1.75	.50
1182	A560	80s ocher, blk & dk car	1.75	.60
	Nos. 1177-1182 (6)		5.00	2.10

Caesar's Mushroom
A561

Designs: Various mushrooms.

1961, Dec. 20   Photo.   Perf. 11
Denominations in Black
1183	A561	2s lemon & red	.25	.25
1184	A561	4s ol grn & red brn	.25	.25
1185	A561	12s bister & red brn	.25	.25
1186	A561	16s lilac & red brn	.25	.25
1187	A561	45s car rose & yel	.45	.25
1188	A561	80s brn org & sepia	.55	.45
1189	A561	1.25 l vio & dk brn	.80	.40
1190	A561	2 l org brn & brn	1.10	.90
	Nos. 1183-1190 (8)		3.90	3.00

Value, denomination in dark grn, imperf set $10 unused or canceled.

Miladinov Brothers and Title Page — A562

1961, Dec. 21   Unwmk.   Perf. 10½
1191	A562	1.25 l olive & blk	1.10	.50

Publication of "Collected Folksongs" by the Brothers Miladinov, Dimitri and Konstantin, cent.

Nos. 1079-1085, 1087, 992, 1023, 1090-1091 and 806 Surcharged

In Black — No. 1192

In Black — No. 1193

In Red — No. 1195

In Red — No. 1197

In Violet — No. 1204

1962, Jan. 1
1192	A533	1s on 10s red brn	.25	.25
1193	A532	1s on 12s red brn	.25	.25
1194	A532	2s on 15s red lilac	.25	.25
1195	A533	2s on 16s dp vio (R)	.25	.25
1196	A533	2s on 20s orange (R)	.25	.25
a.		"2 CT." on 2 lines	.25	.25
1197	A532	3s on 25s brt bl (R)	.25	.25
a.		Black surcharge	12.00	12.00
1198	A532	3s on 28s brt grn (R)	.25	.25
1199	A532	5s on 45s choc (R)	.35	.25
1200	A499	5s on 44s dk bl grn (R)	.25	.25
1201	A509	5s on 44s dp car (V)	.25	.25
1202	A532	10s on 1 l maroon	.45	.25
1203	A532	20s on 2 l dp car	.85	.55
1204	A430	40s on 4 l rose lake (V)	2.10	1.10
	Nos. 1192-1204 (13)		6.00	4.40

Freighter "Varna"
A563

Designs: 5s, Tanker "Komsomoletz." 20s, Liner "G. Dimitrov."

1962, Mar. 1   Photo.   Perf. 10½
1205	A563	1s lt grn & brt bl	.25	.25
1206	A563	5s lt blue & grn	.25	.25
1207	A563	20s gray bl & grnsh bl	.90	.25
	Nos. 1205-1207 (3)		1.50	.75

Dimitrov Working as Printer — A564

13s, Griffin, emblem of state printing works.

1962, Mar. 19   Unwmk.
1208	A564	2s ver, blk & yel	.25	.25
1209	A564	13s red org, blk & yel	.55	.25

80th anniversary (in 1961) of the George Dimitrov state printing works.

Roses — A565

1962, Mar. 28
Various Roses in Natural Colors
1210	A565	1s deep violet	.25	.25
1211	A565	2s salmon & dk car	.25	.25
1212	A565	3s gray & car	.30	.25
1213	A565	4s dark green	.40	.25
1214	A565	5s ultra	.75	.25
1215	A565	6s bluish grn & dk car	.75	.35
1216	A565	8s citron & car	2.00	.75
1217	A565	13s blue	3.50	2.50
	Nos. 1210-1217 (8)		8.20	4.85

For overprint and surcharges see Nos. 1281-1283.

Malaria Eradication Emblem and Mosquito
A566

Design: 20s, Malaria eradication emblem.

1962, Apr. 19
1218	A566	5s org brn, yel & blk	.45	.25
1219	A566	20s emerald, yel & blk	1.50	.60

WHO drive to eradicate malaria. Value, imperf. $5 unused, $1.50 canceled.

Lenin and First Issue of Pravda
A567

1962, May 4   Unwmk.   Perf. 10
1220	A567	5s deep rose & slate	1.50	.95

50th anniversary of Pravda, Russian newspaper founded by Lenin.

Blackboard and Book — A568

1962, May 21   Photo.
1221	A568	5s Prus bl, blk & yel	.40	.25

The 1962 Teachers' Congress.

Soccer Player and Globe
A569

1962, May 26   Perf. 10½
1222	A569	13s brt grn, blk & lt brn	1.40	.65

World Soccer Championship, Chile, May 30-June 17. Value, imperf. in changed colors, $4 unused or canceled.

George Dimitrov
A570

1962, June 18   Photo.
1223	A570	2s dark green	.35	.25
1224	A570	5s turq blue	.70	.25

80th anniv. of the birth of George Dimitrov (1882-1949), communist leader and premier of the Bulgarian Peoples' Republic.

Bishop — A571

1962, July 7   Unwmk.   Perf. 10½

1225	A571	1s shown	.25	.25
1226	A571	2s Rook	.25	.25
1227	A571	3s Queen	.25	.25
1228	A571	13s Knight	1.40	.55
1229	A571	20s Pawn	1.75	.85
		Nos. 1225-1229 (5)	3.90	2.15

15th Chess Olympics, Varna. Nos. 1225-1229 were also issued imperf in changed colors. Value, $6.50 unused.

An imperf. souvenir sheet contains one 20s horizontal stamp showing five chessmen. Size: 75x66mm. Value, $13 unused.

Rila Mountain A572

Designs: 2s, Pirin mountain. 6s, Nesebr, Black Sea. 8s, Danube. 13s, Vidin Castle. 1 l, Rhodope mountain.

1962-63   Perf. 13

1230	A572	1s dk blue grn	.25	.25
1231	A572	2s blue	.25	.25
1232	A572	6s grnsh blue	.25	.25
1233	A572	8s lilac	.25	.25
1234	A572	13s yellow grn	1.25	.25
1234A	A572	1 l dp green ('63)	5.00	1.40
		Nos. 1230-1234A (6)	7.25	2.65

No. 974 Surcharged in Red

1962, July 14   Perf. 13

1235	A493	13s on 44s slate grn	3.50	2.50

25th Bulgarian Esperanto Congress, Burgas, July 14-16.

Girl and Festival Emblem A573

Design: 5s, Festival emblem.

1962, Aug. 18   Photo.   Perf. 10½

1236	A573	5s green, lt bl & pink	.25	.25
1237	A573	13s lilac, lt bl & gray	.75	.25

8th Youth Festival for Peace and Friendship, Helsinki, July 28-Aug. 6, 1962.

Parnassius Apollo — A574

1962, Sept. 13

Various Butterflies in Natural Colors

1238	A574	1s pale cit & dk grn	.25	.25
1239	A574	2s rose & brown	.25	.25
1240	A574	3s buff & red brn	.25	.25
1241	A574	4s gray & brown	.25	.25
1242	A574	5s lt gray & brn	.35	.25
1243	A574	6s gray & black	.70	.25
1244	A574	10s pale grn & blk	2.50	.75
1245	A574	13s buff & red brn	3.00	1.75
		Nos. 1238-1245 (8)	7.55	4.00

Planting Machine — A575

2s, Electric locomotive. 3s, Blast furnace. 13s, Blagoev, Dimitrov & Communist flag.

1962, Nov. 1   Perf. 11½

1246	A575	1s bl grn & dk ol grn	.25	.25
1247	A575	2s bl & Prus bl	.25	.25
1248	A575	3s carmine & brn	.25	.25
1249	A575	13s plum, red & blk	.85	.25
		Nos. 1246-1249 (4)	1.60	1.00

Bulgarian Communist Party, 8th Congress.

Title Page of "Slav-Bulgarian History" — A576

Paisii Hilendarski Writing History A577

1962, Dec. 8   Unwmk.   Perf. 10½

1250	A576	2s olive grn & blk	.25	.25
1251	A577	5s brown org & blk	.25	.25

200th anniv. of "Slav-Bulgarian History."

Aleco Konstantinov (1863-1897), Writer A578

1963, Mar. 5   Photo.   Perf. 11½

1252	A578	5s red, grn & blk	.50	.25

Printed with alternating red brown and black label showing Bai Ganu, hero from Konstantinov's books.

A579

Sofia University — A580

No. 1255, Levski Stadium, Sofia. No. 1256, Arch, Nissaria. No. 1257, Parachutist.

1963, Feb. 20   Unwmk.   Perf. 10

1253	A579	1s brown red	.25	.25
1254	A580	1s red brown	.25	.25
1255	A580	1s blue green	.25	.25
1256	A580	1s dark green	.25	.25
1257	A580	1s brt blue	.25	.25
		Nos. 1253-1257 (5)	1.25	1.25

Vassil Levski A581

1963, Apr. 11   Photo.

1258	A581	13s grnsh blue & buff	1.40	.45

90th anniversary of the death of Vassil Levski, revolutionary leader in the fight for liberation from the Turks.

Boy, Girl and Dimitrov — A582

13s, Girl with book & boy with hammer.

1963, Apr. 25   Unwmk.   Perf. 11½

1259	A582	2s org, ver, red brn & blk		.25	.25
1260	A582	13s bluish grn, brn & blk	.55	.25

10th Congress of Dimitrov's Union of the People's Youth.

Red Squirrel — A583

2s, Hedgehog. 3s, European polecat. 5s, Pine marten. 13s, Badger. 20s, Otter. 2s, 3s, 5s, 13s, horiz.

1963, Apr. 30   Red Numerals

1261	A583	1s grn & brn, *grnsh*	.25	.25
1262	A583	2s grn & blk, *yel*	.25	.25
1263	A583	3s grn & brn, *bis*	.35	.25
1264	A583	5s vio & red brn, *lil*	.70	.25
1265	A583	13s red brn & blk, *pink*	2.50	.70
1266	A583	20s blk & brn, *blue*	2.50	1.40
		Nos. 1261-1266 (6)	6.55	3.10

Sun Coast Promenade A584

Black Sea Resorts: 2s, 3s, 13s, Views of Gold Sand. 5s, 20s, Sun Coast.

1963, Mar. 12   Unwmk.   Perf. 13

1267	A584	1s blue	.25	.25
1268	A584	2s vermilion	.25	.25
1269	A584	2s car rose	2.50	1.25
1270	A584	3s ocher	.25	.25
1271	A584	5s lilac	.25	.25
1272	A584	13s blue green	1.25	.25
1273	A584	20s green	1.25	.25
		Nos. 1267-1273 (7)	6.00	2.75

Freestyle Wrestling A585

Design: 20s, Freestyle wrestling, horiz.

1963, May 31   Perf. 11½

1274	A585	5s yel bister & blk	.35	.25
1275	A585	20s org brn & blk	1.25	.25

15th International Freestyle Wrestling Competitions, Sofia.

"Women for Peace" A586

1963, June 24   Unwmk.   Perf. 11½

1276	A586	20s blue & blk	1.10	.25

World Congress of Women, Moscow, June 24-29.

Esperanto Emblem and Arms of Sofia — A587

1963, June 29   Photo.

1277	A587	13s multicolored	1.00	.25

48th World Esperanto Congress, Sofia, Aug. 3-10.

Moon, Earth and Lunik 4 — A588

2s, Radar equipment. 3s, Satellites and moon.

1963, July 22

1278	A588	1s ultra	.25	.25
1279	A588	2s red lilac	.25	.25
1280	A588	3s greenish blue	.25	.25
		Nos. 1278-1280 (3)	.75	.75

Russia's rocket to the moon, Apr. 2, 1963.

Nos. 1211-1212 and 1215 Ovptd. or Srchd. in Green, Ultra or Black

1963, Aug. 31   Perf. 10½

1281	A565	2s (G)	.35	.25
1282	A565	5s on 3s (U)	.75	.25
1283	A565	13s on 6s	1.40	.35
		Nos. 1281-1283 (3)	2.50	.85

Intl. Stamp Fair, Riccione, Aug. 31.

Women's Relay Race — A589

2s, Hammer thrower. 3s, Women's long jump. 5s, Men's high jump. 13s, Discus thrower.

Perf. 11½
1963, Sept. 13   Photo.   Unwmk.
Flags in National Colors

1284	A589	1s slate green	.25	.25
1285	A589	2s purple	.25	.25
1286	A589	3s Prus blue	.25	.25
1287	A589	5s maroon	.70	.25
1288	A589	13s chestnut brn	2.75	2.10
		Nos. 1284-1288 (5)	4.20	3.10

Balkan Games. A multicolored, 50s, imperf. souvenir sheet shows design of women's relay race. Size: 74x70mm. Value, $5 unused.

"Slav-Bulgarian History" — A590

1963, Sept. 19   Perf. 10½
1289	A590	5s sal pink, slate & yel	.40	.40

5th International Slavic Congress.

Revolutionists
A591

1963, Sept. 22   Perf. 11½
1290	A591	2s brt red & blk	.25	.25

40th anniv. of the September Revolution.

Christo Smirnenski
A592

1963, Oct. 28   Perf. 10½
1291	A592	13s pale lilac & indigo	.70	.25

Christo Smirnenski, poet, 65th birth anniv.

Columbine
A593

1963, Oct. 9   Photo.   Perf. 11½
1292	A593	1s shown	.25	.25
1293	A593	2s Edelweiss	.25	.25
1294	A593	3s Primrose	.25	.25
1295	A593	5s Water lily	.25	.25
1296	A593	6s Tulips	.25	.25
1297	A593	8s Larkspur	.75	.25
1298	A593	10s Alpine clematis	1.50	.25
1299	A593	13s Anemone	2.75	.60
		Nos. 1292-1299 (8)	6.25	2.35

Horses — A594

Designs: 2s, Charioteer and chariot. 3s, Trumpeters. 5s, Woman carrying tray with food. 13s, Man holding bowl. 20s, Woman in armchair. Designs are from a Thracian tomb at Kazanlik.

1963, Dec. 28   Unwmk.   Perf. 10½
1300	A594	1s gray, org & dk red	.25	.25
1301	A594	2s gray, ocher & pur	.25	.25
1302	A594	3s gray, dl yel & sl grn	.25	.25
1303	A594	5s pale grn, ocher & brn	.30	.25
1304	A594	13s pale grn, bis & blk	.75	.35
1305	A594	20s pale grn, org & dk car	1.50	.55
		Nos. 1300-1305 (6)	3.30	1.90

World Map and Emblem
A595

Designs: 2s, Blood transfusion. 3s, Nurse bandaging injured wrist. 5s, Red Cross nurse. 13s, Henri Dunant.

1964, Jan. 27   Perf. 10½
1306	A595	1s lem, blk & red	.25	.25
1307	A595	2s ultra, blk & red	.25	.25
1308	A595	3s gray, sl, blk & red	.25	.25
1309	A595	5s brt bl, blk & red	.25	.25
1310	A595	13s org yel, blk & red	.80	.25
		Nos. 1306-1310 (5)	1.80	1.25

Centenary of International Red Cross.

Speed Skating
A596

Sports: 2s, 50s, Women's figure skating. 3s, Cross-country skiing. 5s, Ski jump. 10s, Ice hockey goalkeeper. 13s, Ice hockey players.

1964, Feb. 21   Unwmk.   Perf. 10½
1311	A596	1s grnsh bl, ind & ocher	.25	.25
1312	A596	2s brt pink, ol grn & dk sl grn	.25	.25
1313	A596	3s dl grn, dk grn & brn	.25	.25
1314	A596	5s bl, blk & yel brn	.25	.25
1315	A596	10s gray, org & blk	.70	.25
1316	A596	13s lil, blk & lil rose	.70	.25
		Nos. 1311-1316 (6)	2.40	1.50

Miniature Sheet
Imperf
1317	A596	50s gray, Prus grn & pink	3.75	3.75

9th Winter Olympic Games, Innsbruck, Jan. 29-Feb. 9, 1964.

Mask of Nobleman, 2nd Century
A597

2s, Thracian horseman. 3s, Ceramic jug. 5s, Clasp & belt. 6s, Copper kettle. 8s, Angel. 10s, Lioness. 13s, Scrub woman, contemporary sculpture.

1964, Mar. 14   Photo.   Perf. 10½
Gray Frame
1318	A597	1s dp green & red	.25	.25
1319	A597	2s ol gray & red	.25	.25
1320	A597	3s bister & red	.25	.25
1321	A597	5s indigo & red	.25	.25
1322	A597	6s org brn & red	.45	.25
1323	A597	8s brn red & red	.70	.25
1324	A597	10s olive & red	.70	.25
1325	A597	13s gray ol & red	.90	.45
		Nos. 1318-1325 (8)	3.80	2.20

2,500 years of Bulgarian art.

"The Unborn Maid"
A598

Fairy Tales: 2s, Grandfather's Glove. 3s, The Big Turnip. 5s, The Wolf and the Seven Kids. 8s, Cunning Peter. 13s, The Wheat Cake.

1964, Apr. 17   Unwmk.   Perf. 10½
1326	A598	1s bl grn, red & org brn	.25	.25
1327	A598	2s ultra, ocher & blk	.25	.25
1328	A598	3s cit, red & blk	.25	.25
1329	A598	5s dp rose, brn & blk	.25	.25
1330	A598	8s yel grn, red & blk	.40	.25
1331	A598	13s lt vio bl, grn & blk	1.25	.25
		Nos. 1326-1331 (6)	2.65	1.50

Ascalaphus Otomanus
A599

Insects: 2s, Nemoptera coa., vert. 3s, Saga natalia (grasshopper). 5s, Rosalia alpina, vert. 13s, Anisoplia austriaca, vert. 20s, Scolia flavitrons.

1964, May 16   Photo.   Perf. 11½
1332	A599	1s brn org, yel & blk	.25	.25
1333	A599	2s dl bl grn, bis & blk	.25	.25
1334	A599	3s gray, grn & blk	.25	.25
1335	A599	5s lt ol grn, blk & vio	.65	.25
1336	A599	13s vio, bis & blk	1.25	.40
1337	A599	20s gray bl, yel & blk	2.25	.85
		Nos. 1332-1337 (6)	4.90	2.25

Soccer — A600

Designs: 13s, Women's volleyball. 60s, Map of Europe and European Women's Volleyball Championship Cup (rectangular, size: 60x69mm).

1964, June 8   Unwmk.   Perf. 11½
1338	A600	2s bl, dk bl, ocher & red	.25	.25
1339	A600	13s bl, dk bl, ocher & red	.90	.40

Miniature Sheet
Imperf
1340	A600	60s ultra, ocher, red & gray	3.00	3.00

Levski Physical Culture Assoc., 50th anniv.

Peter Beron and Title Page of Primer — A601

1964, June 22   Perf. 11½
1341	A601	20s red brn & dk brn, *grysh*	1.75	1.75

140th anniversary of the publication of the first Bulgarian primer.

Robert Stephenson's "Rocket" Locomotive, 1825 — A602

Designs: 2s, Modern steam locomotive. 3s, Diesel locomotive. 5s, Electric locomotive. 8s, Freight train on bridge. 13s, Diesel locomotive and tunnel.

1964, July 1   Photo.   Perf. 11½
1342	A602	1s multicolored	.25	.25
1343	A602	2s multicolored	.25	.25
1344	A602	3s multicolored	.25	.25
1345	A602	5s multicolored	.25	.25
1346	A602	8s multicolored	1.00	.25
1347	A602	13s multicolored	1.00	.25
		Nos. 1342-1347 (6)	3.00	1.50

German Shepherd — A603

1964, Aug. 22   Photo.
1348	A603	1s shown	.25	.25
1349	A603	2s Setter	.25	.25
1350	A603	3s Poodle	.30	.25
1351	A603	4s Pomeranian	.35	.25
1352	A603	5s St. Bernard	.50	.25
1353	A603	6s Terrier	.70	.35
1354	A603	10s Pointer	2.75	1.25
1355	A603	13s Dachshund	3.50	2.25
		Nos. 1348-1355 (8)	8.60	5.10

Partisans — A604

Designs: 2s, People welcoming Soviet army. 3s, Russian aid to Bulgaria. 4s, Blast furnace, Kremikovski. 5s, Combine. 6s, Peace demonstration. 8s, Sentry. 13s, Demeter Blagoev and George Dimitrov.

1964, Sept. 9   Unwmk.   Perf. 11½
Flag in Red
1356	A604	1s lt & dp ultra	.25	.25
1357	A604	2s ol bis & dp ol	.25	.25
1358	A604	3s rose lil & mar	.25	.25
1359	A604	4s lt vio & vio	.25	.25
1360	A604	5s org & red brn	.25	.25
1361	A604	6s bl & dp bl	.25	.25
1362	A604	8s lt grn & grn	.65	.25
1363	A604	13s fawn & red brn	.65	.25
		Nos. 1356-1363 (8)	2.40	2.00

20th anniv. of People's Government of Bulgaria.

No. 967 Surcharged

1964, Sept. 13   Perf. 13
1364	A476	20s on 44s org yel	1.50	.50

International Plovdiv Fair.

Gymnast on Parallel Bars — A606

Sports: 2s, Long jump. 3s, Woman diver. 5s, Soccer. 13s, Women's volleyball. 20s, Wrestling.

1964, Oct. 10 **Perf. 11½**
1366 A606 1s pale grn, grn & red .25 .25
1367 A606 2s pale vio, vio bl & red .25 .25
1368 A606 3s bl grn, brn & red .25 .25
1369 A606 5s pink, pur & red .25 .25
1370 A606 13s bl, Prus grn & red .85 .25
1371 A606 20s yel, grn & red .85 .45
  Nos. 1366-1371 (6) 2.70 1.70

18th Olympic Games, Tokyo. Oct. 10-25. See No. B27.

Vratcata Mountain Road — A607

Bulgarian Views: 2s, Ritlite mountain road. 3s, Pines, Maliovica peak. 4s, Pobitite rocks. 5s, Erkupria. 6s, Rhodope mountain road.

1964, Oct. 26 Photo. **Perf. 12½x13**
1372 A607 1s dk slate grn .25 .25
1373 A607 2s brown .25 .25
1374 A607 3s grnsh blue .25 .25
1375 A607 4s dk red brn .25 .25
1376 A607 5s deep green .25 .25
1377 A607 6s blue violet .60 .25
  Nos. 1372-1377 (6) 1.85 1.50

Mail Coach, Plane and Rocket A608

1964, Oct. 3 Unwmk. **Perf. 11½**
1378 A608 20s greenish blue 1.50 .50

First national stamp exhibition, Sofia, Oct. 3-18. Issued in sheets of 12 stamps and 12 labels (woman's head and inscription, 5x5) arranged around one central label showing stylized bird design. No. 1378 with label, value $2.50.
Exists imperf.

Students Holding Book — A609

1964, Dec. 30 **Photo.**
1379 A609 13s lt blue & blk .75 .35

8th Intl. Students' Congress, Sofia.

500-Year-Old Walnut Tree at Golemo Drenovo — A610

Designs: Various old trees.

1964, Dec. 28
1380 A610 1s blk, buff & cl brn .25 .25
1381 A610 2s blk, pink & dp cl .25 .25
1382 A610 3s blk, yel & dk brn .25 .25
1383 A610 4s blk, lt bl & Prus bl .25 .25
1384 A610 10s blk, pale grn & grn .60 .25
1385 A610 13s blk, pale bis & dk ol grn .90 .25
  Nos. 1380-1385 (6) 2.50 1.50

Soldiers' Monument A611

1965, Jan. 1 **Unwmk.**
1386 A611 2s red & black .40 .40

Bulgarian-Soviet friendship.

Olympic Medal Inscribed "Olympic Glory" A612

1965, Jan. 27 Photo. **Perf. 11½**
1387 A612 20s org brn, gold & blk 1.10 .50

Bulgarian victories in the 1964 Olympic Games.

"Victory Over Fascism" A613

13s, "Fight for Peace" (dove and globe).

1965, Apr. 16 **Perf. 11½**
1388 A613 5s gray, blk & ol bis .25 .25
1389 A613 13s gray, blk & blue .60 .25

Victory over Fascism, 5/9/45, 20th anniv.

Vladimir M. Komarov and Section of Globe — A614

Designs: 2s, Konstantin Feoktistov. 5s, Boris B. Yegorov. 13s, Komarov, Feoktistov and Yegorov. 20s, Spaceship Voskhod.

1965, Feb. 15 **Photo.**
1390 A614 1s pale lil & dk bl .25 .25
1391 A614 2s lt bl, ind & dl vio .25 .25
1392 A614 5s pale grn, grn & ol grn .25 .25
1393 A614 13s pale pink, dp rose & mar .65 .25
1394 A614 20s lt bl, vio bl, grnsh bl & yel 1.10 .25
  Nos. 1390-1394 (5) 2.50 1.25

Russian 3-man space flight, Oct. 12-13, 1964.
Imperfs in changed colors. Four low values se-tenant. Value, set $4 unused, $2 canceled.

Bullfinch — A615

Birds: 2s, European golden oriole. 3s, Common rock thrush. 5s, Barn swallow. 8s, European roller. 10s, European goldfinch. 13s, Rosy pastor starling. 20s, Nightingale.

1965, Apr. 20 Unwmk. **Perf. 11½**
Birds in Natural Colors
1395 A615 1s blue green .25 .25
1396 A615 2s rose lilac .25 .25
1397 A615 3s rose .25 .25
1398 A615 5s brt blue .50 .25
1399 A615 8s citron .55 .45
1400 A615 10s gray 2.10 .55
1401 A615 13s lt vio blue 2.10 1.00
1402 A615 20s emerald 3.00 2.25
  Nos. 1395-1402 (8) 9.00 5.25

Black Sea Fish A616

1965, June 10 Photo. **Perf. 11½**
Gray Frames
1403 A616 1s Sting ray .25 .25
1404 A616 2s Belted bonito .25 .25
1405 A616 3s Hogfish .25 .25
1406 A616 5s Gurnard .35 .25
1407 A616 10s Scad 1.50 .25
1408 A616 13s Turbot 2.00 .50
  Nos. 1403-1408 (6) 4.60 1.75

Plane, Bus, Train, Ship and Whale A617

1965, Apr. 30
1409 A617 13s multicolored 1.10 .65

4th Intl. Conf. of Transport, Dock and Fishery Workers, Sofia, May 10-14.

ITU Emblem and Communications Symbols — A618

1965, May 17
1410 A618 20s multicolored 1.10 .60

Centenary of the ITU.

Col. Pavel Belyayev and Lt. Col. Alexei Leonov — A619

Design: 20s, Leonov floating in space.

1965, May 20 **Unwmk.**
1411 A619 2s gray, dull bl & dk brn .35 .25
1412 A619 20s multicolored 2.75 .85

Space flight of Voskhod 2 and the first man floating in space, Lt. Col. Alexei Leonov.

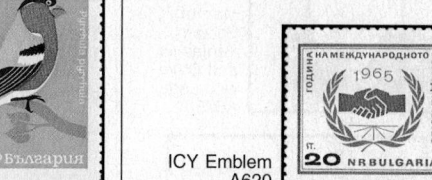

ICY Emblem A620

1965, May 15 **Photo.**
1413 A620 20s org, ol & blk 1.10 .35

International Cooperation Year, 1965.

Corn — A621

1965, Apr. 1 **Perf. 12½x13**
1414 A621 1s shown .25 .25
1415 A621 2s Wheat .25 .25
1416 A621 3s Sunflowers .25 .25
1417 A621 4s Sugar beet .25 .25
1418 A621 5s Clover .25 .25
1419 A621 10s Cotton .35 .25
1420 A621 13s Tobacco 1.10 .25
  Nos. 1414-1420 (7) 2.70 1.75

Marx and Lenin — A622

1965, June **Perf. 10½**
1421 A622 13s red & dk brn 1.50 .25

6th Conference of Postal Ministers of Communist Countries, Peking, June 21-July 15.

Film and UNESCO Emblem A623

1965, June 30
1422 A623 13s dp bl, blk & lt gray .75 .25

Balkan Film Festival, Varna.

Ballerina — A624

1965, July 10   **Photo.**
1423 A624 5s dp lil rose & blk   1.60 .75
2nd Intl. Ballet Competition, Varna.

Map of Balkan Peninsula and Dove with Letter A625

Col. Pavel Belyayev and Lt. Col. Alexei Leonov — A626

2s, Sailboat and modern buildings. 3s, Fish and plants. 13s, Symbolic sun and rocket. 40s, Map of Balkan Peninsula and dove with letter (like 1s).

1965   **Perf. 10½**
1424 A625 1s sil, dp ultra & yel   .25 .25
1425 A625 2s sil, pur & yel   .25 .25
1426 A625 3s gold, grn & yel   .25 .25
1427 A625 13s gold, hn brn & yel   .90 .90
1428 A626 20s sil, bl & brn   1.50 1.50
   Nos. 1424-1428 (5)   3.15 3.15
Miniature Sheet
Imperf
1429 A625 40s gold & brt bl   3.75 2.10
Balkanphila 1965 Philatelic Exhibition, Varna, Aug. 7-15, and visit of Russian astronauts Belyayev and Leonov.
Value, No. 1428 imperf. in changed colors, $1.75.
Issued: 20s, 40s, 8/7; others, 7/23.

Woman Gymnast — A627

Designs: 2s, Woman gymnast on parallel bars. 3s, Weight lifter. 5s, Automobile and chart. 10s, Women basketball players. 13s, Automobile and map of rally.

1965, Aug. 14   **Perf. 10½**
1430 A627 1s crim, brn & blk   .25 .25
1431 A627 2s rose vio, dp cl & blk   .25 .25
1432 A627 3s dp car, brn & blk   .25 .25
1433 A627 5s fawn, red brn & blk   .35 .25
1434 A627 10s dp lil rose, dp cl & blk   .65 .25
1435 A627 13s lilac, claret & blk   .90 .25
   Nos. 1430-1435 (6)   2.65 1.50
Sports events in Bulgaria during May-June, 1965.

No. 989 Surcharged

1965, Aug. 12   **Perf. 13**
1436 A499 2s on 8s orange brn, surcharge 36mm wide   1.50 1.50
  a.   Surcharge 32mm wide   6.00 4.00
1st Natl. Folklore Competition, Aug. 12-15.

Escaping Prisoners — A628

1965, July 23   **Perf. 10½**
1437 A628 2s slate   .40 .40
40th anniversary of the escape of political prisoners from Bolshevik Island.

Fruit — A629

1965, July 1   **Perf. 13**
1438 A629 1s Apples   .25 .25
1439 A629 2s Grapes   .25 .25
1440 A629 3s Pears   .25 .25
1441 A629 4s Peaches   .25 .25
1442 A629 5s Strawberries   .25 .25
1443 A629 6s Walnuts   .30 .25
   Nos. 1438-1443 (6)   1.55 1.50

Horsemanship — A630

1965, Sept. 30   **Unwmk.**   **Perf. 10½**
1444 A630 1s Dressage   .25 .25
1445 A630 2s Three-day test   .25 .25
1446 A630 3s Jumping   .25 .25
1447 A630 5s Race   .45 .25
1448 A630 10s Steeplechase   2.00 .75
1449 A630 13s Hurdle race   2.25 1.10
   Nos. 1444-1449 (6)   5.45 2.85
See No. B28.

Smiling Children — A631

Designs: 2s, Two girl Pioneers. 3s, Bugler. 5s, Pioneer with model plane. 8s, Two singing girls in national costume. 13s, Running boy.

1965, Oct. 24   **Photo.**
1450 A631 1s dk bl grn & yel grn   .25 .25
1451 A631 2s vio & deep rose   .25 .25
1452 A631 3s olive & lemon   .25 .25
1453 A631 5s dp blue & bister   .25 .25
1454 A631 8s olive bister & org   .60 .25
1455 A631 13s rose car & vio   .90 .25
   Nos. 1450-1455 (6)   2.50 1.60
Dimitrov Pioneer Organization.

U-52 Plane over Trnovo A632

2s, 1L-14 over Plovdiv. 3s, Mi-4 Helicopter over Dimitrovgrad. 5s, Tu-104 over Ruse. 13s, IL-18 over Varna. 20s, Tu-114 over Sofia.

1965, Nov. 25   **Perf. 10½**
1456 A632 1s gray, blue & red   .25 .25
1457 A632 2s gray, lilac & red   .25 .25
1458 A632 3s gray, grnsh bl & red   .25 .25
1459 A632 5s gray, org & red   .30 .25
1460 A632 13s gray, bister & red   .90 .25
1461 A632 20s gray, lt grn & red   1.50 .45
   Nos. 1456-1461 (6)   3.45 1.70
Development of Bulgarian Civil Air Transport.

IQSY Emblem, and Earth Radiation Zones A633

Designs (IQSY Emblem and): 2s, Sun with corona. 13s, Solar eclipse.

1965, Dec. 15   **Photo.**   **Perf. 10½**
1462 A633 1s grn, yel & ultra   .25 .25
1463 A633 2s yel, red lil & red   .25 .25
1464 A633 13s bl, yel & blk   .75 .25
   Nos. 1462-1464 (3)   1.25 .75
International Quiet Sun Year, 1964-65.

"North and South Bulgaria" A634

1965, Dec. 6
1465 A634 13s brt yel grn & blk   .70 .45
Union of North and South Bulgaria, cent.

"Martenitsa" Emblem — A635

"Spring" in Folklore: 2s, Drummer. 3s, Bird ornaments. 5s, Dancer "Lazarka." 8s, Vase with flowers. 13s, Bagpiper.

1966, Jan. 10   **Photo.**   **Perf. 10½**
1466 A635 1s rose lil, vio bl & gray   .25 .25
1467 A635 2s gray, blk & crim   .25 .25
1468 A635 3s red, vio & gray   .25 .25
1469 A635 5s lil, blk & crimson   .25 .25
1470 A635 8s rose lil, brn & pur   .50 .25
1471 A635 13s bl, blk & rose lilac   .85 .25
   Nos. 1466-1471 (6)   2.35 1.50

Church of St. John the Baptist, Nessebr A636

Designs: 1s, Christ, fresco from Bojana Church. 2s, Ikon "Destruction of Idols," horiz. 3s, Bratchkovo Monastery. 4s, Zemen Monastery, horiz. 13s, Nativity, ikon from Arbanassi. 20s, Ikon "Virgin and Child," 1342.

1966, Feb. 25   **Litho.**   **Perf. 11½**
1472 A636 1s gray & multi   5.00 1.75
1473 A636 2s gray & multi   .35 .25
1474 A636 3s multicolored   .35 .25
1475 A636 4s multicolored   .35 .25
1476 A636 5s multicolored   .35 .25
1477 A636 13s gray & multi   .70 .25
1478 A636 20s multicolored   1.40 .50
   Nos. 1472-1478 (7)   8.50 3.50
2,500 years of art in Bulgaria.

Georgi Benkovski and T. Kablechkov — A637

1s, Proclamation of April Uprising, Koprivstitsa. 3s, Dedication of flag, Panaguriste. 5s, V. Petleshkov, Z. Dyustabanov. 10s, Botev landing at Kozlodui. 13s, P. Volov, Ilarion Dragostinov.

1966, Mar. 3   **Photo.**   **Perf. 10½**
     Center in Black
1479 A637 1s red brn & gold   .25 .25
1480 A637 2s brt red & gold   .25 .25
1481 A637 3s ol grn & gold   .25 .25
1482 A637 5s steel bl & gold   .25 .25
1483 A637 10s brt rose lil & gold   .55 .25
1484 A637 13s lt vio & gold   .55 .25
   Nos. 1479-1484 (6)   2.10 1.50
April Uprising against the Turks, 90th anniv.

Sofia Zoo Animals A638

1966, May 23   **Litho.**
1485 A638 1s Elephant   .25 .25
1486 A638 2s Tiger   .25 .25
1487 A638 3s Chimpanzee   .25 .25
1488 A638 4s Siberian ibex   .25 .25
1489 A638 5s Polar bear   .65 .25
1490 A638 8s Lion   .80 .50
1491 A638 13s Bison   2.25 1.25
1492 A638 20s Kangaroo   3.00 1.90
   Nos. 1485-1492 (8)   7.70 4.90

WHO Headquarters, Geneva — A639

1966, May 3   **Photo.**
1493 A639 13s deep blue & silver   .80 .35
Inauguration of the WHO Headquarters, Geneva.

Worker
A640

1966, May 9   Photo.   Perf. 10½
1494 A640 20s gray & rose   1.00   .50
Sixth Trade Union Congress.

Yantra River
Bridge,
Biela — A641

No. 1496, Maritsa River Bridge, Svilengrad.
No. 1497, Fountain, Samokov. No. 1498,
Ruins of Fort, Kaskovo. 8s, Old Fort, Ruse.
13s, House, Gabrovo.

1966, Feb. 10   Photo.   Perf. 13
1495 A641 1s Prus blue   .25   .25
1496 A641 1s brt green   .25   .25
1497 A641 2s olive green   .25   .25
1498 A641 2s dk red brown   .25   .25
1499 A641 8s red brown   .35   .25
1500 A641 13s dark blue   .65   .25
          Nos. 1495-1500 (6)   2.00 1.50

Souvenir Sheet

Moon Allegory — A642

1966, Apr. 29   Imperf.
1501 A642 60s blk, plum & sil 4.25 3.50
1st Russian soft landing on the moon by
Luna 9, Feb. 3, 1966.

Steamer Radetzky and Bugler — A643

1966, May 28   Perf. 10½
1502 A643 2s multicolored   .25 .25
90th anniv. of the participation of the Danube steamer Radetzky in the uprising against
the Turks.

Standard Bearer
Nicola Simov-
Kuruto
A644

1966, May 30
1503 A644 5s bister, green & olive .35 .25
Hero of the Turkish War.

UNESCO
Emblem
A645

1966, June 8
1504 A645 20s buff, blk & ver   .85 .35
20th anniv. of UNESCO.

Youth Federation Badge — A646

1966, June 6   Photo.   Perf. 10½
1505 A646 13s silver, bl & blk   .75 .25
7th Assembly of the Intl. Youth Federation.

Soccer — A647

Various soccer scenes. 50s, Jules Rimet
Cup.

1966, June 27
1506 A647 1s gray, yel brn &
                   blk   .25 .25
1507 A647 2s gray, crim & blk   .25 .25
1508 A647 5s gray, ol bis & blk .25 .25
1509 A647 13s gray, ultra & blk .70 .25
1510 A647 20s gray, Prus bl &
                   blk   .80 .25
          Nos. 1506-1510 (5)   2.25 1.25

Miniature Sheet
Imperf
1511 A647 50s gray, dp lil rose &
                   gold   3.75 2.50
World Soccer Cup Championship, Wembley, England, July 11-30. Size of No. 1511:
60x64mm.

Woman Javelin Thrower — A648

No. 1513, Runner. No. 1514, Young man
and woman carrying banners, vert.

1966   Photo.   Perf. 10½
1512 A648 2s grn, yel & ver   .25 .25
1513 A648 13s dp grn, yel & sal
                   pink   .60 .25
1514 A648 13s bl, lt bl & salmon .60 .25
          Nos. 1512-1514 (3)   1.45 .75
Nos. 1512-1513: 3rd Spartacist Games;
issued Aug. 10. No. 1514: 3rd congress of the
Bulgarian Youth Federation; issued May 25.

Wrestlers Nicolas Petrov and Dan
Kolov — A649

1966, July 29
1515 A649 13s bis brn, dk brn &
                   lt ol grn   .75 .35
3rd International Wrestling Championships.

Map of Balkan Countries, Globe and
UNESCO Emblem — A650

1966, Aug. 26   Perf. 10½x11½
1516 A650 13s ultra, lt grn & pink .75 .25
First Congress of Balkanologists.

Children
with
Building
Blocks
A651

2s, Bunny & teddy bear with book. 3s, Children as astronauts. 13s, Children with pails &
shovel.

1966, Sept. 1   Perf. 10½
1517 A651 1s dk car, org & blk   .25 .25
1518 A651 2s emerald, blk &
                   red brn   .25 .25
1519 A651 3s ultra, org & blk   .25 .25
1520 A651 13s blue, rose & blk   1.10 .25
          Nos. 1517-1520 (4)   1.85 1.00
Children's Day.

Yuri A. Gagarin and Vostok 1 — A652

Designs: 2s, Gherman S. Titov, Vostok 2.
3s, Andrian G. Nikolayev, Pavel R. Popovich,
Vostoks 3 & 4. 5s, Valentina Tereshkova,
Valeri Bykovski, Vostoks 5 & 6. 8s, Vladimir M.
Komarov, Boris B. Yegorov, Konstantin Feok-
tistov, Voskhod 1. 13s, Pavel Belyayev, Alexei
Leonov, Voskhod 2.

1966, Sept. 29   Photo.   Perf. 11½x11
1521 A652 1s slate & gray   .25 .25
1522 A652 2s plum & gray   .25 .25
1523 A652 3s yel brn & gray   .25 .25
1524 A652 5s brn red & gray   .25 .25
1525 A652 8s ultra & gray   .30 .25
1526 A652 13s Prus bl & gray   .80 .25
          Nos. 1521-1526,B29 (7)   3.50 1.95
Russian space explorations.

St. Clement,
14th Century
Wood Sculpture
A653

1966, Oct. 27   Photo.   Perf. 11½x11
1527 A653 5s red, buff & brown   .70 .35
1050th anniversary of the birth of St. Clement of Ochrida.

Metodi
Shatorov
A654

Portraits: 3s, Vladimir Trichkov. 5s, Valcho
Ivanov. 10s, Raiko Daskalov. 13s, General
Vladimir Zaimov.

1966, Nov. 8   Perf. 11x11½
Gold Frame, Black Denomination
1528 A654 2s crimson & bl vio   .25 .25
1529 A654 3s magenta & blk   .25 .25
1530 A654 5s car rose & dk bl   .25 .25
1531 A654 10s orange & olive   .45 .25
1532 A654 13s red & brown   .55 .25
          Nos. 1528-1532 (5)   1.75 1.25
Fighters against fascism.

George
Dimitrov — A655

Steel
Worker — A656

1966, Nov. 14   Photo.   Perf. 11½x11
1533 A655 2s magenta & blk   .25 .25
1534 A656 20s fawn, gray & blk   .90 .25
Bulgarian Communist Party, 9th Congress.

Deer's
Head
Drinking
Cup
A667

Gold Treasure: 2s, 6s, 10s, Various Amazon's head jugs. 3s, Ram's head cup. 5s, Circular plate. 8s, Deer's head cup. 13s,
Amphora. 20s, Ram drinking horn.

1966, Nov. 28   Perf. 12x11½
**Vessels in Gold and Brown; Black
Inscriptions**
1535 A667 1s gray & violet   .25 .25
1536 A667 2s gray & green   .25 .25
1537 A667 3s gray & dk bl   .25 .25
1538 A667 5s gray & red brn   .25 .25
1539 A667 6s gray & Prus bl   .25 .25
1540 A667 8s gray & brn ol   .90 .25
1541 A667 10s gray & sepia   .90 .25
1542 A667 13s gray & dk vio bl   1.10 .35
1543 A667 20s gray & vio brn   1.90 .55
          Nos. 1535-1543 (9)   6.05 2.65
The gold treasure from the 4th century B.C.
was found near Panagyurishte in 1949.

Tourist House,
Bansko — A668

Tourist Houses: No. 1545, Belogradchik.
No. 1546, Triavna. 20s, Rila.

1966, Nov. 29   Photo.   Perf. 11x11½
1544 A668 1s dark blue   .25 .25
1545 A668 2s dark green   .25 .25
1546 A668 2s brown red   .25 .25
1547 A668 20s lilac   .65 .25
          Nos. 1544-1547 (4)   1.40 1.00

Decorated Tree A669

Design: 13s, Jug with bird design.

1966, Dec. 12   **Perf. 11**
1548 A669 2s grn, pink & gold   .25 .25
1549 A669 13s brn lake, rose, emer
    & gold   .65 .25
New Year, 1967.

Pencho Slaveikov, Author — A670

Portraits: 2s, Dimcho Debeljanov, author. 3s, P. H. Todorov, author. 5s, Dimitri Dobrovich, painter. 8s, Ivan Markvichka, painter. 13s, Ilya Bezhkov, painter.

1966, Dec. 15   **Perf. 10½x11**
1550 A670 1s blue, olive & org   .25 .25
1551 A670 2s org, brn & gray   .25 .25
1552 A670 3s olive, bl & org   .25 .25
1553 A670 5s gray, red brn &
    org   .25 .25
1554 A670 8s lilac, dk gray & bl   .40 .25
1555 A670 13s blue, vio & lil   .55 .25
    Nos. 1550-1555 (6)   1.95 1.50

Dahlia — A671

Flowers: No. 1557, Clematis. No. 1558, Foxglove. No. 1559, Narcissus. 3s, Snowdrop. 5s, Petunia. 13s, Tiger lily. 20s, Bellflower.

Flowers in Natural Colors

1966, Dec. 29
1556 A671 1s gray & lt brn   .25 .25
1557 A671 1s gray & dull bl   .25 .25
1558 A671 2s gray & dull lil   .25 .25
1559 A671 2s gray & brown   .25 .25
1560 A671 3s gray & dk grn   .35 .25
1561 A671 5s gray & dp ultra   .45 .25
1562 A671 13s gray & brown   1.00 .25
1563 A671 20s gray & ultra   1.00 .35
    Nos. 1556-1563 (8)   3.80 2.10

Ringnecked Pheasant — A672

Game: 2s, Rock partridge. 3s, Gray partridge. 5s, Hare. 8s, Roe deer. 13s, Red deer.

1967, Jan. 28   **Perf. 11x10½**
1564 A672 1s lt ultra, dk brn &
    ocher   .25 .25
1565 A672 2s pale yel grn & dk
    grn   .25 .25
1566 A672 3s lt bl, blk & cr   .25 .25
1567 A672 5s lt grn & blk   .65 .35
1568 A672 8s pale bl, dk brn &
    ocher   2.00 .65
1569 A672 13s bl & dk brn   2.50 1.10
    Nos. 1564-1569 (6)   5.90 2.85

Bulgaria No. 1, 1879 — A673

1967, Feb. 4   **Photo.**   **Perf. 10½**
1570 A673 10s emerald, blk & yel 1.75 1.00
Bulgarian Philatelic Union, 10th Congress.

Thracian Coin, 6th Century, B.C. — A674

Coins: 2s, Macedonian tetradrachma, 2nd cent. B.C. 3s, Tetradrachma of Odessus, 2nd cent. B.C. 5s, Philip II of Macedonia, 4th cent., B.C. 13s, Thracian King Seuthus VII, 4th cent., B.C., obverse and reverse. 20s, Apollonian coin, 5th cent., B.C., obverse and reverse.

1967, Mar. 30   **Perf. 11½x11**
    Size: 25x25mm
1571 A674 1s brn, blk & sil   .25 .25
1572 A674 2s red lil, blk & sil   .25 .25
1573 A674 3s grn, blk & sil   .25 .25
1574 A674 5s brn org, blk & sil   .40 .30
    Size: 37½x25mm
1575 A674 13s brt bl, blk & brnz   1.10 .60
1576 A674 20s vio, blk & sil   2.00 1.00
    Nos. 1571-1576 (6)   4.25 2.65

Partisans Listening to Radio — A675

Design: 20s, George Dimitrov addressing crowd and Bulgarian flag.

1967, Apr. 20   **Perf. 11x11½**
1577 A675 1s red, gold, buff &
    sl grn   .25 .25
1578 A675 20s red, gold, dl red,
    grn & blk   .85 .25

25th anniversary of the Union of Patriotic Front Organizations.

Nikolas Kofardjiev A676

2s, Petko Napetov. 5s, Petko D. Petkov. 10s, Emil Markov. 13s, Traitcho Kostov.

1967, Apr. 24   **Perf. 11½x11**
1579 A676 1s brn red, gray &
    blk   .25 .25
1580 A676 2s ol grn, gray & blk   .25 .25
1581 A676 5s brn, gray & blk   .25 .25
1582 A676 10s dp bl, gray & blk   .25 .25
1583 A676 13s mag, gray & blk   .75 .25
    Nos. 1579-1583 (5)   1.75 1.25

Fighters against fascism.

Symbolic Flower and Flame — A677

1967, May 18   **Photo.**   **Perf. 11x11½**
1584 A677 13s gold, yel & lt grn   .70 .25
First Cultural Congress, May 18-19.

Gold Sand Beach and ITY Emblem A678

20s, Hotel, Pamporovo. 40s, Nessebr Church.

1967, June 12   **Photo.**   **Perf. 11x11½**
1585 A678 13s ultra, yel & blk   .35 .25
1586 A678 20s Prus bl, blk & buff   .75 .30
1587 A678 40s brt grn, blk &
    ocher   1.90 .55
    Nos. 1585-1587 (3)   3.00 1.10

International Tourist Year, 1967.

Angora Cat — A679

Cats: 2s, Siamese, horiz. 3s, Abyssinian. 5s, Black European. 13s, Persian, horiz. 20s, Striped domestic.

    Perf. 11½x11, 11x11½
1967, June 19
1588 A679 1s dl vio, dk brn &
    buff   .25 .25
1589 A679 2s ol, sl & brt bl   .25 .25
1590 A679 3s dull blue & brn   .35 .25
1591 A679 5s grn, blk & yel   1.00 .25
1592 A679 13s dl red brn, sl &
    org   1.40 .25
1593 A679 20s gray grn, brn &
    buff   1.75 .45
    Nos. 1588-1593 (6)   5.00 1.70

Scene from Opera "The Master of Boyana" by K. Iliev A680

Songbird on Keyboard — A681

1967, June 19
1594 A680 5s gray, vio bl & dp
    car   .30 .25
1595 A681 13s gray, dp car & dk
    bl   .55 .25
3rd Intl. Competition for Young Opera Singers.

George Kirkov (1867-1919), Revolutionist — A682

1967, June 24   **Perf. 11x11½**
1596 A682 2s rose red & dk brn   .25 .25

Symbolic Tree and Stars — A683

1967, July 28   **Photo.**   **Perf. 11½x11**
1597 A683 13s dp bl, car & blk   .75 .25
11th Congress of Dimitrov's Union of the People's Youth.

Roses and Distillery A684

Designs: No. 1599, Chick and incubator. No. 1600, Cucumbers and hothouse. No. 1601, Lamb and sheep farm. 3s, Sunflower and oil mill. 4s, Pigs and pig farm. 5s, Hops and hop farm. 6s, Corn and irrigation system. 8s, Grapes and Bolgar tractor. 10s, Apples and cultivated tree. 13s, Bees and honey. 20s, Bee, blossoms and beehives.

1967   **Perf. 11x11½**
1598 A684 1s multicolored   .25 .25
1599 A684 1s dk car, yel & blk   .25 .25
1600 A684 2s vio, lt grn & blk   .25 .25
1601 A684 2s brt grn, gray &
    blk   .25 .25
1602 A684 3s yel grn, yel & blk   .25 .25
1603 A684 4s brt pur, yel & blk   .25 .25
1604 A684 5s ol bis, yel grn &
    blk   .25 .25
1605 A684 6s ol, brt grn & blk   .25 .25
1606 A684 8s grn, bis & blk   .35 .25
1607 A684 10s multicolored   .35 .25
1608 A684 13s grn, bis brn & blk   .70 .25
1609 A684 20s grnsh bl, brt pink
    & blk   .70 .25
    Nos. 1598-1609 (12)   4.10 3.00

Issue dates: Nos. 1598-1601, 1607, 1609, July 15; Nos. 1602-1606, 1608, July 24.

Map of Communist Countries, Spasski Tower A685

2s, Lenin speaking to soldiers. 3s, Fighting at Wlodaja, 1918. 5s, Marx, Engels & Lenin. 13s, Oil refinery. 20s, Vostok communication satellite.

1967, Aug. 25   **Perf. 11**
1610 A685 1s multicolored   .25 .25
1611 A685 2s magenta & olive   .25 .25
1612 A685 3s mag & dull vio   .25 .25
1613 A685 5s magenta & red   .25 .25
1614 A685 13s magenta & ultra   .50 .25
1615 A685 20s magenta & blue   .80 .25
    Nos. 1610-1615 (6)   2.30 1.50

Russian October Revolution, 50th anniv.

Rod, "Fish" and Varna
A686

1967, Aug. 29   Photo.   Perf. 11
1616 A686 10s multicolored   .60   .25
7th World Angling Championships, Varna.

Skiers and Winter Olympics' Emblem — A687

Sports and Emblem: 2s, Ski jump. 3s, Biathlon. 5s, Ice hockey. 13s, Figure skating couple.

1967, Sept. 20   Photo.   Perf. 11
1617 A687 1s dk bl grn, red & blk   .25   .25
1618 A687 2s ultra, blk & ol   .25   .25
1619 A687 3s vio brn, bl & blk   .25   .25
1620 A687 5s green, yel & blk   .25   .25
1621 A687 13s vio bl, blk & buff   .75   .25
       Nos. 1617-1621,B31 (6)   3.75   1.85
10th Winter Olympic Games, Grenoble, France, Feb. 6-18, 1968.

Mountain Peaks — A688

1967, Sept. 25   Engr.   Perf. 11½
1622 A688 1s Bogdan   .25   .25
1623 A688 2s Czerny   .25   .25
1624 A688 3s Ruen, vert.   .25   .25
1625 A688 5s Persenk   .25   .25
1626 A688 10s Botev   .25   .25
1627 A688 13s Rila, vert.   .35   .25
1628 A688 20s Vihren   .65   .25
       Nos. 1622-1628 (7)   2.25   1.75

George Rakovski
A689

1967, Oct. 20   Photo.   Perf. 11
1629 A689 13s yellow grn & blk   .75   .35
Centenary of the death of George Rakovski, revolutionary against Turkish rule.

Yuri A. Gagarin, Valentina Tereshkova and Alexei Leonov — A690

Designs: 2s, Lt. Col. John H. Glenn, Jr., and Maj. Edward H. White. 5s, Earth and Molniya 1. 10s, Gemini 6 and 7. 13s, Luna 13 moon probe. 20s, Gemini 10 and Agena rocket.

1967, Nov. 25
1630 A690 1s Prus bl, blk & yel   .25   .25
1631 A690 2s dl bl, blk & dl yel   .25   .25
1632 A690 5s vio bl, grnsh bl & blk   .25   .25

1633 A690 10s dk bl, blk & red   .70   .25
1634 A690 13s grnsh bl, brt yel & blk   .85   .25
1635 A690 20s dl bl, blk & red   .85   .25
       Nos. 1630-1635 (6)   3.15   1.50
Achievements in space exploration.

Various Views of Trnovo
A691

1967, Dec. 5   Photo.   Perf. 11
1636 A691 1s multicolored   .25   .25
1637 A691 2s multicolored   .25   .25
1638 A691 3s multicolored   .25   .25
1639 A691 5s multicolored   .25   .25
1640 A691 13s multicolored   .50   .25
1641 A691 20s multicolored   .65   .25
       Nos. 1636-1641 (6)   2.15   1.50
Restoration of the ancient capital Veliko Trnovo.

Ratchenitza Folk Dance, by Ivan Markvichka — A692

1967, Dec. 9
1642 A692 20s gold & gray grn   1.60   .85
Belgo-Bulgarian Philatelic Exposition, Brussels, Dec. 9-10. Printed in sheets of 8 stamps and 8 labels. No. 1642 with label, value $2.

Cosmos 186 and 188 Docking — A693

40s, Venera 4 and orbits around Venus.

1968, Jan.
1643 A693 20s multi   .75   .25
1644 A693 40s multi, horiz.   1.75   .50
Docking maneuvers of the Russian spaceships Cosmos 186 and Cosmos 188, Nov. 1, 1967, and the flight to Venus of Venera 4, June 12-Nov. 18, 1967.

Crossing the Danube, by Orenburgski — A694

Paintings: 2s, Flag of Samara, by J. Veschin, vert. 3s, Battle of Pleven by Orenburgski. 13s, Battle of Orlovo Gnezdo, by N. Popov, vert. 20s, Welcome for Russian Soldiers, by D. Gudienov.

Shepherds, by Zlatyn Boyadjiev — A695

Paintings: 2s, Wedding dance, by V. Dimitrov, vert. 3s, Partisans' Song, by Ilya Petrov. 5s, Portrait of Anna Penchovich, by Nikolai Pavlovich, vert. 13s, Self-portrait, by Zachary Zograf, vert. 20s, View of Old Plovdiv, by T. Lavrenov. 60s, St. Clement of Ochrida, by A. Mitov.

1967, Dec.   Litho.   Perf. 11½
Size: 45x38mm, 38x45mm
1650 A695 1s gray & multi   .25   .25
1651 A695 2s gray & multi   .25   .25
Size: 55x35mm
1652 A695 3s gray & multi   .30   .25
Size: 38x45mm, 45x38mm
1653 A695 5s gray & multi   .70   .25
1654 A695 13s gray & multi   1.40   .30
1655 A695 20s gray & multi   1.75   .70
       Nos. 1650-1655 (6)   4.65   2.00
Miniature Sheet
Size: 65x84mm
Imperf
1656 A695 60s multicolored   3.50   2.00

Marx Statue, Sofia — A696

1968, Feb. 20   Photo.   Perf. 11
1657 A696 13s black & red   .70   .25
150th anniversary of birth of Karl Marx.

Maxim Gorky — A697

1968, Feb. 20
1658 A697 13s ver & grnsh blk   .70   .25
Maxim Gorky (1868-1936), Russian writer.

Folk Dancers — A698

5s, Runners. 13s, Doves. 20s, Festival poster, (head, flowers, birds). 40s, Globe & Bulgaria No. 1 under magnifying glass.

1968, Jan. 25   Photo.   Perf. 11
1645 A694 1s gold & dk green   .25   .25
1646 A694 2s gold & dk blue   .25   .25
1647 A694 3s gold & chocolate   .25   .25
1648 A694 13s gold & dk vio   .80   .25
1649 A694 20s gold & Prus grn   1.10   .25
       Nos. 1645-1649 (5)   2.65   1.25
90th anniv. of the liberation from Turkey.

1968, Mar. 20
1659 A698 2s multicolored   .25   .25
1660 A698 5s multicolored   .25   .25
1661 A698 13s multicolored   .70   .25
1662 A698 20s multicolored   .70   .25
1663 A698 40s multicolored   1.20   .65
       Nos. 1659-1663 (5)   3.10   1.65
9th Youth Festival for Peace and Friendship, Sofia, July 28-Aug. 6.

Bellflower — A699

1968, Apr. 25   Perf. 11
1664 A699 1s shown   .25   .25
1665 A699 2s Gentian   .25   .25
1666 A699 3s Crocus   .25   .25
1667 A699 5s Iris   .35   .25
1668 A699 10s Dog-tooth violet   .50   .25
1669 A699 13s Sempervivum   1.00   .25
1670 A699 20s Dictamnus   1.00   .35
       Nos. 1664-1670 (7)   3.60   1.85

"The Unknown Hero," Tale by Ran Bosilek A700

Design: 20s, The Witch and the Young Man (Hans Christian Andersen fairy tale.)

1968, Apr. 25   Photo.   Perf. 10½
1671 A700 13s black & multi   .35   .25
1672 A700 20s black & multi   .70   .50
Bulgarian-Danish Philatelic Exhibition.

Memorial Church, Shipka — A701

1968, May 3
1673 A701 13s multi + label   .85   .25
Bulgarian Stamp Exhibition in Berlin. No. 1673 with label, value $1.25.

Show Jumping A702

Olympic Rings and: 1s, Gymnast on bar. 3s, Fencer. 10s, Boxer. 13s, Woman discus thrower.

1968, June 24   Photo.   Perf. 10½
1674 A702 1s red & black   .25   .25
1675 A702 2s gray, blk & rose brn   .25   .25
1676 A702 3s mag, gray & blk   .25   .25
1677 A702 10s grnsh bl, blk & lem   .50   .25
1678 A702 13s vio bl, gray & pink   1.00   .35
       Nos. 1674-1678,B33 (6)   3.65   1.80
19th Olympic Games, Mexico City, 10/12-27.

Battle of Buzluja A703

Design: 13s, Haji Dimitr and Stefan Karaja.

1968, July 1
1679	A703	2s silver & red brn	.25	.25
1680	A703	13s gold & sl grn	.55	.25

Centenary of the death of the patriots Haji Dimitr and Stefan Karaja.

Lakes of Smolian — A704

Bulgarian Scenes: 2s, Ropotamo Lake. 3s, Erma-Idreleto mountain pass. 8s, Isker River dam. 10s, Slanchev Breg (sailing ship). 13s, Cape Caliacra. 40s, Old houses, Sozopol. 2 l, Chudnite Skali ("Strange Mountains").

1968   **Photo.**   **Perf. 13**
1681	A704	1s Prus green	.25	.25
1682	A704	2s dark green	.25	.25
1683	A704	3s dark brown	.25	.25
1684	A704	8s olive green	.30	.25
1685	A704	10s redsh brown	.35	.25
1686	A704	13s dk olive grn	.25	.25
1687	A704	40s Prus blue	1.10	.40
1688	A704	2 l sepia	3.75	1.25
		Nos. 1681-1688 (8)	6.50	3.15

Sofia Zoo, 80th Anniv. — A705

1968, July 29   **Perf. 10½**
1689	A705	1s Cinereous vulture	.25	.25
1690	A705	2s Crowned crane	.25	.25
1691	A705	3s Zebra	.25	.25
1692	A705	5s Cheetah	.35	.25
1693	A705	13s Indian python	2.10	.90
1694	A705	20s African crocodile	2.75	1.50
		Nos. 1689-1694 (6)	5.95	3.40

Human Rights Flame — A706

1968, July 8
1695	A706	20s dp blue & gold	.90	.35

International Human Rights Year, 1968.

Congress Hall, Varna, and Emblem A707

1968, Sept. 17   **Photo.**   **Perf. 10½**
1696	A707	20s bister, grn & red	.70	.25

56th International Dental Congress, Varna.

Flying Swans A708

Rose A709

Designs: 2s, Jug. 20s, Five Viking ships.

1968   **Photo.**   **Perf. 10½**
1697	A709	2s green & ocher	1.10	1.10
1698	A708	5s dp blue & gray	1.10	1.10
1699	A709	13s dp plum & lil rose	1.10	1.10
a.		Pair, #1698, 1699 + label	2.50	2.50
1700	A708	20s dp vio & gray	1.00	1.00
a.		Pair, #1697, 1700 + label	2.50	2.50
		Nos. 1697-1700 (4)	4.30	4.30

Cooperation with the Scandinavian countries. Issued: 5s, 13s, Sept. 12; 2s, 20s, Nov. 22.

Stag Beetle — A710

No. 1702, Ground beetle (Procerus scabrosus). No. 1703, Ground beetle (Calosoma sycophania). No. 1704, Scarab beetle, horiz. No. 1705, Saturnid moth, horiz.

Perf. 12½x13, 13x12½
1968, Aug. 26
1701	A710	1s brown olive	.25	.25
1702	A710	1s dark blue	.25	.25
1703	A710	1s dark green	.25	.25
1704	A710	1s orange brown	.25	.25
1705	A710	1s magenta	.25	.25
		Nos. 1701-1705 (5)	1.25	1.25

Turks Fighting Insurgents, 1688 — A711

1968, Aug. 22   **Perf. 10½**
1706	A711	13s multicolored	.75	.25

280th anniversary of the Tchiprovtzi insurrection.

Christo Smirnenski (1898-1923), Poet — A712

1968, Sept. 28   **Litho.**   **Perf. 10½**
1707	A712	13s gold, red org & blk	.75	.25

Dalmatian Pelican — A713

Birds: 2s, Little egret. 3s, Crested grebe. 5s, Common tern. 13s, European spoonbill. 20s, Glossy ibis.

1968, Oct. 28   **Photo.**
1708	A713	1s silver & multi	.25	.25
1709	A713	2s silver & multi	.35	.25
1710	A713	3s silver & multi	.35	.25
1711	A713	5s silver & multi	.65	.25
1712	A713	13s silver & multi	1.60	1.25
1713	A713	20s silver & multi	3.25	1.50
		Nos. 1708-1713 (6)	6.45	3.75

Srebirna wild life reservation.

Carrier Pigeon A714

1968, Oct. 19
1714	A714	20s emerald	.90	.75
a.		Sheet of 4 + labels	7.00	3.50

2nd Natl. Stamp Exhib. in Sofia, Oct. 25-Nov. 15. No. 1714a contains 4 No. 1714 and 5 labels. No. 1714 with label, value $1.50.

An imperforate sheet similar to No. 1714a contains stamps in a different color that are not valid for postage.

Man and Woman from Silistra A715

Regional Costumes: 2s, Lovech. 3s, Yambol. 13s, Chirpan. 20s, Razgrad. 40s, Ihtiman.

1968, Nov. 20   **Litho.**   **Perf. 13½**
1715	A715	1s dp org & multi	.25	.25
1716	A715	2s Prus bl & multi	.25	.25
1717	A715	3s multicolored	.25	.25
1718	A715	13s multicolored	.50	.25
1719	A715	20s multicolored	.90	.40
1720	A715	40s green & multi	2.00	.50
		Nos. 1715-1720 (6)	4.15	1.90

St. Arsenius A716

10th cent. Murals & Icons: 2s, Procession with relics of St. Ivan Rilsky, horiz. 3s, St. Michael Torturing the Soul of the Rich Man. 13s, St. Ivan Rilski. 20s, St. John. 40s, St. George. 1 l, Procession meeting relics of St. Ivan Rilsky, horiz.

Perf. 11½x12½, 12½x11½
1968, Nov. 25   **Photo.**
1721	A716	1s gold & multi	.25	.25
1722	A716	2s gold & multi	.25	.25
1723	A716	3s gold & multi	.25	.25
1724	A716	13s gold & multi	.85	.25

1725	A716	20s gold & multi	1.25	.55
1726	A716	40s gold & multi	2.00	.85
		Nos. 1721-1726 (6)	4.85	2.40

Souvenir Sheet
Imperf
1727	A716	1 l gold & multi	3.50	3.00

Millenium of Rila Monastery. No. 1727 also: Sofia 1969 Intl. Phil. Exhib., May 31-June 8, 1969. No. 1727 contains one stamp, size: 57x51mm.

Medlar A717

Herbs: No. 1729, Camomile. 2s, Lily-of-the-valley. 3s, Belladonna. 5s, Mallow. 10s, Butter-cup. 13s, Poppies. 20s, Thyme.

1969, Jan. 2   **Litho.**   **Perf. 10½**
1728	A717	1s blk, grn & org red	.25	.25
1729	A717	1s black, grn & yel	.25	.25
1730	A717	2s blk, emer & grn	.25	.25
1731	A717	3s black & multi	.25	.25
1732	A717	5s black & multi	.25	.25
1733	A717	10s black, grn & yel	.50	.25
1734	A717	13s black & multi	.55	.25
1735	A717	20s black, lil & grn	.85	.25
		Nos. 1728-1735 (8)	3.15	2.00

Silkworms and Spindles A718

Designs: 2s, Silkworm, cocoons and pattern. 3s, Cocoons and spinning wheel. 5s, Cocoons, woof-and-warp diagram. 13s, Silk moth, Cocoon and spinning frame. 20s, Silk moth, eggs and shuttle.

1969, Jan. 30   **Photo.**   **Perf. 10½**
1736	A718	1s bl, grn, sl & blk	.25	.25
1737	A718	2s dp car, sil & blk	.25	.25
1738	A718	3s Prus bl, sil & blk	.25	.25
1739	A718	5s pur, ver, sil & blk	.25	.25
1740	A718	13s red lil, ocher, sil & blk	.40	.25
1741	A718	20s grn, org, sil & blk	.70	.25
		Nos. 1736-1741 (6)	2.10	1.50

Bulgarian silk industry.

Attack and Capture of Emperor Nicephorus A719

Designs (Manasses Chronicle): No. 1742, 1s, Death of Ivan Asen. No. 1746, 3s, Khan Kroum feasting after victory. No. 1748, 13s, Invasion of Bulgaria by Prince Sviatoslav of Kiev. No. 1750, 20s, Russian invasion and campaigns of Emperor John I Zimisces, c. 972 A.D. No. 1752, 40s, Tsar Ivan Alexander, Jesus and Constantine Manasses.

Horizontal designs: No. 1743, 1s, Kings Nebuchadnezzar, Balthazar, Darius and Cyrus. No. 1745, 2s, Kings Cambyses, Gyges and Darius. No. 1747, 5s, King David and Tsar Ivan Alexander. No. 1749, 13s, Persecution of Byzantine army after battle of July 26, 811. No. 1751, 20s, Christening of Bulgarian Tsar Boris, 865. No. 1753, 60s, Arrival of Tsar Simeon in Constantinople and his succeeding surprise attack on that city.

1969   **Photo.**   **Perf. 14x13½, 13½x14**
1742	A719	1s multicolored	.25	.25
1743	A719	1s multicolored	.25	.25
1744	A719	2s multicolored	.25	.25
1745	A719	2s multicolored	.25	.25
1746	A719	3s multicolored	.25	.25
1747	A719	5s multicolored	.25	.25

1748	A719	13s multicolored	.55	.25
1749	A719	13s multicolored	.55	.25
1750	A719	20s multicolored	1.10	.25
1751	A719	20s multicolored	1.10	.25
1752	A719	40s multicolored	1.75	.55
1753	A719	60s multicolored	2.50	.55
		Nos. 1742-1753 (12)	9.05	3.60

Sts. Cyril and Methodius, Mural, Troian Monastery A720

1969, Mar. 23

1754	A720	28s gold & multi	1.40	.60

Post Horn — A721

Designs: 13s, Bulgaria Nos. 1 and 534. 20s, Street fighting at Stackata, 1919.

1969, Apr. 15   Photo.   Perf. 10½

1755	A721	2s green & yel	.25	.25
1756	A721	13s multicolored	.50	.25
1757	A721	20s dk bl & lt bl	.85	.25
		Nos. 1755-1757 (3)	1.60	.75

Bulgarian postal administration, 90th anniv.

The Fox and the Rabbit A722

Puppet theater characters and illustrations from children's books: 2s, Boy reading to hedgehog and squirrel. 13s, Two birds and frog singing together.

1969, Apr. 21

1758	A722	1s emer, org & blk	.25	.25
1759	A722	2s org, lt bl & blk	.25	.25
1760	A722	13s lt bl, ol & blk	.40	.25
		Nos. 1758-1760 (3)	.90	.75

Issued for Week of Children's Books and Arts.

ILO Emblem — A723

1969, Apr. 28

1761	A723	13s dull grn & blk	.50	.25

50th anniv. of the ILO.

St. George and SOFIA 69 Emblem A724

Designs: 2s, Virgin Mary and St. John Bogoslov. 3s, Archangel Michael. 5s, Three Saints. 8s, Jesus Christ. 13s, Sts. George and Dimitrie. 20s, Christ, the Almighty. 40s, St. Dimitrie. 60s, The 40 Martyrs. 80s, The Transfiguration.

1969, Apr. 30   Perf. 11x12

1762	A724	1s gold & multi	.25	.25
1763	A724	2s gold & multi	.25	.25
1764	A724	3s gold & multi	.25	.25
1765	A724	5s gold & multi	.30	.25
1766	A724	8s gold & multi	.30	.25
1767	A724	13s gold & multi	.50	.25
1768	A724	40s gold & multi	.75	.30
1769	A724	40s gold & multi	1.40	1.00
a.		Sheet of 4	9.00	7.75
1770	A724	60s gold & multi	2.00	1.50
1771	A724	80s gold & multi	3.00	1.75
		Nos. 1762-1771 (10)	9.00	6.05

Old Bulgarian art from the National Art Gallery. No. 1769a contains 4 of No. 1769 with center gutter showing Alexander Nevski Shrine. See note on SOFIA 69 after Nos. C112-C120.

St. Cyril Preaching A725

Design: 28s, St. Cyril and followers.

1969, June 20   Litho.   Perf. 10½

1772	A725	2s sil, grn & red	.25	.25
1773	A725	28s sil, dk bl & red	1.25	.45

St. Cyril (827-869), apostle to the Slavs, inventor of Cyrillic alphabet. Issued in sheets of 25 with se-tenant labels; Cyrillic inscription on label of 2s, Glagolitic inscription on label of 28s.

St. Sophia Church — A726

Sofia Through the Ages: 1s, Roman coin with inscription "Ulpia Serdica." 2s, Roman coin with Aesculapius Temple. 4s, Bojana Church. 5s, Sobranie Parliament. 13s, Vasov National Theater. 20s, Alexander Nevski Shrine. 40s, Clement Ochrida University. 1 l, Coat of arms.

1969, May 25   Perf. 13x12½

1774	A726	1s gold & blue	.25	.25
1775	A726	2s gold & ol grn	.25	.25
1776	A726	3s gold & red brn	.25	.25
1777	A726	4s gold & purple	.25	.25
1778	A726	5s gold & plum	.25	.25
1779	A726	13s gold & brt grn	.35	.25

1780	A726	20s gold & vio bl	.55	.25
1781	A726	40s gold & dp car	1.10	.30
		Nos. 1774-1781 (8)	3.25	2.05

Souvenir Sheet
Imperf

1782	A726	1 l grn, gold & red	3.50	2.25

Historic Sofia in connection with the International Philatelic Exhibition, Sofia, 5/31-6/8.

No. 1782 contains one 43½x43½mm stamp. Emblems of 8 preceding philatelic exhibitions in metallic ink in margin; gold inscription.

No. 1782 was overprinted in green "IBRA 73" and various symbols, and released May 4, 1973, for the Munich Philatelic Exhibition. Value $150. The overprint also exists in gray. Value $50.

St. George A727

1969, June 9   Litho.   Perf. 11½

1783	A727	40s sil, blk & pale rose	1.75	.75

38th FIP Congress, June 9-11.

Hand Planting Sapling A728

1969, Apr. 28   Photo.   Perf. 11

1784	A728	2s ol grn, blk & lilac	.25	.25

25 years of the reforestation campaign.

Partisans — A729

Designs: 2s, Combine harvester. 3s, Dam. 5s, Flutist and singers. 13s, Factory. 20s, Lenin, Dimitrov, Russian and Bulgarian flags.

1969, Sept. 9

1785	A729	1s blk, pur & org	.25	.25
1786	A729	2s blk, ol bis & org	.25	.25
1787	A729	3s blk, bl grn & org	.25	.25
1788	A729	5s blk, brn red & org	.25	.25
1789	A729	13s blk, bl & org	.50	.25
1790	A729	20s blk, brn & org	.85	.25
		Nos. 1785-1790 (6)	2.35	1.50

25th anniversary of People's Republic.

Women Gymnasts — A730

1969, Sept.   Photo.   Perf. 11

1791	A730	2s shown	.25	.25
1792	A730	20s Wrestlers	.70	.30

Third National Spartakiad.

Tchanko Bakalov Tcherkovski, Poet. Birth Cent. — A731

1969, Sept. 6

1793	A731	13s multicolored	.60	.25

Woman Gymnast A732

2s, Two women with hoops. 3s, Woman with hoop. 5s, Two women with spheres.

1969, Oct.
Gymnasts in Light Gray

1794	A732	1s green & dk blue	.25	.25
1795	A732	2s blue & dk blue	.25	.25
1796	A732	3s emer & sl grn	.25	.25
1797	A732	5s orange & pur	.25	.25
		Nos. 1794-1797,B35-B36 (6)	2.80	1.75

World Championships for Artistic Gymnastics, Varna.

The Priest Rilski, by Zachary Zograf A733

Paintings from the National Art Gallery. 2s, Woman at Window, by Vasil Stoilov. 3s, Workers at Rest, by Nenko Balkanski, horiz. 4s, Woman Dressing (Nude), by Ivan Nenov. 5s, Portrait of a Woman, by N. Pavlovich. 13s, Falstaff, by Duzunov Kr. Sarafov. No. 1804, Portrait of a Woman, by N. Mihajlov, horiz. No. 1805, Workers at Mealtime, by Stojan Sotirov, horiz. 40s, Self-portrait, by Tcheno Togorov.

Perf. 11½x12, 12x11½
1969, Nov. 10

1798	A733	1s gold & multi	.25	.25
1799	A733	2s gold & multi	.25	.25
1800	A733	3s gold & dk blue	.25	.25
1801	A733	4s gold & multi	.25	.25
1802	A733	5s gold & multi	.35	.25
1803	A733	13s gold & multi	.70	.25
1804	A733	20s gold & multi	1.10	.30
1805	A733	20s gold & multi	1.10	.35
1806	A733	40s gold & multi	1.50	.35
		Nos. 1798-1806 (9)	5.75	2.50

Roman Bronze Wolf — A734

Design: 2s, Roman statue of woman, found at Silistra, vert.

1969, Oct.   Photo.   Perf. 11

1807	A734	2s sil, ultra & gray	.25	.25
1808	A734	13s sil, dk grn & gray	.80	.30

City of Silistra's 1,800th anniversary.

Worker and
Factory
A735

1969 **Perf. 13**
1809 A735 6s ultra & blk .25 .25
25th anniversary of the Engineering Corps.

European Hake — A736

Designs: No. 1811, Deep-sea fishing trawler. Fish: 2s, Atlantic horse mackerel. 3s, Pilchard. 5s, Dentex macrophthalmus. 10s, Chub mackerel. 13s, Otolithes macrognathus. 20s, Lichia vadigo.

1969 **Perf. 11**
1810 A736 1s ol grn & blk .25 .25
1811 A736 1s ultra, ind & gray .25 .25
1812 A736 2s lilac & blk .25 .25
1813 A736 3s vio bl & blk .25 .25
1814 A736 5s rose cl, pink & blk .25 .25
1815 A736 10s gray & blk 1.10 .25
1816 A736 13s ver, sal & blk 1.60 .25
1817 A736 20s ocher & black 2.10 .25
Nos. 1810-1817 (8) 6.05 2.00

Marin
Drinov
A737

1969, Nov. 10 **Litho.** **Perf. 11**
1818 A737 20s black & red org .30 .25
Centenary of the Bulgarian Academy of Science, founded by Marin Drinov.

Trapeze
Artists — A738

Circus Performers: 2s, Jugglers. 3s, Jugglers with loops. 5s, Juggler and bear on bicycle. 13s, Woman and performing horse. 20s, Musical clowns.

1969 **Photo.** **Perf. 11**
1819 A738 1s dk blue & multi .25 .25
1820 A738 2s dk green & multi .25 .25
1821 A738 3s dk violet & multi .25 .25
1822 A738 5s multicolored .25 .25
1823 A738 13s multicolored .50 .25
1824 A738 20s multicolored 1.10 .25
Nos. 1819-1824 (6) 2.60 1.50

Pavel Bania
Sanatorium
A739

Health Resorts: 5s, Chisar Sanatorium. 6s, Kotel Children's Sanatorium. 20s, Narechen Polyclinic.

1969, Dec. **Photo.** **Perf. 10½-14**
1825 A739 2s blue .25 .25
1826 A739 5s ultra .25 .25
1827 A739 6s green .25 .25
1828 A739 20s emerald .55 .25
Nos. 1825-1828 (4) 1.30 1.00

G. S. Shonin, V.
N. Kubasov and
Spacecraft
A740

Designs: 2s, A. V. Filipchenko, V. N. Volkov, V. V. Gorbatko and spacecraft. 3s, Vladimir A. Shatalov, Alexei S. Yeliseyev and spacecraft. 28s, Three spacecraft in orbit.

1970, Jan. **Photo.** **Perf. 11**
1829 A740 1s rose car, ol grn & blk .25 .25
1830 A740 2s bl, dl cl & blk .25 .25
1831 A740 3s grnsh bl, vio & blk .25 .25
1832 A740 28s vio bl, lil rose & lt bl 1.00 .25
Nos. 1829-1832 (4) 1.75 1.00
Russian space flights of Soyuz 6, 7 and 8, Oct. 11-13, 1969.

Khan Krum and Defeat of Emperor
Nicephorus, 811 — A741

Bulgarian History: 1s, Khan Asparuh and Bulgars crossing the Danube (679). 3s, Conversion of Prince Boris to Christianity, 865. 5s, Tsar Simeon and battle of Akhelo, 917. 8s, Tsar Samuel defeating the Byzantines, 976. 10s, Tsar Kaloyan defeating Emperor Baldwin, 1205. 13s, Tsar Ivan Assen II defeating Greek King Theodore Komnine, 1230. 20s, Coronation of Tsar Ivailo, 1277.

1970, Feb. **Perf. 10½**
1833 A741 1s gold & multi .25 .25
1834 A741 2s gold & multi .25 .25
1835 A741 3s gold & multi .25 .25
1836 A741 5s gold & multi .25 .25
1837 A741 8s gold & multi .25 .25
1838 A741 10s gold & multi .45 .25
1839 A741 13s gold & multi .65 .25
1840 A741 20s gold & multi 1.00 .25
Nos. 1833-1840 (8) 3.35 2.00
See Nos. 2126-2133.

Bulgarian Pavilion, EXPO '70 — A742

1970 **Perf. 12½**
1841 A742 20s brown, sil & org 1.40 .75
EXPO '70 International Exposition, Osaka, Japan, Mar. 15-Sept. 13, 1970.

Soccer — A743

Designs: Various views of soccer game.

1970, Mar. 4 **Photo.** **Perf. 12½**
1842 A743 1s blue & multi .25 .25
1843 A743 2s rose car & multi .25 .25
1844 A743 3s ultra & multi .25 .25
1845 A743 5s green & multi .25 .25
1846 A743 20s emerald & multi 1.20 .25
1847 A743 40s red & multi 1.50 .45
Nos. 1842-1847 (6) 3.70 1.70
9th World Soccer Championships for the Jules Rimet Cup, Mexico City, May 30-June 21, 1970. See No. B37.

Lenin (1870-1924) — A744

1970, Apr. 22
1848 A744 2s shown .25 .25
1849 A744 13s Portrait .55 .25
1850 A744 20s Writing 1.20 .25
Nos. 1848-1850 (3) 2.00 .75

Tephrocactus
Alexanderi V.
Bruchii — A745

Cacti: 2s, Opuntia drummondii. 3s, Hatiora cilindrica. 5s, Gymnocalycium vatteri. 8s, Heliantho cereus grandiflorus. 10s, Neochilenia andreaeana. 13s, Peireskia vargasii v. longispina. 20s, Neobesseya rosiflora.

1970 **Photo.** **Perf. 12½**
1851 A745 1s multicolored .25 .25
1852 A745 2s dk green & multi .25 .25
1853 A745 3s multicolored .25 .25
1854 A745 5s blue & multi .25 .25
1855 A745 8s brown & multi .35 .30
1856 A745 10s vio bl & multi 1.75 .40
1857 A745 13s brn red & multi 1.75 .75
1858 A745 20s purple & multi 2.10 .75
Nos. 1851-1858 (8) 6.95 3.20

Rose — A746

Designs: Various Roses.

1970, June 5 **Litho.** **Perf. 13½**
1859 A746 1s gray & multi .25 .25
1860 A746 2s gray & multi .25 .25
1861 A746 3s gray & multi .25 .25
1862 A746 4s gray & multi .35 .25
1863 A746 5s gray & multi .35 .25
1864 A746 13s gray & multi .65 .30
1865 A746 20s gray & multi 1.40 .65
1866 A746 28s gray & multi 2.50 .95
Nos. 1859-1866 (8) 6.00 3.15

Gold Bowl
A747

Designs: Various bowls and art objects from Gold Treasure of Thrace.

1970, June 15 **Photo.** **Perf. 12½**
1867 A747 1s blk, bl & gold .25 .25
1868 A747 2s blk, lt vio & gold .25 .25
1869 A747 3s blk, ver & gold .25 .25
1870 A747 5s blk, yel grn & gold .25 .25
1871 A747 13s blk, org & gold 1.10 .25
1872 A747 20s blk, lil & gold 1.40 .25
Nos. 1867-1872 (6) 3.50 1.50

EXPO Emblem, Rose and Bulgarian
Woman — A748

Designs (EXPO Emblem and): 2s, Three women. 3s, Woman and fruit. 28s, Dancers. 40s, Mt. Fuji and pavilions.

1970, June 20
1873 A748 1s gold & multi .25 .25
1874 A748 2s gold & multi .25 .25
1875 A748 3s gold & multi .25 .25
1876 A748 28s gold & multi 1.10 .30
Nos. 1873-1876 (4) 1.85 1.05
Miniature Sheet
Imperf
1877 A748 40s gold & multi 1.40 .85
EXPO '70 International Exposition, Osaka, Japan, Mar. 15-Sept. 13. No. 1877 contains one stamp with simulated perforations.

Ivan Vasov
A749

1970, Aug. 1 **Photo.** **Perf. 12½**
1878 A749 13s violet blue .75 .25
Ivan Vasov, author, 120th birth anniv.

UN Emblem — A750

1970, Aug. 1
1879 A750 20s Prus bl & gold .75 .25
25th anniversary of the United Nations.

George
Dimitrov — A751

1970, June 8
1880 A751 20s blk, gold & org 1.10 .25
BZNC (Bulgarian Communist Party), 70th anniv.

Retriever
A752

Dogs: 1s, Golden retriever, horiz. 3s, Great Dane. 4s, Boxer. 5s, Cocker spaniel. 13s, Doberman pinscher. 20s, Scottish terrier. 28s, Russian greyhound, horiz.

1970		Photo.	Perf. 12½	
1881	A752	1s multicolored	.25	.25
1882	A752	2s multicolored	.25	.25
1883	A752	3s multicolored	.25	.25
1884	A752	4s multicolored	.40	.25
1885	A752	5s multicolored	.40	.25
1886	A752	13s multicolored	1.10	.40
1887	A752	20s multicolored	2.10	.75
1888	A752	28s multicolored	2.50	1.10
		Nos. 1881-1888 (8)	7.25	3.50

Volleyball
A753

No. 1890, Two women players. No. 1891, Woman player. No. 1892, Man player.

1970, Sept.		Photo.	Perf. 12½	
1889	A753	2s dk red brn, bl & blk	.25	.25
1890	A753	2s ultra, org & blk	.25	.25
1891	A753	20s Prus bl, yel & blk	.90	.25
1892	A753	20s grn, yel & blk	.90	.25
		Nos. 1889-1892 (4)	2.30	1.00

World Volleyball Championships.

Enrico Caruso and "I Pagliacci" by
Ruggiero Leoncavallo — A754

Opera Singers and Operas: 2s, Christina Morfova and "The Bartered Bride" by Bedrich Smetana. 3s, Peter Reitchev and "Tosca" by Giacomo Puccini. 10s, Svetana Tabakova and "The Flying Dutchman" by Richard Wagner. 13s, Katia Popova and "The Masters" by Paroshkev Hadjev. 20s, Feodor Chaliapin and "Boris Godunov" by Modest Musorgski.

1970, Oct. 15		Photo.	Perf. 14	
1893	A754	1s black & multi	.25	.25
1894	A754	2s black & multi	.25	.25
1895	A754	3s black & multi	.25	.25
1896	A754	10s black & multi	.25	.25
1897	A754	13s black & multi	.35	.25
1898	A754	20s black & multi	1.60	.25
		Nos. 1893-1898 (6)	2.95	1.50

Honoring opera singers in their best roles.

Ivan Assen II Coin — A755

Coins from 14th Century with Ruler's Portrait: 2s, Theodor Svetoslav. 3s, Mikhail Chichman. 13s, Ivan Alexander and Mikhail Assen. 20s, Ivan Sratsimir. 28s, Ivan Chichman (initials).

1970, Nov.			Perf. 12½	
1899	A755	1s buff & multi	.25	.25
1900	A755	2s gray & multi	.25	.25
1901	A755	3s multicolored	.25	.25
1902	A755	13s multicolored	.35	.25
1903	A755	20s lt blue & multi	1.00	.25
1904	A755	28s multicolored	1.40	.40
		Nos. 1899-1904 (6)	3.50	1.65

Fire
Protection
A756

1970		Litho.	Perf. 12½	
1905	A756	1s Fireman	.25	.25
1906	A756	3s Fire engine	.25	.25

Bicyclists
A757

1970				Photo.
1907	A757	20s grn, yel & pink	.75	.25

20th Bulgarian bicycle race.

Congress
Emblem — A758

1970
1908 A758 13s gold & multi .60 .25

7th World Congress of Sociology, Varna, Sept. 14-19.

Ludwig van
Beethoven
A759

1970
1909 A759 28s lil rose & dk bl 2.10 1.10

Beethoven (1770-1827), composer.

Friedrich
Engels — A760

1970		Photo.	Perf. 12½	
1910	A760	13s ver, tan & brn	.75	.25

Friedrich Engels (1820-1895), German socialist, collaborator of Karl Marx.

Miniature Sheets

Luna
16
A761

Russian moon mission: 80s, Lunokhod 1, unmanned vehicle on moon, horiz.

1970		Photo.	Imperf.	
1911	A761	80s plum, sil, blk & bl	4.25	4.25
1912	A761	1 l vio bl, sil & red	5.00	4.00

No. 1911 , Lunokhod 1, Nov. 10-17. No. 1912, Luna 16 mission, Sept. 12-24.
Issue dates: 80s, Dec. 18; 1 l, Nov. 10.

Snowflake — A762

1970, Dec. 15		Photo.	Perf. 12½x13	
1913	A762	2s ultra & multi	.25	.25

New Year 1971.

Birds and
Flowers
A763

Folk Art: 2s, Bird and flowers. 3s, Flying birds. 5s, Birds and flowers. 13s, Sun. 20s, Tulips and pansies.

1971, Jan. 25			Perf. 12½x13½	
1914	A763	1s multicolored	.25	.25
1915	A763	2s multicolored	.25	.25
1916	A763	3s multicolored	.25	.25
1917	A763	5s multicolored	.25	.25
1918	A763	13s multicolored	.25	.25
1919	A763	20s multicolored	.75	.25
		Nos. 1914-1919 (6)	2.00	1.50

Spring 1971.

Girl, by Zeko
Spiridonov
A764

Modern Bulgarian Sculpture: 2s, Third Class (people looking through train window), by Ivan Funev. 3s, Bust of Elin Pelin, by Marko Markov. 13s, Bust of Nina, by Andrej Nikolov. 20s, Monument to P. K. Yavorov (kneeling woman), by Ivan Lazarov. 28s, Engineer, by Ivan Funev. 1 l, Refugees, by Sekul Krimov, horiz.

1970, Dec. 28			Perf. 12½	
1920	A764	1s gold & vio	.25	.25
1921	A764	2s gold & dk ol grn	.25	.25
1922	A764	3s gold & rose brn	.25	.25
1923	A764	13s gold & dk grn	.50	.25
1924	A764	20s gold & red brn	.90	.25
1925	A764	28s gold & dk brn	1.00	.25
		Nos. 1920-1925 (6)	3.15	1.50

Souvenir Sheet
Imperf
1926	A764	1 l gold, dk brn & buff	2.25	2.25

Runner
A765

Design: 20s, Woman putting the shot.

1971, Mar. 13		Photo.	Perf. 12½x13	
1927	A765	2s brown & multi	.25	.25
1928	A765	20s dp grn, org & blk	1.40	.35

2nd European Indoor Track and Field Championships.

Bulgarian Secondary School,
Bolgrad — A766

Educators: 20s, Dimiter Mitev, Prince Bogoridi and Sava Radoulov.

1971, Mar. 16			Perf. 12½	
1929	A766	2s silver, brn & grn	.25	.25
1930	A766	2s silver, brn & vio	1.10	.25

First Bulgarian secondary school, 1858, in Bolgrad, USSR.

Communards — A767

1971, Mar. 18		Photo.	Perf. 12½x13	
1931	A767	20s rose mag & blk	.75	.25

Centenary of the Paris Commune.

Dimitrov Facing Goering, Quotation,
FIR Emblem — A768

1971, Apr. 11			Perf. 12½	
1932	A768	2s grn, gold, blk & red	.25	.25
1933	A768	13s plum, gold, blk & red	1.10	.25

Intl. Fed. of Resistance Fighters (FIR), 20th anniv.

George S. Rakovski (1821-1867), Revolutionary Against Turkish Rule — A769

1971, Apr. 14
1934 A769 13s olive & blk brn .60 .25

Edelweiss Hotel, Borovets A770

2s, Panorama Hotel, Pamporovo. 4s, Boats at Albena, Black Sea. 8s, Boats at Rousalka. 10s, Shtastlivetsa Hotel, Mt. Vitosha.

1971 *Perf. 13*
1935 A770 1s brt green .25 .25
1936 A770 2s olive gray .25 .25
1937 A770 4s brt blue .25 .25
1938 A770 8s blue .25 .25
1939 A770 10s bluish green .45 .25
    Nos. 1935-1939 (5) 1.45 1.25

Technological Progress — A771

Designs: 1s, Mason with banner, vert. 13s, Two men and doves, vert.

1971, Apr. 20 Photo. *Perf. 12½*
1940 A771 1s gold & multi .25 .25
1941 A771 2s gray blue & multi .25 .25
1942 A771 13s lt green & multi .85 .25
    Nos. 1940-1942 (3) 1.35 .75

10th Cong. of Bulgarian Communist Party.

Panayot Pipkov and Anthem A772

1971, May 20
1943 A772 13s sil, blk & brt grn .75 .25

Panayot Pipkov, composer, birth cent.

Mammoth A773

Prehistoric Animals: 2s, Bear, vert. 3s, Hipparion (horse). 13s, Platybelodon. 20s, Dinotherium, vert. 28s, Saber-tooth tiger.

1971, May 29 *Perf. 12½*
1944 A773 1s dull bl & multi .25 .25
1945 A773 2s lilac & multi .25 .25
1946 A773 3s multicolored .25 .25
1947 A773 13s multicolored 1.40 .40
1948 A773 20s dp grn & multi 2.10 1.00
1949 A773 28s multicolored 2.50 1.25
    Nos. 1944-1949 (6) 6.75 3.40

Khan Asparuch Crossing Danube, 679 A.D., by Boris Angelushev — A774

Historical Paintings: 3s, Reception at Trnovo, by Ilya Petrov. 5s, Chevartov's Troops at Benkovsky, by P. Morozov. 8s, Russian Gen. Gurko and People in Sofia, 1878, by D. Gudjenko. 28s, People Greeting Red Army, by S. Venov.

1971, Mar. 6 *Perf. 13½x14*
1950 A774 2s gold & multi .25 .25
1951 A774 3s gold & multi .25 .25
1952 A774 5s gold & multi .35 .25
1953 A774 8s gold & multi .70 .25
    a. Souv. sheet of 4, #1950-1953 1.40 .85
1954 A774 28s gold & multi 2.75 1.10
    Nos. 1950-1954 (5) 4.30 2.10

In 1973, No. 1953a was surcharged 1 lev and overprinted "Visitez la Bulgarie," airline initials and emblems, and, on the 5s stamp, "Par Avion."

Freed Black, White and Yellow Men — A775

1971, May 20 Photo. *Perf. 12½*
1955 A775 13s blue, blk & yel .75 .25

Intl. Year against Racial Discrimination.

Map of Europe, Championship Emblem — A776

"XXX" Supporting Barbell — A777

1971, June 19
1956 A776 2s lt blue & multi .25 .25
1957 A777 13s yellow & multi .90 .25

30th European Weight Lifting Championships, Sofia, June 19-27.

Facade, Old House, Koprivnica — A778

Designs: Decorated facades of various old houses in Koprivnica.

1971, July 10 Photo. *Perf. 12½*
1958 A778 1s green & multi .25 .25
1959 A778 2s brown & multi .25 .25
1960 A778 6s violet & multi .25 .25
1961 A778 13s dk red & multi .65 .25
    Nos. 1958-1961 (4) 1.40 1.00

Frontier Guard and German Shepherd A779

1971, July 31 *Perf. 13*
1962 A779 2s green & ol grn .25 .25

25th anniversary of the Frontier Guards.

Congress of Busludja, Bas-relief — A780

1971, July 31 *Perf. 12½*
1963 A780 2s dk red & ol grn .25 .25

80th anniversary of the first Congress of the Bulgarian Social Democratic party.

Young Woman, by Ivan Nenov — A781

Paintings: 2s, Lazarova in Evening Gown, by Stefan Ivanov. 3s, Performer in Dress Suit, by Kyril Zonev. 13s, Portrait of a Woman, by Detchko Uzunov. 20s, Woman from Kalotina, by Vladimir Dimitrov. 40s, Gorjanin (Mountain Man), by Stoyan Venev.

1971, Aug. 2 *Perf. 14x13½*
1964 A781 1s green & multi .25 .25
1965 A781 2s green & multi .25 .25
1966 A781 3s green & multi .25 .25
1967 A781 13s green & multi .70 .25
1968 A781 20s green & multi 1.00 .50
1969 A781 40s green & multi 1.40 .90
    Nos. 1964-1969 (6) 3.85 2.40

National Art Gallery.

Wrestlers A782

Designs: 13s, Wrestlers.

1971, Aug. 27 *Perf. 12½*
1970 A782 2s green, blk & bl .25 .25
1971 A782 13s red org, blk & bl .65 .25

European Wrestling Championships.

Young Workers — A783

1971 *Photo.* *Perf. 13*
1972 A783 2s dark blue .25 .25

25th anniv. of the Young People's Brigade.

Post Horn Emblem A784

1971, Sept. 15 *Perf. 12½*
1973 A784 20s dp green & gold .75 .35

8th meeting of postal administrations of socialist countries, Varna.

FEBS Waves Emblem — A785

1971, Sept. 20
1974 A785 13s black, red & mar .75 .35

7th Congress of European Biochemical Association (FEBS), Varna.

Statue of Republic A786

Design: 13s, Bulgarian flag.

1971, Sept. 20 *Perf. 13x12½*
1975 A786 2s gold, yel & dk red .25 .25
1976 A786 13s gold, grn & red .60 .25

Bulgarian People's Republic, 25th anniv.

Cross Country Skiing and Winter Olympics Emblem A787

Sport and Winter Olympics Emblem: 2s, Downhill skiing. 3s, Ski jump and skiing. 4s, Women's figure skating. 13s, Ice hockey. 28s, Slalom skiing. 1 l, Torch and stadium.

1971, Sept. 25 *Perf. 12½*
1977 A787 1s dk green & multi .25 .25
1978 A787 2s vio blue & multi .25 .25
1979 A787 3s ultra & multi .25 .25
1980 A787 4s dp plum & multi .25 .25
1981 A787 13s dk blue & multi .60 .25
1982 A787 28s multicolored 1.25 .55
    Nos. 1977-1982 (6) 2.85 1.80

Miniature Sheet
Imperf

1983 A787 1 l multicolored 3.50 1.60

11th Winter Olympic Games, Sapporo, Japan, Feb. 3-13, 1972.

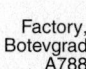

Factory, Botevgrad
A788

Industrial Buildings: 2s, Petro-chemical works, Pleven, vert. 10s, Chemical works, Vratsa. 13s, Maritsa-Istok Power Station, Dimitrovgrad. 40s, Electronics works, Sofia.

1971		**Photo.**	**Perf. 13**	
1984	A788	1s violet	.25	.25
1985	A788	2s orange	.25	.25
1986	A788	10s deep purple	.25	.25
1987	A788	13s lilac rose	.40	.25
1988	A788	40s deep brown	1.25	.25
		Nos. 1984-1988 (5)	2.40	1.25

UNESCO Emblem
A789

1971, Nov. 4			**Perf. 12½**	
1989	A789	20s lt bl, blk, gold & red	.75	.25

25th anniv. of UNESCO.

Soccer Player, by Kyril Zonev (1896-1971)
A790

Paintings by Kyril Zonev: 2s, Landscape, horiz. 3s, Self-portrait. 13s, Lilies. 20s, Landscape, horiz. 40s, Portrait of a Young Woman.

1971, Nov. 10			**Perf. 11x12**	
1990	A790	1s gold & multi	.25	.25
1991	A790	2s gold & multi	.25	.25
1992	A790	3s gold & multi	.25	.25
1993	A790	13s gold & multi	.70	.25
1994	A790	20s gold & multi	1.00	.40
1995	A790	40s gold & multi	1.40	.50
		Nos. 1990-1995 (6)	3.85	1.90

Salyut Space Station — A791

Astronauts Dobrovolsky, Volkov and Patsayev — A792

Designs: 13s, Soyuz 11 space transport. 40s, Salyut and Soyuz 11 joined.

1971, Dec. 20			**Perf. 12½**	
1996	A791	2s dk grn, yel & red	.25	.25
1997	A791	13s multicolored	.35	.25
1998	A791	40s dk blue & multi	1.75	.45
		Nos. 1996-1998 (3)	2.35	.95

Souvenir Sheet
Imperf

1999 A792 80s multicolored 2.25 1.50

Salyut-Soyuz 11 space mission, and in memory of the Russian astronauts Lt. Col. Georgi T. Dobrovolsky, Vladislav N. Volkov and Victor I. Patsayev, who died during the Soyuz 11 space mission, June 6-30, 1971.

Oil Tanker Vihren — A793

1972, Jan. 8		**Photo.**	**Perf. 12½**	
2000	A793	18s lil rose, vio & blk	1.00	.35

Bulgarian shipbuilding industry.

Goce Delchev
A794

5s, Jan Sandanski. 13s, Damjan Gruev.

1972, Jan. 21		**Photo.**	**Perf. 12½**	
2001	A794	2s brick red & blk	.25	.25
2002	A794	5s green & blk	.25	.25
2003	A794	13s lemon & blk	.35	.25
		Nos. 2001-2003 (3)	.85	.75

Centenary of the births of Bulgarian patriots Delchev (1872-1903) and Sandanski, and of Macedonian Gruev (1871-1906).

Gymnast with Hoop, Medals — A795

13s, Gymnast with ball, medals. 70s, Gymnasts with hoops, medals.

1972, Feb. 10				
2004	A795	13s multicolored	.70	.25
2005	A795	18s multicolored	1.00	.25

Miniature Sheet
Imperf

2006 A795 70s multicolored 3.25 2.50

5th World Women's Gymnastic Championships, Havana, Cuba.

View of Melnik, by Petar Mladenov — A796

Paintings from National Art Gallery: 2s, Plower, by Pencho Georgiev. 3s, Funeral, by Alexander Djendov. 13s, Husband and Wife, by Vladimir Dimitrov. 20s, Nursing Mother, by Nenko Balkanski. 40s, Paisii Hilendarski Writing History, by Koio Denchev.

1972, Feb. 20			**Perf. 13½x14**	
2007	A796	1s green & multi	.25	.25
2008	A796	2s green & multi	.25	.25
2009	A796	3s green & multi	.25	.25
2010	A796	13s green & multi	1.25	.25
2011	A796	20s green & multi	1.25	.25
2012	A796	40s green & multi	1.25	.55
		Nos. 2007-2012 (6)	4.50	1.80

Paintings from National Art Gallery.

Worker — A797

1972, Mar. 7			**Perf. 12½**	
2013	A797	13s silver & multi	.60	.30

7th Bulgarian Trade Union Congress.

Singing Harvesters
A798

Designs: Paintings by Vladimir Dimitrov. 3s, 13s, horiz.

1972, Mar. 31		**Perf. 11½x12, 12x11½**		
2014	A798	1s shown	.25	.25
2015	A798	2s Harvester	.25	.25
2016	A798	3s Women Diggers	.25	.25
2017	A798	13s Fabric Dyers	.35	.25
2018	A798	20s "My Mother"	1.40	.25
2019	A798	40s Self-portrait	1.40	.45
		Nos. 2014-2019 (6)	3.90	1.70

Vladimir Dimitrov, painter, 90th birth anniv.

"Your Heart is your Health" — A799

1972, Apr. 30			**Perf. 12½**	
2020	A799	13s red, blk & grn	1.10	.50

World Health Day.

St. Mark's Basilica and Wave — A800

Design: 13s, Ca' D'Oro and wave.

1972, May 6			**Perf. 13x12½**	
2021	A800	2s ol grn, bl grn & lt bl	.25	.25
2022	A800	13s red brn, vio & lt grn	.90	.25

UNESCO campaign to save Venice.

Dimitrov in Print Shop, 1901 — A801

Life of George Dimitrov: 2s, Dimitrov as leader of 1923 uprising. 3s, Leipzig trial, 1933. 5s, As Communist functionary, 1935. 13s, As leader and teacher, 1948. 18s, Addressing youth rally, 1948. 28s, With Pioneers, 1948. 40s, Mausoleum. 80s, Portrait.

1972, May 8		**Photo.**	**Perf. 12½**	
2023	A801	1s shown	.25	.25
2024	A801	2s multicolored	.25	.25
2025	A801	3s multicolored	.25	.25
2026	A801	5s multicolored	.25	.25
2027	A801	13s multicolored	.35	.25
2028	A801	18s multicolored	.35	.25
2029	A801	28s multicolored	.75	.25
2030	A801	40s multicolored	1.50	.45
2031	A801	80s multicolored	4.25	.70
a.		Souvenir sheet	4.50	3.50
		Nos. 2023-2031 (9)	8.20	2.90

90th anniversary of the birth of George Dimitrov (1882-1949), communist leader.

No. 2031a contains one imperf. stamp similar to No. 2031, but in different colors.

Value, No. 2031 imperf. in slightly changed colors, $8.50.

Paisii Hilendarski
A802

Design: 2s, Flame and quotation.

1972, May 12				
2032	A802	2s gold, grn & brn	.25	.25
2033	A802	13s gold, grn & brn	.85	.25

Paisii Hilendarski (1722-1798), monk, writer of Bulgarian-Slavic history.

Canoeing, Motion and Olympic Emblems — A803

Designs (Motion and Olympic emblems and): 2s, Gymnastics. 3s, Swimming, women's. 13s, Volleyball. 18s, Jumping. 40s, Wrestling. 80s, Stadium and sports.

1972, June 25
Figures of Athletes in Silver & Black

2034	A803	1s lt blue & multi	.25	.25
2035	A803	2s orange & multi	.25	.25
2036	A803	3s multicolored	.25	.25
2037	A803	13s yellow & multi	.35	.25
2038	A803	18s multicolored	.70	.25
2039	A803	40s pink & multi	1.40	.40

Nos. 2034-2039 (6) 3.20 1.65

Miniature Sheet
Imperf
Size: 62x60mm

2040	A803	80s gold, ver & yel	3.00	2.00

20th Olympic Games, Munich, 8/26-9/11.

Angel
Kunchev
A804

1972, June 30   Photo.   Perf. 12½

2041	A804	2s mag, dk pur & gold	.30	.30

Centenary of the death of Angel Kunchev, patriot and revolutionist.

Zlatni Pyassatsi
A805

1972, Sept. 16

2042	A805	1s shown	.25	.25
2043	A805	2s Drouzhba	.25	.25
2044	A805	3s Slunchev Bryag	.25	.25
2045	A805	13s Primorsko	.50	.25
2046	A805	28s Roussalka	1.10	.35
2047	A805	40s Albena	1.50	.45

Nos. 2042-2047 (6) 3.85 1.80

Bulgarian Black Sea resorts.

Bronze Medal, Olympic Emblems,
Canoeing — A806

Olympic Emblems and: 2s, Silver medal, broad jump. 3s, Gold medal, boxing. 18s, Gold medal, wrestling. 40s, Gold medal, weight lifting.

1972, Sept. 29

2048	A806	1s Prus bl & multi	.25	.25
2049	A806	2s dk green & multi	.25	.25
2050	A806	3s org brn & multi	.25	.25
2051	A806	18s olive & multi	1.25	.25
2052	A806	40s multicolored	1.25	.55

Nos. 2048-2052 (5) 3.25 1.55

Bulgarian victories in 20th Olympic Games.
For overprint see No. 2066.

Stoj
Dimitrov — A807

Resistance Fighters: 2s, Cvetko Radoinov. 3s, Bogdan Stivrodski. 5s, Mirko Aliev. 13s, Nedelyo Nikolov.

1972, Oct. 30   Photo.   Perf. 12½x13

2053	A807	1s olive & multi	.25	.25
2054	A807	2s multicolored	.25	.25
2055	A807	3s multicolored	.25	.25
2056	A807	5s multicolored	.25	.25
2057	A807	13s multicolored	.45	.25

Nos. 2053-2057 (5) 1.45 1.25

"50
Years
USSR"
A808

1972, Nov. 3   Photo.   Perf. 12½x13

2058	A808	13s gold, red & yel	.60	.25

50th anniversary of Soviet Union.

Turk's-cap
Lily — A809

Protected Plants: 2s, Gentian. 3s, Sea daffodil. 4s, Globe flower. 18s, Primrose. 23s, Pulsatilla vernalis. 40s, Snake's-head.

1972, Nov. 25   Perf. 12½
Flowers in Natural Colors

2059	A809	1s olive bister	.25	.25
2060	A809	2s olive bister	.25	.25
2061	A809	3s olive bister	.25	.25
2062	A809	4s olive bister	.25	.25
2063	A809	18s olive bister	.55	.25
2064	A809	23s olive bister	1.00	.30
2065	A809	40s olive bister	1.40	.50

Nos. 2059-2065 (7) 3.95 2.05

No. 2052 Overprinted in Red

1972, Nov. 27

2066	A806	40s multicolored	1.75	.55

Bulgarian weight lifting Olympic gold medalists.

Dobri Chintulov
A810

1972, Nov. 28   Photo.   Perf. 12½

2067	A810	2s gray, dk & lt grn	.30	.25

Chintulov, writer, 150th birth anniv.

Forehead
Band — A811

Designs (14th-19th Century Jewelry): 2s, Belt buckles. 3s, Amulet. 8s, Pendant. 23s, Earrings. 40s, Necklace.

1972, Dec. 27   Engr.   Perf. 14x13½

2068	A811	1s red brn & blk	.25	.25
2069	A811	2s emerald & blk	.25	.25
2070	A811	3s Prus bl & blk	.25	.25
2071	A811	8s dk red & blk	.35	.25
2072	A811	23s red org & multi	.90	.35
2073	A811	40s violet & blk	1.40	.80

Nos. 2068-2073 (6) 3.40 2.15

Skin Divers
A812

Designs: 2s, Shelf-1 underwater house and divers. 18s, Diving bell and diver, vert. 40s, Elevation balloon and divers, vert.

1973, Jan. 24   Photo.   Perf. 12½

2074	A812	1s lt bl, blk & yel	.25	.25
2075	A812	2s blk, bl & org yel	.25	.25
2076	A812	18s blk, Prus bl & dl org	.60	.25
2077	A812	40s blk, ultra & bister	1.40	.45

Nos. 2074-2077 (4) 2.50 1.20

Bulgarian deep-sea research in the Black Sea.

A souvenir sheet of four contains imperf. 20s stamps in designs of Nos. 2074-2077 with colors changed. Sold for 1 l. Value $5.50 unused, $3 canceled.

Execution of
Levski, by Boris
Angelushev
A813

20s, Vassil Levski, by Georgi Danchev.

1973, Feb. 19   Perf. 13x12½

2078	A813	2s dull rose & Prus grn	.25	.25
2079	A813	20s dull grn & brn	1.25	.25

Centenary of the death of Vassil Levski (1837-1873), patriot, executed by the Turks.

Kukersky Mask,
Elhovo
Region — A814

Kukersky Masks at pre-Spring Festival: 2s, Breznik. 3s, Hissar. 13s, Radomir. 20s, Karnobat. 40s, Pernik.

1973, Feb. 26   Perf. 12½

2080	A814	1s dp rose & multi	.25	.25
2081	A814	2s emerald & multi	.25	.25
2082	A814	3s violet & multi	.25	.25
2083	A814	13s multicolored	.45	.25
2084	A814	20s multicolored	.65	.25
2085	A814	40s multicolored	3.25	1.75

Nos. 2080-2085 (6) 5.10 3.00

Nicolaus
Copernicus — A815

1973, Mar. 21   Photo.   Perf. 12½

2086	A815	28s ocher, blk & clar	1.90	1.00

500th anniversary of the birth of Nicolaus Copernicus (1473-1543), Polish astronomer.

Vietnamese
Worker and
Rainbow
A816

1973, Apr. 16

2087	A816	18s lt blue & multi	.60	.25

Peace in Viet Nam.

Wild
Flowers — A817

1973, May   Photo.   Perf. 13

2088	A817	1s Poppy	.25	.25
2089	A817	2s Daisy	.25	.25
2090	A817	3s Peony	.25	.25
2091	A817	13s Centaury	.45	.25
2092	A817	18s Corn cockle	4.50	2.50
2093	A817	28s Ranunculus	1.25	.75

Nos. 2088-2093 (6) 6.95 4.25

A818

1973, June 2

2094	A818	2s pale grn, buff & brn	.25	.25
2095	A818	18s pale brn, gray & grn	1.00	.55

Christo Botev (1848-1876), poet.

Asen Halachev and
Revolutionists — A819

2s, "Suffering Worker."

1973, June 6   Photo.   Perf. 13

2096	A819	1s gold, red & blk	.25	.25
2097	A819	2s gold, org & dk brn	.25	.25

50th anniversary of Pleven uprising.

Muskrat
A820

Perf. 12½x13, 13x12½

1973, June 29   **Litho.**
2098	A820	1s shown	.25	.25
2099	A820	2s Racoon	.25	.25
2100	A820	3s Mouflon, vert.	.25	.25
2101	A820	12s Fallow deer, vert.	.45	.25
2102	A820	18s European bison	1.25	.60
2103	A820	40s Elk	4.50	2.25
		Nos. 2098-2103 (6)	6.95	3.85

Aleksandr Stamboliski — A821

1973, June 14   **Photo.**   **Perf. 12½**
2104	A821	18s dp brown & org	.35	.25
a.		18s orange	3.50	1.40

Aleksandr Stamboliski (1879-1923), leader of Peasants' Party and premier.

Trade Union
Emblem — A822

1973, Aug. 27   **Photo.**   **Perf. 12½**
2105	A822	2s yellow & multi	.25	.25

8th Congress of World Federation of Trade Unions, Varna, Oct. 15-22.

Stylized Sun,
Olympic
Rings — A823

28s, Emblem of Bulgarian Olympic Committee & Olympic rings. 80s, Soccer, emblems of Innsbruck & Montreal 1976 Games, horiz.

1973, Aug. 29   **Perf. 13**
2106	A823	13s multicolored	1.25	.60
2107	A823	28s multicolored	1.60	.80

Souvenir Sheet
2108	A823	80s multicolored	4.00	2.50

Olympic Congress, Varna. No. 2108 contains one stamp. It also exists imperf, Value $18; also with violet margin, imperf, Value $80.

Revolutionists with Communist
Flag — A824

Designs: 5s, Revolutionists on flatcar blocking train. 13s, Raising Communist flag, vert. 18s, George Dimitrov and Vassil Kolarov.

1973, Sept. 22   **Photo.**   **Perf. 12½**
2109	A824	2s magenta & multi	.25	.25
2110	A824	5s magenta & multi	.25	.25
2111	A824	13s magenta & multi	.40	.25
2112	A824	18s magenta & multi	1.00	.40
		Nos. 2109-2112 (4)	1.90	1.15

50th anniv. of the September Revolution.

Warrior
Saint
A825

Murals from Boyana Church: 1s, Tsar Kaloyan and 2s, his wife Dessislava. 5s, "St. Wystratti." 10s, Tsar Constantine Assen. 13s, Deacon Laurentius. 18s, Virgin Mary. 20s, St. Ephraim. 28s, Jesus. 80s, Jesus in the Temple, horiz.

1973, Sept. 24
2113	A825	1s gold & multi	.25	.25
2114	A825	2s gold & multi	.25	.25
2115	A825	3s gold & multi	.25	.25
2116	A825	5s gold & multi	.40	.25
2117	A825	10s gold & multi	.65	.30
2118	A825	13s gold & multi	.65	.40
2119	A825	18s gold & multi	1.00	.60
2120	A825	20s gold & multi	1.00	.70
2121	A825	28s gold & multi	3.25	1.10
		Nos. 2113-2121 (9)	7.70	4.10

Miniature Sheet
Imperf
2122	A825	80s gold & multi	6.75	6.75

No. 2122 contains one stamp with simulated perforations.

Christo Smirnenski — A826

1973, Sept. 29   **Photo.**   **Perf. 12½**
2123	A826	1s multicolored	.25	.25
2124	A826	2s vio blue & multi	.25	.25

Christo Smirnenski (1898-1923), poet.

Human Rights
Flame — A827

1973, Oct. 10
2125	A827	13s dk bl, red & gold	.50	.25

Universal Declaration of Human Rights, 25th anniv.

Bulgarian History Type

1s, Tsar Theodor Svetoslav receiving Byzantine envoys. 2s, Tsar Mihail Shishman's army in battle with Byzantines. 3s, Tsar Ivan Alexander's victory at Russocastro. 4s, Patriarch Euthimius at the defense of Turnovo. 5s, Tsar Ivan Shishman leading horsemen against the Turks. 13s, Momchil attacking Turks at Umour. 18s, Tsar Ivan Stratsimir meeting King Sigismund's crusaders. 28s, The Boyars Balik, Theodor & Dobrotitsa, meeting ship bringing envoys from Anne of Savoy.

1973, Oct. 23   **Perf. 13**
Silver and Black Vignettes
2126	A741	1s olive bister	.25	.25
2127	A741	2s Prus blue	.25	.25
2128	A741	3s lilac	.25	.25
2129	A741	4s green	.25	.25
2130	A741	5s violet	.25	.25
2131	A741	13s orange & brn	.45	.25
2132	A741	18s olive green	.65	.25
2133	A741	28s yel brn & brn	1.60	.85
		Nos. 2126-2133 (8)	3.95	2.60

Finn
Class — A828

Sailboats: 2s, Flying Dutchman. 3s, Soling class. 13s, Tempest class. 20s, Class 470. 40s, Tornado class.

1973, Oct. 29   **Litho.**   **Perf. 13**
2134	A828	1s ultra & multi	.25	.25
2135	A828	2s green & multi	.25	.25
2136	A828	3s dk blue & multi	.25	.25
2137	A828	13s dull vio & multi	.45	.25
2138	A828	20s gray bl & multi	.65	.45
2139	A828	40s dk blue & multi	3.00	2.50
		Nos. 2134-2139 (6)	4.85	3.95

Value, set imperf. in changed colors, $13.

Village, by Bencho Obreshkov — A829

Paintings: 2s, Mother and Child, by Stoyan Venev. 3s, Rest (woman), by Tsenko Boyadjiev. 13s, Flowers in Vase, by Sirak Skitnik. 18s, Meri Kuneva (portrait), by Ilya Petrov. 40s, Winter in Plovdiv, by Zlatyu Boyadjiev. 13s, 18s, 40s, vert.

Perf. 12½x12, 12x12½
1973, Nov. 10
2140	A829	1s gold & multi	.25	.25
2141	A829	2s gold & multi	.25	.25
2142	A829	3s gold & multi	.25	.25
2143	A829	13s gold & multi	.45	.25
2144	A829	18s gold & multi	.65	.25
2145	A829	40s gold & multi	3.00	1.25
		Nos. 2140-2145 (6)	4.85	2.50

Souvenir Sheet

Paintings by Stanislav Dospevski: a, Domnica Lambreva. b, Self-portrait. Both vert.
2146		Sheet of 2	4.50	2.50
a.	A829	50s gold & multi	1.40	1.00
b.	A829	50s gold & multi	1.40	1.00

Bulgarian paintings. No. 2146 commemorates the 150th birth anniv. of Stanislav Dospevski.

Souvenir Sheet

Soccer — A830

1973, Dec. 10   **Photo.**   **Perf. 13**
2147	A830	28s multicolored	4.50	3.50

No. 2147 sold for 1 l. Exists overprinted for Argentina 78. Value $9.50.

Angel and
Ornaments
A831

1s, Attendant facing right. 2s, Passover table and lamb. 3s, Attendant facing left. 8s, Abraham and ornaments. 13s, Adam and Eve. 28s, Expulsion from Garden of Eden.

1974, Jan. 21   **Photo.**   **Perf. 13**
2148	A831	1s fawn, yel & brn	.25	.25
2149	A831	2s fawn, yel & brn	.25	.25
2150	A831	3s fawn, yel & brn	.25	.25
a.		Strip of 3, #2148-2150	.50	.25
2151	A831	5s slate grn & yel	.25	.25
2152	A831	8s slate grn & yel	.25	.25
a.		Pair, #2151-2152	.65	.50
2153	A831	13s lt brown, yel & ol	.30	.25
2154	A831	28s lt brown, yel & ol	.50	.30
a.		Pair, #2153-2154	1.60	.70
		Nos. 2148-2154 (7)	2.05	1.80

Woodcarvings from Rozhen Monastery, 19th century.

Lenin, by N. Mirtchev — A832

18s, Lenin visiting Workers, by W. A. Serov.

1974, Jan. 28   **Litho.**   **Perf. 12½x12**
2155	A832	2s ocher & multi	.25	.25
2156	A832	18s ocher & multi	.65	.30

50th anniversary of the death of Lenin.

1974, Jan. 28

Demeter Blagoev at Rally, by G. Kowachev.
2157	A832	2s multicolored	.25	.25

50th anniversary of the death of Demeter Blagoev, founder of Bulgarian Communist Party.

Domestic
Animals
A833

1974, Feb. 1   Photo.   *Perf. 13*
2158 A833   1s Sheep   .25   .25
2159 A833   2s Goat   .25   .25
2160 A833   3s Pig   .25   .25
2161 A833   5s Cow   .25   .25
2162 A833 13s Buffalo cow   .80   .25
2163 A833 20s Horse   2.00   .75
      Nos. 2158-2163 (6)   3.80 2.00

Comecon
Emblem
A834

1974, Feb. 11   Photo.   *Perf. 13*
2164 A834 13s silver & multi   .55   .25
   25th anniversary of the Council of Mutual
Economic Assistance.

Soccer — A835

Designs: Various soccer action scenes.

1974, Mar.   Photo.   *Perf. 13*
2165 A835   1s dull grn & multi   .25   .25
2166 A835   2s brt green & multi   .25   .25
2167 A835   3s slate grn & multi   .25   .25
2168 A835 13s olive & multi   .25   .25
2169 A835 28s blue grn & multi   .70   .30
2170 A835 40s emerald & multi   1.75   .75
      Nos. 2165-2170 (6)   3.45 2.05
             Souvenir Sheet
2171 A835   1 l green & multi   3.75 2.00
   World Soccer Championship, Munich, June
13-July 7. No. 2171 exists imperf. Value $70.

Salt
Production
A836

   Children's Paintings: 1s, Cosmic Research
for Peaceful Purposes. 3s, Fire Dancers. 28s,
Russian-Bulgarian Friendship (train and children). 60s, Spring (birds).

1974, Apr. 15   Photo.   *Perf. 13*
2172 A836   1s lilac & multi   .25   .25
2173 A836   2s lt green & multi   .25   .25
2174 A836   3s blue & multi   .25   .25
2175 A836 28s slate & multi   2.00 1.25
      Nos. 2172-2175 (4)   2.75 2.00
          Souvenir Sheet
               Imperf
2176 A836 60s blue & multi   2.75 2.00
   Third World Youth Philatelic Exhibition,
Sofia, May 23-30. No. 2176 contains one
stamp with simulated perforations.
   No. 2176 exists in blue with gray inscriptions, but was not valid for postage. Value $50.

Folk
Singers — A837

   Designs: 2s, Folk dancers (men). 3s, Bagpiper and drummer. 5s, Wrestlers. 13s, Runners (women). 18s, Gymnast.

1974, Apr. 25   *Perf. 13*
2178 A837   1s vermilion & multi   .25   .25
2179 A837   2s org brn & multi   .25   .25
2180 A837   3s brn red & multi   .25   .25
2181 A837   5s blue & multi   .25   .25
2182 A837 13s ultra & multi   .90   .30
2183 A837 18s violet bl & multi   .45   .25
      Nos. 2178-2183 (6)   2.35 1.55

   4th Amateur Arts and Sports Festival

Flowers
A838

1974, May   Photo.   *Perf. 13*
2184 A838   1s Aster   .25   .25
2185 A838   2s Petunia   .25   .25
2186 A838   3s Fuchsia   .25   .25
2187 A838 18s Tulip   .50   .25
2188 A838 20s Carnation   .75   .25
2189 A838 28s Pansy   2.25   .85
      Nos. 2184-2189 (6)   4.25 2.10
          Souvenir Sheet
2190 A838 80s Sunflower   2.00 1.00

Automobiles and Emblems — A839

1974, May 15   Photo.   *Perf. 13*
2191 A839 13s multicolored   .50   .25
   International Automobile Federation (FIA)
Spring Congress, Sofia, May 20-24.

Old and
New
Buildings,
UNESCO
Emblem
A840

1974, June 15
2192 A840 18s multicolored   .50   .25
   UNESCO Executive Council, 94th Session,
Varna.

Postrider
A841

   Designs: 18s, First Bulgarian mail coach.
28s, UPU Monument, Bern.

1974, Aug. 5
2193 A841   2s ocher, blk & vio   .25   .25

2194 A841 18s ocher, blk & grn   .50   .25
           Souvenir Sheet
2195 A841 28s ocher, blk & bl   2.10 1.50
   UPU cent. No. 2195 exists imperf. Value
$60.

Pioneer and
Komsomol
Girl — A842

   Designs: 2s, Pioneer and birds. 60s,
Emblem with portrait of George Dimitrov.

1974, Aug. 12
2196 A842   1s green & multi   .25   .25
2197 A842   2s blue & multi   .25   .25
           Souvenir Sheet
2198 A842 60s red & multi   2.00 1.50
   30th anniversary of Dimitrov Pioneer Organization, Septemvrilche.

"Bulgarian
Communist
Party" — A843

   Symbolic Designs: 2s, Russian liberators.
5s, Industrialization. 13s, Advanced agriculture and husbandry. 18s, Scientific and technical progress.

1974, Aug. 20
2199 A843   1s blue gray & multi   .25   .25
2200 A843   2s blue gray & multi   .25   .25
2201 A843   5s gray & multi   .25   .25
2202 A843 13s gray & multi   .40   .25
2203 A843 18s gray & multi   .65   .25
      Nos. 2199-2203 (5)   1.80 1.25
   30th anniversary of the People's Republic.

Gymnast on
Parallel
Bars — A844

   Design: 13s, Gymnast on vaulting horse.

1974, Oct. 18   Photo.   *Perf. 13*
2204 A844   2s multicolored   .25   .25
2205 A844 13s multicolored   .40   .25
   18th Gymnastic Championships, Varna.

Souvenir Sheet

Symbols of Peace — A845

1974, Oct. 29   Photo.   *Perf. 13*
2206 A845   Sheet of 4   2.50 2.50
   a.   13s Doves   .25   .25
   b.   13s Map of Europe   .25   .25
   c.   13s Olive Branch   .25   .25
   d.   13s Inscription   .25   .25
   1974 European Peace Conference. "Peace"
in various languages written on Nos. 2206a-
2206c. Sold for 60s. Exists imperf. Value $85.
   No. 2206 was overprinted "Europa" and
various cities and dates in 1979. Value $60.

Nib and
Envelope — A846

1974, Nov. 20
2207 A846   2s yellow, blk & grn   .25   .25
   Introduction of postal zone numbers.

Flowers
A847

1974, Dec. 5
2208 A847   2s emerald & multi   .25   .25

St. Todor, Ceramic
Icon — A848

   Designs: 2s, Medallion, Veliko Turnovo. 3s,
Carved capital. 5s, Silver bowl. 8s, Goblet.
13s, Lion's head finial. 18s, Gold plate with
Cross. 28s, Breastplate with eagle.

1974, Dec. 18   Photo.   *Perf. 13*
2209 A848   1s orange & multi   .25   .25
2210 A848   2s pink & multi   .25   .25
2211 A848   3s blue & multi   .25   .25
2212 A848   5s lt vio & multi   .25   .25
2213 A848   8s brown & multi   .25   .25
2214 A848 13s multicolored   .35   .25
2215 A848 18s red & multi   .50   .25
2216 A848 28s ultra & multi   1.40   .65
      Nos. 2209-2216 (8)   3.50 2.40
   Art works from 9th-12th centuries.

Fruit Tree Blossoms — A849

1975, Jan.		Photo.	Perf. 13	
2217	A849	1s Apricot	.25	.25
2218	A849	2s Apple	.25	.25
2219	A849	3s Cherry	.25	.25
2220	A849	19s Pear	.40	.25
2221	A849	28s Peach	1.00	.25
	Nos. 2217-2221 (5)		2.15	1.25

Tree and Book A850

1975, Mar. 25		Photo.	Perf. 13	
2222	A850	2s gold & multi	.25	.25

Forestry High School, 50th anniversary.

Souvenir Sheet

Farmers' Activities (Woodcuts) — A851

1975, Mar. 25

2223	A851	Sheet of 4	1.00	.50
	a.	2s Farmer with ax and flag		
	b.	5s Farmers on guard		
	c.	13s Dancing couple		
	d.	18s Woman picking fruit		

Bulgarian Agrarian Peoples Union, 75th anniv.

Michelangelo, Self-portrait A852

13s, Night, horiz. 18s, Day, horiz. Both designs after sculptures from Medici Tomb, Florence.

1975

2224	A852	2s plum & dk blue	.25	.25
2225	A852	13s vio bl & plum	.40	.25
2226	A852	18s brown & green	.80	.25
	Nos. 2224-2226 (3)		1.45	.75

Souvenir Sheet

2227	A852	2s olive & red	1.75	1.75

Michelangelo Buonarotti (1475-1564), Italian sculptor, painter and architect. No. 2227 issued to publicize ARPHILA 75 Intl. Phil. Exhib., Paris, June 6-16. Sheet sold for 60s. Issued: Nos. 2224-2226, 3/28; No. 2227, 3/31.

Souvenir Sheet

Spain No. 1 and España 75 Emblem — A853

1975, Apr. 4

2228	A853	40s multicolored	5.00	4.00

Espana 75 International Philatelic Exhibition, Madrid, Apr. 4-13.

Gabrov Costume A854

Regional Costumes: 3s, Trnsk. 5s, Vidin. 13s, Gocedelchev. 18s, Risen.

1975, Apr.		Photo.	Perf. 13	
2229	A854	2s blue & multi	.25	.25
2230	A854	3s emerald & multi	.25	.25
2231	A854	5s orange & multi	.25	.25
2232	A854	13s olive & multi	.65	.25
2233	A854	18s multicolored	1.25	.40
	Nos. 2229-2233 (5)		2.65	1.40

Red Star and Arrow — A855

Design: 13s, Dove and broken sword.

1975, May 9

2234	A855	2s red, blk & gold	.25	.25
2235	A855	13s blue, blk & gold	.45	.25

Victory over Fascism, 30th anniversary.

Standard Kilogram and Meter — A856

1975, May 9			Perf. 13x13½	
2236	A856	13s silver, lil & blk	.25	.25

Cent. of Intl. Meter Convention, Paris, 1875.

IWY Emblem, Woman's Head — A857

1975, May 20		Photo.	Perf. 13	
2237	A857	13s multicolored	.35	.25

International Women's Year 1975.

Ivan Vasov — A858

Design: 13s, Ivan Vasov, seated.

1975, May

2238	A858	2s buff & multi	.25	.25
2239	A858	13s gray & multi	.35	.25

125th birth anniversary of Ivan Vasov.

Nikolov and Sava Kokarechkov — A859

2s, Mitko Palaouzov, Ivan Vassilev. 5s, Nicolas Nakev, Stevtcho Kraychev. 13s, Ivanka Pachkoulova, Detelina Mintcheva.

1975, May 30

2240	A859	1s multicolored	.25	.25
2241	A859	2s multicolored	.25	.25
2242	A859	5s multicolored	.25	.25
2243	A859	13s multicolored	.30	.25
	Nos. 2240-2243 (4)		1.05	1.00

Teen-age resistance fighters, killed during World War II.

Mother Feeding Child, by John E. Millais A861

Etchings: 2s, The Dead Daughter, by Goya. 3s, Reunion, by Beshkov. 13s, Seated Nude, by Renoir. 20s, Man in a Fur Hat, by Rembrandt. 40s, The Dream, by Daumier, horiz. 1 l, Temptation, by Dürer.

Photogravure and Engraved

1975, Aug.		Perf. 12x11½, 11½x12		
2248	A861	1s yel grn & multi	.25	.25
2249	A861	2s orange & multi	.25	.25
2250	A861	3s lilac & multi	.25	.25
2251	A861	13s lt blue & multi	.35	.25
2252	A861	20s ocher & multi	.50	.25
2253	A861	40s rose & multi	1.75	.45
	Nos. 2248-2253 (6)		3.35	1.70

Souvenir Sheet

2254	A861	1 l emerald & multi	2.50	1.50

World Graphics Exhibition.

Letter "Z" from 12th Century Manuscript A862

Initials from Illuminated Manuscripts: 2s, "B" from 17th cent. prayerbook. 3s, "V" from 16th cent. Bouhovo Gospel. 8s, "B" from 14th cent. Turnovo collection. 13s, "V" from Dobreisho's Gospel, 13th cent. 18s, "E" from 11th cent. Enina book of the Apostles.

1975, Aug.		Litho.	Perf. 11½	
2255	A862	1s multicolored	.25	.25
2256	A862	2s multicolored	.25	.25
2257	A862	3s multicolored	.25	.25
2258	A862	8s multicolored	.25	.25
2259	A862	13s multicolored	.45	.25
2260	A862	18s multicolored	1.25	.25
	Nos. 2255-2260 (6)		2.70	1.50

Bulgarian art.

Whimsical Globe — A863

1975, Aug.		Photo.	Perf. 13	
2261	A863	2s multicolored	.25	.25

Festival of Humor and Satire.

Lifeboat Dju IV and Gibraltar-Cuba Route — A864

1975, Aug. 5		Photo.	Perf. 13	
2262	A864	13s multicolored	.35	.25

Oceanexpo 75, 1st Intl. Ocean Exhib., Okinawa, July 20, 1975-Jan. 18, 1976.

Sts. Cyril and Methodius — A865

Sts. Constantine and Helena — A866

St. Sophia Church, Sofia, Woodcut by
V. Zahriev — A867

1975, Aug. 21
2263 A865 2s ver, yel & brn   .25   .25
2264 A866 13s green, yel & brn   .40   .25

Souvenir Sheet
2265 A867 50s orange & multi   1.40 1.10
  Balkanphila V, philatelic exhibition, Sofia,
Sept. 27-Oct. 5.

Peace Dove and
Map of
Europe — A868

1975, Nov.   Photo.   Perf. 13
2266 A868 18s ultra, rose & yel   .60   .35
  European Security and Cooperation Conference, Helsinki, Finland, July 30-Aug. 1. No.
2266 printed in sheets of 5 stamps and 4
labels, arranged checkerwise.

Acherontia Atropos — A869

  Moths: 1s, Acherontia atropos. 2s, Daphnis
nerii. 3s, Smerinthus ocellata. 10s, Deilephila
nicea. 13s, Choerocampa elpenor. 18s,
Macroglossum fuciformis.

1975   Photo.   Perf. 13
2267 A869 1s multicolored   .25   .25
2268 A869 2s multicolored   .25   .25
2269 A869 3s multicolored   .25   .25
2270 A869 10s multicolored   .35   .25
2271 A869 13s multicolored   .70   .30
2272 A869 18s multicolored   1.40   .50
  Nos. 2267-2272 (6)   3.20 1.80

Soccer
Player — A870

1975, Sept. 21
2273 A870 2s multicolored   .25   .25
  8th Inter-Toto (soccer pool) Soccer Championships, Varna.

Constantine's Rebellion Against the
Turks, 1403 — A871

  Designs (Woodcuts): 2s, Campaign of
Vladislav III, 1443-1444. 3s, Battles of
Turnovo, 1598 and 1686. 10s, Battle of Liprov-
sko, 1688. 13s, Guerrillas, 17th century. 18s,
Return of exiled peasants.

1975, Nov. 27   Photo.   Perf. 13
2274 A871 1s bister, grn & blk   .25   .25
2275 A871 2s blue, car & blk   .25   .25
2276 A871 3s yellow, lil & blk   .25   .25
2277 A871 10s orange, grn & blk   .25   .25
2278 A871 13s green, lil & blk   .40   .25
2279 A871 18s pink, grn & blk   .75   .25
  Nos. 2274-2279 (6)   2.15 1.50
  Bulgarian history.

Red Cross and First Aid — A872

  Design: 13s, Red Cross and dove.

1975, Dec. 1
2280 A872 2s red brn, red & blk   .25   .25
2281 A872 13s bl grn, red & blk   .40   .25
  90th anniversary of Bulgarian Red Cross.

Egyptian
Galley
A873

  Historic Ships: 2s, Phoenician galley. 3s,
Greek trireme. 5s, Roman galley. 13s, Viking
longship. 18s, Venetian galley.

1975, Dec. 15   Photo.   Perf. 13
2282 A873 1s multicolored   .25   .25
2283 A873 2s multicolored   .25   .25
2284 A873 3s multicolored   .25   .25
2285 A873 5s multicolored   .25   .25
2286 A873 13s multicolored   .40   .25
2287 A873 18s multicolored   .85   .25
  Nos. 2282-2287 (6)   2.25 1.50
  See Nos. 2431-2436, 2700-2705.

Souvenir Sheet

Ethnographical Museum,
Plovdiv — A874

1975, Dec. 17
2288 A874 Sheet of 3   6.00 3.50
  a.   80s grn, yel & dark brn 1.75 1.00
  European Architectural Heritage Year. No.
2288 contains 3 stamps and 3 labels showing
stylized bird.

Dobri
Hristov — A875

1975, Dec.   Perf. 13
2289 A875 5s brt grn, yel & brn   .25   .25
  Dobri Hristov, musician, birth centenary.

United Nations
Emblem — A876

1975, Dec.
2290 A876 13s gold, blk & mag   .35   .25
  United Nations, 30th anniversary.

Glass Ornaments — A877

  13s, Peace dove, decorated ornament.

1975, Dec. 22   Photo.   Perf. 13
2291 A877 2s brt violet & multi   .25   .25
2292 A877 13s gray & multi   .25   .25
  New Year 1976.

Downhill Skiing — A878

  Designs (Winter Olympic Games Emblem
and): 2s, Cross country skier, vert. 3s, Ski
jump. 13s, Biathlon, vert. 18s, Ice hockey, vert.
23s, Speed skating, vert. 80s, Figure skating,
pair, vert.

1976, Jan. 30   Perf. 13½
2293 A878 1s silver & multi   .25   .25
2294 A878 2s silver & multi   .25   .25
2295 A878 3s silver & multi   .25   .25
2296 A878 13s silver & multi   .40   .25
2297 A878 18s silver & multi   .40   .25
2298 A878 23s silver & multi   1.25   .25
  Nos. 2293-2298 (6)   2.80 1.50

Souvenir Sheet
2299 A878 80s silver & multi   2.50 1.50
  12th Winter Olympic Games, Innsbruck,
Austria, Feb. 4-15.

Electric Streetcar, Sofia, 1976 — A879

  Design: 13s, Streetcar and trailer, 1901.

1976, Jan. 12   Photo.   Perf. 13½x13
2300 A879 2s gray & multi   .25   .25
2301 A879 13s gray & multi   .55   .25
  75th anniversary of Sofia streetcars.

Stylized
Bird — A880

  5s, Dates "1976," "1956" & star. 13s, Hammer & sickle. 50s, George Dimitrov.

1976, Mar. 1   Perf. 13
2302 A880 2s gold & multi   .25   .25
2303 A880 5s gold & multi   .25   .25
2304 A880 13s gold & multi   .25   .25
  Nos. 2302-2304 (3)   .75   .75

Souvenir Sheet
2305 A880 50s gold & multi   1.75 3.00
  11th Bulgarian Communist Party Congress.

A. G. Bell and Telephone,
1876 — A881

1976, Mar. 10
2306 A881 18s dk brn, yel &
               ocher   .50   .25
  Centenary of first telephone call by Alexander Graham Bell, Mar. 10, 1876.

Mute Swan — A882

  Waterfowl: 2s, Ruddy shelduck. 3s, Common shelduck. 5s, Garganey teal. 13s, Mallard. 18s, Red-crested pochard.

1976, Mar. 27   Litho.   Perf. 11½
2307 A882 1s vio bl & multi   .25   .25
2308 A882 2s yel grn & multi   .25   .25
2309 A882 3s blue & multi   .25   .25
2310 A882 5s multicolored   1.10   .25
2311 A882 13s purple & multi   1.10   .55
2312 A882 18s green & multi   2.75 1.75
  Nos. 2307-2312 (6)   5.70 3.30

Guerrillas — A883

  Designs (Woodcuts by Stoev): 2s, Peasants
with rifle and proclamation. 5s, Raina Knaginia
with horse and guerrilla. 13s, Insurgents with
cherrywood cannon.

1976, Apr. 5   Photo.   Perf. 13
2313 A883 1s multicolored   .25   .25
2314 A883 2s multicolored   .25   .25
2315 A883 5s multicolored   .25   .25
2316 A883 13s multicolored   .25   .25
  Nos. 2313-2316 (4)   1.00 1.00
  Centenary of uprising against Turkey.

Guard
and Dog
A884

13s, Men on horseback, observation tower.

1976, May 15
2317 A884 2s multicolored .25 .25
2318 A884 13s multicolored .25 .25

30th anniversary of Border Guards.

Construction
Worker — A885

1976, May 20
2319 A885 2s multicolored .25 .25

Young Workers Brigade, 30th anniversary.

Busludja, Bas-
relief
A886

Design: 5s, Memorial building.

1976, May 28 Photo. Perf. 13
2320 A886 2s green & multi .25 .25
2321 A886 5s violet bl & multi .25 .25

First Congress of Bulgarian Social Democratic Party, 85th anniversary.

Memorial
Building — A887

2s, AES Complex. 8s, Thermal power plant.
10s, Chemical plant. 13s, Chemical plant
(diff.). 20s, Hydroelectric station.

1976, Apr. 7
2322 A887 5s green .25 .25
2323 A887 8s maroon .25 .25
2324 A887 10s green .25 .25
2325 A887 13s violet .55 .25
2326 A887 20s brt green .65 .25
Nos. 2322-2326 (5) 1.95 1.25

Five-year plan accomplishments.

Children Playing Around Table — A888

Kindergarten Children: 2s, with doll carriage
& hobby horse. 5s, playing ball. 23s, in
costume.

1976, June 15
2327 A888 1s green & multi .25 .25
2328 A888 2s yellow & multi .25 .25
2329 A888 5s lilac & multi .25 .25
2330 A888 23s rose & multi .40 .25
Nos. 2327-2330 (4) 1.15 1.00

Demeter
Blagoev — A889

1976, May 28
2331 A889 13s bluish blk, red &
gold .50 .25

Demeter Blagoev (1856-1924), writer, political leader, 120th birth anniversary.

Christo Botev — A890

1976, May 25
2332 A890 13s ocher & slate grn .60 .25

Christo Botev (1848-1876), poet, death centenary. Printed se-tenant with yellow green
and ocher label, inscribed with poem.

Boxing, Montreal
Olympic
Emblem — A891

Designs (Montreal Olympic Emblem): 1s,
Wrestling, horiz. 3s, 1 l, Weight lifting. 13s,
One-man kayak. 18s, Woman gymnast. 28s,
Woman diver. 40s, Woman runner.

1976, June 25
2333 A891 1s orange & multi .25 .25
2334 A891 2s multicolored .25 .25
2335 A891 3s lilac & multi .25 .25
2336 A891 13s multicolored .25 .25
2337 A891 18s multicolored .50 .25
2338 A891 28s blue & multi .70 .25
2339 A891 40s lemon & multi 1.00 .50
Nos. 2333-2339 (7) 3.20 2.00

Souvenir Sheet
2340 A891 1 l orange & multi 1.75 1.25

21st Olympic Games, Montreal, Canada,
July 17-Aug. 1.

Belt
Buckle — A892

Thracian Art (8th-4th Centuries): 2s,
Brooch. 3s, Mirror handle. 5s, Helmet cheek
cover. 13s, Gold ornament. 18s, Lion's head

(harness decoration). 20s, Knee guard. 28s,
Jeweled pendant.

1976, July 30 Photo. Perf. 13
2341 A892 1s brown & multi .25 .25
2342 A892 2s blue & multi .25 .25
2343 A892 3s multicolored .25 .25
2344 A892 5s claret & multi .25 .25
2345 A892 13s purple & multi .35 .25
2346 A892 18s multicolored .40 .25
2347 A892 20s multicolored .55 .25
2348 A892 28s multicolored .55 .25
Nos. 2341-2348 (8) 2.85 2.00

Souvenir Sheet

Composite of Bulgarian Stamp
Designs — A893

1976, June 5
2349 A893 50s red & multi 2.75 1.25

International Federation of Philately (F.I.P.),
50th anniversary and 12th Congress.

Partisans at Night, by Ilya
Petrov — A894

Paintings: 5s, Old Town, by Tsanko Lave-
nov. 13s, Seated Woman, by Petrov. vert. 18s,
Seated Boy, by Petrov, vert. 28s, Old Plovdiv,
by Lavrenov, vert. 80s, Ilya Petrov, self-portrait, vert.

1976, Aug. 11 Photo. Perf. 14
2350 A894 2s multicolored .25 .25
2351 A894 5s multicolored .25 .25
2352 A894 13s ultra & multi .35 .25
2353 A894 18s multicolored .65 .25
2354 A894 28s multicolored .80 .25
Nos. 2350-2354 (5) 2.30 1.25

Souvenir Sheet
2354A A894 80s multicolored 1.60 1.25

Souvenir Sheet

Olympic Sports and Emblems — A895

1976, Sept. 6 Photo. Perf. 13
2355 A895 Sheet of 4 2.00 1.50
a. 25s Weight Lifting .35 .25
b. 25s Rowing .35 .25
c. 25s Running .35 .25
d. 25s Wrestling .35 .25

Medalists, 21st Olympic Games, Montreal.

Souvenir Sheet

Fresco and UNESCO Emblem — A896

1976, Dec. 3
2356 A896 50s red & multi 1.75 1.00

UNESCO, 30th anniv.

"The Pianist" by
Jendov — A897

Designs (Caricatures by Jendov): 5s, Imperialist "Trick or Treat." 13s, The Leader, 1931.

1976, Sept. 30 Photo. Perf. 13
2357 A897 2s green & multi .25 .25
2358 A897 5s purple & multi .25 .25
2359 A897 13s magenta & multi .30 .25
Nos. 2357-2359 (3) .80 .75

Alex Jendov (1901-1953), caricaturist.

Fish and
Hook — A898

1976, Sept. 21 Photo. Perf. 13
2360 A898 5s multicolored .25 .25

World Sport Fishing Congress, Varna.

St. Theodore
A899

Frescoes: 3s, St. Paul. 5s, St. Joachim. 13s,
Melchizedek. 19s, St. Porphyrius. 28s, Queen.
1 l, The Last Supper.

1976, Oct. 4 Litho. Perf. 12x12½
2361 A899 2s gold & multi .25 .25
2362 A899 3s gold & multi .25 .25
2363 A899 5s gold & multi .25 .25
2364 A899 13s gold & multi .45 .25

2365	A899	19s gold & multi	.50	.25
2366	A899	28s gold & multi	.70	.25
		Nos. 2361-2366 (6)	2.40	1.50

Miniature Sheet
Perf. 12

| 2367 | A899 | 1 l gold & multi | 1.75 | 1.25 |

Zemen Monastery frescoes, 14th cent.

Document
A900

1976, Oct. 5

| 2368 | A900 | 5s multicolored | .25 | .25 |

State Archives, 25th anniversary.

Cinquefoil
A901

1976, Oct. 14   Photo.   Perf. 13

2369	A901	1s Chestnut	.25	.25
2370	A901	2s Cinquefoil	.25	.25
2371	A901	5s Holly	.25	.25
2372	A901	8s Yew	.25	.25
2373	A901	13s Daphne	.35	.25
2374	A901	23s Judas tree	.85	.25
		Nos. 2369-2374 (6)	2.20	1.50

Dimitri Polianov — A902

1976, Nov. 19

| 2375 | A902 | 2s dk purple & ocher | .25 | .25 |

Dimitri Polianov (1876-1953), poet.

Christo Botev, by Zlatyu Boyadjiev
A903

Paintings: 2s, Partisan Carrying Cherrywood Cannon, by Ilya Petrov. 3s, "Necklace of Immortality" (man's portrait), by Detchko Uzunov. 13s, "April 1876," by Georgi Popoff. 18s, Partisans, by Stoyan Venev. 60s, The Oath, by Svetlin Ruseff.

1976, Dec. 8

2376	A903	1s bister & multi	.25	.25
2377	A903	2s bister & multi	.25	.25
2378	A903	3s bister & multi	.25	.25
2379	A903	13s bister & multi	.25	.25
2380	A903	18s bister & multi	.35	.25
		Nos. 2376-2380 (5)	1.35	1.25

Souvenir Sheet
Imperf

| 2381 | A903 | 60s gold & multi | 1.50 | 1.00 |

Uprising against Turkish rule, centenary.

"Pollution" and Tree
A904

Design: 18s, "Pollution" obscuring sun.

1976, Nov. 10   Perf. 13

| 2382 | A904 | 2s ultra & multi | .25 | .25 |
| 2383 | A904 | 18s blue & multi | .40 | .25 |

Protection of the environment.

Congress Emblem — A904a

Flags — A904b

1976, Nov. 28   Photo.   Perf. 13

| 2384 | A904a | 2s multicolored | .25 | .25 |
| 2384A | A904b | 13s multicolored | .40 | .25 |

33rd BSIS Cong. (Bulgarian Socialist Party).

Tobacco Workers, by Stajkov
A905

Paintings by Stajkov: 2s, View of Melnik. 13s, Shipbuilder.

1976, Dec. 16   Photo.   Perf. 13

2385	A905	1s multicolored	.25	.25
2386	A905	2s multicolored	.25	.25
2387	A905	13s multicolored	.30	.25
		Nos. 2385-2387 (3)	.80	.75

Veselin Stajkov (1906-1970), painter.

Snowflake — A906

1976, Dec. 20

| 2388 | A906 | 2s silver & multi | .25 | .25 |

New Year 1977.

Zachary Stoyanov (1851-1889), Historian — A907

1976, Dec. 30

| 2389 | A907 | 2s multicolored | .25 | .25 |

Bronze Coin of Septimus Severus — A908

Roman Coins: 2s, 13s, 18s, Bronze coins of Caracalla, diff. 23s, Copper coin of Diocletian.

1977, Jan. 28   Photo.   Perf. 13½x13

2390	A908	1s gold & multi	.25	.25
2391	A908	2s gold & multi	.25	.25
2392	A908	13s gold & multi	.25	.25
2393	A908	18s gold & multi	.40	.25
2394	A908	23s gold & multi	.60	.25
		Nos. 2390-2394 (5)	1.75	1.25

Coins struck in Serdica (modern Sofia).

Skis and Compass — A909

1977, Feb. 14   Perf. 13

| 2395 | A909 | 13s ultra, red & lt bl | .25 | .25 |

2nd World Ski Orienteering Championships.

Tourist Congress Emblem — A910

1977, Feb. 24   Photo.   Perf. 13

| 2396 | A910 | 2s multicolored | .25 | .25 |

5th Congress of Bulgarian Tourist Organization.

Bellflower A911

Designs: Various bellflowers.

1977, Mar. 2

2397	A911	1s yellow & multi	.25	.25
2398	A911	2s rose & multi	.25	.25
2399	A911	3s lt blue & multi	.25	.25
2400	A911	13s multicolored	.40	.25
2401	A911	43s yellow & multi	1.50	.30
		Nos. 2397-2401 (5)	2.65	1.30

Vasil Kolarov — A912

1977, Mar. 21   Photo.   Perf. 13

| 2402 | A912 | 2s blue & black | .25 | .25 |

Vasil Kolarov (1877-1950), politician.

Union Congress Emblem — A913

1977, Mar. 25

| 2403 | A913 | 2s multicolored | .25 | .25 |

8th Bulgarian Trade Union Cong., Apr. 4-7.

Wolf — A914

Wild Animals: 2s, Red fox. 10s, Weasel. 13s, European wildcat. 23s, Jackal.

1977, May 16   Litho.   Perf. 12½x12

2404	A914	1s multicolored	.25	.25
2405	A914	2s multicolored	.25	.25
2406	A914	10s multicolored	.30	.25
2407	A914	13s multicolored	.55	.40
2408	A914	23s multicolored	1.25	.60
		Nos. 2404-2408 (5)	2.60	1.75

Diseased Knee — A915

1977, Mar. 31   Photo.   Perf. 13

| 2409 | A915 | 23s multicolored | .60 | .25 |

World Rheumatism Year.

Writers' Congress Emblem A916

1977, June 7

2410 A916 23s lt bl & yel grn   1.00   .50

International Writers Congress: "Peace, the Hope of the Planet." No. 2410 printed in sheets of 8 stamps and 4 labels with signatures of participating writers.

Old Testament Trinity, Sofia, 16th Century A917

Icons: 1s, St. Nicholas, Nessebur, 13th cent. 3s, Annunciation, Royal Gates, Veliko Turnovo, 16th cent. 5s, Christ Enthroned, Nessebur, 17th cent. 13s, St. Nicholas, Elena, 18th cent. 23s, Presentation of the Virgin, Rila Monastery, 18th cent. 35s, Virgin and Child, Tryavna, 19th cent. 40s, St. Demetrius on Horseback, Provadia, 19th cent. 1 l, The 12 Holidays, Rila Monastery, 18th cent.

1977, May 10   Photo.   Perf. 13

2411	A917	1s black & multi	.25	.25
2412	A917	2s green & multi	.25	.25
2413	A917	3s brown & multi	.25	.25
2414	A917	5s blue & multi	.25	.25
2415	A917	13s olive & multi	.35	.25
2416	A917	23s maroon & multi	.60	.25
2417	A917	35s green & multi	.85	.35
2418	A917	40s dp ultra & multi	1.60	.55
	Nos. 2411-2418 (8)		4.40	2.40

Miniature Sheet

Imperf

2419 A917   1 l gold & multi   3.25 3.25

Bulgarian icons. See Nos. 2615-2619.

Souvenir Sheet

St. Cyril — A918

1977, June 7   Photo.   Perf. 13

2420 A918 1 l gold & multi   2.50 2.50

St. Cyril (827-869), reputed inventor of Cyrillic alphabet.

Congress Emblem — A919

1977, May 9

2421 A919 2s red, gold & grn   .25 .25

13th Komsomol Congress.

Newspaper Masthead — A920

1977, June 3   Photo.   Perf. 13

2422 A920 2s multicolored   .25 .25

Cent. of Bulgarian daily press and 50th anniv. of Rabotnichesko Delo newspaper.

Patriotic Front Emblem — A921

1977, May 26

2423 A921 2s gold & multi   .25 .25

8th Congress of Patriotic Front.

Weight Lifting — A922

1977, June 15

2424 A922 13s dp brown & multi   .35 .25

European Youth Weight Lifting Championships, Sofia, June.

Women Basketball Players — A923

1977, June 15   Perf. 13

2425 A923 23s multicolored   .75 .25

7th European Women's Basketball Championships.

Wrestling — A924

Games Emblem and: 13s, Running. 23s, Basketball. 43s, Women's gymnastics.

1977, Apr. 15

2426	A924	2s multicolored	.25	.25
2427	A924	13s multicolored	.25	.25
2428	A924	23s multicolored	.65	.25
2429	A924	43s multicolored	1.00	.40
	Nos. 2426-2429 (4)		2.15	1.15

UNIVERSIADE '77, University Games, Sofia, Aug. 18-27.
No. 2427 exists imperf. Value, $200.

TV Tower, Berlin — A925

1977, Aug. 12   Litho.   Perf. 13

2430 A925 25s blue & dk blue   .75 .25

SOZPHILEX 77 Philatelic Exhibition, Berlin, Aug. 19-28.

Ship Type of 1975

Historic Ships: 1s, Hansa cog. 2s, Santa Maria, caravelle. 3s, Golden Hind, frigate. 12s, Santa Catherina, carrack. 13s, La Corone, galleon. 43s, Mediterranean galleass.

1977, Aug. 29   Photo.   Perf. 13

2431	A873	1s multicolored	.25	.25
2432	A873	2s multicolored	.25	.25
2433	A873	3s multicolored	.25	.25
2434	A873	12s multicolored	.30	.25
2435	A873	13s multicolored	.30	.25
2436	A873	43s multicolored	1.25	.30
	Nos. 2431-2436 (6)		2.60	1.55

Ivan Vasov National Theater A926

Buildings, Sofia: 13s, Party Headquarters. 23s, House of the People's Army. 30s, Clement Ochrida University. 80s, National Gallery. 1 l, National Assembly.

1977, Aug. 30   Photo.   Perf. 13

2437	A926	12s red, *gray*	.25	.25
2438	A926	13s red brn, *gray*	.35	.25
2439	A926	23s blue, *gray*	.55	.25
2440	A926	30s olive, *gray*	.80	.30
2441	A926	80s violet, *gray*	1.25	.70
2442	A926	1 l claret, *gray*	1.75	.90
	Nos. 2437-2442 (6)		4.95	2.65

Map of Europe A927

1977, June 10

2443 A927 23s brown, bl & grn   .60 .25

21st Congress of the European Organization for Quality Control, Varna.

Union of Earth and Water, by Rubens A928

Rubens Paintings: 23s, Venus and Adonis. 40s, Pastoral Scene (man and woman). 1 l, Portrait of a Lady in Waiting.

1977, Sept. 23   Litho.   Perf. 12

2444	A928	13s gold & multi	.40	.25
2445	A928	23s gold & multi	.80	.25
2446	A928	40s gold & multi	1.40	.35
	Nos. 2444-2446 (3)		2.60	.85

Souvenir Sheet

2447 A928 1 l gold & multi   2.50 2.00

Peter Paul Rubens (1577-1640).

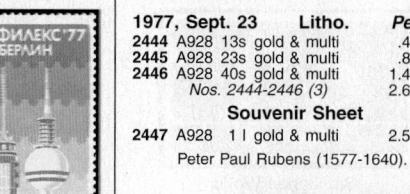

George Dimitrov A929

1977, June 17   Photo.   Perf. 13

2448 A929 13s red & deep claret   .50 .25

George Dimitrov (1882-1947).

Flame with Star — A930

1977, May 17

2449 A930 13s gold & multi   .35 .25

3rd Bulgarian Culture Congress.

Smart Pete on Donkey, by Ilya Beshkov — A931

1977, May 19

2450 A931 2s multicolored   .25 .25

11th National Festival of Humor and Satire Gabrovo.

Elin Pelin — A932

Writers: 2s, Pelin (Dimitur Ivanov Stojanov, (1877-1949). 5s, Peju K. Jaworov (1878-1914).
Artists: 13s, Boris Angelushev (1902-1966), 23s, Ceno Todorov (Ceno Todorov Dikov, 1877-1953). Each printed with label showing scenes from authors' works or illustrations by the artists.

1977, Aug. 26   Photo.   Perf. 13

2451	A932	2s gold & brown	.25	.25
2452	A932	5s gold & gray grn	.25	.25
2453	A932	13s gold & claret	.30	.30
2454	A932	23s gold & blue	.70	.35
	Nos. 2451-2454 (4)		1.50	1.15

13th Canoe World
Championships — A933

1977, Sept. 1　Photo.　Perf. 13
2455　A933　2s shown　.25　.25
2456　A933　23s 2-man canoe　.65　.25

Albena,
Black
Sea —
A933a

1977, Oct. 5　Photo.　Perf. 13
2456A　A933a　35s shown　.85　.35
2456B　A933a　43s Rila Monastery　.85　.35
Sheet contains 4 each plus label.

Dr.
Pirogov — A934

1977, Oct. 14　Photo.　Perf. 13
2457　A934　13s olive, ocher & brn　.35　.25
Centenary of visit by Russian physician N.
J. Pirogov during war of liberation from Turkey.

Peace Decree,
1917 — A935

13s, Lenin, 1917. 23s, "1917" as a flame.

1977, Oct. 21
2458　A935　2s black, buff & red　.25　.25
2459　A935　13s multicolored　.40　.25
2460　A935　23s multicolored　.75　.25
　　　Nos. 2458-2460 (3)　1.40　.75
60th anniv. of Russian October Revolution.

Old Soldier with
Grandchild
A936

Designs (Festival Posters): 13s, "The
Bugler." 23s, Liberation Monument, Sofia
(detail). 25s, Samara flag.

1977, Sept. 30
2461　A936　2s multicolored　.25　.25
2462　A936　13s multicolored　.30　.25
2463　A936　23s multicolored　.70　.25
2464　A936　25s multicolored　.70　.30
　　　Nos. 2461-2464 (4)　1.95　1.05
Liberation from Turkish rule, centenary.

Souvenir Sheet

Games' and Sports Emblems — A937

1977, Aug. 10　Photo.　Perf. 13½x13
2465　A937　1 l multicolored　2.25　1.75
University Games '77, Sofia.

Conference Building — A938

1977, Sept. 12　　　Perf. 13½
2466　A938　23s multicolored　.65　.25
64th Interparliamentary Union Conf., Sofia.

Bulgarian
Worker's
Newspaper,
Anniversaries
A939

1977, Sept. 12　Photo.　Perf. 13
2467　A939　2s yel grn, blk & red　.25　.25

Ornament
A940

New Year 1978: 13s, Different ornament.

1977, Dec. 1
2468　A940　2s gold & multi　.25　.25
2469　A940　13s silver & multi　.40　.25

Railroad Bridge — A941

1977, Nov. 9
2470　A941　13s green, yel & gray　.60　.25
Transport Organization, 50th anniversary.

A942

1977, Nov. 15
2471　A942　8s gold & vio brn　.50　.50
Petko Ratchev Slaveikov (1827-95), poet,
birth sesquicentennial. No. 2471 printed in
sheets of 8 stamps and 8 labels in 4 alternating vertical rows.

A943

Designs: 23s, Soccer player and Games'
emblem. 50s, Soccer players.

1978, Jan. 30　Photo.　Perf. 13
2472　A943　13s multicolored　.50　.25
2473　A943　23s multicolored　.70　.25
Souvenir Sheet
2474　A943　50s ultra & multi　1.75　1.40
11th World Cup Soccer Championship,
Argentina, June 1-25.

Todor Zhivkov
and Leonid I.
Brezhnev
A944

1977, Sept. 7　Photo.　Perf. 13
2475　A944　18s gold, car & brn　.65　.45
Bulgarian-Soviet Friendship. No. 2475
issued in sheets of 3 stamps and 3 labels.

Ostankino Tower,
Moscow,
Bulgarian Post
Emblem — A945

1978, Mar. 1
2476　A945　13s multicolored　.35　.25
Comecon Postal Organization (Council of
Mutual Economic Assistance), 20th anniv.

Leo
Tolstoy — A946

Shipka Pass Monument — A947

5s, Fedor Dostoevski. 13s, Ivan Sergeevich
Turgenev. 23s, Vasili Vasilievich Vereshchagin.
25s, Giuseppe Garibaldi. 35s, Victor Hugo.

1978, Mar. 28　Photo.　Perf. 13
2477　A946　2s yellow & dk grn　.25　.25
2478　A946　5s lemon & brown　.25　.25
2479　A946　13s tan & sl grn　.25　.25
2480　A946　23s gray & vio brn　.35　.25
2481　A946　25s yel grn & blk　.35　.25
2482　A946　35s lt bl & vio bl　.95　.50
　　　Nos. 2477-2482 (6)　2.40　1.75
Souvenir Sheet
2483　A947　50s multicolored　1.10　.80
Bulgaria's liberation from Ottoman rule, cent.

Bulgarian
and
Russian
Colors
A948

1978, Mar. 18
2484　A948　2s multicolored　.25　.25
30th anniv. of Russo-Bulgarian co-operation.

Heart
and
WHO
Emblem
A949

1978, May 12
2485　A949　23s gray, red & org　.75　.25
World Health Day, fight against hypertension.

Goddess
A950

Ceramics (2nd-4th Cent.) & Exhibition
Emblem: 5s, Mask of bearded man. 13s, Vase.
23s, Vase. 35s, Head of Silenus. 53s, Cock.

1978, Apr. 26
2486　A950　2s green & multi　.25　.25
2487　A950　5s multicolored　.25　.25
2488　A950　13s multicolored　.35　.25
2489　A950　23s multicolored　.55　.25
2490　A950　35s multicolored　.80　.45
2491　A950　53s carmine & multi　2.50　.55
　　　Nos. 2486-2491 (6)　4.70　2.00
Philaserdica Philatelic Exhibition.

Nikolai Roerich, by Svyatoslav Roerich — A951 | "Mind and Matter," by Andrei Nikolov — A952

1978, Apr. 5
2492 A951 8s multicolored .25 .25
2493 A952 13s multicolored .35 .25
Nikolai K. Roerich (1874-1947) and Andrei Nikolov (1878-1959), artists.

Bulgarian Flag and Red Star — A953

1978, Apr. 18
2494 A953 2s vio blue & multi .25 .25
Bulgarian Communist Party Congress.

Young Man, by Albrecht Dürer A954

Paintings: 23s, Bathsheba at Fountain, by Rubens. 25s, Portrait of a Man, by Hans Holbein the Younger. 35s, Rembrandt and Saskia, by Rembrandt. 43s, Lady in Mourning, by Tintoretto. 60s, Old Man with Beard, by Rembrandt. 80s, Knight in Armor, by Van Dyck.

1978, June 19 Photo. Perf. 13
2495 A954 13s multicolored .25 .25
2496 A954 23s multicolored .35 .25
2497 A954 25s multicolored .40 .25
2498 A954 35s multicolored .55 .25
2499 A954 43s multicolored .65 .25
2500 A954 60s multicolored .85 .40
2501 A954 80s multicolored 2.00 .65
Nos. 2495-2501 (7) 5.05 2.30
Dresden Art Gallery paintings.

Doves and Festival Emblem — A955

1978, May 31
2502 A955 13s multicolored .35 .25
11th World Youth Festival, Havana, 7/28-8/5.

Fritillaria Stribrnyi — A956

Rare Flowers: 2s, Fritillaria drenovskyi. 3s, Lilium rhodopaeum. 13s, Tulipa urumoffii. 23s, Lilium jankae. 43s, Tulipa rhodopaea.

1978, June 27
2503 A956 1s multicolored .25 .25
2504 A956 2s multicolored .25 .25
2505 A956 3s multicolored .25 .25
2506 A956 13s multicolored .35 .25
2507 A956 23s multicolored .40 .25
2508 A956 43s multicolored 1.25 .50
Nos. 2503-2508 (6) 2.75 1.75

Yacht Cor Caroli and Map of Voyage A957

1978, May 19 Photo. Perf. 13
2509 A957 23s multicolored 1.40 .25
First Bulgarian around-the-world voyage, Capt. Georgi Georgiev, 12/20/76-12/20/77.

Market, by Naiden Petkov — A958

Views of Sofia: 5s, Street, by Emil Stoichev. 13s, Street, by Boris Ivanov. 23s, Tolbukhin Boulevard, by Nikola Tanev. 35s, National Theater, by Nikola Petrov. 53s, Market, by Anton Mitov.

1978, Aug. 28 Litho. Perf. 12½x12
2510 A958 2s multicolored .25 .25
2511 A958 5s multicolored .25 .25
2512 A958 13s multicolored .25 .25
2513 A958 23s multicolored .40 .25
2514 A958 35s multicolored .75 .25
2515 A958 53s multicolored 1.00 .40
Nos. 2510-2515 (6) 2.90 1.65

Miniature Sheet

Sleeping Venus, by Giorgione — A959

1978, Aug. 7 Photo. Imperf.
2516 A959 1 l multicolored 1.75 .85

View of Varna — A960

1978, July 13 Photo. Perf. 13
2517 A960 13s multicolored .60 .30
63rd Esperanto Cong., Varna, 7/29-8/5.

Black Woodpecker A961

Woodpeckers: 2s, Syrian. 3s, Three-toed. 13s, Middle spotted. 23s, Lesser spotted. 43s, Green.

1978, Sept. 1
2518 A961 1s multicolored .25 .25
2519 A961 2s multicolored .25 .25
2520 A961 3s multicolored .25 .25
2521 A961 13s multicolored .60 .30
2522 A961 23s multicolored .90 .50
2523 A961 43s multicolored 2.40 1.25
Nos. 2518-2523 (6) 4.65 2.80

"September 1923" — A962

1978, Sept. 5
2524 A962 2s red & brn .25 .25
55th anniversary of September uprising.

Souvenir Sheet

A963

a, National Theater, Sofia. b, Festival Hall, Sofia. c, Charles Bridge, Prague. d, Belvedere Palace, Prague.

Photogravure and Engraved
1978, Sept. 1 Perf. 12x11½
2525 A963 Sheet of 4 2.50 1.00
a.-d. 40s any single .60 .25
PRAGA '78 and PHILASERDICA '79 Philatelic Exhibitions.

Black and White Hands, Human Rights Emblem — A964

1978, Oct. 3 Photo. Perf. 13x13½
2526 A964 13s multicolored .35 .25
Anti-Apartheid Year.

Gotse Deltchev — A965

1978, Aug. 1 Photo. Perf. 13
2527 A965 13s multicolored .40 .25
Gotse Deltchev (1872-1903), patriot.

Bulgarian Calculator — A966

1978, Sept. 3
2528 A966 2s multicolored .25 .25
International Sample Fair, Plovdiv.

Guerrillas — A967

1978, Aug. 1
2529 A967 5s blk & rose red .25 .25
Ilinden and Preobrazhene revolts, 75th anniv.

"Pipe Line" and Flags A968

1978, Oct. 3
2530 A968 13s multicolored .35 .25
Construction of gas pipe line from Orenburg to Russian border.

A969

1978, Oct. 4 **Perf. 13x13½**
2531 A969 13s Three acrobats .35 .25
3rd World Acrobatic Championships, Sofia, Oct. 6-8.

A970

1978, Sept. 18 **Photo.** **Perf. 13**
2532 A970 2s dp claret & ocher .30 .50
Christo G. Danov (1828-1911), 1st Bulgarian publisher. No. 2532 printed with se-tenant label showing early printing press.

Insurgents, by Todor Panajotov — A971

1978, Sept. 20
2533 A971 2s multicolored .25 .25
Vladaja mutiny, 60th anniversary.

A972

1978, Oct. 11 **Photo.** **Perf. 13**
2534 A972 13s dk brn & org red .35 .25
Salvador Allende (1908-1973), president of Chile.

Human Rights Flame — A973

1978, Oct. 18
2535 A973 23s multicolored .70 .25
Universal Declaration of Human Rights, 30th anniversary.

A974

Burgarian Paintings: 1s, Levski and Matei Mitkaloto, by Kalina Tasseva. 2s, "Strength for my Arm" by Zlatyu Boyadjiev. 3s, Rumena, woman military leader, by Nikola Mirchev, horiz. 13s, Kolju Ficeto, by Elza Goeva. 23s, Family, National Revival Period, by Naiden Petkov.

Perf. 12x12½, 12½x12
1978, Oct. 25 **Litho.**
2536 A974 1s multicolored .25 .25
2537 A974 2s multicolored .25 .25
2538 A974 3s multicolored .25 .25
2539 A974 13s multicolored .35 .25
2540 A974 23s multicolored .65 .25
   Nos. 2536-2540 (5) 1.75 1.25
1300th anniversary of Bulgaria (in 1981).

From late 1978 to 1991, imperf varieties, some overprinted, exist for many sets and souvenir sheets. These were distributed in limited numbers and are described in footnotes following the listed issues.

Souvenir Sheet

A975

Designs: a, Tourism building, Plovdiv. b, Chrelo Tower, Rila Cloister.

1978, Nov. 1 **Photo.** **Perf. 13**
2541 A975 Sheet of 5 + label 4.00 2.00
a.-b. 43s any single .85 .35
Conservation of European architectural heritage. No. 2541 contains 3 No. 2541a & 2 No. 2541b.
Exists overprinted "Essen 1978." Value $32.50.

Ferry, Map of Black Sea with Route A976

1978, Nov. 1 **Photo.** **Perf. 13**
2542 A976 13s multicolored .40 .25
Opening of Ilychovsk-Varna Ferry.

Bird, from Marble Floor, St. Sofia Church — A977

1978, Nov. 20
2543 A977 5s multicolored .35 .25
3rd Bulgaria '78, National Philatelic Exhibition, Sofia. Printed se-tenant with label showing emblems of Bulgaria '78 and Philaserdica '79.

Initial, 13th Century Gospel — A978

Designs: 13s, St. Cyril, miniature, 1567. 23s, Book cover, 16th century. 80s, St. Methodius, miniature, 13th century.

1978, Dec. 15 **Photo.** **Perf. 13**
2544 A978 2s multicolored .25 .25
2545 A978 13s multicolored .30 .25
2546 A978 23s multicolored .65 .25
   Nos. 2544-2546 (3) 1.20 .75
Souvenir Sheet
2547 A978 80s multicolored 1.60 1.00
Cent. of the Cyril and Methodius Natl. Library.

Bulgaria No. 53 A979

Bulgarian Stamps: 13s, #534. 23s, #968. 35s, #1176, vert. 53s, #1223, vert. 1 l, #1.

1978, Dec. 30
2548 A979 2s ol grn & red .25 .25
2549 A979 13s ultra & rose car .25 .25
2550 A979 23s rose lil & ol grn .35 .25
2551 A979 35s brt bl & blk .65 .25
2552 A979 53s ver & sl grn 1.10 .35
   Nos. 2548-2552 (5) 2.60 1.35
Souvenir Sheet
2553 A979 1 l multicolored 1.75 1.25
Philaserdica '79, International Philatelic Exhibition, Sofia, May 18-27, 1979, and centenary of Bulgarian stamps. No. 2553 exists imperf. Value $16.
A larger (63mmx61mm) souvenir sheet was issued in 1979, containing one 1 l stamp, perf 13. Value $4.50. A second souvenir sheet (92mmx125mm), containing one 5 l stamp, perf 13, with reproductions of many stamps of the first Bulgarian issue, was also issued in 1979. Value $35.
See Nos. 2560-2564.

St. Clement of Ochrida — A980

1978, Dec. 8
2554 A980 2s multicolored .25 .25
Clement of Ochrida University, 90th anniv.

Ballet Dancers A981

1978, Dec. 22
2555 A981 13s multicolored .35 .25
Bulgarian ballet, 50th anniversary.

Nikola Karastojanov — A982

1978, Dec. 12
2556 A982 2s multicolored .35 .25
Nikola Karastojanov (1778-1874), printer. No. 2556 printed se-tenant with label showing printing press.

Christmas Tree Made of Birds — A983

1978, Dec. 22
2557 A983 2s shown .25 .25
2558 A983 13s Post horn .25 .25
New Year 1979.

COMECON Building, Moscow, Members' Flags — A984

1979, Jan. 25 **Photo.** **Perf. 13**
2559 A984 13s multicolored .35 .25
Council for Mutual Economic Aid (COMECON), 30th anniversary.

Philaserdica Type of 1978
Designs as Before

1979, Jan. 30
2560 A979 2s brt bl & red .25 .25
2561 A979 13s grn & dk car .25 .25
2562 A979 23s org brn & multi .45 .25
2563 A979 35s dl red & blk .70 .35
2564 A979 53s vio & dk ol .90 .55
   Nos. 2560-2564 (5) 2.55 1.65
Philaserdica '79.

Bank Building, Commemorative
Coin — A985

1979, Feb. 13
2565 A985 2s yel, gray & silver .25 .25
Centenary of Bulgarian People's Bank.

Aleksandr
Stamboliski
A986

1979, Feb. 28
2566 A986 2s orange & dk brn .25 .25
Aleksandr Stamboliski (1879-1923), leader
of peasant's party and premier.

Flower with
Child's Face,
IYC
Emblem — A987

1979, Mar. 8
2568 A987 23s multicolored .65 .25
International Year of the Child.

Stylized Heads,
World
Association
Emblem — A988

1979, Mar. 20
2569 A988 13s multicolored .35 .25
8th World Cong. for the Deaf, Varna, June
20-27.

"75" and Trade
Union
Emblem — A989

1979, Mar. 20
2570 A989 2s slate grn & org .25 .25
75th anniversary of Bulgarian Trade Unions.

Souvenir Sheet

Sculptures in Sofia — A990

Designs: 2s, Soviet Army Monument
(detail). 5s, Mother and Child, Central Railroad
Station. 13s, 23s, 25s, Bas-relief from Monument of the Liberators.

1979, Apr. 2 Photo. Perf. 13
2571 A990 Sheet of 5 + label 1.50 1.00
a. 2s multicolored .25 .25
b. 5s multicolored .25 .25
c. 13s multicolored .35 .25
d. 23s multicolored .45 .25
e. 25s multicolored .50 .25
Centenary of Sofia as capital.

Rocket Launch,
Space Flight
Emblems
A991

Intercosmos & Bulgarian-USSR Flight
Emblems and: 25s, Link-up, horiz. 35s, Parachute descent. 1 l, Globe, emblems & orbit,
horiz.

1979, Apr. 11
2572 A991 12s multicolored .25 .25
2573 A991 25s multicolored .70 .25
2574 A991 35s multicolored .90 .40
Nos. 2572-2574 (3) 1.85 .90
Souvenir Sheet
2575 A991 1 l multicolored 1.75 1.00
1st Bulgarian cosmonaut on Russian space
flight.
A slightly larger imperf. sheet similar to No.
2575 with control numbers at bottom and rockets at sides exists. $100.

Georgi
Ivanov
A992

Design: 13s, Rukavishnikov and Soviet cosmonaut Georgi Ivanov.

1979, May 14 Photo. Perf. 13
2576 A992 2s multicolored .25 .25
2577 A992 13s multicolored .50 .25
Col. Rukavishnikov, 1st Bulgarian astronaut.

Souvenir Sheet

Thracian Gold-leaf Collar — A993

1979, May 16
2578 A993 1 l multicolored 3.50 2.25
48th International Philatelic Federation Congress, Sofia, May 16-17.

Post Horn, Carrier Pigeon, Jet, Globes
and UPU Emblem — A994

Designs (Post Horn, Globes and ITU
Emblem): 5s, 1st Bulgarian and modern tele-
phones. 13s, Morse key and teleprinter. 23s,
Old radio transmitter and radio towers. 35s,
Bulgarian TV tower and satellite. 50s, Ground
receiving station

1979, May 8 Perf. 13½x13
2579 A994 2s multicolored .25 .25
2580 A994 5s multicolored .25 .25
2581 A994 13s multicolored .35 .25
2582 A994 23s multicolored .50 .25
2583 A994 35s multicolored .70 .30
Nos. 2579-2583 (5) 2.05 1.30
Souvenir Sheet
Perf. 13
2584 A994 50s vio, blk & gray 2.00 1.40
Intl. Telecommunications Day and cent. of
Bulgarian Postal & Telegraph Services. Size of
stamp in No. 2584: 39x28mm. No. 2584 exists
imperf. Value $15.

Hotel Vitosha-
New
Otani — A996

1979, May 20
2586 A996 2s ultra & pink .25 .25
Philaserdica '79 Day.

Horseman Receiving Gifts, by Karellia
and Boris Kuklievi — A997

1979, May 23
2587 A997 2s multicolored .25 .25
Bulgarian-Russian Friendship Day.

A998

Man on Donkey, by Boris Angeloushev.

1979, May 23 Photo. Perf. 13½
2588 A998 2s multicolored .25 .25
12th National Festival of Humor and Satire,
Gabrovo.

Durer
Engravings
A999

13s, Four Women. 23s, Three Peasants.
25s, The Cook and his Wife. 35s, Portrait of
Helius Eobanus Hessus. 80s, Rhinoceros,
horiz.

Lithographed and Engraved
1979, May 31 Perf. 14x13½
2589 A999 13s multicolored .35 .25
2590 A999 23s multicolored .45 .25
2591 A999 25s multicolored .60 .25
2592 A999 35s multicolored .90 .25
Nos. 2589-2592 (4) 2.30 1.00
Souvenir Sheet
Imperf
2593 A999 80s multicolored 1.75 1.25
Albrecht Durer (1471-1528), German
engraver and painter.

R. Todorov (1879-1916) — A1000

Bulgarian Writers: No. 2595, Dimitri Dymov
(1909-66). No. 2596, S. A. Kostov (1879-
1939).

1979, June 26 Photo. Perf. 13
2594 A1000 2s multicolored .25 .65
2595 A1000 2s slate grn & yel
grn .25 .65
2596 A1000 2s dp claret & yel .25 .65
Nos. 2594-2596 (3) .75 1.95
Nos. 2594-2596 each printed se-tenant with
label showing title page or character from
writer's work.

Moscow '80
Emblem,
Runners
A1001

Moscow '80 Emblem and: 13s, Pole vault,
horiz. 25s, Discus. 35s, Hurdles, horiz. 43s,
High jump, horiz. 1 l, Long jump.

1979, May 15   ***Perf. 13***
2597 A1001 2s multicolored   .25   .25
2598 A1001 13s multicolored   .35   .25
2599 A1001 25s multicolored   1.00   .25
2600 A1001 35s multicolored   1.00   .35
2601 A1001 43s multicolored   1.40   .45
2602 A1001 1 l multicolored   2.50   .95
        Nos. 2597-2602 (6)   6.50 2.50

Souvenir Sheet

2602A A1001 2 l multicolored   7.00 4.00

22nd Summer Olympic Games, Moscow, July 19-Aug. 3, 1980.

Rocket — A1002

5s, Flags of USSR and Bulgaria. 13s, "35."

1979, Sept. 4   ***Photo.***
2603 A1002 2s multicolored   .25   .25
2604 A1002 5s multicolored   .25   .25
2605 A1002 13s multicolored   .25   .25
        Nos. 2603-2605 (3)   .75   .75

35th anniversary of liberation.

Moscow '80 Emblem, Gymnast A1003

Moscow '80 Emblem & gymnasts.

1979, July 31   ***Photo.***   ***Perf. 13***
2606 A1003 2s multi   .25   .25
2607 A1003 13s multi, horiz.   .25   .25
2608 A1003 25s multi   .40   .25
2609 A1003 35s multi   .80   .35
2610 A1003 43s multi   .80   .35
2611 A1003 1 l multi   2.50 1.00
        Nos. 2606-2611 (6)   5.00 2.45

Souvenir Sheet

2612 A1003 2 l multicolored   7.75 4.00

22nd Summer Olympic Games, Moscow, July 19-Aug. 3, 1980.

A1004

1979, July 8   ***Photo.***   ***Perf. 13***
2613 A1004 13s ultra & blk   .30   .25

Theater Institute, 18th Congress.

A1005

1979, July 17
2614 A1005 8s multicolored   .25   .25

Journalists' Vacation House, Varna, 20th Anniv.

Icon Type of 1977

Virgin and Child from: 13s, 23s, Nesebar, 16th cent., diff. 35s, 43s, Sozopol, 16th cent., diff. 53s, Samokov, 19th cent. Inscribed 1979.

1979, Aug. 7   ***Litho.***   ***Perf. 12½***
2615 A917 13s multicolored   .60   .25
2616 A917 23s multicolored   .60   .25
2617 A917 35s multicolored   .60   .25
2618 A917 43s multicolored   .60   .25
2619 A917 53s multicolored   1.20   .45
        Nos. 2615-2619 (5)   3.60 1.45

Anton Besenschek A1006

1979, Aug. 9   Photo.   Perf. 13x13½
2620 A1006 2s multi   .25   .25

Bulgarian stenography centenary.

A1007

1979, Aug. 28   ***Perf. 13***
2621 A1007 2s multicolored   .25   .25

Bulgarian Alpine Club, 50th anniv.

Public Health Ordinance — A1008

1979, Aug. 31   ***Perf. 13½***
2622 A1008 2s multicolored   .25   .25

Public Health Service centenary. No. 2622 printed with label showing Dimitar Mollov, founder.

Isotope Measuring Device — A1009

1979, Sept. 8   ***Perf. 13½x13***
2623 A1009 2s multicolored   .25   .25

International Sample Fair, Plovdiv.

Games' Emblem A1010

1979, Sept. 20   ***Perf. 13***
2624 A1010 5s multicolored   .25   .25

Universiada '79, World University Games, Mexico City, Sept.

Sofia Locomotive Sports Club, 50th Anniversary — A1011

1979, Oct. 2
2625 A1011 2s blue & org red   .25   .25

Ljuben Karavelov (1837-1879), Poet and Freedom Fighter — A1012

1979, Oct. 4   Photo.   Perf. 13
2626 A1012 2s blue & slate grn   .25   .25

A1013

1979, Oct. 20
2627 A1013 2s Biathlon   .25   .25
2628 A1013 13s Speed skating   .30   .25
2629 A1013 23s Downhill skiing   .50   .25
2630 A1013 43s Luge   1.25   .40
        Nos. 2627-2630 (4)   2.30 1.15

Souvenir Sheet
Imperf

2631 A1013 1 l Slalom   2.00 1.25

13th Winter Olympic Games, Lake Placid, NY, Feb. 12-24.
No. 2631 exists overprinted "Lake Placid 1980," with serial number. Value $100.

A1014

Decko Uzunov, 80th Birthday: 12s, Apparition in Red. 13s, Woman from Thrace. 23s, Composition.

1979, Oct. 31   ***Perf. 14***
2632 A1014 12s multicolored   .30   .25
2633 A1014 13s multicolored   .30   .25
2634 A1014 23s multicolored   .85   .25
        Nos. 2632-2634 (3)   1.45   .75

Swimming, Moscow '80 Emblem — A1016

2s, Two-man kayak, vert. 13s, Swimming, vert. 35s, One-man kayak. 43s, Diving, vert. 1 l, Diving, vert., diff.
2 l, Water polo, vert.

1979, Nov. 30   Photo.   Perf. 13
2636 A1016 2s multicolored   .25   .25
2637 A1016 13s multicolored   .40   .25
2638 A1016 25s shown   1.10   .25
2639 A1016 35s multicolored   1.10   .25
2640 A1016 43s multicolored   1.50   .60
2641 A1016 1 l multicolored   2.25 1.00
        Nos. 2636-2641 (6)   6.60 2.60

Souvenir Sheet

2642 A1016 2 l multicolored   7.75 4.00

22nd Summer Olympic Games, Moscow, July 19-Aug. 3, 1980.

Nikola Vapzarov — A1017

1979, Dec. 7   Photo.   Perf. 13
2643 A1017 2s claret & rose   .30   .30

Vapzarov (1909-1942), poet and freedom fighter. No. 2643 printed with label showing smokestacks.

The First Socialists, by Bojan Petrov — A1018

Paintings: 13s, Demeter Blagoev Reading Newspaper, by Demeter Gjudshenov, 1892. 25s, Workers' Party March, by Sotir Sotirov, 1917. 35s, Dawn in Plovdiv, by Johann Leviev, vert.

Perf. 12½x12, 12x12½

1979, Dec. 10   Litho.
2644 A1018   2s multicolored   .25   .25
2645 A1018   13s multicolored   .30   .25
2646 A1018   25s multicolored   .60   .25
2647 A1018   35s multicolored   .85   .25
    Nos. 2644-2647 (4)   2.00   1.00

Sharpshooting, Moscow '80 Emblem A1019

13s, Judo, horiz. 25s, Wrestling, horiz. 35s, Archery. 43s, Fencing, horiz. 1 l, Fencing. 2 l, Boxing.

1979, Dec. 22   Photo.   Perf. 13
2648 A1019   2s shown   .25   .25
2649 A1019   13s multi   .35   .25
2650 A1019   25s multi   1.00   .25
2651 A1019   35s multi   1.00   .35
2652 A1019   43s multi   1.40   .75
2653 A1019   1 l multi   2.10   1.40
    Nos. 2648-2653 (6)   6.10   3.25

Souvenir Sheet
2654 A1019   2 l multi   7.75   5.00

Procession with Relics, 11th Century Fresco A1020

Frescoes of Sts. Cyril and Methodius, St. Clement's Basilica, Rome: 13s, Reception by Pope Hadrian II. 23s, Burial of Cyril the Philosopher, 18th century. 25s, St. Cyril. 35s, St. Methodius.

1979, Dec. 25
2655 A1020   2s multicolored   .25   .25
2656 A1020   13s multicolored   .25   .25
2657 A1020   23s multicolored   .45   .25
2658 A1020   25s multicolored   .55   .25
2659 A1020   35s multicolored   .85   .25
    Nos. 2655-2659 (5)   2.35   1.25

Bulgarian Television Emblem — A1021

1979, Dec. 29   Perf. 13½
2660 A1021   5s violet bl & lt bl   .30   .30
   Bulgarian television, 25th anniversary. No. 2660 printed with label showing Sofia television tower.

Doves in Girl's Hair A1022

Design: 2s, Children's heads, mosaic, vert.

1979   Perf. 13
2661 A1022   2s multicolored   .25   .25
2662 A1022   13s multicolored   .30   .25
   International Year of the Child. Issue dates: 2s, July 17; 13s, Dec. 14.

Puppet on Horseback, IYC Emblem — A1023

1980, Jan. 22   Photo.   Perf. 13
2663 A1023   2s multicolored   .25   .25
   UNIMA, Intl. Puppet Theater Organization, 50th anniv. (1979); Intl. Year of the Child (1979).

Thracian Rider, Votive Tablet, 3rd Century — A1024

National Archaeological Museum Centenary; 13s, Deines stele, 5th century B.C.

1980, Jan. 29   Photo.   Perf. 13x13½
2664 A1024   2s brown & gold   .25   .25
2665 A1024   13s multicolored   .25   .25

A miniature sheet was issued March 27, 1980, containing six 13s stamps, perf 13, which spelled out "EUROPA." Size 130mmx118mm. Value $30.

Dimitrov Meeting Lenin in Moscow, by Alexander Poplilov A1026

1980, Mar. 28   Perf. 12x12½
2667 A1026   13s multicolored   .30   .25
   Lenin, 110th birth anniversary.

A1027

Circulatory system, lungs enveloped in smoke.

1980, Apr. 7   Perf. 13
2668 A1027   5s multicolored   .25   .25
   World Health Day fight against cigarette smoking.

A1027a

1980, Apr. 10   Photo.   Perf. 13
2669 A1027a   2s Basketball   .25   .25
2670 A1027a   13s Soccer   .35   .25
2671 A1027a   25s Hockey   1.10   .35
2672 A1027a   35s Cycling   1.10   .55
2673 A1027a   43s Handball   1.50   .75
2674 A1027a   1 l Volleyball   2.25   1.10
    Nos. 2669-2674 (6)   6.55   3.25

Souvenir Sheet
2675 A1027a   2 l Weightlifting   7.50   5.00
   22nd Summer Olympic Games, Moscow, July 19-Aug. 3, 1980.

Souvenir Sheet

Intercosmos Emblem, Cosmonauts — A1028

1980, Apr. 22   Perf. 12
2676 A1028   50s multicolored   1.40   .80
   Intercosmos cooperative space program.

Penio Penev (1930-1959), Poet — A1029

1980, Apr. 22   Photo.   Perf. 13
2677 A1029   5s multicolored   .25   .25
   Se-tenant with label showing quote from author's work.

Penny Black — A1030

1980, Apr. 24   Perf. 13
2678 A1030   25s dark red & sepia   .85   .60
   London 1980 International Stamp Exhibition, May 6-14; printed se-tenant with label showing Rowland Hill between every two stamps.
   No. 2678 was overprinted "UPU 1984" in 1982. Value $3.

Demeter H. Tchorbadjiiski, Self-portrait — A1031

1980, Apr. 29
2679 A1031   5s shown   .25   .25
2680 A1031   13s "Our People"   .25   .25

Nikolai Giaurov — A1032

1980, Apr. 30
2681 A1032   5s multicolored   .50   .50
   Nikolai Giaurov (b. 1930), opera singer; printed se-tenant with label showing Boris Godunov.

Raising Red Flag Reichstag Building, Berlin — A1033

Armistice, 35th Anniversary: 13s, Soviet Army memorial, Berlin-Treptow.

1980, May 6   Perf. 13x13½
2682 A1033   5s multicolored   .25   .25
2683 A1033   13s multicolored   .25   .25

Numeral — A1034

1979   Perf. 14
2684 A1034   2s ultra   .25   .25
2685 A1034   5s rose car   .25   .25

A1034a

1980, May 12   Photo.   Perf. 13
2685A A1034a   5s multicolored   .25   .25
   75th Anniv. of Teachers' Union.

Warsaw Pact, 25th Anniv. — A1035

1980, May 14   Photo.   Perf. 13
2686 A1035 13s multicolored   .35 .25

Statues A1036

1980, June 10
2687 A1036 2s multicolored   .25 .25
2688 A1036 13s multicolored   .35 .35
2689 A1036 25s multicolored   1.00 .50
2690 A1036 35s multicolored   1.00 .60
2691 A1036 43s multicolored   1.40 .80
2692 A1036 1 l multicolored   2.10 1.25
  Nos. 2687-2692 (6)   6.10 3.75

Souvenir Sheet
2693 A1036 2 l multicolored   7.50 3.50

22nd Summer Olympic Games, Moscow, July 19-Aug. 3.
In 1981 a souvenir sheet was issued, containing one 50s stamp, perf 13, depicting Olympic medal and lion. Size 100x105mm. Value $18.50.

A1037

1980, Sept.   Photo.   Perf. 13
2694 A1037 13s multicolored   .35 .25

10th Intl. Ballet Competition, Varna.

Hotel Europa, Sofia A1038

Hotels: No. 2696, Bulgaria, Burgas, vert. No. 2697, Plovdiv, Plovdiv. No. 2698, Riga, Russe, vert. No. 2699, Varna, Djuba.

1980, July 11
2695 A1038 23s lt ultra & multi   .45 .25
2696 A1038 23s orange & multi   .45 .25
2697 A1038 23s gray & multi   .45 .25
2698 A1038 23s blue & multi   .45 .25
2699 A1038 23s yellow & multi   .45 .25
  Nos. 2695-2699 (5)   2.25 1.25
  See No. 2766.

Ship Type of 1975

Ships of 16th, 17th Centuries: 5s, Christ of Lubeck, galleon. 8s, Roman galley. 13s, Eagle, Russian galleon. 23s, Mayflower. 35s, Maltese galley. 53s, Royal Louis, galleon.

1980, July 14
2700 A873 5s multicolored   .25 .25
2701 A873 8s multicolored   .25 .25
2702 A873 13s multicolored   .45 .25
2703 A873 23s multicolored   .45 .25
2704 A873 35s multicolored   .80 .25
2705 A873 53s multicolored   1.10 .40
  Nos. 2700-2705 (6)   3.10 1.65

On Aug. 28, 1980, a miniature sheet of six stamps, denominated 5s to 45s, perf 13, was issued. Size: 115mmx135mm. Inscribed "ESSEN 1980" in selvage and serially numbered. Value $40.

Int'l Year of the Child, 1979 — A1040

Designs: Children's drawings and IYC emblem. 43s, Tower. 5s, 25s, 43s, vert.

Perf. 12½x12, 12x12½
1980, Sep. 1   Litho.
2708 A1040 3s multicolored   .25 .25
2709 A1040 5s multicolored   .25 .25
2710 A1040 8s multicolored   .25 .25
2711 A1040 13s multicolored   .25 .25
2712 A1040 25s multicolored   .35 .25
2713 A1040 35s multicolored   .55 .25
2714 A1040 43s multicolored   1.10 .25
  Nos. 2708-2714 (7)   3.00 1.75

Helicopter, Missile Transport, Tank — A1041

1980, Sept. 23   Photo.   Perf. 13
2715 A1041 3s shown   .25 .25
2716 A1041 5s Jet, radar, rocket   .25 .25
2717 A1041 8s Helicopter, ships   .25 .25
  Nos. 2715-2717 (3)   .75 .75

Bulgarian People's Army, 35th anniversary.

St. Anne, by Leonardo da Vinci A1042

Da Vinci Paintings: 8s, 13s, Annunciation (diff.). 25s, Adoration of the Kings. 35s, Lady with the Ermine. 50s, Mona Lisa.

1980, Oct. 10
2718 A1042 5s multicolored   .25 .25
2719 A1042 8s multicolored   .25 .25
2720 A1042 13s multicolored   .25 .25
2721 A1042 25s multicolored   .50 .25
2722 A1042 35s multicolored   .80 .25
  Nos. 2718-2722 (5)   2.05 1.25

Souvenir Sheet
Imperf
2723 A1042 50s multicolored   1.25 .40

International Peace Conference, Sofia — A1043

1980, Sept. 4   Photo.   Perf. 13
2724 A1043 25s multicolored   .45 .25

Yordan Yovkov (1880-1937), Writer — A1044

1980, Sept. 19
2725 A1044 5s multicolored   .25 .25

Se-tenant with label showing scene from Yovkov's work.

International Samples Fair, Plovdiv — A1045

1980, Sept. 24   Perf. 13½x13
2726 A1045 5s multicolored   .25 .25

On Oct. 1, 1980, a souvenir sheet containing one perf 13 50s stamp depicting a map of Europe and dove, was issued. Size: 80mmx80mm. Serially numbered. Value $30.

Blooming Cacti — A1045a

1980, Nov. 4   Photo.   Perf. 13
2726A A1045a 5s multicolored   .25 .25
2726B A1045a 13s multicolored   .25 .25
2726C A1045a 25s multicolored   .55 .25
2726D A1045a 35s multicolored   .85 .45
2726E A1045a 53s multicolored   1.75 .55
  Nos. 2726A-2726E (5)   3.65 1.75

Souvenir Sheet

25th Anniv. of Bulgarian UN Membership — A1045b

1980, Nov. 25
2726F A1045b 60s multicolored   2.50 2.00

World Ski Racing Championship, Velingrad — A1046

1981, Jan. 17   Photo.   Perf. 13
2727 A1046 43s multicolored   .85 .40

Hawthorn A1047

Designs: Medicinal herbs.

1981, Jan.
2728 A1047 3s shown   .25 .25
2729 A1047 5s St. John's wort   .25 .25
2730 A1047 13s Common elder   .35 .25
2731 A1047 25s Blackberries   .65 .25
2732 A1047 35s Lime   .85 .25
2733 A1047 43s Wild briar   1.25 .45
  Nos. 2728-2733 (6)   3.60 1.70

Slalom — A1048

1981, Feb. 27   Photo.   Perf. 13
2734 A1048 43s multicolored   .90 .40

Evian Alpine World Ski Cup Championship, Borovets.

Nuclear Traces, Research Institute — A1049

1981, Mar. 10   **Perf. 13½x13**
2735 A1049 13s gray & blk   .30   .25

Nuclear Research Institute, Dubna, USSR, 25th anniversary.

Congress Emblem — A1050

13s, Stars. 23s, Teletape.
50s, Demeter Blagoev, George Dimitrov.

1981, Mar. 12   **Perf. 13½**
2736 A1050   5s shown   .25   .25
2737 A1050 13s multicolored   .30   .25
2738 A1050 23s multicolored   .40   .30
    Nos. 2736-2738 (3)   .95   .80

Souvenir Sheet

2739 A1050 50s multicolored   1.00   .75

12th Bulgarian Communist Party Congress. Nos. 2736-2738 each printed se-tenant with label.

Paintings by Zachary Zograf — A1050a

1981, Mar. 23   Photo.   Perf. 12x12½
2739A A1050a   5s multicolored   .25   .25
2739B A1050a 13s multicolored   .40   .25
2739C A1050a 23s multicolored   .60   .25
2739D A1050a 25s multicolored   .75   .25
2739E A1050a 35s multicolored   1.10   .25
    Nos. 2739A-2739E (5)   3.10 1.25

Nos. 2739A-2739C are vert.

EXPO '81, Plovdiv — A1050b

1981, Apr. 7
2739F A1050b   5s multicolored   .25   .25
2739G A1050b   8s multicolored   .35   .25
2739H A1050b 13s multicolored   .50   .25
2739J A1050b 25s multicolored   1.20   .25
2739K A1050b 53s multicolored   2.25   .70
    Nos. 2739F-2739K (5)   4.55 1.70

Centenary of Bulgarian Shipbuilding — A1050c

35s, Georgi Dimitrov, liner. 43s, 5th from RMS, freighter. 53s, Khan Asparuch, tanker.

1981, Apr. 15   Photo.   Perf. 13
2739L A1050c 35s multi   .75   .25
2739M A1050c 43s multi   1.10   .25
2739N A1050c 53s multi   1.50   .35
    Nos. 2739L-2739N (3)   3.35   .85

On May 15, 1980, a souvenir sheet commemorating the 125th anniv. of the European Danube Commission was issued. It contains two 25s stamps depicting ships, perf 13, was issued. Size: 90mmx124mm. Serially numbered. Value $24.

A miniature sheet containing eight perf 13 35s stamps depicting ships, was issued Sept. 25, 1981. Size: 109mmx176mm. Value $24.

Arabian Horse A1051

Various breeds.

1980, Nov. 27   Litho.   Perf. 12½x12
2740 A1051   3s multicolored   .25   .25
2741 A1051   5s multicolored   .25   .25
2742 A1051 13s multicolored   .45   .25
2743 A1051 23s multicolored   1.20   .25
2744 A1051 35s multicolored   2.40   .25
    Nos. 2740-2744 (5)   4.55 1.25

Vassil Stoin, Ethnologist, Birth Centenary — A1052

1980, Dec. 5   Photo.   Perf. 13½x13
2745 A1052   5s multicolored   .25   .25

12th Bulgarian Communist Party Congress — A1052a

1980, Dec. 26   Photo.   Perf. 13x13½
2745A A1052a   5s Party symbols   .25   .25

New Year A1053

1980, Dec. 8   **Perf. 13**
2746 A1053   5s shown   .25   .25
2747 A1053 13s Cup, date   .25   .25

Culture Palace, Sofia A1053a

1981, Mar. 13   Photo.   Perf. 13
2747A A1053a   5s multicolored   .25   .25

Vienna Hofburg Palace A1054

1981, May 15   Photo.   Perf. 13
2748 A1054 35s multicolored   .75   .25

WIPA 1981 Intl. Philatelic Exhibition, Vienna, May 22-31.

34th Farmers' Union Congress — A1055

1981, May 18   **Perf. 13½**
2749 A1055   5s shown   .25   .25
2750 A1055   8s Flags   .25   .25
2751 A1055 13s Flags, diff.   .25   .25
    Nos. 2749-2751 (3)   .75   .75

Wild Cat — A1056

1981, May 27
2752 A1056   5s shown   .25   .25
2753 A1056 13s Boar   .35   .25
2754 A1056 23s Mouflon   .65   .30
2755 A1056 25s Mountain goat   .80   .40
2756 A1056 35s Stag   1.00   .40
2757 A1056 53s Roe deer   1.60   .65
    Nos. 2752-2757 (6)   4.65 2.25

Souvenir Sheet
Perf. 13½x13

2758 A1056   1 l Stag, diff.   2.00 1.50

EXPO '81 Intl. Hunting Exhibition, Plovdiv. Nos. 2752-2757 each se-tenant with labels showing various hunting rifles. No. 2758 contains one stamp, size: 48½x39mm.

25th Anniv. of UNESCO Membership A1057

1981, June 11   **Perf. 13**
2759 A1057 13s multicolored   .30   .25

Hotel Type of 1980

23s, Veliko Tirnovo Hotel.

1981, July 13   Photo.   Perf. 13
2766 A1038 23s multi   .45   .25

Flying Figure, Sculpture by Velichko Minekov — A1059

Bulgarian Social Democratic Party Buzludja Congress, 90th Anniv. (Minkov Sculpture): 13s, Advancing Female Figure.

1981, July 16   **Perf. 13½**
2767 A1059   5s multicolored   .25   .25
2768 A1059 13s multicolored   .25   .25

Kukeri, by Georg Tschapkanov A1060

1981, May 28   Photo.   Perf. 13
2769 A1060   5s multicolored   .25   .25

13th Natl. Festival of Humor and Satire.

Statistics Office Centenary A1061

1981, June 9
2770 A1061   5s multicolored   .25   .25

Gold Dish A1063

Designs: Goldsmiths' works, 7th-9th cent.

1981, July 21
2772 A1063   5s multicolored   .25   .25
2773 A1063 13s multicolored   .25   .25
2774 A1063 23s multicolored   .40   .25
2775 A1063 25s multicolored   .45   .35
2776 A1063 35s multicolored   .45   .40
2777 A1063 53s multicolored   1.25   .60
    Nos. 2772-2777 (6)   3.05 2.10

35th Anniv. of Frontier Force — A1064

1981, July 28   **Perf. 13½x13**
2778 A1064   5s multicolored   .25   .25

1300th Anniv. of First Bulgarian
State — A1065

Designs: No. 2779, Sts. Cyril and
Methodius. No. 2780, 9th cent. bas-relief. 8s,
Floor plan, Round Church, Preslav, 10th cent.
12s, Four Evangelists of King Ivan Alexander,
miniature, 1356. No. 2783, King Ivan Asen II
memorial column. No. 2784, Warriors on
horseback. 16s, April uprising, 1876. 23s,
Russian liberators, Tirnovo. 25s, Social Democratic Party founding, 1891. 35s, September
uprising, 1923. 41s, Fatherland Front. 43s,
Prime Minister George Dimitrov, 5th Communist Party Congress, 1948. 50s, Lion, 10th
cent. bas-relief. 53s, 10th Communist Party
Congress. 55s, Kremikovski Metalurgical
Plant. 1 l, Brezhnev, Gen. Todor Zhivkov.

1981, Aug. 10

2779	A1065	5s multicolored	.25	.25
2780	A1065	5s multicolored	.25	.25
2781	A1065	8s multicolored	.25	.25
2782	A1065	12s multicolored	.25	.25
2783	A1065	13s multicolored	.25	.25
2784	A1065	13s multicolored	.30	.25
2785	A1065	16s multicolored	.30	.25
2786	A1065	23s multicolored	.45	.25
2787	A1065	25s multicolored	.55	.25
2788	A1065	35s multicolored	.70	.25
2789	A1065	41s multicolored	.85	.45
2790	A1065	43s multicolored	1.00	.45
2791	A1065	53s multicolored	1.00	.50
2792	A1065	55s multicolored	1.00	.50
	Nos. 2779-2792 (14)		7.40	4.40

Souvenir Sheets

2793	A1065	50s multicolored	.90	.75
2794	A1065	1 l multicolored	2.00	1.50

European
Volleyball
Championship
A1066

1981, Sept. 16   *Perf. 13*
2795 A1066 13s multicolored   .30 .25

Pegasus, Bronze
Sculpture (Word
Day) — A1067

1981, Oct. 2
2796 A1067 5s olive & cream   .25 .25

World Food
Day — A1068

1981, Oct. 16
2797 A1068 13s multicolored   .30 .25

Professional
Theater
Centenary
A1069

1981, Oct. 30
2798 A1069 5s multicolored   .25 .25

Anti-Apartheid Year — A1070

1981, Dec. 2
2799 A1070 5s multicolored   .25 .25

Espana '82
World Cup
Soccer — A1071

Designs: Various soccer players.

1981, Dec.

2800	A1071	5s multicolored	.25	.25
2801	A1071	13s multicolored	.25	.25
2802	A1071	43s multicolored	.70	.25
2803	A1071	53s multicolored	.85	.35
	Nos. 2800-2803 (4)		2.05	1.10

Heritage
Day
A1072

1981, Nov. 21   Photo.   *Perf. 13*
2804 A1072 13s multicolored   .25 .25

Souvenir Sheet
2804A A1072 60s multicolored   4.00 1.90

Bagpipe — A1073

1982, Jan. 14

2805	A1073	13s shown	.25	.25
2806	A1073	25s Flutes	.40	.25
2807	A1073	30s Rebec	.50	.25
2808	A1073	35s Flute, recorder	.55	.25
2809	A1073	44s Mandolin	.75	.30
	Nos. 2805-2809 (5)		2.45	1.30

Public Libraries
and Reading
Rooms, 125th
Anniv — A1074

1982, Jan. 20
2810 A1074 5s dk grn   .25 .25

Souvenir Sheet

Intl. Decade for Women (1975-
1985) — A1075

1982, Mar. 8
2811 A1075 1 l multicolored   1.75 1.00

New Year
1982
A1076

1981, Dec. 22   Photo.   *Perf. 13*
2812 A1076 5s Ornament   .25 .25
2813 A1076 13s Ornament, diff.   .25 .25

The Sofia Plains, by Nicolas Petrov
(1881-1916) — A1077

13s, Girl Embroidering. 30s, Fields of
Peshtera.

1982, Feb. 10   *Perf. 12½*

2814	A1077	5s shown	.25	.25
2815	A1077	13s multicolored	.25	.25
2816	A1077	30s multicolored	.60	.25
	Nos. 2814-2816 (3)		1.10	.75

35th Anniv. of
UNICEF
(1981) — A1078

Mother and Child Paintings: No. 2817, Vladimir Dimitrov. No. 2818, Basil Stoilov. No.
2819, Ivan Milev. No. 2820, Liliana Russeva.

1982, Feb. 25   *Perf. 14*

2817	A1078	53s multi	1.00	.35
2818	A1078	53s multi	1.00	.35
2819	A1078	53s multi	1.00	.35
2820	A1078	53s multi	1.00	.35
	Nos. 2817-2820 (4)		4.00	1.40

Figures, by Vladamir Dimitrov (1882-
1961) — A1079

8s, Landscape. 13s, View of Istanbul. 25s,
Harvesters, vert. 30s, Woman in a Landscape,
vert. 35s, Peasant Woman, vert.
50s, Self-portrait.

1982, Mar. 8   Litho.

2821	A1079	5s shown	.25	.25
2822	A1079	8s multicolored	.25	.25
2823	A1079	13s multicolored	.35	.25
2824	A1079	25s multicolored	.40	.25
2825	A1079	30s multicolored	.40	.25
2826	A1079	35s multicolored	.75	.30
	Nos. 2821-2826 (6)		2.40	1.55

Souvenir Sheet
2827 A1079 50s multicolored   1.00 .75

No. 2827 contains one stamp, size:
54x32mm.

Trade Union Congress — A1080

No. 2828, Dimitrov reading union paper. No.
2829, Culture Palace.

1982, Apr. 8   Photo.   *Perf. 13½*
2828 A1080 5s multicolored   .25 .25
2829 A1080 5s multicolored   .25 .25

Nos. 2828-2829 se-tenant with label showing text.

Medicinal
Plants — A1081

3s, Marsh snowdrop. 5s, Chicory. 8s,
Chamaenerium angustifolium. 13s, Solomon's
seal. 25s, Violets. 35s, Centaury.

1982, Apr. 10   Photo.   *Perf. 13*
2830 A1081 3s shown   .25 .25
2831 A1081 5s multi   .25 .25
2832 A1081 8s multi   .25 .25

2833	A1081	13s multi	.35 .25
2834	A1081	25s multi	.65 .25
2835	A1081	35s multi	1.00 .35
	Nos. 2830-2835 (6)		2.75 1.60

Cosmonauts' Day — A1082

13s, Salyut-Soyuz link-up.

1982, Apr. 12   *Perf. 13½*
2836 A1082 13s multi   .25 .25

Se-tenant with label showing K.E. Tsiolkovsky (space pioneer).

Souvenir Sheet

SOZFILEX Stamp Exhibition — A1083

50s, Dimitrov, emblems.

1982, May 7   *Perf. 13*
2837 A1083 50s multi   2.25 1.25

     Exists imperf. Value, $60.

14th Komsomol Congress (Youth Communists) — A1084

1982, May 25
2838 A1084 5s multicolored   .25 .25

PHILEXFRANCE '82 Intl. Stamp Exhibition, Paris, June 11-21 — A1085

42s, France #1, Bulgaria #1.

1982, May 28
2839 A1085 42s multi   .75 .30

19th Cent. Fresco A1086

Designs: Various floral pattern frescoes.

1982, June 8   *Perf. 11½*
2840 A1086   5s red & multi   .25 .25
2841 A1086   13s green & multi   .25 .25
2842 A1086   25s violet & multi   .35 .25
2843 A1086   30s ol grn & multi   .45 .25
2844 A1086   42s blue & multi   .70 .30
2845 A1086   60s brown & multi   1.40 .45
    Nos. 2840-2845 (6)   3.40 1.75

Souvenir Sheet

George Dimitrov (1882-1949), First Prime Minister — A1087

1982, June 15   *Perf. 13*
2846 A1087 50s multicolored   1.00 .50

9th Congress of the National Front — A1088

1982, June 21   **Photo.**   *Perf. 13*
2847 A1088 5s Dimitrov   .25 .25

35th Anniv. of Balkan Bulgarian Airline — A1089

1982, June 28   *Perf. 13½x13*
2848 A1089 42s multicolored   .65 .50

Nuclear Disarmament A1090

1982, July 15   *Perf. 13*
2849 A1090 13s multicolored   .35 .25

A1091

1982, July   **Photo.**   *Perf. 13*
2850 A1091 5s multicolored   .25 .25
2851 A1091 13s multicolored   .25 .25

Souvenir Sheet
2852 A1091 1 l multicolored   1.50 .75

Ludmila Zhivkova (b. 1942), artist.

5th Congress of Bulgarian Painters — A1092

1982, July 27   *Perf. 13½*
2853 A1092 5s multicolored   .35 .25

   Se-tenant with label showing text.

Flag of Peace Youth Assembly — A1093

Various children's drawings. Frame & inscriptions: 3s, Concert. 5s, Ice Skating. 8s, Children. 13s, Two children celebrating holiday.
   50s, In hot air ballon, vert.

1982, Aug. 10   *Perf. 14*
2853A A1093 3s pink & multi   .25 .25
2853B A1093 5s blue & multi   .25 .25
2853C A1093 8s blue grn & multi   .25 .25
2853D A1093 13s bister & multi   .25 .25
   Nos. 2853A-2853D (4)   1.00 1.00

Souvenir Sheet
Perf. 14
2853E A1093 50s org & multi   1.50 .35
   a.   Imperf.   2.50 1.00

See Nos. 2864-2870, 3052-3058, 3321-3327.

10th Anniv. of UN Conference on Human Environment, Stockholm — A1093a

1982, Nov. 10   *Perf. 13*
2854 A1093a 13s dk blue & grn   .35 .35

A1094

Designs: No. 2855, Park Hotel Moskva, Sofia. No. 2856, Tchernomore, Varna.

1982, Oct. 20   **Photo.**   *Perf. 13*
2855 A1094 32s lt blue & multi   .60 .25
2856 A1094 32s pink & multi   .60 .25

Cruiser Aurora, Vostok I — A1095

1982, Nov. 4
2857 A1095 13s multicolored   .30 .25

   October Revolution, 65th anniv.

60th Anniv. of Institute of Communications A1096

1982, Dec. 9
2858 A1096 5s ultra   .30 .25

60th Anniv. of USSR A1097

1982, Dec. 9
2859 A1097 13s multicolored   .35 .35

The Piano, by Pablo Picasso (1881-1973) A1098

30s, Portrait of Jacqueline. 42s, Maternity. 1 l, Self-portrait.

     Perf. 11½x12½
1982, Dec. 24   *Litho.*
2860 A1098 13s shown   .40 .25
2861 A1098 30s multi   .40 .25
2862 A1098 42s multi   1.25 .45
   Nos. 2860-2862 (3)   2.05 .95

Souvenir Sheet
2863 A1098 1 l multi   2.00 .75

Children's Drawings Type of 1982

   Various children's drawings: 3s, Friends. 5s, Town. 8s, Fairy Tales, vert. 13s, Birds, vert. 25s, Women. 30s, Lion.
   50s, Shaking Hands, vert.

1982, Dec. 28   *Perf. 14*
2864 A1093 3s pale vio & multi   .25 .25
2865 A1093 5s org & multi   .25 .25
2866 A1093 8s blue grn & multi   .25 .25
2867 A1093 13s pink & multi   .25 .25
2868 A1093 25s bister & multi   .50 .25
2869 A1093 30s pale grn & multi   .60 .25
   Nos. 2864-2869 (6)   2.10 1.50

Souvenir Sheet
Perf. 14
2870 A1093 50s turq blue & multi   1.50 .35
   a.   Imperf.   2.00 .75

New Year
A1100

1982, Dec. 28   Photo.   Perf. 13
2872 A1100 5s multicolored   .25 .25
2873 A1100 13s multicolored   .25 .25

A1101

No. 2874, Robert Koch. No. 2875, Simon Bolivar. No. 2876, Rabindranath Tagore (1861-1941).

1982, Dec. 28
2874 A1101 25s multicolored   .45 .25
2875 A1101 30s multicolored   .45 .25
2876 A1101 30s multicolored   .45 .25
    Nos. 2874-2876 (3)   1.35 .75

No. 2874 also for TB bacillus cent.

A1102

1983, Feb. 10   Photo.   Perf. 13x13½
2877 A1102 5s olive & brown   .25 .25

Vassil Levski (1837-73), revolutionary.

Universiade Games — A1103

1983, Feb. 15   Perf. 13
2878 A1103 30s Downhill skiing   .60 .25

Fresh-water Fish — A1104

1983, Mar. 24   Photo.   Perf. 13½x13
2879 A1104 3s Pike   .25 .25
2880 A1104 5s Sturgeon   .25 .25
2881 A1104 13s Chub   .25 .25
2882 A1104 25s Perch   .55 .25
2883 A1104 30s Catfish   .60 .25
2884 A1104 42s Trout   1.50 .55
    Nos. 2879-2884 (6)   3.40 1.80

Karl Marx (1818-1883)
A1105

1983, Apr. 5   Perf. 13x13½
2885 A1105 13s multicolored   .30 .25

Jaroslav Hasek (1883-1923) — A1106

1983, Apr. 20   Photo.   Perf. 13
2886 A1106 13s multicolored   .30 .25

Martin Luther (1483-1546)
A1107

1983, May 10
2887 A1107 13s multicolored   .45 .25

55th Anniv. of Komsomol Youth Movement — A1108

1983, May 13
2888 A1108 5s "PMC"   .25 .25

National Costumes
A1109

1983, May 17   Litho.   Perf. 14
2889 A1109 5s Khaskovo   .25 .25
2890 A1109 8s Pernik   .25 .25
2891 A1109 13s Burgas   .25 .25
2892 A1109 25s Tolbukhin   .55 .25
2893 A1109 30s Blagoevgrad .60 .25
2894 A1109 42s Topolovgrad 1.60 .25
    Nos. 2889-2894 (6)   3.50 1.50

A1111

6th Intl. Satire and Humor Biennial, Gabrovo: Old Man Feeding Chickens.

1983, May 20
2900 A1111 5s multicolored   .25 .25

Christo Smirnensky (1898-1983), Poet — A1112

1983, May 25
2901 A1112 5s multicolored   .25 .25

17th Intl. Geodesists' Congress
A1113

1983, May 27
2902 A1113 30s Emblem   .50 .25

Interarch '83 Architecture Exhibition, Sofia — A1114

1983, June 6
2903 A1114 30s multicolored .60 .25

8th European Chess Championships, Plovdiv
A1115

13s, Chess pieces, map of Europe.

1983, June 20   Photo.   Perf. 13
2904 A1115 13s multi   .35 .25

Souvenir Sheet

BRASILIANA '83 Philatelic Exhibition — A1116

Brazilian and Bulgarian stamps

1983, June 24
2905 A1116 1 l multicolored 1.75 1.25

Social Democratic Party Congress of Russia, 80th Anniv. — A1118

Design: Lenin addressing congress.

1983, July 29   Photo.   Perf. 13
2907 A1118 5s multicolored   .25 .25

Ilinden-Preobrazhensky Insurrection, 80th Anniv. — A1119

5s, Gun, dagger, book.

1983, July 29
2908 A1119 5s multi   .25 .25

Institute of Mining and Geology, Sofia, 30th Anniv. — A1120

1983, Aug. 10
2909 A1120 5s multicolored   .25 .25

60th Anniv. of September 1923 Uprising — A1121

1983, Aug. 19
2910 A1121 5s multicolored   .25 .25
2911 A1121 13s multicolored .25 .25

Angora Cat
A1123

1983, Sept. 26   Perf. 13
2917 A1123 5s shown   .25 .25
2918 A1123 13s Siamese   .35 .25
2919 A1123 20s Abyssinian, vert. .45 .25
2920 A1123 25s Persian   .65 .25
2921 A1123 30s European, vert.   .80 .45
2922 A1123 42s Indochinese 1.25 .55
    Nos. 2917-2922 (6)   3.75 2.00

Animated Film Festival — A1124

1983, Sept. 15 Photo. Perf. 14x13½
2923 A1124 5s Articulation layout .25 .25

Trevethick's Engine, 1804 — A1125

Locomotives: 13s, Blenkinsop's Prince Royal, 1810. 42s, Hedley's Puffing Billy, 1812. 60s, Adler (first German locomotive), 1835.

1983, Oct. 20 Perf. 13
2924 A1125 5s multicolored .25 .25
2925 A1125 13s multicolored .35 .25
2926 A1125 42s multicolored 1.40 .70
2927 A1125 60s multicolored 2.40 .80
Nos. 2924-2927 (4) 4.40 2.00
See Nos. 2983-2987.

Souvenir Sheet

Liberation Monument, Plovdiv — A1126

1983, Nov. 4
2928 A1126 50s multicolored 1.00 .75
Philatelic Federation, 90th anniv.

Sofia Opera, 75th Anniv. — A1127

1983, Dec. 2 Perf. 13x13½
2929 A1127 5s Mask, lyre, laurel .25 .25

Composers' Assoc., 50th Anniv. — A1128

Composers: 5s, Ioan Kukuzel (14th cent.) 8s, Atanasov. 13s, Petko Stainov. 20s, Veselin Stodiov. 25s, Liubomir Pipkov. 30s, Pancho Vladigerov. Se-tenant with labels showing compositions.

1983, Dec. 5
2930 A1128 5s multicolored .25 .25
2931 A1128 8s multicolored .25 .25
2932 A1128 13s multicolored .25 .25
2933 A1128 20s multicolored .35 .25
2934 A1128 25s multicolored .35 .25
2935 A1128 30s multicolored .45 .30
Nos. 2930-2935 (6) 1.90 1.55

New Year 1984 A1129

1983, Dec. 10 Perf. 13
2936 A1129 5s multicolored .25 .25

Angelo Donni, by Raphael A1130

13s, Cardinal. 30s, Baldassare Castiglioni. 42s, Donna Belata. 1 l, Sistine Madonna.

1983, Dec. 22 Perf. 14
2937 A1130 5s shown .25 .25
2938 A1130 13s multicolored .25 .25
2939 A1130 30s multicolored .45 .25
2940 A1130 42s multicolored .70 .30
Nos. 2937-2940 (4) 1.65 1.05

Souvenir Sheet
2941 A1130 1 l multicolored 1.75 1.25

Bat, World Wildlife Emblem — A1131

Various bats and rodents.

1983, Dec. 30 Perf. 13
2942 A1131 12s multicolored .35 .25
2943 A1131 13s multicolored .50 .25
2944 A1131 20s multicolored .80 .25
2945 A1131 30s multicolored 1.25 .25
2946 A1131 42s multicolored 2.50 .50
Nos. 2942-2946 (5) 5.40 1.50

Dmitri Mendeleev (1834-1907), Russian Chemist — A1132

1984, Mar. 14
2947 A1132 13s multicolored .30 .25

Ljuben Karavelov, Poet and Freedom Fighter, Birth Sesquicentenary A1133

1984, Jan. 31
2948 A1133 5s multicolored .25 .25

Tanker Gen. V.I. Zaimov A1137

13s, Mesta. 25s, Veleka. 32s, Ferry. 42s, Cargo ship Rossen.

1984, Mar. 22 Perf. 13½
2959 A1137 5s shown .25 .25
2960 A1137 13s multi .30 .25
2961 A1137 25s multi .55 .25
2962 A1137 32s multi .55 .25
2963 A1137 42s multi 1.10 .35
Nos. 2959-2963 (5) 2.75 1.35

Souvenir Sheet

World Cup Soccer Commemorative of 1982, Spain No. 2281 — A1137a

1984, Apr. 18 Photo. Perf. 13x13½
2963A A1137a 2 l multicolored 5.00 4.00
ESPANA '84.

Dove with Letter over Globe — A1138

1984, Apr. 24 Perf. 13
2964 A1138 5s multicolored .25 .25
World Youth Stamp Exhibition, Pleven, Oct. 5-11.

Berries — A1139

1984, May 5
2965 A1139 5s Cherries .25 .25
2966 A1139 8s Strawberries .25 .25
2967 A1139 13s Blackberries .25 .25
2968 A1139 20s Raspberries .40 .25
2969 A1139 42s Currants 1.20 .30
Nos. 2965-2969 (5) 2.35 1.30

Athlete, Doves — A1140

1984, May 23
2970 A1140 13s multicolored .35 .35
6th Republican Spartikiade games,

Folk Singer, Drum — A1142

1984, June 12
2972 A1142 5s multicolored .25 .25
6th amateur art festival.

Bulgarian-Soviet Relations, 50th Anniv. — A1143

1984, June 27
2973 A1143 13s Initialed seal .30 .25

Doves and Pigeons A1144

1984, July 6 Litho. Perf. 14
2974 A1144 5s Rock dove .25 .25
2975 A1144 13s Stock dove .25 .25
2976 A1144 20s Wood pigeon .40 .25
2977 A1144 30s Turtle dove .65 .25
2978 A1144 42s Domestic pigeon .85 .35
Nos. 2974-2978 (5) 2.40 1.35

1st Natl. Communist Party Congress, 60th Anniv. — A1145

1984, May 18 Photo. Perf. 13½x13
2979 A1145 5s multicolored .25 .25

Souvenir Sheet

Intl. Stamp Exhibition, Essen, May 26-31 — A1146

Europa Conf. stamps: a, 1980. b, 1981.

1984, May 22   **Perf. 13x13½**
2980 A1146   Sheet of 2   6.00 5.00
a.-b.   1.50 l multi   3.00 2.50

Mount Everest
A1147

1984, May 31   **Perf. 13**
2981 A1147 5s multicolored   .25 .25

1st Bulgarian Everest climbing expedition, Apr. 20-May 9.

Souvenir Sheet

UPU Congress, Hamburg — A1148

1984, June 11   **Perf. 13½x13**
2982 A1148   3 l Sailing ship   5.00 4.00

Locomotives Type of 1983

13s, Best Friend of Charleston, 1830, US. 25s, Saxonia, 1836, Dresden. 30s, Lafayette, 1837, US. 42s, Borsig, 1841, Germany. 60s, Philadelphia, 1843, Austria.

1984, July 31   **Perf. 13**
2983 A1125 13s multicolored   .25 .25
2984 A1125 25s multicolored   .45 .25
2985 A1125 30s multicolored   .60 .25
2986 A1125 42s multicolored   .85 .35
2987 A1125 60s multicolored   1.40 .50
    Nos. 2983-2987 (5)   3.55 1.60

September 9 Revolution, 40th Anniv. — A1149

5s, K, production quality emblem. 20s, Victory Monument, Sofia. 30s, Star, "9".

1984, Aug. 4
2988 A1149 5s multicolored   .25 .25
2989 A1149 20s multicolored   .40 .25
2990 A1149 30s multicolored   .60 .45
    Nos. 2988-2990 (3)   1.25 .95

Paintings by Nenko Balkanski (1907-1977) — A1150

5s, Boy Playing Harmonica, vert. 30s, A Paris Window, vert. 42s, Double Portrait. 1 l, Self-portrait, vert.

1984, Sept. 17   **Perf. 14**
2991 A1150 5s multicolored   .25 .25
2992 A1150 30s multicolored   .60 .25
2993 A1150 42s multicolored   1.10 .35
    Nos. 2991-2993 (3)   1.95 .85
Souvenir Sheet
2994 A1150   1 l multicolored   1.75 1.25

MLADPOST '84 International Youth Stamp Exhibition, Pleven — A1151

Buildings in Pleven: 5s, Mausoleum to Russian soldiers, 1877-78 Russo-Turkish War. 13s, Panorama Building.

1984, Sept. 20   **Perf. 13**
2995 A1151 5s multicolored   .25 .25
2996 A1151 13s multicolored   .30 .25

Septembrist Young Pioneers Org., 40th Anniv. — A1152

1984, Sept. 21   Photo.   Perf. 13
2997 A1152 5s multicolored   .25 .25

Nikola Vapzarov A1153

1984, Oct. 2
2998 A1153 5s mar & pale yel   .25 .25

Natl. Soccer, 75th Anniv. A1154

1984, Oct. 3
2999 A1154 42s multicolored   .75 .35

Souvenir Sheet

MLADPOST '84 — A1155

1984, Oct. 5   Photo.   Perf. 13
3000 A1155 50s multicolored   .90 .50

Bridges and Maps — A1156

5s, Devil's Bridge, Arda River. 13s, Koljo-Fitscheto, Bjala. 30s, Asparuchow, Warna. 42s, Bebresch Highway Bridge, Botevgrad. 1 l, Bridge of Friendship, Russia.

1984, Oct. 5   Photo.   Perf. 13½x13
3001 A1156 5s multicolored   .25 .25
3002 A1156 13s multicolored   .40 .25
3003 A1156 30s multicolored   .60 .55
3004 A1156 42s multicolored   1.40 .75
    Nos. 3001-3004 (4)   2.65 1.80
Souvenir Sheet
3005 A1156   1 l multicolored   5.25 2.50

Intl. Olympic Committee, 90th Anniv. — A1158

1984, Oct. 24   Photo.   Perf. 13
3007 A1158 13s multicolored   .30 .25

Pelecanus Crispus A1159

1984, Nov. 2
3008 A1159 5s Adult, young   .35 .25
3009 A1159 13s Two adults   .70 .30
3010 A1159 20s Adult in water   1.10 .70
3011 A1159 32s In flight   2.50 1.00
    Nos. 3008-3011 (4)   4.65 2.25
    World Wildlife Fund.

A1160

1984, Nov. 2
3012 A1160 5s multicolored   .25 .25

Anton Ivanov (1884-1942), labor leader.

Women's Socialist Movement, 70th Anniv. — A1161

1984, Nov. 9
3013 A1161 5s multicolored   .25 .25

Telecommunication Towers — A1162

1984, Nov. 23
3014 A1162 5s Snezhanka   .25 .25
3015 A1162 1 l Orelek   1.60 .75

Snowflakes, New Year 1985 — A1163

5s, Doves, posthorns. 13s, Doves, blossom.

1984, Dec. 5
3016 A1163 5s multicolored   .25 .25
3017 A1163 13s multicolored   .25 .25

Paintings by Stoyan Venev (b. 1904) — A1164

5s, September Nights. 30s, Man with Three Medals. 42s, The Best.

1984, Dec. 10   **Litho.**
3018 A1164 5s multicolored   .25 .25
3019 A1164 30s multicolored   .65 .30
3020 A1164 42s multicolored   1.00 .35
    Nos. 3018-3020 (3)   1.90 .90

Butterflies
A1165

13s, Inachis io. 25s, Papilio machaon. 30s, Brintesia circe. 42s, Anthocaris cardamines. 60s, Vanessa atalanta. 1 l, Limenitis populi.

1984, Dec. 14   *Perf. 11½*
3021	A1165	13s multicolored	.25	.25
3022	A1165	25s multicolored	.45	.25
3023	A1165	30s multicolored	.60	.30
3024	A1165	42s multicolored	.85	.35
3025	A1165	60s multicolored	1.50	.50
		Nos. 3021-3025 (5)	3.65	1.65

Souvenir Sheet
3026	A1165	1 l multicolored	1.50	.75

A1166

1984, Dec. 18   Photo.   *Perf. 13x13½*
3027	A1166	13s multicolored	.30	.25

Cesar Augusto Sandino (1895-1934), Nicaraguan freedom fighter.

A1167

5s, The Three Graces. 13s, Cupid and the Graces. 30s, Original Sin. 42s, La Fornarina. 1 l, Galatea.

1984, Dec. 28   Litho.   *Perf. 14*
3028	A1167	5s multicolored	.25	.25
3029	A1167	13s multicolored	.35	.25
3030	A1167	30s multicolored	.70	.35
3031	A1167	42s multicolored	1.00	.50
		Nos. 3028-3031 (4)	2.30	1.35

Souvenir Sheet
3032	A1167	1 l multicolored	1.75	1.00

Raphael, 500th birth anniv. (1983).

Cruise Ship Sofia, Maiden Voyage — A1168

1984, Dec. 29   Photo.   *Perf. 13*
3033	A1168	13s blue, dk bl & yel	.30	.25

Predators A1170

13s, Conepatus leuconotus. 25s, Prionodon linsang. 30s, Ictonix striatus. 42s, Hemigalus derbyanus. 60s, Galidictis fasciata.

1985, Jan. 17
3035	A1170	13s multicolored	.25	.25
3036	A1170	25s multicolored	.45	.25
3037	A1170	30s multicolored	.55	.25
3038	A1170	42s multicolored	.80	.35
3039	A1170	60s multicolored	1.25	.60
		Nos. 3035-3039 (5)	3.30	1.70

Nikolai Liliev (1885-1960), Poet, UNESCO Emblem — A1171

1985, Jan. 25
3040	A1171	30s multicolored	.50	.30

Zviatko Radojnov (1895-1942), Labor Leader — A1172

1985, Jan. 29
3041	A1172	5s dk red & dk brn	.25	.25

Dr. Assen Zlatarov (1885-1936), Chemist A1173

1985, Feb. 14
3042	A1173	5s multicolored	.25	.25

Souvenir Sheet

Akademik, Research Vessel — A1174

1985, Mar. 1
3043	A1174	80s multicolored	1.50	1.00

UNESCO Intl. Oceanographic Commission, 25th anniv.

Souvenir Sheet

Lenin — A1175

1985, Mar. 12
3044	A1175	50s multicolored	.85	.65

A1176

1985, Mar. 19
3045	A1176	13s multicolored	.25	.25

Warsaw Treaty Org., 30th anniv.

Composers A1177

1985, Mar. 25
3046	A1177	42s Bach	.90	.45
3047	A1177	42s Mozart	.90	.45
3048	A1177	42s Tchaikovsky	.90	.45
3049	A1177	42s Mussorgsky	.90	.45
3050	A1177	42s Verdi	.90	.45
3051	A1177	42s Kutev	.90	.45
		Nos. 3046-3051 (6)	5.40	2.70

Children's Drawings Type of 1982

Various children's drawings: 5s, Girl with bird and rooster. 8s, Children painting. 13s, Girl, bird & flowers. 20s, Two adults, three children. 25s, People with join hands around the globe. 30s, Nurse with stethoscope.
50s, Children dancing, vert.

1985, Mar. 26   Litho.   *Perf. 14*
3052	A1093	5s red & multi	.25	.25
3053	A1093	8s blue & multi	.25	.25
3054	A1093	13s bister & multi	.25	.25
3055	A1093	20s pale vio & multi	.35	.25
3056	A1093	25s blue grn & multi	.45	.25
3057	A1093	30s ochre & multi	.50	.30
		Nos. 3052-3057 (6)	2.05	1.55

Souvenir Sheet
3058	A1093	50s pale grn & multi	1.50	.75

Inscribed 1985. 3rd Flag of Peace Intl. Assembly, Sofia.
No. 3058 exists imperf. with blue control number, same value.

St. Methodius, 1100th Death Anniv. — A1179

1985, Apr. 6   Photo.   *Perf. 13*
3059	A1179	13s multicolored	.50	.25

Victory Parade, Moscow, 1945 — A1180

13s, 11th Infantry on parade, Sofia. 30s, Soviet soldier, orphan. 50s, Soviet flag-raising, Berlin.

1985, Apr. 30   *Perf. 13½*
3060	A1180	5s multicolored	.25	.25
3061	A1180	13s multicolored	.25	.25
3062	A1180	30s multicolored	.60	.25
		Nos. 3060-3062 (3)	1.10	.75

Souvenir Sheet
Perf. 13
3063	A1180	50s multicolored	1.10	.50

Defeat of Nazi Germany, end of World War II, 40th anniv. Nos. 3060-3062 printed se-tenant with labels picturing Soviet (5s, 30s) and Bulgarian medals of honor.

7th Intl. Humor and Satire Biennial — A1181

1985, Apr. 30   *Perf. 13½*
3064	A1181	13s yel, sage grn & red	.25	.25

No. 3064 printed se-tenant with label picturing Gabrovo Cat emblem.

Intl. Youth Year — A1182

1985, May 21   *Perf. 13*
3065	A1182	13s multicolored	.25	.25

Ivan Vazov
(1850-1921),
Poet — A1183

1985, May 30   **Perf. 13½**
3066 A1183 5s tan & sepia   .25   .25
No. 3066 printed se-tenant with label picturing Vasov's birthplace in Sopot.

Soviet
War
Memorial,
Haskovo
City Arms
A1184

1985, June 1   **Perf. 13**
3067 A1184 5s multicolored   .25   .25
Haskovo millennium.

12th World Youth
Festival,
Moscow — A1185

1985, June 25
3068 A1185 13s multicolored   .25   .25

Indira Gandhi (1917-1984), Prime
Minister of India — A1186

1985, June 26
3069 A1186 30s org yel, sep &
      ver   .50   .25

Vasil Aprilov,
Founder — A1187

1985, June 30
3070 A1187 5s multicolored   .25   .25
1st secular school, Gabrovo, 150th anniv.

INTERSTENO '85 — A1188

1985, June 30
3071 A1188 13s multicolored   .25   .25
Congress for the Intl. Union of Stenographers and Typists, Sofia.

Alexander
Nevski
Cathedral
A1189

1985, July 9
3072 A1189 42s multicolored   .65   .35
World Tourism Org., general assembly, Sofia.

UN, 40th
Anniv.
A1190

1985, July 16
3073 A1190 13s multicolored   .25   .25

A1191

1985, July 16
3074 A1191 13s multicolored   .25   .25
Admission of Bulgaria to UN, 30th anniv.

Roses — A1192

5s, Rosa damascena. 13s, Rosa trakijka. 20s, Rosa radiman. 30s, Rosa marista. 42s, Rosa valentina. 60s, Rosa maria.

1985, July 20   **Litho.**
3075 A1192 5s multi   .25   .25
3076 A1192 13s multi   .25   .25
3077 A1192 20s multi   .35   .25
3078 A1192 30s multi   .40   .25
3079 A1192 42s multi   .65   .30
3080 A1192 60s multi   1.00   .35
    a.   Min. sheet of 6, #3075-3080   3.00   2.00
    Nos. 3075-3080 (6)   2.90   1.65

Helsinki Conference, 10th
Anniv. — A1193

1985, Aug. 1   **Photo.**
3081 A1193 13s multicolored   .35   .25

European Swimming Championships,
Sofia — A1194

5s, Butterfly stroke. 13s, Water polo, vert. 42s, Diving, vert. 60s, Synchronized swimming.

1985, Aug. 2   **Litho.**   **Perf. 12½**
3082 A1194 5s multi   .25   .25
3083 A1194 13s multi   .25   .25
3084 A1194 42s multi   .85   .35
3085 A1194 60s multi   1.40   .35
    Nos. 3082-3085 (4)   2.75   1.20

The 60s exists with central design inverted.

Natl.
Tourism
Assoc.,
90th
Anniv.
A1195

1985, Aug. 15   **Photo.**   **Perf. 13**
3086 A1195 5s multicolored   .25   .25

1986 World Cup
Soccer
Championships,
Mexico
A1196

Various soccer plays.

1985, Aug. 29   **Perf. 13**
3087 A1196 5s multicolored   .25   .25
3088 A1196 13s multicolored   .25   .25
3089 A1196 30s multicolored   .55   .25
3090 A1196 42s multicolored   .30   .45
    Nos. 3087-3090 (4)   1.35   1.20

Souvenir Sheet
3091 A1196 1 l multi, horiz.   1.75   1.00

Union of Eastern
Rumelia and
Bulgaria,
1885 — A1197

1985, Aug. 29   **Perf. 14x13½**
3092 A1197 5s multicolored   .25   .25

Computer Design Portraits — A1198

1985, Sept. 23   **Perf. 13**
3093 A1198 5s Boy   .25   .25
3094 A1198 13s Youth   .25   .25
3095 A1198 30s Cosmonaut   .50   .30
    Nos. 3093-3095 (3)   1.00   .80

Intl. Exhibition of the Works of Youth Inventors, Plovdiv.

St. John the
Baptist Church,
Nessebar
A1199

Natl. restoration projects: 13s, Tyrant Hreljo Tower, Rila Monastery. 35s, Soldier, fresco, Ivanovo Rock Church. 42s, Archangel Gabriel, fresco, Bojana Church. 60s, Thracian Woman, fresco, Tomb of Kasanlak, 3rd century B.C. 1 l, The Horseman of Madara, bas-relief.

1985, Sept. 25   **Litho.**   **Perf. 12½**
3096 A1199 5s multicolored   .25   .25
3097 A1199 13s multicolored   .25   .25
3098 A1199 35s multicolored   .65   .30
3099 A1199 42s multicolored   .80   .35
3100 A1199 60s multicolored   1.25   .35
    Nos. 3096-3100 (5)   3.20   1.50

Souvenir Sheet
Imperf
3101 A1199 1 l multicolored   1.75   .90

UNESCO, 40th anniv.

Souvenir Sheet

Ludmila Zhishkova Cultural Palace,
Sofia — A1200

1985, Oct. 8   **Perf. 13**
3102 A1200 1 l multicolored   1.60   1.00
UNESCO 23rd General Assembly, Sofia.

Colosseum, Rome — A1201

1985, Oct. 15   Photo.   Perf. 13½
3103 A1201 42s multicolored   .50   .25
ITALIA '85. No. 3103 printed se-tenant with label picturing the exhibition emblem.

Souvenir Sheet

Cultural Congress, Budapest — A1202

Designs: No. 3104a, St. Cyril, patron saint of Europe. No. 3104b, Map of Europe. No. 3104c, St. Methodius, patron saint of Europe.

Perf. 13, 13 Vert. (#3104b)
1985, Oct. 22   Photo.
3104 A1202 Sheet of 3   2.00   1.25
a.-c.   50s, any single   .65   .40
Helsinki Congress, 10th anniv.
Exists imperf with serial number. Value $27.50.

Flowers — A1203

No. 3105, Gladiolus hybridy. No. 3106, Iris germanica. No. 3107, Convolvulus tricolor.

1985, Oct. 22   Photo.   Perf. 13x13½
3105 A1203 5s rose & rose car   .25   .25
3106 A1203 5s gray blue & dk
             blue   .25   .25
3107 A1203 5s pale vio & vio   .25   .25
      Nos. 3105-3107 (3)   .75   .75
See Nos. 3184-3186.

Historic Sailing Ships A1204

5s, Dutch. 12s, Sea Sovereign, Britain. 20s, Mediterranean. 25s, Royal Prince, Britain. 42s, Mediterranean. 60s, British battleship.

1985, Oct. 28   Photo.   Perf. 13
3108 A1204 5s multicolored   .25   .25
3109 A1204 12s multicolored   .25   .25
3110 A1204 20s multicolored   .30   .25
3111 A1204 25s multicolored   .40   .25
3112 A1204 42s multicolored   .75   .40
3113 A1204 60s multicolored   1.25   .45
      Nos. 3108-3113 (6)   3.20   1.85

Souvenir Sheet

PHILATELIA '85, Cologne — A1205

Designs: a, Cologne Cathedral. b, Alexander Nevski Cathedral, Sofia.

1985, Nov. 4   Imperf.
3114 A1205 Sheet of 2   1.00   .50
a.-b.   30s, any single   .45   .25

Conspiracy to Liberate Bulgaria from Turkish Rule, 150th Anniv. — A1206

Freedom fighters and symbols: No. 3115, Georgi Stojkov Rakowski (1820-76). No. 3116, Batscho Kiro (1835-76). No. 3117, Sword, Bible & hands.

1985, Nov. 6   Perf. 13
3115 A1206 5s multicolored   .25   .25
3116 A1206 5s multicolored   .25   .25
3117 A1206 13s multicolored   .25   .25
      Nos. 3115-3117 (3)   .75   .75

Liberation from Byzantine Rule, 800th Anniv. — A1207

Paintings: 5s, The Revolt 1185, by G. Bogdanov. 13s, The Revolt 1185, by Alexander Tersiev. 30s, Battle Near Klokotnitza, by B. Grigorov and M. Ganowski. 42s, Velika Tarnovo Town Wall, by Zanko Lawrenov. 1 l, St. Dimitriev Church, 12th cent.

1985, Nov. 15   Litho.
3118 A1207 5s multicolored   .25   .25
3119 A1207 13s multicolored   .30   .25
3120 A1207 30s multicolored   .35   .25
3121 A1207 42s multicolored   .35   .55
      Nos. 3118-3121 (4)   1.25   1.30

Souvenir Sheet
Imperf
3122 A1207 1 l multicolored   1.60   .80

Souvenir Sheet

BALKANPHILA '85 — A1208

1985, Nov. 29   Photo.   Perf. 13
3123 A1208 40s Dove, posthorn   .75   .50

Intl. Post and Telecommunications Development Program — A1209

1985, Dec. 2
3124 A1209 13s multicolored   .25   .25

Anton Popov (1915-1942), Freedom Fighter — A1210

1985, Dec. 11   Photo.   Perf. 13
3125 A1210 5s lake   .25   .25

New Year 1986 A1211

5s, Doves, snowflake. 13s, Doves.

1985, Dec. 11   Photo.   Perf. 13
3126 A1211 5s multi   .25   .25
3127 A1211 13s multi   .25   .25

Hunting Dogs and Prey — A1212

5s, Pointer, partridge. 8s, Irish setter, pochard. 13s, English setter, mallard. 20s, Cocker spaniel, woodcock. 25s, German pointer, rabbit. 30s, Balkan hound, boar. 42s, Shorthaired dachshund, fox.

1985, Dec. 27   Litho.   Perf. 13x12½
3128 A1212 5s multicolored   .25   .25
3129 A1212 8s multicolored   .25   .25
3130 A1212 13s multicolored   .25   .25
3131 A1212 20s multicolored   .25   .25
3132 A1212 25s multicolored   .40   .25
3133 A1212 30s multicolored   .55   .25
3134 A1212 42s multicolored   1.10   .35
      Nos. 3128-3134 (7)   3.05   1.85

Intl. Year of the Handicapped — A1213

1985, Dec. 30   Photo.   Perf. 13
3135 A1213 5s multicolored   .25   .25

George Dimitrov (1882-1949) — A1214

1985, Dec. 30   Photo.   Perf. 13
3136 A1214 13s brn lake   .30   .25
7th Intl. Communist Congress, Moscow.

UN Child Survival Campaign — A1215

1986, Jan. 21   Photo.   Perf. 13
3137 A1215 13s multicolored   .30   .25
UNICEF, 40th anniv.

Demeter Blagoev (1856-1924) A1216

1986, Jan. 28   Photo.   Perf. 13
3138 A1216 5s dk lake, car & dk
             red   .25   .25

Intl. Peace Year A1217

1986, Jan. 31   Perf. 13½
3139 A1217 5s multicolored   .25   .25

Orchids — A1218

5s, Dactylorhiza romana. 13s, Epipactis palustris. 30s, Ophrys cornuta. 32s, Limodorum abortivum. 42s, Cypripedium calceolus. 60s, Orchis papilionacea.

1986, Feb. 12   Litho.   Perf. 13x12½
3140 A1218 5s multicolored   .25   .25
3141 A1218 13s multicolored   .25   .25
3142 A1218 30s multicolored   .30   .25
3143 A1218 32s multicolored   .35   .25
3144 A1218 42s multicolored   .55   .25
3145 A1218 60s multicolored   1.10   .25
a.   Min. sheet of 6, #3140-3145   2.75   1.25
      Nos. 3140-3145 (6)   2.80   1.50
Nos. 3140-3145 exist imperf. Value, $7.50.

Hares and
Rabbits
A1219

1986, Feb. 24   *Perf. 12½x12*
3146 A1219 5s multicolored .25 .25
3147 A1219 25s multicolored .45 .25
3148 A1219 30s multicolored .50 .25
3149 A1219 32s multicolored .55 .25
3150 A1219 42s multicolored .70 .25
3151 A1219 60s multicolored .75 .25
Nos. 3146-3151 (6) 3.20 1.50

Exist imperf. Value, set $8.

Bulgarian Eagle, Newspaper, 140th
Anniv. — A1220

Front page of 1st issue & Ivan Bogorov,
journalist.

1986, Feb. 2   **Photo.**   *Perf. 13*
3152 A1220 5s multicolored .25 .25

Souvenir Sheet

Halley's Comet — A1221

Comet's orbit in the Solar System: a, 1980.
b, 1910-86. c, 1916-70. d, 1911.

1986, Mar. 7   *Perf. 13½x13*
3153 A1221 Sheet of 4 1.50 1.10
a.-d. 25s, any single .35 .25

Exists imperf. Value $15.

A1222

1986, Mar. 12   *Perf. 13x13½*
3154 A1222 5s dp bl & bl .25 .25

Vladimir Bachev (1935-1967), poet.

A1223

1986, Mar. 17   *Perf. 13*
3155 A1223 5s Wavy lines .25 .25
3156 A1223 8s Star .25 .25
3157 A1223 13s Worker .25 .25
Nos. 3155-3157 (3) .75 .75

Souvenir Sheet
Imperf
3158 A1223 50s Scaffold, flags .60 .40
13th Natl. Communist Party Congress.

Souvenir Sheet

1st Manned Space Flight, 25th
Anniv. — A1224

Designs: a, Vostok I, 1961. b, Yuri Gagarin
(1934-68), Russian cosmonaut.

1986, Mar. 28   *Perf. 13½x13*
3159 A1224 Sheet of 2 1.25 1.00
a.-b. 50s, any single .60 .50

Exists imperf. Value $12.

April Uprising
against the Turks,
110th
Anniv. — A1225

Monuments: 5s, 1876 Uprising monument,
Panagjuriste. 13s, Christo Botev, Vraca.

1986, Mar. 30   *Perf. 13*
3160 A1225 5s multicolored .25 .25
3161 A1225 13s multicolored .25 .25

A1225a

Levsky-Spartak Sports Club, 75th
Anniv. — A1226

50s, Rhythmic gymnastics.

1986   *Perf. 13*
3161A A1225a 5s multicolored .25 .25
Souvenir Sheet
Imperf
3162 A1226 50s multicolored .60 .40
Issue dates: 5s, Dec. 50s, May 12.

A1227

5s, Congress emblem. 8s, Emblem on
globe. 13s, Flags.

1986, May 19   *Perf. 13*
3163 A1227 5s multicolored .25 .25
3164 A1227 8s multicolored .25 .25
3165 A1227 13s multicolored .25 .25
Nos. 3163-3165 (3) .75 .75

35th Congress of Bulgarian farmers, Sofia.

A1228

1986, May 27   *Perf. 13x13½*
3166 A1228 13s multicolored .25 .25

Conference of Transport Ministers from
Socialist Countries.

17th Intl. Book
Fair,
Sofia — A1229

1986, May 28
3167 A1229 13s blk, brt red &
grysh blk .25 .25

1986 World Cup Soccer
Championships, Mexico — A1230

Various soccer plays; attached labels picture Mexican landmarks.

1986, May 30   *Perf. 13½*
3168 A1230 5s multi, vert. .25 .25
3169 A1230 13s multicolored .25 .25
3170 A1230 20s multicolored .30 .25
3171 A1230 30s multicolored .50 .25
3172 A1230 42s multicolored .70 .25
3173 A1230 60s multi, vert. 1.40 .25
Nos. 3168-3173 (6) 3.40 1.50
Souvenir Sheet
Perf. 13
3174 A1230 1 l Azteca Stadium 1.25 .75
Exist imperf. Value: set $6; souvenir sheet
$10.

Treasures of Preslav — A1231

Gold artifacts: 5s, Embossed brooch. 13s,
Pendant with pearl cross, vert. 20s, Crystal
and pearl pendant. 30s, Embossed shield.
42s, Pearl and enamel pendant, vert. 60s,
Enamel shield.

1986, June 7   *Perf. 13½x13, 13x13½*
3175 A1231 5s multicolored .25 .25
3176 A1231 13s multicolored .25 .25
3177 A1231 20s multicolored .30 .25
3178 A1231 30s multicolored .50 .25
3179 A1231 42s multicolored .70 .30
3180 A1231 60s multicolored .70 .30
Nos. 3175-3180 (6) 2.70 1.60

World Fencing Championships, Sofia,
July 25-Aug. 3 — A1232

1986, July 25   **Photo.**   *Perf. 13*
3181 A1232 5s Head cut, lunge .25 .25
3182 A1232 13s Touche .25 .25
3183 A1232 25s Lunge, parry .45 .25
Nos. 3181-3183 (3) .95 .75

Flower Type of 1985

No. 3184, Ipomoea tricolor. No. 1385,
Anemone coronaria. No. 1386, Lilium
auratum.

1986, July 29   *Perf. 13x13½*
3184 A1203 8s multi .25 .25
3185 A1203 8s multi .25 .25
3186 A1203 32s multi .45 .25
Nos. 3184-3186 (3) .95 .75

A1233

1986, Aug. 25
3187 A1233 42s sepia, sal brn &
lake .45 .30

STOCKHOLMIA '86. No. 3187 printed in
sheets of 3 + 3 labels picturing folk art.

Miniature Sheet

A1234

Environmental Conservation: a, Ciconia
ciconia. b, Nuphar lutea. c, Salamandra salamandra. d, Nymphaea alba.

1986, Aug. 25   **Litho.**   *Perf. 14*
3188 A1234 Sheet of 4 + label 3.00 2.50
a.-d. 30s any single .50 .35

No. 3188 is a miniature sheet containing a
center label picturing the oldest oak tree in
Bulgaria, Granit Village.
Exists imperf. Value $14.

Natl. Arms, Building of the
Sobranie — A1235

1986, Sept. 13   Photo.   Perf. 13
3189 A1235 5s Prus grn, yel grn
     & red   .25   .25

People's Republic of Bulgaria, 40th anniv.

15th Postal Union Congress — A1236

1986, Sept. 24
3190 A1236 13s multicolored   .25   .25

Natl. Youth
Brigade
Movement, 40th
Anniv. — A1237

1986, Oct. 4
3191 A1237 5s multicolored   .25   .25

Intl. Organization
of Journalists,
10th Congress
A1238

1986, Oct. 13
3192 A1238 13s blue & dark blue .25 .25

Sts. Cyril and Methodius,
Disciples — A1239

1986, Oct. 28   Perf. 13½
3193 A1239 13s dark brown &
     buff   .25   .25

Sts. Cyril and Methodius in Bulgaria, 1100th
anniv. No. 3193 se-tenant with inscribed label.

Telephones in Bulgaria,
Cent. — A1240

1986, Nov. 5   Perf. 13
3194 A1240 5s multicolored   .25   .25

World Weight Lifting
Championships — A1241

1986, Nov. 6
3195 A1241 13s multicolored   .25   .25

Ships
A1242

5s, King of Prussia. 13s, East Indiaman,
18th cent. 25s, Shebek, 18th cent. 30s, St
Paul. 32s, Topsail schooner, 18th cent. 42s,
Victory.

1986, Nov. 20
3196 A1242 5s multicolored   .25   .25
3197 A1242 13s multicolored   .25   .25
3198 A1242 25s multicolored   .35   .25
3199 A1242 30s multicolored   .35   .25
3200 A1242 50s multicolored   .50   .30
3201 A1242 42s multicolored   1.10   .40
    Nos. 3196-3201 (6)   2.80   1.70

European Security and Cooperation
Congress, Vienna — A1243

Various buildings and emblems: a, Bulgaria.
b, Austria. c, Donau Park, UN.

Perf. 13, Imperf. x13 (#3202b)
1986, Nov. 27
3202 A1243 Souvenir sheet of 3 2.75 1.25
 a.-c.   50s any single   .75   .40

Exists imperf. bearing control number. Value
$22.50.

Rogozen
Thracian
Pitchers
A1244

1986, Dec. 5   Perf. 13
3203 A1244 10s Facing left   .25   .25
3204 A1244 10s Facing right   .25   .25
 a.   Block, #3203-3204 + 2 labels .65 .65

Union of Bulgarian Philatelists, 14th
Congress.
Exist imperf. Value, block $1.

New Year
1987
A1245

1986, Dec. 9
3205 A1245 5s shown   .25   .25
3206 A1245 13s Snow flakes   .25   .25

Home Amateur Radio Operators in
Bulgaria, 60th Anniv. — A1246

1986, Dec. 10
3207 A1246 13s multicolored   .25   .25

Miniature Sheet

Paintings by Bulgarian
Artists — A1247

a, Red Tree, by Danail Dechev (1891-1962).
b, Troopers Confront Two Men, by Ilya
Beshkov (1901-58). c, View of Melnik, by
Veselin Stajkov (1906-70). d, View of Houses
through Trees, by Kyril Zonev (1896-1961).

1986, Dec. 10   Litho.   Perf. 14
3208 A1247 Sheet of 4   1.75   1.00
 a.-b.   25s any single   .40   .25
 c.-d.   30s any single   .45   .30

Sofia Academy of Art, 90th anniv.

Augusto Cesar Sandino (1893-1934),
Nicaraguan Revolutionary, and
Flag — A1248

1986, Dec. 16   Photo.   Perf. 13
3209 A1248 13s multicolored   .25   .25
Sandinista movement in Nicaragua, 25th
anniv.

Smoyan
Mihylovsky
(b. 1856),
Writer — A1249

Ran Bossilek
(b. 1886)
A1250

Title Page from
Bulgarian
Folk
Songs of the
Miladinov
Brothers — A1251

Annivs. and events: No. 3211, Pentcho
Slaveyckov (b. 1861), writer. No. 3212, Nickola
Atanassov (b. 1886), musician.

1986, Dec. 17
3210 A1249 5s multicolored   .25   .25
3211 A1249 5s multicolored   .25   .25
3212 A1249 8s multicolored   .25   .25
3213 A1250 8s multicolored   .25   .25
3214 A1251 10s multicolored   .25   .25
    Nos. 3210-3214 (5)   1.25   1.25

Paintings by
Titian — A1252

A1253

Various portraits.

1986, Dec. 23   Litho.   Perf. 14
3215 A1252 5s multicolored   .25   .25
3216 A1252 13s multicolored   .25   .25
3217 A1252 20s multicolored   .30   .25
3218 A1252 30s multicolored   .35   .25
3219 A1252 32s multicolored   .55   .25
3220 A1252 42s multicolored   .90   .30
 a.   Min. sheet of 6, #3215-3220 2.25 1.25
    Nos. 3215-3220 (6)   2.60   1.55

Souvenir Sheet
3221 A1253 1 l multicolored   2.00   .75

Rayko Daskalov
(b. 1886),
Politician
A1254

1986, Dec. 23   Photo.   Perf. 13
3222 A1254 5s deep claret   .25   .25

Sports Cars — A1255

742 BULGARIA

1986, Dec. 30   Litho.   Perf. 13½

3223	A1255	5s 1905 Fiat	.25	.25
3224	A1255	10s 1928 Bugatti	.25	.25
3225	A1255	25s 1936 Mercedes	.35	.25
3226	A1255	32s 1952 Ferrari	.45	.25
3227	A1255	40s 1985 Lotus	.55	.30
3228	A1255	42s 1986 McLaren	.90	.30
	Nos. 3223-3228 (6)		2.75	1.60

Varna Railway Inauguration, 120th Anniv. — A1257

1987, Jan. 19   Photo.   Perf. 13½

3229	A1257	5s multicolored	.25	.25
a.		Perf. 11	.40	.40

Dimcho Debelianov (1887-1916), Poet — A1258

1987, Jan. 20   Photo.   Perf. 13

3230	A1258	5s blue, dull yel & dp blue	.25	.25

L.L. Zamenhof, Creator of Esperanto — A1259

1987, Feb. 12

3231	A1259	13s multicolored	.25	.25

Mushrooms A1260

5s, Amanita rubescens. 20s, Boletus regius. 30s, Leccinum aurantiacum. 32s, Coprinus comatus. 40s, Russula vesca. 60s, Cantharellus cibarius.

1987, Feb. 6   Litho.   Perf. 11½

3232	A1260	5s multicolored	.25	.25
3233	A1260	20s multicolored	.25	.25
3234	A1260	30s multicolored	.25	.25
3235	A1260	32s multicolored	.35	.25
3236	A1260	40s multicolored	.45	.25
3237	A1260	60s multicolored	.55	.35
a.		Min. sheet of 6, #3232-3237	2.50	2.50
	Nos. 3232-3237 (6)		2.10	1.60

10th Natl. Trade Unions Congress A1261

1987, Mar. 20   Photo.   Perf. 13

3238	A1261	5s dark red & violet	.25	.25

Rogozen Thracian Treasure A1262

Embossed and gilded silver artifacts: 5s, Plate, Priestess Auge approaching Heracles. 8s, Pitcher, lioness attacking stag. 20s, Plate, floral pattern. 30s, Pitcher, warriors on horseback dueling. 32s, Urn, decorative pattern. 42s, Pitcher (not gilded), winged horses.

1987, Mar. 31

3239	A1262	5s multicolored	.25	.25
3240	A1262	8s multicolored	.25	.25
3241	A1262	20s multicolored	.25	.25
3242	A1262	30s multicolored	.25	.25
3243	A1262	32s multicolored	.35	.25
3244	A1262	42s multicolored	.45	.25
	Nos. 3239-3244 (6)		1.80	1.50

Miniature Sheet

Modern Architecture — A1263

Designs: a, Ludmila Zhivkova conf. center, Varna. b, Ministry of Foreign Affairs, Sofia. c, Interpred Building, Sofia. d, Hotel, Sandanski.

1987, Apr. 7   Perf. 13½x13

3245	A1263	Sheet of 4	1.50	1.00
a.-d.		30s any single	.35	.25

Exists imperf. with black control number. Value $12.

European Freestyle Wrestling Championships A1264

1987, Apr. 22   Perf. 13

3246	A1264	5s multicolored	.25	.25
3247	A1264	13s multi, diff.	.25	.25

CAPEX '87, Toronto A1265

1987, Apr. 24

3248	A1265	42s multicolored	.60	.30

10th Congress of the Natl. Front — A1266

1987, May 11

3249	A1266	5s multicolored	.25	.25

15th Communist Youth Congress — A1267

1987, May 13

3250	A1267	5s George Dimitrov	.25	.25

8th Intl. Humor and Satire Biennial, Gabrovo — A1268

1987, May 15   Perf. 13x13½

3251	A1268	13s multicolored	.25	.25

13th World Rhythmic Gymnastics Championships, Varna — A1269

Gymnasts: 5s, Maria Gigova. 8s, Iliana Raeva. 13s, Anelia Ralenkova. 25s, Pilyana Georgieva. 30s, Lilia Ignatova. 42s, Bianca Panova.
1 l, Neshka Robeva, coach.

1987, Aug. 5   Photo.   Perf. 13

3252	A1269	5s multicolored	.25	.25
3252A	A1269	8s multicolored	.25	.25
3252B	A1269	13s multicolored	.25	.25
3252C	A1269	25s multicolored	.35	.25
3252D	A1269	30s multicolored	.45	.25
3252E	A1269	42s multicolored	.55	.25
	Nos. 3252-3252E (6)		2.10	1.50

Souvenir Sheet
Perf. 13x13½

3252F	A1269	1 l multi	1.50	1.25

Exists imperf. with black control number. Value $7.

Vassil Kolarov — A1270

1987, June 3   Perf. 13

3253	A1270	5s dk red, yel & dk bl	.25	.25

Stela Blagoeva (b. 1887) — A1271

1987, June 4

3254	A1271	5s pink & sepia	.25	.25

Rabotnichesko Delo Newspaper, 60th Anniv. — A1272

1987, May 28

3255	A1272	5s black & lake	.25	.25

Deer A1273

5s, Capreolus capreolus, vert. 10s, Alces alces. 32s, Dama dama, vert. 40s, Cervus nippon, vert. 42s, Cervus elaphus. 60s, Rangifer tarandus, vert.

1987, June 23   Litho.

3256	A1273	5s multicolored	.25	.25
3257	A1273	10s multicolored	.25	.25
3258	A1273	32s multicolored	.45	.25
3259	A1273	40s multicolored	.50	.25
3260	A1273	42s multicolored	.55	.30
3261	A1273	60s multicolored	.80	.35
a.		Min. sheet, #3256-3261, imperf	3.00	2.50
	Nos. 3256-3261 (6)		2.80	1.65

Vassil Levski (1837-73) A1274

Various portraits.

1987, June 19   Photo.

3262	A1274	5s red brn & dark grn	.25	.25
3263	A1274	13s dark grn & red brn	.25	.25

Namibia Day A1275

1987, July 8

3264	A1275	13s org, blk & dark red	.25	.25

Georgi Kirkov
(1867-1919),
Revolutionary
A1276

1987, July 17   *Perf. 13x13½*
3265 A1276 5s clar & dp clar .25 .25

Bees and
Plants — A1277

5s, Phacelia tanacetifolia. 10s, Helianthus annuus. 30s, Robinia pseudoacacia. 32s, Lavandula vera. 42s, Tilia parvifolia. 60s, Onobrychis sativa.

1987, July 29   **Litho.**   *Perf. 13*
3266	A1277	5s multicolored	.25	.25
3267	A1277	10s multicolored	.25	.25
3268	A1277	30s multicolored	.35	.25
3269	A1277	32s multicolored	.35	.25
3270	A1277	42s multicolored	.50	.30
3271	A1277	60s multicolored	.70	.35
a.		Min. sheet of 6, #3266-3271	2.50	2.00
		Nos. 3266-3271 (6)	2.40	1.65

BULGARIA '89 — A1278

1987, Sept. 3   *Perf. 13½x13*
3272 A1278 13s No. 1 .25 .25

HAFNIA
'87 — A1279

1987, Sept. 8   *Perf. 13*
3273 A1279 42s multicolored .45 .25

No. 3273 issued in sheets of 3 plus 2 labels picturing emblems of the HAFNIA '87 and BULGARIA '89 exhibitions, and 1 label with background similar to Denmark Type A32 with castle instead of denomination.

Portrait of a Girl,
by Stefan
Ivanov — A1280

Paintings in the Sofia City Art Galler: 8s, Grape-gatherer, by Bencho Obreshkov. 20s, Portrait of a Lady with a Hat, by David Perets. 25s, Listeners of Marimba, by Kiril Tsonev.

32s, Boy with an Harmonica, by Nenko Balkanski. 60s, Rumyana, by Vasil Stoilov.

1987, Sept. 15   **Litho.**   *Perf. 14*
3274	A1280	5s shown	.25	.25
3275	A1280	8s multicolored	.25	.25
3276	A1280	20s multicolored	.25	.25
3277	A1280	25s multicolored	.30	.25
3278	A1280	32s multicolored	.35	.25
3279	A1280	60s multicolored	.80	.25
		Nos. 3274-3279 (6)	2.20	1.50

Intl. Atomic
Energy
Agency,
30th Anniv.
A1281

1987, Sept. 15 Photo.   *Perf. 13½x13*
3280 A1281 13s red, lt blue & emer .25 .25

Songbirds
A1282

5s, Troglodytes troglodytes. 13s, Emberiza citrinella. 20s, Sitta europaea. 30s, Turdus merula. 42s, Coccothraustes coccothraustes. 60s, Cinclus cinclus.

1987, Oct. 12   **Litho.**   *Perf. 12½x12*
3281	A1282	5s multicolored	.25	.25
3282	A1282	13s multicolored	.25	.25
3283	A1282	20s multicolored	.30	.25
3284	A1282	30s multicolored	.45	.25
3285	A1282	42s multicolored	.65	.30
3286	A1282	60s multicolored	.90	.35
a.		Min. sheet of 6, #3281-3286	3.00	2.00
		Nos. 3281-3286 (6)	2.80	1.65

Balkan
War,
75th
Anniv.
A1283

1987, Sept. 15   **Photo.**   *Perf. 13½*
3287 A1283 5s buff, blk & brt org .25 .25

Newspaper Anniversaries — A1283a

1987, Sept. 24   **Photo.**   *Perf. 13*
3287A A1283a 5s multicolored .25 .25

Rabotnik, 95th anniv.; Rabotnicheski Vstnik, 90th anniv. and Rabotnichesko Delo, 60th anniv.

October Revolution, Russia, 70th
Anniv. — A1284

Lenin and: 5s, Revolutionary. 13s, Cosmonaut.

1987, Oct. 27   **Photo.**   *Perf. 13*
3288 A1284 5s rose brn & red org .25 .25
3289 A1284 13s brt ultra & red org .25 .25

1988 Winter
Olympics,
Calgary
A1285

5s, Biathlon. 13s, Slalom. 30s, Women's figure skating. 42s, 4-Man bobsled. 1 l, Ice hockey.

1987, Oct. 27   **Litho.**   *Perf. 13x13½*
3290	A1285	5s multi	.25	.25
3291	A1285	13s multi	.25	.25
3292	A1285	30s multi	.35	.25
3293	A1285	42s multi	.50	.35
		Nos. 3290-3293 (4)	1.35	1.10

Souvenir Sheet
3294 A1285 1 l multi 1.50 1.25

No. 3294 exists imperf. Value $7.

Souvenir Sheet

Soviet Space Achievements, 1957-
87 — A1286

Designs: No. 3295a, Vega probe. No. 3295b, Mir-Soyuz Space Station.

1987, Dec. 24   **Photo.**   *Perf. 13½x13*
3295 A1286 Sheet of 2 2.00 1.50
a.-b.   50s any single 1.25 .75

Exists imperf. Value $12.

New Year
1988
A1287

Sofia stamp exhibition emblem within folklore patterns.

1987, Dec. 25   *Perf. 13*
3296 A1287 5s multicolored .25 .25
3297 A1287 13s multi, diff. .25 .25

Souvenir Sheet

European Security
Conferences — A1288

Conferences held in Helsinki, 1973, and Vienna, 1987: a, Helsinki Conf. Center. b, Map of Europe. c, Vienna Conf. Center.

Perf. 13x13½ on 2 or 4 Sides
1987, Dec. 30
3298 A1288 Sheet of 3 3.00 2.50
a.-c.   50s any single 1.00 .75

Exists imperf. Value $14.

A1289

1988, Jan. 20
3299 A1289 5s multicolored .25 .25

Christo Kabaktchiev (b. 1878), party leader.

Marine Flowers
A1290

5s, Scilla bythynica. 10s, Geum rhodopaeum. 13s, Caltha polypetala. 25s, Nymphoides peltata. 30s, Cortusa matthioli. 42s, Stratiotes aloides.

1988, Jan. 25   **Litho.**   *Perf. 12*
3300	A1290	5s multicolored	.25	.25
3301	A1290	10s multicolored	.25	.25
3302	A1290	13s multicolored	.25	.25
3303	A1290	25s multicolored	.25	.25
3304	A1290	30s multicolored	.40	.25
3305	A1290	42s multicolored	.60	.45
a.		Min. sheet of 6, #3300-3305	1.75	1.50
		Nos. 3300-3305 (6)	2.00	1.70

Liberation
of
Bulgaria,
110th
Anniv.
A1291

1988, Feb. 15   **Photo.**   *Perf. 13*
3306 A1291 5s Officer, horse .25 .25
3307 A1291 13s Soldiers .25 .25

8th Intl. Civil Servants Congress,
Sofia — A1292

1988, Mar. 22   **Photo.**   *Perf. 13*
3308 A1292 13s multicolored .25 .25

State Railways, Cent. — A1293

Locomotives: 5s, Jantra, 1888. 13s, Christo Botev, 1905. 25s, 0-10-1, 1918. 32s, 4-12-1 heavy duty, 1943. 42s, Diesel, 1964. 60s, Electric, 1979.

1988, Mar. 25   Litho.   *Perf. 11*
3309 A1293 5s multicolored   .25   .25
3310 A1293 13s multicolored   .25   .25
3311 A1293 25s multicolored   .35   .25
3312 A1293 32s multicolored   .45   .25
3313 A1293 42s multicolored   .55   .30
3314 A1293 60s multicolored   .90   .35
a.   Min. sheet of 6, #3309-3314   3.00   1.75
Nos. 3309-3314 (6)   2.75   1.65

Ivan
Nedyalkov
(1880-1925)
A1294

Postal workers, heroes of socialism: 8s, Delcho Spasov (1918-43). 10s, Nikola Ganchev (1915-43). 13s, Ganka Stoyanova Rasheva (1921-44).

1988, Mar. 31   Photo.   *Perf. 13½x13*
3315 A1294 5s buff & dk rose
                    brn   .25   .25
3316 A1294 8s pale ultra & vio
                    blue   .25   .25
3317 A1294 10s pale ol grn & ol
                    grn   .25   .25
3318 A1294 13s pale pink & lake   .25   .25
Nos. 3315-3318 (4)   1.00   1.00

Georgi Traikov (b.
1898), Statesman
A1295

1988, Apr. 8   Litho.   *Perf. 13x13½*
3319 A1295 5s orange & brn   .25   .25

Intl. Red Cross
and Red Crescent
Organizations,
125th
Annivs. — A1296

1988, Apr. 26   Photo.   *Perf. 13*
3320 A1296 13s multicolored   .25   .25

Children's Drawings Type of 1982

Designs: 5s, Girl wearing a folk costume, vert. 8s, Painter at easel, vert. 13s, Children watching clown. 20s, Children releasing doves. 32s, Melodica player, vert. 42s, Cosmonaut, vert. 50s, Assembly emblem.

1988, Apr. 28   Litho.   *Perf. 14*
3321 A1093 5s pink & multi   .25   .25
3322 A1093 8s blue grn & multi   .25   .25
3323 A1093 13s red & multi   .25   .25
3324 A1093 20s apple grn &
                    multi   .30   .25
3325 A1093 32s blue & multi   .40   .25
3326 A1093 42s pale vio & multi   .50   .25
Nos. 3321-3326 (6)   1.95   1.50

Souvenir Sheet

3327 A1093 50s red & multi   1.00   .50

4th Intl. Children's Assembly, Sofia.
No. 3327 exists imperf. Value $2.50.

Karl
Marx
A1297

1988, May 5   *Perf. 13*
3328 A1297 13s multicolored   .25   .25

Birds — A1297a

Designs: No. 3328A, Ciconia ciconia. No. 3328B, Larus argentatus. No. 3328C, Ardea cinerea. No. 3328D, Corvus corone cornix. 10s, Accipiter gentilis. 42s, Bubo bubo.

1988, May 6   Litho.   *Perf. 13x13½*
3328A A1297a 5s multicolored   .25   .25
3328B A1297a 7s multicolored   .25   .25
3328C A1297a 8s multicolored   .25   .25
3328D A1297a 9s multicolored   .25   .25
3328E A1297a 10s multicolored   .40   .25
3328F A1297a 42s multicolored   1.20   .30
Nos. 3328A-3328F (6)   2.60   1.55

Dated 1987.

Sofia
Zoo
A1298

5s, Loxodonta africana. 13s, Ceratotherium simum. 25s, Lycaon pictus. 30s, Pelecanus onocrotalus. 32s, Bucorvus abissinicus. 42s, Nyctea scandiaca.

1988, May 20
3329 A1298 5s multicolored   .25   .25
3330 A1298 13s multicolored   .25   .25
3331 A1298 25s multicolored   .35   .25
3332 A1298 30s multicolored   .45   .25
3333 A1298 32s multicolored   .50   .25
3334 A1298 42s multicolored   .65   .25
a.   Min. sheet of 6, #3329-3334   2.50   1.50
Nos. 3329-3334 (6)   2.45   1.50

FINLANDIA '88 — A1299

1988, June 7
3335 A1299 30s Finland No. 1   .50   .35

No. 3335 printed in miniature sheets of 3 plus 3 labels picturing skyline, SOFIA '89 and FINLANDIA '88 exhibition emblems.
Exists imperf. Value $.90

2nd Joint USSR-
Bulgaria Space
Flight — A1300

1988, June 7
3336 A1300 5s shown   .25   .25
3337 A1300 13s Rocket, globe   .25   .25

EXPO '91, Plovdiv — A1301

1988, June 7   *Perf. 13½x13*
3338 A1301 13s multicolored   .25   .25

1988 European Soccer
Championships — A1302

5s, Corner kick. 13s, Heading the ball. 30s, Referee, player. 42s, Player holding trophy. 1 l, Stadium.

1988, June 10   *Perf. 13*
3339 A1302 5s multi   .25   .25
3340 A1302 13s multi   .25   .25
3341 A1302 30s multi   .40   .25
3342 A1302 42s multi   .55   .25
Nos. 3339-3342 (4)   1.45   1.00

Souvenir Sheet

3343 A1302 1 l multi   1.25   1.00

No. 3343 exists imperf. Value $12.50.

Paintings by
Dechko Usunov
(1899-1986)
A1303

Designs: 5s, Portrait of a Young Girl. 13s, Portrait of Maria Wassilewa. 30s, Self-portrait.

1988, June 14   *Perf. 13x13½*
3344 A1303 5s multicolored   .25   .25
3345 A1303 13s multicolored   .25   .25
3346 A1303 30s multicolored   .40   .25
Nos. 3344-3346 (3)   .90   .75

Souvenir Sheet

1st Woman in Space, 25th
Anniv. — A1304

1988, June 16   *Perf. 13½x13*
3347 A1304 1 l multicolored   1.50   1.00

Valentina Tereshkova's flight, June 16-19, 1963.
Exists imperf. Value $12.50.

Kurdzhali
Region
Religious
Art — A1305

Designs: 5s, St. John the Baptist, 1592. 8s, St. George Slaying the Dragon, 1841.

1988, June 27   *Perf. 13x13½*
3348 A1305 5s multicolored   .25   .25
3349 A1305 8s multicolored   .25   .25

1988 Summer
Olympics,
Seoul — A1306

5s, High jump. 13s, Weight lifting. 30s, Greco-Roman wrestling. 42s, Rhythmic gymnastics. 1 l, Volleyball.

1988, July 25   Litho.   *Perf. 13*
3350 A1306 5s multicolored   .25   .25
3351 A1306 13s multicolored   .25   .25
3352 A1306 30s multicolored   .35   .25
3353 A1306 42s multicolored   .55   .25
Nos. 3350-3353 (4)   1.40   1.00

Souvenir Sheet

3354 A1306 1 l multicolored   1.50   1.00

No. 3354 exists imperf. Value $12.50.

Dimitr
and
Karaja
A1307

1988, July 25   Litho.   *Perf. 13*
3355 A1307 5s blk, dark olive
                    bister & grn   .25   .25

120th anniv. of the deaths of Haji Dimitr and Stefan Karaja, patriots killed during the Balkan Wars.

Problems of Peace and Socialism,
30th Anniv. — A1308

1988, July 26   Photo.
3356 A1308 13s multicolored   .25   .25

Paintings in the Ludmila Zhivkova Art Gallery A1309

Paintings: No. 3357, Harbor, Algiers, by Albert Marquet (1875-1947). No. 3358, Portrait of Hermine David in the Studio, by Jules Pascin (1885-1930). No. 3359, Madonna with Child and Sts. Sebastian and Rocco, by Giovanni Rosso (1494-1540). No. 3360, The Barren Tree, by Roland Oudot (1879-1982).

1988, July 27	Litho.	Perf. 14	
3357 A1309	30s multicolored	.35	.25
3358 A1309	30s multicolored	.35	.25
3359 A1309	30s multicolored	.35	.25
3360 A1309	30s multicolored	.35	.25
Nos. 3357-3360 (4)		1.40	1.00

St. Clement of Ohrid University, Sofia, 100th Anniv. — A1310

1988, Aug. 22		Perf. 13	
3361 A1310	5s blk & pale yel	.25	.25

PRAGA '88 A1311

25s, Czechoslovakia #2 in vermilion.

1988, Aug. 22			
3362 A1311	25s multi	.40	.30

Printed in miniature sheets of 3 plus 3 labels picturing skyline, PRAGA '88 and SOFIA '89 exhibition emblems.
Exists imperf.

OLYMPHILEX '88 — A1312

1988, Sept. 1			
3363 A1312	62s Korea No. 1	1.25	.75

Printed in miniature sheets of 3 plus 3 labels picturing skyline, OLYMPHILEX '88 and SOFIA '89 exhibition emblems.

Exists imperf.

A1313

1988, Sept. 15			
3364 A1313	5s dp bl, lt bl & red	.25	.25

Kremikovtsi steel mill, 25th anniv.

A1314

1988, Sept. 16	Perf. 13½x13		
3365 A1314	13s dark red & ultra	.25	.25

80th Interparliamentary Conference.

Transportation Commission 80th Congress — A1315

1988, Oct. 17			
3366 A1315	13s deep lil rose & blk	.25	.25

Kurdzhali Region Artifacts A1316

5s, Earthenware bowl, 13th-14th cent. 8s, Medieval fortification, Gorna Krepost Village, vert.

1988, Sept. 20		Perf. 13	
3367 A1316	5s multicolored	.25	.25
3368 A1316	8s multicolored	.25	.25

Chiprovo Uprising, 300th Anniv. — A1317

1988, Sept. 23			
3369 A1317	5s multicolored	.25	.25

Bears A1318

Designs: 5s, Ursus arctos. 8s, Thalassarctos maritimus. 13s, Melursus ursinus. 20s, Helarctos malayanus. 32s, Selenarctos thibetanus. 42s, Tremarctos ornatus.

1988, Sept. 26		Perf. 12½	
3370 A1318	5s multicolored	.25	.25
3371 A1318	8s multicolored	.25	.25
3372 A1318	13s multicolored	.25	.25
3373 A1318	20s multicolored	.30	.25
3374 A1318	32s multicolored	.45	.25
3375 A1318	42s multicolored	.70	.25
a.	Min. sheet of 6, #3370-3375	2.00	1.50
Nos. 3370-3375 (6)		2.20	1.50

ECOFORUM for Peace — A1319

1988, Oct. 29		Perf. 13	
3376 A1319	20s multicolored	.30	.25

PLOVDIV '88 — A1320

Design: Amphitheater ruins, PRAGA '88 and PLOVDIV '88 emblems.

1988, Nov. 2			
3377 A1320	5s multicolored	.25	.25

Exists in imperf. sheet of six.

Radio & Television Authority, 25th Anniv. — A1321

1988, Nov. 17	Litho.	Perf. 13	
3378 A1321	5s multicolored	.25	.25

BULGARIA '89 — A1321a

1988, Nov. 22	Litho.	Perf. 13	
3379 A1321a	42s No. 1	.50	.45

Printed in miniature sheets of 3+3 labels picturing exhib. emblem and conf. center.
Exists imperf.

Danube Cruise Excursion Industry, 40th Anniv. — A1321b

1988, Nov. 25		Perf. 13½x13	
3380 A1321b	Sheet of 2	2.50	2.00
a.	1 l Russia	1.25	1.00
b.	1 l Aleksandr Stamboliski	1.25	1.00

Exists imperf. Value $18.

Traffic Safety — A1321c

1988, Nov. 28			
3381 A1321c	5s multicolored	.25	.25

New Year 1989 — A1321d

1988, Dec. 20		Perf. 13	
3382 A1321d	5s shown	.25	.25
3383 A1321d	13s multi, diff.	.25	.25

Hotels in Winter A1322

1988, Dec. 19	Litho.	Perf. 13½x13	
3384 A1322	5s shown	.25	.25
3385 A1322	8s multi, diff.	.25	.25
3386 A1322	13s multi, diff.	.25	.25
3387 A1322	30s multi, diff.	.30	.25
Nos. 3384-3387 (4)		1.05	1.00

Souvenir Sheet

Soviet Space Shuttle Energija-Buran A1322a

1988, Dec. 28		Perf. 13½x13	
3387A A1322a	1 l dark blue	1.50	1.00

Exists imperf. Value $12.50.

BULGARIA '89 — A1322b

Traditional modes of postal conveyance.

1988, Dec. 29		Perf. 13½x13	
3387B A1322b	25s Mail coach	.35	.25
3387C A1322b	25s Biplane	.35	.25
3387D A1322b	25s Truck	.35	.25
3387E A1322b	25s Steam packet	.35	.25
Nos. 3387B-3387E (4)		1.40	1.00

Philatelic Exhibitions — A1323

1989 **Litho.** *Perf. 13*
3388 A1323 42s France No. 1 .75 .60
3389 A1323 62s India No. 200 .75 .60
BULGARIA '89 and PHILEXFRANCE '89 (42s) or INDIA '89 (62s).
Nos. 3388-3389 each printed in sheets of 3 + 3 labels picturing skylines, BULGARIA '89 and PHILEXFRANCE or INDIA exhibition labels. Exist in sheets of 4 also. Exist imperf. Issue dates: 42s, Feb. 23; 62s, Jan. 14.

Souvenir Sheet

Universiade Winter Games, Sofia — A1324

Designs: a, Downhill skiing. b, Ice hockey. c, Cross-country skiing. d, Speed skating.

1989, Jan. 30 **Litho.** *Imperf.*
Simulated Perforations
3390 A1324 Sheet of 4 1.50 .75
a.-d. 25s multicolored .35 .25
No. 3390 exists imperf. without simulated perforations and containing black control number. Value $12.

Humor and Satire Festival, Gabrovo A1325

1989, Feb. 7 *Perf. 13½x13*
3391 A1325 13s Don Quixote .25 .25

Endangered Plant Species — A1326

Designs: 5s, Ramonda serbica. 10s, Paeonia maskula. 25s, Viola perinensis. 30s, Dracunculus vulgaris. 42s, Tulipa splendens. 60s, Rindera umbellata.

1989, Feb. 22 *Perf. 13x13½*
3392 A1326 5s multicolored .25 .25
3393 A1326 10s multicolored .25 .25
3394 A1326 25s multicolored .30 .25
3395 A1326 30s multicolored .40 .25
3396 A1326 42s multicolored .60 .30
3397 A1326 60s multicolored .75 .35
a. Min. sheet of 6, #3392-3397 2.75 1.75
Nos. 3392-3397 (6) 2.55 1.65

World Wildlife Fund A1327

Bats: 5s, Nyctalus noctula. 13s, Rhinolophus ferrumequinum. 30s, Myotis myotis. 42s, Vespertilio murinus.

1989, Feb. 27 *Perf. 13*
3398 A1327 5s multicolored .25 .25
3399 A1327 13s multicolored .25 .25
3400 A1327 30s multicolored .75 .30
3401 A1327 42s multicolored 1.25 .90
a. Min. sheet of 4, #3398-3401 3.50 2.50
Nos. 3398-3401 (4) 2.50 1.70

Aleksandr Stamboliski (1879-1923), Premier — A1328

1989, Mar. 1 *Perf. 13½x13*
3402 A1328 5s brt org & blk .25 .25

Souvenir Sheet

Soviet-Bulgarian Joint Space Flight, 10th Anniv. — A1329

Designs: a, Liftoff. b, Crew.

1989, Apr. 10 *Perf. 13*
3403 A1329 Sheet of 2 2.40 1.25
a.-b. 50s any single 1.10 .60
Exists imperf. Value $15.

EXPO '91 Young Inventors Exhibition, Plovdiv — A1330

1989, Apr. 20 *Perf. 13½x13*
3404 A1330 5s multicolored .25 .25

Petko Enev (b. 1889) A1331

Stanke Dimitrov Marek (b. 1889) — A1332

1989, Apr. 28 *Perf. 13½x13, 13x13½*
3405 A1331 5s scarlet & black .25 .25
3406 A1332 5s scarlet & black .25 .25

Icons — A1333

Paintings by Bulgarian artists: No. 3407, Archangel Michael, by Dimiter Molerov. No. 3408, Mother and Child, by Toma Vishanov. No. 3409, St. John, by Vishanov. No. 3410, St. Dimitri, by Ivan Terziev.

1989, Apr. 28 *Perf. 13x13½*
3407 A1333 30s multicolored .35 .25
3408 A1333 30s multicolored .35 .25
3409 A1333 30s multicolored .35 .25
3410 A1333 30s multicolored .35 .25
Nos. 3407-3410 (4) 1.40 1.00
Nos. 3408, 3410 exist in sheets of four. Nos. 3407-3410 exist in souvenir sheets of four and together in one sheet of four, imperf.

Photocopier A1334

1989, May 5
3411 A1334 5s shown .25 .25
3412 A1334 8s Computer .25 .25
3413 A1334 35s Telephone .40 .30
3414 A1334 42s Dish receiver .55 .35
Nos. 3411-3414 (4) 1.45 1.15
Bulgarian Communications, 110th anniv. Nos. 3411-3413 exist in imperf. sheets of six.

Souvenir Sheet

58th FIP Congress — A1335

1989, May 22
3415 A1335 1 l Charioteer 1.50 .75
Exists imperf. Value $12.

1st Communist Party Congress in Bulgaria, 70th Anniv. — A1336

1989, June 15
3416 A1336 5s mar, blk & dk red .25 .25

Famous Men — A1337

No. 3417, Ilya Blaskov. No. 3418, Sofronii, Bishop of Vratza. No. 3419, Vassil Aprilov (b. 1789), educator, historian. No. 3420, Christo Jassenov (1889-1925). No. 3421, 10s, Stoyan Zagorchinov (1889-1969).

1989
3417 A1337 5s black & gray ol .25 .25
3418 A1337 5s blk, brn blk & pale green .25 .25
3419 A1337 8s lt blue, blk & vio blk .30 .25
3420 A1337 8s tan, blk & dark red brown .25 .25
3421 A1337 10s blk, pale pink & gray blue .30 .25
Nos. 3417-3421 (5) 1.35 1.25
Issued: Nos. 3417-3418, June 15; No. 3419, Aug. 1; No. 3420, Sept. 25; 10s, Aug. 5.

French Revolution, Bicent. — A1338

1989, June 26 *Perf. 13½x13*
3422 A1338 13s Anniv. emblem .25 .25
3423 A1338 30s Jean-Paul Marat .35 .25
3424 A1338 42s Robespierre .50 .25
Nos. 3422-3424 (3) 1.10 .75

7th Army Games — A1339

1989, June 30 *Perf. 13*
3425 A1339 5s Gymnast .25 .25
3426 A1339 13s Equestrian .25 .25
3427 A1339 30s Running .35 .25
3428 A1339 42s Shooting .50 .30
Nos. 3425-3428 (4) 1.35 1.05

22nd World Canoe and Kayak Championships, Plovdiv — A1340

1989, Aug. 11 *Litho.* *Perf. 13*
3429 A1340 13s Woman paddling .25 .25
3430 A1340 30s Man rowing .45 .25

Photography, 150th Anniv. — A1341

1989, Aug. 29 *Perf. 13½x13*
3431 A1341 42s blk, buff & yel .75 .30

September 9 Revolution, 45th Anniv. — A1342

5s, Revolutionaries. 8s, Couple embracing. 13s, Faces in a crowd.

1989, Aug. 30 *Perf. 13*
3432 A1342 5s multicolored .25 .25
3433 A1342 8s multicolored .25 .25
3434 A1342 13s multicolored .25 .25
Nos. 3432-3434 (3) .75 .75

Natural History Museum, Cent. A1343

1989, Aug. 31
3435 A1343 13s multicolored .25 .25

Postal Workers Killed in World War II — A1343a

Designs: 5s, L.D. Dardjikov. 8s, I.B. Dobrev. 10s, N.P. Antonov.

1989, Sept. 22 *Litho.* *Perf. 13*
3436 A1343a 5s multicolored .25 .25
3437 A1343a 8s multicolored .25 .25
3438 A1343a 13s multicolored .25 .25
Nos. 3436-3438 (3) .75 .75

12th Shipping Unions Congress (FIATA) — A1344

1989, Sept. 25 *Litho.* *Perf. 13½x13*
3439 A1344 42s lt blue & dk blue .65 .40

Jawaharlal Nehru, 1st Prime Minister of Independent India — A1346

1989, Oct. 10
3440 A1346 13s blk, pale yel & brn .25 .25

Souvenir Sheet

European Ecology Congress — A1347

1989, Oct. 12 *Perf. 13*
3441 A1347 Sheet of 2 2.75 2.75
a. 50s multicolored .75 .65
b. 1 l multicolored 1.50 1.10

Souvenir sheet exists imperf. Value $15.

Snakes A1368

Designs: 5s, Eryx jaculus turcicus. 10s, Elaphe longissima. 25s, Elaphe situla. 30s, Elaphe quatuorlineata. 42s, Telescopus fallax. 60s, Coluber rubriceps.

1989, Oct. 20 *Litho.* *Perf. 13*
3491 A1368 5s multicolored .25 .25
3492 A1368 10s multicolored .25 .25
3493 A1368 25s multicolored .35 .25
3494 A1368 30s multicolored .45 .30
3495 A1368 42s multicolored .65 .45
3496 A1368 60s multicolored .85 .45
a. Min. sheet of 6, #3491-3496 3.00 2.00
Nos. 3491-3496 (6) 2.80 1.85

Intl. Youth Science Fair, Plovdiv, 1989 — A1369

1989, Nov. 4
3497 A1369 13s multicolored .25 .25

1990 World Soccer Championships, Italy — A1370

Various athletes: No. 3502a, Athletes facing right. No. 3502b, Athletes facing left.

1989, Dec. 1
3498 A1370 5s shown .25 .25
3499 A1370 13s multi, diff. .25 .25
3500 A1370 30s multi, diff. .35 .25
3501 A1370 42s multi, diff. .85 .35
Nos. 3498-3501 (4) 1.70 1.10

Souvenir Sheet
3502 Sheet of 2 1.50 .85
a.-b. A1370 50s any single .75 .40

No. 3502 exists imperf. Value $12.50.

Air Sports A1371

1989, Dec. 8
3503 A1371 5s Glider planes .25 .25
3504 A1371 13s Hang glider .25 .25
3505 A1371 30s Sky diving .55 .30
3506 A1371 42s Three sky divers .55 .30
Nos. 3503-3506 (4) 1.60 1.10
82nd General conference of the FAI, Varna.

Traffic Safety A1372

1989, Dec. 12
3507 A1372 5s multicolored .25 .25

New Year 1990 — A1373

1989, Dec. 25 *Litho.* *Perf. 13*
3508 A1373 5s Santa's sleigh .25 .25
3509 A1373 13s Snowman .25 .25

Cats A1374

No. 3510, Persian. No. 3511, Tiger. 8s, Tabby. No. 3513, Himalayan. No. 3514, Persian, diff. 13s, Siamese. Nos. 3511, 3514-3515 vert.

Perf. 13½x13, 13x13½
1989, Dec. 26 **Background Color**
3510 A1374 5s gray .25 .25
3511 A1374 5s yellow .25 .25
3512 A1374 8s orange .25 .25
3513 A1374 10s blue .25 .25
3514 A1374 10s brown orange .25 .25
3515 A1374 13s red .30 .25
Nos. 3510-3515 (6) 1.55 1.50

Explorers and Their Ships — A1375

1990, Jan. 17 *Perf. 13*
3516 A1375 5s Columbus .25 .25
3517 A1375 8s da Gama .25 .25
3518 A1375 13s Magellan .25 .25
3519 A1375 32s Drake .45 .30
3520 A1375 42s Hudson .70 .45
3521 A1375 60s Cook .90 .45
a. Min. sheet of 6, #3516-3521 3.00 2.25
Nos. 3516-3521 (6) 2.80 1.95

Natl. Esperanto Movement, Cent. — A1376

1990, Feb. 23 *Litho.* *Perf. 13*
3522 A1376 10s multicolored .25 .25

Paintings by Foreign Artists in the Natl. Museum A1377

Artists: No. 3523, Suzanna Valadon (1867-1938). No. 3524, Maurice Brianchon (1899-1978). No. 3525, Moise Kisling (1891-1953). No. 3526, Giovanni Beltraffio (1467-1516).

1990, Mar. 23 *Perf. 14*
3523 A1377 30s multicolored .55 .30
3524 A1377 30s multicolored .55 .30
3525 A1377 30s multicolored .55 .30
3526 A1377 30s multicolored .55 .30
Nos. 3523-3526 (4) 2.20 1.20

1990 World Soccer Championships, Italy — A1378

Various athletes.

1990, Mar. 26 *Perf. 13*
3527 A1378 5s multicolored .25 .25
3528 A1378 13s multi, diff. .25 .25
3529 A1378 30s multi, diff. .45 .25
3530 A1378 42s multi, diff. .75 .30
Nos. 3527-3530 (4) 1.70 1.05

Souvenir Sheet
3531 Sheet of 2 1.75 1.00
a. A1378 50s Three players .85 .40
b. A1378 50s Two players .85 .40

No. 3531 exists imperf. Value $10.

Bavaria
No. 1
A1379

1990, Apr. 6   Litho.   *Perf. 13*
3532 A1379 42s vermilion & blk   .65   .45
   ESSEN '90, Germany, Apr. 12-22. No. 3532 printed in sheets of 3 + 3 labels.

Souvenir Sheet

Penny Black, 150th Anniv. — A1380

1990, Apr. 10
3533 A1380   Sheet of 2   2.00 1.00
  a.   50s Great Britain #1   1.00 .50
  b.   50s Sir Rowland Hill   1.00 .50

Cooperative Farming in Bulgaria,
Cent. — A1381

1990, Apr. 17
3534 A1381 5s multicolored   .25   .25

Dimitar Chorbadjiski-Chudomir (1890-
1967) — A1382

1990, Apr. 24
3535 A1382 5s multicolored   .25   .25

Labor Day,
Cent. — A1383

1990, May 1   *Perf. 13x13½*
3536 A1383 10s multicolored   .25   .25

ITU, 125th Anniv. — A1384

1990, May 13   Litho.   *Perf. 13½x13*
3537 A1384 20s bl, red & blk   .35   .25

Belgium
No. 1
A1385

1990, May 23   *Perf. 13*
3538 A1385 30s multicolored   .60   .35
   Belgica '90. No. 3538 printed in sheets of 3 + 3 labels.

Lamartine (1790-1869), French
Poet — A1386

1990, June 15   *Perf. 13½x13*
3539 A1386 20s multicolored   .35   .25

Dinosaurs — A1387

   5s, Brontosaurus. 8s, Stegosaurus. 13s, Edaphosaurus. 25s, Rhamphorhynchus. 32s, Protoceratops. 42s, Triceratops.

1990, June 19   *Perf. 12½*
3540 A1387   5s multi   .25   .25
3541 A1387   8s multi   .25   .25
3542 A1387   13s multi   .25   .25
3543 A1387   25s multi   .45   .30
3544 A1387   32s multi   .60   .35
3545 A1387   42s multi   .90   .45
  a.   Min. sheet of 6, #3540-3545   3.00 1.60
   Nos. 3540-3545 (6)   2.70 1.85

1992 Summer Olympic Games,
Barcelona — A1388

1990, July 13   *Perf. 13½x13*
3546 A1388   5s Swimming   .25   .25
3547 A1388   13s Handball   .25   .25
3548 A1388   30s Hurdling   .45   .30
3549 A1388   42s Cycling   .75   .30
   Nos. 3546-3549 (4)   1.70 1.10

Souvenir Sheet
3550   Sheet of 2   2.00 1.00
  a.   A1388 50s Tennis, forehand   1.00 .50
  b.   A1388 50s Tennis, backhand   1.00 .50

   No. 3550 exists imperf. Value $10.

Butterflies
A1389

   5s, Zerynthia Polyxena. 10s, Panaxia quadripunctaria. 20s, Proserpinus proserpina. 30s, Hyles lineata. 42s, Thecla betulae. 60s, Euphydryas cynthia.

1990, Aug. 8   Litho.   *Perf. 13*
3551 A1389   5s multicolored   .25   .25
3552 A1389   10s multicolored   .25   .25
3553 A1389   20s multicolored   .25   .25
3554 A1389   30s multicolored   .45   .25
3555 A1389   42s multicolored   .50   .25
3556 A1389   60s multicolored   .85   .45
  a.   Min. sheet of 6, #3551-3556   3.00 1.75
   Nos. 3551-3556 (6)   2.55 1.70

Airplanes — A1390

1990, Aug. 30   Litho.   *Perf. 13½x13*
3557 A1390   5s Airbus A-300   .25   .25
3558 A1390   10s Tu-204   .25   .25
3559 A1390   25s Concorde   .35   .25
3560 A1390   30s DC-9   .35   .30
3561 A1390   42s Il-86   .50   .35
3562 A1390   60s Boeing 747   .85   .55
  a.   Min. sheet of 6, #3557-3562   3.00 2.00
   Nos. 3557-3562 (6)   2.55 1.95

Exarch Joseph I
(1840-1915),
Religious
Leader — A1391

1990, Sept. 27   *Perf. 13*
3563 A1391 5s blk, pur & grn   .25   .25

Intl.
Traffic
Safety
Year
A1392

1990, Oct. 9   Litho.   *Perf. 13*
3564 A1392 5s multicolored   .25   .25

Olymphilex '90,
Varna — A1393

1990, Oct. 16   *Perf. 13x13½*
3565 A1393   5s Shot put   .25   .25
3566 A1393   13s Discus   .25   .25
3567 A1393   42s Hammer throw   .55   .35
3568 A1393   60s Javelin   .75   .60
  a.   Souv. sheet of 4, #3565-3568, imperf.   8.00 6.00
   Nos. 3565-3568 (4)   1.80 1.45

Space Exploration — A1394

   Designs: 5s, Sputnik, 1957, USSR. 8s, Vostok, 1961, USSR. 10s, Voshkod 2, 1965, USSR. 20s, Apollo-Soyuz, 1975, US-USSR. 42s, Space Shuttle Columbia, 1981, US. 60s, Galileo, 1989-1996, US. 1 l, Apollo 11 Moon landing, 1969, US.

1990, Oct. 22   *Perf. 13½x13*
3569 A1394   5s multicolored   .25   .25
3570 A1394   8s multicolored   .25   .25
3571 A1394   10s multicolored   .25   .25
3572 A1394   20s multicolored   .30   .25
3573 A1394   42s multicolored   .70   .35
3574 A1394   60s multicolored   .85   .55
   Nos. 3569-3574 (6)   2.60 1.90

Souvenir Sheet
3575 A1394   1 l multicolored   1.75 1.25

   No. 3575 exists imperf. Value $7.50.

St. Clement of
Ohrid — A1395

1990, Nov. 29   Litho.   *Perf. 13*
3576 A1395 5s multicolored   .25   .25

Christmas
A1396

1990, Dec. 25   Litho.   *Perf. 13*
3577 A1396   5s Christmas tree   .25   .25
3578 A1396   20s Santa Claus   .30   .25

European Figure Skating
Championships, Sofia — A1397

1991, Jan. 18   *Perf. 13½x13*
3579 A1397 15s multicolored   .25   .25

Farm Animals
A1398

1991-92   **Perf. 14x13½**

3581	A1398	20s Sheep	.25	.25
3582	A1398	25s Goose	.25	.25
3583	A1398	30s Hen, chicks	.25	.25
3584	A1398	40s Horse	.25	.25
3585	A1398	62s Goat	.35	.30
3586	A1398	86s Sow	.50	.30
3587	A1398	95s Goat	.35	.25
3588	A1398	1 l Donkey	.50	.35
3589	A1398	2 l Bull	1.00	.75
3590	A1398	5 l Turkey	1.75	1.00
3591	A1398	10 l Cow	3.50	1.00
		Nos. 3581-3591 (11)	8.95	4.95

Issued: 20s, 25s, 40s, 86s, 1 l, 8/21; 10 l, 2/22; 95s, 5/5/92; others, 2/11/91.

Mushrooms
A1399

5s, Amanita phalloides. 10s, Amanita verna. 20s, Amanita pantherina. 32s, Amanita muscaria. 42s, Gyromitra esculenta. 60s, Boletus satanas.

1991, Mar. 19   **Perf. 12½x13**

3597	A1399	5s multicolored	.25	.25
3598	A1399	10s multicolored	.25	.25
3599	A1399	20s multicolored	.25	.25
3600	A1399	32s multicolored	.25	.25
3601	A1399	42s multicolored	.30	.25
3602	A1399	60s multicolored	.70	.25
a.		Min. sheet of 6, #3597-3602	2.00	1.50
		Nos. 3597-3602 (6)	2.00	1.50

French Impressionists
A1400

Designs: 20s, Good Morning, by Gauguin. 43s, Madame Dobini, by Degas. 62s, Peasant Woman, by Pissarro. 67s, Woman with Black Hair, by Manet. 80s, Blue Vase, by Cezanne. 2 l, Jeanny Samari, by Renoir. 3 l, Self portrait, by Van Gogh.

1991, Apr. 1   **Perf. 13**

3603	A1400	20s multicolored	1.10	.35
3604	A1400	43s multicolored	.25	.25
3605	A1400	62s multicolored	.25	.25
3606	A1400	67s multicolored	.25	.25
3607	A1400	80s multicolored	.40	.35
3608	A1400	2 l multicolored	1.10	.35
		Nos. 3603-3608 (6)	3.35	1.80

Miniature Sheet

3609	A1400	3 l multicolored	2.00	1.50

Swiss Confederation, 700th Anniv. — A1401

1991, Apr. 11

3610	A1401	62s multicolored	.60	.35

Philatelic Review, Cent. — A1402

1991, May 7   **Litho.**   **Perf. 13**

3611	A1402	30s multicolored	.25	.25

Europa — A1403

1991, May 10   **Perf. 13x13½**

3612	A1403	43s Meteosat	.70	.40
3613	A1403	62s Ariane rocket	1.00	.55

Horses — A1404

5s, Przewalski's horse. 10s, Tarpan. 25s, Arabian. 35s, Arabian. 42s, Shetland pony. 60s, Draft horse.

1991, May 21   **Perf. 13x12½**

3614	A1404	5s multi	.25	.25
3615	A1404	10s multi	.25	.25
3616	A1404	25s multi	.25	.25
3617	A1404	35s multi	.25	.25
3618	A1404	42s multi	.30	.25
3619	A1404	60s multi	.70	.35
a.		Min. sheet of 6, #3614-3619	2.50	1.50
		Nos. 3614-3619 (6)	2.00	1.60

EXPO 91, Plovdiv — A1405

1991, June 6   **Litho.**   **Perf. 13½x13**

3620	A1405	30s multicolored	.25	.25

Wolfgang Amadeus Mozart
A1406

1991, July 2   **Perf. 13**

3621	A1406	62s multicolored	.50	.30

Space Shuttle Missions, 10th Anniv.
A1407

12s, Columbia. 32s, Challenger. 50s, Discovery. 86s, Atlantis, vert. 1.50 l, Buran, vert. 2 l, Atlantis, diff., vert.
3 l, US shuttle, earth.

1991, July 23   **Litho.**   **Perf. 13**

3622	A1407	12s multi	.25	.25
3623	A1407	32s multi	.25	.25
3624	A1407	50s multi	.40	.25
3625	A1407	86s multi	.40	.25
3626	A1407	1.50 l multi	1.10	.30
3627	A1407	2 l multi	1.10	.35
		Nos. 3622-3627 (6)	3.50	1.65

Souvenir Sheet

3628	A1407	3 l multi	2.00	1.00

No. 3628 exists imperf. Value $6.25.

1992 Winter Olympics, Albertville
A1408

30s, Luge. 43s, Slalom skiing. 67s, Ski jumping. 2 l, Biathlon.
3 l, Two-man bobsled.

1991, Aug. 7   **Litho.**   **Perf. 13x13½**

3629	A1408	30s multi	.25	.25
3630	A1408	43s multi	.30	.25
3631	A1408	67s multi	.45	.30
3632	A1408	2 l multi	1.50	.90
		Nos. 3629-3632 (4)	2.50	1.70

Souvenir Sheet

3633	A1408	3 l multi	2.00	1.00

No. 3633 exists imperf. Value $6.50.

Sheraton Sofia Hotel Balkan
A1409

1991, Sept. 6   **Litho.**   **Perf. 13**

3634	A1409	62s multicolored	.40	.30

Printed in sheets of 3 + 3 labels.

Dogs — A1410

30s, Japanese. 43s, Chihuahua. 62s, Pinscher. 80s, Yorkshire terrier. 1 l, Chinese. 3 l, Pug.

1991, Oct. 11   **Perf. 13x13½**

3635	A1410	30s multi	.25	.25
3636	A1410	43s multi	.25	.25
3637	A1410	62s multi	.40	.25
3638	A1410	80s multi	.40	.25
3639	A1410	1 l multi	.55	.35
3640	A1410	3 l multi	1.50	.75
a.		Min. sheet of 6, #3635-3640	4.00	2.75
		Nos. 3635-3640 (6)	3.35	2.10

Cologne '91, Intl. Philatelic Exhibition
A1411

1991, Oct. 21   **Perf. 13**

3641	A1411	86s multicolored	.60	.45

Printed in sheets of 3 + 3 labels.

Souvenir Sheet

Brandenburg Gate, Bicent. — A1412

1991, Oct. 23

3642	A1412	4 l multicolored	1.75	1.75

Exists imperf. Value $7.50.

Phila Nippon '91
A1413

1991, Nov. 11

3643	A1413	62s Japan #1	.45	.35

Printed in sheets of 3 + 3 labels.

Bulgarian Railroad, 125th Anniv. — A1414

1991, Nov. 30

3644	A1414	30s Locomotive	.25	.25
3645	A1414	30s Passenger car	.25	.25

Medicinal Plants — A1415

Designs: 30s, Pulsatilla vernalis. 40s, Pulsatilla pratensis. 55s, Pulsatilla halleri. 60s, Aquilegia nigricans. 1 l, Hippophae rhamnoides. 2 l, Ribes nigrum.

1991, Nov. 20   **Litho.**   **Perf. 13**

3646	A1415	30s +15s label	.25	.25
3647	A1415	40s multicolored	.25	.25
3648	A1415	55s multicolored	.25	.25
3649	A1415	60s multicolored	.25	.25
3650	A1415	1 l multicolored	.40	.25
3651	A1415	2 l multicolored	.80	.30
a.		Min. sheet of 6, #3646-3651	2.50	1.00
		Nos. 3646-3651 (6)	2.20	1.55

No. 3646 printed se-tenant with label. No. 3651a sold for 5 l, but does not contain the 15s label printed with No. 3646.

Basketball, Cent. A1416

1991, Dec. 6   *Perf. 13½x13*
3652	A1416	43s Ball below rim	.25	.25
3653	A1416	62s Ball at rim	.30	.25
3654	A1416	90s Ball in cylinder	.35	.25
3655	A1416	1 l Ball in basket	.45	.30
	Nos. 3652-3655 (4)		1.35	1.05

El Greco, 450th Birth Anniv. — A1417

Paintings: 43s, Christ Carrying the Cross. 50s, Holy Family with St. Anne. 60s, St. John the Evangelist and St. John the Baptist. 62s, St. Andrew and St. Francis. 1 l, Holy Family with St. Mary Magdalene. 2 l, Cardinal Nino de Guevara. 3 l, Holy Family with St. Anne (detail).

1991, Dec. 13   *Perf. 13*
3656	A1417	43s multicolored	.25	.25
3657	A1417	50s multicolored	.25	.25
3658	A1417	60s multicolored	.30	.25
3659	A1417	62s multicolored	.35	.25
3660	A1417	1 l multicolored	.45	.25
3661	A1417	2 l multicolored	.75	.25
	Nos. 3656-3661 (6)		2.35	1.50

Souvenir Sheet
3662	A1417	3 l multicolored	1.25	.75

No. 3662 contains one 43x53mm stamp.

Christmas — A1418

30s, Snowman, candle, bell, heart. 62s, Star, angel, flower, house, tree.

1991, Dec. 18
3663	A1418	30s multicolored	.25	.25
3664	A1418	62s multicolored	.30	.25

Marine Mammals — A1419

Designs: 30s, Phogophoca graenlandica. 43s, Orcinus orca. 62s, Odobenus rosmarus. 68s, Tursiops truncatus. 1 l, Monachus monachus. 2 l, Phocaena phocaena.

1991, Dec. 24
3665	A1419	30s multicolored	.25	.25
3666	A1419	43s multicolored	.25	.25
3667	A1419	62s multicolored	.25	.25
3668	A1419	68s multicolored	.25	.25
3669	A1419	1 l multicolored	.45	.25
3670	A1419	2 l multicolored	.75	.30
	a.	Min. sheet of #3665-3670	2.10	.75
	Nos. 3665-3670 (6)		2.20	1.55

Settlement of Jews in Bulgaria, 500th Anniv. — A1420

1992, Mar. 5   Litho.   *Perf. 13*
3671	A1420	1 l multicolored	.40	.25

Gioacchino Rossini (1792-1868), Composer — A1421

1992, Mar. 11
3672	A1421	50s multicolored	.25	.25

Plovdiv Fair, Cent. A1422

1992, Mar. 25
3673	A1422	1 l buff & black	.40	.25

Fiat Croma — A1423

Automobiles.

1992, Mar. 26   *Perf. 13½x13*
3674	A1423	30s Volvo 740	.25	.25
3675	A1423	45s Ford Escort	.25	.25
3676	A1423	50s shown	.25	.25
3677	A1423	50s Mercedes 600	.25	.25
3678	A1423	1 l Peugeot 605	.55	.25
3679	A1423	2 l BMW 316	1.00	.30
	Nos. 3674-3679 (6)		2.55	1.55

Francisco de Orellana A1424

Explorers: No. 3681, Vespucci. No. 3682, Magellan. No. 3683, Gonzalo Jimenez de Quesada (1500-1579). 2 l, Drake. 3 l, Pedro de Valdivia (1500-1553). 4 l, Columbus.

1992, Apr. 22   Litho.   *Perf. 13*
3680	A1424	50s multicolored	.25	.25
3681	A1424	50s multicolored	.25	.25
3682	A1424	1 l multicolored	.35	.25
3683	A1424	1 l multicolored	.45	.25
3684	A1424	2 l multicolored	.75	.35
3685	A1424	3 l multicolored	1.10	.35
	Nos. 3680-3685 (6)		3.15	1.70

Souvenir Sheet
3686	A1424	4 l multicolored	1.75	1.00

Granada '92 A1425

1992, Apr. 23
3687	A1425	62s multicolored	.30	.30

No. 3687 printed in sheets of 3 + 3 labels.

Discovery of America, 500th Anniv. — A1426

1992, Apr. 24
3688	1 l Ships, map	.90	.45
3689	2 l Columbus, ship	1.75	.65
	a. A1426 Pair, #3688-3689	3.00	1.50

Europa.

SOS Children's Village A1427

1992, June 15   Litho.   *Perf. 13*
3690	A1427	1 l multicolored	.45	.25

1992 Summer Olympics, Barcelona — A1428

1992, July 15   *Perf. 13½x13*
3691	A1428	50s Swimming	.25	.25
3692	A1428	50s Long jump	.25	.25
3693	A1428	1 l High jump	.35	.25
3694	A1428	3 l Gymnastics	1.10	.35
	Nos. 3691-3694 (4)		1.95	1.10

Souvenir Sheet
Perf. 13x13½
3695	A1428	4 l Torch, vert.	1.50	1.00

Motorcycles — A1429

Designs: 30s, 1902 Laurin & Klement. No. 3697, 1928 Puch 200 Luxus. No. 3698, 1931 Norton CS1. 70s, 1950 Harley Davidson. 1 l, 1986 Gilera SP 01. 2 l, 1990 BMW K1.

1992, July 30   *Perf. 13*
3696	A1429	30s multicolored	.25	.25
3697	A1429	50s multicolored	.25	.25
3698	A1429	50s multicolored	.25	.25
3699	A1429	70s multicolored	.45	.25
3700	A1429	1 l multicolored	.30	.25
3701	A1429	2 l multicolored	.85	.30
	Nos. 3696-3701 (6)		2.35	1.55

Genoa '92 Intl. Philatelic Exhibition A1430

1992, Sept. 18   *Perf. 13*
3702	A1430	1 l multicolored	.45	.25

This is a developing set. Numbers may change.

Insects A1431

1 l, Dragonfly. 2 l, Mayfly. 3 l, Locust. 4 l, Stag beetle. 5 l, Carrion beetle. 7 l, Ant. 20 l, Bee. 50 l, Praying mantis.

1992   Litho.   *Perf. 14x13½*
3710	A1431	1 l multi	.25	
3711	A1431	2 l multi	.45	
3712	A1431	3 l multi	.55	
3713	A1431	4 l multi	.80	
3714	A1431	5 l multi	1.00	
3715	A1431	7 l multi	1.50	
3716	A1431	20 l multi	3.50	
3717	A1431	50 l multi	10.50	
	Nos. 3710-3717 (8)		18.55	

Issued: 7, 20 l, 9/25; 3, 50 l, 11/30; 1, 2, 4, 5 l, 12/15/93.

A1432

1992, Sept. 30   *Perf. 13*
3719	A1432	1 l blk, pink & rose	.45	.25

Higher Institute of Architecture and Building, 50th anniv.

Trees — A1433

No. 3720, Quercus mestensis. No. 3721, Aesculus hippocastanum. No. 3722, Quercus thracica. No. 3723, Pinus peuce. 2 l, Acer heldreichii. 3 l, Pyrus bulgarica.

1992, Oct. 16   *Perf. 13*
3720	A1433	50s multicolored	.25	.25
3721	A1433	50s multicolored	.25	.25
3722	A1433	1 l multicolored	.35	.25
3723	A1433	1 l multicolored	.35	.25
3724	A1433	2 l multicolored	.85	.25
3725	A1433	3 l multicolored	1.10	.30
	Nos. 3720-3725 (6)		3.15	1.55

Ethnographical Museum,
Cent. — A1434

1992, Oct. 23
3726 A1434 1 l multicolored .45 .25

Tanker Bulgaria — A1435

30s, Freighter Bulgaria. 50s, Castor. 1 l, Hero of Sevastopol. 2 l, Aleko Constantinov. 3 l, Varna.

1992, Oct. 30   Litho.   Perf. 13
3727 A1435 30s multicolored .25 .25
3728 A1435 50s multicolored .25 .25
3729 A1435 1 l multicolored .45 .25
3730 A1435 2 l shown .45 .25
3731 A1435 2 l multicolored .45 .25
3732 A1435 3 l multicolored 1.10 .45
Nos. 3727-3732 (6) 2.95 1.70

Bulgarian Merchant Fleet, Cent.

Bulgaria, Member of the Council of
Europe — A1436

1992, Nov. 6   Litho.   Perf. 13
3733 A1436 7 l multicolored 2.50 1.50

Souvenir Sheet

4th World Congress of Popular Sports,
Varna — A1437

1992, Nov. 17   Litho.   Perf. 13
3734 A1437 4 l multicolored 1.50 1.50

Christmas
A1438

1992, Dec. 1   Perf. 13½x13
3735 A1438 1 l Santa Claus .40 .25
3736 A1438 7 l Madonna & Child 2.25 .90

Wild
Cats — A1439

No. 3737, Panthera pardus. No. 3738, Acinonyx jubatus. No. 3739, Panthera onca. No. 3740, Panthera tigris. No. 3741, Felis concolor. No. 3742, Panthera leo.

1992, Dec. 18   Litho.   Perf. 13
3737 A1439 50s multicolored .25 .25
3738 A1439 50s multicolored .25 .25
3739 A1439 1 l multicolored .45 .25
3740 A1439 2 l multicolored .90 .40
3741 A1439 2 l multicolored .90 .40
3742 A1439 3 l multicolored 1.20 .45
Nos. 3737-3742 (6) 3.95 2.00

Sports
A1440

1992, Dec. 18
3743 A1440 50s Baseball .25 .25
3744 A1440 50s Cricket .25 .25
3745 A1440 1 l Polo .50 .25
3746 A1440 1 l Harness racing .50 .25
3747 A1440 2 l Field hockey .80 .45
3748 A1440 3 l Football 1.20 .60
Nos. 3743-3748 (6) 3.50 2.05

Owls
A1441

No. 3749, Aegolius funereus. No. 3750, Strix aluco. No. 3751, Asio otus. No. 3752, Otus scops. No. 3753, Asio flammeus. No. 3754, Tyto alba.

1992, Dec. 23
3749 A1441 30s multi .25 .25
3750 A1441 50s multi .25 .25
3751 A1441 1 l multi .45 .25
3752 A1441 2 l multi .90 .35
3753 A1441 2 l multi .90 .35
3754 A1441 3 l multi 1.40 .45
Nos. 3749-3754 (6) 4.15 1.90

Nos. 3749, 3751, 3753-3754 are vert.

Paintings
Depicting
History of
Bulgaria
A1442

Artists: 50s, Dimiter Gyudzhenov. 1 l, 3 l, Nikolai Pavlovich. 2 l, Dimiter Panchev. 4 l, Mito Ganovski.

1992, Dec. 28
3755 A1442 50s multicolored .25 .25
3756 A1442 1 l multicolored .45 .25
3757 A1442 2 l multicolored .70 .35
3758 A1442 3 l multicolored 1.10 .45
Nos. 3755-3758 (4) 2.50 1.30
Souvenir Sheet
3759 A1442 4 l multi, vert. 1.50 1.50

Archeological
Museum,
Cent. — A1443

1993, Jan. 1   Litho.   Perf. 13x13½
3760 A1443 1 l multicolored .45 .25

1993 World
Biathlon
Championships,
Borovetz — A1444

1 l, Woman aiming rifle. 7 l, Skiing.

1993, Feb. 5
3761 A1444 1 l multi .35 .25
3762 A1444 7 l multi 2.75 1.20

Neophit
Rilski, Birth
Bicent.
A1445

1993, Apr. 22   Litho.   Perf. 13½x13
3763 A1445 1 l hen brn & ol bis .45 .25

Contemporary
Art — A1446

Europa: 3 l, Sculpture of centaur, by Georgi Chapkinov. 8 l, Painting of geometric forms, by D. Bujukliski.

1993, Apr. 29   Perf. 13x13½
3764 A1446 3 l multicolored 1.00 .40
3765 A1446 8 l multicolored 1.75 1.00

Fish
A1447

No. 3766, C.a.j. bicaudatus. No. 3767, Mollienesia velifera. No. 3768, Aphyosemion bivittatum. No. 3769, Pterophyllum eimekei. No. 3770, Symphysodon discus. No. 3771, Trichogaster leeri.

1993, June 29   Litho.   Perf. 13
3766 A1447 1 l multicolored .25 .25
3767 A1447 2 l multicolored .30 .25
3768 A1447 3 l multicolored .45 .25
3769 A1447 3 l multicolored .45 .25
3770 A1447 6 l multicolored .65 .25
3771 A1447 8 l multicolored 1.25 .45
Nos. 3766-3771 (6) 3.35 1.70

Fruit — A1448

No. 3772, Malus domestica. No. 3773, Pyrus sativa. No. 3774, Persica vulgaris. No. 3775, Cydonia oblonga. No. 3776, Punica granatum. No. 3777, Ficus carica.

1993, July 8   Perf. 13x13½
3772 A1448 1 l multicolored .25 .25
3773 A1448 2 l multicolored .30 .25
3774 A1448 3 l multicolored .30 .25
3775 A1448 4 l multicolored .45 .25
3776 A1448 5 l multicolored .85 .25
3777 A1448 8 l multicolored 1.25 .35
Nos. 3772-3777 (6) 3.40 1.60

Claudio Monteverdi (1567-1643),
Composer — A1449

1993, July 20   Litho.   Perf. 13½x13
3778 A1449 1 l multicolored .25 .25

17th
World
Summer
Games
for the
Deaf
A1450

1993, July 20   Perf. 13
3779 A1450 1 l shown .25 .25
3780 A1450 2 l Swimming .30 .25
3781 A1450 3 l Cycling .55 .25
3782 A1450 4 l Tennis .55 .25
Nos. 3779-3782 (4) 1.65 1.00
Souvenir Sheet
3783 A1450 5 l Soccer .75 .75

Miniature Sheet

A1451

Council of Preslav, Cyrillic Alphabet in Bulgaria, 1100th Anniv.: a, Baptism of Christian convert. b, Tsar Boris I (852-889). c, Tsar Simeon (893-927). d, Battle between Bulgarians and Byzantines.

1993, Sept. 16   Litho.   Perf. 13½x13
3784 A1451 5 l Sheet of 4, #a.-d. 3.00 3.00

Alexander of Battenberg (1857-93), Prince of Bulgaria — A1452

1993, Sept. 23   *Perf. 13x13½*
3785   A1452   3 l multicolored   .45   .25

Peter I. Tchaikovsky (1840-93) A1453

1993, Sept. 30   *Perf. 13½x13*
3786   A1453   3 l multicolored   .45   .25

Small Arms — A1454

No. 3787, Crossbow, 16th cent. No. 3788, Pistol, 18th cent. No. 3789, Luger, 1908. No. 3790, Pistol, 1873. No. 3791, Rifle, 1938. No. 3792, Kalashnikov, 1947.

1993, Oct. 22   *Litho.*   *Perf. 13½x14*
3787   A1454   1 l multicolored   .25   .25
3788   A1454   2 l multicolored   .30   .25
3789   A1454   3 l multicolored   .45   .25
3790   A1454   4 l multicolored   .45   .25
3791   A1454   5 l multicolored   .80   .25
3792   A1454   7 l multicolored   1.10   .45
     Nos. 3787-3792 (6)   3.35   1.70

Isaac Newton (1643-1727) A1455

1993, Oct. 29   *Perf. 13½x13*
3793   A1455   1 l multicolored   .25   .25

Organized Philately in Bulgaria, Cent. A1456

1993, Nov. 16
3794   A1456   1 l multicolored   .25   .25

Ecology A1457

1993, Nov. 17
3795   A1457   1 l shown   .25   .25
3796   A1457   7 l Ecology   1.10   .45

Game Animals A1458

No. 3797, Anas platrhynchos. No. 3798, Phasianus colchicus. No. 3799, Vulpes vulpes. No. 3800, Capreolus capreolus. No. 3801, Lepus europaeus. No. 3802, Sus scrofa.

1993, Nov. 25
3797   A1458   1 l multicolored   .25   .25
3798   A1458   1 l multicolored   .25   .25
3799   A1458   2 l multicolored   .25   .25
3800   A1458   3 l multicolored   .40   .25
3801   A1458   6 l multicolored   .80   .30
3802   A1458   8 l multicolored   1.20   .50
     Nos. 3797-3802 (6)   3.15   1.80

Christmas A1459

Signs of Zodiac on sundial: No. 3803a, Taurus, Gemini, Cancer. b, Libra, Virgo, Leo. No. 3804a, Aquarius, Pisces, Aries. b, Capricorn, Sagittarius, Scorpio.

1993, Dec. 1
3803   A1459   1 l Pair, #a.-b.   .45   .25
3804   A1459   7 l Pair, #a.-b.   1.75   .70

When placed together, Nos. 3803-3804 form a complete sundial.

Regional Folk Costumes for Men

A1460   A1461

1993, Dec. 16   *Litho.*   *Perf. 13½x14*
3805   A1460   1 l Sofia   .25   .25
3806   A1461   1 l Plovdiv   .25   .25
3807   A1460   2 l Belogradchik   .25   .25
3808   A1460   3 l Shumen   .30   .25
3809   A1461   2 l Oryakhovitsa   .30   .25
3810   A1461   8 l Kurdzhali   .90   .40
     Nos. 3805-3810 (6)   2.25   1.65

1994 Winter Olympics, Lillehammer A1462

1994, Feb. 8   *Perf. 13*
3811   A1462   1 l Freestlye skiing   .25   .25
3812   A1462   2 l Speed skating   .25   .25
3813   A1462   3 l 2-Man luge   .40   .25
3814   A1462   4 l Hockey   .65   .25
     Nos. 3811-3814 (4)   1.55   1.00

Souvenir Sheet
3815   A1462   5 l Downhill skiing   .65   .65

Nikolai Pavlovich (1835-94) A1463

1994, Feb. 16   *Perf. 13½x13*
3816   A1463   3 l multicolored   .50   .25

Dinosaurs — A1464

No. 3817, Plesiosaurus. No. 3818, Iguanodon. No. 3819, Archaeopteryx. No. 3820, Edmontonia. No. 3821, Styracosaurus. No. 3822, Tyrannosaurus Rex.

1994, Apr. 27   *Litho.*   *Perf. 13*
3817   A1464   2 l multi   .25   .25
3818   A1464   3 l multi   .40   .25
3819   A1464   3 l multi   .40   .25
3820   A1464   4 l multi   .50   .30
3821   A1464   5 l multi   .60   .30
3822   A1464   7 l multi   .90   .45
     Nos. 3817-3822 (6)   3.05

1994 World Cup Soccer Championships, US — A1465

Players in championships of : 3 l, Chile, 1962. 6 l, England, 1966. 7 l, Mexico, 1970. 9 l, West Germany, 1974. No. 3827a, Mexico, 1986, vert. b, US, 1994.

1994, Apr. 28
3823   A1465   3 l multicolored   .35   .25
3824   A1465   6 l multicolored   .75   .25
3825   A1465   7 l multicolored   .85   .30
3826   A1465   9 l multicolored   1.10   .45
     Nos. 3823-3826 (4)   3.05   1.25

Souvenir Sheet
3827   A1465   5 l Sheet of 2, #a.-b.   1.40   .70

For No. 3827 with inscription reading up along the left margin, see No. 3851.

Europa A1466

European Discoveries: 3 l, Axis of symmetry. 15 l, Electrocardiogram.

1994, Apr. 29   *Litho.*   *Perf. 13½*
3828   A1466   3 l multicolored   .70   .30
3829   A1466   15 l multicolored   2.50   1.00

Boris Hristov (1914-93) — A1467

1994, May 18   *Litho.*   *Perf. 13*
3830   A1467   3 l brown & bister   .40   .25

Cricetus Cricetus A1468

Designs: 3 l, In nest. 7 l, Emerging from burrow. 10 l, Standing on hind legs. 15 l, Finding berry.

1994, Sept. 23   *Litho.*   *Perf. 13*
3831   A1468   3 l multicolored   .35   .25
3832   A1468   7 l multicolored   .75   .40
3833   A1468   10 l multicolored   1.20   .55
3834   A1468   15 l multicolored   1.75   .85
     Nos. 3831-3834 (4)   4.05   2.05

World Wildlife Fund.

Space Program — A1469

1994, Nov. 4   *Litho.*   *Perf. 13*
3835   A1469   3 l multicolored   .40   .25

Intl. Olympic Committee, Cent. — A1470

1994, Nov. 7
3836   A1470   3 l multicolored   .40   .25

Icons — A1471

2 l, Christ. 3 l, Christ, the healer. 5 l, Crucifixion. 7 l, Archangel Michael. 8 l, Sts. Cyril, Methodius. 15 l, Madonna & Child.

1994, Nov. 24   *Litho.*   *Perf. 13x13½*
3837   A1471   2 l multicolored   .25   .25
3838   A1471   3 l multicolored   .40   .25
3839   A1471   5 l multicolored   .40   .25
3840   A1471   7 l multicolored   .75   .25
3841   A1471   8 l multicolored   .90   .35
3842   A1471   15 l multicolored   1.90   .35
     Nos. 3837-3842 (6)   4.60   1.75

Christmas A1472

1994, Dec. 1
3843   A1472   3 l Ancient coin   .35   .25
3844   A1472   15 l Coin, diff.   2.00   1.00

Roses A1473

1994, Dec. 12   *Perf. 13*
     Color of Rose
3845   A1473   2 l yellow   .25   .25
3846   A1473   3 l rose red   .35   .25
3847   A1473   5 l white   .55   .25
3848   A1473   7 l salmon   .85   .40
3849   A1473   10 l carmine   1.20   .40
3850   A1473   15 l orange & yellow   1.90   .40
     Nos. 3845-3850 (6)   5.10   1.95

No. 3827 with Addtl. Inscription in Left Sheet Margin

1994, Dec. 15 Litho. Perf. 13
Souvenir Sheet
3851 A1465 5 l Sheet of 2,
#a.-b. 14.00 14.00

Trams — A1474

1994, Dec. 29
3852 A1474 1 l Model 1912 .25 .25
3853 A1474 2 l Model 1928 .25 .25
3854 A1474 3 l Model 1931 .35 .25
3855 A1474 5 l Model 1942 .55 .25
3856 A1474 8 l Model 1951 1.10 .45
3857 A1474 10 l Model 1961 1.20 .50
Nos. 3852-3857 (6) 3.70 1.95

Vassil Petleshkov (1845-76),
Revolutionary — A1475

1995, Feb. 27 Litho. Perf. 13½x13
3858 A1475 3 l multicolored .40 .25

End of World War
II, 50th
Anniv. — A1476

Europa: 15 l, Dove holding olive branch standing on gun barrel.

1995, May 3 Litho. Perf. 13
3859 A1476 3 l multicolored .75 .35
3860 A1476 15 l multicolored 2.50 1.00

Men's World Volleyball League,
Cent. — A1477

Designs: a, 10 l, Player digging ball. b, 15 l, Player spiking ball, vert.

1995, May 25 Litho. Perf. 13
3861 A1477 Sheet of 2, #a.-b. 2.75 1.25

Souvenir Sheet

European Nature Conservation
Year — A1478

Designs: a, 10 l, Pancratium maritimum. b, 15 l, Aquila heliaca.

1995, June 23 Litho. Perf. 13
3862 A1478 Sheet of 2, #a.-b. 3.00 3.00

Antarctic Wildlife — A1479

1 l, Euphausia superba. 2 l, Chaenocephalus. 3 l, Physeter catodon. 5 l, Leptonychotes weddelli. 8 l, Stercorarius skua. 10 l, Aptenodytes forsteri, vert.

1995, June 29
3863 A1479 1 l multicolored .25 .25
3864 A1479 2 l multicolored .25 .25
3865 A1479 3 l multicolored .30 .25
3866 A1479 5 l multicolored .55 .25
3867 A1479 8 l multicolored .90 .45
3868 A1479 10 l multicolored 1.10 .55
Nos. 3863-3868 (6) 3.35 2.00

Stephan Stambolov (1854-95),
Revolutionary Leader,
Politician — A1480

1995, July 6 Litho. Perf. 13
3869 A1480 3 l multicolored .40 .25

1996
Summer
Olympics,
Atlanta
A1481

Designs: 3 l, Pole vault. 7 l, High jump. 10 l, Women's long jump. 15 l, Track.

1995, July 17
3870 A1481 3 l multicolored .30 .25
3871 A1481 7 l multicolored .70 .35
3872 A1481 10 l multicolored 1.10 .35
3873 A1481 15 l multicolored 1.60 .35
Nos. 3870-3873 (4) 3.70 1.30

Legumes — A1482

No. 3874, Pisum sativum. No. 3875, Glicine. No. 3876, Cicer arietinum. No. 3877, Spinacia oleracea. No. 3878, Arachis hypogaea. No. 3879, Lens esculenta.

1995, July 31
3874 A1482 2 l multicolored .55 .35
3875 A1482 3 l multicolored .25 .25
3876 A1482 3 l multicolored .25 .25
3877 A1482 4 l multicolored .55 .30
3878 A1482 5 l multicolored .55 .30
3879 A1482 15 l multicolored 1.50 .40
Nos. 3874-3879 (6) 3.65 1.85

Organized Tourism in Bulgaria,
Cent. — A1483

1995, Aug. 21 Litho. Perf. 13
3880 A1483 3 l multicolored .40 .25

Vassil Zahariev
(1895-1971),
Graphic
Artist — A1484

Designs: 2 l, Woodcut of a man. 3 l, Woodcut of building in valley. 5 l, Self-portrait. 10 l, Carving of two women.

1995, Sept. 4 Litho. Perf. 13
3881 A1484 2 l multicolored .25 .25
3882 A1484 3 l multicolored .35 .25
3883 A1484 5 l multicolored .55 .30
3884 A1484 10 l multicolored 1.10 .55
Nos. 3881-3884 (4) 2.25 1.35

UN, 50th
Anniv.
A1485

1995, Sept. 12
3885 A1485 3 l multicolored .40 .25

Airplanes — A1486

1995, Sept. 26 Litho. Perf. 13
3886 A1486 3 l PO-2 .30 .25
3887 A1486 5 l Li-2 .55 .25
3888 A1486 7 l JU52-3M .75 .35
3889 A1486 10 l FV-58 1.10 .35
Nos. 3886-3889 (4) 2.70 1.20

Motion Pictures,
Cent. — A1487

Designs: 2 l, Charlie Chaplin, Mickey Mouse. 3 l, Marilyn Monroe, Marlene Dietrich. 5 l, Humphrey Bogart. 8 l, Sophia Loren, Liza Minnelli. 10 l, Toshiro Mifune. 15 l, Katya Paskaleva.

1995, Oct. 16
3890 A1487 2 l multicolored .25 .25
3891 A1487 3 l multicolored .30 .25
3892 A1487 5 l multicolored .40 .25
3893 A1487 8 l multicolored 1.00 .25
3894 A1487 10 l multicolored 1.10 .25
3895 A1487 15 l multicolored 1.50 .50
Nos. 3890-3895 (6) 4.55 1.75

Minerals
A1488

1995, Nov. 20 Litho. Perf. 13
3896 A1488 1 l Agate .25 .25
3897 A1488 2 l Sphalerite .25 .25
3898 A1488 5 l Calcite .60 .25
3899 A1488 7 l Quartz .75 .25
3900 A1488 8 l Pyromorphite .90 .25
3901 A1488 10 l Almandine 1.20 .40
Nos. 3896-3901 (6) 3.95 1.65

Christmas
A1489

1995, Dec. 8 Litho. Perf. 13
3902 A1489 3 l shown .40 .25
3903 A1489 15 l Magi 1.90 .25

Southern Fruit, by Cyril Tsonev (1896-
1961) — A1490

1996, Jan. 25 Litho. Perf. 13
3904 A1490 3 l multicolored .40 .25

Martin Luther (1483-1546) — A1491

1996, Feb. 5
3905 A1491 3 l multicolored   .40   .25

Historic
Buildings
A1492

Monasteries: 3 l, Preobragenie. 5 l, Arapov-
sky. 10 l, Drianovo. 20 l, Bachkovo. 25 l,
Troyan. 40 l, Zografski.

1996, Feb. 28   Perf. 14x13½
3906 A1492 3 l green   .25   .25
3907 A1492 5 l red   .25   .25
3908 A1492 10 l blue   .30   .25
3909 A1492 20 l yellow orange .75   .30
3910 A1492 25 l brown   .90   .40
3911 A1492 40 l purple   1.50   .65
   Nos. 3906-3911 (6)   3.95 2.10

5th Meeting of
European Bank
for
Reconstruction
and
Development
A1493

1996, Apr. 15   Litho.   Perf. 13
3912 A1493 7 l shown   .35   .25
3913 A1493 30 l Building, diff. 1.25   .50

Conifers
A1494

Designs: 5 l, Taxus baccata. 8 l, Abies alba.
10 l, Picea abies. 20 l, Pinus silvestris. 25 l,
Pinus heldreichii. 40 l, Juniperus excelsa.

1996, Apr. 23   Perf. 13½x13
3914 A1494 5 l multicolored   .25   .25
3915 A1494 8 l multicolored   .30   .25
3916 A1494 10 l multicolored   .40   .25
3917 A1494 20 l multicolored   .75   .25
3918 A1494 25 l multicolored   .90   .25
3919 A1494 40 l multicolored 1.50   .50
   Nos. 3914-3919 (6)   4.10 1.75

A1495

10 l, People in distress. 40 l, Khristo Botev
(1848-1876), poet, patriot, horiz.

1996, May 1   Perf. 13
3920 A1495 10 l multicolored   .40   .25
3921 A1495 40 l multicolored 1.60   .85

April Uprising, death of Khristo Botev, 120th
anniv.

A1496

Uniforms: 5 l, Light brown dress uniform. 8 l,
Brown combat, helmet. 10 l, Brown uniform,
holding gun with fixed bayonet. 20 l, Early red,
blue dress uniform. 25 l, Officer's early green
dress uniform. 40 l, Soldier's green uniform.

1996, May 6
3922 A1496 5 l multicolored   .90   .25
3923 A1496 8 l multicolored   .25   .25
3924 A1496 10 l multicolored   .25   .25
3925 A1496 20 l multicolored   .60   .30
3926 A1496 25 l multicolored   .75   .35
3927 A1496 40 l multicolored 1.20   .50
   Nos. 3922-3927 (6)   3.95 1.90

Republic of
Bulgaria, 50th
Anniv. — A1497

1996, May 13   Litho.   Perf. 13½
3928 A1497 10 l multicolored   .35   .25

Famous
Women
A1498

Europa: 10 l, Elisaveta Bagriana (1893-
1990), poet. 40 l, Katia Popova (1924-66),
opera singer.

1996, May 29   Litho.   Perf. 13
3929 A1498 10 l multicolored 1.25   .75
   Complete booklet, 5 #3929   8.25
3930 A1498 40 l multicolored 2.00 1.00
   Complete booklet, 5 #3930   12.00

Souvenir Sheet

A1499

10 l, Soccer player. 15 l, Soccer player, diff.

1996, June 4
3931 A1499 Sheet of 2, #a.-b. 1.75   .85

Euro '96, European Soccer Championships,
Great Britain.

A1500

5 l, Wrestling. 8 l, Boxing. 10 l, Women's
shot put. 25 l, Women sculling.
15 l, Pierre de Coubertin.

1996, July 4
3932 A1500 5 l multicolored   .25   .25
3933 A1500 8 l multicolored   .30   .25
3934 A1500 10 l multicolored   .50   .25
3935 A1500 25 l multicolored 1.00   .35
   Nos. 3932-3935 (4)   2.05 1.10

Souvenir Sheet
3936 A1500 15 l multicolored 1.00   .75

1996 Summer Olympic Games, Atlanta.
Olymphilex '96 (No. 3936).

Crabs
A1501

Designs: 5 l, Gammarus arduus. 10 l, Asel-
lus aquaticus. 12 l, Astacus astacus. 25 l,
Palaemon serratus. 30 l, Cumella limicola.
40 l, Carcinus mediterraneus.

1996, July 30
3937 A1501 5 l multicolored   2.00   .75
3938 A1501 10 l multicolored   .35   .25
3939 A1501 12 l multicolored   .35   .25
3940 A1501 25 l multicolored   .35   .25
3941 A1501 30 l multicolored   .35   .25
3942 A1501 40 l multicolored   .35   .25
   Nos. 3937-3942 (6)   3.75 2.00

Francisco Goya
(1746-1828)
A1502

Entire paintings or details: 8 l, Young
Woman with a Letter. 26 l, The Third of May,
1808. 40 l, Neighboring Women on a Balcony.
No. 3947: a, 10 l, The Clothed Maja. b, 15 l,
The Naked Maja.

1996, July 9   Litho.   Perf. 13
3943 A1502 5 l multicolored   .25   .25
3944 A1502 8 l multicolored   .40   .25
3945 A1502 26 l multicolored 1.00   .45
3946 A1502 40 l multicolored 1.50   .75
   Nos. 3943-3946 (4)   3.15 1.70
Souvenir Sheet
Perf. 13½x13
3947 A1502 Sheet of 2, #a.-b. 1.25 1.25

No. 3947 contains two 54x29mm stamps.

St. John of Rila (876-946), Founder of
Rila Monastery — A1503

1996, Sept. 3
3948 A1503 10 l multicolored   .65   .65

Bulgarian
Renaissance
Houses
A1504

Various multi-level houses.

1996, Sept. 12   Litho.   Perf. 14x13½
Background Color
3949 A1504 10 l buff   .25   .25
3950 A1504 15 l orange yellow .30   .25
3951 A1504 30 l yellow green   .60   .25
3952 A1504 50 l red lilac   1.10   .25
3953 A1504 60 l apple green   1.40   .75
3954 A1504 100 l green blue   2.25 1.10
   Nos. 3949-3954 (6)   5.90 2.85

Steam Locomotives — A1505

1996, Sept. 24   Perf. 13
3955 A1505 5 l 1836   .25   .25
3956 A1505 10 l 1847   .40   .25
3957 A1505 12 l 1848   .50   .25
3958 A1505 26 l 1876   1.00   .35
   Nos. 3955-3958 (4)   2.15 1.10

Natl.
Gallery
of Art,
Cent.
A1506

1996, Oct. 14   Litho.   Perf. 13
3959 A1506 15 l multicolored   .60   .25

Defeat of Byzantine Army by Tsar
Simeon, 1100th Anniv. — A1507

10 l, Sword hilt, soldiers on horseback. 40 l,
Sword blade, dagger, fallen soldiers.

1996, Oct. 21
3960	A1507	10 l multicolored	.40	.25
3961	A1507	40 l multicolored	1.60	.25
a.		Pair, #3960-3961	2.00	2.00

No. 3961 is a continuous design.

UNICEF, 50th Anniv. — A1508

Children's drawings: 7 l, Diver, fish. 15 l, Circus performers. 20 l, Boy, artist's pallete. 60 l, Women seated at table.

1996, Nov. 18   Litho.   Perf. 13
3962	A1508	7 l multicolored	.30	.25
3963	A1508	15 l multicolored	.60	.30
3964	A1508	20 l multicolored	.85	.35
3965	A1508	60 l multicolored	2.50	1.20
		Nos. 3962-3965 (4)	4.25	2.10

Christmas A1509

1996, Nov. 26
3966	A1509	15 l Candles on tree	.50	.25
3967	A1509	60 l Church	2.10	1.00

A1510

Painting of Old Bulgarian Town, by Tsanko Lavrenov (1896-1978).

1996, Dec. 11   Litho.   Perf. 13
3968	A1510	15 l multicolored	.50	.25

Puppies A1511

1997, Feb. 25   Litho.   Perf. 13
3969	A1511	5 l Pointer	.25	.25
3970	A1511	7 l Chow chow	.25	.25
3971	A1511	25 l Carakachan dog	.80	.30
3972	A1511	50 l Basset hound	1.60	.65
		Nos. 3969-3972 (4)	2.90	1.45

Alexander Graham Bell (1847-1922) — A1512

1997, Mar. 10
3973	A1512	30 l multicolored	.65	.35

Ivan Milev (1897-1927), Painter — A1513

Paintings: 5 l, Boy drinking from jar. 15 l, Person with head bowed holding up hand. 30 l, Woman. 60 l, Woman carrying child.

1997, Mar. 20
3974	A1513	5 l multicolored	.25	.25
3975	A1513	15 l multicolored	.25	.25
3976	A1513	30 l multicolored	.60	.25
3977	A1513	60 l multicolored	1.50	.45
		Nos. 3974-3977 (4)	2.60	1.20

Stories and Legends — A1514

Europa: 120 l, "March" lady in folk costume, symbol of spring. 600 l, St. George.

1997, Apr. 14
3978	A1514	120 l multicolored	1.25	.75
3979	A1514	600 l multicolored	1.00	.75

Konstantin Kissimov (1897-1965), Actor — A1515

1997, Apr. 16
3980	A1515	120 l multicolored	.25	.25

A1516

1997, Apr. 21
3981	A1516	60 l multicolored	.25	.25

Heinrich von Stephan (1831-97).

A1517

Historical Landmarks: 80 l, Nessebar. 200 l, Ivanovo Rock Churches. 300 l, Boyana Church. 500 l, Madara horseman. 600 l, Tomb of Sveshtari. 1000 l, Tomb of Kazanlak.

1997, May 2   Perf. 13½
3982	A1517	80 l brn & multi	.25	.25
3983	A1517	200 l pur & multi	.25	.25
3984	A1517	300 l bis & multi	.30	.25
3985	A1517	500 l grn & multi	.45	.25
3986	A1517	600 l yel & multi	.75	.30
3987	A1517	1000 l org & multi	1.00	.40
		Nos. 3982-3987 (6)	3.00	1.70

Composers — A1518

Designs: a, Gaetano Donizetti (1797-1848). b, Franz Schubert (1797-1828). c, Felix Mendelssohn (1809-1847). d, Johannes Brahms (1833-1897).

1997, May 29   Litho.   Perf. 13½x13
3988	A1518	120 l Sheet of 4, #a.-d.	1.50	1.10

Plants in Bulgaria's Red Book — A1519

Designs: 80 l, Trifolium rubens. 100 l, Tulipa hageri. 120 l, Inula spiraeifolia. 200 l, Paeonia tenuifolia.

1997, June 24   Perf. 13
3989	A1519	80 l multicolored	.25	.25
3990	A1519	100 l multicolored	.25	.25
3991	A1519	120 l multicolored	.25	.25
3992	A1519	200 l multicolored	.75	.25
		Nos. 3989-3992 (4)	1.50	1.00

A1520

1997, June 29   Litho.   Perf. 13
3993	A1520	120 l multicolored	.25	.25

Civil aviation in Bulgaria, 50th anniv.

A1521

1997, July 3
3994	A1521	120 l multicolored	.25	.25

Evlogy Georgiev (1819-97), banker, philanthopist.

Sofia '97, Modern Pentathlon World Championship — A1522

60 l, Equestrian cross-country, running. 80 l, Fencing, swimming. 100 l, Running, women's fencing. 120 l, Men's shooting, diving. 200 l, Equestrian jumping, women's shooting.

1997, July 25
3995	A1522	60 l multicolored	.40	.35
3996	A1522	80 l multicolored	.40	.35
3997	A1522	100 l multicolored	.40	.35
3998	A1522	120 l multicolored	.40	.35
3999	A1522	200 l multicolored	.40	.35
		Nos. 3995-3999 (5)	2.00	1.75

City of Moscow, 850th Anniv. — A1523

1997, July 30
4000	A1523	120 l multicolored	.60	.60

No. 4000 is printed se-tenant with label for Moscow '97 Intl. Philatelic Exhibition.

Diesel Engine, Cent. A1524

1997, Sept. 8   Litho.   Perf. 13½x13
4001	A1524	80 l Boat	.25	.25
4002	A1524	100 l Tractor	.25	.25
4003	A1524	120 l Truck	.50	.25
4004	A1524	200 l Forklift	.80	.25
		Nos. 4001-4004 (4)	1.80	1.00

43rd General Assembly of Atlantic Club of Bulgaria — A1525

Designs: a, Goddess Tyche. b, Eagle on sphere. c, Building, lion statue, denomination UL. d, Building, denomination UR.

1997, Oct. 2   Perf. 13
4005	A1525	120 l Sheet of 4, #a.-d.	1.25	.90

Miguel de Cervantes (1547-1616) — A1526

1997, Oct. 15
4006	A1526	120 l multicolored	.45	.45

Asen Raztsvetnikov (1897-1951), Poet, Writer — A1527

1997, Nov. 5
4007	A1527	120 l multicolored	.25	.25

Tsar Samuel (d. 1014), Ascension to Throne, 1000th Anniv. A1528

1997, Nov. 18   **Perf. 13½x13**
4008 A1528 120 l Inscription   .25   .25
4009 A1528 600 l Tsar, soldiers   1.50   .65
 a.   Pair, #4008-4009   1.75   .90

Christmas A1529

Designs: 120 l, Snow-covered houses, stars inside shape of Christmas tree, animals. 600 l, Nativity scene.

1997, Dec. 8   **Perf. 13x13½**
4010 A1529 120 l multicolored   .35   .25
4011 A1529 600 l multicolored   1.40   .65

1998 Winter Olympic Games, Nagano A1530

Designs: 60 l, Speed skating. 80 l, Skiing. 120 l, Biathlon. 600 l, Pairs figure skating.

1997, Dec. 17   **Perf. 13½x13**
4012 A1530   60 l multicolored   .25   .25
4013 A1530   80 l multicolored   .25   .25
4014 A1530 120 l multicolored   .25   .25
4015 A1530 600 l multicolored   1.75 1.00
      Nos. 4012-4015 (4)   2.50 1.75

For overprint see No. 4029.

Coat of Arms of Bulgaria A1531

1997, Dec. 22   Litho.   Perf. 13½x13
4016 A1531 120 l multicolored   .25   .25

Souvenir Sheet

Bulgarian Space Program, 25th Anniv. — A1532

1997, Dec. 22   **Perf. 13**
4017 A1532 120 l multicolored   .85   .85

Christo Botev (1848-76), Revolutionary, Poet — A1533

1998, Jan. 6   Litho.   Perf. 13
4018 A1533 120 l multicolored   .25   .25

Bertolt Brecht (1898-1956), Playwright A1534

1998, Feb. 10
4019 A1534 120 l multicolored   .25   .25

Bulgarian Telegraph Agency, Cent. A1535

1998, Feb. 13
4020 A1535 120 l multicolored   .25   .25

Illustrations by Alexander Bozhinov (1878-1968) A1536

Designs: a, Bird wearing bonnet. b, Black bird wearing hat. c, Grandfather Frost, children. d, Girl among flowers looking upward at rain.

1998, Feb. 24   **Perf. 13½x13**
4021 A1536 120 l Sheet of 4,
                    #a.-d.   1.25   .50

Prince Alexander A1537

1998, Feb. 27   **Perf. 13**
4022 A1537 120 l multicolored   .25   .25
4023 A1537 120 l Monument   1.40   .40
 a.   Pair, #4022-4023   1.60   .80

Bulgarian independence from Turkey, 120th anniv.

Easter — A1538

1998, Mar. 27   Litho.   Perf. 13
4024 A1538 120 l multicolored   .25   .25

Bulgarian Olympic Committee, 75th Anniv. — A1539

1998, Mar. 30
4025 A1539 120 l multicolored   .25   .25

PHARE (Intl. Post and Telecommunications Program) — A1540

1998, Apr. 24   Litho.   Perf. 13
4026 A1540 120 l multicolored   .25   .25

National Days and Festivals — A1541

Europa: 120 l, Girls with flowers, "Enyovden." 600 l, Masked men with bells, "Kukery."

1998, Apr. 27
4027 A1541 120 l multicolored   .50   .25
4028 A1541 600 l multicolored   1.75 1.50

No. 4014 Overprinted

1998, Apr. 29   **Perf. 13½x13**
4029 A1530 120 l multicolored   2.25 1.50

Dante and Virgil in Hell, by Eugene Delacroix (1798-1863) A1542

1998, Apr. 30
4030 A1542 120 l multicolored   .25   .25

A1543

1998, May 15   **Perf. 13**
4031 A1543 120 l multicolored   .25   .25

Soccer Team of Central Sports Club of the Army, 50th anniv.

Cats — A1544

60 l, European tabby. 80 l, Siamese. 120 l, Exotic shorthair. 600 l, Birman.

1998, May 25
4032 A1544   60 l multicolored   .25   .25
4033 A1544   80 l multicolored   .25   .25
4034 A1544 120 l multicolored   .25   .25
4035 A1544 600 l multicolored   1.25   .60
      Nos. 4032-4035 (4)   2.00 1.35

Are You Jealous?, by Paul Gauguin (1848-1903) — A1545

1998, June 4
4036 A1545 120 l multicolored   .25   .25

Neophit Hylendarsky-Bozvely (1745-1848), Priest, Author — A1546

1998, June 4
4037 A1546 120 l multicolored   .25   .25

1998 World Cup Soccer Championships, France — A1547

Lion mascot with soccer ball, various stylized soccer plays.

1998, June 10
4038 A1547   60 l multicolored   .25   .25
4039 A1547   80 l multicolored   .25   .25
4040 A1547 120 l multicolored   .35   .25
4041 A1547 600 l multicolored   1.60   .60
      Nos. 4038-4041 (4)   2.45 1.35

Souvenir Sheet

4042 A1547 120 l Mascot, Eiffel
                    Tower   .75   .75

A. Aleksandrov's Flight on Mir, 10th
Anniv. — A1548

1998, June 17   Litho.   Perf. 13
4043 A1548 120 l multicolored   .35   .25

Lisbon '98 — A1549

Designs: a, Map showing route around
Cape of Good Hope, Vasco da Gama (1460-
1524). b, Sailing ship, map of Africa.

1998, June 23
4044 A1549 600 l Sheet of 2,
                 #a.-b. + 2 la-
                 bels   3.50 2.25

Helicopters — A1550

80 l, Focke Wulf FW61, 1937. 100 l, Sikorsky R-4, 1943. 120 l, Mil Mi-12 (V-12), 1970.
200 l, McDonnell-Douglas MD-900, 1995.

1998, July 7   Litho.   Perf. 13
4045 A1550   80 l multicolored   .25   .25
4046 A1550 100 l multicolored   .30   .30
4047 A1550 120 l multicolored   .40   .40
4048 A1550 200 l multicolored   .55   .55
       Nos. 4045-4048 (4)   1.50 1.50

Souvenir Sheet

Intl. Year of the Ocean — A1551

Monachus monachus.

1998, July 14   Litho.   Perf. 13
4049 A1551 120 l multicolored   1.25 1.00

Dimitr Talev (1898-1966),
Writer — A1552

1998, Sept. 14
4050 A1552 180 l multicolored   .45   .25

A1553

1998, Sept. 22
4051 A1553 180 l multicolored   .45   .25
   Declaration of Bulgarian Independence,
90th anniv.

A1554

Butterflies, flowers: 60 l, Limenitis redukta,
ligularia sibirica. 180 l, Vanessa cardui,
anthemis macrantha. 200 l, Vanessa atalanta,
trachelium jacquinii. 600 l, Anthocharis
gruneri, geranium tuberosum.

1998, Sept. 24
4052 A1554   60 l multicolored   .25   .25
4053 A1554 180 l multicolored   .40   .25
4054 A1554 200 l multicolored   .50   .50
4055 A1554 600 l multicolored   1.60 1.60
       Nos. 4052-4055 (4)   2.75 2.60

Christo
Smirnenski
(1898-1923),
Poet — A1555

1998, Sept. 29
4056 A1555 180 l multicolored   .45   .25

Universal Declaration of Human
Rights, 50th Anniv. — A1556

1998, Oct. 26   Litho.   Perf. 13
4057 A1556 180 l multicolored   .45   .25

Giordano Bruno (1548-1600),
Philosopher — A1557

1998, Oct. 26
4058 A1557 180 l multicolored   .45   .25

Greetings
Stamps
A1558

No. 4059, Man diving through flaming heart,
"I Love You." No. 4060, Baby emerging from
chalice, "Happy Birthday." No. 4061, Grape
vine, bird, wine coming from vat, "Happy Holiday." No. 4062, Waiter carrying tray with glass
& ttle of wine, "Happy Name Day."

1998, Nov. 11
4059 A1558 180 l multi   .50   .25
4060 A1558 180 l multi, vert.   .50   .25
4061 A1558 180 l multi, vert.   .50   .25
4062 A1558 180 l multi, vert.   .50   .25
       Nos. 4059-4062 (4)   2.00 1.00

       See No. 4628.

Christmas
A1559

1998, Dec. 2   Litho.   Perf. 13½x13
4063 A1559 180 l multicolored   .45   .25

Ivan Geshov
(1849-1924),
Finance
Minister — A1560

1999, Feb. 8   Litho.   Perf. 13
4064 A1560 180 l multicolored   .35   .25

Third Bulgarian State, 120th
Anniv. — A1561

Designs: a, Reflection of National Assembly. b, Men, paper, Council of Ministers. c,
Scales of Justice, Supreme Court of Appeal.
d, Coins, Bulgarian Natl. Bank. e, Soldiers,
Bulgarian Army. f, Lion, lightpost, Sofia, capital of Bulgaria.

1999, Feb. 10
4065 A1561 180 l Sheet of 6,
                 #a.-f.   2.50 1.25

Bulgarian Culture and Art — A1562

180 l, Georgy Karakashev (1899-1970), set
designer. 200 l, Bencho Obreshkov (1899-
1970), artist. 300 l, Assen Naydenov (1899-
1995), conductor. 600 l, Pancho Vladiguerov
(1899-1978), composer.

1999, Mar. 12   Litho.   Perf. 13
4066 A1562 180 l multicolored   .25   .25
4067 A1562 200 l multicolored   .25   .25
4068 A1562 300 l multicolored   .75   .75
4069 A1562 600 l multicolored   1.50   .85
       Nos. 4066-4069 (4)   2.75 2.10

Bulgaria '99 — A1562a

Parrots: a, Trichoglossus haematodus. b,
Platycercus eximius. c, Melopsittacus undulatus. d, Ara chloroptera.

1999, Mar. 15   Litho.   Perf. 13x13¼
4069A A1562a 600 l Sheet of
                   4, #a.-d.   7.50 7.50

NATO, 50th Anniv. — A1563

1999, Mar. 29   Litho.   Perf. 13
4070 A1563 180 l multicolored   .35   .25

Easter
A1564

1999, Apr. 1
4071 A1564 180 l multicolored   .35   .25

National Parks and Nature
Preserves — A1565

Europa: 180 l, Duck, pond, Ropotamo Preserve. 600 l, Ibex, waterfall, Central Balkan
Natl. Park.

1999, Apr. 13   Litho.   Perf. 13
4072 A1565 180 l multicolored   .65   .25
4073 A1565 600 l multicolored   1.60   .85

IBRA '99, Intl. Philatelic Exhibition, Nuremberg — A1566

1999, Apr. 15
4074 A1566 600 l multicolored 1.50 .75

No. 4074 is divided in half by vert. simulated perfs. and was issued in sheets of 3 + 3 labels.

Council of Europe, 50th Anniv. — A1567

1999, May 5 Litho. *Perf. 13*
4075 A1567 180 l multicolored 1.00 .50

Foreign Culture and Art — A1567a

Designs: 180 l, Honoré de Balzac (1799-1850), novelist. 200 l, Johann Wolfgang von Goethe (1749-1832), poet. 250 l, Aleksandr Pushkin (1799-1837), poet. 600 l, Diego Velázquez (1599-1660), painter.

1999, May 18
4076 A1567a 180 l multi .35 .25
4077 A1567a 200 l multi .70 .25
4078 A1567a 300 l multi .70 .30
4078A A1567a 600 l multi 1.25 .65
Nos. 4076-4078A (4) 3.00 1.45

Bicycles — A1568

Designs: 180 l, Large front-wheeled bicycle, 1867. 200 l, Multi-gear bicycle. 300 l, BMX racing bike. 600 l, Mountain racing bike.

1999, June 1 Litho. *Perf. 13¼*
4079 A1568 180 l multicolored .25 .25
4080 A1568 200 l multicolored .25 .25
4081 A1568 300 l multicolored .85 .25
4082 A1568 600 l multicolored 1.50 .50
Nos. 4079-4082 (4) 2.85 1.25

Sts. Cyril and Methodius — A1569

Various paintings of Sts. Cyril and Methodius standing side by side with denomination at: a, UL. b, UR. c, LL. d, LR.

1999, June 15 Litho. *Perf. 13¼*
4083 A1569 600 l Sheet of 4, #a.-d. 10.00 10.00

Bulgaria '99, European Philatelic Exhibition.

Flowers A1570

a, Oxytropis urumovii. b, Campanula transsilvanica. c, Iris reichenbachii. d, Gentiana punctata.

1999, July 20
4084 A1570 60s Sheet of 4, #a.-d. 12.00 12.00

Bulgaria '99, European Philatelic Exhibition.

Mushrooms — A1571

Designs: a, 10s, Russula virescens. b, 18s, Agaricus campestris. c, 20s, Hygrophorus russula. d, 60s, Lepista nuda.

1999, July 27
4085 A1571 Sheet of 4, #a.-d. 2.75 2.75

Souvenir Sheet

Total Solar Eclipse, Aug. 11, 1999 — A1572

1999, Aug. 10 *Perf. 13*
4086 A1572 20s multicolored 1.50 1.50

A1573

1999, Sept. 23 Litho. *Perf. 13*
4087 A1573 18s multicolored .25 .25

Organized agrarian movement in Bulgaria, 100th anniv.

Souvenir Sheet

A1574

Lion (portion) and: a, No. J2. b, Dove and letter. c, Eastern hemisphere. d, Western hemisphere.

1999, Oct. 5 *Perf. 13x13½*
4088 A1574 60s Sheet of 4, #a.-d. 6.00 6.00

Bulgaria '99, UPU 125th anniv.

Birds, Eggs and Nests — A1575

8s, Lanius minor. 18s, Turdus viscivorus. 20s, Prunella modularis. 60s, Emberiza hortulana.

1999, Oct. 6 *Perf. 13*
4089 A1575 8s multicolored .25 .25
4090 A1575 18s multicolored .25 .25
4091 A1575 20s multicolored .25 .25
4092 A1575 60s multicolored 1.90 1.90
Nos. 4089-4092 (4) 2.65 2.65

Endangered Turtles — A1576

10s, Testudo graeca. 18s, Emys orbicularis. 30s, Testudo hermanni. 60s, Mauremys caspica.

1999, Oct. 8 *Perf. 13*
4093 A1576 10s multicolored .25 .25
4094 A1576 18s multicolored .25 .25
4095 A1576 30s multicolored .85 .85
4096 A1576 60s multicolored 1.50 1.50
Nos. 4093-4096 (4) 2.85 2.85

Olympic Sports A1577

1999, Oct. 10
4097 A1577 10s Boxing .25 .25
4098 A1577 20s High jump .25 .25
4099 A1577 30s Weight lifting .85 .85
4100 A1577 60s Wrestling 1.50 1.50
Nos. 4097-4100 (4) 2.85 2.85

Fountains — A1578

Fountains from: 1s, Sopotski Monastery. 8s, Karlovo. 10s, Koprivshchitsa. 18s, Sandanski. 20s, Karlovo. 60s, Sokolski Monastery.

1999 Litho. *Perf. 13½x14*
Fountain Color
4101 A1578 1s bister .25 .25
4102 A1578 8s green .25 .25
4103 A1578 10s brown .25 .25
4104 A1578 18s light blue .30 .30
4105 A1578 20s dark blue .35 .35
4109 A1578 60s brown 1.00 1.00
Nos. 4101-4109 (6) 2.40 2.40

Issued: 8s, 60s, 11/22/99; others, 1999.

2003, Mar. *Perf. 12¾ Syncopated*
4101a A1578 1s .25 .25
4102a A1578 8s .25 .25
4103a A1578 10s .25 .25
4104a A1578 18s .25 .25
4105a A1578 20s .25 .25
4109a A1578 60s .65 .65
Nos. 4101a-4109a (6) 1.90 1.90

Police Trade Unions' European Council, 10th Anniv. — A1579

1999, Nov. 8 Litho. *Perf. 13*
4113 A1579 18s multi .35 .25

A1580

Various gold artifacts from Panagyurishte.

1999, Nov. 15 *Perf. 13½x14*
4114 A1580 2s multi .25 .25
4115 A1580 3s multi .25 .25
4116 A1580 5s multi .25 .25
4117 A1580 30s multi .45 .25
4118 A1580 1 l multi 1.50 1.25
Nos. 4114-4118 (5) 2.70 2.25

Perf. Perf. 12¾ Syncopated
2003, Mar.
4114a A1580 2s .25 .25
4115a A1580 3s .25 .25
4116a A1580 5s .25 .25
4117a A1580 30s .30 .30
4118a A1580 1 l 1.10 1.10
Nos. 4114a-4118a (5) 2.15 2.15

A1581

1999, Nov. 22 *Perf. 13*
4119 A1581 18s Icon, 1600 .35 .35
4120 A1581 60s Icon, 1607 1.25 1.25

Scouting A1582

10s, Scout, campfire. 18s, Scout assisting another. 30s, Salute. 60s, Scouts, cross.

1999, Dec. 6
4121	A1582	10s multi	.25	.25
4122	A1582	18s multi	.40	.40
4123	A1582	30s multi	.65	.65
4124	A1582	60s multi	1.25	1.25
	Nos. 4121-4124 (4)		2.55	2.55

Expo 2005, Japan — A1583

1999, Dec. 21   *Perf. 13*
4125	A1583	18s multi	.30	.25

Start of Negotiations for Bulgaria's Entry into European Community — A1584

2000, Feb. 15   Litho.   Perf. 13
4126	A1584	18s multi	1.00	1.00

Souvenir Sheet

Ciconia Ciconia — A1585

2000, Mar. 22
4127	A1585	60s multi	2.00	1.25

Petar Beron (1800-71), Scientist — A1586

Zakhari Stoyanov (1850-89), Writer — A1586a

Kolyo Ficheto (1800-81), Architect — A1586b

2000, Mar. 30   Litho.   Perf. 13¼
4128	A1586	10s multi	.25	.25
4129	A1586a	20s multi	.45	.45
4130	A1586b	50s multi	1.10	1.10
	Nos. 4128-4130 (3)		1.80	1.80

Europa A1587

60s, Madonna and child at right.

2000, Apr. 26   Litho.   Perf. 13
4131	A1587	18s shown	.60	.40
4132	A1587	60s multicolored	1.40	1.40

2000 Summer Olympics, Sydney — A1588

2000, Apr. 28   Perf. 13¼x13
4133	A1588	10s Judo	.25	.25
4134	A1588	18s Tennis	.30	.30
4135	A1588	20s Shooting	.40	.35
4136	A1588	60s Long jump	1.10	1.00
	Nos. 4133-4136 (4)		2.05	1.90

Bulgarian Art A1589

Designs: No. 4137, Friends, by Assen Vassilev (1900-81). No. 4138, Landscape from Veliko Turnovo, by Ivan Hristov (1900-87). No. 4139, At the Fountain, sculpture by Ivan Funev (1900-83). No. 4140, All Souls' Day, by Pencho Georgiev (1900-40).

2000, May 23   Perf. 13
4137	A1589	18s multi	.40	.40
4138	A1589	18s multi	.40	.40
4139	A1589	18s multi	.40	.40
4140	A1589	18s multi	.40	.40
	Nos. 4137-4140 (4)		1.60	1.60

Souvenir Sheet

Fairy Tales — A1590

Designs: a, Puss in Boots, by Charles Perrault. b, Little Red Riding Hood, by the Brothers Grimm. c, Thumbelina, by Hans Christian Andersen.

2000, May 23   Perf. 13¼x13
4141	A1590	18s Sheet of 3, #a-c + 3 labels	1.50	1.50

Expo 2000, Hanover — A1591

2000, May 31   Perf. 13
4142	A1591	60s multi + label	1.25	.50

Birth and Death Anniversaries — A1592

Designs: 10s, Johann Gutenberg, inventor of movable type (c. 1400-68). 18s, Johann Sebastian Bach, composer (1685-1750). 20s, Guy de Maupassant, writer (1850-93). 60s, Antoine de Saint-Exupéry, writer (1900-44).

2000, June 20
4143	A1592	10s multi	.25	.25
4144	A1592	18s multi	.40	.40
4145	A1592	20s multi	.50	.50
4146	A1592	60s multi	1.40	1.40
	Nos. 4143-4146 (4)		2.55	2.55

Airships — A1593

Designs: 10s, Le Jaune over Paris. 18s, LZ-13 Hansa over Cologne. 20s, N-1 Norge over Rome. 60s, Graf Zeppelin over Sofia.

2000, July 3   Litho.   Perf. 13¼
4147	A1593	10s multi	.25	.25
4148	A1593	18s multi	.25	.25
4149	A1593	20s multi	.50	.25
4150	A1593	60s multi	1.50	.45
	Nos. 4147-4150 (4)		2.50	1.20

Ivan Vazov (1850-1921), Writer — A1594

2000, July 9
4151	A1594	18s multi	.40	.25

Souvenir Sheet

European Security and Cooperation Conference, Helsinki, 25th Anniv. — A1595

No. 4152: a, Hands. b, Three "e's."

2000, July 19   Litho.   Perf. 13
4152	A1595	20s Sheet of 2, #a-b	2.00	1.50

Churches A1596

Panel colors: 22s, Blue. 24s, Red violet. 50s, Bister. 65s, Bright green. 3 l, Brown. 5 l, Red.

2000, Sept. 1   Perf. 14x13¾
4153-4158	A1596	Set of 6	14.00	4.50

Perf. Perf. 12¾ Syncopated

2003, Mar.
4153a	A1596	22s	.25	.25
4154a	A1596	24s	.55	.55
4155a	A1596	50s	.55	.55
4156a	A1596	65s	.75	.75
	Nos. 4153a-4156a (4)		2.10	2.10

Animals A1597

Designs: 10s, Capra ibex. 22s, Ovis ammon. 30s, Bison bonasus. 65s, Bos grunniens.

2000, Sept. 25   Perf. 13
4159-4162	A1597	Set of 4	2.75	1.60

Flowers — A1598

Designs: 10s, Gladiolus segetum. 22s, Hepatica nobilis. 30s, Adonis vernalis. 65s, Anemone pavonina.

2000, Oct. 17   Perf. 13x13¼
4163-4166	A1598	Set of 4	2.50	.80

European Convention on Human Rights, 50th Anniv. A1599

2000, Nov. 3   **Litho.**   *Perf. 13¼x13*
4167 A1599 65s multi   1.60   .80

Bulgarian Orders — A1600

Designs: 12s, Bravery. 22s, St. Alexander. 30s, Citizen's merit. 65s, Sts. Cyril and Methodius.

2000, Nov. 28   *Perf. 13*
4168-4171 A1600   Set of 4   2.75   .80

Souvenir Sheet

Christianity, 2000th Anniv. — A1601

No. 4172: a, 22s, St. Boris Michael (2000 at UL). b, 22s, St. Sofroni Vrachanski (2000 at LL). c, 65s, Madonna and Child (2000 at UL). d, 65s, Exarch Antim I (2000 at LL).

2000, Nov. 28   *Perf. 13¼x13*
4172 A1601   Sheet of 4, #a-d   4.00 4.00

First Bulgarian Law, 120th Anniv. — A1602

2000, Dec. 8   *Perf. 13x13¼*
4173 A1602 22s multi   .50 .25

Advent of New Millennium — A1603

2001, Jan. 8   *Perf. 13x12¾*
4174 A1603 22s multi   .50 .50

Souvenir Sheet

Electrified City Transport in Bulgaria, Cent. — A1604

No. 4175: a, 22s, Streetcar. b, 65s, Two streetcars.

2001, Jan. 12   *Perf. 13*
4175 A1604   Sheet, 2 each #4175a-4175b   4.00 4.00

Viticulture A1605

Wine glass, wine grapes and buildings: 12s, Muscat, Evxinograd Palace. 22s, Gumza, Baba Vida Fortress. 30s, Wide Melnik, houses in Melnik. 65s, Mavroud, Assenova Fortress.

2001, Feb. 7
4176-4179 A1605   Set of 4   2.75 1.00

Souvenir Sheet

Bulgaria and the Information Society — A1606

No. 4180: a, 22s, Circuits, "@" character. b, 65s, Letters, Dr. John Atanasov (1903-95), computer pioneer.

2001, Mar. 1   *Perf. 13¼x13*
4180 A1606   Sheet of 2, #a-b   7.50 6.50

Souvenir Sheet

"Atlantic" Values, 10th Anniv. — A1607

2001, Apr. 4   *Perf. 13x12¾*
4181 A1607 65s multi   4.00 4.00

Europa A1608

Designs: 22s, Aerial view of Rila Lakes. 65s, Rock bridges, Rhodope Mountains.

2001, Apr. 18   *Perf. 12¾x13*
4182-4183 A1608   Set of 2   14.00 10.00

Todor Kableshkov (1851-1876), Organizer of 1876 April Uprising — A1609

2001, May 1   *Perf. 13*
4184 A1609 22s multi   .50 .25

Protected Species Neophron Percnopterus — A1610

Designs: 12s, Juvenile in flight. 22s, Juvenile with mouth open. 30s, Adult and chick. 65s, Adult and eggs.

2001, May 21   **Litho.**   *Perf. 13*
4185-4188 A1610   Set of 4   2.75 2.75

Souvenir Sheet

Athletes — A1611

No. 4189: a, 22s, Georgi Asparuchov (1943-71), soccer player. b, 30s, Dan Kolov (1892-1940), wrestler. c, 65s, Krum Lekarski (1898-1981), equestrian.

2001, June 29
4189 A1611   Sheet of 3, #a-c, + 3 labels   3.00 3.00

UN High Commissioner for Refugees, 50th Anniv. — A1612

2001, July 11
4190 A1612 65s multi   1.50 1.40

Writers A1613

Designs: 22s, Aleksandr Zhendov (1901-53). 65s, Ilya Beshkov (1901-58).

2001, July 24
4191-4192 A1613   Set of 2   2.00 2.00

Constitutional Court, 10th Anniv. — A1614

2001, Oct. 3
4193 A1614 25s multi   .50 .25

Souvenir Sheet

Sofia Summit 2001 — A1615

Flags of various countries: a, 12s. b, 24s. c, 25s. d, 65s.

2001, Oct. 5   *Perf. 13¼x13*
4194 A1615   Sheet of 4, #a-d   3.00 3.00

Year of Dialogue Among Civilizations A1616

2001, Oct. 9   *Perf. 13*
4195 A1616 65s multi   1.50 .50

Souvenir Sheet

Intl. Black Sea Preservation
Day — A1617

2001, Oct. 31
4196 A1617 65s multi   1.60 1.60

Christmas
A1618

2001, Nov. 19
4197 A1618 25s multi   .50 .25

Lighthouses
A1619

Designs: 25s, Shabla. 32s, Kaliakra.

2001, Nov. 19   *Perf. 14x13½*
4198-4199 A1619 Set of 2   1.10 .50

2003, Mar.   *Perf. 12¾ Syncopated*
4198a-4199a A1619 Set of 2   1.00 1.00
A souvenir sheet containing Nos. 4198a and
4199a dated "2013" and 2 labels was produced in limited quantities and released
8/15/13.

Souvenir Sheet

Zograf Monastery, Mount Athos,
Greece — A1620

No. 4200: a, 25s, Monastery. b, 65s, Icon of
St, George.

2001, Nov. 27
4200 A1620 Sheet of 2, #a-b   2.50 2.50

Cartoons — A1621

2001, Dec. 12 Litho. *Perf. 13¼x13*
4201 A1621 25s multi + label   .60 .60
Printed in sheets of 3 stamps and labels.

Vincenzo Bellini (1801-35), Italian
Composer — A1622

2001, Dec. 17   *Perf. 13*
4202 A1622 25s multi   .60 .25

Builders of the Bulgarian
State — A1623

Designs: 10s, Ancient Bulgarian calendar.
25s, Khans Kubrat (632-51) and Asparukh
(681-700). 30s, Khans Krum (803-14) and
Omurtag (814-31). 65s, King Boris I (852-89)
and Tsar Simeon I (893-927).

2001, Dec. 21
4203-4206 A1623 Set of 4   3.00 1.20

Introduction of Euro Currency in 12
European Nations — A1624

2002, Jan. 3
4207 A1624 65s multi   1.50 1.50

UN
Disarmament
Committee, 50th
Anniv. — A1625

2002, Jan. 23
4208 A1625 25s multi   .60 .60

Souvenir Sheet

Balkanmax 2002 — A1626

No. 4209: a, 25s, Natural bridge. b, 65s,
Buteo rufinus.

2002, Jan. 29
4209 A1626 Sheet of 2, #a-b 17.50 17.50

2002
Winter
Olympics,
Salt Lake
City
A1627

. Designs: 25s, Figure skater. 65s, Speed
skater.

2002, Feb. 5   *Perf. 13¼x13*
4210-4211 A1627 Set of 2   2.00 2.00

10th Natl. Antarctic
Expedition — A1628

2002, Mar. 20
4212 A1628 25s multi + label   .60 .60
Issued in sheets of 3 stamps and 3 different
labels.

Europa
A1629

Circus performers: 25s, Elephant trainer.
65s, Clown.

2002, Mar. 22   *Perf. 13*
4213-4214 A1629 Set of 2   2.50 2.50
See No. 4629 for clown stamp without
"Europa" inscription..

Famous Bulgarians — A1630

Designs: 25s, Veselin Stoyanov (1902-69),
composer. 34s, Angel Karaliichev (1902-72),
writer.

2002, Mar. 27   *Perf. 13¼x13*
4215-4216 A1630 Set of 2   1.25 1.25

Paintings — A1631

Designs: 10s, Industrial Landscape, by Vasil
Barakov, vert. 25s, Illustration for book *Under
the Yoke*, by Boris Angelushev. 65s, The Balcony and the Canary, by Ivan Nenov, vert.

2002, Apr. 17   *Perf. 13*
4217-4219 A1631 Set of 3   2.25 2.25

Stamp
Designers
A1632

Designs: 25s, Stefan Kanchev (1915-2001).
65s, Alexander Popilov (1916-2001).

2002, Apr. 26   *Perf. 13¼x13*
4220-4221 A1632 Set of 2   2.00 2.00

Fruits and
Vegetables
A1633

Designs: 10s, Cucumis melo. 25s, Citrullus
lanatus. 27s, Cucurbita pepo. 65s, Lagenaria
siceraria.

2002, May 8 Litho. *Perf. 13¼x13*
4222-4225 A1633 Set of 4   2.75 2.75

Roosters
A1634

Designs: 10s, Bankivski, vert. 20s, Leghorn.
25s, Bergich Crower. 65s, Plymouth Rock,
vert.

2002, May 10 *Perf. 13x13¼, 13¼x13*
4226-4229 A1634 Set of 4   2.75 2.75

Visit of
Pope
John Paul
II to
Bulgaria
A1635

2002, May 24 Litho.   *Perf. 13*
4230 A1635 65s multi   1.25 1.25

Souvenir Sheet

Chess — A1636

No. 4231: a, 25s, Chess pieces. b, 65s,
Hand moving piece.

2002, May 27
4231 A1636 Sheet of 2, #a-b   2.00 2.00

Admission
to Council
of Europe,
10th
Anniv.
A1637

2002, May 29
4232 A1637 25s multi   .60 .60

Carvings by
Peter Kushlev
A1638

Designs: 6s, Rabbit and fawn. 12s, Deer.
36s, Bird. 44s, Boar.

Perf. 13¾x13½
2002, Aug. 12 **Litho.**
4233-4236 A1638 Set of 4 2.00 2.00
Perf. Perf. 12¾ Syncopated
2003, Mar.
4233a-4236a A1638 Set of 4 1.75 1.75

Ships
A1639

Designs: 12s, Maria Luisa. 36c, Percenk. 49c, Kaliakra. 65c, Sofia.

2002, Oct. 18 **Perf. 13¼x13**
4237-4240 A1639 Set of 4 3.25 2.75

Christmas
A1640

2002, Nov. 20
4241 A1640 36s multi .75 .75

Souvenir Sheet

Invitation to Join NATO — A1641

2002, Nov. 21 **Perf. 13**
4242 A1641 65s multi 1.25 1.25

Souvenir Sheet

Start of European Security and
Cooperation Negotiations, 30th
Anniv. — A1642

2002, Nov. 22 **Perf. 13¼x13**
4243 A1642 65s multi 2.00 2.00

Tsars
A1643

Designs: 18s, Samuel (d. 1014). 36s, Peter II (d. 1197), Assen (d. 1196). 49s, Kaloyan (d. 1207). 65s, Ivan Assen II (d. 1241).

2002, Dec. 6 **Litho.** **Perf. 13¼x13**
4244-4247 A1643 Set of 4 3.50 3.50
See Nos. 4272, 4288-4290.

Europalia, European Culture
Festival — A1644

2003, Jan. 10 **Litho.** **Perf. 13**
4248 A1644 65s multi 1.25 1.25

Paintings
A1645

Designs: 18s, Rose Pickers, by Stoyan Sotirov (1903-84). 36s, The Blind Rebec Player, by Ilya Petrov (1903-75). 65s, Pig Tender, by Zlatyo Boyadjiev (1903-76).

2003, Jan. 28
4249-4251 A1645 Set of 3 2.25 2.25

Souvenir Sheet

Science Fiction — A1646

2003, Feb. 7
4252 A1646 65s multi 1.25 1.25

Re-establishment
of the Bulgarian
State, 125th
Anniv. — A1647

2003, Feb. 28 **Litho.** **Perf. 13**
4253 A1647 36s multi .65 .65

Rescue of Bulgarian Jews, 60th
Anniv. — A1648

2003, Mar. 10
4254 A1648 36s multi .80 .80

Europa — A1649

No. 4255: a, 36s, Woman and birds. b, 65s, Legs, chicken, pig and dog.

2003, Mar. 17
4255 A1649 Vert. pair, #a-b 2.00 2.00

Souvenir Sheet

Vincent van Gogh (1853-90),
Painter — A1650

2003, Mar. 19 **Perf. 13x13¼**
4256 A1650 65s multi 1.40 1.40

Prehistoric
Animals
A1651

2003, Apr. 24 **Perf. 13**
4257 Horiz. strip of 4 3.75 3.75
a. A1651 30s Pterodactylus .60 .60
b. A1651 36s Gorgosaurus .75 .75
c. A1651 49s Mesosaurus 1.00 1.00
d. A1651 65s Monoclonius 1.40 1.40
Booklet, #4257 5.00

Bulgaria 2003 Philatelic
Exhibition — A1652

2003, May 15
4258 A1652 36s multi .80 .80

Bees
A1653

Designs: 20s, Apis mellifera. 30s, Anthidium manicatum. 36s, Bombus subterraneus. 65s, Xylocopa violacea.

2003, June 17 **Litho.** **Perf. 13¼x13**
4259-4262 A1653 Set of 4 3.00 3.00

Water
Plants — A1654

Designs: 20s, Butomus umbellatus. 36s, Sagittaria sagittifolia. 50s, Menyanthes trifoliata. 65s, Iris pseudacorus.

2003, July 25 **Litho.** **Perf. 13**
4263-4266 A1654 Set of 4 3.50 3.50

Goce Delchev (1872-1903),
Patriot — A1655

2003, Aug. 1
4267 A1655 36s multi .75 .75
Ilinden and Preobrazhene Revolts, cent.

Bulgaria
— United
States
Diplomatic
Relations,
Cent.
A1656

2003, Sept. 19 **Litho.** **Perf. 13**
4268 A1656 65s multi 1.25 1.25

Intl Years of Fresh Water, Mountains
and Ecotourism — A1657

2003, Sept. 19
4269 A1657 65s multi + label 1.50 1.50
Printed in sheets of 3 + 3 different labels.

John Atanassov (1903-95), Computer
Pioneer — A1658

2003, Oct. 3 **Litho.** **Perf. 13**
4270 A1658 65s multi + label 1.25 1.25

2003 European
Team Chess
Championships,
Plovdiv — A1659

2003, Oct. 10
4271 A1659 65s multi 1.40 1.40

Tsar Type of 2002

Design: Tsar Ivan Shishman (d. 1396).

2003, Oct. 18
4272 A1643 65s multi 1.40 1.40

New Olympic sports: 20s, Taekwondo. 36s, Mountain biking. 50s, Softball. 65s, Canoe slalom.

2003, Oct. 18
4273-4276 A1660 Set of 4 ...... 3.50 3.50

Bulgarian Olympic Committee, 80th Anniv. — A1660

Christmas
A1661

2003, Nov. 24   *Perf. 13x13¼*
4277 A1661 65s multi 1.25 1.25

Coaches — A1662

Designs: 30s, Man and coach. 36s, Man and woman in coach. 50s, Woman, dog and coach. 65s, Man, woman and coach.

2003, Nov. 28   *Perf. 13*
4278-4281 A1662 Set of 4 ...... 3.50 3.50

FIFA (Fédération Internationale de Football Association), Cent. (in 2004) — A1663

Designs: 20s, FIFA emblem. 25s, Soccer match. 36s, Soccer match, rules. 50s, FIFA Fair Play Trophy, vert. 65s, FIFA World Player Trophy, vert.

2003, Dec. 12
4282-4286 A1663 Set of 5 ...... 4.00 4.00

Re-establisment of Masons in Bulgaria, 10th Anniv. — A1664

2003, Dec. 22   Litho.   *Perf. 13*
4287 A1664 80s multi 1.60 1.60

Tsar Type of 2002

Designs: 30s, Tsar Ivan Alexander (r. 1331-71). 45s, Despot Dosrotitsa (r. 1360-85). 80s, Tsar Ivan Strazhimir (r. 1371-96).

2003, Dec. 23
4288-4290 A1643 Set of 3 ...... 3.00 3.00

Butterflies
A1665

Designs: 40s, Noctua tertia. 45s, Rethera komarovi. 55s, Symtomis marjana. 80s, Arctia caja.

2004, Jan. 15   *Perf. 12¾ Syncopated*
4291-4294 A1665 Set of 4 ...... 4.00 4.00

Perf. 14x13½
4291a-4294a A1665 Set of 4 ...... 30.00 30.00

Issued: Nos 4291a-4294a, Oct.
A souvenir sheet containing Nos. 4291-4294 with inscriptions commemorating the Australia 2013 and Thailand 2013 World Stamp Exhibitions was produced in limited quantities.

Intl. Masquerade Festival, Pernik — A1666

2004, Jan. 23   *Perf. 13*
4295 A1666 80s multi + label 1.60 1.60
Printed in sheets of 3 +3 labels.

Bulgarian Chairmanship of Organization for Security and Cooperation in Europe — A1667

2004, Jan. 30
4296 A1667 80s multi 1.50 1.50

Ivan Vazov National Theater, Cent. — A1668

2004, Feb. 19
4297 A1668 45s multi + label 1.00 1.00

Famous Men
A1669

Designs: 45s, Atanas Dalchev (1904-78), poet. 80s, Lubomir Pipkov (1904-74), composer.

2004, Mar. 25
4298-4299 A1669 Set of 2 ...... 2.50 2.50

Admission to NATO — A1670

2004, Apr. 2
4300 A1670 80s multi 1.75 1.75

Souvenir Sheet

Flight of Georgi Ivanov, First Bulgarian in Space, 25th Anniv. — A1671

2004, Apr. 15
4301 A1671 80s multi 1.50 1.50

Souvenir Sheet

Turnovo Constitution and Restoration of Bulgarian State, 125th Anniv. — A1672

2004, Apr. 16
4302 A1672 45s multi 4.00 4.00

"Bulgarian Dream" Program A1673

2004, May 3
4303 A1673 45s multi .... .90 .90

Souvenir Sheet

Salvador Dali (1904-89), Artist — A1674

2004, May 12   Litho.   *Perf. 13*
4304 A1674 80s multi 2.00 2.00

Artists — A1675

Designs: 45s, Boris Ivanov (1904-93) and Lyuben Dimitrov (1904-2000). 80s, Vassil Stylov (1904-90) and Stoyan Venev (1904-89).

2004, May 21
4305-4306 A1675 Set of 2 ...... 2.50 2.50

Europa — A1676

Designs: 45s, Skiers on mountain. 80s, Parachutist near seaside resort.

2004, May 27
4307-4308 A1676 Set of 2 ...... 2.50 2.50
4308a Booklet pane, 2 each #4307-4308 ...... 5.00 —
Complete booklet, 2 #4308a 10.00

Complete booklet contains one pane with illustrated margins at right and one pane with illustrated margins at left.

Soccer Players — A1677

No. 4309: a, Christo Stoychkov wearing collared shirt, player holding trophy. b, Georgi Asparuchov wearing uncollared shirt, players wearing green and black shorts. c, Krassimir Balakov wearing collared shirt, players wearing white and yellow shirts. d, Nilola Kotkov wearing uncollared shirt, players wearing white shorts.

2004, June 2
4309 A1677 45s Block of 4, #a-d 3.75 3.75

Souvenir Sheet

European Soccer Championships,
Portugal — A1678

2004, June 11
4310   A1678   80s multi   1.50 1.50

Bulgaria —
Austria
Diplomatic
Relations, 125th
Anniv. — A1679

2004, June 23   Litho.   *Perf. 13*
4311   A1679   80s multi   1.50 1.50

Interior Ministry, 125th
Anniv. — A1680

2004, June 26
4312   A1680   45s multi   1.00 1.00

Souvenir Sheet

Bulgarian Postal Service, 125th
Anniv. — A1681

2004, July 16
4313   A1681   45s multi + label   4.00 4.00

Souvenir Sheet

Ecology — A1682

No. 4314: a, 45s, Milvus milvus. b, 80s,
Blennius ocellaris.

2004, July 28
4314   A1682   Sheet of 2, #a-b   3.25 3.25

2004 Summer Olympics,
Athens — A1683

Olympic rings, torch bearer, torch, map of
Bulgaria showing route of torch bearers going
to Olympics in: 10s, Berlin, 1936. 20s, Munich,
1972. 45s, Moscow, 1980. 80s, Athens, 2004.

2004, Aug. 5
4315-4318   A1683   Set of 4   3.25 3.25

Bulgarian Navy, 125th Anniv. — A1684

Designs: 10s, Steamer "Krum." 25s, Torpedo boat "Druski." 45s, Mine sweeper
"Christo Botev." 80s, Frigate "Smeli."

2004, Aug. 6
4319-4322   A1684   Set of 4   3.25 3.25

Masons
in
Bulgaria,
125th
Anniv.
A1685

2004, Sept. 20   Litho.   *Perf. 13*
4323   A1685   45s multi   5.50 5.50

Famous Bulgarians — A1686

Designs: 10s, Patriarch Ephtimius Turnovski
(1327-1402). 20s, Princes Fruzhin (1393-
1460) and Constantine (1396-1422). 45s,
Georgi Peyachevich (1655-1725) and Peter
Partchevich (1612-74), uprising leaders. 80s,
Paisii Hilendarski (1722-73), historian.

2004, Nov. 15
4324-4327   A1686   Set of 4   3.00 3.00

Miniature Sheet

Mushrooms — A1687

No. 4328: a, 10s, Polyporus squamosus. b,
20s, Fomes fomentarius. 45s, Piptoporus
betulinus. 80s, Laetiporus sulphureus.

2004, Nov. 17
4328   A1687   Sheet of 4, #a-d   3.50 3.50

Worldwide Fund for Nature
(WWF) — A1688

No. 4329: a, Two fish, blue background. b,
One fish, yellow green background. c, One
fish, light blue background. d, Large fish eating
small fish, green background.

2004, Nov. 18
4329   Horiz. strip of 4   7.50 7.50
a.-d.   A1688   80s Any single   1.60 1.60
              Complete booklet, 2 #4329   16.00

Christmas — A1689

2004, Nov. 24
4330   A1689   45s multi   1.00 1.00

Souvenir Sheet

Organization for Security and
Cooperation in Europe Ministerial
Council Meeting, Sofia — A1690

2004, Dec. 6   Litho.   *Perf. 13*
4331   A1690   80s multi   1.50 1.50

Self-Portrait of Geo Milev (1895-1925),
Artist, Writer — A1691

2005, Jan. 17
4332   A1691   45s multi   1.00 1.00

Rotary
International,
Cent. — A1692

2005, Feb. 23
4333   A1692   80s multi   1.60 1.60

Souvenir Sheet

Cinema History — A1693

No. 4334: a, 10s, Charlie Chaplin in "The
Gold Rush." b, 20s, "The Battleship Potemkin."
c, 45s, Marlene Dietrich in "The Blue Angel."
d, 80s, Vassil Ghendov in "Bulgaran is a Gal-
lant Man."

2005, Feb. 25   *Perf. 13x13¼*
4334   A1693   Sheet of 4, #a-d   3.00 3.00

Souvenir Sheet

Bulgarian Exarchate, 135th
Anniv. — A1694

2005, Mar. 11   *Perf. 13*
4335   A1694   45s multi   1.00 1.00

Volunteers for
Europe
A1695

2005, Mar. 16
4336   A1695   80s multi   1.60 1.60

Panayot Hitov
(1830-1912) and
Philip Totyo
(1830-1907),
Revolutionaries
A1696

2005, Mar. 21
4337   A1696   45s multi   1.00 1.00

Souvenir Sheet

Polar Explorers — A1697

No. 4338: a, 45s, Admiral Robert Peary (1856-1920). b, 80s, Roald Amundsen (1872-1928).

2005, Mar. 23
4338 A1697 Sheet of 2, #a-b 2.50 2.50

Souvenir Sheet

Fire Trucks — A1698

No. 4339: a, 10s, 1936 Peugeot. b, 20s, 1935 Mercedes. 45s, 1934 Magirus. 80s, 1925 Renault.

2005, Apr. 2 Litho. Perf. 13
4339 A1698 Sheet of 4, #a-d 3.25 3.25

Souvenir Sheet

Hans Christian Andersen (1805-75), Author — A1699

2005, May 20
4340 A1699 80s multi 1.60 1.60

Souvenir Sheet

Introduction of Cyrillic Alphabet to European Union — A1700

2005, May 24
4341 A1700 80s multi 1.60 1.60

Souvenir Sheet

Trains — A1701

No. 4342: a, 45s, Series 46 locomotive. b, 80s, DMV Series 10.

2005, May 26
4342 A1701 Sheet, 2 each #4342a-4342b 5.00 5.00

Child's Drawing of the Radetski A1702

2005, May 27 Litho. Perf. 13
4343 A1702 45s multi 1.00 1.00

Europa A1703

No. 4344: a, Plates of food, apple, gourd. b, Plates of food, wine glass, tomato, scallions.

2005, May 28
4344 Pair 1.75 1.75
a. A1703 45s green & multi .75 .75
b. A1703 80s red & multi 1.00 1.00
c. Booklet pane, 2 each #4344a-4344b 3.50 3.50
Complete booklet, 2 #4344c 7.50

European Philatelic Cooperation, 50th Anniv. (in 2006) — A1704

Designs: 45s, Two stylized people. 80s, Rectangle of stylized people.

2005, May 28
4345-4346 A1704 Set of 2 2.50 2.50
Europa stamps, 50th anniv. (in 2006).

Dragonflies A1705

Designs: 10s, Cordulegaster bidentata. 20s, Erythromma najas, horiz. 45s, Sympetrum pedemontanum, horiz. 80s, Brachytron pratense.

2005, June 29
4347-4350 A1705 Set of 4 3.25 3.25

Elias Canetti (1905-94), 1981 Nobel Laureate in Literature — A1706

2005, July 25
4351 A1706 80s multi 1.75 1.75

Spiders A1707

Designs: 10s, Synema globosum. 20s, Argiope bruennichi. 45s, Eresus cinnaberinus. 80s, Araneus diadematus.

2005, July 29
4352-4355 A1707 Set of 4 3.25 3.25

Organized Tourism in Bulgaria, 110th Anniv. — A1708

2005, Aug. 26 Litho. Perf. 13
4356 A1708 45s multi .90 .90

Union of Bulgaria and Eastern Rumelia, 120th Anniv. — A1709

2005, Sept. 6
4357 A1709 45s multi .90 .90

Women's Folk Costumes A1710

Clothing from region of: 20s, Sofia. 25s, Pleven. 45s, Sliven. 80s, Stara Zagora.

2005, Oct. 15 Litho. Perf. 13
4358-4361 A1710 Set of 4 3.50 3.50

Souvenir Sheet

Stamen Grigoroff (1878-1945) and Microscope — A1711

2005
4362 A1711 80s multi + label 1.25 1.25
a. As #4362, with owl added in UR of stamp, imperf. 12.00 12.00

Grigoroff's discovery of Lactobacillus bulgaricus grigoroff, cent.
Issued: No. 4362, 10/21; No. 4362a, 12/2. No. 4362a has simulated perforations and a perforated serial number.

Antoaneta Stefanova, Female World Chess Champion — A1712

2005, Nov. 10
4363 A1712 80s multi 1.25 1.25

Christmas — A1713

2005, Nov. 30
4364 A1713 45s multi .90 .90

Souvenir Sheet

Admission to the United Nations, 50th Anniv. — A1714

2005, Dec. 14 Litho. Perf. 13
4365 A1714 80s multi 1.50 1.50

Builders of the Bulgarian State — A1715

Designs: 10s, Illarion Makariopolski (1812-75) and Antim I (1816-88), religious leaders. 20s, Georgi Rakovski (1821-67) and Vassil Levski (1837-73), revolutionaries. 45s, Ljuben

Karavelov (1834-79) and Christo Botev (1848-76), poets. 80s, Panayot Volov (1850-76) and Pavel Bobekov (1852-77), revolutionaries.

2005, Dec. 20
4366-4369 A1715   Set of 4   3.00 3.00

Roses — A1716

Designs: 54s, Rosa pendulina. 1.50 l, Rosa gallica. 2 l, Rosa spinosissima. 10 l, Rosa arvensis.

Perf. 13x12¾ Syncopated

2006, Jan. 23			**Litho.**
4370	A1716	54s multi	.85 .50
4371	A1716	1.50 l multi	2.40 1.25
4372	A1716	2 l multi	3.25 1.75
4373	A1716	10 l multi	15.00 10.00
	Nos. 4370-4373 (4)		21.50 13.50

Wolfgang Amadeus Mozart (1756-91), Composer — A1717

2006, Jan. 27   **Perf. 13**
4374 A1717 1 l multi + label   2.50 2.50

Famous Bulgarian Philatelists — A1718

Designs: 35s, Ellin Pellin (1877-1949), novelist. 55s, Lazar Dobrich (1881-1970), circus performer. 60s, Boris Christov (1914-93), opera singer. 1 l, Bogomil Nonev (1920-2002), writer.

2006, Jan. 31   **Litho.**
Stamp + Label
4375-4378 A1718   Set of 4   3.75 3.75

Souvenir Sheet

2006 Winter Olympics, Turin — A1719

No. 4379: a, 55s, Snowboarding. b, 1 l, Figure skating.

2006, Feb. 10   **Perf. 13x13¼**
4379 A1719   Sheet of 2, #a-b   2.50 2.50

Souvenir Sheet

Bulgarian Antarctic Cartography, 10th Anniv. — A1720

2006, Feb. 28   **Perf. 13**
4380 A1720 1 l multi   1.75 1.75

Battle of Nicopolis, 610th Anniv. — A1721

2006, Mar. 14
4381 A1721 1.50 l multi   2.75 2.75

Souvenir Sheet

Ecology — A1722

No. 4382: a, 55s, Martes martes. b, 1.50 l, Ursus arctos.

2006, Mar. 28   **Perf. 13½x13¼**
4382 A1722   Sheet of 2, #a-b + label   3.25 3.25

Europa A1723

Designs: 55c, Person holding star. 1 l, Flower.

Perf. 12¾x13 Syncopated
2006, Apr. 25
4383 A1723 55c multi   1.00 1.00
4384 A1723 1 l multi   2.00 2.00
Booklet Stamps
Perf. 13
4385 A1723 55c multi   3.00 3.00
4386 A1723 1 l multi   8.00 8.00
  a.   Booklet pane, 4 each
      #4385-4386   55.00
      Complete booklet, #4386a   57.50
      Nos. 4383-4386 (4)   14.00 14.00

Souvenir Sheet

Meeting of NATO Foreign Ministers, Sofia — A1724

2006, Apr. 27   **Perf. 13**
4387 A1724 1.50 l multi   2.50 2.50

Trud Newspaper, 70th Anniv. — A1725

2006, Apr. 28
4388 A1725 55s multi   1.25 1.25

Souvenir Sheet

Vesselin Topalov, World Chess Champion — A1726

2006, May 4   **Perf. 13**
4389 A1726 1.50 l multi   2.50 2.50
Exists imperf. with perforated serial number. Value $12.

Palace of Culture, Sofia, 25th Anniv. — A1727

2006, May 5   **Perf. 13¼x13**
4390 A1727 55s multi + label   1.25 1.25

Birds A1728

Designs: 10s, Circus aeruginosus. 35s, Circus cyaneus. 55s, Circus macrourus. 1 l, Circus pygargus.

2006, May 9   **Perf. 13**
4391-4394 A1728   Set of 4   3.75 3.75

Nikola Vaptsarov Naval Academy, 125th Anniv. — A1729

2006, May 20   **Perf. 13¼x13**
4395 A1729 55s multi   1.00 1.00

Souvenir Sheet

2006 World Cup Soccer Championships, Germany — A1730

2006, June 9
4396 A1730 1 l multi   1.75 1.75

Bulgarian Membership in UNESCO, 50th Anniv. — A1731

2006, June 29   **Perf. 13**
4397 A1731 1 l multi   .50 .50

Gena Dimitrova (1941-2005), Opera Singer — A1732

2006, July 18   **Litho.**   **Perf. 13¼**
4398 A1732 1 l multi   2.00 2.00

Flowers A1733

No. 4399: a, Saponaria stranjensis. b, Trachystemon orientalis. c, Hypericum calycinum. d, Rhododendron ponticum.

2006, July 28   **Perf. 13**
4399   Horiz. strip of 4   3.00 3.00
  a.   A1733 10s multi   .25 .25
  b.   A1733 35s multi   .45 .45
  c.   A1733 55s multi   .70 .70
  d.   A1733 1 l multi   1.40 1.40
No. 4399 printed in sheets of 2 strips which are tete-beche.

Bulgarian Automobiles — A1734

Designs: 10s, 1995 Rover Maestro. 35s, 1967 Moskvich. 55s, 1967 Bulgaralpine. 1 l, 1967 Bulgarrenault.

2006, Sept. 29   Litho.   Perf. 13
4400-4403 A1734   Set of 4   3.00 3.00

Souvenir Sheet

Return of the Prodigal Son, by Rembrandt (1606-69) — A1735

2006, Oct. 25
4404 A1735 1 l multi   2.00 2.00

Paintings by Bulgarian Artists — A1736

Designs: 10s, All Souls Day, by Ivan Murkvitchka. 35s, Sozopol - Houses, by Veselin Staykov. 55s, Sofia in Winter, by Nikola Petrov. 1 l, Portrait of T. Popova, by Georgi Popov.

2006, Oct. 27   Perf. 13x13¼
4405-4408 A1736   Set of 4   3.25 3.25

World Sambo Championships, Sofia — A1737

2006, Nov. 3   Perf. 13
4409 A1737 55s multi   .90 .90

Souvenir Sheet

Postal Vans — A1738

2006, Nov. 17   Perf. 13¼
4410 A1738 1 l multi + label   4.00 4.00

Christmas — A1739

2006, Nov. 24   Perf. 13¼x13
4411 A1739 55s multi   .90 .90

2007 Admission of Bulgaria and Romania into European Union — A1740

Designs: 55s, Flags of Bulgaria and Romania, map of Europe, European Union ballot box. 1.50 l, "EU" in colors of Bulgarian and Romanian flags.

2006, Nov. 29   Perf. 13
4412-4413 A1740   Set of 2   3.25 3.25
4413a   Souvenir sheet, #4412-4413   3.25 3.25

See Bulgaria Nos.

Peter Dimkov (1886-1981), Naturopath — A1741

2006, Dec. 20
4414 A1741 55s multi   .90 .90

Builders of the Bulgarian State — A1742

Designs: 10s, Gen. Danail Nikolaev (1852-1942), Gen. Racho Petrov (1861-1942). 35s, Petko Karavelov (1843-1903), Marin Drinov (1838-1906). 55s, Dr. Konstantin Stoylov (1853-1901), Stefan Stambolov (1854-95). 1 l, Prince Alexander I (1857-93).

2006, Dec. 21
4415-4418 A1742   Set of 4   3.25 3.25

Souvenir Sheet

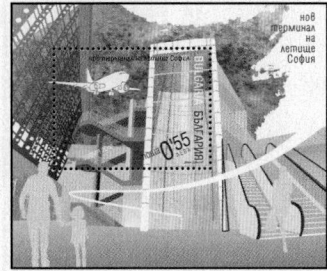

Opening of New Terminal at Sofia Airport — A1743

2006, Dec. 27   Litho.
4419 A1743 55s multi   1.25 1.25
    Exists imperf. with perforated serial number. Value, $15.

Souvenir Sheet

Admission to European Union — A1744

2007, Jan. 31   Perf. 13¼
4420 A1744 1.50 l multi   2.00 2.00

Emilian Stanev (1907-79), Novelist — A1745

2007, Feb. 28   Perf. 13
4421 A1745 55s multi + label   1.00 1.00

Treaty of Rome, 50th Anniv. A1746

2007, Mar. 23   Perf. 13¼x13
4422 A1746 1 l multi   1.60 1.60

Stage Actors — A1747

Designs: 10s, Ivan Dimov (1897-1965). 55s, Sava Ognyanov (1876-1933). 1 l, Krustyo Sarafov (1876-1952).

2007, Mar. 27   Perf. 13
4423-4425 A1747   Set of 3   2.50 2.50

Souvenir Sheet

Launch of Sputnik 1, 50th Anniv. — A1748

2007, Apr. 25   Litho.   Perf. 13¼x13
4426 A1748 1 l multi   1.40 1.40

Europa — A1749

Nos. 4427 and 4428: a, 55s, Scouts around campfire. b, 1.50 l, Scouts reading map.

2007, Apr. 26   Perf. 13 Syncopated
Size: 39x28mm
4427 A1749   Pair, #a-b   3.25 3.25
    Booklet Stamps
    Size: 31x23mm
    Perf. 13
4428 A1749   Pair, #a-b   4.50 4.50
c.   Booklet pane, 4 each #4428a-4428b   18.00 —
    Complete booklet, #4428c   18.00

    Scouting, cent.

Military Aircraft A1750

Designs: 10s, DAR 3, 1937. 35s, DAR 9, 1939. 55s, KB 309, 1939. 1 l, KB 11A, 1940.

2007, Apr. 27   Perf. 13¼x13
4429-4432 A1750   Set of 4   3.00 3.00

Death of King Boris I, 1100th Anniv. A1751

2007, May 2
4433 A1751 55s multi   1.00 1.00

Poets and Painters A1752

Designs: 10s, Dimcho Debelyanov (1887-1916), poet. 35s, Nenko Balkanski (1907-77), painter. 55s, Vera Lukova (1907-74), painter. 1 l, Theodor Trayanov (1882-1945), poet.

2007, May 23   Perf. 13
4434-4437 A1752   Set of 4   3.00 3.00

European Conference of
Transportation Ministers,
Sofia — A1753

2007, May 30 **Perf. 13x13¼**
4438 A1753 1 l multi 1.60 1.60

Monasteries — A1754

Designs: 63s, Lozenski Monastery. 75s,
Obradovski Monastery. 1.20 l, Kremikovski
Monastery. 2.20 l, Chepinski Monastery.

Perf. 12½x12¾ Syncopated
2007, May 30
Color Behind Denomination
4439 A1754 63s yel orange .90 .90
4440 A1754 75s green 1.25 1.25
4441 A1754 1.20 l red 1.90 1.90
4442 A1754 2.20 l blue 3.50 3.50
Nos. 4439-4442 (4) 7.55 7.55

Souvenir Sheet

Diplomatic Relations Between Bulgaria
and Azerbaijan, 15th Anniv. — A1755

2007, June 1 **Perf. 13**
4443 A1755 1 l multi 1.60 1.60

Excavations of
San Clemente
Basilica, Rome,
150th
Anniv. — A1756

2007, May 21 **Litho.** **Perf. 13**
4444 A1756 1 l multi 1.60 1.60

Flowers — A1757

Designs: 10s, Onosma thracica. 45s, Astra-
cantha aitosensis. 55s, Veronica krumovii. 1 l,
Verbascum adrianopolitanum.

Perf. 13x12½ Syncopated
2007, July 6
4445-4448 A1757 Set of 4 3.50 3.50

Vassil Levski
(1837-73),
Patriot — A1758

2007, July 18 **Perf. 13**
4449 A1758 55s multi 1.00 1.00

World Youth
470 Class
Yachting
Championships,
Bourgas
A1759

2007, July 21
4450 A1759 1 l multi 2.00 2.00

Battle of Stara Zagora, 130th
Anniv. — A1760

2007, July 31
4451 A1760 55s multi 1.00 1.00

2007
Rugby
World Cup,
France
A1761

2007, Sept. 5 **Perf. 13¼**
4452 A1761 55s multi 1.00 1.00

Souvenir Sheet

Ropotamo Reserve, 15th
Anniv. — A1762

No. 4453: a, 55s, Lutra lutra. b, 1 l,
Haliaeetus albicilla.

2007, Sept. 10
4453 A1762 Sheet of 2, #a-b 2.50 2.50

Miniature Sheet

Endangered Birds — A1763

No. 4454: a, 10s, Alcedo atthis. b, 35s,
Tichodroma muraria. c, 55s, Bombycilla garrulus. d, 1 l, Phoenicopterus ruber.

2007, Sept. 11 **Perf. 13**
4454 A1763 Sheet of 4, #a-d 3.25 3.25

Great Lodge of
the Old
Freemasons of
Bulgaria, 10th
Anniv. — A1764

2007, Sept. 21
4455 A1764 55s multi 1.75 1.75

Souvenir Sheet

Bulgaria Post Exchange and Sorting
Center, Sofia — A1765

2007, Oct. 9 **Litho.** **Perf. 13¼**
4456 A1765 55s multi 1.00 1.00

World Post Day.

Ivan Hadjiiski
(1907-44),
Psychologist
A1766

2007, Oct. 12 **Perf. 13**
4457 A1766 55s multi 1.00 1.00

Christmas
A1767

2007, Nov. 27 **Litho.** **Perf. 13**
4458 A1767 55s multi 1.00 1.00

Sports
Champions
A1768

Designs: 10s, Rumyana Neykova, European
2000-meter skiff rowing champion. 35s,
Stanka Zlateva, world freestyle wrestling
champion. 1 l, Stefka Kostadinova, women's
world record-holder in high jump.

2007, Dec. 19 **Perf. 13½x13**
4459-4461 A1768 Set of 3 2.25 2.25

Military
Reconnaisance in
Bulgaria,
Cent. — A1769

2007, Dec. 20 **Perf. 13x13¼**
4462 A1769 55s multi 1.00 1.00

Christo Botev (1848-76),
Poet — A1770

2008, Jan. 6 **Litho.** **Perf. 13**
4463 A1770 55s multi 1.00 1.00

Souvenir Sheet

Intl. Polar Year — A1771

No. 4464: a, 55s, Polar bear. b, 1 l,
Penguins.

2008, Jan. 30 **Perf. 13¼**
4464 A1771 Sheet of 2, #a-b, +
2 labels 2.40 2.40

Bulgarian Antarctic expeditions, 20th anniv.

Souvenir Sheet

2008 Summer Olympics,
Beijing — A1772

No. 4465: a, 55s, One volleyball player. b,
1 l, Two volleyball players.

2008, Feb. 25　Litho.　**Perf. 13**
4465　A1772　Sheet of 2, #a-b　2.40 2.40

Independence,
130th
Anniv. — A1773

2008, Feb. 29
4466　A1773　55s multi　1.10 1.10

Europa — A1774

Cover with stamp and: Nos. 4467, 4468,
Postman. Nos. 4469, 4470, Bird.

2008, Apr. 22
4467　A1774　55s grn & multi　1.00 1.00
4468　A1774　55s lilac & multi　1.00 1.00
　a.　Booklet pane of 4　4.00 —
4469　A1774　1 l blue & multi　2.00 2.00
4470　A1774　1 l org yel & multi　3.00 3.00
　a.　Booklet pane of 4　12.00 —
　　Complete booklet, #4468a,
　　4470a　13.00
　Nos. 4467-4470 (4)　7.00 7.00

Stamps in booket panes are tete-beche.

Military Aviators — A1775

No. 4471 — Airplane and: a, 55s, Capt.
Dimitri Spisarevski (1918-43). b, 1 l, Gen.
Stoyan Stoyanov (1913-97).

2008, Apr. 25
4471　A1775　Horiz. pair, #a-b　2.75 2.75

Art — A1776

Designs: 10s, Painting by Boris Kotsev
(1908-59). 35s, Nude, by Eliezer Alsheh

(1908-78). 55s, Nude, by Vera Nedkova (1908-
96). 1 l, Sculpture by Asen Peikov (1908-73).

2008, May 7
4472-4475　A1776　Set of 4　3.75 3.75

Sofia Zoo, 120th Anniv. — A1777

No. 4476: a, 10s, Csalithrix geoffroyi. b, 20s,
Hippopotamus amphibius. c, 35s, Camelus
bactrianus. d, 55s, Suricata suricata. e, 60s,
Ara ararauna. f, 1 l, Lynx lynx.
No. 4477, Like No. 4476d.

2008, May 14　　**Perf. 13**
4476　A1777　Sheet of 6, #a-f　5.00 5.00
Souvenir Sheet
Imperf
4477　A1777　55s multi　22.50 22.50

No. 4477 has simulated perforations. Bulgaria 2009 European Philatelic Exhibition.

Souvenir Sheet

Central Sports Club of the Army
(CSKA) Soccer Team, 60th
Anniv. — A1778

2008, May 7　Litho.　**Perf. 13½x13¼**
4478　A1778　55s multi　1.00 1.00

Souvenir Sheet

Space Flight of Alexander Alexandrov,
20th Anniv. — A1779

2008, June 9　Litho.　**Perf. 13**
4479　A1779　1 l multi　1.75 1.75

Union of Bulgarian Philatelists, 70th
Anniv. — A1780

2008, June 16　Litho.　**Perf. 13**
Stamp With White Border
4480　A1780　60s multi　1.00 1.00

An imperforate souvenir sheet containing
No. 4480 with a colored background sold for
well above face value. Value, $20.

Souvenir Sheet

Wildlife of Strandzha Nature
Park — A1781

No. 4481: a, 60s, Canis aureus. b, 1.50 l,
Aquila pomarina, vert.

2008, July 21　Litho.　**Perf. 13¼**
4481　A1781　Sheet of 2, #a-b　3.50 3.50

Relations
Between Bulgaria
and European
Economic
Community, 20th
Anniv. — A1782

2008, July 30　　**Perf. 13**
4482　A1782　1 l multi　1.75 1.75

Railroad Anniversaries — A1783

No. 4483: a, Orient Express passenger car,
coat of arms of Paris, Munich and Vienna. b,
Locomotive of Bulgarian State Railways, coat
of arms of Belgrade, Sofia and Istanbul.

2008, Sept. 11
4483　Pair　3.50 3.50
　a.　A1783 60s multi　1.00 1.00
　b.　A1783 1.50 l multi　2.40 2.40

Orient Express and Bulgarian State Railways, 130th anniv. No. 4483 printed in sheets
containing four of each stamp + one label.

Nikola (1893-1947) and Dimitar Petkov
(1858-1907), Politicians — A1784

2008, Sept. 18　Litho.　**Perf. 13**
4484　A1784　60s multi　1.20 1.20

Souvenir Sheet

Tsar Ferdinand (1861-1948) — A1785

2008, Sept. 22　　**Perf. 13x13¼**
4485　A1785　60s multi　1.20 1.20

Proclamation of Bulgarian independence,
cent.

Destruction of
the Knights
Templar, 700th
Anniv. — A1786

2008, Sept. 30　　**Perf. 13**
4486　A1786　1 l multi　2.00 2.00

Ferrari Race Cars — A1787

2008, Oct. 16
4487　Pair　20.00 20.00
　a.　A1787 60s 2008 Ferrari　7.00 7.00
　b.　A1787 1 l 1952 Ferrari　10.00 10.00

An imperforate souvenir sheet of the 60s
stamp with simulated perforations exists.

Red Cross in Bulgaria, 130th
Anniv. — A1788

2008, Oct. 24
4488　A1788　60s multi　1.20 1.20

Christmas
A1789

2008, Nov. 21
4489 A1789 60s multi 1.20 1.20

Monastery
Icons — A1790

No. 4490 — Madonna and Child icons from: a, Rila Monastery, 12th cent. b, Troyan Monastery, 18th cent. c, Bachkovo Monastery, 14th cent.

2008, Nov. 21
4490 Horiz. strip of 3 20.00 20.00
  a. A1790 50s multi 3.50 3.50
  b. A1790 60s multi 7.00 7.00
  c. A1790 1 l multi 9.00 9.00

An imperf. souvenir sheet of the 60s stamp with simulated perforations exists.

Sofia St. Clement
of Ohrid
University, 120th
Anniv. — A1791

2008, Nov. 25
4491 A1791 60s multi 1.20 1.20

Famous Men — A1792

No. 4492: a, Andranik Ozanian (1865-1927), Armenian general who particpated in Balkan Wars. b, Peyo Yavorov (1878-1914), Bulgarian poet.

2008, Dec. 10
4492 Horiz. pair 4.00 4.00
  a. A1792 60s multi 1.25 1.25
  b. A1792 1.50 l multi 2.50 2.50

See Armenia No. 789.

Bulgaria
2009
European
Stamp
Exhibition
A1793

2009, Jan. 23
4493 A1793 60s multi 1.20 1.20

Famous Men Born in 1809 — A1794

Designs: 10s, Abraham Lincoln (1809-65), US President. 50s, Nikolai Gogol (1809-52), writer. 60s, Charles Darwin (1809-82), naturalist. 1 l, Edgar Allan Poe (1809-49), writer.

2009, Feb. 6
4494-4497 A1794 Set of 4 4.00 4.00

An imperf. souvenir sheet of No. 4496 with simulated perforations exists.

Birds — A1795

Designs: Nos. 4498a, 4499a, 60s, Scolopax rusticola. Nos. 4498b, 4499b, 1 l, Monticola saxatilis.

2009, Mar. 2 *Perf. 13*
4498 A1795 Horiz. pair, #a-b 3.00 3.00
Souvenir Sheet
Imperf
4499 A1795 Sheet of 2, #a-b 3.00 3.00

No. 4499 has simulated perforations. See Serbia Nos. 457-458.

Amethyst
A1796

2009, Mar. 24 Litho. Perf. 13x13¼
4500 A1796 60s multi 1.20 1.20

Natl. Museum of Natural History, 120th anniv. An imperf. souvenir sheet with simulated perforations exists. Value, $20.

Hagia Sofia
Church and St.
Alexander Nevsky
Cathedral,
Sofia — A1797

2009, Mar. 25 *Perf. 13*
4501 A1797 60s multi 1.00 1.00

Sofia as Bulgarian capital, 130th anniv.

Souvenir Sheet

Preservation of Polar Regions and
Glaciers — A1798

No. 4502: a, 60s, Penguins, head of narwhal. b, 1.50 l, Body of narwhal, polar bear, seal, white-tailed eagle, icebreaker.

2009, Mar. 27
4502 A1798 Sheet of 2, #a-b 4.00 4.00

NATO Anniversaries — A1799

No. 4503 — NATO emblem and flags making up number: a, 60s, "60" (60th anniv. of NATO). b, 1.50s, "5" (5th anniv. of Bulgarian membership in NATO).

2009, Mar. 30
4503 A1799 Horiz. pair, #a-b 4.00 4.00

Bicycles
A1800

Various bicycles.

2009, Mar. 31
4504 Horiz. strip of 4 4.00 4.00
  a. A1800 10s multi .25 .25
  b. A1800 50s multi .70 .70
  c. A1800 60s multi .90 .90
  d. A1800 1 l multi 1.40 1.40

An imperf. souvenir sheet of the 60s with simulated perforations exists. Value, $20.

Souvenir Sheet

Space Flight of First Bulgarian
Cosmonaut Georgi Ivanov, 30th
Anniv. — A1801

2009, Apr. 9 *Perf. 13¼x13*
4505 A1801 60s multi 1.20 1.20

Souvenir Sheet

Restoration of the Bulgarian State,
130th Anniv. — A1802

No. 4506 — Arms of: a, 60s, 1879. b, 1 l, 1997.

2009, Apr. 15
4506 A1802 Sheet of 2, #a-b 2.75 2.75

Cacti — A1803

No. 4507: a, 10s, Rathbunia alamosensis. b, 50s, Mammilaria pseudoperbella. c, 60s, Obregonia degenerii. d, 1.50 l, Astrophitum mayas.

2009, Apr. 24 *Perf. 13*
4507 A1803 Horiz. strip of 4,
    #a-d 5.00 5.00

An imperf souvenir sheet of the 60s with simulated perforations exists. Value, $20.

Europa
A1804

Designs: Nos. 4508, 4510, 60s, IC342 galaxy. Nos. 4509, 4511, 1.50 l, M31 (Andromeda galaxy).

2009, Apr. 28 *Perf. 13 Syncopated*
    Size: 28x40mm
4508-4509 A1804 Set of 2 4.00 4.00
    Size: 25x36mm
    Perf. 13x13¼
4510-4511 A1804 Set of 2 4.00 4.00
4511a Souvenir sheet, 2 each
    #4510-4511 8.00 8.00
4511b Booklet pane of 4, #4510, 3
    #4511 13.00 —
4511c Booklet pane of 4, #4511, 3
    #4510 8.00 —
    Complete booklet, #4511b,
    4511c 24.00

Intl. Year of Astronomy. Nos. 4508-4509 were printed in sheets of 5 + label.

Introduction of the Euro, 10th
Anniv. — A1805

2009, May 20 *Perf. 13*
4512 A1805 1 l multi 2.00 2.00

Art — A1806

Designs: 10s, Landscape, by Vassil Ivanov (1909-75). 50s, Three Vases, by Georgi Kolarov (1909-96). 60s, The Black Sea, by Alexander Mutaffov (1879-1957). 1 l, Cast Shadows, by Konstantin Sturkelov (1889-1961).

2009, May 27 *Litho.*
4513-4516 A1806 Set of 4 4.00 4.00

Lokomotiv Sofia Soccer Team, 80th Anniv. — A1807

2009, May 28   **Perf. 13¼x13**
4517 A1807 60s multi   1.20 1.20

Owls — A1808

No. 4518: a, 10s, Bubo bubo. b, 50s, Athene noctua. c, 60s, Strix uralensis. d, 1.50 l, Glaucidium passerinum.

2009, May 30   **Perf. 13x13¼**
4518 A1808   Horiz. strip or
    block of 4, #a-d   5.00 5.00

Souvenir Sheet

Supermoto European Cup, Pleven — A1809

2009, June 16
4519 A1809 60s multi   1.20 1.20

Captain Petko Voivoda (1844-1900), Hajduk Leader — A1810

2009, June 17   **Perf. 13**
4520 A1810 60s multi   1.20 1.20

Todor Burmov (1834-1906), First Bulgarian Prime Minister — A1811

2009, June 26
4521 A1811 60s multi   1.20 1.20
Ministry of Internal Affairs, 130th anniv.

Souvenir Sheet

Bulgarian Post and Communications Department, 130th Anniv. — A1812

No. 4522 — Hands: a, 60s, Opening air mail letter. b, 1 l, Holding telephone.

2009, June 29   **Perf. 13¼x13**
4522 A1812   Sheet of 2, #a-b   3.00 3.00

Souvenir Sheet

First Man on the Moon, 40th Anniv. — A1813

2009, July 20
4523 A1813 60s multi   1.20 1.20

Bulgarian Academy of Science, 140th Anniv. — A1814

2009, Oct. 9   **Litho.**   **Perf. 13**
4524 A1814 60s multi   1.20 1.20

Souvenir Sheet

Diplomatic Relations Between Bulgaria and Italy, 130th Anniv. — A1815

2009, Oct. 15   **Perf. 13¼x13**
4525 A1815 1 l multi   2.00 2.00
See Italy No. 2970.

Souvenir Sheet

First Establishment of Diplomatic Relations With Foreign Countries, 130th Anniv. — A1816

2009, Nov. 1   **Perf. 13x13¼**
4526 A1816 1 l multi   2.00 2.00

Bulgarian National Television, 50th Anniv. — A1817

2009, Nov. 14   **Perf. 13¼x13**
4527 A1817 60s multi   1.20 1.20

Military Aviation — A1818

No. 4528: a, Fokker E. III and Capt. Marko Parvanov (1892-1962). b, Assen Jordanoff (1896-1967), aeronautical engineer, and Jordanoff 1.

2009, Nov. 18   **Perf. 13**
4528   Horiz. pair   3.00 3.00
   a. A1818 60s multi   1.00 1.00
   b. A1818 1 l multi   1.75 1.75

Nikola Vapzarov (1909-42), Poet — A1819

2009, Nov. 20
4529 A1819 60s multi   1.20 1.20

Christmas A1820

2009, Nov. 20
4530 A1820 60s multi   1.20 1.20

Dimitar Miladinov (1810-62), Poet — A1821

2010, Jan. 7   **Litho.**   **Perf. 13**
4531 A1821 60s multi   1.20 1.20

Bulgarian National Radio, 75th Anniv. — A1822

2010, Jan. 25   **Perf. 13x13¼**
4532 A1822 60s multi   1.20 1.20

Souvenir Sheet

2010 Winter Olympics, Vancouver — A1823

No. 4533: a, 60s, Luge. b, 1 l, Snowboarding.

2010, Feb. 5   **Perf. 13½x13**
4533 A1823   Sheet of 2, #a-b   3.00 3.00

Souvenir Sheet

Frédéric Chopin (1810-49), Composer — A1824

No. 4534 — Chopin with: a, G line of musical staff below blue frame line at bottom. b, Beam connecting four notes below blue frame line below Chopin's tie and lapel.

2010, Mar. 1   **Perf. 13**
4534 A1824 1 l Sheet of 2, #a-b,
    + 4 labels   4.00 4.00

Souvenir Sheet

Peonies — A1825

No. 4535: a, Paeonia suffruticosa subsp. rockii. b, Paeonia officinalis "Rubra Plena."

2010, Mar. 23

4535 A1825 60s Sheet of 2, #a-b 2.25 2.25

Miniature Sheet

Military Commanders — A1826

No. 4536: a, General Georgi Vazov (1860-1934), denomination at left. b, General Ivan Fichev (1860-1931). c, General Stilyan Kovachev (1860-1939). d, Colonel Vladimir Serafimov (1860-1934), denomination at right. e, General Dimitar Geshev (1860-1922).

2010, Mar. 26

4536 A1826 60s Sheet of 5, #a-
    e, + label 5.75 5.75

Souvenir Sheet

FIDE World Chess Championship Match, Sofia — A1827

2010, Apr. 22

4537 A1827 1 l multi 2.00 2.00

Europa A1828

Children's book, tree and: 60s, House, flowers, bird. 1.50s, Rabbit, insect, owl.

2010, Apr. 23 **Litho.** **Perf. 13**

4538 Horiz. pair 4.00 4.00
  a. A1828 60s multi, 29x40mm,
      with white frame 1.10 1.10
  b. A1828 1.50 l multi, 29x40mm,
      with white frame 2.75 2.75

Perf. 13x13¼

4539 Booklet pane of 2 +
      central label 4.00 4.00
  a. A1828 60s multi, 25x36mm,
      with white frame 1.10 1.10
  b. A1828 1.50 l multi, 25x36mm,
      with white frame 2.75 2.75
      Complete booklet, 4 #4539 16.00

Souvenir Sheet
Perf. 13

4540 Sheet of 2 4.00 4.00
  a. A1828 60s multi, 32x43mm,
      without white frame 1.10 1.10
  b. A1828 1.50 l multi, 32x43mm,
      without white frame 2.75 2.75

Expo 2010, Shanghai — A1829

2010, Apr. 30 **Litho.** **Perf. 13**

4541 A1829 1.40 l multi 2.75 2.75

Diplomatic Relations Between Bulgaria and Spain, Cent. A1830

2010, May 4 **Perf. 13½x13**

4542 A1830 1 l multi 2.00 2.00

Souvenir Sheet

Intl. Day of Biological Diversity — A1831

2010, May 21 **Perf. 13¼x13**

4543 A1831 1.50 l multi 3.00 3.00

Souvenir Sheets

Emanuil Manolov (1860-1902), Composer — A1832

Robert Schumann (1810-56), Composer — A1833

No. 4544 — Manolov with: a, Notes above blue frame line at top and below blue frame line at bottom. b, No notes above blue frame line at top, tails of quarter notes below blue frame at bottom.

No. 4545 — Schumann with: a, F line of musical staff below blue frame line at bottom. b, Lines of musical staff and notes below blue frame line at bottom.

2010, June 8 **Litho.** **Perf. 13**

4544 A1832 1 l Sheet of 2, #a-b,
      + 4 labels 4.00 4.00
4545 A1833 1 l Sheet of 2, #a-b,
      + 4 labels 4.00 4.00

Souvenir Sheet

Bulgarian Shepherd — A1834

2010, June 9 **Imperf.**

4546 A1834 60s multi 14.00 14.00

Balkanfila Philatelic Exhibition, Plovdiv.

Souvenir Sheet

2010 World Cup Soccer Championships, South Africa — A1835

2010, June 10 **Perf. 13¼x13**

4547 A1835 2.10 l multi 4.00 4.00

St. Prokopi Varnenski, 200th Anniv. of Death — A1836

2010, June 16 **Perf. 13**

4548 A1836 60s multi 1.20 1.20

Paintings by Jaroslav Veshin (1860-1915) — A1837

No. 4549: a, Maneuvers, 1899. b, Returning from the Market, 1898.

2010, July 23 **Perf. 13¼x13**

4549 A1837 1 l Vert. pair, #a-b, +
      central label 4.00 4.00

Souvenir Sheet

Alphonse Mucha (1860-1939), Illustrator — A1838

No. 4550: a, Summer, Autumn (denomination at left). b, Winter, Spring (denomination at right).

2010, July 23 **Perf. 13¼**

4550 A1838 1 l Sheet of 2, #a-b,
      + central label 4.00 4.00

Youth Olympics, Singapore A1839

2010, July 30 **Perf. 13**

4551 A1839 1.40 l multi 2.75 2.75

Unification of Bulgaria, 125th Anniv. — A1840

2010, Sept. 3 **Litho.** **Perf. 13**

4552 A1840 60s multi 1.00 1.00

These imperforate souvenir sheets with simulated perforations, released in late 2010, were produced in limited quantities.

Miniature Sheet

Pandas — A1841

No. 4553: a, 10s, Head of Ailuropoda melanoleuca. b, 60s, Ailuropoda melanoleuca. c, 1 l, Ailurus fulgens. d, 1.50 l, Head of Ailurus fulgens.

2010, Oct. 28 Litho. *Perf. 13*
4553 A1841 Sheet of 4, #a-d 7.50 7.50

Military Aircraft — A1842

Designs: 50s, Yak-23. 65s, MiG-15. 1 l, MiG-29.

2010, Nov. 12
4554-4556 A1842 Set of 3 4.00 4.00

Christmas — A1843

2010, Nov. 19
4557 A1843 65s multi 1.25 1.25

Miniature Sheet

Tourist Attractions of Northeastern Bulgaria — A1844

No. 4558: a, 10s, Carvings from Thracian Tomb of Sveshtari. b, 50s, Balchik Palace. c, 65s, Srebarna Nature Reserve. d, 1 l, Pobiti Kamani Geological Formation.

2010, Nov. 24 *Perf. 13x13¼*
4558 A1844 Sheet of 4, #a-d 4.25 4.25

Zachary Zograf (1810-53), Painter — A1845

2010, Nov. 26 *Perf. 13*
4559 A1845 1.50 l multi 3.00 3.00

Diplomatic Relations Between Bulgaria and Cuba, 50th Anniv. — A1846

No. 4560: a, 65s, Cuban flag, San Cristobal Church, Havana. b, 1.40 l, Bulgarian flag, St. Alexander Nevsky Cathedral, Sofia.

2010, Dec. 10
4560 A1846 Horiz. pair, #a-b 4.00 4.00

Hydrurga Leptonyx and Map of Antarctica
A1847

2011, Jan. 7 *Perf. 12¾ Syncopated*
4561 A1847 58s multi 1.00 1.00

A souvenir sheet containing 2 stamps + 2 labels was printed in 2013 in limited quantities.

Princess Clementine and 9th Plovdiv Infantry Regiment — A1848

2011, Jan. 24 *Perf. 13*
4562 A1848 65s multi + label 1.25 1.25

9th Plovdiv Infantry Regiment, 125th anniv. Printed in sheets of 4 + 4 labels.

Vanga (Vangelia Pandeva Dimitrova) (1911-96), Mystic
A1849

2011, Jan. 31 Litho.
4563 A1849 65s multi 1.25 1.25

April Fools' Day — A1850

2011, Apr. 1
4564 A1850 65s multi + label 1.25 1.25

Fictional discovery of the Planet of Gabrovo, 35th anniv. Gabrovo is Bulgarian town hosting a humor festival. Printed in sheets of 4 stamps + 4 labels. Horizontal stamp + label strips are tete-beche within the sheet.

Souvenir Sheet

Atlantic Club of Bulgaria, 20th Anniv. — A1851

2011, Apr. 11
4565 A1851 1 l multi 2.00 2.00

Souvenir Sheet

Space Achievements of the Soviet Union, 50th Anniv. — A1852

No. 4566: a, 65s, First manned space flight by Yuri Gagarin. b, 1.50 l, First probe to Venus, Venera 1.

2011, Apr. 12 *Perf. 13x13¼*
4566 A1852 Sheet of 2, #a-b 4.00 4.00

Europa — A1853

Forest and: 65s, Capreolus capreolus in winter. 1.50 l, Scolopax rusticola.

2011, Apr. 28 Litho. *Perf. 13*
Size: 29x54mm

4567 A1853	65s multi	1.25	1.25
4568 A1853	1.50 l multi	3.50	3.50
a.	Souvenir sheet, #4567-4568, perf. 13x13¼	5.00	5.00

Booklet Stamps
Size: 24x44mm
Perf. 13

4569 A1853	65s multi	1.50	1.50
4570 A1853	1.50 l multi	3.75	3.75
a.	Booklet pane of 4, 2 each #4569-4570	10.00	—
	Complete booklet, 2 #4570a	20.00	

Intl. Year of Forests

Souvenir Sheet

Serdica Edict of Religious Toleration, 1700th Anniv. — A1854

2011, Apr. 30 *Perf. 13¼x13*
4571 A1854 65s multi 1.25 1.25

Competition Protection Commission, 20th Anniv. — A1855

2011, May 2   **Perf. 13x12¾**
4572 A1855 65s multi   1.25 1.25

This imperforate souvenir sheet with simulated perforations, released in May 2011, was produced in limited quantities. Value, $15.
Compare with Type A1905.

Miniature Sheet

Tourist Attractions of North Central Bulgaria — A1856

No. 4573: a, 65s, Bear and Woodpecker, Boatin Reserve. b, 65s, Gold ring of Tsar Kaloyan, Church of the Forty Holy Martyrs, Veliko Turnovo. c, 1 l, Glozhene Monastery. d, 1 l, Woman at Etar Architectural and Ethnographic Complex, Gabrovo.

2011, June 10   **Perf. 13x13¼**
4573 A1856 Sheet of 4, #a-d   6.00 6.00

Miniature Sheet

Fish of the Danube River — A1857

No. 4574: a, 65s, Stizostedion lucioperca, Esox lucius, Aspius aspius, Hucho hucho. b, 65s, Abramis brama, Barbus barbus, Ctenopharyngodon idella, Cyprinus carpio, Carassius carassius. c, 1 l, Acipenser ruthenus, Huso huso. d, 1 l, Silurus glanis, Lota lota.

2011, June 29   **Perf. 13¼x13**
4574 A1857 Sheet of 4, #a-d   6.00 6.00

Victory of Khan Krum at Battle of Pliska, 1200th Anniv. A1858

2011, July 26
4575 A1858 65s multi   1.25 1.25

Miniature Sheet

Poisonous Mushrooms — A1859

No. 4576: a, 65s, Rhodophyllus sinuatus. b, 65s, Inocybe patouillardii. c, 1 l, Russula emetica. d, 1 l, Omphalotus olearius.

2011, July 29   **Perf. 13**
4576 A1859 Sheet of 4, #a-d   6.00 6.00

Souvenir Sheet

Waterford, Ireland to Halmstad, Sweden Tall Ships Regatta — A1860

2011, Aug. 25   **Perf. 13¼**
4577 A1860 1 l multi   2.00 2.00

Souvenir Sheet

Fridtjof Nansen (1861-1930), Arctic Explorer — A1861

2011, Oct. 10 Litho.   **Perf. 13¼x13¼**
4578 A1861 1 l multi   2.00 2.00

Franz Liszt (1811-86), Composer — A1862

2011, Oct. 21   **Perf. 13**
4579 A1862 1 l multi + label   4.00 4.00
Printed in sheets of 2 + 2 labels.

Souvenir Sheet

First Bulgarian Railway Line, 145th Anniv. — A1863

No. 4580: a, 65s, William Gladstone (1809-98), British prime minister. b, 1 l, Rail carriage. c, 1.50 l, Locomotive.

2011, Oct. 27   **Perf. 13¼x13**
4580 A1863 Sheet of 3, #a-c, + label   6.00 6.00

Miniature Sheet

Dogs Launched Into Space — A1864

No. 4581: a, 65s, Laika (Nov. 3, 1957). b, 65s, Belka and Strelka (Aug. 19, 1960). c, 1 l, Chernushka (Mar. 9, 1961). d, 1 l, Zvezdochka (Mar. 25, 1961).

2011, Oct. 28   **Perf. 13¼x13**
4581 A1864 Sheet of 4, #a-d   6.00 6.00

A souvenir sheet containing an imperforate example of No. 4581a exists from a limited printing. Value, $17.

First Bulgarians in Dakar Rally, South America — A1865

2011, Oct. 29   **Perf. 13**
4582 A1865 1.50 l multi + label   5.50 5.50
Printed in sheets of 2 + 2 labels.

Souvenir Sheet

Intl. Black Sea Action Day — A1866

No. 4583: a, Scomber scombrus. b, Mytilus galloprovincialis.

2011, Oct. 31   **Perf. 13x13¼**
4583 A1866 1 l Sheet of 2, #a-b   4.00 4.00

Yosif Tsankov (1911-71), Composer — A1867

2011, Nov. 7 Litho.   **Perf. 13¼x13**
4584 A1867 65s multi + label   1.25 1.25

Christmas A1868

2011, Nov. 17   **Perf. 13x13¼**
4585 A1868 65s multi   1.25 1.25

Military Medical Academy, 120th Anniv. — A1869

2011, Dec. 1   **Perf. 13¼x13**
4586 A1869 65s multi   1.25 1.25

Flowers A1870

Designs: 65s, Shown. 1 l, Flowers, diff., vert.

2012, Mar. 16   **Perf. 13 Syncopated**
4587-4588 A1870 Set of 2   1.25 1.25

Disbanding of the Knights Templar, 700th Anniv. — A1871

2012, Mar. 22   **Perf. 13¼x13**
4589 A1871 65s multi   1.25 1.25
No. 4589 was printed in sheets of 5 + label.

Famous People — A1872

Designs: No. 4590, 65s, Dimcho Debelyanov (1887-1916), poet. No. 4591, 65s, Anton Mitov (1862-1930), painter. No. 4592, 1 l, Yana Yazova (1912-74), writer. No. 4593, 1 l, Petya Dubarova (1962-79), poet.

2012, Mar. 28   **Perf. 13¼**
4590-4593 A1872 Set of 4   6.00 6.00

Europa
A1873

Landmarks in Veliko Turnovo: Nos. 4594, 4596a, 65s, Baldwin Tower. Nos. 4595, 4596b, 1.50 l, Patriarchal Cathedral of Tsaravets.

Perf. 13 Syncopated

2012, Apr. 4   **Litho.**
4594-4595 A1873 Set of 2   4.00 4.00

Souvenir Sheet
Perf. 13

4596 A1873 Sheet of 2, #a-b   4.00 4.00
  c.   Booklet pane of 4, #4596a,   perf. 13 on 3 sides   8.00 —
  d.   Booklet pane of 4, #4596b,   perf. 13 on 3 sides   21.00 —
     Complete booklet, #4596c-   4596d   30.00 —

20th National Antarctic
Expedition — A1874

2012, Apr. 7   **Perf. 13¼x13**
4597 A1874 1.40 l multi + label   5.50 5.50

No. 4597 was printed in sheets of 2 + 2 labels. A 65s imperf. souvenir sheet with simulated perforations was produced in limited quantities. Value, $15.

Souvenir Sheet

Sinking of the Titanic, Cent. — A1875

2012, Apr. 10
4598 A1875 1.40 l multi   2.50 2.50

Airplane
Bombardment of
Edirne Railway
Station,
Cent. — A1876

2012, Apr. 12   **Perf. 13x13¼**
4599 A1876 65s multi   1.75 1.75

Parashkev Hadjiev (1912-92),
Composer — A1877

2012, Apr. 27   **Perf. 13¼x13**
4600 A1877 65s multi + label   1.25 1.25

Bulgarian Admission to Council of
Europe, 20th Anniv. — A1878

2012, May 7   **Perf. 13x13¼**
4601 A1878 1 l multi   2.00 2.00

Stara
Zagora
Stone
Relief
Lion, 9th-
11th
Cent.
A1879

2012, May 16   **Perf. 13**
4602 A1879 65s multi   1.25 1.25

Souvenir Sheet

Association of Bulgarian Enterprises
for Intl. road Transport and Roads,
50th Anniv. — A1880

2012, May 30   **Perf. 13¼x13**
4603 A1880 2.10 l multi   4.00 4.00

Souvenir Sheet

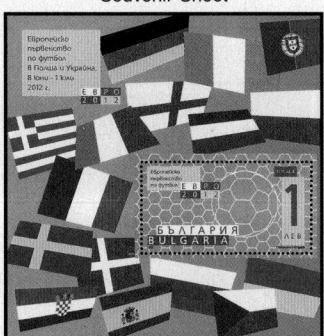

2012 European Soccer
Championships, Poland and
Ukraine — A1881

2012, June 8   **Litho.**   **Perf. 13¼**
4604 A1881 1 l multi   1.75 1.75

Miniature Sheet

Thorny Plants — A1882

No. 4605: a, 65s, Silybum marianum and butterfly. b, 65s, Carduus acanthoides and bee. c, 1 l, Centaurea solstitialis and ladybug. d, 1 l, Dipsacus laciniatus and beetle.

2012, June 14   **Perf. 13**
4605 A1882 Sheet of 4, #a-d   6.00 6.00

A1883

2012, June 22
4606 A1883 65s multi   1.25 1.25

Slavonic-Bulgarian History, by St. Paisios of Hilandar, 250th Anniv. of Publication.

Miniature Sheet

Tourist Attractions of Northwestern
Bulgaria — A1884

No. 4607: a, 65s, Plate and goblet from Rogozen Treasure archaeological find. b, 65s, Drawings from Magura Cave. c, 1 l, Meshchiite Tower, Vratsa. d, 1 l, Baba Vida Fortress, Vidin.

2012, July 12   **Perf. 13x13¼**
4607 A1884 Sheet of 4, #a-d   6.00 6.00

Souvenir Sheet

2012 Summer Olympics,
London — A1885

2012, July 16   **Perf. 13¼x13**
4608 A1885 1.50 l multi   3.00 3.00

Vassil Levski (1837-73), National
Hero — A1886

2012, July 18
4609 A1886 65s multi   1.25 1.25

Claude Debussy (1862-1918),
Composer — A1887

2012, Aug. 22   **Perf. 13**
4610 A1887 1 l multi + label   2.00 2.00

Plovdiv Fair,
120th
Anniv. — A1888

2012, Sept. 24
4611 A1888 65s multi   1.25 1.25

Ivan
Stoyanovich
(1862-1947),
Revolutionary
Leader
A1889

2012, Sept. 25
4612 A1889 65s multi   1.25 1.25

Monument of Liberty, Ruse, by Arnoldo Zocchi (1862-1940)
A1890

2012, Oct. 10   Perf. 13x13¼
4613 A1890 1 l blue   2.00 2.00

Souvenir Sheet

Flora and Fauna of Parangalitsa Preserve — A1891

No. 4614: a, 65s, Primula deorum. b, 1.50 l, Felis silvestris silvestris.

2012, Oct. 18   Perf. 13
4614 A1891 Sheet of 2, #a-b   4.25 4.25

Miniature Sheet

Railroad Mail Cars — A1892

No. 4615: a, 65s, First mail car (blue and red), ships on river. b, 65s, Green and red mail car used from 1888-1904, post offices. c, 1 l, Brown mail car used from 1895-1930, picture postcard depicting Plovdiv area costumes. d, 1 l, Green mail car used from 1909-35, railway map.

2012, Oct. 22
4615 A1892 Sheet of 4, #a-d, +
             2 labels   6.00 6.00

This imperforate souvenir sheet with simulated perforations, released in October 2012, was produced in limited quantities. Value, $15.

A1893

Horses — A1894

No. 4616: a, 65s, Andalusian horse. b, 1 l, Arabian horse.
No. 4617: a, 65s, Irish tinker horse. b, 1 l, Haflinger pony.

2012, Oct. 28
4616 A1893 Pair, #a-b   3.00 3.00
4617 A1894 Pair, #a-b   3.00 3.00
Nos. 4616-4617 each were printed in sheets containing two horizontal pairs and 2 labels.

Ministry of Railways, Posts and Telegraph, Cent. — A1895

2012, Oct. 30
4618 A1895 65s multi   1.25 1.25

Discovery of Artifacts From Grave of Khan Kubrat, Cent. — A1896

2012, Nov. 7
4619 A1896 1 l multi   2.00 2.00

Christmas A1897

2012, Nov. 20
4620 A1897 65s multi   1.25 1.25

Intl. Year of Chemistry — A1898

2012, Nov. 28   Litho.
4621 A1898 65s multi   1.40 1.40

Diplomatic Relations Between Bulgaria and Kazakhstan, 20th Anniv. — A1899

No. 4622: a, 65s, Gold rhyton with design of deer's head, 4th cent. B.C. b, 1.40 l, Gold buckle depicting bird and deer, 8th-7th cent. B.C.

2012, Dec. 12
4622 A1899 Pair, #a-b   4.00 4.00
Printed in sheets containing 3 pairs. See Kazakhstan No. 689.

Souvenir Sheet

Planetary Alignment of Dec. 21, 2012 — A1900

2012, Dec. 21   Perf. 13¼x13
4623 A1900 1 l multi   2.00 2.00

Tourism A1901

2013, Jan. 4   Perf. 13
4624 A1901 1 l multi   2.00 2.00

Maritime Administration, 130th Anniv. — A1902

2013, Feb. 28   Perf. 13¼x13
4625 A1902 65s multi + label   1.25 1.25

Souvenir Sheet

General M. D. Skobelev on Horse, by N. D. Dimitriev-Orenburgsky — A1903

2013, Mar. 5   Perf. 13x13¼
4626 A1903 1.40 l multi   2.75 2.75
End of Russo-Turkish War, 135th anniv. See Russia No. 7436.
An 65s imperforate sheet of type A1903 was printed in limited quantities and issued on Oct. 25. Value, $15.

Salvation of Bulgarian Jews, 70th Anniv. — A1904

2013, Mar. 10
4627 A1904 1.40 l multi + label 2.75 2.75
Printed in sheets containing 2 stamps + 2 labels.

Bird, Grapes and Wine Vat Greetings Type of 1998
Perf. 13 Syncopated
2013, Mar. 29   Litho.
4628 A1558 65s multi   1.50 1.50

No. 4214 Redrawn With Bulgarian Inscription at Lower Left Instead of "Europa"
2013, Mar. 29   Perf. 13 Syncopated
4629 A1629 65s multi   1.50 1.50

Rabbit Mail Carrier A1905

2013, Mar. 29   Perf. 13 Syncopated
4630 A1905 65s multi   1.25 1.25
See footnote after No. 4572.

Bells — A1906

2013, Mar. 29
4631 A1906 1 l multi   2.00 2.00

Cherno More Soccer Team,
Cent. — A1907

2013, Mar. 29   *Perf. 13¼x13*
4632 A1907 65s multi   1.25 1.25
No. 4632 was printed in sheets of 3 + label.

Slavia Soccer Team, Cent. — A1908

2013, Apr. 5   *Perf. 13¼x13*
4633 A1908 65s multi   1.25 1.25
No. 4633 was printed in sheets of 3 + label.

This imperforate souvenir sheet with
simulated perforations, released in Apr.
2013, was produced in limited quantities. Value, $15.

Miniature Sheet

Balkan Wars, Cent. — A1909

Designs: a, 65s, Bulgairan Army in battle. b,
65s, Victory Arch. c, 1 l, Surrender of Adriano-
ple, Mar. 13, 1913. d, 1 l, Tsar Ferdinand on
horse.

2013, Apr. 16   Litho.   *Perf. 13¼x13*
4634 A1909   Sheet of 4, #a-d   6.25 6.25

CSKA Soccer Team, 65th
Anniv. — A1910

2013, Apr. 23
4635 A1910 65s multi   1.50 1.50
No. 4635 was printed in sheets of 3 + label.

Europa — A1911

Bulgarian postal van: Nos. 4636, 4640a,
65s, Facing lower left corner, area in red
behind denomination. Nos. 4637, 4640b,
1.50 l, Facing lower right corner, with red triangle at lower left. No. 4638, Like No. 4636, with
olive green area behind denomination. No.
4639, Like No. 4637, with blue triangle at
lower left.

2013, Apr. 24   *Perf. 13x13¼*
Stamps With White Frames
4636 A1911   65s multi   1.25 1.25
4637 A1911 1.50 l multi   3.00 3.00
Booklet Stamps
Perf. 13 on 3 Sides
4638 A1911   65s multi   1.50 1.50
  a.   Booklet pane of 4   6.00
4639 A1911 1.50 l multi   3.50 3.50
  a.   Booklet pane of 4   14.00
       Complete booklet, #4638a,
       4639a   21.00
Souvenir Sheet
Stamps Without White Frame
Perf. 13x13¼
4640 A1911   Sheet of 2,
                 #a-b   4.25 4.25

Souvenir Sheet

Bulgarian State Railways, 125th
Anniv. — A1912

2013, May 14   *Perf. 13*
4641 A1912 1.40 l multi + label   2.75 2.75

Richard Wagner (1813-83),
Composer — A1913

2013, May 22   *Perf. 13¼x13*
4642 A1913 1 l multi + label   2.00 2.00

Souvenir Sheet

Birds in Mantaritsa Nature
Reserve — A1914

2013, May 22   Litho.
4643 A1914 1.50 l multi   3.00 3.00

St. Ivan Rilski
University of
Mining and
Geology, 60th
Anniv. — A1915

2013, May 28   *Perf. 13x13¼*
4644 A1915 65s multi   1.25 1.25

SOS Children's Villages — A1916

2013, May 30   *Perf. 13*
4645 A1916 65s multi   1.25 1.25

Souvenir Sheet

Soyuz TM-5 Space Flight of Alexander
Alexandrov, 25th Anniv. — A1917

2013, May 30   *Perf. 13¼x13*
4646 A1917 1.50 l multi   3.00 3.00

Souvenir Sheet

Mission of Sts. Cyril and Methodius to
Slavic Lands, 1150th Anniv. — A1918

2013, June 12   *Perf. 13x13¼*
4647 A1918 3.20 l multi   6.25 6.25
See Czech Republic No. 3573, Slovakia No.
666 and Vatican City No. 1536.

Miniature Sheet

Tourist Attractions in Southwestern
Bulgaria — A1919

No. 4648: a, 65s, Building in Kovachevitsa.
b, 65s, Wildlife in Skakavitsa Reserve. c, 1 l,
Fresco, Zemen Monastery. d, 1 l, Church of
St. Petka of the Saddlers, Vassil Levski (1837-
73), national hero.

2013, June 17
4648 A1919   Sheet of 4, #a-d   6.25 6.25

Souvenir Sheet

Tsar Boris III (1894-1943) — A1920

2013, Aug. 30   Litho.   *Perf. 13¼*
4649 A1920 1.50 l multi   3.00 3.00

Diplomatic Relations Between Bulgaria and the United States, 110th Anniv. — A1921

2013, Sept. 12   Litho.   *Perf. 13¼x13*
4650   A1921   1.40 l multi   2.75   2.75

Botev-Plovdiv Soccer Team, Cent — A1922

2013, Oct. 25   Litho.   *Perf. 13*
4651   A1922   65s multi   1.25   1.25

No. 4651 was printed in sheets of 3 + label.

Cat Breeds — A1923

No. 4652: a, 65s, Siamese. b, 1 l, Birman.
No. 4653, horiz.: a, 65s, Scottish Fold. b, 1 l, Somali.

Perf. 13¼x13, 13x13¼
2013, Oct. 26   Pairs, #a-b   Litho.
4652-4653   A1923   Set of 2   6.25   6.25

Miniature Sheet

Orchids — A1924

No. 4654: a, 65s, Cymbidium tridioides. b, 65s, Dendrobium fimbriatum var. occulatum. c, 1 l, Epidendrum radicans. d, 1 l, Dendrobium nobile.

2013, Oct. 26   Litho.   *Perf. 13*
4654   A1924   Sheet of 4, #a-d   6.25   6.25

Souvenir Sheet

Green Balkans Association, 25th Anniv. — A1925

2013, Oct. 27   Litho.   *Perf. 13½x13¼*
4655   A1925   1 l multi   2.00   2.00

Sofia Metro, 15th Anniv. A1926

No. 4656 — Metro cars and: a, Serdika Fortress, Sofia coat of arms. b, Lion's Bridge Station. c, Station, Sofia coat of arms.

2013, Nov. 22   Litho.   *Perf. 13x13¼*
4656   Booklet pane of 3 + label   6.25   —
  a.   A1926 65s multi   1.25   1.25
  b.   A1926 1 l multi   1.75   1.75
  c.   A1926 1.50 l multi   2.75   2.75
    Complete booklet, #4656   6.25

Christmas — A1927

2013, Nov. 22   Litho.   *Perf. 13x13¼*
4657   A1927   65s multi   1.25   1.25

Thracian Artifacts from 4th Cent., B.C. A1928

Designs: No. 4658, 1 l, Silver vial with griffin ornamentation. No. 4659, 1 l, Rhyton with galloping horse.

Perf. 13x12¾ Syncopated
2013, Dec. 18   Litho.
4658-4659   A1928   Set of 2   3.75   3.75

Souvenir Sheet

2014 Winter Olympics, Sochi, Russia — A1929

2014, Jan. 31   Litho.   *Perf. 13¼x13*
4660   A1929   1.40 l multi   2.75   2.75

Mushrooms A1930

Designs: 10s, Boletus pinophilus. 20s, Coprinus picaceus. 50s, Amanita citrina. 1 l, Russula virescens.

Perf. 12¾x12½ Syncopated
2014, Feb. 10   Litho.
4661   A1930   10s multi   .35   .35
4662   A1930   20s multi   .50   .50
4663   A1930   50s multi   1.00   1.00
4664   A1930   1 l multi   2.00   2.00
    Nos. 4661-4664 (4)   3.85   3.85

PFC Levski Sofia Soccer Team, Cent. — A1931

2014, Feb. 21   Litho.   *Perf. 13¼x13*
4665   A1931   65s multi, dated "2013"   1.25   1.25
  a.   Dated "2014"   1.25   1.25

Nos. 4665 and 4665a were each printed in sheets of 3 + label.

Galileo Galilei (1564-1642), Astronomer — A1932

2014, Feb. 21   Litho.   *Perf. 13¼x13*
4666   A1932   1 l multi   2.00   2.00

No. 4666 was printed in sheets of 4.

Diplomatic Relations Between Bulgaria and Romania, 135th Anniv. — A1933

2014, Mar. 7   Litho.   *Perf. 13*
4667   A1933   80s multi   1.60   1.60

Souvenir Sheet

Diplomatic Relations Between Bulgaria and People's Republic of China, 65th Anniv. — A1934

2014, Mar. 14   Litho.   *Perf. 13*
4668   A1934   2.10 l multi   4.00   4.00

St. Sophronius of Vratsa (1739-1813), Bishop — A1935

2014, Mar. 17   Litho.   *Perf. 13*
4669   A1935   65s multi   1.40   1.40

A1936

Bulgarian Parliamentarism, 135th Anniv. — A1937

No. 4670: a, 10s, Turnovo Constitution. b, 20s, Exarch Anthim I (1816-88). c, 30s, Copper bell of 1879 Parliament. d, 65s, 1991 Bulgarian Constitution and current bell of Parliament.
  1 l, Exarch Anthim I, diff.

2014, Apr. 3   Litho.   *Perf. 13¼x13*
4670   A1936   Sheet of 4, #a-d   2.50   2.50
Souvenir Sheet
4671   A1937   1 l multi   2.00   2.00

Miniature Sheet

Famous Men — A1938

No. 4672: a, 65s, Taras Shevchenko (wearing hat) (1814-61), writer. b, 65s, Richard Strauss (1864-1949), composer. c, 1 l, William

Shakespeare (1564-1616), writer. d, 1 l,
Mikhail Lermontov (1814-41), writer.

2014, Apr. 5   Litho.   Perf. 13
4672 A1938   Sheet of 4, #a-d   6.25 6.25
Balkanfila 2014 Intl. Philatelic Exhibition,
Vidin.

Zaria Masonic Lodge, Sofia,
Cent. — A1939

2014, Apr. 15   Litho.   Perf. 13¼x13
4673 A1939 65s multi   1.25 1.25
  a.   Souvenir sheet of 4   3.80 3.80

Launch of STV Kaliakra, 30th
Anniv. — A1940

2014, Apr. 17   Litho.   Perf. 13¼x13
4674 A1940 65s multi + label   1.25 1.25
  No. 4674 was printed in sheets of 2 + 2
labels.

Europa
A1941

Dancers and musicians playing: 65s, Drum.
1.50 l, Shepherd's pipe.

Perf. 13 Syncopated
2014, Apr. 29   Litho.
Stamps With White Frames
4675 A1941 65s multi   1.25 1.25
4676 A1941 1.50 l multi   3.00 3.00
Souvenir Sheet
Stamps Without White Frame
Perf. 13
4677   Sheet of 2   4.25 4.25
  a.   A1941 65s multi   1.25 1.25
  b.   A1941 1.50 l multi   3.00 3.00
Size: 29x39mm
Stamps With White Frames
4678   Booklet pane of 6 + la-
         bel   17.00 —
  a.   A1941 65s multi, perf. 13 vert.   2.50 2.50
  b.   A1941 65s multi, perf. 13 at left   2.50 2.50
  c.   A1941 65s multi, imperf.   2.50 2.50
  d.   A1941 1.50 l multi, perf. 13 vert.   4.50 4.50
  e.   A1941 1.50 l multi, perf. 13 at
         left   4.50 4.50
  f.   A1941 1.50 l multi, imperf.   4.50 4.50
         Complete booklet, #4678   17.00

Souvenir Sheet

Ulmus Minor — A1942

2014, May 12   Litho.   Perf. 13x13¼
4679 A1942 1 l multi   2.50 2.50

Souvenir Sheet

Stephan Parushev (1850-95), First
Postmaster of Bulgarian Post — A1943

2014, May 14   Litho.   Perf. 13
4680 A1943 1 l multi   2.00 2.00
  Bulgarian Post, 135th anniv.

Kozloduy Nuclear Power Plant, 40th
Anniv. — A1944

2014, May 20   Litho.   Perf. 13¼x13
4681 A1944 65s multi   1.25 1.25

Souvenir Sheet

2014 World Cup Soccer
Championships, Brazil — A1945

2014, June 12   Litho.   Perf. 13¼x13
4682 A1945 2.10 l multi   4.50 4.50

Journalism in Bulgaria, 170th
Anniv. — A1946

2014, June 17   Litho.   Perf. 13¼x13
4683 A1946 65s multi   1.25 1.25

Diplomatic Relations Between Bulgaria
and Russia, 135th Anniv.
A1947

2014, July 7   Litho.   Perf. 13
4684 A1947 1.40 l multi   2.75 2.75
  See Russia No. 7542.

Prince Alexander I (1857-93) and
National Guards — A1948

2014, July 10   Litho.   Perf. 13
4685 A1948 65s multi   1.25 1.25
  National Guard Unit of Bulgaria, 135th anniv.

Souvenir Sheet

Peter Deunov (1864-1944), Spiritual
Leader — A1949

2014, July 11   Litho.   Perf. 13x13¼
4686 A1949 1.50 l multi   3.00 3.00

Bulgarian
Customs
Department,
135th
Anniv. — A1950

2014, Aug. 8   Litho.   Perf. 13x13¼
4687 A1950 65s multi   1.25 1.25

Trams
A1951

Tram from: 30s, Berlin, 1900. 65s, Glasgow,
1930. 80s, Melbourne, 1945. 1 l, Sofia, 2014.

2014, Oct. 24   Litho.   Perf. 13
4688-4691 A1951   Set of 4   5.25 5.25
  4691a   Souvenir sheet of 4,
            #4688-4691   5.25 5.25

Birds — A1952

Designs: 30s, Bombycilla garrulus. 50s,
Erythropygia galactotes. 1 l, Melanocorypha
yeltoniensis. 1.50 l, Hippolais icterina.

2014, Oct. 25   Litho.   Perf. 13¼x13
4692-4695 A1952   Set of 4   6.00 6.00
  4695a   Souvenir sheet of 4,
            #4692-4695   6.00 6.00

Miniature Sheet

Tourist Attractions of South Central
Bulgaria — A1953

  No. 4696: a, 65s, Gold coin found at Perper-
ikon archaeological site. b, 65s, Plovdiv
Regional Ethnographic Museum. c, 1 l, Bulga-
rian National Astronomical Observatory,
Rozhen. d, 1 l, Flora and fauna of Kupena
Nature Reserve.

2014, Oct. 25   Litho.   Perf. 13x13¼
4696 A1953   Sheet of 4, #a-d   6.25 6.25

  This imperforate souvenir sheet with
simulated perforations, released in Oct.
2014, was produced in limited quantities. Value, $17.50.

Alexandrovska Hospital, Sofia, 135th
Anniv. — A1954

2014, Oct. 31   Litho.   Perf. 13¼x13
4697 A1954 65s multi   1.25 1.25

Souvenir Sheet

King Wladyslaw III of Poland (1424-44) — A1955

2014, Nov. 10   Litho.   Perf. 13
4698 A1955 1.50 l multi   3.00 3.00

Battle of Varna, 570th anniv.

Diplomatic Relations Between Bulgaria and the Sovereign Military Order of Malta, 20th Anniv. — A1956

2014, Nov. 11   Litho.   Perf. 13x13¼
4699 A1956 1.50 l multi   3.00 3.00

Christmas
A1957

2014, Nov. 20   Litho.   Perf. 13x13¼
4700 A1957 65s multi   1.25 1.25

Souvenir Sheet

Tsar Samuel of Bulgaria — A1958

2014, Nov. 25   Litho.   Perf. 13x13¼
4701 A1958 65s multi   1.40 1.40

Battle of Belasitsa, 1000th anniv.

Consecration of Church of St. Nicholas the Miracle Maker, Sofia, Cent. — A1959

2014, Dec. 5   Litho.   Perf. 13x13¼
4702 A1959 65s multi   1.25 1.25

Artists — A1960

Designs: 30s, Konstantin Sturkelov (1889-1961), painter. 65s, Nikolai Rainov (1889-1954), painter. 80s, Mikhail Katz (1889-1964), sculptor. 1 l, Ivan Lazarov (1889-1952), sculptor.

2014, Dec. 5   Litho.   Perf. 13¼x13
4703-4706 A1960 Set of 4   5.25 5.25

Petar Uvaliev (1915-98), Writer and Radio Commentator — A1961

2015, Jan. 12   Litho.   Perf. 13
4707 A1961 65s multi   1.25 1.25

Bulgarian Cinema, Cent. A1962

2015, Jan. 13   Litho.   Perf. 13¼x13
4708 A1962 65s multi   1.25 1.25

Old Clocks and Watches A1963

Designs: 5s, Astronomical clock. 30s, Table clock. 80s, Pocket watch.

Perf. 12¾x12½ Syncopated
2015, Feb. 20   Litho.
4709 A1963 5s multi   .35   .35
  a.   Perf. 13 horiz.   .60   .60
4710 A1963 30s multi   1.25 1.25
  a.   Perf. 13 horiz.   .40   .40
4711 A1963 80s multi   .90   .90
      Nos. 4709-4711 (3)   2.50 2.50

Bandung 2017 World Stamp Exhibition, Indonesia (Nos. 4709a, 4710a). Issued: Nos. 4709a, 4710a, 7/27/17. Nos. 4709a and 4710a were printed together in sheets of four containing two of each stamp.

Souvenir Sheet

Apollo-Soyuz Joint Space Flight, 40th Anniv. — A1964

2015, Feb. 20   Litho.   Perf. 13
4712 A1964 65s multi   1.25 1.25

Imperforate examples of No. 4712 exist from a limited printing.

Disabled Soldiers' Union, Cent. — A1965

2015, Mar. 27   Litho.   Perf. 13
4713 A1965 65s multi   1.25 1.25

Europa
A1966

Toys: 65s, Rocking horse. 1.50 l, Doll.

Perf. 13 Syncopated
2015, Apr. 20   Litho.
4714 A1966 65s   1.25 1.25
4715 A1966 1.50 l multi   3.00 3.00
Souvenir Sheet
Perf. 13
4716   Sheet of 2   4.25 4.25
  a.   A1966 65s multi   2.75 2.75
  b.   A1966 1.50 l multi   2.75 2.75
Booklet Stamps
Size: 29x39mm
Perf. 13 on 1 Side
4717 A1966 65s   1.25 1.25
  a.   Booklet pane of 4   5.00
4718 A1966 1.50 l multi   3.00 3.00
  a.   Booklet pane of 4   12.00
        Complete booklet, #4717a,
        4718a   17.00

This imperforate souvenir sheet with simulated perforations, released in April 2015, was produced in limited quantities. Value, $15.

Souvenir Sheet

Ecology and Forestry — A1967

2015, May 7   Litho.   Perf. 13¼x13
4719 A1967 1 l multi   2.00 2.00

Medical University of Plovdiv, 70th Anniv. — A1968

2015, May 14   Litho.   Perf. 13¼x13
4720 A1968 65s multi   1.25 1.25

International Telecommunication Union, 150th Anniv. — A1969

2015, May 18   Litho.   Perf. 13¼x13
4721 A1969 1 l multi   1.75 1.75

Marek Soccer Team, Cent. — A1970

2015, May 25   Litho.   Perf. 13
4722 A1970 65s multi   1.25 1.25

No. 4722 was printed in sheets of 3 + label.

Souvenir Sheet

First European Games, Baku — A1971

2015, May 29   Litho.   Perf. 13¼x13
4723 A1971 1.40 l multi   2.75 2.75

Oncology Hospital, 65th
Anniv. — A1972

2015, June 17 Litho.   Perf. 13¼x13
4724 A1972 65s multi   1.25 1.25

Baby, Princess
Marie Louise and
Maichin Dom
Gynecological
Hospital,
Sofia — A1973

2015, Aug. 6 Litho.   Perf. 13x13¼
4725 A1973 65s multi   1.25 1.25

Souvenir Sheet

Stephan Kunchev (1915-2001), Stamp
Designer — A1974

2015, Aug. 6 Litho.   Perf. 13
4726 A1974 1.50 l multi   3.00 3.00

An imperforate souvenir sheet containing a
65s stamp of this design was produced in limited quantities.

Folk Art — A1975

People in costumes at Koprivstitsa Folk Festival: 50s, Men and women. 65s, Men. 1 l,
Women.

2015, Aug. 6 Litho.   Perf. 13¼x13
4727-4729 A1975 Set of 3   4.25 4.25
4729a   Souvenir sheet of 3,
           #4727-4729 + 3 labels 4.25 4.25

Miniature Sheet

Tourist Attractions of Southeastern
Bulgaria — A1976

No. 4730: a, 65s, St. Anastasia Island. b,
65s, Artifact from Kabyle Archaeological
Reserve. c, 1 l, Nestinarstvo dancer on hot
coals. d, 1 l, Grapes and glass of wine.

2015, Aug.15 Litho.   Perf. 13x13¼
4730 A1976   Sheet of 4, #a-d   6.25 6.25

Book
A1977

Dove
A1978

Ferris
Wheel — A1979

Trophy
A1980

Bird on
Branch
and
Ladybugs
A1981

Perf. 13 Syncopated
2015, Sept. 16   Litho.
4731 A1977 65s multi   1.25 1.25
4732 A1978 65s multi   1.25 1.25
4733 A1979 65s multi   1.25 1.25
4734 A1980 1 l multi   2.00 2.00
4735 A1981 1 l multi   2.00 2.00
      Nos. 4731-4735 (5)   7.75 7.75

Alphonse de
Lamartine (1790-
1869),
Writer — A1982

2015, Oct. 21 Litho.   Perf. 13x13¼
4736 A1982 1.50 l multi   3.00 3.00

No. 4736 was printed in sheets of 4 + 2
labels.

Worldwide Fund for Nature
(WWF) — A1983

Canis lupus lupus: Nos. 4737, 4741a, 65s,
Adult and three pups. Nos. 4738, 4741b, 80s,
Wolf with head lowered. Nos. 4739, 4741c,
1.40 l, Wolf with head raised. Nos. 4740,
4741d, 3 l, Four wolves.

2015, Oct. 23 Litho.   Perf. 13
4737-4740 A1983 Set of 4   11.50 11.50
4740a Block or horiz. strip of 4,
       #4737-4740   11.50 11.50
Souvenir Sheet
Perf. 13¼
4741 A1983   Sheet of 4, #a-d 11.50 11.50

No. 4741 contains four 39x29mm stamps.
Nos. 4737-4740 were each printed in sheets
containing 20 stamps + 5 labels. No. 4740a
was printed in a sheet containing two blocks or
strips.

An imperforate souvenir sheet with
simulated perforations containing a 30s
stamp depicting Roald Amundsen and
a 40s stamp depicting Robert Peary,
released Oct. 23, 2015, was produced
in limited quantities.

Flowers — A1984

Designs: 10s, Viola rhodopeia. 50s, Veronica kellereri. 65s, Papaver degenii. 1 l, Col-
chicum borisii.

2015, Nov. 6 Litho.   Perf. 13x13¼
4742-4745 A1984 Set of 4   4.50 4.50
4745a Souvenir sheet of 4,
       #4742-4745   4.50 4.50

National Philatelic Exhibition, Veliko Turnovo
(#4745a).

Souvenir Sheet

Uprising of Peter and Assen, 830th
Anniv. — A1985

2015, Nov. 8 Litho.   Perf. 13½x13¼
4746 A1985 1.50 l multi   2.75 2.75

Locomotives and Railroad
Stations — A1986

No. 4747: a, 65s, 1891 locomotive, Ruse
and Kaspichan stations. b, 1 l, 1897 locomotive, Kaspichan and Varna stations. c, 1.50 l,
1887 locomotive, Tsaribrod and Sofia stations.
d, 2 l, 1890 locomotive, Sofia and Saranbei
stations.

2015, Nov. 18 Litho.   Perf. 13¼x13
4747 A1986   Sheet of 4, #a-d 10.00 10.00

Opening of Sofia
Tech
Park — A1987

2015, Dec. 1 Litho.   Perf. 13x13¼
4748 A1987 1 l multi   2.00 2.00

Christmas — A1988

2015, Dec. 2 Litho.   Perf. 13
4749 A1988 1 l multi   1.75 1.75

Souvenir Sheet

Plovdiv, 2019 European Capital of Culture — A1989

2015, Dec. 21 Litho. *Perf. 13¼*
4750 A1989 1 l multi 2.00 2.00

Emil Dimitrov (1940-2005), Singer — A1990

2015, Dec. 23 Litho. *Perf. 13*
4751 A1990 65s multi 1.25 1.25

Postcrossing — A1991

2015, Dec. 23 Litho. *Perf. 13*
4752 A1991 1 l multi 2.00 2.00

Souvenir Sheet

Surova Folk Festival Mask — A1992

2016, Jan. 28 Litho. *Perf. 13¼x13*
4753 A1992 1.50 l multi 3.00 3.00

This imperforate souvenir sheet with simulated perforations, released in Feb. 2016, was produced in limited quantities. Value, $17.50.

Assen Stareyshiski (1936-91), Artist — A1993

2016, Mar. 30 Litho. *Perf. 13*
4754 A1993 65s multi 1.25 1.25

A1994

Europa A1995

Perf. 13 Syncopated
2016, Apr. 26 Litho.
4755 A1994 1 l multi 2.00 2.00
4756 A1995 2 l multi 4.00 4.00
Souvenir Sheet
Perf. 13
4757 Sheet of 2 6.00 6.00
a. A1994 1 l multi 2.00 2.00
b. A1995 2 l multi 4.00 4.00
Size: 47x29mm
Perf. 13¼ on 2 Sides
4758 A1994 1 l multi 2.00 2.00
a. Tete-beche pair 4.00 4.00
4759 A1995 2 l multi 4.00 4.00
a. Tete-beche pair 8.00 8.00
Think Green Issue.
Nos. 4758 and 4759 were each printed in sheets of 4, with one stamp tete-beche in relation to the other stamps. The stamps include an imperforate margin at left or right. The sheets were sold with, but unattached to, a booklet cover.

Pencho Slaveykov (1866-1912), Poet — A1996

2016, Apr. 27 Litho. *Perf. 13*
4760 A1996 65s multi 1.25 1.25

New Year 2016 (Year of the Monkey) — A1997

2016, Apr. 28 Litho. *Perf. 13*
4761 A1997 2 l multi 4.00 4.00
An imperforate souvenir sheet of type A1997, with the emblem for World Stamp Show 2016 in the upper corner was produced in limited quantities. Value, $17.50.

St. George's Church, Kavarna A1998

Perf. 12¾ Syncopated
2016, May 5 Litho.
4762 A1998 65s multi 1.25 1.25

Ancient Thracian Coins — A1999

Designs: 65s, Silver coin depicting Tsar Sitalk, 444-424 B.C. 1 l, Silver coin depicting Tsar Metok, 407-389 B.C. 1.50 l, Silver coin depicting Hebrizelm, 405-383 B.C. 2 l, Bronze coin depicting Kotis, 383-359 B.C.

2016, May 10 Litho. *Perf. 13*
4763-4766 A1999 Set of 4 10.00 10.00
4766a Sheet of 4, #4763-4766, + 4 labels 10.00 10.00
Nos. 4763-4766 were each issued in sheets of 50 and sheets of 20 + 20 labels.

Alexander Poplilov (1916-2001), Painter — A2000

2016, May 12 Litho. *Perf. 13¼x13*
4767 A2000 65s multi 1.25 1.25

Beroe Soccer Team, Cent. — A2001

2016, May 16 Litho. *Perf. 13*
4768 A2001 65s multi 1.25 1.25
a. Souvenir sheet of 4 3.50 3.50

Hristo Botev (1848-76), Poet, and Steamship Radetski — A2002

2016, May 18 Litho. *Perf. 13*
4769 A2002 65s multi 1.25 1.25
Hijacking of the Radetski by Botev and followers to enter Bulgaria, 140th anniv.

Port of Ruse, 150th Anniv. A2003

2016, May 26 Litho. *Perf. 13¼x13*
4770 A2003 1 l multi 1.50 1.50

Souvenir Sheet

Chess — A2004

2016, July 12 Litho. *Perf. 13x13¼*
4771 A2004 3 l multi 6.25 6.25

White Storks, Flags of Bulgaria and Israel A2005

2016, Sept. 13 Litho. *Perf. 13*
4772 A2005 2.20 l multi 4.50 4.50
See Israel No. 2115.

Exarch Anthim I (1816-88), Chairman of National Assembly of Bulgaria — A2006

2016, Sept. 15 Litho. *Perf. 13¼x13*
4773 A2006 65s multi 1.00 1.00

Souvenir Sheet

Restoration of Trapezitsa Architectural Museum Reserve, Veliko Tarnovo — A2007

2016, Sept. 22   Litho.   Perf. 13¼x13
4774   A2007   1.50 l multi   3.00 3.00

See Azerbaijan No. 1119.

Wiki Loves Earth International Photography Contest — A2008

2016, Oct. 7   Litho.   Perf. 13¼x13
4775   A2008   2 l multi   2.75 2.75

A souvenir sheet containing 4 No. 4775 was prduced in limited quantities.

"Great Is Our Soldier," Bulgarian Army Anthem, Cent. — A2009

2016, Oct. 7   Litho.   Perf. 13¼x13
4776   A2009   2 l multi   4.00 4.00

Worldwide Fund for Nature (WWF) — A2010

Testudo graeca: Nos. 4777, 4781a, 65s, Laying eggs. Nos. 4778, 4781b, 80s, Eggs hatching. Nos. 4779, 4781c, 1.40 l, Adult. Nos. 4780, 4781d, 3 l, Two adults.

2016, Oct. 21   Litho.   Perf. 13
4777-4780   A2010   Set of 4   6.75 6.75
4780a   Block of 4, #4777-4780,
            perf. 13 syncopated   6.75 6.75
Souvenir Sheet
Perf. 13¼
4781   A2010   Sheet of 4, #a-d   6.75 6.75

No. 4781 contains four 39x29mm stamps.

An imperforate souvenir sheet with simulated perforations containing a 65s stamp depicting a cat, released Oct. 10, 2016, was produced in limited quantities.

Motorcycles — A2011

Designs: 65s, BMW R 1200 GS. 1.50 l, Suzuki V-Strom 1000. 2 l, Honda VFR800X Crossrunner. 3 l, Suzuki Multistrada 1200S.

2016, Oct. 22   Litho.   Perf. 13
4782-4785   A2011   Set of 4   8.25 8.25
4785a   Souvenir sheet of 4,
            #4782-4785, perf. 13¼   8.25 8.25

An imperforate souvenir sheet containing No. 4782 with simulated perforations was produced in limited quantities.

Bulgarian Antarctic Expedition, 25th Anniv. — A2012

2016, Nov. 14   Litho.   Perf. 13
4786   A2012   65s multi   .70 .70

Flags of Bulgaria and Switzerland, Louis-Emil Eyer (1865-1916), Physical Education Teacher and Coach — A2013

2016, Nov. 16   Litho.   Perf. 13
4787   A2013   1 l multi   1.10 1.10

Diplomatic relations between Bulgaria and Switzerland, cent.

Christmas A2014

2016, Nov. 16   Litho.   Perf. 13x13¼
4788   A2014   1 l multi   1.10 1.10

Souvenir Sheet

Paintings by Dimitar Dobrovich (1816-1905) — A2015

No. 4789: a, 65s, Self-portrait. b, 2 l, The Spinner Woman.

2016, Nov. 17   Litho.   Perf. 13x13¼
4789   A2015   Sheet of 2, #a-b, +
               2 labels   3.00 3.00

Konstantin Velichkov (1855-1907), Writer and Co-Founder of National Academy of Arts — A2016

2016, Nov. 22   Litho.   Perf. 13¼x13
4790   A2016   65s multi   .70 .70

National Academy of Arts, 120th anniv.

Vasil Yonchev (1916-85), Typographer — A2017

2016, Nov. 22   Litho.   Perf. 13¼x13
4791   A2017   65s multi   .70 .70

Georgi Bonchev (1866-1955), Geologist A2018

2016, Dec. 7   Litho.   Perf. 13x13¼
4792   A2018   65s multi   .70 .70

National Palace of Culture, Sofia, 35th Anniv. — A2019

2016, Dec. 9   Litho.   Perf. 13¼x13
4793   A2019   1.50 l multi + label   1.60 1.60

Souvenir Sheet

Gen. Vladimir Stoychev (1892-1990) Riding Horse — A2020

2017, Feb. 28   Litho.   Perf. 13
4794   A2020   2 l multi   2.25 2.25

An imperforate souvenir sheet with simulated perforations containing a 65s stamp depicting a rooster, released Feb. 28, 2017, was produced in limited quantities.

Bulgarian Civil Aviation, 70th Anniv. — A2021

2017, Mar. 22   Litho.   Perf. 13
4795   A2021   65s multi + label   .70 .70

Rotary Foundation, Cent. — A2022

2017, Apr. 4   Litho.   Perf. 13¼x13
4796   A2022   2 l multi   2.25 2.25

Varna, 2017 European Youth Capital — A2023

2017, Apr. 7   Litho.   Perf. 13
4797   A2023   1 l multi   1.10 1.10

Souvenir Sheet

Plovdiv, 2019 European Capital of Culture — A2024

No. 4798 — Mosaic from Plovdiv depicting: a, 1 l, Pears. b, 1.50 l, Bird.

2017, Apr. 11 Litho. Perf. 13x13¼
4798 A2024 Sheet of 2, #a-b, +
            2 labels   3.00 3.00

Souvenir Sheet

Ella Fitzgerald (1917-96), Jazz
Singer — A2025

2017, Apr. 28 Litho. Perf. 13¼x13
4799 A2025 2 l multi   2.25 2.25

Imperforate examples of No. 4799 with simulated perforations and the emblem of the Finlandia 2017 Philatelic Exhibition in the sheet
margin were printed in limited quantities.

Bulgarian Marine Aviation,
Cent. — A2026

2017, Apr. 29 Litho. Perf. 13¼x13
4800 A2026 65s multi   .75 .75

Arturo Toscanini (1867-1957),
Conductor — A2027

2017, May 4 Litho. Perf. 13
4801 A2027 1 l multi + label   1.25 1.25

Europa
A2028

Designs: 65s, Euxinograd Palace, Varna.
2.10 l, Asen's Fortress.

Perf. 13 Syncopated
2017, May 4   Litho.
4802 A2028   65s multi   .75 .75
4803 A2028   2.10 l multi   2.40 2.40
Booklet Stamps
Perf. 13¼ on 2 or 3 Sides
4804 A2028   65s multi   .75 .75
  a.   Booklet pane of 4   3.00
4805 A2028   2.10 l multi   2.40 2.40
  a.   Booklet pane of 4   9.75 —
        Complete booklet, #4804a,
        4805a   13.00

Souvenir Sheet
Perf. 13¼
4806   Sheet of 2   3.25 3.25
  a.   A2028 65s multi   .75 .75
  b.   A2028 2.10 l multi   2.40 2.40

No. 4806 contains two 39x29mm stamps.

Souvenir Sheet

Battle of Doiran, Cent. — A2029

2017, May 9 Litho. Perf. 13x13¼
4807 A2029 1.50 l multi   1.75 1.75

Souvenir Sheet

Black Sea Marine Life — A2030

No. 4808: a, 65s, Delphinus delphis pon-
ticus. b, 2 l, Barnea candida.

2017, May 22 Litho. Perf. 13
4808 A2030 Sheet of 2, #a-b   3.00 3.00

Grigor Vachkov (1932-80),
Actor — A2031

2017, May 26 Litho. Perf. 13¼x13
4809 A2031 65s multi   .75 .75

Rose Festival,
Kazanlak — A2032

2017, June 2 Litho. Perf. 13x13¼
4810 A2032 65s multi   .75 .75

Carl Djerassi (1923-2015),
Chemist — A2033

2017, June 8 Litho. Perf. 13x13¼
4811 A2033 1 l multi   1.25 1.25

Tsar Simeon II, Chairman of Union of
Bulgarian Philatelists — A2034

2017, June 16 Litho. Perf. 13x13¼
4812 A2034 1.50 l multi + label   1.75 1.75
  a.   Souvenir sheet of 2 + 2 labels 3.50 3.50

Union of Bulgarian Philatelists, 80th anniv.
(in 2018).

Lighthouses
A2035

Designs: 65s, Akhtopol Lighthouse. 1 l,
Shabla Lighthouse. 1.50 l, Burgas Lighthouse.
2 l, Galata Lighthouse.

2017, June 22 Litho. Perf. 13
4813-4816 A2035 Set of 4   6.00 6.00
4816a   Souvenir sheet of 4,
              #4813-4816   6.00 6.00

The Ninth Wave, by Ivan Aivazovsky
(1817-1900) — A2036

2017, July 26 Litho. Perf. 13
4817 A2036 1 l multi   1.25 1.25
  a.   Souvenir sheet of 4   5.00 5.00

Rayna
Knyaginya
(1856-1917),
Seamstress of
Flag of the
Uprising of April
1876 — A2037

2017, July 28 Litho. Perf. 13
4818 A2037 1 l multi   1.25 1.25

Rayko Raychev, Pathologist, Cent. of
Birth — A2038

2017, Aug. 8 Litho. Perf. 13
4819 A2038 65s multi   .80 .80

Souvenir Sheet

International Year of Sustainable
Tourism for Development — A2039

2017, Aug. 28 Litho. Perf. 13½x13
4820 A2039 2.10 l multi   2.60 2.60

Sofia Airport, 80th Anniv. — A2040

2017, Sept. 13 Litho. Perf. 13
4821 A2040 65s multi   .80 .80

Souvenir Sheet

Bulgarian Astronautics Society, 60th
Anniv. — A2041

2017, Oct. 9 Litho. Perf. 13
4822 A2041 65s multi   .80 .80

Souvenir Sheet

80th Birthday of Dimitar Trendafilov,
Painter and Graphic Artist — A2042

2017, Oct. 11 Litho. Perf. 13¼x13½
4823 A2042 65s multi + label   .80 .80

Printed in sheets of 2 stamps + 2 labels.

Souvenir Sheet

002605

Brazil 2017 World Philatelic Exhibition, Brasilia — A2043

Perf. 13¼ Horiz.

2017, Oct. 20   Litho.
4824 A2043 1 l multi + label   1.25 1.25

Miniature Sheet

We the Sparrows — A2044

No. 4825: a, 65s, Passer hispaniolensis. b, 1 l, Passer montanus. c, 1.50 l, Passer domesticus. d, 2 l, Passer petronia.

2017, Oct. 21   Litho.   Perf. 13
4825 A2044   Sheet of 4, #a-d   5.00 5.00

Miniature Sheet

Alternative Transportation — A2045

No. 4826: a, 65s, Rollerblades. b, 1.40 l, Hoverboard. c, 1.50 l, Skateboard. d, 2 l, Scooter.

2017, Oct. 21   Litho.   Perf. 13½x13
4826 A2045   Sheet of 4, #a-d   6.75 6.75

First Bulgarian Presidency of the Council of the European Union — A2046

2017, Nov. 1   Litho.   Perf. 13
4827 A2046 1 l multi   1.25 1.25

Communication Regulation Commission, 20th Anniv. — A2047

2017, Nov. 2   Litho.   Perf. 13¼x13
4828 A2047 65s multi   .80 .80

Christmas A2048

2017, Nov. 16   Litho.   Perf. 13
4829 A2048 1 l multi   1.25 1.25

SEMI-POSTAL STAMPS

Catalogue values for unused stamps in this section are for Never Hinged items.

Regular Issues of 1911-20 Surcharged

a   b

c

Perf. 11½x12, 12x11½

1920, June 20   Unwmk.
B1 A43 (a)   2s + 1s ol grn   .25 .25
B2 A44 (b)   5s + 2½s grn   .25 .25
B3 A44 (b)   10s + 5s rose   .25 .25
B4 A44 (b)   15s + 7½s vio   .25 .25
B5 A44 (b)   25s + 12½s dp bl   .25 .25
B6 A44 (b)   30s + 15s choc   .25 .25
B7 A44 (b)   50s + 25s yel brn   .25 .25
B8 A29 (c)   1 l + 50s dk brn   .45 .25
B9 A37a (a)   2 l + 1 l brn org   .45 .40
B10 A38 (a)   3 l + 1½ l claret   1.20 .80
   Nos. B1-B10 (10)   3.85 3.20

Surtax aided ex-prisoners of war. Value, Nos. B1-B7 imperf., $7.75.

Tsar Boris Type of 1937
Souvenir Sheet

1937, Nov. 22   Photo.   Imperf.
B11 A140 2 l + 18 l ultra   10.00 20.00

19th anniv. of the accession of Tsar Boris III to the throne.

Stamps of 1917-21 Surcharged in Black

1939, Oct. 22   Perf. 12½, 12
B12 A34   1 l + 1 l on 15s slate   .25 .25
B13 A69   2 l + 1 l on 1½ l ol grn   .25 .35
B14 A69   4 l + 2 l on 2 l dp grn   .25 .35
B15 A69   7 l + 4 l on 3 l Prus bl   .80 1.10
B16 A69   14 l + 7 l on 5 l red brn   1.00 2.00
   Nos. B12-B16 (5)   2.55 4.05

Surtax aided victims of the Sevlievo flood. The surcharge on #B13-B16 omits "leva."

Map of Bulgaria SP2

1947, June 6   Typo.   Perf. 11½
B17 SP2 20 l + 1 l dk brn red & grn   .75 .75

30th Jubilee Esperanto Cong., Sofia, 1947.

Postman — SP3   Radio Towers — SP6

#B19, Lineman. #B20, Telephone operators.

1947, Nov. 5
B18 SP3   4 l + 2 l ol brn   .25 .25
B19 SP3   1 l + 5 l brt red   .25 .25
B20 SP3   20 l + 10 l dp ultra   .25 .25
B21 SP6   40 l + 20 l choc   1.00 1.00
   Nos. B18-B21 (4)   1.75 1.75

Christo Ganchev — SP7

Actors' Portraits: 10 l+6 l, Adriana Budevska. 15 l+7 l, Vasil Kirkov. 20 l+15 l, Sava Ognianov. 30 l+20 l, Krostyu Sarafov.

1947, Dec. 8   Litho.   Perf. 10½
B22 SP7   9 l + 5 l Prus grn   .25 .25
B23 SP7   10 l + 6 l car lake   .25 .25
B24 SP7   15 l + 7 l rose vio   .35 .25
B25 SP7   20 l + 15 l ultra   .35 .25
B26 SP7   30 l + 20 l vio brn   1.10 .75
   Nos. B22-B26 (5)   2.30 1.75

National Theater, 50th anniversary.

Souvenir Sheet

Olympic Emblem — SP8

1964, Oct. 10   Litho.   Imperf.
B27 SP8 40s + 20s bis, red & bl   4.00 1.75

18th Olympic Games, Tokyo, Oct. 10-25.

Horsemanship Type of 1965
Miniature Sheet

1965, Sept. 30   Photo.   Imperf.
B28 A630 40s + 20s Hurdle race   4.00 1.75

Space Exploration Type of 1966

Designs: 20s+10s, Yuri A. Gagarin, Alexei Leonov and Valentina Tereshkova. 30s+10s, Rocket and globe.

1966, Sept. 29   Photo.   Perf. 11½x11
B29 A652 20s + 10s pur & gray   1.40 .45
Miniature Sheet
Imperf
B30 A652 30s + 10s gray, fawn & blk   3.00 1.10

Winter Olympic Games Type of 1967

Sports and Emblem: 20s+10s, Slalom. 40s+10s, Figure skating couple.

1967, Sept.   Photo.   Perf. 11
B31 A687 20s + 10s multi   2.00 .60
Souvenir Sheet
Imperf
B32 A687 40s + 10s multi   2.75 .85

Type of Olympic Games Issue, 1968

Designs: 20s+10s, Rowing. 50s+10s, Stadium, Mexico City, and communications satellite.

1968, June 24   Photo.   Perf. 10½
B33 A702 20s + 10s vio bl, gray & pink   1.40 .45
Miniature Sheet
Imperf
B34 A702 50s + 10s gray, blk & Prus bl   3.00 1.50

Sports Type of Regular Issue, 1969

Designs: 13s+5s, Woman with ball. 20s+10s, Acrobatic jump.

Gymnasts in Light Gray

1969, Oct.   Photo.   Perf. 11
B35 A732 13s + 5s brt rose & vio   .80 .35
B36 A732 20s + 10s citron & bl grn   1.00 .40

Miniature Sheet

Soccer Ball — SP9

1970, Mar. 4   Photo.   Imperf.
B37 SP9 80s + 20s multi   3.00 1.75

9th World Soccer Championships for the Jules Rimet Cup, Mexico City, May 30-June 21, 1970.

Souvenir Sheet

Yuri A. Gagarin — SP10

1971, Apr. 12   Photo.   *Imperf.*
B38 SP10 40s + 20s multi   3.00 1.10
10th anniversary of the first man in space.

SP11

Bulgarian lion, magnifying glass, stamp tongs

1971, July 10   Photo.   *Perf. 12½*
B39 SP11 20s + 10s brn org, blk
          & gold   1.25 .40
11th Congress of Bulgarian Philatelists, Sofia, July, 1971.

SP12

Toys: a, Skateboarding. b, Doll, ball. c, Rope. d, Train set.

Souvenir Sheet

1989, Nov. 10   Litho.   *Perf. 13x13½*
B40 Sheet of 4   2.75 1.40
  a.-d. SP12 30s +15s any single   .55   .35
For the benefit of the Children's Foundation. Exists imperf. Value $8.75.

AIR POST STAMPS

Regular Issues of 1925-26 Overprinted in Various Colors

1927-28   Unwmk.   *Perf. 11½*
C1 A76   2 l ol (R) ('28)   1.40 1.40
C2 A74   4 l lake & yel (Bl)   2.00 1.50
C3 A77 10 l brn blk & brn
               org (G) ('28)   55.00 15.00

Overprinted Vertically and Surcharged with New Value

C4 A77   1 l on 6 l dk bl &
               pale lem (C)   1.40 1.40
  a. Inverted surcharge   340.00 275.00
  b. Pair, one without surcharge 440.00
       Nos. C1-C4 (4)   59.80 19.30

Nos. C2-C4 overprinted in changed colors were not issued, value set $14.

Dove Delivering Message — AP1

1931, Oct. 28   Typo.
C5   AP1   1 l dk green   .40   .25
C6   AP1   2 l maroon   .40   .25
C7   AP1   6 l dp blue   .50   .35
C8   AP1 12 l carmine   1.00   .35
C9   AP1 20 l dk violet   1.00   .60
C10 AP1 30 l dp orange   2.00   .75
C11 AP1 50 l orange brn   2.75 1.50
       Nos. C5-C11 (7)   8.05 4.05
Counterfeits exist. See Nos. C15-C18.

Junkers Plane, Rila Monastery — AP2

1932, May 9
C12 AP2 18 l blue grn   40.00 25.00
C13 AP2 24 l dp red   27.50 20.00
C14 AP2 28 l ultra   15.00 17.50
       Nos. C12-C14 (3)   82.50 62.50

> **Catalogue values for unused stamps in this section, from this point to the end of the section, are for Never Hinged items.**

Types of 1931

1938, Dec. 27
C15 AP1   1 l violet brown   .30   .25
C16 AP1   2 l green   .35   .25
C17 AP1   6 l deep rose   1.00   .45
C18 AP1 12 l peacock blue   1.25   .45
       Nos. C15-C18 (4)   2.90 1.40
Counterfeits exist.

Mail Plane — AP3

Plane over Tsar Assen's Tower — AP4

Designs: 4 l, Plane over Bachkovski Monastery. 6 l, Bojurishte Airport, Sofia. 10 l, Plane, train and motorcycle. 12 l, Planes over Sofia Palace. 16 l, Plane over Pirin Valley. 19 l, Plane over Rila Monastery. 30 l, Plane and Swallow. 45 l, Plane over Sofia Cathedral. 70 l, Plane over Shipka Monument. 100 l, Plane and Royal Cipher.

1940, Jan. 15   Photo.   *Perf. 13*
C19 AP3   1 l dk green   .25   .25
C20 AP4   2 l crimson   2.00   .25
C21 AP4   4 l red orange   .25   .25
C22 AP3   6 l dp blue   .35   .25
C23 AP3 10 l dk brown   .40   .25
C24 AP3 12 l dull brown   .80   .35
C25 AP3 16 l brt bl vio   1.10   .50
C26 AP3 19 l sapphire   1.25   .75
C27 AP4 30 l rose lake   2.00 1.00
C28 AP4 45 l gray violet   5.25 1.25
C29 AP4 70 l rose pink   4.00 2.50
C30 AP4 100 l dp slate bl   12.00 5.00
       Nos. C19-C30 (12)   29.65 12.60

Nos. 368 and 370 Overprinted in Black

1945, Jan. 26
C31 A181 1 l bright green   .25   .25
C32 A181 4 l red orange   .25   .25
A similar overprint on Nos. O4, O5, O7 and O8 was privately applied.

Type of Parcel Post Stamps of 1944 Surcharged or Overprinted in Various Colors

Imperf
C37 PP5 10 l on 100 l dl yel
               (Bl)   .25   .25
C38 PP5 45 l on 100 l dl yel (C)   .30   .25
C39 PP5 75 l on 100 l dl yel (G) 1.00   .25
C40 PP5 100 l dl yel (V)   1.00   .35
       Nos. C37-C40 (4)   2.55 1.10

Plane and Sun — AP16

Pigeon with Letter — AP17

Plane, Letter AP18

Wings, Posthorn AP19

Winged Letter — AP20

Plane, Sun — AP21

Pigeon, Posthorn AP22

Mail Plane AP23

Conventionalized Figure Holding Pigeon — AP24

1946, July 15   Litho.   *Perf. 13*
C41 AP16   1 l dull lilac   .25   .25
C42 AP16   2 l slate gray   .25   .25
C43 AP17   4 l violet blk   .25   .25
C44 AP18   6 l blue   .25   .25
C45 AP19 10 l turq green   .25   .25
C46 AP19 12 l yellow brn   .25   .25
C47 AP20 16 l rose violet   .25   .25
C48 AP19 19 l carmine   .25   .25
C49 AP21 30 l orange   .25   .25
C50 AP22 45 l lt ol grn   .25   .25
C51 AP22 75 l red brown   .60   .25
C52 AP23 100 l slate blk   1.60   .60
C53 AP24 100 l red   1.60   .60
       Nos. C41-C53 (13)   6.30 3.95
No. C47 exists imperf. Value $90.

People's Republic

Plane over Plovdiv AP25

1947, Aug. 31   Photo.   *Imperf.*
C54 AP25 40 l dull olive grn   1.20 1.20
Plovdiv International Fair, 1947.

Baldwin's Tower — AP26

1948, May 23   Litho.   *Perf. 11½*
C55 AP26 50 l ol brn, *cr*   1.50 1.50
Stamp Day and the 10th Congress of Bulgarian Philatelic Societies, June 1948.

Romanian and Bulgarian Parliament Buildings AP27

Romanian and Bulgarian Flags, Bridge over Danube AP28

1948, Nov. 3   Photo.
C56 AP27   40 l ol gray, *cr*   .35   .30
C57 AP28 100 l red vio, *cr*   .90   .90
Romanian-Bulgarian friendship.

Mausoleum of Pleven — AP29

1949, June 26
C58 AP29 50 l brown   3.00 3.00
7th Congress of Bulgarian Philatelic Associations, June 26-27, 1949.

Symbols of the UPU — AP30

1949, Oct. 10   *Perf. 11½*
C59 AP30 50 l violet blue   2.00 2.00
75th anniv. of the UPU.

Frontier Guard and Dog — AP31

1949, Oct. 31
C60 AP31 60 l olive black   3.00 3.00

Dimitrov Mausoleum AP32

1950, July 3   Perf. 10½
C61 AP32 40 l olive brown   5.50 2.75
1st anniv. of the death of George Dimitrov.

Belogradchic Rocks — AP33

Air View of Plovdiv Fair — AP34

Designs: 16s, Beach, Varna. 20s, Harvesting grain. 28s, Rila monastery. 44s, Studena dam. 60s, View of Dimitrovgrad. 80s, View of Trnovo. 1 l, University building, Sofia. 4 l, Partisans' Monument.

1954, Apr. 1   Unwmk.   Perf. 13
C62 AP33 8s olive black   .25 .25
C63 AP34 12s rose brown   .25 .25
C64 AP33 16s brown   .25 .25
C65 AP33 20s brn red, *cream*   .25 .25
C66 AP33 28s dp bl, *cream*   .30 .25
C67 AP33 44s vio brn, *cream*   .35 .25
C68 AP33 60s red brn, *cream*   .65 .25
C69 AP34 80s dk grn, *cream*   .70 .30
C70 AP33 1 l dk bl grn, *cream* 2.25 .65
C71 AP34 4 l deep blue   3.75 1.50
    Nos. C62-C71 (10)   9.00 4.20

Glider on Mountainside AP35

60s, Glider over airport. 80s, Three gliders.

1956, Oct. 15   Photo.
C72 AP35 44s brt blue   .35 .25
C73 AP35 60s purple   .35 .25
C74 AP35 80s dk blue grn   1.00 .70
    Nos. C72-C74 (3)   1.70 1.20
30th anniv. of glider flights in Bulgaria.

Passenger Plane — AP36

1957, May 21   Unwmk.   Perf. 13
C75 AP36 80s deep blue   1.00 .45
10th anniv. of civil aviation in Bulgaria.

Sputnik 3 over Earth AP37

1958, Nov. 28   Perf. 11
C76 AP37 80s brt grnsh blue   4.50 3.50
International Geophysical Year, 1957-58. Value, imperf. $12.50.

Lunik 1 Leaving Earth for Moon — AP38

1959, Mar.   Perf. 10½
C77 AP38 2 l brt blue & ocher   7.00 7.00
Launching of 1st man-made satellite to orbit moon. Value, imperf. in slightly different colors, $12.50 unused, $5 canceled.

Statue of Liberty and Tu-110 Airliner AP39

Perf. 10½
1959, Nov. 11   Photo.   Unwmk.
C78 AP39 1 l violet bl & pink   3.00 2.50
Visit of Khrushchev to US. Value, imperf. $7.50.

Lunik 2 and Moon — AP40

1960, June 23   Litho.   Perf. 11
C79 AP40 1.25 l blue, blk & yel   5.00 3.00
Russian rocket to the Moon, Sept. 12, 1959.

Sputnik 5 and Dogs Belka and Strelka — AP41

1961, Jan. 14   Photo.   Perf. 11
C80 AP41 1.25 l brt grnsh bl & org   5.00 3.50
Russian rocket flight of Aug. 19, 1960.

Maj. Yuri A. Gagarin and Vostok 1 AP42

1961, Apr. 26   Unwmk.
C81 AP42 4 l grnsh bl, blk & red   4.00 3.00
First manned space flight, Apr. 12, 1961.

Soviet Space Dogs AP43

1961, June 28   Perf. 11
C82 AP43 2 l slate & dk car   3.50 2.50

Venus-bound Rocket — AP44

1961, June 28
C83 AP44 2 l brt bl, yel & org   7.00 4.50
Soviet launching of the Venus space probe, 2/12/61.

Maj. Gherman Titov AP45

Design: 1.25 l, Spaceship Vostok 2.

1961, Nov. 20   Photo.   Perf. 11x10½
C84 AP45   75s dk ol grn & gray grn   2.25 1.75
C85 AP45 1.25 l vio bl, lt bl & purple   2.75 2.00
1st manned space flight around the world, Maj. Gherman Titov of Russia, 8/6-7/61.

Iskar River Narrows AP46

Designs: 2s, Varna and sailboat. 3s, Melnik. 10s, Trnovo. 40s, Pirin mountains.

1962, Feb. 3   Unwmk.   Perf. 13
C86 AP46 1s bl grn & gray bl   .25 .25
C87 AP46 2s blue & pink   .25 .25
C88 AP46 3s brown & ocher   .25 .25
C89 AP46 10s black & lemon   .50 .25
C90 AP46 40s dk green & green   1.90 .40
    Nos. C86-C90 (5)   3.15 1.40

Ilyushin Turboprop Airliner AP47

1962, Aug. 18   Perf. 11
C91 AP47 13s blue & black   1.10 .35
15th anniversary of TABSO airline.

Konstantin E. Tsiolkovsky and Rocket Launching — AP48

Design: 13s, Earth, moon and rocket on future flight to the moon.

1962, Sept. 24   Perf. 11
C92 AP48 5s dp green & gray   3.50 1.25
C93 AP48 13s ultra & yellow   1.50 .75
13th meeting of the International Astronautical Federation.

Maj. Andrian G. Nikolayev — AP49

Designs: 2s, Lt. Col. Pavel R. Popovich. 40s, Vostoks 3 and 4 in orbit.

1962, Dec. 9   Photo.   Unwmk.
C94 AP49 1s bl, sl grn & blk   .25 .25
C95 AP49 2s bl grn, grn & blk   .50 .25
C96 AP49 40s dk bl grn, pink & blk   2.75 1.75
    Nos. C94-C96 (3)   3.50 2.25
First Russian group space flight of Vostoks 3 and 4, Aug. 12-15, 1962.

Spacecraft "Mars 1" Approaching Mars — AP50

Design: 13s, Rocket launching spacecraft, Earth, Moon and Mars.

1963, Mar. 5   Unwmk.   Perf. 11
C97 AP50 5s multicolored   .70 .35
C98 AP50 13s multicolored   1.40 .70
Launching of the Russian spacecraft "Mars 1," Nov. 1, 1962.

Lt. Col. Valeri F. Bykovski AP51

Designs: 2s, Lt. Valentina Tereshkova. 5s, Globe and trajectories.

1963, Aug. 26   Unwmk.   Perf. 11½
C99 AP51 1s pale vio & Prus bl .25 .25
C100 AP51 2s citron & red brn   .25 .25
C101 AP51 5s rose & dk red   .35 .25
    Nos. C99-C101 (3)   .85 .75

The space flights of Valeri Bykovski, June 14-19, and Valentina Tereshkova, first woman cosmonaut, June 16-19, 1963. An imperf. souvenir sheet contains one 50s stamp showing Spasski tower and globe in lilac and red brown. Light blue border with red brown inscription. Size: 77x67mm. Value $4. See No. CB3.

Nos. C99-C100 Surcharged in Magenta or Green

1964, Aug. 22
C102 AP51 10s on 1s (M)   .35 .25
C103 AP51 20s on 2s   1.00 .40
International Space Exhibition in Riccione, Italy. Overprint in Italian on No. C103.

St. John's Monastery, Rila — AP52

13s, Notre Dame, Paris; French inscription.

1964, Dec. 22   Photo.   Perf. 11½
C104 AP52 5s pale brn & blk   .35   .25
C105 AP52 13s lt ultra & sl bl   .90   .35

The philatelic exhibition at St. Ouen (Seine) organized by the Franco-Russian Philatelic Circle and philatelic organizations in various People's Democracies.

Paper Mill, Bukijovtz AP53

10s, Metal works, Plovdiv. 13s, Metal works, Kremikovtsi. 20s, Oil refinery, Stara-Zagora. 40s, Fertilizer plant, Stara-Zagora. 1 l, Rest home, Meded.

1964-68   Unwmk.   Perf. 13
C106 AP53 8s grnsh blue   .35   .25
C107 AP53 10s red lilac   .50   .25
C108 AP53 13s brt violet   .45   .25
C109 AP53 20s slate blue   1.00   .25
C110 AP53 40s dk olive grn 1.50   .25
C111 AP53 1 l red ('68)   2.75   .55
     Nos. C106-C111 (6)   6.55 1.80

Issue dates: 1 l, May 6. Others, Dec. 7.

Three-master AP54

Means of Communication: 2s, Postal coach. 3s, Old steam locomotive. 5s, Early cars. 10s, Montgolfier balloon. 13s, Early plane. 20s, Jet planes. 40s, Rocket and satellites. 1 l, Postrider.

1969, Mar. 31   Photo.   Perf. 13x12½
C112 AP54 1s gray & multi   .25   .25
C113 AP54 2s gray & multi   .25   .25
C114 AP54 3s gray & multi   .25   .25
C115 AP54 5s gray & multi   .25   .25
C116 AP54 10s gray & multi   .25   .25
C117 AP54 13s gray & multi   .45   .25
C118 AP54 20s gray & multi   .75   .30
C119 AP54 40s gray & multi   1.40   .60
     Nos. C112-C119 (8)   3.85 2.40

Miniature Sheet
Imperf
C120 AP54 1 l gold & org   2.75 2.00

SOFIA 1969 Philatelic Exhibition, Sofia, May 31-June 8.

Veliko Turnovo — AP55

Designs: Historic buildings in various cities.

1973, July 30   Photo.   Perf. 13
C121 AP55 2s shown   .25   .25
C122 AP55 13s Roussalka .50   .25
C123 AP55 20s Plovdiv   2.75 1.50
C124 AP55 28s Sofia   .70   .40
     Nos. C121-C124 (4)   4.20 2.40

Aleksei A. Leonov and Soyuz AP56

Designs: 18s, Thomas P. Stafford and Apollo. 28s, Apollo and Soyuz over earth. 1 l, Apollo Soyuz link-up.

1975, July 15
C125 AP56 13s blue & multi   .35   .25
C126 AP56 18s purple & multi .75   .25
C127 AP56 28s multicolored   1.50   .45
     Nos. C125-C127 (3)   2.60   .95

Souvenir Sheet
C128 AP56 1 l violet & multi 3.25 2.00

Apollo Soyuz space test project (Russo-American cooperation), launching July 15; link-up July 17.

Balloon Over Plovdiv — AP57

1977, Sept. 3
C129 AP57 25s yellow, brn & red .75   .25

Alexei Leonov Floating in Space — AP58

Designs: 25s, Mariner 6, US spacecraft. 35s, Venera 4, USSR Venus probe.

1977, Oct. 14   Photo.   Perf. 13½
C130 AP58 12s multicolored   .35   .25
C131 AP58 25s multicolored   .70   .25
C132 AP58 35s multicolored   1.00   .35
     Nos. C130-C132 (3)   2.05   .85

Space era, 20 years.

TU-154, Balkanair Emblem AP59

1977   Perf. 13
C133 AP59 35s ultra & multi   1.25   .40

30th anniv. of Bulgarian airline, Balkanair. Issued in sheets of 6 stamps + 3 labels (in lilac) with inscription and Balkanair emblem.

Baba Vida Fortress AP60

Design: 35s, Peace Bridge, connecting Rousse, Bulgaria, with Giurgiu, Romania.

1978   Photo.   Perf. 13
C134 AP60 25s multicolored   .50   .50
C135 AP60 35s multicolored   .75   .75

The Danube, European Intercontinental Waterway. Issued in sheets containing 5 each of Nos. C134-C135 and 2 labels, one showing course of Danube, the other hydrofoil and fish.

Red Cross AP61

1978, Mar.   Photo.   Perf. 13
C136 AP61 25s multicolored   .75   .30

Centenary of Bulgarian Red Cross.

AP62

Clock towers.

1979, June 5   Litho.   Perf. 12x12½
C137 AP62 13s Byalla Cherkva   .50   .25
C138 AP62 23s Botevgrad   .50   .25
C139 AP62 25s Pazardgick   .50   .25
C140 AP62 35s Grabovo   .50   .25
C141 AP62 53s Tryavna   1.10   .50
     Nos. C137-C141 (5)   3.10 1.50

1980, Oct. 22   Photo.   Perf. 12x12½
C142 AP62 13s Bjala   .25   .25
C143 AP62 23s Rasgrad   .35   .25
C144 AP62 25s Karnabat   .40   .25
C145 AP62 35s Serlievo   .65   .35
C146 AP62 53s Berkovitza 1.25   .55
     Nos. C142-C146 (5)   2.90 1.65

AP63

1980
C147 AP63 13s shown   .25   .25
C148 AP63 25s Parachutist .60   .25

15th World Parachute Championships, Kazanluk.

DWVY-1 Aircraft — AP64

1981, June 27   Litho.   Perf. 12½
C149 AP64 5s shown   .25   .25
C150 AP64 12s LAS-7   .25   .25
C151 AP64 28s LAS-8   .55   .25

C152 AP64 35s DAR-1   .75   .25
C153 AP64 45s DAR-3   .85   .35
C154 AP64 55s DAR-9   1.10   .45
     Nos. C149-C154 (6)   3.75 1.80

AP65

1983, June 28
C155   Sheet of 2   2.00 1.25
     a.   AP65 50s Valentina Tereshkova   1.00   .60
     b.   AP65 50s Svetlana Savitskaya   1.00   .60

Women in space, 20th anniv.

AP66

5s, TV tower, Tolbukhin. 13s, Postwoman. 30s, TV tower, Mt. Botev.

1983, July 20   Photo.   Perf. 13
C156 AP66 5s multi   .25   .25
C157 AP66 13s multi   .30   .25
C158 AP66 30s multi   .45   .25
     a.   Strip of 3, #C156-C158 1.25   .85

World Communications Year. Emblems of World Communications Year, Bulgarian Post, UPU and ITU on attached margins.

Souvenir Sheet

Geophysical Map of the Moon, Russia's Luna I, II and III Satellites — AP67

1984, Oct. 24   Photo.   Perf. 13
C159 AP67 1 l multicolored   2.00 1.25

Conquest of Space.

Intl. Civil Aviation Org., 40th Anniv. — AP68

42s, Balkan Airlines jet.

1984, Dec. 21   Photo.   Perf. 13
C160 AP68 42s multi   .75   .35

Balkan Airlines — AP69

Design: Helicopter MU-8, passenger jet TU-154 and AN-21 transport plane.

1987, Aug. 25   **Photo.**
C161 AP69 25s multicolored   .50   .30

2nd Joint Soviet-Bulgarian Space Flight — AP70

Cosmonauts: A. Aleksandrov, A. Solovov and V. Savinich.

1989, June 7   **Litho.**   **Perf. 13½x13**
C162 AP70 13s multicolored   .35   .25

AIR POST SEMI-POSTAL STAMPS

Catalogue values for unused stamps in this section are for Never Hinged items.

Statue of Liberty, Plane and Bridge SPAP1

Perf. 11½.
1947, May 24   **Unwmk.**   **Litho.**
CB1 SPAP1 70 l + 30 l red brn   1.50 1.50

5th Philatelic Congress, Trnovo, and CIPEX, NYC, May, 1947.

Bulgarian Worker SPAP2

1948, Feb. 28 Photo.   **Perf. 12x11½.**
CB2 SPAP2 60 l henna brn, cream   .55 .45

2nd Bulgarian Workers' Congress, and sold by subscription only, at a premium of 16 l over face value.

Type of Air Post Stamps, 1963

Valeri Bykovski & Valentina Tereshkova.

1963, Aug. 26 Unwmk.   **Perf. 11½**
CB3 AP51 20s + 10s pale bluish grn & dk grn   1.75 .45

See note after No. C101.

SPECIAL DELIVERY STAMPS

Catalogue values for unused stamps in this section are for Never Hinged items.

Postman on Bicycle SD1   Postman on Motorcycle SD3

Mail Car — SD2

1939 Unwmk. Photo.   **Perf. 13**
E1 SD1 5 l deep blue   1.20 .25
E2 SD2 6 l copper brn   .25 .25
E3 SD3 7 l copper brn   .35 .25
E4 SD2 8 l red orange   1.20 .25
E5 SD1 20 l bright rose   2.50 .40
   Nos. E1-E5 (5)   5.50 1.40

POSTAGE DUE STAMPS

D1

Large Lozenge Perf. 5½ to 6½
1884   **Typo.**   **Unwmk.**
J1 D1 5s orange   600.00 60.00
J2 D1 25s lake   325.00 40.00
J3 D1 50s blue   45.00 30.00
   Nos. J1-J3 (3)   970.00 130.00

1886   **Imperf.**
J4 D1 5s orange   375.00 17.50
J5 D1 25s lake   550.00 16.00
J6 D1 50s blue   19.00 16.00
   Nos. J4-J6 (3)   944.00 49.50

1887   **Perf. 11½**
J7 D1 5s orange   57.50 6.00
J8 D1 25s lake   20.00 6.00
J9 D1 50s blue   20.00 15.00
   Nos. J7-J9 (3)   97.50 27.00

Same, Redrawn
24 horizontal lines of shading in upper part instead of 30 lines
1892   **Perf. 10½, 11, 11½**
J10 D1 5s orange   37.50 6.00
J11 D1 25s lake   20.00 6.00

D2

1893   **Pelure Paper**
J12 D2 5s orange   47.50 15.00

D3

1895   **Imperf.**
J13 D3 30s on 50s blue   22.50 9.00
Perf. 10½, 11½
J14 D3 30s on 50s blue   27.50 9.00

D4

Wmk. Coat of Arms in the Sheet
1896   **Perf. 13**
J15 D4 5s orange   27.50 2.50
J16 D4 10s purple   11.00 3.25
J17 D4 30s green   9.00 2.50
   Nos. J15-J17 (3)   47.50 8.25

Nos. J15-J17 are also known on unwatermarked paper from the edges of sheets. Values about 40% less.
In 1901 a cancellation, "T" in circle, was applied to Nos. 60-65 and used provisionally as postage dues.

D5

1901-04   **Unwmk.**   **Perf. 11½**
J19 D5 5s dl rose   .70 .40
J20 D5 10s yel grn   1.40 .40
J21 D5 20s dl bl ('04)   10.00 .40
J22 D5 30s vio brn   3.50 .40
J23 D5 50s org ('02)   8.50 8.50
   Nos. J19-J23 (5)   24.10 10.10

Nos. J19-J23 exist imperf. and in pairs imperf. between. Value, imperf., $250.

D6

Thin Semi-Transparent Paper
1915   **Unwmk.**   **Perf. 11½**
J24 D6 5s green   .45 .25
J25 D6 10s purple   .45 .25
J26 D6 20s dl rose   .45 .25
J27 D6 30s dp org   2.50 .60
J28 D6 50s dp bl   .85 .35
   Nos. J24-J28 (5)   4.70 1.70

1919-21   **Perf. 11½, 12x11½**
J29 D6 5s emerald   .70 .25
  a. 5s gray green ('21)   .30 .25
J30 D6 10s violet   .70 .25
  a. 10s light violet ('21)   .25 .25
J31 D6 20s salmon   .70 .25
  a. 20s yellow   .25 .25
J32 D6 30s orange   .70 .25
  a. 30s red orange ('21)   .65 .65
J33 D6 50s blue   1.40 .25
J34 D6 1 l emerald ('21)   .25 .25
J35 D6 2 l rose ('21)   .25 .25
J36 D6 3 l brown org ('21)   .35 .25
   Nos. J29-J36 (8)   5.05 2.00

Stotinki values of the above series surcharged 10s or 20s were used as ordinary postage stamps. See Nos. 182-185.
The 1919 printings are on thicker white paper with clean-cut perforations, the 1921 printings on thicker grayish paper with rough perforations.
Most of this series exist imperforate and in pairs imperforate between.

Heraldic Lion — D7

1932, Aug. 15   **Thin Paper**
J37 D7 1 l olive bister   .75 .85
J38 D7 2 l rose brown   .75 .85
J39 D7 6 l brown violet   1.50 1.00
   Nos. J37-J39 (3)   3.00 2.70

Lion of Trnovo — D8   National Arms — D9

1933, Apr. 10
J40 D8 20s dk brn   .25 .25
J41 D8 40s dp bl   .25 .25
J42 D8 80s car rose   .25 .25
J43 D9 1 l org brn   .80 .30
J44 D9 2 l olive   .80 .30
J45 D9 6 l dl vio   .40 .30
J46 D9 14 l ultra   1.00 .50
   Nos. J40-J46 (7)   3.75 2.35

Catalogue values for unused stamps in this section, from this point to the end of the section, are for Never Hinged items.

National Arms — D10

1947, June   **Typo.**   **Perf. 10½**
J47 D10 1 l chocolate   .25 .25
J48 D10 2 l deep claret   .25 .25
J49 D10 8 l deep orange   .30 .25
J50 D10 20 l blue   .85 .25
   Nos. J47-J50 (4)   1.65 1.00

Arms of the People's Republic — D11

1951   **Perf. 11½x10½**
J51 D11 1 l chocolate   .25 .25
J52 D11 2 l claret   .25 .25
J53 D11 8 l red orange   .45 .35
J54 D11 20 l deep blue   1.10 .90
   Nos. J51-J54 (4)   2.05 1.75

OFFICIAL STAMPS

Catalogue values for unused stamps in this section are for Never Hinged items.

Bulgarian Coat of Arms
O1   O2

1942   **Unwmk.**   **Typo.**   **Perf. 13**
O1 O1 10s yel grn   .25 .25
O2 O1 30s red   .25 .25
O3 O1 50s bister   .25 .25
O4 O2 1 l vio bl   .25 .25
O5 O2 2 l dk grn   .25 .25
O6 O2 3 l lilac   .25 .25
O7 O2 4 l rose   .25 .25
O8 O2 5 l carmine   .35 .25
   Nos. O1-O8 (8)   2.10 2.00

1944   **Perf. 10½x11½**
O9 O2 1 l blue   .90 .35
O10 O2 2 l brt red   .90 .35

Lion Rampant
O3   O4

O5

1945   *Imperf.*
O11 O5   1 l pink   .25   .25
      Perf. 10½x11½, Imperf.
O12 O3   2 l blue green   .25   .25
O13 O4   3 l bister brown   .25   .25
O14 O4   4 l light ultra   .25   .25
O15 O5   5 l brown lake   .25   .25
      Nos. O11-O15 (5)   1.25 1.25

In 1950, four stamps prepared for official use were issued as regular postage stamps. See Nos. 724-727.

PARCEL POST STAMPS

> Catalogue values for unused stamps in this section are for Never Hinged items.

Weighing
Packages — PP1

Parcel
Post — PP2

Designs: 3 l, 8 l, 20 l, Parcel post truck. 4 l, 6 l, 10 l, Motorcycle.

Perf. 12½x13½, 13½x12½
1941-42   **Photo.**   **Unwmk.**
Q1   PP1   1 l slate grn   .25   .25
Q2   PP2   2 l crimson   .25   .25
Q3   PP2   3 l dull brn   .25   .25
Q4   PP2   4 l red org   .25   .25
Q5   PP1   5 l deep blue   .35   .25
Q6   PP1   5 l slate grn ('42)   .25   .25
Q7   PP2   6 l red vio   .35   .25
Q8   PP2   6 l henna brn ('42)   .25   .25
Q9   PP1   7 l dark blue   .35   .25
Q10 PP1   7 l dk brn ('42)   .25   .25
Q11 PP2   8 l brt bl grn   .35   .25
Q12 PP2   8 l green ('42)   .25   .25
Q13 PP2   9 l olive gray   .35   .25
Q14 PP2   9 l dp olive ('42)   .35   .25
Q15 PP2 10 l orange   .65   .25
Q16 PP2 20 l gray vio   .65   .25
Q17 PP2 30 l dull blk   1.25   .25
Q18 PP2 30 l sepia ('42)   .90   .25
      Nos. Q1-Q18 (18)   7.55 4.50

Arms of
Bulgaria — PP5

1944   **Litho.**   *Imperf.*
Q21 PP5   1 l dk carmine   .25   .25
Q22 PP5   3 l blue grn   .25   .25
Q23 PP5   5 l dull bl grn   .25   .25
Q24 PP5   7 l rose lilac   .25   .25
Q25 PP5 10 l deep blue   .25   .25
Q26 PP5 20 l orange brn   .25   .25

Q27 PP5 30 l dk brn car   .25   .25
Q28 PP5 50 l red orange   .30   .25
Q29 PP5 100 l blue   .50   .25
      Nos. Q21-Q29 (9)   2.55 2.25

For overprints and surcharges see Nos. 448-454, C37-C40.

POSTAL TAX STAMPS

The use of stamps Nos. RA1 to RA18 was compulsory on letters, etc., to be delivered on Sundays and holidays. The money received from their sale was used toward maintaining a sanatorium for employees of the post, telegraph and telephone services.

View of
Sanatorium
PT1

Sanatorium,
Peshtera
PT2

1925-29   **Unwmk. Typo. Perf. 11½**
RA1 PT1   1 l blk, *grnsh bl*   2.75   .25
RA2 PT1   1 l chocolate ('26)   2.75   .25
RA3 PT1   1 l orange ('27)   3.00   .30
RA4 PT1   1 l pink ('28)   4.50   .30
RA5 PT1   1 l vio, *pnksh* ('29)   4.75   .30
RA6 PT2   2 l blue green   .35   .25
RA7 PT2   2 l violet ('27)   .35   .25
RA8 PT2   5 l deep blue   3.00   .80
RA9 PT2   5 l rose ('27)   3.75   .40
      Nos. RA1-RA9 (9)   25.20 3.10

St.
Constantine
Sanatorium
PT3

1930-33
RA10 PT3   1 l red brn & ol grn   4.00   .25
RA11 PT3   1 l ol grn & yel ('31)   .50   .25
RA12 PT3   1 l red vio & ol brn
                    ('33)   .50   .25
      Nos. RA10-RA12 (3)   5.00   .75

Trojan Rest
Home
PT4

Sanatorium
PT5

1935   **Wmk. 145**   **Perf. 11, 11½**
RA13 PT4   1 l choc & red org   .30   .25
RA14 PT4   1 l emer & indigo   .30   .25
RA15 PT5   5 l red brn & indigo   1.40   .35
      Nos. RA13-RA15 (3)   2.00   .85

St.
Constantine
Sanatorium
PT6

2 l, Children at seashore. 5 l, Rest home.

1941   **Unwmk. Photo.   Perf. 13**
RA16 PT6   1 l dark olive green   .25   .25
RA17 PT6   2 l red orange   .25   .25
RA18 PT6   5 l deep blue   .30   .25
      Nos. RA16-RA18 (3)   .80   .75

See Nos. 702-705 for same designs in smaller size issued as regular postage.

BURKINA FASO

bur-'kē-nə-'fä-sō

Upper Volta

LOCATION — Northwestern Africa, north of Ghana
GOVT. — Republic
AREA — 105,869 sq. mi.
POP. — 11,575,898 (1999 est.)
CAPITAL — Ouagadougou

In 1919 the French territory of Upper Volta was detached from the southern section of Upper Senegal and Niger and made a separate colony. In 1933 the colony was divided among its neighbors: French Sudan, Ivory Coast, and Niger Territory. The Republic of Upper Volta was proclaimed December 11, 1958; the name was changed to Burkina Faso on August 4, 1984.

100 Centimes = 1 Franc

Catalogue values for unused stamps in this country are for Never Hinged items, beginning with Scott 70 in the regular postage section, Scott B1 in the semipostal section, Scott C1 in the airpost section, Scott J21 in the postage due section, and Scott O1 in the official section.

See French West Africa Nos. 67, 84 for additional stamps inscribed "Haute Volta" and "Afrique Occidentale Francaise."

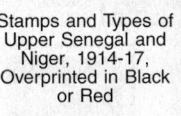

Stamps and Types of Upper Senegal and Niger, 1914-17, Overprinted in Black or Red

1920-28		**Unwmk.**	**Perf. 13½x14**	
1	A4	1c brn vio & vio	.25	.50
2	A4	2c gray & brn vio (R)	.25	.50
3	A4	4c blk & bl	.30	.60
4	A4	5c yel grn & bl grn	1.00	1.00
5	A4	5c ol brn & dk brn ('22)	.25	.50
6	A4	10c red org & rose	2.00	2.00
7	A4	10c yel grn & bl grn ('22)	.25	.50
		Complete booklet, 20 #7		—
8	A4	10c claret & bl ('25)	1.00	1.00
a.		Overprint omitted	240.00	
9	A4	15c choc & org	1.00	1.00
		Complete booklet, 20 #9		—
10	A4	20c brn vio & blk (R)	1.50	1.50
11	A4	25c ultra & bl	2.00	1.40
12	A4	25c blk & bl grn ('22)	1.00	1.00
a.		Overprint omitted	200.00	
13	A4	30c ol brn & brn (R)	4.00	4.50
14	A4	30c red org & rose ('22)	2.00	2.50
15	A4	30c vio & brn red ('25)	1.50	2.00
16	A4	30c dl grn & bl grn ('27)	1.50	2.00
17	A4	35c car rose & vio	1.00	2.00
18	A4	40c gray & car rose	1.00	2.00
19	A4	45c bl & brn (R)	1.00	2.00
20	A4	50c blk & grn	3.50	4.50
21	A4	50c ultra & bl ('22)	1.50	2.50
22	A4	50c red org & bl ('25)	1.50	2.00
a.		Double surcharge, one inverted	1,275.	1,400.
23	A4	60c org red ('26)	1.00	1.50
24	A4	65c bis & pale bl ('28)	2.00	3.00
25	A4	75c org & brn	2.00	2.00
26	A4	1fr brn & brn vio	1.50	2.50
27	A4	2fr grn & bl	2.50	3.00
28	A4	5fr vio & blk (R)	5.00	7.00
		Nos. 1-28 (28)	43.30	56.50

No. 9 Surcharged in Various Colors

1922				
29	A4	0.01c on 15c (Bk)	1.10	1.40
a.		Double surcharge	175.00	250.00
30	A4	0.02c on 15c (Bl)	1.10	1.40
31	A4	0.05c on 15c (R)	1.20	1.50
		Nos. 29-31 (3)	3.40	4.30

Type of 1920 Surcharged

1922				
32	A4	60c on 75c vio, *pnksh*	.75	1.15

Stamps and Types of 1920 Surcharged with New Value and Bars

1924-27				
33	A4	25c on 2fr grn & bl	.80	1.00
34	A4	25c on 5fr vio & blk	.80	1.00
35	A4	65c on 45c bl & brn ('25)	1.50	1.50
36	A4	85c on 75c org & brn ('25)	1.60	2.40
37	A4	90c on 75c brn red & sal pink ('27)	2.25	2.25
38	A4	1.25fr on 1fr dp bl & lt bl (R) ('26)	1.50	2.00
39	A4	1.50fr on 1fr dp bl & ultra ('27)	3.00	3.50
40	A4	3fr on 5fr dl red & brn org ('27)	4.50	5.50
41	A4	10fr on 5fr ol grn & lil rose ('27)	15.00	18.50
42	A4	20fr on 5fr org brn & vio ('27)	22.50	28.00
		Nos. 33-42 (10)	53.45	65.65

Hausa Chief — A5

Hausa Woman — A6

Hausa Warrior A7

1928		**Typo.**	**Perf. 13½x14**	
43	A5	1c indigo & grn	.40	.40
44	A5	2c brn & lil	.40	.40
45	A5	4c blk & yel	.40	.75
46	A5	5c indigo & gray bl	.40	.75
47	A5	10c indigo & pink	1.15	1.15
48	A5	15c brn & bl	1.50	2.25
49	A5	20c brn & grn	1.50	1.60
50	A5	25c brn & yel	1.90	2.40
51	A5	30c dp grn & grn	1.90	2.40
52	A6	40c blk & pink	1.90	2.25
53	A6	45c brn & blue	3.00	3.75
54	A6	50c blk & grn	2.25	2.40
55	A6	65c indigo & bl	3.00	3.75
56	A6	75c blk & lil	2.40	3.00
57	A6	90c brn red & lil	3.00	3.75
		Perf. 14x13½		
58	A7	1fr brn & grn	2.40	2.75
59	A7	1.10fr indigo & lil	3.00	4.00
60	A7	1.50fr ultra & grysh	3.75	4.50
61	A7	2fr blk & bl	4.00	4.75
62	A7	3fr brn & yel	4.00	5.25
63	A7	5fr brn & lil	4.00	5.25
64	A7	10fr blk & grn	20.00	26.00
65	A7	20fr blk & pink	30.00	32.50
		Nos. 43-65 (23)	96.25	116.00

Common Design Types pictured following the introduction.

Colonial Exposition Issue
Common Design Types

1931		**Engr.**	**Perf. 12½**	
Country Name Typo. in Black				
66	CD70	40c dp grn	4.00	4.00
67	CD71	50c violet	4.75	4.75
68	CD72	90c red org	4.75	4.75
69	CD73	1.50fr dull blue	5.50	5.50
		Nos. 66-69 (4)	19.00	19.00

Catalogue values for unused stamps in this section, from this point to the end of the section, are for Never Hinged items.

Republic

President Ouezzin Coulibaly — A8

1959		**Unwmk.** **Engr.**	**Perf. 13**	
70	A8	25fr black & magenta	.55	.40

1st anniv. of the proclamation of the Republic; Ouezzin Coulibaly, Council President, who died in December, 1958.

Imperforates
Most Upper Volta stamps from 1959 onward exist imperforate in issued and trial colors (values two to four times regularly issued stamps), and also in small presentation sheets in issued colors (values four to five times regularly issued stamps).

Deer Mask and Deer — A9

Animal Masks: 1fr, 2fr, 4fr, Wart hog. 5fr, 6fr, 8fr, Monkey. 10fr, 15fr, 20fr, Buffalo. 25fr, Coba (antelope). 30fr, 40fr, 50fr, Elephant. 60fr, 85fr, Secretary bird.

1960				
71	A9	30c rose & violet	.25	.25
72	A9	40c buff & dp claret	.25	.25
73	A9	50c bl grn & gray ol	.25	.25
74	A9	1fr red, blk & red brn	.25	.25
75	A9	2fr emer, yel grn & dk grn	.25	.25
76	A9	4fr bl, vio & ind	.25	.25
77	A9	5fr ol bis, red & brn	.25	.25
78	A9	6fr grnsh bl & vio brn	.25	.25
79	A9	8fr org & red brn	.25	.25
80	A9	10fr lt yel grn & plum	.25	.25
81	A9	15fr org, ultra & brn	.40	.25
82	A9	20fr green & ultra	.40	.35
83	A9	25fr bl, emer & dp clar	.60	.35
84	A9	30fr dk bl grn, blk & brn	.75	.35
85	A9	40fr ultra, ind & dk car	1.00	.50
86	A9	50fr brt pink, brn & grn	1.25	.50
87	A9	60fr org brn & bl	1.50	.65
88	A9	85fr gray ol & dk bl	2.25	1.00
		Nos. 71-88 (18)	10.65	6.45

C.C.T.A. Issue
Common Design Type

1960		**Engr.**	**Perf. 13**	
89	CD106	25fr vio bl & slate	.65	.40

Emblem of the Entente — A9a

1960		**Photo.**	**Perf. 13x13½**	
90	A9a	25fr multicolored	.65	.40

Council of the Entente.

Pres. Maurice Yameogo — A10

1960, May 1		**Engr.**	**Perf. 13**	
91	A10	25fr dk vio brn & slate	.55	.25

Flag, Village and Couple — A11

1960, Aug. 5		**Unwmk.**	**Perf. 13**	
92	A11	25fr red brn, blk & red	.65	.40

Proclamation of independence, Aug. 5, 1960.

World Meteorological Organization Emblem — A12

1961, May 4				
93	A12	25fr blk, bl & red	.90	.45

First World Meteorological Day.

Arms of Republic — A13

1961, Dec. 8		**Photo.**	**Perf. 12x12½**	
94	A13	25fr multicolored	.65	.40

The 1961 independence celebrations.

WMO Emblem, Weather Station and Sorghum Grain — A14

1962, Mar. 23		**Unwmk.**	**Perf. 13**	
95	A14	25fr dk bl, emer & brn	.70	.45

UN 2nd World Meteorological Day, Mar. 23.

Hospital and Nurse — A15

1962, June 23 *Perf. 13x12*
96 A15 25fr multicolored .90 .55
Founding of Upper Volta Red Cross.

Buffalos at Water Hole — A16

Designs: 10fr, Lions, horiz. 15fr, Defassa waterbuck. 25fr, Arly reservation, horiz. 50fr, Diapaga reservation, horiz. 85fr, Buffon's kob.

Perf. 12½x12, 12x12½
1962, June 30 Engr.
97 A16 5fr sepia, bl & grn .40 .25
98 A16 10fr red brn, grn & yel .55 .35
99 A16 15fr sepia, grn & yel 1.45 .50
100 A16 25fr vio brn, bl & grn .95 .70
101 A16 50fr vio brn, bl & grn 1.90 1.65
102 A16 85fr red brn, bl & grn 4.50 2.75
Nos. 97-102 (6) 9.75 6.20

Abidjan Games Issue
Common Design Type
Designs: 20fr, Soccer. 25fr, Bicycling. 85fr, Boxing. All horiz.

1962, July 21 Photo. *Perf. 12½x12*
103 CD109 20fr multicolored .55 .35
104 CD109 25fr multicolored .75 .55
105 CD109 85fr multicolored 1.50 .85
Nos. 103-105 (3) 2.80 1.75

African-Malgache Union Issue
Common Design Type
1962, Sept. 8 Unwmk.
106 CD110 30fr red, bluish grn & gold 1.10 .75

Weather Map and UN Emblem A17

1963, Mar. 23 *Perf. 12x12½*
107 A17 70fr multicolored 1.45 .70
3rd World Meteorological Day, Mar. 23.

Friendship Games, Dakar, Apr. 11-21 — A18

1963, Apr. 11 Engr. *Perf. 13*
108 A18 20fr Basketball .40 .30
109 A18 25fr Discus .60 .30
110 A18 50fr Judo 1.25 .55
Nos. 108-110 (3) 2.25 1.15

Amaryllis A19

Flowers: 50c, Hibiscus. 1fr, Oldenlandia grandiflora. 1.50fr, Rose moss (portulaca). 2fr, Tobacco. 4fr, Morning glory. 5fr, Striga senegalensis. 6fr, Cowpea. 8fr, Lepidagathis heudelotiana. 10fr, Spurge. 25fr, Argyreia nervosa. 30fr, Rangoon creeper. 40fr, Water lily. 50fr, White plumeria. 60fr, Crotalaria retusa. 85fr, Hibiscus.

1963 Photo.
111 A19 50c multi, vert. .25 .25
112 A19 1fr multi, vert. .25 .25
113 A19 1.50fr multi, vert. .25 .25
114 A19 2fr multi, vert. .25 .25
115 A19 4fr multi, vert. .25 .25
116 A19 5fr multi, vert. .30 .25
117 A19 6fr multi, vert. .35 .25
118 A19 8fr multi, vert. .35 .25
119 A19 10fr multi, vert. .35 .25
120 A19 15fr multi .40 .35
121 A19 25fr multi .55 .35
122 A19 30fr multi .75 .35
123 A19 40fr multi 1.25 .50
124 A19 50fr multi 1.40 .50
125 A19 60fr multi 1.75 .80
126 A19 85fr multi 2.25 1.00
Nos. 111-126 (16) 10.95 6.10

Centenary Emblem and Globe — A20

1963, Oct. 21 Unwmk. *Perf. 12*
127 A20 25fr multicolored 1.00 .75
Centenary of International Red Cross.

Scroll — A21

1963, Dec. 10 Photo. *Perf. 13x12½*
128 A21 25fr dp claret, gold & bl .80 .50
15th anniv. of the Universal Declaration of Human Rights.

Sound Wave Patterns A22

1964, Jan. 16 *Perf. 12½x13*
129 A22 25fr multicolored .65 .35
Upper Volta's admission to the ITU.

Recording Rain Gauge and WMO Emblem A23

1964, Mar. 23 Engr. *Perf. 13*
130 A23 50fr dk car rose, grn & bl 1.20 .80
4th World Meteorological Day, Mar. 23.

World Connected by Letters and Carrier Pigeon — A24

60fr, World connected by letters and jet plane.

1964, Mar. 29 Photo. *Perf. 13x12*
131 A24 25fr gray brn & ultra .65 .35
132 A24 60fr gray brn & org 1.10 .90
Upper Volta's admission to the UPU.

IQSY Emblem and Seasonal Allegories — A25

1964, Aug. 17 Engr. *Perf. 13*
133 A25 30fr grn, ocher & car .90 .65
International Quiet Sun Year.

Cooperation Issue
Common Design Type
1964, Nov. 7 Unwmk. *Perf. 13*
134 CD119 70fr dl bl grn, dk brn & car 1.25 .75

Hotel Independance, Ouagadougou — A26

1964, Dec. 11 Litho. *Perf. 12½x13*
135 A26 25fr multicolored 1.90 .90

Pigmy Long-tailed Sunbird — A27

15fr, Olive-bellied Sunbird. 20fr, Splendid Sunbird.

1965, Mar. 1 Photo. *Perf. 13x12½*
Size: 22x36mm
136 A27 10fr shown .90 .35
137 A27 15fr multi 1.10 .50
138 A27 20fr multi 2.00 .90
Nos. 136-138,C20 (4) 24.00 9.25

Comoe Waterfall — A28

25fr, Great Waterfall of Banfora, horiz.

1965 Engr. *Perf. 13*
139 A28 5fr yel grn, bl & red brn .35 .25
140 A28 25fr dk red, brt bl & grn .85 .30
Nos. 139-140 (2) 1.20 .55

Soccer — A29

Designs: 25fr, Boxing gloves and ring. 70fr, Tennis rackets, ball and net.

1965, July 15 Unwmk. *Perf. 13*
141 A29 15fr brn, red & dk grn .40 .25
142 A29 25fr pale org, bl & grn .60 .35
143 A29 70fr dk car & brt grn 1.50 .80
Nos. 141-143 (3) 2.50 1.40
1st African Games, Brazzaville, July 18-25.

Abraham Lincoln — A30

1965, Nov. 3 Photo. *Perf. 13x12½*
144 A30 50fr green & multi .90 .45
Centenary of death of Abraham Lincoln.

Pres. Maurice Yameogo — A31

1965, Dec. 11 Photo. *Perf. 13x12½*
145 A31 25fr multicolored .60 .30

Mantis A32

Wart Hog — A33

1fr, Nemopistha imperatrix. 2fr, Ball python. 4fr, Grasshopper. 6fr, Scorpion. 8fr, Green monkey. 10fr, Dromedary. 15fr, Leopard. 20fr, Cape buffalo. 25fr, Hippopotamus. 30fr, Agama lizard. 45fr, Common puff adder. 50fr, Chameleon. 60fr, Ugada limbata. 85fr, Elephant.

1966 *Perf. 13x12½, 12½x13*
146 A33 1fr multi .25 .25
147 A33 2fr multi .25 .25
148 A32 3fr shown .35 .25
149 A33 4fr multi .35 .25
150 A33 5fr shown .35 .25
151 A32 6fr multi .55 .25
152 A33 8fr multi .65 .25
153 A32 10fr multi .50 .25
154 A33 15fr multi 1.00 .35
155 A32 20fr multi 1.35 .45
156 A33 25fr multi 1.55 .50
157 A32 30fr multi 1.10 .60
158 A33 45fr multi 2.25 .80
159 A32 50fr multi 2.50 1.00
160 A33 60fr multi 2.75 .90
161 A33 85fr multi 3.50 1.25
Nos. 146-161 (16) 19.25 7.85

Headdress — A34

25fr, Plumed headdress. 60fr, Male dancer.

1966, Apr. 9   Photo.   *Perf. 13x12½*
162 A34 20fr yel grn, choc & red   .60   .25
163 A34 25fr multicolored   .65   .30
164 A34 60fr org, dk brn & red   1.50   .60
Nos. 162-164 (3)   2.75   1.15

Intl. Negro Arts Festival, Dakar, Senegal, 4/1-24.

Pô Church
A35

Design: No. 166, Bobo-Dioulasso Mosque.

1966, Apr. 15   *Perf. 12½x13*
165 A35 25fr multicolored   .60   .35
166 A35 25fr bl, cream & red brn   .60   .35

The Red Cross Helping the World — A36

1966, June   Photo.   *Perf. 13x12½*
167 A36 25fr lemon, blk & car   .80   .40

Issued to honor the Red Cross.

Boy Scouts in Camp
A37

15fr, Two Scouts on a cliff exploring the country.

1966, June 15   *Perf. 12½x13*
168 A37 10fr multicolored   .50   .25
169 A37 15fr blk, bis brn, & dl yel   .50   .25

Issued to honor the Boy Scouts.

Cow Receiving Injection
A38

1966, Aug. 16   Photo.   *Perf. 12½x13*
170 A38 25fr yel, blk & blue   1.40   .60

Campaign against cattle plague.

Plowing with Donkey
A39

Design: 30fr, Crop rotation, Kamboince Experimental Station.

1966, Sept. 15   Photo.   *Perf. 12½x13*
171 A39 25fr multicolored   .60   .30
172 A39 30fr multicolored   .60   .30

Natl. and rural education; 3rd anniv. of the Kamboince Experimental Station (No. 172).

UNESCO Emblem and Map of Africa
A40

UNICEF Emblem and Children
A41

1966, Dec. 10   Engr.   *Perf. 13*
173 A40 50fr brt bl, blk & red   .90   .60
174 A41 50fr dk vio, dp lil & dk red   .90   .50

20th anniv. of UNESCO and of UNICEF.

Arms of Upper Volta — A42

1967, Jan. 2   Photo.   *Perf. 12½x13*
175 A42 30fr multicolored   .75   .25

Europafrica Issue

Symbols of Agriculture, Industry, Men and Women — A43

1967, Feb. 4   Photo.   *Perf. 12½*
176 A43 60fr multicolored   1.40   .60

Scout Handclasp and Jamboree Emblem
A44

5fr, Jamboree emblem, Scout holding hat.

1967, June 8   Photo.   *Perf. 12½x13*
177 A44 5fr multicolored   .40   .25
178 A44 20fr multicolored   .85   .50

12th Boy Scout World Jamboree, Farragut State Park, Idaho, Aug. 1-9. See No. C41.

Bank Book and Hands with Coins
A45

1967, Aug. 22   Engr.   *Perf. 13*
179 A45 30fr slate grn, ocher & olive   .60   .30

National Savings Bank.

Mailman on Bicycle — A46

1967, Oct. 15   Engr.   *Perf. 13*
180 A46 30fr dk bl, emer & brn   .90   .45

Stamp Day.

Monetary Union Issue
Common Design Type

1967, Nov. 4   Engr.   *Perf. 13*
181 CD125 30fr dk vio & dl bl   .65   .35

View of Nizier
A47

Olympic Emblem and: 50fr, Les Deux-Alps, vert. 100fr, Ski lift and view of Villard-de-Lans.

1967, Nov. 28
182 A47 15fr brt bl, grn & brn   .45   .25
183 A47 50fr brt bl & slate grn   .80   .40
184 A47 100fr brt bl, grn & red   2.00   1.00
Nos. 182-184 (3)   3.25   1.65

10th Winter Olympic Games, Grenoble, France, Feb. 6-18, 1968.

White and Black Men Holding Human Rights Emblem
A48

1968, Jan. 2   Photo.   *Perf. 12½x13*
185 A48 20fr brt bl, gold & dp car   .60   .25
186 A48 30fr grn, gold & dp car   .75   .35

International Human Rights Year.

Administration School and Student — A49

1968, Feb. 2   Engr.   *Perf. 13*
187 A49 30fr ol bis, Prus bl & brt grn   .65   .35

National School of Administration.

WHO Emblem and Sick People
A50

1968, Apr. 8   Engr.   *Perf. 13*
188 A50 30fr ind, brt bl & car rose   .65   .30
189 A50 50fr brt bl, sl grn & lt brn   .95   .50

WHO, 20th anniversary.

Telephone Office, Bobo-Dioulasso — A51

1968, Sept. 30   Photo.   *Perf. 12½x12*
190 A51 30fr multicolored   .90   .45

Opening of the automatic telephone office in Bobo-Dioulasso.

Grain Pouring over World, Plower and FAO Emblem — A53

1969, Jan. 7   Engr.   *Perf. 13*
192 A53 30fr slate, vio bl & maroon   .70   .35

UNFAO world food program.

Automatic Looms and ILO Emblem
A54

1969, Mar. 15   Engr.   *Perf. 13*
193 A54 30fr brt grn, mar & indigo   .75   .45

ILO, 50th anniversary.

Smith
A55

1969, Apr. 3   Engr.   *Perf. 13*
Size: 36x22mm
194 A55 5fr magenta & blk   .35   .25

See No. C64.

Blood Donor
A56

1969, May 15   Engr.   *Perf. 13*
195 A56 30fr blk, bl & car   1.00   .50

League of Red Cross Societies, 50th anniv.

Nile Pike — A57

Fish: 20fr, Nannocharax gobioides. 25fr, Hemigrammocharax polli. 55fr, Alestes luteus. 85fr, Micralestes voltae.

1969   Engr.   *Perf. 13*
Size: 36x22mm
196 A57 20fr brt bl, brn & yel   1.25   .40
197 A57 25fr slate, brn & dk brn   1.25   .45
198 A57 30fr dk olive & blk   1.50   .75
199 A57 55fr dk grn, yel & ol   2.00   .90
200 A57 85fr slate brn & pink   3.50   1.75
Nos. 196-200,C66-C67 (7)   15.75   7.00

Development Bank Issue
Common Design Type

1969, Sept. 10   Engr.   *Perf. 13*
201 CD130 30fr sl grn, grn & ocher   .65   .30

Millet
A58

Design: 30fr, Cotton.

Weaver
A52

1968, Oct. 30   Engr.   *Perf. 13*
Size: 36x22mm
191 A52 30fr mag, brn & ocher   .70   .30

See No. C58.

1969, Oct. 30   Photo.   Perf. 12½x13
202 A58 15fr dk brn, grn & yel   .50   .25
203 A58 30fr dp claret & brt bl   .80   .35
　　Nos. 202-203,C73-C74 (4)   5.80 2.10

ASECNA Issue
Common Design Type

1969, Dec. 12   Engr.   Perf. 13
204 CD132 100fr brown   1.75 1.00

Niadale
Mask — A59

Carvings from National Museum: 30fr, Niaga. 45fr, Man and woman, Iliu Bara. 80fr, Karan Weeba figurine.

1970, Mar. 5   Engr.   Perf. 13
207 A59 10fr dk car rose, org & dk brn   .30   .25
209 A59 30fr dk brn, brt vio & grnsh bl   .50   .25
211 A59 45fr yel grn, brn & bl   1.00   .45
212 A59 80fr pur, rose lil & brn   1.75   .70
　　Nos. 207-212 (4)   3.55 1.65

African Huts and European City — A60

1970, Apr. 25   Engr.   Perf. 13
213 A60 30fr dk brn, red & bl   .85   .45

Issued for Linked Cities' Day.

Mask for Nebwa Gnomo Dance A61

Designs: 8fr, Cauris dancers, vert. 20fr, Gourmantchés dancers, vert. 30fr, Larllé dancers.

1970, May 7   Photo.   Perf. 13
214 A61 5fr lt brn, vio bl & blk   .55   .25
215 A61 8fr org brn, car & blk   .55   .25
216 A61 20fr dk brn, sl grn & ocher   .85   .25
217 A61 30fr dp car, dk gray & brn 1.05   .35
　　Nos. 214-217 (4)   3.00 1.10

Education Year Emblem, Open Book and Pupils A62

Design: 90fr, Education Year emblem, telecommunication and education symbols.

1970, May 14   Perf. 12½x12
218 A62 40fr black & multi   .60   .25
219 A62 90fr olive & multi   1.40   .60

International Education Year.

UPU Headquarters Issue

Abraham Lincoln, UPU Headquarters and Emblem — A63

1970, May 20   Engr.   Perf. 13
220 A63 30fr dk car rose, ind & red brn   .70   .25
221 A63 60fr dk bl grn, vio & red brn   1.25   .50

See note after CD133, Common Design section.

Ship-building Industry — A64

45fr, Chemical industry. 80fr, Electrical industry.

1970, June 15
222 A64 15fr brt pink, red brn & blk   .90   .40
223 A64 45fr emerald, dp bl & blk 1.00   .40
224 A64 80fr red brn, claret & blk 2.00   .70
　　Nos. 222-224 (3)   3.90 1.50

Hanover Fair.

Cattle Vaccination A65

1970, June 30   Photo.   Perf. 13
225 A65 30fr Prus bl, yel & sepia 1.00   .50

National Veterinary College.

Vaccination and Red Cross — A66

1970, Aug. 28   Engr.   Perf. 12½x13
226 A66 30fr chocolate & car   1.00   .50

Issued for the Upper Volta Red Cross.
For surcharge see No. 252.

Europafrica Issue

Nurse with Child, by Frans Hals — A67

Paintings: 30fr, Courtyard of a House in Delft, by Pieter de Hooch. 150fr, Christina of Denmark, by Hans Holbein. 250fr, Courtyard of the Royal Palace at Innsbruck, Austria, by Albrecht Dürer.

1970, Sept. 25   Litho.   Perf. 13x14
227 A67 25fr multicolored   .80   .25
228 A67 30fr multicolored   .95   .45
229 A67 150fr multicolored   3.25 1.25
230 A67 250fr multicolored   5.00 1.75
　　Nos. 227-230 (4)   10.00 3.70

Citroen A68

Design: 40fr, Old and new Citroen cars.

1970, Oct. 16   Engr.   Perf. 13
231 A68 25fr ol brn, mar & sl grn 1.40   .50
232 A68 40fr brt grn, plum & sl   1.75   .85

57th Paris Automobile Salon.

Professional Training Center A69

1970, Dec. 10   Engr.   Perf. 13
233 A69 50fr grn, bis & brn   .75   .40

Opening of Professional Training Center under joint sponsorship of Austria and Upper Volta.

Upper Volta Arms and Soaring Bird — A70

1970, Dec. 10   Photo.
234 A70 30fr lt blue & multi   .55   .25

Tenth anniversary of independence, Dec. 11.

Political Maps of Africa — A71

1970, Dec. 14   Litho.   Perf. 13½
235 A71 50fr multicolored   .80   .45

10th anniv. of the declaration granting independence to colonial territories and countries.

Beingolo Hunting Horn — A72

Musical Instruments: 15fr, Mossi guitar, vert. 20fr, Gourounsi flutes, vert. 25fr, Lunga drums.

1971, Mar. 1   Engr.   Perf. 13
236 A72 5fr blue, brn & car   .45   .30
237 A72 15fr grn, crim rose & brn .90   .30
238 A72 20fr car rose, bl & gray   1.45   .30
239 A72 25fr brt grn, red brn & ol gray   1.65   .60
　　Nos. 236-239 (4)   4.45 1.50

Voltaphilex I, National Phil. Exhibition.

Four Races — A73

1971, Mar. 21   Engr.   Perf. 13
240 A73 50fr rose cl, lt grn & dk brn   1.60   .50

Intl. year against racial discrimination.

Telephone and Globes A74

1971, May 17   Engr.   Perf. 13
241 A74 50fr brn, gray & dk pur   1.00   .40

3rd World Telecommunications Day.

Cane Field Worker, Banfora Sugar Mill — A75　　Cotton and Voltex Mill Emblem — A76

1971, June 24   Photo.   Perf. 13
242 A75 10fr multicolored   .25   .25
243 A76 35fr multicolored   .50   .25

Industrial development.

Gonimbrasia Hecate — A77

Butterflies and Moths: 2fr, Hamanumida daedalus. 3fr, Ophideres materna. 5fr, Danaus chyrsippus. 40fr, Hypolimnas misippus. 45fr, Danaus petiverana.

1971, June 30
244 A77 1fr blue & multi   .30   .25
245 A77 2fr lt lilac & multi   .60   .25
246 A77 3fr multicolored   .70   .25
247 A77 5fr gray & multi   1.40   .35
248 A77 40fr ocher & multi   6.00 1.65
249 A77 45fr multicolored   11.00 2.10
　　Nos. 244-249 (6)   20.00 4.85

Kabuki Actor — A78

40fr, African mask and Kabuki actor.

1971, Aug. 12   Photo.   Perf. 13
250 A78 25fr multicolored   .50   .25
251 A78 40fr multicolored   .70   .35

Philatokyo 71, Philatelic Exposition, Tokyo, Apr. 19-29.

No. 226 Surcharged

1971   Engr.   Perf. 12½x13
252 A66 100fr on 30fr choc & car   1.60   .85

10th anniversary of Upper Volta Red Cross.

Seed Preparation A79

Designs: 75fr, Old farmer with seed packet, vert. 100fr, Farmer in rice field.

1971, Sept. 30   Photo.   Perf. 13
253 A79 35fr ocher & multi   .45 .25
254 A79 75fr lt blue & multi   .80 .30
255 A79 100fr brown & multi   1.00 .45
  Nos. 253-255 (3)   2.25 1.00

National campaign for seed protection.

Outdoor Classroom A80

Design: 50fr, Mother learning to read.

1971, Oct. 14
256 A80 35fr multicolored   .60 .25
257 A80 50fr multicolored   .80 .45
  Women's education.

Joseph Dakiri, Soldiers Driving Tractors — A81

40fr, Dakiri & soldiers gathering harvest.

1971, Oct. 13   Perf. 12x12½
258 A81 15fr blk, yel & red brn   .60 .25
259 A81 40fr blue & multi   .80 .45

Joseph Dakiri (1938-1971), inaugurator of the Army-Aid-to-Agriculture Program.

Spraying Lake, Fly, Man Leading Blind Women A82

1971, Nov. 26   Photo.   Perf. 13
260 A82 40fr dk brn, yel & bl   .90 .50

Drive against onchocerciasis, roundworm infestation.
For surcharge see No. 295.

Children and UNICEF Emblem — A84

1971, Dec. 11   Perf. 13
262 A84 45fr red, bister & blk   .75 .50
  UNICEF, 25th anniv.

Peulh House A85

Upper Volta Houses: 20fr, Gourounsi house. 35fr, Mossi houses. 45fr, Bobo house, vert. 50fr, Dagari house, vert. 90fr, Bango house, interior.

Perf. 13x13½, 13½x13
1971-72   Photo.
263 A85 10fr ver & multi   .25 .25
264 A85 20fr multicolored   .45 .25
265 A85 35fr brt grn & multi   .60 .45
266 A85 45fr multi ('72)   .70 .25
267 A85 50fr multi ('72)   .85 .45
268 A85 90fr multi ('72)   1.40 .60
  Nos. 263-268 (6)   4.25 2.25

Town Halls of Bobo-Dioulasso and Chalons-sur-Marne — A86

1971, Dec. 23   Perf. 13x12½
269 A86 40fr yellow & multi   .80 .50

Kinship between the cities of Bobo-Dioulasso, Upper Volta, and Chalons-sur-Marne, France.

Louis Armstrong — A87

1972, May 17   Perf. 14x13
270 A87 45fr multicolored   4.50 1.00
  Black musician. See No. C104.

Red Crescent, Cross and Lion Emblems A88

1972, June 23   Perf. 13x14
271 A88 40fr yellow & multi   .75 .50
  World Red Cross Day. See No. C105.

Coiffure of Peulh Woman — A89

Designs: Various hair styles.

1972, July 23   Litho.   Perf. 13
272 A89 25fr blue & multi   .40 .25
273 A89 35fr emerald & multi   .70 .25
274 A89 75fr yellow & multi   1.50 .50
  Nos. 272-274 (3)   2.60 1.00

Classroom A90

15fr, Clinic. 20fr, Factory. 35fr, Cattle. 40fr, Flowers.

1972, Oct. 30   Engr.   Perf. 13
275 A90 10fr sl grn, lt grn & choc   .25 .25
276 A90 15fr brt grn, brn org &
                  brn   .25 .25
277 A90 20fr bl, lt brn & grn   .45 .25
278 A90 35fr grn, brn & brt bl   .80 .25
279 A90 40fr choc, pink & sl grn   .80 .25
  Nos. 275-279 (6)   3.55 2.05
  2nd Five-Year Plan.

West African Monetary Union Issue
Common Design Type
1972, Nov. 2
280 CD136 40fr brn, bl & gray   .60 .25

Lottery Office and Emblem A91

1972, Nov. 6   Litho.
281 A91 35fr multicolored   .80 .40
  5th anniversary of National Lottery.

Domestic Animals — A92

1972, Dec. 4   Litho.   Perf. 13½x12½
282 A92 5fr Donkeys   .25 .25
283 A92 10fr Geese   1.00 .25
284 A92 30fr Goats   1.50 .35
285 A92 50fr Cow   1.90 .50
286 A92 65fr Dromedaries   2.75 .70
  Nos. 282-286 (5)   7.40 2.05

Mossi Woman's Hair Style, and Village — A93

1973, Jan. 24   Engr.   Perf. 13
287 A93 5fr slate grn, org &
                  choc   .25 .25
288 A93 40fr bl, org & chocolate   .70 .25

Eugene A. Cernan and Lunar Module A94

65fr, Ronald E. Evans & splashdown. 100fr, Capsule, in orbit & interior, horiz. 150fr, Harrison H. Schmitt & lift-off. 200fr, Conference & moon-buggy. 500fr, Moon-buggy & capsule, horiz.

Perf. 12½x13½, 13½x12½
1973, Mar. 29   Litho.
289 A94 50fr multi   .50 .25
290 A94 65fr multi   .70 .25
291 A94 100fr multi   1.00 .40
292 A94 150fr multi   1.20 .45
293 A94 200fr multi   1.50 .65
  Nos. 289-293 (5)   4.90 2.00

Souvenir Sheet
294 A94 500fr multi   4.50 3.50
  Apollo 17 moon mission.

No. 260 Srchd. in Red

1973, Apr. 7   Photo.   Perf. 13
295 A82 45fr on 40fr multi   .75 .45
  WHO, 25th anniversary.

Scout Bugler A95

1973, July 18   Litho.   Perf. 12½x13
296 A95 20fr multicolored   .40 .25
  Nos. 296,C160-C163 (5)   4.30 2.25

African Postal Union Issue
Common Design Type
1973, Sept. 12   Engr.   Perf. 13
297 CD137 100fr brt red, mag &
                  dl yel   1.25 .70

Pres. Kennedy, Saturn 5 on Assembly Trailer A96

Pres. John F. Kennedy (1917-1963) and: 10fr, Atlas rocket carrying John H. Glenn. 30fr, Titan 2 rocket and Gemini 3 capsule.

1973, Sept. 12   Litho.   Perf. 12½x13
298 A96 5fr multicolored   .25 .25
299 A96 10fr multicolored   .25 .25
300 A96 30fr multicolored   .40 .25
  Nos. 298-300,C167-C168 (5)   4.40 2.60

Cross-examination — A97

Designs: 65fr, "Diamond Ede." 70fr, Forensic Institute. 150fr, Robbery scene.

1973, Sept. 15   Perf. 13x12½
301 A97 50fr multicolored   .70 .25
302 A97 50fr multicolored   .70 .25
303 A97 70fr multicolored   .85 .35
304 A97 150fr multicolored   1.40 .60
  Nos. 301-304 (4)   3.65 1.45

Interpol, 50th anniversary. See No. C170.

Market Place, Ouagadougou — A98

40fr, Swimming pool, Hotel Independence.

1973, Sept. 30
305	A98	35fr multicolored	.45	.25
306	A98	40fr multicolored	.60	.35
		Nos. 305-306,C171 (3)	2.45	1.40

Tourism. See No. C172.

Protestant Church — A99

Design: 40fr, Ouahigouya Mosque.

1973, Sept. 28   Perf. 13x12½
307	A99	35fr multicolored	.35	.25
308	A99	40fr multicolored	.45	.25
		Nos. 307-308,C173 (3)	3.20	1.70

Houses of worship. See No. C173.

Kiembara Dancers A100

Folklore: 40fr, Dancers.

1973, Nov. 30   Litho.   Perf. 12½x13
309	A100	35fr multicolored	.40	.25
310	A100	40fr multicolored	.50	.25
		Nos. 309-310,C174-C175 (4)	4.25	1.95

Yuri Gagarin and Aries — A101

Famous Men and their Zodiac Signs: 10fr, Lenin and Taurus. 20fr, John F. Kennedy, rocket and Gemini. 25fr, John H. Glenn, orbiting capsule and Cancer. 30fr, Napoleon and Leo. 50fr, Goethe and Virgo. 60fr, Pelé and Libra. 75fr, Charles de Gaulle and Scorpio. 100fr, Beethoven and Sagittarius. 175fr, Conrad Adenauer and Capricorn. 200fr, Edwin E. Aldrin, Jr. (Apollo XI) and Aquarius. 250fr, Lord Baden-Powell and Pisces.

1973, Dec. 15   Litho.   Perf. 13x14
311	A101	5fr multicolored	.25	.25
312	A101	10fr multicolored	.25	.25
313	A101	20fr multicolored	.25	.25
314	A101	25fr multicolored	.25	.25
315	A101	30fr multicolored	.35	.25
316	A101	50fr multicolored	.35	.25
317	A101	60fr multicolored	.55	.25
318	A101	75fr multicolored	.85	.35
319	A101	100fr multicolored	.85	.35
320	A101	175fr multicolored	1.40	.55

321	A101	200fr multicolored	1.75	.55
322	A101	250fr multicolored	2.25	.70
		Nos. 311-322 (12)	9.35	4.25

See Nos. C176-C178.

Rivera with Italian Flag and Championship '74 Emblem — A102

40fr, World Cup, soccer ball, World Championship '74 emblem & Pelé with Brazilian flag.

1974, Jan. 15   Perf. 13x12½
323	A102	5fr multicolored	.25	.25
324	A102	40fr multicolored	.45	.25
		Nos. 323-324,C179-C181 (5)	4.10	1.80

10th World Cup Soccer Championship, Munich, June 13-July 7.

Charles de Gaulle A103

40fr, De Gaulle memorial. 60fr, Pres. de Gaulle.

1974, Feb. 4   Litho.   Perf. 12½x13
325	A103	35fr multicolored	.80	.25
326	A103	40fr multicolored	1.15	.25
327	A103	60fr multicolored	1.30	.35
a.		Strip of 3, Nos. 325-327	3.25	.85
		Nos. 325-327,C183 (4)	6.75	2.60

Gen. Charles de Gaulle (1890-1970), president of France. See No. C184.

N'Dongo and Cameroun Flag A104

World Cup, Emblems and: 20fr, Kolev and Bulgarian flag. 50fr, Keita and Mali flag.

1974, Mar. 19
328	A104	10fr multicolored	.25	.25
329	A104	20fr multicolored	.25	.25
330	A104	50fr multicolored	.45	.25
		Nos. 328-330,C185-C186 (5)	4.30	2.10

10th World Cup Soccer Championship, Munich, June 13-July 7.

Map and Flags of Members A105

1974, May 29   Photo.   Perf. 13x12½
331	A105	40fr blue & multi	.85	.50

15th anniversary of the Council of Accord.

UPU Emblem and Mail Coach — A106

1974, July 23   Litho.   Perf. 13½
332	A106	35fr Mail coach	.40	.25
333	A106	40fr Steamship	.50	.25
334	A106	85fr Mailman	.65	.40
		Nos. 332-334,C189-C191 (6)	6.30	3.40

Universal Postal Union centenary.
For overprints see Nos. 339-341, C197-C200.

Soccer Game, Winner Italy, in France, 1938 — A107

World Cup, Game and Flags: 25fr, Uruguay, in Brazil, 1950. 50fr, West Germany, in Switzerland, 1954.

1974, Sept. 2   Litho.   Perf. 13½
335	A107	10fr multicolored	.25	.25
336	A107	25fr multicolored	.25	.25
337	A107	50fr multicolored	.40	.25
		Nos. 335-337,C193-C195 (6)	5.70	3.30

World Cup Soccer winners.

Map and Farm Woman — A108

1974, Oct. 2   Litho.   Perf. 13x12½
338	A108	35fr yellow & multi	.75	.50

Kou Valley Development.

Nos. 332-334 Overprinted in Red

1974, Oct. 9
339	A106	35fr multicolored	.75	.25
340	A106	40fr multicolored	1.00	.35
341	A106	85fr multicolored	1.15	.55
		Nos. 339-341,C197-C199 (6)	9.75	3.95

Universal Postal Union centenary.

Flowers, by Pierre Bonnard A109

Flower Paintings by: 10fr, Jan Brueghel. 30fr, Jean van Os. 50fr, Van Brussel.

1974, Oct. 31   Litho.   Perf. 12½x13
342	A109	5fr multicolored	.25	.25
343	A109	10fr multicolored	.25	.25
344	A109	30fr multicolored	.25	.25
345	A109	40fr multicolored	.45	.25
		Nos. 342-345,C201 (5)	4.70	2.10

Churchill as Officer of India Hussars — A110

Churchill: 75fr, As Secretary of State for Interior. 100fr, As pilot. 125fr, meeting with Roosevelt, 1941. 300fr, As painter. 450fr, and "HMS Resolution."

1975, Jan. 11   Perf. 13½
346	A110	50fr multicolored	.50	.25
347	A110	75fr multicolored	.60	.25
348	A110	100fr multicolored	.90	.35
349	A110	125fr multicolored	1.00	.45
350	A110	300fr multicolored	2.75	1.25
		Nos. 346-350 (5)	5.75	2.55

Souvenir Sheet
351	A110	450fr multicolored	4.75	1.75

Sir Winston Churchill, birth centenary.

US No. 619 and Minutemen — A111

US Stamps: 40fr, #118 and Declaration of Independence. 75fr, #798 and Signing the Constitution. 100fr, #703 and Surrender at Yorktown. 200fr, #1003 and George Washington. 300fr, #644 and Surrender of Burgoyne at Saratoga. 500fr, #63, 68, 73, 157, 179, 228 and 1483a.

1975, Feb. 17   Litho.   Perf. 11
352	A111	35fr multicolored	.45	.25
353	A111	40fr multicolored	.45	.25
354	A111	75fr multicolored	.80	.25
355	A111	100fr multicolored	1.00	.35
356	A111	200fr multicolored	2.00	.60
357	A111	300fr multicolored	3.00	.95
		Nos. 352-357 (6)	7.70	2.65

Souvenir Sheet
Imperf
358	A111	500fr multicolored	7.50	2.25

American Bicentennial.

"Atlantic" No. 2670, 1904-12 — A112

Locomotives from Mulhouse, France, Railroad Museum: 25fr, No. 2029, 1882. 50fr, No. 2129, 1882.

1975, Feb. 28 Litho. Perf. 13x12½
359 A112 15fr multicolored   .50   .25
360 A112 25fr multicolored   .80   .25
361 A112 50fr multicolored   1.40   .25
      Nos. 359-361,C203-C204 (5)   6.95   1.75

French Flag and Renault Petit Duc, 1910 — A113

Flags and Old Cars: 30fr, US and Ford Model T, 1909. 35fr, Italy and Alfa Romeo "Le Mans," 1931.

1975, Apr. 6   Perf. 14x13½
362 A113 10fr multicolored   .25   .25
363 A113 30fr multicolored   .45   .25
364 A113 35fr multicolored   .50   .25
      Nos. 362-364,C206-C207 (5)   5.20   1.95

Washington and Lafayette — A114

American Bicentennial: 40fr, Washington reviewing troops at Valley Forge. 50fr, Washington taking oath of office. 500fr, British surrender at Yorktown.

1975, May 6   Litho.   Perf. 14
365 A114 30fr multicolored   .25   .25
366 A114 40fr multicolored   .35   .25
367 A114 60fr multicolored   .60   .25
      Nos. 365-367,C209-C210 (5)   5.60   2.90
                Souvenir Sheet
367A A114 500fr multicolored   4.75   2.25

Schweitzer and Pelicans — A115

15fr, Albert Schweitzer and bateleur eagle.

1975, May 25   Litho.   Perf. 13½
368 A115   5fr multicolored   .30   .25
369 A115 15fr multicolored   .50   .25
      Nos. 368-369,C212-C214 (5)   7.05   2.75

Albert Schweitzer, birth centenary.

Apollo and Soyuz Orbiting Earth — A116

Design: 50fr, Apollo and Soyuz near link-up.

1975, July 18
370 A116 40fr multicolored   .35   .25
371 A116 50fr multicolored   .45   .25
      Nos. 370-371,C216-C218 (5)   5.80   2.40

Apollo-Soyuz space test project, Russo-American cooperation, launched July 15, link-up July 17.

Maria Picasso Lopez, Artist's Mother A117

Paintings by Pablo Picasso (1881-1973): 60fr, Self-portrait. 90fr, First Communion.

1975, Aug. 7
372 A117 50fr multicolored   .45   .25
373 A117 60fr multicolored   .70   .25
374 A117 90fr multicolored   .90   .40
      Nos. 372-374,C220-C221 (5)   8.30   2.60

Expo '75 Emblem and Tanker, Idemitsu Maru — A118

Oceanographic Exposition, Okinawa: 25fr, Training ship, Kaio Maru. 45fr, Firefighting ship, Hiryu. 50fr, Battleship, Yamato. 60fr, Container ship, Kamakura Maru.

1975, Sept. 26   Litho.   Perf. 11
375   A118 15fr multicolored   .25   .25
376   A118 25fr multicolored   .35   .25
377   A118 45fr multicolored   .50   .25
377A A118 50fr multicolored   .65   .25
378   A118 60fr multicolored   .85   .30
      Nos. 375-378,C223 (6)   4.60   1.90

Woman, Globe and IWY Emblem — A119

1975, Nov. 20   Photo.   Perf. 13
379 A119 65fr multicolored   .90   .60

International Women's Year.

Msgr. Joanny Thevenoud and Cathedral — A120

65fr, Father Guillaume Templier & Cathedral.

1975, Nov. 20   Engr.   Perf. 13x12½
380 A120 55fr grn, blk & dl red   .90   .45
381 A120 65fr blk, org & dl red   1.00   .60

75th anniv. of the Evangelization of Upper Volta.

Farmer's Hat, Hoe and Emblem A121

1975, Dec. 10   Photo.   Perf. 13x13½
382 A121 15fr buff & multi   .25   .25
383 A121 50fr lt green & multi   .80   .45

Development of the Volta valleys.

Sledding and Olympic Emblem — A122

Innsbruck Background, Olympic Emblem and: 45fr, Figure skating. 85fr, Skiing.

1975, Dec. 16   Litho.   Perf. 13½
384 A122 35fr multicolored   .40   .25
385 A122 45fr multicolored   .60   .25
386 A122 85fr multicolored   .80   .40
      Nos. 384-386,C225-C226 (5)   4.50   2.05

12th Winter Olympic Games, Innsbruck, Austria, Feb. 4-15, 1976.

Gymnast and Olympic Emblem — A123

1976, Mar. 17
387 A123   40fr Gymnastics   .30   .25
388 A123   50fr Sailing   .45   .25
389 A123 100fr Soccer   1.00   .45
      Nos. 387-389,C228-C229 (5)   4.25   1.85

21st Olympic Games, Montreal, Canada, July 17-Aug. 1.

Olympic Emblem and Sprinters A124

Olympic Emblem and: 55fr, Equestrian. 75fr, Hurdles.

1976, Mar. 25   Litho.   Perf. 11
390 A124 30fr multicolored   .30   .25
391 A124 55fr multicolored   .45   .25
392 A124 75fr multicolored   .60   .25
      Nos. 390-392,C231-C232 (5)   4.25   1.80

21st Olympic Games, Montreal.
For overprints see nos. 420-422, C245-C247.

Blind Woman and Man — A125

1976, Apr. 7   Engr.   Perf. 13
393 A125   75fr dk brn, grn & org   1.00   .45
394 A125 250fr dk brn, ocher &
                     org   2.75   1.50

Drive against onchocerciasis, roundworm infestation.

"Deutschland" over Friedrichshafen — A126

Airships: 40fr, "Victoria Louise" over sailing ships. 50fr, "Sachsen" over German countryside.

1976, May 11   Litho.   Perf. 11
395 A126 10fr multicolored   .25   .25
396 A126 40fr multicolored   .40   .25
397 A126 50fr multicolored   .70   .30
      Nos. 395-397,C234-C236 (6)   7.10   3.20

75th anniversary of the Zeppelin.

Viking Lander and Probe on Mars — A127

Viking Mars project: 55fr, Viking orbiter in flight. 75fr, Titan rocket start for Mars, vert.

1976, June 24   Perf. 13½
398 A127 30fr multicolored   .25   .25
399 A127 55fr multicolored   .50   .25
400 A127 75fr multicolored   .75   .25
      Nos. 398-400,C238-C239 (5)   6.15   1.95

World Map, Arms of Upper Volta A128

Design: 100fr, World map, arms and dove.

1976, Aug. 19   Litho.   Perf. 12½
401 A128   55fr brown & multi   .55   .25
402 A128 100fr blue & multi   1.25   .60

5th Summit Conference of Non-aligned Countries, Colombo, Sri Lanka, Aug. 9-19.

Bicentennial, Interphil 76 Emblems
and Washington at Battle of
Trenton — A129

90fr, Bicentennial, Interphil 76 emblems,
Seat of Government, Pennsylvania.

1976, Sept. 30   Perf. 13½
403 A129 60fr multicolored   .65   .25
404 A129 90fr multicolored   .80   .25
    Nos. 403-404,C241-C243 (5)   6.30 2.30

American Bicentennial, Interphil 76, Philadelphia, Pa., May 29-June 6.

UPU and UN Emblems — A130

1976, Dec. 8   Engr.   Perf. 13
405 A130 200fr red, olive & blue   2.25 1.25

UN Postal Administration, 25th anniv.

Arms of
Tenkodogo
A131

Coats of Arms: 20fr, 100fr, Ouagadougou.

1977, May 2   Litho.   Perf. 13
406 A131 10fr multicolored   .25   .25
407 A131 20fr multicolored   .25   .25
408 A131 65fr multicolored   .70   .25
409 A131 100fr multicolored   .90   .45
    Nos. 406-409 (4)   2.10 1.20

Bronze
Statuette — A132

Design: 65fr, Woman with bowl, bronze.

1977, June 13   Photo.   Perf. 13
410 A132 55fr multicolored   .60   .25
411 A132 65fr multicolored   1.00   .35

Nos. 410-411 issued in sheets and coils
with black control number on every 5th stamp.

Granaries
A133

1977, June 20   Photo.   Perf. 13½x13
412 A133 5fr Samo   .25   .25
413 A133 35fr Boromo   .35   .25
414 A133 45fr Banfora   .55   .25
415 A133 55fr Mossi   .75   .25
    Nos. 412-415 (4)   1.90 1.00

Handbags
A134

1977, June 20
416 A134 30fr Gouin   .35   .25
417 A134 40fr Bissa   .35   .25
418 A134 60fr Lobi   .60   .25
419 A134 70fr Mossi   .60   .35
    Nos. 416-419 (4)   1.90 1.10

Nos. 390-392 Overprinted in Gold

(a)

(b)

(c)

1977, July 4   Litho.   Perf. 11
420 A124 (a) 30fr multicolored   .30   .25
421 A124 (b) 55fr multicolored   .50   .45
422 A124 (c) 75fr multicolored   .70   .60
    Nos. 420-422,C245-C246 (5)   4.25 3.00

Winners, 21st Olympic Games.

Crinum
Ornatum — A135

Haemanthus   Hannoa
Multiflorus   Undulata
A136   A137

Flowers, flowering branches and wild fruits:
2fr, Cordia myxa. 3fr, Opilia celtidifolia. 15fr,
Crinum ornatum. 25fr, Haemanthus multiflorus. 50fr, Hannoa undulata. 90fr, Cochlospermum planchonii. 125fr, Clitoria ternatea.
150fr, Cassia alata. 175fr, Nauclea latifolia,
horiz. 300fr, Bombax costatum, horiz. 400fr,
Eulophia cucullata.

1977   Litho.   Perf. 12½
423 A137 2fr multicolored   .25   .25
424 A137 3fr multicolored   .35   .25
425 A135 15fr multicolored   .55   .25
426 A136 25fr multicolored   .60   .25
427 A137 50fr multicolored   .90   .45
428 A135 90fr multicolored   1.40   .55
429 A135 125fr multicolored   2.25   .60
430 A136 150fr multicolored   2.00 1.25
431 A136 175fr multicolored   2.25 1.40
432 A136 300fr multicolored   3.50 1.75
433 A135 400fr multicolored   5.25 2.00
    Nos. 423-433 (11)   19.30 9.00

Issued: 25fr, 150fr, 175fr, 300fr, 8/1; 2fr, 3fr,
50fr, 8/8; 15fr, 90fr, 125fr, 400fr, 8/23.

De Gaulle
and Cross of
Lorraine
A138

Designs: 200fr, King Baudouin of Belgium.

1977, Aug. 16   Perf. 13½x14
434 A138 100fr multicolored   2.50   .75
435 A138 200fr multicolored   1.75   .65

Elizabeth II
A139

Designs: 300fr, Elizabeth II taking salute.
500fr, Elizabeth II after Coronation.

1977, Aug. 16
436 A139 200fr multicolored   1.75   .65
437 A139 300fr multicolored   2.50   .80
Souvenir Sheet
438 A139 500fr multicolored   4.25 2.00

25th anniv. of reign of Queen Elizabeth II.
For overprints see Nos. 478-480.

Lottery Tickets, Cars and Map of
Upper Volta in Flag Colors — A140

1977, Sept. 16   Photo.   Perf. 13
439 A140 55fr multicolored   .70   .50

10th anniversary of National Lottery.

Selma Lagerlof, Literature — A141

Nobel Prize Winners: 65fr, Guglielmo Marconi, physics. 125fr, Bertrand Russell, literature. 200fr, Linus C. Pauling, chemistry. 300fr,
Robert Koch, medicine. 500fr, Albert Schweitzer, peace.

1977, Sept. 22   Litho.   Perf. 13½
440 A141 55fr multicolored   .80   .25
441 A141 65fr multicolored   .50   .30
442 A141 125fr multicolored   1.10   .40
443 A141 200fr multicolored   1.75   .65
444 A141 300fr multicolored   3.25   .95
    Nos. 440-444 (5)   7.40 2.55
Souvenir Sheet
445 A141 500fr multicolored   5.00 2.00

The Three
Graces, by
Rubens
A142

Paintings by Peter Paul Rubens (1577-
1640): 55fr, Heads of Black Men, horiz. 85fr,
Bathsheba at the Fountain. 150fr, The
Drunken Silenus. 200fr, 300fr, Life of Maria de
Medicis, diff.

1977, Oct. 19   Litho.   Perf. 14
446 A142 55fr multicolored   .55   .25
447 A142 65fr multicolored   .65   .25
448 A142 85fr multicolored   .75   .25
449 A142 150fr multicolored   1.50   .55
450 A142 200fr multicolored   1.90   .70
451 A142 300fr multicolored   3.00 1.00
    Nos. 446-451 (6)   8.35 3.00

Lenin in His
Office
A143

85fr, Lenin Monument, Kremlin. 200fr, Lenin
with youth. 500fr, Lenin & Leonid Brezhnev.

1977, Oct. 28   Litho.   Perf. 12
452	A143	10fr multicolored	.45	.25
453	A143	85fr multicolored	1.55	.75
454	A143	200fr multicolored	3.50	1.75
455	A143	500fr multicolored	7.50	3.75
	Nos. 452-455 (4)		13.00	6.50

Russian October Revolution, 60th anniv.

Stadium and Brazil No. C79 — A144

Stadium and: 65fr, Brazil #1144. 125fr, Gt. Britain #458. 200fr, Chile #340. 300fr, Switzerland #350. 500fr, Germany #1147.

1977, Dec. 30   Litho.   Perf. 13½
456	A144	55fr multicolored	.35	.25
457	A144	65fr multicolored	.50	.25
458	A144	125fr multicolored	1.00	.35
459	A144	200fr multicolored	1.60	.50
460	A144	300fr multicolored	2.25	.85
	Nos. 456-460 (5)		5.70	2.20

Souvenir Sheet
461	A144	500fr multicolored	4.25	1.90

11th World Cup Soccer Championship, Argentina.
For overprints see Nos. 486-491.

Jean Mermoz and Seaplane — A145

History of Aviation: 75fr, Anthony H. G. Fokker. 85fr, Wiley Post. 90fr, Otto Lilienthal, vert. 100fr, Concorde. 500fr, Charles Lindbergh and "Spirit of St. Louis."

1978, Jan. 2   Litho.   Perf. 13½
462	A145	65fr multicolored	.65	.25
463	A145	75fr multicolored	.65	.25
464	A145	85fr multicolored	.75	.25
465	A145	90fr multicolored	.95	.25
466	A145	100fr multicolored	1.10	.50
	Nos. 462-466 (5)		4.10	1.50

Souvenir Sheet
467	A145	500fr multicolored	5.00	1.90

Crataeva
Religiosa — A146

1978, Feb. 28   Litho.   Perf. 12½
468	A146	55fr Spider tree	.70	.40
469	A146	75fr Fig tree	.90	.60

Souvenir Sheet

Virgin and Child, by Rubens — A147

1978, May 24   Litho.   Perf. 13½x14
470	A147	500fr multicolored	5.75	1.90

Peter Paul Rubens (1577-1640).

Antenna
and ITU
Emblem
A148

1978, May 30   Perf. 13
471	A148	65fr silver & multi	.70	.50

10th World Telecommunications Day.

Fetish Gate of
Bobo — A149

1978, July 10   Litho.   Perf. 13½
472	A149	55fr Bobo fetish	.70	.35
473	A149	65fr Mossi fetish	.90	.50

Capt. Cook and "Endeavour" — A150

Capt. James Cook (1728-1779) and: 85fr, Death on Hawaiian beach. 250fr, Navigational instruments. 350fr, "Resolution."

1978, Sept. 1   Litho.   Perf. 14½
474	A150	65fr multicolored	.60	.25
475	A150	85fr multicolored	.75	.25
476	A150	250fr multicolored	1.75	.70
477	A150	350fr multicolored	2.75	1.00
	Nos. 474-477 (4)		5.85	2.20

Nos. 436-
438
Overprinted
in Silver

1978, Oct. 24   Litho.   Perf. 13½x14
478	A139	200fr multicolored	1.75	1.00
479	A139	300fr multicolored	2.50	1.40

Souvenir Sheet
480	A139	500fr multicolored	4.75	4.25

25th anniversary of Coronation of Queen Elizabeth II. Overprint in 3 lines on 200fr, in 2 lines on 300fr and 500fr.
Nos. 478-480 exist with overprint in metallic red.

Trent Castle, by Dürer — A151

Paintings by Albrecht Durer (1471-1528): 150fr, Virgin and Child with St. Anne, vert. 250fr, Sts. George and Eustachius, vert. 350fr, Hans Holzschuher, vert.

Perf. 14x13½, 13½x14
1978, Nov. 20   Litho.
481	A151	65fr multicolored	.70	.25
482	A151	150fr multicolored	1.30	.45
483	A151	250fr multicolored	2.25	.90
484	A151	350fr multicolored	3.25	1.25
	Nos. 481-484 (4)		7.50	2.85

Human
Rights
Emblem
A152

1978, Dec. 10   Litho.   Perf. 12½
485	A152	55fr multicolored	.65	.25

Universal Declaration of Human Rights, 30th anniv.

Nos. 456-461 Overprinted in Silver

(a)

(b)

(c)

(d)

(e)

(f)

1979, Jan. 4   Litho.   Perf. 13½
486	A144(a)	55fr multicolored	.45	.25
487	A144(b)	65fr multicolored	.60	.45
488	A144(c)	125fr multicolored	1.00	.70
489	A144(d)	200fr multicolored	1.40	.95
490	A144(e)	300fr multicolored	2.25	1.10
	Nos. 486-490 (5)		5.70	3.45

Souvenir Sheet
491	A144(f)	500fr multicolored	4.50	3.50

Winners, World Soccer Cup Championships 1950-1978.

Radio
Station
A153

Design: 65fr, Mail plane at airport.

1979, Mar. 30   Litho.   Perf. 12½
492	A153	55fr multicolored	.45	.25
493	A153	65fr multicolored	.70	.40

Post and Telecommunications Org., 10th anniv.

Teacher and Pupils, IYC
Emblem — A154

1979, Apr. 9   Perf. 13½
494	A154	75fr multicolored	1.00	.60

International Year of the Child.

Telecommunications — A155

1979, May 17　　Litho.　　Perf. 13
495 A155 70fr multicolored　　　.70　.45
　　11th Telecommunications Day.

Basketmaker and Upper Volta No.
111 — A156

　Design: No. 497, Map of Upper Volta, Concorde, truck and UPU emblem.

1979, June 8　　　　　　Photo.
496 A156 100fr multicolored　　3.50 2.40
497 A156 100fr multicolored　　3.50 2.40
　Philexafrique II, Libreville, Gabon, June 8-17. Nos. 496, 497 each printed in sheets of 10 and 5 labels showing exhibition emblem.

Synodontis
Voltae
A157

　Fresh-water Fish: 50fr, Micralestes comoensis. 85fr, Silurus.

1979, June 10　　Litho.　　Perf. 12½
498 A157 20fr multicolored　　　.75　.25
499 A157 50fr multicolored　　1.50　.25
500 A157 85fr multicolored　　2.00　.60
　　Nos. 498-500 (3)　　　　4.25 1.10

Rowland Hill, Train and Upper Volta
No. 60 — A158

　Sir Rowland Hill (1795-1879), originator of penny postage, Trains and Upper Volta Stamps: 165fr, #59. 200fr, #57. 300fr, #56. 500fr, #55.

1979, June　　Litho.　　Perf. 13½
501 A158 65fr multicolored　　　.65　.25
502 A158 165fr multicolored　　1.50　.55
503 A158 200fr multicolored　　1.90　.65
504 A158 300fr multicolored　　3.25 1.00
　　Nos. 501-504 (4)　　　　7.30 2.45
Souvenir Sheet
505 A158 500fr multicolored　　5.00 1.90

Wildlife Fund
Emblem and
Protected
Animals — A159

　30fr, Waterbuck. 40fr, Roan antelope. 60fr, Caracal. 100fr, African bush elephant. 175fr, Hartebeest. 250fr, Leopard.

1979, Aug. 30　　Litho.　　Perf. 14½
506 A159 30fr multicolored　　1.40　.25
507 A159 40fr multicolored　　2.00　.25
508 A159 60fr multicolored　　2.75　.30
509 A159 100fr multicolored　　3.75　.80
510 A159 175fr multicolored　　6.00 1.00
511 A159 250fr multicolored　14.00 1.25
　　Nos. 506-511 (6)　　　　29.90 3.85

Adult Students and Teacher — A160

　Design: 55fr, Man reading book, vert.

1979, Sept. 8　　Perf. 12½x13, 13x12½
512 A160 55fr multicolored　　　.50　.45
513 A160 250fr multicolored　　2.50 1.50
　　World Literacy Day.

Map of Upper Volta, Telephone
Receiver and Lines, Telecom
Emblem — A161

1979, Sept. 20　　　Perf. 13x12½
514 A161 200fr multicolored　　1.90　.95
　3rd World Telecommunications Exhibition, Geneva, Sept. 20-26.

King
Vulture — A162

1979, Oct. 26　　Litho.　　Perf. 13
515 A162　5fr King vulture　　1.00　.25
516 A162　10fr Hoopoe　　　1.00　.25
517 A162　15fr Bald vulture　1.10　.25
518 A162　25fr Egrets　　　1.75　.35
519 A162　35fr Ostrich　　　2.50　.45
520 A162　45fr Crowned crane　3.00　.55
521 A162 125fr Eagle　　　　7.00 1.90
　　Nos. 515-521 (7)　　　17.35 4.00

Control
Tower,
Emblem,
Jet — A163

1979, Dec. 12　　Photo.　　Perf. 13x12½
522 A163 65fr multicolored　　　.90　.60
　ASECNA (Air Safety Board), 20th anniv.

Central Bank of West African
States — A164

1979, Dec. 28　　Litho.　　Perf. 12½
523 A164 55fr multicolored　　　.70　.45

Eugene
Jamot, Map
of Upper
Volta,
Tsetse
Fly — A165

1979, Dec. 28　　　Perf. 13x13½
524 A165 55fr multicolored　　2.25　.80
　Eugene Jamot (1879-1937), discoverer of sleeping sickness cure.

UPU
Emblem,
Upper Volta
Type D4
under
Magnifier
A166

1980, Feb. 26　　Litho.　　Perf. 12½x13
525 A166 55fr multicolored　　　.80　.35
　　　　Stamp Day.

World
Locomotive
Speed
Record,
25th
Anniversary
A167

1980, Mar. 30　　Litho.　　Perf. 12½
526 A167 75fr multicolored　　2.00　.60
527 A167 100fr multicolored　　2.75 1.25

Pres. Sangoule Lamizana, Pope John
Paul II, Cardinal Pau Zoungrana, Map
of Upper Volta — A168

1980, May 10　　Litho.　　Perf. 12½
528 A168 65fr multicolored　　2.50　.60
Size: 21x36mm
529 A168 100fr Pope John Paul
　　　　　II　　　　　　3.25 1.50
　Visit of Pope John Paul II to Upper Volta.

A169

1980, May 17　　　Perf. 13x12½
530 A169 50fr multicolored　　　.60　.35
　　12th World Telecommunications Day.

Solar
Energy — A170

　65fr, Sun and earth. 100fr, Statue, hills.

1980, June 12　　Litho.　　Perf. 13
531 A170 65fr multicolored　　　.60　.35
532 A170 100fr multicolored　　1.00　.45

Downhill Skiing, Lake Placid '80
Emblem — A171

　65fr, Downhill skiing. 100fr, Women's downhill. 200fr, Figure skating. 350fr, Slalom, vert. 500fr, Speed skating.

1980, June 26　　　　Perf. 14½
533 A171 65fr multi　　　　　.50　.25
534 A171 100fr multi　　　　　.75　.30
535 A171 200fr multi　　　　1.60　.50
536 A171 350fr multi　　　　2.75 1.00
　　Nos. 533-536 (4)　　　5.60 2.05
Souvenir Sheet
537 A171 500fr multi　　　　4.50 1.90
　12th Winter Olympic Game Winners, Lake Placid, NY, Feb. 12-24.

Europafrica Issue

Map of Europe
and Africa,
Jet — A172

1980, July 14　　Litho.　　Perf. 13
538 A172 100fr multicolored　　1.20　.60

Hand Holding Back Sand Dune — A173

Operation Green Sahel: 55fr, Hands holding seedlings.

1980, July 18

539 A173 50fr multicolored .65 .25
540 A173 55fr multicolored .85 .45

Gourmantche Chief Initiation — A174

30fr, Gourmantche chief initiation. 55fr, Moro Naba, Mossi Emperor. 65fr, Princess Guimbe Quattara, vert.

1980, Sept. 12 Litho. *Perf. 14*

541 A174 30fr multicolored .40 .25
542 A174 55fr multicolored .60 .30
543 A174 65fr multicolored .85 .30
Nos. 541-543 (3) 1.85 .85

A175

Gourounsi mask, conference emblem.

1980, Oct. 6 *Perf. 13½x13*

544 A175 65fr multicolored .80 .45

World Tourism Conf., Manila, Sept. 27.

A176

1980, Nov. 5 Litho. *Perf. 12½*

545 A176 55fr Agriculture .40 .25
546 A176 65fr Transportation .50 .35
547 A176 75fr Dam, highway .60 .35
548 A176 100fr Industry 1.00 .50
Nos. 545-548 (4) 2.50 1.45

West African Economic Council, 5th anniv.

20th Anniv. of Independence — A177

1980, Dec. 11 *Perf. 13*

549 A177 500fr multicolored 5.25 3.00

Madonna and Child, by Raphael — A178

Christmas: Paintings of Madonna and Child, by Raphael.

1980, Dec. 22 *Perf. 12½*

550 A178 60fr multicolored .50 .25
551 A178 150fr multicolored 1.40 .50
552 A178 250fr multicolored 2.25 .80
Nos. 550-552 (3) 4.15 1.55

West African Postal Union, 5th Anniv. — A179

1980, Dec. 24 Photo. *Perf. 13½*

553 A179 55fr multicolored .75 .45

Dung Beetle A180

5fr, Dung beetle. 10fr, Crickets. 15fr, Termites. 20fr, Praying mantis, vert. 55fr, Emperor moth. 65fr, Locust, vert.

Perf. 13x13½, 13½x13

1981, Mar. 10 Litho.

554 A180 5fr multicolored .55 .25
555 A180 10fr multicolored .55 .25
556 A180 15fr multicolored 1.15 .25
557 A180 20fr multicolored 2.25 .25
558 A180 55fr multicolored 3.75 .45
559 A180 65fr multicolored 4.00 .55
Nos. 554-559 (6) 12.25 2.00

Antelope Mask, Kouroumba A181

Designs: Various ceremonial masks.

1981, Mar. 20 Litho. *Perf. 13*

560 A181 45fr multicolored .50 .25
561 A181 55fr multicolored .60 .30
562 A181 85fr multicolored .90 .50
563 A181 105fr multicolored 1.25 .60
Nos. 560-563 (4) 3.25 1.65

Notre Dame of Kologh' Naba College, 25th Anniv. A182

1981, Mar. 30

564 A182 55fr multicolored .60 .25

Heinrich von Stephan, UPU Founder, Birth Sesquicentennial — A183

1981, May 4 Litho. *Perf. 13*

565 A183 65fr multicolored .75 .45

13th World Telecommunications Day — A184

1981, May 17 *Perf. 13½x13*

566 A184 90fr multicolored .80 .50

Diesel Train, Abidjan-Niger Railroad — A185

Designs: Trains.

1981, July 6 Litho. *Perf. 13*

567 A185 25fr Diesel train .40 .25
568 A185 30fr Gazelle .70 .25
569 A185 40fr Belier .80 .35
Nos. 567-569 (3) 1.90 .85

Tree Planting Month A186

1981, July 15

570 A186 70fr multicolored 1.10 .50

Natl. Red Cross, 20th Anniv. A187

1981, July 31 *Perf. 12½x13*

571 A187 70fr multicolored 1.00 .50

Intl. Year of the Disabled — A188

1981, Aug. 20 Litho. *Perf. 13x12½*

572 A188 70fr multicolored 1.00 .45

View of Koudougou A189

1981, Sept. 3 Litho. *Perf. 12½*

573 A189 35fr Koudougou .40 .25
574 A189 45fr Toma .50 .25
575 A189 85fr Volta Noire 1.00 .30
Nos. 573-575 (3) 1.90 .80

World Food Day — A190

1981, Oct. 16 *Perf. 13*

576 A190 90fr multicolored 1.10 .70

Elephant A191

Designs: Various protected species.

1981, Oct. 21 Photo. *Perf. 14*

577 A191 5fr multicolored .45 .25
578 A191 15fr multicolored .70 .25
579 A191 40fr multicolored 1.20 .35
580 A191 60fr multicolored 2.25 .65
581 A191 70fr multicolored 2.25 .90
Nos. 577-581 (5) 6.85 2.40

Fight Against Apartheid — A192

1981, Dec. 9 Litho. *Perf. 12½*

582 A192 90fr red orange 1.00 .50

Mangoes — A193

20fr, Papayas, horiz. 35fr, Fruits, vegetables, horiz. 75fr, Mangoes, vert. 90fr, Melons, horiz.

1981, Dec. 15 *Perf. 13x13½, 13½x13*

583 A193 20fr multicolored .60 .25
584 A193 35fr multicolored .55 .25
585 A193 75fr multicolored .90 .50
586 A193 90fr multicolored 1.00 .70
Nos. 583-586 (4) 3.05 1.70

Guinea Hen — A194

Breeding animals. 10fr, 25fr, 70fr, 250fr, 300fr horiz.

1981, Dec. 22　　　　　　　*Perf. 13*
587 A194 10fr Donkey　　　　　.25　.25
588 A194 25fr Pig　　　　　　　.35　.25
589 A194 70fr Cow　　　　　　　.90　.25
590 A194 90fr Guinea hen　　1.00　.45
591 A194 250fr Rabbit　　　　2.75 1.10
　　　Nos. 587-591 (5)　　　5.25 2.30
　　　　Souvenir Sheet
592 A194 300fr Sheep　　　　4.25 4.00

West African Rice
Development
Assoc., 10th
Anniv. — A195

1981, Dec. 29
593 A195 90fr multicolored　　1.10　.50

20th Anniv. of
World Food
Program — A196

1982, Jan. 18
594 A196 50fr multicolored　　.60　.25

Traditional Houses — A197

30fr, Morhonaba Palace, vert. 70fr, Bobo.
100fr, Gourounsi. 200fr, Peulh. 250fr, Dagari.

1982, Apr. 23　Litho.　*Perf. 12½*
595 A197 30fr multicolored　　.35　.25
596 A197 70fr multicolored　　.70　.25
597 A197 100fr multicolored　1.10　.35
598 A197 200fr multicolored　2.00　.75
599 A197 250fr multicolored　2.00　.90
　　　Nos. 595-599 (5)　　　6.15 2.50

14th World Telecommunications
Day — A198

1982, May 17
600 A198 125fr multicolored　　1.20　.60

Water Lily — A199

25fr, Water lily. 40fr, Kapoks. 70fr, Frangipani. 90fr, Cochlospermum planchonii. 100fr,
Cotton.

1982, Sept. 22　　　*Perf. 13x12½*
601 A199 25fr multi　　　.25　.25
602 A199 40fr multi　　　.50　.25
603 A199 70fr multi　　　.85　.25
604 A199 90fr multi　　　1.10　.45
605 A199 100fr multi　　1.20　.60
　　　Nos. 601-605 (5)　　3.90 1.80

African
Postal
Union
A200

1982, Oct. 7
606 A200 70fr multicolored　　.60　.25
607 A200 90fr multicolored　1.00　.50

25th Anniv. of
Cultural Aid
Fund — A201

1982, Nov. 10　　*Perf. 12½x13*
608 A201 70fr multicolored　　.80　.45

Map, Hand
Holding
Grain,
Steer Head
A202

1982　　　　　　*Perf. 12½*
609 A202 90fr multicolored　　.95　.45

Traditional
Hairstyle
A203

1983, Jan.　Litho.　*Perf. 12½*
610 A203 90fr lt green & multi　.90　.35
611 A203 120fr lt blue & multi　1.25　.45
612 A203 170fr pink & multi　1.90　.70
　　　Nos. 610-612 (3)　　4.05 1.50

For overprints see Nos. 884-886.

8th Film Festival,
Ouagadougou — A204

90fr, Scene. 500fr, Filmmaker Dumarou
Ganda.

1983, Feb. 10　Litho.　*Perf. 13x12½*
613 A204 90fr multi　　　1.40　.80
614 A204 500fr multi　　7.00 3.50

UN Intl. Drinking
Water and
Sanitation
Decade, 1981-
90 — A205

1983, Apr. 21　Litho.　*Perf. 13½x13*
615 A205 60fr Water drops　　.50　.25
616 A205 70fr Carrying water　1.00　.50

Manned Flight
Bicentenary
A206

Portraits and Balloons: 15fr, J.M.
Montgolfier, 1783. 25fr, Etienne Montgolfier's
balloon, 1783, Pilatre de Rozier. 70fr, Charles
& Roberts flight, 1783, Jacques Charles. 90fr,
Flight over English Channel, John Jeffries.
100fr, Testu-Brissy's horseback flight,
Wilhemine Reichardt. 250fr, Andree's Spitz-
bergen flight, 1897, S.A. Andree. 300fr, Pic-
card's stratosphere flight, 1931, August
Piccard.
No. 623A, J. M. and J. E. Montgolfier, bal-
loon, horiz. No. 623B, John Wise, balloon.

1983, Apr. 15　Litho.　*Perf. 13½*
617 A206 15fr multicolored　　.25　.25
618 A206 25fr multicolored　　.25　.25
619 A206 70fr multicolored　　.70　.25
620 A206 90fr multicolored　　.90　.30
621 A206 100fr multicolored　1.10　.35
622 A206 250fr multicolored　2.25　.80
　　　Nos. 617-622 (6)　　5.45 2.20
　　　　Souvenir Sheet
623 A206 300fr multicolored　3.50 1.25
　　　　Size: 57x39mm
623A A206 1500fr gold & multi　18.00 18.00
　　　　Souvenir Sheet
623B A206 1500fr gold & multi　25.00 25.00
　　No. 623 contains one stamp 38x47mm.
Nos. 621-623 airmail.
　　No. 623B contains one 39x57mm stamp.
Nos. 623A-623B are airmail.

World
Communications
Year — A207

30fr, Man reading letter. 45fr, Aircraft over
stream. 90fr, Girl on telephone.

1983, May 26　Litho.　*Perf. 12½*
624 A207 30fr multi　　　.25　.25
625 A207 35fr Like No. 624　.45　.25
626 A207 45fr multi　　　.65　.25
627 A207 90fr multi　　　.90　.40
　　　Nos. 624-627 (4)　　2.25 1.15

Fishing
Resources
A208

20fr, Synadontis gambiensis. 30fr,
Palmotochromis. 40fr, Boy fishing, vert. 50fr,
Fishing with net. 75fr, Fishing with basket.

1983, July 28　Litho.　*Perf. 13*
628 A208 20fr multicolored　　.60　.25
629 A208 30fr multicolored　　.80　.25
630 A208 40fr multicolored　1.00　.35
631 A208 50fr multicolored　1.10　.35
632 A208 75fr multicolored　1.75　.45
　　　Nos. 628-632 (5)　　5.25 1.65

Anti-deforestation — A209

10fr, Planting saplings. 50fr, Tree nursery.
100fr, Prevent forest fires. 150fr, Woman cooking. 200fr, Prevent felling, vert.

1983, Sept. 13　Litho.　*Perf. 13*
633 A209 10fr multicolored　　.25　.25
634 A209 50fr multicolored　　.50　.25
635 A209 100fr multicolored　1.10　.25
636 A209 150fr multicolored　2.00　.60
637 A209 200fr multicolored　2.25　.90
　　　Nos. 633-637 (5)　　6.10 2.25

Fresco Detail, by Raphael — A210

Paintings: 120fr, Self-portrait, by Pablo
Picasso, 1901, vert. 185fr, Self-portrait at the
palette, by Manet, 1878, vert. 350fr, Fresco
Detail, diff., by Raphael. 500fr, Goethe, by
George Oswald May, 1779, vert.

1983, Nov.　Litho.　*Perf. 13*
638 A210 120fr multicolored　1.50　.45
639 A210 185fr multicolored　1.75　.55
640 A210 300fr multicolored　2.50　.75
641 A210 350fr multicolored　2.75 1.00
642 A210 500fr multicolored　4.50 1.50
　　　Nos. 638-642 (5)　　13.00 4.25

25th
Anniv. of
the
Republic
A211

1983, Dec. 9　Litho.　*Perf. 14*
643 A211 90fr Arms　　　.70　.25
644 A211 500fr Family, flag　4.00 1.50

A212

1984, May 29　Litho.　*Perf. 12½*
645 A212 90fr multicolored　　.80　.30
646 A212 100fr multicolored　　.90　.40

Council of Unity, 25th anniv.

Flowers and
Fungi — A213

25fr, Polystictus leoninus. 185fr, Pterocarpus Lucens. 200fr, Phlebopus colossus
sudanicus. 250fr, Cosmos sulphureus. 300fr,
Trametes versicolor. 400fr, Ganoderma
lucidum.

600fr, Leucocoprinus cepaestipes.

1984, June 15　Litho.　*Perf. 13½*
647 A213 25fr multicolored　　.40　.25
648 A213 185fr multicolored　3.00　.60
649 A213 200fr multicolored　3.25　.70
650 A213 250fr multicolored　4.75　.75

651	A213	300fr multicolored	4.00 .80
652	A213	400fr multicolored	6.00 1.10
		Nos. 647-652 (6)	21.40 4.20

Souvenir Sheet

653	A213	600fr multicolored	6.25 2.25

Nos. 647-653 have Scouting emblem. Nos. 651-653 are airmail. For overprints see Nos. 669-674.

Wildlife
A214

Wildlife — A215

15fr, Cheetah, four cubs. 35fr, Two adults. 90fr, One adult. 120fr, Cheetah, two cubs. 300fr, Baboons. 400fr, Vultures. 1000fr, Antelopes.

1984, July 19

654	A214	15fr multicolored	.50 .25
655	A214	35fr multicolored	1.10 .50
656	A214	90fr multicolored	2.75 .70
657	A214	120fr multicolored	3.00 1.00
658	A214	300fr multicolored	3.50 1.10
659	A214	400fr multicolored	3.50 1.15
		Nos. 654-659 (6)	14.35 4.70

Souvenir Sheet

660	A215	1000fr multicolored	10.00 2.00

World Wildlife Fund (Nos. 654-657); Rotary Intl. (Nos. 658, 660); Natl. Boy Scouts (No. 659). Nos. 658-660 are airmail.

Sailing Ships and Locomotives — A216

1984, Aug. 14   *Perf. 12½*

661	A216	20fr Maiden Queen	.25 .25
662	A216	40fr CC 2400 ch	.45 .25
663	A216	60fr Scawfell	.70 .25
664	A216	100fr PO 1806	1.00 .25
665	A216	120fr Harbinger	1.25 .45
666	A216	145fr Livingstone	1.40 .60
667	A216	400fr True Briton	4.25 1.50
668	A216	450fr Pacific C51	4.50 1.10
		Nos. 661-668 (8)	13.80 4.65

Burkina Faso

Natl. Defense — A216a

Design: 120fr, Capt. Sankara, crowd, horiz.

1984, Nov. 21   Litho.   *Perf. 13½*

668A	A216a	90fr multicolored	45.00 —
668B	A216a	120fr multicolored	65.00 —

No. 635
Overprinted

Aide au Sahel 84

Methods and Perfs As Before

1984

668C	A209	100fr multi	80.00 75.00

Nos. 647-652
Overprinted

1985, Mar. 5   Litho.   *Perf. 13½*

669	A213	25fr multicolored	.50 .25
670	A213	185fr multicolored	3.25 1.10
671	A213	200fr multicolored	5.00 1.50
672	A213	250fr multicolored	4.50 1.60
673	A213	300fr multicolored	6.00 2.25
674	A213	400fr multicolored	7.50 3.00
		Nos. 669-674 (6)	26.75 9.70

A217

Designs: 5fr, 120fr, Flag. 15fr, 150fr, Natl. Arms, vert. 90fr, 185fr, Map.

1985, Mar. 8   Litho.   *Perf. 12½*

675	A217	5fr multicolored	.45 .25
676	A217	15fr multicolored	.65 .30
677	A217	90fr multicolored	2.10 .80
678	A217	120fr multicolored	1.40 .60
679	A217	150fr multicolored	2.00 .75
680	A217	185fr multicolored	2.25 .90
		Nos. 675-680 (6)	8.85 3.60

Nos. 678-680 are airmail.

1986 World Cup Soccer Championships, Mexico — A218

Various soccer plays and Aztec artifacts.

1985, Apr. 20   Litho.   *Perf. 13*

681	A218	25fr multicolored	.25 .25
682	A218	45fr multicolored	.30 .25
683	A218	90fr multicolored	.55 .25
684	A218	100fr multicolored	.60 .30
685	A218	150fr multicolored	.90 .55
686	A218	200fr multicolored	1.25 .85
687	A218	250fr multicolored	1.60 1.00
		Nos. 681-687 (7)	5.45 3.45

Souvenir Sheet

688	A218	500fr multicolored	6.75 1.25

Nos. 681-685 vert. No. 684-688 are airmail. No. 688 contains one 40x32mm stamp.

Motorcycle, Cent. — A220

50fr, Steam tricycle, G.A. Long. 75fr, Pope. 80fr, Manet-90. 100fr, Ducati. 150fr, Jawa. 200fr, Honda. 250fr, B.M.W.

1985, May 26

689	A220	50fr multi	.35 .25
690	A220	75fr multi	.50 .25
691	A220	80fr multi	.60 .25
692	A220	100fr multi	.80 .30
693	A220	150fr multi	1.10 .45
694	A220	200fr multi	1.60 .65
695	A220	250fr multi	1.75 .80
		Nos. 689-695 (7)	6.70 2.95

Nos. 692-695 are airmail.

Reptiles
A221

5fr, Chamaeleon dilepis. 15fr, Agama stellio. 35fr, Lacerta Lepida. 85fr, Hiperolius marmoratus. 100fr, Echis leucogaster. 150fr, Kinixys erosa. 250fr, Python regius.

1985, June 20

696	A221	5fr multicolored	.25 .25
697	A221	15fr multicolored	.25 .25
698	A221	35fr multicolored	.50 .25
699	A221	85fr multicolored	1.40 .30
700	A221	100fr multicolored	1.50 .30
701	A221	150fr multicolored	1.80 .45
702	A221	250fr multicolored	2.90 .60
		Nos. 696-702 (7)	8.60 2.40

Nos. 696-697 vert. Nos. 700-702 are airmail.

A222

A222a

Queen Mother, 85th Birthday
A222a

75fr, On pony bobs. 85fr, Wedding, 1923. 500fr, Holding infant Elizabeth, 1926. 600fr, Coronation of King George VI, 1937. 1000fr, Christening of Prince William, 1982. No. 707A, Christening of Prince Harry, 1985.

1985, June 21   *Perf. 13½*

703	A222	75fr multicolored	.90 .45
704	A222	85fr multicolored	1.00 .45
705	A222	500fr multicolored	4.00 1.50
706	A222	600fr multicolored	5.25 1.75
		Nos. 703-706 (4)	11.15 4.15

Litho. & Embossed

Perf. 13¼

706A	A222a	1500fr gold & multi	12.50 —

Souvenir Sheets

Litho.

707	A222	1000fr multi	10.00 10.00

Litho. & Embossed

707A	A222a	1500fr gold & multi	12.50 —

Nos. 705-707A are airmail.

Vintage Autos and Aircraft — A223

5fr, Benz Victoria, 1893. 25fr, Peugeot 174, 1927. 45fr, Louis Bleriot. 50fr, Breguet 14. No. 712, Bugatti Coupe Napoleon T41 Royale. No. 713, Airbus A300-P4. No. 714, Mercedes-Benz 540K, 1938. No. 715, Airbus A300B. No. 716, Louis Bleriot, Karl Benz.

1985, June 21

708	A223	5fr multicolored	.25 .25
709	A223	25fr multicolored	.45 .25
710	A223	45fr multicolored	.60 .25
711	A223	50fr multicolored	.60 .25
712	A223	500fr multicolored	5.00 1.00
713	A223	500fr multicolored	4.00 1.00
714	A223	600fr multicolored	5.00 1.25
715	A223	600fr multicolored	5.00 1.25
		Nos. 708-715 (8)	20.90 5.50

Souvenir Sheet

716	A223	1000fr multicolored	9.50 2.25

Automobile, cent. Nos. 712-716 are airmail.

Audubon
Birth
Bicent.
A224

Illustrations of No. American bird species by Audubon and scouting trefoil: 60fr, Aix sponsa. 100fr, Mimus polyglotos. 300fr, Icterus galbula. 400fr, Sitta carolinensis. 500fr, Asyndesmus lewis. 600fr, Buteo cagopus. 1000fr, Columba leucocephala.

1985, June 21

717	A224	60fr multicolored	.55 .25
718	A224	100fr multicolored	.85 .30
719	A224	300fr multicolored	2.75 .80
720	A224	400fr multicolored	3.50 1.00
721	A224	500fr multicolored	3.75 1.00
722	A224	600fr multicolored	4.50 1.25
		Nos. 717-722 (6)	15.90 4.60

Souvenir Sheet

723	A224	1000fr multicolored	11.00 2.25

Nos. 721-723 are airmail.

ARGENTINA '85, Buenos Aires — A225

Various equestrians: 25fr, Gaucho, piebald. 45fr, Horse and rider, Andes Mountains. 90fr, Rodeo. 100fr, Andes background. 150fr, Gauchos, 3 horses. 200fr, Rider beside mount. 250fr, Contest. 500fr, Foal.

1985, July 5   *Perf. 13*

724	A225	25fr multicolored	.40 .25
725	A225	45fr multicolored	.65 .25
726	A225	90fr multicolored	1.15 .25
727	A225	100fr multicolored	.80 .25
728	A225	150fr multicolored	1.20 .25
729	A225	200fr multicolored	1.60 .40
730	A225	250fr multicolored	2.25 .60
		Nos. 724-730 (7)	8.05 2.25

Souvenir Sheet

731	A225	500fr multicolored	4.50 1.40

Nos. 727-731 are airmail.

Locomotives — A226

50fr, 105-30 electric, tank wagon. 75fr, Diesel shunting locomotive. 80fr, Diesel locomotive. 100fr, Diesel railcar. 150fr, No. 6093. 200fr, No. 105 diesel railcar. 250fr, Diesel, passenger car.

1985, July 23

732	A226	50fr multicolored	.70	.25
733	A226	75fr multicolored	.95	.25
734	A226	80fr multicolored	1.10	.25
735	A226	100fr multicolored	.80	.25
736	A226	150fr multicolored	1.20	.30
737	A226	200fr multicolored	1.60	.45
738	A226	250fr multicolored	2.10	.60
		Nos. 732-738 (7)	8.45	2.35

Nos. 735-738 are airmail.

Artifacts — A227

Designs: 10fr, 4-legged jar, Tikare. 40fr, Lidded pot with bird handles, P. Bazega. 90fr, Mother and child, bronze statue, Ouagadougou. 120fr, Drummer, bronze statue, Ouagadougou.

1985, July 27   Perf. 13x12½

739-742	A227	Set of 4	4.00	1.50

No. 742 is airmail.

Fungi — A228

15fr, Philiota mutabilis. 20fr, Hypholoma (nematoloma) fasciculare. 30fr, Ixocomus granulatus. 60fr, Agaricus campestris. 80fr, Trachypus scaber. 150fr, Armillaria mellea. 250fr, Marasmius scorodonius.

1985, Aug. 8   Perf. 13

743	A228	15fr multicolored	.25	.25
744	A228	20fr multicolored	.25	.25
745	A228	30fr multicolored	.30	.25
746	A228	60fr multicolored	.60	.25
747	A228	80fr multicolored	1.00	.30
748	A228	150fr multicolored	2.10	.45
749	A228	250fr multicolored	2.25	.60
		Nos. 743-749 (7)	6.75	2.35

Nos. 748 is airmail.

ITALIA '85
A228a

Paintings by Botticelli: 25fr, Virgin and Child. 45fr, Portrait of a Man. 90fr, Mars and Venus. 100fr, Birth of Venus. 150fr, Allegory of the Calumny. 200fr, Pallas and the Centaur. 250fr,

Allegory of Spring. 500fr, The Virgin of Melagrana.

1985, Oct. 25   Litho.   Perf. 12½x13

749A	A228a	25fr multicolored	.35	.25
749B	A228a	45fr multicolored	.60	.25
749C	A228a	90fr multicolored	1.20	.30
749D	A228a	100fr multicolored	.75	.30
749E	A228a	150fr multicolored	.85	.30
749F	A228a	200fr multicolored	1.50	.45
749G	A228a	250fr multicolored	2.00	.70
		Nos. 749A-749G (7)	7.25	2.55

Souvenir Sheet

749H	A228a	500fr multicolored	3.00	1.50

No. 749D-749H are airmail.

Intl. Red Cross in Burkina Faso, 75th Anniv. A229

40f, Helicopter. 85fr, Ambulance. 150fr, Henri Dunant. 250fr, Physician, patient.

1985, Nov. 10

750	A229	40f multi	1.55	.35
751	A229	85fr multi	3.25	.40
752	A229	150fr multi	.85	.35
753	A229	250fr multi	1.25	.40
		Nos. 750-753 (4)	6.90	1.50

Nos. 752-753 are vert. and airmail.

Child Survival
A230

1986, Jan. 6

754	A230	90fr Breast-feeding	1.25	.50

Dated 1985.

Dodo Carnival — A231

20fr, Three children, drummer. 25fr, Lion, 4 dancers. 40fr, Two dancers, two drummers. 45fr, Three dancers. No. 759, Zebra, ostrich, dancers. No. 760, Elephant, dancer.

1986, Jan. 6   Perf. 12½

755	A231	20fr multicolored	.25	.25
756	A231	25fr multicolored	.25	.25
757	A231	40fr multicolored	.45	.25
758	A231	45fr multicolored	.50	.25
759	A231	90fr multicolored	1.10	.45
760	A231	90fr multicolored	1.10	.45
		Nos. 755-760 (6)	3.65	1.90

Dated 1985.

Christophe Columbus (1451-1506) — A232

Columbus: 250fr, At Court of King of Portugal, the Nina. 300fr, Using astrolabe, the Santa Maria. 400fr, Imprisonment at Hispanola, 1500, the Santa Maria. 450fr, At San Salvador, 1492, the Pinta. 1000fr, Fleet departing Palos harbor, 1492.

1986, Feb. 10   Perf. 13½

761	A232	250fr multicolored	2.25	.60
762	A232	300fr multicolored	2.40	.75
763	A232	400fr multicolored	3.25	.90
764	A232	450fr multicolored	3.50	1.50
		Nos. 761-764 (4)	11.40	3.75

Souvenir Sheet

765	A232	1000fr multicolored	6.50	2.25

Nos. 764-765 are airmail. Dated 1985.

Railroad Construction — A233

90fr, Man, woman carrying rail. 120fr, Laying rails. 185fr, Diesel train on new tracks. 500fr, Adler locomotive, 1835. 1000fr, Electric train, Series 290 diesel.

1986, Feb. 10

766	A233	90fr multicolored	1.00	.45
767	A233	120fr multicolored	1.10	.50
768	A233	185fr multicolored	1.60	.60
769	A233	500fr multicolored	4.75	1.50
		Nos. 766-769 (4)	8.45	3.05

Souvenir Sheet

770	A233	500fr multicolored	9.00	2.25

German Railways, sesquicentennial. Nos. 769-770 are airmail. Dated 1985.

Intl. Peace Year — A234

1986, Oct. 10   Photo.   Perf. 12½x13

771	A234	90fr blue	1.50	.45

World Health by the Year 2000 — A235

Designs: 100fr, Primary care medicine. 150fr, Mass inoculations.

1986, Aug. 8   Litho.   Perf. 13

772	A235	90fr multicolored	1.10	.40

Size: 26x38mm

Perf. 12½x13

773	A235	100fr multicolored	1.10	.50
774	A235	120fr multicolored	1.50	.55
		Nos. 772-774 (3)	3.70	1.45

Insects — A236

15fr, Phryneta aurocinta. 20fr, Sternocera interrupta. 40fr, Prosoprocera lactator. 45fr, Gonimbrasia hecate. 85fr, Charaxes epijasius.

1986, Sept. 10   Litho.   Perf. 12½x13

775	A236	15fr multicolored	.35	.25
776	A236	20fr multicolored	.35	.25
777	A236	40fr multicolored	.90	.35

778	A236	45fr multicolored	.95	.35
778A	A236	85fr multicolored	1.90	.70
		Nos. 775-778A (5)	4.45	1.90

World Post Day — A237

1986, Oct. 9   Perf. 13

779	A237	120fr multicolored	1.50	.45

UN Child Survival Campaign — A238

Designs: 30fr, Mother feeding child. 60fr, Adding medicines to food. 90fr, Nurse vaccinating child. 120fr, Nurse weighing child.

1986, Oct. 8   Litho.   Perf. 11½x12

780	A238	30fr multicolored	.50	.25
781	A238	60fr multicolored	.80	.35
782	A238	90fr multicolored	1.10	.50
783	A238	120fr multicolored	1.60	.60
		Nos. 780-783 (4)	4.00	1.70

Mammals A239

Designs: 50fr, Warthog. 65fr, Hyena. 90fr, Antelope. 100fr, Gazelle. 120fr, Bushbuck. 145fr, Kudu. 500fr, Gazelle, diff.

1986, Nov. 3   Litho.   Perf. 13x12½

784	A239	50fr multicolored	.50	.25
784A	A239	65fr multicolored	.60	.30
784B	A239	90fr multicolored	.75	.40
784C	A239	100fr multicolored	.75	.50
784D	A239	120fr multicolored	.85	.55
784E	A239	145fr multicolored	1.15	.65
784F	A239	500fr multicolored	4.00	2.00
		Nos. 784-784F (7)	8.60	4.65

Traditional Dances — A240

Designs: 10fr, Namende. 25fr, Mouhoun. 90fr, Houet. 105fr, Seno. 120fr, Ganzourgou.

1986, Nov. 3   Litho.   Perf. 12½x13

785	A240	10fr multicolored	.35	.25
785A	A240	25fr multicolored	.50	.25
785B	A240	90fr multicolored	1.75	.45
785C	A240	105fr multicolored	1.75	.45
785D	A240	120fr multicolored	2.25	.60
		Nos. 785-785D (5)	6.60	2.00

Hairstyles A241

1986, Nov. 4　Litho.　Perf. 12½x13
788 A241 35fr Peul　.35　.25
789 A241 75fr Dafing　.90　.40
790 A241 90fr Peul, diff.　1.40　.50
791 A241 120fr Mossi　1.75　.65
792 A241 185fr Peul, diff.　2.50　.90
　　Nos. 788-792 (5)　6.90　2.70

10th African Film Festival — A242

90fr, Maps, cameras. 120fr, Jolson, cameramen. 185fr, Charlie Chaplin.

1987, Feb. 21　Litho.　Perf. 12x12½
793 A242 90fr multi　1.25　.60
794 A242 120fr multi　2.25　.90
795 A242 185fr multi　3.25　1.40
　　Nos. 793-795 (3)　6.75　2.90

60th Anniv. of the film *The Jazz Singer* (120fr); 10th anniv. of the death of Charlie Chaplin (185fr).

Intl Women's Day — A243

1987, Mar. 8　　　Perf. 13½
796 A243 90fr multicolored　1.00　.40

Flora — A244

70fr, Calotropis procera. 75fr, Acacia seyal. 85fr, Parkia biglobosa. 90fr, Sterospermum kunthianum. 100fr, Dichrostachys cinerea. 300fr, Combretum paniculatum.

1987, June 6　Litho.　Perf. 12½x13
797 A244 70fr multicolored　1.00　.35
798 A244 75fr multicolored　1.00　.35
799 A244 85fr multicolored　1.25　.55
800 A244 90fr multicolored　1.25　.55
801 A244 100fr multicolored　1.60　.55
802 A244 300fr multicolored　3.75　1.00
　　Nos. 797-802 (6)　9.85　3.35

Fight Against Leprosy — A245

Raoul Follereau (1903-1977) and: 90fr, Doctors examining African youth. 100fr, Laboratory research. 120fr, Gerhard Hansen (1841-1912), microscope, bacillus under magnification. 300fr, Follereau embracing cured leper.

1987, Aug. 6　　　Perf. 13
803 A245 90fr multicolored　1.15　.45
804 A245 100fr multicolored　1.20　.45
805 A245 120fr multicolored　1.40　.60
806 A245 300fr multicolored　3.25　1.50
　　Nos. 803-806 (4)　7.00　3.00

World Environment Day — A246

1987, Aug. 18　Litho.　Perf. 13x12½
807 A246 90fr shown　1.10　.50
808 A246 145fr Emblem, huts　1.65　.75

Pre-Olympic Year — A247

75fr, High jump. 85fr, Tennis, vert. 90fr, Ski jumping. 100fr, Soccer. 145fr, Running. 350fr, Pierre de Coubertin, tennis, vert.

1987, Aug. 31　　　Perf. 12½
809 A247 75fr multicolored　.90　.45
810 A247 85fr multicolored　1.00　.45
811 A247 90fr multicolored　1.00　.60
812 A247 100fr multicolored　1.10　.60
813 A247 145fr multicolored　1.60　.75
814 A247 350fr multicolored　3.75　1.60
　　Nos. 809-814 (6)　9.35　4.45

Pierre de Coubertin (1863-1937).

World Post Day — A248

1987, Oct. 5　Litho.　Perf. 12½x13
815 A248 90fr multicolored　1.00　.45

Fight Against Apartheid — A249

100fr, Luthuli, book, 1962.

1987, Nov. 11　Litho.　Perf. 13
816 A249 90fr shown　1.00　.45
817 A249 100fr multicolored　1.20　.45

Albert John Luthuli (1898-1967), South African reformer, author and 1960 Nobel Peace Prize winner. No. 817 incorrectly inscribed "1899-1967."

Traditional Costumes — A250

1987, Dec. 4　Litho.　Perf. 11½x12
818 A250 10fr Dagari　.25　.25
819 A250 30fr Peul　.30　.25
820 A250 90fr Mossi　.75　.25

821 A250 200fr Senoufo　1.60　.90
822 A250 500fr Mossi　4.00　2.10
　　Nos. 818-822 (5)　6.90　3.75

Traditional Musical Instruments A251

20fr, Xylophone. 25fr, 3-Stringed lute, vert. 35fr, Zither. 90fr, Conical drum. 1000fr, Calabash drum, vert.

Perf. 12x11½, 11½x12
1987, Dec. 4　　　Litho.
823 A251 20fr multicolored　.30　.25
824 A251 25fr multicolored　.30　.25
825 A251 35fr multicolored　.40　.25
826 A251 90fr multicolored　1.00　.45
827 A251 1000fr multicolored　10.00　4.00
　　Nos. 823-827 (5)　12.00　5.20

Intl. Year of Shelter for the Homeless — A252

1987, Dec. 4　Litho.　Perf. 13
828 A252 90fr multicolored　1.00　.45

Five-year Natl. Development Plan — A253

40fr, Small businesses. 55fr, Agriculture. 60fr, Constructing schools. 90fr, Transportation and communications. 100fr, Literacy. 120fr, Animal husbandry.

1987, Dec. 15　　　Perf. 13½
829 A253 40fr multicolored　.40　.25
830 A253 55fr multicolored　.65　.25
831 A253 60fr multicolored　.65　.25
832 A253 90fr multicolored　1.00　.30
833 A253 100fr multicolored　1.10　.55
834 A253 120fr multicolored　1.40　.60
　　Nos. 829-834 (6)　5.20　2.20

World Health Organization, 40th Anniv. — A254

1988, Mar. 31　Litho.　Perf. 12½x13
835 A254 120fr multicolored　1.25　.45

1988 Summer Olympics, Seoul A255

1988, May 5　　　Perf. 13x12½
836 A255 30fr shown　.25　.25
837 A255 160fr Torch, vert.　1.25　.60
838 A255 175fr Soccer　1.50　.70
839 A255 235fr Volleyball, vert.　2.00　1.00
840 A255 450fr Basketball, vert.　3.50　2.00
　　Nos. 836-840 (5)　8.50　4.55

Souvenir Sheet
Perf. 12½x13
841 A255 500fr Runners　6.50　5.25

No. 841 contains one stamp, size: 40x52mm plus two labels.

Ritual Masks A256

10fr, Epervier, Houet. 20fr, Jeunes Filles, Oullo. 30fr, Bubale, Houet. 40fr, Forgeron, Mouhoun. 120fr, Nounouma, Ouri. 175fr, Chauve-souris, Ouri.

1988, May 30　Litho.　Perf. 13
842 A256 10fr multicolroed　.25　.25
843 A256 20fr multicolored　.25　.25
844 A256 30fr multicolored　.30　.25
845 A256 40fr multicolored　.35　.25
846 A256 120fr multicolored　1.00　.45
847 A256 175fr multicolored　1.50　.75
　　Nos. 842-847 (6)　3.65　2.20

Nos. 842-846 vert.

Handicrafts A257

5fr, Kieriebe ceramic pitcher, vert. 15fr, Mossi basket. 25fr, Gurunsi chair. 30fr, Bissa basket. 45fr, Ougadougou leather box. 85fr, Ougadougou bronze statue, vert. 120fr, Ougadougou leather valise.

1988, Aug. 22　Litho.　Perf. 13½
848 A257 5fr multicolored　.25　.25
849 A257 15fr multicolored　.25　.25
850 A257 25fr multicolored　.25　.25
851 A257 30fr multicolored　.30　.25
852 A257 45fr multicolored　.50　.25
853 A257 85fr multicolored　.80　.35
854 A257 120fr multicolored　1.25　.55
　　Nos. 848-854 (7)　3.60　2.15

World Post Day — A258

1988, Oct. 9　Litho.　Perf. 13
855 A258 120fr multicolored　1.35　.45

Aquatic Fauna A259

1988, Oct. 31　　　Perf. 12
856 A259 70fr Angler martin　.80　.25
857 A259 100fr Mormyrus rume　1.10　.45
858 A259 120fr Frog　1.50　.55
859 A259 160fr Duck　2.10　.70
　　Nos. 856-859 (4)　5.50　1.95

Civil Rights and Political Activists A260

Designs: 80fr, Mohammed Ali Jinnah (1876-1948), 1st Governor General of Pakistan.

120fr, Mahatma Gandhi (1869-1948), India. 160fr, John F. Kennedy. 235fr, Martin Luther King, Jr.

1988, Nov. 22   Litho.   Perf. 14
860	A260	80fr multicolored	.80	.35
861	A260	120fr multicolored	1.25	.55
862	A260	160fr multicolored	1.75	.70
863	A260	235fr multicolored	2.25	1.10
		Nos. 860-863 (4)	6.05	2.70

No. 863 is airmail.

Christmas — A261

Stained-glass windows: 120fr, Adoration of the shepherds. 160fr, Adoration of the Magi. 450fr, Madonna and child. 1000fr, Flight into Egypt.

1988, Dec. 2   Perf. 12
864	A261	120fr multicolored	1.25	.45
865	A261	160fr multicolored	1.50	.45
866	A261	450fr multicolored	4.50	1.80
867	A261	1000fr multicolored	9.50	4.50
		Nos. 864-867 (4)	16.75	7.40

A262

No. 869, Ababacar Makharam. No. 870, Jean Tchissoukou. No. 871, Paulin Vieyra.

1989, Feb. 25   Litho.   Perf. 14
868	A262	75fr shown	1.10	.35
869	A262	500fr muticolored	5.00	1.75
870	A262	500fr multicolored	5.00	1.75
871	A262	500fr multicolored	5.00	1.75
		Nos. 868-871 (4)	16.10	5.60

Souvenir Sheet
872	Sheet of 3	16.00	14.00
a.-c.	A262 500fr like #869-871, inscribed in gold	4.00	1.75

Panafrican Film Festival (FESPACO), 20th anniv. Nos. 869-872 are airmail.

World Fight Against AIDS A263

1989, Apr. 7   Litho.   Perf. 13
873	A263	120fr multicolored	1.25	.50

Council for Rural Development, 30th Anniv. — A264

1989, May 3   Litho.   Perf. 15x14
874	A264	75fr multicolored	.90	.45

Parasitic Plants — A265

Legumes and cereals: 20fr, Striga generiodes. 50fr, Striga hermonthica. 235fr, Striga aspera. 450fr, Alectra vogelii.

1989, Oct. 9   Litho.   Perf. 11½
Granite Paper
875	A265	20fr multicolored	.25	.25
876	A265	50fr multicolored	.35	.25
877	A265	235fr multicolored	1.75	1.10
878	A265	450fr multicolored	3.00	1.50
		Nos. 875-878 (4)	5.35	3.10

Dogs A266

1989, Oct. 9   Perf. 15x14½
879	A266	35fr Sahel	.55	.25
880	A266	50fr Puppy	.65	.25
881	A266	60fr Hunting dog	.90	.25
882	A266	350fr Guard dog	4.00	2.00
		Nos. 879-882 (4)	6.10	2.75

Solidarity with the Palestinian People — A267

1989, Nov. 15   Perf. 13
883	A267	120fr Monument, Place de la Palestine	1.50	.45

Nos. 610-612 Overprinted

1988, Dec. 21   Litho.   Perf. 12½
884	A203	90fr multicolored	.90	.30
885	A203	120fr multicolored	1.10	.30
886	A203	170fr multicolored	1.75	.50
		Nos. 884-886 (3)	3.75	1.10

Visit of Pope John Paul II A268

120fr, Our Lady of Yagma. 160fr, Pope, crowd.

1990, Jan. 1   Litho.   Perf. 15x14
887	A268	120fr multi	1.25	.55
888	A269	160fr multi	1.75	.90

150th Anniv. of the Postage Stamp A269

500fr, Penny Black, ship.

1990, Mar. 20   Litho.   Perf. 15x14
889	A269	120fr multicolored	1.40	.60

Souvenir Sheet
Perf. 14x15
890	A269	500fr multicolored	4.75	4.25

Stamp World London '90.

World Cup Soccer Championships, Italy — A270

1990, Apr. 26   Litho.   Perf. 11½
891	A270	30fr multicolored	.30	.25
892	A270	150fr multi, diff.	2.10	.70

Souvenir Sheet
893	A270	1000fr multi, horiz.	10.00	8.50

Intl. Literacy Year A271

1990, July 10   Litho.   Perf. 13
894	A271	40fr multicolored	.50	.25
895	A271	130fr multicolored	1.45	.60

Mushrooms — A272

10fr, Cantharellus cibarius. 15fr, Psalliota bispora. 60fr, Amanita caesarea. 190fr, Boletus badius.

1990, May 17   Litho.   Perf. 11½
896	A272	10fr multicolored	.30	.25
897	A272	15fr multicolored	.50	.25
898	A272	60fr multicolored	1.10	.80
899	A272	190fr multicolored	3.50	1.75
a.	Souv. sheet of 4, #896-899	19.50	6.25
		Nos. 896-899 (4)	5.40	3.05

Intl. Exposition of Handicrafts — A273

35fr, Masks, fans, vert. 270fr, Rattan chair, vert.

1990, Sept. 25   Litho.   Perf. 13
900	A273	35fr multi	.30	.25
901	A273	45fr shown	.40	.25
902	A273	270fr multi	2.50	1.00
		Nos. 900-902 (3)	3.20	1.50

Gen. Charles de Gaulle (1890-1970) A274

1990, Nov. 22   Litho.   Perf. 13
903	A274	200fr multicolored	2.25	.90

Minerals A275

1991, Feb. 4   Litho.   Perf. 15x14
904	A275	20fr Quartz	.35	.25
905	A275	50fr Granite	.60	.25
906	A275	280fr Amphibolite	3.25	1.40
		Nos. 904-906 (3)	4.20	1.90

African Film Festival — A276

1991, Feb. 20   Perf. 11½
907	A276	150fr multicolored	2.00	.90

Souvenir Sheet
908	A276	1000fr Award	14.00	10.00

Fight Against Drugs — A277

1991, Feb. 20
909	A277	130fr multicolored	1.35	.60

Samuel F.B. Morse (1791-1872), Inventor — A278

1991, May 17   Litho.   Perf. 13
910	A278	200fr multicolored	2.00	.90

Native Girl — A279

1991-94   Litho.   Perf. 14½x15
911	A279	5fr gray & multi	.25	.25
912	A279	10fr yellow & multi	.25	.25
913	A279	25fr lilac rose & multi	.25	.25
914	A279	50fr red lilac & multi	.25	.25
915	A279	130fr blue & multi	1.25	.55
916	A279	150fr multicolored	1.50	.60

920 A279 200fr multicolored 1.90 .80
922 A279 330fr orange & multi 3.25 1.40
Nos. 911-922 (8) 8.90 4.35

Issued: 150fr, 200fr, 6/20/91; 130fr, 330fr, 1/15/93; 5-50fr, 5/3/94.

Flowers
A280

5fr, Grewia tenax. 15fr, Hymenocardia acide. 60fr, Cassia sieberiana, vert. 100fr, Adenium obesum. 300fr, Mitragyna inermis.

1991, July 31 **Litho.** **Perf. 11½**
926 A280 5fr multicolored .25 .25
927 A280 15fr multicolored .25 .25
928 A280 60fr multicolored .65 .25
929 A280 100fr multicolored 1.00 .40
930 A280 300fr multicolored 3.00 1.25
Nos. 926-930 (5) 5.15 2.40

Traditional Dance
Costumes
A281

1991, Aug. 20 **Perf. 12½**
931 A281 75fr Warba .90 .40
932 A281 130fr Wiskamba 1.35 .70
933 A281 280fr Pa-zenin 3.50 1.50
Nos. 931-933 (3) 5.75 2.60

World Post
Day — A282

1991, Oct. 9 **Perf. 13½**
934 A282 130fr multicolored 1.35 .50

Cooking
Utensils
A283

45fr, Pancake fryer. 130fr, Cooking pot, vert. 310fr, Mortar & pestle, vert. 500fr, Ladle, calabash.

1992, Jan. 8 **Litho.** **Perf. 11½**
935 A283 45fr multicolored .50 .25
936 A283 130fr multicolored 1.50 .45
937 A283 310fr multicolored 3.50 1.25
938 A283 500fr multicolored 5.50 2.00
Nos. 935-938 (4) 11.00 3.95

1992 African
Soccer
Championships,
Senegal — A284

50fr, Yousouf Fofana. 100fr, Francois-Jules Bocande. 500fr, Trophy.

1992, Jan. 17 **Perf. 13½**
939 A284 50fr multicolored .65 .25
940 A284 100fr multicolored 1.25 .40

Souvenir Sheet
Perf. 13x12½
941 A284 500fr multicolored 5.50 2.00

UN Decade For the
Handicapped — A285

1992, Mar. 31 **Litho.** **Perf. 12½**
942 A285 100fr multicolored 1.10 .40

World Health
Day — A286

1992, Apr. 7 **Perf. 13**
943 A286 330fr multicolored 5.00 1.40

Discovery
of America,
500th
Anniv.
A287

50fr, Columbus, Santa Maria. 150fr, Ships, natives. 350fr, Map.

1992, Aug. 12 **Litho.** **Perf. 12½**
944 A287 50fr multicolored 1.00 .25
945 A287 150fr multicolored 2.50 .65

Souvenir Sheet
946 A287 350fr multicolored 4.75 1.50
Genoa '92. No. 946 contains one 52x31mm stamp.

Insects
A288

20fr, Dysdercus voelkeri. 40fr, Rhizopertha dominica. 85fr, Orthetrum microstigma. 500fr, Apis mellifera.

1992, Aug. 17 **Perf. 15x14**
947 A288 20fr multicolored .25 .25
948 A288 40fr multicolored .55 .25
949 A288 85fr multicolored 1.10 .35
950 A288 500fr multicolored 6.50 2.25
Nos. 947-950 (4) 8.40 3.10

A289

Christmas: 10fr, Boy, creche. 130fr, Children decorating creche. 1000fr, Boy holding painting of Madonna and Child.

1992, Dec. 21 **Litho.** **Perf. 11½**
951 A289 10fr multicolored .25 .25
952 A289 130fr multicolored 1.40 .50
953 A289 1000fr multicolored 10.00 4.00
Nos. 951-953 (3) 11.65 4.75

Invention of
the Diesel
Engine,
Cent.
A290

1993, Jan. 25 **Litho.** **Perf. 11½**
954 A290 1000fr multicolored 11.50 4.00

Paris '94,
Philatelic
Exhibition
A291

1993, July 15
955 A291 400fr multicolored 5.00 1.75
956 A291 650fr multi, diff. 7.00 2.75

African Film
Festival — A292

Designs: 250fr, Monument to the cinema. 750fr, M. Douta (1919-1991), comedian, horiz.

Perf. 11½x12, 12x11½
1993, Feb. 16 **Litho.**
957 A292 250fr multicolored 2.75 1.00
958 A292 750fr multicolored 8.25 3.00

Birds — A293

100fr, Mycteria ibis. 200fr, Leptoptilos crumeniferus. 500fr, Ephippiorhynchus senegalensis.

1993, Mar. 31 **Perf. 11½x12**
959 A293 100fr multicolored 1.00 .40
960 A293 200fr multicolored 2.00 .80
961 A293 500fr multicolored 5.25 2.00
a. Souvenir sheet of 3, #959-961 13.00 4.75
Nos. 959-961 (3) 8.25 3.20

No. 961a sold for 1200fr.

1994 World Cup Soccer
Championships, U.S. — A294

1000fr, Players, US flag.

1993, Apr. 8 **Perf. 15**
962 A294 500fr shown 6.50 2.00
963 A294 1000fr multi 13.50 4.00

Fruit
Trees — A295

150fr, Saba senegalensis, vert. 300fr, Butyrospermum parkii. 600fr, Adansonia digitata, vert.

1993, June 2 **Litho.** **Perf. 11½**
964 A295 150fr multicolored 1.75 .95
965 A295 300fr multicolored 3.50 1.90
966 A295 600fr multicolored 7.50 4.00
Nos. 964-966 (3) 12.75 6.85

Traditional
Jewelry
A296

200fr, Ring for hair. 250fr, Agate necklace, vert. 500fr, Bracelet.

1993, Sept. 25 **Litho.** **Perf. 11½**
967 A296 200fr multi 1.75 .85
968 A296 250fr multi 2.25 1.00
969 A296 500fr multi 4.50 2.00
Nos. 967-969 (3) 8.50 3.85

Gazella
Rufifrons
A297

1993, Dec. 10 **Litho.** **Perf. 14½**
970 A297 30fr shown 1.15 .25
971 A297 40fr Two facing left 1.15 .25
972 A297 60fr Two standing 2.25 .75
973 A297 100fr Young gazelle 4.50 1.25
a. Souvenir sheet, #970-973 8.00 6.50
Nos. 970-973 (4) 9.05 2.50

World Wildlife Fund (Nos. 970-973). No. 973a sold for 400fr.

Kingfishers — A298

600fr, Halcyon senegalensis. 1200fr, Halcyon chelicuti. 2000fr, Ceyx picta.

1994, Mar. 8 **Litho.** **Perf. 11½**
974 A298 600fr multicolored 4.00 1.75
975 A298 1200fr multicolored 8.50 3.75

Souvenir Sheet
976 A298 2000fr multicolored 17.00 9.75

1994 World Cup Soccer
Championships, U.S. — A299

1000fr, Players, US map. 1800fr, Soccer ball, players.

1994, Mar. 28
977 A299 1000fr multicolored 5.00 2.00
978 A299 1800fr multicolored 8.00 4.00
a. Souvenir sheet of 1 10.00 8.50

No. 978a sold for 2000fr.

First Manned
Moon Landing,
25th
Anniv. — A300

No. 979, Astronaut, flag. No. 980, Lunar module, earth.

1994, July 15   Litho.   Perf. 11½
979	A300	750fr multi	3.25	1.90
980	A300	750fr multi	3.25	1.90
a.		Pair, #979-980	7.00	3.75

No. 980a is a continuous design.

First Stamp Exhibition, Paris, 1994 — A301

1994, Apr. 28
981	A301	1500fr Dogs	7.25	3.75
a.		Souvenir sheet of 1	10.00	8.25

Legumes — A302

40fr, Hibiscus sabdariffa. 45fr, Solanum aethiopicum. 75fr, Solanum melongena. 100fr, Hibiscus esculentus.

1994   Litho.   Perf. 11½
982	A302	40fr multicolored	.25	.25
983	A302	45fr multicolored	.35	.25
984	A302	75fr multicolored	.60	.25
985	A302	100fr multicolored	.75	.25
		Nos. 982-985 (4)	1.95	1.00

Intl. Olympic Committee, Cent. — A303

1994, Oct. 10   Perf. 15
986	A303	320fr multicolored	1.90	.80

Domestic Animals — A304

150fr, Pig, horiz. 1000fr, Capra hircus. 1500fr, Ovis aries, horiz.

1994, Oct. 10   Perf. 11½
987	A304	150fr multi	.75	.35
988	A304	1000fr multi	4.75	2.50
989	A304	1500fr multi	7.00	3.00
		Nos. 987-989 (3)	12.50	5.85

Elvis Presley (1935-77) — A305

A305a

Portraits in feature films: 300fr, Loving You. 500fr, Jailhouse Rock. 1000fr, Blue Hawaii. 1500fr, Marilyn Monroe, Presley.

1995   Litho.   Perf. 13½
990-992	A305	Set of 3	10.00	4.75

Souvenir Sheets
993	A305	1500fr multi	7.50	6.50

Litho. & Embossed
993A	A305a	3000fr gold & multi	17.50	11.00

Nos. 990-992 exist in souvenir sheets of one. No. 993 contains one 51x42mm stamp with continuous design. No. 993A, exists in souvenir sheets of silver & multi with different designs in sheet margin.
Issued: No. 993A, 2/24/95.
See Nos. 1012-1015A.

Crocodile — A306

1995, Feb. 6   Litho.   Perf. 15x14½
994	A306	10fr brown & multi	.25	.25
995	A306	20fr lilac & multi	.25	.25
996	A306	25fr olive brn & multi	.25	.25
997	A306	30fr green & multi	.25	.25
998	A306	40fr red brn & multi	.25	.25
999	A306	50fr gray & multi	.25	.25
1000	A306	75fr gray vio & multi	.35	.25
1001	A306	100fr gray brn & multi	.50	.25
1002	A306	150fr olive & multi	.75	.40
1003	A306	175fr gray bl & multi	.90	.45
1004	A306	250fr brn lake & multi	1.25	.65
1005	A306	400fr bl grn & multi	1.50	1.00
		Nos. 994-1005 (12)	6.75	4.50

World Tourism Organization, 20th Anniv. — A307

Designs: 150fr, Man riding donkey, vert. 350fr, Bobo-Dioulasso railroad station. 450fr, Grand Mosque, Bani. 650fr, Gazelle, map.

1995, Jan. 26   Litho.   Perf. 11½
1006	A307	150fr multicolored	.75	.40
1007	A307	350fr multicolored	1.75	.90
1008	A307	450fr multicolored	2.25	1.10
1009	A307	650fr multicolored	3.25	1.60
		Nos. 1006-1009 (4)	8.00	4.00

FESPACO '95 — A308

Motion pictures: 150fr, "Rabi," Gaston Kabore. 250fr, "Tilai," Idrissa Ouedraogo.

1995   Perf. 13½
1010	A308	150fr multicolored	.80	.40
1011	A308	250fr multicolored	1.40	.70

Nos. 1010-1011 exist in souvenir sheets of one. Motion pictures, cent.

Traditional Houses — A308a

1995   Litho.   Perf. 13½
1011A	A308a	70fr Mossi	.30	.25
1011B	A308a	100fr Kassena	.55	.25
1011C	A308a	200fr Bobo	1.00	.40
1011D	A308a	250fr Peulh	1.50	.60
		Nos. 1011A-1011D (4)	3.35	1.50

Stars of Motion Pictures Type of 1995

Marilyn Monroe in feature films: 400fr, The Joyful Parade. 650fr, The Village Tramp. 750fr, Niagara.
1500fr, The Seven Year Itch. 3000fr, Marilyn Monroe (1926-62).

1995   Litho.   Perf. 13½
1012-1014	A305	Set of 3	9.00	3.25

Souvenir Sheets
1015	A305	1500fr multi	8.25	4.00

Litho. & Embossed
1015A	A305a	3000fr gold & multi	17.50	11.00

Nos. 1012-1014 exist in souvenir sheets of 1. No. 1015 contains one 42x51mm stamp with continuous design. No. 1015A exists in souvenir sheets of silver & multi with different designs in sheet margin.

Birds — A309

Designs: 450fr, Laniarius barbarus. 600fr, Estrilda bengala. 750fr, Euplectes afer.

1995, Apr. 5   Litho.   Perf. 11½
1016	A309	450fr multicolored	2.25	.75
1017	A309	600fr multicolored	3.25	1.40
1018	A309	750fr multicolored	4.00	1.75
a.		Souv. sheet, #1016-1018	9.75	4.50
		Nos. 1016-1018 (3)	9.50	3.90

No. 1018a sold for 2000fr.

Reptiles — A310

Designs: 450fr, Psammophis sibilans. 500fr, Eryx muelleri. 1500fr, Turtle.

1995, Dec. 31
1019	A310	450fr multicolored	3.00	1.00
1020	A310	500fr multicolored	3.00	1.10
1021	A310	1500fr multicolored	9.00	3.50
		Nos. 1019-1021 (3)	15.00	5.60

1996 Summer Olympics, Atlanta — A311

150fr, Basketball. 250fr, Baseball. 650fr, Tennis. 750fr, Table tennis.
1500fr, Equestrian event. 3000fr, Tennis, diff.

1995, Sept. 20   Litho.   Perf. 13½
1022	A311	150fr multi	.65	.25
1023	A311	250fr multi	1.00	.30
1024	A311	650fr multi	2.50	.60

1025	A311	750fr multi	3.50	1.25
a.		Souv. sheet, #1022-1025	50.00	—
		Nos. 1022-1025 (4)	7.65	2.40

Souvenir Sheets
1026	A311	1500fr multi	7.75	7.00

Litho. & Embossed
1026A	A311	3000fr gold & multi	16.00	10.00

No. 1026A also exists as a silver & multi souvenir sheet with different design in sheet margin. Both the gold & silver stamps also exist together in a souvenir sheet of 2.

Sports Figures — A312

Ayrton Senna (1960-94), World Driving Champion — A313

Designs: 300fr, Juan Manuel Fangio, race car driver, 1955 Mercedes W 196. 400fr, Andre Agassi, US tennis player. 500fr, Ayrton Senna (1960-94), race car driver, McLaren MP 4/6 Honda. 1000fr, Michael Schumacher, race car driver, 1995 Benetton B 195.
1500fr, Enzo Ferrari, 412 TR, F40.

1995, Sept. 20
1027	A312	300fr multi	1.50	1.00
1028	A312	400fr multi	1.65	.50
1029	A312	500fr multi	2.25	.50
1030	A312	1000fr multi	4.25	1.00
a.		Souvenir sheet of 3, #1027, 1029-1030	13.00	7.25
		Nos. 1027-1030 (4)	9.65	3.00

Souvenir Sheets
1031	A312	1500fr multicolored	7.25	6.00

Litho. & Embossed
1032	A313	3000fr gold & multi	15.00	10.00

Nos. 1027-1030 exist in souvenir sheets of 1. No. 1031 contains one 55x48mm stamp. No. 1032 also exists as a silver & multi souvenir sheet with different design in sheet margin. Both the gold and silver stamps also exist together in a souvenir sheet of 2.
For surcharge see No. 1078.

Souvenir Sheets

John Lennon (1940-1980) — A314

Designs: No. 1033, With guitar, circular pattern with name "LENNON," portrait. No. 1034, With guitar, emblem, portrait.

1995   Litho. & Embossed   Perf. 13½
1033	A314	3000fr gold & multi	15.00	6.00
1034	A314	3000fr gold & multi	15.00	6.00

Nos. 1033-1034 each exist in souvenir sheets of silver & multi. Souvenir sheets of one gold and one silver exist in same designs and one of each design.

1995 Boy Scout Jamboree, Holland A315

Mushrooms: 150fr, Russula nigricans. 250fr, Lepiota rhacodes. 300fr, Xerocomus subtomentos. 400fr, Boletus erythropus. 500fr, Russula sanguinea. 650fr, Amanita rubescens. 750fr, Amanita vaginata. 1000fr, Geastrum sessil.

No. 1043, 1500fr, Amanita muscaria. No. 1044, 1500fr, Morchella esculenta.

1996, Feb. 20	**Litho.**		**Perf. 13½**
1035-1042	A315	Set of 8	17.50 8.00
1041a		Sheet of 4, #1035, 1037, 1040-1041	15.00 12.50
1042a		Sheet of 4, #1036, 1038-1039, 1042	15.00 12.50

Souvenir Sheets

1043-1044	A315	Set of 2	15.00 6.00

Mushrooms — A316

Designs: 175fr, Hygrophore perroquet. 250fr, Pleurote en huitre. 300fr, Pezize (oreille d'ane). 450fr, Clavaire jolie.

1996, Jan. 24			
1045-1048	A316	Set of 4	6.50 2.25
1048a		Souv. sheet, #1045-1048	16.00 2.25

Nos. 1045-1048 each exist in souv. sheets of 1.

UN, 50th Anniv. A317

Designs: 500fr, UN headquarters, New York. 1000fr, UN emblem, people, vert.

1995, Dec. 20			**Perf. 11½**
1049	A317	500fr multicolored	2.50 1.25
1050	A317	1000fr multicolored	4.50 2.25

Christmas A318

Designs: 150fr, Christmas tree, children pointing to picture of nativity scene. 450fr, Yagma Grotto. 500fr, Flight into Egypt. 1000fr, Adoration of the Magi.

1995, Dec. 18			
1051	A318	150fr multicolored	.80 .40
1052	A318	450fr multicolored	2.40 1.25
1053	A318	500fr multicolored	2.75 1.40
1054	A318	1000fr multicolored	5.00 2.25
		Nos. 1051-1054 (4)	10.95 5.30

Entertainers — A319

Portraits: 150fr, Michael Jackson. 250fr, Prince. 300fr, Madonna. 400fr, Mick Jagger. 500fr, Bob Marley. 650fr, The Beatles. 750fr, Marilyn Monroe. 1000fr, Elvis Presley wearing black jacket. No. 1062, Elvis Presley, smiling. No. 1063, 1500fr, Presley, hand under chin. No. 1064, 1500fr, Stevie Wonder.

1996, May 14	**Litho.**		**Perf. 13½**
1055	A319	150fr multi	.80 .25
1056	A319	250fr multi	1.25 .25
1057	A319	300fr multi	1.50 .35
1058	A319	400fr multi	2.00 .35
1059	A319	500fr multi	2.50 .50
1060	A319	650fr multi	2.50 .50
1061	A319	750fr multi	4.00 .60
1061A	A319	1000fr multi	5.00 .60
		Nos. 1055-1061A (8)	19.55 3.40

Souvenir Sheets

1062-1064	A319	Set of 3	20.00 10.00

Dated 1995.

Butterflies and Insects A320

100fr, Epiphora bauhiniae. 150fr, Kraussella amabile. 175fr, Charaxes epijasius. 250fr, Locusta migratoria.

1996	**Litho.**		**Perf. 13½**
1065	A320	100fr multi, vert.	.50 .25
1066	A320	150fr multi, vert.	.85 .35
1067	A320	175fr multi, vert.	.85 .35
1068	A320	250fr multi	1.10 .50
		Nos. 1065-1068 (4)	3.30 1.45

Two souvenir sheets containing Nos. 1065, 1067 and Nos. 1066, 1068, respectively, exist.

Butterflies A321

Designs: 150fr, Morpho rega. 250fr, Hypolymnas misippus. 450fr, Pseudacraea boisduvali. 600fr, Charaxes castor. 1500fr, Antanartia delius.

1996, June 28	**Litho.**		**Perf. 13½**
1069	A321	150fr multicolored	.80 .35
1070	A321	250fr multicolored	1.25 .55
1071	A321	450fr multicolored	2.25 1.00
1072	A321	600fr multicolored	3.25 2.75
		Nos. 1069-1072 (4)	7.55 4.65

Souvenir Sheet

1073	A321	1500fr multicolored	8.25 6.00
a.		Ovptd. in sheet margin	8.25 5.50

Overprint in silver in sheet margin of No. 1073a contains Hong Kong '97 Exhibition

emblem and two line inscription in Chinese. Issued in 1997.

Insects — A321a

c, 25fr, Sauterelle. d, 75fr, Schistocerca gregaria. e, 300fr, Pardolata haasi. f, 400fr, Psammomys obesus.

1996, June 28	**Litho.**		**Perf. 13½**
1073B	A321a	Strip of 4, #c.-f.	4.25 1.40

1998 World Cup Soccer Championships, France — A322

Various soccer plays.

1996	**Litho.**		**Perf. 13**
1074	A322	50fr multi	.25 .25
1075	A322	150fr multi, vert.	.90 .25
1076	A322	250fr multi, vert.	1.10 .50
1077	A322	450fr multi, vert.	2.25 1.00
		Nos. 1074-1077 (4)	4.50 2.00

No. 1028 Ovptd. in Metallic Red

1996	**Litho.**		**Perf. 13½**
1078	A312	400fr multicolored	8.25 .80

No. 1078 exists in souvenir sheet of 1.

Wild Cats — A323

Designs: 100fr, Panthera leo. 150fr, Acinonyx jubatus. 175fr, Lynx caracal. 250fr, Panthera pardus.

1996			**Perf. 12½x12**
1079	A323	100fr multicolored	.75 .25
1080	A323	150fr multicolored	.85 .30
1081	A323	175fr multicolored	.90 .35
1082	A323	250fr multicolored	1.50 .40
		Nos. 1079-1082 (4)	4.00 1.30

Summit of France and African Nations, Ouagadougou A323a

1996	**Litho.**		**Perf. 11¾**
1082A	A323a	150fr pink & multi	— 1.00
1082B	A323a	250fr yel & multi	— 1.50

Orchids — A324

Various orchids.

1996, Aug. 30	**Litho.**		**Perf. 12½x13**
1083	A324	100fr blue & multi	.75 .25
1084	A324	175fr lilac & multi	1.10 .30
1085	A324	250fr orange & multi	1.50 .40
1086	A324	300fr olive & multi	2.00 .75
		Nos. 1083-1086 (4)	5.35 1.70

UNICEF, 50th Anniv. — A324a

Design: 70fr, Child drinking near water pump, horiz. 75fr, Child reading book. 150fr, Mother nursing child. 250fr, Vaccination of child.

1996	**Litho.**		**Perf. 11¾**
1086A	A324a	70fr multi	4.00 2.00
1086B	A324a	75fr multi	4.00 2.00
1086C	A324a	150fr multi	4.00 2.00
1086D	A324a	250fr multi	8.00 5.00
		Nos. 1086A-1086D (4)	20.00 11.00

Birds — A325

Designs: 500fr, Falco peregrinus. 750fr, Crossoptilon mantchuricum. 1000fr, Branta canadensis. 1500fr, Pelecanus crispus.

1996, June 25			**Perf. 12½x12**
1087	A325	500fr multicolored	1.90 .80
1088	A325	750fr multicolored	2.60 1.00
1089	A325	1000fr multicolored	3.25 1.50
1090	A325	1500fr multicolored	5.25 2.00
		Nos. 1087-1090 (4)	13.00 5.30

Nos. 1087-1090 each printed se-tenant with labels.

Diana,
Princess of
Wales (1961-
97) — A325a

Various portraits, color of sheet margin: No. 1090A, blue. No. 1090K, deep pink.
No. 1090U, 2000fr, In yellow. No. 1090V, 2000fr, Wearing tiara.

Sheets of 9

1997	Litho.	Perf. 13½	
1090A	A325a 150fr #Ab-Aj	6.75	2.40
1090K	A325a 180fr #Kl-Kt	8.25	3.00

Souvenir Sheets

1090U-1090V A325a Set of 2	25.00	7.00

Nos. 1090U-1090V each contain one 41x46mm stamp.
See Nos. 1125U-1128.

Flowers —
A325b

Design: 150fr, Cienfuegosia digitata, vert. 175fr, Costus pectabilis. 250fr, Cerathoteca sesamoides, vert. 400fr, Crotalaria retusa, vert.

Perf. 13¼x13, 13x13¼

1997, Dec. 22		Litho.	
1090W	A325b 150fr multi	3.50	1.50
1090X	A325b 175fr multi	4.00	1.50
1090Y	A325b 250fr multi	6.00	1.50
1090Z	A325b 400fr multi	9.50	1.50
	Nos. 1090W-1090Z (4)	23.00	6.00

A326

Various portraits, color of sheet margin: No. 1091, Pale pink. No. 1092, Pale blue. No. 1093, Pale yellow.
No. 1094, 1500fr, In white dress, serving food to child (in sheet margin). No. 1095, 1500fr, Wearing wide-brimmed hat.

Sheets of 6

1998	Litho.	Perf. 14	
1091	A326 425fr #a.-f.	11.00	4.50
1092	A326 530fr #a.-f.	13.00	5.50
1093	A326 590fr #a.-f.	15.00	6.00

Souvenir Sheets

1094-1095 A326 Set of 2	18.00	5.00

Diana, Princess of Wales (1961-97).

A327

1998	Litho.	Perf. 14	
1096	A327 260fr shown	1.80	.30

Souvenir Sheet

1097	A327 1500fr Portrait, diff.	10.00	2.50

Mother Teresa (1910-97). No. 1096 was issued in sheets of 6. Nos. 1096-1097 have birth date inscribed "1907."

Birds — A328

5fr, White-winged triller. 10fr, Golden sparrow. 100fr, American goldfinch. 170fr, Red-legged thrush. 260fr, Willow warbler. 425fr, Blue grosbeak.
No. 1104: a, Bank swallow. b, Kirtland's warbler. c, Long-tailed minivet. d, Blue-gray gnatcatcher. e, Reed-bunting. f, Black-collared apalis. g, American robin. h, Cape long-claw. i, Wood thrush.
No. 1105: a, Song sparrow. b, Dartford warbler. c, Eastern bluebird. d, Rock thrush. e, Northern mockingbird. f, Northern cardinal. g, Eurasian goldfinch. h, Varied thrush. i, Northern oriole.
No. 1106, 1500fr, Golden whistler. No. 1107, 1500fr, Barn swallow, horiz.

1998, Oct. 1	Litho.	Perf. 13½	
1098-1103 A328 Set of 6		7.00	2.00

Sheets of 9

1104	A328 260fr #a.-i.	13.50	4.50
1105	A328 425fr #a.-i.	20.00	8.00

Souvenir Sheets

1106-1107 A328 Set of 2	18.00	6.00

Butterflies
and Moths
A329

No. 1108: a, Arctia caja. b, Nymphalis antiopa. c, Brahmaea wallichii. d, Issoria lathonia. e, Speyeria cybele. f, Vanessa virginiensis. g, Rothchildia orizaba. h, Cethosia hypsea. i, Marpesia petreus.
No. 1109: a, Agraulis vanillae. b, Junonia coenia. c, Danaus gilippus. d, Polygonia comma. e, Anthocharis cardamines. f, Heliconius aoede. g, Atlides halesus. h, Mesosemia croseus. i, Automeris io.
No. 1110, 1500fr, Papilio xuthus. No. 1111, 1500fr, Pterourus multicaudatus. No. 1112, 1500fr, Pterourus troilus. No. 1113, 1500fr, Papilio machaon.

1998, Oct. 25		Sheets of 9	
1108	A329 170fr #a.-i.	9.00	3.75
1109	A329 530fr #a.-i.	24.00	9.00

Souvenir Sheets

1110-1113 A329 Set of 4	36.00	12.00

Nos. 1110-1113 each contain one 56x42mm stamp.

Christmas
— A330

Fauna, flora with Christmas items: 100fr, Tersina viridis, holly, vert. 170fr, Citherias menander, present, vert. 260fr, Chrysanthemum, reindeer, sleigh, vert. 425fr, Swallowtail butterfly, greeting card. 530fr, European bee eater, Santa Claus, snowman.
No. 1119, 1500fr, Anthemis tinctoria, sleigh. No. 1120, 1500fr, Papilio ulysses, greeting card.

1998, Dec. 1	Litho.	Perf. 14	
1114-1118 A330 Set of 5		7.75	2.75

Souvenir Sheets

1119-1120 A330 Set of 2	18.00	5.50

Handicrafts
A330a

Design: No. 1120A, Wooden carved stool, vert. No. 1120B, Stool with carved heads. 50fr, Peul hat. 70fr, Basket with handle, vert. 75fr, Bronze figurine of woman milk seller and child, vert. No. 1120F, Bronze figurine of Mossi chief on horseback. No. 1120G, Dagari stool. 150fr, Basket, vert. 170fr, Wooden statue, Pasoré region, vert. 260fr, Wooden statue, Kaya region, vert.

1996-98	Litho.	Perf. 11¾	
1120A	A330a 25fr multi	6.00	1.50
1120B	A330a 25fr multi	6.00	1.50
1120C	A330a 50fr multi	6.00	1.50
1120D	A330a 70fr multi	6.00	1.50
1120E	A330a 75fr multi	6.00	1.50
1120F	A330a 100fr multi	6.00	1.50
1120G	A330a 100fr multi	6.00	1.50
1120H	A330a 150fr multi	6.00	1.50
1120I	A330a 170fr multi	6.00	1.50
1120J	A330a 260fr multi	6.00	1.50
	Nos. 1120A-1120J (10)	60.00	15.00

Issued: No. 1120A, 50fr, 70fr, 75fr, No. 1120F, 150fr, 11/13/96. No. 1120B, 1120G, 170fr, 260f, 6/20/98.

34th Organization for African Unity
Summit, Ouagadougou — A330b

1998, May 20	Litho.	Perf. 13x13¼	
1120K	A330b 170fr red & multi	1.75	.40
1120L	A330b 425fr blue & multi	4.25	1.00

Protected Wildlife
— A330c

Designs: 170fr, Leptoptilos crumeniferus. 200fr, Acionyx jubatus. 260fr, Orycteropus afer. 530fr, Struthio camulus. 590fr, Hippopotamus amphibus, horiz.

Perf. 13¼x13, 13x13¼

1998, May 20		Litho.	
1120M	A330c 170fr multi	1.00	.40
1120N	A330c 200fr multi	1.00	.50
1120O	A330c 260fr multi	1.25	.60
1120P	A330c 530fr multi	2.75	1.25
1120Q	A330c 590fr multi	3.00	1.50
	Nos. 1120M-1120Q (5)	9.00	4.25

15th FESPACO Film
Festival — A330d

Film: 150fr, Enfance et Jeunesse. 250fr, Etalon de Yennega.

1997, Feb. 5	Litho.	Perf. 11½x11¾	
1120R	A330d 150fr multi	.90	.40
1120S	A330d 250fr multi	1.50	.50

Wild Animals —
A330e

Design: 25fr, Redunca. 50fr, Cob Defassa (Defassa waterbuck). 150fr, Bubale. 250fr, Buffle (buffalo).

Perf. 11½x11¾

1997, Mar. 20		Litho.	
1120T	A330e 25fr multi	.25	.25
1120U	A330e 50fr multi	—	.25
1120V	A330e 150fr multi	.70	.45
1120W	A330e 250fr multi	—	.75
x.	Souvenir sheet, #1120T-1120W	—	2.50

No. 1120Wx sold for 500fr.

Heinrich
Von
Stephan
(1831-97),
Founder of
UPU —
A320f

1997, Apr. 8	Litho.	Perf. 11¾	
1120Y	A320f 250fr multi	13.00	1.50

Trains —
A331

No. 1121: a, CDR No. 19, Ireland. b, EMD "F" Series Bo-Bo, US. c, Class 72000, France. d, Class AE 4/4 Bo-Bo, Switzerland. e, Class 277, Spain. f, ET 403 four car train, West Germany. g, Class EM2 Co-Co, UK. h, Europe Dutch Swiss Tee.
No. 1122: a, DF 4 East Wind IV Co-Co, China. b, Union Pacific Railroad, US. c, No. 3.641, Norway. d, Class GE 4/4 Bo-Bo, Switzerland. e, Class GE Bo-Bo, South Africa. f, WDM-2 Co-Co, India. g, Kraus Mafeei Co-Co, US. h, RTG Four-car transit, France.
No. 1123, 1500fr, ETR 401 Pendolino, Italy. No. 1124, 1500fr, No. 12 Sarah Siddons, UK.

1998, Nov. 10		Sheets of 8	
1121	A331 170fr #a.-h.	8.00	3.00
1122	A331 425fr #a.-h.	21.00	8.00

Souvenir Sheets

1123-1124 A331 Set of 2	18.00	7.50

Intl. Fund for Agricultural Development,
20th Anniv. — A331a

Design: 150fr, Restoration of degraded soils. 400fr, "20," wheat stalk.

Perf. 13½x13¼

1998, Mar. 20		Litho.	
1124A	A331a 150fr multi	.70	.30
1125	A331a 400fr multi	1.75	.80

Masks — A331b

Design: 75fr, Buffalo mask, vert. 150fr, Duck mask. 200fr, Kob mask. 250fr, Mask with panels, vert.

1997, May 20	Litho.		Perf. 13¼	
1125A	A331b	75fr multi	6.50	1.50
1125B	A331b	150fr multi	13.00	2.00
1125C	A331b	200fr multi	18.00	3.00
1125D	A331b	250fr multi	22.50	3.00
Nos. 1125A-1125D (4)			60.00	9.50

Ceramics — A331c

Design: 100fr, Millet container. 150fr, Decorated covered baking pot. 250fr, Beer mug. 450fr, Vase.

	Perf. 11½x11¾			
1997, Sept. 11		Litho.		
1125E	A331c	100fr multi	—	.50
1125F	A331c	150fr multi	—	.75
1125G	A331c	250fr multi	—	1.00
1125H	A331c	450fr multi	2.75	1.50

Fish — A331d

Design: 100fr, Aplocheiolichthys pfaffi. 150fr, Fundulosoma thierryi. 175fr, Sarotherodon galilaeus. 250fr, Epiplatys spilargyreius.

1997, Nov. 20	Litho.		Perf. 13¼	
1125I	A331d	100fr multi	.45	.25
1125J	A331d	150fr multi	—	—
1125K	A331d	175fr multi	—	—
1125L	A331d	250fr multi	—	—

African Soccer Championships — A331e

Design: 175fr, Goalie making save. 150fr, Four players. 250fr, Soccer player, stylized person holding food bowl, vert. 500fr, Soccer ball, trophy, map of Africa, vert.

	Perf. 13x13¼, 13¼x13			
1998, Jan. 20		Litho.		
1125M	A331e	150fr multi	.70	.30
1125N	A331e	175fr multi	.85	.30
1125O	A331e	250fr multi	—	—
1125P	A331e	500fr multi	—	—

No. 1125P is dated 1997.

Traditional Costumes — A331f

Design: 150fr, Peulh (Togore). 175fr, Mossi (Banague). 250fr, Peulh (Boodi). 450fr, Bissa (Gangadruku).

1998, Feb. 20	Litho.		Perf. 13½x13	
1125Q	A331f	150fr multi	3.00	.25
1125R	A331f	175fr multi	4.00	.50
1125S	A331f	250fr multi	5.00	.75
1125T	A331f	450fr multi	6.00	1.00
Nos. 1125Q-1125T (4)			18.00	2.50

An additional stamps were released in this set. The editors would like to examine them.

Diana, Princess of Wales Type

Designs: 260fr, Diana wearing tiara. 425fr, Diana in white blouse. 590fr, Diana with Pope John Paul II. No. 1127A: various portraits, color of sheet margin is violet.

1500fr, Diana speaking, American Red Cross emblem in sheet margin. 2000fr, Diana wearing Japanese kimono.

1997	Litho.		Perf. 13½	
1125U	A325a	260fr multi	—	—
1126	A325a	425fr multi	1.60	1.60
1127	A325a	590fr multi	2.25	1.10
	Sheet of 9			
1127A	A325a	180fr #b-j	6.00	3.00
	Souvenir Sheets			
1127K	A325a	1500fr multi	11.00	2.75
1128	A325a	2000fr multi	12.00	3.75

No. 1127 was issued in sheets of 9. No. 1127K contains one 41x46mm stamp.

Airplanes A332

No. 1129: a, Sukhoi Su-24. b, Yakovlev Yak-38. c, Tupolev Blackjack. d, Antonov An-26. e, Antonov An-22 Anteus. f, Antonov An-124. 1000fr, Ilyushin Il-76T.

1999, Sept. 8	Litho.		Perf. 14	
1129	A332	425fr Sheet of 6,		
		#a.-f.	12.50	6.00
	Souvenir Sheet			
1130	A332	1000fr multicolored	6.00	4.00

No. 1130 contains one 57x43mm stamp.

Ships A333

No. 1131: a, Portland. b, Goethe. c, Fulton. No. 1132: a, CSS Nashville. b, Cutty Sark. c, Brilliant. d, Eagle. e, Red Jacket. f, USS Columbia. g, HMS Rose. h, Resolution. i, 1000-ton paquebot. j, Mayflower. No. 1133: a, USS Tennessee. b, HMS Alacrity. c, Bismarck. d, Yamoto. e, Aurora. f, Iowa class battleship. g, Liberty Ship. h, F209. i, Star. j, Big Eagle. Each 1000fr: No. 1134, Batavia. No. 1135, Grand Voilier.

1999, Sept. 8	**Sheets of 3 and 10**			
1131	A333	170fr #a.-c.	2.75	1.75
1132	A333	100fr #a.-j.	5.75	3.25
1133	A333	200fr #a.-j.	12.50	6.50
	Souvenir Sheets			
1134-1135	A333	Set of 2	12.00	6.50

Domesticated Animals — A334

5fr, Tabby cat, vert. 10fr, Chinchilla. 20fr, Yorkshire terriers. 25fr, Cocker spaniels. No. 1140, vert.: a, Afghan hound. b, Fox terrier. c, Pug. d, Dalmatian. e, Boston terrier. f, Cocker spaniel. No. 1141: a, American wirehaired. b, Tabby. c, Blue Burmese. d, Abyssinian. e, Lilac Burmese. f, Siamese. No. 1142, 1000fr, Persian. No. 1143, 1000fr, Japanese bobtail, vert. No. 1144, 1000fr, Labrador retriever, vert. No. 1145, 1000fr, Labrador retrievers, vert.

1999, Oct. 4				
1136-1139	A334	Set of 4	1.25	.80
	Sheets of 6			
1140	A334	260fr #a.-f.	7.75	3.00
1141	A334	530fr #a.-f.	16.00	10.00
	Souvenir Sheets			
1142-1145	A334	Set of 4	22.00	12.00

Domesticated Animals — A335

No. 1146 — Horses: a, Gelderlander. b, Trait lourd. c, Vladimir. d, Percheron. e, Sumba. f, Dartmoor. No. 1147 — Dogs: a, French bulldog. b, Bernese. c, Griffon. d, King Charles spaniel. e, Spitz. f, Yorkshire terrier. No. 1148 — Cats: a, American wirehaired. b, Japanese bobtail. c, Himalayan. d, LaPerm. e, Lilac Siamese colorpoint. f, Norwegian forest cat. No. 1149, 1000fr, Shetland pony, vert. No. 1150, 1000fr, Basset hound, vert. No. 1151, 1000fr, Japanese bobtail, diff., vert.

1999, Oct. 4			**Sheets of 6**	
1146	A335	170fr #a.-f.	5.25	3.50
1147	A335	425fr #a.-f.	11.00	9.00
1148	A335	590fr #a.-f.	15.00	13.00
	Souvenir Sheets			
1149-1151	A335	Set of 3	16.50	9.00

Fight Against Hunger — A337

1999, Dec.	Litho.		Perf. 14	
1157	A337	350fr multi	1.75	1.00

Issued in sheets of 5.

FESPACO '99 Film Festival A338

Award winning film: 170fr, Tilai, by Idrissa Ouédraogo. 260fr, Map of Africa, camera, clapper board, vert. 425fr, Buud Yam, by Gaston Kaboré.

1999	Litho.		Perf. 13x13¼, 13¼x13	
1158	A338	170fr multi	.70	.30
1159	A338	260fr multi	1.25	.45
1159A	A338	425fr multi	2.00	.75

Issued: 1159A, 2/22/99.

Council of the Entente, 40th Anniv. A338a

Denomination color: 170fr, Black. 260fr, Green.

1999, May 5	Litho.		Perf. 13x13¼	
1160-1161	A338a	Set of 2	1.90	.75

Lions A338b

Panel colors: 170fr, blue; 260fr, red; 425fr, green; 530fr, orange; 590fr, purple.

1999, May 26	Litho.		Perf. 13x13¼	
1161A-1161E	A338b	Set of 5	28.00	3.50

Philex France 99.

Orchids — A339

No. 1162, each 260fr: a, Angraecum orchid cape. b, Disa kirstenbosck pride. c, Disa blackii. d, Angraecum long icalear. e, Bulbophyllum falcatum. f, Phragmipedium schlimii (two flowers). g, Polystachya affinis. h, Jumellea sagittata (with leaves).
No. 1163, each 260fr: a, Angraecum sesquipedale. b, Oeceoclades maculata. c, Ancistrochilus childianus. d, Polystachyabella. e, Bulbophyllum lepidum. f, Vanilla imperialis. g, Tridactyle tridactylites. h, Eulophia guineensis.
No. 1164, each 260fr: a, Ansellia africana. b, Aerangis luteo-alba. c, Disa uniflora. d, Angraecum distichum. e, Bulbophyllum falcatum. f, Phragmepedium schlimii (pink flower). g, Polystachya affinis. h, Jumellea sagittata (without leaves).
No. 1165, 1500fr, Disa tripetaloides, horiz. No. 1166, 1500fr, Liparis guineensis, horiz. No. 1167, 1500fr, Bolusiella talbotii, horiz.

2000, Jan. 10	Litho.		Perf. 14	
	Sheets of 8, #a.-h.			
1162-1164	A339	Set of 3	35.00	20.00
	Souvenir Sheets			
1165-1167	A339	Set of 3	27.50	16.00

Space Exploration A340

No. 1168: a, Robert H. Goddard and 1926 rocket. b, Sputnik 1. c, X-15. d, Chinese, inventors of rockets. e, V-2. f, Explorer 1.
No. 1169: a, Vostok 1. b, Friendship 7. c, Soyuz 1. d, Freedom 7. e, Gemini 4. f, Apollo 7.
No. 1170, horiz.: a, Gemini 8. b, Agena target vehicle. c, Soyuz 11. d, Salyut 1. e, Apollo 18. f, Soyuz 19.
No. 1171, 1500fr, Tacsat satellite. No. 1172, 1500fr, Hubble Space Telescope. No. 1173, 1500fr, Viking Lander, horiz.

2000, Jan. 10			**Sheets of 6**	
1168	A340	350fr #a.-f.	12.50	7.50
1169	A340	425fr #a.-f.	14.50	9.00
1170	A340	530fr #a.-f.	19.00	11.00
	Souvenir Sheets			
1171-1173	A340	Set of 3	18.00	13.00

No. 1173 contains one 57x42mm stamp.

Peter Pan — A341

Designs: a, 75fr, Fairy, red flowers. b, 75fr, Parrot. c, 75fr, Moon, Wendy, Michael, John. d, 75fr, White flower. e, 80fr, Fairy, pink flower. f, 80fr, Butterflies. g, 80fr, Peter Pan. h, 80fr, Fairy. i, 90fr, Red flower. j, 90fr, Butterflies. k, 90fr, Egret. l, 90fr, White flower. m, 100fr, Mermaid. n, 100fr, Pirate ship, crocodile's tail. o, 100fr, Crocodile's head. p, 100fr, Captain Hook.

2000, Jan. 10			Perf. 12¼	
1174	A341	Sheet of 16, #a.-p.	8.25	4.25

2000 Summer Olympics,
Sydney — A343

No. 1191: a, Hannes Kohlemainen. b, Runner. c, US flag, Fulton County Stadium, Atlanta. d, Discus thrower.

2000, Nov. 12		**Litho.**		**Perf. 14**	
1191	A343	350fr Sheet of 4, #a-d		8.00	3.75

First Zeppelin Flight, Cent. — A344

No. 1192, 350fr: a, LZ-1, b, LZ-2 (dark gray at left). c, LZ-2 (white at left) d, LZ-5. e, LZ-8. f, LZ-7.
No. 1193, 350fr: a, LZ-9. b, LZ-10. c, LZ-11. d, LZ-127. e, LZ-129. f, LZ-130.
No. 1194, 1500fr, LZ-1. No. 1195, 1500fr, LZ-4.

2000, Nov. 12		**Sheets of 6, #a-f**		
1192-1193	A344	Set of 2	23.00	11.00
Souvenir Sheets				
1194-1195	A344	Set of 2	18.00	8.00

Berlin Film Festival, 50th
Anniv. — A345

No. 1196: a, Le Grand Blond Avec Une Chaussure Noire. b Ruy Guerra. c, Mario Monicelli. d, Mudhur Jaffrey. e, Orökbefogadás. f, Palermo Oder Wolfsburg.

2000, Nov. 12		**Litho.**		**Perf. 14**	
Sheet of 6					
1196	A345	420fr #a-f		14.00	7.00
Souvenir Sheet					
1197	A345	1500fr Platoon		9.25	4.50

Souvenir Sheets

Public Railways, 175th Anniv. — A346

No. 1198: a, George Stephenson, Locomotion No. 1. b, Stourbridge Lion.
No. 1199: a, George Stephenson, Brusselton inclined plane. b, Robert Stephenson, turnpike crossing near Darlington. c, Locomotive built by George Stephenson. d, Experimental passenger coach built by Robert Stephenson.

2000, Nov. 12		**Sheets of 2 and 4**		
1198	A346	550fr #a-b	7.00	3.25
1199	A346	800fr #a-d	17.00	9.25

Fruits — A347

95fr, Parkia biglobosa. 100fr, Baobab. 170fr, Tamarind, horiz. 425fr, Vitellaria paradoxa.

2000		**Litho.**		**Perf. 14¾**	
1200	A347	95fr multicolored		2.75	.25
1201	A347	100fr multicolored		2.75	.25
1202	A347	170fr multicolored		5.00	.30
1203	A347	425fr multicolored		12.00	.60
		Nos. 1200-1203 (4)		22.50	1.40

Issued: 170fr, 2/23.
The editors suspect that other stamps of this type were issued and would like to examine any examples.

Elephants
A348

2000, Mar. 22		**Litho.**		**Perf. 14¾**	
1204	A348	200fr Facing left		9.00	1.00
1205	A348	425fr multi, vert.		19.00	1.25
1206	A348	500fr Facing right		26.00	1.50
		Nos. 1204-1206 (3)		54.00	3.75

National Culture
Week — A349

Designs: 120fr, Sidari Troupe, Sidéradougou, vert. 130fr, Dancer and drummer, vert. 260fr, Dancer and xylophone player, vert. 425fr, Dancers and drummer. 530fr, Musicians. 590fr, Dancers.

2000		**Litho.**	**Perf. 13½x13, 13x13½**		
1207	A349	120fr multi		3.00	.50
1208	A349	130fr multi		3.00	.50
1209	A349	260fr multi		6.50	1.00
1210	A349	425fr multi		10.00	1.50
1211	A349	530fr multi		12.50	2.00
1212	A349	590fr multi		14.00	2.00
		Nos. 1207-1212 (6)		49.00	7.50

Molluscs
and
Crustaceans
A350

Designs: 30fr, Limnaea natalensis. 170fr, Caelastura teretiscula. 250fr, Achatina achatina. 260fr, Biomphalaria pfeifferi. 425fr, Potamonautes macleay.

2000, Apr. 28		**Litho.**		**Perf. 13x13¼**	
1213	A350	30fr multi		.65	.25
1214	A350	170fr multi		6.00	.40
1215	A350	250fr multi		9.00	.75
1216	A350	260fr multi		9.50	.75
1217	A350	425fr multi		15.00	1.00
		Nos. 1213-1217 (5)		40.15	3.15

Belem-Yegre
Museum — A351

Designs: 170fr, Dougui mask, vert. 260fr, Main entrance. 425fr, Monuments. 530fr, Tombstone, vert.

2000		**Litho.**	**Perf. 15x14¾, 14¾x15**		
1218	A351	170fr multi		3.75	.50
1219	A351	260fr multi		6.00	.60
1220	A351	425fr multi		10.00	1.00
1221	A351	530fr multi		12.50	1.25
		Nos. 1218-1221 (4)		32.25	3.35

Items in National
Museum — A352

Designs: 170fr, Kurumba statuettes. 260fr, Mossi statuette. 425fr, Loulouka pot. 530fr, Mossi du Kourwéogo statuette. 590fr, San statuette.

2001		**Litho.**	**Perf. 13¼x13**		
1222	A352	170fr multi		4.00	.40
1223	A352	260fr multi		7.00	.50
1224	A352	425fr multi		10.00	1.00
1224A	A352	530fr multi		13.00	1.25
1225	A352	590fr multi		15.00	1.75
		Nos. 1222-1225 (5)		49.00	4.90

Birds
A353

Designs: 25fr, Anaplectes rubriceps. 50fr, Dendrocygna viduata. 95fr, Ploceus cucullatus, vert. 170fr, Bubulcus ibis, vert. 425fr, Campethera masculosa, vert. 590fr, Francolinus bicalcaratus, vert.

2001		**Litho.**	**Perf. 13x13¼, 13¼x13**		
1226	A353	25fr multi		1.25	.25
1227	A353	50fr multi		1.75	.25
1227A	A353	95fr multi		3.75	.25
1228	A353	170fr multi		6.75	.50
1228A	A353	425fr multi		17.50	1.00
1229	A353	590fr multi		24.00	1.50
		Nos. 1226-1229 (6)		55.00	3.75

Tourism
A354

Designs: 170fr, Karfiguéla Waterfall, vert. 260fr, Sand dune, Oursi. 425fr, Laongo granite sculptures, vert. 530fr, Decorated homes, Tiébélé. 590fr, Sindou Peaks.

2001		**Litho.**	**Perf. 13¼x13, 13x13¼**		
1230	A354	170fr multi		3.75	.50
1231	A354	260fr multi		7.00	.75
1232	A354	425fr multi		10.00	1.00
1233	A354	530fr multi		12.00	1.25
1234	A354	590fr multi		14.00	1.50
		Nos. 1230-1234 (5)		46.75	5.00

Fish
A355

Designs: 25fr, Gymnarchus niloticus. 40fr, Bagrus docmak. 50fr, Hemisynedontis membranenceus. 170fr, Oreochromis niloticus niloticus. 425fr, Lates niloticus. 530fr, Heterotis niloticus.

2001		**Litho.**		**Perf. 13x13½**	
1235	A355	25fr multi		1.40	.50
1236	A355	40fr multi		1.75	.75
1237	A355	50fr multi		1.90	1.00
1238	A355	170fr multi		6.50	1.25
1239	A355	425fr multi		17.00	1.50
1240	A355	530fr multi		21.00	2.00
		Nos. 1235-1240 (6)		49.55	7.00

Insects
A356

Designs: 5fr, Helicoverpa armigera. 10fr, Poekilocerus bufonius hieroglyphicus. 20fr, Diopsls thoracica. 100fr, Psalydolitta sp. 170fr, Ptinus fur, vert. 200fr, Bruchidius atralineatus, vert. 260fr, Dysdercus sp., vert. 500fr, Lygus lineolaris. 1000fr, Doryphora. 1500fr, Acantboscelides obtectus say, vert.

		Perf. 13x13½, 13½x13			
2002, Apr. 4				**Litho.**	
1241	A356	5fr multi		1.00	.25
1242	A356	10fr multi		1.00	.25
1243	A356	20fr multi		1.00	.25
1244	A356	100fr multi		3.00	.75
1245	A356	170fr multi		3.50	.80
1246	A356	200fr multi		4.00	1.00
1247	A356	260fr multi		5.00	1.25
1248	A356	500fr multi		10.00	2.50
1249	A356	1000fr multi		20.00	5.00
1250	A356	1500fr multi		24.00	2.25
		Nos. 1241-1250 (10)		72.50	14.30

Crafts — A357

Design: 100fr, Long-headed Pouni mask. 170fr, Figurine of Mossi tom-tom player. 425fr, Calao Pouni mask, horiz.

2003, June 30		**Litho.**		**Perf. 13½x13**	
1251	A357	100fr multi		2.50	.75
1252	A357	170fr multi		4.00	1.00
		Perf. 13x13½			
1253	A357	425fr multi		13.00	3.50

Intl. Fund for Agricultural Development, 25th Anniv. — A358

2003, Sept. 20   Litho.   Perf. 13x13¼
1254 A358 170fr multi   5.00 1.25

Burkina Faso - Taiwan Cooperation — A359

Designs: 5fr, 10fr, 20fr, 100fr, 170fr, Kou Valley rice farm. 200fr, 260fr, 425fr, 530fr, 590fr, Bagré Aqueduct.

2003, Oct. 10   Litho.   Perf. 13x13½
Frame Color
1255 A359 5fr red   .50   .25
1256 A359 10fr blue   .50   .25
1257 A359 20fr brown   .50   .25
1258 A359 100fr blue   1.75   .25
1259 A359 170fr black   2.75   .25
1260 A359 200fr dark red   3.50   .55
1261 A359 260fr blue   4.50   .60
1262 A359 425fr brown   8.00 1.00
1263 A359 530fr blue   9.50 1.25
1264 A359 590fr black   11.00 1.50
       Nos. 1255-1264 (10)   42.50 6.15

Musical Instruments A360

Design: 30fr, Bwaba balaphone, horiz. 40fr, Nouni flute. 150fr, Mossi funerary drum, horiz.

2004, Mar. 27   Litho.   Perf. 13½x13
1265 A360 30fr multi
1266 A360 40fr multi   1.50 1.50
1268 A360 150fr multi

One additional stamp was issued in this set. The editors would like to examine any examples.

National Pardon Day — A361

2004, Mar. 30   Litho.   Perf. 13¼x13
1269 A361 170fr tan & multi   2.00 2.00
1270 A361 530fr red & multi   5.00 5.00

An additional stamp was issued in this set. The editors would like to examine it.

Tenth Francophone Summit, Ouagadougou A362

2004, Nov. 1   Litho.   Perf. 13½x13
1271 A362 425fr lil, brn & multi   3.25 2.75
1272 A362 530fr red, grn &
                multi   4.00 3.50
1273 A362 590fr blue & multi   5.00 4.50
       Nos. 1271-1273 (3)   12.25 10.75

Mediator of Faso, 10th Anniv. — A363

Design: 100fr, Mediator grasping two men. 330fr, Mediator grasping two men.

2005, Jan. 20   Litho.   Perf. 13½x13
1274 A363 100fr grn & multi   1.00 1.00
1276 A363 330fr blue & multi   4.00 3.00

Two additional stamps were issued in this set. The editors would like to examine any examples.

Hoes — A363a

Designs: 5p, Peulh hoe, Dou, vert. 10fr, Dagari hoe, eastern region. 30fr, Dagari hoe. 70fr, Mossi plateau hoe. 100fr, Mossi hoe, Zitenga, horiz.

Perf. 13½x13, 13x13½
2005, Nov. 16   Litho.
1276B A363a 5fr multi   3.25 1.00
1276C A363a 10fr multi   3.25 1.00
1276D A363a 30fr multi   3.25 1.00
1276E A363a 70fr multi   3.25 1.00
1276F A363a 100fr multi   3.25 1.00
       Nos. 1276B-1276F (5)   16.25 5.00

Hats — A363b

Designs: 265fr, Peulh du Seno hat, horiz. 300fr, Mossi chief's hat. 500fr, Yatenga banded hat. 690fr, Crooked Yatenga hat.

2005, Nov. 16   Litho.   Perf. 13½x13
1276G A363b 265fr multi   2.50 1.50
1276H A363b 300fr multi   3.00 1.50
1276I   A363b 500fr multi   4.50 1.50
1276J A363b 690fr multi   6.75 1.50
       Nos. 1276G-1276J (4)   16.75 6.00
       See Nos. 1285-1291.

Léopold Sédar Senghor (1906-2001), First President of Senegal — A364

2006, Mar. 2   Litho.   Perf. 13x13½
1277 A364 100fr red & multi   .75   .75
1278 A364 200fr bl grn & multi   1.50 1.50
1279 A364 1000fr pur & multi   7.50 7.50
       Nos. 1277-1279 (3)   9.75 9.75

Cooperation Between Burkina Faso and Germany — A365

2006   Litho.   Perf. 13x13¼
1280 A365 200fr multi   2.50 2.50

Burkina EMS Chronopost, 5th Anniv. — A366

2006, June 9   Litho.   Perf. 13½x13
1281 A366 200fr org & multi   2.00 2.00
1282 A366 330fr red brn & multi   3.00 3.00
1283 A366 690fr red vio & multi   5.00 5.00

Hats Type of 2005

Design: 5fr, 10fr, 20fr, 40fr, 50fr, 75fr, 1000fr, 1500fr, Peulh du Seno hat, horiz.

2006, Nov. 6   Litho.   Perf. 13x13¼
1284 A363b 5fr rose &
                 multi   1.00 1.00
1285 A363b 10fr lt blue &
                 multi   1.00 1.00
1286 A363b 20fr org & multi   1.00 1.00
1287 A363b 40fr blue & mul-
                 ti   1.00 1.00
1288 A363b 50fr green &
                 multi   1.00 1.00
1289 A363b 75fr lt blue &
                 multi   1.25 1.25
1290 A363b 1000fr ol & multi   10.00 10.00
1291 A363b 1500fr yel brn &
                 multi   15.00 15.00
       Nos. 1284-1291 (8)   31.25 31.25
       Dated 2006.

Lions International, 90th Anniv. — A367

Denomination color: 330fr, Blue; 690fr, Pink.

2007   Litho.   Perf. 13¼
1292 A367 330fr multi   3.00 3.00
1293 A367 690fr multi   7.00 7.00

Wrestling A368

Designs: 5fr, Parade of wrestlers. 30fr, Wrestlers in attack position. 200fr, Wrestlers grabbing each other's thighs, vert. 690fr, Wrestler grabbing opponent's leg.

2008, Mar. 17   Litho.   Perf. 13x13¼
1294 A368 5fr multi   .25   .25
1295 A368 30fr multi   .30   .25
1296 A368 200fr multi   2.00   .50
1297 A368 690fr multi   6.50 2.00
       Nos. 1294-1297 (4)   9.05 3.00

Safari Animals and Shelters A369

Designs: 10fr, Nerwaya Safari hut, lion. 25fr, Express Safari hut, duck. 75fr, Sahel shelter, bird, vert. 100fr, Safari Chasse hut, leopard.

Perf. 13x13¼, 13¼x13
2008, June 6   Litho.
1298 A369 10fr multi   1.25 1.00
1299 A369 25fr multi   1.50 1.00
1300 A369 75fr multi   3.25 1.50
1301 A369 100fr multi   4.50 2.00
1302 A369 200fr multi   9.50 4.00
       Nos. 1298-1302 (5)   20.00 9.50

Dances — A370

Designs: 50fr, Bissa dance. 200fr, Gourmatché dance. 500fr, Mossi Kiegba dance. 690fr, Kassena dance.

2008, July 1   Litho.   Perf. 13¼x13
1303 A370 50fr multi   .35   .25
1304 A370 200fr multi   1.40   .50
1305 A370 500fr multi   3.50 1.50
1306 A370 690fr multi   5.00 1.75
       Nos. 1303-1306 (4)   10.25 4.00

Burkina Faso Federation of Associations for Promotion of the Handicapped — A371

2008, Oct. 31   Litho.   Perf. 13x13¼
1307 A371 200fr blue & multi   3.00 1.00
1308 A371 690fr green & multi   12.00 3.00

Independence, 48th Anniv. — A372

2008, Dec. 5   Litho.   Perf. 13¼x13
1309 A372 200fr green & multi   4.00 1.00
1310 A372 690fr blue & multi   16.00 4.00

FESPACO 2009 Film Festival A373

Designs: 690fr, Sembene Ousmane (1923-2007), writer and film director. 1000fr, 40th anniversary emblem.

2009, Feb. 20   Perf. 13x13¼
Granite Paper
1311-1312 A373 Set of 2   13.00 13.00

Traditional Foods
A374

Designs: 20fr, Millet fritters. 300fr, Tô de mais. 1500fr, Bean fritters.

2009   Litho.   Granite Paper
1313-1315 A374 Set of 3   15.00 7.50

Agricultural Work
A375

Designs: 200fr, Planting. 690fr, Hoeing. 1000fr, Millet harvesting.

2009   Litho.   Perf. 13x13¼
1316-1318 A375 Set of 3   20.00 10.00

Traditional Occupations — A376

Designs: 40fr, Blacksmith. 200fr, Weaver. 1500fr, Cotton spinner.

2009   Litho.   Perf. 13x13¼
Granite Paper
1319-1321 A376 Set of 3   20.00 10.00

Transportation — A378

Designs: 30fr, Woman on bicycle. 70fr, Man on donkey cart.

2010, Aug. 16   Litho.   Perf. 13x13¼
1325-1326 A378 Set of 2   5.00 2.50

World Health Day
A379

Designs: 100fr, Blood donation. 160fr, Campaign against malaria.

2010, Oct. 15   Granite Paper
1327-1328 A379 Set of 2   7.00 2.50

Domesticated Animals — A381

Designs: 100fr, Donkey. 265fr, Horse. 300fr, Dromedary.

2011, Feb. 1   Litho.   Perf. 13x13¼
1331-1333 A381 Set of 3   3.50 1.75
Dated 2010.

Campaign Against AIDS, 30th Anniv.
A382

Designs: 200fr, Man, woman, letter carrier with Post Office AIDS campaign poster. 690fr, People in post office. Post Office AIDS campaign poster.

2011, Aug. 8
1334-1335 A382 Set of 2   5.25 2.75

Poultry
A383

Designs: 100fr, Ducks (canard). 160fr, Turkeys (dindon). 265fr, Rooster and hen (coq).

2011, Oct. 12
1336-1338 A383 Set of 3   3.50 1.75

Vegetable Cultivation
A384

Designs: 30fr, Onions. 70fr, Cabbages. 100fr, Carrots.

2011, Nov. 7
1339-1341 A384 Set of 3   3.50 1.75

Cooperation Between Burkina Faso and Germany, 50th Anniv. — A385

Background color: 200fr, Blue. 690fr, Yellow orange.

2011, Dec. 23   Perf. 14½x14¼
1342-1343 A385 Set of 2   7.00 3.50

National Assembly, 20th Anniv.
A386

Background color: 200fr, Blue. 690fr, Brown.

2012, Apr. 20   Litho.   Perf. 13x13¼
1344-1345 A386 Set of 2   5.50 3.00

Everyday Life in Ouagadougou — A387

Designs: 100fr, Street traffic. 330fr, Roadside restaurant.

2012, Oct. 16   Litho.   Perf. 13x13¼
1346-1347 A387 Set of 2   3.50 3.50

Cooking Implements
A388

Designs: 500fr, Portable hearth for cooking pancakes. 690fr, Hearth for preparing millet beer.

2012, Nov. 30   Litho.   Perf. 13x13¼
1348-1349 A388 Set of 2   10.00 10.00

Riches of the Forest
A389

Designs: 100fr, Jujubes. 200fr, Detarium microcarpa. 500fr, Karité (shea nuts). 1500fr, Plums.

2012, Nov. 30   Litho.   Perf. 13x13¼
1350-1353 A389 Set of 4   19.50 19.50

Village Life
A390

Designs: 200fr, Women at water pump. 330fr, Women cooking. 690fr, Women at grain mill. 1000fr, Women crushing millet.

2012, Dec. 13   Litho.   Perf. 13x13¼
1354-1357 A390 Set of 4   19.00 19.00

Food Storage Containers
A391

Designs: 200fr, Gourd. 690fr, Canari (pot).

2012, Dec. 18   Litho.   Perf. 13x13¼
1358-1359 A391 Set of 2   7.50 7.50

United Nations, 70th Anniv.
A401

2015, Oct. 24   Litho.   Perf. 13x13¼
1377 A401 690fr multi   —   —

Economic Community of West African States, 40th Anniv.
A402

2015, Dec. 17   Litho.   Perf. 13x13¼
1378 A402 200fr multi   —   —

African Philatelic Hub — A403

2016, Sept. 23 Litho.   Perf. 13¼x13
1379 A403 690fr multi   —   —

Old Tenkodogo Post Office
A404

2016, Oct. 5   Litho.   Perf. 13x13¼
1380 A404 200fr multi   —   —

Tour de Faso Bicycle Race
A405

2016, Oct. 27   Litho.   Perf. 13x13¼
1381 A405 200fr multi   —   —

Bomavé Konate, Sculptor — A406

2016, Dec. 2   Litho.   Perf. 13¼x13
1382 A406 690fr multi   —   —

Gnassogoni Troglodyte Village — A407

2016, Dec. 17   Litho.   Perf. 13¼x13
1383 A407 500fr multi   —   —

SEMI-POSTAL STAMPS

Catalogue values for unused stamps in this section are for Never Hinged items.

Anti-Malaria Issue
Common Design Type
Perf. 12½x12
1962, Apr. 7   Engr.   Unwmk.
B1 CD108 25fr + 5fr red org   .75 .70

Freedom from Hunger Issue
Common Design Type
1963, Mar. 21   Perf. 13
B2 CD112 25fr + 5fr dk grn, bl &
           brn   .75 .70

CAN '96 (African Nations) Soccer
Championships — SP1

Designs: 150fr+25fr, Stallions, soccer ball.
250fr+25fr, Map of Africa, soccer player.

1996, Jan. 2	Litho.		Perf. 11½	
B3	SP1 150fr +25fr multi		1.25	.50
a.	Souvenir sheet of 1		2.75	2.00
B4	SP1 250fr +25fr multi		2.50	.90

No. B3a sold for 500fr.

AIR POST STAMPS

Catalogue values for unused
stamps in this section are for
Never Hinged items.

Plane over Map Showing Air
Routes — AP1

200fr, Plane at airport, Ouagadougou.
500fr, Champs Elysees, Ouagadougou.

Unwmk.

1961, Mar. 4	Engr.		Perf. 13	
C1	AP1 100fr multicolored		1.45	.70
C2	AP1 200fr multicolored		4.50	1.40
C3	AP1 500fr multicolored		10.50	4.00
	Nos. C1-C3 (3)		16.45	6.10

Air Afrique Issue
Common Design Type

1962, Feb. 17				
C4	CD107 25fr brt pink, dk pur & lt grn		3.50	1.75

UN Emblem and Upper Volta
Flag — AP2

Perf. 13½x12½

1962, Sept. 22		Photo.		
C5	AP2 50fr multicolored		.75	.40
C6	AP2 100fr multicolored		1.75	.80

Admission to UN, second anniversary.

Post Office, Ouagadougou — AP3

1962, Dec. 11			Perf. 13x12	
C7	AP3 100fr multicolored		1.50	.70

Jet
Over
Map
AP4

1963, June 24				
C8	AP4 200fr multicolored		5.00	1.50

First jet flight, Ouagadougou to Paris.
For surcharge see No. C10.

African Postal Union Issue
Common Design Type

1963, Sept. 8	Unwmk.		Perf. 12½	
C9	CD114 85fr dp vio, ocher & red		1.50	.75

No. C8 Surcharged in Red

1963, Nov. 19			Perf. 13x12	
C10	AP4 50fr on 200fr multi		1.40	.80

See note after Mauritania No. C26.

Europafrica Issue
Common Design Type

50fr, Sunburst & Europe linked with Africa.

1964, Jan. 6			Perf. 12x13	
C11	CD116 50fr multicolored		1.50	.80

Ramses II, Abu
Simbel — AP5

1964, Mar. 8	Engr.		Perf. 13	
C12	AP5 25fr dp green & choc		.75	.50
C13	AP5 100fr brt bl & brn		2.75	2.00

UNESCO world campaign to save historic
monuments of Nubia.

Greek Sculptures
AP6

15fr, Greek Portrait Head. 25fr, Seated
boxer. 85fr, Victorious athlete. 100fr, Venus of
Milo.

1964, July 1	Unwmk.		Perf. 13	
C14	AP6 15fr multicolored		.45	.25
C15	AP6 25fr multicolored		.60	.25
C16	AP6 85fr multicolored		1.40	1.00
C17	AP6 100fr multicolored		2.00	1.10
a.	Min. sheet of 4, #C14-C17		10.00	10.00
	Nos. C14-C17 (4)		4.45	2.60

18th Olympic Games, Tokyo, Oct. 10-25.

West African
Gray
Woodpecker
AP7

1964, Oct. 1	Engr.		Perf. 13	
C18	AP7 250fr multicolored		10.00	5.00

President John F.
Kennedy (1917-
1963)
AP8

1964, Nov. 25	Photo.		Perf. 12½	
C19	AP8 100fr orange, brn & lil		2.25	1.50
a.	Souvenir sheet of 4		10.00	8.00

Bird Type of Regular Issue, 1965

1965, Mar. 1	Photo.		Perf. 13	
	Size: 27x48mm			
C20	A27 500fr Abyssinian roller		20.00	7.50

Earth and Sun — AP9

1965, Mar. 23		Engr.		
C21	AP9 50fr multicolored		.85	.45

5th World Meteorological Day.

Hughes Telegraph, ITU Emblem and
Dial Telephone — AP10

1965, May 17	Unwmk.		Perf. 13	
C22	AP10 100fr red, sl grn & bl grn		1.90	1.00

ITU, centenary.

Intl. Cooperation Year — AP10a

1965, June 21	Photo.		Perf. 13	
C23	AP10a 25fr multicolored		.45	.25
C24	AP10a 100fr multicolored		1.40	.50
a.	Min. sheet, 2 each #C23-C24		3.75	3.00

Sacred Sabou Crocodile — AP11

1965, Aug. 9	Engr.		Perf. 13	
C25	AP11 60fr shown		3.00	1.00
C26	AP11 85fr Lion, vert.		3.75	1.10

Early Bird
Satellite over
Globe — AP12

1965, Sept. 15	Unwmk.		Perf. 13	
C27	AP12 30fr brt bl, brn & brn red		.75	.30

Space communications.

Tiros Satellite
and Weather
Map — AP13

1966, Mar. 23	Engr.		Perf. 13	
C28	AP13 50fr dk car, brt bl & blk		.90	.60

6th World Meteorological Day.

FR-1 Satellite over Ouagadougou
Space Tracking Station — AP14

1966, Apr. 28			Perf. 13	
C29	AP14 250fr mag, ind & org brn		4.75	2.50

Inauguration of WHO Headquarters,
Geneva — AP15

1966, May 3		Photo.		
C30	AP15 100fr yel, blk & bl		2.00	.95

Air Afrique Issue
Common Design Type

1966, Aug. 31	Photo.		Perf. 13	
C31	CD123 25fr tan, blk & yel grn		.75	.50

Sir Winston Churchill, British Lion and
"V" Sign — AP16

1966, Nov. 5   Engr.   Perf. 13
C32 AP16 100fr slate grn & car
          rose   2.00 .85
Sir Winston Spencer Churchill (1874-1965),
statesman and WWII leader.

Pope Paul VI, Peace Dove, UN
General Assembly and
Emblem — AP17

1966, Nov. 5
C33 AP17 100fr dk blue & pur   2.00 .85
Pope Paul's appeal for peace before the UN
General Assembly, Oct. 4, 1965.

Blind Man and Lions Emblem — AP18

1967, Feb. 28   Engr.   Perf. 13
C34 AP18 100fr dk vio bl, brt bl &
          dk brn   2.00 .85
50th anniversary of Lions Intl.

UN Emblem and
Rain over
Landscape
AP19

1967, Mar. 23   Engr.   Perf. 13
C35 AP19 50fr ultra, dk grn & bl
          grn   1.10 .60
7th World Meteorological Day.

Diamant
Rocket — AP20

French Spacecraft: 20fr, FR-1 satellite,
horiz. 30fr, D1-C satellite. 100fr, D1-D satellite, horiz.

1967, Apr. 18   Engr.   Perf. 13
C36 AP20 5fr brt bl, sl grn &
          org   .25 .25
C37 AP20 20fr lilac & slate blue   .50 .25
C38 AP20 30fr red brn, brt bl &
          emer   .75 .25
C39 AP20 100fr emer & dp claret   1.50 .85
     Nos. C36-C39 (4)   3.00 1.60
     For overprint see No. C69.

Albert Schweitzer
(1875-1965),
Medical
Missionary and
Organ
Pipes — AP21

1967, May 12   Engr.   Perf. 13
C40 AP21 250fr claret & blk   4.75 2.50

World Map and 1967 Jamboree
Emblem — AP22

1967, June 8   Photo.
C41 AP22 100fr multicolored   1.75 .85
12th Boy Scout World Jamboree, Farragut
State Park, Idaho, Aug. 1-9.

Madonna
and Child,
15th
Century
AP23

Paintings: 20fr, Still life by Paul Gauguin.
50fr, Pietà, by Dick Bouts. 60fr, Anne of
Cleves, by Hans Holbein the Younger. 90fr,
The Money Lender and his Wife, by Quentin
Massys (38x40mm). 100fr, Blessing of the
Risen Christ, by Giovanni Bellini. 200fr, The
Handcart, by Louis Le Nain, horiz. 250fr, The
Four Evangelists, by Jacob Jordaens.

Perf. 12½x12, 12x12½, 13½ (90fr)
1967-68   Photo.
C42 AP23 20fr multi ('68)   .45 .35
C43 AP23 30fr multi   .70 .35
C44 AP23 50fr multi   1.00 .50
C45 AP23 60fr multi ('68)   .85 .60
C46 AP23 90fr multi   1.25 .95
C47 AP23 100fr multi   1.50 1.00
C48 AP23 200fr multi ('68)   2.75 2.10
C49 AP23 250fr multi   4.25 2.50
     Nos. C42-C49 (8)   12.75 8.35
     See Nos. C70-C72.

African Postal Union Issue, 1967
Common Design Type
1967, Sept. 9   Engr.   Perf. 13
C50 CD124 100fr multicolored   1.80 .70

Caravelle "Ouagadougou" — AP24

1968, Feb. 29   Engr.   Perf. 13
C51 AP24 500fr bl, dp cl & blk   10.00 5.50

WMO Emblem, Sun, Rain,
Wheat — AP25

1968, Mar. 23   Engr.   Perf. 13
C52 AP25 50fr dk red, ultra &
          gray grn   1.10 .50
8th World Meteorological Day.

Europafrica Issue

Clove Hitch — AP25a

1968, July 20   Photo.   Perf. 13
C53 AP25a 50fr yel bis, blk & dk
           red   .90 .50
See note after Niger No. C89.

Vessel in Form of Acrobat with Bells,
Colima Culture — AP26

Mexican Sculptures: 30fr, Ballplayer, Vera-
cruz, vert. 60fr, Javelin thrower, Colima, vert.
100fr, Seated athlete with cape, Jalisco.

1968, Oct. 14   Engr.   Perf. 13
C54 AP26 10fr dk red, ocher &
          choc   .55 .25
C55 AP26 30fr bl grn, brt grn &
          dk brn   .70 .25
C56 AP26 60fr ultra, ol & mar   1.40 .55
C57 AP26 100fr brt grn, bl & mar 1.90 .90
     Nos. C54-C57 (4)   4.55 1.95
19th Olympic Games, Mexico City, 10/12-27.

Artisan Type of Regular Issue
1968, Oct. 30   Engr.   Perf. 13
Size: 48x27mm
C58 A52 100fr Potter   1.60 .75

PHILEXAFRIQUE Issue

Too Late or
The Letter,
by Armand
Cambon
AP27

1968, Nov. 22   Photo.   Perf. 12½
C59 AP27 100fr multicolored   3.50 3.00
PHILEXAFRIQUE, Phil. Exhib., Abidjan,
Feb. 14-23, 1969. Printed with alternating rose
claret label.

Albert John
Luthuli — AP28

Design: No. C61, Mahatma Gandhi.

1968, Dec. 16   Photo.   Perf. 12½
C60 AP28 100fr dk grn, yel grn &
          blk   1.50 1.25
C61 AP28 100fr dk grn, yel & blk 1.50 1.00
a.   Min. sheet, 2 each #C60-C61 9.00 9.00
     Exponents of non-violence.

2nd PHILEXAFRIQUE Issue
Common Design Type
50fr, Upper Volta #59, dancers & musicians.

1969, Feb. 14   Engr.   Perf. 13
C62 CD128 50fr pur, bl car & brn 4.00 3.25

Weather Sonde, WMO Emblem, Mule
and Cattle in Irrigated Field — AP29

1969, Mar. 24   Engr.   Perf. 13
C63 AP29 100fr dk brn, brt bl &
          grn   3.25 2.00
9th World Meteorological Day.

Artisan Type of Regular Issue
Design: 150fr, Basket weaver.

1969, Apr. 3   Engr.   Perf. 13
Size: 48x27mm
C64 A55 150fr brn, bl & blk   2.75 1.25

Lions Emblem, Eye and Blind
Man — AP30

1969, Apr. 30   Photo.
C65 AP30 250fr red & multi   3.50 1.75
12th Congress of District 403 of Lions Intl.,
Ouagadougou, May 2-3.

Fish Type of Regular Issue

Designs: 100fr, Phenacogrammus pabrensis. 150fr, Upside-down catfish.

1969		**Engr.**	**Perf. 13**	
		Size: 48x27mm		
C66	A57	100fr slate, pur & yel	2.25	1.00
C67	A57	150fr org brn, gray & slate	4.00	1.75

Earth and Astronaut — AP31

Embossed on Gold Foil

1969		**Die-cut Perf. 10½x10**	
C68	AP31	1000fr gold	25.00 25.00

Apollo 8 mission, which put the first man into orbit around the moon, Dec. 21-27, 1968.

No. C39 Overprinted in red with Lunar Landing Module and

1969, July 25		**Engr.**	**Perf. 13**
C69	AP20	100fr emer & dp claret	4.00 4.00

See note after Mali No. C80.

Painting Type of 1967-68

Paintings: 50fr, Napoleon Crossing Great St. Bernard Pass, by Jacques Louis David. 150fr, Napoleon Awarding the First Cross of the Legion of Honor, by Jean-Baptiste Debret. 250fr, Napoleon Before Madrid, by Carle Vernet.

1969, Aug. 18		**Photo.**	**Perf. 12½x12**
C70	AP23	50fr carmine & multi	2.25 1.00
C71	AP23	150fr violet & multi	5.75 2.50
C72	AP23	250fr green & multi	8.00 4.50
		Nos. C70-C72 (3)	16.00 8.00

Napoleon Bonaparte (1769-1821).

Agriculture Type of Regular Issue

1969, Oct. 30		**Photo.**	**Perf. 12½x13**
		Size: 47½x27mm	
C73	A58	100fr Peanuts	1.25 .50
C74	A58	200fr Rice	3.25 1.00

AP32

Tree of Life, symbols of science, agriculture and industry.

1969, Nov. 21		**Photo.**	**Perf. 12x13**
C75	AP32	100fr multicolored	1.10 .80

See note after Mauritania No. C28.

AP33

Designs: 20fr, Lenin. 100fr, Lenin Addressing Revolutionaries in Petrograd, by V. A. Serov, horiz.

1970, Apr. 22		**Photo.**	**Perf. 12½**
C76	AP33	20fr ocher & brn	.80 .50
C77	AP33	100fr blk, lt grn & red	1.90 1.25

Lenin (1870-1924), Russian communist leader.

Pres. Roosevelt with Stamp Collection — AP34

10fr, Franklin Delano Roosevelt, vert.

1970, June 4		**Photo.**	**Perf. 12½**
C78	AP34	10fr dk brn, emer & red brn	.25 .25
C79	AP34	200fr vio bl, gray & dk car	2.25 1.10

Soccer Game and Jules Rimet Cup — AP35

100fr, Goalkeeper catching ball, globe.

1970, June 4		**Engr.**	**Perf. 13**
C80	AP35	40fr olive, brt grn & brn	.60 .45
C81	AP35	100fr blk, lil, brn & grn	1.50 .80

9th World Soccer Championships for the Jules Rimet Cup, Mexico City, 5/30-6/21/70.

EXPO Emblem, Monorail and "Cranes at the Seashore" AP36

Design: 150fr, EXPO emblem, rocket, satellites and "Geisha."

1970, Aug. 7		**Photo.**	**Perf. 12½**
C82	AP36	50fr multicolored	1.60 .80
C83	AP36	150fr green & multi	2.60 1.00

Issued to publicize EXPO '70 International Exhibition, Osaka, Japan, Mar. 15-Sept. 13.

UN Emblem, Dove and Star — AP37

250fr, UN emblem and doves, horiz.

1970, Oct. 2		**Engr.**	**Perf. 13**
C84	AP37	60fr dk bl, bl & grn	.50 .35
C85	AP37	250fr dk red brn, vio bl & ol	3.25 1.25

25th anniversary of the United Nations.

Holy Family — AP38

Silver Embossed

1970, Nov. 27		**Die-Cut Perf. 10**	
C86	AP38	300fr silver	8.00 8.00

Gold Embossed

C87	AP38	1000fr gold	20.00 20.00

Christmas.

Family and Upper Volta Flag — AP39

Litho.; Gold Embossed

1970, Dec. 10			**Perf. 12½**
C88	AP39	500fr gold, blk & red	6.00 3.00

10th anniversary of independence, Dec. 11.

UN "Key to a Free World" — AP40

1970, Dec. 14		**Engr.**	**Perf. 13**
C89	AP40	40fr red, bister & blue	.90 .50

UN Declaration of Independence for Colonial Peoples, 10th anniv.

Gamal Abdel Nasser — AP41

1971, Jan. 30		**Photo.**	**Perf. 12½**
C90	AP41	100fr green & multi	1.10 .50

Nasser (1918-1970), president of Egypt.

Herons, Egyptian Art, 1354 — AP42

250fr, Page from Koran, Egypt, 1368-1388.

1971, May 13		**Photo.**	**Perf. 13**
C91	AP42	100fr multi	1.25 .80
C92	AP42	250fr multi, vert.	3.25 2.00

Olympic Rings and Various Sports — AP43

1971, June 10		**Engr.**	**Perf. 13**
C93	AP43	150fr vio bl & red	3.25 1.60

Pre-Olympic Year.

Boy Scout and Buildings — AP44

1971, Aug. 12		**Photo.**	**Perf. 12½**
C94	AP44	45fr multicolored	1.10 .60

13th Boy Scout World Jamboree, Asagiri Plain, Japan, Aug. 2-10.

De Gaulle, Map of Upper Volta, Cross of Lorraine — AP45

Charles de Gaulle — AP46

1971, Nov. 9   Photo.   Perf. 13x12
C95 AP45 40fr lt brn, grn &
            blk   .90   .50

**Lithographed; Gold Embossed
Perf. 12½**
C96 AP46 500fr gold & grn   11.00 10.00
    Gen. Charles de Gaulle (1890-1970), presi-
dent of France.

**African Postal Union Issue, 1971
Common Design Type**
Design: 100fr, Mossi dancer and UAMPT
building, Brazzaville, Congo.

1971, Nov. 13   Perf. 13x13½
C97 CD135 100fr bl & multi   1.50   .70

Gen. Sangoule
Lamizana
AP47

1971, Dec. 11   Perf. 12½
C98 AP47 35fr sep, blk, gold & ultra .90 .60
Inauguration of 2nd Republic of Upper Volta.

Kabuki Actor and
Ice
Hockey — AP48

1972, Feb. 15   Engr.   Perf. 13
C99 AP48 150fr red, bl & pur   2.50   1.25
    11th Winter Olympic Games, Sapporo,
Japan, Feb. 3-13.

Music, by
Pietro
Longhi
AP49

Design: 150fr, Gondolas and general view,
by Ippolito Caffi, horiz.

1972, Feb. 28   Photo.   Perf. 13
C100 AP49 100fr gold & multi   2.25   1.00
C101 AP49 150fr gold & multi   3.25   1.50
    UNESCO campaign to save Venice.

Running and
Olympic
Rings — AP50

Design: 200fr, Discus and Olympic rings.

1972, May 5   Engr.   Perf. 13
C102 AP50 65fr dp bl, brn & grn   .70   .60
C103 AP50 200fr dp bl & brn   2.25   1.50
    a.   Min. sheet of 2, #C102-C103   3.00   3.00
    20th Olympic Games, Munich, 8/26-9/10.

Musician Type of Regular Issue
Design: 500fr, Jimmy Smith and keyboard.

1972, May 17   Photo.   Perf. 14x13
C104 A87 500fr green & multi   9.00   4.75

Red Crescent Type of Regular Issue
1972, June 23   Perf. 13x14
C105 A88 100fr yellow & multi 1.40   .60

2nd Plan Type of Regular Issue
Design: 85fr, Road building machinery.

1972, Oct. 30   Engr.   Perf. 13
C106 A90 85fr brick red, bl & blk 1.00   .80

Presidents Pompidou and
Lamizana — AP51

Design: 250fr, Presidents Pompidou and
Lamizana, different design.

**1972, Nov. 20   Photo.   Perf. 13
Size: 48x37mm**
C107 AP51 40fr gold & multi   2.00   2.00

**Photogravure; Gold Embossed
Size: 56x36mm**
C108 AP51 250fr yel grn, dk grn
            & gold   7.00   6.25
    Visit of Pres. Georges Pompidou of France,
Nov. 1972.

Skeet-shooting, Scalzone,
Italy — AP52

    Gold-medal Winners: 40fr, Pentathlon,
Peters, Great Britain. 45fr, Dressage, Meade,
Great Britain. 50fr, Weight lifting, Talts, USSR.
60fr, Boxing, light-weight, Seales, US. 65fr,
Fencing, Ragno-Lonzi, Italy. 75fr, Gymnastics,
rings, Nakayama, Japan. 85fr, Gymnastics,
Touritcheva, USSR. 90fr, 110m high hurdles,
Milburn, US. 150fr, Judo, Kawaguchi, Japan.
200fr, Sailing, Finn class, Maury, France.
250fr, Swimming, Spitz, US (7 gold). 300fr,
Women's high jump, Meyfarth, West Ger-
many. 350fr, Field Hockey, West Germany.
400fr, Javelin, Wolfermann, West Germany.
No. C124, Women's diving, King, US. No.
C125, Cycling, Morelon, France. No. C126,

Individual dressage, Linsenhoff, West
Germany.

1972-73   Litho.   Perf. 12½
C109 AP52 35fr multi ('73)   .40   .25
C110 AP52 40fr multi   .40   .25
C111 AP52 45fr multi ('73)   .45   .30
C112 AP52 50fr multi ('73)   .40   .30
C113 AP52 60fr multi ('73)   .65   .45
C114 AP52 65fr multi   .65   .45
C115 AP52 75fr multi ('73)   .65   .55
C116 AP52 85fr multi   .95   .55
C117 AP52 90fr multi ('73)   .70   .55
C118 AP52 150fr multi ('73)   1.15   .70
C119 AP52 200fr multi   1.75   .80
C120 AP52 250fr multi ('73)   2.00   .80
C121 AP52 300fr multi   3.00   1.50
C122 AP52 350fr multi ('73)   2.60   1.50
C123 AP52 400fr multi ('73)   3.50   1.50
    Nos. C109-C123 (15)   19.25 10.45

Souvenir Sheets
C124 AP52 500fr multi   7.50   5.00
C125 AP52 500fr multi   7.50   5.00
C126 AP52 500fr multi ('73)   7.50   5.00
    20th Olympic Games, Munich.

Nativity, by Della Notte — AP53

    Christmas: 200fr, Adoration of the Kings, by
Albrecht Dürer.

1972, Dec. 23   Photo.   Perf. 13
C127 AP53 100fr gold & multi   1.25   .90
C128 AP53 200fr gold & multi   2.75   2.00

Madonna
and Child,
by Albrecht
Dürer
AP54

    Christmas: 75fr, Virgin Mary, Child and St.
John, by Joseph von Führich. 100fr, The Vir-
gin of Grand Duc, by Raphael. 125fr, Holy
Family, by David. 150fr, Madonna and Child,
artist unknown. 400fr, Flight into Egypt, by
Gentile da Fabriano, horiz.

1973, Mar. 22   Litho.   Perf. 12½x13
C129 AP54 50fr multi   .45   .25
C130 AP54 75fr multi   .60   .35
C131 AP54 100fr multi   .90   .45
C132 AP54 125fr multi   1.10   .55
C133 AP54 150fr multi   1.40   .55
    Nos. C129-C133 (5)   4.45   2.15

Souvenir Sheet
C134 AP54 400fr multi   5.25   4.00

Manned Lunar Buggy on
Moon — AP55

    Moon Exploration: 65fr, Lunakhod, Russian
unmanned vehicle on moon. 100fr, Lunar
module returning to orbiting Apollo capsule.
150fr, Apollo capsule in moon orbit. 200fr,
Space walk. 250fr, Walk in Sea of Tranquillity.

1973, Apr. 30   Litho.   Perf. 13x12½
C135 AP55 50fr multi   .45   .25
C136 AP55 65fr multi   .70   .25
C137 AP55 100fr multi   1.00   .45

C138 AP55 150fr multi   1.25   .60
C139 AP55 200fr multi   2.00   .80
    Nos. C135-C139 (5)   5.40   2.35

Souvenir Sheet
C140 AP55 250fr multi   3.50   2.50

Giraffes
AP56

    African Wild Animals: 150fr, Elephants.
200fr, Leopard, horiz. 250fr, Lion, horiz. 300fr,
Rhinoceros, horiz. 500fr, Crocodile, horiz.

Perf. 12½x13, 13x12½
1973, May 3   Litho.
C141 AP56 100fr multi   1.00   .30
C142 AP56 150fr multi   1.50   .60
C143 AP56 200fr multi   2.00   1.10
C144 AP56 250fr multi   2.25   1.10
C145 AP56 500fr multi   5.00   2.75
    Nos. C141-C145 (5)   11.75   5.85

Souvenir Sheet
C146 AP56 300fr multi   4.00   4.00

Europafrica Issue

Girl
Reading
Letter, by
Jan
Vermeer
AP57

    Paintings: 65fr, Portrait of a Lady, by Roger
van der Weyden. 100fr, Young Lady at her
Toilette, by Titian. 150fr, Jane Seymour, by
Hans Holbein. 200fr, Mrs. Williams, by John
Hoppner. 250fr, Milkmaid, by Jean-Baptiste
Greuze.

1973, June 7   Litho.   Perf. 12½x13
C147 AP57 50fr multi   .45   .25
C148 AP57 65fr multi   .70   .25
C149 AP57 100fr multi   1.00   .45
C150 AP57 150fr multi   1.25   .60
C151 AP57 200fr multi   2.00   .90
    Nos. C147-C151 (5)   5.40   2.35

Souvenir Sheet
C152 AP57 250fr multi   3.75   1.50
    For overprint see No. C165-C166.

Africa
Encircled by
OAU Flags
AP58

1973, June 7
C153 AP58 45fr multi   .75   .40
    10th anniv. of Org. for African Unity.

Locomotive "Pacific" 4546, 1908 — AP59

Locomotives from Railroad Museum, Mulhouse, France: 40fr, No. 242, 1927. 50fr, No. 2029, 1882. 150fr, No. 701, 1885-92. 250fr, "Coupe-Vent" No. C145, 1900. 350fr, Buddicomb No. 33, Paris to Rouen, 1884.

1973, June 30 ***Perf. 13x12½***

C154 AP59 10fr multi .35 .25
C155 AP59 40fr multi .55 .25
C156 AP59 50fr multi .60 .25
C157 AP59 150fr multi 1.75 .60
C158 AP59 250fr multi 3.00 .90
Nos. C154-C158 (5) 6.25 2.25

Souvenir Sheet

C159 AP59 350fr multi 4.00 2.75

Boy Scout Type of 1973

40fr, Flag signaling. 75fr, Skiing. 150fr, Cooking. 200fr, Hiking. 250fr, Studying stars.

1973, July 18 Litho. ***Perf. 12½x13***

C160 A95 40fr multi .45 .25
C161 A95 75fr multi .70 .45
C162 A95 150fr multi 1.25 .60
C163 A95 200fr multi 1.50 .70
Nos. C160-C163 (4) 3.90 2.00

Souvenir Sheet

C164 A95 250fr multi 4.00 1.25

Nos. C148 and C150 Surcharged in Silver

1973, Aug. 16

C165 AP57 100fr on 65fr multi 1.75 1.50
C166 AP57 200fr on 150fr multi 3.50 2.25

Drought relief.

Kennedy Type, 1973

John F. Kennedy and: 200fr, Firing Saturn 1 rocket, Apollo program. 300fr, First NASA manned space capsule. 400fr, Saturn 5 countdown.

1973, Sept. 12 Litho. ***Perf. 12½x13***

C167 A96 200fr multi 1.40 .80
C168 A96 300fr multi 2.10 1.05

Souvenir Sheet

C169 A96 400fr multi 4.25 2.50

10th death anniv. of Pres John F. Kennedy.

Interpol Type of 1973

Souvenir Sheet

Design: Victim in city street.

1973, Sept. 15 ***Perf. 13x12½***

C170 A97 300fr multi 3.25 1.10

Tourism Type of 1973

1973, Sept. 30

C171 A98 100fr Waterfalls 1.40 .80

Souvenir Sheet

C172 A98 275fr Elephant 4.25 1.25

House of Worship Type of 1973

Cathedral of the Immaculate Conception.

1973, Sept. 28

C173 A99 200fr multi 2.40 1.20

Folklore Type of 1973

100fr, 225fr, Bobo masked dancers, diff.

1973, Nov. 30 Litho. ***Perf. 12½x13***

C174 A100 100fr multi 1.35 .50
C175 A100 225fr multi 2.00 .95

Zodiac Type of 1973

Souvenir Sheets

Zodiacal Light and: No. C176, 1st 4 signs of Zodiac. No. C177, 2nd 4 signs. No. C178, Last 4 signs.

1973, Dec. 15 ***Perf. 13x14***

C176 A101 250fr multi 3.00 1.10
C177 A101 250fr multi 3.00 1.10
C178 A101 250fr multi 3.00 1.10

Nos. C176-C178 have multicolored margin showing night sky and portraits: No. C176, Louis Armstrong; No. C177, Mahatma Gandhi; No. C178, Martin Luther King.

Soccer Championship Type, 1974

Championship '74 emblem and: 75fr, Gento, Spanish flag. 100fr, Bereta, French flag. 250fr, Best, British flag. 400fr, Beckenbauer, West German flag.

1974, Jan. 15 Litho. ***Perf. 13x12½***

C179 A102 75fr multi .60 .25
C180 A102 100fr multi .90 .25
C181 A102 250fr multi 1.90 .80
Nos. C179-C181 (3) 3.40 1.30

Souvenir Sheet

C182 A102 400fr multi 8.00 3.25

De Gaulle Type, 1974

300fr, De Gaulle, Concorde, horiz. 400fr, De Gaulle, French space shot.

Perf. 13x12½, 12½x13

1974, Feb. 4 Litho.

C183 A103 300fr multi 3.50 1.75

Souvenir Sheet

C184 A103 400fr multi 7.00 1.90

Soccer Cup Championship Type, 1974

World Cup, Emblems and: 150fr, Brindisis, Argentinian flag. No. C186, Kenko, Zaire flag. No. C187, Streich, East German flag. 400fr, Cruyff, Netherlands flag.

1974, Mar. 19 ***Perf. 12½x13***

C185 A104 150fr multi 1.10 .45
C186 A104 300fr multi 2.25 .90

Souvenir Sheets

C187 A104 300fr multi 4.00 1.50
C188 A104 400fr multi 4.00 1.50

UPU Type, 1974

UPU Emblem and: 100fr, Dove carrying mail. 200fr, Air Afrique 707. 300fr, Dish antenna. 500fr, Telstar satellite.

1974, July 23 ***Perf. 13½***

C189 A106 100fr multi 1.00 .50
C190 A106 200fr multi 1.50 .75
C191 A106 300fr multi 2.25 1.25
Nos. C189-C191 (3) 4.75 2.50

Souvenir Sheet

C192 A106 500fr multi 4.75 1.90

For overprint see No. C197-C200.

Soccer Cup Winners Type, 1974

World Cup, Game and Flags: 150fr, Brazil, in Sweden, 1958. 200fr, Brazil, in Chile, 1962. 250fr, Brazil, in Mexico, 1970. 450fr, England, in England, 1966.

1974, Sept. 2

C193 A107 150fr multi 1.05 .55
C194 A107 200fr multi 1.50 .75
C195 A107 250fr multi 2.25 1.25
Nos. C193-C195 (3) 4.80 2.55

Souvenir Sheet

C196 A107 450fr multi 4.00 1.90

Nos. C189-C192 Overprinted in Red

1974, Oct. 9

C197 A106 100fr multi 1.35 .60
C198 A106 200fr multi 2.00 .90
C199 A106 300fr multi 3.50 1.30
Nos. C197-C199 (3) 6.85 2.80

Souvenir Sheet

C200 A106 500fr multi 4.00 1.90

Universal Postal Union, centenary.

Flower Type of 1974

Flower Paintings by: 300fr, Auguste Renoir. 400fr, Carl Brendt.

1974, Oct. 31 Litho. ***Perf. 12½x13***

C201 A109 300fr multi 3.50 1.10

Souvenir Sheet

C202 A109 400fr multi 5.25 1.60

Locomotive Type of 1975

Locomotives from Railroad Museum. Mulhouse, France: 100fr, Crampton No. 80, 1852. 200fr, No. 701, 1885-92. 300fr, "Forquenot," 1882.

1975, Feb. 28 Litho. ***Perf. 13x12½***

C203 A112 100fr multi 1.50 .35
C204 A112 200fr multi 2.75 .65

Souvenir Sheet

C205 A112 300fr multi 5.25 2.25

Old Cars Type, 1975

Flags and Old Cars: 150fr, Germany and Mercedes-Benz, 1929. 200fr, Germany and Maybach, 1936. 400fr, Great Britain and Rolls Royce Silver Ghost, 1910.

1975, Apr. 6 ***Perf. 14x13½***

C206 A113 150fr multi 1.75 .50
C207 A113 200fr multi 2.25 .70

Souvenir Sheet

C208 A113 400fr multi 3.75 1.75

American Bicentennial Type

200fr, Washington crossing Delaware. 300fr, Hessians Captured at Trenton.

1975, May 6 Litho. ***Perf. 14***

C209 A114 200fr multi 2.00 .90
C210 A114 300fr multi 2.40 1.25

Schweitzer Type of 1975

Albert Schweitzer and: 150fr, Toucan. 175fr, Vulturine guinea fowl. 200fr, King vulture. 450fr, Crested corythornis.

1975, May 25 Litho. ***Perf. 13½***

C212 A115 150fr multi 1.50 .60
C213 A115 175fr multi 2.00 .70
C214 A115 200fr multi 2.75 .95
Nos. C212-C214 (3) 6.25 2.25

Souvenir Sheet

C215 A115 450fr multi 6.25 2.25

Apollo Soyuz Type of 1975

100fr, Apollo, Soyuz near link-up. 200fr, Cosmonauts Alexei Leonov, Valeri Kubasov. 300fr, Astronauts Donald K. Slayton, Vance Brand, Thomas P. Stafford. 500fr, Apollo Soyuz emblem, U.S., USSR flags.

1975, July 18 Litho. ***Perf. 13½***

C216 A116 100fr multi 1.00 .25
C217 A116 200fr multi 1.50 .65
C218 A116 300fr multi 2.50 1.00
Nos. C216-C218 (3) 5.00 1.90

Souvenir Sheet

C219 A116 500fr multi 5.00 2.25

Picasso Type of 1975

Picasso Paintings: 150fr, El Prado, horiz. 350fr, Couple in Patio. 400fr, Science and Charity.

1975, Aug. 7

C220 A117 150fr multi 2.25 .70
C221 A117 350fr multi 4.00 1.00

Souvenir Sheet

C222 A117 400fr multi 3.50 1.60

EXPO '75 Type of 1975

Expo '75 emblem and: 150fr, Passenger liner Asama Maru. 300fr, Future floating city Aquapolis.

1975, Sept. 26 Litho. ***Perf. 11***

C223 A118 150fr multi 2.00 .60

Souvenir Sheet

Perf. 13½

C224 A118 300fr multi 3.75 1.25

Winter Olympic Games Type of 1975

Innsbruck Background, Olympic Emblem and: 100fr, Ice hockey. 200fr, Ski jump. 300fr, Speed skating.

1975, Dec. 15 ***Perf. 13½***

C225 A122 100fr multi .95 .45
C226 A122 200fr multi 1.75 .70

Souvenir Sheet

C227 A122 300fr multi 4.25 1.50

Olympic Games Type of 1976

Olympic Emblem and: 125fr, Heavyweight judo. 150fr, Weight lifting. 500fr, Sprint.

1976, Mar. 17 Litho. ***Perf. 13½***

C228 A123 125fr multi 1.00 .35
C229 A123 150fr multi 1.50 .55

Souvenir Sheet

C230 A123 500fr multi 4.25 2.25

Summer Olympic Games Type of 1976

Olympic emblem and: 150fr, Pole vault. 200fr, Gymnast on balance beam. 500fr, Two-man sculls.

1976, Mar. 25 ***Perf. 11***

C231 A124 150fr multi 1.15 .45
C232 A124 200fr multi 1.75 .60

Souvenir Sheet

C233 A124 500fr multi 4.25 2.25

For overprint see No. C245-C247.

Zeppelin Type of 1976

Airships: 100fr, Graf Zeppelin over Swiss Alps. 200fr, LZ-129 over city. 300fr, Graf Zeppelin. 500fr, Zeppelin over Bodensee.

1976, May 11

C234 A126 100fr multi 1.00 .45
C235 A126 200fr multi 2.00 .75
C236 A126 300fr multi 2.75 1.20
Nos. C234-C236 (3) 5.75 2.40

Souvenir Sheet

C237 A126 500fr multi 4.75 2.25

Viking Mars Type of 1976

Designs: 200fr, Viking lander assembly. 300fr, Viking orbiter in descent on Mars. 450fr, Viking in Mars orbit.

1976, June 24 Litho. ***Perf. 13½***

C238 A127 200fr multi 1.90 .45
C239 A127 300fr multi 2.75 .75

Souvenir Sheet

C240 A127 450fr multi 4.25 2.25

American Bicentennial Type

Bicentennial and Interphil '76 Emblems and: 100fr, Siege of Yorktown. 200fr, Battle of Cape St. Vincent. 300fr, Peter Francisco's bravery. 500fr, Surrender of the Hessians.

1976, Sept. 30 Litho. ***Perf. 13½***

C241 A129 100fr multi 1.00 .35
C242 A129 200fr multi 1.60 .65
C243 A129 300fr multi 2.25 .80
Nos. C241-C243 (3) 4.85 1.80

Souvenir Sheet

C244 A129 500fr multi 6.50 2.25

Nos. C231-C233 Overprinted in Gold

a. VAINQUEUR 1976 / TADEUSZ SLUSARSKI / POLOGNE
b. VAINQUEUR 1976 / NADIA COMANECI / ROUMANIE

(c)

1977, July 4   Litho.   Perf. 11
C245 A124(a) 150fr multi   1.00 .70
C246 A124(b) 200fr multi   1.75 1.00

Souvenir Sheet

C247 A124(c) 500fr multi   4.25 2.25

Winners, 21st Olympic Games.

UPU Emblem over Globe — AP60

1978, Aug. 8   Litho.   Perf. 13
C248 AP60 350fr multi   3.50 2.00

Congress of Paris, establishing UPU, cent.

Jules Verne, Apollo 11 Emblem,
Footprint on Moon, Neil
Armstrong — AP61

Space Conquest: 50fr, Yuri Gagarin and
moon landing. 100fr, Montgolfier hot air balloon and memorial medal, 1783; Bleriot's
monoplane, 1909.

1978, Sept. 27   Litho.   Perf. 13x12½
C249 AP61 50fr multi   .55 .30
C250 AP61 60fr multi   .60 .25
C251 AP61 100fr multi   1.10 .55
    Nos. C249-C251 (3)   2.25 1.05

Anti-Apartheid
Year — AP62

1978, Oct. 12   Litho.   Perf. 13
C252 AP62 100fr blue & multi   1.10 .60

Philexafrique II-Essen Issue
Common Design Types

No. C253, Hippopotamus, Upper Volta
#C18. No. C254, Kingfisher, Hanover #1.

1978, Nov. 1   Litho.   Perf. 12½
C253 CD138 100fr multi   2.40 1.40
C254 CD139 100fr multi   2.40 1.40

Nos. C253-C254 printed se-tenant.

Sun God Horus
with Sun — AP63

300fr, Falcon with cartouches, UNESCO
emblem.

1978, Dec. 4
C255 AP63 200fr multi   1.75 .80
C256 AP63 300fr multi   2.50 1.25

UNESCO Campaign to safeguard monuments at Philae.

Jules Verne and
Balloon — AP64

1978, Dec. 10   Engr.   Perf. 13
C257 AP64 200fr multi   2.50 1.40

Verne (1828-1905), science fiction writer.

Bicycling, Olympic Rings — AP65

Designs: Bicycling scenes.

1980   Perf. 14½
C258 AP65 65fr multi   .70 .25
C259 AP65 150fr multi, vert.   1.25 .50
C260 AP65 250fr multi   2.50 .80
C261 AP65 350fr multi   3.50 1.25
    Nos. C258-C261 (4)   7.95 2.80

Souvenir Sheet

C262 AP65 500fr multi   6.00 1.90

22nd Summer Olympic Games, Moscow,
July 19-Aug. 3.

**Nos. C258-C262 Overprinted with
Name of Winner and Country**

1980, Nov. 22   Litho.   Perf. 14½
C263 AP65 65fr multi   .70 .40
C264 AP65 150fr multi, vert.   1.60 .85
C265 AP65 250fr multi   2.75 1.50
C266 AP65 350fr multi   3.50 1.75
    Nos. C263-C266 (4)   8.55 4.50

Souvenir Sheet

C267 AP65 500fr multi   6.00 3.50

1982 World
Cup — AP66

Designs: Various soccer players.

1982, June 22   Litho.   Perf. 13½
C268 AP66 70fr multi   .60 .25
C269 AP66 90fr multi   .80 .35
C270 AP66 150fr multi   1.40 .50
C271 AP66 300fr multi   2.50 1.00
    Nos. C268-C271 (4)   5.30 2.10

Souvenir Sheet

C272 AP66 500fr multi   4.75 1.60

Anniversaries and Events — AP67

90fr, Space Shuttle. 120fr, World Soccer
Cup. 300fr, Cup, diff. 450fr, Royal Wedding.
500fr, Prince Charles, Lady Diana.

1983, June   Litho.   Perf. 13½
C273 AP67 90fr multicolored   .80 .25
C274 AP67 120fr multicolored   1.10 .45
C275 AP67 300fr multicolored   2.50 .80
C276 AP67 450fr multicolored   3.50 1.10
    Nos. C273-C276 (4)   7.90 2.60

Souvenir Sheet

C277 AP67 500fr multicolored   4.75 1.75

Pre-Olympics, 1984 Los
Angeles — AP68

90fr, Sailing. 120fr, Type 470. 300fr, Wind
surfing. 400fr, Wind surfing, diff.
500fr, Soling Class, Wind surfing.

1983, Aug. 1   Litho.   Perf. 13
C278 AP68 90fr multicolored   .90 .25
C279 AP68 120fr multicolored   1.10 .35
C280 AP68 300fr multicolored   2.90 .80
C281 AP68 400fr multicolored   3.75 1.00
    Nos. C278-C281 (4)   8.65 2.40

Souvenir Sheet

C282 AP68 500fr multicolored   6.00 1.75

Christmas
AP69

Rubens Paintings: 120fr, Adoration of the
Shepherds. 350fr, Virgin of the Garland. 500fr,
Adoration of the Kings.

1983   Litho.   Perf. 13
C283 AP69 120fr multicolored   1.00 .45
C284 AP69 350fr multicolored   3.00 .90
C285 AP69 500fr multicolored   4.00 1.40
    Nos. C283-C285 (3)   8.00 2.75

1984 Summer Olympics — AP70

1984, Mar. 26   Litho.   Perf. 12½
C286 AP70 90fr Handball, vert.   .70 .25
C287 AP70 120fr Volleyball, vert. 1.00 .35
C288 AP70 150fr Handball, diff.   1.40 .45
C289 AP70 250fr Basketball   2.25 .60
C290 AP70 300fr Soccer   2.75 1.00
    Nos. C286-C290 (5)   8.10 2.65

Souvenir Sheet

C291 AP70 500fr Volleyball, diff.   4.75 1.75

Local Birds — AP71

90fr, Phoenicopterus roseus. 185fr, Chori-
otis kori, vert. 200fr, Buphagus
erythrorhynchus, vert. 300fr, Bucorvus
leadbeateri.

1984, May 14   Litho.   Perf. 12½
C292 AP71 90fr multicolored   1.40 .55
C293 AP71 185fr multicolored 2.50 1.25
C294 AP71 200fr multicolored 2.50 1.40
C295 AP71 300fr multicolored 3.50 2.25
    Nos. C292-C295 (4)   9.90 5.45

AP72

Famous Men — AP73

Designs: 5fr, Houari Boumediene (1927-
1978), president of Algeria 1965-78. 125fr,
Gottlieb Daimler (1834-1900), German auto-
motive pioneer, and 1886 Daimler. 250fr,
Louis Bleriot (1872-1936), French aviator, first
to fly the English Channel in a heavier-than-air
craft. 300fr, Abraham Lincoln. 400fr, Henri
Dunant (1828-1910), founder of the Red
Cross. 450fr, Auguste Piccard (1884-1962),
Swiss physicist, inventor of the bathyscaphe
Trieste, 1948. 500fr, Robert Baden-Powell
(1856-1941), founder of Boy Scouts. 600fr,
Anatoli Karpov, Russian chess champion.
1000fr, Paul Harris (1868-1947), founder of
Rotary Intl.

1984, May 21 Litho. Perf. 13½

C296	AP72	5fr multi	.25	.25
C297	AP72	125fr multi	1.10	.35
C298	AP72	250fr multi	2.25	.60
C299	AP72	300fr multi	2.75	.80
C300	AP72	400fr multi	3.50	1.00
C301	AP72	450fr multi	4.00	1.00
C302	AP72	500fr multi	4.50	1.25
C303	AP72	600fr multi	4.75	1.50
	Nos. C296-C303 (8)		23.10	6.75

Souvenir Sheet

C304	AP73	1000fr multi	9.00	2.00

No. C304 contains one 51x30mm stamp.

Burkina Faso

Butterflies — AP73a

10fr, Graphium pylades. 120fr, Hypolimnas misippus. 400fr, Danaus chrysippus. 450fr, Papilio demodocus.

1984, May 23 Perf. 13½

C305	AP73a	10fr multicolored	.25	.25
C306	AP73a	120fr multicolored	1.75	.80
C307	AP73a	400fr multicolored	5.50	2.25
C308	AP73a	450fr multicolored	5.75	2.50
	Nos. C305-C308 (4)		13.25	5.60

Philexafrica '85, Lome — AP74

No. C309, Solar & wind energy. No. C310, Children.

1985, May 20 Litho. Perf. 13

C309	AP74	200fr multi	2.40	1.25
C310	AP74	200fr multi	2.40	1.25
a.	Pair, #C309-C310 + label		5.00	2.50

PHILEXAFRICA '85, Lome — AP75

National development: No. C311, Youth. No. C312, Communications and transportation.

1985, Nov. 16 Litho. Perf. 13

C311	AP75	250fr multi	4.25	1.50
C312	AP75	250fr multi	4.25	1.50
a.	Pair, #C311-C312 + label		10.50	4.00

Intl. Youth Year (No. C311).

French Revolution, Bicent. — AP76

Designs: 150fr, Oath of the Tennis Court, by David. 200fr, Storming of the Bastille, by Thevenin. 600fr, Rouget de Lisle Singing La Marseillaise, by Pils.

1989, May 3 Litho. Perf. 13

C313	AP76	150fr multi	1.75	.70
C314	AP76	200fr multi	2.10	1.00
C315	AP76	600fr multi	7.00	2.75
	Nos. C313-C315 (3)		10.85	4.45

PHILEXFRANCE '89.

POSTAGE DUE STAMPS

Postage Due Stamps of Upper Senegal and Niger, 1914, Overprinted in Black or Red

1920 Unwmk. Perf. 14x13½

J1	D2	5c green	.40	.80
J2	D2	10c rose	.40	.80
J3	D2	15c gray	.75	.80
J4	D2	20c brown (R)	.75	.80
J5	D2	30c blue	.75	.80
J6	D2	50c black (R)	1.25	1.60
J7	D2	60c orange	1.25	1.60
J8	D2	1fr violet	2.25	2.25
	Nos. J1-J8 (8)		7.80	9.45

Type of 1914 Issue Surcharged

1927

J9	D2	2fr on 1fr lilac rose	3.50	3.50
J10	D2	3fr on 1fr orange brn	6.00	4.50

D3

1928 Typo.

J11	D3	5c green	.40	.80
J12	D3	10c rose	.80	.80
J13	D3	15c dark gray	1.25	1.60
J14	D3	20c dark brown	1.25	1.60
J15	D3	30c dark blue	1.75	2.50
J16	D3	50c black	3.50	4.00
J17	D3	60c orange	4.00	4.75
J18	D3	1fr dull violet	6.50	7.25
J19	D3	2fr lilac rose	11.00	11.00
J20	D3	3fr orange brn	15.00	19.00
	Nos. J11-J20 (10)		45.45	53.30

Catalogue values for unused stamps in this section, from this point to the end of the section, are for Never Hinged items.

Republic

D4

1962, Jan. 31 Perf. 14x13½
Denomination in Black

J21	D4	1fr bright blue	.25	.25
J22	D4	2fr orange	.25	.25
J23	D4	5fr brt vio blue	.25	.25
J24	D4	10fr red lilac	.35	.35
J25	D4	20fr emerald	.80	.80
J26	D4	50fr rose red	1.75	1.75
	Nos. J21-J26 (6)		3.65	3.65

OFFICIAL STAMPS

Catalogue values for unused stamps in this section are for Never Hinged items.

Elephant — O1

Perf. 12½
1963, Feb. 1 Unwmk. Photo.
Center in Sepia

O1	O1	1fr red brown	.25	.25
O2	O1	5fr yel green	.25	.25
O3	O1	10fr deep vio	.25	.25
O4	O1	15fr red org	.35	.35
O5	O1	25fr brt rose lilac	.80	.80
O6	O1	50fr brt green	1.25	1.25
O7	O1	60fr brt red	1.40	1.40
O8	O1	85fr dk slate grn	2.25	2.25
O9	O1	100fr brt blue	3.50	3.50
O10	O1	200fr bright rose	5.25	5.25
	Nos. O1-O10 (10)		15.55	15.55

BURMA

'bər-mə

Myanmar

LOCATION — Bounded on the north by China; east by China, Laos and Thailand; south and west by the Bay of Bengal, Bangladesh and India.
GOVT. — Republic
AREA — 261,228 sq. mi.
POP. — 60,584,850 (2012 est.)
CAPITAL — Naypyidaw Myodaw

Burma was part of India from 1826 until April 1, 1937, when it became a self-governing unit of the British Commonwealth and received a constitution. On January 4, 1948, it achieved full independence as the Union of Burma. In 1989 it became known as the Republic of the Union of Myanmar.

12 Pies = 1 Anna
16 Annas = 1 Rupee
100 Pyas = 1 Kyat (1953)

Catalogue values for unused stamps in this country are for Never Hinged items, beginning with Scott 35 in the regular postage section and Scott O28 in the official section.

Watermarks

Wmk. 196 — Multiple Stars

Wmk. 254 — Elephant Heads

Wmk. 257 — Curved Wavy Lines

George V Stamps of India 1926-36 Overprinted in Black

Wmk. 196
1937, Apr. 1 Typo. Perf. 14

1	A46	3p slate	1.25	.25
2	A71	½a green	.65	.25
3	A68	9p dark green	.65	.25
4	A72	1a dark brown	2.75	.25
5	A49	2a ver	.65	.25
6	A57	2a6p buff	.55	.25
7	A51	3a carmine rose	2.75	.50
8	A70	3a6p deep blue	4.25	.25
9	A52	4a olive green	.75	.25
10	A53	6a bister	.75	.60
11	A54	8a red violet	2.25	.25
12	A55	12a claret	8.50	3.50

Overprint is at the bottom on No. 7.

Overprinted in Black

13	A56	1r green & brown	35.00	5.50
14	A56	2r brn org & car rose	29.00	27.50
15	A56	5r dk violet & ultra	32.50	30.00
16	A56	10r car & green	135.00	125.00
17	A56	15r ol grn & ultra	450.00	250.00
18	A56	25r blue & ocher	750.00	550.00
	Nos. 1-18 (18)		1,457.	994.85
	Set, never hinged		2,600.	

For overprints see Nos. O1-O14, 1N1-1N3, 1N25-1N26, 1N47.

King George VI
A1   A2

Royal Barge — A3

Elephant Moving Teak Log — A4

Farmer Plowing Rice Paddy — A5

Sailboat on Irrawaddy River — A6

George VI and
Peacock — A7

George VI — A8

Perf. 13½x14

1938-40		Litho.		**Wmk. 254**	
18A	A1	1p	red org ('40)	2.25	2.00
19	A1	3p	violet	.25	3.00
20	A1	6p	ultramarine	.65	.25
21	A1	9p	yel green	1.50	2.00
22	A2	1a	brown violet	.25	.25
23	A2	1½a	turq grn	1.20	3.75
24	A2	2a	carmine	2.25	1.00

Perf. 13

25	A3	2a6p	rose lake	10.00	3.75
26	A4	3a	dk violet	10.00	3.75
27	A5	3a6p	dp bl & brt bl	2.50	9.50
28	A2	4a	slate blue,		
			perf. 13½x14	2.40	.25
29	A6	8a	slate green	2.75	.50

Perf. 13½

30	A7	1r	brt ultra & dk		
			violet	3.00	
31	A7	2r	dk vio & red		
			brown	16.00	6.00
32	A8	5r	car & dull vio	42.50	55.00
33	A8	10r	gray grn & brn	47.50	80.00
		Nos. 18A-33 (16)		145.00	172.00
		Set, never hinged		240.00	

See Nos. 51-65. For overprints and surcharges see Nos. 34-50, O15-O27, 1N4-1N11, 1N28-1N30, 1N37-1N46, 1N48-1N49.

No. 25
Surcharged
in Black

1940, May 6				**Perf. 13**	
34	A3	1a on 2a6p	rose lake	3.00	.250
		Never hinged		4.50	

Centenary of first postage stamp.

> Catalogue values for unused stamps in this section, from this point to the end of the section, are for Never Hinged items.

Nos. 18A to 33 Overprinted in Black

a

b

1945

35	A1(a)	1p	red orange	.25	.25
a.	Pair, one without overprint			1,850.	
36	A1(a)	3p	violet	.25	1.60
37	A1(a)	6p	ultramarine	.25	.35
38	A1(a)	9p	yel green	.35	1.40
39	A2(a)	1a	brown violet	.25	.25
40	A2(a)	1½a	turq green	.25	.25
41	A2(a)	2a	carmine	.25	.25
42	A3(b)	2a6p	rose lake	2.25	2.50
43	A4(b)	3a	dk violet	1.75	.25
44	A5(b)	3a6p	dp bl & brt bl	.25	.85
45	A2(a)	4a	slate blue	.25	.85

46	A6(b)	8a	slate green	.25	1.60
47	A7(b)	1r	brt ultra & dk		
			vio	.70	.70
48	A7(b)	2r	dk vio & red		
			brown	.70	1.50
49	A8(b)	5r	car & dull vio	.75	1.50
50	A8(b)	10r	gray grn &		
			brn	.75	1.50
		Nos. 35-50 (16)		9.50	15.60

Types of 1938

Perf. 13½x14

1946, Jan. 1		Litho.		**Wmk. 254**	
51	A1	3p	brown	.25	3.75
52	A1	6p	violet	.25	.40
53	A1	9p	dull green	.25	5.75
54	A2	1a	deep blue	.25	.25
55	A2	1½a	salmon	.25	.25
56	A2	2a	rose lake	.25	.60

Perf. 13

57	A3	2a6p	greenish blue	3.25	6.75
58	A4	3a	blue violet	7.00	9.50
59	A5	3a6p	ultra & gray blk	2.25	4.50
60	A2	4a	rose lil, perf.		
			13½x14	.60	1.00
61	A6	8a	deep magenta	2.00	6.25

Perf. 13½

62	A7	1r	dp mag & dk		
			vio	2.10	3.25
63	A7	2r	sal & red brn	9.00	6.25
64	A8	5r	red brn & dk		
			grn	10.00	25.00
65	A8	10r	dk vio & car	25.00	37.50
		Nos. 51-65 (15)		62.70	111.00

For overprints see Nos. 70-84, O28-O42.

Burmese
Man — A9

Burmese
Woman — A10

Mythological
Leogyph
Chinthe — A11

Elephant Hauling
Teak — A12

1946, May 2				**Perf. 13**	
66	A9	9p	peacock green	.30	.25
67	A10	1½a	brt violet	.30	.25
68	A11	2a	carmine	.30	.25
69	A12	3a6p	ultramarine	.70	.55
		Nos. 66-69 (4)		1.60	1.30

Victory of the Allied Nations in WWII.

**Nos. 51-65 Overprinted
in Black**

1947, Oct. 1			**Perf. 13½x14, 13, 13½**		
70	A1	3p	brown	1.75	.85
71	A1	6p	violet	.25	.40
72	A1	9p	dull green	.25	.40
a.	Inverted overprint			26.00	37.50
73	A2	1a	deep blue	.25	.40
74	A2	1½a	salmon	2.40	.25
75	A2	2a	rose lake	.40	.30
76	A3	2a6p	greenish bl	2.40	1.75
77	A4	3a	blue violet	4.50	2.00
78	A5	3a6p	ultra & gray blk	1.75	3.50
79	A2	4a	rose lilac	2.50	.50
80	A6	8a	dp magenta	2.50	3.50
81	A7	1r	dp mag & dk vio	8.25	3.75
82	A7	2r	sal & red brn	8.25	8.25
83	A8	5r	red brn & dk grn	8.25	8.00
84	A8	10r	dk vio & car	5.50	8.00
		Nos. 70-84 (15)		49.20	41.85

The overprint is slightly larger on Nos. 76 to 78 and 80 to 84. The Burmese characters read "Interim Government."

Other denominations are known with the overprint inverted or double.

Issues of the Republic

U Aung San Map
and Chinze — A13

Perf. 12½x12

1948, Jan. 6		Litho.		**Unwmk.**	
85	A13	½a	emerald	.25	.25
86	A13	1a	deep rose	.25	.25
87	A13	2a	carmine	.35	.25
88	A13	3½a	blue	.55	.25
89	A13	8a	lt chocolate	.85	.25
		Nos. 85-89 (5)		2.25	1.25

Attainment of independence, Jan. 4, 1948.

Martyrs'
Memorial — A14

1948, July 19		Engr.		**Perf. 14x13½**	
90	A14	3p	ultramarine	.25	.25
91	A14	6p	green	.25	.25
92	A14	9p	dp carmine	.25	.25
93	A14	1a	purple	.25	.25
94	A14	2a	lilac rose	.25	.25
95	A14	3½a	dk slate green	.35	.25
96	A14	4a	yel brown	.45	.25
97	A14	8a	orange red	.50	.25
98	A14	12a	claret	.70	.25
99	A14	1r	blue green	1.25	.25
100	A14	2r	deep blue	2.00	.35
101	A14	5r	chocolate	5.50	.80
		Nos. 90-101 (12)		12.00	3.65

1st anniv. of the assassination of Burma's leaders in the fight for independence.

Ball Game
(Chin-lone)
A15

Bell
A16

Mythical Duck (Shwe
hintha) — A17

Rice
Planting
A18

Royal
Throne — A19

Designs: 6p, Dancer. 9p, Musician. 3a, Spinning. 3a6p, Royal Palace. 4a, Cutting teak. 8a, Plowing rice field.

Perf. 12½ (A15-A17), 12x12½ (A18), 13 (A19)

1949, Jan. 4					
102	A15	3p	ultramarine	1.90	.45
103	A15	6p	green	.25	.25
104	A15	9p	carmine	.25	.25
105	A16	1a	red orange	.40	.25
106	A17	2a	orange	1.00	.25
107	A18	2a6p	lilac rose	.40	.25
108	A18	3a	purple	.40	.25
109	A18	3a6p	dk slate grn	.65	.25
110	A16	4a	chocolate	.65	.25
111	A18	8a	carmine	.85	.25
112	A19	1r	blue green	1.60	.25
a.	Perf. 14			6.00	4.00
113	A19	2r	deep blue	2.90	.25
114	A19	5r	chocolate	6.25	1.50
115	A19	10r	orange red	12.50	2.75
		Nos. 102-115 (14)		30.00	7.80

See Nos. 122-135, 139-152.
For overprints see O56-O67.

UPU Monument,
Bern — A20

1949, Oct. 9			**Unwmk.**	**Perf. 13**	
116	A20	2a	orange	.45	.40
117	A20	3½a	olive grn	.55	.40
118	A20	6a	lilac	.80	.40
119	A20	8a	crimson	1.10	1.00
120	A20	12½a	ultra	2.00	1.25
121	A20	1r	blue green	2.40	1.90
		Nos. 116-121 (6)		7.30	5.35

75th anniv. of the UPU.

Types of 1949

Designs as before.

Perf. 13½x14, 14x13½, 13

1952-53		Litho.		**Wmk. 254**	
122	A15	3p	brown orange	1.00	.40
123	A15	6p	deep plum	.25	.25
124	A15	9p	blue	.25	.25
125	A16	1a	violet bl	.25	.25
126	A17	2a	green ('52)	.90	.25
127	A18	2a6p	green	.35	.25
128	A18	3a	sal pink ('52)	.40	.25
129	A18	3a6p	brown orange	.65	.25
130	A18	4a	vermilion	.65	.25
131	A18	8a	lt blue ('52)	.80	.50
132	A19	1r	rose violet	1.00	.75
133	A19	2r	yel green	2.00	.85
134	A19	5r	ultramarine	5.75	2.00
135	A19	10r	aquamarine	12.00	4.50
		Nos. 122-135 (14)		26.25	11.00

Map of Burma and
Monument — A21

1953, Jan. 4				**Perf. 14**	
136	A21	14p	green	.85	.25

Perf. 13

Size: 36½x26mm

137	A21	20p	salmon pink	1.10	.30
138	A21	25p	ultramarine	1.25	.40

Fifth anniversary of independence.
For surcharge see No. 166.

Types of 1949

Designs: 2p, Dancer. 3p, Musician. 20p, Spinning. 25p, Royal Palace. 30p, Cutting teak. 50p, Plowing rice field.

1954, Jan. 4		**Perf. 14x13½, 13, 14**			
139	A15	1p	brown orange	1.40	.25
140	A15	2p	plum	.25	.25
141	A15	3p	blue	.25	.25

142	A16	5p ultramarine	.25	.25
143	A18	10p yel green	.25	.25
144	A17	15p green	.65	.25
145	A18	20p vermilion	.45	.25
146	A18	25p lt red org	.45	.25
147	A18	30p vermilion	.65	.25
148	A18	50p blue	.75	.25
149	A19	1k rose violet	1.60	.50
150	A19	2k green	2.75	.75
151	A19	5k ultramarine	7.00	1.00
152	A19	10k light blue	17.50	1.50
		Nos. 139-152 (14)	34.20	6.25

For overprints and surcharges see Nos. 163-165, 173-175, O68-O79, O80-O81, O83, O85, O87.

Peace Pagoda, Monks' Hostels and Meeting-cave — A22

Designs: 10p, Sangha (community) of Cambodia. 15p, Council meeting. 50p, Sangha of Thailand. 1k, Sangha of Ceylon. 2k, Sangha of Laos.

1954		Typo.	Perf. 13	
153	A22	10p deep blue	.25	.25
154	A22	15p deep claret	.30	.25
155	A22	35p dark brown	.60	.25
156	A22	50p green	.80	.25
157	A22	1k carmine	1.75	.50
158	A22	2k violet	3.00	1.30
		Nos. 153-158 (6)	6.70	3.00

6th Buddhist Council, Rangoon, 1954-56.

Marble Markers of 5th Buddhist Council A23

Designs: 40p, Thatbyinnyu Pagoda. 60p, Shwedagon Pagoda, Rangoon. 1.25k, Aerial View of 6th Buddhist Council, Yegu.

		Perf. 11x11½		
1956, May 24			Unwmk.	
159	A23	20p blue & gray olive	.45	.25
160	A23	40p blue & brt yel grn	.75	.30
161	A23	60p green & lemon	1.10	.60
162	A23	1.25k gray blue & yel	2.25	.90
		Nos. 159-162 (4)	4.55	1.95

2500th anniv. of the Buddhist Era.

Nos. 146, 149-150 Srchd. or Ovptd.

1959, Nov. 9		Wmk. 254	Perf. 13, 14	
163	A18	15p on 25p lt red org	.50	.25
164	A19	1k rose violet	1.50	1.00
165	A19	2k green	3.00	1.75
		Nos. 163-165 (3)	5.00	3.00

Centenary of Mandalay, former capital.
The two lines of overprint are 4mm apart on No. 163; 7mm on Nos. 164-165.

No. 136 Surcharged

1961, June			Perf. 14	
166	A21	15p on 14p green	3.00	.40

Children playing hurdles — A24

Unwmk.

1961, Dec. 11		Litho.	Perf. 13	
167	A24	15p claret & rose claret	1.25	.25

15th anniversary of UNICEF.

Runner with Torch — A25

Soccer, Pole Vault and Shot Put — A26

Designs: 50p, Women runners. 1k, Hurdling, weight lifting, boxing, bicycling and swimming.

		Perf. 14x13, 13x14		
1961, Dec. 11			Photo.	
168	A25	15p red & ultra	.35	.25
169	A26	25p dk green & ocher	.60	.25
170	A26	50p vio blue & pink	1.10	.35
171	A25	1k brt green & yel	1.75	.75
		Nos. 168-171 (4)	3.80	1.60

2nd South East Asia Peninsular Games, Rangoon.

Map and Flag of Burma — A27

1963, Mar. 2		Engr.	Perf. 13	
172	A27	15p red	2.75	.25

First anniversary of new government.

Nos. 143 and 148 Ovptd. in Violet or Red

1963, Mar. 21		Wmk. 254	Litho.	
173	A18	10p yel green (V)	2.00	.60
174	A18	50p blue (R)	4.00	1.25

FAO "Freedom from Hunger" campaign. No. 173 is known with a red overprint.

No. 145 Overprinted

1963, May 1			Wmk. 254	
175	A18	20p vermilion	2.50	.50

Issued for May Day.

White-browed Fantail Flycatcher — A28

Indian Roller — A29

Birds: 20p, Red-whiskered bulbul. 25p, Crested serpent eagle. 50p, Sarus crane. 1k,

---

Oriental pied hornbill. 2k, Kalij pheasant. 5k, Green peafowl.

Perf. 13½

1964, Apr. 16		Unwmk.	Photo.	
		Size: 25x21mm		
176	A28	1p gray	.55	.25
177	A28	2p carmine rose	.65	.25
178	A28	3p blue green	.65	.25
		Size: 22x26½mm		
		Perf. 13½x13, 13 (#182)		
179	A29	5p violet blue	.75	.30
180	A29	10p orange brn	.85	.30
181	A29	15p olive	1.00	.45
		Size: 35x25mm		
182	A28	20p rose & brn	1.25	.45
		Size: 27x36½mm, 36½x27mm		
183	A29	25p yel & brown	1.40	.45
184	A29	50p red, blk & gray	2.25	.65
185	A29	1k gray, ind & yel	6.00	1.50
186	A28	2k pale ol, ind & red	12.50	4.00
187	A29	5k citron, dk bl & red	27.50	10.00
		Nos. 176-187 (12)	55.35	18.85

See Nos. 197-208. For overprints see Nos. O82, O84, O86, O88-O93, O94-O115.

ITU Emblem, Old and New Communication Equipment — A30

1965, May 17		Litho.	Perf. 15	
		Size: 32x22mm		
188	A30	20p bright pink	2.50	.25
		Perf. 13		
		Size: 34x24½mm		
189	A30	50p dull green	3.50	.50

Centenary of the ITU.

ICY Emblem A31

1965, July 1		Unwmk.	Perf. 13	
190	A31	5p violet blue	.90	.25
191	A31	10p brown orange	1.40	.25
192	A31	15p olive	3.00	.50
		Nos. 190-192 (3)	5.30	1.00

International Cooperation Year.

Rice Farmer — A32

1966, Mar. 2			Perf. 13½x13	
193	A32	15p multicolored	4.25	.40

Issued for Farmers' Day.

Cogwheel and Hammer — A33

1967, May 1		Litho.	Unwmk.	
194	A33	15p lt blue, yel & black	4.25	.50

Issued for Labor Day, May 1.

Aung San, Tractor and Farmers A34

1968, Jan. 4		Unwmk.	Perf. 13½	
195	A34	15p sky bl, blk & ocher	4.25	.40

20th anniversary of independence.

Largest Burmese Pearl — A35

1968, Mar. 4		Litho.	Perf. 13½	
196	A35	15p blue, ultra, gray & yel	7.50	.40

Burmese pearl industry.

Bird Types of 1964 in Changed Sizes

Designs as before.

Unwmk.

1968, July 1		Photo.	Perf. 14	
		Size: 21x17mm		
197	A28	1p gray	.65	.30
198	A28	2p carmine rose	.65	.30
199	A28	3p blue green	.70	.40
		Size: 23½x28mm		
200	A29	5p violet blue	.70	.40
201	A29	10p orange brown	.75	.55
202	A29	15p olive	.95	.60
		Size: 38½x21, 21x38½mm		
203	A28	20p rose & brown	1.10	.60
204	A29	25p yel & brown	1.50	1.25
205	A29	50p ver, blk, & gray	2.50	1.25
206	A29	1k gray, ind & yel	17.50	1.25
207	A28	2k dull cit, ind & red	15.00	3.25
208	A29	5k yel, dk blue & red	30.00	14.00
		Nos. 197-208 (12)	72.00	24.15

For overprints see Nos. O92-O102.

Paddy Rice — A36

1969, Mar. 2		Litho.	Perf. 13	
209	A36	15p blue, emerald & yel	4.25	.30

Issued for Peasant's Day.

ILO Emblem A37

1969, Oct. 29			Photo.	
210	A37	15p dk blue grn & gold	.75	.25
211	A37	50p dp carmine & gold	1.75	.55

50th anniv. of the ILO.

824

BURMA

Soccer — A38

Designs: 25p, Runner, horiz. 50p, Weight lifter. 1k, Women's volleyball.

Perf. 12½x13, 13x12½

1969, Dec. 1 Litho.
212 A38 15p brt olive & multi .40 .25
213 A38 25p brown & multi .60 .25
214 A38 50p brt green & multi 1.30 .30
215 A38 1k blue, yel grn & blk 2.40 .50
Nos. 212-215 (4) 4.70 1.30

5th South East Asia Peninsular Games, Rangoon.

Burmese Flags and Marching Soldiers — A39

1970, Mar. 27 Perf. 13
216 A39 15p multicolored 2.50 .30
Issued for Armed Forces Day.

Solar System and UN Emblem A40

1970, June 26 Photo. Unwmk.
217 A40 15p lt ultra & multi 4.25 .40
25th anniversary of the United Nations.

Scroll, Marchers, Peacock Emblem — A41

Designs: 25p, Students' boycott demonstration. 50p, Banner and marchers at Shwedagon Camp.

1970, Nov. 23 Litho. Perf. 13
218 A41 15p ultra & multi .75 .25
219 A41 25p multicolored 1.25 .25
220 A41 50p lt blue & multi 2.00 .50
Nos. 218-220 (3) 4.00 1.00

50th National Day (Students' 1920 uprising).

Workers, Farmers, Technicians — A42

15p, Burmese of various races, & flags. 25p, Hands holding document. 50p, Red party flag.

1971, June 28 Litho. **Perf. 13½**
221 A42 5p blue & multi .75 .25
222 A42 15p blue & multi 1.25 .25
223 A42 25p blue & multi 1.50 .30
224 A42 50p blue & multi 2.00 .50
a. Souvenir sheet of 4, #221-224 22.50 22.50
Nos. 221-224 (4) 5.50 1.30

1st Congress of Burmese Socialist Program Party.

Child Drinking Milk — A43

UNICEF, 25th Anniv.: 50p, Marionettes.

1971, Dec. 11 **Perf. 14½**
225 A43 15p lt ultra & multi 1.25 .30
226 A43 50p emerald & multi 2.00 .60

Aung San, Independence Monument, Panglong — A44

Union Day, 25th Anniv.: 50p, Bogyoke Aung San and people in front of Independence Monument. 1k, Map of Burma with flag pointing to Panglong, vert.

1972, Feb. 12 Perf. 14
227 A44 15p ocher & multi .75 .25
228 A44 50p blue & multi 1.25 .35
229 A44 1k green, ultra & red 3.50 .65
Nos. 227-229 (3) 5.50 1.25

Burmese and Double Star A45

1972 Litho. Perf. 14
230 A45 15p bister & multi 2.10 .25
Revolutionary Council, 10th anniversary.

"Your Heart is your Health" — A46

1972, Apr. 7 Perf. 14x14½
231 A46 15p yellow, red & black 2.40 .30
World Health Day.

Burmese of Various Ethnic Groups A47

1973, Feb. 12 Litho. Perf. 14
232 A47 15p multicolored 2.40 .45
1973 census.

In 1973, the Government Security Printing Works located at Wazi assumed control of the production of Burma's postage stamps and bank notes. Unless otherwise mentioned, all subsequent issues were printed at that location. Collectors should note that the printing is often poor and the gauge of perforations may vary from the gauge stated in the catalogue listings.

Casting Vote — A48

Natl. Referendum: 10p, Voters holding map of Burma. 15p, Farmer & soldier holding ballots.

Perf. 14x14½, 14½x14
1973, Dec. 15 Litho.
233 A48 5p deep org & black .80 .25
234 A48 10p blue & multi .85 .30
235 A48 15p blue & multi, vert. .90 .45
Nos. 233-235 (3) 2.55 1.00

Open-air Meeting A49

Designs: 15p, Regional flags. 1k, Scales of justice and Burmese emblem.

1974, Mar. 2 Photo. **Perf. 13½**
Size: 80x26mm
236 A49 15p blue & multi 1.10 .30
Size: 37x25mm
237 A49 50p blue & multi 1.75 .50
238 A49 1k lt blue, bis & blk 2.65 .95
Nos. 236-238 (3) 5.50 1.75

First meeting of People's Assembly.

Carrier Pigeon and UPU Emblem A50

UPU Cent.: 20p, Mother reading letter to child, vert. 50p, Simulated block of stamps, vert. 1k, Burmese doll, vert. 2k, Mailman delivering letter to family.

1974, May 22 Perf. 13x13½, 13½x13
239 A50 15p grn, lt grn & org .75 .25
240 A50 20p multicolored 1.00 .25
241 A50 50p green & multi 1.75 .40
242 A50 1k ultra & multi 2.75 .75
243 A50 2k blue & multi 5.00 1.50
Nos. 239-243 (5) 11.25 3.15

Kachins A51 Man and Woman A52

Designs: 3p, Tribal woman. 5p, 15p, Man and woman. 10p, Tribal man and woman (like 1p). 50p, Woman with fan. 1k, Seated woman. 5k, Tribal man with drum.

Inscribed: Socialist Republic of the Union of Burma

Perf. 13, 13x13½ (#248-251)
1974-78 Photo.
244 A51 1p rose & lilac rose .55 .25
245 A51 3p dk brown & pink .70 .25

246 A51 5p pink & violet .75 .25
246A A51 10p Prus blue ('76) 1.00 .25
247 A51 15p lt grn & ol ('75) 1.00 .25
248 A52 20p lt blue & multi 1.50 .25
249 A52 50p ocher & multi 2.50 .50
250 A52 1k brt rose & multi .50 1.25
251 A52 5k ol green & multi 16.00 5.00
Nos. 244-251 (9) 29.00 8.25

For different country names see Nos. 298-303.

IWY Emblem, Woman and Globe A53

IWY: 2k, Symbolic flower, globe and IWY emblem, vert.

1975, Dec. 15 Photo. Perf. 13
252 A53 50p green & black 1.00 .30
253 A53 2k black & blue 3.75 1.10

Burmese with Raised Fists A54

Constitution Day: 50p, Demonstrators with banners and emblem. 1k, People and map of Burma, emblem.

1976, Jan. 3 Perf. 14
254 A54 20p blue & black 1.30 .25
255 A54 50p blue, blk & brn 1.70 .50
Size: 56x20mm
256 A54 1k blue & multi 4.00 1.00
Nos. 254-256 (3) 7.00 1.75

Students, Campaign Emblem — A55

Abacus A56

Intl. Literacy Year: 50p, Campaign emblem. 1k, Emblem, book and globe.

1976, Sept. 8 Photo. Perf. 14
257 A55 10p salmon & black .65 .30
258 A56 15p blue grn & multi .85 .45
259 A56 50p ultra, org & blk 2.00 .75
260 A55 1k multicolored 3.50 1.50
Nos. 257-260 (4) 7.00 3.00

Steam Locomotive A57

Diesel Train Emerging from Tunnel — A58

Cent. of Burma's Railroad: 20p, Early train and oxcart. 25p, Old and new trains approaching station. 50p, Railroad bridge.

1977, May 1   **Perf. 13½**
261 A57 15p multicolored   11.00   1.75

Size: 38x26, 26x38mm
262 A57 20p multicolored   3.50   .60
263 A57 25p multicolored   5.25   .85
264 A57 50p multicolored   6.50   1.75
265 A58 1k multicolored   15.00   2.50
    Nos. 261-265 (5)   41.25   7.45

Karaweik Pagoda A59

Design: 1k, Karaweik Pagoda, front view.

1977
266 A59 50p light brown   1.75   .55

Size: 78x25mm
267 A59 1k multicolored   4.25   .95

Jade Dragon — A60

Precious Jewelry: 20p, Gold bird with large pear in beak. 50p, Hand holding pearl necklace with pendant. 1k, Gold dragon, horiz.

1978   **Photo.**   **Perf. 13**
268 A60 15p green & yel grn   1.00   .25
269 A60 20p multicolored   2.00   .35
270 A60 50p multicolored   4.00   .75

Size: 55x20mm
Perf. 14
271 A60 1k multicolored   9.00   1.50
    Nos. 268-271 (4)   16.00   2.85

Satellite over Map of Asia A61

1979, Feb., 12   **Photo.**   **Perf. 13**
272 A61 25p multicolored   4.25   .60

IYC Emblem in Map of Burma — A62

1979, Dec.   **Photo.**   **Perf. 13½**
273 A62 25p multicolored   1.25   .30
274 A62 50p multicolored   3.25   .60
   International Year of the Child.

Weather Balloon, WMO Emblem — A63

50p, Weather satellite, cloud.

1980, Mar. 23   **Photo.**   **Perf. 13½**
275 A63 25p shown   1.25   .25
276 A63 50p red, grn & blk   2.75   .45
   World Meteorological Day.

Weight Lifting, Olympic Rings A64

1980, Dec.   **Litho.**   **Perf. 14**
277 A64 20p Weight lifting   .85   .25
278 A64 50p Boxing   1.50   .40
279 A64 1k Soccer   2.40   .65
    Nos. 277-279 (3)   4.75   1.30
22nd Summer Olympic Games, Moscow, July 19-Aug. 3.

13th World Telecommunications Day — A65

1981, May 17   **Photo.**   **Perf. 13½**
280 A65 25p orange & black   3.75   .40

World Food Day A66

25p, Livestock, produce. 50p, Farmer, rice, produce. 1k, Emblems.

1981, Oct. 16   **Photo.**   **Perf. 13½**
281 A66 25p multi   1.25   .25
282 A66 50p multi   2.50   .45
283 A66 1k multi   3.25   .85
    Nos. 281-283 (3)   7.00   1.55

Intl. Year of the Disabled A67

1981, Dec. 12
284 A67 25p multicolored   3.00   .35

World Communications Year — A68

1983, Sept. 15   **Litho.**   **Perf. 14½x14**
285 A68 15p pale blue & black   .55   .25
286 A68 25p dull lake & black   1.00   .30
287 A68 50p grn, pale grn, blk & lake   2.50   .65
288 A68 1k buff, blk, beige & yel grn   4.00   .95
    Nos. 285-288 (4)   8.05   2.15

Fish, Ship, Globe, FAO Emblem — A69

1983, Oct. 16   **Photo.**   **Perf. 14x14½**
289 A69 15p brt blue, bister & blk   .75   .25
290 A69 25p yel grn, pale org & blk   1.25   .30
291 A69 50p org, pale grn & blk   2.75   .95
292 A69 1k yel, ultra & black   4.75   1.75
    Nos. 289-292 (4)   9.50   3.25
   World Food Day.

Stylized Trees, Hemispheres and Log — A70

1984, Oct. 16   **Perf. 14½x14**
293 A70 15p org, black & blue   .80   .25
294 A70 25p pale yel, blk & lt vio   1.20   .30
295 A70 50p pale pink, blk & lt grn   2.00   1.20
296 A70 1k yel, blk & lt rose vio   4.50   2.50
    Nos. 293-296 (4)   8.50   4.25
   World Food Day.

Intl. Youth Year — A71

1985, Oct. 15   **Perf. 14x14½**
297 A71 15p multicolored   2.40   .30

Types of 1974
Inscribed: Union of Burma

1989   **Photo.**   **Perf. 13½**
298 A51 15p olive & lt green   .80   .30
298A A52 20p lt blue & multi   *60.00*
299 A52 50p violet & brown   1.90   .75
300 A52 1k multicolored   3.00   1.25
    Nos. 298,299-300 (3)   5.70   2.30
Issued: 15p, 6/26; 50p, 6/12; 1k, 9/6.
No. 298A was prepared but not issued. A quantity was accidentally supplied to the Shan State post office in July 1995, and these stamps were sold to the public. A limited quantity was subsequently made available to collectors in Yangon.

UNION OF MYANMAR
Inscribed: Union of Myanmar

1990-91   **Photo.**   **Perf. 13½**
301 A51 15p olive & lt green   .80   .30
301A A52 20p brn, grnsh blue & blk ('91)   *30.00*
302 A52 50p violet & brown   2.00   .55
303 A52 1k multicolored   3.00   1.25
   Issued: 15p, May 26; 50p, May 12.

Fountain, Natl. Assembly Park — A74

1990, May 27   **Litho.**   **Perf. 14½x14**
304 A74 1k multicolored   6.50   1.25
State Law and Order Restoration Council.

A75

1990, Dec. 20   **Litho.**   **Perf. 14x14½**
305 A75 2k multicolored   7.00   1.75
   UN Development Program, 40th anniv.

Nawata Ruby — A76

1991, Jan. 26
306 A76 50p multi   7.50   1.25

Painting of Freedom Fighters — A77

Bronze Statue — A78

1992, Jan. 4   **Litho.**   **Perf. 14x14½**
307 A77 50p multicolored   1.00   .60
308 A78 2k multicolored   3.50   2.00

National Sports Festival — A79

1992, Apr. 10   **Litho.**   **Perf. 14x14½**
309 A79 50p multicolored   2.25   .60

A80

1992, Dec. 1   **Litho.**   **Perf. 14x14½**
310 A80 50p red   2.75   .50
   World Campaign Against AIDS.

A81

1992, Dec. 5   Litho.   Perf. 14x14½
Background Color
311 A81 50p pink .75 .30
312 A81 1k yellow 1.25 .65
313 A81 3k orange 3.50 1.50
314 A81 5k green 6.50 2.50
Nos. 311-314 (4) 12.00 4.95
Intl. Conference on Nutrition, Rome.

Artifacts — A82

1993, Sept. 1   Litho.   Perf. 14x14½
315 A82 5k Golden goose
(Hintha) 6.00 2.00
316 A82 10k Lawkanatt 12.00 4.50

Natl.
Constitutional
Convention
A83

1993, Jan. 1   Litho.   Perf. 14x14½
317 A83 50p multicolored .75 .30
318 A83 3k multicolored 3.75 1.50

Equestrian Festival — A84

1993, Oct. 23   Litho.   Perf. 14½x14
319 A84 3k multicolored 5.50 1.50

Environment
Day — A85

1994, June 5   Litho.   Perf. 14
320 A85 4k multicolored 5.50 2.00

A86

1994, Sept. 15   Litho.   Perf. 14
321 A86 3k multicolored 5.00 2.00
Union of Solidarity & Development, 1st anniv.

Armed
Forces,
50th
Anniv.
A87

1995, Mar. 27   Litho.   Perf. 14½x14
322 A87 50p multicolored 1.50 .50

Prevent Drug
Abuse — A88

1995, June 26   Litho.   Perf. 14
323 A88 2k multicolored 3.50 1.50

A89

1995, Oct. 17   Litho.   Perf. 14x14½
324 A89 50p multicolored 2.00 .50
Myanmar motion pictures, 60th anniv.

UN, 50th
Anniv. — A90

1995, Oct. 24
325 A90 4k multicolored 6.25 3.25

A91

1995, Nov. 1
326 A91 50p pink & multi .80 .50
327 A91 2k green & multi 3.25 1.75
University of Yangon (Rangoon), 75th anniv.

Visit
Myanmar
Year
A92

Designs: 50p, Couple in boat on Inlay Lake
with food bowl for Buddha, Buddhist monks.
4k, Decorated royal barge on Kandawgyi
(Royal Lake), Yangoon. 5k, Royal moat,
entrance of Yadanabon (Mandalay), vert.

Perf. 14½x14, 14x14½
1996, Mar. 1   Litho.
328 A92 50p multicolored .85 .50
329 A92 4k multicolored 5.50 3.00
330 A92 5k multicolored 7.00 4.00
Nos. 328-330 (3) 13.35 7.50

UNICEF, 50th
Anniv. — A93

Stylized designs: 1k, Mother breastfeeding.
2k, Vaccinating child. 4k, Girls going to school.

1996, Dec. 11   Litho.   Perf. 14x14½
331 A93 1k multicolored 1.40 1.00
332 A93 2k multicolored 2.75 2.00
333 A93 4k multicolored 5.50 3.00
Nos. 331-333 (3) 9.65 6.00

Intl. Letter
Writing
Week
A94

Designs: 2k, Men in canoe. 5k, Stylized
figures forming pyramid, flag, map, vert.

1996, Oct. 7   Perf. 14½x14, 14x14½
334 A94 2k multicolored 2.50 2.00
335 A94 5k multicolored 5.00 4.00

A95

1997, July 24   Litho.   Perf. 14x14½
336 A95 1k blue & multi 1.50 1.50
337 A95 2k yellow & multi 3.00 3.00
Assoc. of Southeast Asian Nations
(ASEAN), 30th anniv.

A96

1998, Jan. 4   Litho.   Perf. 14x14½
338 A96 2k multicolored 3.50 3.50
Independence, 50th anniv.

Musical
Instruments
A97

5k, Xylophone. 10k, Mon brass gongs. 20k,
Rakhine (drum). 30k, Harp. 50k, Shan pot
drum. 100k, Kachin brass gong.

1998-2001   Photo.   Perf. 13¼
339 A97 5k multicolored 1.00 .60
340 A97 10k multicolored 1.25 1.00
341 A97 20k multicolored 2.00 1.75
342 A97 30k multicolored 3.25 2.75
343 A97 50k multicolored 6.00 5.00
344 A97 100k multicolored 8.00 6.50
Nos. 339-344 (6) 21.50 17.60
Caution: Market prices for Nos. 339-344
have been speculative for the past 10 years.
Issued: 5k, 8/28; 10k, 10/9; 20k, 2/12/99;
30k, 4/18/01; 50k, 11/15/99; 100k, 2/12/00.
See No. 413.

Decade of
Disabled Persons
(1993-2002)
A98

1999, Jan. 10   Litho.   Perf. 14
345 A98 2k yellow & multi 2.50 2.00
346 A98 5k apple green & multi 5.00 4.00

UPU, 125th
Anniv. — A99

1999, Dec. 20   Litho.   Perf. 14x14¼
347 A99 2k blue & multi 2.75 2.00
348 A99 5k purple & multi 5.25 4.00

Independence,
52nd
Anniv. — A100

2000, Jan. 4
349 A100 2k multi 3.50 3.50

World Meteorological Day — A101

Perf. 14x14¼, 14¼x14
2000, Mar. 23   Photo.
350 A101 2k Anemometer,
vert. 2.50 2.50
351 A101 5k shown 6.00 6.00
352 A101 10k Cloud, sun 11.00 11.00
Nos. 350-352 (3) 19.50 19.50

Diplomatic Relations with People's
Republic of China, 50th Anniv. — A102

2000, June 8   Litho.   Perf. 14¼x14
353 A102 5k multi   9.00 9.00

Myanmar postal officials have
declared as "illegal" the following items
inscribed "Union of Myanmar."
Sheets of nine stamps of various
denominations depicting:
Personalities of the 20th Century,
Musical stars, Orchids with Rotary
emblems, Mushrooms with Rotary
emblems, Cats and dogs with Scout
emblems, Chess, Fish, Owls, and
Trains (two different).
Sheets of six stamps of various
denominations depicting:
Bruce Lee, Horror movie scenes, and
Marilyn Monroe (two different).
Souvenir sheets of two stamps of
various denominations depicting:
Formula 1 race cars (two different),
Golfers (six different), and Classic cars
(eight different).
Souvenir sheets of one depicting:
Dutch royal wedding, Bruce Lee
(three different), Tiger Woods (three dif-
ferent), Impressionist paintings (six dif-
ferent), Elvis Presley (six different), and
Chess (twelve different).

Campaign
Against
Drugs — A103

2000, June 26   Litho.   Perf. 14x14¼
354 A103 2k multi   3.75 3.75

Independence,
53rd
Anniv. — A104

2001, Jan. 4
355 A104 2k multi   4.00 4.00

Independence,
54th
Anniv. — A105

Inscriptions in: (2k), Burmese. 30k, English.

2002, Jan. 4
356-357 A105   Set of 2   13.00 13.00

Independence,
55th
Anniv. — A106

Inscriptions in: (2k), Burmese. 30k, English.

2003, Jan. 4
358-359 A106   Set of 2   12.00 12.00

Flora — A107

Designs: No. 360, 30k, Black orchide. No.
361, 30k, Mango.

2004, Feb. 11
360-361 A107   Set of 2   10.00 10.00

FIFA (Fédération Internationale de
Football Association), Cent. — A108

2004, May 5   Perf. 14¼x14
362 A108 2k multi   5.00 5.00

World Buddhist Summit — A109

Designs: 5k, Emblem, temples. 30k,
Emblem, temples, diff.

2004, Dec. 9   Litho.   Perf. 14¼x14
363-364 A109   Set of 2   6.25 6.25

Myanmar postal authorities have
declared overprints of No. 362 with Burmese inscriptions for the 2006 World
Cup to be illegal.

Independence,
59th
Anniv. — A110

Statues, star and: (2k), Flag, Burmese
inscriptions. 5k, Map, English inscriptions.

2007, Jan. 4   Litho.   Perf. 14x14¼
365-366 A110   Set of 2   4.00 4.00

A111

A112

National Convention — A113

2007, Aug. 13   Litho.   Perf. 14¼x14
367 A111 20k multi   1.25 1.25
368 A112 30k multi   2.50 2.50
369 A113 50k multi   3.00 3.00
      Nos. 367-369 (3)   6.75 6.75

Miniature Sheet

ASEAN Joint Stamp Issue

Association of South East Asian
Nations (ASEAN), 40th Anniv. — A114

No. 370: a, Secretariat Building, Bandar
Seri Begawan, Brunei. b, National Museum of
Cambodia. c, Fatahillah Museum, Jakarta,
Indonesia. d, Typical house, Laos. e, Malayan
Railway Headquarters Building, Kuala
Lumpur, Malaysia. f, Yangon Post Office,
Myanmar. g, Malacañang Palace, Philippines.
h, National Museum of Singapore. i,
Vimanmek Mansion, Bangkok, Thailand. j,
Presidential Palace, Hanoi, Viet Nam.

2007, Oct. 19
370 A114 50k Sheet of 10,
            #a-j   18.50 18.50

See Brunei No. 607, Cambodia No. 2339,
Indonesia Nos. 2120-2121, Laos Nos. 1717-
1718, Malaysia No. 1170, Philippines Nos.
3103-3105, Singapore No. 1265, Thailand No.
2315, and Viet Nam Nos. 3302-3311.

A115

Independence, 60th Anniv. — A116

2008, Jan. 4   Litho.   Perf. 14¼x14
371 A115 50k multi   2.00 2.00
372 A116 100k multi   3.25 3.25

Constitutional Referendum — A117

Designs: No. 373, 100k, Map of Burma,
people, statues, ballot box. No. 374, 100k,
Line of people casting ballots, statues. 200k,
Map of Burma, hand depositing ballot, vert.

Perf. 14¼x14, 14x14¼
2008, May 9   Litho.
373-375 A117   Set of 3   6.00 6.00

A118

Independence, 61st Anniv. — A119

2009, Jan. 4   Litho.   Perf. 14¼x14
376 A118 200k multi   4.00 4.00
377 A119 300k multi   6.00 6.00

The values for the stamps are based
on official exchange rates set by the
Myanmar government. Actual exchange
rates appear to differ significantly.

A120

Independence, 62nd Anniv. — A121

2010, Jan. 4   Litho.   Perf. 14¼x14
378 A120 100k multi   7.00 7.00
379 A121 200k multi   7.00 7.00

Diplomatic Relations Between
Myanmar and People's Republic of
China, 60th Anniv. — A122

2010, June 8   Litho.   Perf. 14¼x14
380 A122 100k multi   4.00 4.00

General Elections — A123

2010, Nov. 7
381 A123 500k multi   3.00 3.00

Souvenir Sheet

Vienna Convention for the Protection
of the Ozone Layer, 25th
Anniv. — A124

2010, Nov. 18
382 A124 100k multi   5.00 5.00

Independence, 63rd Anniv. — A125

2011, Jan. 4   Litho.   Perf. 14¼x14
383 A125 100k multi   5.00 5.00

Union Assembly Building — A126

President's Office Building — A127

2011, June 16   Litho.   Perf. 14¼x14
384 A126 500k multi   7.00 7.00
385 A127 500k multi   7.00 7.00
Celebrating the renaming of the country as
the Republic of the Union of Myanmar.

A128

Independence, 64th Anniv. — A129

2012, Jan. 4
386 A128 500k multi   3.00 3.00
387 A129 1200k multi   7.00 7.00

Miniature Sheet

11th ASEAN Telecommunications and
Information Technology Ministers
Meeting, Nay Pyi Taw — A130

No. 388: a, 100k, Line of flags, emblem,
building. b, 100k, Circle of flags around
emblem, building. c, 100k, Emblem, buildings
in circle. d, 200k, Like #388a. e, 200k, Like
#388b. f, 200k, Like #388c.

2012, Mar. 19
388 A130 Sheet of 6, #a-f   7.00 7.00

A131

Second Leaders Retreat of Asian
Telecommunications Senior Officials
and Asian Telecommunications
Regulators Council, Bangkok,
Thailand — A132

2012, Oct. 1
389 A131 500k multi   5.00 5.00
390 A132 500k multi   5.00 5.00

A133

Independence, 65th Anniv. — A134

2013, Jan. 4
391 A133 100k multi   2.75 2.75
392 A134 100k multi   2.75 2.75

Diplomatic Relations Between
Myanmar and Russia, 65th
Anniv. — A135

2013, Apr. 10
393 A135 500k multi   3.50 3.50

Miniature Sheet

27th South East Asia Games,
Naypyidaw — A136

No. 394: a, 100k, Emblem of 2013 Games.
b, 100k, Owl holding torch. c, 100k, Two owls.
d, 100k, Six owls. e, 500k, Like #394a. f, 500k,
Like #394b. g, 500k, Like #394c. h, 500k, Like
#394d.

2013, Sept. 2   Litho.   Perf. 14¼x14
394 A136 Sheet of 8, #a-h   14.00 14.00

A137

A138

Independence, 66th Anniv. — A139

2014, Jan. 4   Litho.   Perf. 14¼x14
395 A137 100k multi   2.25 2.25
396 A138 200k multi   4.50 4.50

Souvenir Sheet
397 A139 100k multi   4.25 4.25

A140

A141

Census — A142

2014, Feb. 24   Litho.   Perf. 14¼x14
398 A140 200k multi   1.75 1.75

English Text
399 A141 200k green & multi   1.75 1.75
400 A141 200k blue & multi   1.75 1.75

Burmese Text
401 A142 200k green & multi   1.75 1.75
402 A142 200k blue & multi   1.75 1.75
     Nos. 398-402 (5)   8.75 8.75

A143

A144

A145

Census
A146

2014, Mar. 10   Litho.   Perf. 14x14¼
403 A143 100k multi   1.75 1.75

Perf. 14¼x14
404 A144 100k multi   1.75 1.75

English Text
405 A145 100k green & multi   1.75 1.75
406 A145 100k blue & multi   1.75 1.75

Burmese Text
407 A146 100k green & multi   1.75 1.75
408 A146 100k blue & multi   1.75 1.75
     Nos. 403-408 (6)   10.50 10.50

A147

2014 ASEAN Summit,
Naypyidaw — A148

2014, May 8   Litho.   Perf. 14¼x14
409 A147 100k multi   2.60 2.60
410 A148 100k multi   2.60 2.60

Announcement of Five Principles of
Peaceful Co-existence Between
Burma, China and India, 60th
Anniv. — A149

Temple, Myanmar, Great Wall of China and
Taj Mahal with background color of: 100k,
Green. 500k, Orange brown.

2014, June 28   Litho.   Perf. 14¼x14
411-412 A149 Set of 2   7.25 7.25

**Musical Instrument Type of 1998-
2000 Inscribed "Republic of the
Union of Myanmar"**

2014 ?   Litho.   Perf. 14x14¼
413 A97 100k Kachin brass gong 1.60 1.60

A150

A151

A152

Independence, 67th Anniv. — A152

2015, Jan. 4   Litho.   Perf. 14¼x14
414 A150 100k multi   2.00 2.00
415 A151 100k multi   2.00 2.00
416 A152 200k multi   4.00 4.00
    Nos. 414-416 (3)   8.00 8.00

ASEAN Emblem and
Flags — A153

Denominations: 100k, 500k.

2015, Aug. 8   Litho.   Perf. 14¼x14
417-418 A153 Set of 2   9.00 9.00

See Brunei No. 656, Cambodia No. , Indo-
nesia No. 2428, Laos No. , Malaysia No. 1562,
Philippines No. 3619, Singapore No. 1742,
Thailand No. 2875, Viet Nam No. 3529.

K 100
A154

K100
A155

K 100
K 200

Independence, 68th
Anniv. — A156

2016, Jan. 4   Litho.   Perf. 14¼x14
419 A154 100k multi   2.00 2.00
420 A155 100k multi   2.00 2.00
421 A156 200k multi   4.00 4.00
    Nos. 419-421 (3)   8.00 8.00

100 K   MYANMAR
A157

K 200
A158

500 K   MYANMAR
A159

Union Peace Conference,
Naypyidaw — A159

2016, Aug. 29   Litho.   Perf. 14¼x14
422 A157 100k multi   1.50 1.50
423 A158 200k multi   3.00 3.00
424 A159 500k multi   7.50 7.50
    Nos. 422-424 (3)   12.00 12.00

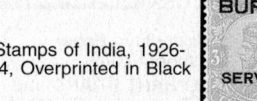

K 500

Bogyoke Aung
San (1915-47),
Politician — A162

2017, Mar. 17   Litho.   Perf. 14x14¼
428 A162 500k multi   7.00 7.00

Ministry of Foreign Affairs, 70th anniv.

OFFICIAL STAMPS

Stamps of India, 1926-
34, Overprinted in Black

1937   Wmk. 196   Perf. 14
O1 A46 3p gray   2.75 .25
O2 A71 ½a green   14.00 .30
O3 A68 9p dark green   4.75 1.00
O4 A72 1a dark brown   7.00 .35
O5 A49 2a vermilion   14.00 .40
O6 A57 2a6p buff   7.00 3.75
O7 A52 4a olive grn   7.00 .35

O8 A53 6a bister   7.00 12.00
O9 A54 8a red violet   7.00 2.00
O10 A55 12a claret   7.00 10.00

Overprinted

O11 A56 1r green & brown   17.50 9.00
O12 A56 2r buff & car rose 35.00 60.00
O13 A56 5r dk vio & ultra 120.00 85.00
O14 A56 10r car & green   300.00 240.00
    Nos. O1-O14 (14)   550.00 425.00
    Set, never hinged   775.00

For overprint see No. 1N27.

Regular Issue of 1938
Overprinted in Black

1939   Wmk. 254   Perf. 14
O15 A1 3p violet   .30 .30
O16 A1 6p ultramarine   .30 .30
O17 A1 9p yel green   3.50 3.50
O18 A2 1a brown violet   .30 .35
O19 A2 1½a turquoise green 3.25 2.00
O20 A2 2a carmine   1.00 .30
O21 A2 4a slate blue   3.50 3.50

Overprinted

Perf. 13½x13
O22 A3 2a6p rose lake   17.00 17.00
O23 A6 8a slate green   15.00 5.00
Perf. 14
O24 A7 1r brt ultra & dk
          vio   15.00 6.00
O25 A7 2r dk vio & red
          brn   30.00 15.00
O26 A8 5r car & dull vio 25.00 40.00
O27 A8 10r gray grn & brn 110.00 50.00
    Nos. O15-O27 (13)   224.15 143.25
    Set, never hinged   375.00

For overprints see Nos. 1N12-1N16, 1N31-
1N36, 1NO1.

> **Catalogue values for unused
> stamps in this section, from this
> point to the end of the section, are
> for Never Hinged items.**

**Nos. 51-56, 60 Overprinted Like
Nos. O15-O21**
1946   Perf. 13½x14
O28 A1 3p brown   3.75 2.75
O29 A1 6p violet   2.75 2.00
O30 A1 9p dull green   .70 3.50
O31 A2 1a deep blue   .30 2.25
O32 A2 1½a salmon   .30 .35
O33 A2 2a rose lake   .35 2.25
O34 A2 4a rose lilac   .35 .90

**Nos. 57, 61-65 Ovptd.
Like Nos. O22-O27**
Perf. 13, 13½
O35 A3 2a6p greenish blue 2.50 4.75
O38 A6 8a deep magenta   4.50 2.50
O39 A7 1r dp mag & dk
          vio   1.90 3.75
O40 A7 2r salmon & red
          brn   10.00 35.00
O41 A8 5r red brn & dk
          grn   19.00 45.00
O42 A8 10r dk violet & car 20.00 65.00
    Nos. O28-O42 (13)   66.40 170.00

Nos. O28 to
O42
Overprinted
in Black

1947
O43 A1 3p brown   2.00 .45
O44 A1 6p violet   4.00 .25
O45 A1 9p dull green   7.00 1.20
O46 A2 1a deep blue   7.00 1.00
O47 A2 1½a salmon   10.00 .40
O48 A2 2a rose lake   7.00 .30
O49 A3 2a6p greenish bl 35.00 15.00
O50 A6 4a rose lilac   24.00 .50
O51 A6 8a dp magenta   24.00 4.50
O52 A7 1r dp mag & dk
          vio   20.00 3.00
O53 A7 2r sal & red brn 20.00 22.50
O54 A8 5r red brn & dk
          grn   20.00 22.50
O55 A8 10r dk vio & car 20.00 35.00
    Nos. O43-O55 (13)   200.00 106.60

The overprint is slightly larger on Nos. O49
and O51 to O55. The Burmese characters
read "Interim Government."

Issues of the Republic

Nos. 102-106, 109-115
Overprinted in Carmine
or Black

a. Overprint 13mm long.
b. Overprint 15mm long.
1949   Unwmk.   Perf. 12½, 13
O56 A15(a) 3p ultra (C)   1.25 .25
O57 A15(a) 6p green (C)   .50 .25
O58 A15(a) 9p carmine   .50 .25
O59 A16(a) 1a red orange   .50 .25
O60 A17(a) 2a orange   .60 .25
O61 A18(b) 3a6p dk sl grn (C) .60 .25
O62 A18(a) 4a chocolate   .60 .25
O63 A18(b) 8a carmine   .60 .25
O64 A19(b) 1r blue green
              (C)   1.25 .25
O65 A19(b) 2r dp blue (C)   2.60 1.00
O66 A19(b) 5r chocolate   8.00 2.50
O67 A19(b) 10r orange red   22.50 6.00
    Nos. O56-O67 (12)   39.50 11.75

**Same Overprint in Black on Nos.
139-142, 144-152**
Perf. 14x13½, 13, 14
1954-57   Wmk. 254
O68 A15(a) 1p brown org   .30 .25
O69 A15(a) 2p plum   .30 .25
O70 A15(a) 3p blue   .30 .25
O71 A16(a) 5p ultra   .30 .25
O72 A17(a) 15p green   .30 .25
O72A A18(b) 20p ver ('57)   .50 .25
O73 A18(b) 25p lt red org   .50 .25
O74 A16(a) 30p vermilion   .50 .25
O75 A18(b) 50p blue   1.25 .30
O76 A19(b) 1k rose violet   1.75 .40
O77 A19(b) 2p dk blue   4.25 .75
O78 A19(b) 5k ultra   7.00 1.25
O79 A19(b) 10k light blue 22.50 3.50
    Nos. O68-O79 (13)   39.75 8.20

No. 141 Ovptd.   *Service*

1964   Litho.   Perf. 14
O80 A15 3p blue   20.00 12.50

Nos. 139, 141-142, 144,
177-179, 181, 183
Ovptd.

1964-65   Overprint: 11½mm
O81 A15 1p brown orange   8.00 1.00
O82 A28 2p carmine rose
          ('65)   7.00 1.00
O83 A15 3p blue   8.00 1.00
O84 A28 3p blue green ('65) 8.00 1.00
O85 A16 5p ultramarine   8.00 1.00
O86 A28 5p violet blue ('65) 7.00 1.00
O87 A17 15p green   8.00 1.00
O88 A28 15p olive ('65)   7.00 1.00
O89 A29 25p yel & brn ('65) 8.00 1.00
    Nos. O81-O89 (9)   68.00 9.00

အစိုးရတိန္ဓ   အစိုးရကိစ္စ
#176-178   #181
Ovptd.   Ovptd.

1966   **Overprint: 15mm**
O90 A28 1p black   11.00 3.00
O91 A28 2p carmine rose   11.00 3.00
O92 A28 3p blue green   11.00 3.00
                            Overprint: 12mm
O93 A29 15p olive   11.00 3.00

Nos. 176-179, 181-187 Overprinted in Black or Red

1967 Unwmk. Photo. Perf. 13½
Overprint: 15mm
Size: 25x21mm
O94 A28 1p gray   .50   .40
O95 A28 2p carmine rose   .90   .50
O96 A28 3p blue green   .90   .65
Size: 22x26½mm
O97 A29 5p violet blue   1.10 .70
O98 A29 15p olive   1.10 .80
Size: 35x25mm
O99 A28 20p rose & brown   2.00 .90
Size: 27x36½mm, 36½x27mm
O100 A29 25p yel & brown (R)   2.50 1.00
O101 A29 50p red, blk & gray   4.00 1.25
O102 A29 1k gray, ind & yel (R)   9.25 1.90
O103 A28 2k pale ol, ind & red (R) 15.50 3.00
O104 A29 5k cit, dk bl & red   40.00 15.00
   Nos. O94-O104 (11)   77.75 26.10

Similar Overprint on Nos. 197-200, 202-208 in Black or Red
1968   Perf. 14
Size: 21x17mm
Overprint: 13mm
O105 A28 1p gray   .50   .25
O106 A28 2p carmine rose   1.00   .25
O107 A28 3p blue green   1.10   .40
Size: 23½x28mm
Overprint: 15mm
O108 A29 5p violet blue   1.25   .40
O109 A29 15p olive   1.25   .40
Size: 38½x21mm, 21x38½mm
Overprint: 14mm
O110 A28 20p rose & brn   2.00   .50
O111 A29 25p yel & brown (R)   4.00   .50
O112 A29 50p ver, blk & gray   5.00   .75
O113 A29 1k gray, ind & yel (R)   7.75 1.00
O114 A28 2k dl cit, ind & red   12.50 2.00
O115 A29 5k yel, dk bl & red (R) 19.00 5.75
   Nos. O105-O115 (11)   55.35 12.20

OCCUPATION STAMPS

Issued by Burma Independence Army (in conjunction with Japanese occupation officials)

Henzada Issue
Stamps of Burma, 1937-40, Overprinted in Black Blue, or Red; Nos. 1, 3, 5 Overprinted in Blue or Black

Henzada Type I

1942, May   Wmk. 196   Perf. 14
1N1 A46 3p slate   5.00 25.00
1N2 A68 9p dark green   30.00 80.00
1N3 A49 2a vermilion   130.00 225.00
On 1938-40 George VI Issue
Perf. 13½x14
Wmk. 254
1N4 A1 1p red orange   275.00 400.00
1N5 A1 3p violet   47.50 95.00
1N6 A1 6p ultra   30.00 65.00

1N7   A1 9p yel green   1,100.
1N8   A1 1a brown violet   11.00 50.00
1N9   A2 1½a turq green   25.00 85.00
1N10 A2 2a carmine   25.00 85.00
1N11 A2 4a slate blue   50.00 120.00
On Official Stamps of 1939
1N12 A1 3p violet   150.00 300.00
1N13 A1 6p ultra   175.00 300.00
1N14 A2 1½a turq green   200.00 350.00
1N15 A2 2a carmine   425.00 550.00
1N16 A2 4a slate blue   1,350.

Authorities believe this overprint was officially applied only to postal stationery and that the adhesive stamps existing with it were not regularly issued. It has been called "Henzada Type II."

Myaungmya Issue
1937 George V Issue Overprinted in Black

Myaungmya Type I

1942, May   Wmk. 196   Perf. 14
1N25 A68 9p dk green   130.00
1N26 A70 3a6p deep blue   85.00
On Official Stamp of 1937, No. O8
1N27 A53 6a bister   95.00
On 1938-40 George VI Issue
Perf. 13½x14
Wmk. 254
1N28 A1 9p yel green   175.00
1N29 A2 1a brown vio   650.00
1N30 A2 4a sl blue (blk ovpt. over red) 190.00
On Official Stamps of 1939
1N31 A1 3p violet   42.50 110.00
1N32 A1 6p ultra   27.00 80.00
1N33 A2 1a brown vio   28.00 65.00
1N34 A2 1½a turq green   900.00 1,350.
1N35 A2 2a carmine   40.00 120.00
1N36 A2 4a slate blue   40.00 95.00

1938-40 George VI Issue Overprinted

Myaungmya Type II

1942, May
1N37 A1 3p violet   22.00 90.00
1N38 A1 6p ultra   60.00 130.00
1N39 A1 9p yel green   27.00 85.00
1N40 A2 1a brown vio   17.50 80.00
1N41 A2 2a carmine   32.50 100.00
1N42 A2 4a slate blue   60.00 130.00

Nos. 30-31 Overprinted

Myaungmya Type III

1N43 A7 1r brt ultra & dk vio 450.00 750.00
1N44 A7 2r dk vio & red brn   275.00 550.00

Pyapon Issue

No. 5 and 1938-40 George VI Issue Overprinted

1942, May
1N45 A1 6p ultra   100.00
1N46 A2 1a brown vio   120.00 300.00
1N47 A49 2a vermilion   100.00
1N48 A2 2a carmine   160.00 350.00
1N49 A2 4a slate blue   850.00 850.00
   Nos. 1N45-1N49 (5)   1,330.
   Nos. 1N47-1N49 are valued in faulty condition.
   Counterfeits of the peacock overprints exist.

OCCUPATION OFFICIAL STAMP

Myaungmya Issue
Burma No. O23 Overprinted in Black

1942, May   Wmk. 254   Perf. 13
1NO1 A6 8a slate green   110.00 300.00
Overprint characters translate: "Office use." Two types of overprint differ mainly in base of peacock which is either 5mm or 8mm.

ISSUED UNDER JAPANESE OCCUPATION

Yano Seal — OS1

Wmk. ABSORBO DUPLICATOR and Outline of Elephant in Center of Sheet
Handstamped
1942, June 1   Perf. 12x11
Without Gum
2N1 OS1 1(a) vermilion   75.00 120.00
This stamp is the handstamped impression of the personal chop or seal of Shizuo Yano, chairman of the committee appointed to re-establish the Burmese postal system. It was prepared in Rangoon on paper captured from the Burma Government Offices. Not every stamp shows a portion of the watermark.

Farmer Plowing — OS2

Vertically Laid Paper
Without Gum
Wmk. ELEPHANT BRAND and Outline of Trumpeting Elephant Covering Several Stamps
1942, June 15   Litho.   Perf. 11x12
2N2 OS2 1a scarlet   30.00 35.00
   See illustration OS4.

Same, Surcharged with New Value
1942, Oct. 15
2N3 OS2 5c on 1a scarlet   26.00 30.00

Stamps of Japan, 1937-42, as shown, Handstamp Surcharged with New Value in Black

½A.   1R.

Rice Harvest A83

General Nogi A84

Power Plant A85

Admiral Togo A86

Diamond Mountains, Korea — A89

Meiji Shrine, Tokyo — A90

Yomei Gate, Nikko — A91

Mount Fuji and Cherry Blossoms A94

Torii of Miyajima Shrine — A96

1942, Sept.   Wmk. 257   Perf. 13
2N4   A83 ¼a on 1s fawn   50.00 52.50
2N5   A84 1a on 2s crim   55.00 55.00
2N6   A85 ¾a on 3s green   85.00 90.00
2N7   A86 1a on 5s brn lake   82.50 72.50
2N8   A89 3a on 7s dp green   130.00 150.00
2N9   A86 4a on 4s dk green   65.00 72.50
 a. 4a on 4s + 2s dk green (#B5) 190.00 200.00
2N10 A90 8a on 8s dk pur & pale vio 180.00 180.00
 a. Red surcharge   300.00 325.00
2N11 A91 1r on 10s lake   29.00 37.50
2N12 A94 2r on 20s ultra   60.00 60.00
 a. Red surcharge   60.00 60.00
2N13 A96 5r on 30s pck bl   19.00 32.50
 a. Red surcharge   30.00 37.50
   Nos. 2N4-2N13 (10)   755.50 802.50
Numerous double, inverted, etc., surcharges exist.

Re-surcharged in Black

15 C.

1942, Oct. 15
2N14 A83 1c on ¼a on 1s   65.00 65.00
2N15 A84 2c on ½a on 2s   65.00 65.00
2N16 A85 3c on ¾a on 3s   65.00 65.00
 a. "3C." in blue   225.00
2N17 A86 5c on 1a on 5s   90.00 77.50
2N18 A89 10c on 3a on 7s   170.00 150.00

2N19	A86	15c on 4a on 4s	.55.00	60.00
2N20	A90	20c on 8a on 8s (#2N10)	900.00	750.00
a.		On #2N10a	400.00	200.00
		Nos. 2N14-2N20 (7)	1,410.	1,233.

No. 2N16a was issued in the Shan States. Done locally, numerous different handstamps of each denomination can exist.

Stamps of Japan, 1937-42, Handstamp Surcharged with New Value in Black

15 C.

1942, Oct. 15

2N21	A83	1c on 1s fawn	40.00	24.00
2N22	A84	2c on 2s crim	65.00	45.00
2N23	A85	3c on 3s green	100.00	65.00
a.		"3C." in blue	110.00	120.00
2N24	A86	5c on 5s brn lake	100.00	60.00
a.		"5C." in violet	180.00	200.00
2N25	A89	10c on 7s dp grn	140.00	82.50
2N26	A86	15c on 4s dk grn	30.00	30.00
2N27	A90	20c on 8s dk pur & pale vio	210.00	110.00
		Nos. 2N21-2N27 (7)	685.00	416.50

Nos. 2N23a and 2N24a were issued in the Shan States.

Burma State Government Crest — OS3

Unwmk.
1943, Feb. 15   Litho.   Perf. 12
Without Gum

2N29	OS3	5c carmine	29.00	35.00
a.		Imperf.	29.00	35.00

This stamp was intended to be used to cover the embossed George VI envelope stamp and generally was sold affixed to such envelopes. It is also known used on private envelopes.

Farmer Plowing — OS4

1943, Mar.   Typo.   Without Gum

2N30	OS4	1c deep orange	6.00	10.00
2N31	OS4	2c yel green	1.50	1.20
2N32	OS4	3c blue	5.00	1.20
a.		Laid paper	24.00	40.00
2N33	OS4	5c carmine	4.00	8.00
a.		Small "5c"	32.00	21.00
b.		Imperf, pair	130.00	
2N34	OS4	10c violet brown	9.50	9.50
2N35	OS4	15c red violet	.75	4.50
a.		Laid paper	7.25	25.00
2N36	OS4	20c dull purple	.75	1.20
2N37	OS4	30c blue green	1.25	3.00
		Nos. 2N30-2N37 (8)	28.75	38.60

Small "c" in Nos. 2N34 to 2N37.

Burmese Soldier Carving "Independence" OS5 | **Farmer Rejoicing OS6**

Boy with Burmese Flag — OS7

Hyphen-hole Perf., Pin-Perf. x Hyphen-hole Perf.

1943, Aug. 1   Typo.

2N38	OS5	1c orange	1.50	2.10
a.		Perf. 11	15.00	20.00
2N39	OS6	3c blue	3.00	4.00
a.		Perf. 11	15.00	20.00
2N40	OS7	5c rose	3.50	4.25
a.		Perf. 11	23.00	11.00
		Nos. 2N38-2N40 (3)	8.00	10.35

Declaration of the independence of Burma by the Ba Maw government, Aug. 1, 1943.

Burmese Girl Carrying Water Jar — OS8 | **Elephant Carrying Teak Log — OS9**

Watch Tower of Mandalay Palace — OS10

1943, Oct. 1   Litho.   Perf. 12½

2N41	OS8	1c dp salmon	24.00	18.00
2N42	OS8	2c yel green	1.00	2.40
2N43	OS8	3c violet	1.00	2.75
2N44	OS9	5c rose	1.00	1.00
2N45	OS9	10c blue	2.25	1.25
2N46	OS9	15c vermilion	1.20	3.50
2N47	OS9	20c yel green	1.20	2.10
2N48	OS9	30c brown	1.20	2.40
2N49	OS10	1r vermilion	.75	2.40
2N50	OS10	2r violet	.75	2.75
		Nos. 2N41-2N50 (10)	34.35	38.55

No. 2N49 exists imperforate. Canceled to order examples of Nos. 2N42-2N50 same values as unused.

Bullock Cart OS11 | **Shan Woman OS12**

1943, Oct. 1   Perf. 12½

2N51	OS11	1c brown	45.00	47.50
2N52	OS11	2c yel green	50.00	47.50
2N53	OS11	3c violet	8.00	14.00
2N54	OS11	5c ultra	3.50	8.50
2N55	OS12	10c blue	18.00	22.50
2N56	OS12	20c rose	47.50	22.50
2N57	OS12	30c brown	27.50	75.00
		Nos. 2N51-2N57 (7)	199.50	237.50

For use only in the Shan States. Perak No. N34 also used in Shan States. Canceled-to-order stamps are valued at ½ used value.

Surcharged in Black

1944, Nov. 1

2N58	OS11	1c brown	5.00	10.00
2N59	OS11	2c yel green	1.00	6.50
a.		Inverted surcharge	500.00	850.00
2N60	OS11	3c violet	2.75	8.50
2N61	OS11	5c ultra	3.00	4.00
2N62	OS12	10c blue	4.00	3.00
2N63	OS12	20c rose	.85	2.00
2N64	OS12	30c brown	1.50	2.25
		Nos. 2N58-2N64 (7)	18.10	36.25

Top line of surcharge reads: "Bama naing ngan daw" (Burma State). Bottom line repeats denomination in Burmese. Surcharge applied when the Shan States came under Burmese government administration, Dec. 24, 1943. Canceled-to-order stamps same value as unused.

BURUNDI
bu-'rün-dē

LOCATION — Central Africa, adjoining the ex-Belgian Congo Republic, Rwanda and Tanzania
GOVT. — Republic
AREA — 10,759 sq. mi.
POP. — 5,735,937 (1999 est.)
CAPITAL — Bujumbura

Burundi was established as an independent country on July 1, 1962. With Rwanda, it had been a UN trusteeship territory (Ruanda-Urundi) administered by Belgium. A military coup overthrew the monarchy November 28, 1966.

100 Centimes = 1 Franc

Catalogue values for all unused stamps in this country are for Never Hinged items.

Flower Issue of Ruanda-Urundi, 1953 Overprinted

Perf. 11½
1962, July 1   Unwmk.   Photo.
Flowers in Natural Colors

1	A27	25c dk grn & dull org	.25	.25
2	A27	40c grn & salmon	.25	.25
3	A27	60c blue grn & pink	.40	.40
4	A27	1.25fr dk grn & blue	19.00	19.00
5	A27	1.50fr vio & apple grn	.65	.55
6	A27	5fr dp plum & lt bl grn	1.60	1.10
7	A27	7fr dk grn & fawn	2.50	1.90
8	A27	10fr dp plum & pale ol	3.50	3.25
		Nos. 1-8 (8)	28.15	26.70

Animal Issue of Ruanda-Urundi, 1959-61 with Similar Overprint or Surcharge in Black or Violet Blue
Size: 23x33mm, 33x23mm

9	A29	10c multicolored	.25	.25
10	A30	20c multicolored	.25	.25
11	A29	40c multicolored	.25	.25
12	A30	50c multicolored	.25	.25
a.		Larger overprint and bar	1.50	.25
b.		As "a," ovpt. "Royaume du Royaume"	12.50	
13	A29	1fr multicolored	.25	.25
14	A30	1.50fr multi (VB)	.25	.25
15	A29	2fr multicolored	.25	.25
16	A30	3fr multicolored	.25	.25
17	A30	3.50fr on 3fr multi	.25	.25
18	A30	4fr on 10fr multi ("XX" 6mm wide)	.30	.25
a.		"XX" 4mm wide	1.40	.60
19	A30	5fr multicolored	.35	.25
20	A30	6.50fr multicolored	.35	.25
a.		Ovpt. "Royume du Royaume"	12.50	
21	A30	8fr multicolored	1.25	.55
a.		Violet blue overprint	2.25	1.25
22	A30	10fr multicolored	1.00	.55

Size: 45x26½mm

23	A30	20fr multicolored	2.50	1.10
24	A30	50fr multi (ovpt. bars 2mm wide)	4.00	1.90
a.		Overprint bars 4mm wide	4.50	2.75
		Nos. 9-24 (16)	12.00	7.10

On No. 12a, "Burundi" is 13mm long; bar is continuous line across sheet. On No. 12, "Burundi" is 10mm; bar is 29mm. No. 12a was issued in 1963.
Two types of overprint exist on 10c, 40c, 1fr and 2fr: I, "du" is below "me"; bar 22½mm. II, "du" below "oy"; bar 20mm.
The 50c and 3fr exist in two types, besides the larger 50c overprint listed as No. 12: I, "du" is closer to "Royaume" than to "Burundi"; bar is less than 29mm; wording is centered above bar. II, "du" is closer to "Burundi"; bar is more than 30mm; wording is off-center leftward.

King Mwami Mwambutsa IV and Royal Drummers — A1

Flag and Arms of Burundi — A2

2fr, 8fr, 50fr, Map of Burundi and King.

Unwmk.
1962, Sept. 27   Photo.   Perf. 14

25	A1	50c dull rose car & dk brn	.25	.25
26	A2	1fr dk grn, red & emer	.25	.25
27	A1	2fr brown ol & dk brn	.25	.25
28	A1	3fr vermilion & dk brn	.25	.25
29	A2	4fr Prus bl, red & emer	.25	.25
30	A1	8fr violet & dk brn	.25	.25
31	A1	10fr brt green & dk brn	.25	.25
32	A2	20fr brown, red & emer	.60	.25
33	A1	50fr brt pink & dk brn	1.75	.25
		Nos. 25-33 (9)	4.10	2.25

Burundi's independence, July 1, 1962. Exist imperf. Value set, $20.
See Nos. 47-50. For overprints see Nos. 45-46, 51-52.

Ruanda-Urundi Nos. 151-152 Srchd.

Photogravure, Surcharge Engraved
1962, Oct. 31   Perf. 11½
Inscription in French

34	A31	3.50fr on 3fr ultra & red	.25	.25
35	A31	6.50fr on 3fr ultra & red	.30	.25
36	A31	10fr on 3fr ultra & red	.65	.35

Inscription in Flemish

37	A31	3.50fr on 3fr ultra & red	.30	.25
38	A31	6.50fr on 3fr ultra & red	.50	.30
39	A31	10fr on 3fr ultra & red	.65	.45
		Nos. 34-39 (6)	2.65	1.75

Dag Hammarskjold, Secretary General of the United Nations, 1953-61.

King Mwami Mwambutsa IV, Map of Burundi and Emblem — A3

1962, Dec. 10   Photo.   Perf. 14

40	A3	8fr yel, bl grn & blk brn	.50	.25
41	A3	50fr gray grn, bl grn & blk brn	2.00	1.00

WHO drive to eradicate malaria. Exist imperf. Value set, $24.
Stamps of type A3 without anti-malaria emblem are listed as Nos. 27, 30 and 33.

Sowing Seed over Africa — A4

1963, Mar. 21   *Perf. 14x13*

42	A4	4fr olive & dull pur	.25	.25
43	A4	8fr dp org & dull pur	.25	.25
44	A4	15fr emerald & dull pur	.30	.25
		Nos. 42-44 (3)	.80	.75

FAO "Freedom from Hunger" campaign. Exist imperf. Value set, $25.

Nos. 27 and 33 Overprinted in Dark Green

1963, June 19   **Unwmk.**   *Perf. 14*

45	A1	2fr brn olive & dk brn	2.25	2.25
46	A1	50fr brt pink & dk brn	3.50	3.50

Conquest and peaceful use of outer space.

Types of 1962 Inscribed: "Premier Anniversaire" in Red or Magenta

1963, July 1   **Photo.**

47	A2	4fr olive, red & emer (R)	.25	.25
48	A1	8fr orange & dk brn (M)	.25	.25
49	A1	10fr lilac & dk brn (M)	.30	.25
50	A2	20fr gray, red & emer (R)	1.00	.25
		Nos. 47-50 (4)	1.80	1.00

First anniversary of independence. Exist imperf. Value set, $15.

Nos. 26 and 32 Surcharged in Brown

1963, Sept. 24   **Unwmk.**   *Perf. 14*

51	A2	6.50fr on 1fr multi	.55	.25
52	A2	15fr on 20fr multi	.90	.25

Red Cross Flag over Globe with Map of Africa — A5

1963, Sept. 26   *Perf. 14x13*

53	A5	4fr emer, car & gray	.25	.25
54	A5	8fr brn ol, car & gray	.40	.25
55	A5	10fr blue, car & gray	.70	.25
56	A5	20fr lilac, car & gray	1.60	.50
		Nos. 53-56 (4)	2.95	1.25

Centenary of International Red Cross. Exist imperf. Value set, $20. See No. B7.

"1962", Arms of Burundi, UN and UNESCO Emblems — A6

UN Agency Emblems: 8fr, ITU. 10fr, World Meteorological Organization. 20fr, UPU. 50fr, FAO.

1963, Nov. 4   **Unwmk.**   *Perf. 14*

57	A6	4fr yel, ol grn & blk	.25	.25
58	A6	8fr pale lil, Prus bl & blk	.35	.25
59	A6	10fr blue, lil & blk	.45	.25
60	A6	20fr yel grn, grn & blk	.90	.25
61	A6	50fr yel, red brn & blk	1.50	.35
a.		Souvenir sheet of 2	5.75	5.75
		Nos. 57-61 (5)	3.45	1.35

1st anniv. of Burundi's admission to the UN. Exist imperf. Value set, $20. No. 61a contains two imperf. stamps with simulated perforations similar to Nos. 60-61. The 20fr stamp shows the FAO and the 50fr the WMO emblems.

UNESCO Emblem, Scales and Map — A7

Designs: 3.50fr, 6.50fr, Scroll, scales and "UNESCO." 10fr, 20fr, Abraham Lincoln, broken chain and scales.

1963, Dec. 10   **Litho.**   *Perf. 14x13½*

62	A7	50c pink, lt bl & blk	.25	.25
63	A7	1.50fr org, lt bl & blk	.25	.25
64	A7	3.50fr fawn, lt grn & blk	.25	.25
65	A7	6.50fr lt vio, lt grn & blk	.25	.25
66	A7	10fr blue, bis & blk	.30	.25
67	A7	20fr pale brn, ocher, bl & blk	.55	.25
		Nos. 62-67 (6)	1.85	1.50

15th anniv. of the Universal Declaration of Human Rights and the cent. of the American Emancipation Proclamation (Nos. 66-67). Exist imperf. Value set, $6.

Ice Hockey — A8

3.50fr, Women's figure skating. 6.50fr, Torch. 10fr, Men's speed skating. 20fr, Slalom.

Unwmk.

1964, Jan. 25   **Photo.**   *Perf. 14*

68	A8	50c olive, blk & gold	.25	.25
69	A8	3.50fr lt brown, blk & gold	.25	.25
70	A8	6.50fr pale gray, blk & gold	.60	.25
71	A8	10fr gray, blk & gold	1.50	.30
72	A8	20fr tan, blk & gold	2.00	.50
		Nos. 68-72 (5)	4.60	1.55

Issued to publicize the 9th Winter Olympic Games, Innsbruck, Jan. 29-Feb. 9, 1964. Exist imperf. Value set, $80.

A souvenir sheet contains two stamps (10fr+5fr and 20fr+5fr) in tan, black and gold. Value: perf $12, unused or used; imperf $13, unused or used.

Canceled to Order

Starting about 1964, values in the used column are for "canceled to order" stamps. Postally used stamps sell for much more.

Impala — A9

Animals: 1fr, 5fr, Hippopotamus, horiz. 1.50fr, 10fr, Giraffe. 2fr, 8fr, Cape buffalo, horiz. 3fr, 6.50fr, Zebra, horiz. 3.50fr, 15fr, Defassa waterbuck. 20fr, Cheetah. 50fr, Elephant. 100fr, Lion.

Perf. 14x13, 13x14

1964, Feb. 10   *Litho.*

Size: 21½x35mm, 35x21½mm

73	A9	50c multi	.25	.25
74	A9	1fr multi	.25	.25
75	A9	1.50fr multi	.25	.25
76	A9	2fr multi	.35	.25
77	A9	3fr multi	.50	.25
78	A9	3.50fr multi	.60	.25

Size: 26x42mm, 42x26mm

79	A9	4fr multi	.25	.25
80	A9	5fr multi	.35	.25
81	A9	6.50fr multi	.40	.35
82	A9	8fr multi	.50	.35
83	A9	10fr multi	.80	.40
84	A9	15fr multi	1.00	.50

Perf. 14

Size: 53x33mm

85	A9	20fr multi	1.75	.50
86	A9	50fr multi	3.50	.80
87	A9	100fr multi	7.00	1.10
		Nos. 73-87,C1-C7 (22)	30.25	8.70

Exist imperf. Value set (22), $48.

Burundi Dancer — A10

Designs: Various Dancers and Drummers.

Unwmk.

1964, Aug. 21   **Litho.**   *Perf. 14*

Dancers Multicolored

88	A10	50c gold & emerald	.25	.25
89	A10	1fr gold & vio blue	.25	.25
90	A10	4fr gold & brt blue	.25	.25
91	A10	6.50fr gold & red	.30	.25
92	A10	10fr gold & brt blue	.50	.25
93	A10	15fr gold & emerald	.70	.25
94	A10	20fr gold & red	.95	.50
a.		Souvenir sheet of 3, #92-94	4.25	4.25
		Nos. 88-94 (7)	3.20	2.00

Exist imperf. Value set, $9; souvenir sheet, $5.50.

1964, Sept. 10

Dancers Multicolored

88a	A10	50c silver & emerald	.25	.25
89a	A10	1fr silver & violet blue	.25	.25
90a	A10	4fr silver & bright blue	.25	.25
91a	A10	6.50fr silver & red	.30	.25
92a	A10	10fr silver & bright blue	.50	.25
93a	A10	15fr silver & emerald	.65	.30
94b	A10	20fr silver & red	.95	.50
c.		Souvenir sheet of 3, #92a-94b	3.50	3.50
		Nos. 88a-94b (7)	3.15	2.05

New York World's Fair, 1964-65. Exist imperf. Value set, $9; souvenir sheet, $4.

Pope Paul VI and King Mwami Mwambutsa IV — A11

22 Sainted Martyrs — A12

4fr, 14fr, Pope John XXIII and King Mwami.

1964, Nov. 12   **Photo.**   *Perf. 12*

95	A11	50c brt bl, gold & red brn	.25	.25
96	A12	1fr mag, gold & slate	.25	.25
97	A11	4fr pale rose lil, gold & brn	.25	.25
98	A12	8fr red, gold & brn	.30	.25
99	A11	14fr lt grn, gold & brn	.60	.25
100	A11	20fr red brn, gold & grn	.90	.35
		Nos. 95-100 (6)	2.55	1.60

Canonization of 22 African martyrs, 10/18/64. Exist imperf. Value set, $15.

Shot Put — A13

Sports: 1fr, Discus. 3fr, Swimming. 4fr, Running. 6.50fr, Javelin, woman. 8fr, Hurdling. 10fr, Broad jump. 14fr, Diving, woman. 18fr, High jump. 20fr, Vaulting.
3fr, 8fr, 10fr, 18fr, 20fr are horiz.

1964, Nov. 18   **Litho.**   *Perf. 14*

101	A13	50c olive & multi	.25	.25
102	A13	1fr brt pink & multi	.25	.25
103	A13	3fr multi	.25	.25
104	A13	4fr multi	.25	.25
105	A13	6.50fr multi	.25	.25
106	A13	8fr lt bl & multi	.40	.25
107	A13	10fr multi	.45	.25
108	A13	14fr multi	.60	.25
109	A13	18fr bister & multi	.85	.35
110	A13	20fr gray & multi	.90	.50
		Nos. 101-110 (10)	4.45	2.95

18th Olympic Games, Tokyo, Oct. 10-25, 1964. Exist imperf. Value set, $15. See No. B8.

African Purple
Gallinule — A14

Birds: 1fr, 5fr, Little bee eater. 1.50fr, 6.50fr,
Secretary bird. 2fr, 8fr, Yellow-billed stork. 3fr,
10fr, Congo peacock. 3.50fr, 15fr, African anhinga. 20fr, Saddle-billed stork. 50fr, Abyssinian
ground hornbill. 100fr, Crowned crane.

Birds in Natural Colors

1965		Unwmk.	Perf. 14	
Size: 21x35mm				
111	A14	50c tan, grn & blk	.25	.25
112	A14	1fr pink, mag & blk	.25	.25
113	A14	1.50fr blue & blk	.25	.25
114	A14	2fr yel grn, dk grn & blk	.25	.25
115	A14	3fr yellow, brn & blk	.25	.25
116	A14	3.50fr yel grn, dk grn & blk	.35	.25
Size: 26x43mm				
117	A14	4fr tan, grn & blk	.45	.25
118	A14	5fr pink, mag & blk	.55	.25
119	A14	6.50fr blue & blk	.70	.25
120	A14	8fr yel grn, dk grn & blk	.90	.25
121	A14	10fr yel, brn & blk	1.10	.35
122	A14	15fr yel grn, dk grn & blk	1.75	.35
Size: 33x53mm				
123	A14	20fr rose lilac & blk	2.25	.45
124	A14	50fr yellow, brn & blk	4.50	.90
125	A14	100fr green, yel & blk	9.00	1.75
		Nos. 111-125 (15)	22.80	6.30

Issue dates: Nos. 111-116, Mar. 31. Nos.
117-122, Apr. 16. Nos. 123-125, Apr. 30.
For overprints see Nos. 174-184, C35A-
C35I.

Relay Satellite
and Morse
Key — A15

3fr, Telstar & old telephone handpiece. 4fr,
Luna satellite & old wall telephone. 6.50fr,
Orbiting Geophysical Observatory & radar
screen. 8fr, Telstar II & headphones. 10fr,
Sputnik II & radar aerial. 14fr, Syncom & transmission aerial. 20fr, Interplanetary Explorer &
tracking aerial.

1965, July 3		Litho.	Perf. 13	
126	A15	1fr multi	.25	.25
127	A15	3fr multi	.25	.25
128	A15	4fr multi	.25	.25
129	A15	6.50fr multi	.25	.25
130	A15	8fr multi	.25	.25
131	A15	10fr multi	.25	.25
132	A15	14fr multi	.25	.25
133	A15	20fr multi	.30	.25
		Nos. 126-133 (8)	2.05	2.00

Cent. of the ITU. Exist imperf. Value, set
$7.50.
Perf. and imperf. souv. sheets of 2 contain
Nos. 131, 133. Size: 120x86mm. Value, both
sheets, $7.50.

Globe and ICY Emblem — A16

Designs: 4fr, Map of Africa and UN development emblem. 8fr, Map of Asia and Colombo
Plan emblem. 10fr, Globe and UN emblem.
18fr, Map of the Americas and Alliance for
Progress emblem. 25fr, Map of Europe and
EUROPA emblems. 40fr, Map of Outer Space
and satellite with UN wreath.

1965, Oct. 1		Litho.	Perf. 13	
134	A16	1fr ol green & multi	.25	.25
135	A16	4fr dull blue & multi	.25	.25
136	A16	8fr pale yellow & multi	.25	.25
137	A16	10fr lilac & multi	.25	.25
138	A16	18fr salmon & multi	.45	.25
139	A16	25fr gray & multi	.75	.25
140	A16	40fr blue & multi	1.25	.25
a.		Souvenir sheet of 3, #138-140	4.50	4.50
		Nos. 134-140 (7)	3.45	1.75

International Cooperation Year.
Exist imperf. Values: set $7.50; souvenir
sheet $5.50.

Protea
A17

Flowers: 1fr, 5fr, Crossandra. 1.50fr, 6.50fr,
Ansellia. 2fr, 8fr, Thunbergia. 3fr, 10fr,
Schizoglossum. 3.50fr, 15fr, Dissotis. 4fr, 20fr,
Protea. 50fr, Gazania. 100fr, Hibiscus. 150fr,
Markhamia.

1966		Unwmk.	Perf. 13½	
Size: 26x26mm				
141	A17	50c multi	.25	.25
142	A17	1fr multi	.25	.25
143	A17	1.50fr multi	.25	.25
144	A17	2fr multi	.25	.25
145	A17	3fr multi	.25	.25
146	A17	3.50fr multi	.25	.25
Size: 31x31mm				
147	A17	4fr multi	.25	.25
148	A17	5fr multi	.35	.25
149	A17	6.50fr multi	.45	.25
150	A17	8fr multi	.90	.25
151	A17	10fr multi	1.00	.25
152	A17	15fr multi	1.10	.25
Size: 39x39mm				
153	A17	20fr multi	1.60	.25
154	A17	50fr multi	3.50	.30
155	A17	100fr multi	5.25	.50
156	A17	150fr multi	7.50	.70
		Nos. 141-156,C17-C25 (25)	39.60	8.10

Issue dates: Nos. 141-147, Feb. 28; Nos.
148-153, May 18; Nos. 154-156, June 15.
Exist imperf. Value set (25), $55.
For overprints see Nos. 159-173, C27-C35.

Souvenir Sheets

Allegory of Prosperity and Equality
Tapestry by Peter Colfs — A18

1966, Nov. 4		Litho.	Perf. 13½	
157	A18	Sheet of 7 (1.50fr)	2.75	.95
a.-g.		Any single	.25	.25
158	A18	Sheet of 7 (4fr)	4.50	1.50
a.-g.		Any single	.25	.25

20th anniv. of UNESCO. Each sheet contains 6 stamps showing a reproduction of the
Colfs tapestry from the lobby of the General
Assembly Building, NYC, and one stamp with
the UNESCO emblem plus a label. The labels
on Nos. 157-158 and C26 are inscribed in
French or English. The 3 sheets with French
inscription have light blue marginal border.
The 3 sheets with English inscription have
pink border. See No. C26.
Exist imperf. Value each sheet, $15.

Republic

Nos. 141-152,
154-156
Overprinted

1967		Litho.	Perf. 13½	
Size: 26x26mm				
159	A17	50c multi	.25	.25
160	A17	1fr multi	.25	.25
161	A17	1.50fr multi	.25	.25
162	A17	2fr multi	.25	.25
163	A17	3fr multi	.25	.25
164	A17	3.50fr multi	.25	.25
Size: 31x31mm				
165	A17	4fr multi	1.60	.30
166	A17	5fr multi	.25	.25
167	A17	6.50fr multi	.35	.25
168	A17	8fr multi	.35	.25
169	A17	10fr multi	.60	.25
170	A17	15fr multi	.80	.25
Size: 39x39mm				
171	A17	50fr multi	3.50	.90
172	A17	100fr multi	11.00	2.75
173	A17	150fr multi	11.00	2.75
		Nos. 159-173,C27-C35 (24)	57.30	14.95

Nos. 111, 113, 116, 118-125
Overprinted "REPUBLIQUE DU
BURUNDI" and Horizontal Bar

1967		Litho.	Perf. 14	
Birds in Natural Colors				
Size: 21x35mm				
174	A14	50c multi	2.75	2.75
175	A14	1.50fr blue & black	.60	.60
176	A14	3.50fr multi	.75	.75
Size: 26x43mm				
177	A14	5fr multi	.90	.90
178	A14	6.50fr blue & black	1.00	1.00
179	A14	8fr multi	1.25	1.25
180	A14	10fr yel, brn & blk	1.75	1.75
181	A14	15fr multi	2.25	2.25
Size: 33x53mm				
182	A14	20fr multi	4.00	4.00
183	A14	50fr multi	7.00	7.00
184	A14	100fr multi	12.00	12.00
		Nos. 174-184 (11)	34.25	34.25

Haplochromis Multicolor — A19

Various Tropical Fish.

1967		Photo.	Perf. 13½	
Size: 42x19mm				
186	A19	50c multi	.25	.25
187	A19	1fr multi	.25	.25
188	A19	1.50fr multi	.25	.25
189	A19	2fr multi	.30	.25
190	A19	3fr multi	.30	.25
191	A19	3.50fr multi	.40	.25
Size: 50x25mm				
192	A19	4fr multi	.60	.25
193	A19	5fr multi	.75	.25
194	A19	6.50fr multi	.85	.25
195	A19	8fr multi	1.40	.25
196	A19	10fr multi	2.25	.25
197	A19	15fr multi	2.75	.25
Size: 59x30mm				
198	A19	20fr multi	4.00	.35
199	A19	50fr multi	6.75	.45
200	A19	100fr multi	11.00	.65
201	A19	150fr multi	15.00	1.00
		Nos. 186-201,C46-C54 (25)	96.60	8.25

Issue Dates: Nos. 186-191, Apr. 4; Nos.
192-197, Apr. 28; Nos. 198-201, May 18.

Ancestor Figures,
Ivory
Coast — A20

African Art: 1fr, Seat of Honor, Southeast
Congo. 1.50fr, Antelope head, Aribinda
Region. 2fr, Buffalo mask, Upper Volta. 4fr,
Funeral figures, Southwest Ethiopia.

1967, June 5		Photo.	Perf. 13½	
202	A20	50c silver & multi	.25	.25
203	A20	1fr silver & multi	.25	.25
204	A20	1.50fr silver & multi	.25	.25
205	A20	2fr silver & multi	.25	.25
206	A20	4fr silver & multi	.25	.25
		Nos. 202-206,C36-C40 (10)	3.70	2.80

Exists imperf. Value set, $9.

Scouts on Hiking Trip — A21

Designs: 1fr, Cooking at campfire. 1.50fr,
Lord Baden-Powell. 2fr, Boy Scout and Cub
Scout giving Scout sign. 4fr, First aid.

1967, Aug. 9		Photo.	Perf. 13½	
207	A21	50c silver & multi	.25	.25
208	A21	1fr silver & multi	.35	.25
209	A21	1.50fr silver & multi	.50	.25
210	A21	2fr silver & multi	.65	.25
211	A21	4fr silver & multi	.80	.25
		Nos. 207-211,C41-C45 (10)	12.80	2.65

60th anniv. of the Boy Scouts and the 12th
Boy Scout World Jamboree, Farragut State
Park, Idaho, Aug. 1-9.
Exists imperf. Value set, $20.

The
Gleaners,
by
Francois
Millet
A22

Paintings Exhibited at EXPO '67: 8fr, The
Water Carrier of Seville, by Velazquez. 14fr,
The Triumph of Neptune and Amphitrite, by
Nicolas Poussin. 18fr, Acrobat Standing on a
Ball, by Picasso. 25fr, Marguerite van Eyck, by
Jan van Eyck. 40fr, St. Peter Denying Christ,
by Rembrandt.

1967, Oct. 12		Photo.	Perf. 13½	
212	A22	4fr multi	.25	.25
213	A22	8fr multi	.25	.25
214	A22	14fr multi	.45	.25
215	A22	18fr multi	.50	.25
216	A22	25fr multi	.80	.25
217	A22	40fr multi	1.00	.25
a.		Souvenir sheet of 2, #216-217	2.25	2.25
		Nos. 212-217 (6)	3.25	1.50

EXPO '67 International Exhibition, Montreal,
Apr. 28-Oct. 27. Printed in sheets of 10
stamps and 2 labels inscribed in French or
English.

Exists imperf. Value: set $5.50; souvenir sheet $2.25.

Place de la Revolution and Pres. Michel Micombero — A23

Designs: 5fr, President Michel Micombero and flag. 14fr, Formal garden and coat of arms. 20fr, Modern building and coat of arms.

1967, Nov. 23   *Perf. 13½*

218	A23	5fr multi	.25	.25
219	A23	14fr multi	.40	.25
220	A23	20fr multi	.70	.25
221	A23	30fr multi	.90	.25
		Nos. 218-221 (4)	2.25	1.00

First anniversary of the Republic.
Exists imperf. Value set, $5.

Madonna by Carlo Crivelli — A24

Designs: 1fr, Adoration of the Shepherds by Juan Bautista Mayno. 4fr, Holy Family by Anthony Van Dyck. 14fr, Nativity by Maitre de Moulins.

1967, Dec. 7   **Photo.**   *Perf. 13½*

222	A24	1fr multi	.25	.25
223	A24	4fr multi	.25	.25
224	A24	14fr multi	.60	.25
225	A24	26fr multi	1.00	.30
a.		Sheetlet of 4, #222-225	3.00	3.00
		Nos. 222-225 (4)	2.10	1.05

Christmas 1967. Exists imperf. Value: set $4; souvenir sheet, $3.50.
Printed in sheets of 25 and one corner label inscribed "Noel 1967" and giving name of painting and painter.

Slalom — A25

10fr, Ice hockey. 14fr, Women's skating. 17fr, Bobsled. 26fr, Ski jump. 40fr, Speed skating. 60fr, Hand holding torch, and Winter Olympics emblem.

1968, Feb. 16   **Photo.**   *Perf. 13½*

226	A25	5fr silver & multi	.25	.25
227	A25	10fr silver & multi	.30	.25
228	A25	14fr silver & multi	.55	.25
229	A25	17fr silver & multi	.65	.25
230	A25	26fr silver & multi	.95	.25
231	A25	40fr silver & multi	1.20	.25
232	A25	60fr silver & multi	1.65	.25
a.		Souvenir sheet of 2, types of #231-232 inscribed "Poste Aerienne"	3.00	2.25
		Nos. 226-232 (7)	5.55	1.75

Issued to publicize the 10th Winter Olympic Games, Grenoble, France, Feb. 6-18. Issued in sheets of 10 stamps and label.

Exists imperf. Values: set, $10; souvenir sheet, $3.

The Lacemaker, by Vermeer A26

Paintings: 1.50fr, Portrait of a Young Man, by Botticelli. 2fr, Maja Vestida, by Goya, horiz.

1968, Mar. 29   **Photo.**   *Perf. 13½*

233	A26	1.50fr gold & multi	.25	.25
234	A26	2fr gold & multi	.25	.25
235	A26	4fr gold & multi	.30	.25
		Nos. 233-235,C59-C61 (6)	3.70	2.35

Issued in sheets of 6.
Exists imperf. Value set, $6.50.

Moon Probe A27

Designs: 6fr, Russian astronaut walking in space. 8fr, Mariner satellite, Mars. 10fr, American astronaut walking in space.

1968, May 15   **Photo.**   *Perf. 13½*
Size: 35x35mm

236	A27	4fr silver & multi	.25	.25
237	A27	6fr silver & multi	.30	.25
238	A27	8fr silver & multi	.40	.25
239	A27	10fr silver & multi	.50	.25
		Nos. 236-239,C62-C65 (8)	5.50	2.35

Issued to publicize peaceful space explorations. Exist imperf. Value, set $7.
A souvenir sheet contains one 25fr stamp in Moon Probe design and one 40fr in Mariner satellite design. Stamp size: 41x41mm. Value: perf $3.50; imperf $4.

Salamis Aethiops A28

Butterflies: 1fr, 5fr, Graphium ridleyanus. 1.50fr, 6.50fr, Cymothoe. 2fr, 8fr, Charaxes eupale. 3fr, 10fr, Papilio bromius. 3.50fr, 15fr, Teracolus annae. 20fr, Salamis aethiops. 50fr, Papilio zonobia. 100fr, Danais chrysippus. 150fr, Salamis temora.

1968   **Size: 30x33½mm**

240	A28	50c gold & multi	.25	.25
241	A28	1fr gold & multi	.25	.25
242	A28	1.50fr gold & multi	.35	.25
243	A28	2fr gold & multi	.45	.25
244	A28	3fr gold & multi	.60	.25
245	A28	3.50fr gold & multi	.75	.25

Size: 33½x37½mm

246	A28	4fr gold & multi	.90	.25
247	A28	5fr gold & multi	1.10	.25
248	A28	6.50fr gold & multi	1.60	.25
249	A28	8fr gold & multi	2.00	.25
250	A28	10fr gold & multi	2.75	.30
251	A28	15fr gold & multi	3.50	.35

Size: 41x46mm

252	A28	20fr gold & multi	4.50	.40
253	A28	50fr gold & multi	7.75	.60
254	A28	100fr gold & multi	15.00	1.00
255	A28	150fr gold & multi	20.00	1.50
		Nos. 240-255,C66-C74 (25)	117.10	12.85

Issue dates: Nos. 240-245, June 7; Nos. 246-251, June 28; Nos. 252-255, July 19.

Women, Along the Manzanares, by Goya — A29

Paintings: 7fr, The Letter, by Pieter de Hooch. 11fr, Woman Reading a Letter, by Gerard Terborch. 14fr, Man Writing a Letter, by Gabriel Metsu.

1968, Sept. 30   **Photo.**   *Perf. 13½*

256	A29	4fr multi	.25	.25
257	A29	7fr multi	.25	.25
258	A29	11fr multi	.40	.25
259	A29	14fr multi	.50	.25
		Nos. 256-259,C84-C87 (8)	8.05	2.40

International Letter Writing Week.
Exists imperf. Value set, $9.

Soccer — A30

1968, Oct. 24

260	A30	4fr shown	.25	.25
261	A30	7fr Basketball	.25	.25
262	A30	13fr. High jump	.25	.25
263	A30	24fr Relay race	.35	.25
264	A30	40fr Javelin	.75	.30
		Nos. 260-264,C88-C92 (10)	8.45	3.00

19th Olympic Games, Mexico City, Oct. 12-27. Printed in sheets of 8.
Exists imperf. Value set, $15.

Virgin and Child, by Fra Filippo Lippi — A31

Paintings: 5fr, The Magnificat, by Sandro Botticelli. 6fr, Virgin and Child, by Albrecht Durer. 11fr, Madonna del Gran Duca, by Raphael.

1968, Nov. 26   **Photo.**   *Perf. 13½*

265	A31	3fr multi	.25	.25
266	A31	5fr multi	.25	.25
267	A31	6fr multi	.25	.25
268	A31	11fr multi	.35	.25
a.		Souvenir sheet of 4, #265-268	1.60	1.25
		Nos. 265-268,C93-C96 (8)	3.75	2.25

Christmas 1968. Exist imperf. Value: set (8) $5; souvenir sheets $5.
For overprints see Nos. 272-275, C100-C103.

WHO Emblem and Map of Africa — A32

1969, Jan. 22

269	A32	5fr gold, dk grn & yel	.25	.25
270	A32	5fr gold, vio & ver	.35	.25
271	A32	11fr gold, pur & red lil	.50	.25
		Nos. 269-271 (3)	1.10	.75

20th anniv. of WHO in Africa.
Exist imperf. Value set, $2.50.

Nos. 265-268 Overprinted in Silver

1969, Feb. 17   **Photo.**   *Perf. 13½*

272	A31	3fr multi	.25	.25
273	A31	5fr multi	.25	.25
274	A31	6fr multi	.35	.25
275	A31	11fr multi	.55	.25
		Nos. 272-275,C100-C103 (8)	4.15	2.30

Man's 1st flight around the moon by the US spacecraft Apollo 8, Dec. 21-27, 1968. Exist imperf. Value set (8), $6.50.

Map of Africa, and CEPT Emblem A33

Designs: 14fr, Plowing with tractor. 17fr, Teacher and pupil. 26fr, Maps of Europe and Africa and CEPT (Conference of European Postal and Telecommunications Administrations) emblem, horiz.

1969, Mar. 12   **Photo.**   *Perf. 13*

276	A33	5fr multi	.25	.25
277	A33	14fr multi	.45	.25
278	A33	17fr multi	.55	.25
279	A33	26fr multi	.90	.25
		Nos. 276-279 (4)	2.15	1.00

5th anniv. of the Yaounde (Cameroun) Agreement, creating the European and African-Malgache Economic Community. Exist imperf. Value set, $4.

Resurrection, by Gaspard Isenmann — A34

Paintings: 14fr, Resurrection by Antoine Caron. 17fr, Noli me Tangere, by Martin Schongauer. 26fr, Resurrection, by El Greco.

1969, Mar. 24

280	A34	11fr gold & multi	.35	.25
281	A34	14fr gold & multi	.45	.25
282	A34	17fr gold & multi	.60	.25
283	A34	26fr gold & multi	.75	.25
a.		Souvenir sheet of 4, #280-283	2.25	2.25
		Nos. 280-283 (4)	2.15	1.00

Easter 1969. Exist imperf. Values: set $3; souvenir sheet $2.

Potter — A35

ILO Emblem and: 5fr, Farm workers. 7fr, Foundry worker. 10fr, Woman testing corn crop.

1969, May 17   Photo.   *Perf. 13½*

284	A35	3fr multicolored	.25	.25
285	A35	5fr multicolored	.25	.25
286	A35	7fr multicolored	.25	.25
287	A35	10fr multicolored	.35	.25
		Nos. 284-287 (4)	1.10	1.00

50th anniv. of the ILO. Exist imperf. Value set, $2.50.

Industry and Bank's Emblem A36

African Development Bank Emblem and: 17fr, Communications. 30fr, Education. 50fr, Agriculture.

1969, July 29   Photo.   *Perf. 13½*

288	A36	10fr gold & multi	.30	.25
289	A36	17fr gold & multi	.50	.25
290	A36	30fr gold & multi	.80	.40
291	A36	50fr gold & multi	1.40	.75
a.		Souvenir sheet of 4, #288-291	4.00	4.00
		Nos. 288-291 (4)	3.00	1.65

African Development Bank, 5th anniv. Exist imperf. Values: set $7; souvenir sheet $4.50.

Girl Reading Letter, by Vermeer A37

Paintings: 7fr, Graziella (young woman), by Auguste Renoir. 14fr, Woman writing a letter, by Gerard Terborch. 26fr, Galileo Galilei, painter unknown. 40fr, Ludwig van Beethoven, painter unknown.

1969, Oct. 24   Photo.   *Perf. 13½*

292	A37	4fr multicolored	.25	.25
293	A37	7fr multicolored	.25	.25
294	A37	14fr multicolored	.45	.25
295	A37	26fr multicolored	.75	.25
296	A37	40fr multicolored	1.10	.25
a.		Souvenir sheet of 2, #295-296	3.00	3.00
		Nos. 292-296 (5)	2.80	1.25

Intl. Letter Writing Week, Oct. 7-13. Exist imperf. Values: set $6; souvenir sheet $3.

Rocket Launching A38

Moon Landing: 6.50fr, Rocket in space. 7fr, Separation of landing module from capsule. 14fr, 26fr, Landing module landing on moon. 17fr, Capsule in space. 40fr, Neil A. Armstrong leaving landing module. 50fr, Astronaut on moon.

1969, Nov. 6   Photo.   *Perf. 13½*

297	A38	4fr blue & multi	.25	.25
298	A38	6.50fr vio blue & multi	.25	.25
299	A38	7fr vio blue & multi	.50	.25
300	A38	14fr black & multi	1.00	.25
301	A38	17fr vio blue & multi	1.75	.30
		Nos. 297-301,C104-C106 (8)	12.00	2.55

Souvenir Sheet

302		Sheet of 3	13.50	13.50
a.		A38 26fr multicolored	1.75	1.75
b.		A38 40fr multicolored	2.50	2.50
c.		A38 50fr multicolored	3.50	3.50

Exist imperf. Values: set $14; souvenir sheet $15.

See note after Algeria No. 427.

Madonna and Child, by Rubens — A39

Paintings: 6fr, Madonna and Child with St. John, by Giulio Romano. 10fr, Magnificat Madonna, by Botticelli.

1969, Dec. 2   Photo.

303	A39	5fr gold & multi	.25	.25
304	A39	6fr gold & multi	.25	.25
305	A39	10fr gold & multi	.40	.25
a.		Souvenir sheet of 3, #303-305	1.25	1.25
		Nos. 303-305,C107-C109 (6)	5.60	1.60

Christmas 1969. Exist imperf. Values: set (6) $7; souvenir sheets (2) $6.

Sternotomis Bohemani — A40

Designs: Various Beetles and Weevils.

1970   Size: 39x28mm   *Perf. 13½*

306	A40	50c multicolored	.25	.25
307	A40	1fr multicolored	.25	.25
308	A40	1.50fr multicolored	.25	.25
309	A40	2fr multicolored	.25	.25
310	A40	3fr multicolored	.30	.25
311	A40	3.50fr multicolored	.40	.25

Size: 46x32mm

312	A40	4fr multicolored	.50	.25
313	A40	5fr multicolored	.65	.25
314	A40	6.50fr multicolored	.75	.25
315	A40	8fr multicolored	.90	.25
316	A40	10fr multicolored	1.50	.25
317	A40	15fr multicolored	2.00	.30

Size: 52x36mm

318	A40	20fr multicolored	3.25	.40
319	A40	50fr multicolored	6.00	.50
320	A40	100fr multicolored	10.50	.75
321	A40	150fr multicolored	15.00	1.00
		Nos. 306-321,C110-C118 (25)	78.70	9.90

Issue dates: Nos. 306-313, Jan. 20; Nos. 314-318, Feb. 17; Nos. 319-321, Apr. 3.

Jesus Condemned to Death — A41

Stations of the Cross, by Juan de Aranoa y Carredano: 1.50fr, Jesus carries His Cross. 2fr, Jesus falls the first time. 3fr, Jesus meets His mother. 3.50fr, Simon of Cyrene helps carry the cross. 4fr, Veronica wipes the face of Jesus. 5fr, Jesus falls the second time.

1970, Mar. 16   Photo.   *Perf. 13½*

322	A41	1fr gold & multi	.25	.25
323	A41	1.50fr gold & multi	.25	.25
324	A41	2fr gold & multi	.25	.25
325	A41	3fr gold & multi	.25	.25
326	A41	3.50fr gold & multi	.25	.25
327	A41	4fr gold & multi	.25	.25
328	A41	5fr gold & multi	.25	.25
a.		Souv. sheet, #322-328 + label	1.60	1.60
		Nos. 322-328,C119-C125 (14)	7.65	4.15

Easter 1970. Exists imperf. Values: set (14) $10; souvenir sheets (2) $10.

Parade and EXPO '70 Emblem — A42

Designs (EXPO '70 Emblem and): 6.50fr, Aerial view. 7fr, African pavilions. 14fr, Pagoda, vert. 26fr, Recording pavilion and pool. 40fr, Tower of the Sun, vert. 50fr, Flags of participating nations.

1970, May 5   Photo.   *Perf. 13½*

329	A42	4fr gold & multi	.25	.25
330	A42	6.50fr gold & multi	.25	.25
331	A42	7fr gold & multi	.25	.25
332	A42	14fr gold & multi	.45	.25
333	A42	26fr gold & multi	.90	.25
334	A42	40fr gold & multi	1.25	.25
335	A42	50fr gold & multi	1.40	.30
		Nos. 329-335 (7)	4.75	1.80

EXPO '70 Intl. Exhibition, Osaka, Japan, Mar. 15-Sept. 13, 1970. Exists imperf. Value $6.

See No. C126.

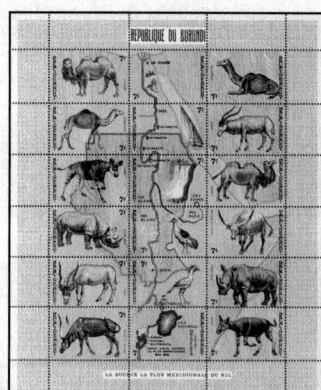

Fauna and Map of the Nile — A43

Fauna: a, i, Camel. c, d, Dromedary. g, r, Okapi. f, m, Addax. j, o, Rhinoceros. l, p, Burundi cow (each animal in 2 different poses).

Map of the Nile: b, Delta and pyramids. e, dhow. h, Falls. k, Blue Nile and crowned crane. n, Victoria Nile and secretary bird. q, Lake Victoria and source of Nile on Mt. Gikizi. Continuous design.

1970, July 8   Photo.   *Perf. 13½*

336	A43	Sheet of 18	45.00	24.50
a.-r.		7fr any single	2.50	.35

Publicizing the southernmost source of the Nile on Mt. Gikizi in Burundi. Exists imperf. Value $55.

See No. C127.

Winter Wren, Firecrest, Skylark and Crested Lark — A44

Birds: 2fr, 3.50fr, 5fr, vert.; others horiz.

1970, Sept. 30   Photo.   *Perf. 13½*
Stamp Size: 44x33mm

337	A44	Block of 4	2.50	.60
a.		2fr Northern shrike	.60	.25
b.		2fr European starling	.60	.25
c.		2fr Yellow wagtail	.60	.25
d.		2fr Bank swallow	.60	.25
338	A44	Block of 4	3.00	.70
a.		3fr Winter wren	.65	.25
b.		3fr Firecrest	.65	.25
c.		3fr Skylark	.65	.25
d.		3fr Crested lark	.65	.25
339	A44	Block of 4	4.00	.80
a.		3.50fr Woodchat shrike	.75	.25
b.		3.50fr Common rock thrush	.75	.25
c.		3.50fr Black redstart	.75	.25
d.		3.50fr Ring ouzel	.75	.25
340	A44	Block of 4	5.50	1.00
a.		4fr European Redstart	1.00	.25
b.		4fr Hedge sparrow	1.00	.25
c.		4fr Gray wagtail	1.00	.25
d.		4fr Meadow pipit	1.00	.25
341	A44	Block of 4	6.50	1.10
a.		5fr Eurasian hoopoe	1.15	.25
b.		5fr Pied flycatcher	1.15	.25
c.		5fr Great reed warbler	1.15	.25
d.		5fr Eurasian kingfisher	1.15	.25
342	A44	Block of 4	7.75	1.25
a.		6.50fr House martin	1.50	.30
b.		6.50fr Sedge warbler	1.50	.30
c.		6.50fr Fieldfare	1.50	.30
d.		6.50fr European Golden oriole	1.50	.30
		Nos. 337-342,C132-C137 (12)	152.25	19.20

Nos. 337-342 are printed in sheets of 16.

Library, UN Emblem — A45

Designs: 5fr, Students taking test, and emblem of University of Bujumbura. 7fr, Students in laboratory and emblem of Ecole Normale Superieure of Burundi. 10fr, Students with electron-microscope and Education Year emblem.

1970, Oct. 23

343	A45	3fr gold & multi	.25	.25
344	A45	5fr gold & multi	.25	.25
345	A45	7fr gold & multi	.30	.25
346	A45	10fr gold & multi	.40	.25
		Nos. 343-346 (4)	1.20	1.00

Issued for International Education Year. Exists imperf. Value set, $1.50.

Pres. and Mrs. Michel Micombero — A46

Designs: 7fr, Pres. Michel Micombero and Burundi flag. 11fr, Pres. Micombero and Revolution Memorial.

1970, Nov. 28   Photo.   Perf. 13½
347 A46 4fr gold & multi   .25 .25
348 A46 7fr gold & multi   .35 .25
349 A46 11fr gold & multi   .45 .25
 a.   Souvenir sheet of 3   1.25 1.25
    Nos. 347-349 (3)   1.05 .75

4th anniv. of independence. No. 349a contains 3 stamps similar to Nos. 347-349, but inscribed "Poste Aerienne."
Exist imperf. Value: set $1.25; souvenir sheet, $1.25.
See Nos. C140-C142.

Lenin with Delegates
A47

Designs (Lenin, Paintings): 5fr, addressing crowd. 6.50fr, with soldier and sailor. 15fr, speaking from balcony. 50fr, Portrait.

1970, Dec. 31   Photo.   Perf. 13½
Gold Frame
350 A47 3.50fr dk red brown   .55 .25
351 A47 5fr dk red brown   .70 .25
352 A47 6.50fr dk red brown   .85 .25
353 A47 15fr dk red brown   1.40 .40
354 A47 50fr dk red brown   3.50 .50
    Nos. 350-354 (5)   7.00 1.65

Lenin's birth centenary (1870-1924). Exist imperf. Value set, $8.

Lion — A48

1971, Mar. 19   Photo.   Perf. 13½
Size: 38x38mm
355 Strip of 4   2.00 .80
 a.   A48 1fr Lion   .35 .25
 b.   A48 1fr Cape buffalo   .35 .25
 c.   A48 1fr Hippopotamus   .35 .25
 d.   A48 1fr Giraffe   .35 .25
356 Strip of 4   2.75 .90
 a.   A48 2fr Hartebeest   .45 .25
 b.   A48 2fr Black rhinoceros   .45 .25
 c.   A48 2fr Zebra   .45 .25
 d.   A48 2fr Leopard   .45 .25
357 Strip of 4   3.25 1.00
 a.   A48 3fr Grant's gazelles   .55 .25
 b.   A48 3fr Cheetah   .55 .25
 c.   A48 3fr African white-backed
         vultures   .55 .25
 d.   A48 3fr Johnston's okapi   .55 .25
358 Strip of 4   3.75 1.10
 a.   A48 5fr Chimpanzee   .60 .25
 b.   A48 5fr Elephant   .60 .25
 c.   A48 5fr Spotted hyenas   .60 .25
 d.   A48 5fr Beisa   .60 .25
359 Strip of 4   4.75 1.50
 a.   A48 6fr Gorilla   .95 .30
 b.   A48 6fr Gnu   .95 .30
 c.   A48 6fr Wart hog   .95 .30
 d.   A48 6fr Cape hunting dog   .95 .30
360 Strip of 4   5.75 1.75
 a.   A48 11fr Sable antelope   1.10 .35
 b.   A48 11fr Caracal lynx   1.10 .35
 c.   A48 11fr Ostriches   1.10 .35
 d.   A48 11fr Bongo   1.10 .35
    Nos. 355-360,C146-C151
      (12)   90.75 15.70

Nos. 355a-355d, 356a-356d, 357a-357d, 358a-358d and 359a-359d exist with gold line under country name.
For overprints and surcharges see Nos. C152, CB15-CB18.

The Resurrection, by Il Sodoma — A49

Paintings: 6fr, Resurrection, by Andrea del Castagno. 11fr, Noli me Tangere, by Correggio.

1971, Apr. 2
361 A49 3fr gold & multi   .25 .25
362 A49 6fr gold & multi   .25 .25
363 A49 11fr gold & multi   .50 .25
 a.   Souvenir sheet of 3, #361-363 1.75 1.75
    Nos. 361-363,C143-C145 (6)   5.60 1.60

Easter 1971. Exist imperf. Value: set (6) $4.75; souvenir sheets, $5.75.

Young Venetian Woman, by Dürer — A50

Dürer Paintings: 11fr, Hieronymus Holzschuher. 14fr, Emperor Maximilian I. 17fr, Holy Family, from Paumgartner Altar. 26fr, Haller Madonna. 31fr, Self-portrait, 1498.

1971, Sept. 20
364 A50 6fr multicolored   .30 .25
365 A50 11fr multicolored   .40 .25
366 A50 14fr multicolored   .55 .25
367 A50 17fr multicolored   1.00 .40
368 A50 26fr multicolored   1.25 .50
369 A50 31fr multicolored   1.50 .60
 a.   Souvenir sheet of 2, #368-369 3.50 3.50
    Nos. 364-369 (6)   5.00 2.25

International Letter Writing Week. Albrecht Dürer (1471-1528), German painter and engraver.
Exist imperf. Values: set $9; souvenir sheet $4.

Nos. 364-369, 369a Overprinted in Black and Gold: "VIème CONGRES / DE L'INSTITUT INTERNATIONAL / DE DROIT D'EXPRESSION FRANCAISE"

1971, Oct. 8
370 A50 6fr multicolored   .25 .25
371 A50 11fr multicolored   .35 .25
372 A50 14fr multicolored   .50 .25
373 A50 17fr multicolored   .75 .25
374 A50 26fr multicolored   1.10 .45
375 A50 31fr multicolored   1.40 .25
 a.   Souvenir sheet of 2   3.00 3.00
    Nos. 370-375 (6)   4.35 1.50

6th Cong. of the Intl. Legal Institute of the French-speaking Area, Bujumbura, 8/10-19. Exists imperf. Values: set $9; souvenir sheet $3.50.

Madonna and Child, by Il Perugino — A51

Paintings of the Madonna and Child by: 5fr, Andrea del Sarto. 6fr, Luis de Morales.

Lunar Orbiter A52

1971, Nov. 2   Photo.   Perf. 13½
376 A51 3fr dk green & multi   .30 .25
377 A51 5fr dk green & multi   .30 .25
378 A51 6fr dk green & multi   .35 .25
 a.   Souvenir sheet of 3, #376-378 4.50 4.50
    Nos. 376-378,C153-C155 (6)   3.85 1.60

Christmas 1971.
Exist imperf. Value: set (6) $4.50; souvenir sheets, $9.
For surcharges see Nos. B49-B51, CB19-CB21.

Designs: 11fr, Vostok. 14fr, Luna 1. 17fr, Apollo 11 astronaut on moon. 26fr, Soyuz 11. 40fr, Lunar Rover (Apollo 15).

1972, Jan. 15
379 A52 6fr gold & multi   .25 .25
380 A52 11fr gold & multi   .40 .25
381 A52 14fr gold & multi   .60 .25
382 A52 17fr gold & multi   .70 .25
383 A52 26fr gold & multi   1.25 .30
384 A52 40fr gold & multi   2.00 .50
 a.   Souvenir sheet of 6   5.50 5.50
    Nos. 379-384 (6)   5.20 1.80

Conquest of space.
No. 384a contains one each of Nos. 379-384 inscribed "APOLLO 16."
Exist imperf. Value: set $11; souvenir sheet, $11.
See No. C156.

Slalom and Sapporo '72 Emblem — A53

Sapporo '72 Emblem and: 6fr, Figure skating, pairs. 11fr, Figure skating, women's. 14fr, Ski jump. 17fr, Ice hockey. 24fr, Speed skating, men's. 26fr, Snow scooter. 31fr, Downhill skiing. 50fr, Bobsledding.

1972, Feb. 3
385 A53 5fr silver & multi   .25 .25
386 A53 6fr silver & multi   .25 .25
387 A53 11fr silver & multi   .35 .25
388 A53 14fr silver & multi   .45 .25
389 A53 17fr silver & multi   .60 .25
390 A53 24fr silver & multi   .75 .25
391 A53 26fr silver & multi   .90 .25
392 A53 31fr silver & multi   1.00 .25
393 A53 50fr silver & multi   1.75 .30
    Nos. 385-393 (9)   6.30 2.30

11th Winter Olympic Games, Sapporo, Japan, Feb. 3-13. Printed in sheets of 12. See No. C157.
Exists imperf. Value: set $37.50.
Issued: Nos. 385-390, 2/1; Nos. 391-393, 2/21.

Ecce Homo, by Quentin Massys — A54

Paintings: 6.50fr, Crucifixion, by Rubens. 10fr, Descent from the Cross, by Jacopo da Pontormo. 18fr, Pieta, by Ferdinand Gallegos. 27fr, Trinity, by El Greco.

1972, Mar. 20   Photo.   Perf. 13½
394 A54 3.50fr gold & multi   .25 .25
395 A54 6.50fr gold & multi   .45 .25
396 A54 10fr gold & multi   .70 .25
397 A54 18fr gold & multi   1.50 .25
398 A54 27fr gold & multi   1.75 .25
 a.   Souv. sheet of 5, #394-398 + label 7.00 7.00
    Nos. 394-398 (5)   4.65 1.25

Easter 1972. Printed in sheets of 8 with label.
Exist imperf. Value: set $6; souvenir sheet $7.

Gymnastics, Olympic Rings and "Motion" A55

1972, May 19
399 A55 5fr shown   .25 .25
400 A55 6fr Javelin   .35 .25
401 A55 11fr Fencing   .70 .25
402 A55 14fr Bicycling   .90 .25
403 A55 17fr Pole vault   1.10 .25
    Nos. 399-403,C158-C161 (9)   11.50 2.60

Souvenir Sheet
404   Sheet of 2   4.00 3.75
 a.   A55 31fr Discus   1.50 1.50
 b.   A55 40fr Soccer   1.50 1.50

20th Olympic Games, Munich, 8/26-9/11.
Exist imperf. Values: set (9) $9; souvenir sheet $5.

Prince Rwagasore, Pres. Micombero, Burundi Flag, Drummers A56

7fr, Rwagasore, Micombero, flag, map of Africa, globe. 13fr, Micombero, flag, globe.

1972, Aug. 24   Photo.   Perf. 13½
405 A56 5fr silver & multi   .25 .25
406 A56 7fr silver & multi   .25 .25
407 A56 13fr silver & multi   .45 .25
    Nos. 405-407,C162-C164 (6)   2.65 1.70

10th anniversary of independence.
Exist imperf. Values: set $3.50; souvenir sheets $2.

Madonna and Child, by Andrea Solario — A57

Paintings of the Madonna and Child by: 10fr, Raphael. 15fr, Botticelli.

1972, Nov. 2
408 A57 5fr lt blue & multi   .30 .25
409 A57 10fr lt blue & multi   .60 .25
410 A57 15fr lt blue & multi   1.10 .25
 a.   Souvenir sheet of 3, #408-410 2.75 2.75
    Nos. 408-410,C165-C167 (6)   8.00 1.65

Christmas 1972. Sheets of 20 stamps + label.
Exist imperf. Values: set (6) $7; souvenir sheets $8.50.
For surcharges see Nos. B56-B58, CB26-CB28.

Orchids — A58

50c, Platycoryne Crocea. 1fr, Cattleya trianaei. 2fr. Eulophia cucullata. 3fr, Cymbidium hamsey. 4fr, Thelymitra pauciflora. 5fr, Miltassia. 6fr, Miltonia.

1972		**Size: 33x33mm**		
411	A58	50c shown	.40	.25
412	A58	1fr multicolored	.50	.25
413	A58	2fr multicolored	.60	.25
414	A58	3fr multicolored	.75	.25
415	A58	4fr multicolored	.90	.25
416	A58	5fr multicolored	1.25	.25
417	A58	6fr multicolored	1.50	.25
		Size: 38x38mm		
418	A58	7fr Like 50c	1.75	.25
419	A58	8fr Like 1fr	2.00	.25
420	A58	9fr Like 2fr	2.50	.25
421	A58	10fr Like 3fr	3.00	.25
	Nos. 411-421,C168-C174 (18)		41.90	5.35

Issued: Nos. 411-417, 11/6; Nos. 418-421, 11/29.

Henry Morton Stanley — A59

Designs: 7fr, Porters, Stanley's expedition. 13fr, Stanley entering Ujiji.

1973, Mar. 19		**Photo.**	**Perf. 13½**	
422	A59	5fr gold & multi	.35	.25
423	A59	7fr gold & multi	.50	.25
424	A59	13fr gold & multi	.85	.25
	Nos. 422-424,C175-C177 (6)		5.05	1.60

Exploration of Africa by David Livingstone (1813-1873) and Henry Morton Stanley (John Rowlands; 1841-1904).
Exist imperf. Values: set (6) $4.50; souvenir sheets $3.50.

Crucifixion, by Roger van der Weyden — A60

Easter (Paintings): 5fr, Flagellation of Christ, by Caravaggio. 13fr, The Burial of Christ, by Raphael.

1973, Apr. 10				
425	A60	5fr gold & multi	.25	.25
426	A60	7fr gold & multi	.35	.25
427	A60	13fr gold & multi	.65	.25
a.	Souvenir sheet of 3, #425-427		3.75	3.00
	Nos. 425-427,C178-C180 (6)		5.80	1.65

Exist imperf. Values: set (6) $6; souvenir sheets $7.

INTERPOL Emblem, Flag — A61

Design: 10fr, INTERPOL flag and emblem. 18fr, INTERPOL Headquarters and emblem.

1973, May 19		**Photo.**	**Perf. 13½**	
428	A61	5fr silver & multi	.25	.25
429	A61	10fr silver & multi	.35	.25
430	A61	18fr silver & multi	.60	.25
	Nos. 428-430,C181-C182 (5)		4.05	1.55

Intl. Criminal Police Organization, 50th anniv.
Exist imperf. Value set, $5.50.

Signs of the Zodiac, Babylon — A62

Designs: 5fr, Greek and Roman gods representing planets. 7fr, Ptolemy (No. 433a) and Ptolemaic solar system. 13fr, Copernicus (No. 434a) and heliocentric system.
a, UL. b, UR. c, LL. d, LR.

1973, July 27		**Photo.**	**Perf. 13½**	
431	A62	3fr Block of 4, #a.-d.	1.10	.40
432	A62	5fr Block of 4, #a.-d.	1.75	.60
433	A62	7fr Block of 4, #a.-d.	2.50	.60
434	A62	13fr Block of 4, #a.-d.	3.50	1.00
e.	Souvenir sheet of 4, #431-434		25.00	25.00
	Nos. 431-434,C183-C186 (8)		31.60	7.60

500th anniversary of the birth of Nicolaus Copernicus (1473-1543), Polish astronomer.
Exist imperf. Values: set (8) $60; souvenir sheets $95.

Flowers and Butterflies — A63

Block of 4 containing 2 flower & 2 butterfly designs. The 1fr, 2fr, 5fr and 11fr have flower designs listed as "a" and "d" numbers, butterflies as "b" and "c" numbers; the arrangement is reversed for the 3fr and 6fr.

1973, Sept. 3		**Photo.**	**Perf. 13**	
		Stamp Size: 34x41½mm		
435	A63	Block of 4	1.75	.40
a.	1fr Protea cynaroides		.30	.25
b.	1fr Precis octavia		.30	.25
c.	1fr Epiphora bauhiniae		.30	.25
d.	1fr Gazania longiscapa		.30	.25
436	A63	Block of 4	3.50	.40
a.	2fr Kniphofia		.60	.25
b.	2fr Cymothoe coccinata		.60	.25
c.	2fr Nudaurelia zambesina		.60	.25
d.	2fr Freesia refracta		.60	.25
437	A63	Block of 4	5.50	.40
a.	3fr Calotis eupompe		.90	.25
b.	3fr Narcissus		.90	.25
c.	3fr Cineraria hybrida		.90	.25
d.	3fr Cyrestis camillus		.90	.25
438	A63	Block of 4	9.00	.40
a.	5fr Iris tingitana		1.50	.25
b.	5fr Pappilio demodocus		1.50	.25
c.	5fr Catopsilia avelaneda		1.50	.25
d.	5fr Nerine sarniensis		1.50	.25
439	A63	Block of 4	10.00	.45
a.	6fr Hypolimnas dexithea		1.75	.25
b.	6fr Zantedeschia tropicalis		1.75	.25
c.	6fr Sandersonia aurantiaca		1.75	.25
d.	6fr Drurya antimachus		1.75	.25
440	A63	Block of 4	12.50	.50
a.	11fr Nymphaea capensis		2.00	.25
b.	11fr Pandoriana pandora		2.00	.25
c.	11fr Precis orythia		2.00	.25
d.	11fr Pelargonium domestica		2.00	.25
	Nos. 435-440,C187-C192 (12)		141.25	7.10

Virgin and Child, by Giovanni Bellini — A64

Virgin and Child by: 10fr, Jan van Eyck. 15fr, Giovanni Boltraffio.

1973, Nov. 13		**Photo.**	**Perf. 13**	
441	A64	5fr gold & multi	.50	.25
442	A64	10fr gold & multi	1.00	.25
443	A64	15fr gold & multi	1.25	.25
a.	Souvenir sheet of 3, #441-443		2.50	2.00
	Nos. 441-443,C193-C195 (6)		7.50	1.55

Christmas 1973.
Exist imperf. Values: set $8; souvenir sheets $8.
For surcharges see Nos. B59-B61, CB29-CB31.

Pietá, by Paolo Veronese — A65

Paintings: 10fr, Virgin and St. John, by van der Weyden. 18fr, Crucifixion, by van der Weyden. 27fr, Burial of Christ, by Titian. 40fr, Pietá, by El Greco.

1974, Apr. 19		**Photo.**	**Perf. 14x13½**	
444	A65	5fr gold & multi	.25	.25
445	A65	10fr gold & multi	.40	.25
446	A65	18fr gold & multi	1.10	.25
447	A65	27fr gold & multi	1.60	.25
448	A65	40fr gold & multi	2.50	.35
a.	Souvenir sheet of 5, #444-448		5.75	5.00
	Nos. 444-448 (5)		5.85	1.35

Easter 1974.
Exist imperf. Values: set $6.50; souvenir sheet $8.

Fish — A66

1974, May 30		**Photo.**	**Perf. 13**	
		Stamp Size: 35x35mm		
449	A66	Block of 4	4.50	.55
a.	1fr Haplochromis multicolor		.80	.25
b.	1fr Pantodon buchholzi		.80	.25
c.	1fr Tropheus duboisi		.80	.25
d.	1fr Distichodus sexfasciatus		.80	.25
450	A66	Block of 4	6.00	.40
a.	2fr Pelmatochromis kribensis		.90	.25
b.	2fr Nannaethiops tritaeniatus		.90	.25
c.	2fr Polycentropsis abbreviata		.90	.25
d.	2fr Hemichromis bimaculatus		.90	.25
451	A66	Block of 4	6.50	.65
a.	3fr Ctenopoma acutirostre		1.00	.25
b.	3fr Synodontis angelicus		1.00	.25
c.	3fr Tilapia melanopleura		1.00	.25
d.	3fr Aphyosemion bivittatum		1.00	.25
452	A66	Block of 4	10.00	.70
a.	5fr Monodactylus argenteus		1.60	.25
b.	5fr Zanclus canescens		1.60	.25
c.	5fr Pygoplites diacanthus		1.60	.25
d.	5fr Cephalopholis argus		1.60	.25
453	A66	Block of 4	12.50	.75
a.	6fr Priacanthus arenatus		2.25	.25
b.	6fr Pomacanthus arcuatus		2.25	.25
c.	6fr Scarus guacamaia		2.25	.25
d.	6fr Zeus faber		2.25	.25
454	A66	Block of 4	25.00	1.90
a.	11fr Lactophrys quadricornis		4.50	.45
b.	11fr Balistes vetula		4.50	.45

c.	11fr Acanthurus bahianus	4.50	.45
d.	11fr Holocanthus ciliaris	4.50	.45
Nos. 449-454,C207-C212 (12)		144.00	13.15

Soccer and Cup A67

Designs: Various soccer scenes and cup.

1974, July 4		**Photo.**	**Perf. 13**	
455	A67	5fr gold & multi	.30	.25
456	A67	6fr gold & multi	.40	.25
457	A67	11fr gold & multi	.75	.25
458	A67	14fr gold & multi	1.10	.30
459	A67	17fr gold & multi	1.50	.30
a.	Souvenir sheet of 3		7.25	6.00
	Nos. 455-459,C196-C198 (8)		10.05	2.65

World Soccer Championship, Munich, June 13-July 7. No. 459a contains 3 stamps similar to Nos. C196-C198 without "Poste Aerienne."
Exist imperf. Values: set (8) $8; souvenir sheet $10.

Flags over UPU Headquarters, Bern — A68

No. 460b, G.P.O., Bujumbura. No. 461a, Mailmen ("11F" in UR). No. 461b, Mailmen ("11F" in UL). No. 462a, UPU emblem. No. 462b, Means of transportation. No. 463a, Pigeon over globe showing Burundi. No. 463b, Swiss flag, pigeon over map showing Bern. Pairs are continuous designs.

1974, July 23				
460	A68	6fr Pair, #a.-b.	.85	.25
461	A68	11fr Pair, #a.-b.	1.25	.25
462	A68	14fr Pair, #a.-b.	1.75	.25
463	A68	17fr Pair, #a.-b.	2.10	.25
c.	Souvenir sheet of 8, #460-463		20.00	20.00
	Nos. 460-463,C199-C202 (8)		19.95	3.35

Cent. of UPU.
Exist imperf. Value set, $30.

St. Ildefonso Writing Letter, by El Greco A69

Paintings: 11fr, Lady Sealing Letter, by Chardin. 14fr, Titus at Desk, by Rembrandt. 17fr, The Love Letter, by Vermeer. 26fr, The Merchant G. Gisze, by Holbein. 31fr, Portrait of Alexandre Lenoir, by David.

1974, Oct. 1		**Photo.**	**Perf. 13**	
468	A69	6fr gold & multi	.35	.25
469	A69	11fr gold & multi	.60	.30
470	A69	14fr gold & multi	.70	.35
471	A69	17fr gold & multi	1.00	.35
472	A69	26fr gold & multi	1.10	.45
473	A69	31fr gold & multi	1.50	.60
a.	Souvenir sheet of 2, #472-473		4.00	4.00
	Nos. 468-473 (6)		5.25	2.30

International Letter Writing Week, Oct. 6-12.
Exist imperf. Values: set $7; souvenir sheet $4.

Virgin and Child, by Bernaert van Orley — A70

Paintings of the Virgin and Child: 10fr, by Hans Memling. 15fr, by Botticelli.

1974, Nov. 7   Photo.   Perf. 13
474	A70	5fr gold & multi	.65	.25
475	A70	10fr gold & multi	1.20	.25
476	A70	15fr gold & multi	1.50	.25
a.		Souvenir sheet of 3, #474-476	4.00	4.00
		Nos. 474-476,C213-C215 (6)	8.75	1.75

Christmas 1974. Sheets of 20 stamps and one label.
Exist imperf. Values: set (6) $7.50; souvenir sheets $9.

Apollo-Soyuz Space Mission and Emblem — A71

1975, July 10   Photo.   Perf. 13
477	A71	Block of 4	4.00	2.75
a.		26fr A.A. Leonov, V.N. Kubasov, Soviet flag	.65	
b.		26fr Soyuz and Soviet flag	.65	
c.		26fr Apollo and American flag	.65	
d.		26fr D.K. Slayton, V.D. Brand, T.P. Stafford, American flag	.65	
478	A71	Block of 4	5.00	3.25
a.		31fr Apollo-Soyuz link-up	.95	
b.		31fr Apollo, blast-off	.95	
c.		31fr Soyuz, blast-off	.95	
d.		31fr Kubasov, Leonov, Slayton, Brand, Stafford	.95	
		Nos. 477-478,C216-C217 (4)	18.00	12.00

Apollo Soyuz space test project (Russo-American cooperation), launching July 15; link-up, July 17.
Exist imperf. Value set, $16.

Addax — A72

1975, July 31   Photo.   Perf. 13½
479		Strip of 4	1.50	.65
a.	A72	1fr shown	.30	.25
b.	A72	1fr Roan antelope	.30	.25
c.	A72	1fr Nyala	.30	.25
d.	A72	1fr White rhinoceros	.30	.25
480		Strip of 4	2.40	.65
a.	A72	2fr Mandrill	.45	.25
b.	A72	2fr Eland	.45	.25
c.	A72	2fr Salt's dik-dik	.45	.25
d.	A72	2fr Thomson's gazelles	.45	.25
481		Strip of 4	4.00	.65
a.	A72	3fr African small-clawed otter	.65	.25
b.	A72	3fr Reed buck	.65	.25
c.	A72	3fr Indian civet	.65	.25
d.	A72	3fr Cape buffalo	.65	.25
482		Strip of 4	6.00	1.10
a.	A72	5fr White-tailed gnu	1.10	.25
b.	A72	5fr African wild asses	1.10	.25
c.	A72	5fr Black-and-white colobus monkey	1.10	.25
d.	A72	5fr Gerenuk	1.10	.25
483		Strip of 4	8.75	1.10
a.	A72	6fr Dama gazelle	1.60	.25
b.	A72	6fr Black-backed jackal	1.60	.25
c.	A72	6fr Sitatungas	1.60	.25
d.	A72	6fr Zebra antelope	1.60	.25

484		Strip of 4	12.00	1.10
a.	A72	11fr Fennec	2.25	.25
b.	A72	11fr Lesser kudus	2.25	.25
c.	A72	11fr Blesbok	2.25	.25
d.	A72	11fr Serval	2.25	.25
		Nos. 479-484,C218-C223 (12)	94.90	11.30

For overprints see Nos. C224-C227.

Jonah, by Michelangelo — A73

Paintings from Sistine Chapel: No. 485b, Libyan Sybil. No. 486a, Prophet Isaiah. No. 486b, Delphic Sybil. No. 487a, Daniel. No. 487b, Cumaean Sybil.

1975, Dec. 3   Photo.   Perf. 13
485	A73	5fr Pair, #a.-b.	1.50	.50
486	A73	13fr Pair, #a.-b.	3.50	.60
487	A73	27fr Pair, #a.-b.	6.00	.70
c.		Souvenir sheet of 6, #485-487	12.00	9.00
		Nos. 485-487,C228-C230 (6)	30.50	4.30

Michelangelo Buonarotti (1475-1564), Italian sculptor, painter and architect. Printed in sheets of 18 stamps + 2 labels.
Exist imperf. Values: set (6) $30; souvenir sheets $28.
For surcharges see Nos. B65-B67, CB35-CB37.

Speed Skating — A74

Designs (Innsbruck Games Emblem and): 24fr, Figure skating, women's. 26fr, Two-man bobsled. 31fr, Cross-country skiing.

1976, Jan. 23 Photo.   Perf. 14x13½
491	A74	17fr dp bl & multi	.70	.25
492	A74	24fr multi	1.00	.25
493	A74	26fr multi	1.25	.25
494	A74	31fr plum & multi	1.50	.35
a.		Souvenir sheet of 3, perf. 13½	5.50	3.50
		Nos. 491-494,C234-C236 (7)	9.35	2.50

12th Winter Olympic Games, Innsbruck, Austria, Feb. 4-15.
No. 494a contains stamps similar to Nos. C234-C236, without "POSTE AERIENNE."
Exist imperf. Values: set (7) $10; souvenir sheets $10.

Basketball — A75

Montreal Games Emblem and: Nos. 495a, 498b, 499c, Basketball. Nos. 495b, 497a, 499b, Pole vault. Nos. 496a, 497b, 499d, Running. Nos. 496b, 498a, 499a, Soccer.

1976, May 3   Litho.   Perf. 13½
495	A75	14fr Pair, #a.-b.	1.50	1.00
496	A75	17fr Pair, #a.-b.	2.25	1.50
497	A75	28fr Pair, #a.-b.	3.50	2.25
498	A75	40fr Pair, #a.-b.	9.00	4.00
		Nos. 495-498,C237-C239 (7)	34.25	20.90

Souvenir Sheet
499		Sheet of 4	13.50	13.50
a.	A75	14fr red & multi	3.00	3.00
b.	A75	17fr olive & multi	3.00	3.00
c.	A75	28fr blue & multi	3.00	3.00
d.	A75	40fr magenta & multi	3.00	3.00

21st Olympic Games, Montreal, Canada, July 17-Aug. 1.
Exist imperf. Values: set (7) $30; souvenir sheets $50.

Virgin and Child, by Dirk Bouts — A76

Virgin and Child by: 13fr, Giovanni Bellini. 27fr, Carlo Crivelli.

1976, Oct. 18   Photo.   Perf. 13½
504	A76	5fr gold & multi	.85	.25
505	A76	13fr gold & multi	1.10	.25
506	A76	27fr gold & multi	2.00	.25
a.		Souvenir sheet of 3, #504-506	4.00	3.50
		Nos. 504-506,C250-C252 (6)	11.20	1.75

Christmas 1976. Sheets of 20 stamps and descriptive label.
Exist imperf. Values: set (6) $10; souvenir sheets $11.
For surcharges see Nos. B71-B73, CB41-CB43.

St. Veronica, by Rubens A77

Paintings by Rubens: 21fr, Christ on the Cross. 27fr, Descent from the Cross. 35fr, The Deposition.

1977, Apr. 5   Photo.   Perf. 13
507	A77	10fr gold & multi	1.50	1.50
508	A77	21fr gold & multi	3.00	3.00
509	A77	27fr gold & multi	3.25	3.25
510	A77	35fr gold & multi	4.00	4.00
a.		Souvenir sheet of 4	10.00	10.00
		Nos. 507-510 (4)	11.75	11.75

Easter 1977. Sheets of 30 stamps and descriptive label. No. 510a contains 4 stamps similar to Nos. 507-510 inscribed "POSTE AERIENNE."
Exist imperf. Values: set $14; souvenir sheet $12.

A78

No. 511a, Alexander Graham Bell. Nos. 511b, Intelsat Satellite, Modern & Old Telephones. No. 512a, Switchboard operator, c. 1910, wall telephone. No. 512b, Intelsat, radar. No. 513a, A.G. Bell, 1st telephone. No. 513b, Satellites around globe, videophone.

1977, May 17   Photo.   Perf. 13
511	A78	10fr Pair, #a.-b.	1.25	1.25
512	A78	17fr Pair, #a.-b.	2.50	2.50
513	A78	26fr Pair, #a.-b.	4.50	4.50
		Nos. 511-513,C253-C254 (5)	13.90	13.90

Centenary of first telephone call by Alexander Graham Bell, Mar. 10, 1876.
Exist imperf. Value set (5), $9.

Wildlife — A80

1977, Aug. 22 Photo.   Perf. 14x14½
517	A80	Strip of 4	2.25	.25
a.		2fr Buffon's Kob	.50	.25
b.		2fr Marabous	.50	.25
c.		2fr Brindled gnu	.50	.25
d.		2fr River hog	.50	.25

518	A80	Strip of 4	3.75	.50
a.		5fr Zebras	.75	.25
b.		5fr Shoebill	.75	.25
c.		5fr Striped hyenas	.75	.25
d.		5fr Chimpanzee	.75	.25
519	A80	Strip of 4	6.00	.60
a.		8fr Flamingos	1.25	.25
b.		8fr Nile crocodiles	1.25	.25
c.		8fr Green mamba	1.25	.25
d.		8fr Greater kudus	1.25	.25
520	A80	Strip of 4	12.00	.70
a.		11fr Hyrax	2.25	.25
b.		11fr Cobra	2.25	.25
c.		11fr Jackals	2.25	.25
d.		11fr Verreaux's eagles	2.25	.25
521	A80	Strip of 4	17.50	1.00
a.		21fr Honey badger	3.25	.25
b.		21fr Harnessed antelopes	3.25	.25
c.		21fr Secretary bird	3.25	.25
d.		21fr Klipspringer	3.25	.25
522	a80	Strip of 4	22.50	1.50
a.		27fr African big-eared fox	4.75	.30
b.		27fr Elephants	4.75	.30
c.		27fr Vulturine guineafowl	4.75	.30
d.		27fr Impalas	4.75	.30
		Nos. 517-522,C258-C263 (12)	184.50	13.45

Exist imperf.

The Goose Girl, by Grimm — A81

Fairy Tales: 5fr, by Grimm Brothers. 11fr, by Aesop. 14fr, by Hans Christian Andersen. 17fr, by Jean de La Fontaine. 26fr, English fairy tales.

1977, Sept. 14   Perf. 14
523		Block of 4	5.50	.65
a.	A81	5fr shown	1.00	.25
b.	A81	5fr The Two Wanderers	1.00	.25
c.	A81	5fr The Man of Iron	1.00	.25
d.	A81	5fr Snow White and Rose Red	1.00	.25
524		Block of 4	11.50	.65
a.	A81	11fr The Quarreling Cats	2.00	.25
b.	A81	11fr The Blind and the Lame	2.00	.25
c.	A81	11fr The Hermit and the Bear	2.00	.25
d.	A81	11fr The Fox and the Stork	2.00	.25
525		Block of 4	14.50	.65
a.	A81	14fr The Princess and the Pea	2.50	.25
b.	A81	14fr The Old Tree Mother	2.50	.25
c.	A81	14fr The Ice Maiden	2.50	.25
d.	A81	14fr The Old House	2.50	.25
526		Block of 4	18.00	1.00
a.	A81	17fr The Oyster and the Suitors	3.50	.25
b.	A81	17fr The Wolf and the Lamb	3.50	.25
c.	A81	17fr Hen with the Golden Egg	3.50	.25
d.	A81	17fr The Wolf as Shepherd	3.50	.25
527		Block of 4	24.00	1.25
a.	A81	26fr Three Heads in the Well	4.00	.25
b.	A81	26fr Mother Goose	4.00	.25
c.	A81	26fr Jack and the Beanstalk	4.00	.25
d.	A81	26fr Alice in Wonderland	4.00	.25
		Nos. 523-527 (5)	73.50	4.20

Exist imperf. Value (set), $80.

Security Council Chamber, UN Nos. 28, 46, 37, C7 — A82

UN Stamps and: 8fr, UN General Assembly, interior. 21fr, UN Meeting Hall.

1977, Oct. 10   Photo.   Perf. 13½
528	A82	Block of 4	3.50	2.50
a.		8fr No. 25	.90	.50
b.		8fr No. C5	.90	.50
c.		8fr No. 23	.90	.50
d.		8fr No. 28	.90	.50
529	A82	Block of 4	5.25	3.50
a.		10fr No. 28	1.00	.75
b.		10fr No. 46	1.00	.75
c.		10fr No. 37	1.00	.75
d.		10fr No. C7	1.00	.75
530	A82	Block of 4	8.75	6.00
a.		21fr No. 45	1.60	1.25
b.		21fr No. 42	1.60	1.25
c.		21fr No. 17	1.60	1.25

d. 21fr No. 13   1.60   1.25
e. Souvenir sheet of 3   4.00   4.00
Nos. 528-530,C264-C266 (6)   41.00   35.50

25th anniv. (in 1976) of the UN Postal Administration. No. 530e contains 8fr in design of No. 529d, 10fr in design of No. 530b, 21fr in design of No. 528c.
Exist imperf. Value (set), $55.

Virgin and Child — A83

Paintings of the Virgin and Child: 5fr, By Meliore Toscano. 13fr, By J. Lombardos. 27fr, By Emmanuel Tzanes, 1610-1680.

1977, Oct. 31   Photo.   Perf. 14x13
531 A83 5fr multicolored   1.10   .30
532 A83 13fr multicolored   2.25   .60
533 A83 27fr multicolored   3.25   .75
a. Souvenir sheet of 3, #531-533   6.00   6.00
Nos. 531-533,C267-C269 (6)   14.60   6.65

Christmas 1977. Sheets of 24 stamps with descriptive label.
Exist imperf. Values: set (6) $15; souvenir sheets $9.
For surcharges see Nos. B74-B76, CB44-CB46.

Cruiser Aurora, Russia Nos. 211, 303, 1252, 187 — A84

Russian Stamps and: 8fr, Kremlin, Moscow. 11fr, Pokrovski Cathedral, Moscow. 13fr, Labor Day parade, 1977 and 1980 Olympic Games emblem.

1977, Nov. 14   Photo.   Perf. 13
534 A84 Block of 4   4.00   .60
a. 5fr No. 211   .85   .25
b. 5fr No. 303   .85   .25
c. 5fr No. 1252   .85   .25
d. 5fr No. 187   .85   .25
535 A84 Block of 4   7.75   .60
a. 8fr No. 856   1.25   .25
b. 8fr No. 1986   1.25   .25
c. 8fr No. 908   1.25   .25
d. 8fr No. 2551   1.25   .25
536 A84 Block of 4   10.50   .60
a. 11fr No. 3844b   1.75   .25
b. 11fr No. 3452   1.75   .25
c. 11fr No. 3382   1.75   .25
d. 11fr No. 3837   1.75   .25
537 A84 Block of 4   13.00   .90
a. 13fr No. 4446   2.10   .25
b. 13fr No. 3497   2.10   .25
c. 13fr No. 2926   2.10   .25
d. 13fr No. 2365   2.10   .25
Nos. 534-537 (4)   35.25   2.70

60th anniv. of Russian October Revolution.
Exist imperf. Value (set), $30.00.

Ship at Dock, Arms and Flag — A85

Burundi Arms and Flag and: 5fr, Men at lathes. 11fr, Male leopard dance. 14fr, Coffee harvest. 17fr, Government Palace.

1977, Nov. 25   Photo.   Perf. 13½
538 A85 1fr sil & multi   .25   .25
539 A85 5fr sil & multi   .25   .25
540 A85 11fr sil & multi   .70   .25
541 A85 14fr sil & multi   1.10   .25
542 A85 17fr sil & multi   1.40   .30
Nos. 538-542 (5)   3.70   1.30

15th anniversary of independence.
Exist imperf. Value (set), $4.

A86

Paintings of the Virgin and Child by: 13fr, Rubens. 17fr, Solario. 27fr, Tiepolo. 31fr, Gerard David. 40fr, Bellini.

1979, Feb.   Photo.   Perf. 14x13
543 A86 13fr multi   1.75   1.10
544 A86 17fr multi   2.10   1.25
545 A86 27fr multi   3.50   2.10
546 A86 31fr multi   4.50   2.75
547 A86 40fr multi   6.00   3.75
Nos. 543-547 (5)   17.85   10.95

Christmas 1978. See Nos. B77-B81, C270, CB47.
Exist imperf. Value (set), $19.

Birds — A87

Designs: 1fr, Buceros abyssinicus. 2fr, Anhinga rufa. 3fr, Phoeniconais minor. 5fr, Phoeniconais minor. 8fr, Afropavo congenis. 10fr, Porphyrio alba. 20fr, Polemaethus bellicosus. 27fr, Ibis ibis. 50fr, Ephippiorhynchus senegalensis.

1979   Photo.   Perf. 13½x13
548 A87 1fr multicolored   .60   .60
549 A87 2fr multicolored   .65   .65
550 A87 3fr multicolored   .75   .75
551 A87 5fr multicolored   1.10   1.00
552 A87 8fr multicolored   1.90   1.75
553 A87 10fr multicolored   2.25   2.00
554 A87 20fr multicolored   4.75   4.50
555 A87 27fr multicolored   5.25   5.00
556 A87 50fr multicolored   10.50   10.00
Nos. 548-556,C273-C281 (18)   91.50   65.90

See No. 585F.

Mother and Infant, IYC Emblem A88

IYC Emblem and: 20fr, Infant. 27fr, Girl with doll. 50fr, Children in Children's Village.

1979, July 19   Photo.   Perf. 14
557 A88 10fr multi   .90   .90
558 A88 20fr multi   2.10   1.75
559 A88 27fr multi   2.75   2.75
560 A88 50fr multi   4.25   4.25
Nos. 557-560 (4)   10.00   9.65

Exist imperf. Value set, $10.
See No. B82.

A89

Virgin and Child by: 20fr, del Garbo. 27fr, Giovanni Penni. 31fr, G. Romano. 50fr, Jacopo Bassano.

1979, Oct. 12
561 A89 20fr multi   2.00   1.00
562 A89 27fr multi   3.75   2.00
563 A89 31fr multi   5.25   2.50
564 A89 50fr multi   6.50   2.75
Nos. 561-564,B83-B86 (8)   39.50   16.50

Christmas 1979. See Nos. C271, CB48.
Exist imperf. Value set (8), $35.

A90

Designs: 20fr, Rowland Hill, Penny Black. Stamps of Burundi: 27fr, German East Africa Nos. 17, N17. 31fr, Nos. 4, 24. 40fr, Nos. 29, 294. 60fr, Heinrich von Stephan, No. 462.

1979, Nov. 6
565 A90 20fr multi   1.35   .75
566 A90 27fr multi   1.90   1.00
567 A90 31fr multi   2.10   1.10
568 A90 40fr multi   3.50   1.90
569 A90 60fr multi   5.00   2.75
Nos. 565-569 (5)   13.85   7.50

Sir Rowland Hill (1795-1879), originator of penny postage.
Exist imperf. Vale, set $14.
See No. C272.

A91

No. 570: a, 110-meter hurdles. b, Hurdles, Thomas Munkelt. c, Hurdles, R.D.A.
No. 571: a, Discus. b, Discus, V. Rasshchupkin. c, Discus, U.R.S.S.
No. 572: a, Soccer (player preparing to kick ball) b, Soccer (ball in air) c, Soccer, (ball being blocked by hands).

1980, Oct. 24   Photo.   Perf. 13x13½
570 A91 20fr Strip of 3, #a.-c.   10.00   4.00
571 A91 30fr Strip of 3, #a.-c.   16.00   6.00
572 A91 40fr Strip of 3, #a.-c.   23.00   9.50
Nos. 570-572 (3)   49.00   19.50

22nd Summer Olympic Games, Moscow, July 19-Aug. 3.
Exist imperf. Value set, $49.
See No. C282.

Virgin and Child, by Mainardi A92

Christmas 1980 (Paintings): 30fr, Holy Family, by Michelangelo. 40fr, Virgin and Child, by di Cosimo. 45fr, Holy Family, by Fra Bartolomeo.

1980, Dec. 12   Photo.   Perf. 13½x13
579 A92 10fr multi   1.50   .65
580 A92 30fr multi   3.00   1.25
581 A92 40fr multi   6.50   3.00
582 A92 45fr multi   9.00   4.00
Nos. 579-582,B87-B90 (8)   42.10   17.80

Exist imperf. Value set, $45.
See No. CB49.

UPRONA Party National Congress, 1979 — A93

1980, Dec. 29   Perf. 14x13½
583 A93 10fr multi   .90   .65
584 A93 40fr multi   2.75   2.10
585 A93 45fr multi   3.00   2.40
Nos. 583-585 (3)   6.65   5.15

Exist imperf. Value set, $6.

Birds Type of 1979

Designs: 5fr, Buceros abyssinicus. 30fr, Melittophagus pusillus. 40fr, Phoeniconaias minor. 50fr, Porphyrio alba.

1980   Photo.   Perf. 13½x13
Brown Frame
585A A87 5fr multi   —
585C A87 30fr multi   —
585D A87 40fr multi   —
585F A87 50fr multi   —
Metallic Blue Frame
585L A87 50fr Like #585F   —

Seven additional stamps were issued in this set. The editors would like to examine any examples.

Johannes Kepler, Dish Antenna A94

1981, Feb. 12   Perf. 14
586 A94 10fr shown   2.75   1.00
587 A94 40fr Satellite   6.00   1.90
588 A94 45fr Satellite, diff.   8.25   2.50
a. Souvenir sheet of 3, #586-588   17.50   13.00
Nos. 586-588 (3)   17.00   5.40

350th death anniv. of Johannes Kepler and 1st earth satellite station in Burundi.
Exist imperf. Values: set $16; souvenir sheet $19.

Lion A95

3fr, Giraffes. 5fr, Rhinoceros. 10fr, Cape buffalo. 20fr, Elephant. 25fr, Hippopotamus. 30fr, Zebra. 50fr, Warthog. 60fr, Oryx. 65fr, Wild dog. 70fr, Cheetah. 75fr, Wildebeest. 85fr, Hyena.

1983, Apr. 22   Photo.   Perf. 13
589 A95 2fr shown   4.50   11.00
590 A95 3fr multi   4.50   11.00
591 A95 5fr multi   6.00   11.00
592 A95 10fr multi   7.50   15.00
593 A95 20fr multi   11.00   15.00
594 A95 25fr multi   15.00   30.00
595 A95 30fr multi   22.50   30.00
596 A95 50fr multi   30.00   55.00
597 A95 60fr multi   15.00   67.50
598 A95 65fr multi   19.00   75.00
599 A95 70fr multi   22.50   90.00
600 A95 75fr multi   30.00   110.00
601 A95 85fr multi   1,100.   525.00
Nos. 589-601 (13)   1,288.   1,046.

Nos. 589-601 Overprinted in Silver with World Wildlife Fund Emblem

1983   **Photo.**   **Perf. 13**

589a	A95	2fr multi	10.00	5.00
590a	A95	3fr multi	10.00	6.00
591a	A95	5fr multi	10.00	6.50
592a	A95	10fr multi	10.00	15.00
593a	A95	20fr multi	25.00	22.50
594a	A95	25fr multi	40.00	27.50
595a	A95	30fr multi	50.00	40.00
596a	A95	50fr multi	75.00	60.00
597a	A95	60fr multi	90.00	67.50
598a	A95	65fr multi	110.00	75.00
599a	A95	70fr multi	130.00	80.00
600a	A95	75fr multi	180.00	90.00
601a	A95	85fr multi	260.00	100.00
	Nos. 589a-601a (13)		1,000.	595.00

Apparently there is speculation in these two sets. Both sets exist imperf, offered at prices 5-7 times the values shown above.

20th Anniv. of Independence, July 1, 1982 — A96

Flags, various arms, map or portrait.

1983   **Perf. 14**

602	A96	10fr multi	1.00	.65
603	A96	25fr multi	3.25	2.25
604	A96	30fr multi	3.75	2.50
605	A96	50fr multi	5.25	3.25
606	A96	65fr multi	6.75	4.50
	Nos. 602-606 (5)		20.00	13.15

Exist imperf. Value set, $22.50.

Christmas 1983 — A97

Virgin and Child paintings: 10fr, by Luca Signorelli (1450-1523). 25fr, by Esteban Murillo (1617-1682). 30fr, by Carlo Crivelli (1430-1495). 50fr, by Nicolas Poussin (1594-1665).

1983, Oct. 3   **Litho.**   **Perf. 14½x13½**

607	A97	10fr multi	4.50	1.25
608	A97	25fr multi	6.50	1.75
609	A97	30fr multi	12.00	3.50
610	A97	50fr multi	17.00	9.00
	Nos. 607-610,B91-B94 (8)		89.50	31.00

Exist imperf. Value set, $110.
See Nos. C285, CB50.

Butterflies — A98

No. 611a, Cymothoe coccinata. No. 611b, Papilio zalmoxis. No. 612a, Asterope pechueli. No. 612b, Papilio antimachus. No. 613a, Papilio hesperus. No. 613b, Bebearia mardania. No. 614a, Euphaedra neophron. No. 614b, Euphaedra perseis. No. 615a, Euphaedra imperialis. No. 615b, Pseudocraea striata.

1984, June 29   **Photo.**   **Perf. 13**

611	A98	5fr Pair, #a.-b.	13.00	3.75
612	A98	10fr Pair, #a.-b.	22.00	4.50
613	A98	30fr Pair, #a.-b.	62.50	18.00
614	A98	35fr Pair, #a.-b.	67.50	29.00
615	A98	65fr Pair, #a.-b.	150.00	50.00
	Nos. 611-615 (5)		315.00	105.25

Exist imperf. Value set, $1,600.
For surcharges see No. 654D.

19th UPU Congress, Hamburg A99

UPU emblem and: 10fr, German East Africa, #17, N17. 30fr, #4, 24. 35fr, #294, 595. 65fr, Dr. Heinrich von Stephan, #464-465.

1984, July 14   **Litho.**   **Perf. 13x13½**

621	A99	10fr multi	2.75	.60
622	A99	30fr multi	6.00	2.75
623	A99	35fr multi	7.25	3.75
624	A99	65fr multi	8.75	4.50
	Nos. 621-624 (4)		24.75	11.60

Exist imperf. Value set, $27.50.
See No. C286.

1984 Summer Olympics — A100

Gold medalists: 10fr, Jesse Owens, US, track and field, Berlin, 1936. 30fr, Rafer Johnson, US, decathlon, 1960. 35fr, Bob Beamon, US, long jump, 1968. 65fr, Kipchoge Keino, Kenya, 3000-meter steeplechase, 1972.

1984, Aug. 6   **Perf. 13½x13**

625	A100	10fr multi	2.75	.90
626	A100	30fr multi	7.25	2.75
627	A100	35fr multi	8.75	3.00
628	A100	65fr multi	14.50	6.00
	Nos. 625-628 (4)		33.25	12.65

Exist imperf. Value set, $32.50.
See No. C287.

Christmas 1984 — A101

Paintings: 10fr, Rest During the Flight into Egypt, by Murillo (1617-1682). 25fr, Virgin and Child, by R. del Garbo. 30fr, Virgin and Child, by Botticelli (1445-1510). 50fr, The Adoration of the Shepherds, by Giacomo da Bassano (1517-1592).

1984, Dec. 15   **Perf. 13½**

629	A101	10fr multi	3.25	1.00
630	A101	25fr multi	7.50	2.50
631	A101	30fr multi	9.00	3.00
632	A101	50fr multi	13.00	4.75
	Nos. 629-632,B95-B98 (8)		60.75	22.50

Exist imperf. Value set (8), $65.
See Nos. C288, CB51.

Flowers — A102

1986, July 31   **Photo.**   **Perf. 13x13½**

633	A102	2fr Thunbergia	.50	.40
634	A102	3fr Saintpaulia	.75	.50
635	A102	5fr Clivia	1.25	.75
636	A102	10fr Cassia	3.25	1.60
637	A102	20fr Strelitzia	6.50	4.00
638	A102	35fr Gloriosa	9.75	5.75
	Nos. 633-638,C289-C294 (12)		120.00	77.50

For surcharges see Nos. 654A-654B.

Intl. Peace Year — A103

10fr, Rockets as housing. 20fr, Atom as flower. 30fr, Handshake. 40fr, Globe, chicks.

1986, May 1   **Litho.**   **Perf. 14**

639	A103	10fr multicolored	1.00	.55
640	A103	20fr multicolored	2.00	1.10
641	A103	30fr multicolored	3.25	2.00
642	A103	40fr multicolored	4.75	2.75
a.	Souvenir sheet of 4, #639-642		11.50	6.25
	Nos. 639-642 (4)		11.00	6.40

No. 642a exists imperf. Value $11.

Great Lake Nations Economic Community (CEPGI), 10th Anniv. — A104

Outline maps of Lake Tanganyika, CEPGI emblem and: 5fr, Aviation. 10fr, Agriculture. 15fr, Industry. 25fr, Electrification. 35fr, Flags of Burundi, Rwanda and Zaire.

1986, May 1   **Photo.**   **Perf. 13½x14½**

643	A104	5fr multi	2.75	.50
644	A104	10fr multi	6.50	1.90
645	A104	15fr multi	10.50	2.50
646	A104	25fr multi	14.50	3.75
647	A104	35fr multi	21.00	60.00
a.	Souv. sheet, #643-647 + label		70.00	27.50
	Nos. 643-647 (5)		55.25	68.65

No. 647a exists imperf. Value $70.

Intl. Year of Shelter for the Homeless A105

10fr, Hovel. 20fr, Drain pipe shelter. 80fr, Shoveling sand. 150fr, Children, house model.

1987, June   **Litho.**   **Perf. 14**

648	A105	10fr multicolored	2.50	.55
649	A105	20fr multicolored	4.50	1.25
650	A105	80fr multicolored	10.00	4.50
651	A105	150fr multicolored	18.00	7.75
a.	Souvenir sheet of 4, #648-651		35.00	17.50
	Nos. 648-651 (4)		35.00	14.05

Exist imperf. Values: set $35; souvenir sheet $35.

A106

1987(?)   **Litho.**   **Perf. 14**

652	A106	5fr shown	1.45	.50
653	A106	20fr, Skull, lungs	9.00	2.40
654	A106	80fr Cigarette, face	24.00	7.50
	Nos. 652-654 (3)		34.45	10.40

WHO Anti-smoking campaign.
Exist imperf. Value set, $35.

Nos. 633-634 Srchd. in Silver and Black

Methods and Perfs As Before

1989

654A	A102	20fr on 2fr #633	—
654B	A102	20fr on 3fr #634	—

An additional stamp was issued in this set. The editors would like to examine any example.

No. 613 Surcharged

1989   **Photo.**   **Perf. 13**

654D	A98	80fr on 30fr, Pair, #e.-f.	—

Numbers have been reserved for additional values in this set.

Visit of Pope John Paul II — A107

1990   **Litho.**   **Perf. 14**

655	A107	5fr red lil & multi	1.15	.30
656	A107	10fr blue & multi	1.75	.50
657	A107	20fr gray & multi	3.25	1.25
658	A107	30fr ol grn & multi	5.25	2.25
659	A107	50fr brt blue & multi	7.25	3.25
660	A107	80fr grn bl & multi	11.50	5.50
a.	Souv. sheet of 6, #655-660, perf. 13½		30.00	15.00
	Nos. 655-660 (6)		30.15	13.05

No. 660a exists imperf. Value $37.50.

Animals A108

5fr, Hippopotamus. 10fr, Chickens. 20fr, Lion. 30fr, Elephant. 50fr, Guinea fowl. 80fr, Crocodile.

1991, Oct. 4   **Litho.**   **Perf. 14**

661	A108	5fr multicolored	1.10	.45
662	A108	10fr multicolored	1.40	.75
663	A108	20fr multicolored	3.00	2.10
664	A108	30fr multicolored	4.25	2.25
665	A108	50fr multicolored	6.00	3.75
666	A108	80fr multicolored	5.25	5.25
a.	Souv. sheet of 6, #661-666, perf. 13½		27.50	17.50
	Nos. 661-666 (6)		27.75	14.55

No. 666a exists imperf. Value $30.

Flowers — A108a

15fr, Impatiens petersiana. 20fr, Lachenalia aloides. 30fr, Nymphaea lotus. 50fr, Clivia miniata.

1992, June 2   Litho.   Perf. 14
666B	A108a	15fr multicolored	3.00	.70
666C	A108a	20fr multicolored	4.25	1.40
666D	A108a	30fr multicolored	6.75	1.75
666E	A108a	50fr multicolored	8.50	3.00
f.		Souvenir sheet of 4, #666B-666E, perf. 13½	22.50	6.50
		Nos. 666B-666E (4)	22.50	6.85

No. 666Ef exists imperf. Value $22.50.

A109

Native Music and Dancing A110

15fr, Native drummer. 30fr, Two dancers. 115fr, Drummers. 200fr, Five dancers.

1992, Apr. 2   Litho.   Perf. 14
667	A109	15fr multicolored	1.25	.40
668	A109	30fr multicolored	2.00	.85
669	A110	115fr multicolored	7.75	2.50
670	A110	200fr multicolored	11.50	4.50
a.		Souvenir sheet	22.50	13.50
		Nos. 667-670 (4)	22.50	8.25

No. 670a contains one each of Nos. 667-668, perf. 13x13½, and Nos. 669-670, perf. 13½x13.
No. 670a exists imperf. Value $22.50.

Independence, 30th Anniv. — A111

30fr, 140fr, People with flag. 85fr, 115fr, Natl. flag. 110fr, 200fr, Monument. 120fr, 250fr, Map.

1992, June 30   Litho.   Perf. 15
671	A111	30fr multi	.50	.30
672	A111	85fr multi	1.75	1.10
673	A111	110fr multi, vert.	2.00	1.50
674	A111	115fr multi, vert.	2.50	1.90
675	A111	120fr multi, vert.	2.75	2.00
676	A111	140fr multi	3.00	2.25
677	A111	200fr multi, vert.	4.25	3.00
678	A111	250fr multi, vert.	5.25	4.25
		Nos. 671-678 (8)	22.00	16.30

Discovery of America, 500th Anniv. A112

Columbus' fleet, globe and: 200fr, Pre-Columbian artifacts. 400fr, Fruits and vegetables.

1992, Oct. 12   Litho.   Perf. 15
679	A112	200fr multicolored	6.50	3.25
680	A112	400fr multicolored	11.00	7.00

Felis Serval A113

130fr, Two seated. 200fr, One standing, one lying. 220fr, Two faces.

1992, Oct. 16
681	A113	30fr shown	1.10	.50
682	A113	130fr multi	5.75	3.25
683	A113	200fr multi	8.00	4.25
684	A113	220fr multi	10.00	5.50
		Nos. 681-684 (4)	24.85	13.50

World Wildlife Fund.
Each stamp in this set was issued in 1997 with a 50fr surcharge and overprinted 'CAROLOPHILEX 97.' Value, set $120.

Mushrooms A114

Designs: 10fr, Russula ingens. 15fr, Russula brunneorigida. 20fr, Amanita zambiana. 30fr, Russula subfistulosa. 75fr, 85fr, Russula meleagris. 100fr, Russula immaculata. 110fr, like No. 685. 115fr, like No. 686. 120fr, 130fr, Russula sejuncta. 250fr, Afroboletus luteolus.

1992-93   Perf. 11½x12
Granite Paper
685	A114	10fr multicolored	.25	.25
686	A114	15fr multicolored	.40	.25
687	A114	20fr multicolored	.45	.30
688	A114	30fr multicolored	1.00	.90
689	A114	75fr multicolored	2.50	1.90
690	A114	85fr multicolored	3.00	2.50
691	A114	100fr multicolored	4.00	2.75
691A	A114	110fr multicolored	3.50	2.50
691B	A114	115fr multicolored	4.50	3.25
692	A114	120fr multicolored	5.25	3.25
693	A114	130fr multicolored	6.50	3.75
694	A114	250fr multicolored	12.50	7.75
		Nos. 685-694 (12)	43.85	29.35

Issued: 110fr, 115fr, 1993; others, 9/30/92.
For surcharges see Nos. 781-783.

1992 Summer Olympics, Barcelona A115

1992, Nov. 6   Perf. 15
695	A115	130fr Runners	4.00	2.00
696	A115	500fr Hurdler	13.50	8.50

A116

Christmas (Details of Adoration of the Kings, by Gentile da Fabriano): a, 100fr,

Crowd, horses. b, 130fr, Kings. c, 250fr, Nativity scene.

1992, Dec. 7   Litho.   Perf. 11½
697	A116	Strip of 3, #a.-c.	11.50	5.00
d.		Souvenir sheet of 3, #697a-697c	11.50	5.50

Nos. 697a-697c have white border. No. 697d has continuous design and sold for 580fr.

A116a

Designs: 200fr, Emblems. 220fr, Profile of person made from fruits and vegetables.

1992, Dec. 5   Litho.   Perf. 15
697E	A116a	200fr multicolored	8.50	4.00
697F	A116a	220fr multicolored	10.00	5.25

Intl. Conference on Nutrition, Rome.

European Common Market A117

Designs: 130fr, Flags, stars. 500fr, Europe, Africa, clasped hands, stars.

1993, Mar. 29   Litho.   Perf. 15
698	A117	130fr multicolored	3.00	1.50
699	A117	500fr multicolored	11.50	7.50

1994 World Cup Soccer Championships, US — A118

Players, stadium, US flag and: 130fr, Statue of Liberty. 200fr, Golden Gate Bridge.

1993, July 5   Litho.   Perf. 15
700	A118	130fr multicolored	5.50	2.50
701	A118	200fr multicolored	7.00	3.50

Traditional Musical Instruments — A119

1993, Apr. 30   Litho.   Perf. 15
702	A119	200fr Indonongo	3.50	3.25
703	A119	220fr Ingoma	4.00	3.50
704	A119	250fr Ikembe	4.50	3.75
705	A119	300fr Umuduri	5.25	4.50
		Nos. 702-705 (4)	17.25	15.00

A120

130fr, Papilio bromius. 200fr, Charaxes eupale. 250fr, Cymothoe caenis. 300fr, Graphium ridleyanus.

1993, June 4   Litho.   Perf. 11½
706	A120	130fr multicolored	3.50	3.00
707	A120	200fr multicolored	5.25	4.50
708	A120	250fr multicolored	6.75	6.25
709	A120	300fr multicolored	7.50	6.25
a.		Souvenir sheet of 4, #706-709	25.00	25.00
		Nos. 706-709 (4)	23.00	20.00

No. 709a sold for 980fr.

Farm Animals — A121

1993, Dec. 9   Perf. 14
710	A121	100fr Cattle	2.10	1.75
711	A121	120fr Sheep	2.50	2.40
712	A121	130fr Pigs	3.00	2.50
713	A121	250fr Goats	5.00	4.25
		Nos. 710-713 (4)	12.60	10.90

Christmas — A122

Natives adoring Christ Child: a, 100fr, Woman carrying baby, two people kneeling. b, 130fr, With Christ Child. 250fr, c, Woman carrying baby, three other people.

1993, Dec. 10   Perf. 11½
714	A122	Strip of 3, #a.-c.	12.00	12.00
d.		Souvenir sheet of 3, #714a-714c	12.00	12.00

Nos. 714a-714c have white border. No. 714d has continuous design and sold for 580fr.

Rock Stars — A123

60fr, Elvis Presley. 115fr, Mick Jagger. 120fr, John Lennon. 200fr, Michael Jackson.

1994   Litho.   Perf. 15
715	A123	60fr multi	2.00	1.75
716	A123	115fr multi	4.00	3.50
717	A123	120fr multi	4.00	3.50
718	A123	200fr multi	7.25	6.50
a.		Souvenir sheet, #715-718	17.50	16.00
		Nos. 715-718 (4)	17.25	15.25

No. 718a sold for 600fr.

A124

1994, Oct. 10   Litho.   Perf. 15
719	A124	150fr multicolored	9.00	6.00

Intl. Olympic Committee, cent.

A125

Christmas (Madonna and Child): a, 115fr, Chinese. b, 120fr, Japanese. c, 250fr, Polish.

1994, Dec. 14　Photo.　Perf. 15
720　A125　Strip of 3, #a.-c.　12.50 12.50
　d.　Souvenir sheet of 1, #720c　9.00 9.00

A126

115fr, FAO, 50th anniv. 120fr, UN, 50th anniv.

1995, Feb. 21　Litho.　Perf. 11½
721　A126　115fr multicolored　3.00 3.00
722　A126　120fr multicolored　3.00 3.00

A127

Flowers: 15fr, Cassia didymobotrya. 20fr, Mitragyna rubrostipulosa. 30fr, Phytolacca dodecandra. 85fr, Acanthus pubescens. 100fr, Bulbophyllum comatum. 110fr, Angraecum evradianum. 115fr, Eulophia burundiensis. 120fr, Habenaria adolphii.

Granite Paper

1995　Litho.　Perf. 11½
723　A127　15fr multicolored　.25 .25
724　A127　20fr multicolored　.45 .25
725　A127　30fr multicolored　.85 .45
726　A127　85fr multicolored　2.00 1.40
727　A127　100fr multicolored　2.50 1.60
728　A127　110fr multicolored　2.75 2.10
729　A127　115fr multicolored　3.50 2.75
730　A127　120fr multicolored　4.25 3.25
　Nos. 723-730 (8)　16.55 12.05

Transportation Methods — A128

30fr, Otraco bus. 115fr, Transintra semi truck. 120fr, Arnolac tugboat. 250fr, Air Burundi airplane.

1995, Nov. 16　Litho.　Perf. 11½
731　A128　30fr multicolored　.50 .35
732　A128　115fr multicolored　2.10 1.60
733　A128　120fr multicolored　2.40 1.90
734　A128　250fr multicolored　5.00 4.25
　Nos. 731-734 (4)　10.00 8.10

A129

Christmas (African sculpture): a, 100fr, Boy with panga, basket on head. b, 130fr, Boy carrying sheaf of wheat. c, 250fr, Mother, children.

1995, Dec. 26　Litho.　Perf. 11½x12
735　A129　Strip of 3, #a.-c.　10.00 10.00
　d.　Souvenir sheet of 3, #735a-735c　11.00 11.00

A130

Athlete, national flag: 130fr, Venuste Niyongabo. 500fr, Arthemon Hatungimana.

1996, June 28　Litho.　Perf. 14
736　A130　130fr multicolored　3.00 2.75
737　A130　500fr multicolored　9.50 8.50

1996 Summer Olympic Games, Atlanta.

Birds
A131

Designs: 15fr, Hagedashia hagedash. 20fr, Alopochen aegyptiacus. 30fr, Haliaeetus vocifer. 120fr, Ardea goliath. 165fr, Balearica regulorum. 220fr, Actophilornis africana.

1996　Litho.　Perf. 14
740　A131　15fr multicolored　.40 .40
741　A131　20fr multicolored　.55 .55
742　A131　30fr multicolored　.65 .65
743　A131　120fr multicolored　2.00 2.00
744　A131　165fr multicolored　4.00 4.00
745　A131　220fr multicolored　5.50 5.50
　Nos. 740-745 (6)　13.10 13.10

Fish of Lake Tanganyika
A132

Designs: 30fr, Julidochromis malieri. 115fr, Cyphotilapia frontosa. 120fr, Lamprologus brichardi. 250fr, Synodonis petricola.

1996, June 4　Litho.　Perf. 11¾x11½
746　A132　30fr multicolored　.65 .55
747　A132　115fr multicolored　2.10 2.00
748　A132　120fr multicolored　2.50 2.10
749　A132　250fr multicolored　4.50 4.50
　a.　Souv. sheet, #746-749, perf 11¾　11.00 11.00
　Nos. 746-749 (4)　9.75 9.15

No. 749a sold for 615fr.
Although ostensibly issued in 1996, this set was not available in the philatelic marketplace until 1999.

SOS Children's Village, 50th Anniv. — A133

100fr, Children in Village. 250fr, Children, flags. 270fr, Children around flagpole.

1998, Dec. 26　Litho.　Perf. 14
750　A133　100fr multicolored　1.00 1.00
751　A133　250fr multicolored　2.40 2.40
752　A133　270fr multicolored　2.50 2.50
　Nos. 750-752 (3)　5.90 5.90

Christmas — A134

Various paintings of Madonna and Child.

1999, Jan. 19　Perf. 11¾
Frame color
753　A134　100fr green　1.40 1.40
754　A134　130fr yellow brown　2.00 2.00
755　A134　250fr rose　3.50 3.50
　a.　Souvenir sheet of 3, #753-755　9.00 9.00
　Nos. 753-755 (3)　6.90 6.90

Nos. 753-755 are dated "1996," "1997," and "1998," respectively.
No. 755a sold for 580fr.

Diana, Princess of Wales (1961-97)
A135

Denominations: a, 100fr. b, 250fr. c, 300fr.

1999, Sept. 30　Perf. 13¾
756　A135　Sheet of 6, 2 each #a.-c.　12.00 12.00

Fight Against Hunger — A136

2000, Feb. 28　Litho.　Perf. 14
757　A136　350fr Danny Kaye　2.50 2.50
　Issued in sheets of 5.

Second Republic, 10th Anniv. (in 1986) — A136a

Designs: 70fr, Coffee pickers, statue. 80fr, Pres. Jean-Baptiste Bagaza, arms of Burundi. 200fr, Children at school, statue.

2000 ?　Photo.　Perf. 13¾x14
757B　A136a　200fr multi　—
757C　A136a　70fr multi　—
757D　A136a　80fr multi　—

One additional stamp was issued in this set. The editors would like to examine any examples.

Space — A137

No. 758, horiz.: a, Space plane (2003). b, Reuseable space plane. c, Future space ship. d, Galileo. e, Space telescope. f, Space platform. g, Satellite launched Feb. 17, 1996. h, Cassini. i, Solar probe. j, Vehicle without fenders. k, Vehicle with fenders. l, Spacecraft for Mars.
1500fr, Newton's telescope.

2000, July 24　Litho.　Perf. 14
758　A137　165fr Sheet of 12, #a-l　20.00 20.00
Souvenir Sheet
759　A137　1500fr multi　20.00 20.00

Flowers — A138

Design: 150fr, Dodecatheon. 200fr, Fremonto dendron. 250fr, Rudbeckia laciniata. 350fr, Helianthus amnus. 400fr, Lilium longiflorum.

2002, Apr. 4　Litho.　Perf. 13x12¾
760　A138　150fr multi　—
761　A138　200fr multi　—
762　A138　250fr multi　—
764　A138　350fr multi　—
765　A138　400fr multi　—

One additional stamp was issued in this set. The editors would like to examine any examples.

Orchids, Mushrooms, Birds and Butterflies — A139

No. 766, 650fr — Orchids: a, Angraceum eburnum. b, Disa cardinalis. c, Bulbophyllum guttulatum. d, Aerangis luteoalba. e, Disa diores. f, Disa kirstenbosch.
No. 767, 650fr, horiz. — Mushrooms: a, Stropharia aerugurosa. b, Inocybe rimosa. c,

Cortinarius alboviolaceus. d, Hypholoma fasciculare. e, Cortinarius purpurascens. f, Hebeloma crustuliniforme.

No. 768, 650fr — Birds: a, Phalacrocorax carbo. b, Threskiornis aethiopicus. c, Nycticorax nycticorax. d, Phoeniconaias minor. e, Balaeniceps rex. f, Balearica regulorum.

No. 769, 650fr, horiz. — Butterflies: a, Papilio antenor. b, Graphium policenes. c, Papilio bromius. d, Graphium ridleyanus. e, Eurytides xanticles. f, Papilio gallienus.

No. 770, 2500fr, Aerangis citrata. No. 771, 2500fr, Coprinus picaceus. No. 772, 2500fr, Dendrocygna viduata. No. 773, 2500fr, Papilio dardanus, horiz.

2004, Nov. 8   Litho.   Perf. 14
Sheets of 6, #a-f
766-769 A139 Set of 4   45.00 45.00
Souvenir Sheets
770-773 A139 Set of 4   30.00 30.00

Worldwide Fund for Nature
(WWF) — A140

No. 774 — Sitatunga: a, Pair, both without horns. b, One, with horns. c, One, without horns. d, Pair, one with horns.

2004, Nov. 8   Perf. 13¼
774 A140 500fr Block or strip
              of 4, #a-d   13.00 13.00
  e. Sheet, 2 each #774a-774d   25.00 25.00
Frames vary.
No. 774e exists imperf. Value $90.

Tourism
A141

Designs: 150fr, Source of the Nile River (Luvironza River). 250fr, Monument to Burton and Speke, Nyanza. 500fr, Shanga Waterfall, Karera. 1000fr, Monument to Stanley and Livingstone, Mugere.

2007, May 8   Litho.   Perf. 13x13½
775-778 A141 Set of 4   15.00 15.00

24th UPU
Congress
A142

2007, Oct. 16   Litho.   Perf. 13x13½
779 A142 730fr multi   7.00 7.00
780 A142 730fr +20fr multi   8.00 8.00

The 24th UPU Congress was moved to Geneva from Nairobi because of political unrest.

No. 692
Surcharged in
White and Black

Methods and Perfs As Before
2007
781 A114 1200fr on 120fr #692 12.00 12.00
782 A114 1300fr on 120fr #692 13.00 13.00
783 A114 2500fr on 120fr #692 25.00 25.00
  Nos. 781-783 (3)   50.00 50.00

2008 Summer
Olympics,
Beijing — A144

2008, Aug. 1   Litho.   Perf. 13½x13
787 A144 500fr multi   6.00 6.00

Flowers
and Birds
A145

Designs: 90fr, Erythrina flowers. 150fr, Maracuja flower. 500fr, Werner flowers, vert. 810fr, Heron, vert. 1000fr, Aigle royal (golden eagle), vert.

2008, Dec. 24   Perf. 13x13½, 13½x13
788-792 A145 Set of 5   25.00 25.00

Birds
A146

Designs: 290fr, Hieraaetus spilogaster. 295fr, Falco eleonorae. 505fr, Falco subbuteo. 515fr, Falco biarmicus. 555fr, Bubo africanus. 590fr, Milvus migrans aegyptius. 710fr, Haliaeetus vocifer. 730fr, Trigonoceps occipitalis. 810fr, Gypohierax angolensis.

2009, July 6   Litho.   Perf. 13x13½
Granite Paper
793-801 A146 Set of 9   50.00 50.00
801a   Sheet of 9, #793-801 50.00 50.00

Owls — A147

Various owls: 860fr, 1010fr, 1030fr, 1100fr.

2009, July 8   Perf. 13½x13
Granite Paper
802-805 A147 Set of 4   45.00 45.00
805a   Souvenir sheet of 4,
               #802-805   45.00 45.00

A148

A149

A150

A151

A152

A153

A154

A155

Butterflies
A156

2009, July 13   Perf. 13x13½
Granite Paper
806 A148 500fr multi   4.00 4.00
807 A149 500fr multi   4.00 4.00
808 A150 500fr multi   4.00 4.00
809 A151 500fr multi   4.00 4.00
810 A152 500fr multi   4.00 4.00
811 A153 500fr multi   4.00 4.00
812 A154 500fr multi   4.00 4.00
813 A155 500fr multi   4.00 4.00
814 A156 500fr multi   4.00 4.00
  a. Sheet of 9, #806-814   40.00 40.00
      Nos. 806-814 (9)   36.00 36.00

Miniature Sheet

Fish — A157

No. 815: a, Astatoreochromis straeleni. b, Brycinus imberi. c, Amphilius jacksonii. d, Gnathonemus longibarbis. e, Citharinus gibbosus. f, Orthochromis malagaraziensis. g, Hapiochromis sp. h, Hydrocynus vittatus. i, Hippopotamyrus dischorhynchus. j, Labeobarbus sp. k, Malapterurus tanganyikaensis. l, Mormyrus longirostris. m, Petrocephalus catastoma. n, Ctenopoma muriei. o, Oreochromis niloticus eduardianus.

2009, Aug. 1   Granite Paper
815 A157 400fr Sheet of 15,
                  #a-o   50.00 50.00

Miniature Sheet

Traditional Hairstyles — A158

No. 816: a, Close-up of bearded man. b, Man with neckerchief and bag with letter "A." c, Bearded man, hand holding stick in background. d, Man with back of head shaved, with pipe in mouth, facing right. e, Man wearing patterned neckerchief with pipe in mouth, facing right. f, Man with necklace and bracelet.

2010, Jan. 1   Perf. 13¾x13¼
816 A158 500fr Sheet of 6, #a-
                  f   18.00 18.00

Souvenir Sheet

Traditional Houses — A159

No. 817: a, Family and house. b, House.

2010, Jan. 1   Perf. 13¼x13¾
817 A159 500fr Sheet of 2, #a-b 6.50 6.50

Miniature Sheet

Art and Culture — A160

No. 818: a, Dancers. b, Busts. c, Two women, spears, sculpture, flowers. d, Woman with bowls and containers. e, Large decorated pot. f, Man with stick and pot. g, Woman with head on hand, vert. h, Sculptures. i, Woman with necklace and headcovering, vert.

Perf. 13x13½, 13½x13 (#818g, 818i)
2010, June 1   **Granite Paper**
818   A160   500fr   Sheet of 9, #a-
     i   24.00 24.00
Pan-African Postal Union, 30th anniv.

Primates
A161

Designs: 730fr, Chimpanzee. 1000fr, Baboons. 2500, Gorillas.

2011, Mar. 15   *Perf. 13x13¼*
819-821   A161   Set of 3   20.00 20.00
821a   Souvenir sheet of 3,
       #819-821   20.00 20.00

Animals
A162

Hippopotamus amphibius: 1000fr, Three animals. 1020fr, Three animals, diff. No. 824, 3000fr, Three animals with open mouths. No. 825, 3000fr, Two animals.
No. 826: a, 1090fr, One animal facing right. b, 1090fr, One animal facing left. c, 3000fr, One animal facing forward. d, 3000fr, One animal facing left.

2011, Dec. 1   *Perf. 13x13½*
822-825   A162   Set of 4   15.00 15.00
Miniature Sheet
Perf. 13½
826   A162   Sheet of 4, #a-d   15.00 15.00

Primates

Designs: 1020fr, Pan troglodytes. No. 828, 1090fr, Papio anubis. No. 829, 3000fr, Two Colobus angolensis. No. 830, 3000fr, Two Chlorocebus pygerythrus.
No. 831: a, 1090fr, Two Chlorocebus pygerythrus, diff. b, 1090fr, Pan troglodytes, diff. c, 3000fr, Papio anubis, diff. d, 3000fr, Adult, juvenile and head of Colobus angolensis.

Perf. 13x13½
827-830   A162   Set of 4   15.00 15.00
Miniature Sheet
Perf. 13½
831   A162   Sheet of 4, #a-d   15.00 15.00

Rhinoceroses

Designs: No. 832, 1090fr, Diceros bicornis. No. 833, 1090fr, Ceratotherium simum. No. 834, 3000fr, Diceros bicornis facing right. No. 835, 3000fr, Ceratotherium simum facing left.
No. 836: a, 1020fr, Ceratotherium simum, diff. b, 1120fr, Diceros bicornis, diff. c, 3000fr, Adult and juvenile Ceratotherium simum. d, 3000fr, Diceros bicornis facing left.

832-835   A162   Set of 4   15.00 15.00
Miniature Sheet
Perf. 13½
836   A162   Sheet of 4, #a-d   15.00 15.00

Bats

Designs: No. 837, 1020fr, Epomops franqueti. No. 838, 1020fr, Nyctalus noctula. No. 839, 3000fr, Desmodus rotundus. No. 840, 3000fr, Plecotus austriacus, name at LR.
No. 841: a, 1000fr, Nyctalus noctula, diff. b, 1120fr, Rhinolophus hipposideros. c, 3000fr, Plecotus austriacus, name at UL. d, 3000fr, Nyctophilus corbeni.

Perf. 13x13½
837-840   A162   Set of 4   15.00 15.00
Miniature Sheet
Perf. 13½
841   A162   Sheet of 4, #a-d   15.00 15.00

Cats

Designs: 1000fr, Acinonyx jubatus. No. 843, 1090fr, Leptailurus serval. No. 844, 3000fr, Panthera pardus facing left. No. 845, 3000fr, Panthera leo.
No. 846: a, 1020fr, Acinonyx jubatus, diff. b, 1090fr, Panthera leo, diff. c, 3000fr, Felis silvestris. d, 3000fr, Panthera pardus facing right.

Perf. 13x13½
842-845   A162   Set of 4   15.00 15.00
Miniature Sheet
Perf. 13½
846   A162   Sheet of 4, #a-d   15.00 15.00

Elephants

Loxodonta afrciana: No. 847, 1000fr, Adult and juvenile. 1120fr, Adult facing right. No. 849, 3000fr, Adult facing left, animal name at UR. No. 850, 3000fr, Adult and juvenile, diff.
No. 851: a, 1000fr, Adult, animal name at left. b, 1000fr, Adult, animal name at UR. c, 3000fr, Adult facing right, animal name at LR. d, 3000fr, Adult facing left, animal name at LL.

Perf. 13x13½
847-850   A162   Set of 4   15.00 15.00
Miniature Sheet
Perf. 13½
851   A162   Sheet of 4, #a-d   15.00 15.00

Dolphins

Designs: No. 852, 1020fr, Lagenorhynchus albirostris. 1090fr, Grampus griseus. No. 854, 3000fr, Delphinus delphis. No. 855, 3000fr, Lagenorhynchus cruciger.
No. 856: a, 1000fr, Tursiops truncatus. b, 1020fr, Stenella attenuata. c, 3000fr, Stenella longirostris. d, 3000fr, Stenella frontalis.

Perf. 13x13½
852-855   A162   Set of 4   15.00 15.00
Miniature Sheet
Perf. 13½
856   A162   Sheet of 4, #a-d   15.00 15.00

Whales

Designs: No. 857, 1020fr, Balaenoptera musculus. No. 858, 1020fr, Balaenoptera physalus. No. 859, 3000fr, Orcinus orca. No. 860, 3000fr, Eschrichtius robustus.
No. 861: a, 1000fr, Eschrichtius robustus, diff. b, 1000fr, Balaenoptera musculus, diff. c, 3000fr, Megaptera novaeangliae. d, 3000fr, Delphinopterus leucas.

Perf. 13x13½
857-860   A162   Set of 4   15.00 15.00
Miniature Sheet
Perf. 13½
861   A162   Sheet of 4, #a-d   15.00 15.00

Birds of Prey

Designs: 1000fr, Gypohierax angolensis. No. 863, 1090fr, Pandion haliaetus. No. 864, 3000fr, Torgos tracheliotos. No. 865, 3000fr, Aquila wahlbergi.
No. 866: a, 1020fr, Lophaetus occipitalis. b, 1090fr, Necrosyrtes monachus. c, 3000fr, Falco tinnunculus. d, 3000fr, Polemaetus bellicosus.

Perf. 13x13½
862-865   A162   Set of 4   15.00 15.00
Miniature Sheet
Perf. 13½
866   A162   Sheet of 4, #a-d   15.00 15.00

Birds

Designs: 1000fr, Pelecanus onocrotalus. 1090fr, Phalacrocorax carbo. No. 869, 3000fr, Podiceps cristatus. No. 870, 3000fr, Mycteria ibis.
No. 871: a, 1020fr, Microcarbo africanus. b, 1020fr, Nettapus auritus. c, 3000fr, Phoenicopterus minor. d, 3000fr, Balaeniceps rex.

Perf. 13x13½
867-870   A162   Set of 4   15.00 15.00
Miniature Sheet
Perf. 13½
871   A162   Sheet of 4, #a-d   15.00 15.00

Parrots

Designs: No. 872, 1000fr, Agapornis fischeri. No. 873, 1000fr, Poicephalus meyeri. No. 874, 3000fr, Psittacus erithacus, name at UL. No. 875, 3000fr, Poicephalus robustus, name at right.
No. 876: a, 1000fr, Agapornis pullarius. b, 1090fr, Agapornis fischeri, diff. c, 3000fr, Poicephalus robustus, name at left. d, 3000fr, Psittacus erithacus, name at right.

Perf. 13x13½
872-875   A162   Set of 4   15.00 15.00
Miniature Sheet
Perf. 13½
876   A162   Sheet of 4, #a-d   15.00 15.00

Owls

Designs: No. 877, 1090fr, Tyto alba. No. 878, 1090fr, Tyto capensis. No. 879, 3000fr, Asio capensis, name at top. No. 880, 3000fr, Bubo africanus.
No. 881: a, 1020fr, Tyto capensis, diff. b, 1090fr, Bubo africanus, diff. c, 3000fr, Asio capensis, name at LR. d, 3000fr, Otus scops.

Perf. 13x13½
877-880   A162   Set of 4   15.00 15.00
Miniature Sheet
Perf. 13½
881   A162   Sheet of 4, #a-d   15.00 15.00

Bees

Designs: 1000fr, Bombus mixtus. 1090fr, Xylocopa virginica. No. 884, 3000fr, Bombus lapidarius. No. 885, 3000fr, Thyreus nitidulus.
No. 886: a, 1020fr, Osmia ribifloris. b, 1020fr, Apis mellifera. c, 3000fr, Anthidium florentinum. d, 3000fr, Apis mellifera scutellata.

Perf. 13x13½
882-885   A162   Set of 4   15.00 15.00
Miniature Sheet
Perf. 13½
886   A162   Sheet of 4, #a-d   15.00 15.00

Butterflies

Designs: 1090fr, Papilio torquatus. No. 888, 1120fr, Boloria dia. No. 889, 3000fr, Lasiommata megera. No. 890, 3000fr, Papilio menatius.
No. 891: a, 1020fr, Salamis temora. b, 1120fr, Charaxes castor. c, 3000fr, Acraea acrita. d, 3000fr, Papilio demodocus.

Perf. 13x13½
887-890   A162   Set of 4   15.00 15.00
Miniature Sheet
Perf. 13½
891   A162   Sheet of 4, #a-d   15.00 15.00

Fish and Marine Life

Designs: No. 892, 1000fr, Rhinobatos lentiginosus. 1090fr, Anoplogaster cornuta. No. 894, 3000fr, Stegostoma fasciatum. No. 895, 3000fr, Ocypode quadrata.
No. 896: a, 1000fr, Carcarhinus limbatus. b, 1020fr, Myliobatis californica. c, 3000fr, Hippocampus ingens. d, 3000fr, Mola mola.

Perf. 13x13½
892-895   A162   Set of 4   15.00 15.00
Miniature Sheet
Perf. 13½
896   A162   Sheet of 4, #a-d   15.00 15.00

Turtles

Designs: No. 897, 1020fr, Pelusios sinuatus. 1120fr, Stigmochelys pardalis. No. 899, 3000fr, Pelusios subniger. No. 900, 3000fr, Pelomedusa subrufa, name at UL.
No. 901: a, 1000fr, Stigmochelys pardalis, diff. b, 1020fr, Pelusios subniger, diff. c, 3000fr, Pelomedusa subrufa, name at UR. d, 3000fr, Pelusios sinuatus, diff.

Perf. 13x13½
897-900   A162   Set of 4   15.00 15.00
Miniature Sheet
Perf. 13½
901   A162   Sheet of 4, #a-d   15.00 15.00

Frogs

Designs: 1020fr, Leptopelis kivuensis. 1090fr, Hyperolius discodactylus. No. 904, 3000fr, Phrynobatrachus versicolor. No. 905, 3000fr, Hyperolius castaneus.

No. 906: a, 1000fr, Hyperolius viridiflavus. b, 1120fr, Bubbling kassina. c, 3000fr, Common plantannia. d, 3000fr, Hyperolius marmoratus.

Perf. 13x13½
902-905   A162   Set of 4   15.00 15.00
Miniature Sheet
Perf. 13½
906   A162   Sheet of 4, #a-d   15.00 15.00

Prehistoric Crocodiles

Designs: No. 907, 1020fr, Shansisuchus. 1090fr, Desmatosuchus. No. 909, 3000fr, Luperosuchus. No. 910, 3000fr, Araripesuchus.
No. 911: a, 1020fr, Baurusuchus. b, 1120fr, Champsosaurus. c, 3000fr, Dokosaursus. d, 3000fr, Geosaurus.

Perf. 13x13½
907-910   A162   Set of 4   15.00 15.00
Miniature Sheet
Perf. 13½
911   A162   Sheet of 4, #a-d   15.00 15.00

Dinosaurs

Designs: No. 912, 1090fr, Giganotosaurus. No. 913, 1090fr, Ankylosaurus. No. 914, 3000fr, Temnodontosaurus. No. 915, 3000fr, Triceratops.
No. 916: a, 1000fr, Stegosaurus. b, 1120fr, Pterosaur. c, 3000fr, Chasmatosaursus. d, 3000fr, Scutosaurus.

Perf. 13x13½
912-915   A162   Set of 4   15.00 15.00
Miniature Sheet
Perf. 13½
916   A162   Sheet of 4, #a-d   15.00 15.00

Worldwide
Fund for
Nature
(WWF)
A163

Laniarius mufumbiri: No. 917, 1120fr, Three birds. No. 918, 1120fr, One bird facing right. No. 919, 3000fr, One bird, facing left. No. 920, 3000fr, Two birds.

2011, Dec. 1   *Perf. 13x13½*
917-920   A163   Set of 4   15.00 15.00
920a   Souvenir sheet of 4,
       #917-920, perf. 13½   15.00 15.00

Organizations, People and
Events — A164

Scouting: No. 921, 1020fr, Six Scouts, purple emblem at LR. No. 922, 1020fr, Five scouts hunting and examining butterflies, green emblem at UR. No. 923, 3000fr, Scouts starting fire, green emblem at LR. No. 924, 3000fr, Kenyan Scouts, purple emblem at UL.
No. 925: a, 1000fr, Lord Robert Baden-Powell, scouts on rope bridge. b, 1090fr, Scout saluting, Scouts cooking, purple emblem at UL. c, 1090fr, Scouts around pile of sticks for campfire, green emblem at LR. d, 3000fr, Scout examining flower, Scouts in tower, purple emblem at LR.

2011, Dec. 30   **Litho.**   *Perf. 13x13½*
921-924   A164   Set of 4   15.00 15.00
Miniature Sheet
Perf. 13½
925   A164   Sheet of 4, #a-d   15.00 15.00

Humanitarian Organizations

Designs: No. 926, 1020fr, International Red Cross emblem, relief efforts in Obo, Central African Republic. No. 927, 1020fr, Rotary International emblem, Rotary recruitment, Méru, Kenya. No. 928, 3000fr, Lions International emblem, planting of trees in China. No. 929, 3000fr, UNICEF emblem, relief efforts to Pakistan flood victims.
No. 930: a, 1020fr, Lions International emblem, food distribution to Philippine typhoon victims. b, 1120fr, UNICEF emblem, Vietnamese school children. c, 3000fr, International Red Cross emblem, first aid, Rio de

Janeiro. d, 3000fr, Rotary International emblem, Saint Jude School, Tanzania.

Perf. 13x13½

926-929 A164 Set of 4 15.00 15.00

Miniature Sheet

Perf. 13½

930 A164 Sheet of 4, #a-d 15.00 15.00

Pope John Paul II

Pope John Paul II and: 1000fr, Sisters Marie Simon Pierre and Tobianna carrying relics of Pope John Paul II. 1020fr, Crowd holding banners. No. 933, 3000fr, Pope Benedict XVI holding infant. No. 929, 3000fr, Beatification ceremony for Pope John Paul II.

No. 935 — Pope John Paul II and: a, 1090fr, Pope Benedict XVI blessing crowd. b, 1090fr, Crowd holding banners, diff. c, 3000fr, Crowd holding banners and United States flag. d, 3000fr, Pope John Paul II waving to crowd.

Perf. 13x13½

931-934 A164 Set of 4 15.00 15.00

Miniature Sheet

Perf. 13½

935 A164 Sheet of 4, #a-d 15.00 15.00

Pope Benedict XVI

Pope Benedict XVI and works by Michelangelo: 1000fr, Ezekiel. 1120fr, Christ Carrying the Cross. No. 938, 3000fr, Zacharias. No. 939, 3000fr, Delphic Sybil.

No. 940 — Pope Benedict and works by Michelangelo: a, 1090fr, Libyan Sibyl. b, 1090fr, Joel. c, 3000fr, Creation of the Earth, Moon and Planets. d, 3000fr, Last Judgment.

Perf. 13x13½

936-939 A164 Set of 4 15.00 15.00

Miniature Sheet

Perf. 13½

940 A164 Sheet of 4, #a-d 15.00 15.00

Pierre-Auguste Renoir

Renoir and his works: No. 941, 1000fr, The Laundrywoman, 1891. No. 942, 1000fr, The Seine at Asnières, 1897. No. 943, 3000fr, Coucher de Soleil sur la Mer, 1879. No. 944, 3000fr, The Children of Monsieur Caillebotte, 1895.

No. 945 — Renoir and his works: a, 1000fr, Children on a Guernsey Beach, 1883. b, 1020fr, Oarsmen at Chatou, 1879. c, 1090fr, La Grenouillère, 1869. d, 3000fr, Luncheon of the Boating Party, 1880-81.

Perf. 13x13½

941-944 A164 Set of 4 15.00 15.00

Miniature Sheet

Perf. 13½

945 A164 Sheet of 4, #a-d 15.00 15.00

Pablo Picasso

Picasso and his works: No. 946, 1090fr, Child with a Dove, 1901. No. 947, 1090fr, Lecture, 1932. No. 948, 3000fr, Mother and Child, 1905. No. 949, 3000fr, Seated Woman in a Garden, 1938.

No. 950 — Picasso and his works: a, 1090fr, Guitar (I Love Eva), 1912. b, 1120fr, Head of a Woman, 1960. c, 3000fr, Jacqueline with Flowers, 1954. d, 3000fr, At the Lapin Agile, 1905.

Perf. 13x13½

946-949 A164 Set of 4 15.00 15.00

Miniature Sheet

Perf. 13½

950 A164 Sheet of 4, #a-d 15.00 15.00

Film Actors and Actresses

Designs: No. 951, 1000fr, James Dean. 1090fr, Marlene Dietrich. No. 953, 3000fr, Grace Kelly. No. 954, 3000fr, Clark Gable.

No. 955: a, 1000fr, John Wayne. b, 1120fr, Elizabeth Taylor. c, 3000fr, Romy Schneider. d, 3000fr, Marlon Brando.

Perf. 13x13½

951-954 A164 Set of 4 15.00 15.00

Miniature Sheet

Perf. 13½

955 A164 Sheet of 4, #a-d 15.00 15.00

Marilyn Monroe

Monroe: No. 956, 1020fr, With legs crossed. No. 957, 1020fr, With arms extended and leg raised. No. 958, 3000fr, With child on lap. No. 959, 3000fr, Holding drink.

No. 960: a, 1000fr, Seated, wearing gown. b, 1120fr, Seated on pilings, wearing bathing suit. c, 3000fr, Playing guitar. d, 3000fr, With skirt blowing up.

Perf. 13x13½

956-959 A164 Set of 4 15.00 15.00

Miniature Sheet

Perf. 13½

960 A164 Sheet of 4, #a-d 15.00 15.00

Elvis Presley

Presley: No. 961, 1090fr, Holding microphone, denomination at UL. No. 962, 1090fr, No microphone, denomination at UR. No. 963, 3000fr, Two images, microphone on stand, denomination at UR. No. 964, 3000fr, Two images, holding microphone, denomination at UR.

No. 965 — Presley: a, 1020fr, No microphone. b, 1120fr, Holding microphone. c, 3000fr, Three images, holding microphone, denomination at UR. d, 3000fr, Three images, no microphone, denomination at UL.

Perf. 13x13½

961-964 A164 Set of 4 15.00 15.00

Miniature Sheet

Perf. 13½

965 A164 Sheet of 4, #a-d 15.00 15.00

Singers

Designs: No. 966, 1090fr, Jimi Hendrix. No. 967, 1090fr, Paul McCartney. No. 968, 3000fr, Mick Jagger. No. 969, 3000fr, Ray Charles.

No. 970: a, 1020fr, Bob Marley. b, 1090fr, Tina Turner. c, 3000fr, Fats Domino. d, 3000fr, Stevie Wonder.

Perf. 13x13½

966-969 A164 Set of 4 15.00 15.00

Miniature Sheet

Perf. 13½

970 A164 Sheet of 4, #a-d 15.00 15.00

Composers

Designs: No. 971, 1000fr, Wolfgang Amadeus Mozart and memorial to Mozart, Vienna. 1090fr, Ludwig van Beethoven and Beethoven Monument, Bonn. No. 973, 3000fr, Antonio Vivaldi, and St. John the Baptist Church, Venice. No. 974, 3000fr, Frédéric Chopin, violin and bow.

No. 975: a, 1000fr, Mozart and keyboard. b, 1020fr, Beethoven and pipe organ. c, 3000fr, Vivaldi holding violin, churches. d, 3000fr, Chopin and piano.

Perf. 13x13½

971-974 A164 Set of 4 15.00 15.00

Miniature Sheet

Perf. 13½

975 A164 Sheet of 4, #a-d 15.00 15.00

Table Tennis Players

Designs: 1000fr, Wang Hao. 1120fr, Zhang Yining. No. 978, 3000fr, Guo Yue. No. 979, 3000fr, Werner Schlager.

No. 980: a, 1020fr, Ding Ning. b, 1090fr, Zhang Jike. c, 3000fr, Wang Liqin. d, 3000fr, Wang Nan.

Perf. 13x13½

976-979 A164 Set of 4 15.00 15.00

Miniature Sheet

Perf. 13½

980 A164 Sheet of 4, #a-d 15.00 15.00

Soccer Players

Designs: No. 981, 1000fr, Wayne Rooney, Municipal Stadium, Wroclaw, Poland. 1020fr, Bastian Schweinsteiger, National Stadium, Warsaw, Poland. No. 983, 3000fr, Samuel Eto'o, Poznan Stadium, Poznan, Poland. No. 984, 3000fr, Karim Benzema, Olympic Stadium, Kyiv, Ukraine.

No. 985: a, 1000fr, Cristiano Ronaldo, Olympic Stadium, Kyiv. b, 1090fr, Lionel Messi, Metalist Stadium, Kharkiv, Ukraine. c, 3000fr, Kaká, PGE Arena, Gdansk. d, 3000fr, Manuel Neuer, Donbass Arena, Donetsk, Ukraine.

Perf. 13x13½

981-984 A164 Set of 4 15.00 15.00

Miniature Sheet

Perf. 13½

985 A164 Sheet of 4, #a-d 15.00 15.00

Chess Players

Designs: 1020fr, Stan Vaughan. 1120fr, Emanuel Lasker. No. 988, 3000fr, Paul Morphy. No. 989, 3000fr, Alexandra Kosteniuk.

No. 990: a, 1090fr, François-André Danican Philidor. b, 1090fr, Domenico Ercole Del Rio. c, 3000fr, Howard Staunton. d, 3000fr, Johannes Zukertort.

Perf. 13x13½

986-989 A164 Set of 4 15.00 15.00

Miniature Sheet

Perf. 13½

990 A164 Sheet of 4, #a-d 15.00 15.00

Famous Africans

Designs: No. 991, 1020fr, Bishop Desmond Tutu. 1090fr, Wangari Maathai and Salamis temora butterfly. No. 993, 3000fr, Patrice Lumumba and Aerangis modesta flowers. No. 994, 3000fr, Kofi Annan.

No. 995: a, 1020fr, Nelson Mandela and Malachite. b, 1020fr, Léopold Sédar Senghor and Acraea acrita butterfly. c, 3000fr, Albert Lutuli and Precis sophia butterfly. d, 3000fr, Maathai and Fluorite.

Perf. 13x13½

991-994 A164 Set of 4 15.00 15.00

Miniature Sheet

Perf. 13½

995 A164 Sheet of 4, #a-d 15.00 15.00

Aviators

Designs: No. 996, 1020fr, Orville Wright and Wright biplane. No. 997, 1020fr, Adolphe Pégoud and Blériot monoplane. No. 998, 3000fr, Bert Hinkler and Puss Moth. No. 999, 3000fr, Richard E. Byrd and Curtiss-Wright biplane.

No. 1000: a, 1000fr, William Boeing, Boeing 787 and Boeing 80. b, 1090fr, Louis Blériot and Blériot XI. c, 3000fr, Charles Lindbergh and Spirit of St. Louis. d, 3000fr, Anthony Fokker and Fokker F-27 and Fokker Spin.

Perf. 13x13½

996-999 A164 Set of 4 15.00 15.00

Miniature Sheet

Perf. 13½

1000 A164 Sheet of 4, #a-d 15.00 15.00

Wedding of Prince William and Catherine Middleton

Prince William, Catherine Middleton and: 1090fr, Arms, British flag. No. 1002, 1120fr, Couple walking. No. 1003, 3000fr, Arms and Prince Harry. No. 1004, 3000fr, British flag, denomination at UR.

No. 1005 — Prince William, Catherine Middleton and: a, 1020fr, British flag, diff. b, 1120fr, British flag, diff. c, 3000fr, British flag, denomination at UL. d, 3000fr, British flag, denomination at UR, Prince wearing military cap.

Perf. 13x13½

1001-1004 A164 Set of 4 15.00 15.00

Miniature Sheet

Perf. 13½

1005 A164 Sheet of 4, #a-d 15.00 15.00

The Titanic

Titanic: No. 1006, 1000fr, At sea, denomination at UR in black. 1120fr, Near tugboats. No. 1008, 3000fr, Striking iceberg, denomination at UR in white, "Titanic" at UL in white. No. 1009, 3000fr, With Captain Edward Smith in ship's wheel, denomination at UR in black, "Titanic" at UL in black.

No. 1010 — Titanic: a, 1000fr, Sinking near lifeboat and iceberg. b, 1020fr, Sending up distress flares. c, 3000fr, At sea, denomination at UR in white, "Titanic" at UR in white. d, 3000fr, At sea, denomination at UR in black, "Titanic" at UR in black.

Perf. 13x13½

1006-1009 A164 Set of 4 12.50 12.50

Miniature Sheet

Perf. 13½

1010 A164 Sheet of 4, #a-d 12.00 12.00

Christmas

Paintings: No. 1011, 1020fr, Adoration of the Shepherds, by Gerrit van Honthorst. No. 1012, 1020fr, Adoration of the Shepherds, by Louis Le Nain. No. 1013, 3000fr, Nativity, by Georges de La Tour. No. 1014, 3000fr, Adoration of the Shepherds, by Bartolomé Esteban Murillo.

No. 1015: a, 1000fr, The Third Joyful Mystery, by Lorenzo Lotto. b, 1000fr, Adoration of the Child, by van Honthorst. c, 3000fr, Song of the Angels, by William Adolphe Bouguereau. d, 3000fr, Holy Family, by Lorenzo Costa.

Perf. 13x13½

1011-1014 A164 Set of 4 12.50 12.50

Miniature Sheet

Perf. 13½

1015 A164 Sheet of 4, #a-d 12.00 12.00

New Year 2012 (Year of the Dragon)

Dragon color: No. 1016, 1020fr, Red, tail at left. No. 1017, 1020fr, Green, tail at right. No.

1018, 3000fr, Blue, tail at UR. No. 1019, 3000fr, Brown, tail at LR.

No. 1020: a, 1090fr, Red, tail at left. b, 1090fr, Red and green, tail at right. c, 3000fr, Green and red, tail at right. d, 3000fr, Blue and red, tail at UL.

Perf. 13x13½

1016-1019 A164 Set of 4 12.50 12.50

Miniature Sheet

Perf. 13½

1020 A164 Sheet of 4, #a-d 12.50 12.50

A165

Sports Personalities — A166

No. 1021 — Muhammad Ali and scenes from fights with: a, 1070fr, Floyd Patterson. b, 1070fr, Doug Jones. c, 3000fr, Sonny Liston. d, 3000fr, Leon Spinks

No. 1022: a, 1070fr, He Chong, diving. b, 1070fr, Jordyn Marie Wieber, gymnastics. c, 1070fr, Olha Saladukha, triple jump. d, 5000fr, Pawel Wojciechowski, pole vault.

No. 1023: a, 1070fr, Lance Armstrong, cyclist. b, 1070fr, Martina Navratilova, tennis. c, 1070fr, Brian Lara, cricket. d, 5000fr, Pelé, soccer.

No. 1024: a, 1070fr, Lionel Messi, soccer. b, 1070fr, Novak Djokovic, tennis. c, 1070fr, Martin Kaymer, golf. d, 5000fr, Usain Bolt, track.

No. 1025, 7500fr, Muhammad Ali and Joe Frazier. No. 1026, 7500fr, Eric Guay, skiing. No. 1027, 7500fr, Carl Lewis, track. No. 1028, 7500fr, Magnus Carlsen, chess.

2012, Mar. 30 Litho. Perf. 13¼

Sheets of 4, #a-d

1021-1024 A165 Set of 4 50.00 50.00

Souvenir Sheets

1025-1028 A166 Set of 4 47.50 47.50

A167

Paintings — A168

No. 1029 — Paintings of Ivan Aivazovsky: a, 1070fr, Portrait of the Fleet on the Northern Sea, 1849. b, 1070fr, The Great Roads at Kronstadt, 1836, vert. c, 3000fr, Brig Mercury Attacked by Two Turkish Ships, 1892. d, 3000fr, The Battle in the Chios Channel, 1848, vert.

No. 1030 — Paintings of Camille Pissarro: a, 1070fr, Pont Boieldieu at Sunset, 1896. b, 1070fr, Woman Hanging Laundry, 1887, vert.

c, 3000fr, Boulevard Montmartre on a Cloudy Morning, 1897. d, 3000fr, The Old Market in Rouen, 1898, vert.

No. 1031 — Paintings of Edgar Degas: a, 1070fr, Hall of the Opera Ballet, 1874. b, 1070fr, Dance Examination, 1880, vert. c, 3000fr, Dance School, 1873. d, 3000fr, Singer with a Glove, 1878, vert.

No. 1032 — Paintings of Paul Cézanne: a, 1070fr, Rideau, Couchon et Compotier, 1893-94. b, 1070fr, The Village of Gardanne, 1886, vert. c, 3000fr, The Card Players, 1893-96. d, 3000fr, Forest Near the Rocky Caves Above the Chateau Noir, 1904, vert.

No. 1033 — Paintings of Claude Monet: a, 1070fr, Arrival of the Normandy Train, Gare Saint-Lazare, 1877. b, 1070fr, The Boat Studio, 1876, vert. c, 3000fr, Impression, Sunrise, 1872. d, 3000fr, Woman with Parasol, 1875, vert.

No. 1034 — Paintings of Frédéric Bazille: a, 1070fr, Family Reunion, 1867. b, 1070fr, The Rose Dress, 1864, vert. c, 3000fr, The Banks of the Lez, 1870. d, 3000fr, La Diseuse de Bonne Aventure, 1869, vert.

No. 1035 — Paintings of Berthe Morisot: a, 1070fr, Interior, 1872. b, 1070fr, At the Ball, 1875, vert. c, 3000fr, Lady at her Toilette, 1875. d, 3000fr, Young Girl with Cage, 1885, vert.

No. 1036 — Paintings of Armand Guillaumin: a, 1070fr, Sunset at Ivry, 1873. b, 1070fr, Hollow in the Snow, 1869, vert. c, 3000fr, La Place Valhubert, 1875. d, 3000fr, Outskirts of Paris, 1875, vert.

No. 1037 — Paintings of Gustave Caillebotte: a, 1070fr, The Boating Party, 1877-78. b, 1070fr, Interior, 1880, vert. c, 3000fr, The Floor Scrapers, 1875. d, 3000fr, A Balcony, 1880, vert.

No. 1038 — Paintings of Edouard Manet: a, 1070fr, Racecourse in the Bois de Boulogne, 1872. b, 1070fr, Café Concert, 1878, vert. c, 3000fr, Bar at the Folies-Bergère, 1881-82. d, 3000fr, Portrait of Irma Brunner, 1882, vert.

No. 1039 — Paintings of Ivan Shishkin: a, 1070fr, Rye Field, 1869. b, 1070fr, Bratzevo, 1869, vert. c, 1070fr, Morning in a Pine Forest, 1886 (bears on trees, title incorrect on stamp). d, 5000fr, Birch Grove, 1896, vert.

No. 1040 — Paintings of Alfred Sisley: a, 1070fr, Flood at Port-Marly, 1876. b, 1070fr, Snow at Louveciennes, 1874, vert. c, 1070fr, The Seine at Port-Marly Sand Piles, 1875. d, 5000fr, Street in Ville d'Avray, 1873, vert.

No. 1041 — Paintings of Pierre-Auguste Renoir: a, 1070fr, Moulin de la Galette, 1876 (artist and title omitted on stamp). b, 1070fr, Two Sisters on the Terrace, 1881, vert. c, 1070fr, Madame Charpentier and Her Children, 1878. d, 5000fr, The Theater Box, 1874, vert.

No. 1042 — Paintings of Mary Cassatt: a, 1070fr, Cup of Tea, 1879 (title omitted on stamp). b, 1070fr, Portrait of a Lady of Seville, 1873, vert. c, 1070fr, A Woman and a Girl Driving, 1881. d, 5000fr, Spanish Dancer Wearing a Lace Mantilla Box, 1873, vert.

No. 1043 — Tingatina paintings by: a, 1070fr, Saidi Omary. b, 1070fr, Noel Kapanda, vert. c, 1070fr, George Lilanga. d, 5000fr, Iddi Issa, vert.

No. 1044 — Paintings depicting Joan of Arc: a, 1070fr, Joan of Arc Kissing the Sword of Deliverance, by Dante Gabriel Rossetti, 1863. b, 1070fr, Joan of Arc During the Siege of Orleans, by Jules Eugene Lenepveu, 1889, vert. c, 1070fr, Capture of Joan of Arc, by Adolphe Alexandre Dillens, 1850. d, 5000fr, Joan of Arc at the Coronation of Charles VII in the Cathedral of Reims, by Jean Auguste Dominique Ingres, 1854, vert.

No. 1045, 7500fr, A Ship in the Stormy Sea, 1887, by Aivazovsky. No. 1046, 7500fr, The Poultry Market at Pontoise, 1882, by Pissarro. No. 1047, 7500fr, The Green Dancer, 1879, by Degas. No. 1048, 7500fr, Harlequin, 1888-90, by Cézanne. No. 1049, 7500fr, Rouen Cathedral, Magic in Blue, 1894, by Monet. No. 1050, 7500fr, Village View, 1868, by Bazille. No. 1051, 7500fr, In the Dining Room, 1875, by Morisot. No. 1052, 7500fr, Vase of Chrysanthemums, 1885, by Guillaumin. No. 1053, 7500fr, Young Man at His Window, 1876, by Caillebotte. No. 1054, 7500fr, Spring (Jeanne de Marsy), 1881, by Manet. No. 1055, 7500fr, Evening, 1892, by Shishkin. No. 1056, 7500fr, Grande Rue, Argenteuil, 1872, by Sisley. No. 1057, 7500fr, In the Garden, 1885, by Renoir. No. 1058, 7500fr, Woman with a Pearl Necklace in a Theater Box, 1879, by Cassatt. No. 1059, 7500fr, Paon sur un Baobab, 1972, by Edward Saidi Tingatinga. No. 1060, 7500fr, Joan of Arc in Battle, 1843, by Hermann Anton Stilke.

2012, Mar. 30   *Perf. 13¼*
     Sheets of 4, #a-d
1029-1044 A167   Set of 16   200.00 200.00
       Souvenir Sheets
1045-1060 A168   Set of 16   190.00 190.00

Transportation and Space
Flight — A169

No. 1061 — Boats: a, 1070fr, Anna Tunnicliffe sailing boat in 2008 Olympics. b, 1070fr, Yacht in Yarmouth Regatta. c, 3000fr, Europa, horiz. d, 3000fr, Colvin Gazelle, horiz.

No. 1062 — Steam trains: a, 1070fr, Venezia Santa Lucia. b, 1070fr, Class A4 Silver Fox. c, 3000fr, Flying Scotsman Express, horiz. d, 3000fr, Denver, Leadville and Gunnison train, horiz.

No. 1063 — French trains: a, 1070fr, TGV-PSE. b, 1070fr, Z-TER (Z 21561). c, 3000fr, Thalys PBKA, horiz. d, 3000fr, La Gironde and Joseph Eugène Schneider, horiz.

No. 1064 — German trains: a, 1070fr, ICE TD (Class 605). b, 1070fr, DB Class 614. c, 3000fr, RS-1 Regio Shuttle, horiz. d, 3000fr, Saxonia and Johann Andreas Schubert, horiz.

No. 1065 — Japanese trains: a, 1070fr, JRW Shinkansen Series 500 W1. b, 1070fr, Tobu 100. c, 3000fr, Shinkansen Superexpress Series 700, horiz. d, 3000fr, Shinkansen Series E5, horiz.

No. 1066 — Chinese trains: a, 1070fr, CRH5. b, 1070fr, CRH2. c, 3000fr, CRH2A, horiz. d, 3000fr, CRH3C, horiz.

No. 1067 — Bicycles: a, 1070fr, Mountain biker climbing hill. b, 1070fr, Mountain bikers descending hill. c, 3000fr, Road cycling (cyclisme sur route), horiz. d, 3000fr, Track cycling (cyclisme sur piste), horiz.

No. 1068 — Formula 1 race cars and drivers: a, 1070fr, AT&T Williams team car, Ayrton Senna, Brazilian flag. b, 1070fr, Mercedes GP Petronas team car, Michael Schumacher, German flag. c, 3000fr, Alfa Romeo 158, Giuseppe Farina, Italian flag, horiz. d, 3000fr, Mercedes-Benz W 196 R, Juan Manuel Fangio, Argentine flag, horiz.

No. 1069 — Helicopters: a, 1070fr, Boeing AH-64 Apache. b, 1070fr, Boeing CH-47 Chinook. c, 3000fr, Bell UH-1, horiz. d, 3000fr, MBB/Kawasaki BK 117 C2, horiz.

No. 1070 — Concorde: a, 1070fr, Two airplanes, line drawing of aiplane's nose. b, 1070fr, Two airplanes, line drawing of airplane's tail. c, 3000fr, Denomination at UR, horiz. d, 3000fr, Denomination at UL, horiz.

No. 1071 — Ships and Amerigo Vespucci: a, 1070fr, Vespucci at right, horiz. b, 1070fr, Vespucci at left. c, 1070fr, Vespucci at right. d, 5000fr, Vespucci at right, horiz.

No. 1072 — Horses and carriages: a, 1070fr, Lewis Tompkins driving carriage, horiz. b, 1070fr, Queen Elizabeth II and Prince Philip in carriage. c, 1070fr, Horse's head and omnibus carriage. d, 5000fr, Horse-drawn ambulance, horiz.

No. 1073 — Balloons and their creators: a, 1070fr, Balloon of Francesco Lana de Terzi, horiz. b, 1070fr, Balloon of Jean-Pierre Blanchard. c, 1070fr, Balloon of André-Jacques Garnerin, ascending. d, 5000fr, Balloon of Garnerin descending, horiz.

No. 1074 — The Hindenburg and Ferdinand von Zeppelin: a, 1070fr, Hindenburg in flight, horiz. b, 1070fr, Hindenburg and Empire State Building. c, 1070fr, Hindenburg on fire. d, 5000fr, People around Hindenburg, horiz.

No. 1075 — Centenary of London to Paris flight of Henri Salmet: a, 1070fr, Salmet in cockpit of Blériot monoplane, plane in flight facing left, horiz. b, 1070fr, Salmet at left, post card depicting his plane in flight. c, 1070fr, Salmet at right, post card depicting his plane on ground. d, 5000fr, Salmet in cockpit, plane in flight facing right, horiz.

No. 1076 — Opel Automobile Company, 150th Anniv.: a, 1070fr, Adam Opel, Opel emblem, sewing machine, horiz. b, 1070fr, Fritz Opel on Opel bicycle, bicycle emblem. c, 1070fr, 1899 Opel automobile, automobile emblem. d, 5000fr, 1935 Opel Olympia and emblem, horiz.

No. 1077 — Fire-fighting vehicles: a, 1070fr, 1870 Tozer pumper, horiz. b, 1070fr, 1883 Valiant pumper. c, 1070fr, Ladder truck and

motorcycle with sidecar. d, 5000fr, Ladder truck, horiz.

No. 1078 — Soviet space pioneers and vehicles: a, 1070fr, Dogs Belka and Strelka, horiz. b, 1070fr, Alexei Leonov. c, 1070fr, Valentina Tereshkova. d, 5000fr, Lunokhod 1, horiz.

No. 1079 — Sergei Krikalev and space vehicles: a, 1070fr, Space Shuttle Endeavour, horiz. b, 1070fr, Soyuz TM-7, denomination at UL. c, 1070fr, Soyuz TM-7, denomination at UR. d, 5000fr, Space Shuttle Flight STS-60 landing, horiz.

No. 1080, 7500fr, Viking drakkar, horiz. No. 1081, 7500fr, LNER Class A4 locomotive, Mallard commemorative plaque, horiz. No. 1082, 7500fr, TGV Duplex train, France, horiz. No. 1083, 7500fr, ICE 3 (Class 407), Germany, horiz. No. 1084, 7500fr, SL Yamaguchi C571 locomotive, Japan, horiz. No. 1085, 7500fr, CRH1 train, China, horiz. No. 1086, 7500fr, Arthur Zimmerman, world champion cyclist, 1893, horiz. No. 1087, 7500fr, Red Bull Formula 1 race cars, Sebastian Vettel, flag of Germany, horiz. No. 1088, 7500fr, Sikorsky S-70A Firehawk helicopter, horiz. No. 1089, 7500fr, Concorde, horiz. No. 1090, 7500fr, Ship and Vespucci, horiz. No. 1091, 7500fr, United States horse-drawn mail wagon, 1911, horiz. No. 1092, 7500fr, Balloon of Jacques Etienne Montgolfier, horiz. No. 1093, 7500fr, Zeppelin, Hindenburg in flight, horiz. No. 1094, 7500fr, Salmet in cockpit, plane in flight, horiz. No. 1095, 7500fr, 2011 Opel RAK e concept automobile, horiz. No. 1096, 7500fr, Firemen and pumper, 1903, horiz. No. 1097, 7500fr, Yuri Gagarin and Vostok 1, horiz. No. 1098, 7500fr, Krikalev and Mir Space Station, horiz.

2012, May 30   **Litho.**
     Sheets of 4, #a-d
1061-1079 A169   Set of 19 225.00 225.00
       Souvenir Sheets
1080-1098 A169   Set of 19 200.00 200.00

Miniature Sheets

Leaders of Burundi — A170

No. 1099 — King Mwambutsa IV Bangiricenge (1912-77): a, 270fr. b, 550fr. c, 1090fr. d, 2050fr.

No. 1100 — Prince Louis Rwagasore (1932-61), Prime Minister: a, 270fr. b, 550fr. c, 1090fr. d, 2050fr.

No. 1101 — Charles Ndizeye (King Ntare V) (1947-72): a, 270fr. b, 550fr. c, 1090fr. d, 2050fr.

No. 1102 — President Michel Micombero (1940-83): a, 270fr. b, 550fr. c, 1090fr. d, 2050fr.

No. 1103 — President Jean-Baptiste Bagaza: a, 270fr. b, 550fr. c, 1090fr. d, 2050fr.

No. 1104 — President Pierre Buyoya: a, 270fr. b, 550fr. c, 1090fr. d, 2050fr.

No. 1105 — President Melchior Ndadaye (1953-93): a, 270fr. b, 550fr. c, 1090fr. d, 2050fr.

No. 1106 — President Cyprien Ntaryamira (1955-94): a, 270fr. b, 550fr. c, 1090fr. d, 2050fr.

No. 1107 — President Sylvestre Ntibantunganya: a, 270fr. b, 550fr. c, 1090fr. d, 2050fr.

No. 1108 — President Domitien Ndayizeye: a, 270fr. b, 550fr. c, 1090fr. d, 2050fr.

No. 1109 — President Pierre Nkurunziza: a, 270fr. b, 550fr. c, 1090fr. d, 2050fr.

2012, Aug. 1   *Perf. 13¼*
     Sheets of 4, #a-d
1099-1109 A170   Set of 11   62.50 62.50
Nos. 1099c and 1099d lack king's name.

Nature Protection — A171

No. 1110 — Commerce in endangered wild animals: a, 1070fr, Two Panthera tigris in cage. b, 1070fr, Pongo pygmaeus abelii. c, 3000fr, Nycticebus sp. d, 3000fr, Gavialis gangeticus.

No. 1111 — Deforestation: a, 1070fr, Agalychnis callidryas. b, 1070fr, Harpia harpyja. c, 3000fr, Pongo pygmaeus. d, 3000fr, Ramphastos sulfuratus.

No. 1112 — Habitat fragmentation: a, 1070fr, Ceratotherium simum. b, 1070fr, Ursus arctos. c, 3000fr, Camelus dromedarius. d, 3000fr, Panthera leo and vans.

No. 1113 — Destruction of the Antarctic ozone layer: a, 1070fr, Orcinus orca, map of Antarctica. b, 1070fr, Balaenoptera musculus, scientific balloon launch. c, 3000fr, Megaleledone setebos, Antarctic research station. d, 3000fr, Leptonychotes weddellii, map of Antarctica.

No. 1114 — Warming of the climate: a, 1070fr, Bubo scandiacus. b, 1070fr, Sterna paradisaea. c, 3000fr, Pygoscelis adeliae. d, 3000fr, Odobenus rosmarus.

No. 1115 — Sea of plastic waste in North Pacific: a, 1070fr, Fish in net. b, 1070fr, Oceanographic vessel Kaisei and rubber raft. c, 3000fr, Map of Pacific Ocean, turtles ensnared in plastic packaging. d, 3000fr, Seals and plastic waste.

No. 1116 — Species extinct or threatened in the wild: a, 1070fr, Gallirallus owstoni. b, 1070fr, Nectophrynoides asperginis. c, 3000fr, Elaphurus davidianus. d, 3000fr, Brachylagus idahoensis.

No. 1117 — Endangered mammals: a, 1070fr, Panthera tigris facing right. b, 1070fr, Panthera leo on ground and in tree. c, 3000fr, Equus quagga. d, 3000fr, Adult and juvenile Ceratotherium simum.

No. 1118 — Sharks and pinnipeds: a, 1070fr, Carcharodon carcharias, Phocidae, "Phocidae" in black. b, 1070fr, Carcharodon carcharias, Phocidae, "Phocidae" in white. c, 3000fr, Carcharodon carcharias, name in black. d, 3000fr, Carcharodon carcharias, Phocidae, names in white.

No. 1119 — Dolphins: a, 1070fr, Stenella frontalis. b, 1070fr, Tursiops truncatus. c, 3000fr, Tursiops truncatus, denomination at UL. d, 3000fr, Tursiops truncatus, denomination at UR.

No. 1120 — Orcinus orca and Carcharodon carcharias with denomination at a, 1070fr, White. b, 1070fr, Black. c, 3000fr, White. d, 3000fr, Black.

No. 1121 — Whales: a, 1070fr, Physeter macrocephalus. b, 1070fr, Megaptera novaeangliae. c, 3000fr, Eschrichtius robustus. d, 3000fr, Balaenoptera acutorostrata.

No. 1122 — Birds and air pollution: a, 1070fr, Cuculus canorus. b, 1070fr, Grus americana. c, 3000fr, Crax rubra. d, 3000fr, Carduelis cucullata.

No. 1123 — Endangered birds: a, 1070fr, Anodorhynchus hyacintinus, Ara militaris. b, 1070fr, Merops orientalis. c, 3000fr, Aquila rapax. d, 3000fr, Strix nebulosa.

No. 1124 — Endangered plants and insects: a, 1070fr, Lobelia bridgesii, Cerambyx dux. b, 1070fr, Begonia samhaensis, Chlorophorus aegyptiacus. c, 3000fr, Sarracenia flava, Ampedus cardinalis. d, 3000fr, Echinocactus grusonii, Magicicada cassini.

No. 1125 — Endangered butterflies: a, 1070fr, Papilio palinurus. b, 1070fr, Idea iasonia. c, 3000fr, Parides hahneli. d, 3000fr, Euphaedra themis.

No. 1126 — Endangered fish: a, 1070fr, Cheilochromis euchilus. b, 1070fr, Pomacanthus imperator. c, 3000fr, Apolemichthys xanthotis. d, 3000fr, Cephalopholis miniata.

No. 1127 — Endangered reptiles: a, 1070fr, Calumma tarzan. b, 1070fr, Astrochelys yniphora. c, 3000fr, Crotalus catalinensis. d, 3000fr, Acanthodactylus beershebensis.

No. 1128 — Dinosaurs: a, 1070fr, Pachyrhinosaurus. b, 1070fr, Tropeognathus. c, 3000fr, Lystrosaurus. d, 3000fr, Arrhinoceratops.

No. 1129 — Acid rain and mushrooms: a, 1070fr, Gyromitra esculenta. b, 1070fr, Calvatia gigantea. c, 3000fr, Chorioactis. d, 3000fr, Hydnellum peckii.

No. 1130, 7500fr, Nycticebus pygmaeus. No. 1131, 7500fr, Danaus plexippus. No. 1132, 7500fr, Odocoileus virginianus clavium. No. 1133, 7500fr, Aptenodytes forsteri, airplanes over iceberg, globe. No. 1134, 7500fr,

Ursus maritimus. No. 1135, 7500fr, *Zalophus californianus* ensnared in net. No. 1136, 7500fr, *Oryx dammah.* No. 1137, 7500fr, *Cebus flavius.* No. 1138, 7500fr, *Carcharodon carcharias, Otariidae,* vert. No. 1139, 7500fr, *Delphinus delphis.* No. 1140, 7500fr, *Orcinus orca and Carhcharodon carcharias,* diff. No. 1141, 7500fr, *Megaptera novaeangliae,* diff. No. 1142, 7500fr, *Cacatua sulphurea citrinocristata.* No. 1143, 7500fr, *Strix occidentalis.* No. 1144, 7500fr, *Latania loddegesii, Buprestis splendens.* No. 1145, 7500fr, *Diaethria eluina.* No. 1146, 7500fr, *Pomacanthus maculosus.* No. 1147, 7500fr, *Glyptemys insculpta.* No. 1148, 7500fr, *Compsognathus.* No. 1149, 7500fr, *Entoloma hochstetteri* and acid rain.

2012, Aug. 31   **Litho.**
Sheets of 4, #a-d
1110-1129 A171   Set of 20   225.00 225.00
Souvenir Sheets
1130-1149 A171   Set of 20   210.00 210.00

Egg House, Moscow, and Fabergé Eggs — A172

No. 1150 — Egg House and: a, Red egg with three portraits of Emperor Nicholas II and two daughters at top. b, Jeweled frame with portraits of Emperor Nicholas II and Empress Alexandra, c, Egg with portrait of Emperor Nicholas II. d, Egg with portrait of Empress Alexandra at top. e, Egg with mounted horseman. f, Ship inside open egg.
No. 1151, 5000fr, Egg House, egg and coach. No. 1152, 5000fr, Egg House, blue egg, 12 pendants.

2012, Oct. 15 Litho. Perf. 12¾x13¼
1150 A172 1190fr Sheet of 6,
     #a-f   9.75 9.75
Souvenir Sheets
1151-1152 A172   Set of 2   13.50 13.50
Rossica 2013 Intl. Philatelic Exhibition, Moscow.

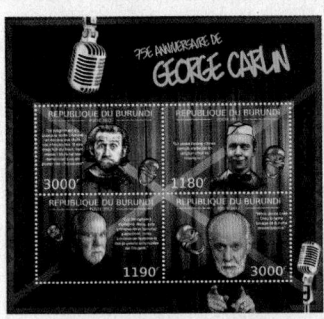

A173

No. 1153 — George Carlin (1937-2008), comedian, mask and text in French beginning with: a, 1180fr, "La seule bonne chose. . ." b, 1190fr, "J'ai finalement accepté Jésus. . ." c, 3000fr, "La religion est en quelque sorte. . ." d, 3000fr, "Nous avons créé Dieu. . ."
No. 1154 — Neil Armstrong (1930-2012), first man to walk on Moon, and: a, 1180fr, Apollo 11 emblem. b, 1190fr, Apollo command and service modules. c, 3000fr, Apollo 11 command, service and lunar modules. d, 3000fr, Astronaut and flag.
No. 1155 — Exploration of Mars: a, 1180fr, Artist's conception of Mars Exploration Rover. b, 1190fr, Curiosity rover. c, 3000fr, Satellite orbiting Mars. d, 3000fr, Sojourner rover.
No. 1156 — Impressionists and their paintings: a, 1180fr, The Soda Fountain, by William Glackens. b, 1190fr, In a Daisy Field, by Theodore Robinson. c, 3000fr, The Ballet Dancers, by William Metcalf. d, 3000fr, Portrait of a Woman, by Albert Henry Collings.
No. 1157 — Alexander Graham Bell (1847-1922), inventor of the telephone, and: a, 1180fr, AEA Silver Dart airplane. b, 1190fr, Examination of the wounded Pres. James A. Garfield. c, 3000fr, Magneto telephone. d, 3000fr, Columbia gramophone.
No. 1158 — Scenes from films adapted from works written by Ray Bradbury (1920-2012): a, 1180fr, Moby Dick (television play), 1956. b, 1190fr, The Illustrated Man (movie), 1969. c, 3000fr, Something Wicked This Way

Comes (movie), 1983. d, 3000fr, *The Beast from 20,000 Fathoms* (movie), 1953.
No. 1159 — Marilyn Monroe (1926-62), actress, and: a, 1180fr, Arthur Miller (1915-2005), playwright and Monroe's husband. b, 1190fr, Second image of Monroe. c, 3000fr, Brooklyn Bridge, Pres. John F. Kennedy (1917-63). d, 3000fr, Frank Sinatra (1915-98), singer.
No. 1160 — Musicians: a, 1180fr, B.B. King. b, 1190fr, Stevie Ray Vaughan. c, 3000fr, Tina Turner. d, 3000fr, Cher.
No. 1161 — Khadja Nin, musician: a, 1180fr, Two images of Nin. b, 1190fr, One image of Nin. c, 3000fr, Stevie Wonder. d, 3000fr, Montserrat Caballe.
No. 1162 — Princess Diana (1961-97), and: a, 1180fr, Prince William. b, 1190fr, Land mine sign. c, 3000fr, Princes William and Harry. d, 3000fr, Princes Charles and William.
No. 1163 — Pope John Paul II (1920-2005): a, 1180fr, And dove flying to right. b, 1190fr, And dove flying to left. c, 3000fr, Praying, dove at LL. d, 3000fr, With hand raised.
No. 1164 — Sergio Pininfarina (1926-2012), automobile designer and: a, 1180fr, Peugeot 504 Cabriolet. b, 1190fr, Lancia Montecarlo. c, 3000fr, Rolls-Royce Hyperion. d, 3000fr, Ferrari F40.
No. 1165 — Sports of the 2012 Summer Olympics, London: a, 1180fr, Judo. b, 1190fr, Soccer. c, 3000fr, Table tennis. d, 3000fr, Cycling.
No. 1166 — Minerals: a, 1180fr, Tanzanite and Vanadinite. b, 1190fr, Diamond and Vanadinite. c, 3000fr, Liddicoatite tourmaline and Tanzanite. d, 3000fr, Liddicoatite tourmaline.
No. 1167 — Pigeons, with inscription: a, 1180fr, Pigeon Hirondelle. b, 1190fr, Le "Cravaté Africain." c, 3000fr, "Le Dragon." d, 3000fr, Le Pigeon Souabe.
No. 1168 — Somniosus microcephalus, with diagonal line running from: a, 1180fr, UL to LR. b, 1190fr, LL to UR. c, 3000fr, LL to UR. d, 3000fr, UL to LR.
No. 1169 — Festivals: a, 1180fr, Diwali, India. b, 1190fr, New Year, China. c, 3000fr, Octoberfest, Germany. d, 3000fr, Feast of San Fermin, Spain.
No. 1170 — Burundi coffee production: a, 1180fr, Hands holding coffee cherries, coffee bean sorters. b, 1190fr, Harvesters, bags of coffee beans. c, 3000fr, Women drinking coffee. d, 3000fr, Harvester with basket, hands holding coffee cherries.
No. 1171 — Royal Drummers and Dancers of Burundi, with diagonal line running from: a, 1180fr, UL to LR. b, 1190fr, LL to UR. c, 3000fr, LL to UR. d, 3000fr, UL to LR.
No. 1172, 7500fr, Carlin and mask. No. 1173, 7500fr, Armstrong and bald eagle from Apollo 11 emblem. No. 1174, 7500fr, Curiosity landing on Mars. No. 1175, 7500fr, Portrait of Miss Dora Wheeler, by William Merritt Chase. No. 1176, 7500fr, First telephone invented by Bell. No. 1177, 7500fr, Bradbury and scene from miniseries adapted from *The Martian Chronicles.* No. 1178, 7500fr, Monroe and Joe DiMaggio (1914-99), baseball player and Monroe's husband. No. 1179, 7500fr, Bob Marley (1945-81), musician. No. 1180, 7500fr, Nin and Wonder. No. 1181, 7500fr, Princess Diana and Red Cross flag. No. 1182, 7500fr, Pope John Paul II and dove, diff. No. 1183, 7500fr, Pininfarina and Maserati GranTurismo S. No. 1184, 7500fr, Swimmer. No. 1185, 7500fr, Tanzanite and Vanadinite, diff. No. 1186, 7500fr, Two pigeons. No. 1187, 7500fr, Somniosus microcephalus, diff. No. 1188, 7500fr, Carnaval, Rio de Janeiro. No. 1189, 7500fr, Woman, coffee bush and beans. No. 1190, 7500fr, Royal Drummers and Dancers of Burundi, diff.

2012, Oct. 15 Litho. Perf. 13¼
Sheets of 4, #a-d
1153-1171 A173   Set of 19   220.00 220.00
Souvenir Sheets
1172-1190 A173   Set of 19   195.00 195.00

A174

No. 1191 — Hystrix africaeaustralis: a, 1180fr, Facing left. b, 1190fr, Facing right. c, 3000fr, Facing right, diff. d, 3000fr, Facing left, diff.
No. 1192 — Pangolins: a, 1180fr, Manis temminckii. b, 1190fr, Manis gigantea. c, 3000fr, Manis javanica. d, 3000fr, Manis temminckii, diff.
No. 1193 — Gorilla gorilla: a, 1180fr, Walking. b, 1190fr, Sitting. c, 3000fr, On back, denomination in black. d, 3000fr, Head, denomination in white.
No. 1194 — Pan troglodytes: a, 1180fr, On one tree branch. b, 1190fr, Holding two trees. c, 3000fr, Adult and juvenile. d, 3000fr, Adult.
No. 1195 — Lions International emblem and Panthera leo: a, 1180fr, Two females. b, 1190fr, Male running. c, 3000fr, Male walking. d, 3000fr, Male and female.
No. 1196 — Loxodonta africana: a, 1180fr, Adult and juvenile. b, 1190fr, Adult. c, 3000fr, Adults, animal name in black. d, 3000fr, Adult, animal name in white.
No. 1197 — Dolphins: a, 1180fr, Cephalorhynchus hectori maui. b, 1190fr, Lipotes vexillifer. c, 3000fr, Delphinus delphis . d, 3000fr, Orcaella brevirostris.
No. 1198 — Whales: a, 1180fr, Caperea marginata. b, 1190fr, Physeter catodon. c, 3000fr, Balaeniptera physalus. d, 3000fr, Balaenoptera musculus.
No. 1199 — Birds of prey: a, 1180fr, Elanus caeruleus. b, 1190fr, Milvus aegypticus. c, 3000fr, Haliaeetus vocifer. d, 3000fr, Milvus milvus.
No. 1200 — Owls: a, 1180fr, Bubo virginianus. b, 1190fr, Bubo africanus. c, 3000fr, Bubo bubo, Bubo africanus. d, 3000fr, Otus asio, Ptilopsis leucotis.
No. 1201 — Vultures: a, 1180fr, Vultur gryphus. b, 1190fr, Sarcogyps calvus. c, 3000fr, Necrosyrtes monachus. d, 3000fr, Gypaetus barbatus.
No. 1202 — Parrots: a, 1180fr, Psittacus erithacus. b, 1190fr, Agapornis fischeri. c, 3000fr, Poicephalus robustus. d, 3000fr, Agapornis personatus.
No. 1203 — Chrysolophus pictus: a, 1180fr, In flight. b, 1190fr, Two males. c, 3000fr, Male and female, denomination at LR. d, 3000fr, Two males and female, denomination at LL.
No. 1204 — Bees and wasps: a, 1180fr, Apis cerana. b, 1190fr, Vespula germanica. c, 3000fr, Apis mellifera. d, 3000fr, Vespa orientalis.
No. 1205 — Dragonflies: a, 1180fr, Trithemis arteriosa. b, 1190fr, Trithemis arteriosa, diff. c, 3000fr, Orthetrum chrysostigma. d, 3000fr, Schnura senegalensis.
No. 1206 — Butterflies: a, 1180fr, Belenois calypso. b, 1190fr, Graphium angolanus. c, 3000fr, Graphium ridleyanus. d, 3000fr, Papilio dardanus antinorii.
No. 1207 — Butterflies: a, 1180fr, Papilio demodocus. b, 1190fr, Cymothoe mabillei. c, 3000fr, Eurema hecabe. d, 3000fr, Euphaedra janetta.
No. 1208 — Goldfish breeds: a, 1180fr, Panda Moor. b, 1190fr, Celestial Eye. c, 3000fr, Bubble Eye. d, 3000fr, Black Moor.
No. 1209 — Fish: a, 1180fr, Pelvicachromis pulcher. b, 1190fr, Neochromis omnicaeruleus. c, 3000fr, Ptyochromis sp. d, 3000fr, Paralabidochromis sp.
No. 1210 — Shells: a, 1180fr, Chlamyis varia, Cardita calcyculata. b, 1190fr, Jujubinus exasperatus, Marmarostoma. c, 3000fr, Ovula ovum, Cymathium rubeculum. d, 3000fr, Epitionium commune, Solemya togata.
No. 1211 — Sea turtles: a, 1180fr, Dermochelys coriacea. b, 1190fr, Caretta caretta. c, 3000fr, Natator depressus. d, 3000fr, Eretmochelys imbricata.
No. 1212 — Cacti and animals: a, 1180fr, Euphorbia trigona, Varanus albigularis. b, 1190fr, Opuntia ficu-indica, hyaena hyaena. c, 3000fr, Euphorbia tortilis, Suricata suricatta. d, 3000fr, Euphorbia trigona var. rubra, Naja haje.
No. 1213 — Edible mushrooms: a, 1180fr, Amanita rubescens. b, 1190fr, Morchella conica. c, 3000fr, Cantharellus cibarius. d, 3000fr, Boletus edulis.
No. 1214 — Poisonous mushrooms: a, 1180fr, Entoloma sinuatum. b, 1190fr, Amanita verna, Amanita muscaria. c, 3000fr, Russula emetica. d, 3000fr, Amanita phalloides, Paxillus involutus.
No. 1215 — Minerals: a, 1180fr, Orthose. b, 1190fr, Agate. c, 3000fr, Galena. d, 3000fr, Topaz.
No. 1216, 7500fr, Hystrix africaeaustralis, diff. No. 1217, 7500fr, Manis tricuspis. No. 1218, 7500fr, Gorilla gorilla gorilla. No. 1219, 7500fr, Pan troglodytes, diff. No. 1220, 7500fr, Lions International emblem and Panthera leo, diff. No. 1221, 7500fr, Loxodonta africana, diff. No. 1222, 7500fr, Platanista gangetica. No. 1223, 7500fr, Delphinapterus leucas. No. 1224, 7500fr, Haliaeetus vocifer, diff. No. 1225, 7500fr, Tyto alba. No. 1226, 7500fr, Sarcoramphus papa. No. 1227, 7500fr, Poicephalus meyeri. No. 1228, 7500fr, Chrysolophus pictus, diff. No. 1229, 7500fr, Apis mellifera, diff. No. 1230, 7500fr, Crocothemis erythraea. No. 1231, 7500fr, Papilio dardanus cenea. No. 1232, 7500fr, Hypolycaena antifaunus. No. 1233, 7500fr, Pearlscale goldfish. No. 1234, 7500fr,

Lithochromis rufus. No. 1235, 7500fr, *Melo aethiopicus, Hippopus hippopus.* No. 1236, 7500fr, *Caretta caretta,* diff. No. 1237, 7500fr, *Opuntia robusta, Vulpes zerda.* No. 1238, 7500fr, *Amanita caesarea.* No. 1239, 7500fr, *Boletus satanas.* No. 1240, 7500fr, *Calcite.*

2012, Dec. 21 Litho. Perf. 13¼
Sheets of 4, #a-d
1191-1215 A174   Set of 25   275.00 275.00
Souvenir Sheets
1216-1240 A174   Set of 25   245.00 245.00

Transportation and Space — A175

No. 1241 — Dog and sleds: a, 1180fr, Dogs, sled and driver. b, 1190fr, Dogs, sled and driver, diff. c, 3000fr, Sled dog, statue of Balto. d, 3000fr, Two dogs and sled.
No. 1242 — Paintings of horses and wagons by: a, 1180fr, Charles Cooper Henderson. b, 1190fr, James Pollard. c, 3000fr, Pollard, diff. d, 3000fr, John Nost Sartorius.
No. 1243 — Medieval ships: a, 1180fr, Norman ship, 11th cent. b, 1190fr, Venetian merchant ship, 1250. c, 3000fr, Galley, 1280. d, 3000fr, Nostra Senora, 1275.
No. 1244 — Discovery of America by Christopher Columbus, 520th anniv.: a, 1180fr, Columbus Before the Queen, painting by Emanuel Gottlieb Leutze. b, 1190fr, Columbus Landing at Guanahani, painting by John Vanderlyn. c, 3000fr, Columbus and ship, Santa Maria. d, 3000fr, The Death of Columbus, painting by Louis Prang.
No. 1245 — Steamboats, 225th anniv.: a, 1180fr, John Fitch and his steamboat. b, 1190fr, James Watt and steam engine. c, 3000fr, Robert Fulton and diagram of steamboat. d, 3000fr, Steamboat Washington.
No. 1246 — Warships: a, 1180fr, Prinz Eugen. b, 1190fr, Bismarck. c, 3000fr, Yamato. d, 3000fr, Georgy Pobedonosets.
No. 1247 — Invention of the locomotive: a, 1180fr, Limmat 4-2-2. b, 1190fr, The General 4-4-0. c, 3000fr, Statue of Richard Trevithick, Trevithick's 1804 locomotive. d, 3000fr, Statue of George Stephenson, Stockton & Darlington Railroad locomotive.
No. 1248 — Aerotrains: a, 1180fr, Prototype #02. b, 1190fr, Prototype Rohr. c, 3000fr, Experimental train 01. d, 3000fr, I-80 HV.
No. 1249 — Snowmobiles: a, 1180fr, BRP Ski-Doo Rev XP. b, 1190fr, Arctic Cat ProClimb M1100 Sno Pro Limited. c, 3000fr, Yamaha FX Nytro RMX. d, 3000fr, Polaris RMK 700.
No. 1250 — Fire trucks: a, 1180fr, 1915 American La France. b, 1190fr, 1985 Pierce Arrow. c, 3000fr, 2002 Pierce. d, 3000fr, 1946 Bickle Seagrave.
No. 1251 — Buses: a, 1180fr, 1940 Greyhound. b, 1190fr, 1954 Bristol double-decker. c, 3000fr, JCK 892. d, 3000fr, 1940 General American Autocoach.
No. 1252 — Automobiles: a, 1180fr, 1906 Mercedes-Benz race car. b, 1190fr, Mercedes-Benz W196 race car. c, 3000fr, 1935 Mercedes-Benz Roadster. d, 3000fr, 1923 Lancia Lambda Torpedo.
No. 1253 — Taxis: a, 1180fr, Coco taxi, Havana, Cuba. b, 1190fr, 1834 fiacre, England. c, 3000fr, 1912 Unic taxi, London. d, 3000fr, Maybach taxi, Moscow.
No. 1254 — Stock cars and NASCAR drivers: a, 1180fr, 2012 Chevrolet, Tony Stewart. b, 1190fr, 1983 Ford, Dale Earnhardt. c, 3000fr, 2012 Dodge, Brad Keselowski. d, 3000fr, 1957 Oldsmobile, Richard Petty.
No. 1255 — Harley-Davidson motorcycles: a, 1180fr, 2012 FLTRX Road Glide Custom. b, 1190fr, 1942 WLA. c, 3000fr, 2010 CVO Fat Bob FXDFSE2. d, 3000fr, 2010 VRSCB V-Rod.
No. 1256 — Disappearance of Amelia Earhart (1897-1937), pilot: a, 1180fr, Earhart sitting on nose of plane. b, 1190fr, Earhart parachuting. c, 3000fr, Earhart in front of plane, denomination in white. d, 3000fr, Earhart in front of plane, denomination in black.
No. 1257 — Supersonic aircraft: a, 1180fr, Tupolev Tu-144, flying right. b, 1190fr, British Airways Concorde. c, 3000fr, Air France Concorde. d, 3000fr, Tupolev Tu-144, flying left.
No. 1258 — Air ambulances: a, 1180fr, Victoria Hawker Beechcraft B200C King Air. b, 1190fr, LAHAK MBB Bo-105CBS-4 helicopter. c, 3000fr, Eurocopter-Kawasaki EC-145 (BK-117C-2) helicopter. d, 3000fr, King Air B350.
No. 1259 — Military aircraft: a, 1180fr, Boeing B-52H Stratofortress. b, 1190fr, Boeing

Bird of Prey, Boeing F/A-18E. c, 3000fr, Lockheed YF-117A Nighthawk, Lockheed F-117A Nighthawk. d, 3000fr, Northrop YB-35.

No. 1260 — American X-Planes: a, 1180fr, Northrup Grumman X-47A Pegasus. b, 1190fr, Boeing X-50 Dragonfly. c, 3000fr, McDonnell Douglas/Boeing X-36. d, 3000fr, Grumman X-29.

No. 1261 — Space tourism: a, 1180fr, White Knight One. b, 1190fr, Virgin Atlantic Global Flyer. c, 3000fr, Richard Branson and SpaceShip One. d, 3000fr, White Knight Two.

No. 1262 — Voyager 2, 35th anniv.: a, 1180fr, Voyager 2 and Neptune. b, 1190fr, Voyageer 2 and Saturn. c, 3000fr, Voyager 2 and Uranus. d, 3000fr, Storms on Jupiter, Jupiter's moons Callisto and Io.

No. 1263 — Mail transportation: a, 1180fr, Vespa scooter. b, 1190fr, Pacific Air Transport 840 biplane. c, 3000fr, Panhard Dyna van. d, 3000fr, 1931 Ford postal truck.

No. 1264 — Cargo transportation: a, 1180fr, Airbus Skylink A-300 B4-608ST Beluga. b, 1190fr, Cargo ship Irina Trader. c, 3000fr, Scania R620 trucks. d, 3000fr, Class 7100 electric locomotive.

No. 1265 — Electric vehicles: a, 1180fr, Heathrow Airport transport pods. b, 1190fr, Policeman on Segway personal transporter. c, 3000fr, Series 500 Shinkansen train. d, 3000fr, 2009 Nisan Denki concept vehicle.

No. 1266, 7500fr, Dogs, sled and driver, diff. No. 1267, 7500fr, Painting of Royal Mail coach by John Frederick Herring, Sr. No. 1268, 7500fr, Fortune, 1300 (ship). No. 1269, 7500fr, Santa Maria, statue of Columbus, Madrid. No. 1270, 7500fr, John Fitch and 1790 steamboat model. No. 1271, 7500fr, German battleship Scharnhorst. No. 1272, 7500fr, Stephenson's Rocket, 1829. No. 1273, 7500fr, Aerotrain I-80 HV on bridge. No. 1274, 7500fr, Arctic Cat Firecat F7 snowmobile. No. 1275, 7500fr, Pierce 105-foot rear mount ladder firetruck. No. 1276, 7500fr, 1951 Bristol Royal Blue LL6B bus. No. 1277, 7500fr, 1886 Benz automobile. No. 1278, 7500fr, London taxi, 1950-82. No. 1279, 7500fr, Chevrolet and Jimmie Johnson. No. 1280, 7500fr, 2008 Harley-Davidson VRSCA V-Rod motorcycle. No. 1281, 7500fr, Earhart airplane wing and compass rose, vert. No. 1282, 7500fr, Tupolev Tu-144, diff. No. 1283, 7500fr, Canadair CL-600-2B16 Challenger 604 air ambulance. No. 1284, 7500fr, Lockheed F-117A Nighthawk, diff. No. 1285, 7500fr, NASA X-38. No. 1286, 7500fr, SpaceShip Two. No. 1287, 7500fr, Antenna of Voyager 2. No. 1288, 7500fr, Royal Air Mail automobile. No. 1289, 7500fr, Cargo ship Angeln. No. 1290, 7500fr, Solar Impulse solar-powered airplane.

2012, Dec. 28   Litho.   Perf. 13¼
Sheets of 4, #a-d
1241-1265 A175   Set of 25   275.00   275.00
Souvenir Sheets
1266-1290 A175   Set of 25   245.00   245.00

Famous People — A176

No. 1291 — Frank Sinatra (1915-98), singer: a, 90fr, Wearing hat. b, 1180fr, Holding microphone. c, 3000fr, Standing near microphone. d, 3000fr, Wearing hat, diff.

No. 1292 — Johann Sebastian Bach (1685-1750), composer: a, 90fr, Wearing blue cravat. b, 1190fr, Playing organ. c, 3000fr, With cello and bow. d, 3000fr, Wearing red cravat.

No. 1293 — Robert Schumann (1810-56), composer: a, 90fr, Wearing blue jacket. b, 1190fr, Reviewing score. c, 3000fr, At piano. d, 3000fr, Wearing blue jacket, diff.

No. 1294 — Georges Lemmen (1865-1916), painter: a, 90fr, Lemmen. b, 1190fr, The Carousel, by Lemmen, 1896. c, 3000fr, Houses at La Hulpe, by Lemmen, 1888. d, 3000fr, Plage à Heist, by Lemmen, 1891.

No. 1295 — Paul Signac (1863-1935), painter: a, 90fr, Signac. b, 1190fr, Woman at her Toilette Wearing a Purple Corset, by Signac, 1893. c, 3000fr, Lighthouse at Grox,

by Signac, 1923. d, 3000fr, Portrait of Félix Fénéon, by Signac, 1890.

No. 1296 — Brigitte Bardot, actress: a, 90fr, Wearing hat. b, 1190fr, Holding mask. c, 3000fr, Without hat. d, 3000fr, Scene from Viva Maria!

No. 1297 — Ludwig van Beethoven (1770-1827), composer: a, 1020fr, Wearing red cravat. b, 1180fr, As conductor. c, 3000fr, Holding paper. d, 3000fr, Wearing white cravat.

No. 1298 — Wolfgang Amadeus Mozart (1756-91), composer: a, 1020fr, Playing harpsichord. b, 1180fr, Portrait. c, 3000fr, Playing violin. d, 3000fr, Playing harpsichord with woman.

No. 1299 — Franz Schubert (1797-1828), composer: a, 1020fr, Wearing blue shirt. b, 1180fr, Playing piano. c, 3000fr, Playing guitar. d, 3000fr, Wearing red cravat.

No. 1300 — Richard Wagner (1813-83), composer: a, 1020fr, Facing right, wearing red cravat. b, 1180fr, Playing piano. c, 3000fr, Writing at desk. d, 3000fr, Facing forward, wearing red cravat.

No. 1301 — Charlie Chaplin (1889-1977), actor: a, 1020fr, Wearing cap. b, 1180fr, With dog. c, 3000fr, Holding "Little Tramp" doll. d, 3000fr, Without hat.

No. 1302 — John Wayne (1907-79), actor: a, 1020fr, Wearing red neckerchief. b, 1180fr, On horse. c, 3000fr, Holding rifle, wearing badge. d, 3000fr, Wearing hat.

No. 1303 — Greta Garbo (1905-90), actress: a, 1020fr, With Herbert Marshall in The Painted Veil. b, 1180fr, Wearing blue dress. c, 3000fr, With Conrad Nagel in The Mysterious Lady. d, 3000fr, Wearing crown.

No. 1304 — Marilyn Monroe (1926-62), actress: a, 1020fr, Wearing yellow dress and red scarf. b, 1180fr, Wearing top hat. c, 3000fr, Seated, wearing blue dress. d, 3000fr, Holding money.

No. 1305 — Georges Seurat (1859-91), painter: a, 1020fr, Seurat. b, 1190fr, Chahut, by Seurat, 1889-90. c, 3000fr, The Eiffel Tower, by Seurat, 1889. d, 3000fr, Bathers at Asnières, by Seurat, 1884.

No. 1306 — Paul Sérusier (1864-1927), painter: a, 1020fr, Sérusier. b, 1190fr, The Flowered Barrier, by Sérusier, 1889. c, 3000fr, The Garland of Roses, by Sérusier, 1898. d, 3000fr, L'Averse, by Sérusier, 1893.

No. 1307 — Grace Kelly (1929-82), actress and princess: a, 1090fr, Wearing fur stole. b, 1180fr, Seated, wearing white gown. c, 3000fr, Wearing white blouse and blue pants. d, 3000fr, Wearing white dress.

No. 1308 — James Dean (1931-55), actor: a, 1090fr, With Julie Harris in East of Eden. b, 1180fr, Wearing dark shirt and jacket. c, 3000fr, Wearing t-shirt and jacket. d, 3000fr, With Elizabeth Taylor in Giant.

No. 1309 — Jane Fonda, actress: a, 1090fr, Holding weapon. b, 1180fr, Wearing striped blouse. c, 3000fr, Wearing nurse's cap. d, 3000fr, Saluting, holding space helmet.

No. 1310 — Paul Gauguin (1843-1903), painter: a, 1090fr, Gauguin. b, 1190fr, Agony in the Garden, by Gauguin, 1889. c, 3000fr, Picking Lemons, by Gauguin, 1891. d, 3000fr, Peasant Woman and Cows in a Landscape, by Gauguin, 1890.

No. 1311 — Vincent van Gogh (1853-90), painter: a, 1090fr, Van Gogh. b, 1190fr, Olive Picking, by van Gogh, 1889. c, 3000fr, The Good Samaritan, by van Gogh, 1890. d, 3000fr, Avenue of Poplars in Autumn, by van Gogh, 1884.

No. 1312 — Henri de Toulouse-Lautrec (1864-1901), painter: a, 1090fr, Toulouse-Lautrec. b, 1190fr, At the Circus Fernando - The Rider, by Toulouse-Lautrec, 1888. c, 3000fr, Woman with an Umbrella, by Toulouse-Lautrec, 1889. d, 3000fr, The Clowness Cha U Ka O at the Moulin Rouge, by Toulouse-Lautred, 1895.

No. 1313 — Félix Vallotton (1865-1925), painter: a, 1090fr, Vallotton. b, 1190fr, Woman Reading, by Vallotton, 1922. c, 3000fr, Still Life with Flowers, by Vallotton, 1925. d, 3000fr, Still Life with Marigolds and Tangerines, by Vallotton, 1924.

No. 1314 — Pierre Bonnard (1867-1947), painter: a, 1090fr, Bonnard. b, 1190fr, Woman with a Parrot, by Bonnard, 1910. c, 3000fr, View of Cannet, by Bonnard, 1927. d, 3000fr, Jeune Fillesà la Mouette, by Bonnard, 1917.

No. 1315 — Elvis Presley (1935-77), musician: a, 1090fr, With guitar. b, 1190fr, Wearing white shirt and blue jacket. c, 3000fr, Wearing striped jacket and green shirt. d, 3000fr, In Hawaiian shirt playing ukulele.

No. 1316, 7500fr, Sinatra, diff. No. 1317, 7500fr, Bach, diff. No. 1318, 7500fr, Schumann, diff. No. 1319, 7500fr, Lemmen, diff. No. 1320, 7500fr, Signac, diff. No. 1321, 7500fr, Bardot and Lino Ventura in Rum Runners. No. 1322, 7500fr, Beethoven, diff. No. 1323, 7500fr, Mozart, diff. No. 1324, 7500fr, Schubert, diff. No. 1325, 7500fr, Wagner, diff. No. 1326, 7500fr, Chaplin, diff. No. 1327, 7500fr, Wayne, diff. No. 1328, 7500fr, Garbo, diff. No. 1329, 7500fr, Monroe, diff. No. 1330, 7500fr, Seurat, diff. No. 1331, 7500fr, Sérusier, diff. No. 1332, 7500fr, Kelly, diff. No. 1333, 7500fr, Dean with Natalie Wood in Rebel Without a Cause. No. 1334, 7500fr, Fonda, diff. No. 1335, 7500fr, Gauguin, diff. No. 1336, 7500fr, Van Gogh, diff. No. 1337,

7500fr, Toulouse-Lautred, diff. No. 1338, 7500fr, Vallotton, diff. No. 1339, 7500fr, Bonnard, diff. No. 1340, 7500fr, Presley, diff.

2013, July 5   Litho.   Perf. 13¼
Sheets of 4, #a-d
1291-1315 A176   Set of 25   260.00   260.00
Souvenir Sheets
1316-1340 A176   Set of 25   245.00   245.00

A177

No. 1341 — Intl. Red Cross, 150th anniv.: a, 90fr, Rescue dog. b, 1180fr, Red Cross doctor examining patient. c, 3000fr, Red Cross worker giving food box to child. d, 3000fr, Rescue dog, diff.

No. 1342 — Paul P. Harris (1868-1947), founder of Rotary International: a, 90fr, Rotary emblem, Harris, Laeliocattleya ridolfiana. b, 1180fr, Rotary and Rotary Foundation emblems, owl, books, mortarboard and diploma. c, 3000fr, Rotary emblem, needle with polio vaccine, brain of boy. d, 3000fr, Rotary emblem, Harris, Selenipedium grande.

No. 1343 — Edvard Munch (1863-1944), painter, and: a, 90fr, The Haymaker, 1917. b, 1180fr, The Scream, 1893. c, 3000fr, Red and White, 1899-1900. d, 3000fr, Self-portrait with a Wine Bottle, 1906.

No. 1344 — 50th anniv. of space flight of Valentina Tereshkova, first woman in space: a, 90fr, Tereshkova in space suit, space capsule. b, 1190fr, Tereshkova on wheel, Tereshkova in military uniform. c, 3000fr, Tereshkova in space suit, Tershkova in military uniform. d, 3000fr, Tereshkova being examined by technicians, Tereshkova in space suit.

No. 1345 — Haroun Tazieff (1914-88), geologist and vulcanologist: a, 90fr, Tazieff and Nyiragongo Volcano, Congo. b, 1190fr, Tyrannosaurus and Redoubt Volcano, Alaska. c, 3000fr, Compsognathus and Ulawun Volcano, Papua New Guinea. d, 3000fr, Tazieff and Mount Etna, Sicily.

No. 1346 — Magnus Carlsen, chess grand master: a, 1020fr, Wearing red suit. b, 1180fr, Playing against Garry Kasparov. c, 3000fr, Playing against Levon Aronian. d, 3000fr, Wearing red suit, diff.

No. 1347 — Shenzhou 10: a, 1020fr, Astronaut Nie Haisheng. b, 1180fr, Astronaut Wang Yaping. c, 3000fr, Astronaut Zhang Xiaoguang. d, 3000fr, Shenzhou 10 docking with Tiangong 1.

No. 1348 — Butterflies and Scouts: a, 1020fr, Ornithoptera paradisea, Lord Robert Baden-Powell (1857-1941), founder of Scouting movement. b, 1190fr, Chrysiridia rhipheus, Scout hiking. c, 3000fr, Appias nero, Scout leaning on walking stick. d, 3000fr, Rhetus periander, Baden-Powell.

No. 1349 — Campaign against malaria: a, 1020fr, Line of people, malaria detection test strip. b, 1190fr, Campaign emblem, man receiving package. c, 3000fr, Red Cross workers. d, 3000fr, World Malaria Day emblem, Anopheles stephensi.

No. 1350 — Joan Miró (1893-1983), painter, and: a, 1020fr, Still Life II - The Carbide Lamp, 1922-23. b, 1190fr, Vineyards and Olive Trees, 1919. c, 3000fr, Abstract painting, 1933. d, 3000fr, The Smile of the Flamboyant Wings, 1953.

No. 1351 — Paintings in Rijksmuseum, Amsterdam: a, 1020fr, The Windmill at Wijkbij-Duurstede, by Jacob van Ruysdael. b, 1190fr, Children of the Sea, by Jozef Israels. c, 3000fr, The Damrak in Amsterdam, by George Hendrik Breitner. d, 3000fr, The Art Gallery of Jan Gildemeester, by Adriaan de Lelie.

No. 1352 — Resignation of Pope Benedict XVI: a, 1020fr, Pope Benedict XVI holding censer, statue of angel holding cross. b, 1190fr, Pope Benedict XVI with clasped hands, St. Peter's Basilica. c, 3000fr, Pope Benedict XVI waving, St. Peter's Basilica. d, 3000fr, Pope Benedict XVI wearing miter and holding cross, statue of angel.

No. 1353 — Election of Pope Francis: a, 1090fr, Pope Francis waving. b, 1180fr, Pope Francis consecrating host. c, 3000fr, Pope Francis with children. d, 3000fr, Popes Francis and Benedict XVI.

No. 1354 — Coronation of Queen Elizabeth II, 60th anniv: a, 1090fr, Queen Elizabeth II as young woman on throne. b, 1180fr, Queen Elizabeth II as older woman on throne. c,

3000fr, Queen Elizabeth II with attendant lifting cape. d, 3000fr, Queen Elizabeth II and Prince Philip.

No. 1355 — Miles Joseph Berkeley (1803-89), mycologist: a, 1090fr, Boletus appendiculatus, Uroglaux dimorpha. b, 1180fr, Berkeley, Cortinarius caperatus. c, 3000fr, Berkeley, Amanita muscaria. d, 3000fr, Hypholoma faciculare, Tyto alba.

No. 1356 — Pierre de Coubertin (1863-1937), founder of International Olympic Committee: a, 1090fr, Coubertin, cycling. b, 1180fr, Diving, running. c, 3000fr, Watching women's gymnastics. d, 3000fr, Men's gymnastics, rhythmic gymnastics.

No. 1357 — New Year 2014 (Year of the Horse): a, 1090fr, Horse leaping. b, 1180fr, Head of horse. c, 3000fr, Head of horse, diff. d, 3000fr, Horse galloping.

No. 1358 — Airships: a, 1090fr, Early propellor-driven dirigible. b, 1190fr, 2005 dirigible concept. c, 3000fr, High-altitude dirigible. d, 3000fr, Hindenburg.

No. 1359 — Mohandas K. Gandhi (1869-1948), Indian nationalist leader, and butterflies: a, 1090fr, Troides aeacus. b, 1190fr, Teinopalypus imperialis. c, 3000fr, Papilio krishna. d, 3000fr, Junonia almana.

No. 1360 — Diplomatic relations between Burundi and the People's Republic of China, 50th anniv.: a, 1090fr, Flags of China and Burundi, Mao Zedong and King Mwambutsa IV. b, 1190fr, Jia Qinglin meeting with Gabriel Ntisezerana, 2012. c, 3000fr, Jia Qinglin and Pierre Nkurunziza shaking hands, 2006. d, 3000fr, Flags of China and Burundi, Mao Zedong and King Mwambutsa IV, diff.

No. 1361, 7500fr, Red Cross worker holding child, Henry Dunant, founder of Red Cross. No. 1362, 7500fr, Rotary emblems throughout the years. No. 1363, 7500fr, Munch and Evening on the Avenue Karl-Johan, 1892. No. 1364, 7500fr, Tereshkova and Yuri Gagarin. No. 1365, 7500fr, Tazieff, Mount Etna, Pteranodon. No. 1366, 7500fr, Carlsen playing Viswanathan Anand. No. 1367, 7500fr, Shenzhou 10 astronauts in capsule. No. 1368, 7500fr, Hebomoia leucippe, group of Scouts. No. 1369, 7500fr, Red Cross patient, Anopheles stephensi. No. 1370, 7500fr, Miró and Burnt Canvas I, 1973. No. 1371, 7500fr, Still Life, by Floris van Dyck. No. 1372, 7500fr, Pope Benedict XVI and his coat of arms. No. 1373, 7500fr, Pope Francis and his coat of arms, St. Peter's Basilica. No. 1374, 7500fr, Queen Elizabeth II, Buckingham Palace. No. 1375, 7500fr, Berkeley, Boletus regineus, Boletus edulis. No. 1376, 7500fr, Discus and high jump. No. 1377, 7500fr, Horse galloping, diff. No. 1378, 7500fr, Ferdinand von Zeppelin (1838-1917), airship manufacturer, and Graf Zeppelin. No. 1379, 7500fr, Gandhi and Parnassius maharaja. No. 1380, 7500fr, Hospital in Bubanza, Burundi, flags of Burundi and China.

2013, Aug. 5   Litho.   Perf. 13¼
Sheets of 4, #a-d
1341-1360 A177   Set of 20   210.00   210.00
Souvenir Sheets
1361-1380 A177   Set of 20   195.00   195.00

Rossica 2013 Intl. Philatelic Exhibition, Moscow (#1344, 1364); 2013 China Intl. Collection Expo, Beijing (#1360, 1380).

A178

No. 1381 — African animals: a, 90fr, Loxodonta africana. b, 1180fr, Panthera onca. c, 3000fr, Giraffa camelopardalis. d, 3000fr, Gorilla gorilla gorilla.

No. 1382 — Wild dogs and cacti: a, 90fr, Lycaon pictus, Opuntia ovata. b, 1190fr, Canis lupus dingo, Ferocactus echidne. c, 3000fr, Canis lupus dingo, Ferocactus pileus. d, 3000fr, Cuon alpinus, Cylindropuntia fulgida.

No. 1383 — Fish: a, 90fr, Sphaeramia nematoptera. b, 1190fr, Pterapogon kauderni. c, 3000fr, Balistapus undulatus. d, 3000fr, Synchiropus splendidus.

No. 1384 — Snakes: a, 90fr, Elaphe obsoleta quadrivittata. b, 1190fr, Lampropeltis triangulum. c, 3000fr, Diadophis punctatus. d, 3000fr, Opheodrys vernalis.

No. 1385 — Minerals: a, 90fr, Brazilian carnelian agate. b, 1190fr, Malachite. c, 3000fr, Spirit quartz (amethyst). d, 3000fr, Blue azurite.

No. 1386 — Pope John Paul II (1920-2005), and: a, 90fr, His coat of arms. b, 1190fr, St. Peter's Basilica. c, 3000fr, Colonnades in St. Peter's Square. d, 3000fr, Doves.

No. 1387 — Cat breeds: a, 1020fr, Bambino. b, 1180fr, Persian. c, 3000fr, Sphynx. d, 3000fr, Abyssinian.

No. 1388 — Birds: a, 1020fr, Buteo augur. b, 1180fr, Gyps africnus. c, 3000fr, Aquila verreauxii. d, 3000fr, Aquila nipalensis.

No. 1389 — Dinosaurs: a, 1020fr, Tyrannosaurus rex. b, 1180fr, Nasutoceratops. c, 3000fr, Stegosaurus. d, 3000fr, Plateosaurus.

No. 1390 — Human ancestors: a, 1020fr, Homo erectus hunting. b, 1180fr, Homo neanderthalensis drawing on cave wall. c, 3000fr, Homo neanderthalensis, drawing of mammoth. d, 3000fr, Homo floresiensis hunting.

No. 1391 — Impressionist paintings: a, 1020fr, A Cloudy Day, by Julian Onderdonk. b, 1180fr, Woman Reading in the Garden, by Richard E. Miller. c, 3000fr, Summer Fragrance, by Edward Alfred Cucuel. d, 3000fr, Out to Sea, by Guy Rose.

No. 1392 — Giuseppe Verdi (1813-1901), composer, and costumes from: a, 1020fr, Aida. b, 1180fr, Rigoletto. c, 3000fr, Aida, diff. d, 3000fr, Don Carlos.

No. 1393 — Mao Zedong (1893-1976), Chinese communist leader: a, 1020fr, At desk. b, 1180fr, With arm raised. c, 3000fr, With hands together. d, 3000fr, Reading newspaper and giving speech.

No. 1394 — 95th birthday of Nelson Mandela, President of South Africa: a, 1020fr, Mandela with Mother Teresa. b, 1180fr, Mandela waving. c, 3000fr, Mandela with hands together. d, 3000fr, Mandela with Pope John Paul II.

No. 1395 — Turtles: a, 1020fr, Rhinoclemmys funerea, Leucocephalon yuwonoi. b, 1190fr, Heosemys spinosa. c, 3000fr, Eretmochelys imbricata. d, 3000fr, Chelonia mydas.

No. 1396 — Cricket players: a, 1020fr, Travis Birt. b, 1190fr, Graeme Swann. c, 3000fr, M. S. Dhoni. d, 3000fr, Misbah-ul-Haq.

No. 1397 — Dolphins: a, 1090fr, Sotalia fluviatilis. b, 1180fr, Stenella coeruleoalba. c, 3000fr, Steno bredanensis. d, 3000fr, Lagenorhynchus obscurus.

No. 1398 — Bees and flowers: a, 1090fr, Apis mellifera mellifera, Camellia japonica. b, 1180fr, Apis cerana, Primula sinensis. c, 3000fr, Apis mellifera, Rhododendron maximum. d, 3000fr, Apis florea, Syringa vulgaris.

No. 1399 — Fire trucks: a, 1090fr, Mercedes-Benz Atego LF 10/6 Ziegler. b, 1180fr, Ford F-350. c, 3000fr, Kronenburg MAC 11. d, 3000fr, Scania P270 FJ 07 ANP.

No. 1400 — Visit of Pope Francis to Brazil: a, 1090fr, Pope Francis, flag of Brazil, youth, World Youth Day emblem. b, 1180fr, Pope Francis, flag of Brazil, Aparecida Cathedral. c, 3000fr, Pope Francis, World Youth Day emblem and stage. d, 3000fr, Pope Francis, World Youth Day emblem, Christ the Redeemer statue, flags.

No. 1401 — Owls: a, 1090fr, Asio otus. b, 1190fr, Pseudoscops clamator. c, 3000fr, Asio flammeus. d, 3000fr, Strix aluco aluco.

No. 1402 — Endangered animals: a, 1090fr, Cercopithecus hamlyni. b, 1190fr, Eidolon helvum. c, 3000fr, Phataginus tricuspis. d, 3000fr, Felis margarita.

No. 1403 — Shells and lighthouses: a, 1090fr, Chicoreus palmarosae, Boca Chita Lighthouse, Florida. b, 1190fr, Lobatus gigas, Peggys Point Lighthouse, Nova Scotia. c, 3000fr, Cardium costatum, La Martre Lighthouse, Quebec. d, 3000fr, Columbarium pagoda pagoda, Maota Pagoda Lighthouse, China.

No. 1404 — Paintings by Pablo Picasso (1881-1973): a, 1090fr, Dying Bull, 1934. b, 1190fr, Mandolin and Guitar, 1924. c, 3000fr, Interior with a Girl Drawing, 1935. d, 3000fr, Les Demoiselles d'Avignon, 1907.

No. 1405 — High-speed trains: a, 1180fr, SNCF TGV Atlantique. b, 1190fr, BR Class 395 Javelin. c, 3000fr, NTV Alstom AGV ETR 575. d, 3000fr, Hitachi Super Express.

No. 1406, 7500fr, Ceratotherium simum. No. 1407, 7500fr, Cuon alpinus, Hylocereus undatus. No. 1408, 7500fr, Nemateleotris magnifica. No. 1409, 7500fr, Regina rigida sinicola. No. 1410, 7500fr, Variscite. No. 1411, 7500fr, Pope John Paul II, statue. No. 1412, 7500fr, Siberian cat. No. 1413, 7500fr, Terathopius ecaudatus. No. 1414, 7500fr, Dollodon. No. 1415, 7500fr, Homo neanderthalensis drawing on cave wall, diff. No. 1416, 7500fr, The Bowdoin, Monhegan Island, by Edward Willis Redfield. No. 1417, 7500fr, Verdi and scene from Aida. No. 1418, 7500fr, Mao Zedong and Chinese writing. No. 1419, 7500fr, Mandela, map of Africa. No. 1420, 7500fr, Psammobates geometricus. No. 1421, 7500fr, Adam Gilchrist. No. 1422, 7500fr, Cephalorhynchus commerssonii. No. 1423, 7500fr, Vespula germanica, Hydrangea macrophylla. No. 1424, 7500fr, Rosenbauer fire truck. No. 1425, 7500fr, Pope Francis, youths raising cross, flag of Brazil. No. 1426, 7500fr, Bubo virginianus. No. 1427, 7500fr, Varecia rubra. No. 1428, 7500fr, Charonia tritonis, Sambro Island Lighthouse, Nova Scotia. No. 1429, The Old Guitarist, by Picasso,

1903. No. 1430, 7500fr, Siemens Velaro ICE 3DB Class 407.

2013, Aug. 20   Litho.   Perf. 13¼
Sheets of 4, #a-d
1381-1405 A178 Set of 25 260.00 260.00
Souvenir Sheets
1406-1430 A178 Set of 25 245.00 245.00

Brasiliana 2013 Intl. Philatelic Exhibition, Rio (#1400, 1425).

SEMI-POSTAL STAMPS

Prince Louis Rwagasore — SP1

Prince and Stadium SP2

Nos. B3, B6, Prince, memorial monument.

Perf. 14x13, 13x14
1963, Feb. 15   Photo.   Unwmk.

B1	SP1	50c + 25c brt vio	.25	.25
B2	SP2	1fr + 50c red org & dk bl	.25	.25
B3	SP2	1.50fr + 75c lem & dk vio	.25	.25
B4	SP1	3.50fr + 1.50fr lil rose	.25	.25
B5	SP2	5fr + 2fr rose pink & dk bl	.25	.25
B6	SP2	6.50fr + 3fr gray ol & dk vio	.25	.25
		Nos. B1-B6 (6)	1.50	1.50

Issued in memory of Prince Louis Rwagasore (1932-61), son of King Mwami Mwambutsa IV and Prime Minister. The surtax was for the stadium and monument in his honor.
Exist imperf. Value set, $18.

Red Cross Type of Regular Issue
Souvenir Sheet
1963, Sept. 26   Litho.   Imperf.

B7		Sheet of 4	5.00 5.00
a.	A5 4fr + 2fr fawn, red & black		1.00 1.00
b.	A5 8fr + 2fr green, red & black		1.00 1.00
c.	A5 10fr + 2fr gray, red & black		1.00 1.00
d.	A5 20fr + 2fr ultra, red & black		1.00 1.00

Surtax for Red Cross work in Burundi.

Olympic Type of Regular Issue
Souvenir Sheet
Designs: 18fr+2fr, Hurdling, horiz. 20fr+5fr, Vaulting, horiz.

1964, Nov. 18   Perf. 13½

B8		Sheet of 2	12.00 12.00
a.	A13 18fr + 2fr lt grn & multi		5.00 4.00
b.	A13 20fr + 5fr brt pink & multi		5.00 4.00

Exists imperf. Value $12.

Scientist with Microscope and Map of Burundi — SP3

Lithographed and Photogravure
1965, Jan. 28   Unwmk.   Perf. 14½

B9	SP3	2fr + 50c multi	.25	.25
B10	SP3	4fr + 1.50fr multi	.25	.25
B11	SP3	5fr + 2.50fr multi	.30	.25
B12	SP3	8fr + 3fr multi	.40	.25
B13	SP3	10fr + 5fr multi	.65	.30
		Nos. B9-B13 (5)	1.85	1.30

Souvenir Sheet
Perf. 13x13½

B14	SP3	10fr + 10fr multi	1.50 1.50

Issued for the fight against tuberculosis.
Exist imperf. Values: set $5; souvenir sheet $2.

Coat of Arms, 10fr Coin, Reverse SP4

Designs (Coins of Various Denominations): 4fr+50c, 8fr+50c, 15fr+50c, 40fr+50c, King Mwambutsa IV, obverse.

Lithographed; Embossed on Gilt Foil
1965, Aug. 9   Imperf.
Diameter: 39mm

B15	SP4	2fr + 50c crim & org	.25	.25
B16	SP4	4fr + 50c ultra & ver	.30	.30

Diameter: 45mm

B17	SP4	6fr + 50c org & gray	.50	.50
B18	SP4	8fr + 50c bl & mag	.65	.65

Diameter: 56mm

B19	SP4	12fr + 50c lt grn & red lil	.95	.95
B20	SP4	15fr + 50c yel grn & lt lil	1.10	1.10

Diameter: 67mm

B21	SP4	25fr + 50c vio bl & buff	2.10	2.10
B22	SP4	40fr + 50c brt pink & red brn	4.00	4.00
		Nos. B15-B22 (8)	9.85	9.85

Stamps are backed with patterned paper in blue, orange and pink engine-turned design.

Prince Louis Rwagasore and Pres. John F. Kennedy SP5

4fr+1fr, 20fr+5fr, Prince Louis, memorial. 20fr+2fr, 40fr+5fr, Pres. John F. Kennedy, library shelves. 40fr+2fr, King Mwambutsa IV at Kennedy grave, Arlington, vert.

1966, Jan. 21   Photo.   Perf. 13½

B23	SP5	4fr + 1fr gray bl & dk brn	.25	.25
B24	SP5	10fr + 1fr pale grn, ind & brn	.25	.25
B25	SP5	20fr + 2fr lil & dp grn	.50	.25
B26	SP5	40fr + 2fr gray grn & dk brn	1.10	.55
		Nos. B23-B26 (4)	2.10	1.30

Souvenir Sheet

B27		Sheet of 2	3.25 3.75
a.	SP5 20fr + 5fr gray bl & dk brn		1.50 1.50
b.	SP5 40fr + 5fr lilac & dp grn		1.50 1.50

Issued in memory of Prince Louis Rwagasore and President John F. Kennedy.
Exist imperf. Values: set $6; souvenir sheet $3.50.

Republic

Winston Churchill and St. Paul's, London SP6

Designs: 15fr+2fr, Tower of London and Churchill. 20fr+3fr, Big Ben and Churchill.

1967, Mar. 23   Photo.   Perf. 13½

B28	SP6	4fr + 1fr multi	.30	.25
B29	SP6	15fr + 2fr multi	.50	.25
B30	SP6	20fr + 3fr multi	.65	.40
		Nos. B28-B30 (3)	1.45	.90

Issued in memory of Sir Winston Churchill (1874-1965), statesman and World War II leader.
Exist imperf. Value $4.50.
A souvenir sheet contains one airmail stamp, 50fr+5fr, with Churchill portrait centered. Size: 80x80mm. Exists perf and imperf. Value, each sheet, $2.

Nos. B28-B30 Overprinted

1967, July 14   Photo.   Perf. 13½

B31	SP6	4fr + 1fr multi	.70	.25
B32	SP6	15fr + 2fr multi	1.00	.40
B33	SP6	20fr + 3fr multi	1.25	.50
		Nos. B31-B33 (3)	2.95	1.15

50th anniversary of Lions International.
Exist with dates transposed. Value, set $30.
Both the regular set imperf and the souvenir sheets described below No. B30 also received this Lions overprint. Value: set $8.50; souvenir sheet, each $3. Also exists imperf. Value, set $50.

Blood Transfusion and Red Cross — SP7

Designs: 7fr+1fr, Stretcher bearers and wounded man. 11fr+1fr, Surgical team. 17fr+1fr, Nurses tending blood bank.

1969, June 26   Photo.   Perf. 13½

B34	SP7	4fr + 1fr multi	.25	.25
B35	SP7	7fr + 1fr multi	.35	.25
B36	SP7	11fr + 1fr multi	.40	.25
B37	SP7	17fr + 1fr multi	.60	.25
		Nos. B34-B37,CB9-CB11 (7)	5.55	2.25

League of Red Cross Societies, 50th anniv.
Exist imperf. Value set (7), $9.

Pope Paul VI and Map of Africa — SP8

3fr+2fr, 17fr+2fr, Pope Paul VI. 10fr+2fr, Flag made of flags of African Nations. 14fr+2fr, View of St. Peter's, Rome. 40fr+2fr, 40fr+5fr, Martyrs of Uganda. 50fr+2fr, 50fr+5fr, Pope on Throne.

1969, Sept. 12   Photo.   Perf. 13½

B38	SP8	3fr + 2fr multi, vert.	.25	.25
B39	SP8	5fr + 2fr multi	.25	.25
B40	SP8	10fr + 2fr multi	.35	.25
B41	SP8	14fr + 2fr multi	.75	.25
B42	SP8	17fr + 2fr multi, vert.	1.25	.30
B43	SP8	40fr + 2fr multi	1.75	.60
B44	SP8	50fr + 2fr multi	2.00	.65
		Nos. B38-B44 (7)	6.60	2.55

Souvenir Sheet

B45		Sheet of 2	4.50 4.50
a.	SP8 40fr + 5fr multi		2.00 2.00
b.	SP8 50fr + 5fr multi		2.00 2.00

Visit of Pope Paul VI to Uganda, 7/31-8/2.
Exist imperf. Values: set $11; souvenir sheet $4.50.

Virgin and Child, by Albrecht Dürer — SP9

Christmas (Paintings): 11fr+1fr, Madonna of the Eucharist, by Sandro Botticelli. 20fr+1fr, Holy Family, by El Greco.

1970, Dec. 14   Photo.   Perf. 13½
Gold Frame

B46	SP9	6.50fr + 1fr multi	.70 .25
B47	SP9	11fr + 1fr multi	1.00 .25
B48	SP9	20fr + 1fr multi	1.25 .35
a.		Souv. sheet of 3, #B46-B48	3.50 3.50
		Nos. B46-B48,CB12-CB14 (6)	6.95 2.15

Exist imperf. Values: set (6) $6.50; souvenir sheets $6.75.

Nos. 376-378 Surcharged in Gold and Black

1971, Nov. 27

B49	A51	3fr + 1fr multi	.25 .25
B50	A51	5fr + 1fr multi	.65 .25
B51	A51	6fr + 1fr multi	.75 .25
a.		Souvenir sheet of 3	4.00 4.00
		Nos. B49-B51,CB19-CB21 (6)	5.45 1.80

UNICEF, 25th anniv. No. B51a contains 3 stamps similar to Nos. B49-B51 with 2fr surtax each.

Exist imperf. Values: set (6) $5.50; souvenir sheets $8.

"La Polenta," by Pietro Longhi SP10

Designs: 3fr+1fr, Archangel Michael, Byzantine icon from St. Mark's 6fr+1fr, "Gossip," by Pietro Longhi. 11fr+1fr, "Diana's Bath," by Giovanni Batista Pittoni. All stamps inscribed UNESCO.

1971, Dec. 27

B52	SP10	3fr + 1fr gold & multi	.25 .25
B53	SP10	5fr + 1fr gold & multi	.35 .25
B54	SP10	6fr + 1fr gold & multi	.45 .25
B55	SP10	11fr + 1fr gold & multi	.70 .25
a.		Souvenir sheet of 4	3.00 3.00
		Nos. B52-B55,CB22-CB25 (8)	5.80 2.20

The surtax was for the UNESCO campaign to save the treasures of Venice. No. B55a contains 4 stamps similar to Nos. B52-B55, but with 2fr surtax.

Exist imperf. Values: set (8) $7.50; souvenir sheets $10.

Nos. 408-410 Surcharged in Silver

1972, Dec. 12   Photo.   Perf. 13½

B56	A57	5fr + 1fr multi	.55 .25
B57	A57	10fr + 1fr multi	1.00 .25
B58	A57	15fr + 1fr multi	1.60 .25
a.		Souvenir sheet of 3	3.00 3.00
		Nos. B56-B58,CB26-CB28 (6)	8.40 1.95

Christmas 1972. No. B58a contains 3 stamps similar to Nos. B56-B58, but with 2fr surtax.

Exist imperf. Values: set (6) $10; souvenir sheets $16.

Nos. 441-443 Surcharged "+1F" in Silver

1973, Dec. 14   Photo.   Perf. 13

B59	A64	5fr + 1fr multi	.70 .25
B60	A64	10fr + 1fr multi	.90 .25
B61	A64	15fr + 1fr multi	1.10 .25
a.		Souvenir sheet of 3	4.00 4.00
		Nos. B59-B61,CB29-CB31 (6)	6.60 1.95

Christmas 1973. No. B61a contains 3 stamps similar to Nos. B59-B61 with 2fr surtax each.

Exist imperf. Values: set (6) $7.50; souvenir sheets $8.

Christmas Type of 1974
1974, Dec. 2   Photo.   Perf. 13

B62	A70	5fr + 1fr multi	1.00 .25
B63	A70	10fr + 1fr multi	1.40 .30
B64	A70	15fr + 1fr multi	2.10 .40
a.		Souvenir sheet of 3	5.50 5.50
		Nos. B62-B64,CB32-CB34 (6)	10.10 2.85

No. B64a contains 3 stamps similar to Nos. B62-B64 with 2fr surtax each.

Exist imperf. Values: set (6) $11; souvenir sheets $17.

Nos. 485-487 Surcharged "+ 1F" in Silver and Black

1975, Dec. 22   Photo.   Perf. 13
Pairs, #a.-b.

B65	A73	5fr + 1fr #485	3.25 .25
B66	A73	13fr + 1fr #486	6.50 .30
B67	A73	27fr + 1fr #487	10.00 .60
c.		Souvenir sheet of 6	16.50 16.50
		Nos. B65-B67,CB35-CB37 (6)	41.50 2.55

Michelangelo Buonarroti (1475-1564), 500th birth anniversary. No. B67c contains 6 stamps similar to Nos. B65a-B67b with 2fr surcharge each.

Exist imperf. Values: set (6) $28; souvenir sheets $26.

Nos. 504-506 Surcharged "+1f" in Silver and Black

1976, Nov. 25   Photo.   Perf. 13½

B71	A76	5fr + 1fr multi	.95 .25
B72	A76	13fr + 1fr multi	1.50 .25
B73	A76	27fr + 1fr multi	3.00 .60
a.		Souvenir sheet of 3	5.50 5.50
		Nos. B71-B73,CB41-CB43 (6)	12.55 2.35

Christmas 1976. No. B73a contains 3 stamps similar to Nos. B71-B73 with 2fr surtax each.

Exist imperf. Values: set (6) $11; souvenir sheets $10.

Nos. 531-533 Surcharged "+1fr" in Silver and Black

1977   Photo.   Perf. 14x13

B74	A83	5fr + 1fr multi	.90 .25
B75	A83	13fr + 1fr multi	2.50 .25
B76	A83	27fr + 1fr multi	3.00 .25
a.		Souvenir sheet of 3	6.50 6.50
		Nos. B74-B76,CB44-CB46 (6)	14.40 2.25

Christmas 1977. No. B76a contains 3 stamps similar to Nos. B74-B76 with 2fr surtax each.

Exist imperf. Values: set (6) $12; souvenir sheets $13.

Christmas Type of 1979
1979, Feb.   Photo.   Perf. 14x13

B77	A86	13fr + 1fr multi	1.50 1.25
B78	A86	17fr + 1fr multi	1.90 1.60
B79	A86	27fr + 1fr multi	3.50 2.50

B80	A86	31fr + 1fr multi	4.00 3.50
B81	A86	40fr + 1fr multi	5.25 4.50
		Nos. B77-B81 (5)	16.15 13.35

Exist imperf. Value $12.

IYC Type of 1979
1979, July 19   Photo.   Perf. 14

B82		Sheet of 4	11.00 11.00
a.	A88	10fr + 2fr like #557	2.50 2.50
b.	A88	20fr + 2fr like #558	2.50 2.50
c.	A88	27fr + 2fr like #559	2.50 2.50
d.	A88	50fr + 2fr like #560	2.50 2.50

Exist imperf. Value $12.50.

Christmas Type of 1979
1979, Dec. 10   Photo.   Perf. 13½

B83	A89	20fr + 1fr like #561	2.50 1.00
B84	A89	27fr + 1fr like #562	4.75 2.00
B85	A89	31fr + 1fr like #563	6.50 2.50
B86	A89	50fr + 2fr like #564	8.25 2.75
		Nos. B83-B86 (4)	22.00 8.25

Christmas Type of 1980
1981, Jan. 16   Photo.   Perf. 13½x13

B87	A92	10fr + 1fr like #579	1.60 .65
B88	A92	30fr + 1fr like #580	3.25 1.25
B89	A92	40fr + 1fr like #581	7.25 3.00
B90	A92	50fr + 1fr like #582	10.00 4.00
		Nos. B87-B90 (4)	22.10 8.90

Christmas Type of 1983
1983, Nov. 2   Litho.   Perf. 14½x13½

B91	A97	10fr + 1fr like #607	5.50 1.25
B92	A97	25fr + 1fr like #608	8.00 1.75
B93	A97	30fr + 1fr like #609	15.00 3.50
B94	A97	50fr + 1fr like #610	21.00 9.00
		Nos. B91-B94 (4)	49.50 15.50

Christmas Type of 1984
1984, Dec. 15   Perf. 13½

B95	A101	10fr + 1fr like #629	2.75 1.00
B96	A101	25fr + 1fr like #630	6.50 2.50
B97	A101	30fr + 1fr like #631	7.75 3.00
B98	A101	50fr + 1fr like #632	11.00 4.75
		Nos. B95-B98 (4)	28.00 11.25

Multi-party Elections, 1st Anniv.
SP11　　　　SP12

30fr+10fr, Pres. Buyoya handing Baton of Power to Pres. Ndadaye. 110fr+10fr, Pres. Ndadaye giving inauguration speech. 115fr+10fr, Arms, map of Burundi. 120fr+10fr, Warrior, flag of Burundi, trees, map of Burundi.

1994, Oct. 20   Litho.   Perf. 15

B99	SP11	30fr +10fr multi	1.00 .75
B100	SP11	110fr +10fr multi	3.50 2.75
B101	SP12	115fr +10fr multi	4.00 2.75
B102	SP12	120fr +10fr multi	4.00 2.75
		Nos. B99-B102 (4)	12.50 9.00

AIR POST STAMPS

Animal Type of Regular Issue

6fr, Zebra. 8fr, Cape buffalo (bubalis). 10fr, Impala. 14fr, Hippopotamus. 15fr, Defassa waterbuck. 20fr, Cheetah. 50fr, Elephant.

Unwmk.
1964, July 2   Litho.   Perf. 14
Size: 42x21mm, 21x42mm

C1	A9	6fr multi	.40 .25
C2	A9	8fr multi	.50 .25
C3	A9	10fr multi, vert.	.70 .25
C4	A9	14fr multi	1.05 .30
C5	A9	15fr multi, vert.	1.35 .40

Size: 53x32½mm

C6	A9	20fr multi	2.50 .50
C7	A9	50fr multi	6.00 .75
		Nos. C1-C7 (7)	12.50 2.70

Exists imperf.

Bird Type of Regular Issue

Birds: 6fr, Secretary bird. 8fr, African anhinga. 10fr, African peacock. 14fr, Bee eater. 15fr, Yellow-billed stork. 20fr, Saddle-billed stork. 50fr, Abyssinian ground hornbill. 75fr, Martial eagle. 130fr, Lesser flamingo.

1965, June 10   Litho.   Perf. 14
Size: 26x43mm

C8	A14	6fr multi	.25 .25
C9	A14	8fr multi	.35 .25
C10	A14	10fr multi	.45 .25
C11	A14	14fr multi	.75 .30
C12	A14	15fr multi	.95 .40

Size: 33x53mm

C13	A14	20fr multi	1.90 .45
C14	A14	50fr multi	3.00 .65
C15	A14	75fr multi	4.50 1.00
C16	A14	130fr multi	7.75 1.60
		Nos. C8-C16 (9)	19.90 5.15

For overprints see Nos. C35A-C35I.

Flower Type of Regular Issue

Flowers: 6fr, Dissotis. 8fr, Crossandra. 10fr, Ansellia. 14fr, Thunbergia. 15fr, Schizoglossum. 20fr, Gazania. 50fr, Protea. 75fr, Hibiscus. 130fr, Markhamia.

1966, Oct. 10   Unwmk.   Perf. 13½
Size: 31x31mm

C17	A17	6fr multi	.35 .25
C18	A17	8fr multi	.50 .25
C19	A17	10fr multi	.60 .25
C20	A17	14fr multi	.75 .25
C21	A17	15fr multi	1.00 .25

Size: 39x39mm

C22	A17	20fr multi	1.25 .25
C23	A17	50fr multi	2.25 .35
C24	A17	75fr multi	3.50 .50
C25	A17	130fr multi	6.00 1.00
		Nos. C17-C25 (9)	16.20 3.35

For overprints see Nos. C27-C35.

Tapestry Type of Regular Issue
Souvenir Sheet

1966, Nov. 4   Unwmk.   Perf. 13½

C26	A18	Sheet of 7 (14fr)	9.00 6.50

See note after No. 158.

REPUBLIC

Nos. C17-C25 Overprinted

1967   Litho.   Perf. 13½
Size: 31x31mm

C27	A17	6fr multi	.25 .25
C28	A17	8fr multi	.35 .25
C29	A17	10fr multi	.50 .25
C30	A17	14fr multi	.75 .25
C31	A17	15fr multi	1.00 .25

Size: 39x39mm

C32	A17	20fr multi	2.00 .35
C33	A17	50fr multi	5.00 .90
C34	A17	75fr multi	8.00 1.50
C35	A17	130fr multi	8.50 1.50
		Nos. C27-C35 (9)	26.35 5.50

Nos. C8-C16 Overprinted

1967   Litho.   Perf. 14
Size: 26x43mm

C35A	A14	6fr multi	.50 .40
C35B	A14	8fr multi	1.00 .50
C35C	A14	10fr multi	1.50 .60
C35D	A14	14fr multi	2.00 .75
C35E	A14	15fr multi	2.75 .90

Size: 33x53mm

C35F	A14	20fr multi	4.00 2.00
C35G	A14	50fr multi	8.50 4.00
C35H	A14	75fr multi	12.50 5.00
C35I	A14	130fr multi	18.00 7.50
		Nos. C35A-C35I (9)	50.75 21.65

African Art Type of Regular Issue

10fr, Spirit of Bakutu figurine, Equatorial Africa. 14fr, Pearl throne of Sultan of the Bamum, Cameroun. 17fr, Bronze head of Mother Queen of Benin, Nigeria. 24fr, Statue of 109th Bakouba king, Kata-Mbula, Central Congo. 26fr, Baskets and lances, Burundi.

1967, June 5		**Photo.**	*Perf. 13½*	
C36	A20	10fr gold & multi	.25	.25
C37	A20	14fr gold & multi	.30	.25
C38	A20	17fr gold & multi	.45	.25
C39	A20	24fr gold & multi	.55	.50
C40	A20	26fr gold & multi	.90	.50
	Nos. C36-C40 (5)		2.45	1.55

Boy Scout Type of Regular Issue

10fr, Scouts on hiking trip. 14fr, Cooking at campfire. 17fr, Lord Baden-Powell. 24fr, Boy Scout & Cub Scout giving Scout sign. 26fr, First aid.

1967, Aug. 9			*Perf. 13½*	
C41	A21	10fr gold & multi	1.25	.25
C42	A21	14fr gold & multi	1.50	.25
C43	A21	17fr gold & multi	1.75	.25
C44	A21	24fr gold & multi	2.75	.25
C45	A21	26fr gold & multi	3.00	.40
	Nos. C41-C45 (5)		10.25	1.40

A souvenir sheet of 2 contains one each of Nos. C44-C45 and 2 labels in the designs of Nos. 208-209 with commemorative inscriptions was issued 1/8/68. Size: 100x100mm. Value, $8 unused, $5 used.

Fish Type of Regular Issue

Designs: Various Tropical Fish

1967, Sept. 8		**Photo.**	*Perf. 13½*	
		Size: 50x23mm		
C46	A19	6fr multi	.95	.25
C47	A19	8fr multi	1.40	.25
C48	A19	10fr multi	1.90	.25
C49	A19	14fr multi	2.25	.25
C50	A19	15fr multi	2.00	.25
		Size: 58x27mm		
C51	A19	20fr multi	3.75	.25
C52	A19	50fr multi	7.75	.30
C53	A19	75fr multi	11.50	.35
C54	A19	130fr multi	18.00	.60
	Nos. C46-C54 (9)		49.50	2.80

Boeing 707 of Air Congo and ITY Emblem — AP1

Designs: 14fr, Boeing 727 of Sabena over lake. 17fr, Vickers VC10 of East African Airways over lake. 26fr, Boeing 727 of Sabena over airport.

1967, Nov. 3		**Photo.**	*Perf. 13*	
C55	AP1	10fr blk, yel brn & sil	.35	.25
C56	AP1	14fr blk, org & sil	.60	.25
C57	AP1	17fr blk, brt bl & sil	.70	.30
C58	AP1	26fr blk, brt rose lil & sil	1.40	.55
	Nos. C55-C58 (4)		3.05	1.35

Opening of the jet airport at Bujumbura and for International Tourist Year, 1967. Exist imperf. Value set, $7.

Paintings Type of Regular Issue

Paintings: 17fr, Woman with Cat, by Renoir. 24fr, The Jewish Bride, by Rembrandt, horiz. 26fr, Pope Innocent X, by Velazquez.

1968, Mar. 29		**Photo.**	*Perf. 13½*	
C59	A26	17fr multi	.65	.30
C60	A26	24fr multi	1.00	.40
C61	A26	26fr multi	1.25	.90
	Nos. C59-C61 (3)		2.90	1.60
	Issued in sheets of 6.			

Space Type of Regular Issue

14fr, Moon Probe. 18fr, Russian astronaut walking in space. 25fr, Mariner satellite, Mars. 40fr, American astronaut walking in space.

1968, May 15		**Photo.**	*Perf. 13½*	
		Size: 41x41mm		
C62	A27	14fr sil & multi	.60	.25
C63	A27	18fr sil & multi	.80	.25
C64	A27	25fr sil & multi	.90	.25
C65	A27	40fr sil & multi	1.75	.60
	Nos. C62-C65 (4)		4.05	1.35

Butterfly Type of Regular Issue

Butterflies: 6fr, Teracolus annae. 8fr, Graphium ridleyanus. 10fr, Cymothoe. 14fr, Charaxes eupale. 15fr, Papilio bromius. 20fr, Papilio zenobia. 50fr, Salamis aethiops. 75fr, Danais chrysippus. 130fr, Salamis temora.

1968, Sept. 9		**Photo.**	*Perf. 13½*	
		Size: 38x42mm		
C66	A28	6fr gold & multi	1.10	.25
C67	A28	8fr gold & multi	2.00	.25
C68	A28	10fr gold & multi	2.25	.30
C69	A28	14fr gold & multi	2.75	.40
C70	A28	15fr gold & multi	3.00	.50
		Size: 44x49mm		
C71	A28	20fr gold & multi	4.25	.75
C72	A28	50fr gold & multi	7.50	1.00
C73	A28	75fr gold & multi	12.50	1.25
C74	A28	130fr gold & multi	20.00	1.50
	Nos. C66-C74 (9)		55.35	6.20

Painting Type of Regular Issue

Paintings: 17fr, The Letter, by Jean H. Fragonard. 26fr, Young Woman Reading Letter, by Jan Vermeer. 40fr, Lady Folding Letter, by Elisabeth Vigée-Lebrun. 50fr, Mademoiselle Lavergne, by Jean Etienne Liotard.

1968, Sept. 30		**Photo.**	*Perf. 13½*	
C84	A29	17fr multi	.65	.30
C85	A29	26fr multi	1.25	.30
C86	A29	40fr multi	2.00	.40
C87	A29	50fr multi	2.75	.40
	Nos. C84-C87 (4)		6.65	1.40

A souvenir sheet containing examples of Nos. C86-C87 with changed colors exists perf and imperf. Value, each $6.50.

Olympic Games Type

1968, Oct. 24				
C88	A30	10fr Shot put	.25	.25
C89	A30	17fr Running	.45	.25
C90	A30	26fr Hammer throw	.90	.25
C91	A30	50fr Hurdling	1.75	.40
C92	A30	75fr Broad jump	3.25	.55
	Nos. C88-C92 (5)		6.60	1.70

Christmas Type of 1968

Paintings: 10fr, Virgin and Child, by Correggio. 14fr, Nativity, by Federigo Barocci. 17fr, Holy Family, by El Greco. 26fr, Adoration of the Magi, by Maino.

1968, Nov. 26		**Photo.**	*Perf. 13½*	
C93	A31	10fr multi	.35	.25
C94	A31	14fr multi	.45	.25
C95	A31	17fr multi	.60	.25
C96	A31	26fr multi	1.25	.50
a.		Souv. sheet of 4, #C93-C96	3.00	2.25
	Nos. C93-C96 (4)		2.65	1.25

For overprints see Nos. C100-C103.

Human Rights Flame, Hand and Globe — AP2

1969, Jan. 22				
C97	AP2	10fr multi	.35	.25
C98	AP2	14fr multi	.55	.25
C99	AP2	26fr lil & multi	.90	.25
	Nos. C97-C99 (3)		1.80	.75

International Human Rights Year, 1968. Exist imperf. Value set, $4.50.

Nos. C93-C96 Overprinted in Silver

(blank - third column middle)

1969, Feb. 17		**Photo.**	*Perf. 13½*	
C100	A31	10fr multi	.45	.25
C101	A31	14fr multi	.60	.25
C102	A31	17fr multi	.70	.30
C103	A31	26fr multi	1.00	.50
	Nos. C100-C103 (4)		2.75	1.30

Man's 1st flight around the moon by the US spacecraft Apollo 8, Dec. 21-27, 1968.

Moon Landing Type of 1969

Designs: 26fr, Neil A. Armstrong leaving landing module. 40fr, Astronaut on moon. 50fr, Splashdown in the Pacific.

1969, Nov. 6		**Photo.**	*Perf. 13½*	
C104	A38	26fr gold & multi	1.75	.30
C105	A38	40fr gold & multi	2.50	.45
C106	A38	50fr gold & multi	4.00	.50
	Nos. C104-C106 (3)		8.25	1.25

Christmas Type of 1969

Paintings: 17fr, Madonna and Child, by Benvenuto da Garofalo. 26fr, Madonna and Child, by Jacopo Negretti. 50fr, Madonna and Child, by Il Giorgione. All horizontal.

1969, Dec. 2			**Photo.**	
C107	A39	17fr gold & multi	.70	.25
C108	A39	26fr gold & multi	1.25	.25
C109	A39	50fr gold & multi	2.75	.35
a.		Souv. sheet of 3, #C107-C109	4.25	3.50
	Nos. C107-C109 (3)		4.70	.85

Insect Type of Regular Issue

Designs: Various Beetles and Weevils.

1970		**Size: 46x32mm**	*Perf. 13½*	
C110	A40	6fr gold & multi	.65	.25
C111	A40	8fr gold & multi	.80	.25
C112	A40	10fr gold & multi	1.00	.25
C113	A40	14fr gold & multi	1.25	.25
C114	A40	15fr gold & multi	1.50	.25
		Size: 52x36mm		
C115	A40	20fr gold & multi	3.00	.40
C116	A40	50fr gold & multi	5.75	.55
C117	A40	75fr gold & multi	8.50	.75
C118	A40	130fr gold & multi	13.50	1.25
	Nos. C110-C118 (9)		35.95	4.20

Issued: Nos. C110-C115, 1/20; Nos. C116-C118, 2/27.

Easter Type of 1970

Stations of the Cross, by Juan de Aranoa y Carredano: 8fr, Jesus meets the women of Jerusalem. 10fr, Jesus falls a third time. 14fr, Jesus stripped. 15fr, Jesus nailed to the cross. 18fr, Jesus dies on the cross. 20fr, Descent from the cross. 50fr, Jesus laid in the tomb.

1970, Mar. 16		**Photo.**	*Perf. 13½*	
C119	A41	8fr gold & multi	.30	.25
C120	A41	10fr gold & multi	.40	.25
C121	A41	14fr gold & multi	.55	.25
C122	A41	15fr gold & multi	.65	.25
C123	A41	18fr gold & multi	.90	.30
C124	A41	20fr gold & multi	1.00	.40
C125	A41	50fr gold & multi	2.10	.70
a.		Souv. sheet of 7, #C119-C125 + label	7.25	6.00
	Nos. C119-C125 (7)		5.90	2.40

EXPO '70 Type of Regular Issue
Souvenir Sheet

Designs: 40fr, Tower of the Sun, vert. 50fr, Flags of participating nations, vert.

1970, May 5		**Photo.**	*Perf. 13½*	
C126		Sheet of 2	3.00	3.00
a.		A42 40fr multi	1.00	1.00
b.		A42 50fr multi	1.25	1.25

Rhinoceros Type of Regular Issue

Fauna: a, i, Camel. c, d, Dromedary. g, r, Okapi. f, m, Addax. j, o, Rhinoceros. l, p, Burundi cow (each animal in 2 different poses).

Map of the Nile: b, Delta and pyramids. e, dhow. h, Falls. k, Blue Nile and crowned crane. n, Victoria Nile and secretary bird. q, Lake Victoria and source of Nile on Mt. Gikizi. Continuous design.

1970, July 8		**Photo.**	*Perf. 13½*	
C127		Sheet of 18	50.00	25.00
a.-r.		A43 14fr any single	2.00	.35

Publicizing the southernmost source of the Nile on Mt. Gikizi in Burundi.

UN Emblem and Headquarters, NYC — AP3

25th Anniv. of the UN (UN Emblem and): 11fr, Security Council and mural by Per Krohg. 26fr, Pope Paul VI and U Thant. 40fr, Flags in front of UN Headquarters, NYC.

1970, Oct. 23		**Photo.**	*Perf. 13½*	
C128	AP3	7fr gold & multi	.25	.25
C129	AP3	11fr gold & multi	.35	.25
C130	AP3	26fr gold & multi	.85	.25
C131	AP3	40fr gold & multi	1.10	.40
a.		Souvenir sheet of 2	3.75	3.75
	Nos. C128-C131 (4)		2.55	1.15

No. C131a contains 2 stamps similar to Nos. C130-C131 but without "Poste Aerienne." Exist imperf. Values: set $4; souvenir sheet $7.

Bird Type of Regular Issue

8fr, 14fr, 30fr, vert.; 10fr, 20fr, 50fr, horiz.

1970		**Photo.**	*Perf. 13½*	
		Stamp size: 52x44mm		
C132	A44	Block of 4	13.50	1.50
a.		8fr Northern shrike	2.75	.25
b.		8fr European starling	2.75	.25
c.		8fr Yellow wagtail	2.75	.25
d.		8fr Bank swallow	2.75	.25
C133	A44	Block of 4	16.50	1.75
a.		10fr Winter wren	3.25	.30
b.		10fr Firecrest	3.25	.30
c.		10fr Skylark	3.25	.30
d.		10fr Crested lark	3.25	.30
C134	A44	Block of 4	20.00	2.00
a.		14fr Woodchat shrike	4.00	.35
b.		14fr Common rock thrush	4.00	.35
c.		14fr Black redstart	4.00	.35
d.		14fr Ring ouzel	4.00	.35
C135	A44	Block of 4	18.00	2.25
a.		20fr European redstart	3.75	.40
b.		20fr Hedge sparrow	3.75	.40
c.		20fr Gray wagtail	3.75	.40
d.		20fr Meadow pipit	3.75	.40
C136	A44	Block of 4	22.50	2.75
a.		30fr Eurasian hoopoe	4.50	.45
b.		30fr Pied flycatcher	4.50	.45
c.		30fr Great reed warbler	4.50	.45
d.		30fr Eurasian kingfisher	4.50	.45
C137	A44	Block of 4	32.50	3.50
a.		50fr House martin	7.00	.60
b.		50fr Sedge warbler	7.00	.60
c.		50fr Fieldfare	7.00	.60
d.		50fr European Golden oriole	7.00	.60
	Nos. C132-C137 (6)		123.00	13.75

Queen Fabiola and King Baudouin of Belgium AP4

Designs: 20fr, Pres. Michel Micombero and King Baudouin. 40fr, Pres. Micombero and coats of arms of Burundi and Belgium.

1970, Nov. 28		**Photo.**	*Perf. 13½*	
C140	AP4	6fr multicolored	1.00	.25
C141	AP4	20fr multicolored	2.60	.65
C142	AP4	40fr multicolored	5.25	1.10
a.		Souvenir sheet of 3	9.00	9.00
	Nos. C140-C142 (3)		8.85	2.00

Visit of the King and Queen of Belgium. No. C142a contains 3 stamps similar to Nos. C140-C142, but without "Poste Aerienne." Exist imperf. Values: set $10; souvenir sheet $9.

Easter Type of Regular Issue

Paintings of the Resurrection: 14fr, by Louis Borrassá. 17fr, Piero della Francesca. 26fr, Michel Wohlgemuth.

1971, Apr. 2   Photo.   Perf. 13½

C143	A49 14fr gold & multi	.95	.25
C144	A49 17fr gold & multi	1.25	.25
C145	A49 26fr gold & multi	2.40	.35
a.	Souv. sheet of 3, #C143-C145	5.00	5.00
	Nos. C143-C145 (3)	4.60	.85

Easter 1971.

Animal Type of Regular Issue

1971   Photo.   Perf. 13½
Size: 44x44mm

C146	Strip of 4	8.50	.85
a.	A48 10fr Lion	1.60	.25
b.	A48 10fr Cape buffalo	1.60	.25
c.	A48 10fr Hippopotamus	1.60	.25
d.	A48 10fr Giraffe	1.60	.25
C147	Strip of 4	9.50	1.00
a.	A48 14fr Hartebeest	1.90	.25
b.	A48 14fr Black rhinoceros	1.90	.25
c.	A48 14fr Zebra	1.90	.25
d.	A48 14fr Leopard	1.90	.25
C148	Strip of 4	10.50	1.00
a.	A48 17fr Grant's gazelles	2.10	.25
b.	A48 17fr Cheetah	2.10	.25
c.	A48 17fr African white-backed vultures	2.10	.25
d.	A48 17fr Johnston's okapi	2.10	.25
C149	Strip of 4	12.00	1.50
a.	A48 24fr Chimpanzee	2.25	.30
b.	A48 24fr Elephant	2.25	.30
c.	A48 24fr Spotted Hyenas	2.25	.30
d.	A48 24fr Beisa	2.25	.30
C150	Strip of 4	13.50	1.90
a.	A48 26fr Gorilla	2.50	.40
b.	A48 26fr Gnu	2.50	.40
c.	A48 26fr Warthog	2.50	.40
d.	A48 26fr Cape hunting dog	2.50	.40
C151	Strip of 4	14.50	2.40
a.	A48 31fr Sable antelope	3.00	.50
b.	A48 31fr Caracal lynx	3.00	.50
c.	A48 31fr Ostriches	3.00	.50
d.	A48 31fr Bongo	3.00	.50
	Nos. C146-C151 (6)	68.50	8.65

For overprint and surcharges see Nos. C152, CB15-C18.

No. C146 Overprinted in Gold and Black

1971, July 20   Photo.   Perf. 13½

C152	Strip of 4	5.00	3.00
a.	A48 10fr Lion	1.10	.25
b.	A48 10fr Cape buffalo	1.10	.25
c.	A48 10fr Hippopotamus	1.10	.25
d.	A48 10fr Giraffe	1.10	.25

Intl. Year Against Racial Discrimination.

Christmas Type of Regular Issue

Paintings of the Madonna and Child by: 14fr, Cima de Conegliano. 17fr, Fra Filippo Lippi. 31fr, Leonardo da Vinci.

1971, Nov. 2   Photo.   Perf. 13½

C153	A51 14fr red & multi	.60	.25
C154	A51 17fr red & multi	.80	.25
C155	A51 31fr red & multi	1.50	.35
a.	Souv. sheet of 3, #C153-C155	3.00	3.00
	Nos. C153-C155 (3)	2.90	.85

Christmas 1971.
For surcharges see Nos. CB19-CB21.

Spacecraft Type of Regular Issue
Souvenir Sheet

1972, Jan. 15   Photo.   Perf. 13½

C156	Sheet of 6	7.00	7.00
a.	A52 6fr Lunar Orbiter	.75	.75
b.	A52 11fr Vostok	.75	.75
c.	A52 14fr Luna 1	.75	.75
d.	A52 17fr Apollo 11 astronaut on moon	.75	.75
e.	A52 26fr Soyuz 11	.75	.75
f.	A52 40fr Lunar rover (Apollo 15)	.75	.75

Sapporo '72 Type of Regular Issue
Souvenir Sheet

Emblem and: 26fr, Snow scooter. 31fr, Downhill skiing. 50fr, Bobsledding.

1972, Feb. 3

C157	Sheet of 3	6.00	5.00
a.	A53 26fr silver & multi	1.50	1.25
b.	A53 31fr silver & multi	1.50	1.25
c.	A53 50fr silver & multi	1.50	1.25

Olympic Games Type of 1972

1972, July 24   Photo.   Perf. 13½

C158	A55 24fr Weight lifting	1.60	.25
C159	A55 26fr Hurdles	1.75	.25
C160	A55 31fr Discus	2.10	.40
C161	A55 40fr Soccer	2.75	.45
	Nos. C158-C161 (4)	8.20	1.35

Independence Type of 1972

Designs: 15fr, Prince Rwagasore, Pres. Micombero, Burundi flag, drummers. 18fr, Rwagasore, Micombero, flag, map of Africa, globe. 27fr, Micombero, flag, globe.

1972, Aug. 24   Photo.   Perf. 13½

C162	A56 15fr gold & multi	.40	.25
C163	A56 18fr gold & multi	.50	.30
C164	A56 27fr gold & multi	.80	.40
a.	Souv. sheet of 3, #C162-C164	2.00	2.00
	Nos. C162-C164 (3)	1.70	.95

Christmas Type of 1972

Paintings of the Madonna and Child by: 18fr, Sebastiano Mainardi. 27fr, Hans Memling. 40fr, Lorenzo Lotto.

1972, Nov. 2   Photo.   Perf. 13½

C165	A57 18fr dk car & multi	1.50	.25
C166	A57 27fr dk car & multi	1.75	.25
C167	A57 40fr dk car & multi	2.75	.40
a.	Souv. sheet of 3, #C165-C167	6.00	4.75
	Nos. C165-C167 (3)	6.00	.90

For surcharges see Nos. CB26-CB28.

Orchid Type of Regular Issue

13fr, Thelymitra pauciflora. 14fr, Miltassia. 15fr, Miltonia. 18fr, Platycoryne crocea. 20fr, Cattleya trinaei. 27fr, Eulophia cucullata. 36fr, Cymbidium hamsey.

1973, Jan. 18   Photo.   Perf. 13½
Size: 38x38mm

C168	A58 13fr multi	2.50	.25
C169	A58 14fr multi	2.75	.25
C170	A58 15fr multi	3.00	.30
C171	A58 18fr multi	3.50	.35
C172	A58 20fr multi	4.00	.40
C173	A58 27fr multi	5.00	.45
C174	A58 36fr multi	6.00	.60
	Nos. C168-C174 (7)	26.75	2.60

African Exploration Type of 1973

Designs: 15fr, Livingstone writing his diary. 18fr, "Dr. Livingstone, I presume." 27fr, Livingstone and Stanley discussing expedition.

1973, Mar. 19   Photo.   Perf. 13½

C175	A59 15fr gold & multi	.85	.25
C176	A59 18fr gold & multi	1.00	.25
C177	A59 27fr gold & multi	1.50	.35
a.	Souv. sheet of 3	4.00	4.00
	Nos. C175-C177 (3)	3.35	.85

No. C177a contains 3 stamps similar to Nos. C175-C177, but without "Poste Aerienne."

Easter Type of 1973

Paintings: 15fr, Christ at the Pillar, by Guido Reni. 18fr, Crucifixion, by Mathias Grunewald. 27fr, Descent from the Cross, by Caravaggio.

1973, Apr. 10

C178	A60 15fr gold & multi	1.25	.25
C179	A60 18fr gold & multi	1.40	.30
C180	A60 27fr gold & multi	1.90	.35
a.	Souv. sheet of 3, #C178-C180	4.75	3.75
	Nos. C178-C180 (3)	4.55	.90

INTERPOL Type of Regular Issue

Designs: 27fr, INTERPOL emblem and flag. 40fr, INTERPOL flag and emblem.

1973, May 19   Photo.   Perf. 13½

C181	A61 27fr gold & multi	1.25	.30
C182	A61 40fr gold & multi	1.60	.50

Copernicus Type of Regular Issue

Designs: 15fr, Copernicus (C183a), Earth, Pluto, and Jupiter. 18fr, Copernicus (No. C184a), Venus, Saturn, Mars. 27fr, Copernicus (No. C185a), Uranus, Neptune, Mercury. 36fr, Earth and various spacecraft.
a, UL. b, UR. c, LL. d, LR.

1973, July 27   Photo.   Perf. 13½

C183	A62 15fr Block of 4, #a.-d.	3.50	1.75
C184	A62 18fr Block of 4, #a.-d.	4.25	.75
C185	A62 27fr Block of 4, #a.-d.	6.50	1.25
C186	A62 36fr Block of 4, #a.-d.	8.50	1.25
e.	Souv. sheet, #C183-C186	25.00	25.00
	Nos. C183-C186 (4)	22.75	5.00

Flower-Butterfly Type of 1973

Designs: Each block of 4 contains 2 flower and 2 butterfly designs. The 10fr, 14fr, 24fr and 31fr have flower designs listed as "a" and "d" numbers, butterflies as "b" and "c" numbers; the arrangement is reversed for the 17fr and 26fr.

1973, Sept. 28   Photo.   Perf. 13
Stamp Size: 35x45mm

C187	A63 Block of 4	18.00	.40
a.	10fr Protea cynaroides	3.00	.25
b.	10fr Precis octavia	3.00	.25
c.	10fr Epiphora bauhiniae	3.00	.25
d.	10fr Gazania longiscapa	3.00	.25
C188	A63 Block of 4	12.50	.40
a.	14fr Kniphofia	2.00	.25
b.	14fr Cymothoe coccinata	2.00	.25
c.	14fr Nudaurelia zambesina	2.00	.25
d.	14fr Freesia refracta	2.00	.25
C189	A63 Block of 4	14.50	.75
a.	17fr Calotis eupompe	2.25	.25
b.	17fr Narcissus	2.25	.25
c.	17fr Cineraria hybrida	2.25	.25
d.	17fr Cyrestis camillus	2.25	.25
C190	A63 Block of 4	16.00	.75
a.	24fr Iris tingitana	2.50	.25
b.	24fr Papilio demodocus	2.50	.25
c.	24fr Catopsilia avelaneda	2.50	.25
d.	24fr Nerine sarniensis	2.50	.25
C191	A63 Block of 4	18.00	1.00
a.	26fr Hypolimnas dexithea	2.75	.25
b.	26fr Zantedeschia tropicalis	2.75	.25
c.	26fr Sandersonia aurantiaca	2.75	.25
d.	26fr Drurya antimachus	2.75	.25
C192	A63 Block of 4	20.00	1.25
a.	31fr Nymphaea capensis	3.00	.25
b.	31fr Pandoriana pandora	3.00	.25
c.	31fr Precis orythia	3.00	.25
d.	31fr Pelargonium domestica	3.00	.25
	Nos. C187-C192 (6)	99.00	4.55

Christmas Type of 1973

Virgin and Child by: 18fr, Raphael. 27fr, Pietro Perugino. 40fr, Titian.

1973, Nov. 19

C193	A64 18fr gold & multi	.85	.25
C194	A64 27fr gold & multi	1.50	.25
C195	A64 40fr gold & multi	2.40	.30
a.	Souv. sheet of 3, #C193-C195	5.00	4.50
	Nos. C193-C195 (3)	4.75	.80

For surcharges see Nos. CB239-CB31.

Soccer Type of Regular Issue

Designs: Various soccer scenes and cup.

1974, July 4   Photo.   Perf. 13

C196	A67 20fr gold & multi	1.50	.30
C197	A67 26fr gold & multi	1.75	.45
C198	A67 40fr gold & multi	2.75	.55
	Nos. C196-C198 (3)	6.00	1.30

For souvenir sheet see No. 459a.

UPU Type of 1974

No. C199a, Flags over UPU Headquarters, Bern. No. C199b, G.P.O., Bujumbura. No. C200a, Mailmen ("26F" in UR). No. C200b, Mailmen ("26F" in UL). No. C201a, UPU emblem. No. C201b, Means of transportation. No. C202a, Pigeon over globe showing Burundi. No. C202b, Swiss flag, pigeon over map showing Bern.

1974, July 23

C199	A68 24fr Pair, #a.-b.	2.75	.50
C200	A68 26fr Pair, #a.-b.	3.00	.50
C201	A68 31fr Pair, #a.-b.	3.25	.60
C202	A68 40fr Pair, #a.-b.	5.00	.75
c.	Souv. sheet, #C199-C202	27.50	27.50
	Nos. C199-C202 (4)	14.00	2.35

Fish Type of 1974

1974, Sept. 9   Photo.   Perf. 13
Size: 35x35mm

C207	A66 Block of 4	4.75	.60
a.	10fr Haplochromis multicolor	.90	.25
b.	10fr Pantodon buchholzi	.90	.25
c.	10fr Tropheus duboisi	.90	.25
d.	10fr Distichodus sexfasciatus	.90	.25
C208	A66 Block of 4	7.75	.85
a.	14fr Pelmatochromis kribensis	1.50	.25
b.	14fr Nannaethiops tritaeniatus	1.50	.25
c.	14fr Polycentropsis abbreviata	1.50	.25
d.	14fr Hemichromis bimaculatus	1.50	.25
C209	A66 Block of 4	10.50	1.25
a.	17fr Ctenopoma acutirostre	1.90	.25
b.	17fr Synodontis angelicus	1.90	.25
c.	17fr Tilapia melanopleura	1.90	.25
d.	17fr Aphyosemion bivittatum	1.90	.25
C210	A66 Block of 4	14.50	1.50
a.	24fr Monodactylus argenteus	2.75	.30
b.	24fr Zanclus canescens	2.75	.30
c.	24fr Pygoplites diacanthus	2.75	.30
d.	24fr Cephalopholis argus	2.75	.30
C211	A66 Block of 4	18.00	1.90
a.	26fr Premnas arenatus	3.50	.35
b.	26fr Premnas arcutus	3.50	.35
c.	26fr Scarus guacamaia	3.50	.35
d.	26fr Zeus faber	3.50	.35
C212	A66 Block of 4	24.00	2.10
a.	31fr Lactophrys quadricornis	4.50	.45
b.	31fr Balistes vetula	4.50	.45
c.	31fr Acanthurus bahianus	4.50	.45
d.	31fr Holocanthus ciliaris	4.50	.45
	Nos. C207-C212 (6)	79.50	8.20

Christmas Type of 1974

Paintings of the Virgin and Child: 18fr, by Hans Memling. 27fr, by Filippino Lippi. 40fr, by Lorenzo di Gredi.

1974, Nov. 7   Photo.   Perf. 13

C213	A70 18fr gold & multi	1.25	.25
C214	A70 27fr gold & multi	1.75	.30
C215	A70 40fr gold & multi	2.40	.45
a.	Souv. sheet of 3, #C213-C215	5.00	4.00
	Nos. C213-C215 (3)	5.40	1.00

Christmas 1974. Sheets of 20 stamps and one label.

Apollo-Soyuz Type of 1975

1975, July 10   Photo.   Perf. 13

C216	A71 Block of 4	4.00	2.75
a.	27fr A.A. Leonov, V.N. Kubasov, Soviet flag	.65	
b.	27fr Soyuz and Soviet flag	.65	
c.	27fr Apollo and American flag	.65	
d.	27fr Slayton, Brand, Stafford, American flag	.65	
C217	A71 Block of 4	5.00	3.25
a.	40fr Apollo-Soyuz link-up	.95	
b.	40fr Apollo, blast-off	.95	
c.	40fr Soyuz, blast-off	.95	
d.	40fr Kubasov, Leonov, Slayton, Brand, Stafford	.95	

Nos. C216-C217 are printed in sheets of 32 containing 8 blocks of 4.

Animal Type of 1975

1975, Sept. 17   Photo.   Perf. 13½

C218	Strip of 4	5.00	.25
a.	A72 10fr Addax	.90	.25
b.	A72 10fr Roan antelope	.90	.25
c.	A72 10fr Nyala	.90	.25
d.	A72 10fr White rhinoceros	.90	.25
C219	Strip of 4	6.75	.65
a.	A72 14fr Mandrill	1.25	.25
b.	A72 14fr Eland	1.25	.25
c.	A72 14fr Salt's dik-dik	1.25	.25
d.	A72 14fr Thomson's gazelles	1.25	.25
C220	Strip of 4	10.00	.65
a.	A72 17fr African small-clawed otter	1.75	.25
b.	A72 17fr Reed buck	1.75	.25
c.	A72 17fr Indian civet	1.75	.25
d.	A72 17fr Cape buffalo	1.75	.25
C221	Strip of 4	11.50	1.40
a.	A72 24fr White-tailed gnu	2.00	.30
b.	A72 24fr African wild asses	2.00	.30
c.	A72 24fr Black-and-white colobus monkey	2.00	.30
d.	A72 24fr Gerenuk	2.00	.30
C222	Strip of 4	13.00	1.40
a.	A72 26fr Dama gazelle	2.25	.30
b.	A72 26fr Black-backed jackal	2.25	.30
c.	A72 26fr Sitatungas	2.25	.30
d.	A72 26fr Zebra antelope	2.25	.30
C223	Strip of 4	14.00	1.60
a.	A72 31fr Fennec	2.50	.35
b.	A72 31fr Lesser kudus	2.50	.35
c.	A72 31fr Blesbok	2.50	.35
d.	A72 31fr Serval	2.50	.35
	Nos. C218-C223 (6)	60.25	6.05

Nos. C218-C219 Ovptd. in Black & Silver

1975, Nov. 19   Photo.   Perf. 13½

C224	Strip of 4	4.50	2.50
a.	A72 10fr Addax	.85	.40
b.	A72 10fr Roan antelope	.85	.40
c.	A72 10fr Nyala	.85	.40
d.	A72 10fr White rhinoceros	.85	.40
C225	Strip of 4	7.00	4.50
a.	A72 14fr Mandrill	1.50	.75
b.	A72 14fr Oryx	1.50	.75
c.	A72 14fr Dik-dik	1.50	.75
d.	A72 14fr Thomson's gazelles	1.50	.75

International Women's Year 1975.

Nos. C222-C223 Ovptd. in Black and Silver

1975, Nov. 19

C226	Strip of 4	13.00	12.00
a.	A72 26fr Dama gazelle	2.25	2.00
b.	A72 26fr Wild dog	2.25	2.00
c.	A72 26fr Sitatungas	2.25	2.00
d.	A72 26fr Striped duiker	2.25	2.00

C227		Strip of 4	17.00	15.00
a.	A72	31fr Fennec	3.00	2.50
b.	A72	31fr Lesser kudus	3.00	2.50
c.	A72	31fr Blesbok	3.00	2.50
d.	A72	31fr Serval	3.00	2.50

United Nations, 30th anniversary.

Michelangelo Type of 1975

Paintings from Sistine Chapel: No. C228a, Zachariah. No. C228b, Joel. No. C229a, Erythrean Sybil. No. C229b, Prophet Ezekiel. No. C230a, Persian Sybil. No. C230b, Prophet Jeremiah.

1975, Dec. 3		**Photo.**	**Perf. 13**	
C228	A73	18fr Pair, #a.-b.	4.50	.60
C229	A73	31fr Pair, #a.-b.	6.00	.90
C230	A73	40fr Pair, #a.-b.	9.00	1.00
c.		Souv. sheet of 6, #C228-C230	16.00	12.00
		Nos. C228-C230 (3)	19.50	2.50

Printed in sheets of 18 stamps + 2 labels.
For surcharges see Nos. CB35-CB37.

Olympic Games Type, 1976

Designs (Olympic Games Emblem and): 18fr, Ski jump. 36fr, Slalom. 50fr, Ice hockey.

1976, Jan. 23		**Photo.**	**Perf. 14x13½**	
C234	A74	18fr ol brn & multi	.90	.25
C235	A74	36fr grn & multi	1.75	.50
C236	A74	50fr pur & multi	2.25	.65
a.		Souvenir sheet of 4	5.00	4.00
		Nos. C234-C236 (3)	4.90	1.40

No. C236a contains 4 stamps similar to Nos. 491-494, perf. 13½, inscribed "POSTE AERIENNE."

21st Olympic Games, Montreal, Canada, July 17-Aug. 1 — AP5

Montreal Games Emblem and: Nos. C237b, C239a, C240b, High jump. Nos. C238a, C239b, C240a, Athlete on rings. Nos. C237a, C238b, C240c, Hurdles.

1976, May 3		**Litho.**	**Perf. 13½**	
C237	AP5	27fr Pair, #a.-b.	3.75	2.40
C238	AP5	31fr Pair, #a.-b.	4.75	3.25
C239	AP5	50fr Pair, #a.-b.	9.50	6.50
		Nos. C237-C239 (3)	18.00	12.15

Souvenir Sheet

C240	AP5	Sheet of 3, #a.-c.	13.50	13.50

Battle of Bunker Hill, by John Trumbull — AP6

Paintings: 26fr, Franklin, Jefferson and John Adams. 36fr, Declaration of Independence, by John Trumbull.

1976, July 16		**Photo.**	**Perf. 13**	
C244	AP6	18fr Pair, #a.-b.	2.00	.35
C245	AP6	26fr Pair, #a.-b.	3.00	.45
C246	AP6	36fr Pair, #a.-b.	3.75	.85
c.		Souv. sheet of 6, #C244-C246	9.00	9.00
		Nos. C244-C246 (3)	8.75	1.65

American Bicentennial.
Exist imperf. Values: set $11; souvenir sheet $10.

Christmas Type of 1976

Paintings: 18fr, Virgin and Child with St. Anne, by Leonardo da Vinci. 31fr, Holy Family with Lamb, by Raphael. 40fr, Madonna of the Basket, by Correggio.

1976, Oct. 18		**Photo.**	**Perf. 13½**	
C250	A76	18fr gold & multi	1.75	.25
C251	A76	26fr gold & multi	2.25	.30
C252	A76	40fr gold & multi	3.25	.45
a.		Souv. sheet of 3, #C250-C252	7.50	1.00
		Nos. C250-C252 (3)	7.25	1.00

Christmas 1976. Sheets of 20 stamps and descriptive label.
For surcharges see Nos. CB41-CB43.

A.G. Bell Type of 1977

10fr, A.G. Bell and 1st telephone. No. C253a, 17fr, A.G. Bell speaking into microphone. Nos. C253b, C255e, Satellites around globe, videophone. No. C254a, Switchboard operator, c.1910, wall telephone. No. C254b, 26fr, Intelsat satellite, modern & old telephones. No. C255c, Intelsat, radar.

1977, May 17		**Photo.**	**Perf. 13**	
C253	A78	18fr Pair, #a.-b.	1.90	1.90
C254	A78	36fr Pair, #a.-b.	3.75	3.75
C255		Sheet of 5	7.00	7.00
a.		A78 10fr multi	1.00	1.00
b.		A78 17fr multi	1.00	1.00
c.		A79 18fr multi	1.00	1.00
d.		A79 26fr multi	1.00	1.00
e.		A79 36fr multi	1.00	1.00

#C255c, C255e are air post stamps.

Animal Type of 1977

1977, Aug. 22		**Photo.**	**Perf. 14x14½**	
C258	A80	Strip of 4	5.00	.35
a.		9fr Buffon's kob	.95	.25
b.		9fr Marabous	.95	.25
c.		9fr Brindled gnu	.95	.25
d.		9fr River hog	.95	.25
C259	A80	Strip of 4	7.50	.80
a.		13fr Zebras	1.40	.25
b.		13fr Shoebill	1.40	.25
c.		13fr Striped hyenas	1.40	.25
d.		13fr Chimpanzee	1.40	.25
C260	A80	Strip of 4	12.00	1.50
a.		30fr Flamingos	2.25	.25
b.		30fr Nile Crocodiles	2.25	.25
c.		30fr Green mamba	2.25	.25
d.		30fr Greater kudus	2.25	.25
C261	A80	Strip of 4	21.00	1.75
a.		35fr Hyrax	4.00	.35
b.		35fr Cobra	4.00	.35
c.		35fr Jackals	4.00	.35
d.		35fr Verreaux's eagles	4.00	.35
C262	A80	Strip of 4	30.00	2.00
a.		54fr Honey badger	6.00	.45
b.		54fr Harnessed antelopes	6.00	.45
c.		54fr Secretary bird	6.00	.45
d.		54fr Klipspringer	6.00	.45
C263	A80	Strip of 4	45.00	2.50
a.		70fr African big-eared fox	8.50	.55
b.		70fr Elephants	8.50	.55
c.		70fr Vulturine guineafowl	8.50	.55
d.		70fr Impalas	8.50	.55
		Nos. C258-C263 (6)	120.50	8.90

UN Type of 1977

Designs (UN Stamps and): 24fr, UN buildings by night. 27fr, UN buildings and view of Manhattan. 35fr, UN buildings by day.

1977, Oct. 10		**Photo.**	**Perf. 13½**	
C264	A82	Block of 4	6.00	6.00
a.		24fr No. 77	1.20	1.20
b.		24fr No. 78	1.20	1.20
c.		24fr No. 40	1.20	1.20
d.		24fr No. 32	1.20	1.20
C265	A82	Block of 4	7.00	7.00
a.		27fr No. 50	1.40	1.40
b.		27fr No. 21	1.40	1.40
c.		27fr No. 30	1.40	1.40
d.		27fr No. 44	1.40	1.40
C266	A82	Block of 4	10.50	10.50
a.		35fr No. C6	2.00	2.00
b.		35fr No. 105	2.00	2.00
c.		35fr No. 1	2.00	2.00
d.		35fr No. 1	2.00	2.00
e.		Souvenir sheet of 3	2.00	2.00
		Nos. C264-C266 (3)	23.50	23.50

No. C266e contains 24fr in design of No. C265b, 27fr in design of No. C266a, 35fr in design of No. C264c.

Christmas Type of 1977

Paintings of the Virgin and Child: 18fr, Master of Moulins. 31fr, Workshop of Lorenzo de Credi. 40fr, Palma Vecchio.

1977, Oct. 31		**Photo.**	**Perf. 14x13**	
C267	A83	18fr multi	1.75	1.00
C268	A83	31fr multi	2.75	1.75
C269	A83	40fr multi	3.50	2.25
a.		Souv. sheet of 3, #C267-C269	6.00	6.00
		Nos. C267-C269 (3)	8.00	5.00

Sheets of 24 stamps and descriptive label.
For surcharges see Nos. CB44-CB46.

Christmas 1978 Type of 1979
Souvenir Sheet

1979, Feb.		**Photo.**	**Perf. 14x13½**	
C270		Sheet of 5	12.00	10.00
a.		A86 13fr like #543	2.00	2.00
b.		A86 17fr like #544	2.00	2.00
c.		A86 27fr like #545	2.00	2.00
d.		A86 31fr like #546	2.00	2.00
e.		A86 40fr like #547	2.00	2.00

Christmas Type of 1979
Souvenir Sheet

1979, Oct. 12			**Perf. 13½**	
C271		Sheet of 4	12.50	12.50
a.		A89 20fr like #561	2.50	2.50
b.		A89 27fr like #562	2.50	2.50
c.		A89 31fr like #563	2.50	2.50
d.		A89 50fr like #564	2.50	2.50

Hill Type of 1979
Souvenir Sheet

1979, Nov. 6				
C272		Sheet of 5	11.00	8.00
a.		A90 20fr like #565	2.00	1.40
b.		A90 27fr like #566	2.00	1.40
c.		A90 30fr like #567	2.00	1.40
d.		A90 40fr like #568	2.00	1.40
e.		A90 60fr like #569	2.00	1.40

Bird Type of 1979

1979		**Photo.**	**Perf. 13½x3**	
C273	A87	6fr like #548	1.25	.65
C274	A87	13fr like #549	2.25	1.50
C275	A87	18fr like #550	3.75	2.00
C276	A87	26fr like #551	5.00	3.00
C277	A87	31fr like #552	5.75	4.00
C278	A87	36fr like #553	7.25	5.00
C279	A87	40fr like #554	9.00	6.00
C280	A87	54fr like #555	13.00	7.50
C281	A87	70fr like #556	16.50	10.00
		Nos. C273-C281 (9)	63.75	39.65

Olympic Type of 1980
Souvenir Sheet

1980, Oct. 24		**Photo.**	**Perf. 13½**	
C282		Sheet of 9	35.00	25.00
a.		A91 20fr like #570a	3.50	2.00
b.		A91 20fr like #570b	3.50	2.00
c.		A91 20fr like #570c	3.50	2.00
d.		A91 30fr like #571a	3.50	2.00
e.		A91 30fr like #571b	3.50	2.00
f.		A91 30fr like #571c	3.50	2.00
g.		A91 40fr like #572a	3.50	2.00
h.		A91 40fr like #572b	3.50	2.00
i.		A91 40fr like #572c	3.50	2.00

Christmas Type of 1980
Souvenir Sheet

1980, Dec. 12		**Photo.**	**Perf. 13½x13**	
C283		Sheet of 4	22.00	10.00
a.		A92 10fr like #579	4.00	2.00
b.		A92 30fr like #580	4.00	2.00
c.		A92 40fr like #581	4.00	2.00
d.		A92 45fr like #582	4.00	2.00

UPRONA Type of 1980
Souvenir Sheet

1980, Dec. 29			**Perf. 14½x13½**	
C284		Sheet of 3	6.50	4.50
a.		A93 10fr like #583	1.60	1.00
b.		A93 40fr like #584	1.60	1.00
c.		A93 45fr like #585	1.60	1.00

Christmas Type of 1983
Souvenir Sheet

1983, Oct. 3		**Litho.**	**Perf. 14½x13½**	
C285		Sheet of 4	75.00	75.00
a.		A97 10fr like #607	15.00	15.00
b.		A97 25fr like #608	15.00	15.00
c.		A97 30fr like #609	15.00	15.00
d.		A97 50fr like #610	15.00	15.00

UPU Congress Type of 1984
Souvenir Sheet

1984, July 14			**Perf. 13x13½**	
C286		Sheet of 4	25.00	25.00
a.		A99 10fr like #621	5.00	5.00
b.		A99 30fr like #622	5.00	5.00
c.		A99 35fr like #623	5.00	5.00
d.		A99 65fr like #624	5.00	5.00

Summer Olympics Type of 1984
Souvenir Sheet

1984, Aug. 6			**Perf. 13½x13**	
C287		Sheet of 4	30.00	30.00
a.		A100 10fr like #625	6.25	6.25
b.		A100 30fr like #626	6.25	6.25
c.		A100 35fr like #627	6.25	6.25
d.		A100 65fr like #628	6.25	6.25

Christmas Type of 1984
Souvenir Sheet

1984, Dec. 15			**Perf. 13½**	
C288		Sheet of 4	30.00	12.00
a.		A101 10fr like #629	6.00	2.40
b.		A101 25fr like #630	6.00	2.40
c.		A101 30fr like #631	6.00	2.40
d.		A101 50fr like #632	6.00	2.40

Flower Type of 1986 with Dull Lilac Border

1986, July 31		**Photo.**	**Perf. 13x13½**	
C289	A102	70fr like #633	11.50	8.50
C290	A102	75fr like #634	13.00	9.00
C291	A102	80fr like #635	14.00	10.00
C292	A102	85fr like #636	15.50	11.00
C293	A102	100fr like #637	18.00	12.00
C294	A102	150fr like #638	26.00	14.00
		Nos. C289-C294 (6)	98.00	64.50

Animals
AP8

100fr, M. nemestrina. 115fr, Equus grevyi. 200fr, Long horn cattle. 220fr, Pelecanus onocrotalus.

1992, June 2		**Litho.**	**Perf. 14**	
C298	AP8	100fr multicolored	3.50	2.25
C299	AP8	115fr multicolored	4.50	2.50
C300	AP8	200fr multicolored	10.00	6.00
C301	AP8	220fr multicolored	12.00	7.00
a.		Souvenir sheet of 4, #C298-C301, perf. 13½	30.00	
		Nos. C298-C301 (4)	30.00	17.75

No. C301a exists imperf. Value, $30.

AIR POST SEMI-POSTAL STAMPS

Coin Type of Semi-Postal Issue

Designs (Coins of Various Denominations): 3fr+1fr, 11fr+1fr, 50fr+1fr, Coat of Arms, reverse. 5fr+1fr, 14fr+1fr, 30fr+1fr, 100fr+1fr, King Mwambutsa IV, obverse.

Lithographed; Embossed on Gilt Foil

1965, Nov. 15			**Imperf.**	
		Diameter: 39mm		
CB1	SP4	3fr + 1fr lt & dk vio	.25	.25
CB2	SP4	5fr + 1fr pale grn & red	.35	.35
		Diameter: 45mm		
CB3	SP4	11fr + 1fr org & lilac	.55	.55
CB4	SP4	14fr + 1fr red & emer	.70	.70
		Diameter: 56mm		
CB5	SP4	20fr + 1fr ultra & blk	.90	.90
CB6	SP4	30fr + 1fr dp org & mar	1.25	1.25
		Diameter: 67mm		
CB7	SP4	50fr + 1fr bl & vio bl	2.50	2.50
CB8	SP4	100fr+ 1fr rose & dp cl	4.50	4.50
		Nos. CB1-CB8 (8)	11.00	11.00

Stamps are backed with patterned paper in blue, orange, and pink engine-turned design.

Red Cross Type of Semi-Postal Issue

Designs: 26fr+3fr, Laboratory. 40fr+3fr, Ambulance and thatched huts. 50fr+3fr, Red Cross nurse with patient.

1969, June 26		**Photo.**	**Perf. 13½**	
CB9	SP7	26fr + 3fr multi	.95	.25
CB10	SP7	40fr + 3fr multi	1.25	.40
CB11	SP7	50fr + 3fr multi	1.75	.60
		Nos. CB9-CB11 (3)	3.95	1.25

Perf. and imperf. souvenir sheets exist containing 3 stamps similar to Nos. CB9-CB11, but without "Poste Aerienne." Size: 90½x97mm

Christmas Type of Semi-Postal Issue

Paintings: 14fr+3fr, Virgin and Child, by Velázquez. 26fr+3fr, Holy Family, by Joos van Cleve. 40fr+3fr, Virgin and Child, by Rogier van der Weyden.

1970, Dec. 14		**Photo.**	**Perf. 13½**	
CB12	SP9	14fr + 3fr multi	.75	.25
CB13	SP9	26fr + 3fr multi	1.25	.45
CB14	SP9	40fr + 3fr multi	2.00	.60
a.		Souv. sheet of 3, #CB12-CB14	4.00	4.00
		Nos. CB12-CB14 (3)	4.00	1.30

No. C147 Surcharged in Gold and Black

1971, Aug. 9		**Photo.**	**Perf. 13½**	
CB15		Strip of 4	11.00	4.00
a.	A48	14fr+2fr Hartebeest	2.40	.25
b.	A48	14fr+2fr Black rhinoceros	2.40	.25
c.	A48	14fr+2fr Zebra	2.40	.25
d.	A48	14fr+2fr Leopard	2.40	.25

UNESCO campaign against illiteracy.

No. C148 Surcharged in Gold and Black

1971, Aug. 9
CB16   Strip of 4   14.00 5.00
  a. A48 17fr+1fr Grant's gazelles   3.00 .25
  b. A48 17fr+1fr Cheetah   3.00 .25
  c. A48 17fr+1fr African white-
    backed vultures   3.00 .25
  d. A48 17fr+1fr Johnston's okapi   3.00 .25

International help for refugees.

Nos. C150-C151 Surcharged in Black and Gold

a

b

1971, Aug. 16
CB17   Strip of 4   14.00 4.00
  a. A48(a) 26fr+1fr Gorilla   3.00 .90
  b. A48(a) 26fr+1fr Gnu   3.00 .90
  c. A48(a) 26fr+1fr Warthog   3.00 .90
  d. A48(a) 26fr+1fr Cape hunting
    dog   3.00 .90
CB18   Strip of 4   17.50 5.00
  a. A48(b) 31fr+1fr Sable antelope   3.50 1.10
  b. A48(b) 31fr+1fr Caracal lynx   3.50 1.10
  c. A48(b) 31fr+1fr Ostriches   3.50 1.10
  d. A48(b) 31fr+1fr Bongo   3.50 1.10

75th anniv. of modern Olympic Games
(#CB17); Olympic Games, Munich, 1972
(#CB18).

Nos. C153-C155
Surcharged

1971, Nov. 27   Photo.   Perf. 13½
CB19   A51 14fr + 1fr multi   .80 .35
CB20   A51 17fr + 1fr multi   1.25 .35
CB21   A51 31fr + 1fr multi   1.75 .35
    Nos. CB19-CB21 (3)   3.80 1.05
  a. Souvenir sheet of 3   4.00 3.25

25th anniv. of UNICEF.
No. CB21a contains 3 stamps similar to
#CB19-CB21 with 2 fr surcharge each.

Casa
D'Oro,
Venice
SPAP1

Views in Venice: 17fr+1fr, Doge's Palace.
24fr+1fr, Church of Sts. John and Paul.
31fr+1fr, Doge's Palace and Piazzetta at Feast
of Ascension, by Canaletto.

1971, Dec. 27
CB22   SPAP1 10fr + 1fr multi   .45 .25
CB23   SPAP1 17fr + 1fr multi   .80 .25
CB24   SPAP1 24fr + 1fr multi   1.20 .35
CB25   SPAP1 31fr + 1fr multi   1.60 .35
    Nos. CB22-CB25 (4)   4.05 1.20
  a. Souvenir sheet of 4   4.50 4.50

Surtax for the UNESCO campaign to save
the treasures of Venice. No. CB25a contains 4
stamps similar to Nos. CB22-CB25, but with
2fr surtax.
Nos. CB22-CB25a exist imperf. Value: set
$6.50; souvenir sheet $8.

Nos. C165-
C167, C193-
C195 Srchd. in
Silver

1972, Dec. 12   Photo.   Perf. 13½
CB26   A57 18fr + 1fr multi   1.00 .25
CB27   A57 27fr + 1fr multi   1.75 .35
CB28   A57 40fr + 1fr multi   2.50 .60
  a. Souvenir sheet of 3   6.00 5.00
    Nos. CB26-CB28 (3)   5.25 1.20

Christmas 1972. No. CB28a contains 3
stamps similar to Nos. CB26-CB28 but with
2fr surtax.

1973, Dec. 14   Photo.   Perf. 13
CB29   A64 18fr + 1fr multi   .90 .30
CB30   A64 27fr + 1fr multi   1.25 .40
CB31   A64 40fr + 1fr multi   1.75 .50
  a. Souvenir sheet of 3   4.50 4.00
    Nos. CB29-CB31 (3)   3.90 1.20

Christmas 1973. No. CB31a contains 3
stamps similar to Nos. CB29-CB31 with 2fr
surtax each.

Christmas Type of 1974

1974, Dec. 2   Photo.   Perf. 13
CB32   A70 18fr + 1fr multi   1.10 .30
CB33   A70 27fr + 1fr multi   1.75 .60
CB34   A70 40fr + 1fr multi   2.75 1.00
  a. Souvenir sheet of 3   6.00 6.00
    Nos. CB32-CB34 (3)   5.60 1.90

Christmas 1974. No. CB34a contains 3
stamps similar to Nos. CB32-CB34 with 2fr
surtax.

Nos. C228-C230 Srchd. in Silver and Black

1975, Dec. 22   Photo.   Perf. 13
CB35   A73 18fr +1fr Pair, #a-b   5.00 .30
CB36   A73 31fr +1fr Pair, #a-b   6.75 .50
CB37   A73 40fr +1fr Pair, #a-b   10.00 .60
  c. Souvenir sheet of 6   19.00 19.00
    Nos. CB35-CB37 (3)   21.75 1.40

Michelangelo Buonarroti (1475-1564). No.
CB37c contains 6 stamps similar to Nos.
CB35-CB37 with 2fr surtax each.

Nos. C250-C252 Surcharged "+1f" in Silver and Black

1976, Nov. 25   Photo.   Perf. 13½
CB41   A76 18fr + 1fr multi   1.60 .25
CB42   A76 31fr + 1fr multi   2.25 .35
CB43   A76 40fr + 1fr multi   3.25 .65
  a. Souvenir sheet of 3   7.00 7.00
    Nos. CB41-CB43 (3)   7.10 1.25

Christmas 1976. No. CB43a contains 3
stamps similar to Nos. CB41-CB43 with 2fr
surtax each.

Nos. C267-C269 Surcharged "+1fr" in Silver and Black

1977   Photo.   Perf. 14x13
CB44   A83 18fr + 1fr multi   1.50 .30
CB45   A83 31fr + 1fr multi   2.75 .40
CB46   A83 40fr + 1fr multi   3.75 .55
  a. Souvenir sheet of 3   12.00 12.00
    Nos. CB44-CB46 (3)   8.00 1.25

Christmas 1977. No. CB46a contains 3
stamps similar to Nos. CB44-CB46 with 2fr
surtax each.

Christmas 1978 Type
Souvenir Sheet

1979, Feb.   Photo.   Perf. 14x13
CB47   Sheet of 5   22.00 12.00
  a. A86 13fr + 2fr multi   3.75 1.75
  b. A86 17fr + 2fr multi   3.75 1.75
  c. A86 27fr + 2fr multi   3.75 1.75
  d. A86 31fr + 2fr multi   3.75 1.75
  e. A86 40fr + 2fr multi   3.75 1.75

Christmas Type of 1979
Souvenir Sheet

1979, Dec. 10   Photo.   Perf. 13½
CB48   Sheet of 4   22.00 12.00
  a. A89 20fr + 2fr like #561   3.75 2.00
  b. A89 27fr + 2fr like #562   3.75 2.00
  c. A89 31fr + 2fr like #563   3.75 2.00
  d. A89 50fr + 2fr like #564   3.75 2.00

Exists imperf. Value $13.

Christmas Type of 1980
Souvenir Sheet

1981, Jan. 16   Photo.   Perf. 13½x13
CB49   Sheet of 4   22.00 22.00
  a. A92 10fr + 2fr like #579   3.75 3.75
  b. A92 30fr + 2fr like #580   3.75 3.75
  c. A92 40fr + 2fr like #581   3.75 3.75
  d. A92 50fr + 2fr like #582   3.75 3.75

Exists imperf. Value $13.

Christmas Type of 1983
Souvenir Sheet

1983, Nov. 2   Litho.   Perf. 14½x13½
CB50   Sheet of 4   16.00 16.00
  a. A97 10fr + 2fr like #607   1.25 1.00
  b. A97 25fr + 2fr like #608   2.00 1.75
  c. A97 30fr + 2fr like #609   4.00 3.50
  d. A97 50fr + 2fr like #610   5.50 5.00

Exists imperf. Value $13.

Christmas Type of 1984
Souvenir Sheet

1984, Dec. 15   Perf. 13½
CB51   Sheet of 4   15.00 15.00
  a. A101 10fr + 2fr like #629   3.00 3.00
  b. A101 25fr + 2fr like #630   3.00 3.00
  c. A101 30fr + 2fr like #631   3.00 3.00
  d. A101 50fr + 2fr like #632   3.00 3.00

BUSHIRE

bü-'shir

LOCATION — On Persian Gulf

Bushire is an Iranian port that British
troops occupied Aug. 8, 1915.

20 Chahis (or Shahis) = 1 Kran
10 Krans = 1 Toman

Watermark

Wmk. 161 — Lion

ISSUED UNDER BRITISH OCCUPATION

Basic Iranian Designs

Iranian Stamps of
1911-13 Overprinted
in Black

Perf. 11½, 11½x11
Typo. & Engr.
1915, Aug. 15   Unwmk.
N1   A32 1c green & org   175.00 120.00
N2   A32 2c red & sepia   175.00 120.00
N3   A32 3c gray brn &
    grn   200.00 150.00
N4   A32 5c brown & car   1,250. 1,100.
N5   A32 6c green & red
    brn   165.00 100.00
N6   A32 9c grn & red
    vio   200.00 150.00
  a. Double overprint
N7   A32 10c red & org
    brn   250.00 200.00
N8   A32 12c grn & ultra   250.00 200.00
N9   A32 1k ultra & car   265.00 240.00
  a. Double overprint   7,500.
N10   A32 24c vio & grn   275.00 225.00
N11   A32 2k grn & red
    vio   700.00 600.00
N12   A32 3k vio & blk   750.00 650.00
N13   A32 5k red & ultra   650.00 550.00
N14   A32 10k ol bis & cl   700.00 600.00
    Nos. N1-N14 (14)   6,005. 5,005.

Nos. N1-N14, except No. N4, exist without
period after "Occupation." This variety sells for
more. See the *Scott Classic Catalogue of
Stamps and Covers* for listings.
Forged overprints exist of Nos. N1-N29.
The Bushire overprint exists on Iran No. 537
but is considered a forgery.

On Iranian Stamps of 1915

No. N15

No. N26

No. N29

Perf. 11, 11½
1915, Sept.   Wmk. 161
N15   A33 1c car & indigo   1,000. 1,000.
N16   A33 2c blue & car   15,000. 15,000.
N17   A33 3c dk grn   1,100. 1,100.
N18   A33 5c red   22,000. 12,500.
N19   A33 6c ol grn & car   10,000. 10,000.
N20   A33 9c yel brn & vio   1,600. 1,600.
N21   A33 10c bl grn & yel
    brn   2,500. 2,500.
N22   A33 12c ultra   4,700. 4,700.
N23   A34 1k sil, yel brn &
    gray   1,700. 1,700.
N24   A33 24c yel brn & dk
    brn   1,400. 1,400.
N25   A34 2k sil, bl & rose   1,400. 1,400.
N26   A34 3k sil, vio & brn   1,400. 1,400.
N27   A34 5k sil, brn & grn   2,100. 2,100.
  a. Inverted overprint   —   25,000.
N28   A35 1t gold, pur &
    blk   2,500. 2,500.
N29   A35 3t gold, cl & red
    brn   7,800. 7,800.

Persia (Iran) resumed administration of
Bushire post office Oct. 16, 1915.

GET SOMEONE STARTED COLLECTING!

Thinking about starting a stamp collection? Here are the albums and the resources to get started.

MINUTEMAN ALBUM

America's number one stamp album makes collecting easy and fun. Album spaces are identified by Scott numbers and many of the spaces feature historic vignettes about the stamps. The three ring binder has been custom designed for the album pages. Now even the intermediate or beginner collector can have an album to fit their collecting interest without spending a small fortune. Save even more when you take advantage of money saving packages that are available!

ITEM	DESCRIPTION (PAGES ONLY)	RETAIL	AA*
180PMM19	**19th Century 1840-1899**	$19.99	**$16.99**
180PMM20	**20th Century 1900-1999**	$69.99	**$59.49**
180PMM21	**21st Century 2000-2003**	$49.99	**$42.49**
180PMM21A	**Pages 2004-2009**	$69.99	**$59.49**

(Part and kit pages fit 3-ring binder only.)

MINUTEMAN ALBUM KIT

Includes all Minuteman album pages covering U.S. Stamps 1840-2015, as well as two Minuteman 3-ring binders.

ITEM	DESCRIPTION	RETAIL	AA*
180MMKIT	**Minuteman Kit**	$219.99	**$169.99**

MINUTEMAN 20TH CENTURY ALBUM KIT

Includes Minuteman pages covering U.S. stamps from 1900 - 1999, as well as Minuteman 3-ring binder.

ITEM	DESCRIPTION	RETAIL	AA*
180AMM20	**20th Century Album Plus 3-Ring Binder**	$69.99	**$59.49**

MINUTEMAN SUPPLEMENTS & ACCESSORIES

ITEM	DESCRIPTION	RETAIL	AA*
180S010	**2010 Supplement** (pages only)	$19.99	**$16.99**
180S011	**2011 Supplement** (pages only)	$19.99	**$16.99**
180S012	**2012 Supplement** (pages only)	$19.99	**$16.99**
180S013	**2013 Supplement** (pages only)	$19.99	**$16.99**
180S014	**2014 Supplement** (pages only)	$19.99	**$16.99**
180S015	**2015 Supplement** (pages only)	$19.99	**$16.99**
180S016	**2016 Supplement** (pages only)	$22.99	**$19.99**
180S017	**2017 Supplement** (pages only)	$22.99	**$19.99**
180Z003	**Minuteman Blank Pages Pack** Fits both 2-post and 3-ring binders	$19.99	**$16.99**

Starting with 2003, supplements fit both the 2-post Minuteman and 3-ring binders.

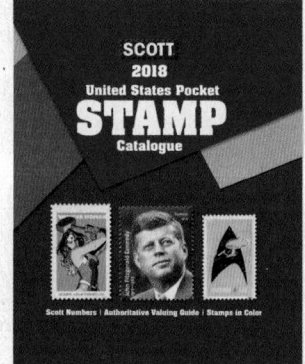

2018 U.S. STAMP POCKET CATALOGUE

With pages designed to be a convenient inventory checklist, the Scott U.S. Pocket Stamp Catalogue is a perfect compact companion at shows, club meetings, and your desk. Full-color stamp illustrations accompany listings and values for more than 4,000 U.S. stamps, all identified by Scott catalog numbers. Get your copy today!

ITEM	DESCRIPTION	RETAIL	AA*
P112018	**2018 U.S. Pocket Stamp Catalogue**	$32.50	**$26.99**

Get yours today by visiting AmosAdvantage.com

Or Call **1-800-572-6885** Outside U.S. & Canada Call: **1-937-498-0800**

P.O. Box 4129, Sidney, OH 45365

Illustrated Identifier

This section pictures stamps or parts of stamp designs that will help identify postage stamps that do not have English words on them.

Many of the symbols that identify stamps of countries are shown here as well as typical examples of their stamps.

See the Index and Identifier for stamps with inscriptions such as "sen," "posta," "Baja Porto," "Helvetia," "K.S.A.," etc.

Linn's Stamp Identifier is now available. The 144 pages include more than 2,000 inscriptions and more than 500 large stamp illustrations. Available from Linn's Stamp News, P.O. Box 4129, Sidney, OH 45365-4129, or amosadvantage.com

1. HEADS, PICTURES AND NUMERALS

GREAT BRITAIN

Great Britain stamps never show the country name, but, except for postage dues, show a picture of the reigning monarch.

Victoria

Edward VII   George V   Edward VIII

George VI

Elizabeth II

Some George VI and Elizabeth II stamps are surcharged in annas, new paisa or rupees. These are listed under Oman.

Silhouette (sometimes facing right, generally at the top of stamp)

The silhouette indicates this is a British stamp. It is not a U.S. stamp.

VICTORIA

Queen Victoria

INDIA

Other stamps of India show this portrait of Queen Victoria and the words "Service" (or "Postage") and "Annas."

AUSTRIA

YUGOSLAVIA

(Also BOSNIA & HERZEGOVINA if imperf.)

BOSNIA & HERZEGOVINA

Denominations also appear in top corners instead of bottom corners.

HUNGARY

Another stamp has posthorn facing left

BRAZIL

AUSTRALIA

Kangaroo and Emu

GERMANY

Mecklenburg-Vorpommern

SWITZERLAND

PALAU

2. ORIENTAL INSCRIPTIONS

CHINA

Any stamp with this one character is from China (Imperial, Republic or People's Republic). This character appears in a four-character overprint on stamps of Manchukuo. These stamps are local provisionals, which are unlisted. Other overprinted Manchukuo stamps show this character, but have more than four characters in the overprints. These are listed in People's Republic of China.

Some Chinese stamps show the Sun.

Most stamps of Republic of China show this series of characters.

Stamps with the China character and this character are from People's Republic of China.
人

Calligraphic form of People's Republic of China

（一）	（二）	（三）	（四）	（五）	（六）
1	2	3	4	5	6
（七）	（八）	（九）	（十）	（一十）	（二十）
7	8	9	10	11	12

Chinese stamps without China character

REPUBLIC OF CHINA

PEOPLE'S REPUBLIC OF CHINA

Mao Tse-tung

MANCHUKUO

Temple   Emperor Pu-Yi

The last 3 characters are common to
other Manchukuo stamps.

Orchid Crest

Manchukuo
stamp
without
these
elements

JAPAN

Chrysanthemum Crest   Country Name

Japanese stamps without these elements

The number of characters in the
center and the design of dragons on
the sides will vary.

RYUKYU ISLANDS

Country Name

PHILIPPINES
(Japanese Occupation)

Country Name

NETHERLANDS INDIES
(Japanese Occupation)

Indicates Japanese Occupation

Java   Sumatra

Country Name   Country Name

Moluccas, Celebes and
South Borneo

Country Name

NORTH BORNEO
(Japanese Occupation)

Indicates Japanese   Country
Occupation   Name

MALAYA
(Japanese Occupation)

Indicates Japanese   Country
Occupation   Name

The first 3 characters are common to
many Manchukuo stamps.

BURMA
Union of Myanmar

ပြည်ထောင်စုမြန်မာနိုင်ငံတော်
Union of Myanmar
(Japanese Occupation)

Indicates Japanese
Occupation

Country
Name

Other Burma Japanese Occupation stamps
without these elements

Burmese Script

KOREA

These two characters, in any order,
are common to stamps from the
Republic of Korea (South Korea) or of
the People's Democratic Republic of
Korea (North Korea).

This series of four characters can be found
on the stamps of both Koreas.
Most stamps of the Democratic People's
Republic of Korea (North Korea)
have just this inscription.

Indicates Republic of Korea (South Korea)

South Korean postage stamps issed after
1952 do not show currency expressed
in Latin letters. Stamps wiith "
HW," "HWAN," "WON,"
"WN," "W" or "W" with two lines through it,
if not illustrated in listings of stamps
before this date, are revenues.
North Korean postage stamps do not have
currency expressed in Latin letters.

Yin Yang appears on some stamps.

South Korean stamps show Yin Yang and
starting in 1966, 'KOREA" in Latin letters

Example of South Korean stamps lacking
Latin text, Yin Yang and standard Korean
text of country name. North Korean stamps
never show Yin Yang and starting in 1976
are inscribed "DPRK" or "DPR KOREA" in
Latin letters.

THAILAND

Country Name

King Chulalongkorn

King Prajadhipok and
Chao P'ya Chakri

3. CENTRAL AND EASTERN ASIAN INSCRIPTIONS

INDIA - FEUDATORY STATES

Alwar

Bhor

Bundi

Similar stamps come with
different designs in corners
and differently drawn daggers
(at center of circle).

Dhar   Duttia

Faridkot

Hyderabad

Similar stamps exist with
different central design which is
inscribed "Postage"
or "Post & Receipt."

Indore

Jammu & Kashmir

Text varies.

Jasdan

Jhalawar

Kotah

Size and text varies

Nandgaon

Nowanuggur

Poonch

Similar stamps exist
in various sizes with different text

Rajasthan

Rajpeepla

Soruth

Tonk

BANGLADESH

Country Name

NEPAL

Similar stamps are smaller, have squares in
upper corners and have five or nine
characters in central bottom panel.

TANNU TUVA   ISRAEL

GEORGIA

This inscription
is found on other
pictorial stamps.

Country Name

ARMENIA

The four characters are found somewhere
on pictorial stamps. On some stamps only
the middle two are found.

4. AFRICAN INSCRIPTIONS

ETHIOPIA

5. ARABIC INSCRIPTIONS

١ ٢ ٣ ٤ ٥
1 2 3 4 5

٧ ٨ ٩ ٠
7 8 9 0 (6 ٦)

AFGHANISTAN

Many early Afghanistan stamps show Tiger's head, many of these have ornaments protruding from outer ring, others show inscriptions in black.

Arabic Script

Crest of King Amanullah

Mosque Gate & Crossed Cannons

افغانستان

The four characters are found somewhere on pictorial stamps. On some stamps only the middle two are found.

BAHRAIN

EGYPT

Postage

IRAN

Country Name

Royal Crown

Lion with Sword

Symbol

Emblem

IRAQ

JORDAN

LEBANON

Similar types have
denominations at top
and slightly different
design.

LIBYA

Country Name in various styles

Other Libya stamps show Eagle and
Shield (head facing either direction) or
Red, White and Black Shield (with or with-
out eagle in center).

Without Country Name

SAUDI ARABIA

Tughra (Central design)

← Palm Tree and Swords

SYRIA

Arab Government Issues

THRACE   YEMEN

PAKISTAN

PAKISTAN - BAHAWALPUR

Country Name in top panel, star and crescent

TURKEY

Star & Crescent is a device found on many Turkish stamps, but is also found on stamps from other Arabic areas (see Pakistan-Bahawalpur)

Tughra (similar tughras can be found on stamps of Turkey in Asia, Afghanistan and Saudi Arabia)

Mohammed V

Mustafa Kemal

Plane, Star and Crescent

TURKEY IN ASIA

Other Turkey in Asia pictorials show star & crescent. Other stamps show tughra shown under Turkey.

6. GREEK INSCRIPTIONS

GREECE

Country Name in various styles
(Some Crete stamps overprinted with the Greece country name are listed in Crete.)

Lepta

Drachma   Drachmas   Lepton
Abbreviated Country Name
Other forms of Country Name

No country name

CRETE

Country Name

Crete stamps with a surcharge that have the year "1922" are listed under Greece.

EPIRUS

Similar stamps have text above the eagle.

IONIAN IS.

---

7. CYRILLIC INSCRIPTIONS

RUSSIA

Postage Stamp   Imperial Eagle

Postage in various styles

Abbreviation   Abbreviation   Russia
for Kopeck   for Ruble

Abbreviation for Russian Soviet
Federated Socialist Republic
RSFSR stamps were overprinted
(see below)

Abbreviation for Union of Soviet
Socialist Republics

This item is footnoted in Latvia

RUSSIA - Army of the North

"OKCA"

RUSSIA - Wenden

RUSSIAN OFFICES IN THE TURKISH EMPIRE

These letters appear
on other stamps of the
Russian offices.

The unoverprinted ver-
sion of this stamp and a
similar stamp were over-
printed by various coun-
tries (see below).

ARMENIA

BELARUS

FAR EASTERN REPUBLIC

Country Name

FINLAND

Circles and Dots
on stamps similar
to Imperial
Russia issues

SOUTH RUSSIA

Country Name

BATUM

Forms of Country Name

TRANSCAUCASIAN FEDERATED REPUBLICS

Abbreviation for
Country Name

KAZAKHSTAN

Country Name

KYRGYZSTAN

Country
Name

ROMANIA

TAJIKISTAN

Country Name & Abbreviation

UKRAINE

Country Name in various forms

The trident appears
on many stamps,
usually as
an overprint.

Abbreviation for
Ukrainian
Soviet
Socialist
Republic

WESTERN UKRAINE

Abbreviation for
Country Name

AZERBAIJAN

AZƏRBAYCAN

Country Name

A.C.C.P.

Abbreviation for Azerbaijan
Soviet Socialist Republic

MONTENEGRO

ЦРНЕГОРЕ

ЦРНА ГОРА

Country Name in various forms

ЦРГОРЕ

Abbreviation
for country
name

No country name
(A similar Montenegro
stamp without coun-
try name has same
vignette.)

SERBIA

СРПСКА   **СРБИЈА**

Country Name in various forms

СРП   **К. С.**

Abbreviation for country name

No country name

MACEDONIA

МАКЕДОНИЈА

Country Name

МАКЕДОНСКИ
11 Октомври   1997

Different form of Country Name

SERBIA & MONTENEGRO

YUGOSLAVIA

ЈУГОСЛАВИЈА

Showing country name

No Country Name

BOSNIA & HERZEGOVINA
(Serb Administration)

РЕПУБЛИКА СРПСКА

Country Name

РЕПУБЛИКЕ СРПСКЕ

Different form of Country Name

No Country Name

BULGARIA

Country Name   Postage

Stotinka

Stotinki (plural)   Abbreviation for
Stotinki

Country Name in various forms and styles

No country name

  Abbreviation
for Lev, leva

MONGOLIA

Country name in   Tugrik in Cyrillic
one word

Country name in   Mung in Cyrillic
two words

Mung
in Mongolian

Tugrik
in Mongolian

Arms

No Country Name

COVER SUPPLIES

COVER BINDERS AND PAGES

Padded, durable, 3-ring binders will hold up to 100 covers. Features the "D" ring mechanism on the right hand side of album so you don't have to worry about creasing or wrinkling covers when opening or closing binder. Cover pages sold separately. **Binders and pages are also sold in a money saving sets. Call or go online for more details.**

Item	Retail	AA*
COVER BINDERS	$16.99	**$12.99**

Choose from four classic colors:
Black (CBBK); Blue (CBBL);
Red/Burgundy (CBRD);
Gray (CBGY)

COVER ALBUM PAGES WITH BLACK BACKGROUNDS

Item	Description	Retail	AA*
T2	Double-sided Page, 2 Pocket (25/pack)	$9.99	**$8.99**
SS2PG1B	Supersafe Page, 1 Pocket (10/pack)	$5.75	**$4.75**

COVER SLEEVES

Clear polyethylene sleeves protect your covers. **Sold in packages of 100.**

U.S. POSTAL CARD

3¹¹⁄₁₆"
5¾"

Item	Retail	AA*
CVB05	$2.75	**$2.25**

U.S. FIRST DAY COVER #6

3¹⁵⁄₁₆"
6⅞"

Item	Retail	AA*
CVB06	$3.25	**$2.75**

CONTINENTAL POSTCARD

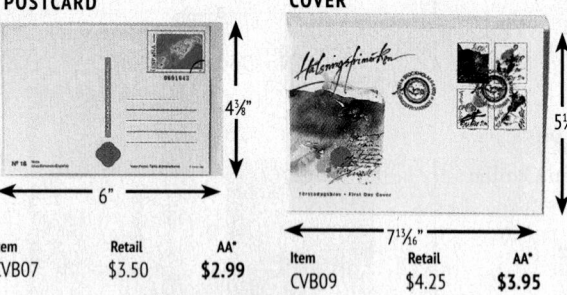

4⅜"
6"

Item	Retail	AA*
CVB07	$3.50	**$2.99**

EUROPEAN FIRST DAY COVER

5⅛"
7¹³⁄₁₆"

Item	Retail	AA*
CVB09	$4.25	**$3.95**

#10 BUSINESS ENVELOPE

4¼"
9⅝"

Item	Retail	AA*
CVB10	$5.75	**$4.95**

MINT SHEET BINDERS & PAGES

Keep those mint sheets intact in a handsome, 3-ring binder. Just like the cover album, the Mint Sheet album features the "D" ring mechanism on the right hand side of binder so you don't have to worry about damaging your stamps when turning the pages.
Binders and pages are also sold in a money saving sets. Call or go online for more details.

Item		Retail	AA*
MBRD	Red (Burgundy)	$21.99	**$17.99**
MBBL	Blue	$21.99	**$17.99**
MBGY	Gray	$21.99	**$17.99**
MBBK	Black	$21.99	**$17.99**
MS1	BLACK Mint Sheet Pages (25 per pack)	$16.99	**$14.99**
SSMP3C	CLEAR Mint Sheet Pages (12 per pack)	$9.95	**$8.95**

GLASSINE ENVELOPES

Perfect for organizing duplicates and sending approvals or mailing stamps. **Sold in packages of 100.**

Item	Size (Dimensions)	Retail	AA*
GEO1	#1 (1¾" x 2⅞")	$4.99	**$4.49**
GEO2	#2 (2⁵⁄₁₆" x 3⅝")	$5.49	**$4.99**
GEO3	#3 (2½" x 4¼")	$5.99	**$5.49**
GEO4	#4 (3¼" x 4⅞")	$6.99	**$5.99**
GE4H	#4½ (3⅛" x 5¹⁄₁₆")	$5.95	**$5.25**
GE05	#5 (3½" x 6")	$8.99	**$7.99**
GE06	#6 (3¾" x 6¾")	$9.50	**$8.50**
GE07	#7 (4⅛" x 6¼")	$10.00	**$9.00**
GE08	#8 (4½" x 6⅝")	$10.50	**$9.50**
GE10	#10 (4⅛" x 9½")	$16.99	**$14.99**
GE11	#11 (4½" x 10⅜")	$17.99	**$16.99**

GLASSINE BAGS

These larger glassine bags are ideal for storing panes, covers or prestige booklets. A handy accessory to keep around for all your collecting needs. Available in five different sizes. **Sold in packages of 100.**

Item	Size (Dimensions)	Retail	AA*
GB12	#12 (4⅝" x 6⅝")	$8.99	**$7.99**
GB13	#13 (5¾" x 7¾")	$9.99	**$8.99**
GB13A	#13A (6¾" x 9")	$10.99	**$9.99**
GB14	#14 (7¾" x 9¾")	$16.99	**$14.99**
GB15	#15 (8½" x 11")	$18.99	**$15.99**
GB16	#16 (11½" x 14")	$33.99	**$28.99**

Glassines are also available in boxes of 1,000 – call for pricing.

PRINZ CORNER MOUNTS

Clear, self-adhesive corner mounts are ideal for postal cards and covers. Mounts measure ⅞" each side and are made from transparent glass foil. There are 250 mounts in each pack.

Item	Retail	AA*
ACC176	$11.99	**$8.99**

AmosAdvantage.com • 1-800-572-6885

Outside U.S. and Canada, call (937) 498-0800
Mail to PO Box 4129, Sidney, OH 45365-4129

NEW WORLD OF TECHNOLOGY

6-IN-1 LED POCKET MAGNIFIER/MICROSCOPE (55X)

A powerful LED microscope (up to 55X magnification) teams up with two aspheric Perspex lenses (3X magnification large and 10X magnification small) to examine objects at various levels of detail. Built-in focus wheel ensures clarity. View objects even in low-light conditions with three lighting functions: three LED flashlight, simple UV light, one white LED. Black composite housing.

Item	Retail	AA*
MG61LED	$21.95	$19.95

SCHAUBEK 10X LED & UV COMBO MAGNIFIER

This pocket-sized magnifier boasts 10X magnification with both LED and UV longwave light. Battery powered for maximum portability. Handy carrying case protects the 21mm magnifier while on the go.

Item	Retail	AA*
MG10XLUV	$39.99	$34.99

ZOOM 20X-40X MICROSCOPE WITH LED

This practical zoom microscope provides what collectors have been waiting for – outstanding clarity and resolution. Magnification is continuously adjustable between 20X and 40X. Powerful LED lighting illuminates the stage (3 #LR44 batteries included). Stand, examination slides, and slide covers also included.

Item	Retail	AA*
LHPM3	$29.95	$21.95

ZOOM 10X-300X USB DIGITAL MICROSCOPE, 5.0 MEGAPIXEL

The industry-leading 5.0 megapixel resolution makes the smallest details on coins and stamps visible on your computer screen via the included USB cable. Up to 10x - 300x magnification available with this high-end digital microscope

Item	Retail	AA*
LHDM4	$179.95	$169.95

5-IN-1 MULTI-FUNCTION POCKET MAGNIFIER 2.5X-10X LED

A sturdy stainless steel frame houses two aspheric lenses: 2.5X rectangular and 10X round, plus three lighting functions: 3-LED side flashlight, 1-LED research light, simple 395nm long-wave UV light. A mini ballpoint pen, available to take notes, tucks inside the acrylic housing. Leatherette case & 3 #LR927 batteries included.

Item	Retail	AA*
MG51	$15.95	$13.95

3.2X LED ILLUMINATED MAGNIFIER

This 7" aluminum 3.2X magnifier is both beautiful and functional. Six LEDs surround the 1.375" lens to provide glare-free illumination. Zippered protective case and 2 AA batteries included.

Item	Retail	AA*
MG32XL	$35.95	$31.95

BLACK TRUE COLOR LIGHT

A versatile, compact light that provides superior image and color rendering while reducing glare and eye strain. Technologically advanced light produces a precise blend of light for contrast and brightness that makes colors vibrant and details incredibly clear. The lamp comes with an "E"(electronic) tube for a quicker starting time. This does plug into an outlet for long uses.

Item	Retail	AA*
ACC191BB	$79.99	$49.99

LIGHTHOUSE DUAL WAVE ULTRAVIOLET LAMP

Examine your collectibles for both fluorescence (long wave) and phosphorescence (short wave) using one versatile ultraviolet lamp. Flip a switch to change quickly and easily between short and long UV rays (254 and 380nm). Short wave exposes tagging, while long wave reveals faults, tears, and repairs. Battery operated; requires 4x AA batteries (not included).

Item	Retail	AA*
LHL81	$71.95	$59.95

10X POCKET MAGNIFIER

This compact, portable and easy-to-use 10x pocket magnifier comes with its own illumination from a brilliant white LED. The glass lens is 18mm (3/4") in diameter.

Item	Retail	AA*
MG10XLED	$12.95	$11.95

13W DUOFLEX MAGNIFIER DESK LAMP

The OttLite DuoFlex has a two-pronged approach to enhance your vision. First, the large 3X-5X magnifier enlarges your subject. Then the energy-efficient 13w "E" bulb spotlights the field. Flexible arms allow nearly infinite positioning. Long-term bulb is rated to last up to 10,000 hours.

Item	Retail	AA*
ACC213W	$109.99	$59.99

PHONESCOPE DIGITAL MICROSCOPE

Clip this compact Lighthouse Phonescope lens on your smartphone or tablet to transform it into a powerful digital microscope. See the smallest details and instantly capture high-quality images and videos. The precision macro glass lens offers up to 60X magnification and requires no batteries. Field of view: 1/2" (13mm). Phonescope works with all popular smartphones without scratching display. Image resolution and zoom function dependent upon your device.

Item	Retail	AA*
LHSCOPE	$25.99	$21.99

SHIPPING & HANDLING: United States: Order total $0-$10.00 charged $3.99 shipping. United States - Order total $10.01-$79.99 charged $7.99 shipping. United States - Order total $80.00 or more charged 10% of order total for shipping. Maximum Freight Charge $45.00. Canada: 20% of order total. Minimum charge $19.99 Maximum charge $200.00. Foreign orders are shipped via FedExl Intl. or USPS and billed actual freight.

ORDERING INFORMATION: *AA prices apply to paid subscribers of Amos Media titles, or orders placed online. Prices, terms and product availability subject to change. Taxes will apply in CA, OH, & IL. Shipping and handling rates will apply. See below.

Vols. 1A-1B Number Additions, Deletions & Changes

Number in 2018 Catalogue	Number in 2019 Catalogue
United States	
new	2492k
new	3283b
new	5158a
Computer Vended Postage	
CVP88C	CVP84C
new	CVP87Bc
Stamped Envelopes/Wrappers	
new	UO84a
Canal Zone	
new	71f
new	86i
new	91d
Ryukyu Islands	
new	17h
Annam & Tonkin	
new	4
Argentina	
new	B20a
new	B21a
new	CB15a
new	CB16a
Australia	
new	17b
Austria	
new	291i
Azerbaijan	
new	1A-10A
Bahrain	
new	225a-227a
new	228b
new	229Ab
new	231a-235a
new	236a-236b
new	237a-240a
new	238b-238d
MR1	RA1
MR2	RA2
new	RA3
new	RA4
Bangladesh	
852	851
new	852
Barbados	
new	180a
Bhutan	
new	1409A
new	1409B
Botswana	
new	157b
new	160b
new	166b
new	167b
new	909g
Brazil	
new	37c
new	287a
new	296a
new	357b
new	358a
new	376d
new	388a
new	426a

Number in 2018 Catalogue	Number in 2019 Catalogue
Brazil	
new	667a
new	669a
new	670a
1822	1822A
new	1822Ab-1822Ad
2000a	2000A
new	2000Ab-2000Ad
new	2064a
new	2065b
new	2067b
new	2068b
2088	2088A
new	2088Ab
new	2088Ac
new	2880a
new	2932a
new	2968a
new	2983a
new	3008a
new	C5a
new	C6c
new	C7b-C7c
new	C17a
new	C18a
new	C19a
new	C20a
new	C21a
new	C22a
new	C23a-C23c
new	C24a-C24b
new	C25a-C25c
new	C30c
new	C45d-C45f
new	E1b
new	J18c
new	J19c-J19d
new	J20c-J20d
new	J21a
new	J21c
new	J21e
new	J22c
new	J22e
new	J23d
new	J24d
new	J43a
new	J44a
new	J45a
new	J46a
new	J58a
new	J66a
new	J72a
new	P19b-P19c
new	P20b-P20c
new	P21b-P21c
new	P22e
new	P24e-P24f
new	P24h
new	P24j
new	RA1a
British Honduras	
new	195a
Brunei	
new	201b
new	204b
new	206b
Bulgaria	
new	2870a

ScottMounts

ITEM	W x H (mm)	DESCRIPTION	MOUNTS	RETAIL	AA*
PRE-CUT SINGLE MOUNTS					
901	40 x 25	U.S. Standard Comm. Hor. Water Activated	40	$3.50	$2.39
902	25 x 40	U.S. Standard Comm. Vert. Water Activated	40	$3.50	$2.39
903	25 x 22	U.S. Regular Issue – Hor. Water Activated	40	$3.50	$2.39
904	22 x 25	U.S. Regular Issue – Vert. Water Activated	40	$3.50	$2.39
905	41 x 31	U.S. Semi-Jumbo – Horizontal	40	$3.50	$2.39
906	31 x 41	U.S. Semi-Jumbo – Vertical	40	$3.50	$2.39
907	50 x 31	U.S. Jumbo – Horizontal	40	$3.50	$2.39
908	31 x 50	U.S. Jumbo – Vertical	40	$3.50	$2.39
909	25 x 27	U.S. Famous Americans/Champions Of Liberty	40	$3.50	$2.39
910	33 x 27	United Nations	40	$3.50	$2.39
911	40 x 27	United Nations	40	$3.50	$2.39
976	67 x 25	Plate Number Coils, Strips of Three	40	$6.25	$3.99
984	67 x 34	Pacific '97 Triangle	10	$3.50	$2.39
985	111 x 25	Plate Number Coils, Strips of Five	25	$6.25	$3.99
986	51 x 36	U.S. Hunting Permit/Express Mail	40	$6.25	$3.99
1045	40 x 26	U.S. Standard Comm. Hor. Self-Adhesive	40	$3.50	$2.39
1046	25 x 41	U.S. Standard Comm. Vert. Self-Adhesive	40	$3.50	$2.39
1047	22 x 26	U.S. Definitives Vert. Self Adhesive	40	$3.50	$2.39
966		Value Pack (Assortment pre-cut sizes)	320	$23.25	$15.25
975		Best Pack (Assortment pre-cut sizes - Black Only)	160	$14.75	$9.99
PRE-CUT PLATE BLOCK, FDC, POSTAL CARD MOUNTS					
912	57 x 55	Regular Issue Plate Block	25	$6.25	$3.99
913	73 x 63	Champions of Liberty	25	$6.25	$3.99
914	106 x 55	Rotary Press Standard Commemorative	20	$6.25	$3.99
915	105 x 57	Giori Press Standard Commemorative	20	$6.25	$3.99
916	127 x 70	Giori Press Jumbo Commemorative	10	$6.25	$3.99
917	165 x 94	First Day Cover	10	$6.25	$3.99
918	140 x 90	Postal Card Size/Submarine Booklet Pane	10	$6.25	$3.99
1048	152 x 107	Large Postal Cards	8	$10.25	$6.99
STRIPS 215MM LONG					
919	20	U.S. 19th Century, Horizontal Coil	22	$7.99	$5.25
920	22	U.S. Early Air Mail	22	$7.99	$5.25
921	24	U.S., Vertical Coils, Christmas (#2400, #2428 etc.)	22	$7.99	$5.25
922	25	U.S. Commemorative and Regular	22	$7.99	$5.25
1049	26	U.S. Commemorative and Regular	22	$7.99	$5.25
923	27	U.S. Famous Americans	22	$7.99	$5.25
924	28	U.S. 19th Century, Liechtenstein	22	$7.99	$5.25
1050	29	Virginia Dare, British Empire, etc.	22	$7.99	$5.25
925	30	U.S. 19th Century; Jamestown, etc; Foreign	22	$7.99	$5.25
926	31	U.S. Horizontal Jumbo and Semi-Jumbo	22	$7.99	$5.25
927	33	U.S. Stampin' Future, UN	22	$7.99	$5.25
1054	34	U.S. American Landmarks, Eclipse	22	$7.99	$5.25
928	36	U.S. Hunting Permit, Canada	15	$7.99	$5.25
1051	37	U.S., British Colonies	22	$7.99	$5.25
929	39	U.S. Early 20th Century	15	$7.99	$5.25
930	41	U.S. Vert. Semi-Jumbo ('77 Lafayette, Pottery, etc.)	15	$7.99	$5.25
931		Multiple Assortment: One strip of each size 22-41 above (SMKB) (2 x 25mm strips)	12	$7.99	$5.25
1052	42	U.S., British Colonies	22	$7.99	$5.25
1053	43	U.S., British Colonies	22	$7.99	$5.25
932	44	U.S. Vertical Coil Pair Garden Flowers Booklet Pane	15	$7.99	$5.25
933	48	U.S. Farley, Gutter Pair	15	$7.99	$5.25
934	50	U.S. Jumbo (Lyndon Johnson, '74 U.P.U., etc.)	15	$7.99	$5.25
935	52	U.S. Standard Commemorative Block (Butterflies)	15	$7.99	$5.25
936	55	U.S. Standard Plate Block – normal margins	15	$7.99	$5.25
937	57	U.S. Standard Plate Block - wider margins	15	$7.99	$5.25
938	61	U.S. Blocks, Israel Tabs, '99 Christmas Madonna Pane	15	$7.99	$5.25
STRIPS 240MM LONG					
939	63	U.S. Jumbo Commemorative Horizontal Block	10	$9.25	$5.99
940	66	U.S. CIPEX Souvenir Sheet, Self-Adhesive Booklet Pane (#2803a, 3012a)	10	$9.25	$5.99
941	68	U.S. ATM Booklet Pane, Farley Gutter Pair & Souvenir Sheet	10	$9.25	$5.99
942	74	U.S. TIPEX Souvenir Sheet	10	$9.25	$5.99
943	80	U.S. Standard Commemorative Vertical Block	10	$9.25	$5.99
944	82	U.S. Blocks of Four, U.N. Chagall	10	$9.25	$5.99
945	84	Israel Tab Block, Mars Pathfinder Sheetlet	10	$9.25	$5.99
946	89	Submarine Booklet, Souvenir Sheet World Cup, Rockwell	10	$9.25	$5.99
947	100	U.S. '74 U.P.U. Block, U.N. Margin Inscribed Block	7	$9.25	$5.99
948	120	Various Souvenir Sheets and Blocks	7	$9.25	$5.99
STRIPS 265MM LONG					
1035	25	U.S. Coils Strips of 11	12	$9.25	$5.99
949	40	U.S. Postal People Standard Standard & Semi-Jumbo Commemorative Strip	10	$9.25	$5.99
981	44	U.S. Long self-adhesive booklet panes	10	$9.25	$5.99
1030	45	Various (Canada Scott #1725-1734)	10	$9.25	$5.99
1036	46	U.S. Long self adhesive booklet panes of 15	10	$9.25	$5.99
950	55	U.S. Regular Plate Block or Strip of 20	10	$9.25	$5.99
951	59	U.S. Double Issue Strip	10	$9.25	$5.99
952	70	U.S. Jumbo Commemorative Plate Block	10	$12.50	$8.50
1031	72	Various (Canada Scott #1305a-1804a)	10	$12.50	$8.50
1032	75	Plate Blocks: Lance Armstrong, Prehistoric Animals, etc.	10	$12.50	$8.50
1060	76	U.S. 1994 Stamp Printing Centennial Souvenir Sheet, etc.	10	$12.50	$8.50
953	91	U.S. Self-Adhesive Booklet Pane '98 Wreath, '95 Santa	10	$12.50	$8.50
1033	95	Mini-Sheet Plate Blocks w/top header	10	$12.50	$8.50
1061	96	U.S., Foreign	10	$12.50	$8.50
954	105	U.S. Standard Semi-Jumbo Commemorative Plate Number Strip	10	$12.50	$8.50
955	107	Same as above–wide margin	10	$12.50	$8.50
956	111	U.S. Gravure-Intaglio Plate Number Strip	10	$14.75	$9.99
1062	115	Foreign Small Sheets	10	$17.50	$11.99
957	127	U.S. 2000 Space S/S, World War II S/S	10	$17.50	$11.99
1063	131	Looney Tunes sheets; World War II Souvenir Sheet Plate Block	10	$17.50	$11.99
1064	135	U.S., Japan Gifts of Friendship sheet	10	$17.50	$11.99
958	137	Great Britain Coronation	10	$17.50	$11.99
1065	139	Sheets: Soda Fountain, Lady Bird Johnson, Earthscapes, etc.	10	$17.50	$11.99
1066	143	Sheets: Merchant Marine Ships, 2013 Hanukkah, etc.	10	$17.50	$11.99
1067	147	Sheets: Pickup Trucks, Animal Rescue, Washington D.C., etc.	10	$17.50	$11.99
1068	151	Sheets: Go Green, Bicycling, Happy New Year, Ben Franklin, etc.	10	$17.50	$11.99

ITEM	W x H (mm)	DESCRIPTION	MOUNTS	RETAIL	AA*
STRIPS 265MM LONG, continued					
959	158	American Glass, U.S. Football Coaches Sheets	10	$17.99	$12.50
1069	163	Sheets: Modern Architecture, UN Human Rights, etc.	5	$12.50	$8.50
1070	167	Sheets: John F. Kennedy, Classics Forever, Made in America, etc.	5	$12.50	$8.50
1071	171	Film Directors, Foreign Souvenir Sheets	5	$12.50	$8.50
960	175	Large Block, Souvenir Sheet	5	$12.50	$8.50
1072	181	Sheets: Jimi Hendrix, Johnny Cash, American Photography, etc.	5	$17.50	$11.99
1073	185	Frank Sinatra, Ronald Reagan, Arthur Ashe, Creast Cancer, etc.	5	$17.50	$11.99
1074	188	Sheets: Yoda, 9/11 Heroes, Andy Warhol, Frida Kahlo, etc	5	$17.50	$11.99
1075	198	Sheets: Modern American Art, Super Heroes, Baseball Sluggers, etc.	5	$17.50	$11.99
1076	215	Celebrity Chefs sheets; Foreign sheets	5	$17.50	$11.99
961	231	U.S. Full Post Office Pane Regular and Commemorative	5	$17.99	$12.50
SOUVENIR SHEETS/SMALL PANES					
962	204 x 153	New Year 2000, U.S. Bicentennial S/S	4	$9.25	$5.99
963	187 x 144	55¢ Victorian Love Pane, U.N. Flag Sheet	9	$15.50	$10.25
964	160 x 200	U.N., Israel Sheet	10	$15.50	$10.25
965	120 x 207	U.S. AMERIPEX Presidential Sheet	4	$6.25	$3.99
968	229 x 131	World War II S/S Plate Block Only	5	$9.25	$5.99
970	111 x 91	Columbian Souvenir Sheet	6	$6.25	$4.75
972	148 x 196	Apollo Moon Landing/Carnivorous Plants	4	$7.99	$5.25
989	129 x 122	U.S. Definitive Sheet: Harte, Hopkins, etc.	8	$10.25	$6.99
990	189 x 151	Chinese New Year	5	$10.25	$6.99
991	150 x 185	Breast Cancer/Fermi/Soccer/'96 Folk Heroes	5	$10.25	$6.99
992	198 x 151	Cherokee Strip Sheet	5	$10.25	$6.99
993	185 x 151	Bernstein/NATO/Irish/Lunt/Gold Rush Sheets	5	$10.25	$6.99
994	198 x 187	Postal Museum	4	$10.25	$6.99
995	156 x 187	Sign Language/Statehood	5	$10.25	$6.99
996	188 x 197	Illustrators, '98 Music: Folk, Gospel; Country/Western	4	$10.25	$6.99
997	151 x 192	Olympic	5	$10.25	$6.99
998	174 x 185	Buffalo Soldiers	5	$10.25	$6.99
999	130 x 198	Silent Screen Stars	5	$10.25	$6.99
1000	190 x 199	Stars Stripes/Baseball/Insects & Spiders/Legends West/Aircraft, Comics, '96 Olympics, Civil War	4	$10.25	$6.99
1001	178 x 181	Cranes	4	$10.25	$6.99
1002	183 x 212	Wonders of the Sea, We the People	3	$10.25	$6.99
1003	156 x 264	$14 Eagle	4	$10.25	$6.99
1004	159 x 270	$9.95 Moon Landing	4	$10.25	$6.99
1005	159 x 259	$2.90 Priority/$9.95 Express Mail	4	$10.25	$6.99
1006	223 x 187	Hubble, Hollywood Legends, O'Keefe Sheets	3	$10.25	$6.99
1007	185 x 181	Deep Sea Creatures, Olmsted Sheets	4	$10.25	$6.99
1008	152 x 228	Indian Dances/Antique Autos	5	$10.25	$6.99
1009	165 x 150	River Boat/Hanukkah	6	$10.25	$6.99
1010	275 x 200	Dinosaurs/Large Gutter Blocks	2	$10.25	$6.99
1011	161 x 160	Pacific '97 Triangle Mini Sheets	6	$10.25	$6.99
1012	174 x 130	Road Runner, Daffy, Bugs, Sylvester & Tweety	6	$10.25	$6.99
1013	196 x 158	Football Coaches	4	$10.25	$6.99
1014	184 x 184	American Dolls, Flowering Trees Sheets	4	$10.25	$6.99
1015	186 x 230	Classic Movie Monsters	3	$10.25	$6.99
1016	187 x 160	Trans-Mississippi Sheet	4	$10.25	$6.99
1017	192 x 230	Celebrate The Century	3	$10.25	$6.99
1018	156 x 204	Space Discovery	5	$10.25	$6.99
1019	182 x 209	American Ballet	5	$10.25	$6.99
1020	139 x 151	Christmas Wreaths	5	$10.25	$6.99
1021	129 x 126	Justin Morrill, Henry Luce	8	$10.25	$6.99
1022	184 x 165	Baseball Fields, Bright Eyes	4	$10.25	$6.99
1023	185 x 172	Shuttle Landing Pan Am Invert Sheets	4	$10.25	$6.99
1024	172 x 233	Sonoran Desert	3	$10.25	$6.99
1025	150 x 166	Prostate Cancer	5	$10.25	$6.99
1026	201 x 176	Famous Trains	4	$10.25	$6.99
1027	176 x 124	Canada - Historic Vehicles	5	$10.25	$6.99
1028	245 x 114	Canada - Provincial Leaders	5	$10.25	$6.99
1029	177 x 133	Canada - Year of the Family	5	$10.25	$6.99
1034	181 x 213	Arctic Animals	3	$10.25	$6.99
1037	179 x 242	Louise Nevelson	3	$10.25	$6.99
1038	179 x 217	Library Of Congress	3	$10.25	$6.99
1039	182 x 232	Youth Team Sports	3	$10.25	$6.99
1040	183 x 216	Lucille Ball Scott #3523	3	$10.25	$6.99
1041	182 x 244	American Photographers	3	$10.25	$6.99
1042	185 x 255	Andy Warhol	3	$10.25	$6.99
1043	165 x 190	American Film Making	4	$10.25	$6.99
1044	28 x 290	American Eagle PNC Strips of 11	12	$9.25	$5.99

Available in clear or black backgrounds. Please specify color choice when ordering.

2017 NATIONAL, MINUTEMAN OR ALL-AMERICAN SUPPLEMENT MOUNT PACKS

ITEM	DESCRIPTION	RETAIL	AA*
2017 B	2017 National, Minuteman or All-American Supplement Mount Pack - BLACK	$49.99	$39.99
2017 C	2017 National, Minuteman or All-American Supplement Mount Pack - CLEAR	$49.99	$39.99

Currency Conversion

Country	Dollar	Pound	S Franc	Yen	HK $	Euro	Cdn $	Aus $
Australia	1.3140	1.7709	1.3459	0.0117	0.1682	1.5632	1.0351	—
Canada	1.2695	1.7109	1.3003	0.0113	0.1625	1.5102	—	0.9661
European Union	0.8406	1.1329	0.8610	0.0075	0.1076	—	0.6622	0.6397
Hong Kong	7.8119	10.528	8.0015	0.0697	—	9.2932	6.1535	5.9451
Japan	112.13	151.12	114.85	—	14.354	133.39	88.326	85.335
Switzerland	0.9763	1.3158	—	0.0087	0.1250	1.1614	0.7690	0.7430
United Kingdom	0.7420	—	0.7600	0.0066	0.0950	0.8827	0.5845	0.5647
United States	—	1.3477	1.0243	0.0089	0.1280	1.1896	0.7877	0.7610

Country	Currency	U.S. $ Equiv.
Austria	euro	1.1896
Azerbaijan	manat	.5888
Bahamas	dollar	1.0000
Bahrain	dinar	2.6518
Bangladesh	taka	.0121
Barbados	dollar	.5000
Barbuda	East Caribbean dollar	.3704
Belarus	ruble	.4968
Belgium	euro	1.1896
Belize	dollar	.5004
Benin	Community of French Africa (CFA) franc	.0018
Bermuda	dollar	1.0000
Bhutan	ngultrum	.0155
Bolivia	boliviano	.1447
Bosnia & Herzegovina	convertible mark	.6084
Botswana	pula	.0965
Brazil	real	.3069
British Antarctic Territory	British pound	1.3477
British Indian Ocean Territory	British pound	1.3477
Brunei	dollar	.7422
Bulgaria	lev	.6081
Burkina Faso	CFA franc	.0018
Burma	kyat	.0007
Burundi	franc	.0006

Source: **xe.com** Dec. 1, 2017. Figures reflect values as of Dec. 1, 2017.

INDEX TO ADVERTISERS
2019 VOLUME 1B

Take an Excursion

with a Scott International stamp album

The Scott International album is one of the broadest and far reaching worldwide albums available. The acid-free pages are printed on two sides, to conveniently save space. In addition, all the illustrations come with a Scott number for easy identification. Embark on a philatelic adventure today!

Binders are sold separately.

2019
VOLUME 1B
DEALER DIRECTORY
YELLOW PAGE LISTINGS

This section of your Scott Catalogue contains advertisements to help you conveniently find what you need, when you need it...!

Albania

**WORLDSTAMPS/
FRANK GEIGER PHILATELISTS**
PO Box 4743
Pinehurst, NC 28374
PH: 910-295-2048
info@WorldStamps.com
www.WorldStamps.com

Andorra

**WORLDSTAMPS/
FRANK GEIGER PHILATELISTS**
PO Box 4743
Pinehurst, NC 28374
PH: 910-295-2048
info@WorldStamps.com
www.WorldStamps.com

Appraisals

**DR. ROBERT FRIEDMAN &
SONS STAMP & COIN
BUYING CENTER**
2029 W. 75th St.
Woodridge, IL 60517
PH: 800-588-8100
FAX: 630-985-1588
stampcollections@drbobstamps.com
www.drbobfriedmanstamps.com

MILLER'S STAMP COMPANY
12 Douglas Lane, Suite 11
Waterford, CT 06385
Stamps@millerstamps.com
PH: 860-908-6200

Argentina

GUILLERMO JALIL
Maipu 466,local 4
1006 Buenos Aires
Argentina
guillermo@jalilstamps.com
philatino@philatino.com
www.philatino.com
www.jalilstamps.com

Auctions

DUTCH COUNTRY AUCTIONS
The Stamp Center
4115 Concord Pike
Wilmington, DE 19803
PH: 302-478-8740
FAX: 302-478-8779
auctions@dutchcountryauctions.com
www.dutchcountryauctions.com

Australia

COLONIAL STAMP COMPANY
5757 Wilshire Blvd. PH #8
Los Angeles, CA 90036
PH: 323-933-9435
FAX: 323-939-9930
Toll Free in North America
PH: 877-272-6693
FAX: 877-272-6694
info@colonialstampcompany.com
www.colonialstampcompany.com

Australia

**WORLDSTAMPS/
FRANK GEIGER PHILATELISTS**
PO Box 4743
Pinehurst, NC 28374
PH: 910-295-2048
info@WorldStamps.com
www.WorldStamps.com

Austria

**WORLDSTAMPS/
FRANK GEIGER PHILATELISTS**
PO Box 4743
Pinehurst, NC 28374
PH: 910-295-2048
info@WorldStamps.com
www.WorldStamps.com

**HENRY GITNER
PHILATELISTS, INC.**
PO Box 3077-S
Middletown, NY 10940
PH: 845-343-5151
PH: 800-947-8267
FAX: 845-343-0068
hgitner@hgitner.com
www.hgitner.com

Bangkok

COLONIAL STAMP COMPANY
5757 Wilshire Blvd. PH #8
Los Angeles, CA 90036
PH: 323-933-9435
FAX: 323-939-9930
Toll Free in North America
PH: 877-272-6693
FAX: 877-272-6694
info@colonialstampcompany.com
www.colonialstampcompany.com

Belarus

**WORLDSTAMPS/
FRANK GEIGER PHILATELISTS**
PO Box 4743
Pinehurst, NC 28374
PH: 910-295-2048
info@WorldStamps.com
www.WorldStamps.com

Belgium

**WORLDSTAMPS/
FRANK GEIGER PHILATELISTS**
PO Box 4743
Pinehurst, NC 28374
PH: 910-295-2048
info@WorldStamps.com
www.WorldStamps.com

Bermuda

COLONIAL STAMP COMPANY
5757 Wilshire Blvd. PH #8
Los Angeles, CA 90036
PH: 323-933-9435
FAX: 323-939-9930
Toll Free in North America
PH: 877-272-6693
FAX: 877-272-6694
info@colonialstampcompany.com
www.colonialstampcompany.com

Bhutan

**WORLDSTAMPS/
FRANK GEIGER PHILATELISTS**
PO Box 4743
Pinehurst, NC 28374
PH: 910-295-2048
info@WorldStamps.com
www.WorldStamps.com

Bosnia

**WORLDSTAMPS/
FRANK GEIGER PHILATELISTS**
PO Box 4743
Pinehurst, NC 28374
PH: 910-295-2048
info@WorldStamps.com
www.WorldStamps.com

British Asia

THE STAMP ACT
PO Box 1136
Belmont, CA 94002
PH: 650-703-2342
thestampact@sbcglobal.net

British Commonwealth

**COLLECTORS EXCHANGE
ORLANDO STAMP SHOP**
1814A Edgewater Drive
Orlando, FL 32804
PH: 407-620-0908
PH: 407-947-8603
FAX: 407-730-2131
jlatter@cfl.rr.com
www.BritishStampsAmerica.com
www.OrlandoStampShop.com

**WORLDSTAMPS/
FRANK GEIGER PHILATELISTS**
PO Box 4743
Pinehurst, NC 28374
PH: 910-295-2048
info@WorldStamps.com
www.WorldStamps.com

**ARON R. HALBERSTAM
PHILATELISTS, LTD.**
PO Box 150168
Van Brunt Station
Brooklyn, NY 11215-0168
PH: 718-788-3978
arh@arhstamps.com
www.arhstamps.com

ROY'S STAMPS
PO Box 28001
600 Ontario Street
St. Catharines, ON
CANADA L2N 7P8
Phone: 905-934-8377
Email: roystamp@cogeco.ca

THE STAMP ACT
PO Box 1136
Belmont, CA 94002
PH: 650-703-2342
thestampact@sbcglobal.net

British Commonwealth

British E. Africa

COLONIAL STAMP COMPANY
5757 Wilshire Blvd. PH #8
Los Angeles, CA 90036
PH: 323-933-9435
FAX: 323-939-9930
Toll Free in North America
PH: 877-272-6693
FAX: 877-272-6694
info@colonialstampcompany.com
www.colonialstampcompany.com

British Guiana

COLONIAL STAMP COMPANY
5757 Wilshire Blvd. PH #8
Los Angeles, CA 90036
PH: 323-933-9435
FAX: 323-939-9930
Toll Free in North America
PH: 877-272-6693
FAX: 877-272-6694
info@colonialstampcompany.com
www.colonialstampcompany.com

Burundi

**WORLDSTAMPS/
FRANK GEIGER PHILATELISTS**
PO Box 4743
Pinehurst, NC 28374
PH: 910-295-2048
info@WorldStamps.com
www.WorldStamps.com

Buying

**DR. ROBERT FRIEDMAN &
SONS STAMP & COIN
BUYING CENTER**
2029 W. 75th St.
Woodridge, IL 60517
PH: 800-588-8100
FAX: 630-985-1588
stampcollections@drbobstamps.com
www.drbobfriedmanstamps.com

Canada

CANADA STAMP FINDER
PO Box 92591
Brampton, ON L6W 4R1
PH: 514-238-5751
Toll Free in North America:
877-412-3106
FAX: 323-315-2635
canadastampfinder@gmail.com
www.canadastampfinder.com

Canada

ROY'S STAMPS
PO Box 28001
600 Ontario Street
St. Catharines, ON
CANADA L2N 7P8
Phone: 905-934-8377
Email: roystamp@cogeco.ca

China - PRC

THE STAMP ACT
PO Box 1136
Belmont, CA 94002
PH: 650-703-2342
thestampact@sbcglobal.net

Classics

GARY POSNER, INC.
265 Sunrise Hwy. Ste. 1-308
Rockville Centre, NY 11570
Toll Free: 800-323-4279
Cell: 917-538-8133
FAX: 516-599-2145
garyposnerinc@aol.com
www.garyposnerinc.com

Collections

**DR. ROBERT FRIEDMAN &
SONS STAMP & COIN
BUYING CENTER**
2029 W. 75th St.
Woodridge, IL 60517
PH: 800-588-8100
FAX: 630-985-1588
stampcollections@drbobstamps.com
www.drbobfriedmanstamps.com

GARY POSNER, INC.
265 Sunrise Hwy. Ste. 1-308
Rockville Centre, NY 11570
Toll Free: 800-323-4279
Cell: 917-538-8133
FAX: 516-599-2145
garyposnerinc@aol.com
www. garyposnerinc.com

Ducks

MICHAEL JAFFE
PO Box 61484
Vancouver, WA 98666
PH: 360-695-6161
PH: 800-782-6770
FAX: 360-695-1616
mjaffe@brookmanstamps.com
www.brookmanstamps.com

Europe-Western

**HENRY GITNER
PHILATELISTS, INC.**
PO Box 3077-S
Middletown, NY 10940
PH: 845-343-5151
PH: 800-947-8267
FAX: 845-343-0068
hgitner@hgitner.com
www.hgitner.com

German Colonies

COLONIAL STAMP COMPANY
5757 Wilshire Blvd. PH #8
Los Angeles, CA 90036
PH: 323-933-9435
FAX: 323-939-9930
Toll Free in North America
PH: 877-272-6693
FAX: 877-272-6694
info@colonialstampcompany.com
www.colonialstampcompany.com

Great Britain

COLONIAL STAMP COMPANY
5757 Wilshire Blvd. PH #8
Los Angeles, CA 90036
PH: 323-933-9435
FAX: 323-939-9930
Toll Free in North America
PH: 877-272-6693
FAX: 877-272-6694
info@colonialstampcompany.com
www.colonialstampcompany.com

New Issues

DAVIDSON'S STAMP SERVICE
Personalized Service since 1970
PO Box 36355
Indianapolis, IN 46236-0355
PH: 317-826-2620
ed-davidson@earthlink.net
www.newstampissues.com

**WORLDSTAMPS/
FRANK GEIGER PHILATELISTS**
PO Box 4743
Pinehurst, NC 28374
PH: 910-295-2048
info@WorldStamps.com
www.WorldStamps.com

Stamp Stores

California

**BROSIUS STAMP, COIN &
SUPPLIES**
2105 Main St.
Santa Monica, CA 90405
PH: 310-396-7480
FAX: 310-396-7455
brosius.stamp.coin@hotmail.com

COLONIAL STAMP COMPANY
5757 Wilshire Blvd. PH #8
Los Angeles, CA 90036
PH: 323-933-9435
FAX: 323-939-9930
Toll Free in North America
PH: 877-272-6693
FAX: 877-272-6694
info@colonialstampcompany.com
www.colonialstampcompany.com

Connecticut

MILLER'S STAMP COMPANY
12 Douglas Lane, Suite 11
Waterford, CT 06385
www.millerstamps.com
PH: 860-908-6200

Delaware

DUTCH COUNTRY AUCTIONS
The Stamp Center
4115 Concord Pike
Wilmington, DE 19803
PH: 302-478-8740
FAX: 302-478-8779
auctions@dutchcountryauctions.com
www.dutchcountryauctions.com

Florida

**DR. ROBERT FRIEDMAN &
SONS STAMP & COIN
BUYING CENTER**
PH: 800-588-8100
FAX: 630-985-1588
stampcollections@drbobstamps.com
www.drbobfriedmanstamps.com

Stamp Stores

Illinois

**DR. ROBERT FRIEDMAN &
SONS STAMP & COIN
BUYING CENTER**
2029 W. 75th St.
Woodridge, IL 60517
PH: 800-588-8100
FAX: 630-985-1588
stampcollections@drbobstamps.com
www.drbobfriedmanstamps.com

Indiana

KNIGHT STAMP & COIN CO.
237 Main St.
Hobart, IN 46342
PH: 219-942-4341
PH: 800-634-2646
knight@knightcoin.com
www.knightcoin.com

New Jersey

**BERGEN STAMPS &
COLLECTIBLES**
306 Queen Anne Rd.
Teaneck, NJ 07666
PH: 201-836-8987
bergenstamps@gmail.com

TRENTON STAMP & COIN CO
Thomas DeLuca
Store: Forest Glen Plaza
1804 Highway 33
Hamilton Square, NJ 08690
Mail: PO Box 8574
Trenton, NJ 08650
PH: 609-584-8100
FAX: 609-587-8664
TOMD4TSC@aol.com

New York

CHAMPION STAMP CO., INC.
432 West 54th St.
New York, NY 10019
PH: 212-489-8130
FAX: 212-581-8130
championstamp@aol.com
www.championstamp.com

CK STAMPS
42-14 Union St. # 2A
Flushing, NY 11355
PH: 917-667-6641
ckstampsllc@yahoo.com

Ohio

HILLTOP STAMP SERVICE
Richard A. Peterson
PO Box 626
Wooster, OH 44691
PH: 330-262-8907 (O)
PH: 330-262-5378 (H)
hilltop@bright.net
www.hilltopstamps.com

Supplies

**BROOKLYN GALLERY COIN &
STAMP, INC.**
8725 4th Ave.
Brooklyn, NY 11209
PH: 718-745-5701
FAX: 718-745-2775
info@brooklyngallery.com
www.brooklyngallery.com

Topicals

**WORLDSTAMPS/
FRANK GEIGER PHILATELISTS**
PO Box 4743
Pinehurst, NC 28374
PH: 910-295-2048
info@WorldStamps.com
www.WorldStamps.com

E. JOSEPH McCONNELL, INC.
PO Box 683
Monroe, NY 10949
PH: 845-783-9791
FAX: 845-782-0347
ejstamps@gmail.com
www.EJMcConnell.com

Topicals - Columbus

MR. COLUMBUS
PO Box 1492
Fennville, MI 49408
PH: 269-543-4755
David@MrColumbus1492.com
www.MrColumbus1492.com

United Nations

BRUCE M. MOYER
Box 99
East Texas, PA 18046
PH: 610-395-8410
FAX: 610-421-8020
moyer@unstamps.com
www.unstamps.com

United States

KEITH WAGNER
ACS Stamp Company
2914 W 135th Ave
Broomfield, Colorado 80020
303-841-8666
www.ACSStamp.com

BROOKMAN STAMP CO.
PO Box 90
Vancouver, WA 98666
PH: 360-695-1391
PH: 800-545-4871
FAX: 360-695-1616
info@brookmanstamps.com
www.brookmanstamps.com

**WORLDSTAMPS/
FRANK GEIGER PHILATELISTS**
PO Box 4743
Pinehurst, NC 28374
PH: 910-295-2048
info@WorldStamps.com
www.WorldStamps.com

**HENRY GITNER
PHILATELISTS, INC.**
PO Box 3077-S
Middletown, NY 10940
PH: 845-343-5151
PH: 800-947-8267
FAX: 845-343-0068
hgitner@hgitner.com
www.hgitner.com

MILLER'S STAMP COMPANY
12 Douglas Lane, Suite 11
Waterford, CT 06385
www.millerstamps.com
PH: 860-908-6200

GARY POSNER, INC.
265 Sunrise Hwy. Ste. 1-308
Rockville Centre, NY 11570
Toll Free: 800-323-4279
Cell: 917-538-8133
FAX: 516-599-2145
garyposnerinc@aol.com
www. garyposnerinc.com

U.S. Classics/Moderns

BARDO STAMPS
PO Box 7437
Buffalo Grove, IL 60089
PH: 847-634-2676
jfb7437@aol.com
www.bardostamps.com

U.S.-Collections Wanted

DUTCH COUNTRY AUCTIONS
The Stamp Center
4115 Concord Pike
Wilmington, DE 19803
PH: 302-478-8740
FAX: 302-478-8779
auctions@dutchcountryauctions.com
www.dutchcountryauctions.com

**DR. ROBERT FRIEDMAN &
SONS STAMP & COIN
BUYING CENTER**
2029 W. 75th St.
Woodridge, IL 60517
PH: 800-588-8100
FAX: 630-985-1588
stampcollections@drbobstamps.com
www.drbobfriedmanstamps.com

MILLER'S STAMP COMPANY
12 Douglas Lane, Suite 11
Waterford, CT 06385
www.millerstamps.com
PH: 860-908-6200

U.S. - Errors, Freaks & Oddities

GARY POSNER, INC.
265 Sunrise Hwy. Ste. 1-308
Rockville Centre, NY 11570
Toll Free: 800-323-4279
Cell: 917-538-8133
FAX: 516-599-2145
garyposnerinc@aol.com
www. garyposnerinc.com

U.S. - Plate Blocks

GARY POSNER, INC.
265 Sunrise Hwy. Ste. 1-308
Rockville Centre, NY 11570
Toll Free: 800-323-4279
Cell: 917-538-8133
FAX: 516-599-2145
garyposnerinc@aol.com
www. garyposnerinc.com

U.S. - Rare Stamps

GARY POSNER, INC.
265 Sunrise Hwy. Ste. 1-308
Rockville Centre, NY 11570
Toll Free: 800-323-4279
Cell: 917-538-8133
FAX: 516-599-2145
garyposnerinc@aol.com
www. garyposnerinc.com

Want Lists - British Empire 1840-1935 German Cols./Offices

COLONIAL STAMP COMPANY
5757 Wilshire Blvd. PH #8
Los Angeles, CA 90036
PH: 323-933-9435
FAX: 323-939-9930
Toll Free in North America
PH: 877-272-6693
FAX: 877-272-6694
info@colonialstampcompany.com
www.colonialstampcompany.com

Want Lists - U.S.

GARY POSNER, INC.
265 Sunrise Hwy. Ste. 1-308
Rockville Centre, NY 11570
Toll Free: 800-323-4279
Cell: 917-538-8133
FAX: 516-599-2145
garyposnerinc@aol.com
www. garyposnerinc.com

Wanted - Worldwide Collections

DUTCH COUNTRY AUCTIONS
The Stamp Center
4115 Concord Pike
Wilmington, DE 19803
PH: 302-478-8740
FAX: 302-478-8779
auctions@dutchcountryauctions.com
www.dutchcountryauctions.com

Wanted - U.S.

GARY POSNER, INC.
265 Sunrise Hwy. Ste. 1-308
Rockville Centre, NY 11570
Toll Free: 800-323-4279
Cell: 917-538-8133
FAX: 516-599-2145
garyposnerinc@aol.com
www. garyposnerinc.com

Websites

KEITH WAGNER
ACS Stamp Company
2914 W 135th Ave
Broomfield, Colorado 80020
303-841-8666
www.ACSStamp.com

MILLER'S STAMP COMPANY
12 Douglas Lane, Suite 11
Waterford, CT 06385
www.millerstamps.com
PH: 860-908-6200

Wholesale - Dealers

HENRY GITNER PHILATELISTS, INC.
PO Box 3077-S
Middletown, NY 10940
PH: 845-343-5151
PH: 800-947-8267
FAX: 845-343-0068
hgitner@hgitner.com
www.hgitner.com

GARY POSNER, INC.
265 Sunrise Hwy. Ste. 1-308
Rockville Centre, NY 11570
Toll Free: 800-323-4279
Cell: 917-538-8133
FAX: 516-599-2145
garyposnerinc@aol.com
www. garyposnerinc.com

Worldwide-Collections

DR. ROBERT FRIEDMAN & SONS STAMP & COIN BUYING CENTER
2029 W. 75th St.
Woodridge, IL 60517
PH: 800-588-8100
FAX: 630-985-1588
stampcollections@drbobstamps.com
www.drbobfriedmanstamps.com